S0-AGN-642

Indiana Teacher's Edition

IN

HOLT McDOUGAL

Biology

Stephen Nowicki

HOLT McDOUGAL

HOUGHTON MIFFLIN HARCOURT

HOLT MCDOUGAL BIOLOGY

Teacher's Edition Acknowledgments

2b *mouse* AP/Wide World Photos; *fMRI* © Dr. Scott T. Grafton/Visuals Unlimited; *adaptation* © Bill Beatty/Visuals Unlimited; *design* Illustration by Argosy; **34b** *pitcher plant* U. S. Botanic Garden; *squid* © 2003 haddock@mbari.org; *atoms* **68b** *cell wall* © Dennis Kunkel/Phototake; *amoeba* © K. W. Jeon/Visuals Unlimited; *cell structure* Illustration by Bart Vallecoccia; *transport* Illustration by Argosy; **98b** *weightlifter* © 2006 JupiterImages Corporation; *volvox* © Roland Birke/Peter Arnold, Inc.; *ATP-ADP cellular energy* Illustration by Argosy; **132b** *skin cancer* National Cancer Institute; *leaf cross-section* © Steve Gschmeissner/Photo Researchers, Inc.; *cell cycle* Illustration by Argosy; *cell cycle, left* © Carolina Biological/Phototake; *cell cycle, right* © Carolina Biological/Phototake; **166b** *offspring* © 2006 JupiterImages Corporation; *Mendel* © Bettmann/Corbis; *meiosis* © Adrian T. Sumner/Photo Researchers, Inc.; *Mendel's experiments* Illustration by Concord Consortium; **198b** *squirrel* © Gregory K. Scott/Photo Researchers, Inc.; *chromosome* © Adrian T. Sumner/Photo Researchers, Inc.; *Punnett* © Elliott Kimmel, Science Teacher; **224b** *mRNA* © Dr. Elena Kiseleva/Photo Researchers, Inc.; *disease* © Dr. Ken Greer/Visuals Unlimited; *protein* Illustration by Argosy; **262b** *gel* © Tek Image/Photo Researchers, Inc.; *rooster* © Reuters/Corbis; *DNA* © David Parker/Photo Researchers, Inc.; **296b** *finch* © Kevin Schafer/Corbis; *Darwin* © Bettmann/Corbis; *vestigial* Illustration by Stephen Durke; *natural* Illustration by Argosy; **326b** *flamingo* © Tom Brakefield/Corbis; *elk* © Albert Copley/Visuals Unlimited; *evolutionary* Illustration by Argosy; **358b** *dragonfly* © Layne Kennedy/Corbis; *chimpanzee* © Jupiter Images; *fossil formation* Illustration by Peter Bull; *geologic* Illustration by Argosy; **394b** *beaver* © Ilene MacDonald/Alamy Images; *reef* © 2006 JupiterImages Corporation; *levels* Illustration by Richard Bonson/Wildlife Art Ltd.; *food web* Illustration by Argosy; **426b** *dolphins* © Alexis Rosenfeld/SPL/Photo Researchers, Inc.; *river bed* © 2006 JupiterImages Corporation; *ecological* © David A. Northcott/Corbis; *limits* Illustration by Argosy; **454b** *field* © Art Wolfe/The Image Bank/Getty Images; *rainforest* © Pete Saloutos/Corbis; *biomes* © MapQuest.com, Inc.; *marine* Illustration by Argosy; **482b** *trees* © Rob & Ann Simpson/Visuals Unlimited; *wildlife* © Wally Bauman/Alamy Images; *greenhouse* Illustration by Stephen Durke; *human effects* Illustration by Argosy; **516b** *sea cucumber* © Brian J. Skerry/NGSImages.com; *red handfish* © Gary Bell/oceanwideimages.com; *Linnaean* Illustration by Peter Bull; *cladogram* Illustration by Argosy; **542b** *bacteria* © Photo Researchers, Inc.; *Ebola* © David Murray/Corbis; *bacteriophage* Illustration by Stephen Durke; *antibiotics* Illustration by Argosy; **572b** *Giardia* © Dr. Fred Hossler/Visuals Unlimited; *fungi* © Jupiter Images; *protist phylogenetic tree* Illustration by Peter Bull; *protist and fungus life cycles* Illustration by Tata Interactive; **610b** *dogwood* © Images.com/Jupiter Images; *bat* © Claus Meyer/Minden Pictures; *adaptations* Illustration by Debbie Maizels; *plants and pollinators* Illustration by Argosy; **638b** *tendril* © Kevin Schafer/Corbis; *cactus* © AbleStock.com/Jupiter Images; *model* Illustration by Peter Bull; *key* © LEAF - Wisconsin's K-12 Forestry Education Program; **662b** *Venus flytrap* © D. Heuclin/Peter Arnold, Inc.; *butterfly* © 2006 JupiterImages Corporation; *life cycle* Illustration by Debbie Maizels; *seed* Illustration by Argosy; **694b** *jellyfish* George Grall/National Geographic Image Collection; *tongue snail* Paige Gill/Florida Keys National Marine Sanctuary/NOAA Photo Library; *symmetry* © Sue Daly/naturepl.com; *structures* Illustration by Argosy; **728b** *mantis* © Jose B. Ruiz/naturepl.com; *fly eye* © Dr. Robert Calentine/Visuals Unlimited; *arachnid* Illustration by Robin Boutell; *arthropod* Illustration by Argosy; **756b** *lionfish* © Paul Osmond/www.deepseaimages.com; *axolotyl* © Jane Burton/naturepl.com; *anatomy* Illustration by Peter Bull; *fish types* Illustration by Argosy; **786b** *pelican* © 2006 JupiterImages Corporation; *monkey* © Frans Lanting/Minden Pictures; *phylogenetic* Illustration by Alan Male; *beak shape* John J. Mosesso/NBII; **816b** *swans* © Peter Lane Taylor/Visuals Unlimited; *weaver nest* © John Cancalosi/Ardea London Ltd.; *cognition* © Jim Wallace/Duke University Photography; *behavioral* Illustration by Lionbridge Technologies; **850b** *alveolar* © Arnold Brody/Photo Researchers, Inc.; *sweat pore* © Steve Gschmeissner/Photo Researchers, Inc.; *feedback* Illustration by Peter Bull; *homeostasis* Illustration by Argosy; **872b** *spinal cord* © Steve Gschmeissner/Photo Researchers, Inc.; *brain scan* © Yves Forestier/Corbis; *reflex arc* Illustration by Sharon & Joel Harris; *disorders* Illustration by Argosy; **908b** *bronchi* © Innerspace Imaging/Photo Researchers, Inc.; *artery* © SPL/Photo Researchers, Inc.; *alveoli* Illustration by Stephen Durke; *systems* Illustration by Argosy; **938b** *phagocytosis* © Gopal Murti/Phototake; *antibody* © Institut Pasteur/Phototake; *HIV* Illustration by Stephen Durke; *immune responses* Illustration by Argosy; **970b** *kidney* © Susumu Nishinaga/Photo Researchers, Inc.; *microvilli* © Susumu Nishinaga/Photo Researchers, Inc.; *glomeruli* Illustration by Sharon & Joel Harris; *digestive* Illustration by Argosy; **998b** *knee x-ray* © Zephyr/Photo Researchers, Inc.; *bone* © Andrew Syred/Photo Researchers, Inc.; *muscle* Illustration by Sharon & Joel Harris; *joints* Illustration by Argosy; **1022b** *embryo* © Dr. Yorgos Nikas/Photo Researchers, Inc.; *fetus* © Du Cane Medical Imaging Ltd./Photo Researchers, Inc.; *menstrual cycle* Illustration by Peter Bull; *timeline* Illustration by Argosy.

Printed in China.

ISBN-13: 978-0-547-41444-7

2 3 4 5 6 7 8 9 10 0940 19 18 17 16 15 14 13 12 11 10

4500238034 ^ B C D E F G

Biology

A State of the Art Textbook

provides a clear, approachable writing style, engaging visuals, and shorter sections for easier comprehension. Unsurpassed chapter reviews contain targeted practice for Standards-Based Assessment.

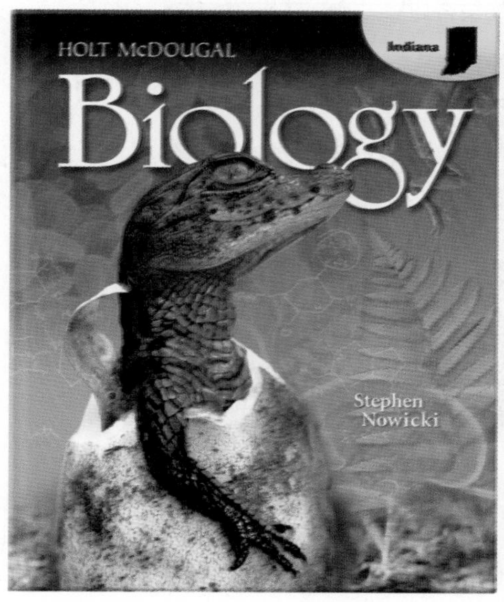

Innovative Technology

saves you time, makes teaching easier, and connects your students to the world of biology.

A Library of Classroom-Proven Labs

teach key concepts and support inquiry-based learning through easy-to-use labs and activities.

Universal Access

through a variety of multi-media tools, classroom materials and leveled content connect every student to the community of learning.

Custom Assessment and Remediation Tools

help your students master the biology standards.

Innovative Technology

SELECT the engaging, interactive technology tools that **CONNECT** the world of biology to your students' lives.

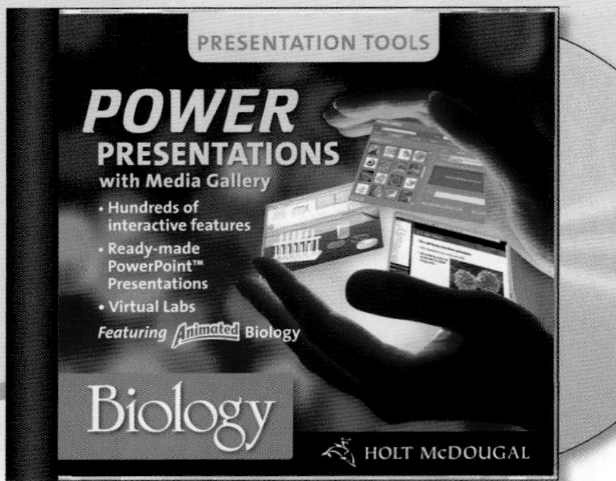

Power Presentations *featuring* Media Gallery

contains hundreds of exciting photos, animations, video clips, and PowerPoint™ slides that you can edit and adapt to your needs. PowerPoint™ presentations are ready to go right away, and are fully editable to make classroom lectures engaging and meaningful.

With a keyword search you can easily find the right image at the right time.

The ability to write your own caption makes every slide show unique.

Choose from thousands of images, graphics, videos, and animations to create slide shows that bring your classroom presentations alive.

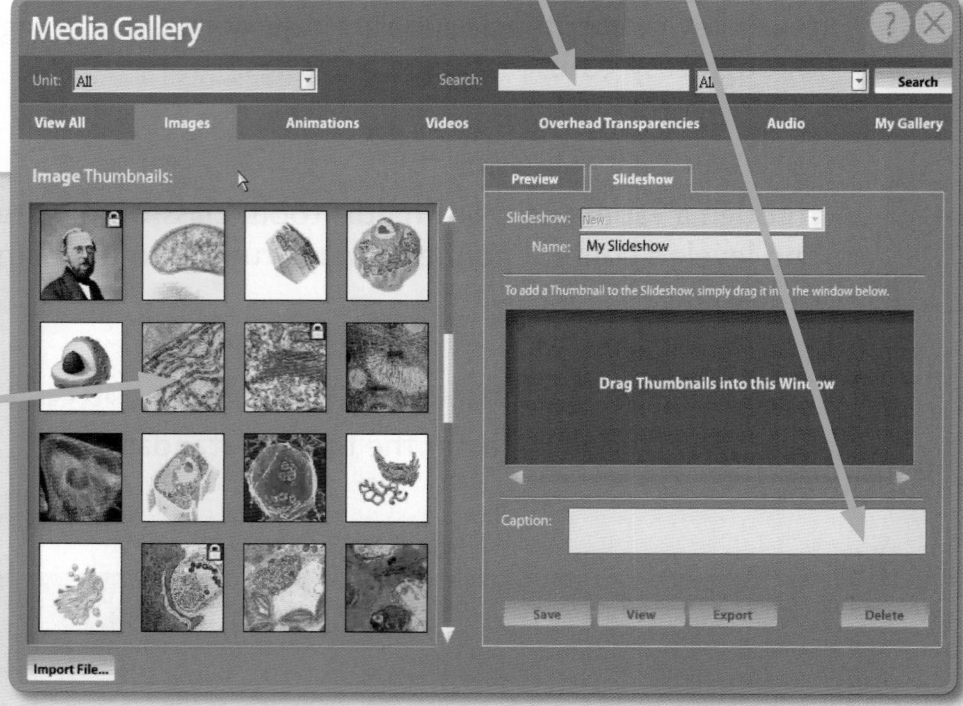

An Online Magazine connects students to the latest biology news through live newsfeeds, up-to-the-minute articles, and features about cutting-edge issues, technologies and careers.

Available at CLASSZONE.COM

Feature articles give students and teachers the opportunity to extend their learning and connect to the world of biology happening around them.

Simple navigation and engaging artwork make difficult concepts come alive at the click of a button.

Provides simulations and animations that let students visualize and interact with concepts and processes.

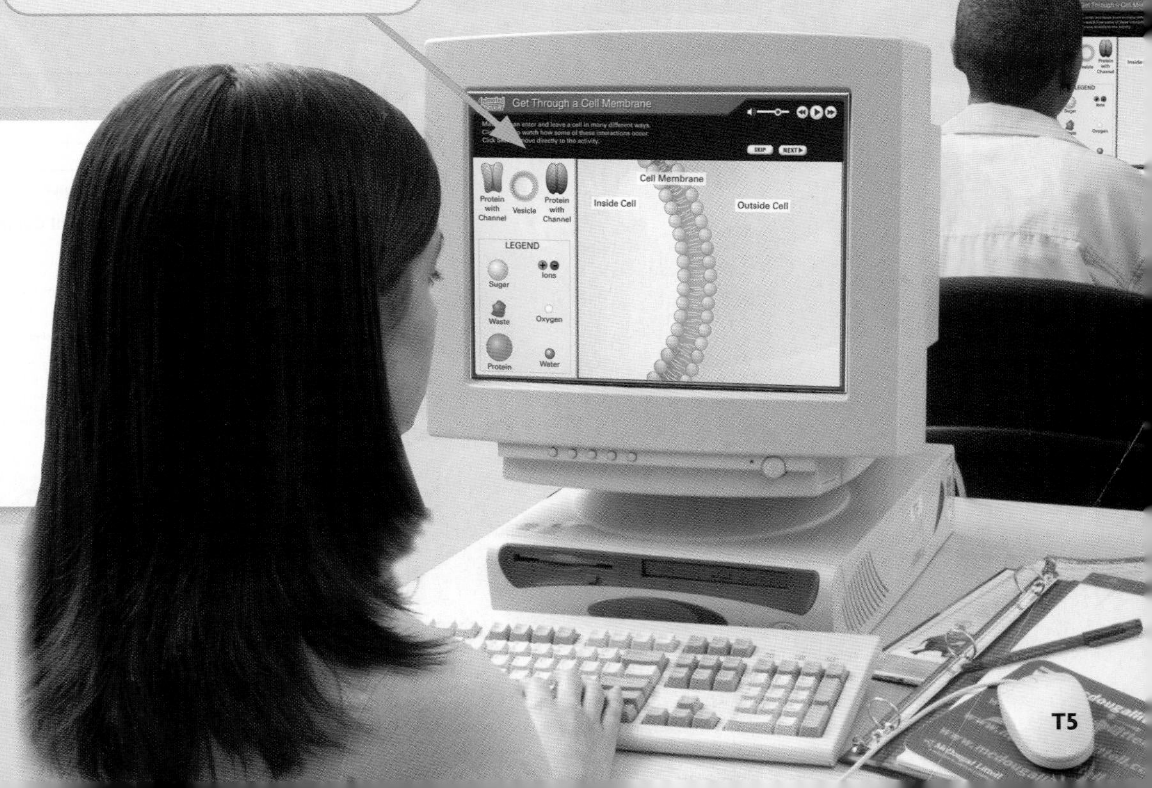

Classroom-Proven Labs

SELECT the quick, easy-to-use lab activities that **CONNECT** your students to the concepts they are learning.

Lab Binder

featuring

Lab Generator with Virtual Labs

Allows you to select, edit, and adapt ready-made labs or design your own—all correlated standards. Labs feature quick, easy-to-find materials.

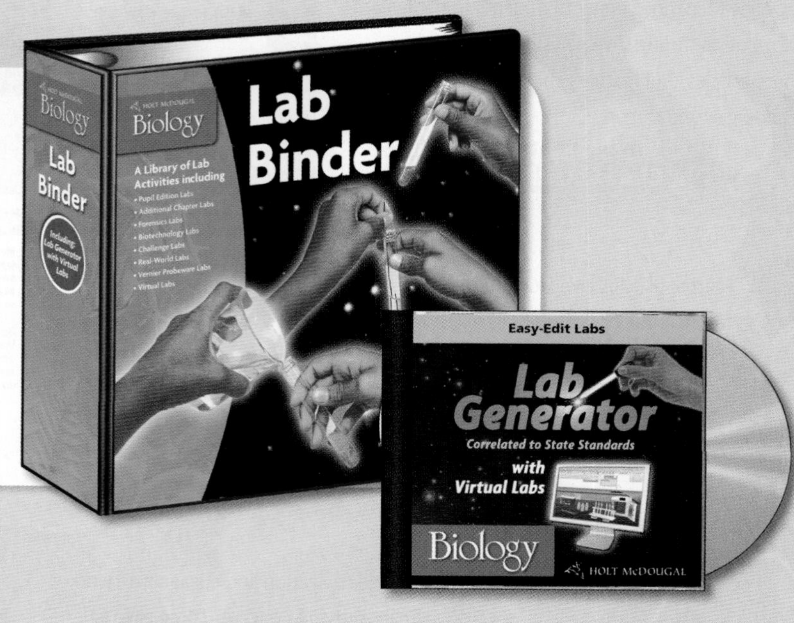

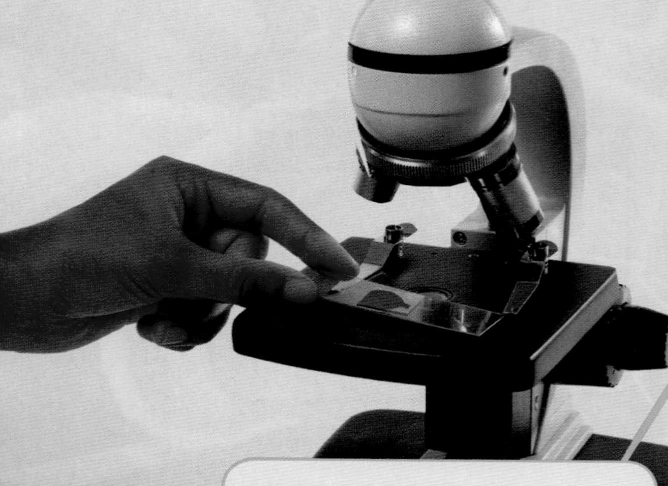

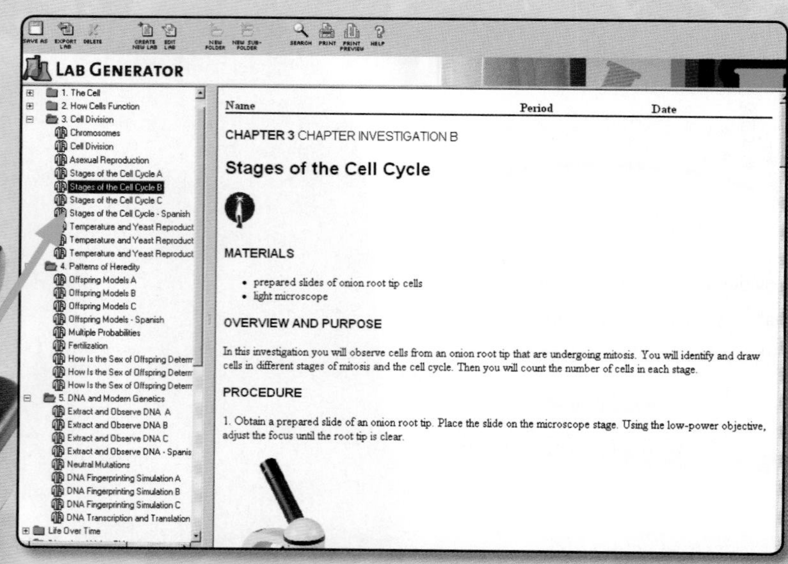

With the most comprehensive lab program, the Lab generator gives instant access to a library of fully editable labs.

Data Analysis

Interpret data with questions that ensure comprehension and understanding.

Available at CLASSZONE.COM

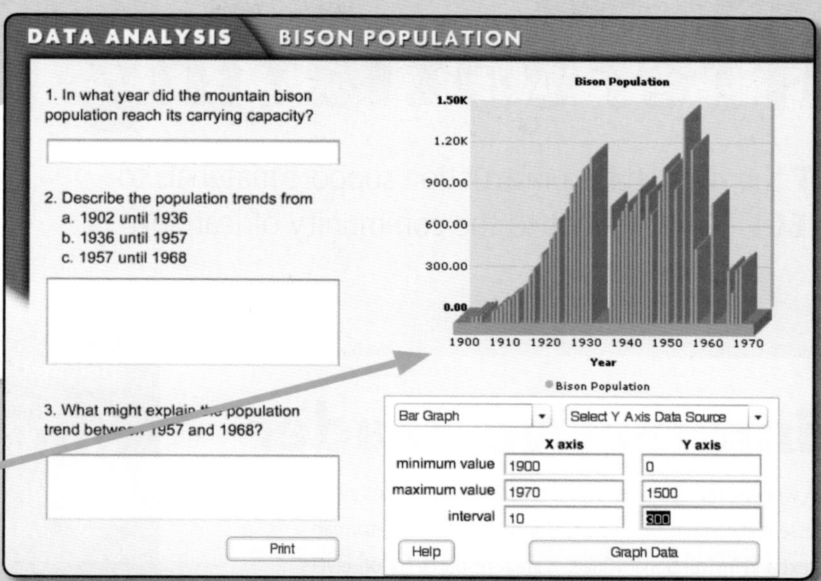

A dynamic graphic program allows students to easily build their own graphs and immediately see the results.

Virtual Labs

Engage your students with high interest labs that simulate real experiments, provide a wide range of choice, and advance written, verbal and visual comprehension.

Available at CLASSZONE.COM

Differentiating Instruction

SELECT the right leveled-instruction support materials to **CONNECT** every student to the community of learning.

Interactive Reader

A working text for below-level readers that presents all essential content from the textbook through easy-to-read text and instructional visuals. A great resource for on-level students to review key concepts.

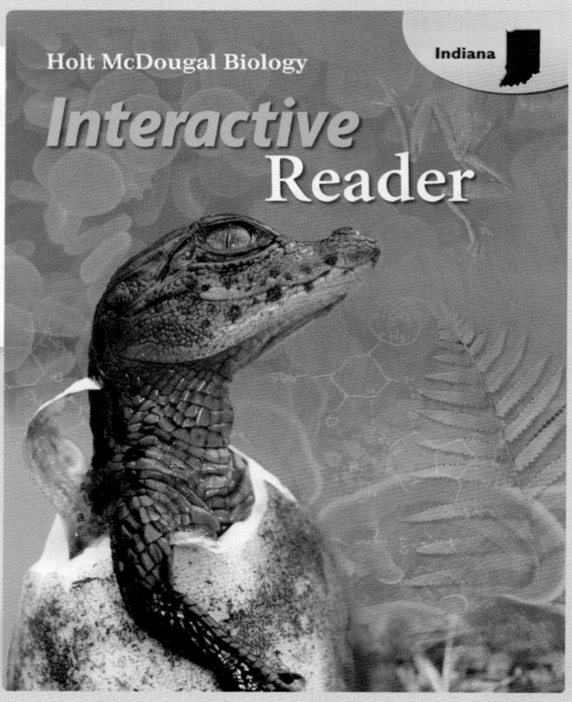

Student Resources

Study Guide

Student workbook provides chapter review worksheets and reteaching exercises.

Standards Review and Practice

Comprehensive worksheets help students prepare for standardized tests.

Provides a fun, online environment where students can review chapter material through custom-designed activities, games, and quizzes.

Custom Assessment

SELECT the assessment and remediation tools that
CONNECT your students to the standards.

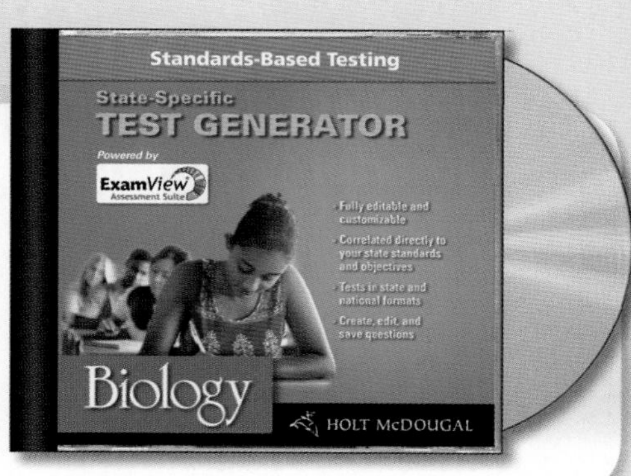

ExamView Test Generator

The Test Generator provides a searchable database of items from all tests and quizzes, including leveled questions. Correlations to state standards and full edit capability give you the flexibility to customize assessments to your students' needs.

The **Houghton Mifflin Harcourt Assessment System** is a flexible, web-based program that allows you to use assessment as a teaching tool. This seamless testing and remediation system gives you a fast and easy way to:

TEST
Unique testing is custom-built to standards.

SCORE
Automatic scoring gives you results in minutes.

REPORT
Diagnostic reports show you what standards were missed.

RETEACH
Personalized remediation helps you target reteaching.

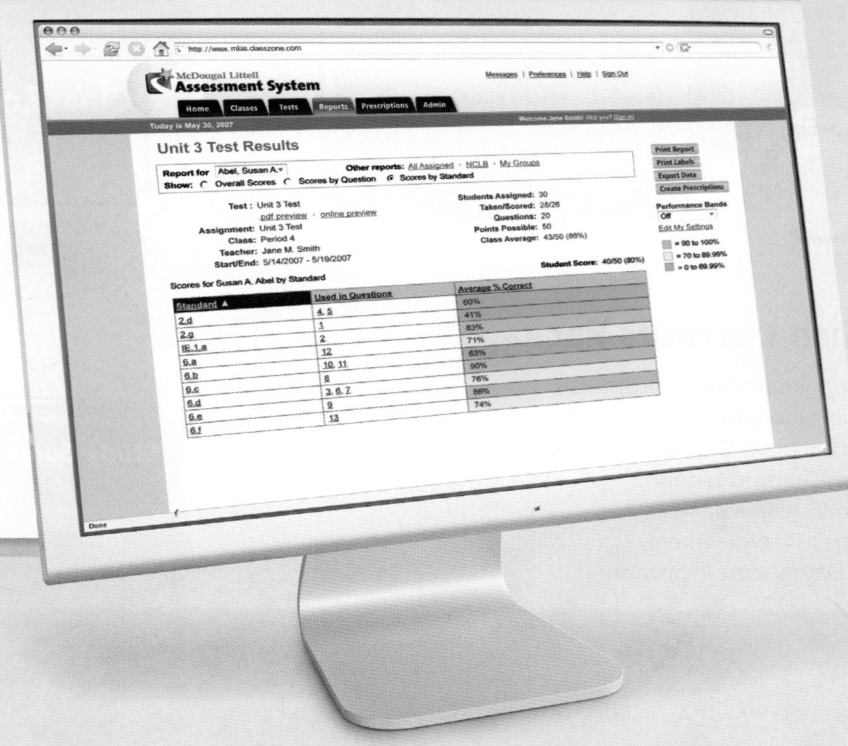

Student Resources

A complete program of technology and print resources provide support for individual student learning.

Core Student Resources include

- Pupil Edition
- Biology Interactive Reader
- Pupil Edition Audio Readings
- e-Edition Interactive Textbook

ClassZone.com

Companion website includes student support with

- BioZine Interactive Magazine
- Animated Biology
- Interactive Review
- Virtual Labs
- Data Analysis Activities
- Scilinks
- WebQuests

English Learners Package

- Biología Pupil Edition in Spanish
- Pupil Edition Audio Readings in Spanish
- Multilanguage Glossary
- Study Guide in Spanish
- Spanish Assessment
- Spanish Reinforcement
- Lab Data Sheets in Spanish

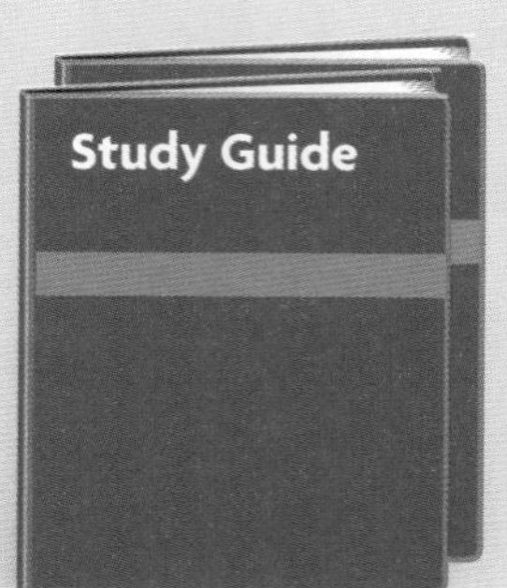

Student Workbooks

- Study Guide
- Interactive Reader

Teacher Resources

Time-saving, easy-to-use teacher resources make lesson planning and preparation simple.

Key Teaching Resources include

- Teacher's Edition
- Easy Planner DVD
- Biology Lab Binder featuring Lab Generator with Virtual Labs DVD

Multimedia Presentation Kit

- Power Presentations with Media Gallery DVD
- DVD Video Series
- Transparency Book

Biology Toolkit

Classroom tools for

- Differentiating Instruction
- Science and Process Skills
- Reading and Notetaking Strategies
- Vocabulary
- Writing
- Presenting and Analyzing Data
- Teach with Technology

Assessment Package

- Assessment Book
- Test Generator CD-ROM

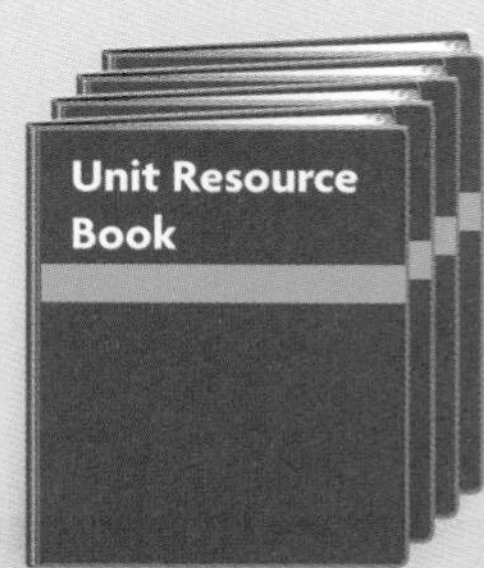

Resource Manager

- Lesson Plan Book
- Introducing Biology Unit Resource Book
- Cells Unit Resource Book
- Genetics Unit Resource Book
- Evolution Unit Resource Book
- Ecology Unit Resource Book
- Classification and Diversity Unit Resource Book
- Plants Unit Resource Book
- Animals Unit Resource Book
- Human Biology Unit Resource Book

Guide to Indiana Biology I Standards Coverage

Correlation to Indiana Biology I Standards T13

Indiana Table of Contents IN8

Indiana Student Guide IN35

Overview of the Indiana Standards IN36
Biology I Standards IN37

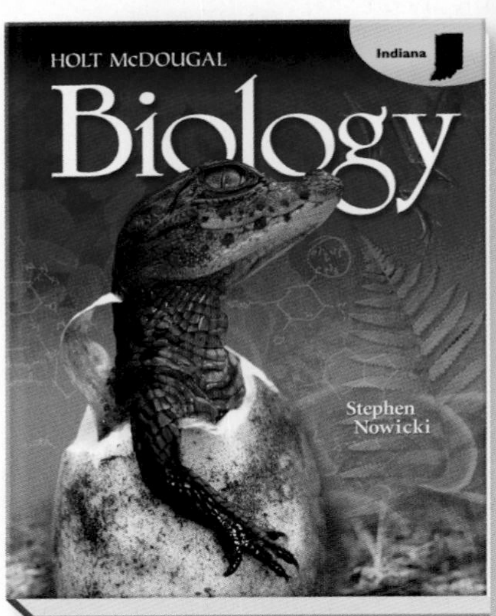

Embedded Standards Support

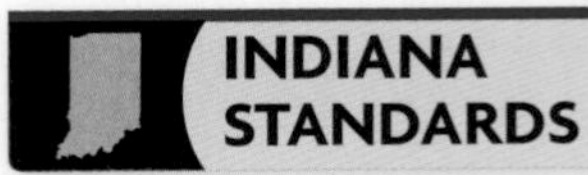

Look for the Indiana Standards symbol throughout the book. It tells you which standards are covered in each section.

Holt McDougal Biology correlated to The Indiana Academic Standards for Science Biology I

Indiana Academic Standards		Student/Teacher Edition Pages
Biology I		
Students should understand that scientific knowledge is gained from observation of natural phenomena and experimentation, by designing and conducting investigations guided by theory, and by evaluating and communicating the results of those investigations according to accepted procedures. Thus, scientific knowledge is scientists' best explanations for the data from many investigations. Further, ideas about objects in the microscopic world that we cannot directly sense are often understood in terms of concepts developed to understand objects in the macroscopic world that we can see and touch. In the science classroom student work should align with this process of science and should be guided by the following principles. These should be woven throughout the daily work that students are doing when learning the content presented in the standard indicators.		
NOS.1	Develop explanations based on reproducible data and observations gathered during laboratory investigations.	28, 57, 88, 106–107, 116, 124, 126, 127, 142, 143, 172, 210, 229, 234, 282, 308, 315, 320, 334, 339, 352, 364, 384, 405, 435, 438, 442, 448, 461, 475, 477, 493, 497, 529, 546, 562, 566, 595, 600, 623, 647, 656, 669, 676–677, 684, 709, 721, 742, 750, 772, 780, 792, 830, 836, 840, 857, 865, 884, 886, 895, 902, 921, 925, 932, 933, 981, 985, 992, 993, 1012, 1014, 1033, 1038
NOS.2	Recognize that their explanations must be based both on their data and other known information from investigations of others.	18, 226–228, 334, 364, 399, 435, 438, 460, 475, 529, 628, 676–677, 742, 836, 895, 985, 1014
NOS.3	Clearly communicate their ideas and results of investigations verbally and in written form using tables, graphs, diagrams, and photographs.	18, 22, 28, 57, 58, 88, 92, 93, 106–107, 124, 126, 127, 142, 143, 147, 156, 210, 229, 268, 282, 308, 315, 321, 334, 352, 375, 384, 399, 405, 435, 438, 449, 461, 475, 493, 506, 560, 562, 566, 610, 620, 623, 632, 647, 657, 669, 676, 685, 709, 723, 733, 739, 742, 750, 751, 770, 772, 776, 792, 804, 810, 824, 830, 836, 840, 857, 866, 902, 921, 928, 932, 933, 949, 981, 992, 1012, 1016, 1017, 1031, 1033, 1044
NOS.4	Regularly evaluate the work of their peers and in turn have their work evaluated by their peers.	18, 28, 353, 364, 460, 475, 676–677
NOS.5	Apply standard techniques in laboratory investigations to measure physical quantities in appropriate units and convert known quantities to other units as necessary.	18, 28, 57, 88, 126, 127, 156, 460, 475, 477, 493, 676–677, 772, 804, 857, 921, 981, 1012
NOS.6	Use analogies and models (mathematical and physical) to simplify and represent systems that are difficult to understand or directly experience due to their size, time scale, or complexity, and recognize the limitations of analogies and models.	18, 22, 51, 83, 93, 156, 192, 238, 257, 268, 278, 286, 315, 334, 337, 352, 364, 381, 385, 420, 421, 435, 476, 496, 507, 536, 567, 772, 861, 932, 943, 964, 983, 1011
NOS.7	Focus on the development of explanatory models based on their observations during laboratory investigations.	18, 57, 83, 238, 268, 278, 315, 334, 364, 435, 496, 772, 861, 943
NOS.8	Explain that the body of scientific knowledge is organized into major theories, which are derived from and supported by the results of many experiments, and allow us to make testable predictions.	16–17, 70–71, 298–301, 302–303, 310–314, 316–319

Indiana Academic Standards		Student/Teacher Edition Pages
NOS.9	Recognize that new scientific discoveries often lead to a re-evaluation of previously accepted scientific knowledge and of commonly held ideas.	16–17, 70–71, 177, 209, 226–228, 231–232, 298–301, 302–303, 518, 533–535, 575–576
NOS.10	Describe how scientific discoveries lead to the development of new technologies, and conversely how technological advances can lead to scientific discoveries through new experimental methods and equipment.	19–23, 64–66, 70–71, 162–163, 280–283, 292–294, 390–392, 512–514, 606–608, 690–692, 846–848, 1050–1052
NOS.11	Explain how scientific knowledge can be used to guide decisions on environmental and social issues.	24–27, 64–66, 279, 512–514
Standard 1: Cellular Chemistry		
Core Standard Describe the basic molecular structure and function of the four major categories of organic compounds (carbohydrates, lipids, proteins and nucleic acids) essential to cellular function.		
Core Standard Describe how the work done in cells is performed by a variety of organic molecules, especially proteins, whose functions depend on the sequence of their monomers and the consequent shape of the molecule.		
B.1.1	Describe the structure of the major categories of organic compounds which make up living organisms in terms of their building blocks and the small number of chemical elements (carbon, hydrogen, nitrogen, oxygen, phosphorous, and sulfur) from which they are composed.	36–39, 40–43, 44–48
B.1.2	Understand that the shape of a molecule determines its role in the many different types of cellular processes including metabolism, homeostasis, growth and development, and heredity, and understand that the majority of these processes involve proteins that act as enzymes.	18, 54–56, 57, 59, 75–77, 79, 104–105, 113–115, 235–238, 239–242, 243–247, 248–251, 265–266, 269–271, 981
B.1.3	Explain and give examples of how the function and differentiation of cells is influenced by their external environment, including temperature, acidity and the concentration of certain molecules, and that changes in these conditions may affect how a cell functions.	18, 40–43, 57
Standard 2: Cellular Structure		
Core Standard Describe features that are common to all cells and contrast those with distinctive features that allow cells to carry out specific functions.		
B.2.1	Describe features common to all cells that are essential for growth and survival, and explain their functions.	5–6, 8–9, 72, 73–79, 92, 93
B.2.2	Describe the structure of a cell membrane and explain how it regulates the transport of materials into and out of the cell and prevents harmful materials from entering the cell.	81–84, 85–87, 88, 89–91, 93, 156
B.2.3	Explain that most cells contain mitochondria, the key sites of cellular respiration, where stored chemical energy is converted into useable energy for the cell and some cells, including many plant cells, contain chloroplasts, the key sites of photosynthesis, where the energy of light is captured for use in chemical work.	77, 79, 104–105, 108–112, 113–115, 117–121
B.2.4	Explain that all cells contain ribosomes, the key sites for protein synthesis, where genetic material is decoded in order to form unique proteins.	76, 245–247

Indiana Academic Standards		Student/Teacher Edition Pages
B.2.5	Explain that cells use proteins to form structures, including cilia, flagella, which allow them to carry out specific functions, including movement, adhesion, and absorption.	78, 556, 578–579
B.2.6	Investigate a variety of different cell types and relate the proportion of different organelles within these cells to their functions.	73–75, 77, 78, 79, 92, 93, 97(#5)
Standard 3: Matter Cycles and Energy Transfer		
Core Standard Describe how the sun's energy is captured and used to construct sugar molecules which can be used as a form of energy or serve as building blocks of organic molecules.		
Core Standard Diagram how matter and energy cycle through an ecosystem.		
B.3.1	Describe how some organisms capture the sun's energy through the process of photosynthesis by converting carbon dioxide and water into high energy compounds and releasing oxygen.	103–105, 106–107, 108–112, 116, 406–407, 414
B.3.2	Describe how most organisms can combine and recombine the elements contained in sugar molecules into a variety of biologically essential compounds by utilizing the energy from cellular respiration.	100–102, 113–115, 117–121, 126
B.3.3	Recognize and describe that metabolism consists of all of the biochemical reactions that occur inside cells, including the production, modification, transport, and exchange of materials that are required for the maintenance of life.	6, 50–53, 100–102, 103–105, 108–112, 113–115, 117–121, 122–125
B.3.4	Describe how matter cycles through an ecosystem by way of food chains and food webs and how organisms convert that matter into a variety of organic molecules to be used in part in their own cellular structures.	408–411, 412–416
B.3.5	Describe how energy from the sun flows through an ecosystem by way of food chains and food webs and only a small portion of that energy is used by individual organisms while the majority of energy is lost as heat.	408–411, 417–419
Standard 4: Interdependence		
Core Standard Describe the relationship between living and nonliving components of ecosystems and describe how that relationship is in flux due to natural changes and human actions.		
B.4.1	Explain that the amount of life an environment can support is limited by the available energy, water, oxygen, and minerals, and by the ability of ecosystems to recycle the remains of dead organisms.	402–404, 405, 406–407, 408–411, 412–416, 441–444, 456–457, 596
B.4.2	Describe how human activities and natural phenomena can change the flow and of matter and energy in an ecosystem and how those changes impact other species.	445–447, 448, 484–487, 488–492, 493, 494–496, 498–501, 502–505, 512–514, 846–848
B.4.3	Describe the consequences of introducing non-native species into an ecosystem and identify the impact it may have on that ecosystem.	500–501

Indiana Academic Standards		Student/Teacher Edition Pages
B.4.4	Describe how climate, the pattern of matter and energy flow, the birth and death of new organisms, and the interaction between those organisms contribute to the long term stability of an ecosystem.	406–407, 408–411, 412–416, 417–419, 428–430, 431–434, 435, 440–444, 445–447, 458–461, 470, 472, 475, 484–487, 488–492, 493, 494–496, 498–501, 509–510, 559–561, 596, 598–599
Standard 5: Molecular Basis of Heredity		
Core Standard Describe the basic structure of DNA and how this structure enables DNA to function as the hereditary molecule that directs the production of RNA and proteins.		
Core Standard Understand that proteins largely determine the traits of an organism.		
B.5.1	Describe the relationship between chromosomes and DNA along with their basic structure and function.	138–139, 168–171, 230–233
B.5.2	Describe how hereditary information passed from parents to offspring is encoded in regions of DNA molecules called genes.	23, 170–171, 177–179, 180–182, 209–211
B.5.3	Describe the process by which DNA directs the production of protein within a cell.	239–242, 243–247, 257
B.5.4	Explain how the unique shape and activity of each protein is determined by the sequence of its amino acids.	47–48, 75, 243–247
B.5.5	Understand that proteins are responsible for the observable traits of an organism and for most of the functions within an organism.	75
B.5.6	Recognize that traits can be structural, physiological or behavioral and can include readily observable characteristics at the organismal level or less recognizable features at the molecular and cellular level.	177–179, 180–182
Standard 6: Cellular Reproduction		
Core Standard Explain the processes, both mitosis and meiosis, by which new cells are formed from existing cells and how in multicellular organisms, groups of cells cooperate to perform essential functions within an organism.		
Core Standard Explain the cellular processes that occur to generate natural genetic variations between parents and offspring.		
B.6.1	Describe the process of mitosis and explain that this process ordinarily results in daughter cells with a genetic make-up identical to the parent cells.	134–137, 138–142
B.6.2	Understand that most cells of a multicellular organism contain the same genes, but develop from a single cell (e.g., a fertilized egg) in different ways due to differential gene expression.	151–155, 248–251, 852–856
B.6.3	Explain that in multicellular organisms the zygote produced during fertilization undergoes a series of cell divisions that lead to clusters of cells that go on to specialize and become the organism's tissues and organs.	151–155, 852–856, 1036–1037
B.6.4	Describe and model the process of meiosis and explain the relationship between the genetic make-up of the parent cell and the daughter cells (gametes).	168–171, 173–176, 192
B.6.5	Explain how, in sexual reproduction, crossing over, independent assortment, and random fertilization, result in offspring that are genetically different from the parents.	189–191

Indiana Academic Standards		Student/Teacher Edition Pages
Standard 7: Genetics		
Core Standard Explain how the genetic information from parents determines the unique characteristics of their offspring.		
B.7.1	Distinguish between dominant and recessive alleles and determine the phenotype that would result from the different possible combinations of alleles in an offspring.	180–182, 183–187, 193
B.7.2	Describe dominant, recessive, codominant, sex-linked, incompletely dominant, multiply allelic, and polygenic traits and illustrate their inheritance patterns over multiple generations.	181–182, 183–187, 193, 200–203, 204–207, 208, 212–217, 218, 219
B.7.3	Determine the likelihood of the appearance of a specific trait in an offspring given the genetic make-up of the parents.	180–182, 183–187, 193, 200–203, 204–207, 208, 212–217, 218, 219, 287
B.7.4	Explain the process by which a cell copies its DNA and identify factors that can damage DNA and cause changes in its nucleotide sequence.	235–238, 252–255, 256
B.7.5	Explain and demonstrate how inserting, substituting or deleting segments of a DNA molecule can alter a gene, which is then passed to every cell that develops from it and that the results may be beneficial, harmful or have little or no effect on the organism.	252–255, 275–279, 286
Standard 8: Evolution		
Core Standard Describe how biochemical, fossil, anatomical, developmental, and genetic findings are used to determine relationships among organisms, producing modern classification systems.		
Core Standard Describe how modern evolutionary theory provides an explanation of the history of life on earth and the similarities between organisms that exist today.		
B.8.1	Explain how anatomical and molecular similarities among organisms suggests that life on earth began as simple, one-celled organisms about 4 billion years ago and multicellular organisms evolved later.	370–371, 372–374, 376–378, 612–613
B.8.2	Explain how organisms are classified and named based on their evolutionary relationships into taxonomic categories.	524–528, 533–535, 536, 537, 574–576, 617–622, 696–698, 699–704, 758–762
B.8.3	Use anatomical and molecular evidence to establish evolutionary relationships between organisms.	311–314, 528, 529, 530–532, 536, 537, 556–557, 612–613, 699–704, 730–731, 758–762, 793–797
B.8.4	Understand that molecular evidence supports the anatomical evidence for these evolutionary relationships and provides additional information about the order in which different lines of descent branched.	317–318
B.8.5	Describe how due to genetic variations, environmental forces, and reproductive pressures, organisms with beneficial traits are more likely to survive, reproduce, and pass on their genetic information.	302, 304–309, 315, 321, 330–333, 334, 338, 352, 353
B.8.6	Explain how genetic variation within a population (a species) can be attributed to mutations as well as a random assortment of existing genes.	328–329, 335–337
B.8.7	Describe the modern scientific theory of the origins and history of life on earth, and evaluate the evidence that supports it.	310–314, 316–319, 360–363, 364, 365–367, 368–371, 372–374, 376–378, 379–383

Holt McDougal Biology

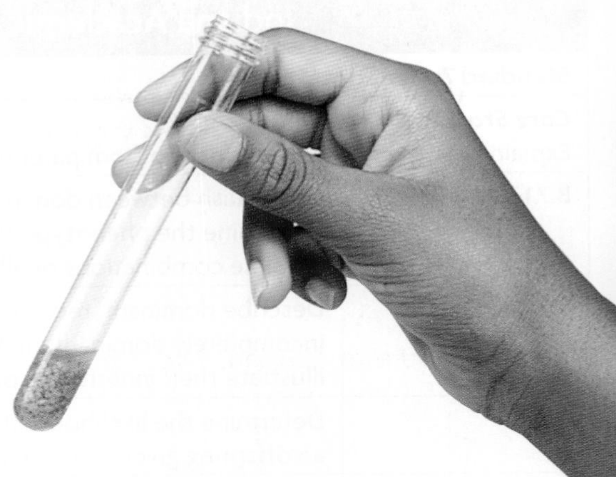

Indiana Lab Program

Featuring

Safety in the Biology Lab

Lab Materials List

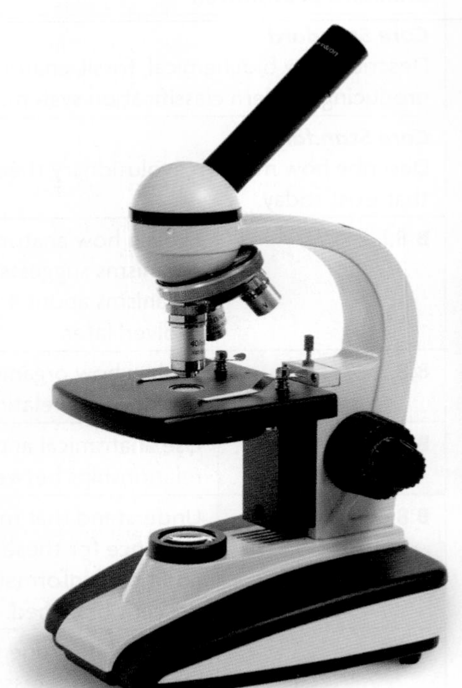

Safety in the Biology Lab

The investigations and activities in *Holt McDougal Biology* are designed to involve students in the process of science. Some of the investigations involve chemicals, glassware, and sharp tools. Some involve live animals or prepared specimens. Your insistence on everyone's adherence to safe lab practices will ensure students get the most out of their laboratory and field-work experiences.

BE PREPARED

Be sure to familiarize yourself with federal, state, and local safety regulations. It is your responsibility to provide students with a safe working environment. Post the student safety guidelines and dress code in a prominent place in the room.

Facilities Make sure all equipment is in good working order before school begins and plan a regular schedule of inspection for the school year. Inspect all safety equipment, such as the fume hood, eyewash station, and emergency shower, as well as fire equipment, such as fire extinguishers and smoke detectors. Make sure that the electrical outlets are protected with ground fault interrupters. Familiarize yourself with the location of the master shut-off valves and switches for the lab.

Storeroom and Supplies Make sure you have the supplies you need. Detailed material lists appear in the **Teacher's Edition**, **Lab Binder**, and can be generated using the **Lab Generator.** Check for shelf-life dates or dates of purchase on existing stock. Generally, chemicals should not be stored longer than two years. Organize stock so that incompatible reagents, such as acids and bases, are stored separately. It is safer to store solid reagents on upper shelves and liquid reagents on lower shelves, however, any large containers should be stored at or near floor level. Check glassware for chips and cracks.

As you review and restock your inventory, be sure that you have Material Safety Datasheets for all the chemicals in your storeroom, including household items such as bleach. Make sure you have a chemical spill kit in stock.

Biological materials, such as seeds or culture media, should be stored apart from chemical supplies. Any refrigerator intended to store laboratory materials should have a sign prohibiting personal use or food storage.

Waste Disposal Review federal, state, and local regulations for disposal and recycling of chemical and biological waste. Make sure the school has the proper containers for storage and the necessary means for removal.

Student Safety Equipment Make sure you have enough safety goggles, gloves, and aprons available for every student in class. If the same goggles will be used by students in different classes, have a plan for sanitizing the goggles after each use.

First Aid Have a first aid kit available for minor injuries, with antiseptics, bandages, ointments, tapes, and gauze pads. In the case of more serious injuries, post in the lab and place on your phone the numbers of poison control, and local police and fire departments. Be prepared to document any incident.

SAFETY ICONS

Apron

Fumes

Animal Safety

General Safety

Breakage

Gloves

Chemical Safety

Hand Washing

Disposal

Heating Safety

Electrical Safety

Hot/Glove

Safety Goggles

Poison

Fire Safety

Sharp Objects

GETTING STARTED

At the beginning of the school year, and before students conduct their first investigation, go over the safety regulations and dress code for the lab. Show students where the information is posted, point out fire exits and alarms, and discuss fire evacuation procedures. Discuss the safety equipment in the lab—how it works and when it is appropriate to use.

Discuss the list of safety symbols at the front of the textbook and go over the material in the Lab Handbook on pages R2–R13. The **Lab Binder** includes a safety quiz, as well as a safety contract, which students should sign and return before their first lab. Be certain students understand that they must report any incident of student injury or report any situation or condition that could lead to injury. Tell students that a positive attitude about safety is critical—they should be not be afraid to do an investigation, but they should recognize the potential for hazards where they exist.

Make sure you are aware of any medical problems or allergies that might cause problems for a student in conducting certain labs. You might want to have parents provide a card with such information, as well as their home and work phone numbers. Also think about any accommodations you will need to make for students with special needs.

Remind students why food and drink are not allowed in the lab. Explain that edible substances used in a lab must not be eaten or placed in their mouths. Stress the importance of washing their hands with soap and water after handling lab materials of any sort, and go over the proper handling and disposal of unused materials or lab wastes.

ON LAB DAY

Have just the supplies and equipment available that you need for the lab. Make sure all chemicals and solutions are clearly labeled and that the MSDS is on hand for each. Discuss with students any special safety concerns you have and also mention any special handling needed of unused or waste materials. Go over any questions students may have on the pre-lab assignment if you gave one.

Limit the size of the groups working on an activity to a number that can productively and safely work together. Give students a timetable for the lab period and outline your expectations. Be sure to allow sufficient time for students to perform the investigation, write down data and observations, and still have enough time left over for clean up.

Make sure students keep work stations from becoming cluttered; only materials needed for an investigation should be brought to the lab station. Model the behavior you want to see in your students, wearing gloves and goggles when you expect them to do so. Encourage students to ask questions if there is any part of a procedure they are uncertain about. Remind students that it is their responsibility to make sure the lab room is clean before they leave and that all equipment has been turned off and all supplies properly stored. Be sure that the storage room and lab room are locked when you leave.

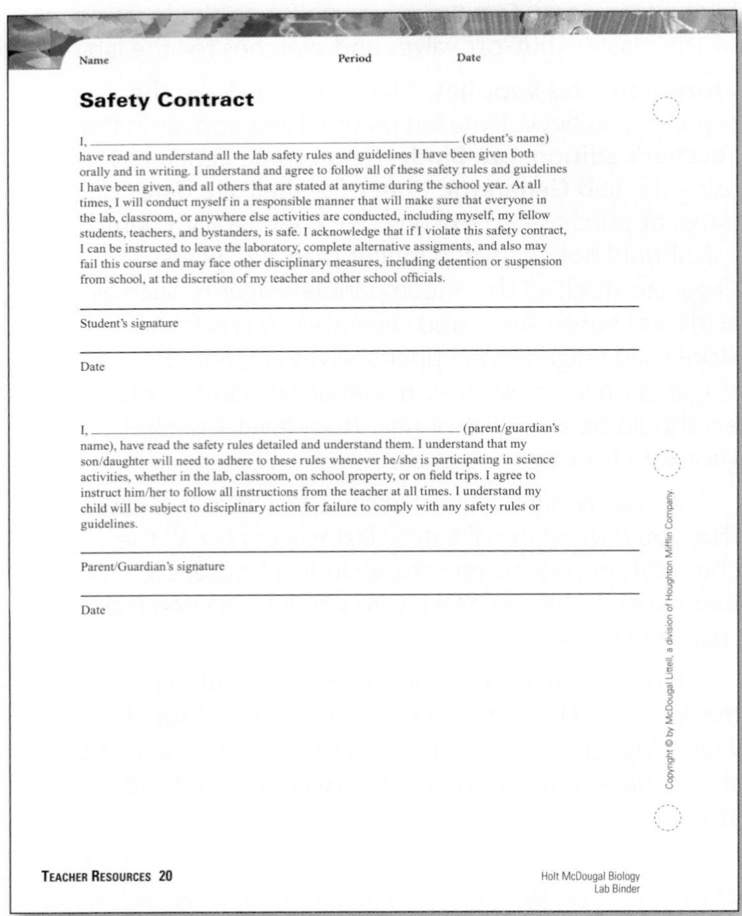

Name Period Date

Safety Contract

I, ______________________________ (student's name) have read and understand all the lab safety rules and guidelines I have been given both orally and in writing. I understand and agree to follow all of these safety rules and guidelines I have been given, and all others that are stated at anytime during the school year. At all times, I will conduct myself in a responsible manner that will make sure that everyone in the lab, classroom, or anywhere else activities are conducted, including myself, my fellow students, teachers, and bystanders, is safe. I acknowledge that if I violate this safety contract, I can be instructed to leave the laboratory, complete alternative assigments, and also may fail this course and may face other disciplinary measures, including detention or suspension from school, at the discretion of my teacher and other school officials.

____
Student's signature

____
Date

I, ______________________________ (parent/guardian's name), have read the safety rules detailed and understand them. I understand that my son/daughter will need to adhere to these rules whenever he/she is participating in science activities, whether in the lab, classroom, on school property, or on field trips. I agree to instruct him/her to follow all instructions from the teacher at all times. I understand my child will be subject to disciplinary action for failure to comply with any safety rules or guidelines.

____
Parent/Guardian's signature

____
Date

TEACHER RESOURCES 20 — Holt McDougal Biology Lab Binder

FIELD STUDY

If you plan to conduct any field work, be sure the activities fall within the school's guidelines for outside activities and additional supervision. Visit the site ahead of time to assess the potential for hazards and also to address any accommodations needed for special needs students.

Make sure all student permission forms are turned in the day before the trip. Go over assignments and protocols for the handling and use of equipment. Students should know what their responsibilities are and what you expect them to record in the way of data or observations. Warn students of any potential allergens at the site and tell students that they should not handle any animals or plants unless instructed to do so. Make sure to bring a first-aid kit.

WORKING WITH ORGANISMS

The Lab Binder for each unit of *Holt McDougal Biology* has specific instructions for working with organisms required for a given investigation. See the section entitled "Handling and Care of Organisms" for that unit. Also included is a reprint of the NSTA position statement "Animals: Responsible Use of Live Animals and Dissection in the Science Classroom."

Bacteria The NSTA now recommends that bacteria not be cultured in the classroom, given the risk of inadvertently culturing resistant bacteria along with the target bacteria.

Plants Make sure any plant material is stored and kept separate from other lab materials. Use store-bought plants, seeds, and soil. Farm products may be treated with fertilizer; wild plants may contain allergens. When possible, students should wear gloves when handling plants and always wash their hands thoroughly after handling them. Dead plants may be discarded in the trash as long as they have not been treated with chemicals that require special disposal.

Animals Live animals to be used in investigations should be kept separate from other lab materials and from students. Refer to federal, state, and local laws and regulations regarding the acquisition, handling, and care of animals. Future care or disposal of animals must be considered before making an acquisition. Remind students that animals used for an investigation must be handled in a humane way, with every effort made to minimize harm. Students should wear gloves and wash their hands thoroughly after handling the animals.

Consider student attitudes when planning a dissection. Students should see a clear purpose to the activity.

With the exception of human hair suggested for a forensic lab, no human fluids, tissues, or cells are used in the investigations in the *Holt McDougal Biology* program.

TEACHER-TESTED LABS 

The investigations included in the **Pupil Edition** of *Holt McDougal Biology* were tested by teachers in a classroom setting and revised based upon recommendations of those teachers. Still, it is important that you preview the labs to determine how well they will work for you in your classroom. In addition to the information provided in the **Teacher's Edition**, more information is available on the **Pupil Edition** investigations in the **Lab Binder** that accompanies the program. An editable version of each investigation is available in the **Lab Generator**.

The **Lab Binder** and **Lab Generator** also have additional labs, including forensic and probeware labs.

Lab Materials List

The following chart lists the materials for the Pupil Edition labs by unit. The labs are identified by type and chapter number, using the abbreviations QL (Quick Lab), CI (Chapter Investigation), and OI (Options for Inquiry). Full details of the materials needed for each lab is provided in the Holt McDougal Lab Binder. The Lab Binderalso includes a full complement of additional labs, including challege labs, virtual labs, and probeware labs. To create a customized materials list based on the actual labs you plan to perform, use the Holt McDougal Biology Lab Generator.

*Quantities are listed per group of four students. Lab aprons, safety goggles, water, books, paper, pens, pencils, metric rulers, scissors, calculators, and microscopes are assumed to be available for all labs.

Unit 1 Introducing Biology

MATERIAL	QUANTITY PER GROUP PER LAB*	LAB
CONSUMABLES		
marbles	4	CI-1
marker	1	CI-2, OI-2
marker, permanent	1	OI-1
tape, masking	10 cm	OI-1
newspaper	1	OI-1
string	1 m	OI-1
wooden sticks	3	OI-1
detergent	9 mL	CI-1
gelatin	1 box (teacher)	CI-1
lemon juice	5 mL	OI-2
mouthwash	5 mL	OI-2
vinegar	5 mL	OI-2
window cleaner	5 mL	OI-2
bean plants	3	OI-1
pond water	1 drop	QL-1
LAB CONSUMABLES		
pH indicator paper	6 strips	OI-2
pH buffer solution 3	1 bottle (teacher)	CI-2
pH buffer solution 4	1 bottle (teacher)	CI-1
pH buffer solution 5	1 bottle (teacher)	CI-2
pH buffer solution 7	1 bottle (teacher)	CI-1, CI-2
pH buffer solution 9	1 bottle (teacher)	CI-2
pH buffer solution 10	1 bottle (teacher)	CI-1
pH buffer solution 11	1 bottle (teacher)	CI-2
catalase	6 mL	CI-2
3% hydrogen peroxide solution	1 mL	CI-2
LAB EQUIPMENT		
eyedropper	1	QL-1
beaker, 250-mL	1	OI-1
graduated cylinder, 10-mL	up to 7	CI-1, CI-2, OI-2
graduated cylinder, 100-mL	4	CI-1
light source	1	OI-1
magnets	2	QL-2
microscope slide	1	QL-1
test tube	up to 6	CI-2, OI-2
test tube rack	1	OI-2
INTERNET ACCESS		
computer	1	OI-1, OI-2

Unit 2 Cells

MATERIAL	QUANTITY PER GROUP PER LAB*	LAB
CONSUMABLES		
balloon, round	up to 3	OI-3, QL-4, OI-4
beads	12	OI-3
cellophane (red, green, blue)	1 sheet	CI-4
erasers, different sizes	3	OI-3

hole punch	1	CI-4
marker	1	CI-3, OI-4
marker, permanent	1	OI-3
pipe cleaners, different colors	2	QL-3
rubber bands, varying sizes	1 box (teacher)	QL-3, CI-3, OI-4
string	1 m, 30 cm	OI-4, QL-4
tape, masking	10 cm	CI-3
baking soda	1/8 tsp	CI-4
beverages, varying sugar content	1, 2	OI-4, QL-4
celery piece	1	OI-3
chicken eggs	2	CI-3
cotton plugs	6	OI-4
cotton swabs	50	QL-3
cup, 12-oz plastic	2	CI-3
detergent	1 drop	CI-4
food coloring	1 package (teacher)	OI-4
food, sugar-based	1 package	OI-4
gelatin jigglers	5	OI-3
onion	1 (teacher)	OI-3
paper towels	1 roll (teacher)	OI-4, OI-5
plastic bottles,	up to 3	QL-4, OI-4
plastic knife	1	OI-5
plastic spoon	1	OI-5
plastic wrap	20 cm	CI-3
salt (NaCl)	4 g (teacher), 25 g	OI-5, CI-3
sandwich bags, resealable	2	OI-3
sponges, two colors	6 slices each	OI-3
stirrer, coffee	10	OI-3
straw, drinking	up to 5	QL-3, OI-3
sugar (glucose)	50 g	CI-3
vinegar	bottle	CI-3
yeast	1 package	OI-4, QL-4
Elodea leaf	1	OI-3
ivy leaves	3	CI-4
seeds	12	OI-4

LAB CONSUMABLES		
prepared slides		
normal cells	1	QL-5
cancerous cells	1	QL-5
human cheek cells	1	OI-3
onion root cells	1	CI-5
distilled water	up to 1 L	CI-3, OI-5
potassium hydroxide (KOH) powder	1.5 tsp	OI-4
methylene blue stain	1 dropper bottle	OI-3
agar	20 g (teacher)	OI-5
phenol	1 g (teacher)	OI-5
ethanol	100 mL (teacher)	OI-5
sodium hydroxide solution	100 mL	OI-5
LAB EQUIPMENT		
balance	1	CI-3, OI-4
beaker, 100-mL	up to 2	CI-4, OI-4
beaker, 250-mL	up to 2	QL-4, OI-5
beaker, 500-mL	1	CI-3
eyedropper	1	OI-3
forceps	1	CI-4
graduated cylinder, 100-mL	up to 2	QL-4, OI-4, OI-5
lamp, desk	1	CI-4
lamp, strong white light	1	CI-4
microscope coverslip	2	OI-3
microscope slide	2	OI-3
plastic syringe, 10 cc	1	CI-4
razor tool	1	OI-3
spatula	2	OI-4
stopwatch	1	CI-4
test tube	3	OI-4
timer	1	OI-5
INTERNET ACCESS		
computer	1	OI-5

Unit 3 Genetics

MATERIAL	QUANTITY PER GROUP PER LAB*	LAB
CONSUMABLES		
coins	2	QL-7
colored pencil, red	1	OI-9
colored pencil, yellow	1	OI-9
construction paper, 5 colors	1 set	OI-8
hook-and-loop tab, 2-cm piece	2	OI-6
index card	1	OI-6, QL-7
marker	1	OI-6, QL-7, OI-8
markers, colored	1 set	OI-6
pennies	2	OI-6
pipe cleaner, white	4	OI-6
ribbon	60 cm	OI-8
stapler	1	OI-8
tape, clear	up to 20 cm	QL-9, OI-9
tape, masking	up to 10 cm	OI-6, QL-7
yarn, 5-cm pieces	15	QL-9
aluminum foil	20 cm	CI-9
baking soda	30 g (teacher)	CI-9
detergent	5 mL	CI-8
food coloring, four colors	1 box (teacher)	CI-9
glycerol	10 mL	CI-9
isopropyl alcohol	10 mL	CI-8
meat tenderizer	3 g	CI-8
paper plate, white	4	OI-8
plastic soap dish (rectangular)	1	CI-9
raw wheat germ	10 g	CI-8
salt (NaCl)	8 g	CI-8
sandwich bags, resealable plastic	2	QL-8
sunscreen, different ratings	3	OI-8

LAB CONSUMABLES		
agarose	10 g (teacher)	CI-9
battery, 9-volt	5	CI-9
distilled water	125 mL	CI-8
foam tray	1	CI-9
UV beads	12	OI-8
LAB EQUIPMENT		
balance	1	CI-8
eyedropper	2	CI-8
glass stirring rod	1	CI-8
graduated cylinder, 10-mL	up to 4	CI-8, CI-9
graduated cylinder, 100-mL	2	CI-9
pipettes	5	CI-9
spatula	1	CI-8
test tube	up to 5	CI-8, CI-9
test tube rack	1	CI-8, CI-9
UV light box	1	OI-8
wires with alligator clips	2	CI-9

Unit 4 Evolution

MATERIAL	QUANTITY PER GROUP PER LAB*	LAB
CONSUMABLES		
bag	1	CI-10
construction paper, blue	1 sheet	CI-10
construction paper, green	1 sheet	CI-10
construction paper, orange	1 sheet	CI-10, CI-11
construction paper, red	1 sheet	CI-10, CI-11
construction paper, yellow	1 sheet	CI-10, CI-11
deck of cards	1	QL-11
envelope	1	CI-11
fabric	1	CI-10
graph paper	1 sheet	CI-12, OI-12
paper clip, ribbed large	15	OI-11
paper clip, small	10	OI-11
paper clip, smooth large	15	OI-11

pencils, colored	3	CI-12
pennies	10	CI-12
picture, cut into strips	1	QL-10
aluminum pie plate	1	OI-10
chopsticks	1 pair	OI-10
clothespins	1	OI-10
cup	1	OI-11
sunflower seeds	1/2 c	OI-10
tongs	1	OI-10
wood screw	1	OI-11
wooden block	1	OI-11
LAB EQUIPMENT		
forceps	1	OI-10
Petri dishes	4	OI-10
stopwatch	1	OI-10

Unit 5 Ecology

MATERIAL	QUANTITY PER GROUP PER LAB*	LAB
CONSUMABLES		
beads	16	QL-16
cardboard container	1	OI-15
containers	2	OI-13
craftstick	1	OI-16
erasers	500 (teacher)	QL-13
glass marking pencil	1	OI-14
graph paper	1 sheet	QL-14, OI-16
graph paper, 21 x 27 cm^2	1	CI-14
marker	1	CI-13, OI-15, CI-16, QL-16, OI-16
marker, permanent	1	OI-15
obituary section of a newspaper	1	QL-14
paper clips	600 (teacher)	QL-13
pencils, colored	1 set	OI-14
pencils	500 (teacher)	QL-13
plastic bag, large sealable	1	OI-13
plastic wrap, blue	60 cm	CI-13
plastic wrap, red	60 cm	CI-13
plastic wrap, yellow	60 cm	CI-13
rubber band, large	2	CI-15
shoebox	1	OI-16
stapler	1	OI-15
string	1 m	OI-16
tape, masking	up to 20 cm	CI-13, OI-15, QL-16, OI-16
baby food jar, with lid	3	OI-14
bowl, plastic	2	CI-15
cheesecloth	60-cm piece	CI-13
cup, paper, large	1	QL-16
cup, paper, medium	2	QL-16
cup, paper, small	4	QL-16
cup, plastic	up to 4	CI-13, OI-15, CI-16, OI-16
glass jar with lid	1	OI-13
plastic food wrap	1000-cm piece	CI-15
plastic fork	800 (teacher)	QL-13
plastic spoon	1000 (teacher)	QL-13
rice grains	400	CI-14
salt	400 mL	QL-16
toothpick	1	CI-14, OI-16
tray, plastic or aluminum	1	OI-15
wax paper	100-cm piece	CI-15
camera (optional)	1	OI-14
Elodea leaves	8 sprigs	CI-15
gravel	up to 2 c	CI-13, OI-13
household-plant liquid fertilizer	10 mL	CI-13

pond water	200 mL	OI-14
seedling, raddish	4	CI-13, CI-16
refrigerator access	1	OI-15
sample water and sedi-ment	500 mL	CI-15
sand	2 c, 2c	CI-13, OI-15
seed, lima bean	10	OI-15
seed, raddish	4 (teacher)	CI-16
seed, sunflower	5	OI-15
seed, wheatgrass	30	OI-15
soil, potting	up to 2 c	CI-13, OI-13, OI-15, OI-15
soil, potting, bag	20 lb	CI-16
terrarium plants	6	OI-13
LAB CONSUMABLES		
algal culture	5 mL	OI-14
ammonium sulfate	1 g (teacher)	OI-14
chlorine test strips	2	OI-16
copper test strips	2	OI-16
dissolved oxygen kits	1	CI-15
iron test strips	2	OI-16
nitrate test strips	2	OI-16
nitrite test strips	2	OI-16
pH strips	14 strips	CI-15
pH3 buffer solution	1 bottle (teacher)	CI-16
pH7 buffer solution	1 bottle (teacher)	CI-16
trisodium phosphate	1 g (teacher)	OI-14
LAB EQUIPMENT		
balance	1 (teacher)	OI-14
beaker, 250-mL	1	CI-16
beaker, 500-mL	1	QL-16
eyedropper	3	OI-14
graduated cylinder, 10-mL	1 (teacher)	OI-14
graduated cylinder, 50-mL	1	OI-14
graduated cylinder, 100-mL	2, 1, 2, 2	CI-13, OI-13, OI-15, OI-16
hand lens	1	OI-14
lamp	1	OI-15
light source	1	OI-13, OI-15
measuring cup	1	OI-13
quadrat	1	QL-13
stopwatch	1	QL-15
thermometer	2, 1, 2	CI-15, QL-15, OI-15

Unit 6 Classification and Diversity

MATERIAL	QUANTITY PER GROUP PER LAB*	LAB
CONSUMABLES		
clay	1 box of 4 colors	OI-18
marker	1 set	OI-18
marker, permanent	1	CI-18
paper, construction	1 package (teacher)	OI-18
paper, white	3 sheets, 1/2 sheet	OI-18, CI-19
pencil, colored	1 set	OI-17
pipe cleaner	1 bag	OI-18
tape, transparent	10 cm, 20 cm	CI-18, OI-18
6-oz yogurt	1 (teacher)	QL-18
cooking oil	2 mL	OI-18
drain cleaner, enzymatic, 3 types	2 mL each	OI-18
hairspray	1 bottle	CI-19
mushroom	1	CI-19
plastic bag, sealable	1	OI-19
plastic cup	1	CI-19
plastic knife	1	CI-19
toothpick	1, 12	QL-18, OI-18
water, spring	4 drops	QL-19
white bread	1 slice	OI-19

limpet shells (or photographs)	1 set	CI-17
straw, cut into pieces	1	OI-19
LAB CONSUMABLES		
0.02% tetrazolium indicator solution	2 mL	OI-18
agar	1 bottle (teacher)	CI-18
culture of Amoeba	1 drop	QL-19
culture of Euglena	1 drop	QL-19
M9 salts	1 bottle (teacher)	CI-18
methanol	100 mL (teacher)	CI-18
methylcellulose solution	3 drop	QL-19
nutrient agar/tryptic soy agar	1 bottle (teacher)	CI-18
LAB EQUIPMENT		
eyedropper	up to 4	QL-19, OI-19
graduated cylinders, 10-mL	3	OI-18
grid, clear plastic	1	OI-19
magnifying glass or dissecting scope	1	CI-19
microscope coverslip	up to 2	QL-18, QL-19
microscope slide	up to 3	QL-18, QL-19
Petri dish	2	CI-18
plastic dropper	5	OI-18
scale	1	OI-19
test tube rack	1	OI-18
test tubes, 10-mL, with caps	4	OI-18
INTERNET ACCESS		
computer	1	OI-17, OI-18

Unit 7 Plants

MATERIAL	QUANTITY PER GROUP PER LAB*	LAB
CONSUMABLES		
coin	1	OI-21
marker, waterproof	1	CI-22
paper clip	2	OI-21
pencil, colored	1 set	QL-22
tape, clear	5 cm	CI-21
apple	1 piece	OI-22
bananas, unripe	3	OI-22
clear fingernail polish	1 bottle	CI-21
container	1	CI-22
paper towel	1	CI-22, OI-22
pea pod	1	OI-22
peach	1 piece	OI-22
pear	1 piece	OI-22
plastic bag, large sealable	3	OI-22
spinach leaves	1 handful	QL-21
flower	1	QL-22
leaf, green	2	OI-21
leaf, red	1	OI-21
leaf, tree	1	CI-21
plant leaf, thick cuticle	1	CI-20
plant leaf, thin cuticle	1	CI-20
plant root, stem, root	1	OI-21
plant, flowering	1	OI-20
plant, herbacious	1	OI-20
plant, woody stem	1	OI-20
seeds, radish	14	CI-22
LAB CONSUMABLES		
prepared slides		
nonvascular plant tissue	1	QL-20
vascular plant tissue	1	QL-20

chromatography paper	2 strips	OI-21
filter paper	1 piece	QL-21
isopropyl alcohol	5 mL	OI-21
methanol	10 mL	QL-21
LAB EQUIPMENT		
graduated cylinder, 10-mL	1	QL-21, OI-21
beaker	1	QL-21
dissecting microscope	1	OI-20, OI-22
dissecting tray	1	OI-22
eyedropper	1	QL-21, OI-21
flashlight	1	QL-21
lamp, fluorescent	1	CI-22
forceps	1	CI-20, CI-22
funnel	1	QL-21
hand lens	1	CI-20, CI-22
eyedropper, large	1	CI-22
test tubes, large, with rubber stoppers	2	OI-21
magnifying glass	1	QL-22
microscope coverslips	up to 3	CI-20, OI-21
microscope slides	up to 3	CI-20, CI-21, OI-21
mortar	1	QL-21
pestle	1	QL-21
Petri dishes	2	CI-22
grid, plastic	2	CI-22
razor tool	1	CI-20, OI-21
scalpel	1	OI-22
test tube	1	QL-21
test tube rack	1	QL-21, OI-21
tweezers	1	QL-22, OI-22
INTERNET ACCESS		
computer	1	OI-20

Unit 8 Animals

MATERIAL	QUANTITY PER GROUP PER LAB*	LAB
CONSUMABLES		
bead, clear	100	CI-25
bead, colored	20	CI-25
graph paper	1	CI-25, CI-27
map, North America	1	OI-26
map, United States	1	OI-25
marker	1	OI-27
paper, dark-colored	1 sheet	OI-27
paper, light-colored	1 sheet	OI-27
pencil, colored	1 set	OI-25, OI-26
shoebox lid	1	OI-27
aluminum foil	up to 25 cm	CI-24, OI-27
baking soda	2 g	CI-24
bone, beef	1	CI-26
bone, chicken	1	CI-26
bone, duck or turkey	1	CI-26
bottle, clear plastic with lid	3	CI-24
chicken egg	1	OI-26
cotton swab	1	OI-24
cup, clear plastic	3	CI-24
large bowl	1	CI-25
paper towel	1 roll (teacher)	QL-23, OI-23, OI-24, OI-25, OI-26, OI-27
petroleum jelly	1 tube (teacher)	OI-24
plastic spoon	1	CI-24
sea salt	40 g (teacher)	CI-24

spring water	1000 mL	CI-24, OI-24
tissues	1 box	OI-24
toothpick	1	CI-23
vinegar	10 mL	CI-24
water, spring	1 bottle (teacher)	CI-23
wrap, clear plastic	20 cm	CI-24
hammer	1	CI-26
screwdriver	1	QL-23

LAB CONSUMABLES

prepared slides		
mite	1	QL-24
mosquito	1	QL-24
spider	1	QL-24
tick	1	QL-24
brine shrimp eggs	0.1 g	CI-24
clam specimen, preserved	1	QL-23
crayfish specimen, preserved	1	OI-24
culture of Daphnia magna	1 drop	CI-23
culture of Daphnia magna	1 drop	OI-24
culture of Hydra	1 drop	CI-23
feather, contour	1	QL-26
feather, down	1	QL-26
feather, quill	1	QL-26
frog embryo, tadpoles, preserved specimen	1 set	QL-25
perch, preserved	1	OI-25
pill bugs	12	OI-27
sea star specimen, preserved	1	OI-23
3% hydrogen peroxide	1 mL (teacher)	OI-24
filter paper disks	10	OI-23
hydrogen peroxide solution	1 drop	OI-24
pH duo-test paper	1 box	CI-24

LAB EQUIPMENT

balance	1	CI-24, CI-26
dissecting forceps	1	OI-26
dissecting microscope	1	OI-23, CI-23, CI-24, OI-24, QL-25
dissecting needle	1	OI-23, OI-24, OI-25, OI-26
dissecting pins	12	QL-23, OI-23, OI-24, OI-25
dissecting tray	1	QL-23, OI-23, OI-24, OI-25, OI-26
eyedropper	up to 5	OI-23, CI-24, OI-24
eyedropper, large	2	CI-23
fine scissors	1	OI-26
forceps	1	QL-23, OI-23, OI-24, OI-25
graduated cylinder, 10-mL	1	OI-27
graduated cylinder, 100-mL	1	CI-24, CI-26
hand lens	1	QL-23, CI-23, OI-23, OI-24, OI-25, CI-26
lamp	1	CI-24
light source	1	OI-27
microscope coverslip	1	OI-24
microscope slide	1	OI-24
Petri dish	up to 10	CI-23, OI-23, CI-24, QL-25
probe	1	QL-23
scalpel	1	QL-23, OI-25
spatula	1	QL-25
stopwatch	1	OI-24

INTERNET ACCESS		
computer	1	OI-27

Unit 9 Human Biology

MATERIAL	QUANTITY PER GROUP PER LAB*	LAB
CONSUMABLES		
glue stick	1	OI-31
marker	1	OI-30, CI-32, OI-32
marker, colored	1 set	OI-31, CI-34
tape	10 cm	CI-32, OI-32
tape, clear	15 cm	OI-30
white paper	1 sheet	OI-30, OI-31
antacid, 4 different types	1 box (per class)	OI-32
baking soda	1 g (teacher)	QL-31
beef jerky	4 pieces	CI-32
bottle, 1-liter	1	OI-30
construction paper	1 set	OI-31
cup, 8-oz paper	1	QL-31
cup, paper, large	4	QL-32, OI-32
cup, paper, small	1	OI-30
knife	1	OI-32
milk, lactose-free	20 drops	OI-32
milk, nonfat	20 drops	OI-32
paper towels	8	QL-32
pecans	4	CI-32
straw, bendable plastic	1 (per person)	OI-30
potato	4 pieces	CI-32
straw	4	CI-30
stirrer, coffee	2	OI-32
toothpicks	3	QL-29
white vinegar	100 mL	OI-32
CD player	1	OI-30
clock	1	CI-30, OI-30, CI-32
deck of cards	1	OI-29
jump rope	1	CI-28
soft blindfold/bandana	1	QL-29
stopwatch	1	CI-28, OI-29
tennis ball	1	CI-33
timer	1	QL-32, OI-32, CI-33
VCR player or DVD player	1	OI-30
videos, DVDs or CDs	1	OI-30
LAB CONSUMABLES		
prepared slides		
blood cells	1	OI-28, QL-30, OI-33
liver tissue	1	CI-31
liver tissue, cirrhosis	1	CI-31
lung tissue	1	CI-31
lung, cancereous tissue	1	CI-31
lymph tissue	1	CI-31
lymph tissue, diseased	1	CI-31
mammalian egg cells	1	QL-34
mammalian sperm cells	1	QL-34
nerve cells	1	OI-28
red blood cells	1	CI-31
red blood cells, anemic	1	CI-31
sea star blastula	1	O-34
sea star embryo, early cleavage	1	OI-34
sea star embryo, late cleavage	1	OI-34
sea star gastrula	1	OI-34
skeletal muscle	1	OI-28, OI-33
smooth muscle	1	OI-33
tendon tissue	1	OI-33
ligament tissue	1	OI-33

skin cells	1	OI-33
stomach tissue	1	CI-31
stomach tissue, ulcerous	1	CI-31
0.4% NaOH solution	50 mL	CI-30
1% hydocholoric acid solution	80 mL	CI-32
bromothymol blue	10 mL	CI-30
glucose test strips	4	OI-32
lactase	2 drops	OI-32
model skull	1	QL-33
pepsin	80 mL	CI-32
pH test strips	8	OI-32
phenolphthalein	3 drops	QL-31

LAB EQUIPMENT

balance	1	CI-32
beaker, 100-mL	4	CI-32
beaker, 250-mL	1	CI-30
eyedropper	up to 2	CI-30, QL-31, OI-
graduated cylinder, 50-mL	1	OI-32
graduated cylinder, 100-mL	up to 3	CI-30, CI-32
mortar and pestle	1	OI-32
scale	1	OI-32
test tubes	2	OI-32
thermometer	1	CI-32

INTERNET ACCESS

computer	1	OI-28, OI-29, OI-31, OI-34

HOLT McDOUGAL

Indiana

Biology

Stephen Nowicki

HOLT McDOUGAL

HOUGHTON MIFFLIN HARCOURT

Acknowledgments for Covers
Front cover and Title Page *caiman in shell* © Ingo Arndt/naturepl.com; *red blood cells* © William Fowle/Electron Microscopy Center, Northeastern University; *all others* © Getty Images; **Back cover** © Nick Greaves/Bruce Coleman Inc./Alamy Images.

2012 Edition

Printed in the U.S.A.

ISBN 13: 978-0-547-41443-0

1 2 3 4 5 6 7 8 9 10 0868 19 18 17 16 15 14 13 12 11 10

4500237636 ^ B C D E F G

© Jim Wallace/Duke University Photography

Stephen Nowicki, Ph.D.

Stephen Nowicki grew up with a strong interest in music and at one time wanted to be a classical musician. A biology course in college sparked his excitement for biology, leading him to major in both biology and music. Nowicki obtained his bachelor's and master's degrees from Tufts University. He received his doctorate in neurobiology and behavior from Cornell University in 1985.

Nowicki is now Dean of the Natural Sciences, as well as Bass Fellow and Professor in the departments of Biology, Psychology, and Neurobiology at Duke University. He has taught at Duke since 1989, where he directed a complete redesign of the introductory biology program. Nowicki's research interests center on animal behavior and how communication systems evolve. His work combines both field studies and laboratory experiments. He uses birdsong as a model system and studies topics such as the structure, function, and evolution of animal communication systems. In the past, Nowicki and his students have studied behavior in a wide variety of organisms, including insects, lobsters, lizards, squirrels, and primates.

Nowicki's research has been published in more than 70 articles in scientific journals, including *Science, Nature,* and *Animal Behavior.* He also coauthored the book *The Evolution of Animal Communication: Reliability and Deception in Signaling Systems.* In addition, he is the author of a video lecture series based on the introductory biology course he taught at Duke. He serves regularly on proposal review panels for the National Science Foundation.

Outside of his professional interests, Nowicki enjoys music. He has played the trombone since the fourth grade, and played for two seasons with the Duke University Pep Band at basketball games. Juggling and cooking are other hobbies that Nowicki enjoys in his free time. Nowicki is married to Susan Peters, who also studies animal communication, and they have one son, Schuyler. Nowicki and his family live in Durham, North Carolina.

IN3

Content Reviewers

Mark Baustian, Ph.D.
President
West Hill Biological Resources
Spencer, NY

John Beaver, Ph.D.
Professor Emeritus
College of Education and Human Services
Western Illinois University
Macomb, IL

Elizabeth A. De Stasio, Ph.D.
Associate Professor and Raymond H. Herzog Professor of Science
Department of Biology
Lawrence University
Appleton, WI

Dan Franck, Ph.D.
Botany Education Consultant
Chatham, NY

Linda Graham, Ph.D.
Professor of Botany
Department of Botany
University of Wisconsin
Madison, WI

David Harbster, M.A. in Biology Education
Professor of Biology
Paradise Valley Community College
Phoenix, AZ

C. Leon Harris, Ph.D.
Professor Emeritus
Department of Biological Sciences
State University of New York at Plattsburgh
Plattsburgh, NY

Anthony Ippolito, Ph.D.
Visiting Assistant Professor
Department of Biological Sciences
DePaul University
Chicago, IL

Sönke Johnsen, Ph.D.
Assistant Professor
Department of Biology
Duke University
Durham, NC

Paula Lemons, Ph.D.
Assistant Professor of the Practice
Department of Biology
Duke University
Durham, NC

Lori Marino, Ph.D.
Senior Lecturer
Neuroscience and Behavioral Biology Program
Emory University
Atlanta, GA

Louise McCullough, M.D./Ph.D.
Director of Stroke Research
Department of Neurology
University of Connecticut Health Center
Farmington, CT

Elizabeth Panter, R.D.
Dietitian
Clinical Nutrition Department
Johns Hopkins Bayview Medical Center
Baltimore, MD

Sheila Patek, Ph.D.
Assistant Professor
Department of Integrative Biology
University of California
Berkeley, CA

Adam Savage, B.S., M.F.A.
Science Consultant
Chicago, IL

F. Daniel Vogt, Ph.D.
Professor
Department of Biological Sciences
State University of New York at Plattsburgh
Plattsburgh, NY

Jerry Waldvogel, Ph.D.
Associate Professor
Department of Biological Sciences
Clemson University
Clemson, SC

Safety Reviewer

Juliana Texley, Ph.D.
Former K–12 Science Teacher and School Superintendent
Boca Raton, FL

Program Consultant

Laine Gurley, Ph.D.
Biology Teacher
Rolling Meadows High School
Rolling Meadows, IL

IN4

Indiana Teacher Reviewers

Marva Moore
Hamilton Southeastern High School
Fishers, IN

David Dowell
Carmel, IN

Jan Carroll Weir
Science Department Chairman
Indianapolis, IN

Roberta C. Harnish
Crown Point, IN

Teacher Reviewers and Lab Evaluators

Elaine Armstrong
Battle Ground High School
Battle Ground, WA

Amy Bell
Arcadia High School
Phoenix, AZ

Jerry Bell
Desert Vista High School
Phoenix, AZ

Bonnie Brenner
Niles West High School
Niles, IL

Shirley Bryant
Granada Hills Charter High School
Granada Hills, CA

Jason Campbell
Schaumburg High School
Schaumburg, IL

Christopher Dignam
Lane Tech High School
Chicago, IL

Jennifer Ellberg
Maine West High School
Des Plaines, IL

Charles Ellwood
Pebblebrook High School
Mableton, GA

Barry Feldman
Corona del Sol High School
Tempe, AZ

Gerry Foster
Desert Vista High School
Phoenix, AZ

Riley Greenwood
Valley Center High School
Valley Center, KS

Michelle Hadden
La Joya High School
Avondale, AZ

Randy Hein
Floyd Central High School
Floyds Knobs, IN

Stephen Hobbs
Seton Catholic High School
Chandler, AZ

Janet Jones
Sullivan High School
Chicago, IL

Karen Klafeta
Morton East High School
Cicero, IL

Robert Kolenda
Neshaminy High School
Langhorne, PA

Tina Lanquist
Moorpark High School
Moorpark, CA

Michael McDowell
Napa New Technology High School
Napa, CA

Wanda Miller
Martinsburg High School
Martinsburg, WV

Birgit Musheno
Desert Vista High School
Phoenix, AZ

Kenneth Nealy
Windsor Public Schools
Windsor, CT

Lonnie Newton
Arvada West Senior High
Arvada, CO

Palak Patel
Wheaton North High School
Wheaton, IL

Heather Pereira
Amador Valley High School
Pleasanton, CA

Yvonne Perry
Douglas County High School
Douglasville, GA

Tracy Rader
Fulton Jr-Sr High School
Indianapolis, IN

Kathey Roberts
Lakeside High School
Hot Springs, AR

Cassandra Ross
Redan High School
Stone Mountain, GA

Lori Ruter
Lake Norman High School
Mooresville, NC

James Rutkowski
Erie School District
Erie, PA

Sara Sagmeister
Maine South High School
Park Ridge, IL

Jackie Snow
Lee's Summit North High School
Lee's Summit, MO

Laura Spitznogle
Williamsville East High School
East Amherst, NY

George Wandiko
Rialto High School
Rialto, CA

Jason Wikman
Charlotte High School
Punta Gorda, FL

IN5

Indiana

Overview of Indiana Student Edition

Indiana Table of Contents IN8

Indiana Student Guide IN35

Overview of Indiana Standards IN36

INDIANA STANDARDS

Look for the Indiana Standards symbol throughout the book. It tells you which standards are covered in each section.

©Alexey Stiop/Alamy

Contents in Brief

Unit 1 Introducing Biology 1

1 Biology in the 21st Century
2 Chemistry of Life

Unit 2 Cells 67

3 Cell Structure and Function
4 Cells and Energy
5 Cell Growth and Division

Unit 3 Genetics 165

6 Meiosis and Mendel
7 Extending Mendelian Genetics
8 From DNA to Proteins
9 Frontiers of Biotechnology

Unit 4 Evolution 295

10 Principles of Evolution
11 The Evolution of Populations
12 The History of Life

Unit 5 Ecology 393

13 Principles of Ecology
14 Interactions in Ecosystems
15 The Biosphere
16 Human Impact on Ecosystems

Unit 6 Classification and Diversity 515

17 The Tree of Life
18 Viruses and Prokaryotes
19 Protists and Fungi

Unit 7 Plants 609

20 Plant Diversity
21 Plant Structure and Function
22 Plant Growth, Reproduction, and Response

Unit 8 Animals 693

23 Invertebrate Diversity
24 A Closer Look at Arthropods
25 Vertebrate Diversity
26 A Closer Look at Amniotes
27 Animal Behavior

Unit 9 Human Biology 849

28 Human Systems and Homeostasis
29 Nervous and Endocrine Systems
30 Respiratory and Circulatory Systems
31 Immune System and Disease
32 Digestive and Excretory Systems
33 Protection, Support, and Movement
34 Reproduction and Development

UNIT 1

Introducing Biology

INDIANA

Unit Focus

Unit 1 gives you a general understanding of what modern biology is all about and reviews and explains the chemistry of living systems. You will explore scientific thinking, methods, equipment, and experimentation.

Chapter 1 Biology in the 21st Century 2

	1.1	The Study of Life	4
	1.2	Unifying Themes of Biology	7
		DATA ANALYSIS *Qualitative and Quantitative*	12
NOS.8, NOS.9	1.3	Scientific Thinking and Processes	13
NOS.10	1.4	Biologists' Tools and Technology	19
NOS.11	1.5	Biology and Your Future	24
QUICK LAB		Life Under a Microscope	22
INVESTIGATION		Manipulating Independent Variables	18
OPTIONS FOR INQUIRY		Lab: Manipulating Plant Growth	28
		Lab: Biology in the News	29
		Online: Animated BIOLOGY, WebQuest, Data Analysis	29
INDIANA		ISTEP+ Test Prep *B.1.3, B.8.5, NOS.1, NOS.4, NOS.6*	33

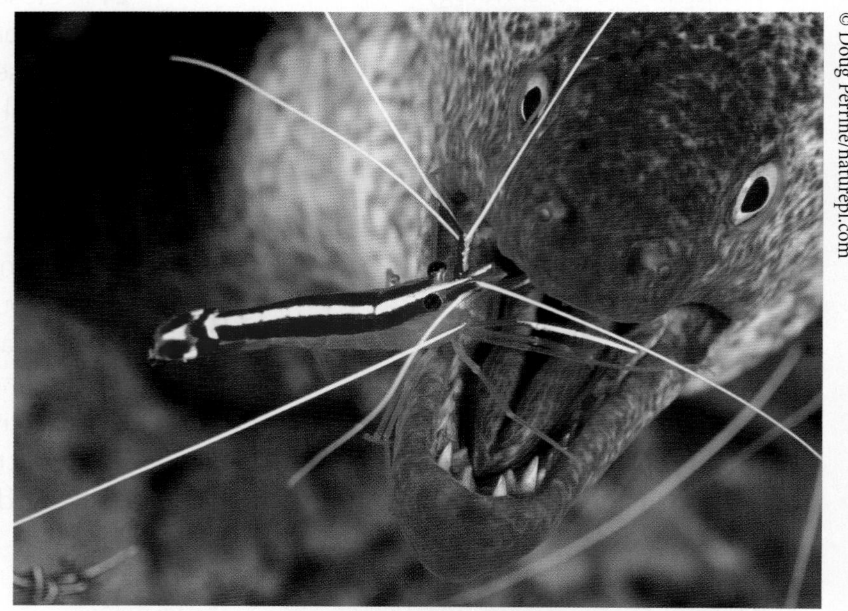

Moray eel and cleaner shrimp, *p. 7*

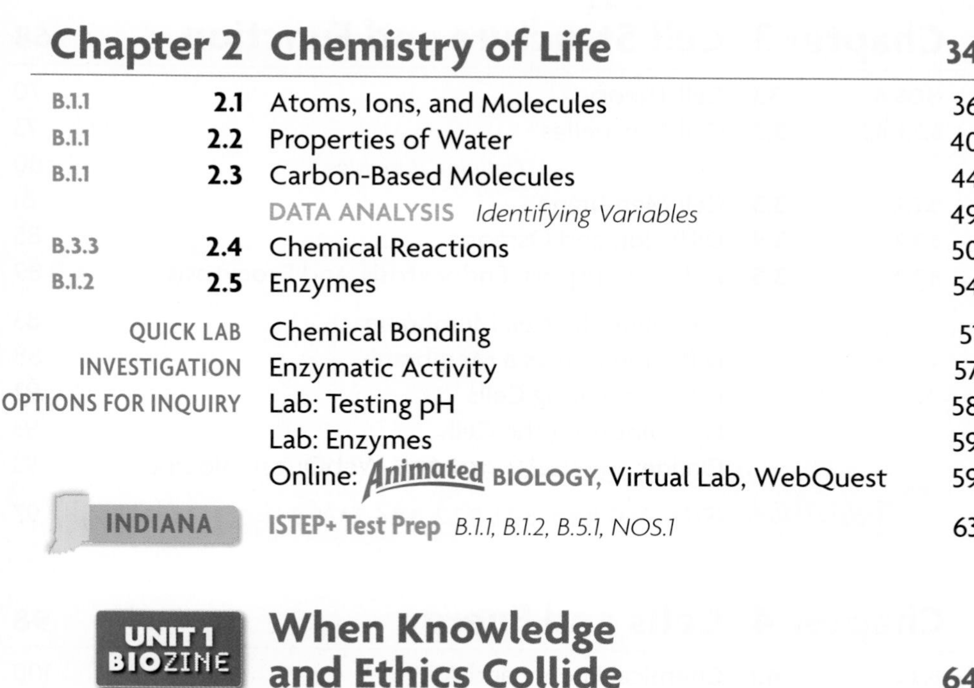

Chapter 2 Chemistry of Life 34

B.1.1 **2.1** Atoms, Ions, and Molecules 36
B.1.1 **2.2** Properties of Water 40
B.1.1 **2.3** Carbon-Based Molecules 44
DATA ANALYSIS *Identifying Variables* 49
B.3.3 **2.4** Chemical Reactions 50
B.1.2 **2.5** Enzymes 54

QUICK LAB Chemical Bonding 51
INVESTIGATION Enzymatic Activity 57
OPTIONS FOR INQUIRY Lab: Testing pH 58
Lab: Enzymes 59
Online: Animated BIOLOGY, Virtual Lab, WebQuest 59

INDIANA **ISTEP+ Test Prep** *B.1.1, B.1.2, B.5.1, NOS.1* 63

UNIT 1 BIOZINE **When Knowledge and Ethics Collide** 64

Technology Genetic Testing
Careers Geneticist

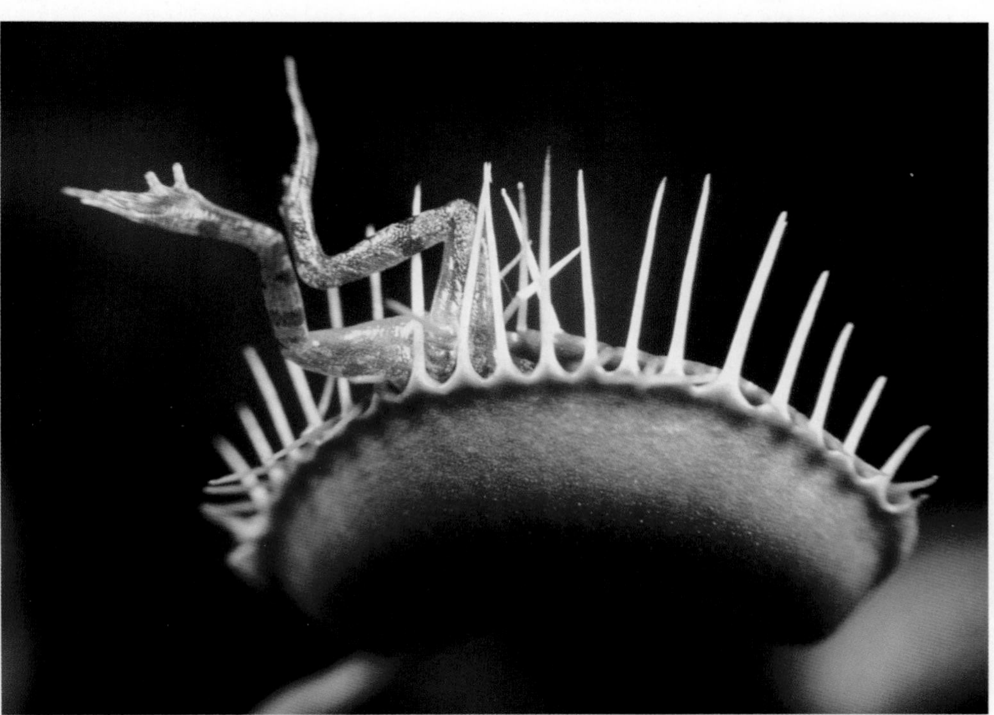

Venus flytrap and frog, *pp. 34–35*

© OSF/Photolibrary.com

CLASSZONE.COM

VIRTUAL LAB

Chapter 2 Calorimetry

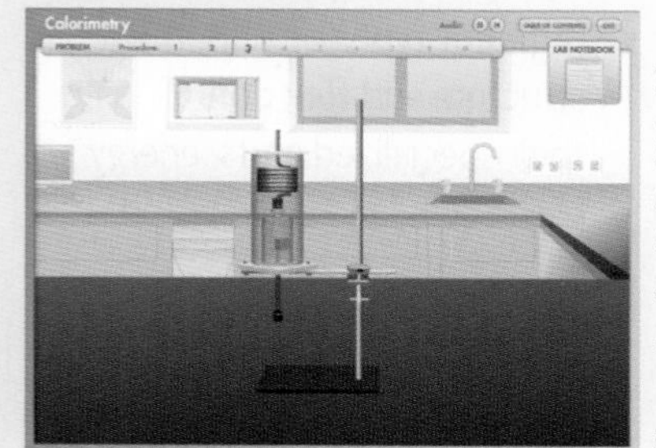

Illustration by Six Red Marbles

Animated BIOLOGY

Chapter 1 Cells Through Different Microscopes, Experimental Design

Chapter 2 Hydrogen Bonding, Energy and Chemical Reactions, Atoms and Bonding

WEBQUEST

Chapter 1 Bioethics

Chapter 2 Prions and Public Health

Interactive Review

REVIEW Key Concepts, Vocabulary Games, Concept Maps, Animated Biology, Online Quiz

BIOZINE

INTERNET MAGAZINE

Explore today's world of biology online at ClassZone.com.

UNIT 2

INDIANA

Cells

Unit Focus

In Unit 2, you will learn about different types of cells, the structure and function of their specialized parts, energy use in cells, and cell division.

Chapter 3 Cell Structure and Function 68

NOS.8	3.1	Cell Theory	70
B.2.1, B.2.4	3.2	Cell Organelles	73
		DATA ANALYSIS *Defining Variables*	80
B.2.2	3.3	Cell Membrane	81
B.2.2	3.4	Diffusion and Osmosis	85
B.2.2	3.5	Active Transport, Endocytosis, and Exocytosis	89
QUICK LAB		Modeling the Cell Membrane	83
INVESTIGATION		Diffusion Across a Membrane	88
OPTIONS FOR INQUIRY		Lab: Comparing Cells	92
		Lab: Modeling the Cell	93
		Online: Animated BIOLOGY, WebQuest, BioZine	93
INDIANA		ISTEP+ Test Prep *B.2.1, B.2.2, B.2.6, NOS.8*	97

Chapter 4 Cells and Energy 98

B.3.2	4.1	Chemical Energy and ATP	100
B.3.1	4.2	Overview of Photosynthesis	103
B.3.1	4.3	Photosynthesis in Detail	108
B.3.2	4.4	Overview of Cellular Respiration	113
		DATA ANALYSIS *Interpreting Graphs*	116
B.3.2	4.5	Cellular Respiration in Detail	117
B.3.3	4.6	Fermentation	122
QUICK LAB		Fermentation	124
INVESTIGATION		Rates of Photosynthesis	106
OPTIONS FOR INQUIRY		Lab: Cellular Respiration	126
		Lab: Investigating Fermentation in Foods	127
		Online: Animated BIOLOGY, Virtual Lab, WebQuest	127
INDIANA		ISTEP+ Test Prep *B.2.3, B.3.1, B.3.2, B.3.4*	131

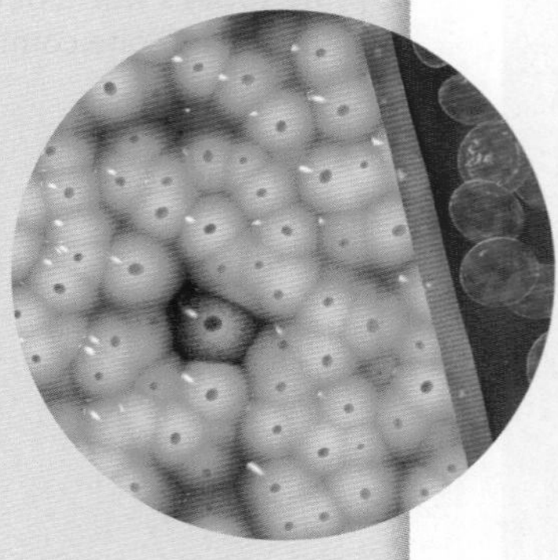

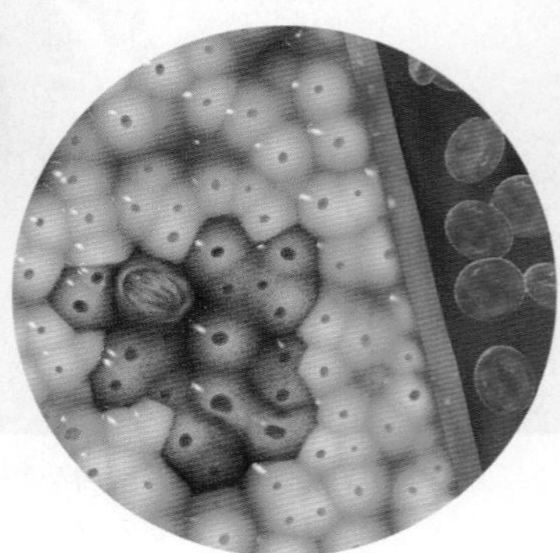

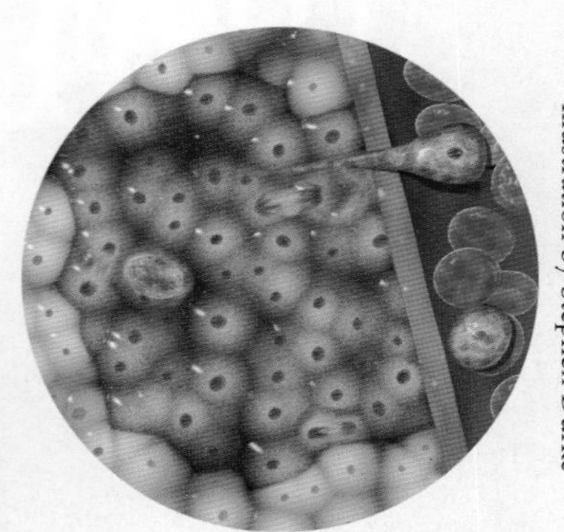

Illustration by Stephen Durke

Cancer cells, *p. 146*

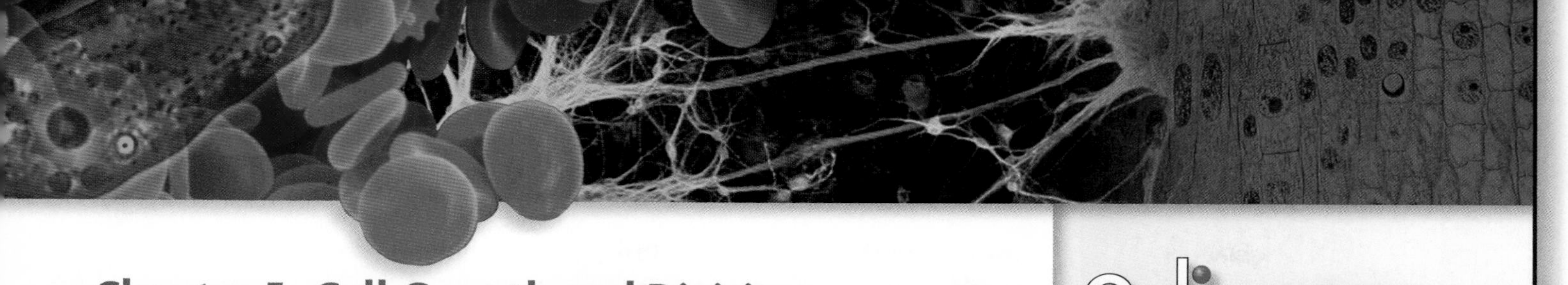

Chapter 5 Cell Growth and Division 132

B.6.1	5.1	The Cell Cycle	134
B.6.1	5.2	Mitosis and Cytokinesis	138
		DATA ANALYSIS *Constructing Data Tables*	142
	5.3	Regulation of the Cell Cycle	144
	5.4	Asexual Reproduction	148
B.6.2	5.5	Multicellular Life	151

QUICK LAB	Cancer	147
INVESTIGATION	Mitosis in Onion Root Cells	143
OPTIONS FOR INQUIRY	Lab: Modeling Cell Surface-Area-to-Volume Ratio	156
	Lab: Apoptosis	157
	Online: Animated BIOLOGY, Virtual Lab, WebQuest	157
INDIANA	ISTEP+ Test Prep *B.6.1, B.6.2, B.6.3, NOS.1*	161

UNIT 2 BIOZINE

Stem Cell Research—Potential Solutions, Practical Challenges 162

Technology Somatic Cell Nuclear Transfer
Careers Cell Biologist

Vesicles in a cell, *p. 77*

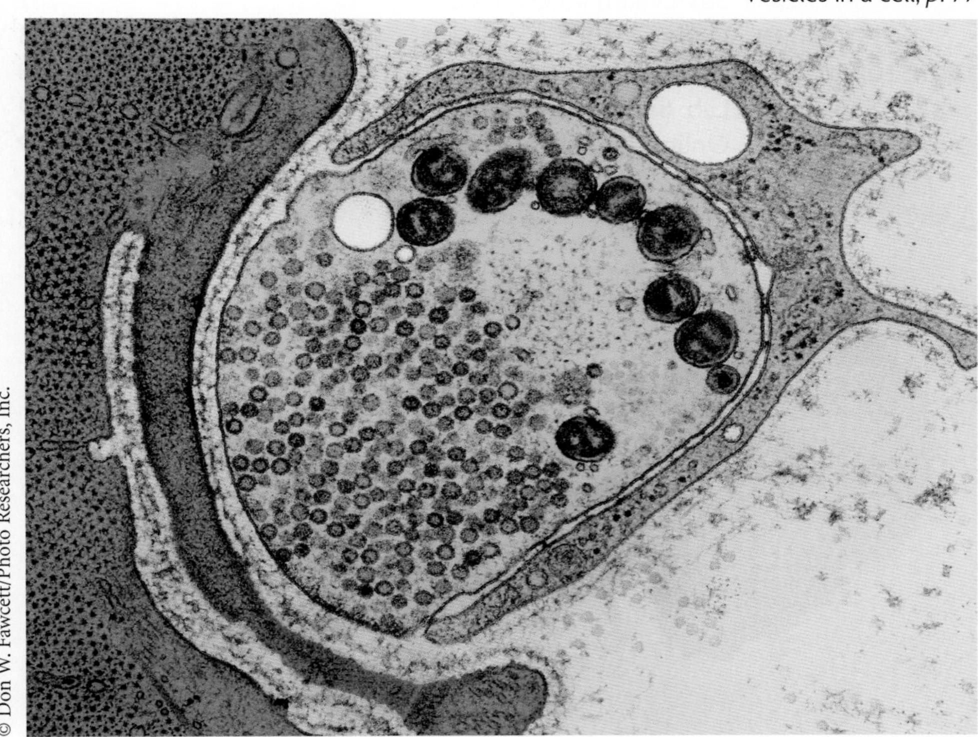

CLASSZONE.COM

VIRTUAL LAB

Chapter 4 Carbon Dioxide Transfer Through Snails and Elodea

Chapter 5 Investigating Bacterial Growth

Animated BIOLOGY

Chapter 3 Cell Organelles, Get Through a Cell Membrane

Chapter 4 Photosynthesis, Cellular Respiration, Mirror Processes

Chapter 5 Mitosis, Binary Fission, Mitosis Stage Matching Game

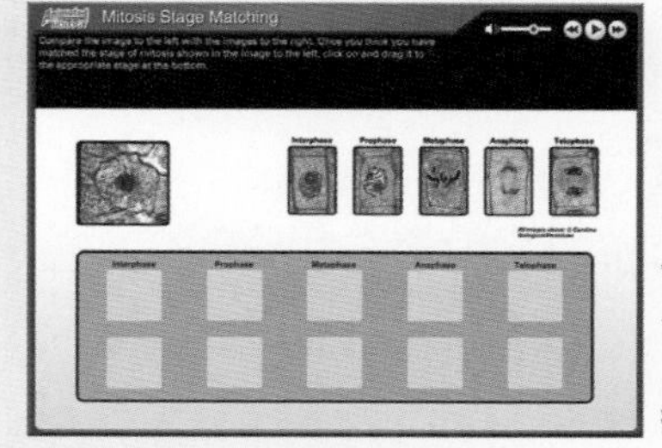

WEBQUEST

Chapter 3 Organelle Dysfunction

Chapter 4 Energy and Athletic Training

Chapter 5 Skin Cancer

Interactive Review

REVIEW Key Concepts, Vocabulary Games, Concept Maps, Animated Biology, Online Quiz

BIOZINE

INTERNET MAGAZINE

Explore today's world of biology online at ClassZone.com.

UNIT 3

INDIANA

Genetics

Unit Focus

In Unit 3, you will learn about sources of genetic variation, how the genetic makeup of an individual is determined, how the genetic code is eventually translated into proteins, and how biotechnology can change an organism's DNA.

Chapter 6 Meiosis and Mendel 166

B.6.4	6.1	Chromosomes and Meiosis	168
		DATA ANALYSIS *Interpreting Bar Graphs*	172
B.6.4	6.2	Process of Meiosis	173
B.5.2	6.3	Mendel and Heredity	177
B.5.2	6.4	Traits, Genes, and Alleles	180
B.7.1, B.7.3	6.5	Traits and Probability	183
B.6.5	6.6	Meiosis and Genetic Variation	189
	QUICK LAB	Using a Testcross to Determine Genotype	185
	INVESTIGATION	Allele Combinations and Punnett Squares	188
	OPTIONS FOR INQUIRY	Lab: Modeling Meiosis	192
		Lab: Probability Practice	193
		Online: Animated BIOLOGY, Virtual Lab, WebQuest	193
	INDIANA	ISTEP+ Test Prep *B.5.2, B.6.5*	197

Chapter 7 Extending Mendelian Genetics 198

B.7.2	7.1	Chromosomes and Phenotype	200
B.7.2	7.2	Complex Patterns of Inheritance	204
B.5.2	7.3	Gene Linkage and Mapping	209
		DATA ANALYSIS *Constructing Bar Graphs*	210
B.7.3	7.4	Human Genetics and Pedigrees	212
	QUICK LAB	Sex-Linked Inheritance	202
	INVESTIGATION	Codominance	208
	OPTIONS FOR INQUIRY	Lab: Pedigree Analysis	218
		Lab: Incomplete Dominance	219
		Online: Animated BIOLOGY, WebQuest, Data Analysis	219
	INDIANA	ISTEP+ Test Prep *B.6.5, B.7.1, B.7.2*	223

Royal blue and green betta fish, *p. 205*

Photos by Atison Phumchoosri

IN12

Chapter 8 From DNA to Proteins 224

NOS.9	8.1	Identifying DNA as the Genetic Material	226
B.5.1	8.2	Structure of DNA	230
		DATA ANALYSIS *Interpreting Histograms*	234
B.7.4	8.3	DNA Replication	235
B.5.3	8.4	Transcription	239
B.5.3	8.5	Translation	243
B.6.2	8.6	Gene Expression and Regulation	248
B.7.5	8.7	Mutations	252
	QUICK LAB	Replication	238
	INVESTIGATION	Extracting DNA	229
	OPTIONS FOR INQUIRY	Lab: UV Light and Skin Cancer	256
		Lab: Modeling Transcription	257
		Online: Animated BIOLOGY, WebQuest, Data Analysis	257
	INDIANA	ISTEP+ Test Prep *B.5.3, B.5.4, NOS.2*	261

Chapter 9 Frontiers of Biotechnology 262

	9.1	Manipulating DNA	264
	9.2	Copying DNA	269
	9.3	DNA Fingerprinting	272
B.7.5	9.4	Genetic Engineering	275
NOS.10	9.5	Genomics and Bioinformatics	280
		DATA ANALYSIS *Constructing Histograms*	282
	9.6	Genetic Screening and Gene Therapy	284
	QUICK LAB	Modeling Plasmids and Restriction Enzymes	278
	INVESTIGATION	Modeling Forensics	268
	OPTIONS FOR INQUIRY	Lab: Modeling Genetic Engineering	286
		Lab: Genetic Screening	287
		Online: Animated BIOLOGY, Virtual Lab, WebQuest	287
	INDIANA	ISTEP+ Test Prep *B.5.2, B.7.2, B.7.5, NOS.1*	291

UNIT 3 BIOZINE Medical Technology—The Genetic Forefront 292

Technology Biochips
Careers Cancer Geneticist

CLASSZONE.COM

VIRTUAL LAB

Chapter 6 Breeding Mutations in Fruit Flies

Chapter 9 Gel Electrophoresis, Bacterial Transformation

Animated BIOLOGY

Chapter 6 Meiosis, Genotypes and Phenotypes, Mendel's Experiment

Chapter 7 Human Chromosomes, Tracking Traits

Chapter 8 DNA Replication, Build a Protein

Chapter 9 Restriction Enzymes, Polymerase Chain Reaction

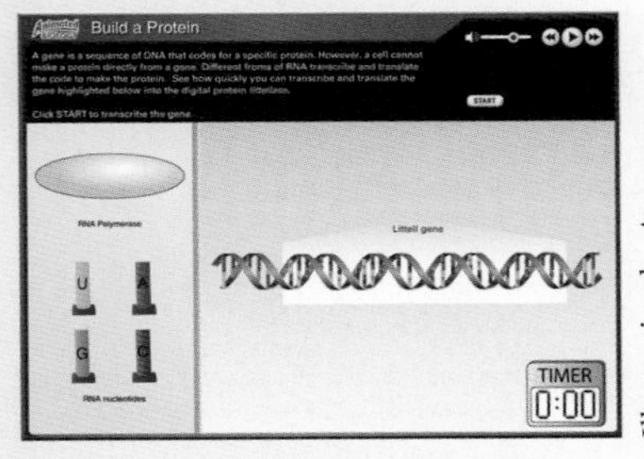

Illustration by Argosy

WEBQUEST

Chapter 6 Selective Breeding

Chapter 7 Genetic Heritage

Chapter 8 Transgenic Organisms

Chapter 9 Animal Cloning

Interactive Review

REVIEW Key Concepts, Vocabulary Games, Concept Maps, Animated Biology, Online Quiz

BIOZINE

INTERNET MAGAZINE

Explore today's world of biology online at ClassZone.com.

UNIT 4

INDIANA

Unit Focus

The focus of Unit 4 includes the basic principles of evolution and natural selection, how populations evolve, and the history of life on Earth.

Evolution

Chapter 10 Principles of Evolution 296

NOS.9	10.1	Early Ideas About Evolution	298
B.8.5	10.2	Darwin's Observations	302
B.8.5	10.3	Theory of Natural Selection	304
		DATA ANALYSIS *Interpreting Line Graphs*	308
B.8.7	10.4	Evidence of Evolution	310
B.8.7	10.5	Evolutionary Biology Today	316
QUICK LAB		Piecing Together Evidence	313
INVESTIGATION		Predator-Prey Pursuit	315
OPTIONS FOR INQUIRY		Lab: Using Patterns to Make Predictions	320
		Lab: Adaptations in Beaks	321
		Online: Animated BIOLOGY, WebQuest, Data Analysis	321
INDIANA		**ISTEP+ Test Prep** *B.8.1, B.8.5, B.8.6*	325

Chapter 11 The Evolution of Populations 326

B.8.6	11.1	Genetic Variation Within Populations	328
B.8.5	11.2	Natural Selection in Populations	330
	11.3	Other Mechanisms of Evolution	335
		DATA ANALYSIS *Identifying Patterns*	339
	11.4	Hardy-Weinberg Equilibrium	340
	11.5	Speciation Through Isolation	344
	11.6	Patterns in Evolution	347
QUICK LAB		Genetic Drift	337
INVESTIGATION		Natural Selection in African Swallowtails	334
OPTIONS FOR INQUIRY		Lab: Investigating an Anole Lizard Population	352
		Lab: Exploring Adaptations	353
		Online: Animated BIOLOGY, WebQuest, Data Analysis	353
INDIANA		**ISTEP+ Test Prep** *B.8.5, B.8.6*	357

Chapter 12 The History of Life 358

B.8.7 **12.1** The Fossil Record 360
B.8.7 **12.2** The Geologic Time Scale 365
B.8.7 **12.3** Origin of Life 368
B.8.7 **12.4** Early Single-Celled Organisms 372
DATA ANALYSIS *Calculating Axes Intervals* 375
B.8.7 **12.5** Radiation of Multicellular Life 376
B.8.7 **12.6** Primate Evolution 379

QUICK LAB Geologic Clock 381
INVESTIGATION Radioactive Decay 364
OPTIONS FOR INQUIRY Lab: Stride Inferences 384
Lab: Understanding Geologic Time 385
Online: Animated BIOLOGY, Virtual Lab, WebQuest 385

INDIANA ISTEP+ Test Prep *B.8.7, NOS.1, NOS.2, NOS.6* 389

UNIT 4 BIOZINE **Drug-Resistant Bacteria— A Global Health Issue** 390

Technology New Drug Delivery System
Careers Evolutionary Biologist

© Michael & Patricia Fodgen/Corbis

Tarsiers, *p. 379*

Online BIOLOGY
CLASSZONE.COM

VIRTUAL LAB
Chapter 12 Comparing Hominoid Skulls

Animated BIOLOGY
Chapter 10 Natural Selection Principles, Simulate Natural Selection
Chapter 11 Mechanisms of Evolution, Founder Effect, Evolutionary Arms Race
Chapter 12 Endosymbiosis, Geologic Time Scale

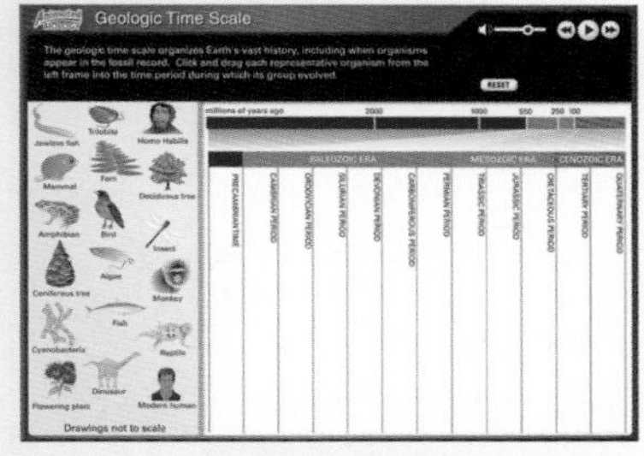

Illustration by Argosy

WEBQUEST
Chapter 10 Dinosaur Descendants
Chapter 11 Speciation in Action
Chapter 12 Geologic Dating

Interactive Review
REVIEW Key Concepts, Vocabulary Games, Concept Maps, Animated Biology, Online Quiz

BIOZINE
INTERNET MAGAZINE
Explore today's world of biology online at ClassZone.com.

UNIT 5

INDIANA

Ecology

Unit Focus

In Unit 5, ecology is defined as the study of interactions among living and nonliving things in an ecosystem. You will learn about various types of interactions and how scientists study them, how Earth is divided into biomes, and how humans can impact ecosystems within these biomes.

Chapter 13 Principles of Ecology 394

	13.1	Ecologists Study Relationships	396
		DATA ANALYSIS *Populations and Samples*	401
B.4.1	13.2	Biotic and Abiotic Factors	402
B.4.1	13.3	Energy in Ecosystems	406
B.3.5	13.4	Food Chains and Food Webs	408
B.3.4	13.5	Cycling of Matter	412
B.3.5	13.6	Pyramid Models	417
	QUICK LAB	Quadrat Sampling	399
	INVESTIGATION	Abiotic Factors and Plant Growth	405
	OPTIONS FOR INQUIRY	Lab: Random Sampling	420
		Lab: Build a Terrarium	421
		Online: Animated BIOLOGY, Virtual Lab, WebQuest	421
	INDIANA	ISTEP+ Test Prep *B.3.4, B.3.5, B.4.2, B.4.4*	425

Chapter 14 Interactions in Ecosystems 426

B.4.4	14.1	Habitat and Niche	428
B.4.4	14.2	Community Interactions	431
	14.3	Population Density and Distribution	436
B.4.1	14.4	Population Growth Patterns	440
		DATA ANALYSIS *Reading Combination Graphs*	442
B.4.2	14.5	Ecological Succession	445
	QUICK LAB	Survivorship Curves	438
	INVESTIGATION	Modeling Predation	435
	OPTIONS FOR INQUIRY	Lab: Limiting Nutrients for Algae	448
		Lab: Making a Local Field Guide	449
		Online: Animated BIOLOGY, WebQuest, Data Analysis	449
	INDIANA	ISTEP+ Test Prep *B.4.1, B.4.2, B.4.3, B.4.4*	453

Industrial pollution, *p. 491*

Chapter 15 The Biosphere 454

B.4.1	15.1	Life in the Earth System	456
B.4.4	15.2	Climate	458
		DATA ANALYSIS *Constructing Combination Graphs*	461
	15.3	Biomes	462
	15.4	Marine Ecosystems	468
	15.5	Estuaries and Freshwater Ecosystems	471
	QUICK LAB	Microclimates	460
	INVESTIGATION	Winter Water Chemistry	475
	OPTIONS FOR INQUIRY	Lab: Modeling Biomes	476
		Lab: Heating and Cooling Rates of Water and Soil	477
		Online: Animated BIOLOGY, WebQuest, Data Analysis	477
	INDIANA	**ISTEP+ Test Prep** *B.3.1, B.4.1, B.4.2, B.4.4, B.8.5, NOS.1*	481

Chapter 16 Human Impact on Ecosystems 482

B.4.2	16.1	Human Population Growth and Natural Resources	484
B.4.2	16.2	Air Quality	488
B.4.2	16.3	Water Quality	494
		DATA ANALYSIS *Discrete and Continuous Data*	497
B.4.2	16.4	Threats to Biodiversity	498
B.4.2	16.5	Conservation	502
	QUICK LAB	Modeling Biomagnification	496
	INVESTIGATION	Acid Rain	493
	OPTIONS FOR INQUIRY	Lab: Water Quality Testing	506
		Lab: Contamination of Groundwater	507
		Online: Animated BIOLOGY, WebQuest, Data Analysis	507
	INDIANA	**ISTEP+ Test Prep** *B.3.4, B.4.2, B.4.3, NOS.6*	511

UNIT 5 BIOZINE Global Warming—Changing the Planet 512

Technology Deep Sea Sediment Coring
Careers Oceanographer

CLASSZONE.COM

VIRTUAL LAB

Chapter 13 Estimating Population Size

Animated BIOLOGY

Chapter 13 Distribution of Producers, Build a Food Web

Chapter 14 Survive within a Niche, What Limits Population Growth?

Chapter 15 Lake Turnover, Where Do They Live?

Chapter 16 Human Population Growth, Global Warming, Human Effects on a Food Web

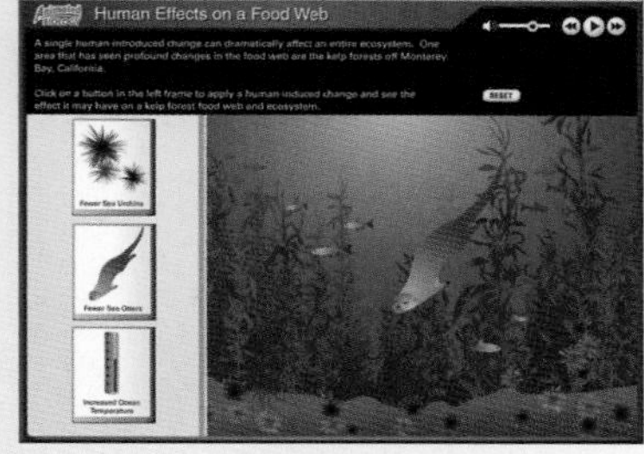

Illustration by Argosy

WEBQUEST

Chapter 13 Keystone Species

Chapter 14 Environmental Stress

Chapter 15 Explore an Ecosystem

Chapter 16 Invasive Species

Interactive Review

REVIEW Key Concepts, Vocabulary Games, Concept Maps, Animated Biology, Online Quiz

BIOZINE

INTERNET MAGAZINE

Explore today's world of biology online at ClassZone.com.

UNIT 6

INDIANA

Classification and Diversity

Unit Focus

Unit 6 first introduces the way in which scientists classify living things. Next it begins the exploration of diversity of living things with viruses and prokaryotes, and then protists and fungi.

Chapter 17 The Tree of Life 516

	17.1	The Linnaean System of Classification	518
B.8.2	17.2	Classification Based on Evolutionary Relationships	524
		DATA ANALYSIS *Transforming Data*	529
B.8.3	17.3	Molecular Clocks	530
B.8.2	17.4	Domains and Kingdoms	533
	QUICK LAB	Construct a Cladogram	525
	INVESTIGATION	Creating a Dichotomous Key for Limpet Shells	522
	OPTIONS FOR INQUIRY	Lab: Modeling DNA Hybridization	536
		Lab: Defining Species	537
		Online: Animated BIOLOGY, WebQuest, BioZine	537
	INDIANA	ISTEP+ Test Prep *B.8.2, B.8.6, NOS.9*	541

Chapter 18 Viruses and Prokaryotes 542

	18.1	Studying Viruses and Prokaryotes	544
		DATA ANALYSIS *Choosing Data Representation*	546
	18.2	Viral Structure and Reproduction	547
	18.3	Viral Diseases	552
B.8.3	18.4	Bacteria and Archaea	555
B.4.4	18.5	Beneficial Roles of Prokaryotes	559
	18.6	Bacterial Diseases and Antibiotics	563
	QUICK LAB	Examining Bacteria in Yogurt	560
	INVESTIGATION	Leaf Print Bacteria	562
	OPTIONS FOR INQUIRY	Lab: Using Bacteria to Break Down Oil	566
		Lab: Modeling Viruses	567
		Online: Animated BIOLOGY, Virtual Lab, WebQuest	567
	INDIANA	ISTEP+ Test Prep *B.4.1, B.8.2, B.8.5, NOS.1*	571

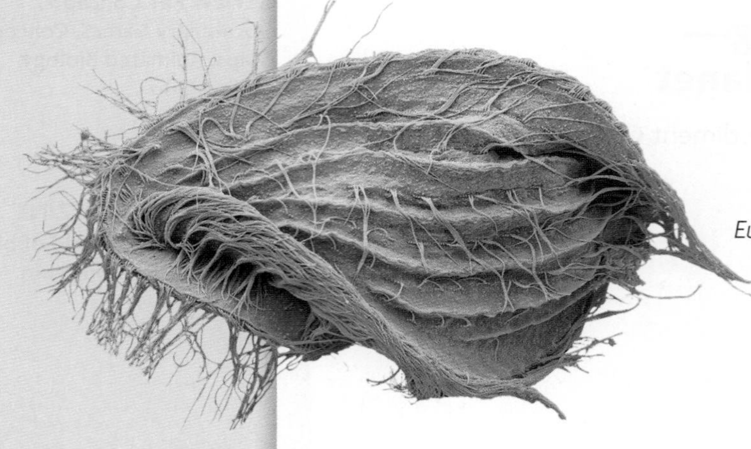

Euplotes, an animal-like protist, *p. 575*

Chapter 19 Protists and Fungi 572

B.8.2	19.1	Diversity of Protists	574
	19.2	Animal-like Protists	577
	19.3	Plantlike Protists	581
		DATA ANALYSIS *Analyzing Experimental Design*	586
	19.4	Funguslike Protists	587
	19.5	Diversity of Fungi	589
B.4.4	19.6	Ecology of Fungi	596
	QUICK LAB	Investigating Motion in Protists	579
	INVESTIGATION	Exploring Mushroom Anatomy	595
	OPTIONS FOR INQUIRY	Lab: Quantifying Mold Growth	600
		Lab: Algae in Products	601
		Online: Animated BIOLOGY, WebQuest, Data Analysis	601

INDIANA ISTEP+ Test Prep *B.3.4, B.4.1, B.8.2, NOS.9* 605

UNIT 6 BIOZINE
Pandemics—Is the Next One on the Way? 606

Technology Dissecting a Virus
Careers Epidemiologist

White oak, *p. 519*

Online BIOLOGY
CLASSZONE.COM

VIRTUAL LAB

Chapter 18 Testing Antibacterial Products

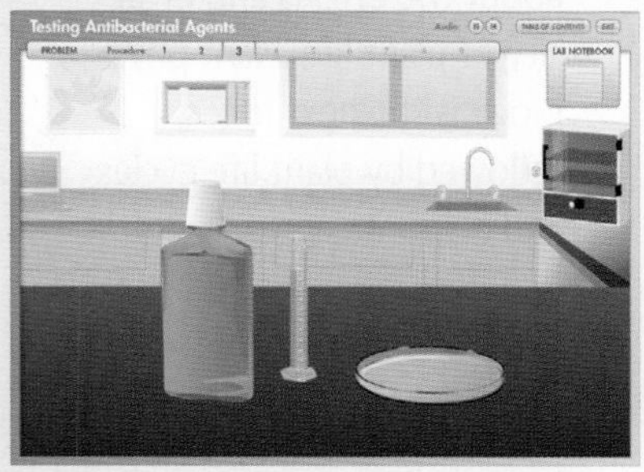

Animated BIOLOGY

Chapter 17 Molecular Clock, Build a Cladogram

Chapter 18 Viral Infections, What Would You Prescribe?

Chapter 19 Protist Movement, Algae Concentrations, Protist and Fungus Life Cycles

WEBQUEST

Chapter 17 Classify a Sea Cucumber

Chapter 18 Antibiotics in Agriculture

Chapter 19 Sickening Protists

Interactive Review

REVIEW Key Concepts, Vocabulary Games, Concept Maps, Animated Biology, Online Quiz

BIOZINE

INTERNET MAGAZINE

Explore today's world of biology online at ClassZone.com.

UNIT 7

Plants

INDIANA

Unit Focus

In Unit 7, you will first learn about the origins and diversity of plant life. Plant physiology is the next focus, followed by plant life cycles and responses.

Chapter 20 Plant Diversity 610

B.8.3 **20.1** Origins of Plant Life 612
B.8.2 **20.2** Classification of Plants 617
20.3 Diversity of Flowering Plants 624
DATA ANALYSIS *Mean, Median, and Mode* 628
20.4 Plants in Human Culture 629

QUICK LAB Classifying Plants as Vascular or Nonvascular 620
INVESTIGATION Habitat Clues 623
OPTIONS FOR INQUIRY Lab: Comparing Monocots and Dicots 632
Lab: Investigating Medicinal Plants 633
Online: Animated BIOLOGY, WebQuest, BioZine 633
INDIANA **ISTEP+ Test Prep** *B.8.5, NOS.1, NOS.9* 637

Chapter 21 Plant Structure and Function 638

21.1 Plant Cells and Tissues 640
21.2 The Vascular System 643
21.3 Roots and Stems 648
DATA ANALYSIS *Identifying the Importance of Repeated Trials* 649
21.4 Leaves 652

QUICK LAB Chlorophyll Fluorescence 654
INVESTIGATION Density of Stomata 647
OPTIONS FOR INQUIRY Lab: Photosynthesis and Red Leaves 656
Lab: Connecting Form to Function 657
Online: Animated BIOLOGY, Virtual Lab, WebQuest 657
INDIANA **ISTEP+ Test Prep** *B.2.1, B.3.1, NOS.1* 661

Double samaras, *p. 673*

Chapter 22 Plant Growth, Reproduction, and Response 662

22.1	Plant Life Cycles	664
22.2	Reproduction in Flowering Plants	668
22.3	Seed Dispersal and Germination	673
	DATA ANALYSIS *Identifying Experimental Design Flaws*	674
22.4	Asexual Reproduction	678
22.5	Plant Hormones and Responses	680
QUICK LAB	A Closer Look at Flowers	669
INVESTIGATION	Seed Germination	676
OPTIONS FOR INQUIRY	Lab: Investigating Plant Hormones	684
	Lab: Fruit Dissection	685
	Online: Animated BIOLOGY, Virtual Lab, WebQuest	685
INDIANA	**ISTEP+ Test Prep** *B.6.4, B.6.5, B.8.5, NOS.1, NOS.4*	689

UNIT 7 BIOZINE

Genetically Modified Foods—Do Potential Problems Outweigh Benefits? 690

Technology Gene Gun
Careers Research Engineer

Prickly pear cactus, *p. 678*

CLASSZONE.COM

VIRTUAL LAB

Chapter 21 Plant Transpiration

Chapter 22 Exploring Plant Responses

Animated BIOLOGY

Chapter 20 Plant and Pollinator Matching Game

Chapter 21 Movement Through a Plant, Name That Tree

Chapter 22 Seed Dispersal

WEBQUEST

Chapter 20 Endangered Plants

Chapter 21 Plant Adaptations

Chapter 22 Plants in Space

Interactive Review

REVIEW Key Concepts, Vocabulary Games, Concept Maps, Animated Biology, Online Quiz

BIOZINE

INTERNET MAGAZINE

Explore today's world of biology online at ClassZone.com.

UNIT 8

Animals

INDIANA

Unit Focus

Unit 8 begins by discussing the common characteristics of all animals. Animal diversity, including invertebrate and vertebrate diversity, is explored. Then the focus shifts to animal behavior.

Chapter 23 Invertebrate Diversity 694

B.8.2	23.1	Animal Characteristics	696
B.8.2	23.2	Animal Diversity	699
	23.3	Sponges and Cnidarians	705
	23.4	Flatworms, Mollusks, and Annelids	710
	23.5	Roundworms	716
	23.6	Echinoderms	718
		DATA ANALYSIS *Analyzing Scatterplots*	721
	QUICK LAB	Anatomy of a Clam	714
	INVESTIGATION	Feeding *Hydra*	709
	OPTIONS FOR INQUIRY	Lab: Anatomy of a Sea Star	722
		Lab: Anatomy of an Annelid	723
		Online: Animated BIOLOGY, WebQuest, BioZine	723
	INDIANA	ISTEP+ Test Prep *B.5.1, B.6.4, B.8.3, B.8.6, NOS.2, NOS.9*	727

Chapter 24 A Closer Look at Arthropods 728

B.8.3	24.1	Arthropod Diversity	730
	24.2	Crustaceans	735
	24.3	Arachnids	740
		DATA ANALYSIS *Constructing Scatterplots*	742
	24.4	Insect Adaptations	743
	24.5	Arthropods and Humans	747
	QUICK LAB	Comparing Arthropods	733
	INVESTIGATION	Hatching Brine Shrimp	739
	OPTIONS FOR INQUIRY	Lab: Daphnia and Heart Rate	750
		Lab: Inside a Crayfish	751
		Online: Animated BIOLOGY, Virtual Lab, WebQuest	751
	INDIANA	ISTEP+ Test Prep *B.3.5, B.4.1, B.8.5, NOS.1, NOS.2*	755

Chapter 25 Vertebrate Diversity 756

B.8.3	25.1	Vertebrate Origins	758
	25.2	Fish Diversity	763
	25.3	A Closer Look at Bony Fish	768
		DATA ANALYSIS *Constructing Scatterplots*	770
	25.4	Amphibians	773
	25.5	Vertebrates on Land	778
	QUICK LAB	Frog Development	776
	INVESTIGATION	Fish Reproduction	772
	OPTIONS FOR INQUIRY	Lab: Anatomy of a Bony Fish	780
		Lab: Vanishing Amphibian—an Indicator Species	781
		Online: Animated BIOLOGY, WebQuest, Data Analysis	781
	INDIANA	ISTEP+ Test Prep *B.8.2, B.8.3, NOS.1, NOS.3, NOS.8*	785

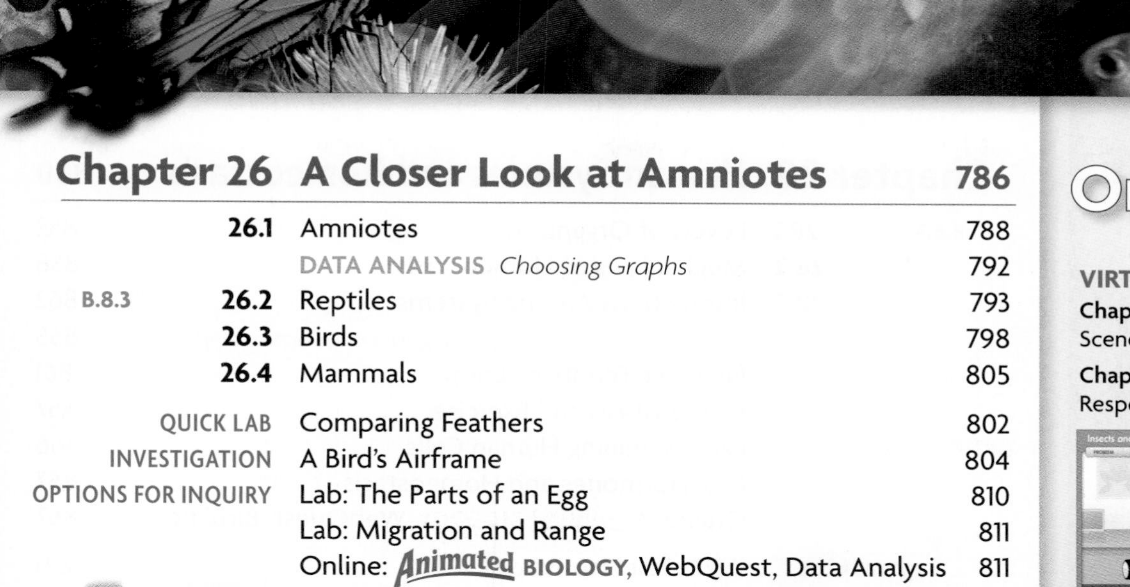

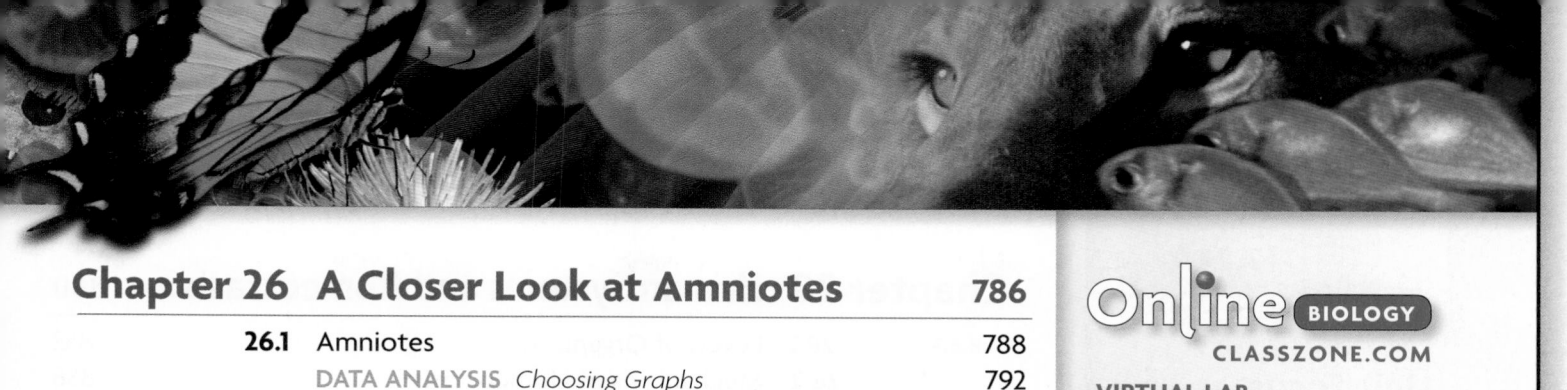

Chapter 26 A Closer Look at Amniotes 786

	26.1	Amniotes	788
		DATA ANALYSIS *Choosing Graphs*	792
B.8.3	26.2	Reptiles	793
	26.3	Birds	798
	26.4	Mammals	805
QUICK LAB		Comparing Feathers	802
INVESTIGATION		A Bird's Airframe	804
OPTIONS FOR INQUIRY		Lab: The Parts of an Egg	810
		Lab: Migration and Range	811
		Online: Animated BIOLOGY, WebQuest, Data Analysis	811
INDIANA		ISTEP+ Test Prep *B.1.2, B.8.3, B.8.5, NOS.1*	815

Chapter 27 Animal Behavior 816

	27.1	Adaptive Value of Behavior	818
	27.2	Instinct and Learning	822
	27.3	Evolution of Behavior	827
	27.4	Social Behavior	831
		DATA ANALYSIS *Constructing Bar Graphs*	836
	27.5	Animal Cognition	837
QUICK LAB		Human Behavior	824
INVESTIGATION		Using an Ethogram to Describe Animal Behavior	830
OPTIONS FOR INQUIRY		Lab: Pill Bug Behavior	840
		Lab: Animal Cognition	841
		Online: Animated BIOLOGY, Virtual Lab, WebQuest	841
INDIANA		ISTEP+ Test Prep *B.3.5, B.7.1, B.8.5, NOS.8*	845

UNIT 8 BIOZINE **The Loss of Biodiversity** 846

Technology Bioremediation
Careers Conservation Biologist

© Dwight Kuhn

Pill bugs, *p. 840*

CLASSZONE.COM

VIRTUAL LAB

Chapter 24 Insects and Crime Scene Analysis

Chapter 27 Interpreting Bird Response

Animated BIOLOGY

Chapter 23 Digestive Tract Formation, Shared Body Structures

Chapter 24 Molting Cicada, Insect Metamorphosis, What Type of Arthropod?

Chapter 25 Gas Exchange in Gills, Frog Metamorphosis, What Type of Fish Is It?

Chapter 26 Bird Flight, Beak Shape and Diet

Chapter 27 Spider Mating Habits, Animal Cognition, Behavioral Costs and Benefits

WEBQUEST

Chapter 23 Parasites

Chapter 24 Field Guide

Chapter 25 Fisheries on the Brink

Chapter 26 Sea Turtles

Chapter 27 Animal Cognition

Interactive Review

REVIEW Key Concepts, Vocabulary Games, Concept Maps, Animated Biology, Online Quiz

BIOZINE

INTERNET MAGAZINE

Explore today's world of biology online at ClassZone.com.

UNIT 9

Human Biology

INDIANA

Unit Focus

In Unit 9, you will learn about how your body systems work together to maintain a stable internal environment. Structures and functions of all the major body systems are addressed.

Chapter 28 Human Systems and Homeostasis 850

B.6.3 **28.1** Levels of Organization 852
28.2 Mechanisms of Homeostasis 858
28.3 Interactions Among Systems 862
DATA ANALYSIS *Interpreting Inverse Relationships* 865
QUICK LAB Negative Feedback Loop 861
INVESTIGATION Homeostasis and Exercise 857
OPTIONS FOR INQUIRY Lab: Examining Human Cells 866
Lab: Hormones and Homeostasis 867
Online: Animated BIOLOGY, WebQuest, BioZine 867
INDIANA **ISTEP+ Test Prep** *NOS.5* 871

Chapter 29 Nervous and Endocrine Systems 872

29.1 How Organ Systems Communicate 874
29.2 Neurons 876
29.3 The Senses 880
29.4 Central and Peripheral Nervous Systems 885
29.5 Brain Function and Chemistry 891
DATA ANALYSIS *Correlation or Causation* 895
29.6 The Endocrine System and Hormones 896
QUICK LAB The Primary Sensory Cortex 886
INVESTIGATION The Stroop Effect 884
OPTIONS FOR INQUIRY Lab: Reaction Time 902
Lab: Brain-Based Disorders 903
Online: Animated BIOLOGY, WebQuest, Data Analysis 903
INDIANA **ISTEP+ Test Prep** *NOS.4* 907

Chapter 30 Respiratory and Circulatory Systems 908

30.1 Respiratory and Circulatory Functions 910
30.2 Respiration and Gas Exchange 914
30.3 The Heart and Circulation 917
30.4 Blood Vessels and Transport 922
DATA ANALYSIS *Forming a Null Hypothesis* 925
30.5 Blood 926
30.6 Lymphatic System 930
QUICK LAB Blood Cells 928
INVESTIGATION Carbon Dioxide and Exercise 921
OPTIONS FOR INQUIRY Lab: Making and Using a Respirometer 932
Lab: Stimuli and Heart Rate 933
Online: Animated BIOLOGY, Virtual Lab, WebQuest 933
INDIANA **ISTEP+ Test Prep** *NOS.1* 937

Chapter 31 Immune System and Disease 938

31.1	Pathogens and Human Illness	940
31.2	Immune System	945
	DATA ANALYSIS *Identifying Experimental Design Flaws*	947
31.3	Immune Responses	950
31.4	Immunity and Technology	955
31.5	Overreactions of the Immune System	957
31.6	Diseases that Weaken the Immune System	960
QUICK LAB	How Pathogens Spread	943
INVESTIGATION	Observing Normal and Diseased Tissue	949
OPTIONS FOR INQUIRY	Lab: Modeling T Cell Activation	964
	Lab: What Is an Autoimmune Disease?	965
	Online: Animated BIOLOGY, WebQuest, Data Analysis	965
INDIANA	ISTEP+ Test Prep *NOS.1, NOS.8*	969

Chapter 32 Digestive and Excretory Systems 970

32.1	Nutrients and Homeostasis	972
32.2	Digestive System	977
32.3	Absorption of Nutrients	982
	DATA ANALYSIS *Identifying Outliers*	985
32.4	Excretory System	986
QUICK LAB	Villi in the Small Intestine	983
INVESTIGATION	Testing a Digestive Enzyme	981
OPTIONS FOR INQUIRY	Lab: Antacid Effectiveness	992
	Lab: Digesting Milk	993
	Online: Animated BIOLOGY, WebQuest, Data Analysis	993
INDIANA	ISTEP+ Test Prep *NOS.6*	997

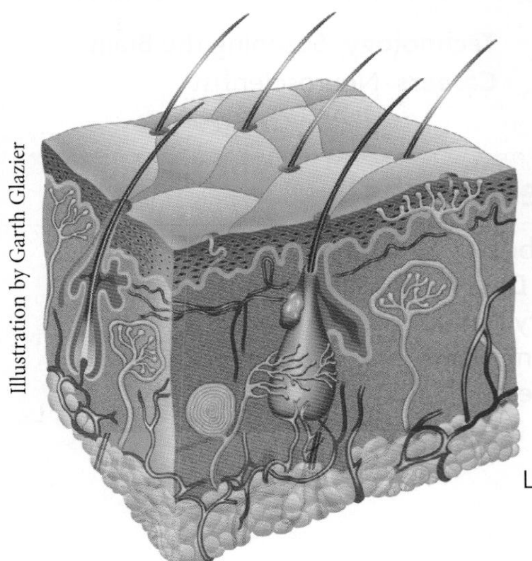

Layers of skin, *p. 883*

Online BIOLOGY
CLASSZONE.COM

VIRTUAL LAB

Chapter 30 Blood Typing

Animated BIOLOGY

Chapter 28 Human Organ Systems, Keep an Athlete Running

Chapter 29 Nerve Impulse Transmission, Reflex Arc, Diagnose a Hormone Disorder

Chapter 30 How You Breathe, How the Heart Pumps Blood, Build the Circulatory and Respiratory Systems

Chapter 31 Vaccines and Active Immunity, Destroy the Invaders

Chapter 32 Digestive System, Run the Digestive System

Chapter 33 Muscle Contraction, What Kind of Joint Is It?

Chapter 34 Embryonic Development, Human Aging, Developmental Timeline

WEBQUEST

Chapter 28 Hypothermia

Chapter 29 Drug Addiction

Chapter 30 Asthma

Chapter 31 HIV and AIDS

Chapter 32 Obesity

Chapter 33 Muscular Dystrophy

Chapter 34 Healthy Diet, Healthy Baby

Interactive Review

REVIEW Key Concepts, Vocabulary Games, Concept Maps, Animated Biology, Online Quiz

BIOZINE

INTERNET MAGAZINE

Explore today's world of biology online at ClassZone.com.

IN25

Human Biology *continued*

INDIANA

© D. Philips/Photo Researchers, Inc.

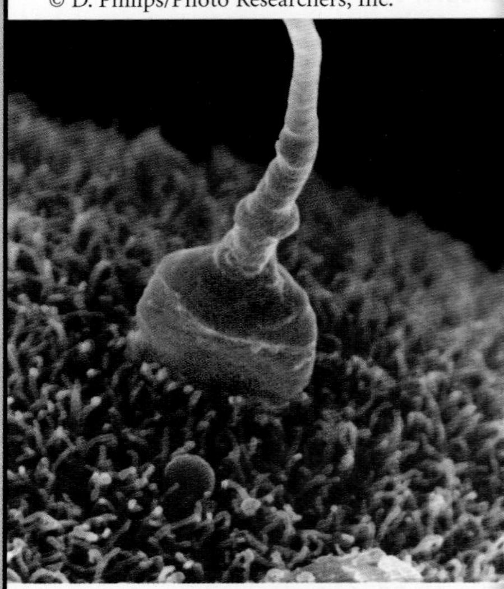

Sperm and egg, *p. 1031*

Chapter 33 Protection, Support, and Movement 998

33.1	Skeletal System	1000
33.2	Muscular System	1006
33.3	Integumentary System	1013
	DATA ANALYSIS *Analyzing Trends in Data*	1014
QUICK LAB	Muscles and Bones of the Skull	1011
INVESTIGATION	Muscle Fatigue	1012
OPTIONS FOR INQUIRY	Lab: Muscles in Action	1016
	Lab: Bone and Muscle Cells	1017
	Online: Animated BIOLOGY, WebQuest, Data Analysis	1017
INDIANA	**ISTEP+ Test Prep** *NOS.6*	1021

Chapter 34 Reproduction and Development 1022

34.1	Reproductive Anatomy	1024
34.2	Reproductive Processes	1027
B.6.3 **34.3**	Fetal Development	1034
	DATA ANALYSIS *Interpreting Graphs*	1038
34.4	Birth and Development	1040
QUICK LAB	Human Sex Cells	1031
INVESTIGATION	Hormones in the Human Menstrual Cycle	1033
OPTIONS FOR INQUIRY	Lab: Development of an Embryo	1044
	Lab: Effects of Chemicals on Reproductive Organs	1045
	Online: Animated BIOLOGY, WebQuest, Data Analysis	1045
INDIANA	**ISTEP+ Test Prep** *B.5.2, B.6.4, NOS.1*	1049

UNIT 9 BIOZINE

Brain Science—We Are Wired to Learn! 1050

Technology Scanning the Brain
Careers Neuroscientist

Student Resources R1

Lab Handbook	R2
Math and Data Analysis Handbook	R14
Vocabulary Handbook	R18
Note-taking Handbook	R22
Appendices	R25
Glossary	R40
Index	R75

Biology Online

BIOZINE at ClassZone.com

This online companion to the BioZine pages in your textbook keeps you up to date with cutting-edge advances in biology. The BioZine provides the latest information about biology topics, issues, and technology. It also features news feeds, opinion polls, and much more about careers in biology.

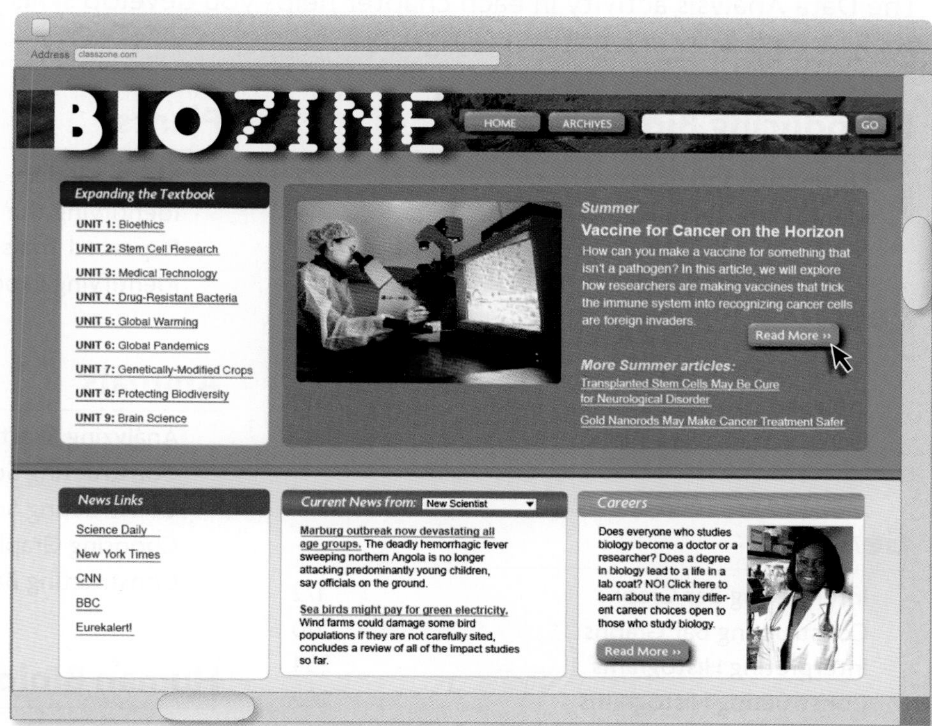

BIOZINE Features in the Pupil Edition

UNIT 1 When Knowledge and Ethics Collide 64
Technology: Genetic Testing
Careers: Geneticist

UNIT 2 Stem Cell Research—Potential Solutions, Practical Challenges 162
Technology: Somatic Cell Nuclear Transfer
Careers: Cell Biologist

UNIT 3 Medical Technology—The Genetic Forefront 292
Technology: Biochips
Careers: Cancer Geneticist

UNIT 4 Drug-Resistant Bacteria—A Global Health Issue 390
Technology: New Drug Delivery System
Careers: Evolutionary Biologist

UNIT 5 Global Warming—Changing the Planet 512
Technology: Deep Sea Sediment Coring
Careers: Oceanographer

UNIT 6 Pandemics—Is the Next One on the Way? 606
Technology: Dissecting a Virus
Careers: Epidemiologist

UNIT 7 Genetically Modified Foods—Do Potential Problems Outweigh Benefits? 690
Technology: Gene Gun
Careers: Research Engineer

UNIT 8 The Loss of Biodiversity 846
Technology: Bioremediation
Careers: Conservation Biologist

UNIT 9 Brain Science—We Are Wired to Learn! 1050
Technology: Scanning the Brain
Careers: Neuroscientist

Data Analysis

The Data Analysis activity in each chapter helps you develop skills you need to analyze data from scientific investigations.

Introducing Biology

Qualitative and Quantitative 12
Identifying Variables 49

Cells

Defining Variables 80
Interpreting Graphs 116
Constructing Data Tables 142

Genetics

Interpreting Bar Graphs 172
Constructing Bar Graphs 210
Interpreting Histograms 234
Constructing Histograms 282

Evolution

Interpreting Line Graphs 308
Identifying Patterns 339
Calculating Axes Intervals 375

Ecology

Populations and Samples 401
Reading Combination Graphs 442
Constructing Combination Graphs 461
Discrete and Continuous Data 497

Classification and Diversity

Transforming Data 529
Choosing Data Representation 546
Analyzing Experimental Design 586

Plants

Mean, Median, and Mode 628
Identifying the Importance of Repeated Trials 649
Identifying Experimental Design Flaws 674

Animals

Analyzing Scatterplots 721
Constructing Scatterplots 742
Constructing Scatterplots 770
Choosing Graphs 792
Constructing Bar Graphs 836

Human Biology

Interpreting Inverse Relationships 865
Correlation or Causation 895
Forming a Null Hypothesis 925
Identifying Experimental Design Flaws 947
Identifying Outliers 985
Analyzing Trends in Data 1014
Interpreting Graphs 1038

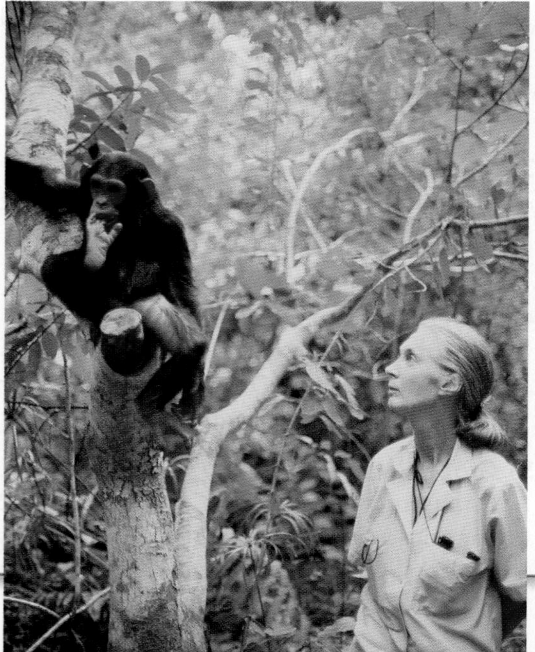

Jane Goodall and chimpanzee

Quick Labs

Explore key concepts and develop basic lab skills using these Quick Labs.

Introducing Biology

Life Under a Microscope Observing 22
Chemical Bonding Modeling 51

Cells

Modeling the Cell Membrane Modeling 83
Fermentation Designing Experiments 124
Cancer Observing 147

Genetics

Using a Testcross Inferring 185
Sex-Linked Inheritance Predicting 202
Replication Modeling 238
Modeling Plasmids and Restriction Enzymes Modeling 278

Evolution

Piecing Together Evidence Inferring 313
Genetic Drift Modeling 337
Geologic Clock Modeling 381

Ecology

Quadrat Sampling Sampling 399
Survivorship Curves Interpreting Data 438
Microclimates Observing 460
Modeling Biomagnification Modeling 496

Classification and Diversity

Construct a Cladogram Classifying 525
Examining Bacteria in Yogurt Observing 560
Investigating Motion in Protists Observing 579

Plants

Classifying Plants as Vascular or Nonvascular Classifying 620
Chlorophyll Fluorescence Analyzing 654
A Closer Look at Flowers Dissecting 669

Animals

Anatomy of a Clam Observing 714
Comparing Arthropods Comparing 733
Frog Development Observing 776
Comparing Feathers Observing 802
Human Behavior Observing 824

Human Biology

Negative Feedback Loop Modeling 861
The Primary Sensory Cortex Designing Experiments 886
Blood Cells Observing 928
How Pathogens Spread Modeling 943
Villi in the Small Intestine Designing Experiments 983
Muscles and Bones of the Skull Interpreting Graphics 1011
Human Sex Cells Observing 1031

IN29

Chapter Investigations

Connect content to the scientific process with design-your-own investigations or guided inquiry with real-world applications.

Unit 1 Introducing Biology

1 Manipulating Independent Variables Measuring, Modeling 18

2 Enzymatic Activity Identifying Variables, Observing, Measuring, Collecting Data, Interpreting Data 57

Unit 2 Cells

3 Diffusion Across a Membrane Designing Experiments, Analyzing Data 88

4 Rates of Photosynthesis Designing Experiments, Analyzing, Calculating, Graphing, Inferring 106

5 Mitosis in Onion Root Cells Observing, Collecting Data, Concluding 143

Unit 3 Genetics

6 Allele Combinations and Punnett Squares Calculating, Analyzing 188

7 Codominance Inferring, Predicting 208

8 Extracting DNA Observing, Analyzing 229

9 Modeling Forensics Modeling, Analyzing, Concluding, Predicting 268

Unit 4 Evolution

10 Predator-Prey Pursuit Modeling, Observing, Predicting 315

11 Natural Selection in African Swallowtails Modeling, Graphing, Interpreting Data 334

12 Radioactive Decay Analyzing, Interpreting Data, Modeling 364

Unit 5 Ecology

13 Abiotic Factors and Plant Growth Designing Experiments, Collecting Data 405

14 Modeling Predation Modeling, Analyzing Data 435

15 Winter Water Chemistry Designing Experiments, Collecting Data, Analyzing Data 475

16 Acid Rain Designing Experiments, Hypothesizing, Collecting Data, Analyzing Data 493

Chapter Investigations

Hydra (LM; magnification 20×)

Unit 6 Classification and Diversity

17 Creating a Dichotomous Key for Limpet Shells Observing, Identifying, Classifying 522

18 Leaf Print Bacteria Observing, Evaluating Outcomes 562

19 Exploring Mushroom Anatomy Observing, Predicting, Inferring 595

Unit 7 Plants

20 Habitat Clues Observing, Analyzing, Classifying 623

21 Density of Stomata Observing, Collecting Data, Analyzing Data 647

22 Seed Germination Observing, Measuring, Collecting, Interpreting Data 676

Unit 8 Animals

23 Feeding *Hydra* Observing, Collecting Data 709

24 Hatching Brine Shrimp Designing Experiments, Collecting Data, Analyzing, Predicting 739

25 Fish Reproduction Modeling 772

26 A Bird's Airframe Observing, Measuring, Analyzing 804

27 Using an Ethogram to Describe Animal Behavior Observing, Graphing Data 830

Unit 9 Human Biology

28 Homeostasis and Exercise Observing, Collecting Data 857

29 The Stroop Effect Observing, Collecting Data, Inferring 884

30 Carbon Dioxide and Exercise Observing, Measuring, Analyzing 921

31 Observing Normal and Diseased Tissue Observing, Analyzing 949

32 Testing a Digestive Enzyme Analyzing Data 981

33 Muscle Fatigue Collecting Data, Analyzing Data, Graphing 1012

34 Hormones in the Human Menstrual Cycle Graphing, Interpreting Graphs 1033

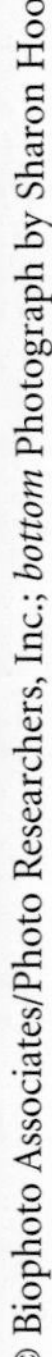

IN31

Additional Inquiry Opportunities

The Options for Inquiry pages at the end of each chapter give you a choice of two hands-on labs and three online activities.

Indiana Standards for both investigations are listed in the left column.

Online Activities include
- Virtual Labs
- Animated Biology
- WebQuests
- Data Analysis

CHAPTER 8 **OPTIONS FOR INQUIRY**

Use these inquiry-based labs and online activities to deepen your understanding of DNA.

INDIANA STANDARDS

B.5.3 Describe the process by which DNA directs the production of protein within a cell.
B.7.4 Explain the process by which a cell copies its DNA and identify factors that can damage DNA and cause changes in its nucleotide sequence.
NOS.6 Use analogies and models (mathematical and physical) to simplify and represent systems that are difficult to understand or directly experience due to their size, time scale, or complexity, and recognize the limitations of analogies and models.

DESIGN YOUR OWN INVESTIGATION

UV Light and Skin Cancer

Exposure to the ultraviolet (UV) radiation in sunlight can lead to skin cancer caused by mutations in the DNA of skin cells. The most common type of damage from UV light is the formation of thymine dimers, or pairs of thymine bases bonded together. These mutations interfere with both replication and transcription. Sunscreens receive ratings based on the amount of protection from UV radiation they provide. The higher the sun protection factor (SPF), the more radiation the lotion blocks.

MATERIALS
- 3 different kinds of sunscreen
- sunlight or UV light box
- 12 UV beads

UV beads

SKILLS Collecting Data, Defining Operational Variables

PROBLEM Which sunscreen blocks more UV rays?

PROCEDURE
1. Choose either three different brands of sunscreen or three samples of the same brand with different SPFs.
2. Design an experiment using the UV beads to test the effectiveness of each of the sunscreens. Remember to include a control group and multiple trials.
3. Identify the independent and dependent variables and any constants in your procedure.
4. Once your teacher has approved your experimental design, carry out your procedure. Record your results in a data table.

ANALYZE AND CONCLUDE
1. **Analyze** What can you conclude about the effectiveness of the sunscreens?
2. **Apply** Identify the operational definition of your variable in this experiment.
3. **Evaluate** What was the importance of having a control in this procedure?
4. **Experimental Design** Identify sources of unavoidable error and reasons for inconsistent results.

EXTEND YOUR INVESTIGATION
Exposure to high levels of UV radiation during the teenage years is a major risk factor for skin cancer, but the cancer itself generally does not develop until many years later. Use what you have learned about mutations to propose a reasonable explanation for why skin cancer usually appears later in life.

256 Unit 3: Genetics

INVESTIGATION

Modeling Transcription

During the process of transcription, a strand of mRNA that complements the base sequence on a strand of DNA is made.

SKILL Modeling

MATERIALS
- metric ruler
- 60 cm piece of wide ribbon
- scissors
- construction paper of 5 colors
- marker
- stapler

PROBLEM How can you model transcription?

PROCEDURE
1. Cut two pieces of ribbon, each about 30 cm long.
2. Choose five colors of construction paper to represent each of the bases in DNA and RNA.
3. Write out a sequence of 12 bases on a strand of DNA. Cut out corresponding squares of construction paper for each base. Use the marker to label each base.
4. Staple each base along the edge of one piece of ribbon so that they are an equal distance apart. This piece represents a single strand of DNA in the nucleus.
5. Write out the set of complementary bases that will make up the strand of mRNA. Cut out corresponding squares of construction paper for each base. Use the marker to label each base.
6. Staple each base in the correct order along the edge of the second piece of ribbon.

ANALYZE AND CONCLUDE
1. **Compare** How is your model similar to the process of transcription?
2. **Apply** Explain what happens when mRNA leaves the nucleus of a eukaryotic cell.
3. **Evaluate** How would you continue to model translation using the materials in this lab?
4. **Experimental Design** What are some limitations of the model you used in this lab?

Online BIOLOGY CLASSZONE.COM

ANIMATED BIOLOGY
Build a Protein
Can you build a protein from a DNA code? Use enzymes, nucleotides, ribosomes, and transfer RNA to synthesize protein.

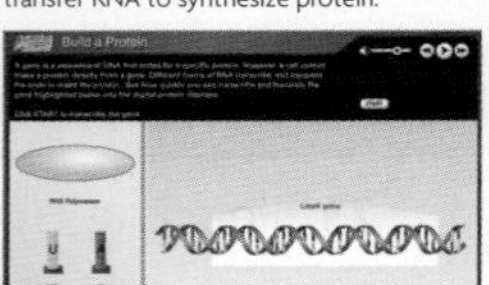

WEBQUEST
What do *Bt* corn and a fluorescent mouse have in common? They both produce proteins with genes from other organisms. In this WebQuest, you will learn more about transgenic organisms. Explore the potential benefits and risks involved when one organism is engineered to produce a protein from another organism.

DATA ANALYSIS ONLINE
Erwin Chargaff showed that the proportion of certain base pairs always had a consistent relationship, although the amount of each might vary across species. This idea that A = T and C = G is known as Chargaff's rules. Graph the percentage of bases in four different species to put Chargaff's rules to the test.

Chapter 8: From DNA to Proteins 257

Labs These additional inquiry activities offer labs of all types, including Design Your Own and dissections.

Options for Inquiry

Photographs by Sharon Hoogstraten

Introducing Biology

Manipulating Plant Growth	28
Biology in the News	29
Testing pH	58
Enzymes	59

Cells

Comparing Cells	92
Modeling the Cell	93
Cellular Respiration	126
Investigate Fermentation in Foods	127
Modeling Cell Surface Area–to–Volume Ratio	156
Apoptosis	157

Genetics

Modeling Meiosis	192
Probability Practice	193
Pedigree Analysis	218
Incomplete Dominance	219
UV Light and Skin Cancer	256
Modeling Transcription	257
Modeling Genetic Engineering	286
Genetic Screening	287

Evolution

Using Patterns to Make Predictions	320
Adaptations in Beaks	321
Investigating an Anole Lizard Population	352
Exploring Adaptations	353
Stride Inferences	384
Understanding Geologic Time	385

Ecology

Random Sampling	420
Build a Terrarium	421
Limiting Nutrients for Algae	448
Making a Local Field Guide	449
Modeling Biomes	476
Heating and Cooling Rates of Water and Soil	477
Water Quality Testing	506
Contamination of Groundwater	507

Classification and Diversity

Modeling DNA Hybridization	536
Defining Species	537
Using Bacteria to Break Down Oil	566
Modeling Viruses	567
Quantifying Mold Growth	600
Algae in Products	601

Options for Inquiry

Photograph by Sharon Hoogstraten

Plants

Comparing Monocots and Dicots 632
Investigating Medicinal Plants 633
Photosynthesis and Red Leaves 656
Connecting Form to Function 657
Investigating Plant Hormones 684
Fruit Dissection 685

Animals

Anatomy of a Sea Star 722
Anatomy of an Annelid 723
Daphnia and Heart Rate 750
Inside a Crayfish 751
Anatomy of a Bony Fish 780
Vanishing Amphibian—an Indicator Species 781
The Parts of an Egg 810
Migration and Range 811
Pill Bug Behavior 840
Animal Cognition 841

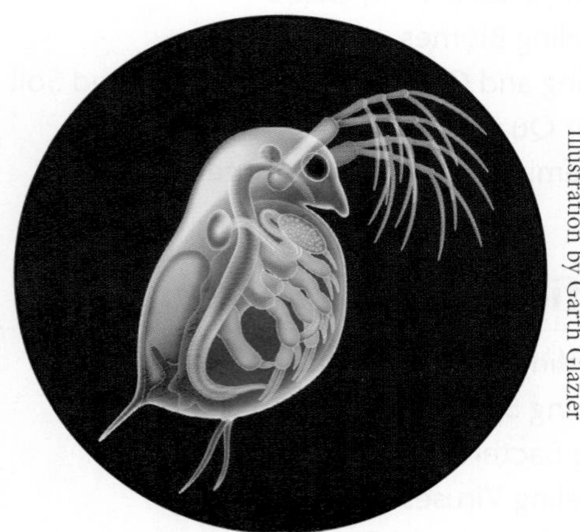

Illustration by Garth Glazier

Daphnia

Human Biology

Examining Human Cells 866
Hormones and Homeostasis 867
Reaction Time 902
Brain-Based Disorders 903
Making and Using a Respirometer 932
Stimuli and Heart Rate 933
Modeling T Cell Activation 964
What Is an Autoimmune Disease? 965
Antacid Effectiveness 992
Digesting Milk 993
Muscles in Action 1016
Bone and Muscle Cells 1017
Development of an Embryo 1044
Effects of Chemicals on Reproductive Organs 1045

IN34

Indiana

Indiana Student Guide

Overview of Indiana Standards IN36

Biology I Standards IN37

INDIANA STUDENT GUIDE

©Alexey Stiop/Alamy

Overview of the Indiana Standards

The Indiana State Standards outline what you should know and be able to do at each grade level. Your textbook is closely aligned to the State Standards. This section lists all of the State Standards and gives examples of how they are tested.

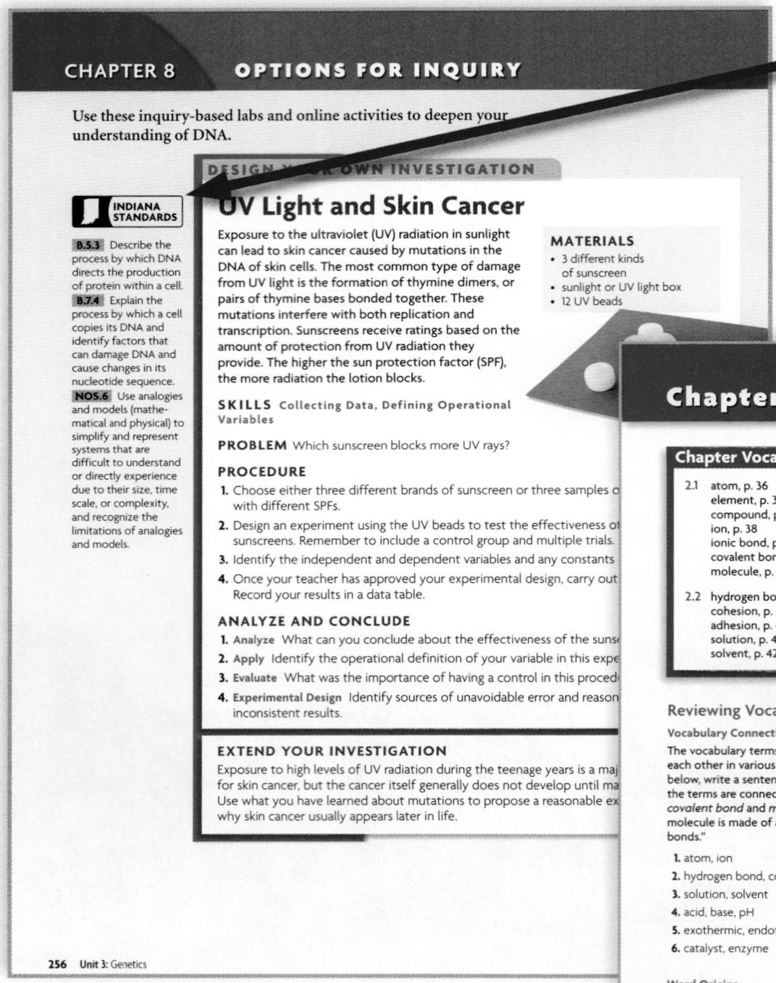

CHAPTER 8 **OPTIONS FOR INQUIRY**

Use these inquiry-based labs and online activities to deepen your understanding of DNA.

INDIANA STANDARDS

B.5.3 Describe the process by which DNA directs the production of protein within a cell.
B.7.4 Explain the process by which a cell copies its DNA and identify factors that can damage DNA and cause changes in its nucleotide sequence.
NOS.6 Use analogies and models (mathematical and physical) to simplify and represent systems that are difficult to understand or directly experience due to their size, time scale, or complexity, and recognize the limitations of analogies and models.

DESIGN YOUR OWN INVESTIGATION

UV Light and Skin Cancer

Exposure to the ultraviolet (UV) radiation in sunlight can lead to skin cancer caused by mutations in the DNA of skin cells. The most common type of damage from UV light is the formation of thymine dimers, or pairs of thymine bases bonded together. These mutations interfere with both replication and transcription. Sunscreens receive ratings based on the amount of protection from UV radiation they provide. The higher the sun protection factor (SPF), the more radiation the lotion blocks.

MATERIALS
- 3 different kinds of sunscreen
- sunlight or UV light box
- 12 UV beads

SKILLS Collecting Data, Defining Operational Variables

PROBLEM Which sunscreen blocks more UV rays?

PROCEDURE
1. Choose either three different brands of sunscreen or three samples o with different SPFs.
2. Design an experiment using the UV beads to test the effectiveness of sunscreens. Remember to include a control group and multiple trials.
3. Identify the independent and dependent variables and any constants
4. Once your teacher has approved your experimental design, carry out Record your results in a data table.

ANALYZE AND CONCLUDE
1. **Analyze** What can you conclude about the effectiveness of the suns
2. **Apply** Identify the operational definition of your variable in this expe
3. **Evaluate** What was the importance of having a control in this procedu
4. **Experimental Design** Identify sources of unavoidable error and reason inconsistent results.

EXTEND YOUR INVESTIGATION
Exposure to high levels of UV radiation during the teenage years is a maj for skin cancer, but the cancer itself generally does not develop until ma Use what you have learned about mutations to propose a reasonable ex why skin cancer usually appears later in life.

256 Unit 3: Genetics

Standards Alignment
Throughout your textbook you will see standards listed. This shows what standards are covered in that section.

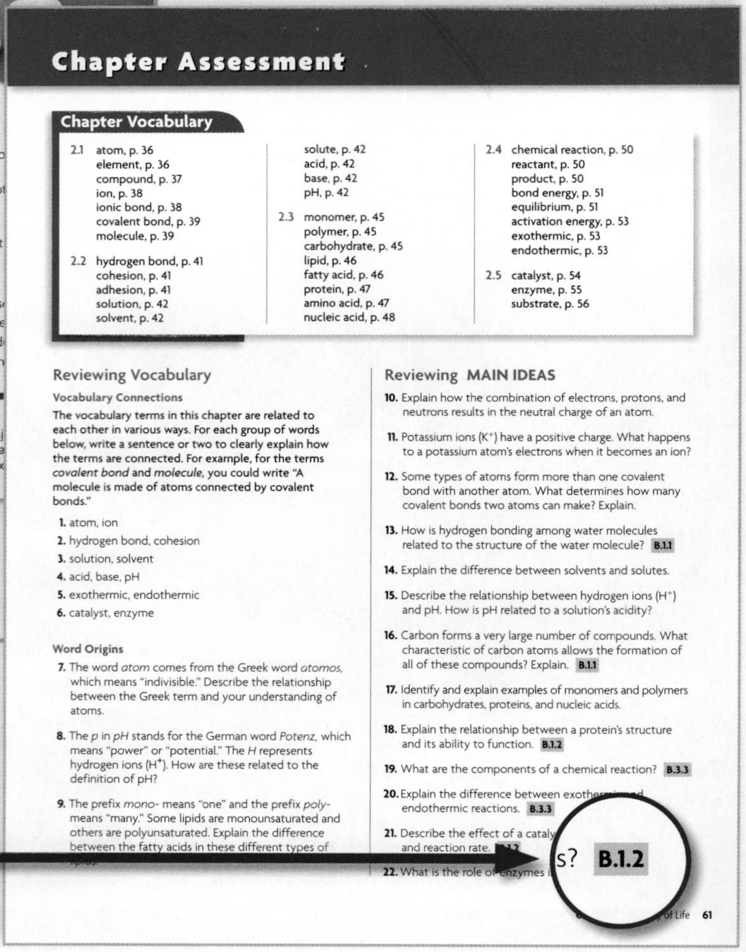

Chapter Assessment

Chapter Vocabulary

2.1 atom, p. 36
element, p. 36
compound, p. 37
ion, p. 38
ionic bond, p. 38
covalent bond, p. 39
molecule, p. 39

2.2 hydrogen bond, p. 41
cohesion, p. 41
adhesion, p. 41
solution, p. 42
solvent, p. 42
solute, p. 42
acid, p. 42
base, p. 42
pH, p. 42

2.3 monomer, p. 45
polymer, p. 45
carbohydrate, p. 45
lipid, p. 46
fatty acid, p. 46
protein, p. 47
amino acid, p. 47
nucleic acid, p. 48

2.4 chemical reaction, p. 50
reactant, p. 50
product, p. 50
bond energy, p. 51
equilibrium, p. 51
activation energy, p. 53
exothermic, p. 53
endothermic, p. 53

2.5 catalyst, p. 54
enzyme, p. 55
substrate, p. 56

Reviewing Vocabulary

Vocabulary Connections
The vocabulary terms in this chapter are related to each other in various ways. For each group of words below, write a sentence or two to clearly explain how the terms are connected. For example, for the terms *covalent bond* and *molecule*, you could write "A molecule is made of atoms connected by covalent bonds."

1. atom, ion
2. hydrogen bond, cohesion
3. solution, solvent
4. acid, base, pH
5. exothermic, endothermic
6. catalyst, enzyme

Word Origins

7. The word *atom* comes from the Greek word *atomos*, which means "indivisible." Describe the relationship between the Greek term and your understanding of atoms.
8. The *p* in *pH* stands for the German word *Potenz*, which means "power" or "potential." The *H* represents hydrogen ions (H^+). How are these related to the definition of pH?
9. The prefix *mono-* means "one" and the prefix *poly-* means "many." Some lipids are monounsaturated and others are polyunsaturated. Explain the difference between the fatty acids in these different types of lipids.

Reviewing MAIN IDEAS

10. Explain how the combination of electrons, protons, and neutrons results in the neutral charge of an atom.
11. Potassium ions (K^+) have a positive charge. What happens to a potassium atom's electrons when it becomes an ion?
12. Some types of atoms form more than one covalent bond with another atom. What determines how many covalent bonds two atoms can make? Explain.
13. How is hydrogen bonding among water molecules related to the structure of the water molecule? **B.1.1**
14. Explain the difference between solvents and solutes.
15. Describe the relationship between hydrogen ions (H^+) and pH. How is pH related to a solution's acidity?
16. Carbon forms a very large number of compounds. What characteristic of carbon atoms allows the formation of all of these compounds? Explain. **B.1.1**
17. Identify and explain examples of monomers and polymers in carbohydrates, proteins, and nucleic acids.
18. Explain the relationship between a protein's structure and its ability to function. **B.1.2**
19. What are the components of a chemical reaction? **B.3.3**
20. Explain the difference between exothe and endothermic reactions. **B.3.3**
21. Describe the effect of a cataly and reaction rate.
22. What is the role of enzymes i s? **B.1.2**

of Life 61

Indiana Standards Review
Small codes next to items in the Section Assessment and Chapter Assessment indicate questions that address a standard.
Every item in the ***ISTEP+ Test Prep*** *at the end of each chapter addresses a standard.*

Indiana Academic Standards for Science: Biology I

INDIANA STANDARD

Nature of Science

Students should understand that scientific knowledge is gained from observation of natural phenomena and experimentation, by designing and conducting investigations guided by theory, and by evaluating and communicating the results of those investigations according to accepted procedures. Thus, scientific knowledge is scientists' best explanations for the data from many investigations. Further, ideas about objects in the microscopic world that we cannot directly sense are often understood in terms of concepts developed to understand objects in the macroscopic world that we can see and touch. In the science classroom student work should align with this process of science and should be guided by the following principles. These should be woven throughout the daily work that students are doing when learning the content presented in the standard indicators.

WHAT IT MEANS TO YOU

When scientists observe the natural world, they often think of a question or problem. But scientists don't just guess at answers. Instead, they follow series of steps called the scientific method. Scientific methods are a series of steps that scientists use to answer questions and solve problems. Although scientific methods have several steps, there is not a set procedure. Scientists may use all of the steps or just some of the steps. They may even repeat some of the steps or do them in a different order. The goal of scientific methods is to come up with reliable answers and solutions. Scientists use scientific methods to gain insight into the problems they investigate.

NOS.1 Develop explanations based on reproducible data and observations gathered during laboratory investigations.

NOS.2 Recognize that their explanations must be based both on their data and other known information from investigations of others.

NOS.3 Clearly communicate their ideas and results of investigations verbally and in written form using tables, graphs, diagrams, and photographs.

NOS.4 Regularly evaluate the work of their peers and in turn have their work evaluated by their peers.

NOS.5 Apply standard techniques in laboratory investigations to measure physical quantities in appropriate units and convert known quantities to other units as necessary.

NOS.6 Use analogies and models (mathematical and physical) to simplify and represent systems that are difficult to understand or directly experience due to their size, time scale, or complexity, and recognize the limitations of analogies and models.

NOS.7 Focus on the development of explanatory models based on their observations during laboratory investigations.

NOS.8 Explain that the body of scientific knowledge is organized into major theories, which are derived from and supported by the results of many experiments, and allow us to make testable predictions.

IN37

NOS.9 Recognize that new scientific discoveries often lead to a re-evaluation of previously accepted scientific knowledge and of commonly held ideas.

NOS.10 Describe how scientific discoveries lead to the development of new technologies, and conversely how technological advances can lead to scientific discoveries through new experimental methods and equipment.

NOS.11 Explain how scientific knowledge can be used to guide decisions on environmental and social issues.

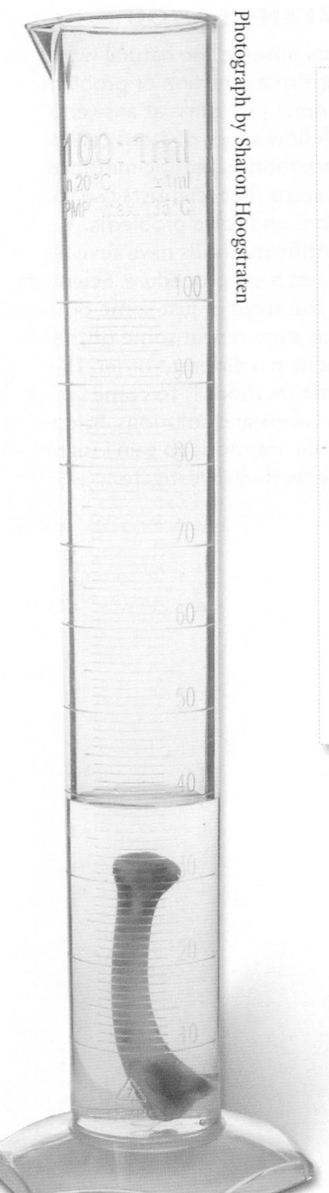

Photograph by Sharon Hoogstraten

SAMPLE QUESTIONS

1 Experimental results that do not support a hypothesis can often be very valuable. Why?

A They can be labeled as a theory instead of a law.
B They can be changed to match the hypothesis for the published article.
C They can cause scientists to develop new experiments that produce additional data.
D They can cause incompetent scientists to lose their jobs and make room for better scientists.

2 What happens when an observation is submitted for peer review?

A The article is proofread before it is published.
B A professor gives a lecture based on a published article.
C The results are looked at closely by other scientific experts.
D Information on the experimental design is included in published works.

Answer: 1C, 2C

INDIANA STANDARD 1

Cellular Chemistry

Core Standard

Describe the basic molecular structure and function of the four major categories of organic compounds (carbohydrates, lipids, proteins and nucleic acids) essential to cellular function.

Core Standard

Describe how the work done in cells is performed by a variety of organic molecules, especially proteins, whose functions depend on the sequence of their monomers and the consequent shape of the molecule.

B.1.1 Describe the structure of the major categories of organic compounds which make up living organisms in terms of their building blocks and the small number of chemical elements (carbon, hydrogen, nitrogen, oxygen, phosphorous, and sulfur) from which they are composed.

B.1.2 Understand that the shape of a molecule determines its role in the many different types of cellular processes including metabolism, homeostasis, growth and development, and heredity, and understand that the majority of these processes involve proteins that act as enzymes.

B.1.3 Explain and give examples of how the function and differentiation of cells is influenced by their external environment, including temperature, acidity and the concentration of certain molecules, and that changes in these conditions may affect how a cell functions.

WHAT IT MEANS TO YOU

Biological molecules are the building blocks of all your body's cells. Chemical reactions in and around the cells in your body break down the food you eat to obtain the proteins, carbohydrates, lipids, water, vitamins, and minerals needed to function. Your body must maintain a delicate balance of conditions at all times in order to function properly.

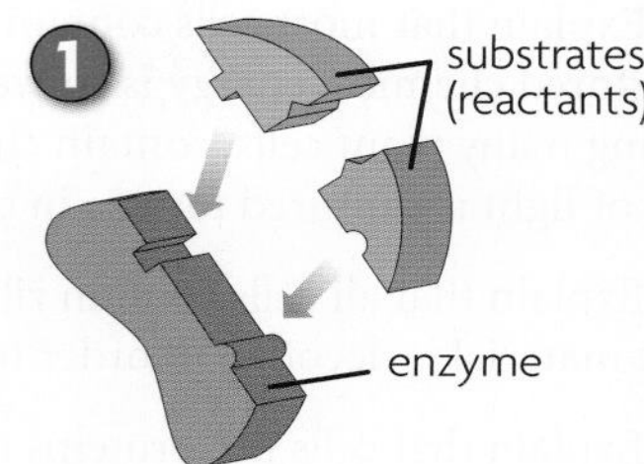

Substrates bind to an enzyme at certain places called active sites.

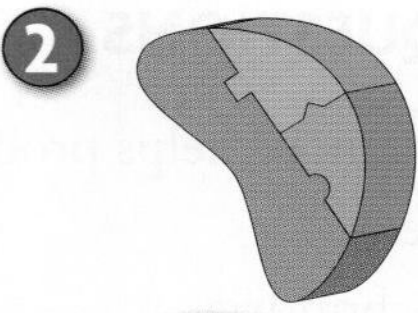

The enzyme brings substrates together and weakens their bonds.

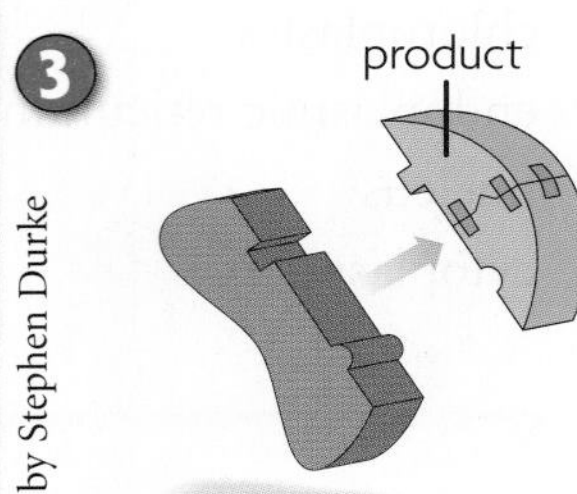

The catalyzed reaction forms a product that is released from the enzyme.

Illustration by Stephen Durke

SAMPLE QUESTIONS

1 Enzymes are special molecules that help chemical reactions take place. Which of the following is the most true about enzymes?

- **A** Enzymes require high temperatures to work.
- **B** Enzymes must be replaced after each reaction.
- **C** Enzymes need to increase the pH of a solution to work.
- **D** Enzymes decrease the amount of energy needed to start a chemical reaction.

2 Cell membranes consist of a double layer of phospholipids. A variety of other molecules, including proteins, are embedded within the phospholipids layers. These proteins most likely function in

- **A** helping the cell divide successfully.
- **B** producing DNA for the cell.
- **C** helping material cross the membrane.
- **D** converting energy into forms the cell can use.

Answer: 1A, 2C

INDIANA STUDENT GUIDE

Cellular Structure

Core Standard

Describe features that are common to all cells and contrast those with distinctive features that allow cells to carry out specific functions.

B.2.1 Describe features common to all cells that are essential for growth and survival, and explain their functions.

B.2.2 Describe the structure of a cell membrane and explain how it regulates the transport of materials into and out of the cell and prevents harmful materials from entering the cell.

B.2.3 Explain that most cells contain mitochondria, the key sites of cellular respiration, where stored chemical energy is converted into useable energy for the cell and some cells, including many plant cells, contain chloroplasts, the key sites of photosynthesis, where the energy of light is captured for use in chemical work.

B.2.4 Explain that all cells contain ribosomes, the key sites for protein synthesis, where genetic material is decoded in order to form unique proteins.

B.2.5 Explain that cells use proteins to form structures, including cilia, flagella, which allow them to carry out specific functions, including movement, adhesion, and absorption.

B.2.6 Investigate a variety of different cell types and relate the proportion of different organelles within these cells to their functions.

WHAT IT MEANS TO YOU

All living things are made up of one or more cells. In fact, your body is made of millions of cells that together carry out all of your life functions. As you read these words, muscle cells allow your eyes to scan the page. Nerve cells transmit chemical and electrical signals from your eyes to your brain.

SAMPLE QUESTIONS

1 What organelle helps produce chemical energy in the plant's green leaves?

A nucleus
B mitochondria
C chloroplast
D membrane

2 Where in the eukaryotic cell are proteins and lipids produced?

A chloroplastss
B endoplasmic reticulum
C nucleus
D cytoplasm

Answer: 1C, 2B

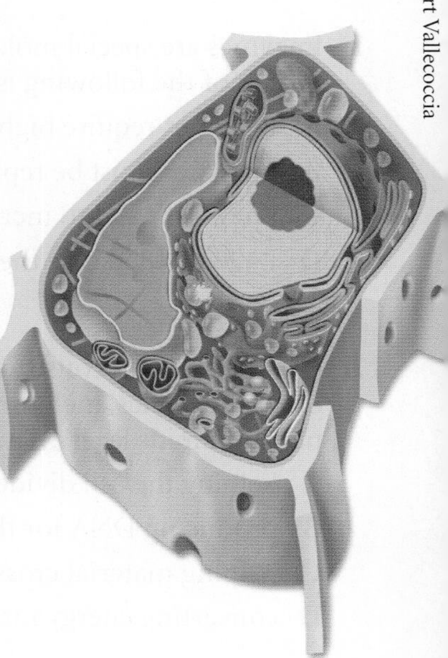

Illustration by Bart Vallecoccia

INDIANA
STANDARD 3

Matter Cycles and Energy Transfer

Core Standard
Describe how the sun's energy is captured and used to construct sugar molecules which can be used as a form of energy or serve as building blocks of organic molecules.

Core Standard
Diagram how matter and energy cycle through an ecosystem.

WHAT IT MEANS TO YOU

Energy is required by all living things. When you consume food, that food is broken down and used to produce energy. Your body uses that energy to maintain homeostasis, for motion, for cell repair, and numerous other tasks. Much of the energy consumed by organisms is released into the atmosphere as heat. Energy can be neither created or destroyed–just converted from one form to another.

B.3.1 Describe how some organisms capture the sun's energy through the process of photosynthesis by converting carbon dioxide and water into high energy compounds and releasing oxygen.

B.3.2 Describe how most organisms can combine and recombine the elements contained in sugar molecules into a variety of biologically essential compounds by utilizing the energy from cellular respiration.

B.3.3 Recognize and describe that metabolism consists of all of the biochemical reactions that occur inside cells, including the production, modification, transport, and exchange of materials that are required for the maintenance of life.

B.3.4 Describe how matter cycles through an ecosystem by way of food chains and food webs and how organisms convert that matter into a variety of organic molecules to be used in part in their own cellular structures.

B.3.5 Describe how energy from the sun flows through an ecosystem by way of food chains and food webs and only a small portion of that energy is used by individual organisms while the majority of energy is lost as heat.

INDIANA STUDENT GUIDE

SAMPLE QUESTIONS

1 Which of the following is necessary in order for plants to undergo photosynthesis?

A nitrogen
B ATP
C carbon dioxide
D oxygen

Answer: 1C

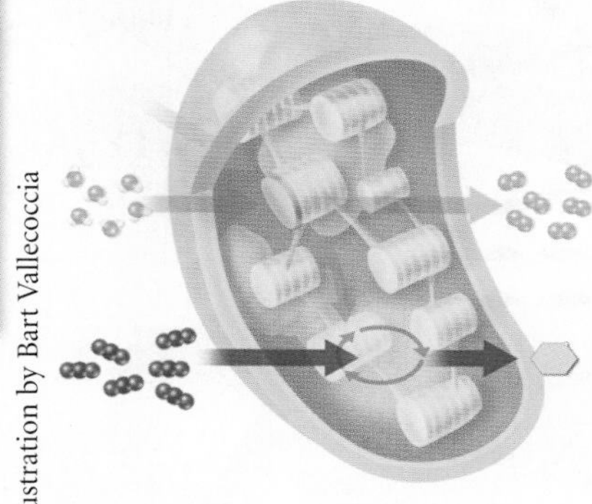

Illustration by Bart Vallecoccia

IN41

Interdependence

Core Standard

Describe the relationship between living and nonliving components of ecosystems and describe how that relationship is in flux due to natural changes and human actions.

WHAT IT MEANS TO YOU

You are part of an ecosystem, which includes all of the living and nonliving things in an area. Ecology is the study of interactions among these living and nonliving things. Most of your daily actions have some kind of effect on the ecosystems in which you live and those you visit. Some actions can even affect ecosystems on a global scale.

B.4.1 Explain that the amount of life an environment can support is limited by the available energy, water, oxygen, and minerals, and by the ability of ecosystems to recycle the remains of dead organisms.

B.4.2 Describe how human activities and natural phenomena can change the flow and of matter and energy in an ecosystem and how those changes impact other species.

B.4.3 Describe the consequences of introducing non-native species into an ecosystem and identify the impact it may have on that ecosystem.

B.4.4 Describe how climate, the pattern of matter and energy flow, the birth and death of new organisms, and the interaction between those organisms contribute to the long term stability of an ecosystem.

Illustration by Richard Bonson/Wildlife Art Ltd.

IN42

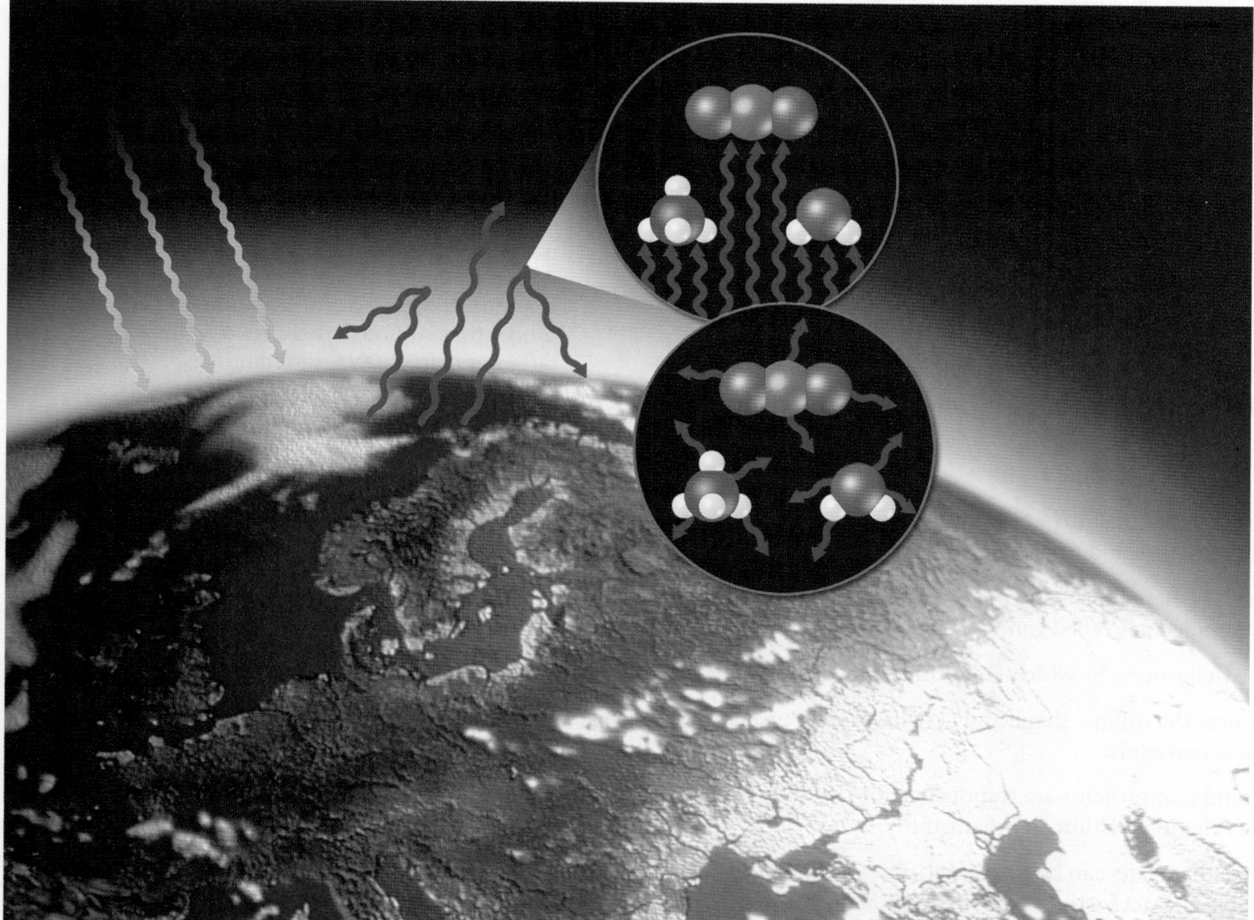

SAMPLE QUESTIONS

1 Kudzu is a vine that was introduced to the United States from Japan in 1876 to help control erosion. It grew so quickly that it was declared a weed in 1972. Kudzu destroys forests by smothering trees and preventing access to sunlight. In this scenario, kudzu is best defined as a

A predatory species

B emigrating species

C symbiotic species

D nonnative species

2 Fungi make stored nutrients available to other organisms. What is this process called?

A predation

B decomposition

C photosynthesis

D competition

Answer: 1D, 2B

IN43

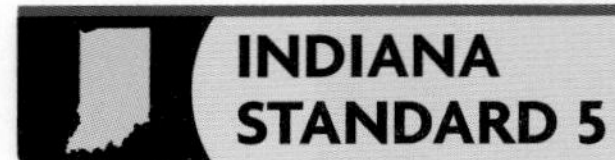

Molecular Basis of Heredity

Core Standard

Describe the basic structure of DNA and how this structure enables DNA to function as the hereditary molecule that directs the production of RNA and proteins.

Core Standard

Understand that proteins largely determine the traits of an organism.

WHAT IT MEANS TO YOU

If the DNA in each of your cells were stretched out from end to end, it would measure more than two meters. A single DNA molecule is a chain of repeating units that carries code that controls protein production. Although there are only four different units in DNA, different combinations and sequences of these units produce the genetic diversity of all life as we know it.

B.5.1 Describe the relationship between chromosomes and DNA along with their basic structure and function.

B.5.2 Describe how hereditary information passed from parents to offspring is encoded in regions of DNA molecules called genes.

B.5.3 Describe the process by which DNA directs the production of protein within a cell.

B.5.4 Explain how the unique shape and activity of each protein is determined by the sequence of its amino acids.

B.5.5 Understand that proteins are responsible for the observable traits of an organism and for most of the functions within an organism.

B.5.6 Recognize that traits can be structural, physiological or behavioral and can include readily observable characteristics at the organismal level or less recognizable features at the molecular and cellular level.

SAMPLE QUESTIONS

1 During transcription, what type of RNA transports the copy of the DNA message?

A mRNA
B tRNA
C rRNA
D dRNA

2 CCAGCAUAUGCC

A strand of messenger RNA contains the sequence shown above. How many amino acids are coded for in this sequence?

A 3
B 4
C 6
D 12

Answer: 1A, 2B

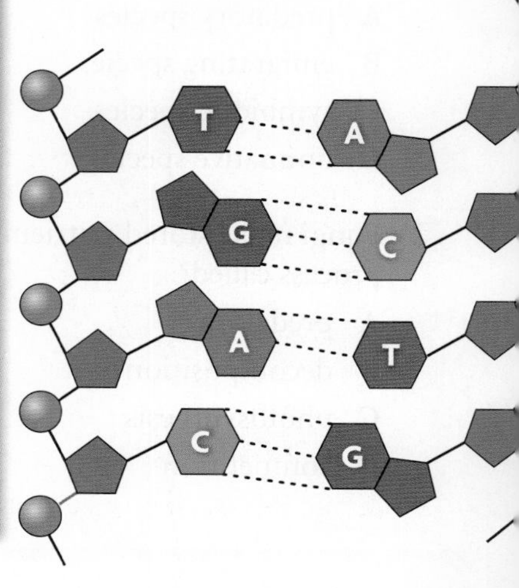

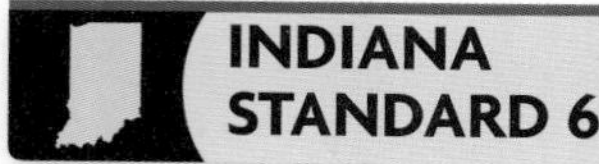

INDIANA STANDARD 6

Cellular Reproduction

Core Standard
Explain the processes, both mitosis and meiosis, by which new cells are formed from existing cells and how in multicellular organisms, groups of cells cooperate to perform essential functions within an organism.

Core Standard
Explain the cellular processes that occur to generate natural genetic variations between parents and offspring.

B.6.1 Describe the process of mitosis and explain that this process ordinarily results in daughter cells with a genetic make-up identical to the parent cells.

B.6.2 Understand that most cells of a multicellular organism contain the same genes, but develop from a single cell (e.g., a fertilized egg) in different ways due to differential gene expression.

B.6.3 Explain that in multicellular organisms the zygote produced during fertilization undergoes a series of cell divisions that lead to clusters of cells that go on to specialize and become the organism's tissues and organs.

B.6.4 Describe and model the process of meiosis and explain the relationship between the genetic make-up of the parent cell and the daughter cells (gametes).

B.6.5 Explain how, in sexual reproduction, crossing over, independent assortment, and random fertilization, result in offspring that are genetically different from the parents.

WHAT IT MEANS TO YOU

All cells in multicellular organisms were created by the replication of one original cell. So all the cells in the organism contain the same DNA. Yet these cells differ in shape and function because they are specialized. Each cell expresses only the genes necessary for its function. Gene expression is regulated so that not only are certain proteins produced at specific times, but the amount produced is also controlled to meet the needs of the cell.

SAMPLE QUESTIONS

1 The cells that make up the skin of an individual have some functions different from the cells that make up the liver because

A all cells have a common ancestor.
B different cells have different genetic material.
C environment and past history have no influence on cell function.
D different parts of genetic instructions are used in different types of cells.

2 After a series of cell divisions, an embryo develops different types of body cells such as muscle cells, nerve cells, and blood cells. This development occurs because

A the genetic code changes as the cells divide.
B different segments of the genetic instructions are used to produce different types of cells.
C different genetic instructions are synthesized to meet the needs of new types of cells.
D some parts of the genetic materials are lost as a result of fertilization.

Answer: 1D, 2B

INDIANA STUDENT GUIDE

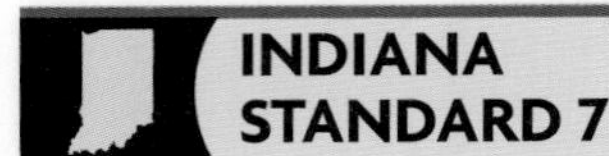

Genetics

Core Standard

Explain how the genetic information from parents determines the unique characteristics of their offspring.

B.7.1 Distinguish between dominant and recessive alleles and determine the phenotype that would result from the different possible combinations of alleles in an offspring.

B.7.2 Describe dominant, recessive, codominant, sex-linked, incompletely dominant, multiply allelic, and polygenic traits and illustrate their inheritance patterns over multiple generations.

B.7.3 Determine the likelihood of the appearance of a specific trait in an offspring given the genetic make-up of the parents.

B.7.4 Explain the process by which a cell copies its DNA and identify factors that can damage DNA and cause changes in its nucleotide sequence.

B.7.5 Explain and demonstrate how inserting, substituting or deleting segments of a DNA molecule can alter a gene, which is then passed to every cell that develops from it and that the results may be beneficial, harmful or have little or no effect on the organism.

WHAT IT MEANS TO YOU

You may look more like one of your parents than the other, or you may be a perfect blend of both of your parents. If you've ever wondered why, the answers lie within Mendel's laws. These laws explain how chance and probability affect which traits you received. So even if both of your parents are very tall with dark hair, there may be a chance that you are short with light hair.

SAMPLE QUESTIONS

1 Mendel proposed that the probability of an offspring getting one gene does not affect the probability of getting a different gene. Today we know that this is not always true. Which statement best describes why two genes might always be inherited together?

A Some genes are near each other on the same chromosome.

B Some chromosomes always bond with specific genes at the centromere.

C Some DNA gets repeated, causing a gene to appear on more than one chromosome.

D Some centromeres store additional genes that always get passed on during meiosis.

Answer: 1A

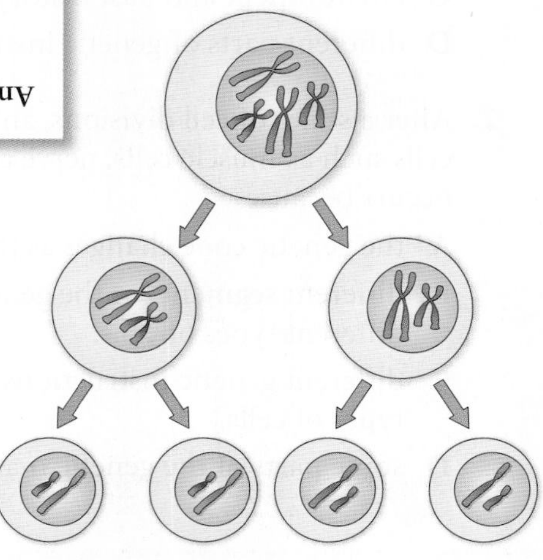

INDIANA STANDARD 8

Evolution

Core Standard
Describe how biochemical, fossil, anatomical, developmental, and genetic findings are used to determine relationships among organisms, producing modern classification systems.

Core Standard
Describe how modern evolutionary theory provides an explanation of the history of life on earth and the similarities between organisms that exist today.

WHAT IT MEANS TO YOU

All of the living things in your environment have adaptations that arose through natural selection. The wings of birds, the compound eyes of ants, and the shapes of leaves are all traits that are advantageous in certain environments. As traits are selected for, and others are selected against, the genetic makeup of species changes over time.

B.8.1 Explain how anatomical and molecular similarities among organisms suggests that life on earth began as simple, one-celled organisms about 4 billion years ago and multicellular organisms evolved later.

B.8.2 Explain how organisms are classified and named based on their evolutionary relationships into taxonomic categories.

B.8.3 Use anatomical and molecular evidence to establish evolutionary relationships between organisms.

B.8.4 Understand that molecular evidence supports the anatomical evidence for these evolutionary relationships and provides additional information about the order in which different lines of descent branched.

B.8.5 Describe how due to genetic variations, environmental forces, and reproductive pressures, organisms with beneficial traits are more likely to survive, reproduce, and pass on their genetic information.

B.8.6 Explain how genetic variation within a population (a species) can be attributed to mutations as well as a random assortment of existing genes.

B.8.7 Describe the modern scientific theory of the origins and history of life on earth, and evaluate the evidence that supports it.

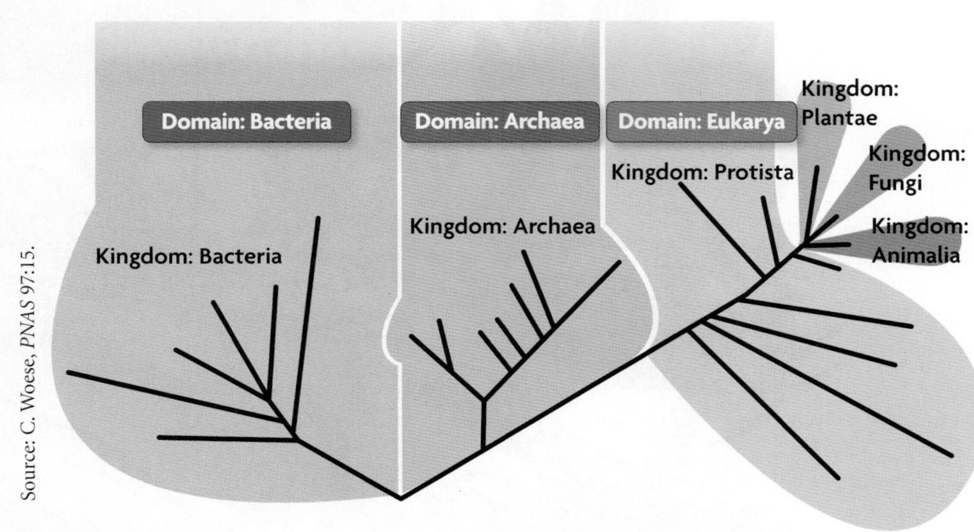

Source: C. Woese, *PNAS* 97:15.

INDIANA STUDENT GUIDE

SAMPLE QUESTIONS

1 Herbicides are used to keep weeds from growing in farm fields and gardens. After many years, farmers might find that a weed species is no longer affected by a particular herbicide. This occurred because the herbicide

A killed most of the plants in the population.

B caused mutations in the plant species' gene pool

C caused another plant to go extinct

D selected for plants that were able to survive and reproduce

2 A species of tropical bird carries a dominant gene that causes it to lay bright-colored eggs. The bright color of the shells makes the eggs more visible to predators. What will most likely occur in this population over time?

A Birds who lay bright-colored eggs will increase in number.

B Birds who lay bright-colored eggs will decrease in number.

C The number of bright-colored egg laying birds will remain the same.

D This species of tropical bird will become extinct.

Answer: 1D, 2B

Illustration by Alan Male

UNIT 1

Introducing Biology

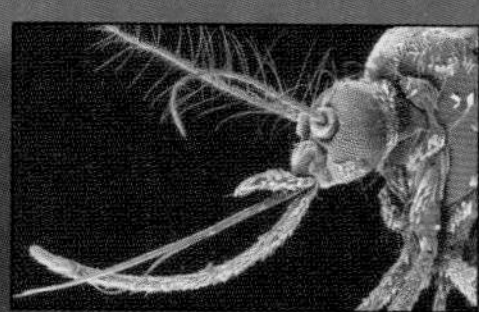

CHAPTER 1
Biology in the 21st Century 2

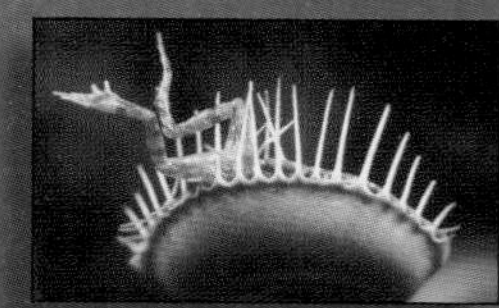

CHAPTER 2
Chemistry of Life 34

INTERNET MAGAZINE
When Knowledge and Ethics Collide 64

TECHNOLOGY Genetic Testing

CAREER Geneticist

Unit Project

Purpose **Understand how to structure and write a formal laboratory report.**

Overview Students will write a formal laboratory report based on either Louis Pasteur's or Francesco Redi's experiments on spontaneous generation. Students will

- conduct a literature search to find information on the experiments
- identify the problem or question each scientist was trying to answer and write the hypothesis, experimental procedure, data and observations, and conclusions for his experiment
- write a laboratory report based on the chosen experiment

Preparation Make a copy of the project description and rubric for each student (*Unit Resource Book,* pp. 61–62), and generate a timetable. A description of the experiments is included as an optional student handout.

Project Management Allow two weeks for the completion of the project. Students will need to use some creativity when writing the materials list, procedure, and safety concerns.

Unit Resource Book Unit 1 Project, pp. 61–64

CHAPTER 1

Indiana Resource Preview

Print Resources

Biology in the 21st Century

INDIANA STANDARDS		Sections	PAGES and PACING	UNIT RESOURCE BOOK
	1.1	**The Study of Life** **KEY CONCEPT** Biologists study life in all its forms.	pp. 4–6 30 minutes	URB pages 1–4
	1.2	**Unifying Themes of Biology** **KEY CONCEPT** Unifying themes connect concepts from many fields of biology.	pp. 7–11 30 minutes	URB pages 5–8
		DATA ANALYSIS: Qualitative and Quantitative Types of Data	p. 12 30 minutes	URB page 21
NOS.8, NOS.9	1.3	**Scientific Thinking and Processes** **KEY CONCEPT** Science is a way of thinking, questioning, and gathering evidence.	pp. 13–17 30 minutes	URB pages 9–12
B.1.2, NOS.4, NOS.5		CHAPTER INVESTIGATION: Manipulating Independent Variables	p. 18 45 minutes	**Lab Binder** Introducing Biology pages 1–4
NOS.10	1.4	**Biologists' Tools and Technology** **KEY CONCEPT** Technology continually changes the way biologists work.	pp. 19–23 30 minutes	URB pages 13–16
NOS.11	1.5	**Biology and Your Future** **KEY CONCEPT** Understanding biology can help you make informed decisions.	pp. 24–27 30 minutes	URB pages 17–20
NOS.1, NOS.4		OPTIONS FOR INQUIRY	pp. 28–29 45 minutes, 45 minutes	**Lab Binder** Introducing Biology pages 5–8
		Chapter Review	pp. 30–33	**Assessment Book** Chapter Tests A, B pages 11–18

INDIANA STANDARDS

B.1.2 Understand that the shape of a molecule determines its role in the many different types of cellular processes including metabolism, homeostasis, growth and development, and heredity, and understand that the majority of these processes involve proteins that act as enzymes.

NOS.1 Develop explanations based on reproducible data and observations gathered during laboratory investigations.

NOS.4 Regularly evaluate the work of their peers and in turn have their work evaluated by their peers.

NOS.8 Explain that the body of scientific knowledge is organized into major theories, which are derived from and supported by the results of many experiments, and allow us to make testable predictions.

NOS.9 Recognize that new scientific discoveries often lead to a re-evaluation of previously accepted scientific knowledge and of commonly held ideas.

NOS.10 Describe how scientific discoveries lead to the development of new technologies, and conversely how technological advances can lead to scientific discoveries through new experimental methods and equipment.

NOS.11 Explain how scientific knowledge can be used to guide decisions environmental and social issues.

Labs

PUPIL EDITION LABS

Manipulating Independent Variables, p. 18 Students investigate how pH or enzyme concentration affects the breakdown of protein. **Lab Binder** pp. 1–4	**Time:** 45 minutes **Materials:** 4 graduated cylinders with gelatin, 4 marbles, metric ruler, 10 mL water, 2 10-mL graduated cylinders, 10 mL detergent (10%, 30% or 50%), 10 mL detergent (pH 4, 7, and 10)
Life Under a Microscope, Section 4, p. 22 Students observe and describe the characteristics of organisms found in a drop of pond water. **Lab Binder** pp. 9–10	**Time:** 20 minutes **Materials:** 1 drop pond water, eyedropper, microscope slide, cover slip, microscope

OPTIONS FOR INQUIRY

Manipulating Plant Growth, p. 28 Students test how plants grow in response to external stimuli. **Lab Binder** pp. 5–6	**Time:** 45 minutes **Materials:** 3 bean plants, 10 cm masking tape, permanent marker, light source, 3 wooden sticks, 1 m string, metric ruler, water, 250-mL beaker
Biology in the News, p. 29 Students analyze a biology news story. **Lab Binder** pp. 7–8	**Time:** 45 minutes **Materials:** newspaper

LAB BINDER Unit 1 Introducing Biology

Additional Investigation: Measuring Microscopic Objects, pp. 11–15

Biotechnology Labs: Biotechnology in Food Products, pp. 29–32; Fruit Preservation, pp. 33–36

LAB GENERATOR

A searchable CD of all labs in the program in editable format, including forensic, probeware, and biotechnology labs.

Presentation Tools

POWER PRESENTATIONS

Presentation Chapter 1
PowerPresentations for each section incorporate images and clips from the Media Gallery. Includes Note Navigator for each section.

MEDIA GALLERY

Contains the following images and video clips, as well as animations, simulations, and forms of visuals from the book.

Adaptation

Experimental design

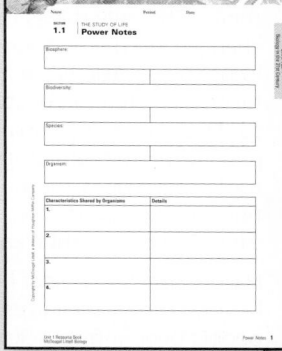

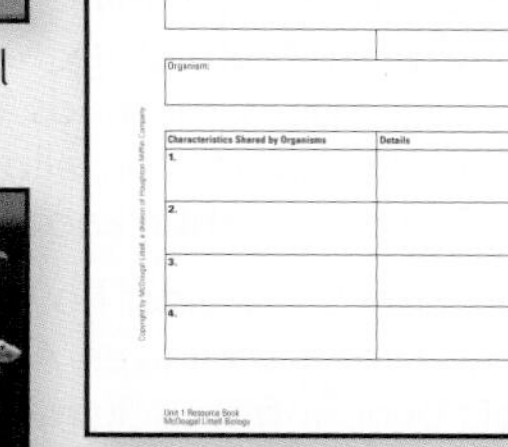

Power Notes

TEM

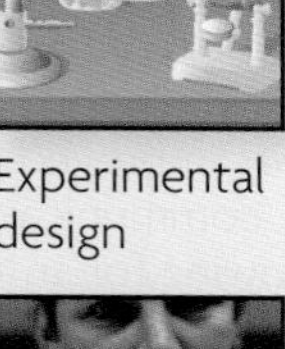
Mouse growing ear

VIDEO

View a series of short video clips in which researchers use the scientific method to explore a problem.

ANIMATED BIOLOGY

Cells Through Different Microscopes

Experimental Design

TRANSPARENCIES

Scientific Thinking T1

Online BIOLOGY CLASSZONE.COM

BioZine
Animated Biology
Interactive Review
SciLinks
Resource Centers

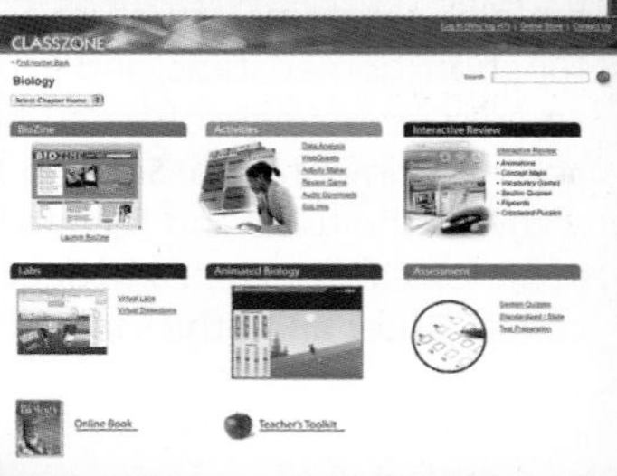

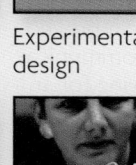

CHAPTER 1

▼ Focus and Motivate

What is biology in the 21st century?

Explain to students that even in the 21st century, biology is still the study of living things. The only things that have changed are the methods used to study living things. **Ask,** What changes have taken place that make studying biology so different now compared with in the past? Modern technology has improved tools, techniques, methods, communication, and transportation, allowing for an explosion of scientific knowledge.

Have students consider how the study of biology affects their lives. **Ask,** How do people benefit from scientific advancements in biology? The knowledge helps people understand the nature of life, and prepares them to make informed decisions about health, medicine, genetics, and the environment.

BIOZINE ClassZone.com

Students can access BioZine at **ClassZone.com** to learn about some of the latest research in the biological sciences.

In a Hurry?

Students may be familiar with the material in **Section 1.1** on the characteristics of life. The critical material in this chapter is found in **Sections 1.2** and **1.3,** which introduce unifying themes of biology—systems, structure and function, homeostasis, and evolution—and discuss aspects of scientific thinking and experimentation. **Section 1.4** covers some of the tools and technology used in biological research, and **Section 1.5** covers issues and ethics in biology.

CHAPTER 1 Biology in the 21st Century

KEY CONCEPTS

1.1 The Study of Life
Biologists study life in all its forms.

1.2 Unifying Themes of Biology
Unifying themes connect concepts from many fields of biology.

1.3 Scientific Thinking and Processes
Science is a way of thinking, questioning, and gathering evidence.

1.4 Biologists' Tools and Technology
Technology continually changes the way biologists work.

1.5 Biology and Your Future
Understanding biology can help you make informed decisions.

Online BIOLOGY CLASSZONE.COM

Animated BIOLOGY
View animated chapter concepts.
- Cells Through Different Microscopes
- Experimental Design

BIOZINE
Keep current with biology news.
- Featured stories
- News feeds
- Careers

RESOURCE CENTER
Get more information on
- Biodiversity
- Scientific Tools and Technology

Student Activity

Purpose **Have students recognize that the organization of matter and use of energy in living things is distinctly different from the interaction of energy and matter in nonliving things.**

Materials (per team)

Each team will need either pictures or physical samples of various objects, such as the following:

- crystal, rock, or mineral
- plant or insect
- apple, apple seed
- wood or shell

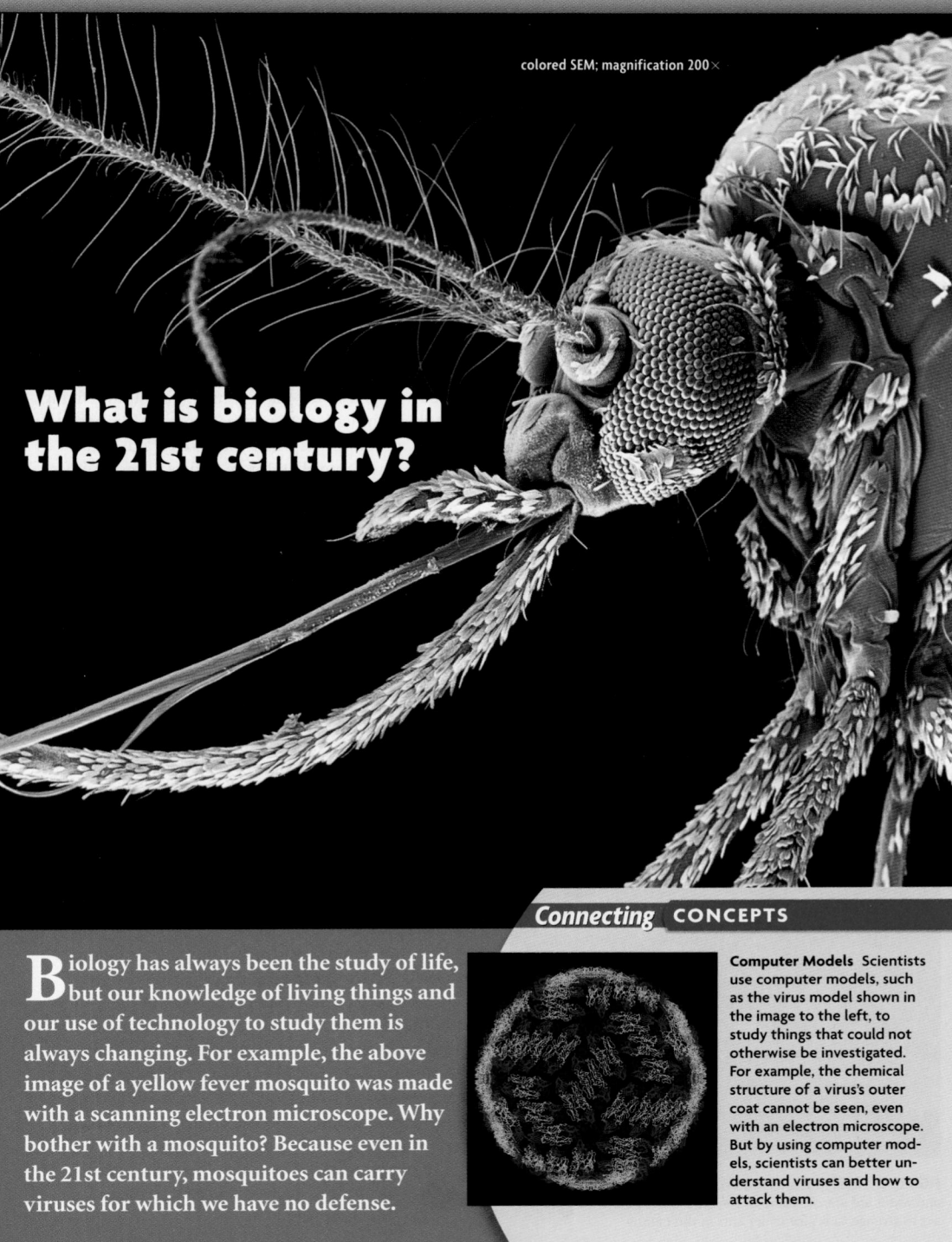

colored SEM; magnification 200×

What is biology in the 21st century?

Connecting CONCEPTS

Biology has always been the study of life, but our knowledge of living things and our use of technology to study them is always changing. For example, the above image of a yellow fever mosquito was made with a scanning electron microscope. Why bother with a mosquito? Because even in the 21st century, mosquitoes can carry viruses for which we have no defense.

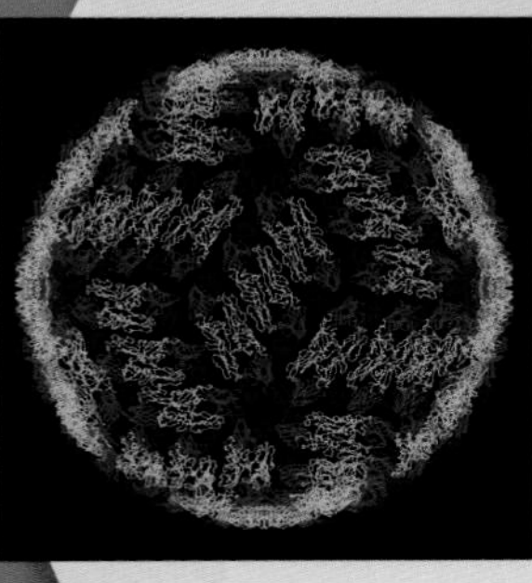

Computer Models Scientists use computer models, such as the virus model shown in the image to the left, to study things that could not otherwise be investigated. For example, the chemical structure of a virus's outer coat cannot be seen, even with an electron microscope. But by using computer models, scientists can better understand viruses and how to attack them.

Introduce Point out that in the specimens provided, matter has been organized with an input of energy. Have students consider which of their specimens are alive or have been. Ask them to identify what is distinctive about the behavior of matter and energy in living things as opposed to nonliving things.

Discuss Have teams summarize their conclusions. Compare a crystal to a shell. **Ask,** How are these objects alike, how are they different? Neither is alive yet both "grow" as energy and matter interact in an organized way; however the living organism that produced the shell is capable of ongoing, self-organizing and self-maintaining activity.

Discuss a seed. It is not living in the ordinary sense, as a plant is, but it has the potential to grow into a plant given the proper conditions. **Ask,** Why is reproduction considered a characteristic of life when not all living things reproduce? Life comes from life; reproduction is necessary for the continuity of life.

Activate Prior Knowledge

Point to the title of the chapter. **Ask,** Why would biology of the 21st century be any different from the biology of the 1990s? An accumulation of new information as well as reinterpretation of old information change the way biologists think about biological processes. Also, technology and techniques improve constantly.

Preview Vocabulary

Greek and Latin Word Origins Point out to students the Vocabulary Handbook, pages R18–19 at the end of the book, includes a selection of Greek and Latin word parts common to biology.

Academic Vocabulary Point out the list of Academic Vocabulary in the Vocabulary Handbook on pages R20–21. Tell students that, in addition to the science vocabulary highlighted in the text, there are words they need to know when reading, writing, or speaking about any academic subject. Two such words used in Chapter 1 are *unity* and *diversity*. Have students define these antonyms in their own words and think of other words with a similar appearance or meaning.

Similar words that appear in the text include *diversity, variety, different, biodiversity, variability, variable, unity,* and *unifying*. Encourage students to look for words they can add to each word family as they read the text and to note the different ways and contexts in which the words are used.

English Learners It is important to start a conversation with the English learners in your classroom. **Ask**

- What words do you associate with science?
- Are they very different when spoken in your home language?

As you listen, assess students' language level. You may need to adapt your language level in the classroom to be sure that what you say is understood by all students.

▼ Plan and Prepare

Objectives

- Define and give examples of Earth's biodiversity.
- Summarize the characteristics that all living things share.

Section Resources

Unit Resource Book Study Guide pp. 1–2 Power Notes p. 3 Reinforcement p. 4
Interactive Reader Chapter 1 **Spanish Study Guide** pp. 1–2
Biology Toolkit pp. C1, C26
Technology Power Presentation 1.1 Media Gallery DVD Online Quiz 1.1

Activate Prior Knowledge Students are probably familiar with the term *diversity* as it relates to the variation of physical traits seen in human beings. **Ask,** What do you think a biologist means by the word *biodiversity?* Students will probably mention all the different forms of life on Earth. Help students understand that diversity can exist across a species, which offers the opportunity for adaptation. It also exists as species diversity across an ecosystem.

▼ Teach

TEACH FROM VISUALS

FIGURE 1.1 Some honeypot ants in a colony gorge themselves with food, hang from the ceiling of their nest, and regurgitate food for the worker ants. **Ask,** How do honeypot ants survive in a hostile environment? Some of the ants store food and water for the rest of the colony.

1.1 The Study of Life

KEY CONCEPT Biologists study life in all its forms.

MAIN IDEAS

- Earth is home to an incredible diversity of life.
- All organisms share certain characteristics.

VOCABULARY

biosphere, p. 4
biodiversity, p. 5
species, p. 5
biology, p. 5
organism, p. 5
cell, p. 5
metabolism, p. 6
DNA, p. 6

Connect It's a warm summer evening. Maybe you're laughing and joking while waiting to eat at a family barbecue. As you sit down for dinner, mosquitoes flying around have the same idea. But their dinner is you, not the barbecue. Probably the most attention that you pay to mosquitoes is when you take careful aim before smacking them. Biologists have a somewhat different view of mosquitoes, unless of course they are the ones being bitten. But in those times of logic and reason, a biologist can see a mosquito as just one example of the great diversity of life found on Earth.

MAIN IDEA

Earth is home to an incredible diversity of life.

In Yellowstone National Park, there are pools of hot water as acidic as vinegar. It might be difficult to believe, but those pools are also full of life. Life is found in the darkness at the deepest ocean floors and in thousands-of-years-old ice in Antarctica. Not only are living things found just about anywhere on Earth but they also come in a huge variety of shapes and sizes. Plants, for example, include tiny mosses and giant redwood trees on which moss can grow. There are massive animals such as the blue whale, which is the largest animal living on Earth. There are tiny animals such as the honeypot ant in **FIGURE 1.1**, which can store so much food for other ants that it swells to the size of a grape.

FIGURE 1.1 Honeypot ants live in deserts where food and water are scarce. Some of the ants in the colony act as storage tanks for other ants in the colony.

The Biosphere

All living things and all the places they are found on Earth make up the **biosphere.** Every part of the biosphere is connected, however distantly, with every other part of the biosphere. The biosphere includes land environments such as deserts, grasslands, and different types of forests. The biosphere also includes saltwater and freshwater environments, as well as portions of the atmosphere. And different types of plants, animals, and other living things are found in different areas of the biosphere. Even the inside of your nose, which is home to bacteria and fungi, is a part of the biosphere.

Differentiated Instruction

ENGLISH LEARNERS

Have students write definitions of the vocabulary terms in their notebooks in their home language and then in English. Refer them to the *Multilanguage Glossary* to check their work and, if necessary, revise their definitions. The *Multilanguage Glossary* includes all key terms in the text and their definitions in English, as well as in Spanish, Chinese, Vietnamese, Khmer, Laotian, Arabic, Haitian Creole, Russian, and Portuguese.

BELOW LEVEL

Have students survey their textbooks by completing the following tasks:

- Read the unit and chapter titles in the Contents and note how chapters are organized into units.
- Turn to several chapters and note how the subheadings are related to the main ideas listed under the Key Concepts.
- Locate a list of vocabulary words, and then find each of them within the chapter.

Biology Toolkit, Textbook Survey, p. C1

Biodiversity

Across the biosphere, the variety of life is called biological diversity, or **biodiversity.** Biodiversity generally increases from Earth's poles to the equator. This means that greater biodiversity is found in warmer areas. Why is biodiversity greater closer to the equator? More living things are able to survive in consistently warm temperatures than in areas that have large temperature changes during a year. Because more living things, especially plants, can survive in warm areas, those areas provide a larger, more consistent food supply for more species.

VISUAL VOCAB

Across the **biosphere,** the variety of life is called **biodiversity.**

Biodiversity is **greater** closer to the equator.

biosphere = everywhere life exists

There are several different ways *species* can be defined. One definition of **species** is a particular type of living things that can reproduce by interbreeding among themselves. About 2 million different living species have been identified, but biologists estimate that tens of millions of species remain to be discovered. Over half of the known species are insects, but no one knows how many insect species actually exist.

TAKING NOTES

Use a two-column chart to help you summarize vocabulary terms and concepts.

term or concept	meaning

Every year, biologists discover about 10,000 new species. In contrast, some scientists estimate that over 50,000 species die out, or become extinct, every year. Occasionally, however, a species thought to be extinct is found again. For example, the ivory-billed woodpecker was thought to have become extinct in 1944, but a team of scientists reported seeing it in Arkansas in 2004.

A Apply Describe biodiversity in terms of species.

MAIN IDEA

All organisms share certain characteristics.

Biology is the scientific study of all forms of life, or all types of organisms. An **organism** is any individual living thing. All organisms on Earth share certain characteristics, but an actual definition of life is not simple. Why? The categories of living and nonliving are constructed by humans, and they are not perfect. For example, some things, such as viruses, fall into a middle range between living and nonliving. They show some, but not all, of the characteristics of living things.

Cells All organisms are made up of one or more cells. A **cell** is the basic unit of life. In fact, microscopic, single-celled organisms are the most common forms of life on Earth. A single-celled, or unicellular, organism carries out all of the functions of life, just as you do. Larger organisms that you see every day are made of many cells, and are called multicellular organisms. Different types of cells in a multicellular organism have specialized functions, as shown in **FIGURE 1.2.** Your muscle cells contract and relax, your stomach cells secrete digestive juices, and your brain cells interpret sensory information. Together, specialized cells make you a complete organism.

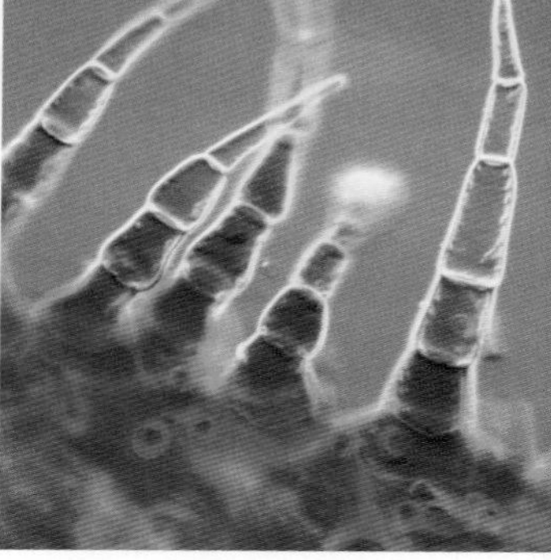

FIGURE 1.2 Cells can work together in specialized structures, such as these leaf hairs that protect a leaf from insects. (LM; magnification 700×)

PRE-AP*

Suggest that students take notes by using the Cornell note-taking method. Have them mark a heavy line about two inches from the left side of their paper, and another across the bottom about two inches from the edge. They should take abbreviated notes in outline form in the large square on the right, and note key points in the column on the left.

As soon after class as possible, students should use the bottom area to summarize in their own words the content of the page of notes.

*Pre-AP is a registered trademark of the College Board, which was not involved in the production of and does not endorse this product.

Biology Toolkit, Cornell Notes, p. C26

ONLINE BIOLOGY Go to the chapter Resource Center at **ClassZone.com** for additional resources and information on biodiversity. Students can also do an analysis of biodiversity of marine organisms in Options for Inquiry on page 29.

Take It Further

The moment of extinction occurs when the last individual of a species dies. Considering the history of life on Earth, it is common for a species to go extinct within 10 million years of its first appearance, although some species have continued to exist for hundreds of millions of years. In some cases, new species, or **daughter species,** evolve from a parent species. These organisms would have most of the parent species' genetic information. Extinction of a parent species when daughter species or subspecies still exist is called **pseudo-extinction.** For example, biologists categorize dinosaurs as *pseudoextinct* because some of their descendants, birds, survive today. Students will learn about patterns of extinction in Chapter 12.

TEACH FROM VISUALS

FIGURE 1.2 Point out that the leaf hairs are made up of several specialized epidermal cells. Tell students that a multicellular organism's specialized cells develop through the processes of cell determination and differentiation, which are covered in Chapter 34.

Answers

A Apply Biodiversity is the number of different species in a given area, from a single community to the entire Earth.

▼ Teach *continued*

Take It Further

Tell students that the behavior of the male jaw fish shown in **FIGURE 1.3** is an example of **paternal mouth brooding.** Males may "churn" eggs by spitting them out, then taking them back in quickly. This is done to remove debris as well as to rotate and aerate the eggs so the embryos develop properly. Behaviors such as this are referred to **reproductive strategies,** even though the behavior may be instinctive and not learned. Students will learn more about animal behavior in Chapter 27.

Answers

A Summarize All living things are made of one or more cells, need energy, respond to the environment, and have the ability to reproduce.

▼ Assess and Reteach

Assess Use the Online Quiz or Section Quiz (*Assessment Book,* p. 5).

Reteach Introduce students to the Note-taking Handbook at the back of their textbook. Use the graphic organizer Supporting Main Ideas on page R22 to review the section. Copy each of the two blue main-idea headings into a box and then have students provide supporting details taken from the text.

***Connecting* CONCEPTS**

Cells and Energy You will read in **Chapter 4** about different processes used by cells to capture and release energy—photosynthesis, chemosynthesis, and cellular respiration.

Need for energy All organisms need a source of energy for their life processes. Energy is the ability to cause a change or to do work. The form of energy used by all living things, from bacteria to ferrets to ferns, is chemical energy. Some organisms use chemicals from their environment to make their own source of chemical energy. Some organisms, such as plants, algae, and some bacteria, absorb energy from sunlight and store some of it in chemicals that can be used later as a source of energy. Animals get their source of energy by eating other organisms. In all organisms, energy is important for **metabolism,** or all of the chemical processes that build up or break down materials.

Response to environment All organisms must react to their environment to survive. Light, temperature, and touch are just a few of the physical factors, called stimuli, to which organisms must respond. Think about how you respond to light when you leave a dimly lit room and go into bright sunlight. One of your body's responses is to contract the pupils of your eyes. Your behavior might also change. You might put on sunglasses or raise your hand to shade your eyes. Other organisms also respond to changes in light. For example, plants grow toward light. Some fungi need light to form the structures that you know as mushrooms.

Reproduction and development Members of a species must have the ability to produce new individuals, or reproduce. When organisms reproduce, they pass their genetic material to their offspring. In all organisms, the genetic material is a molecule called deoxyribonucleic acid (dee-AHK-see-RY-boh-noo-KLEE-ihk), or **DNA.**

Single-celled organisms can reproduce when one cell divides into two cells. Both new cells have genetic information that is identical to the original cell. Many multicellular organisms, such as the gold-specs jawfish in **FIGURE 1.3,** reproduce by combining the genetic information from two parents. In both cases, the instructions for growth and development of organisms, from bacteria to people, are carried by the same chemicals—DNA and ribonucleic acid (RNA). The process of development allows organisms to mature and gain the ability to reproduce.

FIGURE 1.3 Reproductive strategies differ among species. The male gold-specs jawfish protects unhatched eggs by holding them in his mouth.

A Summarize What characteristics are shared by all living things?

1.1 ASSESSMENT

ONLINE QUIZ ClassZone.com

REVIEWING MAIN IDEAS

1. How are **species** related to the concept of **biodiversity**?
2. How do the characteristics of living things contribute to an **organism's** survival?

CRITICAL THINKING

3. **Apply** Describe the relationship between **cells** and organisms.
4. **Synthesize** How does biodiversity depend on a species' ability to reproduce?

***Connecting* CONCEPTS**

5. **Human Biology** You respond automatically to many different stimuli, such as loud noises. Why might a quick response to a sound be important?

1.1 ASSESSMENT

1. Biodiversity is the variety and number of species in a given area.
2. The cells that are the basic unit of life carry out the functions needed to support and maintain life, for which they require a continual supply of energy. The ability to respond to the environment helps an organism to avoid injury and death, as well as meet material needs. Reproduction and development enables species survival.
3. All organisms are made of one or more cells, which are the functional units of life, carrying out the activities that support life.
4. Without the ability to reproduce, a species would become extinct, which would lead to a decrease in biodiversity.
5. A quick response could protect against hearing damage or a physical threat.

1.2 Unifying Themes of Biology

KEY CONCEPT Unifying themes connect concepts from many fields of biology.

MAIN IDEAS
- All levels of life have systems of related parts.
- Structure and function are related in biology.
- Organisms must maintain homeostasis to survive in diverse environments.
- Evolution explains the unity and diversity of life.

VOCABULARY
system, p. 7
ecosystem, p. 7
homeostasis, p. 9
evolution, p. 10
adaptation, p. 10

Connect What do you think about when you hear the term *theme*? Maybe you think about the music at the start of your favorite TV show. Maybe you think about the colors and organization of a computer desktop. In both cases, that theme shows up over and over again. In biology, you will see something similar. That is, some concepts come up time after time, even in topics that might seem to be completely unrelated. Understanding these themes, or concepts, can help you to connect the different areas of biology.

MAIN IDEA

All levels of life have systems of related parts.

Think about the separate parts of a car—tires, engine, seats, and so on. Even if you have a complete set of car parts, you might not have a functioning car. Only when all of the parts that make up a car are put together in the correct way do you have a working car. A car is a system. A **system** is an organized group of related parts that interact to form a whole. Like any other system, a car's characteristics come from the arrangement and interaction of its parts.

Systems exist on all scales in biology, from molecules that cannot be seen, to cells that can be seen only with a microscope, to the entire biosphere. In just one heart muscle cell, for example, many chemicals and processes interact in a precise way so that the cell has energy to do its work. Moving up a level, heart muscle, valves, arteries, and veins help form a system in your body—the circulatory system.

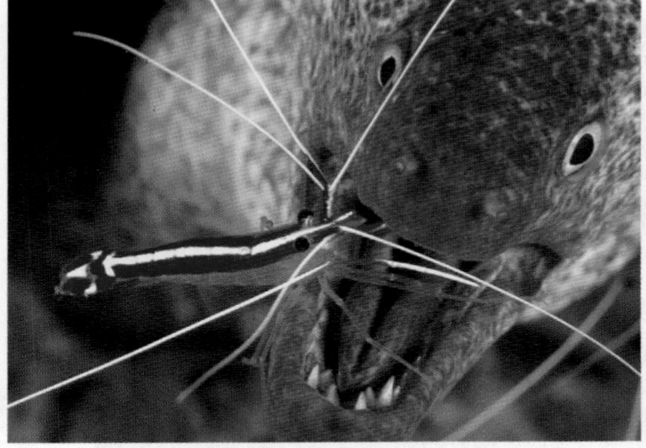

FIGURE 1.4 The moray eel and the cleaner shrimp are parts of a system in which both organisms benefit. The shrimp cleans the eel's mouth and gets food and protection in return.

Two organisms that interact can also be a system, as you can see in **FIGURE 1.4.** On a larger scale, you are a part of a biological system—an ecosystem—that has living and nonliving parts. An **ecosystem** is a physical environment with different species that interact with one another and with nonliving things. When you hear the term *ecosystem,* you might think about a large region, such as a desert, a coral reef, or a forest. But an ecosystem can also be a very small area, such as an individual tree.

Differentiated Instruction

ENGLISH LEARNERS

Figurative language, such as "keep your eye on the ball" or "give me a hand" may be perplexing to students. Scan the text before students begin to read so you can anticipate confusion. Engage students in a discussion about the literal and figurative meanings of certain expressions. For example, **Section 1.2** uses "information" and "message" to describe electrochemical functions of nerve cells. Of course, the messages are not written or spoken, but rather are electrical impulses.

One way to reinforce figurative meanings is to respond visibly to such phrases. For example, respond to "give me a hand" by applauding or by offering a helping hand to demonstrate the meaning in context. Tell students they can often find context clues that will help them understand figurative meanings, such as *like, as,* and *as if,* in preceding or subsequent phrases. Make sure students can differentiate between figurative language and analogies.

Biology Toolkit, Context Clues, p. D10

SECTION 1.2

Plan and Prepare

Objectives

- Summarize four major unifying themes of biology.
- Give an example of each of the themes of biology.

Section Resources

Unit Resource Book
Study Guide pp. 5–6
Power Notes p. 7
Reinforcement p. 8
Pre-AP Activity pp. 23–24

Interactive Reader Chapter 1
Spanish Study Guide pp. 3–4

Biology Toolkit pp. C18, D9, D10

Technology
Power Presentation 1.2
Media Gallery DVD
Online Quiz 1.2

Activate Prior Knowledge Write on the board *How I Spent My Summer Vacation.* **Ask**
- If each person in the class wrote a paper on this subject, would all the papers be the same? no
- What are some of the things you did during your summer vacation? List responses under the title.
- How are the activities related to the title? The title is a theme and is the unifying element in a broad array of vacation activities.

Point out that similar relationships exist in biology.

Teach

TEACH FROM VISUALS

FIGURE 1.4 Explain that this is a symbiotic relationship called mutualism, which students will learn about in Chapter 14. Have students survey this section's Main Idea headings, which summarize some of the basic principles of biology. **Ask,** Which of these themes are related to the interaction of the moray eel and the cleaner shrimp? systems, structure and function, homeostasis, evolution

▼ Teach *continued*

Vocabulary

Academic Vocabulary The term **system** is commonly used in science and means a group of interacting, interrelated, or interdependent elements forming a complex whole. Examples: *ecosystem, digestive system, open system, closed system, solar system, weather system.*

Integrating Systems Biology

All biologists study living systems at some level. This includes studying organisms as part of an ecosystem; studying cells, tissues and organs as part of an organism; and studying molecules as part of a cell. Relatively new to the field of biology is **systems biology,** which extends the continuum to include the analysis of gene regulation and the effects of proteins in defining what an organism is and how it develops and functions.

A systems biologist is interested in the metabolic network and pathways that sustain life—somewhat like the underlying circuitry in a computer chip. This approach to the study of biology has been made possible by scientific advancements in molecular biology, computer technology, and genome sequencing. One obvious application of systems biology is using computer simulations of cellular models to test new drugs for effectiveness and possible side effects.

Answers

A Connect Students, teacher, and all the instructional materials interact to form the whole class.

Often, different biologists study different systems. For example, a person studying DNA might focus on very specific chemical interactions that take place in a cell. A person studying behavior in birds might focus on predator–prey relationships in an ecosystem. However, more and more biologists are working across different system levels. For example, some scientists study how chemicals in the brain affect social interactions.

A Connect Describe how your biology class could be considered a system.

MAIN IDEA

Structure and function are related in biology.

Think about a car again. In a car, different parts have different structures. The structure of a car part gives the part a specific function. For example, a tire's function is directly related to its structure. No other part of the car can perform that function. Structure and function are also related in living things. What something does in an organism is directly related to its shape or form. For example, when you eat, you probably bite into food with your sharp front teeth. Then you probably chew it mostly with your grinding molars. All of your teeth help you eat, but different types of teeth have different functions.

Structure and function are related at the level of chemicals in cells. For example, membrane channels and enzymes are both proteins, but they have very different structures and functions. A channel is a protein molecule that extends through the membrane, or outer layer, of a cell. It has a structure like a tube that allows specific chemicals to pass into and out of a cell. Enzymes are protein molecules that make chemical processes possible in living things. These proteins have shapes that allow them to attach to only certain chemicals and then cause the chemicals to react with each other.

Different types of cells also have different functions that depend on their specialized structures. For example, cells in your brain process information. They have many branches that receive information from other cells. They also have long extensions that allow them to send messages to other cells. Red blood cells are very different. They are much smaller, disk-shaped, and are

Connecting CONCEPTS

Biochemistry Proteins are a type of molecule found in all living things. Proteins have many different functions, which you will read about in **Chapter 2.**

FIGURE 1.5 The snout beetle (below) has specialized prongs and pads on its tarsi (right) that allow it to easily walk on both smooth and rough surfaces. (colored SEMs; magnifications: beetle 20×; tarsus 100×)

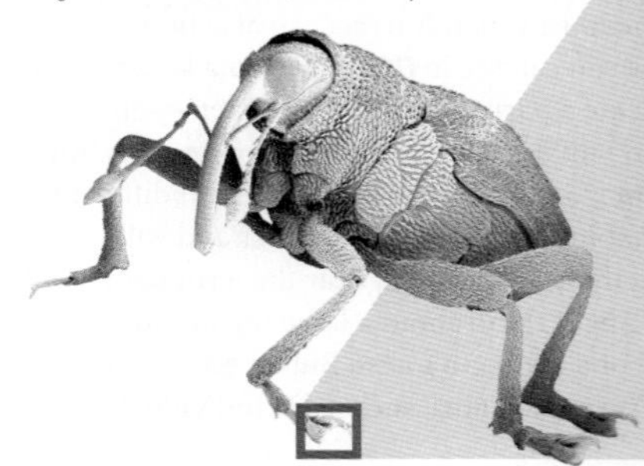

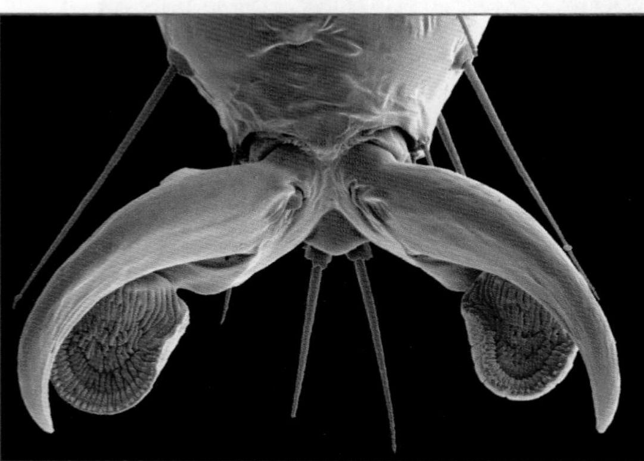

Differentiated Instruction

ENGLISH LEARNERS

Remember to enunciate clearly when presenting material to students. Speak naturally, but separate words so they can be clearly understood. Because words can seem to blend together when spoken, students need plenty of cues from your mouth positions and facial expressions. To assess whether you are getting your message across, do a quick check of comprehension. Ask some simple questions as you teach, and have students write a quick response that they can hold up for you to see.

Biology Toolkit, Slates, p. C18

BELOW LEVEL

On page 8, a car tire is given as an example of the relationship between structure and function. On page 9, an analogy is made between the cruise control mechanism in a car and homeostasis in an animal. Point out the structure of an analogy: A is to B as C is to D. Explain that analogies are word/concept relationships. Have students form their own analogies as they read through the section.

Biology Toolkit, Analogies, p. D9

specialized to carry oxygen. Their structure allows them to fit through even the smallest blood vessels to deliver oxygen throughout your body. Of course, a cell from your brain cannot take the place of one of your red blood cells.

Structure and function are also related on the level of the organism. For example, your foot structure allows you to walk easily on rough, fairly level surfaces. Walking on a surface such as ice is more difficult, and walking up a wall is impossible for you. The beetle in **FIGURE 1.5** is different. Its tarsi, or "feet," have sharp prongs that can grip smooth or vertical surfaces, as well as soft pads for walking on rough surfaces. The beetle's tarsus has a different structure and function than your foot has, but both are specialized for walking.

A Infer Do you think heart muscle has the same structure as arm muscle? Explain.

MAIN IDEA

Organisms must maintain homeostasis to survive in diverse environments.

Temperature and other environmental conditions are always changing, but the conditions inside organisms usually stay quite stable. How does the polar bear in **FIGURE 1.6** live in the arctic? How can people be outside when the temperature is below freezing, but still have a stable body temperature around 37°C (98.6°F)? Why do you shiver when you are cold, sweat when you are hot, and feel thirsty when you need water?

Homeostasis (HOH-mee-oh-STAY-sihs) is the maintenance of constant internal conditions in an organism. Homeostasis is important because cells function best within a limited range of conditions. Temperature, blood sugar, acidity, and other conditions must be controlled. Breakdowns in homeostasis are often life-threatening.

Homeostasis is usually maintained through a process called negative feedback. In negative feedback, a change in a system causes a response that tends to return that system to its original state. For example, think about how a car's cruise control keeps a car moving at a constant set speed. A cruise control system has sensors that monitor the car's speed and then send that information to a computer. If the car begins to go faster than the set speed, the computer tells the car to slow down. If the car slows below the set speed, the computer tells the car to speed up. Similarly, if your body temperature drops below normal, systems in your body act to return your temperature to normal. Your muscles cause you to shiver, and blood vessels near your skin's surface constrict. If your body temperature rises above normal, different responses cool your body.

Behavior is also involved in homeostasis. For example, animals regulate their temperature through behavior. If you feel cold, you may put on a jacket. Reptiles sit on a warm rock in sunlight if they get too cold, and they move into shade if they get too warm.

B Summarize What is homeostasis, and why is it important?

FIGURE 1.6 The polar bear can maintain homeostasis in very cold climates. Its hollow hair is one adaptation that helps the bear retain its body heat. (SEM; magnification 450×)

TEACH FROM VISUALS

FIGURE 1.6 Direct students' attention to the cross section of the hair of the polar bear. **Ask**

- What about the structure of the polar bear's hair relates to how it functions? Thickness offers insulation while the hollow core enables air within to be kept warm by body heat.
- What other observation can you make about the polar bear in this picture that relates structure and function and homeostasis? The bear has fat deposits that help it retain warmth.

Point out that the polar bear's skin, as evidenced by its nose, is black. Black absorbs heat and helps to keep the bear warm.

Science Trivia

- The hair of a polar bear is transparent. It appears white because it reflects visible light, in much the same way that snow and ice do.
- Polar bears at the San Diego and the Singapore zoos turned green when algae infested the hollow cores of their hairs.
- A polar bear at a zoo in Argentina turned purple in response to a medical treatment given to clear up a case of dermatitis.

HANDS-ON ACTIVITY

To explore the unifying theme of homeostasis, have volunteers submerse one hand in a beaker of water that is 10 to 15 degrees colder than room temperature for several minutes. When students remove their hands, have them take their oral temperature with a thermometer. Then have students compare their skin temperature to their internal body temperature. Students should find that even though skin temperature decreased, internal temperature did not.

Answers

A Infer Both types of tissue are made up of muscle cells. However since the heart and arm function differently—the heart is a pump and the arm enables movement—one would expect the tissues and cells to be structured differently.

B Summarize Homeostasis is the maintenance of constant conditions within an organism. It is important because cells function best within a certain range of conditions.

The Inside Story

Geneticist and evolutionary biologist **Theodosius Dobzhansky** said "Nothing in biology makes sense except in the light of evolution." The idea of evolution by natural selection began to take shape for **Charles Darwin,** following his voyage on HMS *Beagle.* Closely associated with that trip and typically cited as a prime example of the phenomenon of natural selection are 13 species of finches known today as **Darwin's finches.**

It is often assumed that the finches Darwin observed on the Galápagos Islands played a pivotal role in the formation of his theory, but this is not the case. Darwin did not use the finches to buttress his argument for natural selection in *On the Origin of Species by Natural Selection.* In fact, some of the birds were so different in character, he didn't think they were finches at all.

It was not until much later that **Peter** and **Rosemary Grant** demonstrated conclusively that natural selection is alive and well and happening routinely in the species of finches known as Darwin's finches. Beginning in 1973, the Grants spent many years tracking thousands of individual finches across generations to show how individual finch species change in response to altered environments.

TEACH FROM VISUALS

FIGURE 1.7 Tell students that the adaptations shown in the photographs are called mimicry. They will learn more about such adaptations in Chapter 14.

MAIN IDEA

Evolution explains the unity and diversity of life.

Connecting CONCEPTS

Evolution The processes of evolution, natural selection, and adaptation are described in more detail in **Unit 4**.

Evolution is the change in living things over time. More specifically, evolution is a change in the genetic makeup of a subgroup, or population, of a species. The concept of evolution links observations from all levels of biology, from cells to the biosphere. A wide range of scientific evidence, including the fossil record and genetic comparisons of species, show that evolution is continuing today.

Adaptation

One way evolution occurs is through natural selection of adaptations. In natural selection, a genetic, or inherited, trait helps some individuals of a species survive and reproduce more successfully than other individuals in a particular environment. An inherited trait that gives an advantage to individual organisms and is passed on to future generations is an **adaptation.** Over time, the makeup of a population changes because more individuals have the adaptation. Two different populations of the same species might have different adaptations in different environments. The two populations may continue to evolve to the point at which they are different species.

Consider the orchid and the thorn bug in **FIGURE 1.7.** Both organisms have adapted in ways that make them resemble other organisms. The orchid that looks like an insect lures other insects to it. The insects that are attracted to the orchid can pollinate the flower, helping the orchid to reproduce. The thorn bug's appearance is an adaptation that makes predators less likely to see and eat it.

FIGURE 1.7 Through evolution, some orchids (left) have flowers that look like insects and some insects, such as the thorn bug (right), look like parts of plants.

Differentiated Instruction

INCLUSION

To improve the teaching environment for students who are hearing impaired:

- Allow students access to your lecture notes.
- Avoid speaking when facing the board.
- Provide seating where students can hear best or lip-read.
- Allow group work during oral assignments.
- Obtain close-captioned films.
- Provide classroom partners.
- Rephrase instructions. Some sounds may be heard or understood better than others.

This adaptation allows the thorn bug to survive and reproduce. In different environments, however, you would find other orchid and insect species that have different adaptations.

Adaptation in evolution is different from the common meaning of adaptation. For example, if you say that you are adapting to a new classroom or to a new town, you are not talking about evolution. Instead, you are talking about consciously getting used to something new. Evolutionary adaptations are changes in a species that occur over many generations due to environmental pressures, not through choices made by organisms. Evolution is simply a long-term response to the environment. The process does not necessarily lead to more complex organisms, and it does not have any special end point. Evolution continues today, and it will continue as long as life exists on Earth.

Unity and Diversity

Evolution is a unifying theme of biology because it accounts for both the diversity and the similarities, or the unity, of life. As you study biology, you will see time after time that organisms are related to one another. When you read about cells in Unit 2 and genetics in Unit 3, you will see that all organisms have similar cell structures and chemical processes. These shared characteristics result from a common evolutionary descent.

Humans and bacteria have much more in common than you may think. Both human and bacterial genetics are based on the same molecules—DNA and RNA. Both human and bacterial cells rely upon the same sources of energy, and they have similar cell structures. Both human and bacterial cells have membranes made mostly of fats that protect the inside of the cell from the environment outside the cell.

Now think about the vast number of different types of organisms. All of the species now alive are the result of billions of years of evolution and adaptation to the environment. How? Natural selection of genetic traits can lead to the evolution of a new species. In the end, this genetic diversity is responsible for the diversity of life on Earth.

A Analyze **How does evolution lead to both the diversity and the unity of life?**

1.2 ASSESSMENT

ONLINE QUIZ ClassZone.com

REVIEWING ▶ MAIN IDEAS

1. Describe a biological **system.**
2. Give an example of how structure is related to function in living things.
3. Why is **homeostasis** essential for living things?
4. What is the relationship between **adaptation** and natural selection?

CRITICAL THINKING

5. **Analyze** How are structure and function related to adaptation?
6. **Apply** How is the process of natural selection involved in **evolution**?

***Connecting* CONCEPTS**

7. **Cells** Do you think homeostasis is necessary at the level of a single cell? Explain.

1.2 ASSESSMENT

1. A system is a group of interrelated, interacting parts that make up a whole.
2. Structure determines function; the snout beetle's feet have prongs and pads to walk on both smooth and rough surfaces.
3. It enables organisms to survive in diverse and changing environments.
4. Natural selection leads to different adaptations in different environments.
5. An adaptation is a genetic change that can affect the structure of some aspect of an organism's body and how well it functions in a given environment.
6. Natural selection of different adaptations in different environments can lead to new species.
7. Stable conditions within a cell are necessary for the cell's survival, whether in a unicellular or multicellular organism. If homeostasis is not maintained within a cell, cell functions can be disrupted. In turn, this can disrupt functions at higher levels of organization.

Take It Further

A change in an individual in response to environmental conditions is **acclimation.** Individuals acclimate; populations adapt. For example, climbers can take days or weeks to acclimate to oxygen levels at higher elevations. To acclimate, climbers stay a few days at base camp. They climb to the next camp where they spend a night, and then return to base camp. This process is repeated several times, extending the time spent at the higher elevation. Once a climber is used to that elevation, the process starts over at a higher camp. The golden rule for high altitude climbers is "climb high, sleep low." This means climbers can ascend more than 300 meters (1000 ft) per day as long as they descend to a lower elevation no more than 300 meters (1000 ft) from their starting elevation to sleep.

Answers

A Analyze Adaptations to different environments account for diversity; similarities among all organisms suggest a common evolutionary ancestor, that which unites all living things.

Assess and Reteach ▼

Assess Use the Online Quiz or Section Quiz (*Assessment Book,* p. 6).

Reteach Assign students to four cooperative groups and assign each group one of the following topics: systems, structure and function, homeostasis, or evolution. Ask students to collaborate in summarizing, in their own words, the unifying theme they were assigned and then to write a summary. Have each group designate a speaker to present its summary to the class. After each presentation, have group members answer questions from the class.

DATA ANALYSIS

Introduce

Every scientific investigation involves gathering and recording data. Some data are qualitative and subjective, meaning that the data could be interpreted differently depending on the person gathering the data. Some data are quantitative, or are objective measurements. **Ask**

- In the photograph of the jackals, how would you record data about the age of the individuals qualitatively and quantitatively? Qualitative age data could be notes that the jackals appear to be young or old. Quantitative age data could be records of their exact ages based on when each jackal was born.
- If qualitative data depend on the subjective observations of the observer, are qualitative data less valuable in research? No, qualitative data often describe behaviors and other qualities that cannot be easily quantified, such as color.

Discuss

Often, scientists use both types of data in their research. **Ask,** If you were studying the pod of dolphins, how could you use both qualitative and quantitative data in your research? Most research begins with observations. Qualitative data can lead to questions and hypotheses that can be tested quantitatively. Here are some examples.

Qualitative data: Observations show that female dolphins begin to engage in mating behavior at a young age.

Quantitative data: From observing female bottlenose dolphins from birth, data indicate that mating behavior begins at an average age of nine years.

Unit Resource Book, Data Analysis, p. 21

Types of Data

Scientists collect two different types of data: qualitative data and quantitative data.

Qualitative data Qualitative data are descriptions in words of what is being observed. They are based on some quality of an observation, such as color, odor, or texture.

Quantitative data Quantitative data are numeric measurements. The data are objective—they are the same no matter who measures them. They include measurements such as mass, volume, temperature, distance, concentration, time, or frequency.

EXAMPLE

Suppose that a marine biologist observes the behavior and activities of dolphins. She identifies different dolphins within the group and observes them every day for a month. She records detailed observations about their behaviors. Some of her observations are qualitative data, and some are quantitative data.

Qualitative data examples

- Dolphin colors range from gray to white.
- Dolphins in a pod engage in play behavior.
- Dolphins have smooth skin.

Quantitative data examples

- There are nine dolphins in this pod.
- Dolphins eat the equivalent of 4–5 percent of their body mass each day.
- The sonar frequency most often used by the dolphins is around 100 kHz.

Notice that the qualitative data are descriptions. The quantitative data are objective numerical measurements.

IDENTIFY DATA TYPES

Suppose that you are a biologist studying jackals in their natural habitat in Africa. You observe their behaviors and interactions, and take photographs of their interactions to study later. Examine the photograph of the jackals shown to the right.

1. **Analyze** Give three examples of qualitative data that could be obtained from the photograph of the jackals.
2. **Analyze** Give three examples of quantitative data that could be obtained from the photograph of the jackals.

Answers

1. *Sample Answer:* The jackals are young; the jackals are playing; the jackals appear healthy.
2. *Sample Answer:* There are five jackals in the group; two jackals are engaged in play behavior; one jackal is on its back.

1.3 Scientific Thinking and Processes

KEY CONCEPT Science is a way of thinking, questioning, and gathering evidence.

MAIN IDEAS
- Like all science, biology is a process of inquiry.
- Biologists use experiments to test hypotheses.
- A theory explains a wide range of observations.

VOCABULARY
observation, p. 13
data, p. 14
hypothesis, p. 14
experiment, p. 16
independent variable, p. 16
dependent variable, p. 16
constant, p. 16
theory, p. 16

INDIANA STANDARDS

NOS.8 Explain that the body of scientific knowledge is organized into major theories, which are derived from and supported by the results of many experiments, and allow us to make testable predictions.

NOS.9 Recognize that new scientific discoveries often lead to a re-evaluation of previously accepted scientific knowledge and of commonly held ideas.

Connect What does the study of fungus have in common with the study of human heart disease? How is research in a laboratory similar to research in a rain forest? Biologists, like all scientists, ask questions about the world and try to find answers through observation and experimentation. How do your daily observations help answer questions that you have about the world?

MAIN IDEA

Like all science, biology is a process of inquiry.

Science is a human process of trying to understand the world around us. There is no one method used by all scientists, but all scientific inquiry is based on the same principles. Scientific thinking is based on both curiosity and skepticism. Skepticism is the use of critical and logical thinking to evaluate results and conclusions. Scientific inquiry also requires evidence. One of the most important points of science is that scientific evidence may support or even overturn long-standing ideas. To improve our understanding of the world, scientists share their findings with each other. The open and honest exchange of data is extremely important in science.

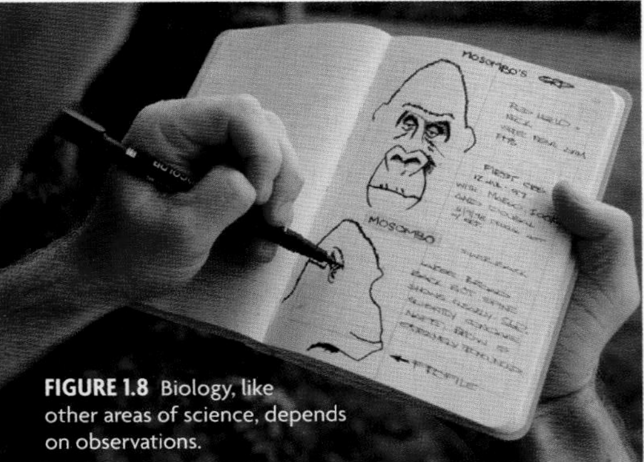
FIGURE 1.8 Biology, like other areas of science, depends on observations.

Observations, Data, and Hypotheses

All scientific inquiry begins with careful and systematic observations. Of course, **observation** includes using our senses to study the world, but it may also involve other tools. For example, scientists use computers to collect measurements or to examine past research results. Much early biological research was based on observing, describing, and categorizing the living world. By themselves, description and categorization are not as common in research today due to advances in technology, but they are still very important in biology. For example, how could someone study the interactions of gorillas without observing and describing their behavior, as in **FIGURE 1.8**?

Differentiated Instruction

ENGLISH LEARNERS

Remind students that people ask questions to get information. Provide practice with clarification techniques by using phrases such as the following:

I didn't understand what you said.

Could you repeat that, please?

Does ___ mean ___?

Also, have students ask questions related to what they have read or you have explained. Review the question words *What, Who, When, Where, Why,* and *How.*

Model this technique for students by asking some questions about the nature of scientific thinking, such as the following:

What makes a scientist a scientist?

How do scientists approach their work?

Why do scientists do experiments?

Ask students to form their own questions about **Section 1.3** to ask one another in groups. Tell students that you consider their questions a sign of critical thinking, and emphasize that the questions are an excellent tool for making meaning clear.

Plan and Prepare

Objectives

- Identify the different elements of scientific inquiry.
- Differentiate between theories and hypotheses.

Section Resources

Unit Resource Book
Study Guide pp. 9–10
Power Notes p. 11
Reinforcement p. 12

Interactive Reader Chapter 1
Spanish Study Guide pp. 5–6

Biology Toolkit pp. C7, C10

Technology
Power Presentation 1.3
Media Gallery DVD
Online Quiz 1.3

Activate Prior Knowledge Quiz students on the nature of a hypothesis. **Ask,** Is this a hypothesis: "If I keep a plant from getting any sunlight, it will die." No, it's a prediction. Discuss the difference between a prediction and a hypothesis. Remind students that a hypothesis is worded in such a way as to show a relationship that can be tested. **Ask,** How can you reframe the prediction about the plant to make it a hypothesis? "If sunlight is necessary to the survival of a plant, then when a plant is deprived of sunlight, it will die." Point out that a hypothesis implies a question to be answered.

Teach

Vocabulary

Academic Vocabulary Point out that a scientist typically describes a hypothesis in terms of **validity,** rather than **truth.** *Validity* implies a proposition or an argument is well grounded or logically derived. *Truth* is, more simply, the quality of being real, genuine, or factual.

▼ Teach *continued*

History of Science

The scientific tradition began in ancient Greece and is generally attributed to **Aristotle.** He was the first individual we know of to explain biological phenomena in terms of natural causes, as opposed to supernatural or mythical causes. He used the power of logic to find explanations for cause and effect, and form and function. Aristotle's most powerful tools consisted of his powers of observation and reasoning.

Aristotle and the natural philosophers who followed him established a set of widely held assumptions about the natural world and how it functioned. Typically, answers to specific questions had to fit within this framework of assumptions, which provided a predetermined explanation. One such assumption was that the Sun and all the other stars and planets revolved around Earth.

With the **Scientific Revolution** of the 17th century, a new methodology came into being. This new scientific method started with data and observations, from which an explanation was derived, and incorporated experimentation to test assumptions. In 1620, **Francis Bacon** outlined the approach in his work *Novum Organum,* which carried the subtitle *True Suggestions for the Interpretation of Nature.* In 1637, **René Descartes** framed the principles of scientific thinking in his *Discourse on Method.* Descartes described reconstructing the accepted body of knowledge, piece by piece, trusting only that which could be seen to be beyond any doubt.

Vocabulary

Academic Vocabulary The term **significant** commonly means "important," but in statistics, *significant* means "not likely due to chance." Explain that a finding may be statistically significant without being important in the real world. When statisticians say that a result is **statistically significant,** they mean that a change in a dependent variable is probably due to manipulation of the independent variable. That probability is typically 95 percent.

***Connecting* CONCEPTS**

Data Analysis Biology relies on the analysis of scientific data. Use the Data Analysis activities in each chapter in this book to build your data analysis skills.

Scientific questions often come from observations, whether the observations are one's own or someone else's. Observations can also be recorded as **data** that can be analyzed. Scientists collect two general types of data: qualitative data and quantitative data. As you learned on page 12, qualitative data are descriptions of a phenomenon that can include sights, sounds, and smells. This type of data is often useful to report what happens but not how it happens. In contrast, quantitative data are characteristics that can be measured or counted, such as mass, volume, and temperature. Anything that is expressed as a number, from time to a rating scale on a survey, is quantitative data that can be used to explore how something happens.

Scientists use observations and data to form a hypothesis. A **hypothesis** (plural, *hypotheses*) is a proposed answer for a scientific question. A hypothesis must be specific and testable. You probably form and test many hypotheses every day, even though you may not be aware of it. Suppose you oversleep. You needed to get up at 7 A.M., but when you wake up you observe that it is 8 A.M. What happened? Did the alarm not go off? Was it set for the wrong time? Did it go off but you slept through it? You just made three hypotheses to explain why you overslept—the alarm did not go off, the alarm was set for the wrong time, or the alarm went off but you did not hear it.

Testing Hypotheses

A hypothesis leads to testable predictions of what would happen if the hypothesis is valid. How could you use scientific thinking to test a hypothesis about oversleeping? If you slept late because the alarm was set for the wrong time, you could check the alarm to find out the time for which it was set. Suppose the alarm was actually set for 7 P.M. In this case, your hypothesis would be supported by your data, and you could be certain that the alarm was set for the wrong time.

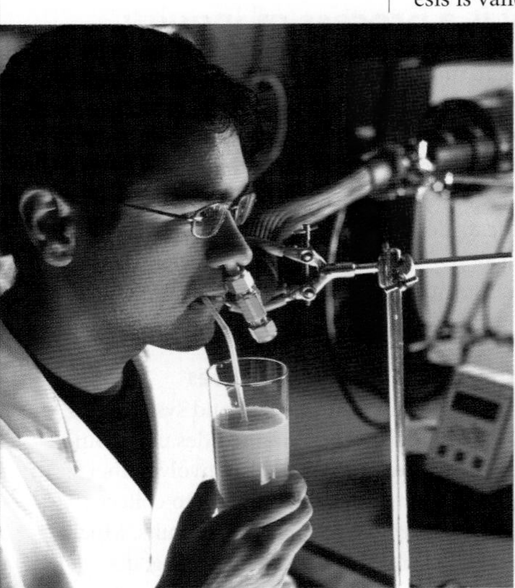

FIGURE 1.9 In this experiment, a scientist studies how chemicals are detected in the mouth and nose to produce taste.

For scientists, just one test of a hypothesis is usually not enough. Most of the time, it is only by repeating tests that scientists can be more certain that their results are not mistaken or due to chance. Why? Biological systems are highly variable. By repeating tests, scientists take this variability into account and try to decrease its effects on the experimental results.

After scientists collect data, they use statistics to mathematically analyze whether a hypothesis is supported. There are two possible outcomes of statistical analysis.

- **Nonsignificant** The data show no effect, or an effect so small that the results could have happened by chance.
- **Statistically significant** The data show an effect that is likely not due to chance.

When data do not support a hypothesis, it is rejected. But these data are still useful because they often lead to new hypotheses.

Experimental methods and results are evaluated by other scientists in a process called peer review. How was an experiment done and how were the data analyzed? Do the data support the conclusions of the experiment?

Differentiated Instruction

BELOW LEVEL

Tell students that there are different strategies for previewing a section. Introduce students to the PLAN strategy: Predict, Locate, Add, and Note. Have students predict what the section will be about by reading the headings and locating key vocabulary. They should write down their predictions and any questions they have. As they read, they can add details and note how the material addresses their questions.

Biology Toolkit, PLAN, p. C7

FIGURE 1.10 Scientific Thinking

Science is a cycle. The steps are shown in a certain order, but the cycle does not begin or end at any one point, and the steps may take place in various orders.

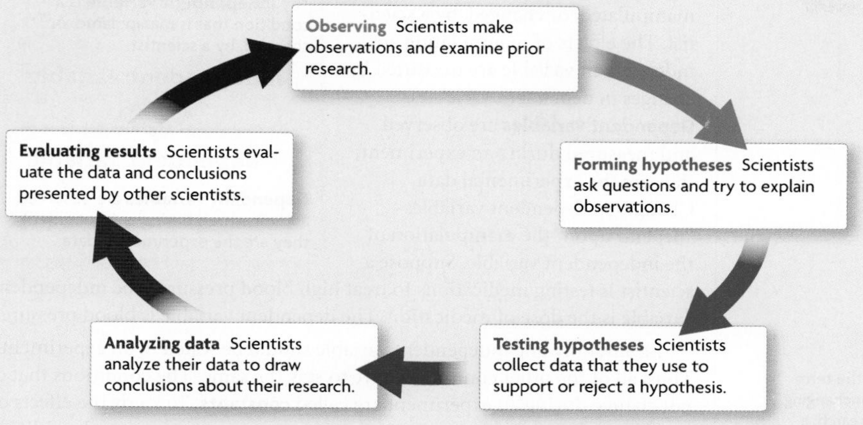

Observing Scientists make observations and examine prior research.

Forming hypotheses Scientists ask questions and try to explain observations.

Testing hypotheses Scientists collect data that they use to support or reject a hypothesis.

Analyzing data Scientists analyze their data to draw conclusions about their research.

Evaluating results Scientists evaluate the data and conclusions presented by other scientists.

A Synthesize Where in the cycle would retesting a hypothesis fit? Explain.

Is there bias in the experimental design or in the conclusions? Only after this review process is complete are research results accepted. Whether the results support an existing theory or disagree with earlier research, they are often used as a starting point for new questions. In **FIGURE 1.10**, you see the cycle of observing, forming hypotheses, testing hypotheses, analyzing data, and evaluating results that keeps scientific inquiry going.

B Synthesize Why is there no one correct process of scientific investigation?

MAIN IDEA

Biologists use experiments to test hypotheses.

You have read about the importance of observations in science. Observational studies help biologists describe and explain something in the world. But in observational studies, scientists try not to interfere with what happens. They try to simply observe a phenomenon. One example involves the endangered white stork. The number of white storks has decreased sharply over the last 50 years. To help protect the storks, biologists have studied the migration patterns of the birds. What can observational studies tell a biologist about stork populations and migration? The studies can show changes in migration path and distance. They can show where storks breed and how many eggs they lay. Observational studies can answer all of these questions. But there is one question that observations cannot answer: What causes any changes that might be observed? The only way to answer that question is through an experiment.

Take It Further

Tell students that a hypothesis cannot be proved, only tested. Applying logic, if something cannot be proved, then it cannot be disproved. Data either support or do not support a hypothesis, and the hypothesis is accepted or rejected—not proved.

Part of establishing support for a hypothesis is to subject experimental results and data to **peer review.** It is rare for one researcher to spot every mistake or flaw in a complicated investigation. Errors and opportunities for improvement may stand out only to another scientist with special expertise, increasing the probability that weaknesses in an experiment will be identified and fixed.

Answers

A Synthesize during "testing hypotheses" (to repeat the experiment) and after "analyzing data" (if the hypothesis is rejected) or "evaluating results" (if other data agree or disagree)

B Synthesize The steps can occur in different orders and depend on what is being investigated.

INCLUSION

A science class offers a variety of students important information that will help them function in an increasingly technological society. Below is a list of ways to accommodate all students in a comfortable learning environment:

- Provide a daily, unvarying routine so your expectations are clear.
- Establish special teaching procedures that take into account a short attention span and restlessness.
- Make certain that students understand instructions before they start work.
- Seat students where classroom distractions are minimized.
- Be selective about which concepts students should master.
- Encourage repeated efforts.
- Within reasonable expectations, evaluate students' grasp of concepts, not spelling, punctuation, or sentence structure.

▼ Teach *continued*

Vocabulary

Academic Vocabulary Point out that in everyday use, an **observation** may be "a comment based on something seen." In this use, an interpretation, or inference, has been made. In science, an observation must be detectable with the senses or a measurement tool. Show students an apple and then have them identify the following statements as observations or inferences.

1. The skin is red. observation
2. The apple is edible. inference
3. There are seeds inside. inference
4. It can make you healthy. inference
5. It feels smooth. observation

Take It Further

Researchers involved in experiments that test human reactions often apply an added system of control to their investigations. This is because a test subject's expectations can affect the results. For example, in a clinical trial for a new drug, just the knowledge that a person is receiving an active drug may produce some benefit or cause a doctor to look for improvement. In such an instance, investigators use a randomized, double-blind, placebo-controlled study. This ensures that psychological factors do not affect the results.

The study employs two drugs, the active one that researchers expect to be an effective treatment and a **placebo,** a substance that has no treatment value but outwardly appears identical to the active drug. The study is made **random** by using a computer to randomly determine who receives the drug and who receives the placebo. The procedure is **double blind** because neither the participating doctors nor their test subjects know which drug (active or placebo) the subject is receiving.

Answers

A Infer A change in the independent variable is potentially the cause of a measured effect in the dependent variable.

Scientific experiments allow scientists to test hypotheses and find out how something happens. In **experiments,** scientists study factors called independent variables and dependent variables to find cause-and-effect relationships. The **independent variable** in an experiment is a condition that is manipulated, or changed, by a scientist. The effects of manipulating an independent variable are measured by changes in dependent variables. **Dependent variables** are observed and measured during an experiment; they are the experimental data. Changes in dependent variables "depend upon" the manipulation of the independent variable. Suppose a scientist is testing medications to treat high blood pressure. The independent variable is the dose of medication. The dependent variable is blood pressure.

VISUAL VOCAB

The **independent variable** is a condition that is manipulated, or changed, by a scientist.

independent variable

affects

dependent variable

Dependent variables are observed and measured during an experiment; they are the experimental data.

VOCABULARY

In common usage, the term *constant* means "unchanging." In experimental research, a constant is a condition or factor that is controlled so that it does not change.

Ideally, only one independent variable should be tested in an experiment. Thus, all of the other conditions have to stay the same. The conditions that do not change during an experiment are called **constants.** To study the effects of an independent variable, a scientist uses a control group or control condition. Subjects in a control group are treated exactly like experimental subjects except for the independent variable being studied. The independent variable is manipulated in experimental groups or experimental conditions.

Constants in the blood pressure medication experiment include how often the medication is given, and how the medication is taken. To control the experiment, these factors must remain the same, or be held constant. For example, the medication could be tested with 0, 25, 50, or 100 milligram doses, twice a day, taken by swallowing a pill. By changing only one variable at a time—the amount of medication—a scientist can be more confident that the results are due to that variable.

A Infer How do experiments show cause-and-effect relationships?

MAIN IDEA

A theory explains a wide range of observations.

Many words have several different meanings. Depending on the context in which a word is used, its meaning can change completely. For example, the word *right* could mean "correct," or it could refer to a direction. Similarly, the word *theory* has different meanings. Usually, the word *theory* in everyday conversation means a speculation, or something that is imagined to be true. In science, the meaning of *theory* is very different.

Recall that a hypothesis is a proposed answer for a scientific question. A **theory** is a proposed explanation for a wide range of observations and experimental results that is supported by a wide range of evidence. Eventually, a theory may be broadly accepted by the scientific community. Natural

Differentiated Instruction

TEACH WITH TECHNOLOGY

To hone students' powers of observation, find a videoclip that shows an interesting and complex event. It might be a magic trick or a visually arresting advertisement. Play the clip, then ask students to write down all that they saw. Play the clip again, asking them to observe the event more carefully. Then have students share what they saw, comparing their first perception of the event to their second.

PRE-AP

Working in small groups, have students consider how a theory provides a framework for the way scientific investigations are conducted. They should identify a theory that served for a time and then was supplanted by another, for example, the geocentric and heliocentric theories; spontaneous generation and the cell theory. Students should compile what they know about the theories, the effect a wrong theory has, and a theory's predictive value. Then discuss the results in class.

Biology Toolkit, Round Table, p. C10

selection is a scientific theory. It is supported by a large amount of data, and it explains many observations of life on Earth. Theories are not easily accepted in science, and by definition they are never proved. Scientific hypotheses and theories may be supported or refuted, and they are always subject to change. New theories that better explain observations and experimental results can replace older theories.

Theories can change based on new evidence. One example of how scientific understanding can change involves the cause of disease. Until the mid 1800s, illnesses were thought to be related to supernatural causes or to imbalances of the body's "humours," or fluids. Then scientific research suggested that diseases were caused by microscopic organisms, such as bacteria. The germ theory of disease was born, but it has changed over the years. For example, an early addition to the germ theory stated that it must be possible to grow a disease-causing microorganism in a laboratory.

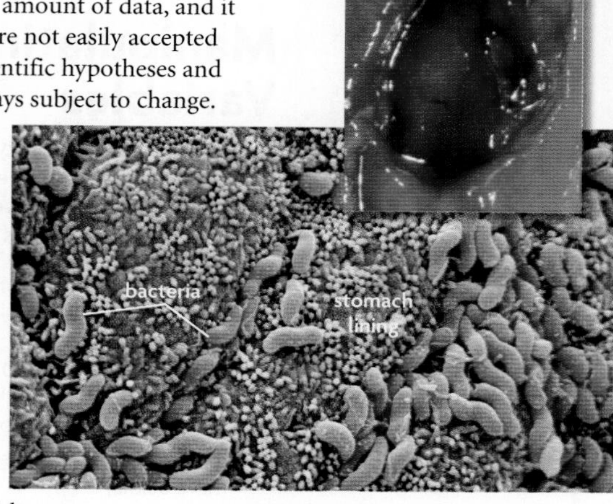

FIGURE 1.11 For many years, scientific evidence indicated that stomach ulcers (top) were caused by stress. Then, new evidence showed that the ulcers are actually caused by a type of bacteria called *Helicobacter pylori* (bottom). (colored SEM; magnification 4000×)

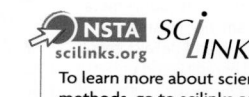

Now, we know that viruses and prions do not completely fit the germ theory of disease because they are not living organisms. A virus has some of the characteristics of life, but it cannot reproduce itself without infecting a living cell. Prions are even less like organisms—they are just misfolded proteins. The link between prions and disease was not even suggested until the early 1980s, but much evidence points to prions as the cause of mad cow disease and, in humans, Creutzfeldt–Jakob disease.

The details of germ theory have changed as our knowledge of biology has grown, but the basic theory is still accepted. Scientists must always be willing to revise theories and conclusions as new evidence about the living world is gathered. Science is an ongoing process. New experiments and observations refine and expand scientific knowledge, as you can see in **FIGURE 1.11.** Our understanding of the world around us has changed dramatically over the past few decades, and the study of biology has changed and expanded as well.

To learn more about scientific methods, go to scilinks.org. **Keycode: MLB001**

Ⓐ **Summarize** **What is a scientific theory?**

1.3 ASSESSMENT

ONLINE QUIZ ClassZone.com

NOS.8; NOS.9

REVIEWING MAIN IDEAS

1. What role do **hypotheses** play in scientific inquiry?
2. What is the difference between an **independent variable** and a **dependent variable**?
3. How is the meaning of **theory** in science different from the everyday use of the term?

CRITICAL THINKING

4. **Compare and Contrast** How are hypotheses and theories related?
5. **Apply** Give examples of different ways in which **observations** are used in scientific inquiry.

Connecting CONCEPTS

6. **Scientific Process** Why is the statement "All life is made of cells" an example of a theory? Explain.

Address Misconceptions

Common Misconception Students may think that all questions can be answered by using scientific methods.

Correcting the Misconception Explain that scientific methods apply only to the study of phenomena that can be observed and measured. Appreciation of beauty and personal tastes, for example, are outside of the realm of scientific investigation.

Answers

Ⓐ **Summarize** a well-accepted explanation for a wide range of observations and experimental results, supported by a body of evidence

Assess and Reteach ▼

Assess Use the Online Quiz or Section Quiz (*Assessment Book,* p. 7).

Reteach Work with students to incorporate the key vocabulary of the section into either a cluster diagram or concept map. You can print out a description of each graphic organizer, and a blank, from the *Biology Toolkit*.

1.3 ASSESSMENT

1. A hypothesis provides a testable explanation for an observation.
2. An independent variable is manipulated, a dependent variable shows the effect of that manipulation.
3. A scientific theory is a widely accepted explanation that is supported by evidence. In everyday language, a theory is a guess.
4. Hypotheses and theories are both proposed explanations for a scientific question. Observations and data collected in testing hypotheses contribute to the broader question that is addressed by a theory. A theory, in turn, provides the framework for new hypotheses.
5. Scientific questions are developed from initial observations. Observations are also made to test hypotheses.
6. When first proposed, the idea that all life is made of cells changed the way scientists thought about what defines an organism. Not only did it encompass all accumulated evidence, but it also provided a framework for new investigations.

INVESTIGATION

Time 45 minutes	TEACHER TESTED
Teacher Preparation	
Student Difficulty	
Lab Binder Introduction, pp. 1–4	

Purpose Investigate how pH or enzyme concentration affects the breakdown of protein.

Overview Students will assess the breakdown of protein by measuring the distance a marble sinks into gelatin exposed to three different solutions of detergent. They will test either pH or concentration of the solutions.

LAB PREPARATION

- Prepare detergent solutions before class.
- Prepare and refrigerate graduated cylinders with gelatin the day before.

LAB MANAGEMENT

- Have students place marbles on top of the gelatin before adding a detergent solution.

Safety Remind students never to taste lab materials. Make sure they wash their hands before leaving the lab.

Teacher Notes

"I review enzymes in depth with the students beforehand."

"It was nice to utilize the detergents, which made it relevant and authentic."

POST-LAB DISCUSSION

Discuss results. **Ask,** How do you know which was the independent variable and dependent variable? independent: concentration of pH because it was manipulated; dependent: distance because it was measured **Ask,** Can you conclude from this experiment why the marble sank? No, the data only show that gelatin breaks down, not why.

Manipulating Independent Variables

Some chemicals, called enzymes, help break down substances into smaller molecules. Some laundry detergents contain enzymes that help break down protein stains in clothing. In this investigation, you will test how different conditions affect the activity of the enzymes in laundry detergent.

MATERIALS

- 4 graduated cylinders with gelatin
- 4 marbles
- metric ruler
- 10 mL water
- 2 10-mL graduated cylinders
- 10 mL detergent (10%)
- 10 mL detergent (30%)
- 10 mL detergent (50%)

OR

- 10 mL detergent (pH 4)
- 10 mL detergent (pH 7)
- 10 mL detergent (pH 10)

PROCESS SKILLS

- **Measuring**
- **Modeling**

INDIANA STANDARDS

B.1.2 Understand that the shape of a molecule determines its role in the many different types of cellular processes including metabolism, homeostasis, growth and development, and heredity, and understand that the majority of these processes involve proteins that act as enzymes.

NOS.4 Regularly evaluate the work of their peers and in turn have their work evaluated by their peers.

NOS.5 Apply standard techniques in laboratory investigations to measure physical quantities in appropriate units and convert known quantities to other units as necessary.

PROBLEM How is enzyme activity affected by changes in conditions?

PROCEDURE

1. Obtain four graduated cylinders filled with gelatin. One of the cylinders is for the control condition. The other three are for the experimental conditions.
2. Decide which variable you would like to test.
   - pH (pH is a measurement of acidity, and a lower pH means that a substance is more acidic)
   - detergent concentration
3. The dependent variable is the amount of gelatin broken down by the enzyme in the detergent. Measure the dependent variable by placing a marble on top of the gelatin and measuring how far the marble sinks into the gelatin.
4. Identify the independent variable in your experiment. Form a hypothesis that explains the effect of the independent variable on the dependent variable.
5. Pour 10 mL of water onto the gelatin in one graduated cylinder. This graduated cylinder represents the control condition. Pour 10 mL of each different detergent solution into each of the other graduated cylinders. These graduated cylinders represent the experimental conditions.
6. Place a marble on the top of the gelatin in each graduated cylinder. Wait five minutes, then measure the distance that the marble has sunk into the gelatin.
7. Construct a data table like the one shown below, and record your data.

TABLE 1. EFFECT OF DETERGENT ON GELATIN

Condition	Distance (cm)
Water	
Solution 1	
Solution 2	
Solution 3	

ANALYZE AND CONCLUDE

1. **Analyze** Use a bar graph to plot your data. What trends exist in your data? Explain whether your results supported your hypothesis.
2. **Communicate** Share the results of your experiment with other groups in your class. Did other groups that manipulated the same independent variable obtain similar results? Why or why not?

EXTEND YOUR INVESTIGATION

Some areas have "hard" water, or water with a high mineral content. Other areas have "soft" water, or water with a low mineral content. Design an experiment to test the effect of the mineral content of water on detergent activity.

18 Unit 1: Introducing Biology

Answers

Expected Results

Students in the test group used concentration and reported that the distance the marble sank increased with increasing concentration. Results with different detergents will vary. Higher pH typically denatures enzymes; however, detergents with protease have an optimal pH between 7.5 and 10.5.

Analyze and Conclude

1. Bar graphs should show independent variable vs. distance (in cm). Support of the initial hypothesis will depend on students' measurements.
2. Answers may include the idea that different procedures and random error produced different results.

Extend Your Investigation

The procedure would be similar, except for using water with varying mineral concentrations.

1.4 Biologists' Tools and Technology

KEY CONCEPT Technology continually changes the way biologists work.

MAIN IDEAS
- Imaging technologies provide new views of life.
- Complex systems are modeled on computers.
- The tools of molecular genetics give rise to new biological studies.

VOCABULARY
microscope, p. 19
gene, p. 23
molecular genetics, p. 23
genomics, p. 23

INDIANA STANDARDS

NOS.10 Describe how scientific discoveries lead to the development of new technologies, and conversely how technological advances can lead to scientific discoveries through new experimental methods and equipment.

Connect Can you imagine life without cars, computers, or cell phones? Technology changes the way we live and work. Technology also plays a major part in the rapid increase of biological knowledge. Today, technology allows biologists to view tiny structures within cells and activity within a human brain. Technology allows biologists to study and change genes. What will technology allow next?

MAIN IDEA

Imaging technologies provide new views of life.

Until the late 1600s, no one knew about cells or single-celled organisms. Then the microscope was invented. Scientists suddenly had the ability to study living things at a level they never knew existed. Thus, the microscope was the first in a long line of technologies that have changed the study of biology.

Microscopes

A **microscope** provides an enlarged image of an object. Some of the most basic concepts of biology—such as the fact that cells make up all organisms—were not even imaginable before microscopes. The first microscopes magnified objects but did not produce clear images. By the 1800s, most microscopes had combinations of lenses that provided clearer images. Today's light microscopes, such as the one in **FIGURE 1.12** that you might use, are still based on the same principles. They are used to see living or preserved specimens, and they provide clear images of cells as small as bacteria. Light microscopes clearly magnify specimens up to about 1500 times their actual size, and samples are often stained with chemicals to make details stand out.

Electron microscopes, developed in the 1950s, use beams of electrons instead of light to magnify objects. These microscopes can be used to see cells, but they produce much higher magnifications, so they can also show much smaller things. Electron microscopes can clearly magnify specimens more than 100,000 times their actual size. They can even be used to directly study individual protein molecules. However, electron microscopes, unlike light microscopes, cannot be used to study living organisms because the specimens being studied have to be in a vacuum.

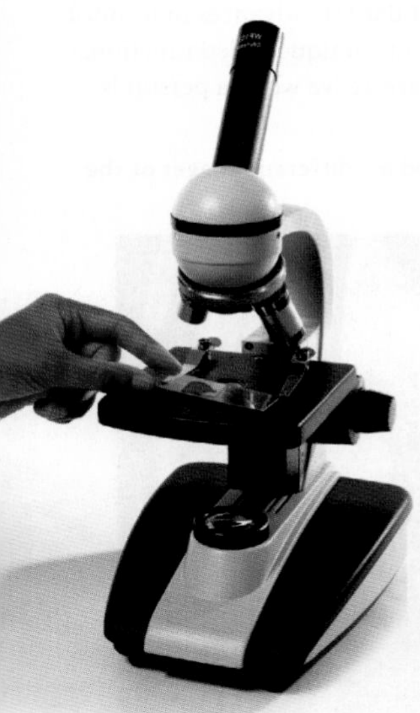

FIGURE 1.12 Biologists use microscopes to study cells, which are too small to be seen with the naked eye.

Differentiated Instruction

HANDS-ON ACTIVITY

Set up five numbered stations, each with two microscopes. Prepare slides to view ahead of time, and place a slide of a different object on each microscope. Make slides of ordinary things that students can quickly identify, such as an insect leg or wing, a fingernail clipping, a hair follicle, or a letter cut out of a newspaper. Ask students to work in pairs to focus on the objects, using the adjustment knobs. Have students view each slide under both low and high power and then identify, sketch, and label each object.

Allow students no more than ten minutes at each station. Tell students that the slides and cover slips are delicate and can be broken if the high-power objective is pressed onto the slide with the coarse adjustment. Have alcohol swabs at each station and tell students to wipe the eyepiece before using the microscope. When students are finished, let them compare notes to see if they identified the objects correctly.

Plan and Prepare

Objectives

- Describe the usefulness of modern imaging technologies.
- Explain the usefulness of computer models in studying biological systems.
- Summarize how modern computer-based technologies have advanced the study of genetics.

Section Resources

Unit Resource Book
Study Guide pp. 13–14
Power Notes p. 15
Reinforcement p. 16
Pre-AP Activity pp. 25–26

Interactive Reader Chapter 1
Spanish Study Guide pp. 7–8

Biology Toolkit pp. C17, C19

Technology
Power Presentation 1.4
Media Gallery DVD
Online Quiz 1.4

Activate Prior Knowledge Have students define technology. **Ask,** Does a magnifying glass represent technology? a microscope? Both do. Technology is an application or innovation that allows humans to manipulate their material environment. Point out that technology need not be scientific in nature. A sewing needle represents technology.

Teach

TEACH FROM VISUALS

FIGURE 1.12 Use the photograph to review the parts of a microscope. Refer students to pages R8–R10 in the Lab Handbook for more detailed information on the parts of a microscope, as well as information on magnification and specimen size.

▼ Teach *continued*

ONLINE BIOLOGY Go to the chapter Resource Center at **ClassZone.com** for additional resources and information on scientific tools and technology.

Vocabulary

Academic Vocabulary Students may associate the term **resolution** with a course of action.

resolve, to make a firm decision about or bring to a successful conclusion

In chemistry and mathematics, resolve can mean "to separate into parts or coordinate components." In physics, *resolve* can refer to the capacity to make an image visible or distinct.

The *resolution* of a microscope is the minimum distance that two points can be seen as being separate. The resolution of a light microscope is limited by the shortest wavelength of visible light. Electron microscopes produce images using beams of electrons, which can have even shorter wavelengths and produce a much greater resolution.

Take It Further

A **scanning electron microscope** (SEM) uses a beam of electrons instead of light, but it yields information similar to that of a light microscope. SEMs, however, can magnify objects up to 500,000 times. Different types of SEMs can yield four types of information:

- topography (surface features of an object)
- morphology (shape, size, and arrangement of an object's particles)
- composition (elements and compounds and their relative ratios)
- crystallographic information (arrangement and degree of order of the atoms)

Answers

A **Compare and Contrast** In SEMs, electrons deflect off specimens. In TEMs, electrons pass through specimens.

There are two main types of electron microscopes.

- A scanning electron microscope (SEM) scans the surface of a specimen with a beam of electrons. Usually, the specimen's surface is coated with a very thin layer of a metal that deflects the electrons. A computer forms a three-dimensional image from measurements of the deflected electrons.
- A transmission electron microscope (TEM) transmits electrons through a thin slice of a specimen. The TEM makes a two-dimensional image similar to that of a light microscope, but a TEM has a much higher magnification.

Often, SEM and TEM images are colorized with computers so that certain details are easier to see, as shown in **FIGURE 1.14.** Any time you see an SEM or TEM image in color, it has been given that color artificially.

Connecting **CONCEPTS**

Imaging Biologists use several types of micrographs, or images from microscopes. Whenever you see a micrograph in this book, LM stands for "light micrograph," SEM stands for "scanning electron micrograph," and TEM stands for "transmission electron micrograph."

Medical Imaging

Imaging technology is not limited to microscopes. In fact, technology used to study tissues inside living humans is commonly used in research and medicine. For example, doctors or dentists have probably taken x-ray images of you several times. An x-ray image is formed by x-rays, which pass through soft tissues, such as skin and muscle, but are absorbed by bones and teeth. Thus, x-ray images are very useful for looking at the skeleton but not so useful for examining soft tissues such as ligaments, cartilage, or the brain.

What if a doctor wants to examine ligaments in a person's knee? Another imaging technology called magnetic resonance imaging (MRI) is used. MRI uses a strong magnetic field to produce a cross-section image of a part of the body. A series of MRI images can be put together to give a complete view of all of the tissues in that area, as you can see in **FIGURE 1.13.** Advances in technology have led to new uses for MRI. For example, a technique called functional MRI (fMRI) can show which areas of the brain are active while a person is doing a particular task.

A Compare and Contrast **How do SEMs and TEMs produce different images of the same specimen?**

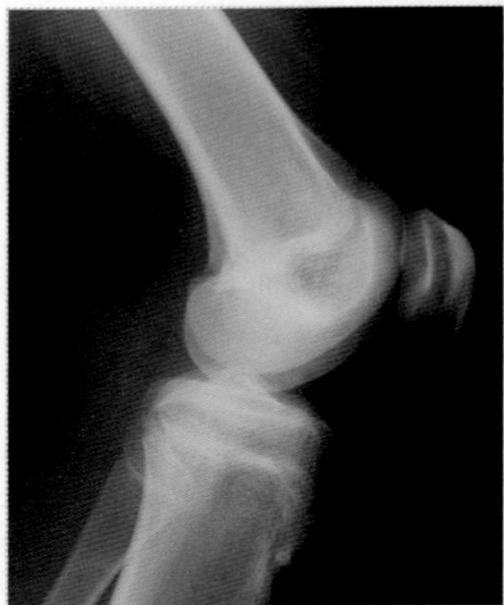

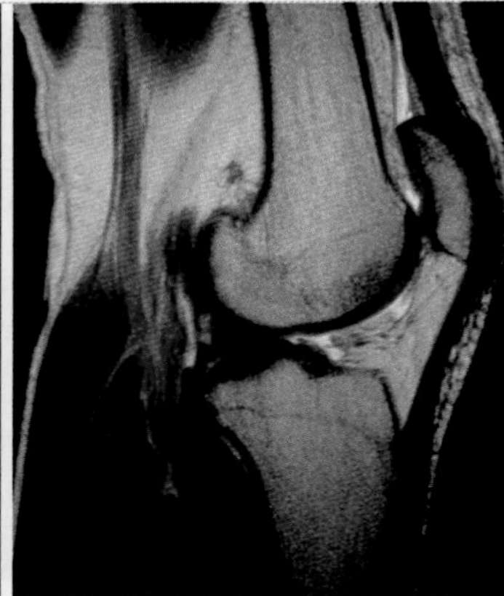

FIGURE 1.13 An x-ray of the human knee (left) shows dense tissues, such as bone, in detail. An MRI of the human knee (right) shows both soft and dense tissues in detail.

Differentiated Instruction

ENGLISH LEARNERS

English learners may be at a disadvantage in comprehending the text's language, but they are as competent as native speakers in interpreting images. Start with **FIGURE 1.13.** Have students describe what they see. Ask how the images are alike and different. Then apply the same technique to **FIGURE 1.14.**

Biology Toolkit, Connect to Content through Visuals, p. C17

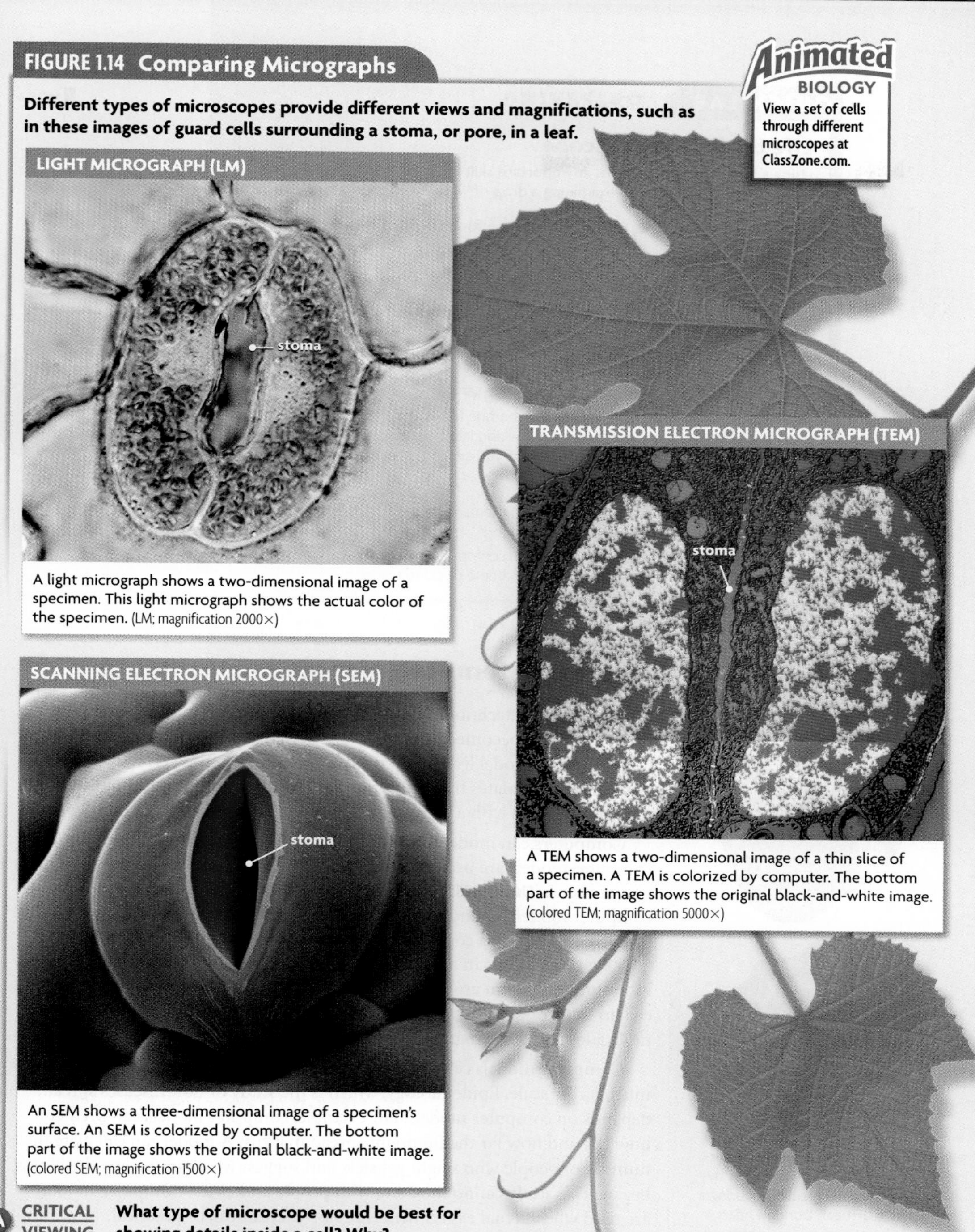

FIGURE 1.14 Comparing Micrographs

Different types of microscopes provide different views and magnifications, such as in these images of guard cells surrounding a stoma, or pore, in a leaf.

A light micrograph shows a two-dimensional image of a specimen. This light micrograph shows the actual color of the specimen. (LM; magnification 2000×)

A TEM shows a two-dimensional image of a thin slice of a specimen. A TEM is colorized by computer. The bottom part of the image shows the original black-and-white image. (colored TEM; magnification 5000×)

An SEM shows a three-dimensional image of a specimen's surface. An SEM is colorized by computer. The bottom part of the image shows the original black-and-white image. (colored SEM; magnification 1500×)

A CRITICAL VIEWING **What type of microscope would be best for showing details inside a cell? Why?**

TEACH FROM VISUALS

FIGURE 1.14 Have students read the captions of each image. **Ask**

- Which image has the highest magnification? the TEM
- Which image is seen in its actual color? the light micrograph
- Why don't SEMs and TEMs yield images in color? Color is part of the visible light region of the electromagnetic spectrum. SEMs and TEMs use electrons, not light.

Integrating Forensic Science

Forensic science is a term used to describe the actions taken by investigators during the examination of crime scenes and the gathering of evidence to be used in the prosecution of criminals. The SEM is an important tool in modern forensic science due to its wide range of applications. The SEM allows the rapid analysis of very small specimens of many materials that are important as evidence. Paint particles, natural and artificial fibers, fingerprints, gunshot residue, counterfeit money, and forged documents are all examples of specimens that can be analyzed with a SEM.

Answers

A **Critical Viewing** A TEM would be best because it shows the interior of a specimen at a high magnification.

TEACH WITH TECHNOLOGY

Show students more advanced microscopy techniques. If you have microscopes with oil-immersion objective lenses, show students how to use them. Explain that because light is refracted every time it passes through a medium with a different refractive index (air to glass or vice versa), the quality of the image is reduced. Immersion oil has been formulated so that it has a refractive index identical to that of glass. Thus, there is no refraction of light when it passes from glass to oil.

To demonstrate, remove the glass dropper rod from the oil, and then replace it. **Ask,** What happens to the image of the glass rod? It vanishes. Using oil immersion will enable students to view objects at 1000×. Furnish them will prepared slides of bacteria to view and sketch.

▼ Teach *continued*

QUICK LAB

Time 20 minutes	TEACHER TESTED
Lab Binder Introduction, pp. 9–10	

Purpose Observe and describe the characteristics of organisms found in a drop of pond water.

LAB MANAGEMENT

- Collect pond water less than 24 hours before the lab. To improve the chance of getting photosynthetic organisms, collect water from the surface of the pond. Keep the water aerated with a battery-powered aquarium aerator.
- Use a plankton net to obtain a more concentrated sample of organisms.
- Review with students the basic characteristics of protists, plants, and animals before the lab. Provide references for identifying microorganisms.
- Demonstrate how to tilt the cover slip and lower it carefully into place on the slide to help eliminate bubbles that might obscure students' views.

Safety Caution students to handle the glass slides carefully, and remind them to wipe eyepieces with alcohol wipes after using them. Make sure students wash their hands before leaving the lab.

Teacher Notes "This activity provides a good opportunity to address the plant-like and animal-like characteristics of euglena."

Answers

Analyze and Conclude

1. Answers could include observations of a cell membrane, responses to stimuli, movement, endocytosis, exocytosis, and fission.
2. Answers will vary depending on the organisms observed.

Answers

A Infer Some phenomena cannot be studied directly due to ethics, practicality, scale, complexity, or safety.

QUICK LAB **OBSERVING** NOS.3

Life Under a Microscope

Using a microscope properly is an important skill for many biologists. In this lab, you will review microscope skills by examining a drop of water from the surface of a local pond.

PROBLEM What types of organisms can be found in pond water?

MATERIALS
- 1 drop pond water
- eyedropper
- microscope slide
- cover slip
- microscope

PROCEDURE

1. Make a wet mount slide. Place a drop of pond water in the center of a microscope slide and carefully put a cover slip over the water. For more information on making a wet mount, see page R8.
2. View the pond water sample under low power on the microscope. Use the coarse focus knob to bring the sample into focus. Draw and label any organisms that you see in the sample.
3. View the slide under high power. Use the fine focus knob to bring portions of the sample into focus. Draw and label any organisms, including details of their structures, that you see in the sample.

ANALYZE AND CONCLUDE

1. **Connect** Describe how organisms in the sample exhibit the characteristics of living things.
2. **Compare and Contrast** Make a table to compare and contrast the characteristics of organisms in the sample of pond water.

MAIN IDEA

Complex systems are modeled on computers.

Normal heartbeat

Heart attack

FIGURE 1.15 This computer-generated model shows that heart activity (red) is tightly regulated during a normal heartbeat. During a heart attack, heart activity is widespread and disorganized.

Computer-based technology has greatly expanded biological research. As computers have become faster and more powerful, biologists have found ways to use them to model living systems that cannot be studied directly. A computer model simulates the interactions among many different variables to provide scientists with a general idea of how a biological system may work.

Computers can model complex systems within organisms. For example, computer models are used to study how medicines might affect the body or, as you can see in **FIGURE 1.15**, the effects of a heart attack. Scientists have even used computer models to find out how water molecules travel into and out of cells. The scientists made a computer program that took into account more than 50,000 virtual atoms in a virtual cell. The computer model showed that water molecules must spin around in the middle of a channel, or a passage into the cell, to fit through the channel. Water molecules had a specific fit that other molecules could not match.

Computer models can also help biologists study complex systems on a much larger scale. Epidemiology, which is the study of how diseases spread, depends on computer models. For example, computer models can predict how fast and how far the flu might spread in a city. A model can calculate the number of people who might get sick, and suggest where in the city the illness began. This study cannot be done with people and cities. Computer models are used when actual experiments are not safe, ethical, or practical.

A Infer **What are some reasons why biologists use computer models?**

Differentiated Instruction

BELOW LEVEL

Remind students of the importance of making observations in science. Have students write for five minutes on the question of how technology affects our ability or capacity to make observations, using examples from this section. Tell students to write continually during the whole time and not to worry about style.

Biology Toolkit, Quick-Write, p. C19

MAIN IDEA

The tools of molecular genetics give rise to new biological studies.

Computer-based technologies, such as those shown in **FIGURE 1.16**, have led to major changes in biology. But perhaps the greatest leap forward in our knowledge of life has happened in genetics. In just 40 years, we have gone from learning how the genetic code works, to changing genes, to implanting genes from one species into another. What is a gene? A **gene** is nothing more than a segment of DNA that stores genetic information. Our understanding of the DNA molecule has led to many technologies that were unimaginable when your parents were in high school—genetically modified foods, transgenic plants and animals, even replacement of faulty genes. These advances come from molecular genetics. **Molecular genetics** is the study and manipulation of DNA on a molecular level. Molecular genetics is used to study evolution, ecology, biochemistry, and many other areas of biology.

Entirely new areas of biology have arisen from combining molecular genetics with computer technology. For example, computers are used to quickly find DNA sequences. Through the use of computers, the entire DNA sequences, or genomes, of humans and other organisms have been found. **Genomics** (juh-NOH-mihks) is the study and comparison of genomes both within and across species. Here again, biologists need to use computers.

All of the information from genomics is managed by computer databases. By searching computer databases, a process called data mining, a biologist can find patterns, similarities, and differences in biological data. Suppose a biologist identifies a molecule that prevents the growth of cancerous tumors. The biologist could use computer databases to search for similar molecules.

This is the cutting edge of biology today. Where will biology be when your children are in high school?

A Connect **What does the term *genetics* mean to you? Why?**

FIGURE 1.16 Robots are used to speed up research into the human genome (top). Computers are used to sequence human DNA (bottom).

***Connecting* CONCEPTS**

Genetics You will learn much more about these and other genetics topics in **Unit 3**.

***Connecting* CONCEPTS**

Genetics The **Human Genome Project** (HGP) is the international research program with the goal of completely mapping all the genes of human beings. The HGP has revealed that there are probably somewhere between 30,000 and 40,000 human genes. This is the basic set of inheritable instructions for the development and function of a human being. The full sequence of genetic information (all of the DNA in the human genome) was completed in April 2003, many years ahead of schedule due mainly to the simultaneous development of computer programs that could very quickly analyze the genetic information. Another major component of the HGP is devoted to the analysis of the ethical, legal, and social implications of this new genetic knowledge. The Human Genome Project is discussed in more detail in Chapter 9.

Answers

A Connect Answers may include topics from popular culture, such as cloning, forensics, and mutation.

1.4 ASSESSMENT

ONLINE QUIZ ClassZone.com

NOS.10

REVIEWING MAIN IDEAS

1. How do light **microscopes** differ from electron microscopes?
2. Why is computer modeling used in biological studies?
3. How does **molecular genetics** add to our understanding of **genes**?

CRITICAL THINKING

4. **Apply** Viruses are smaller than cells. What types of microscopes could be used to study them? Explain.
5. **Synthesize** Provide an example of how technology has helped biologists gain a better understanding of life.

***Connecting* CONCEPTS**

6. **Evolution** **Genomics** can be used to study the genetic relationships among species. Why might genomics be important for evolution research? Explain.

Assess and Reteach

Assess Use the Online Quiz or Section Quiz (*Assessment Book,* p. 8).

Reteach Remind students that one way to define technology is an innovation that allows humans to manipulate their environment. Have students go through the different forms of technology discussed in this section and describe what form that manipulation takes and how it benefits us.

1.4 ASSESSMENT

1. Light microscopes use light to view specimens, including living specimens. Electron microscopes use electrons to view specimens at higher magnifications but cannot examine living specimens.
2. to model anything that is not practical or ethical to do in the real world
3. Molecular genetics is the study of inheritance on a molecular level. DNA is the molecule that encodes genetic information. A gene is a segment of DNA.
4. Light microscopes are not powerful enough to clearly view viruses, so electron microscopes would need to be used.
5. Answers could include imaging technologies showing more details of cells, computer analysis of genes and genomes, and computer models.
6. By comparing the genomes of different species, scientists can establish how closely related species are by finding occurrences of shared DNA sequences and genes.

SECTION 1.5

▼ Plan and Prepare

Objectives

- Evaluate the importance of biology in making informed decisions.
- Summarize the benefits and risks of the application of biotechnology.
- Explain how advances in technology might affect the future of biology.

Section Resources

Unit Resource Book
Study Guide pp. 17–18
Power Notes p. 19
Reinforcement p. 20

Interactive Reader Chapter 1
Spanish Study Guide pp. 9–10

Biology Toolkit p. C11

Technology
Power Presentation 1.5
Media Gallery DVD
Online Quiz 1.5

Activate Prior Knowledge Discuss the steps that people take when making important decisions. **Ask,** How would you characterize some of the factors you take into account when making an important decision? social, economic, ethical, moral Explain that knowing as much as they can about biology can help them make informed decisions about their health, the environment, how they vote, and how they act as citizens.

▼ Teach

Take It Further

Allergic reactions to peanuts range from itching or swelling of the lips, tongue, or mouth to shortness of breath and a drop in blood pressure. Sometimes the allergy is so severe that even cross-contaminated equipment in the food processing facility can cause a deadly reaction. Because of this, companies sometimes put warning statements such as "may contain peanuts" on the label. Foods without these labels could be unsafe for people with a peanut allergy.

1.5 Biology and Your Future

KEY CONCEPT Understanding biology can help you make informed decisions.

MAIN IDEAS

- Your health and the health of the environment depend on your knowledge of biology.
- Biotechnology offers great promise but also raises many issues.
- Biology presents many unanswered questions.

VOCABULARY

biotechnology, p. 26
transgenic, p. 26

NOS.11 Explain how scientific knowledge can be used to guide decisions on environmental and social issues.

Connect Should brain imaging technology be used to tell if someone is lying? Is an endangered moth's habitat more important than a new highway? Would you vote for or against the pursuit of stem cell research? An informed answer to any of these questions requires an understanding of biology and scientific thinking. And although science alone cannot answer these questions, gathering evidence and analyzing data can help every decision maker.

MAIN IDEA

Your health and the health of the environment depend on your knowledge of biology.

Decisions are based on opinions, emotions, education, experiences, values, and logic. Many of your decisions, now and in the future, at both personal and societal levels, involve biology. Your knowledge of biology can help you make informed decisions about issues involving endangered species, biotechnology, medical research, and pollution control, to name a few. How will your decisions affect the future of yourself and others?

TAKING NOTES

Use a mind map to take notes about the importance of studying biology.

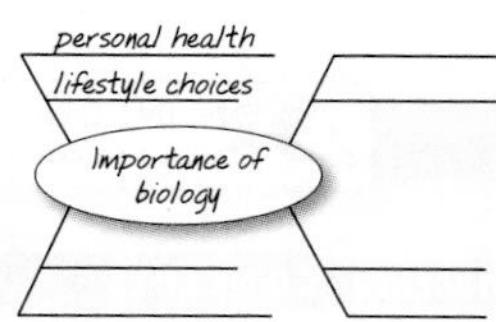

Biology and Your Health

What you eat and drink is directly related to your health. But you may not think twice about the possibility of contaminated food or water, or a lack of vitamins in your diet. Not long ago, diseases caused by vitamin deficiencies were still fairly common. The first vitamins were identified less than 100 years ago, but today the vitamins found in foods are printed on labels.

Even today we still face food-related causes of illness. For example, you might hear about an outbreak of food poisoning, and mad cow disease was only recognized in the late 1980s. Of perhaps greater concern to you are food allergies. Many people suffer from severe, even life-threatening, allergies to foods such as peanuts and shellfish. Beyond questions about the sources of food are questions and concerns about what people eat and how much they eat. For example, scientists estimate that more than 60 percent of adults in the United States are overweight or obese. The health consequences of obesity include increased risks of diabetes, stroke, heart disease, breast cancer, colon cancer, and other health problems. Biology can help you to better understand all of these health-related issues.

Differentiated Instruction

PRE-AP

Have students brainstorm designing a decision-making model with at least four steps. Give students the first step: Identify the issue or question. Subsequent steps could include gathering information about both sides of the issue, identifying options, listing benefits and consequences, considering personal values, deciding, and acting. Display the model and suggest a question to which students can apply the model.

Biology Toolkit, Brainstorming, p. C11

An understanding of biology on many different levels—genetic, chemical, and cellular, for example—can help you make any number of lifestyle choices that affect your health. Why is it important to use sunscreen? What are the benefits of exercise? What are the effects of using alcohol, illegal drugs, and tobacco? Cigarette smoke does not just affect the lungs; it can also change a person's body chemistry, as you can see in **FIGURE 1.17**. Lower levels of monoamine oxidase in the brain can affect mood, and lower levels in the liver could contribute to high blood pressure.

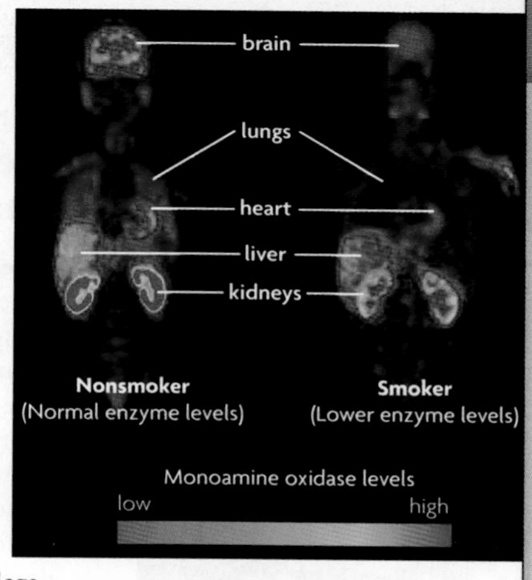

FIGURE 1.17 As compared with nonsmokers, smokers have much lower levels of an enzyme called monoamine oxidase throughout their bodies.

Biology and the World Around You

In 1995, some middle school students from Minnesota were walking through a wetland and collecting frogs for a school project. The students stopped to look at the frogs, and what they saw shocked them. Many of the frogs had deformities, including missing legs, extra legs, and missing eyes. What caused the deformities? Scientists investigated that question by testing several hypotheses. They studied whether the deformities could have been caused by factors such as a chemical in the water, ultraviolet radiation, or some type of infection.

Why would frog deformities such as that in **FIGURE 1.18** provoke such scientific interest? The frogs are a part of an ecosystem, so whatever affected them could affect other species in the area. If the deformities were caused by a chemical in the water, might the chemical pose a risk to people living in the area? In other regions of the United States, parasites caused similar deformities in frogs. Might that parasite also be present in Minnesota? If so, did it pose a risk to other species?

Scientists still do not know for sure what caused the frog deformities in Minnesota. No parasitic infection was found, so that hypothesis was rejected. However, evidence indicates that the water contained a chemical very similar to a chemical in frogs that helps control limb development. It is not known whether the chemical is the result of pollution or if it occurs naturally.

Suppose that the chemical comes from a factory in the area. Is it reasonable to ban the chemical? Should the factory be closed or fined? In any instance like this, political, legal, economic, and biological concerns have to be considered. What is the economic impact of the factory on the area? Is there any evidence of human health problems in the area? Is there a different chemical that could be used? Without an understanding of biology, how could you make an informed decision related to any of these questions?

These are the types of questions that people try to answer every day. Biologists and other scientists research environmental issues such as pollution, biodiversity, habitat preservation, land conservation, and natural resource use, but decisions about the future are not in the hands of scientists. It is up to everyone to make decisions based on evidence and conclusions from many different sources.

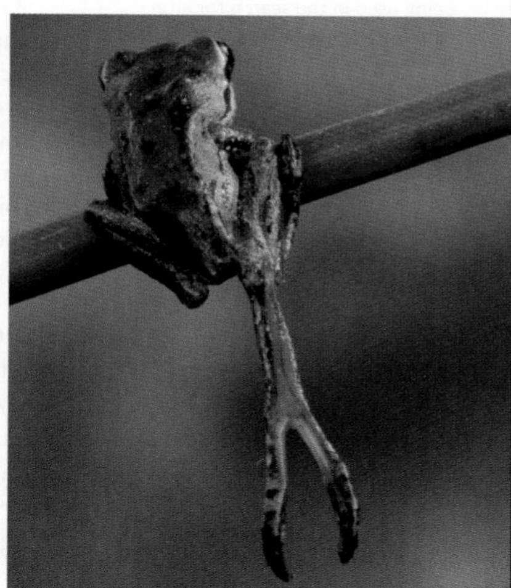

FIGURE 1.18 Deformities in frogs can be an indication of chemical pollution in an ecosystem.

Ⓐ Connect **How might biology help you to better understand environmental issues?**

ENGLISH LEARNERS

Use the section Biology and the World Around You to model how to interpret text. Ask volunteers to read the text aloud and then read through parts of it again to establish what happened, why it was important, what concerns were raised, and what we know so far. Use direct sentence structure when talking about or paraphrasing the material. Place main clauses before subordinate ones, use short and simple sentences, and avoid interrupting clauses.

TEACH FROM VISUALS

FIGURE 1.18 Tell students that research has shown that abnormalities are rare among laboratory-reared frogs—less than 0.05 percent. **Ask,** What can you infer from this fact? An environmental factor is the cause of the abnormalities.

Take It Further

In the two years that followed the discovery of the Minnesota **frog deformities** in 1995, reports of deformities increased but were restricted to one species, the northern leopard frog. In 1997, the number of reports and species involved increased. Six species of deformed frogs have been documented at more than 150 sites across 54 counties in Minnesota. The malformations found include missing or additional feet, legs, toes, and eyes, as well as musculoskeletal and urogenital defects. The incidence of abnormalities was as high as 60 percent among some frog populations.

Integrating Epidemiology

Epidemiology is the study of factors that cause illness and disease in populations. Epidemiologists are consulted when acute conditions or diseases affect a small number of people in the same community, because most diseases are not randomly distributed. For example, epidemiologists investigated cancer clusters reported in Toms River, New Jersey, and Woburn, Massachusetts, that were believed to be caused by industrial pollutants. An epidemiologist uses scientific inquiry and experimentation to determine the relationship between a disease and its cause and the implications to public health. Principles of science, statistics, philosophy, anthropology, psychology, and social policy are integrated into epidemiological investigations.

Answers

Ⓐ **Connect** Answers should indicate a knowledge of the interactions among living things in an ecosystem.

▼ Teach *continued*

ONLINE BIOLOGY For more on bioethics, see the WebQuest in Options for Inquiry on page 29.

Take It Further

In 1963, **Thomas Starzl** performed the first liver transplant. Starzl has since become known as the father of transplantation. More than 100,000 people are alive today due to organ transplants, with more than 92,000 Americans on waiting lists.

To address the lack of human organs available for transplant, Starzl researched **xenotransplantation,** which is the transfer of cells, tissues, or organs from one species to another. Between 1963 and 1993, Starzl transplanted into humans six baboon kidneys, three chimpanzee livers, and two baboon livers. All of the transplants were unsuccessful. Starzl does not view xenotransplants as permanent replacements, just temporary fixes until an appropriate human organ is located. The risks of xenotransplants are organ rejection and infection spread from donor animals to humans.

MAIN IDEA

Biotechnology offers great promise but also raises many issues.

Biotechnology is the use and application of living things and biological processes. Biotechnology includes a very broad range of products, processes, and techniques. In fact, some forms of biotechnology have been around for centuries, such as the use of microorganisms to make bread and cheese. Today, biotechnology is used in medicine, agriculture, forensic science, and many other fields. For example, people wrongly convicted of crimes have been freed from prison when DNA testing has shown that their DNA did not match DNA found at crime scenes. Biotechnology has great potential to help solve a variety of modern problems, such as the search for alternative energy sources like the algae shown in **FIGURE 1.19.** However, along with the advances in biotechnology come questions about its uses.

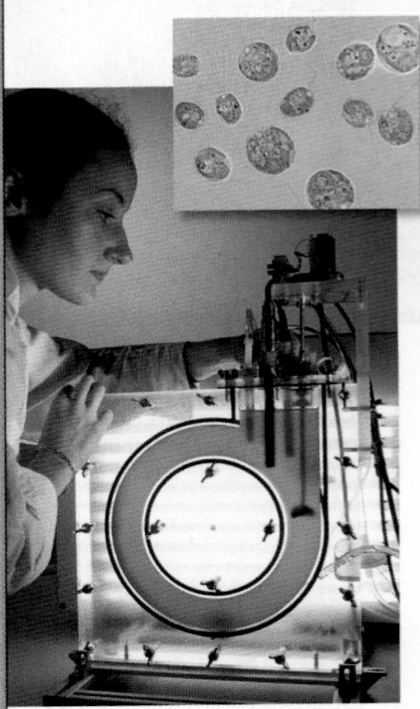

FIGURE 1.19 Biotechnology is being used in the search for alternative energy sources, as shown in this bioreactor that uses algae (inset) to produce hydrogen gas. (LM; magnification 400×)

Benefits and Biological Risks

All domestic plants and animals are the result of centuries of genetic manipulation through selective breeding. Today, genetic manipulation can mean the transfer of genetic information from one organism to a very different organism. Organisms that have genes from more than one species, or have altered copies of their own genes, are called **transgenic** organisms. Transgenic bacteria can make human insulin to treat people with diabetes. Transgenic sheep and cows can make human antibodies and proteins. When you hear about genetically modified foods, you are hearing about transgenic organisms.

Genetically modified foods have many potential benefits. Crop plants are changed to increase the nutrients and yield of the plants and to resist insects. Insect-resistant crops could reduce or end the need for chemical pesticides. However, the long-term effects of genetically modified crops are not fully known. Is it safe to eat foods with genetically modified insect resistance? What if genetically modified plants spread undesirable genes, such as those for herbicide resistance, to wild plants? Around the world, the benefits and risks of biotechnology are debated. Understanding these benefits and risks requires knowledge of ecosystems, genetic principles, and even the functions of genes.

Benefits and Ethical Considerations

Another form of biotechnology is human genetic screening, which is the analysis of a person's genes to identify genetic variations. Genetic screening can indicate whether individuals or their potential offspring may be at risk for certain diseases or genetic disorders. Genetic screening has the potential for early diagnosis of conditions that can be treated before an illness occurs.

Genetic screening also raises ethical concerns. For example, who should have access to a person's genetic information? Some people are concerned that insurance companies might refuse health insurance to someone with a gene that might cause a disease. Suppose genetic screening reveals that a child might have a genetic disorder. How should that information be used? Genetic screening has the potential to eliminate some disorders, but what should be

Connecting CONCEPTS

Genetics You will learn more about genetic screening and how it is used in **Chapter 9.**

Differentiated Instruction

HANDS-ON ACTIVITY

Introduce social issues and current science topics into the science classroom by having students bring in articles on life science and biotechnology from newspapers and magazines. Set aside class time regularly to discuss the articles.

Tell students that the study of life science will introduce topics about which there will be different points of view. Solicit their help in creating an environment in which students are expected to respect the right of others to express those views.

considered a disorder? Of greater concern is the possibility that people might use genetic screening to choose the characteristics of their children. Is it ethical to allow people to choose to have only brown-eyed male children who would be at least six feet tall?

A Predict How might genetically modified crops affect biodiversity?

MAIN IDEA

Biology presents many unanswered questions.

About 50 years ago, the structure of DNA was discovered. By 2003, the entire human DNA sequence was known. Over the last 50 years, our biological knowledge has exploded. But even today there are more questions than answers. Can cancer be prevented or cured? How do viruses mutate? How are memories stored in the brain? One of the most interesting questions is whether life exists on planets other than Earth. Extreme environments on Earth are home to living things like the methane worms in **FIGURE 1.20.** Thus, it is logical to suspect that other planets may also support life. But even if life exists elsewhere in the universe, it may be completely different from life on Earth. How might biological theories change to take into account the characteristics of those organisms?

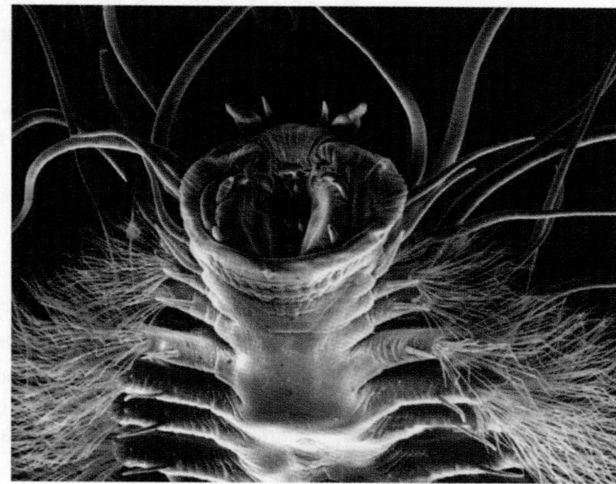

FIGURE 1.20 Methane worms live in frozen methane gas at the bottom of the Gulf of Mexico. Because some organisms can live in such extreme environments, some scientists hypothesize that life exists, or once existed, on the planet Mars. (SEM; magnification 20×)

A huge number of questions in biology are not just unanswered—they are unasked. Before the microscope was developed, no one investigated anything microscopic. Before the middle of the 20th century, biologists did not know for sure what the genetic material in organisms was made of. As technology and biology advance, who knows what will be discovered in the next 20 years?

B Evaluate Do you think technology can help answer all biological questions? Explain your views.

1.5 ASSESSMENT

ONLINE QUIZ ClassZone.com

NOS.11

REVIEWING MAIN IDEAS

1. Give three examples of ways in which biology can help inform everyday decisions.
2. What are some of the potential benefits and potential risks of **biotechnology**?
3. What are some of the unanswered questions in biology?

CRITICAL THINKING

4. **Synthesize** Scientists disagree on whether genetically modified foods are safe to eat. What type of scientific evidence would be needed to show that a genetically modified food is unsafe?
5. **Connect** How might your study of biology help inform you about your lifestyle choices?

Connecting CONCEPTS

6. **Ecology** What effects might genetically modified plants and animals have on an ecosystem if they breed with wild plants and animals?

1.5 ASSESSMENT

1. *Sample Answer:* Knowledge of biology can inform decisions about diet, using sunscreen, and exercise.
2. benefits: treatment and prevention of disease and illness, improving crop growth; risks: ethical concerns, privacy, potential negative health and environmental effects.
3. Answers could include questions about life on other planets, cancer, viruses, or memory.
4. *Sample Answer:* long-term feeding trials comparing health of animals that do and do not eat GM foods. The best evidence will be collected over time with humans. Over several years, there will be more data about the health of people who eat GM foods compared with people who do not.
5. A knowledge of biology helps to make informed decisions about lifestyle choices that could affect your health and quality of life and the health of the environment.
6. They could decrease biodiversity and affect an ecosystem in unpredictable ways.

Take It Further

Discuss with students that like the methane worms in **FIGURE 1.20,** many organisms alive on Earth today are hardy enough to withstand, even flourish, in extremely harsh environments. *Thermophilic bacteria* live in pools of boiling water at Yellowstone National Park, where water boils at 92°C (198°F). Dense colonies of mussels form around the edge of extremely salty holes in the ocean floor. The **brine pools** are so salty and dense that submersible vehicles such as the Alvin can sit on top of them with its engines off.

Answers

A Predict If only a few varieties of crop plants are used, biodiversity will decrease.

B Evaluate No, because at this time we can only directly study a limited number of biological phenomena, even with advances in technology. There are always questions to be asked and investigated, and technology is a part of the search for answers.

Assess and Reteach ▼

Assess Use the Online Quiz or Section Quiz (*Assessment Book,* p. 9).

Reteach Have students recall recent news stories of developments in the biological sciences. Discuss whether these developments have the potential to raise social or ethical questions, as well as scientific ones. Discuss the question of science literacy in evaluating these stories.

OPTIONS FOR INQUIRY

INVESTIGATION

Time 45 minutes	TEACHER TESTED
Teacher Preparation	
Student Difficulty	
Lab Binder Introduction, pp. 5–6	

Purpose Test how plants grow in response to external stimuli.

Overview Students will design a test of one stimulus—light, gravity, or touch, and observe plant growth responses. Students will

- write an experimental procedure that describes how they will test their independent variable
- define constants and use a control
- design an appropriate data table and record their observations in it

LAB PREPARATION

- Purchase germinated bean plants that have about one week's growth.
- If you germinate seeds yourself, do not use the bush variety. Use beans that have tendrils to grasp a support.

LAB MANAGEMENT

- Students testing light need to decide if they will test amount of growth using evenly distributed light or pattern of growth using directional light.
- Students testing gravity need to provide evenly distributed light.
- Students testing touch need to insert a small support, such as a drinking straw, into the soil near the plants.

Teacher Note "I've never done gravity before, so that aspect of the activity was interesting."

POST-LAB DISCUSSION

Discuss the results. **Ask,** Why do plants respond to external stimuli? To survive, plants must be able to grow in ways that allow them to get light and nutrients.

Use these inquiry-based labs and online activities to deepen your understanding of biology and scientific experiments.

INDIANA STANDARDS

NOS.1 Develop explanations based on reproducible data and observations gathered during laboratory investigations.

NOS.4 Regularly evaluate the work of their peers and in turn have their work evaluated by their peers.

DESIGN YOUR OWN INVESTIGATION

Manipulating Plant Growth

The direction in which plants grow is affected by conditions such as light, gravity, and contact with an object. In this lab, you will design your own experiment to determine how changing an independent variable affects a dependent variable.

SKILLS Designing Experiments, Observing, Collecting Data, Analyzing Data, Inferring

PROBLEM How does changing an external condition affect plant growth?

MATERIALS

- 3 bean plants
- 10 cm masking tape
- permanent marker
- light source
- 3 wooden sticks
- 1 m string
- metric ruler
- water
- 250-mL beaker

PROCEDURE

1. Label three bean plants A, B, and C.
2. Decide which condition you will test: light, gravity, or contact with an object.
3. Design your experiment and identify your independent variable. Use one plant as the control condition. Use the other two plants as experimental conditions. For example, gravity can be tested by placing an experimental plant on its side.
4. Identify the constants in your experiment, such as the amount of water you will give the plants.
5. Determine the operational definition for the dependent variable; that is, decide how you will measure the dependent variable. For example, it could be the number of leaves facing in a certain direction each day.
6. Record your observations once a day for five days in a table like the one shown below. Remember to wash your hands after handling the plants.
7. Have your teacher approve your procedure. Carry out your experiment.

TABLE 1. EFFECT OF __________ ON PLANT GROWTH

Day	Plant A Growth (mm)	Plant B Growth (mm)	Plant C Growth (mm)
1			
2			

ANALYZE AND CONCLUDE

1. **Analyze** How did your independent variable affect plant growth? How did you measure the dependent variable? Do the data support your hypothesis? Explain.
2. **Infer** Why is it important to have control groups and constants in an experiment?
3. **Communicate** Share your results with other groups. How did different independent variables affect plant growth? Did your results agree with the results of other groups that tested the same variable? If not, what might have caused that difference?
4. **Design Experiments** Review the design of your experiment. What changes could you make to the procedure to reduce the variability in your data?
5. **Ask Questions** From your data, what new questions do you have about plant growth?

Answers

Sample Data

For a sample of student data from this lab, go to page R101.

Analyze and Conclude

1. Answers will vary depending on the variable tested. Plants should have grown toward the light, against gravity, or away from contact. Dependent variable may have been measured using a ruler. Whether data support a hypothesis depends on the hypothesis and collected data.
2. to ensure that changes in the dependent variable resulted only from changes in the independent variable
3. Answers will vary. For groups who tested the same variable, differences may result from differences in experimental design or random error.
4. Constants could be better maintained, or measurement could be standardized.
5. Answers should suggest questions about what causes the change in the plant that makes it respond in the way that it does.

INVESTIGATION

Biology in the News

Every day, newspapers print articles related to biology. Maybe someone has reported a previously unknown species, such as the Goodman's mouse lemur, discovered on the island of Madagascar in 2005. Maybe it's a story about the effect of a low-fat diet on the risk of developing cancer. Some articles discuss biology-related questions or problems, such as the use of a mercury-based preservative in certain vaccines. What biology news stories interest you?

SKILL Researching

PROBLEM What types of biology-based problems are reported in the news?

PROCEDURE

1. Find a news story about a biology-based problem in the newspaper or from one of the news feeds in the BioZine at ClassZone.com. Because medical research is the most common topic discussed in news articles, find an article about a different topic in biology.
2. Read the article and answer the following questions:
   - What is the topic of the article?
   - What is the problem, discovery, or event?
   - What is being decided?
   - Who are the people involved in making the decision?
   - What are all of the possible consequences of the decision?
   - What factors may be influencing the decision?
   - What new questions are raised as a result of the discovery, situation, or research?
   - How is knowledge of biology useful for understanding this topic?

Goodman's mouse lemur was discovered in 2005.

Online BIOLOGY
CLASSZONE.COM

ANIMATED BIOLOGY

Experimental Design

How do you test a hypothesis? Use items in a lab to design a valid experiment for a sample hypothesis, and identify all of the factors in your investigation.

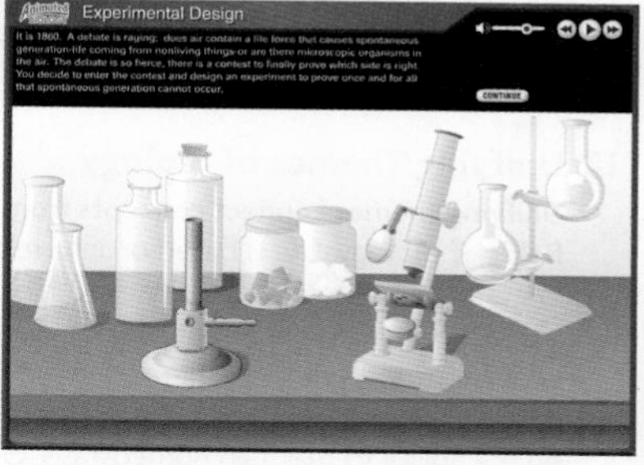

WEBQUEST

Is it always ethical to conduct scientific research, ask for a person's DNA, or use all of the biotechnology that we have? In this WebQuest, you will explore bioethics. First, learn how scientists think ethically. Then, explore a situation and determine for yourself if it was handled in an ethical manner.

BIOLOGY TODAY

Scientist Suspected of Bioethics Violations

DATA ANALYSIS ONLINE

Earth has a great, ever-changing diversity of life. The types and numbers of organisms have changed over time. Graph the estimated number of different categories of marine organisms over the past 550 million years to analyze the trends in Earth's biodiversity.

Answers

2. Answers will vary depending on students' articles. Below are sample answers on the discovery of Goodman's mouse lemur:
   - new lemurs found in Madagascar
   - discovery of a new species of lemur in the rain forest of Madagascar
   - the importance of conserving Madagascar's rapidly disappearing rain forests
   - Dr. Steve Goodman of the World Wildlife Fund and Chicago's Field Museum of Natural History; scientists with the German Primate Center and the University of Göttingen; Malagasy collaborators
   - greater knowledge about the fauna of Madagascar, and protection of the rain forest
   - desire to protect the lemurs' habitat
   - What other species are still undiscovered?
   - The species was identified by analyzing its DNA. An understanding of DNA and human impact on rain forests is necessary to understand this article.

Online Biology ▼

ANIMATED BIOLOGY Use this interactive animation to reinforce the concepts in **Section 1.3.**

WEBQUEST The WebQuest takes one full class period. Students complete the activity online and will need access to a printer to print their answers. Sample answers, teacher notes, and alternative assessment ideas are available on **ClassZone.com.** Use with **Section 1.5.**

DATA ANALYSIS ONLINE
Students will see that diversity of species grows rather steadily over time, though there are some extinction events. Use with **Section 1.1.**

INVESTIGATION

Time 45 minutes	TEACHER TESTED
Teacher Preparation	
Student Difficulty	
Lab Binder Introduction, pp. 7–8	

Purpose Analyze a biology news story.

Overview Students will review a biology-related newspaper article or a news article from the BioZine at **ClassZone.com.**

LAB PREPARATION

- Arrange for access to computers and other sources of news stories.

POST-LAB DISCUSSION

Allow time for students to discuss what they learned in their research.

CHAPTER REVIEW

Interactive Review

Encourage students go to **ClassZone.com** for a detailed review of each section, including visuals and vocabulary practice.

Unit Resource Book, Vocabulary Practice, pp. 27–30

CHAPTER 1 **Interactive Review** @ CLASSZONE.COM

KEY CONCEPTS | Vocabulary Games | Concept Maps | Animated Biology | Online Quiz

1.1 The Study of Life

Biologists study life in all its forms. Everywhere that organisms are found on Earth is considered to be the biosphere. The biosphere includes millions of diverse species. Organisms are made of one or more cells, need energy for all of their functions, respond to their environment, and reproduce by passing on their genetic information to offspring.

1.2 Unifying Themes of Biology

Unifying themes connect concepts from many fields of biology. Life is based on interrelated systems, from chemical processes within cells to interactions among different species in an ecosystem. Individual organisms depend on the relationship between structure and function, and on the ability to maintain homeostasis. Over billions of years, evolution and adaptation have given rise to all of the species on Earth.

1.3 Scientific Thinking and Processes

Science is a way of thinking, questioning, and gathering evidence. Scientists test hypotheses, or proposed explanations, through observation and experimentation. In a scientific experiment, a scientist controls constants, manipulates independent variables, and measures dependent variables. A scientific theory explains a wide range of observations and experimental results. A theory is supported by a wide range of evidence, and it is widely accepted by the scientific community.

1.4 Biologists' Tools and Technology

Technology continually changes the way biologists work. Imaging technologies have had a major influence on biology. Microscopes, from the light microscope to today's electron microscopes, allow biologists to study tiny details of cells. The development of fast, powerful computers has given scientists the ability to model aspects of life that cannot be studied directly. Technology also allows the study, comparison, and manipulation of genes at the molecular level.

1.5 Biology and Your Future

Understanding biology can help you make informed decisions. An understanding of biology can help you to make important decisions about your own health and lifestyle, as well as decisions that will shape the world around you. The development of biotechnology and genetic manipulation is just one issue in biology that will affect you and the rest of society in the coming years.

Synthesize Your Notes

Content Frame Identify relationships between the characteristics of living things and the unifying themes of biology. Use your notes to make content frame organizers like the one below to summarize the relationships.

Characteristic	Theme	Example
Cells	Systems	Cells work together in multicellular organisms.
	Structure and Function	

Concept Map Use concept maps like the one below to visualize general relationships among topics in biology.

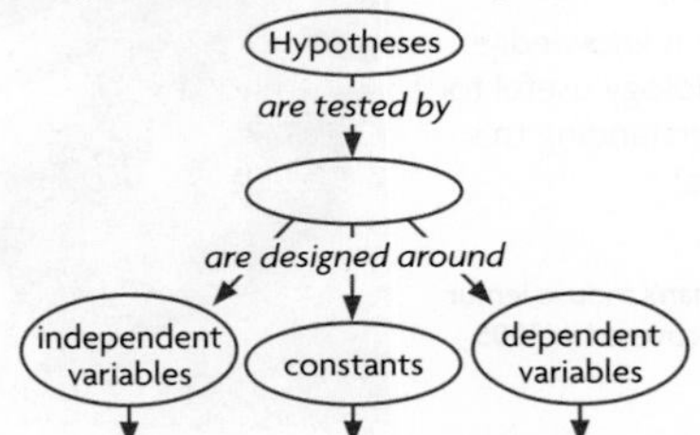

Reviewing Vocabulary

1. Organisms live in both; the biosphere contains all ecosystems.
2. Both propose answers to a scientific question, but a theory encompasses a large quantity of observations and experimental results, and a hypothesis applies to just one experiment.
3. Scientists control both; the independent variable is manipulated, and constants are unchanging.
4. What is it that natural selection acts upon to bring about evolution?
5. Observations are typically qualitative in nature: what do scientists collect to measure natural phenomena?
6. What part of the DNA sequence in a genome contains genetic information?
7. All of the terms relate to the study of living things.
8. stopping change to internal conditions, keeping them at the same point

Chapter Assessment

Chapter Vocabulary

1.1 biosphere, p. 4
biodiversity, p. 5
species, p. 5
biology, p. 5
organism, p. 5
cell, p. 5
metabolism, p. 6
DNA, p. 6

1.2 system, p. 7
ecosystem, p. 7
homeostasis, p. 9
evolution, p. 10
adaptation, p. 10

1.3 observation, p. 13
data, p. 14
hypothesis, p. 14
experiment, p. 16
independent variable, p. 16
dependent variable, p. 16
constant, p. 16
theory, p. 16

1.4 microscope, p. 19
gene, p. 23
molecular genetics, p. 23
genomics, p. 23

1.5 biotechnology, p. 26
transgenic, p. 26

Reviewing Vocabulary

Compare and Contrast

Describe one similarity and one difference between the two terms in each of the following pairs.

1. biosphere, ecosystem
2. hypothesis, theory
3. independent variable, constant

Write Your Own Questions

Think about the relationship between each word pair below. Then write a question about the first term that uses the second term as the answer. For the pair *organism, cell,* the question could be "What is the basic building block of all organisms?" Answer: the cell

4. evolution, adaptation **B.8.5**
5. observation, data
6. DNA, gene **B.5.2**

Greek and Latin Word Origins

7. The prefix *bio-* means "life." How does this meaning relate to the definitions of terms in the chapter that contain the prefix *bio-*?

8. The prefix *homeo-* comes from a Greek word that means "same." The suffix *-stasis* comes from a Greek word that means "stoppage," or "standstill." How are these definitions related to the meaning of *homeostasis*?

Reviewing MAIN IDEAS

9. In general, greater biodiversity exists closer to Earth's equator than in areas closer to Earth's poles. What does this mean in terms of the number of species that are found in these regions?

10. Briefly describe the basic characteristics that all living things on Earth have in common.

11. Give an example of how structure and function are related in an organism.

12. How does negative feedback act to maintain homeostasis in living things?

13. Evidence shows that hippos and whales are closely related organisms. How might evolution and adaptation account for similarities and differences between them?

14. Explain how scientists use observations and data to develop a hypothesis.

15. How does the manipulation of an independent variable during a scientific experiment allow a scientist to find a cause-and-effect relationship between variables?

16. What is the difference between a hypothesis and a theory? **NOS.8**

17. Briefly describe why the development of the microscope was important in biology. **NOS.10**

18. How can an understanding of biology play a role in your health? in the health of your environment? **NOS.11**

19. Describe an example of biotechnology, including its benefits and risks.

CHAPTER REVIEW

Reviewing Main Ideas

9. A greater number of different species is found in those regions.
10. They all have one or more cells, which are the basic units of life. They all need energy to carry out cell functions. They all need to respond to the environment to survive. They must be able to reproduce to maintain the species.
11. Molecules with different structures have different functions; specialized cells have structures that allow them to perform their functions; different parts of multicellular organisms are specialized to perform different functions.
12. It acts to reverse a change in conditions to bring the conditions back to normal levels.
13. Due to environmental changes, one population of animals was better adapted to land and a different population was better adapted to water, so evolution resulted in the two different species.
14. Scientists propose explanations for observations and data to form hypotheses.
15. If only one factor is changing and a dependent variable is affected, the change in the dependent variable is probably due to the independent variable.
16. A hypothesis accounts for one observation (or experiment); a theory accounts for many.
17. Different types of microscopes allow the study of things too small to be seen with the human eye. The development of the microscope led to the discovery of cells and micro-organisms. Modern microscopes show the internal structure of cells.
18. It allows you to make informed decisions on health and environmental concerns such as smoking, diet, exercise, sunscreen use, pollution, habitat preservation, and natural-resource use.
19. *Sample Answers:* GM foods (benefits: improved crop yield; risks: loss of biodiversity and possible long-term health effects); genetic screening (benefits: detection of genetic diseases; risk: privacy).

ITEM CORRELATIONS

Standard	Items
B.5.2	6
B.8.5	4
NOS.8	16
NOS.10	17
NOS.11	18

Critical Thinking

20. The loss of species may destroy sources of new medicines.
21. Banning DDT allowed affected populations of fish and birds to recover. Humans are part of the same ecosystems as fish and birds, and toxins that affect those animals may also affect humans. Removing a toxic chemical from the environment decreases risks to human health.
22. Systems: Different parts work together to form a whole. Structure and Function: The general structures and functions are the same, but a more complex structure also comes with more complex functions. Homeostasis: Circulatory systems are needed to maintain stable conditions in the organisms. Evolution: Adaptations have led to the evolution of the different circulatory systems in different species.
23. no, because two variables were manipulated and it is not possible to determine which one produced the effect
24. Light microscopes use light, produce a two-dimensional image, and can be used to study living specimens; SEMs use electrons and provide a highly magnified three-dimensional view of a specimen's surface, but cannot be used with living specimens; TEMs also use electrons and provide a highly magnified two-dimensional view of a specimen's interior, but cannot be used with living specimens.

Interpreting Visuals

25. At all points of the scientific thinking cycle; observations help scientists carefully consider information and data.
26. Students could draw a diagram that indicates that the steps can take place in any order or by drawing arrows between different steps, such as between testing hypotheses and observing.

Critical Thinking

20. Predict Many medications used to treat human illnesses are based on substances found in other organisms. How might a decrease in biodiversity affect medical discoveries and treatments?

21. Synthesize In 1973, the insecticide called DDT was banned in the United States due to concerns that it was toxic to fish and that it may have affected birds. There is little scientific evidence that DDT is directly harmful to humans. How could banning DDT be beneficial to human health?

22. Synthesize Birds and mammals have complex circulatory systems that pump and carry blood to all parts of their bodies. Insects have much simpler circulatory systems. Select two unifying themes of biology from Section 1.2, and describe how they apply to the circulatory systems of animals.

23. Evaluate Suppose a scientist is investigating plant growth. During the experiment, both the type of light and the type of plant are manipulated. The scientist concludes that the results are caused only by changes in the light. Is this an appropriate conclusion? Why or why not?

24. Compare and Contrast Describe the similarities and differences among images from light microscopes, scanning electron microscopes, and transmission electron microscopes.

Interpreting Visuals

Use the diagram below to answer the next two questions.

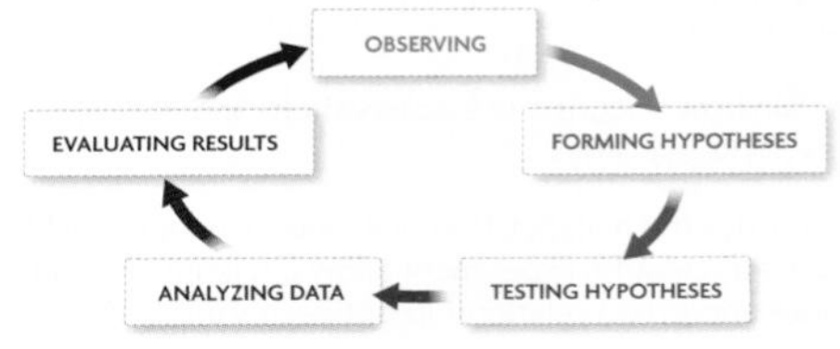

25. Apply Observing is shown at only one point during the cycle. At what other points during the cycle is observing necessary? Explain.

26. Analyze As shown, the cycle of scientific thinking goes in one step-by-step direction. Where could you add arrows to the diagram to show a more complete description of the scientific process? Explain.

Analyzing Data

Use the information below to answer the next three questions.

Suppose a team of scientists is studying the migration of animal species in Africa. One of the scientists takes the photograph below.

27. Apply Give three examples of qualitative data that could be collected during this research.

28. Apply Give three examples of quantitative data that could be collected during this research.

29. Synthesize Suppose the scientists wanted to change the number of species present in this study. Could this manipulation be done? If so, how? If not, why not?

Connecting CONCEPTS

30. Write an Analogy Earlier in the chapter, a car's cruise control system was used as an analogy for negative feedback and homeostasis in an organism. Think of your own analogy to describe one of the other unifying themes of biology. Write a paragraph using that analogy to explain that theme. Be sure to also describe any ways in which your analogy does not fit the theme.

31. Synthesize The yellow fever mosquito shown on page 3 is just one type of mosquito that can pass disease-causing viruses to people. Mosquitoes can also carry other diseases such as malaria, Dengue fever, and West Nile virus. And even if mosquitoes do not carry dangerous viruses, they are certainly pests. On the other hand, mosquitoes are a source of food for many types of animals. Suppose you developed a way to rid Earth of mosquitoes. Do you think it should be used? Why or why not?

Analyzing Data

27. Answers could include a description of landscape and climate, and behavior of animals and their distribution.
28. Answers include anything that could be measured, for example, number of different species and number of animals of each species, and relative proportion of one species to another.
29. Only by computer modeling, because it is not ethically or realistically possible to alter the number of species in an ecosystem.

INDIANA ISTEP+ Test Prep

B.1.3; B.8.5; NOS.1; NOS.4; NOS.6

Test Practice
For more test practice, go to ClassZone.com.

1 Which of the following is the ***best*** example of a scientific model?

A a group of zoo monkeys to represent behavior in a natural environment

B a computer simulation of Earth's climate changes

C an x-ray showing multiple fractures in a bone

D a salt-water aquarium in the home of a fish enthusiast

2

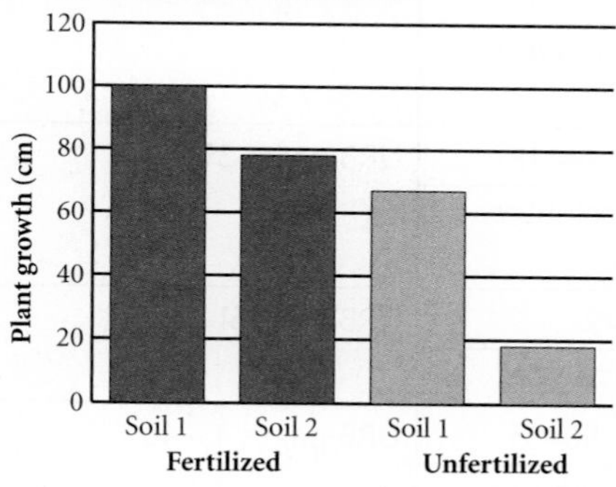

A scientist wants to know how a certain fertilizer affects the growth of tomato plants growing in two different soils. What conclusion can be drawn from the graph shown here?

A Soil 1 and Soil 2 are the same.

B The fertilizer has a greater effect in Soil 1.

C The fertilizer has a greater effect in Soil 2.

D Soil 1 absorbed more fertilizer than Soil 2.

THINK THROUGH THE QUESTION

Conclusions based on scientific research must be supported by the data collected. Conclusions are very specific to the data, so statements that appear to be very general are unlikely to be the right answers.

3 Students hypothesized that water pollution affects the growth of fish. In an experiment, they added the same amount of food to ponds polluted by fertilizers and industrial waste. They measured fish growth and found that most fish grow slowly in each of these environments. What part of their experiment did they forget to include?

A a group to serve as a control

B a hypothesis to test

C a theory to explain their results

D a procedure to follow

4 Finch species in the Galapagos Islands have a wide variety of beak shapes. The theory of natural selection suggests that these differences arose because

A changes occurred over a short period of time.

B finches with certain beak shapes survived in greater numbers.

C conscious decisions let certain finches survive.

D individual finches adapted to their environment.

5

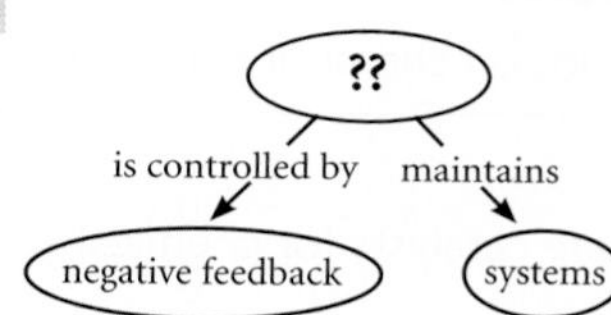

Which of the following ***best*** completes this concept map?

A biodiversity

B homeostasis

C evolution

D adaptation

6 Explain the concept of evolution by natural selection.

CHAPTER REVIEW

Standards-Based Assessment

1. B	4. B
2. C	5. B
3. A	6. See Below

TEST DOCTOR

Question 2 Answer C is correct. Answer A is incorrect because the graph shows that plant growth differs based on the type of soil. Answer B is incorrect because plant growth changes only about 33 cm (from about 67 cm to 100 cm) with fertilizer in soil 1, as opposed to a change of about 60 cm (from about 18 cm to about 78 cm) with fertilizer in soil 2. Answer D is incorrect because fertilizer absorption cannot be determined from the graph.

Question 3 Answer A is correct. Answer B is incorrect because the hypothesis is that water pollution affects fish growth. Answer C is incorrect because a theory is a proposed explanation for a wide range of observations and experimental results. Answer D is incorrect because the students' procedure is to add food and measure fish growth.

Question 6 Organisms best suited to their environment reproduce more successfully than other organisms. Over generations the proportion of organisms with favorable traits increases in a population.

Connecting Concepts

30. Answers should indicate knowledge of the other unifying themes of biology (systems, structure and function, and evolution).
31. Students should describe the effects of removing mosquitoes from Earth in terms of biodiversity, ecosystems, the biosphere, and risks and benefits.

ITEM CORRELATIONS

Standard	Items
B.1.3	5
B.8.5	4, 6
NOS.1	2
NOS.4	3
NOS.6	1

CHAPTER 2

Indiana Resource Preview

Print Resources

Chemistry of Life

INDIANA STANDARDS		Sections	PAGES and PACING	UNIT RESOURCE BOOK
B.1.1	2.1	**Atoms, Ions, and Molecules** **KEY CONCEPT** All living things are based on atoms and their interactions.	pp. 36–39 45 minutes	URB pages 31–34
B.1.1	2.2	**Properties of Water** **KEY CONCEPT** Water's unique properties allow life to exist on Earth.	pp. 40–43 30 minutes	URB pages 35–38
B.1.1	2.3	**Carbon-Based Molecules** **KEY CONCEPT** Carbon-based molecules are the foundation of life.	pp. 44–48 30 minutes	URB pages 39–42
		DATA ANALYSIS: Identifying Variables Independent and Dependent Variables	p. 49 15 minutes	URB page 51
B.3.3	2.4	**Chemical Reactions** **KEY CONCEPT** Life depends on chemical reactions.	pp. 50–53 30 minutes	URB pages 43–46
B.1.2	2.5	**Enzymes** **KEY CONCEPT** Enzymes are catalysts for chemical reactions in living things.	pp. 54–56 30 minutes	URB pages 47–50
B.1.3, NOS.7		CHAPTER INVESTIGATION: Enzymatic Activity	p. 57 45 minutes	**Lab Binder** Introducing Biology pages 17–20
B.1.2, NOS.3		OPTIONS FOR INQUIRY	pp. 58–59 45 minutes, 45 minutes	**Lab Binder** Introducing Biology pages 21–23
		Chapter Review	pp. 60–63	**Assessment Book** Chapter Tests A, B pages 31–38

INDIANA STANDARDS

B.1.1 Describe the structure of the major categories of organic compounds essential to living organisms in terms of their building blocks, and the small number of chemical elements (carbon, hydrogen, nitrogen, oxygen, phosphorous, and sulfur) from which they are composed.

B.1.2 Understand that the shape of a molecule determines its role in the many different types of cellular processes including metabolism, homeostasis, growth and development, and heredity, and understand that the majority of these processes involve proteins that act as enzymes.

B.1.3 Explain and give examples of how the function and differentiation of cells is influenced by their external environment, including temperature, acidity and the concentration of certain molecules, and that changes in these conditions may affect how a cell functions.

B.3.3 Recognize and describe that metabolism consists of all the biochemical reactions that occur inside cells, including the production, modification, transport, and exchange of materials that are required for the maintenance of life.

NOS.3 Clearly communicate their ideas and results of investigations verbally and in written form using tables, graphs, diagrams, and photographs.

NOS.7 Focus on the development of explanatory models based on their observations during laboratory investigations.

Labs

PUPIL EDITION LABS

Chemical Bonding, Section 4, p. 51 Students model the formation of a chemical bond. **Lab Binder** p. 24	**Time:** 10 minutes **Materials:** 2 flat magnets
Enzymatic Activity, p. 57 Students determine the pH at which the enzyme catalase functions best. **Lab Binder** pp. 17–20	**Time:** 45 minutes **Materials:** 5 test tubes; test tube rack; marker; 7 10-mL graduated cylinders; 4 mL each of solutions of pH 3, 5, 7, 9, and 11; 2 mL 60% catalase solution; 1 mL 3% hydrogen peroxide solution; metric ruler

OPTIONS FOR INQUIRY

Testing pH, p. 58 Students determine the pH of some household products. **Lab Binder** pp. 21–22	**Time:** 45 minutes **Materials:** 6 test tubes, test tube rack, 6 10-mL graduated cylinders, lemon juice, vinegar, mouthwash, window cleaner, 2 unknown solutions, pH indicator paper
Enzymes, p. 59 Students research the effects of enzyme deficiency. **Lab Binder** p. 23	**Time:** 45 minutes **Materials:** Computer with Internet access

LAB BINDER Unit 1 Introducing Biology

Additional Investigation: Modeling Biochemical Compounds, pp. 25–28

Challenge Lab: The Biochemistry of Compost Bins, pp. 37–40; Action of Yeast, pp. 41–44

Vernier Probeware Labs: Acids and Bases, pp. 45–50; Enzyme Action, pp. 51–56

Virtual Lab Worksheet: Calorimetry, p. 57

LAB GENERATOR

A searchable CD of all labs in the program in editable format, including forensic, probeware, and biotechnology labs.

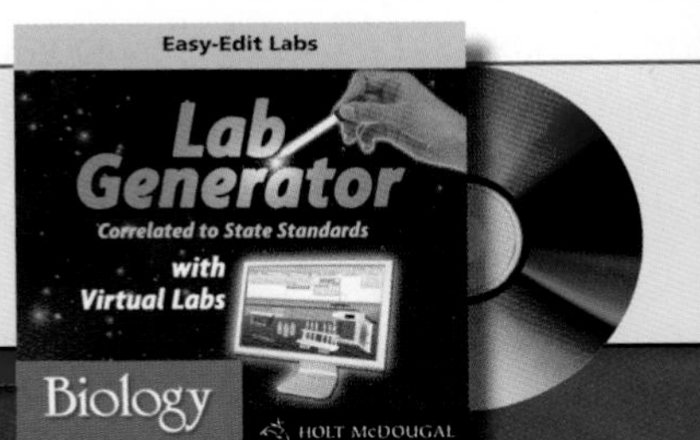

Presentation Tools

POWER PRESENTATIONS

Presentation Chapter 2
PowerPresentations for each section incorporate images and clips from the Media Gallery. Includes Note Navigator for each section.

MEDIA GALLERY

Contains the following images and video clips, as well as animations, simulations, and forms of visuals from the book.

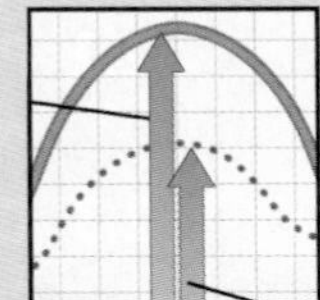
Catalyst

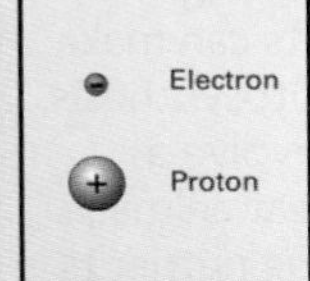

Atoms

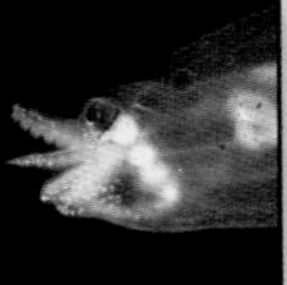
Bioluminescent squid

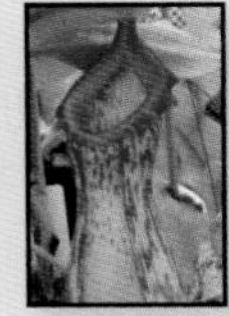
Pitcher plant

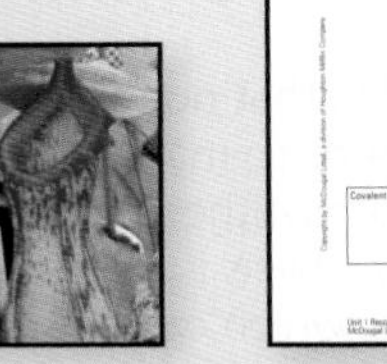

Power Notes

VIDEO

Explore a set of short video clips on atoms and bonding.

ANIMATED BIOLOGY

Hydrogen Bonding
Energy and Chemical Reactions
Atoms and Bonding

TRANSPARENCIES

Atom Models T2
Ionic and Covalent Bonds T3
Hydrogen Bonds T4
Understanding pH T5
Carbon-Based Molecules T6
Energy and Chemical Reactions T7
Enzymes T8

Online BIOLOGY CLASSZONE.COM

BioZine
Animated Biology
Interactive Review
SciLinks
Resource Centers

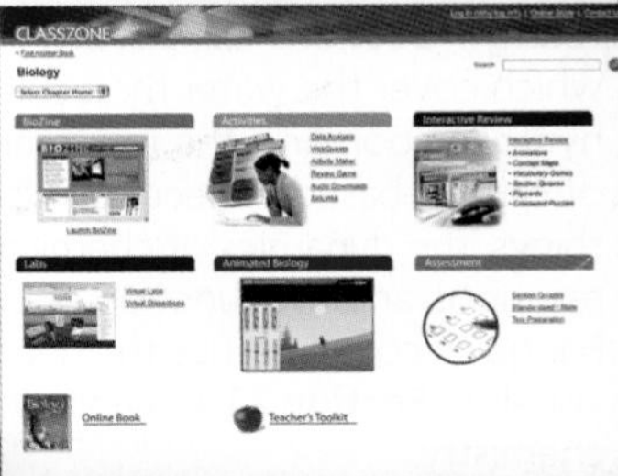

CHAPTER 2

▼ Focus and Motivate

How can this plant digest a frog?

Have students read the explanation in the caption. The more interesting question is why. **Ask,** If plants can make their own food through photosynthesis, why would a plant species evolve a mechanism to capture and eat animals? The animal must be supplying nutrients that the plant cannot get from other sources.

Discuss with students that not all the materials a plant needs to maintain itself are supplied by photosynthesis. The end product of photosynthesis is a simple sugar called glucose, which can be broken down to yield energy. Most plants absorb additional nutrients from the soil, such as compounds containing nitrogen and phosphorus, which are needed to make molecules that make up a plant's cells and tissues. Venus flytraps grow in swampy areas that have nitrogen-poor soil. These plants get the nitrogen they need by trapping and digesting animals.

BIOZINE ClassZone.com

Students can access BioZine at **ClassZone.com** to check the daily science news feeds.

In a Hurry?

The critical material of the chapter is found in **Sections 2.2, 2.3, 2.4,** and **2.5**—which cover the water molecule and hydrogen bonding, the four main types of carbon-based molecules in living things, the dynamics of chemical reactions, and the function of enzymes. For quick coverage, use the headings and visuals in **Section 2.1** as a review of basic chemistry.

CHAPTER 2

Chemistry of Life

KEY CONCEPTS

2.1 Atoms, Ions, and Molecules
All living things are based on atoms and their interactions.

2.2 Properties of Water
Water's unique properties allow life to exist on Earth.

2.3 Carbon-Based Molecules
Carbon-based molecules are the foundation of life.

2.4 Chemical Reactions
Life depends on chemical reactions.

2.5 Enzymes
Enzymes are catalysts for chemical reactions in living things.

Online BIOLOGY CLASSZONE.COM

Animated BIOLOGY
View animated chapter concepts.
- Hydrogen Bonding
- Energy and Chemical Reactions
- Calorimetry
- Atoms and Bonding

BIOZINE
Keep current with biology news.
- News feeds
- Careers
- Polls

RESOURCE CENTER
Get more information on
- Elements of Life
- Acids, Bases, and pH

Teacher Demo

Eye Opener Demonstrate the dehydration of sucrose.

Materials
- 100-mL beaker of heat resistant glass
- 20 g powdered sugar
- 5 mL concentrated sulfuric acid
- safety goggles

Safety Make sure the beaker has no cracks. The reaction is exothermic, producing fumes from burning sugar. Perform in a well-ventilated area, where the beaker can be left untouched as it cools. Do not touch the beaker once the reaction begins. Refer to the MSDS on sulfuric acid.

How can this plant digest a frog?

Connecting CONCEPTS

Like other carnivores, the Venus flytrap eats animals to get nutrients that it needs to make molecules such as proteins and nucleic acids. Other chemical compounds made by the plant's cells enable the Venus flytrap to digest the animals that it eats. These chemicals are similar to the chemicals that allow you to digest the food that you eat.

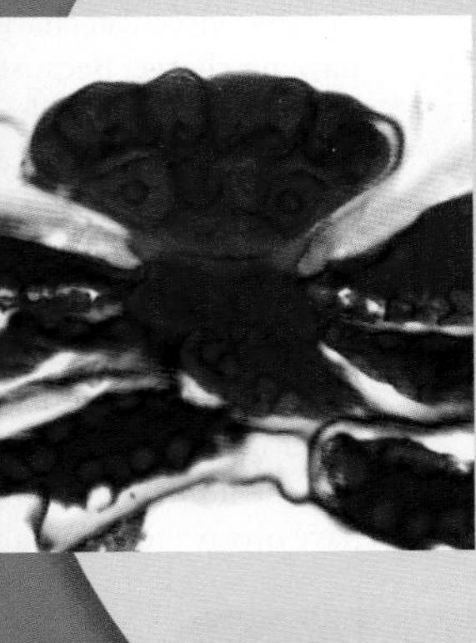

Cell Function The Venus flytrap has specialized cells on the surfaces of its leaves. Some of these cells allow the plant to snap shut on its prey within 0.5 seconds. Other cells, such as those that appear purple in this light micrograph, secrete digestive chemicals that allow the plant to consume its prey. (LM; magnification 500×)

Demonstrate Place sugar into the beaker. As you proceed, point out the safety precautions you are taking. With goggles on, slowly add sulfuric acid to the sugar. A column of carbon will rise up from the beaker, as steam is released.

Discuss Point out that students have just observed a chemical reaction involving the dehydration of the organic compound sucrose, a sugar. **Ask**

- What effect did the sulfuric acid have upon sugar? caused the release of water in the form of steam—dehydration, leaving behind a mass of carbon material
- What is the defining characteristic of an organic compound? contains carbon
- Was the reaction exothermic or endothermic, and what does that indicate? exothermic, releases energy

Activate Prior Knowledge

Point out that sometimes to understand how something works, one needs get down to basics. **Ask,** What does it take to master a computer game, perform a dance move, or sink a penalty shot in the back of the net? One needs to know how it works, break it down into components, study it. Discuss the fact that much of what happens in biology, at a basic level, relates to chemistry.

Preview Vocabulary

Word Origins Sometimes word parts can help students remember meaning:

mono = one *poly* = many

Other times, word roots are too similar, which is true for *solvent/solute/solution.* In such instances, students should look for other ways to associate meaning with words so similar in appearance.

Academic Vocabulary Students will be studying different elements and their properties. Point out that the word *unique* as applied to an element has a meaning distinct from words that describe atoms as *individual* or *specific.*

unique, being the only one of its kind
specific, distinguishing a type
individual, a single member

English Learners Tell students that in this chapter they will be dealing with words that are not a regular part of everyday conversation. Suggest that students use the strategy of word squares to help them learn key vocabulary. This strategy, described on page D4 of the *Biology Toolkit,* includes a picture, a student definition as well as a dictionary definition, and use in a sentence. Have English learners pair up to teach another the words.

Integrating Biomechanics

The Venus flytrap can capture prey even though it has no muscles or nervous system. When one of six tiny trigger hairs is touched, the plant responds by moving water in its cells to change the curvature of the leaves. The convex leaf halves become concave and snap shut in less than 0.5 seconds.

SECTION 2.1

▼ Plan and Prepare

Objectives

- Identify elements common to living things.
- Describe how ions form.
- Compare ionic and covalent bonding.

Section Resources

Unit Resource Book
- Study Guide pp. 31–32
- Power Notes p. 33
- Reinforcement p. 34

Interactive Reader Chapter 2
Spanish Study Guide pp. 11–12

Biology Toolkit pp. C2, C22, C40

Technology
- Power Presentation 2.1
- Media Gallery DVD
- Online Quiz 2.1

Activate Prior Knowledge Tell students that six elements are found in substantial quantities in the human body, with traces of 22 others. **Ask,** What are some examples of things that are complex yet made up of simple units? Students might mention 0s and 1s of binary computer code or the 26 letters of the alphabet. Discuss that chemical reactions that occur in living matter produce almost unlimited variety.

▼ Teach

Science Trivia

- The four most common elements in the human body and their mass percents are oxygen (65.0), carbon (18.0), hydrogen (10.0), and nitrogen (3.0).
- The mass percent of the most common trace elements in the body are calcium (1.5), phosphorus (1.0), potassium (0.35), sulfur (0.25), and sodium (0.15).

2.1 Atoms, Ions, and Molecules

KEY CONCEPT All living things are based on atoms and their interactions.

MAIN IDEAS
- Living things consist of atoms of different elements.
- Ions form when atoms gain or lose electrons.
- Atoms share pairs of electrons in covalent bonds.

VOCABULARY
atom, p. 36
element, p. 36
compound, p. 37
ion, p. 38
ionic bond, p. 38
covalent bond, p. 39
molecule, p. 39

Review
cell, organism

INDIANA STANDARDS

B.1.1 Describe the structure of the major categories of organic compounds essential to living organisms in terms of their building blocks, and the small number of chemical elements (carbon, hydrogen, nitrogen, oxygen, phosphorus, and sulfur) from which they are composed.

TAKING NOTES

Use a main idea web to help you make connections among elements, atoms, ions, compounds, and molecules.

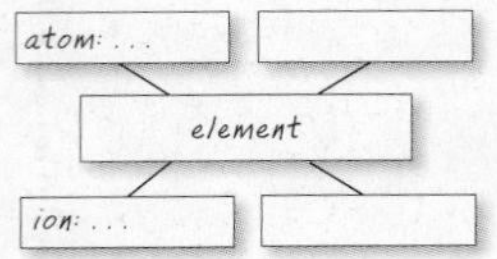

Connect The Venus flytrap produces chemicals that allow it to consume and digest insects and other small animals, including an unlucky frog. Frogs also produce specialized chemicals that allow them to consume and digest their prey. In fact, all organisms depend on many chemicals and chemical reactions. For this reason, the study of living things also involves the study of chemistry.

MAIN IDEA

Living things consist of atoms of different elements.

What do a frog, a skyscraper, a car, and your body all have in common? Every physical thing you can think of, living or not, is made of incredibly small particles called atoms. An **atom** is the smallest basic unit of matter. Millions of atoms could fit in a space the size of the period at the end of this sentence. And it would take you more than 1 trillion (1,000,000,000,000, or 10^{11}) years to count the number of atoms in a single grain of sand.

Atoms and Elements

Although there is a huge variety of matter on Earth, all atoms share the same basic structure. Atoms consist of three types of smaller particles: protons, neutrons, and electrons. Protons and neutrons form the dense center of an atom—the atomic nucleus. Electrons are much smaller particles outside of the nucleus. Protons have a positive electrical charge, and electrons have a negative electrical charge. Neutrons, as their name implies, are neutral—they have no charge. Because an atom has equal numbers of positively charged protons and negatively charged electrons, it is electrically neutral.

An **element** is one particular type of atom, and it cannot be broken down into a simpler substance by ordinary chemical means. An element can also refer to a group of atoms of the same type. A few familiar elements include the gases hydrogen and oxygen and the metals aluminum and gold. Because all atoms are made of the same types of particles, what difference among atoms makes one element different from other elements? Atoms of different elements differ in the number of protons they have. All atoms of a given element have a specific number of protons that never varies. For example, all hydrogen atoms have one proton, and all oxygen atoms have eight protons.

Differentiated Instruction

ENGLISH LEARNERS

Remind students to preview each section by first looking for main ideas and key vocabulary. Vocabulary terms appear at the top of the first page of each section and are highlighted in yellow in the text. The blue headings in each section are the main ideas written as sentences; each is signaled by a small red triangle and the words "Main Idea." The paragraphs under them further explain the ideas, and the smaller black headings are key supporting details.

Biology Toolkit, Section Preview, p. C2

PRE-AP

Tell students that they will see different types of models used to show atoms and molecules. The model used depends on the characteristic that is of interest: specifically chemical formula, orbital configuration, or three-dimensional shape. Have students set up a table to compare different models used in this section and throughout the chapter.

Biology Toolkit, Content Frame, p. C22

The electrons in the atoms of each element determine the properties of that element. As **FIGURE 2.1** shows, electrons are considered to be in a cloud around the nucleus. The simplified models of a hydrogen atom and an oxygen atom on the left side of **FIGURE 2.2** illustrate how electrons move around the nucleus in regions called energy levels. Different energy levels can hold different numbers of electrons. For example, the first energy level can hold two electrons, and the second energy level can hold eight electrons. Atoms are most stable when they have a full outermost energy level.

Of the 91 elements that naturally occur on Earth, only about 25 are found in organisms. Just 4 elements—carbon (C), oxygen (O), nitrogen (N), and hydrogen (H)—make up 96 percent of the human body's mass. The other 4 percent consists of calcium (Ca), phosphorus (P), potassium (K), sulfur (S), sodium (Na), and several other trace elements. Trace elements are found in very small amounts in your body, but you need them to survive. For example, iron (Fe) is needed to transport oxygen in your blood. Chromium (Cr) is needed for your cells to break down sugars for usable energy.

FIGURE 2.1 The exact position of electrons cannot be known. They are somewhere in a three-dimensional electron cloud around the nucleus.

FIGURE 2.2 Representing Atoms

BOHR'S ATOMIC MODEL

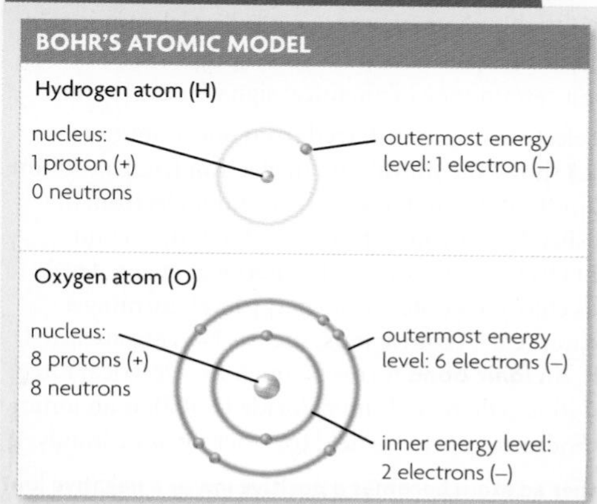

SIMPLIFIED MODEL

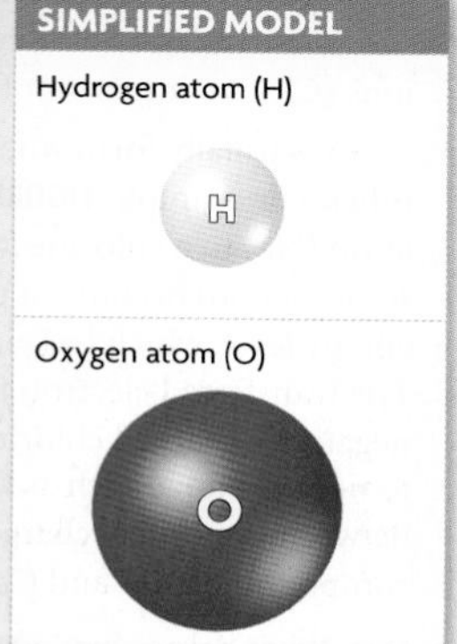

The model of the atom developed by Niels Bohr (left) shows that an atom's electrons are located outside the nucleus in regions called energy levels. Different types of atoms have different numbers of electrons and energy levels.

Often, atoms are shown as simplified spheres (right). Different types of atoms are shown in different sizes and colors.

A Apply How many electrons would need to be added to fill the outermost energy level of hydrogen? of oxygen?

Compounds

The atoms of elements found in organisms are often linked, or bonded, to other atoms. A **compound** is a substance made of atoms of different elements bonded together in a certain ratio. Common compounds in living things include water (H_2O) and carbon dioxide (CO_2). A compound's properties are often different from the properties of the elements that make up the compound. At temperatures on Earth, for example, hydrogen and oxygen are both gases. Together, though, they can form water. Similarly, a diamond is pure carbon, but carbon atoms are also the basis of sugars, proteins, and millions of other compounds.

B Contrast How are elements different from compounds?

BELOW LEVEL

Work with students to create a concept map that shows the relationship between atoms, elements, compounds, and molecules. Have them suggest ways to incorporate all the key vocabulary of the section.

Biology Toolkit, Concept Map, p. C40

ONLINE BIOLOGY Go to the chapter Resource Center at **ClassZone.com** for additional resources and information on the elements of life.

History of Science

Over the past 200 years, various models of the atom have been proposed. In 1808, **John Dalton** proposed that all matter is composed of tiny indivisible particles called atoms. Then in 1897, **J. J. Thomson** discovered the electron and announced that atoms are divisible into even smaller particles. He proposed a model of a spherical, positively charged atom in which negatively charged electrons were embedded like raisins in plum pudding.

In 1910, **Ernest Rutherford's** experiments showed that an atom is mostly empty space. Within the space is a tiny, dense nucleus that contains almost all the atom's mass. **Niels Bohr** introduced his model of the atom in 1913, and along with it, the concept of energy levels.

The current **quantum-mechanical model** describes an atom with electrons that move with wavelike motion in locations that cannot be exactly known. Just as different tools are needed for different jobs, each model adds different information to the scientific understanding of the atom.

Answers

A Apply 1; 6

B Contrast Elements are composed of only one type of atom; compounds are composed of different types of atoms.

▼ Teach *continued*

TEACH FROM VISUALS

FIGURE 2.3 Explain that the relative sizes of the subatomic particles shown in the figure are not accurate. They are drawn this way to illustrate the concepts of ion formation. Actually, electrons are about 1000 times smaller than protons and neutrons and are much farther away from the nucleus than shown in the diagram. **Ask**

- Why is the sodium ion shown smaller than the sodium atom? It has lost its outer energy level.
- How does the size of the chlorine atom compare with the size of the chloride ion? The ion is much larger than the atom.

Explain to students that when an atom loses an electron, the nuclear charge pulls the remaining electrons closer. When an atom gains an electron, the electron cloud takes up more space.

Address Misconceptions

Common Misconception Students often think that a positive ion can bond only with the negative ion to which it donated its electron.

Correcting the Misconception A positive ion can bond with any negative ion. An ionic bond is simply the electrostatic attraction between oppositely charged ions. Make sure students do not think an ionic bond is a physical connection between two ions.

Answers

A Apply Atoms with few outer electrons tend to lose electrons and so form positive ions; atoms with almost full outer energy levels tend to gain electrons and form negative ions.

MAIN IDEA

Ions form when atoms gain or lose electrons.

***Connecting* CONCEPTS**

Cell Structure and Function Several different ions are transported across cell membranes during cell processes. You will learn how this transport occurs in **Chapters 3** and **4**.

An **ion** is an atom that has gained or lost one or more electrons. An ion forms because an atom is more stable when its outermost energy level is full; the gain or loss of electrons results in a full outermost energy level. An atom becomes an ion when its number of electrons changes and it gains an electrical charge. This charge gives ions certain properties. For example, compounds consisting only of ions—ionic compounds—easily dissolve in water.

Some ions are positively charged, and other ions are negatively charged. The type of ion that forms depends on the number of electrons in an atom's outer energy level. An atom with few electrons in its outer energy level tends to lose those electrons. An atom that loses one or more electrons becomes a positively charged ion because it has more protons than electrons. In contrast, an atom with a nearly full outer energy level tends to gain electrons. An atom that gains one or more electrons becomes a negatively charged ion because it has more electrons than protons.

Ions play large roles in organisms. For example, hydrogen ions (H^+) are needed for the production of usable chemical energy in cells. Calcium ions (Ca^{2+}) are necessary for every muscle movement in your body. And chloride ions (Cl^-) are important for a certain type of chemical signal in the brain.

Ions usually form when electrons are transferred from one atom to another. For example, **FIGURE 2.3** shows the transfer of an electron from a sodium atom (Na) to a chlorine atom (Cl). When it loses its one outer electron, the sodium atom becomes a positively charged sodium ion (Na^+). Its second energy level, which has eight electrons, is now a full outermost energy level. The transferred electron fills chlorine's outermost energy level, forming a negatively charged chloride ion (Cl^-). Positive ions, such as Na^+, are attracted to negative ions, such as Cl^-. An **ionic bond** forms through the electrical force between oppositely charged ions. Salt, or sodium chloride (NaCl), is an ionic compound of Na^+ and Cl^-. Sodium chloride is held together by ionic bonds.

A Apply **What determines whether an atom becomes a positive ion or a negative ion?**

FIGURE 2.3 IONS AND IONIC BONDS

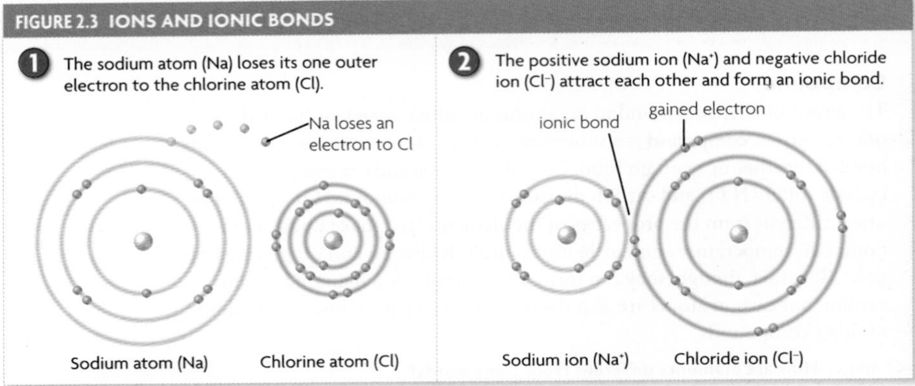

1 The sodium atom (Na) loses its one outer electron to the chlorine atom (Cl).
Na loses an electron to Cl
Sodium atom (Na)
Chlorine atom (Cl)
2 The positive sodium ion (Na+) and negative chloride ion (Cl−) attract each other and form an ionic bond.
ionic bond
gained electron
Sodium ion (Na+)
Chloride ion (Cl−)

Differentiated Instruction

INCLUSION

Physical representations of **FIGURES 2.3** and **2.4** can be made to help students who are visually impaired. Copy the figures onto a piece of cardboard. Squeeze white glue onto the electrons and their energy levels, then sprinkle with coarse sand. When the glue dries, this will be a tactile learning tool.

MAIN IDEA

Atoms share pairs of electrons in covalent bonds.

Not all atoms easily gain or lose electrons. Rather, the atoms of many elements share pairs of electrons. The shared pairs of electrons fill the outermost energy levels of the bonded atoms. A **covalent bond** forms when atoms share a pair of electrons. Covalent bonds are generally very strong, and depending on how many electrons an atom has, two atoms may form several covalent bonds to share several pairs of electrons. **FIGURE 2.4** illustrates how atoms of carbon and oxygen share pairs of electrons in covalent bonds. All three atoms in a molecule of carbon dioxide (CO_2) have full outer energy levels.

VOCABULARY

The prefix *co-* means "together," and *valent* comes from a Latin word that means "power" or "strength."

FIGURE 2.4 COVALENT BONDS

A carbon atom needs four electrons to fill its outer energy level. An oxygen atom needs two electrons to fill its outer energy level. In carbon dioxide, carbon makes a double bond, or shares two pairs of electrons, with each oxygen atom.

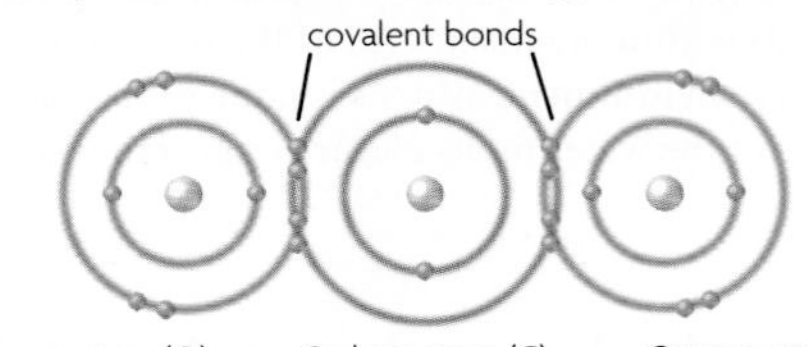

A **molecule** is two or more atoms held together by covalent bonds. In the compound carbon dioxide, each oxygen atom shares two pairs of electrons (four electrons) with the carbon atom. Some elements occur naturally in the form of diatomic, or "two-atom," molecules. For example, a molecule of oxygen (O_2) consists of two oxygen atoms that share two pairs of electrons. Almost all of the substances that make up organisms, from lipids to nucleic acids to water, are molecules held together by covalent bonds.

A Summarize What happens to electrons in outer energy levels when two atoms form a covalent bond?

ONLINE BIOLOGY Students can simulate building their own atoms. See Animated Biology in Options for Inquiry on page 59.

TEACH FROM VISUALS

FIGURE 2.4 Have students look closely at the energy levels. **Ask**

- How many electrons does a single oxygen atom have in its outer energy level? 6 a carbon atom? 4
- What is the significance of the number of electrons in the outer energy levels of oxygen and carbon in a molecule of carbon dioxide? Each atom shares enough electrons to complete the outer level; oxygen gains 2 and carbon gains 4.

Answers

A Summarize Atoms share pairs of outer energy level electrons.

2.1 ASSESSMENT

ONLINE QUIZ ClassZone.com

B.1.1

REVIEWING MAIN IDEAS

1. What distinguishes one **element** from another?
2. Describe the formation of an **ionic compound.**
3. What is the difference between an **ionic bond** and a **covalent bond**?

CRITICAL THINKING

4. **Compare and Contrast** How does a **molecule** differ from an **atom**?
5. **Apply** Explain why a hydrogen atom can become either an **ion** or a part of a molecule.

***Connecting* CONCEPTS**

6. **Chemistry** A sodium atom has one outer electron, and a carbon atom has four outer electrons. How might this difference be related to the types of compounds formed by atoms of these two elements?

Assess and Reteach

Assess Use the Online Quiz or Section Quiz (*Assessment Book,* p. 25).

Reteach Use **FIGURES 2.3** and **2.4** to review the material in the section. Have students describe what is happening in each figure, using the key vocabulary from the section.

2.1 ASSESSMENT

1. the number of protons in the nucleus
2. *Sample Answer:* In sodium chloride, a sodium atom loses an electron to a chlorine atom. The oppositely charged ions are attracted to each other and form an ionic bond.
3. An ionic bond is formed due to the electrical attraction between oppositely charged ions. A covalent bond is formed by shared pairs of electrons.
4. A molecule is made up of two or more atoms held together by covalent bonds.
5. A hydrogen atom has one unpaired electron in its outer energy level. The electron can be lost to form an ion or shared to form a covalent bond.
6. An atom that has a nearly full or nearly empty outer energy level (such as sodium) tends to form ions. An atom in between (such as carbon) tends to share electrons.

▼ Plan and Prepare

Objectives

- Recognize the importance of hydrogen bonding
- Explain why many compounds dissolve in water.
- Compare acids and bases.

Section Resources

Unit Resource Book Study Guide pp. 35–36 Power Notes p. 37 Reinforcement p. 38 Pre-AP Activity pp. 53–54
Interactive Reader Chapter 2 **Spanish Study Guide** pp. 13–14
Biology Toolkit pp. C17, C23, C26
Technology Power Presentation 2.2 Media Gallery DVD Online Quiz 2.2

Activate Prior Knowledge When astronomers look for evidence of life on other planets, they typically search for evidence of water. **Ask,** Why is water so important to life? Students may recognize water as the main component of cytoplasm and blood. Discuss that water is also the medium in which the chemical reactions in cells take place.

▼ Teach

Vocabulary

Academic Vocabulary A **pole** is, in simple terms, a rod. When applied to a rotating body, as in the rotation of Earth, the pole becomes an **axis** around which a body rotates. The word **polar** is often used to describe the extreme ends of a body. This relates to the description of water as a *polar* molecule.

With a magnet, each end of the pole has an opposite charge, which is analogous to what happens with a polar molecule. Because of the two different charges, the pole is often referred to as a **dipole.**

2.2 Properties of Water

KEY CONCEPT Water's unique properties allow life to exist on Earth.

MAIN IDEAS

- Life depends on hydrogen bonds in water.
- Many compounds dissolve in water.
- Some compounds form acids or bases.

VOCABULARY

hydrogen bond, p. 41
cohesion, p. 41
adhesion, p. 41
solution, p. 42
solvent, p. 42
solute, p. 42
acid, p. 42
base, p. 42
pH, p. 42

Review
ion, molecule

B.1.1 Describe the structure of the major categories of organic compounds essential to living organisms in terms of their building blocks, and the small number of chemical elements (carbon, hydrogen, nitrogen, oxygen, phosphorous, and sulfur) from which they are composed.

Connect When you are thirsty, you need to drink something that is mostly water. Why is the water you drink absolutely necessary? Your cells, and the cells of every other living thing on Earth, are mostly water. Water gives cells structure and transports materials within organisms. All of the processes necessary for life take place in that watery environment. Water's unique properties, which are related to the structure of the water molecule, are important for living things.

MAIN IDEA

Life depends on hydrogen bonds in water.

How do fish survive a cold winter if their pond freezes? Unlike most substances, water expands when it freezes. Water is less dense as a solid (ice) than as a liquid. In a pond, ice floats and covers the water's surface. The ice acts as an insulator that allows the water underneath to remain a liquid. Ice's low density is related to the structure of the water molecule.

Water and Hydrogen Bonds

Water is a polar molecule. You can think about polar molecules in the same way that you can think about a magnet's poles. That is, polar molecules have a region with a slight positive charge and a region with a slight negative charge. Polar molecules, such as the water molecule shown in **FIGURE 2.5,** form when atoms in a molecule have unequal pulls on the electrons they share. In a molecule of water, the oxygen nucleus, with its eight protons, attracts the shared electrons more strongly than do the hydrogen nuclei, with only one proton each. The oxygen atom gains a small negative charge, and the hydrogen atoms gain small positive charges. Other molecules, called nonpolar molecules, do not have these charged regions. The atoms in nonpolar molecules share electrons more equally.

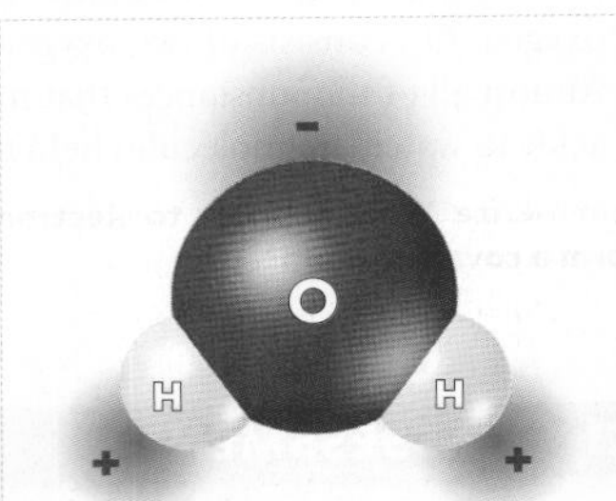

FIGURE 2.5 In water molecules, the oxygen atom has a slightly negative charge, and the hydrogen atoms have slightly positive charges.

Differentiated Instruction

PRE-AP

Have students use Cornell notes to outline the section. They should include a diagram for each key vocabulary term.

Biology Toolkit, Cornell Notes, p. C26

BELOW LEVEL

Point out to students that among the vocabulary terms in this section are words that can be paired and compared.

cohesion	*adhesion*
solvent	*solute*
acid	*base*

Suggest students use diagrams to compare and contrast these terms.

Biology Toolkit, Combination Notes, p. C23

Opposite charges of polar molecules can interact to form hydrogen bonds. A **hydrogen bond** is an attraction between a slightly positive hydrogen atom and a slightly negative atom, often oxygen or nitrogen. Hydrogen bonding is shown among water molecules in **FIGURE 2.6**, but these bonds are also found in many other molecules. For example, hydrogen bonds are part of the structures of proteins and of DNA, which is the genetic material for all organisms.

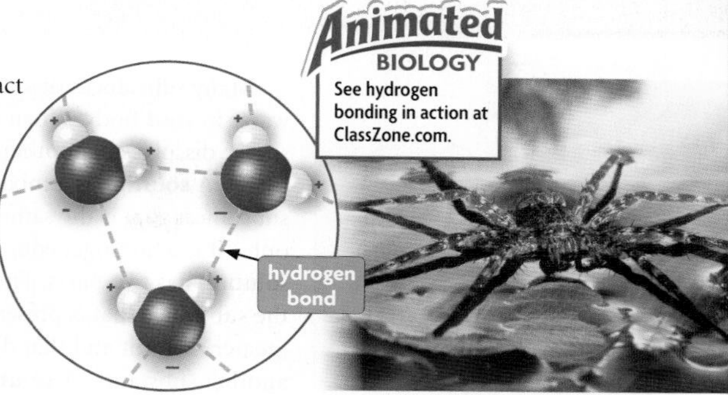
Animated BIOLOGY
See hydrogen bonding in action at ClassZone.com.
hydrogen bond

FIGURE 2.6 Water's surface tension comes from hydrogen bonds (left) that cause water molecules to stick together.

Properties Related to Hydrogen Bonds

Individual hydrogen bonds are about 20 times weaker than typical covalent bonds, but they are relatively strong among water molecules. As a result, a large amount of energy is needed to overcome the attractions among water molecules. Without hydrogen bonds, water would boil at a much lower temperature than it does because less energy would be needed to change liquid water into water vapor. Water is a liquid at the temperatures that support most life on Earth only because of hydrogen bonds in water. Hydrogen bonds are responsible for three important properties of water.

- **High specific heat** Hydrogen bonds give water an abnormally high specific heat. This means that water resists changes in temperature. Compared to many other compounds, water must absorb more heat energy to increase in temperature. This property is very important in cells. The processes that produce usable chemical energy in cells release a great deal of heat. Water absorbs the heat, which helps to regulate cell temperatures.
- **Cohesion** The attraction among molecules of a substance is **cohesion.** Cohesion from hydrogen bonds makes water molecules stick to each other. You can see this when water forms beads, such as on a recently washed car. Cohesion also produces surface tension, which makes a kind of skin on water. Surface tension keeps the spider in **FIGURE 2.6** from sinking.
- **Adhesion** The attraction among molecules of different substances is called **adhesion.** In other words, water molecules stick to other things. Adhesion is responsible for the upward curve on the surface of the water in **FIGURE 2.7** because water molecules are attracted to the glass of the test tube. Adhesion helps plants transport water from their roots to their leaves because water molecules stick to the sides of the vessels that carry water.

FIGURE 2.7 The water's surface (left, dyed red) is curved down because water has greater adhesion than cohesion. The surface of the mercury (right) is curved up because mercury has greater cohesion than adhesion.

A Compare How are hydrogen bonds similar to ionic bonds?

MAIN IDEA

Many compounds dissolve in water.

Molecules and ions cannot take part in chemical processes inside cells unless they dissolve in water. Important materials such as sugars and oxygen cannot be transported from one part of an organism to another unless they are dissolved in blood, plant sap, or other water-based fluids.

INCLUSION

For students who are literal thinkers, help them visualize hydrogen bonding by using cardboard cutouts of water molecules, labeling the positive and negative ends. Have students arrange the cutouts with opposite charges together to make an array of molecules that represent the organization of water.

Integrating Physics

Hydrogen bonding is a special case of **dipole-dipole attractions** that occur between polar molecules. Hydrogen bonds form between molecules that consist of hydrogen atoms and atoms with high electronegativities, such as oxygen and nitrogen. The bonds within these molecules are very polar, and the hydrogen atom is so small that the molecules can get very close to one another. A hydrogen bond is not as strong as an ionic bond. In relative terms, it is only about 1/10 as strong.

Vocabulary

Greek and Latin Word Origins The Latin root that is the base of **adhere** and **cohere** is

haerere = to cling

The prefixes that differentiate the two words might not seem to offer much help: *ad-* means "toward," and *co-* means "together." Students could think of *adhesive* tape as holding together two separate and different things.

Students might think of a different set of words. An *adversary* is one who opposes or differs in point of view. Compare this to a *coworker, copilot,* or *cocaptain,* who are people who share similar views and goals.

Answers

A Compare Hydrogen bonds are attractions due to charged regions; ionic bonds are bonds formed by the attraction of oppositely charged ions.

▼ Teach *continued*

Vocabulary

Word Origins The words **solution, solvent,** and **solute** all share the same root, meaning "to loosen." To distinguish among the words, have students make associations that will help them remember the terms. For example, *dilute/solute* suggests a small amount spread out. Students can associate the *v* in *solvent* with a wedge that splits and separates the *solute.* Once they have sorted that out, they have their *solution.*

Address Misconceptions

Common Misconception Students often think that all solutes are solids and all solvents are liquids.

Correcting the Misconception Solutions can involve different states of matter.

- Air is made up of roughly 78 percent nitrogen, 21 percent oxygen, and a mix of argon, carbon dioxide, and other gases. **Ask,** Which gas is the solvent, and why? nitrogen, because it is present in the greatest amount
- Brass is a metal alloy, a solid dissolved in a solid, typically 67 percent copper and 33 percent zinc. **Ask,** Which is the solvent? copper the solute? zinc
- Vinegar contains about 5 percent acetic acid and 95 percent water. **Ask,** Which is the solute? acetic acid

Take It Further

Solutes that dissolve in water disrupt the hydrogen bonds between water molecules, replacing them with attractions between solute and water. If the attractions between solute particles are stronger than those between solute and water, the compound will not dissolve. Nonpolar molecules do not dissolve in water because the attraction among the nonpolar molecules is greater than the attraction between water molecules and the nonpolar molecules.

Answers

Ⓐ Connect Answers will vary, but typically the solvent is water; the solutes include sugars, ions, and proteins.

Many substances dissolve in the water in your body. When one substance dissolves in another, a solution forms. A **solution** is a mixture of substances that is the same throughout—it is a homogeneous mixture. A solution has two parts. The **solvent** is the substance that is present in the greater amount and that dissolves another substance. A **solute** is a substance that dissolves in a solvent. The amount of solute dissolved in a certain amount of solvent is a solution's concentration. One spoonful of a drink mix in water has little flavor because it has a low concentration. But a solution with four spoonfuls in the same amount of water tastes stronger because it has a higher concentration.

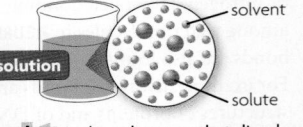

VISUAL VOCAB

The **solvent** is the substance that is present in the greatest amount, and is the substance that dissolves solutes.

A **solute** is the substance that dissolves.

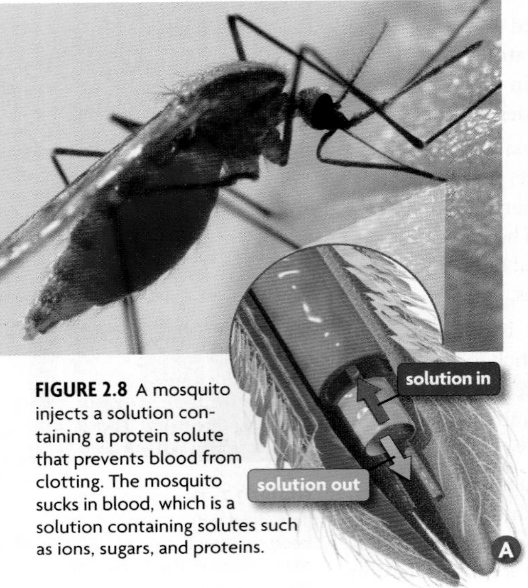

FIGURE 2.8 A mosquito injects a solution containing a protein solute that prevents blood from clotting. The mosquito sucks in blood, which is a solution containing solutes such as ions, sugars, and proteins.

The liquid part of your blood, called plasma, is about 95 percent water. Therefore, the solvent in plasma is water and all of the substances dissolved in it are solutes. Most of these solutes, such as sugars and proteins, dissolve in the water of blood plasma because they are polar. Polar molecules dissolve in water because the attraction between the water molecules and the solute molecules is greater than the attraction among the molecules of the solute. Similarly, ionic compounds, such as sodium chloride, dissolve in water because the charges of the water molecules attract the charges of the ions. The water molecules surround each ion and pull the compound apart.

Nonpolar substances, such as fats and oils, rarely dissolve in water. Nonpolar molecules do not have charged regions, so they are not attracted to polar molecules. Polar molecules and nonpolar molecules tend to remain separate, which is why we say, "Oil and water don't mix." But nonpolar molecules will dissolve in nonpolar solvents. For example, some vitamins, such as vitamin E, are nonpolar and dissolve in fat in your body.

Ⓐ **Connect What are the solvent and solutes in a beverage you drink?**

MAIN IDEA

Some compounds form acids or bases.

Some compounds break up into ions when they dissolve in water. An **acid** is a compound that releases a proton—a hydrogen ion (H^+)—when it dissolves in water. An acid increases the concentration of H^+ ions in a solution. **Bases** are compounds that remove H^+ ions from a solution. When a base dissolves in water, the solution has a low H^+ concentration. A solution's acidity, or H^+ ion concentration, is measured by the **pH** scale. In **FIGURE 2.9** you can see that pH is usually between 0 and 14. A solution with a pH of 0 is very acidic, with a high H^+ concentration. A solution with a pH of 14 is very basic, with a low H^+ concentration. Solutions with a pH of 7 are neutral—neither acidic nor basic.

Differentiated Instruction

ENGLISH LEARNERS

Point out that the **VISUAL VOCAB** note reinforces definitions given in the text. Use questions to work through this figure as well as **FIGURE 2.9.** Ask questions to help students interpret the diagram, discussing the use of color, number, shape, and direction. Have them sketch the diagram of the pH scale in their science notebooks and then add labels. Point out that a low pH is associated with a high number of hydrogen ions.

Biology Toolkit, Connect to Content Through Visuals, p. C17

FIGURE 2.9 Understanding pH

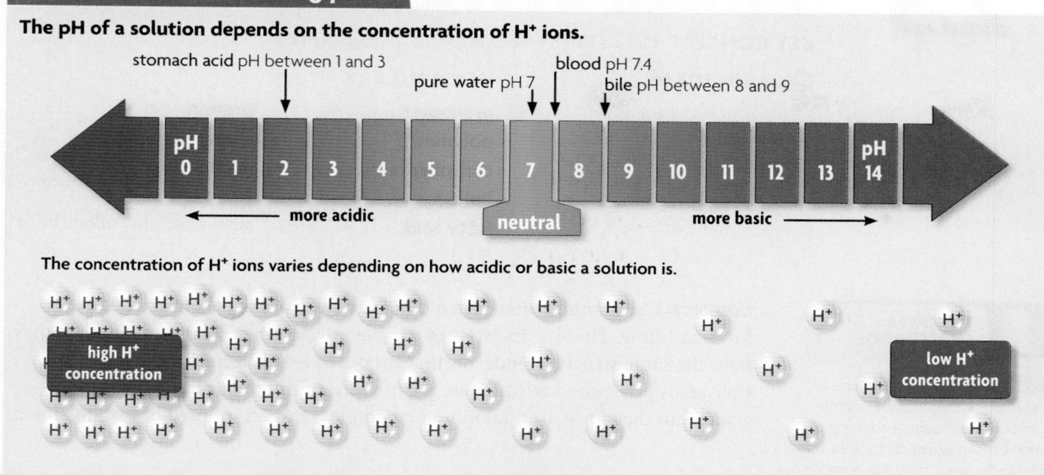

A Summarize **Describe the relationship between the H^+ concentration and the pH value.**

Most organisms, including humans, need to keep their pH within a very narrow range around neutral (pH 7.0). However, some organisms need a very different pH range. The azalea plant thrives in acidic (pH 4.5) soil, and a microorganism called *Picrophilus* survives best at an extremely acidic pH of 0.7. For all of these different organisms, pH must be tightly controlled.

One way pH is regulated in organisms is by substances called buffers. A buffer is a compound that can bind to an H^+ ion when the H^+ concentration increases, and can release an H^+ ion when the H^+ concentration decreases. In other words, a buffer "locks up" H^+ ions and helps to maintain homeostasis. For example, the normal pH of human blood is between 7.35 and 7.45, so it is slightly basic. Just a small change in pH can disrupt processes in your cells, and a blood pH greater than 7.8 or less than 6.8, for even a short time, is deadly. Buffers in your blood help prevent any large changes in blood pH.

B Apply **Cells have higher H^+ concentrations than blood. Which has a higher pH? Why?**

Connecting **CONCEPTS**

Human Biology In the human body, both the respiratory system and the excretory system help regulate pH. You will learn about human systems and homeostasis in **Chapter 28**.

ONLINE BIOLOGY Go to the chapter Resource Center at **ClassZone.com** for additional resources and information on acids, bases, and pH.

TEACH FROM VISUALS

FIGURE 2.9 To explain why the concentration of hydrogen ions decreases the larger the pH number becomes, explain that the pH scale is a negative logarithm. A pH of 1 is equal to the log of a H^+ ion concentration of 10^{-1}, whereas a pH of 10 is equal to the log of a H^+ ion concentration of 10^{-10}. There is a tenfold difference in H^+ ion concentration from one pH value to the next. **Ask,** What is the difference in H^+ ion concentration between lemon juice (pH 2) and tomato juice (pH 4)? Lemon juice has a H^+ concentration 100 times greater than tomato juice.

Answers

A Summarize The higher the H^+ concentration, the lower the pH.

B Apply blood, because a lower H^+ concentration means a higher pH

2.2 ASSESSMENT

ONLINE QUIZ ClassZone.com

B.1.1

REVIEWING MAIN IDEAS

1. How do polar molecules form **hydrogen bonds**?
2. What determines whether a compound will dissolve in water?
3. Make a chart that compares **acids** and **bases.**

CRITICAL THINKING

4. **Compare and Contrast** How do polar molecules differ from nonpolar molecules? How does this difference affect their interactions?
5. **Connect** Describe an example of **cohesion** or **adhesion** that you might observe during your daily life.

Connecting **CONCEPTS**

6. **Cellular Respiration** When sugars are broken down to produce usable energy for cells, a large amount of heat is released. Explain how the water inside a cell helps to keep the cell's temperature constant.

Assess and Reteach

Assess Use the Online Quiz or Section Quiz (*Assessment Book,* p. 26).

Reteach Have students use the example of dropping a sugar cube into a glass of water to diagram the interaction of a solute and solvent. Then have students compare this to pouring oil into water.

2.2 ASSESSMENT

1. The oppositely charged regions of a polar molecule attract other polar molecules, allowing a positvely charged hydrogen atom to bond to a negatively charged atom.
2. Compounds that have charges, such as ionic compounds and polar molecules, will dissolve in water.
3. Answers will vary but should indicate the following: acids donate protons (hydrogen ions), and bases accept hydrogen ions in solution; acids in solution have a high hydrogen ion concentration and a pH below 7; bases in solution have a low hydrogen ion concentration and a pH above 7.
4. Polar molecules have charged regions due to unequal sharing of electrons. Nonpolar molecules do not have charged regions because electrons are shared more equally. The charge differences tend to keep the molecules separate.
5. *Sample Answer:* Cohesion: water beading on a surface; adhesion: water sticking to the side of a glass.
6. Water has a high specific heat; water in a cell can absorb a large amount of energy before its temperature increases.

SECTION 2.3

▼ Plan and Prepare

Objectives

- Describe the bonding properties of carbon atoms.
- Compare carbohydrates, lipids, proteins, and nucleic acids.

Section Resources

Unit Resource Book Study Guide pp. 39–40 Power Notes p. 41 Reinforcement p. 42
Interactive Reader Chapter 2 **Spanish Study Guide** pp. 15–16
Biology Toolkit pp. C22, C30, D10
Technology Power Presentation 2.3 Media Gallery DVD Online Quiz 2.3

Activate Prior Knowledge Students may not realize that the word *organic* is related to carbon-based molecules. **Ask,** What do you think of when you hear the word *organic?* Students may mention organic food and farming. For a long time, the term *organic* was strictly associated with the chemistry of life. Until scientists gained the ability to synthesize carbon compounds, the only "factories" making carbon compounds were living organisms, hence the connection to "all natural."

▼ Teach

TEACH FROM VISUALS

FIGURE 2.10 Tell students the molecular formulas in the figure do not show all bonds as lines. For example, CH_3 has three hydrogens bonded to carbon. **Ask,** What is common to all the carbons shown in the figure? Each has four bonds.

2.3 Carbon-Based Molecules

KEY CONCEPT Carbon-based molecules are the foundation of life.

MAIN IDEAS

- Carbon atoms have unique bonding properties.
- Four main types of carbon-based molecules are found in living things.

VOCABULARY

monomer, p. 45
polymer, p. 45
carbohydrate, p. 45
lipid, p. 46
fatty acid, p. 46
protein, p. 47
amino acid, p. 47
nucleic acid, p. 48

Review
atom, molecule, covalent bond

INDIANA STANDARDS

B.1.1 Describe the structure of the major categories of organic compounds essential to living organisms in terms of their building blocks, and the small number of chemical elements (carbon, hydrogen, nitrogen, oxygen, phosphorous, and sulfur) from which they are composed.

Connect Car manufacturers often build several types of cars from the same internal frame. The size and style of the cars might differ on the outside, but they have the same structure underneath. Carbon-based molecules are similar, but they are much more varied. There are millions of different carbon-based molecules, but they form around only a few simple frames composed of carbon atoms.

MAIN IDEA

Carbon atoms have unique bonding properties.

Carbon is often called the building block of life because carbon atoms are the basis of most molecules that make up living things. These molecules form the structure of living things and carry out most of the processes that keep organisms alive. Carbon is so important because its atomic structure gives it bonding properties that are unique among elements. Each carbon atom has four unpaired electrons in its outer energy level. Therefore, carbon atoms can form covalent bonds with up to four other atoms, including other carbon atoms.

As **FIGURE 2.10** shows, carbon-based molecules have three fundamental structures—straight chains, branched chains, and rings. All three types of molecules are the result of carbon's ability to form four covalent bonds. Carbon chains can bond with carbon rings to form very large, very complex molecules. These large molecules can be made of many small molecules that are bonded together. In a sense, the way these molecules form is similar to the way in which individual links of metal come together to make a bicycle chain.

FIGURE 2.10 CARBON CHAINS AND RINGS

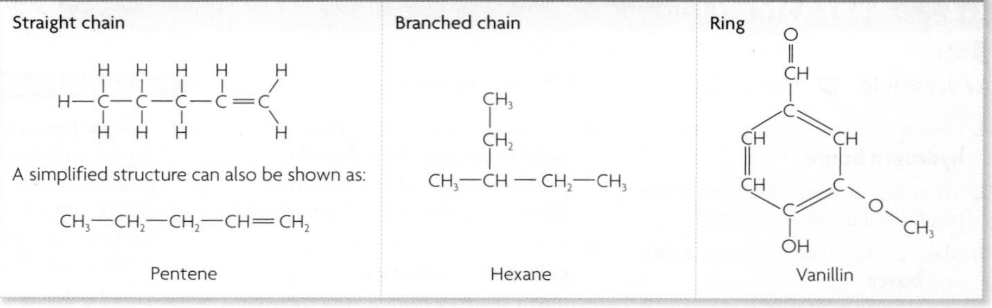

Differentiated Instruction

BELOW LEVEL

To reinforce the concept of polymers (many) made from repeating monomers (one), write this chart on the board. Have students expand the chart in their science notebooks to include Example and Function as suggested in their text on page 45.

Monomer	Polymer
monosaccharides (simple sugars)	polysaccharides
amino acid	proteins
nucleotides	nucleic acids
fatty acids	lipids (triglycerides)*

*Tell students that lipids are smaller than true polymers and are not all made of repeating units.

Biology Toolkit, Content Frame, p. C22

In many carbon-based molecules, small molecules are subunits of an entire molecule, like links in a chain. Each subunit in the complete molecule is called a **monomer.** When monomers are linked, they form molecules called polymers. A **polymer** is a large molecule, or macromolecule, made of many monomers bonded together. All of the monomers in a polymer may be the same, as they are in starches, or they may be different, as they are in proteins.

VISUAL VOCAB

Each smaller molecule is a subunit called a **monomer.**

mono- = one
poly- = many

monomer

polymer

A **polymer** is a molecule that contains many monomers bonded together.

A Synthesize **Write your own analogy for the formation of a polymer from monomers.**

MAIN IDEA

Four main types of carbon-based molecules are found in living things.

All organisms are made of four types of carbon-based molecules: carbohydrates, lipids, proteins, and nucleic acids. These molecules have different structures and functions, but all are formed around carbon chains and rings.

TAKING NOTES

Use a content frame to help you understand monomers and polymers in carbon-based molecules.

Monomer	Polymer	Example	Function

Carbohydrates

Fruits and grains are in different food groups, but they both contain large amounts of carbohydrates. **Carbohydrates** are molecules composed of carbon, hydrogen, and oxygen, and they include sugars and starches. Carbohydrates can be broken down to provide a source of usable chemical energy for cells. Carbohydrates are also a major part of plant cell structure.

The most basic carbohydrates are simple sugars, or monosaccharides (MAHN-uh-SAK-uh-RYDZ). Many simple sugars have either five or six carbon atoms. Fruits contain a six-carbon sugar called fructose. Glucose, one of the sugars made by plant cells during photosynthesis, is another six-carbon sugar. Simple sugars can be bonded to make larger carbohydrates. For example, two sugars bonded together make the disaccharide you know as table sugar, shown in **FIGURE 2.11.** Many glucose molecules can be linked to make polysaccharides (PAHL-ee-SAK-uh-RYDZ), which are polymers of monosaccharides.

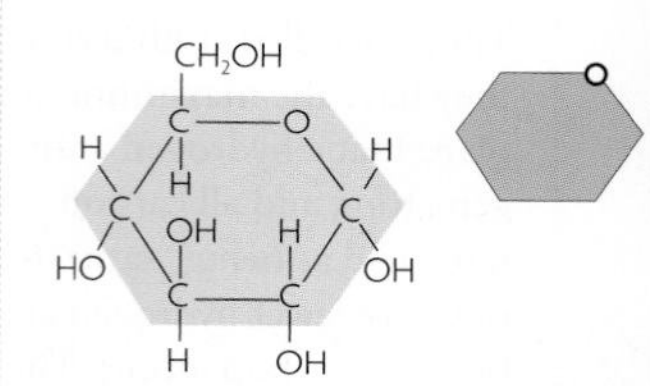

Glucose ($C_6H_{12}O_6$) can be ring shaped and is often shown as a simplified hexagon.

Starches, glycogen, and cellulose are polysaccharides. Starches and glycogen are similar, but they differ from cellulose because their glucose monomers are bonded together differently. Most starches are branched chains of glucose molecules. Starches are made and stored by plants, and they can be broken down as a source of energy by plant and animal cells. Glycogen, which is made and stored in animals, is more highly branched than plant starches.

FIGURE 2.11 Household sugar (sucrose) is a disaccharide, or two-sugar molecule, of glucose (inset) and fructose.

The Inside Story

Early chemists believed in **vitalism**—the idea that a spiritual, vital force existed inside the molecules of living things. Then in 1828, **Friedrich Wöhler** heated ammonium and cyanate ions—inorganic "mineral-world" substances—and produced urea, an organic "living-world" compound. Wöhler wrote, "I must tell you that I can prepare urea without requiring a kidney of an animal, either man or dog." This was the beginning of organic chemistry.

The distinction of an organic compound being the product of a living organism is no longer a meaningful one. Scientists now regularly synthesize organic compounds in the lab, such as the medicinal compounds originally found in plants.

Answers

A Synthesize Answers should indicate an understanding of linking units together to make a whole, such as a string of holiday lights, beads on a necklace or bracelet, or links in a chain.

Vocabulary

carbohydrate The word *carbohydrate* literally means "watered carbon." This can be explained by the ratio of carbon atoms to hydrogen and oxygen atoms in a carbohydrate: 1:2:1. However, the general formula CH_2O creates a false impression that the oxygen is supplied by water. The oxygen in a carbohydrate comes from oxygen gas. The hydrogens come from a molecule of water, but only after releasing the oxygen.

ENGLISH LEARNERS

Suggest that students use context clues to identify which terms used in the text relate to monomers and which to the polymer itself. Model for students how you interpret the text describing carbohydrates on page 45. Point out the words associated with *monomer: monosaccharides, fructose, glucose;* and those associated with *polymer: polysaccharides, starch, glycogen, cellulose.* You might want to use a cluster diagram to show the relationship.

Biology Toolkit, Context Clues, p. D10; Cluster Diagram, p. C30

INCLUSION

You can help students who are hearing impaired as you discuss the material in the section if you signal for them the key ideas or identify the particular compounds you want them to know. Arrange with them a phrase that will act as the signal, such as "important idea." Be consistent in using the phrase, being sure to look directly at students when you speak.

Integrating Chemistry

Some polymers form through a process of **dehydration,** that is, a molecule of water is released as one monomer bonds to another. One provides a hydrogen (—H) and the other provides a hydroxyl group (—OH). Some polymers can also be broken down in a reverse reaction, called **hydrolysis.** The bonds between the monomers are broken by the addition of water molecules.

▼ Teach *continued*

Take It Further

Few animals have the enzymes that allow them to hydrolyze **cellulose.** The structure of cellulose plays a role, but it is the amount and type of available enzymes that determines whether or not cellulose is broken down. Cows and termites are able to obtain energy from grass, hay, or wood because protists and bacteria that live in their bodies hydrolyze the cellulose to glucose. Although humans cannot digest cellulose, it does play an important role in our diets as insoluble fiber.

Science Trivia

- Cellulose is the most abundant organic molecule on Earth.
- Plants produce almost 10^{11} (100 billion) tons of cellulose a year.

Integrating Chemistry

Point out that biological macromolecules such as starches are similar in structure to polymers that students use every day. Many of these polymers are based on organic molecules from petroleum. **Ask,** What polymers do you commonly use? Plastics, nylon, polyesters, and Teflon are examples.

Vocabulary

Academic Vocabulary The word **saturate** shares the same sense of being full or complete as the words **satiate** and **satisfy.** However, *satiate* means to "satisfy fully, to excess," whereas *satisfy* suggests something that is "sufficient, adequate" in filling a need.

FIGURE 2.12 CARBOHYDRATE STRUCTURE

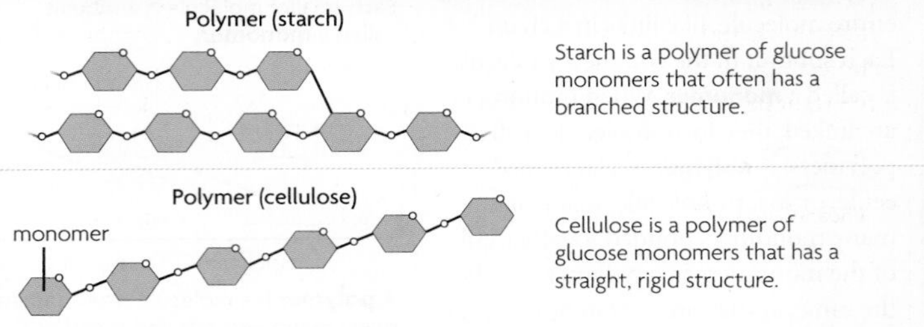

Polymer (starch)

Starch is a polymer of glucose monomers that often has a branched structure.

Polymer (cellulose)

monomer

Cellulose is a polymer of glucose monomers that has a straight, rigid structure.

***Connecting* CONCEPTS**

Cell Structure A cell wall made of cellulose surrounds the membrane of plant cells. You will learn more about cell walls in **Chapter 3.**

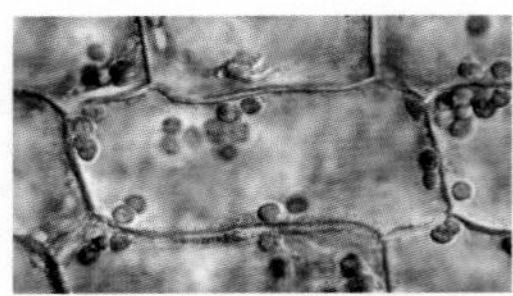

Cellulose is somewhat different from starch and glycogen. Its straight, rigid structure, shown in **FIGURE 2.12,** makes the cellulose molecule a major building block in plant cell structure. Cellulose makes up the cell wall that is the tough outer covering of plant cells. You have eaten cellulose in the stringy fibers of vegetables such as celery, so you know that it is tough to chew and break up.

Lipids

Lipids are nonpolar molecules that include fats, oils, and cholesterol. Like carbohydrates, most lipids contain chains of carbon atoms bonded to oxygen and hydrogen atoms. Some lipids are broken down as a source of usable energy for cells. Other lipids are parts of a cell's structure.

Fats and oils are two familiar types of lipids. They store large amounts of chemical energy in organisms. Animal fats are found in foods such as meat and butter. You know plant fats as oils, such as olive oil and peanut oil. The structures of fats and oils are similar. They both consist of a molecule called glycerol (GLIHS-uh-RAWL) bonded to molecules called fatty acids. **Fatty acids** are chains of carbon atoms bonded to hydrogen atoms. Two different types of fatty acids are shown in **FIGURE 2.13.**

Many lipids, both fats and oils, contain three fatty acids bonded to glycerol. They are called triglycerides. Most animal fats are saturated fats, which means they have the maximum number of hydrogen atoms possible. That is, every place that a hydrogen atom can bond to a carbon atom is filled with a hydrogen atom, and all carbon–carbon bonds are single bonds. You can think of the fatty acid as being "saturated" with hydrogen atoms. In contrast, fatty acids in oils have fewer hydrogen atoms because there is at least one double bond between carbon atoms. These lipids are called unsaturated fats because the fatty acids are not saturated with hydrogen atoms. Fats and oils are very similar, but why are animal fats solid and plant oils liquid? The double bonds in unsaturated fats make kinks in the fatty acids. As a result, the molecules cannot pack together tightly enough to form a solid.

FIGURE 2.13 Fatty acids can be either saturated or unsaturated.

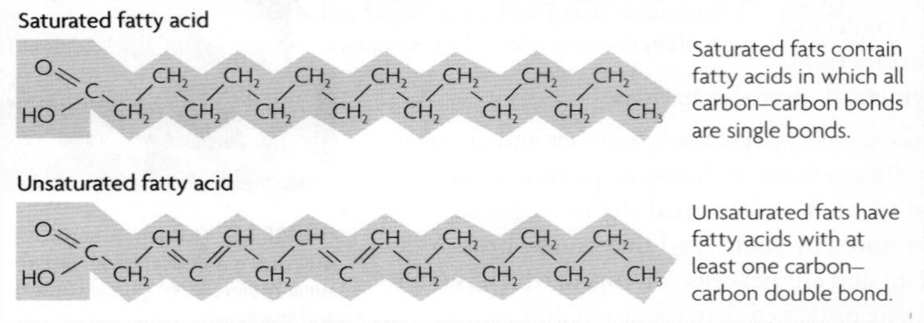

Saturated fatty acid

Saturated fats contain fatty acids in which all carbon–carbon bonds are single bonds.

Unsaturated fatty acid

Unsaturated fats have fatty acids with at least one carbon–carbon double bond.

Differentiated Instruction

PRE-AP

Remind students to expand their table describing models used for atoms and molecules, as suggested in the Pre-AP note on page 36. Have them include the molecular formulas shown in this section.

All cell membranes are made mostly of another type of lipid, called a phospholipid (FAHS-foh-LIHP-ihd). A phospholipid consists of glycerol, two fatty acids, and a phosphate group (PO_4^-) that is part of the polar "head" of the molecule. The fatty acids are the nonpolar "tails" of a phospholipid. Compare the structure of a phospholipid to the structure of a triglyceride in **FIGURE 2.14**.

FIGURE 2.14 LIPID STRUCTURE

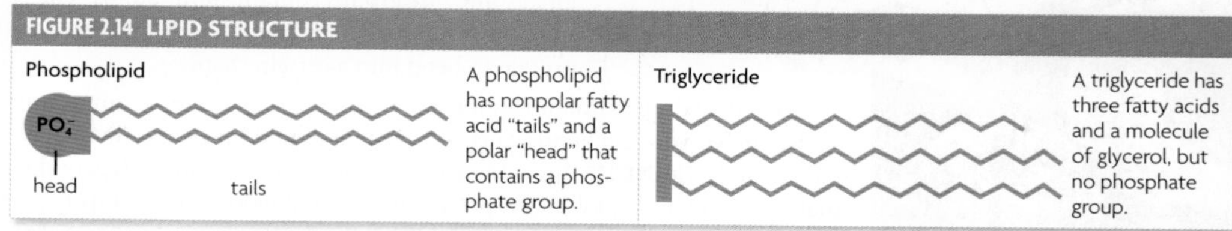

A phospholipid has nonpolar fatty acid "tails" and a polar "head" that contains a phosphate group.

A triglyceride has three fatty acids and a molecule of glycerol, but no phosphate group.

Cholesterol (kuh-LEHS-tuh-RAWL) is a lipid that has a ring structure. You may hear about dangers of eating foods that contain a lot of cholesterol, such as eggs, but your body needs a certain amount of it to function. For example, cholesterol is a part of cell membranes, and your body uses it to make chemicals called steroid hormones. Cholesterol-based steroids have many functions. Some regulate your body's response to stress. Others, such as testosterone and estrogen, control sexual development and the reproductive system.

Proteins

Proteins are the most varied of the carbon-based molecules in organisms. In movement, eyesight, or digestion, proteins are at work. A **protein** is a polymer made of monomers called amino acids. **Amino acids** are molecules that contain carbon, hydrogen, oxygen, nitrogen, and sometimes sulfur. Organisms use 20 different amino acids to build proteins. Your body can make 12 of the amino acids. The others come from foods you eat, such as meat, beans, and nuts.

FIGURE 2.15 Serine is one of 20 amino acids that make up proteins in organisms.

Look at **FIGURE 2.15** to see the amino acid serine. All amino acids have similar structures. As **FIGURE 2.16** shows, each amino acid monomer has a carbon atom that is bonded to four other parts. Three of these parts are the same in every amino acid: a hydrogen atom, an amino group (NH_2), and a carboxyl group (COOH). Amino acids differ only in their side group, or the R-group.

Amino acids form covalent bonds, called peptide bonds, with each other. The bonds form between the amino group of one amino acid and the carboxyl group of another amino acid. Through peptide bonds, amino acids are linked into chains called polypeptides. A protein is one or more polypeptides.

FIGURE 2.16 AMINO ACID AND PROTEIN STRUCTURE

All amino acids have a carbon atom bonded to a hydrogen atom, an amino group (NH_2), and a carboxyl group (COOH). Different amino acids have different side groups (R).

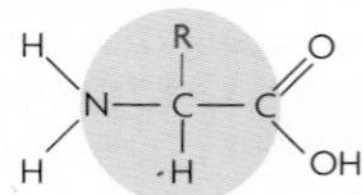

Monomer (amino acid)

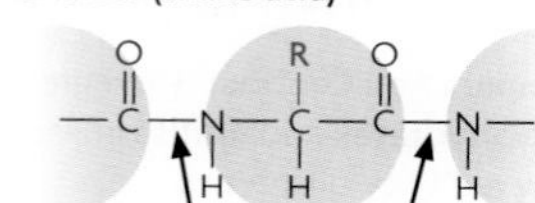

Peptide bonds form between the amino group of one amino acid and the carboxyl group of another amino acid.

Polymer (protein)

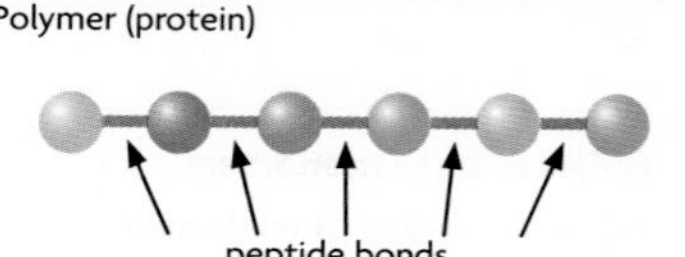

A polypeptide is a chain of precisely ordered amino acids linked by peptide bonds. A protein is made of one or more polypeptides.

TEACH FROM VISUALS

FIGURE 2.14 Point out the two parts of a phospholipid. **Ask**

- How would the polar head of a phospholipid respond to water molecules? attracted to water
- How would the nonpolar tails respond to water molecules? repelled by water

Point out that the phosphate group is a polyatomic ion. A group of atoms that are covalently bonded together may collectively lose or gain one or more electrons. A polyatomic ion stays together as a unit during reactions.

Integrating Medical Science

Lipoproteins are clusters of lipids (including cholesterol) and proteins that travel in blood plasma. They carry lipids to the cells in the body, where they are used to make membranes and steroid hormones. There are two main kinds of lipoproteins, distinguished by how dense, or compact, they are. **Low-density lipoproteins** (LDLs), commonly called "bad cholesterol," have been implicated in high blood pressure and heart disease because they are deposited on the walls of arteries as plaque and can block the flow of blood through the arteries. **High-density lipoproteins** (HDLs), called "good cholesterol," are beneficial. HDLs remove cholesterol from the arteries and return it to the liver.

TEACH WITH TECHNOLOGY

Computer-generated molecular models can help students visualize the types of macromolecules discussed in this section. Exploring carbohydrates and proteins in three dimensions will add to students' understanding. Computer programs such as Chem3D allow representation of molecules in three dimensions. Go to **ClassZone.com** for links.

▼ Teach continued

ONLINE BIOLOGY Students can learn what happens when proteins are malformed. Have students do the WebQuest on prions in Options for Inquiry on page 59.

Take It Further

Proteins have several levels of structure. The **primary structure** is the sequence of amino acids in the chain. The **secondary structure** is the arrangement of the amino acid chain in space. The two most common arrangements are the alpha helix, in which hydrogen bonding occurs between every fourth amino acid, and the beta sheet, in which amino acids in two parallel regions of the chain form hydrogen bonds. The **tertiary structure** is the overall shape of the protein after the secondary structure folds. Shape can be partially due to covalent bonding between sulfur atoms in some side groups, as well as to hydrogen bonding.

Answers

A Apply Proteins are polymers of amino acids that are assembled based on genetic information in nucleic acids.

▼ Assess and Reteach

Assess Use the Online Quiz or Section Quiz (*Assessment Book*, p. 27).

Reteach Use the figures to reteach the section, referring to the different ways molecules are represented. Each model serves a different purpose: to show the three-dimensional shape, the atomic structure of a molecule, bonding, and even to provide a simplified symbol for easier identification. Have students look at the figures and explain how the different models are used.

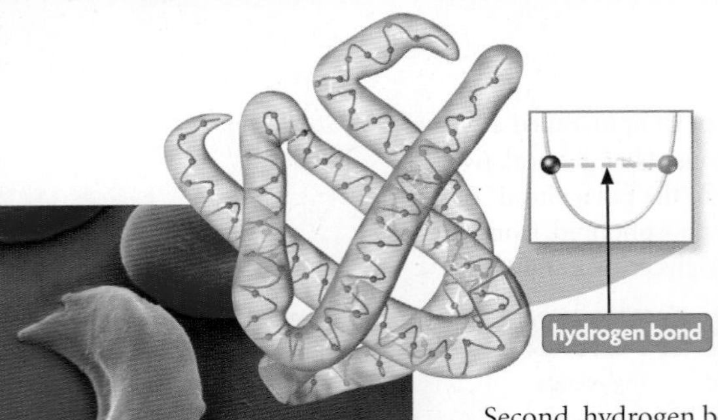

FIGURE 2.17 Hemoglobin in red blood cells transports oxygen. The structure of hemoglobin depends on hydrogen bonds between specific amino acids. Just one amino acid change causes red blood cells to have the curved shape characteristic of sickle cell anemia. (colored SEM; magnification 3500×)

Proteins differ in the number and order of amino acids. The specific sequence of amino acids determines a protein's structure and function. Two types of interactions between the side groups of some amino acids are especially important in protein structure. First, some side groups contain sulfur atoms. The sulfur atoms can form covalent bonds that force the protein to bend into a certain shape.

Second, hydrogen bonds can form between the side groups of some amino acids. These hydrogen bonds cause the protein to fold into a specific shape. For example, **FIGURE 2.17** shows the structure of one of the four polypeptides that makes up hemoglobin, the protein in your red blood cells that transports oxygen. Each of the four polypeptides contains an iron atom that bonds to an oxygen molecule. The four polypeptides are folded in a way that puts the four oxygen-carrying sites together in a pocketlike structure inside the molecule. If a protein has incorrect amino acids, the structure may change in a way that prevents the protein from working properly. Just one wrong amino acid of the 574 amino acids in hemoglobin causes the disorder sickle cell anemia.

Nucleic Acids

Detailed instructions to build proteins are stored in extremely long carbon-based molecules called nucleic acids. **Nucleic acids** are polymers that are made up of monomers called nucleotides. A nucleotide is composed of a sugar, a phosphate group, and a nitrogen-containing molecule called a base. There are two general types of nucleic acids: DNA and RNA.

Nucleic acids differ from the other types of carbon-based molecules. Carbohydrates, lipids, and proteins have a large number of structures and functions. Nucleic acids have just one function. They work together to make proteins. DNA stores the information for putting amino acids together to make proteins, and RNA helps to build proteins. DNA is the basis of genes and heredity, but cannot do anything by itself. Instead, the structure of DNA—the order of nucleotides—provides the code for the proper assembly of proteins. You will learn more about nucleic acids and how they build proteins in Unit 3.

For more information on carbon-based molecules, visit scilinks.org.
Keycode: MLB002

A Apply What is the relationship between proteins and nucleic acids?

2.3 ASSESSMENT

ONLINE QUIZ ClassZone.com

B.1.1

REVIEWING ▶ MAIN IDEAS

1. What is the relationship between a **polymer** and a **monomer**?
2. Explain how both **nucleic acids** and **proteins** are polymers. Be sure to describe the monomers that make up the polymers.

CRITICAL THINKING

3. **Compare and Contrast** How are **carbohydrates** and **lipids** similar? How are they different?
4. **Infer** Explain how the bonding properties of carbon atoms result in the large variety of carbon-based molecules in living things.

Connecting CONCEPTS

5. **Biochemistry** Why might **fatty acids, amino acids,** and nucleic acids increase the hydrogen ion (H^+) concentration of a solution? Explain your answer.

2.3 ASSESSMENT

1. A polymer is a large molecule made up of smaller units, called monomers, which are linked together.
2. Both are made of smaller units that are bonded together. Proteins are polymers of amino acids; nucleic acids are polymers of nucleotides.
3. Answers should include the following information: both are made of carbon, hydrogen, and oxygen; both are broken down as a source of energy; both have some structural functions; carbohydrates include sugars and starches, and lipids include fats and oils.
4. Carbon atoms are able to form four covalent bonds with other atoms including other carbon atoms; many other types of atoms can bond to carbon, and many different combinations are possible.
5. The molecules are acids; acids increase the H^+ ion concentration in a solution and lower the pH.

DATA ANALYSIS ClassZone.com

Independent and Dependent Variables

In an experiment, a scientist determines the effect one variable has on another. A scientist changes, or manipulates, the **independent variable** and measures or observes the **dependent variables.** Therefore, data from an experiment are measurements of dependent variables. Changes in dependent variables "depend upon" the independent variable.

EXAMPLE
A scientist studied the effect of jogging on the number of Calories used. (The Calories in food are kilocalories, or 1000 calories.) People jogged for three different lengths of time—10 minutes, 20 minutes, and 30 minutes. The number of Calories used was measured, recorded, and plotted on a graph like the one shown on the right. What are the independent and dependent variables?

- The independent variable is the length of time spent jogging (10 minutes, 20 minutes, or 30 minutes).
- The dependent variable is the number of Calories used while jogging—the number of Calories "depends on" time.

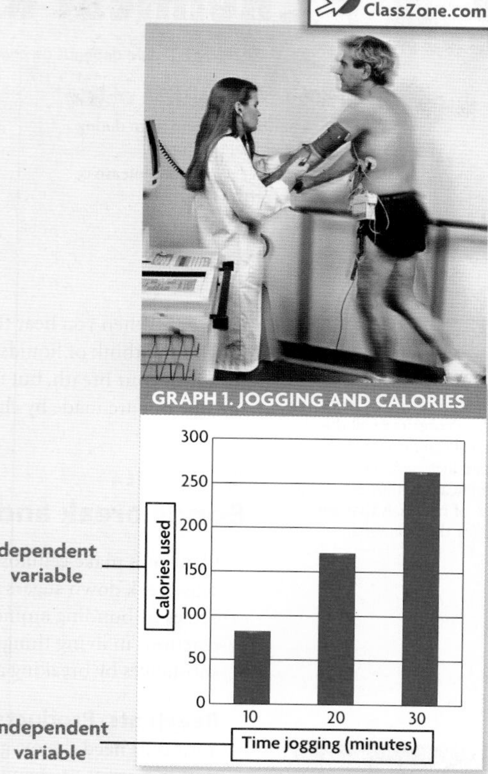

IDENTIFY VARIABLES
A company that makes nutritional products is developing a new type of protein drink for athletes. A scientist at the company is studying the pH at which a digestive enzyme best breaks down the different proteins in the drink. The scientist uses the following experimental procedure:

- Five test tubes each contain 2 mL of the protein drink.
- Five different solutions contain the digestive enzyme, but each solution has a different pH—1.5, 2.0, 2.5, 3.0, and 3.5. One enzyme solution is added to each test tube of protein drink.
- Protein levels are measured in each of the five test tubes.

1. **Identify** What are the independent and dependent variables in the experiment? Explain your answers.
2. **Apply** Time is often used as a dependent variable in experiments. Describe how time could be used as a dependent variable in this experiment.

Answers

1. The independent variable is pH because pH is manipulated. The dependent variable is the protein concentration because it is the variable that is measured.
2. Time could be used as a dependent variable if the amount of time needed to break down the protein was measured.

DATA ANALYSIS

Introduce

Explain what is implied by the term *rate*. **Ask**

- How many units of measure are involved in a rate? at least two
- What measurements should you make to find your heart rate? number of beats and time

Have students measure their heart rate by taking their pulse. Show students how to place their second and third fingers (not the thumb) of one hand on the inside of the wrist of the other hand. **Ask,** In what units should you express your heart rate? beats per minute

Discuss

Discuss the variables in the example. **Ask**

- What variables must be held constant in this experiment for the results to be valid? how fast the subject jogs
- What would the graph look like if *Time* was plotted on the vertical axis and *Calories* on the horizontal axis? The bars would be horizontal.
- What do the data tell you? The longer you jog, the more energy is used.

Unit Resource Book, Data Analysis, p. 51

SECTION 2.4

Plan and Prepare

Objectives

- Describe how bonds break and reform during chemical reactions.
- Explain why chemical reactions release or absorb energy.

Section Resources

Unit Resource Book
Study Guide pp. 43–44
Power Notes p. 45
Reinforcement p. 46

Interactive Reader Chapter 2
Spanish Study Guide pp. 17–18

Biology Toolkit p. C19

Technology
Power Presentation 2.4
Media Gallery DVD
Online Quiz 2.4

Activate Prior Knowledge Have students think of pedaling a bike along a level surface, then up a hill, and then down. Make the analogy to the energy involved in a chemical reaction. **Ask,** At what point is more energy needed? when leaving the level surface to reach the top of the hill Relate this to the energy of activation. **Ask,** How does it feel when you crest the hill and head down? Extra energy is no longer needed to cover the distance back down.

Teach

Take It Further

Point out that the chemical equation shown in the text for cellular respiration describes the overall process. The equation is a summary of many chemical reactions. The products of the first reaction, in which some of the bonds in glucose are broken, become the reactants in the next reaction, and so on. Oxygen does not take part in the process until the final reaction.

2.4 Chemical Reactions

KEY CONCEPT Life depends on chemical reactions.

MAIN IDEAS

- Bonds break and form during chemical reactions.
- Chemical reactions release or absorb energy.

VOCABULARY

chemical reaction, p. 50
reactant, p. 50
product, p. 50
bond energy, p. 51
equilibrium, p. 51
activation energy, p. 53
exothermic, p. 53
endothermic, p. 53

Review
atom, molecule

B.3.3 Recognize and describe that metabolism consists of all the biochemical reactions that occur inside cells, including the production, modification, transport, and exchange of materials that are required for the maintenance of life.

Connect When you hear the term *chemical reaction,* what comes to mind? Maybe you think of liquids bubbling in beakers. You probably do not think of the air in your breath, but most of the carbon dioxide and water vapor that you breathe out are made by chemical reactions in your cells.

MAIN IDEA

Bonds break and form during chemical reactions.

Plant cells make cellulose by linking simple sugars together. Plant and animal cells break down sugars to get usable energy. And all cells build protein molecules by bonding amino acids together. These are just a few of the chemical reactions in living things. **Chemical reactions** change substances into different substances by breaking and forming chemical bonds.

Reactants, Products, and Bond Energy

Your cells need the oxygen molecules that you breathe in. Oxygen (O_2) plays a part in a series of chemical reactions that provides usable energy for your cells. These reactions, which are described in detail in Chapter 4, break down the simple sugar glucose ($C_6H_{12}O_6$). The process uses oxygen and glucose and results in carbon dioxide (CO_2), water (H_2O), and usable energy. Oxygen and glucose are the reactants. **Reactants** are the substances changed during a chemical reaction. Carbon dioxide and water are the products. **Products** are the substances made by a chemical reaction. Chemical equations are used to show what happens during a reaction. The overall equation for the process that changes oxygen and glucose into carbon dioxide and water is

$$\underbrace{6O_2 + C_6H_{12}O_6}_{\text{Reactants}} \underbrace{\longrightarrow}_{\text{Direction}} \underbrace{6CO_2 + 6H_2O}_{\text{Products}}$$

The reactants are on the left side of the equation, and the products are on the right side. The arrow shows the direction of the reaction. This process, which is called cellular respiration, makes the carbon dioxide and water vapor that you breathe out. But for carbon dioxide and water to be made, bonds must be broken in the reactants, and bonds must form in the products. What causes bonds in oxygen and glucose molecules to break? And what happens when new bonds form in carbon dioxide and water?

FIGURE 2.18 The breakdown of glucose provides chemical energy for all activities, including speed skating.

Differentiated Instruction

ENGLISH LEARNERS

Students who have been educated in their home languages can transfer some content language because many science terms derived from Latin are similar across languages. For example, ask students how the terms *equilibrium, exothermic,* and *endothermic* are expressed in their home language to check for cognates, or shared roots.

PRE-AP

Explain that the coefficients in the equation for cellular respiration show the number of molecules taking part in the reaction. The law of conservation of mass states that matter cannot be created or destroyed in a chemical reaction. Have students take five minutes to describe how this relates to the chemical equation shown in the text.

Biology Toolkit, Quick-Write, p. C19

QUICK LAB MODELING NOS.6

Chemical Bonding

You use energy to put things together, but chemical bonding is different. Energy is added to break bonds, and energy is released when bonds form.

MATERIALS
2 flat magnets

PROBLEM How is chemical bonding similar to the interaction between two magnets?

PROCEDURE

1. Bring the magnets close to each other until they snap together.
2. Pull the magnets away from each other.

ANALYZE AND CONCLUDE

1. **Infer** How is bond formation represented by the snapping sound?
2. **Apply** How is bond energy related to your separation of the magnets?

First, energy is added to break bonds in molecules of oxygen and glucose. **Bond energy** is the amount of energy that will break a bond between two atoms. Bonds between different types of atoms have different bond energies. A certain amount of energy is needed to break bonds in an oxygen molecule. A different amount of energy is needed to break bonds in a glucose molecule.

Energy is released when bonds form, such as when molecules of water and carbon dioxide are made. When a bond forms, the amount of energy released is equal to the amount of energy that breaks the same bond. For example, energy is released when hydrogen and oxygen atoms bond to form a water molecule. The same amount of energy is needed to break apart a water molecule.

Chemical Equilibrium

Some reactions go from reactants to products until the reactants are used up. However, many reactions in living things are reversible. They move in both directions at the same time. These reactions tend to go in one direction or the other depending on the concentrations of the reactants and products. One such reaction lets blood, shown in **FIGURE 2.19**, carry carbon dioxide. Carbon dioxide reacts with water in blood to form a compound called carbonic acid (H_2CO_3). Your body needs this reaction to get rid of carbon dioxide waste from your cells.

$$CO_2 + H_2O \rightleftharpoons H_2CO_3$$

The arrows in the equation above show that the reaction goes in both directions. When the carbon dioxide concentration is high, as it is around your cells, the reaction moves toward the right and carbonic acid forms. In your lungs, the carbon dioxide concentration is low. The reaction goes in the other direction, and carbonic acid breaks down.

When a reaction takes place at an equal rate in both directions, the reactant and product concentrations stay the same. This state is called equilibrium. **Equilibrium** (EE-kwuh-LIHB-ree-uhm) is reached when both the reactants and products are made at the same rate.

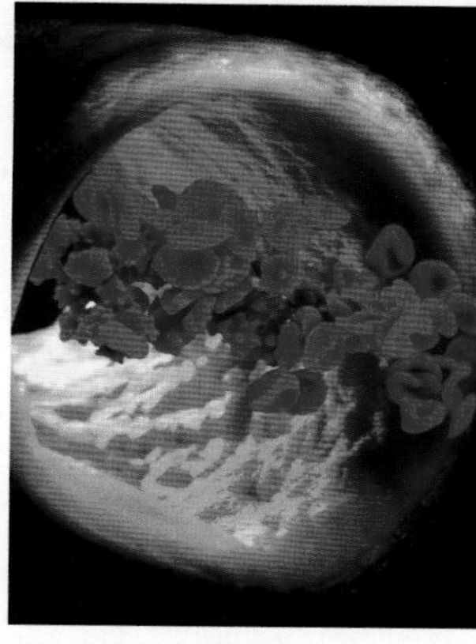

FIGURE 2.19 Blood cells and plasma transport materials throughout the body. Carbonic acid dissolves in the blood so that carbon dioxide can be transported to the lungs. (composite colored SEM; magnification 1000×)

A Apply Explain why concentration is important in a chemical reaction.

BELOW LEVEL

Explain that the term *equilibrium* means "balanced." Have two students pull with equal force on opposite ends of a rope so they are balanced. **Ask,** Are the students in equilibrium? Explain why or why not. The students are in equilibrium because they are pulling with balanced forces. **Ask,** Is it correct to say that nothing is happening? Explain why or why not. No, the students are exerting forces. Because the forces are balanced, neither student moves.

QUICK LAB

Time 10 minutes	
Lab Binder	Introduction, p. 24

Purpose Model the formation and breaking of a chemical bond.

LAB MANAGEMENT

- Make sure students understand the nature of the model. Atoms do not make a snapping sound when they form a bond; the sound is symbolic.

Analyze and Conclude

1. The sound represents the energy released when a bond forms.
2. In order to pull the magnets apart, effort (energy) is needed. Similarly, energy is required to break bonds.

Address Misconceptions

Common Misconception Students often think that energy is released when chemical bonds are broken.

Correcting the Misconception The opposite is true. Energy is always required to break bonds, and energy is always released when new bonds form. However, the net change in energy can be either an overall release or absorption of energy. You can compare bond breaking within molecules to the physical energy required in opening a sealed jar.

Answers

A Apply Concentration can alter the equilibrium of a chemical reaction. A higher concentration of reactants means that more of the reactants are available to react.

▼ Teach *continued*

Take It Further

Point out that living systems maintain a **dynamic equilibrium.** Reactants are always being delivered to cells and products removed. If this movement of materials stops, the cell dies. For example, as long as a cell receives a steady supply of oxygen and glucose and gets rid of carbon dioxide waste, the product of one reaction in cellular respiration becomes the reactant of the next reaction. Cells do not reach a state of equilibrium, but carry on chemical activity continually.

TEACH FROM VISUALS

FIGURE 2.20 Explain that the energy curves in these graphs are steeper than they are in actual reactions. The graphs represent idealized situations.

Point out on the graphs that the bond energies of the products are not equal to the bond energies of the reactants. **Ask,** How does the energy of the products compare with the energy of the reactants in each type of reaction? Energy of products is lower in an exothermic reaction and higher in an endothermic reaction.

Answers

A Critical Viewing No, the bond energies of reactants and products determine whether a reaction is exothermic or endothermic.

FIGURE 2.20 Energy and Chemical Reactions

Energy is required to break bonds in reactants, and energy is released when bonds form in products. Overall, a chemical reaction either absorbs or releases energy.

Animated
BIOLOGY
Watch exothermic and endothermic reactions at ClassZone.com.

ACTIVATION ENERGY

When enough activation energy is added to the reactants, bonds in the reactants break and the reaction begins.

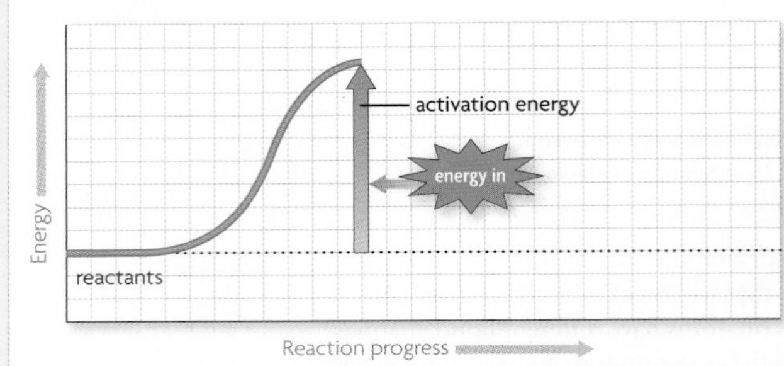

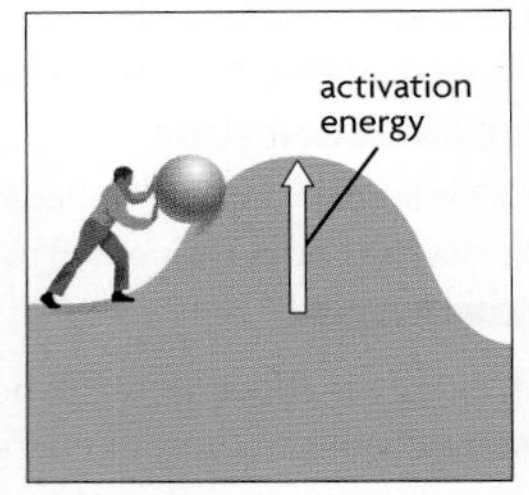

EXOTHERMIC REACTION Energy Released

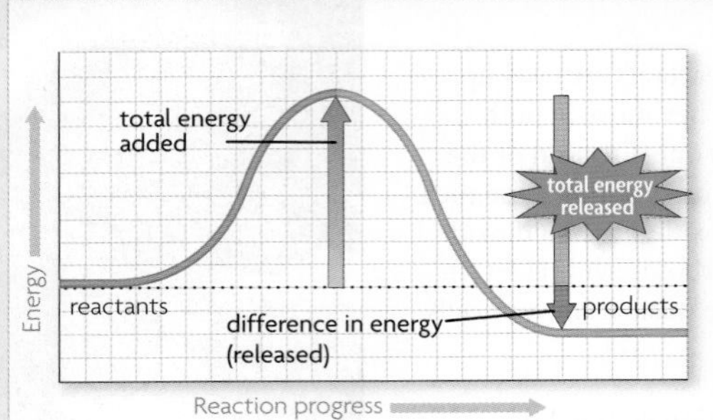

The products in an exothermic reaction have a lower bond energy than the reactants, and the difference in bond energy is released to the surroundings.

ENDOTHERMIC REACTION Energy Absorbed

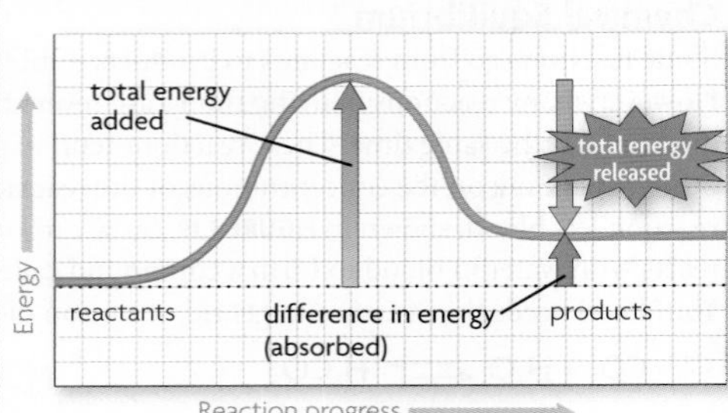

The products in an endothermic reaction have a higher bond energy than the reactants, and the difference in bond energy is absorbed from the surroundings.

A CRITICAL VIEWING **Is the amount of activation energy related to whether a reaction is exothermic or endothermic? Why or why not?**

Differentiated Instruction

TEACH WITH TECHNOLOGY

Use a temperature probe to demonstrate an exothermic or endothermic reaction.

Exothermic Place a temperature probe in a jar. Cover jar. After five minutes, record temperature. Remove probe. Soak a piece of steel wool in vinegar for one minute. Then squeeze out the excess vinegar. Wrap the wool around the probe, and place the wool/probe in jar. Cover jar. After five minutes, record the temperature. (When iron rusts, four atoms of solid iron react with three molecules of oxygen gas to form two molecules of solid iron oxide).

Endothermic Pour 25 mL of a citric acid solution (any strength) into a plastic-foam coffee cup. Use a temperature probe to record the initial temperature. Stir in about 15 g of baking soda (sodium bicarbonate). Record the change in temperature. The reaction mixture can be rinsed down the drain. (In this reaction, one molecule of citric acid reacts with three molecules of sodium bicarbonate to form three molecules of carbon dioxide, three molecules of water, and one molecule of sodium citrate.)

MAIN IDEA

Chemical reactions release or absorb energy.

All chemical reactions involve changes in energy. Energy that is added to the reactants breaks their chemical bonds. When new bonds form in the products, energy is released. This means that energy is both absorbed and released during a chemical reaction. Some chemical reactions release more energy than they absorb. Other chemical reactions absorb more energy than they release. Whether a reaction releases or absorbs energy depends on bond energy.

Some energy must be absorbed by the reactants in any chemical reaction. **Activation energy** is the amount of energy that needs to be absorbed for a chemical reaction to start. Activation energy is like the energy you would need to push a rock up a hill. Once the rock is at the top of the hill, it rolls down the other side by itself. A graph of the activation energy that is added to start a chemical reaction is shown at the top of **FIGURE 2.20.**

An **exothermic** chemical reaction releases more energy than it absorbs. If the products have a lower bond energy than the reactants, the reaction is exothermic. The excess energy—the difference in bond energy between the reactants and products—is often given off as heat or light. Some animals, such as squids and fireflies, give off light that comes from exothermic reactions, as shown in **FIGURE 2.21.** Cellular respiration, the process that uses glucose and oxygen to provide usable energy for cells, is also exothermic. Cellular respiration releases not only usable energy for your cells but also heat that keeps your body warm.

An **endothermic** chemical reaction absorbs more energy than it releases. If products have a higher bond energy than reactants, the reaction is endothermic. Energy must be absorbed to make up the difference. One of the most important processes for life on Earth, photosynthesis, is endothermic. During photosynthesis, plants absorb energy from sunlight and use that energy to make simple sugars and complex carbohydrates.

A Analyze **How is activation energy related to bond energy?**

VOCABULARY

The prefix *exo-* means "out," and the prefix *endo-* means "in." Energy "moves out of" an exothermic reaction, and energy "moves into" an endothermic reaction.

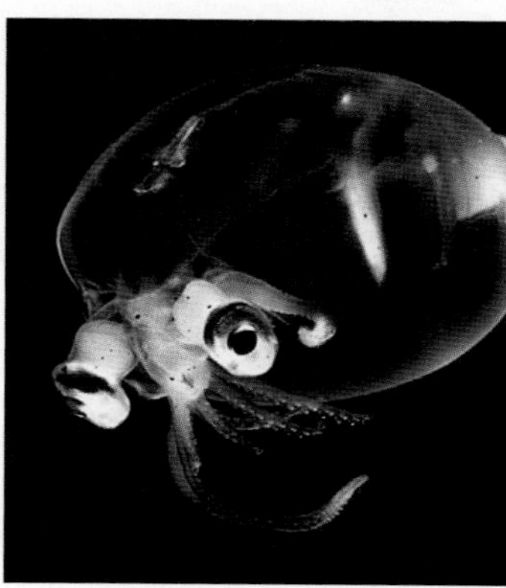

FIGURE 2.21 The glow of the bugeye squid comes from an exothermic reaction that releases light.

2.4 ASSESSMENT

ONLINE QUIZ ClassZone.com

B.3.3

REVIEWING MAIN IDEAS

1. Hydrogen peroxide (H_2O_2) breaks down into water (H_2O) and oxygen (O_2). Explain why this is a **chemical reaction.** What are the **reactants** and the **products** in the reaction?
2. How do **endothermic** and **exothermic** reactions differ?

CRITICAL THINKING

3. **Infer** The process below is exothermic. What must be true about the **bond energies** of the reactants and the products? Explain.

$$6O_2 + C_6H_{12}O_6 \rightarrow 6CO_2 + 6H_2O$$

4. **Evaluate** Why might it not always be possible to determine the reactants and the products in a reaction? Explain your answer in terms of chemical **equilibrium.**

Connecting CONCEPTS

5. **Biochemistry** A chemical reaction can start when enough **activation energy** is added to the reactants. Do you think the activation energy for chemical reactions in living things is high or low? Explain your answer.

ONLINE BIOLOGY Have students use the Virtual Lab in Options for Inquiry to explore how much energy food provides. See page 59.

Integrating Physics

When a bond is made, not all of the activation energy that is used to make the bond ends up in the bond. Some spreads out into the surroundings as heat, according to the **second law of thermodynamics.** If this energy did not disperse, it would simply flow back into the bond and undo it. Heat dispersal ensures that the molecules that are formed stay together in a stable state.

Answers

A Analyze The amount of activation energy required depends on the bond energy of the reactants.

Assess and Reteach

Assess Use the Online Quiz or Section Quiz (*Assessment Book*, p. 28).

Reteach Have students give examples of an exothermic and an endothermic reaction. Exothermic: the burning of paper, cellular respiration; endothermic: reaction in a cold pack, photosynthesis Have students draw an energy graph for each reaction. **Ask,** What form does the energy take in each reaction? The burning of paper releases both heat and light; cellular respiration releases heat and chemical energy (ATP). A cold pack absorbs heat; photosynthesis absorbs light energy from sunlight.

2.4 ASSESSMENT

1. It is a chemical reaction because different substances are formed. The reactant is hydrogen peroxide, and the products are oxygen and water.
2. Endothermic reactions absorb energy because the products have a higher bond energy than the reactants have. Exothermic reactions release energy because the products have a lower bond energy than the reactants have.
3. The bond energies of the reactants must be higher than those of the products because excess energy is released.
4. Depending on the concentrations of the reactants and the products, both reactants and products may be formed at the same time if the reaction is reversible. At equilibrium, reactants and products are formed at the same rate.
5. The activation energy for reactions must be relatively low because temperature cannot be greatly increased in living things.

SECTION 2.5

Plan and Prepare

Objectives

- Explain the effect of a catalyst on activation energy.
- Describe how enzymes regulate chemical reactions.

Section Resources

Unit Resource Book
Study Guide pp. 47–48
Power Notes p. 49
Reinforcement p. 50
Pre-AP Activity pp. 55–56

Interactive Reader Chapter 2
Spanish Study Guide pp. 19–20

Biology Toolkit pp. C19, D5

Technology
Power Presentation 2.5
Media Gallery DVD
Online Quiz 2.5

Activate Prior Knowledge Discuss how leaving a newspaper in sunlight will eventually cause the paper to yellow. If you set a match to the newspaper, it burns quickly. **Ask,** What does adding energy to a reaction do? It increases the kinetic energy of the reactant molecules, so more frequent and forceful collisions result in a faster reaction. Discuss that adding energy to reactions in a cell could destroy the cell. A solution to the problem is to lower the amount of energy needed to start the reaction.

Teach

TEACH FROM VISUALS

FIGURE 2.22 Point out that a catalyst lowers the activation energy of a slowly occurring reaction so that it occurs more quickly. It cannot cause a reaction that would never occur otherwise.

2.5 Enzymes

KEY CONCEPT Enzymes are catalysts for chemical reactions in living things.

MAIN IDEAS
- A catalyst lowers activation energy.
- Enzymes allow chemical reactions to occur under tightly controlled conditions.

VOCABULARY
catalyst, p. 54
enzyme, p. 55
substrate, p. 56

Review
chemical reaction, activation energy, protein, hydrogen bond

INDIANA STANDARDS

B.1.2 Understand that the shape of a molecule determines its role in the many different types of cellular processes including metabolism, homeostasis, growth and development, and heredity, and understand that the majority of these processes involve proteins that act as enzymes.

Connect Just how can a Venus flytrap digest a frog? It happens through the action of proteins called enzymes. Enzymes help to start and run chemical reactions in living things. For example, enzymes are needed to break down food into smaller molecules that cells can use. Without enzymes, a Venus flytrap couldn't break down its food, and neither could you.

MAIN IDEA

A catalyst lowers activation energy.

Remember what you learned about activation energy in Section 2.4. Activation energy for a chemical reaction is like the energy that is needed to push a rock up a hill. When enough energy is added to get the rock to the top of a hill, the rock can roll down the other side by itself. Activation energy gives a similar push to a chemical reaction. Once a chemical reaction starts, it can continue by itself, and it will go at a certain rate.

Often, the activation energy for a chemical reaction comes from an increase in temperature. But even after a chemical reaction starts, it may happen very slowly. The reactants may not interact enough, or they may not be at a high enough concentration, to quickly form the products of the reaction. However, both the activation energy and rate of a chemical reaction can be changed by a chemical catalyst, as shown in **FIGURE 2.22.** A **catalyst** (KAT-l-ihst) is a substance that decreases the activation energy needed to start a chemical reaction and, as a result, also increases the rate of the chemical reaction.

FIGURE 2.22 CATALYSTS AND ACTIVATION ENERGY

Under normal conditions, a certain amount of activation energy is needed to start a chemical reaction. A catalyst decreases the activation energy needed.

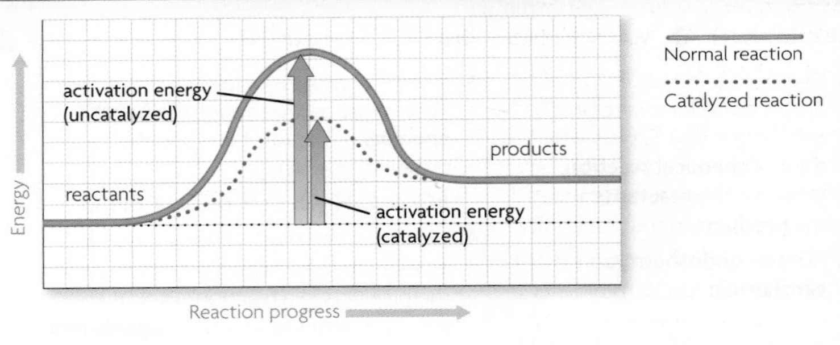

Differentiated Instruction

ENGLISH LEARNERS

Have students use a 2 × 2 word square for the vocabulary in this section. They should place the term at the center of the square and then in the four cells, include a definition, characteristics, examples, and nonexamples.

Biology Toolkit, Frayer Model, p. D5

BELOW LEVEL

Have students review the three parts of the lock-and-key model shown on page 56. Have them write for five minutes, describing the analogy. They should consider why the model is described as a lock and key. Have them identify the different parts and what happens to each part after the reaction is completed.

Biology Toolkit, Quick-Write, p. C19

Compare the activation energies and the reaction rates in the graph in **FIGURE 2.22.** Under normal conditions, the reaction requires a certain amount of activation energy, and it occurs at a certain rate. When a catalyst is present, less energy is needed and the products form faster. Although catalysts take part in chemical reactions, catalysts are not considered to be either reactants or products because catalysts are not changed or used up during a reaction.

A Summarize Describe two functions of catalysts in chemical reactions.

MAIN IDEA

Enzymes allow chemical reactions to occur under tightly controlled conditions.

Chemical reactions in organisms have to take place at an organism's body temperature. Often, reactants are found in low concentrations. Because the reactions must take place very quickly, they usually need a catalyst. **Enzymes** are catalysts for chemical reactions in living things. Enzymes, like other catalysts, lower the activation energy and increase the rate of chemical reactions. In reactions that are reversible, such as the carbon dioxide and carbonic acid reaction described in Section 2.4, enzymes do not affect chemical equilibrium. This means that enzymes do not change the direction of a reaction—they just change the amount of time needed for equilibrium to be reached.

Enzymes are involved in almost every process in organisms. From breaking down food to building proteins, enzymes are needed. For example, amylase is an enzyme in saliva that breaks down starch into simpler sugars. This reaction occurs up to a million times faster with amylase than without it. Enzymes are also an important part of your immune system, as shown in **FIGURE 2.23.**

Almost all enzymes are proteins. These enzymes, like other proteins, are long chains of amino acids. Each enzyme also depends on its structure to function properly. Conditions such as temperature and pH can affect the shape and function, or activity, of an enzyme. Enzymes work best in a small temperature range around the organism's normal body temperature. At only slightly higher temperatures, the hydrogen bonds in an enzyme may begin to break apart. The enzyme's structure changes and it loses its ability to function. This is one reason why a very high fever is so dangerous to a person. A change in pH can also affect the hydrogen bonds in enzymes. Many enzymes in humans work best at the nearly neutral pH that is maintained within cells of the human body.

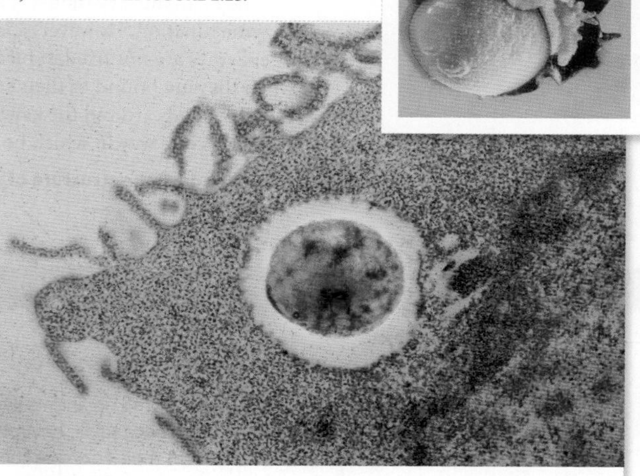

FIGURE 2.23 The inset micrograph (top) shows a white blood cell engulfing an invading pathogen. The larger micrograph shows a pathogen after it has been captured. Once inside a white blood cell, enzymes are used to destroy the pathogen. (inset image: colored SEM; magnification about 3000×; large image: colored TEM; magnification 11,000×)

TEACH WITH TECHNOLOGY

Use an oxygen probe to track the effect of an enzyme on a reaction. One such reaction uses liver extract, which contains the enzyme catalase, to convert hydrogen peroxide (H_2O_2) to oxygen gas and water. In another reaction, an extract of ground raw potato becomes darkened in the presence of catechol and oxygen, in the same way a cut potato darkens. The change in absorbance (optical density) at 540 nm can be tracked with a probe.

Answers

A Summarize Catalysts decrease activation energy and increase reaction rate.

Vocabulary

Academic Vocabulary The word **catalyst** is used in everyday language to describe someone or something that sets a process in motion. The root of the word means "to loosen." A related concept is that of a **threshold.** In everyday terms, a *threshold* is a point of entry. When applied in science, it refers to the point at which an effect can be seen or differentiated. An enzyme acting as a catalyst effectively lowers the threshold for the energy of activitation in a chemical reaction.

History of Science

All enzymes were thought to be proteins until 1982, when **Thomas Cech** and **Sidney Altman** discovered the catalytic activity of RNA. These RNAs were named **ribozymes.** They resemble enzymes in their action and the presence of an active site. More than 500 ribozymes are now known. Altman and Cech were awarded the Nobel Prize in Chemistry in 1989 for their work.

Integrating Genetics

By switching genes on and off, a cell can control which metabolic reactions take place in that cell. In addition, some genes code for enzyme inhibitors and regulatory molecules. Some inhibitors work on specific enzymes, others are nonspecific, and still others compete with the substrate for the active site. By controlling the production of enzymes and inhibitors, the cell regulates its metabolism.

▼ Teach *continued*

Take It Further

The lock-and-key model is a good way to begin to understand enzyme function, but it has been largely replaced by the **inducible fit model,** which is described in the last paragraph of the text. The main difference is the understanding that the enzyme itself changes shape as it interacts with its substrate. In the inducible fit model, the bending of the enzyme gives insight into one mechanism by which bonds in the substrate are weakened. The enzyme resists bending and puts a molecular force on the substrate. (Electrostatic and hydrophobic/hydrophilic interactions between side chains of the protein also weaken bonds.)

Answers

A Apply If the structure of an enzyme changes, its function will change.

▼ Assess and Reteach

Assess Use the Online Quiz or Section Quiz (*Assessment Book,* p. 29).

Reteach Relate the lock-and-key model shown on page 56 to **FIGURE 2.22** to summarize how an enzyme acts as a catalyst.

***Connecting* CONCEPTS**

Biochemistry The order of amino acids determines the structure and function of an enzyme. An enzyme's structure often depends on hydrogen bonds between amino acids.

Enzyme structure is important because each enzyme's shape allows only certain reactants to bind to the enzyme. The specific reactants that an enzyme acts on are called **substrates.** For example, amylase only breaks down starch. Therefore, starch is the substrate for amylase. Substrates temporarily bind to enzymes at specific places called active sites. Like a key fits into a lock, substrates exactly fit the active sites of enzymes. This is why if an enzyme's structure changes, it may not work at all. This idea of enzyme function, which is called the lock-and-key model, is shown below.

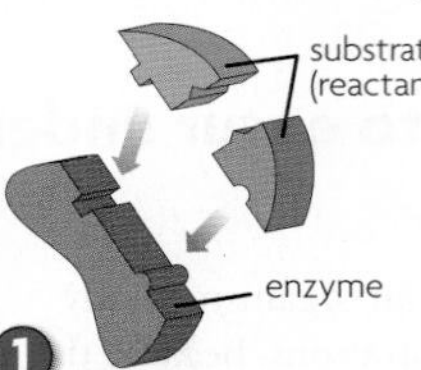

Substrates bind to an enzyme at certain places called active sites.

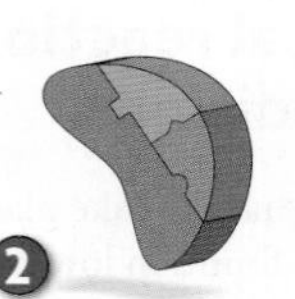

The enzyme brings substrates together and weakens their bonds.

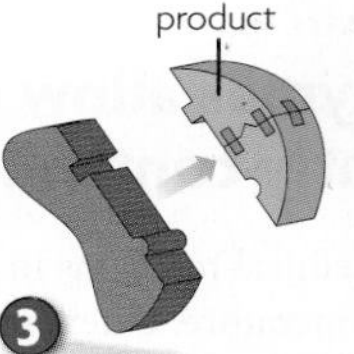

The catalyzed reaction forms a product that is released from the enzyme.

The lock-and-key model helps explain how enzymes work. First, enzymes bring substrate molecules close together. Because of the low concentrations of reactants in cells, many reactions would be unlikely to take place without enzymes bringing substrates together. Second, enzymes decrease activation energy. When substrates bind to the enzyme at the enzyme's active site, the bonds inside these molecules become strained. If bonds are strained, or stretched slightly out of their normal positions, they become weaker. Less activation energy is needed for these slightly weakened bonds to be broken.

The lock-and-key model is a good starting point for understanding enzyme function. However, scientists have recently found that the structures of enzymes are not fixed in place. Instead, enzymes actually bend slightly when they are bound to their substrates. In terms of a lock and key, it is as if the lock bends around the key to make the key fit better. The bending of the enzyme is one way in which bonds in the substrates are weakened.

A Apply How does the structure of an enzyme affect its function?

2.5 ASSESSMENT

ONLINE QUIZ ClassZone.com

B.1.2

REVIEWING MAIN IDEAS

1. How does a **catalyst** affect the activation energy of a chemical reaction?
2. Describe how the interaction between an **enzyme** and its **substrates** changes a chemical reaction.

CRITICAL THINKING

3. **Infer** Some organisms live in very hot or very acidic environments. Would their enzymes function in a person's cells? Why or why not?
4. **Predict** Suppose that the amino acids that make up an enzyme's active site are changed. How might this change affect the enzyme?

***Connecting* CONCEPTS**

5. **Homeostasis** Organisms need to maintain homeostasis, or stable internal conditions. Why is homeostasis important for the function of enzymes?

2.5 ASSESSMENT

1. A catalyst reduces the activation energy required to start the reaction.
2. An enzyme brings substrates close together so that they can react, and slightly alter (weaken) the bonds within the substrates by changing the shapes of the molecules.
3. No, those enzymes function under different conditions than are found in humans.
4. The substrates would likely not bond to the enzyme because the shape of the active site would change.
5. If homeostatic conditions, such as temperature or pH, are not maintained, then the hydrogen bonds that keep an enzyme in its correct shape will weaken or break and the enzyme's structure will change. This will affect its function.

MATERIALS
- 5 test tubes
- test tube rack
- marker
- 7 10-mL graduated cylinders
- 4 mL each of solutions of pH 3, 5, 7, 9, and 11
- 2 mL 60% catalase solution
- 1 mL 3% hydrogen peroxide solution
- metric ruler

PROCESS SKILLS
- **Identifying Variables**
- **Observing**
- **Measuring**
- **Collecting Data**
- **Interpreting Data**

B.1.3 Explain and give examples of how the function and differentiation of cells is influenced by their external environment, including temperature, acidity and the concentration of certain molecules, and that changes in these conditions may affect how a cell functions.

NOS.7 Focus on the development of explanatory models based on their observations during laboratory investigations.

Enzymatic Activity

Enzymes are necessary for many processes, including digestion and fighting disease. Conditions such as temperature and pH must be tightly controlled so that enzymes can function properly. In this lab, you will study an enzyme called catalase that helps break down hydrogen peroxide into water and oxygen.

PROBLEM How does pH affect enzymatic activity?

PROCEDURE
1. Label 5 test tubes pH 3, pH 5, pH 7, pH 9, pH 11. Place them in the test tube rack.
2. Add 4 mL of the appropriate pH solution to each test tube. Be sure to use a different graduated cylinder for each of the solutions.
3. Add 2 mL of the catalase enzyme solution to each of the test tubes. Gently swirl the test tubes to mix the solutions. Allow the test tubes to sit for 5 minutes.
4. Design a data table that has rows labeled with the independent variable and columns labeled with the dependent variable. Read step 6 to determine whether the foam height is the independent variable or the dependent variable.
5. Add 1 mL of the hydrogen peroxide solution to each test tube. Allow 5 minutes for the solutions to react. Foam should appear on the solution tops.

Caution: Avoid skin contact with hydrogen peroxide.

6. Measure the distance in millimeters from the bottom of each test tube to the top of the foam in the test tube. Record your measurements in your data table.

ANALYZE AND CONCLUDE
1. **Identify Variables** What are the independent and dependent variables? What is the operational definition of the dependent variable?
2. **Analyze** Choose a type of graph to appropriately display your data. Construct your graph.
3. **Analyze** How is the enzymatic activity of catalase related to pH? What does this tell you about the pH of your cells?
4. **Infer** The activity of an enzyme depends upon its structure. What do your results suggest about the effect of pH on the structure of catalase? Explain.
5. **Experimental Design** Why is it important that each test tube have the same amount of each solution? What other sources of experimental error may have existed?
6. **Apply** Gelatin recipes that include fruit often say not to use pineapple. Gelatin is mostly protein. Pineapple contains an enzyme that is often used in meat tenderizers. What effect might pineapple have on gelatin? Why?

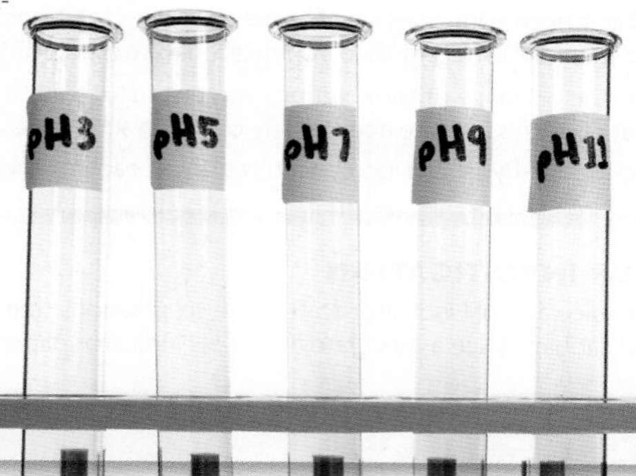

Answers

Sample Data
For a sample graph, go to page R101.

Analyze and Conclude
1. independent variable: pH of solution; dependent variable: amount of oxygen produced; operational definition: height of foam
2. Students should use a bar graph, with the height of the solution plus foam (in mm) on the y-axis and pH on the x-axis.
3. Catalase works best at a nearly neutral pH (7) and will not function at high or low pH. Students should report a decline on both sides of the neutral solution and indicate that their cells have a pH of approximately 7.
4. Answers should indicate that when pH is too high or too low, the structure of catalase changes and the enzyme cannot function properly.
5. The amounts must be controlled so that another variable is not introduced.
6. The enzyme in pineapple breaks down the protein in gelatin, preventing it from solidifying.

INVESTIGATION

Time 45 minutes (TEACHER TESTED)
Teacher Preparation
Student Difficulty
Lab Binder Introduction, pp. 17–20

Purpose Determine the pH at which the enzyme catalase functions best.

Overview Students will observe the breakdown of hydrogen peroxide by catalase to form oxygen and water. They will vary pH as the independent variable to determine the optimum pH for this enzyme.

LAB PREPARATION
- Keep catalase refrigerated to prevent denaturing.
- Liver extract can be used in place of catalase solution. Homogenize raw liver and water in a blender, and then refrigerate.

LAB MANAGEMENT
- Contents of tubes can be flushed down the drain with water.

Safety Remind students to wash their hands. Hydrogen peroxide is harmful if swallowed and can be irritating to eyes.

Inclusion Students who are visually impaired will hear fizzing, indicating the chemical reaction. They can measure the length of time they hear fizzing in each tube.

POST-LAB DISCUSSION
Tell students that many reactions in the body produce hydrogen peroxide as a byproduct. **Ask,** Why do you think cells have catalase? Hydrogen peroxide is toxic to cells. Catalase is needed to break it down into harmless products. Discuss that the pH of a cell is about 7, which is the optimum pH for the action of many enzymes, including catalase.

Teacher Note "Just about all the students obtained the outcome and drew the graph correctly."

OPTIONS FOR INQUIRY

INVESTIGATION

Time	45 minutes (TEACHER TESTED)
Teacher Preparation	
Student Difficulty	
Lab Binder	Introduction, pp. 21–22

Purpose Determine the pH of some household products.

Overview Students will test the pH of some household products. They will

- use pH indicator paper to determine the pH
- construct a pH scale

LAB PREPARATION

- Place the solutions in labeled containers.
- The ammonia is household ammonia used for cleaning.

LAB MANAGEMENT

- Clear plastic cups can be used instead of test tubes.

Safety Remind students to always use great caution when testing unknowns. Have MSDS sheets on hand for any material you use.

Teacher Note "I utilized a pH test-strip lab with all students and a cabbage lab with advanced students."

POST-LAB DISCUSSION

Discuss the significance of pH. **Ask**

- What does pH measure? concentration of hydrogen ions in solution
- Is pH an absolute measure or a relative measure? relative measure

Use these inquiry-based labs and online activities to deepen your understanding of the importance of chemistry in biology.

INDIANA STANDARDS

B.1.2 Understand that the shape of a molecule determines its role in the many different types of cellular processes including metabolism, homeostasis, growth and development, and heredity, and understand that the majority of these processes involve proteins that act as enzymes.

NOS.3 Clearly communicate their ideas and results of investigations verbally and in written form using tables, graphs, diagrams, and photographs.

INVESTIGATION

Testing pH

Universal indicator paper changes color depending on the pH of the solution being tested. Many substances around your home are acids and have a low pH. Others are bases and have a high pH. In this lab you will use pH indicator paper to investigate the pH of several common substances.

SKILLS Observing, Analyzing, Inferring

PROBLEM How acidic or basic are household substances?

MATERIALS

- 6 test tubes
- test tube rack
- 6 10-mL graduated cylinders
- lemon juice
- vinegar
- mouthwash
- window cleaner
- 2 unknown solutions
- pH indicator paper

PROCEDURE

1. Use a different graduated cylinder to pour 5 mL of each of the six solutions into each of six test tubes.
2. Test the pH of each known solution with a different strip of pH indicator paper. Use the color scale on the indicator paper package to estimate the pH of each solution. Record the pH of the known solutions.
3. Construct a pH scale ranging from 0 (very acidic) to 14 (very basic), with 7 (neutral) in the center. Label your pH scale with the known solutions.
4. Test the pH of both unknown solutions with different strips of pH indicator paper, and record the pH of each.
5. Add labels for the unknown solutions to the pH scale that you made in step 3.

ANALYZE AND CONCLUDE

1. **Identify** Find out from your teacher what the unknown solutions are. Is the pH of any of the solutions different than you might have expected? Why or why not?
2. **Apply** What is the pH range of the solutions you tested? Are any of them very acidic or basic? What does this indicate about many common substances found in the home?
3. **Analyze** Describe the hydrogen ion concentrations in each of the six solutions.

EXTEND YOUR INVESTIGATION

Use red cabbage juice as a pH indicator to test the six solutions that you tested earlier. Is the red cabbage juice as accurate as the pH indicator paper? Explain.

Answers

Sample Data

Knowns:

Known	pH
Lemon juice	2.3
Vinegar	3.0
Window cleaner	10.0–11.5

Possible unknowns:

Possible unknown	pH
Orange juice	3.0
Mouthwash	4.3–6.5
Shampoo	4.5–7.0
Milk	6.8
Toothpaste	9.9
Ammonia	12.0

Analyze and Conclude

1. Answers will vary depending on the solutions selected as the unknowns.
2. Most household substances are neither strongly acidic nor strongly basic. The usual range is between a pH of 3 and 12.
3. Answers should indicate an understanding of the inverse relationship between pH and H^+ concentration.

Extend Your Investigation

Cabbage juice is not as accurate as pH paper because it does not show as many variations in color.

INVESTIGATION

Enzymes

As in all organisms, enzymes are critical for chemical reactions in humans. One reaction produces melanin, which gives skin a dark color. Melanin helps protect skin cells from ultraviolet radiation—the greater the exposure to ultraviolet radiation, the greater the production of melanin. Melanin is made from the amino acid tyrosine by an enzyme called tyrosinase. Without tyrosinase, the reaction cannot take place. This causes a condition called albinism.

SKILL Communicating

PROBLEM What happens if an enzyme is missing or defective?

RESEARCH

Research the effect of one of the following enzyme deficiencies:

- phenylketonuria
- galactosemia
- lactose intolerance

For the enzyme deficiency that you have selected:

1. Identify the enzyme involved and its function.
2. Examine how a person's health is affected by this enzyme deficiency.
3. Find out how the deficiency is diagnosed.
4. Describe the effects of not treating the deficiency.

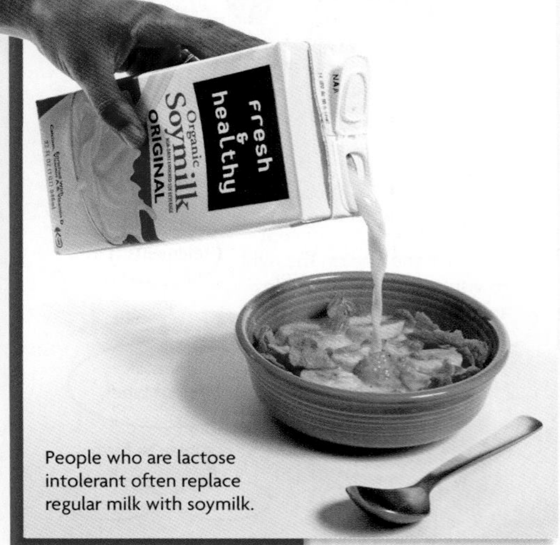

People who are lactose intolerant often replace regular milk with soymilk.

Online BIOLOGY CLASSZONE.COM

VIRTUAL LAB

Calorimetry

How much energy is in the food you eat? In this interactive lab, you will burn different food items and measure the number of Calories each releases.

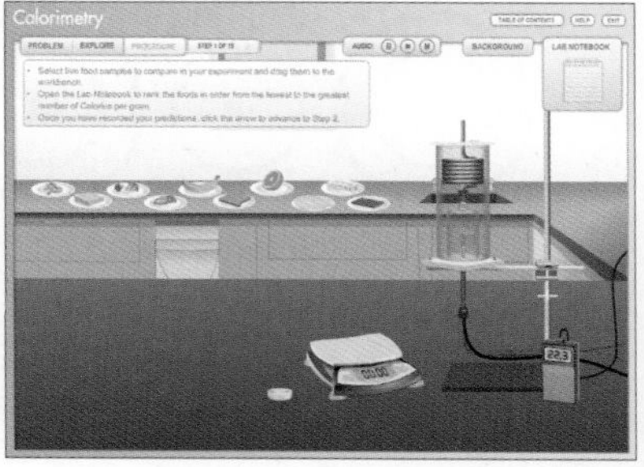

ANIMATED BIOLOGY

Atoms and Bonding

Build atoms from a bank of protons, neutrons, and electrons. Then explore how two or more atoms interact to form compounds.

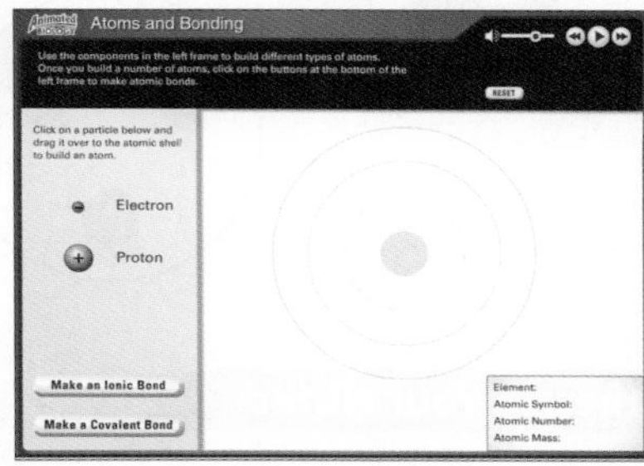

WEBQUEST

Prions are misfolded proteins that cause mad cow disease and, in humans, new variant Creutzfeldt-Jakob disease. In this WebQuest, you will learn about prions and how they infect people and other animals. Determine if the drastic steps taken to prevent the spread of prions actually keep people safe.

Online Biology ▼

VIRTUAL LAB Use this lab to reinforce concepts in **Section 2.4.**

ANIMATED BIOLOGY Students will be able to make ionic and covalent compounds. Use with **Section 2.1.**

WEBQUEST The WebQuest takes one full class period. Students complete the activity online and will need access to a printer to print their answers. Sample answers, teacher notes, and alternative assessment ideas are available on **ClassZone.com.** Use with **Section 2.3.**

INVESTIGATION
Time 45 minutes
Teacher Preparation (1 flask)
Student Difficulty (1 flask)
Lab Binder Introduction, p. 23

POST-LAB DISCUSSION

Remind students that most metabolic processes consist of several reactions. **Ask,** What happens if one enzyme in a pathway is missing or defective? The entire pathway is shut down. The products in the reaction before the blocked reaction will accumulate. These accumulated products may be toxic.

Answers

Phenylketonuria (PKU) results when the enzyme phenylalanine hydroxylase cannot be produced. The enzyme is needed to change phenylalanine into tyrosine. If untreated, phenylalanine builds up in the blood, causing rashes, seizures, and severe mental retardation. In most states, newborns are given a blood test to screen for PKU. Treatment includes a diet that generally excludes phenylalanine.

Galactosemia results when the enzyme needed to break down the simple sugar galactose (found in milk) is absent. Symptoms in untreated newborns who are fed milk include vomiting, jaundice, poor weight gain, and convulsions. If left untreated, liver and brain damage will occur. A diagnosis is made through blood and urine tests. Treatment includes a lifelong restriction of milk and milk products from the diet.

Lactose intolerance results when the enzyme lactase, used to break down the sugar lactose, is not produced. Symptoms include diarrhea, gas, and abdominal cramps after consuming dairy products. Treatment includes lactase supplements and avoiding dairy products.

CHAPTER REVIEW

Interactive Review

Encourage students to go to **ClassZone.com** for a detailed review of each section, including visuals and vocabulary practice.

Unit Resource Book, Vocabulary Practice, pp. 57–60

CHAPTER 2 Interactive Review @ CLASSZONE.COM

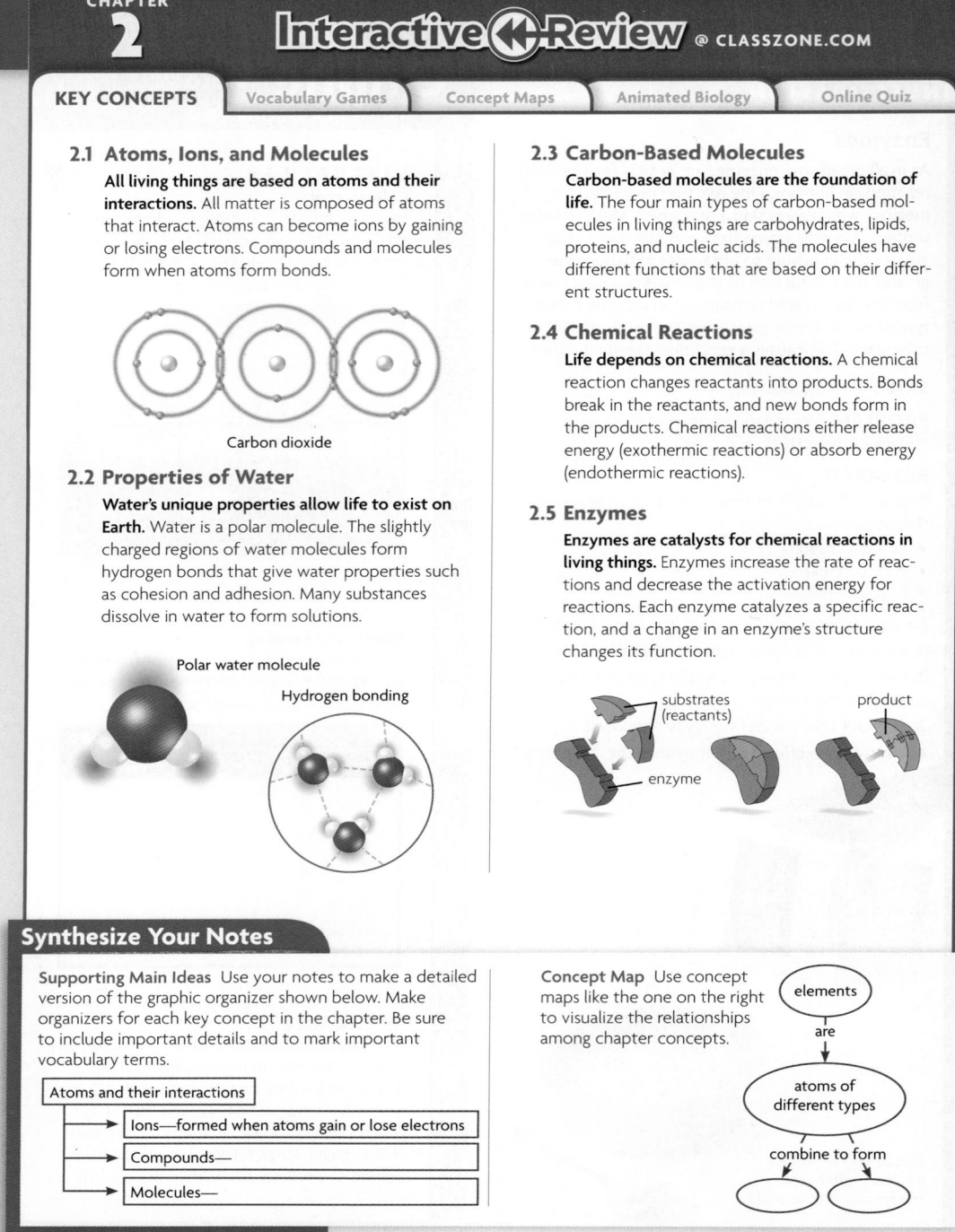

KEY CONCEPTS | Vocabulary Games | Concept Maps | Animated Biology | Online Quiz

2.1 Atoms, Ions, and Molecules

All living things are based on atoms and their interactions. All matter is composed of atoms that interact. Atoms can become ions by gaining or losing electrons. Compounds and molecules form when atoms form bonds.

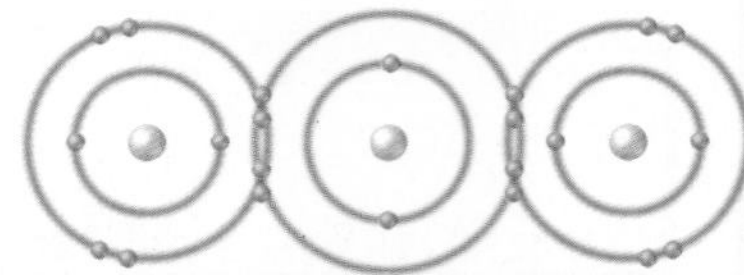

Carbon dioxide

2.2 Properties of Water

Water's unique properties allow life to exist on Earth. Water is a polar molecule. The slightly charged regions of water molecules form hydrogen bonds that give water properties such as cohesion and adhesion. Many substances dissolve in water to form solutions.

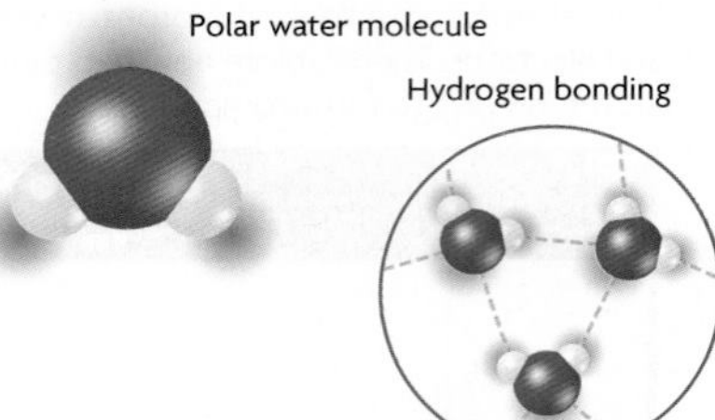

2.3 Carbon-Based Molecules

Carbon-based molecules are the foundation of life. The four main types of carbon-based molecules in living things are carbohydrates, lipids, proteins, and nucleic acids. The molecules have different functions that are based on their different structures.

2.4 Chemical Reactions

Life depends on chemical reactions. A chemical reaction changes reactants into products. Bonds break in the reactants, and new bonds form in the products. Chemical reactions either release energy (exothermic reactions) or absorb energy (endothermic reactions).

2.5 Enzymes

Enzymes are catalysts for chemical reactions in living things. Enzymes increase the rate of reactions and decrease the activation energy for reactions. Each enzyme catalyzes a specific reaction, and a change in an enzyme's structure changes its function.

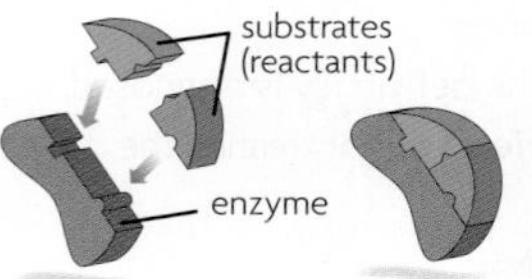

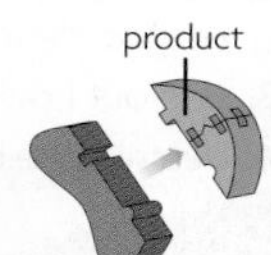

Synthesize Your Notes

Supporting Main Ideas Use your notes to make a detailed version of the graphic organizer shown below. Make organizers for each key concept in the chapter. Be sure to include important details and to mark important vocabulary terms.

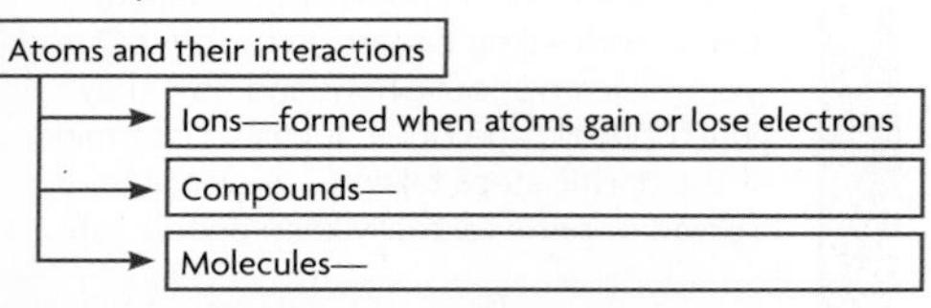

Concept Map Use concept maps like the one on the right to visualize the relationships among chapter concepts.

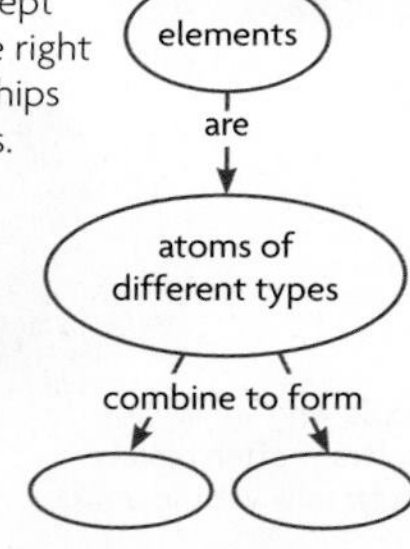

Reviewing Vocabulary

1. Atoms are the basic unit of matter. An atom that gains or loses electrons and has a charge is an ion.
2. Cohesion in water is the result of hydrogen bonds that form from one polar water molecule being attracted to another.
3. A solvent dissolves other substances to form a solution.
4. Acids have a high concentration of hydrogen ions and a low pH. Bases have a low concentration of hydrogen ions and a high pH.
5. Exothermic reactions release more energy than they absorb. Endothermic reactions absorb more energy than they release.
6. A catalyst is a substance that increases the rate of a chemical reaction. Enzymes are biological catalysts.
7. An atom is the basic unit of matter. It cannot be broken down by normal chemical means.
8. It is the strength or concentration of hydrogen ions that makes a solution acidic or basic.
9. A monounsaturated lipid has one unsaturated carbon in its fatty acid tail(s); a polyunsaturated lipid has two or more unsaturated carbons in its fatty acid tail(s).

Chapter Assessment

Chapter Vocabulary

2.1	atom, p. 36 element, p. 36 compound, p. 37 ion, p. 38 ionic bond, p. 38 covalent bond, p. 39 molecule, p. 39		solute, p. 42 acid, p. 42 base, p. 42 pH, p. 42	2.4	chemical reaction, p. 50 reactant, p. 50 product, p. 50 bond energy, p. 51 equilibrium, p. 51 activation energy, p. 53 exothermic, p. 53 endothermic, p. 53
2.2	hydrogen bond, p. 41 cohesion, p. 41 adhesion, p. 41 solution, p. 42 solvent, p. 42	2.3	monomer, p. 45 polymer, p. 45 carbohydrate, p. 45 lipid, p. 46 fatty acid, p. 46 protein, p. 47 amino acid, p. 47 nucleic acid, p. 48	2.5	catalyst, p. 54 enzyme, p. 55 substrate, p. 56

Reviewing Vocabulary

Vocabulary Connections

The vocabulary terms in this chapter are related to each other in various ways. For each group of words below, write a sentence or two to clearly explain how the terms are connected. For example, for the terms *covalent bond* and *molecule*, you could write "A molecule is made of atoms connected by covalent bonds."

1. atom, ion
2. hydrogen bond, cohesion
3. solution, solvent
4. acid, base, pH
5. exothermic, endothermic
6. catalyst, enzyme

Word Origins

7. The word *atom* comes from the Greek word *atomos,* which means "indivisible." Describe the relationship between the Greek term and your understanding of atoms.
8. The *p* in *pH* stands for the German word *Potenz,* which means "power" or "potential." The *H* represents hydrogen ions (H^+). How are these related to the definition of pH?
9. The prefix *mono-* means "one" and the prefix *poly-* means "many." Some lipids are monounsaturated and others are polyunsaturated. Explain the difference between the fatty acids in these different types of lipids.

Reviewing MAIN IDEAS

10. Explain how the combination of electrons, protons, and neutrons results in the neutral charge of an atom.
11. Potassium ions (K^+) have a positive charge. What happens to a potassium atom's electrons when it becomes an ion?
12. Some types of atoms form more than one covalent bond with another atom. What determines how many covalent bonds two atoms can make? Explain.
13. How is hydrogen bonding among water molecules related to the structure of the water molecule? **B.1.1**
14. Explain the difference between solvents and solutes.
15. Describe the relationship between hydrogen ions (H^+) and pH. How is pH related to a solution's acidity?
16. Carbon forms a very large number of compounds. What characteristic of carbon atoms allows the formation of all of these compounds? Explain. **B.1.1**
17. Identify and explain examples of monomers and polymers in carbohydrates, proteins, and nucleic acids.
18. Explain the relationship between a protein's structure and its ability to function. **B.1.2**
19. What are the components of a chemical reaction? **B.3.3**
20. Explain the difference between exothermic and endothermic reactions. **B.3.3**
21. Describe the effect of a catalyst on activation energy and reaction rate. **B.1.2**
22. What is the role of enzymes in organisms? **B.1.2**

CHAPTER REVIEW

16. Carbon atoms have four unpaired electrons in their outermost energy level, so they can form four covalent bonds.
17. Carbohydrates—Simple sugars (for example, glucose) are monomers that are bonded to form polysaccharides (for example, cellulose). Proteins—Amino acids are monomers that are bonded to form proteins. Nucleic acids—Nucleotides are monomers that are bonded to form nucleic acids.
18. The specific function of a protein is dependent on its precise structure. A change in protein structure changes its function.
19. Substances that are changed in a chemical reaction are reactants; substances made are products.
20. If a reaction has a net gain of energy (that is, it absorbs more energy than it releases), it is an endothermic reaction and the products have a higher bond energy than the reactants have. If a reaction has a net release of energy (that is, it releases more energy than it absorbs), it is an exothermic reaction and the products have a lower bond energy than the reactants have.
21. A catalyst decreases activation energy and increases reaction rate.
22. Enzymes allow reactions to occur at high rates under the tightly controlled conditions found in organisms.

Reviewing Main Ideas

10. Neutrons have no charge. Each proton has a charge of +1, and each electron has a charge of −1. Atoms are neutral when the number of protons and electrons are equal.
11. loses one electron
12. If atoms need more than one electron to fill their outermost energy levels, they can share more than one electron pair.
13. The larger oxygen atom pulls electrons away from the hydrogen atoms, producing charged regions that result in hydrogen bonding.
14. Solvents are present in greater concentrations and dissolve solutes.
15. There is an inverse relationship—the greater the hydrogen ion concentration, the lower the pH, the more acidic the solution.

ITEM CORRELATIONS

Standard	Items
B.1.1	13, 16, 23, 27, 28
B.1.2	18, 21, 22, 29, 30-32
B.3.3	19, 20

Critical Thinking

23. Phospholipids have fatty acid chains bonded to glycerol as do triglycerides; however, a third fatty acid is replaced by a phosphate group, which gives the molecule a polar head and two nonpolar tails.
24. Both bonds involve attraction between positive and negative charges. Ionic bonds are very strong attractions between oppositely charged ions that result in a compound. Hydrogen bonds are relatively weak attractions between partial positive and negative charges that do not form a compound.
25. For medication to travel in the body, it must dissolve in the blood. To dissolve easily, the molecules of the medication must be polar.
26. A protein's function might be disrupted if hydrogen bonds break and the protein's structure changes due to changes in pH or temperature.
27. Starch and cellulose are both polysaccharides of glucose. Starches are branched and are used by plants to store chemical energy. Cellulose has a straight, rigid structure and makes up plant cell walls.
28. Lipids are a major component of cell membranes, they store energy, and they are used to make hormones.
29. In raw foods, enzyme structures are still intact and can be reused. When foods are cooked, the enzyme structure is destroyed, and it loses its function.

Interpreting Visuals

30. A substrate (B) binds to the active site of the enzyme (A); a chemical reaction occurs due to the reactants' weakened bonds; products (C and D) are released from the enzyme.
31. It decreases the amount of activation energy needed because the weakened bonds of the substrate are easier to break.
32. Buffers help keep pH stable. Conditions such as pH need to be tightly controlled so that hydrogen bonds between amino acids in enzymes can remain intact.

Critical Thinking

23. **Compare and Contrast** How are phospholipids similar to lipids such as triglycerides? How are they different? **B.1.1**

24. **Compare and Contrast** Briefly describe the similarities and differences between hydrogen bonds and ionic bonds. Which type of bond do you think is stronger? Why?

25. **Infer** Suppose that you have a cold. What characteristics must cold medicine have that allow it to be transported throughout your body? Explain.

26. **Predict** Homeostasis involves the maintenance of constant conditions in an organism. What might happen to a protein if homeostasis is disrupted? Why?

27. **Compare and Contrast** Describe the structures and functions of starch and cellulose. How are the molecules similar? How are they different? **B.1.1**

28. **Apply** Suppose you had a friend who wanted to entirely avoid eating fats. What functions of lipids could you describe to convince that person of the importance of fats to his or her health? **B.1.1**

29. **Infer** The human body can reuse some of the enzymes found in raw fruits and vegetables. Why is this not the case for cooked fruits and vegetables? **B.1.2**

Interpreting Visuals

The diagram below shows the lock-and-key model of enzyme function. Use it to answer the next three questions.

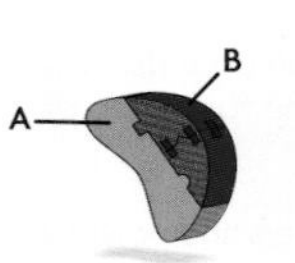

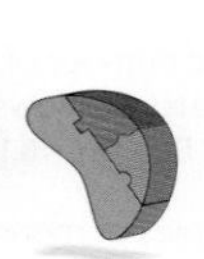
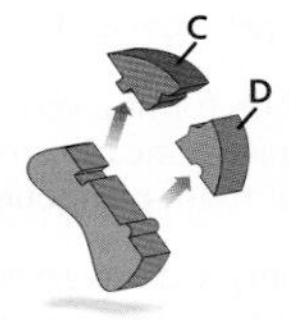

30. **Summarize** Briefly explain what is happening at each step of the process. Be sure to identify each of the substances (A–D) shown in each step of the process. **B.1.2**

31. **Apply** How does Substance A affect the amount of activation energy needed by the process? Explain. **B.1.2**

32. **Synthesize** Describe the importance of buffers in solutions in allowing the process shown above to take place. **B.1.2**

Analyzing Data

Use the graph below to answer the next three questions.

ENERGY IN A CHEMICAL REACTION

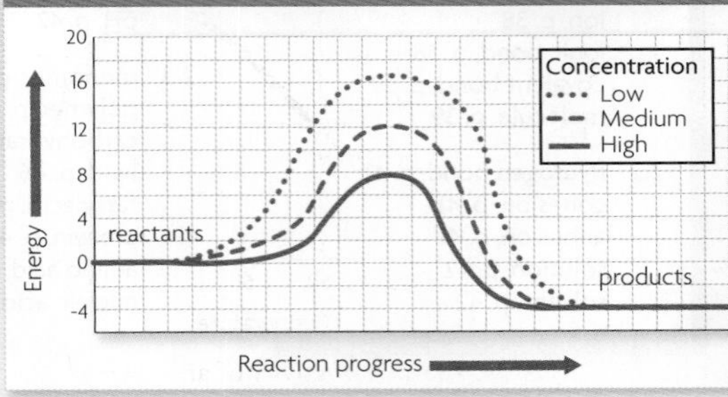

33. **Apply** Suppose the graph was constructed from data collected during an experiment. What were the independent and dependent variables in the experiment? Explain.

34. **Analyze** How much activation energy is needed to start the chemical reaction represented by each line on the graph? How much energy is released from each reaction?

35. **Apply** Explain whether each of the chemical reactions shown on the graph is endothermic or exothermic.

Connecting CONCEPTS

36. **Write About Chemical Equilibrium** Carbon dioxide reacts with water in blood plasma to form carbonic acid. The equation for this reaction is shown on page 51. Suppose that you are a molecule of carbon dioxide. Describe the chemical reactions that take place when you enter the blood and when you leave the blood. Explain what determines how these reactions occur. Be sure to include all terms from the chapter that are related to the chemical reaction.

37. **Apply** The Venus flytrap shown in the photograph on page 35 uses enzymes to digest its prey. Describe how pH, solutions, and chemical reactions all play important roles inside the trap of this carnivorous plant.

Analyzing Data

33. The independent variable is enzyme (or catalyst) concentration; the dependent variable is energy required.
34. 17 units needed/21 units released; 12 units needed/16 units released; 8 units needed/12 units released
35. They are all exothermic because they release more energy than they absorb.

INDIANA ISTEP+ Test Prep

B.1.1; B.1.2; B.5.1; NOS.1

Test Practice For more test practice, go to ClassZone.com.

1

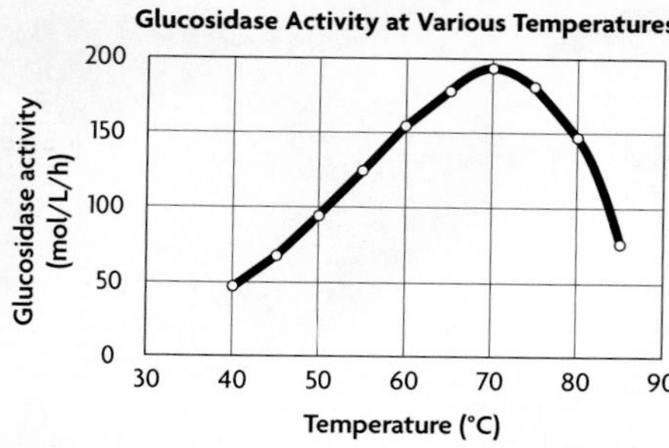

This graph shows the activity of an enzyme called glucosidase. What can you conclude from these data?

A Glucosidase breaks down glucose substrates.
B Glucosidase functions best around 70°C.
C Glucosidase does not function below 70°C.
D Glucosidase is not affected by temperature.

2 Proteins are long molecules that are built from various combinations of

A carbohydrates.
B nucleic acids.
C lipids.
D amino acids.

3

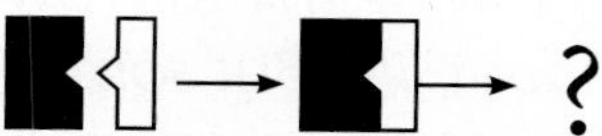

The diagram shows how an enzyme (black) binds to a substrate (white) during a chemical reaction. When this reaction is complete, the

A enzyme's shape will be different.
B surrounding temperature will have increased.
C hydrogen ion concentration will have decreased.
D substrate will be a different molecule.

4 An animal's stomach contains enzymes that break down food into smaller molecules that the animal's cells can use. Enzymes perform this function by

A participating in chemical reactions.
B increasing the temperature.
C changing the ionic concentration.
D lowering the pH.

5 The primary function of DNA is to

A provide energy for a cell.
B transmit messages between cells.
C translate the codes in RNA.
D store information for building proteins.

6 Explain how an enzyme works to speed up a chemical reaction.

Standards-Based Assessment

1. B	4. A
2. D	5. D
3. D	6. See Below

Question 1 Answer B is correct because glucosidase activity peaks (about 195 mol/L/h) at 70°C. Answer A is incorrect because the substrate of glucosidase cannot be determined from the graph. Answer C is incorrect because the graph shows glucosidase activity from 40°C to 85°C. Answer D is incorrect because the graph shows that glucosidase activity changes in response to changes in temperature.

Question 2 Answer D is correct because proteins are macromolecules made up of amino acids. Answer A is incorrect because carbohydrates are macromolecules made up of carbon, hydrogen, and oxygen that often form rings. Answer B is incorrect because nucleic acids are macromolecules made up of DNA and RNA. Answer C is incorrect because lipids are macromolecules made up of carbon chains bonded to oxygen and hydrogen atoms.

Question 3 Answer D is correct. Answer A is incorrect because the enzyme is unchanged by the reaction. Answer B is incorrect because it is not known whether this is an exothermic or endothermic reaction. Answer C is incorrect because it is not known whether the hydrogen ion concentration is affected.

Question 6 Enzymes bring substrates closer together and weaken their chemical bonds. Less energy is needed to break these bonds than without the enzyme.

Connecting Concepts

36. Answers will vary, but they should include information about reactants (H_2O, CO_2 or H_2CO_3), products (H_2CO_3 or H_2O, CO_2), solvent (water), solute (carbon dioxide), solution (blood), chemical equilibrium, and concentration. Answers should imply that the carbon dioxide molecule enters the blood at the cells and leaves at the lungs.

37. Answers will vary, but they should say that enzymes work at specific pH, that the enzymes and the digestive products are in solution, and that chemical reactions take place in the trap. Additional information about enzyme structure and function and about the role of enzymes in chemical reactions in living things could be included.

ITEM CORRELATIONS

Standard	Items
B.1.1	2
B.1.2	3, 4, 6
B.5.1	5
NOS.1	1

UNIT

1

Introduce

Tell students that advances in knowledge and technology have been tied to ethical considerations since ancient times. The Hippocratic Oath, written in ancient Greece, described the ethical obligations of physicians. Today physicians traditionally take a modern version of the Hippocratic Oath. Sometimes codes of ethics are written in response to ethical issues that arise. For example, the Nuremberg Code was written to establish ethics involving research on humans in response to abuses during World War II.

Scientists, especially those with careers in fields such as biotechnology, genetics, and medicine, must take the ethical issues of their work into account. Some scientists make decisions about their work based on their own values. Other decisions are based on guidelines and laws that regulate research or how knowledge gained from research is used.

As more complicated ethical, legal, and social issues arise, time and money is spent in studying and debating these issues. Individuals and groups take grievances into the court system, bills are introduced into Congress, congressional hearings are held, and, for some issues, state and federal laws are passed. As students read about scientific advances, they should consider what ethical issues could be involved.

Discuss with students how ethical issues affect scientists and how scientific research raises ethical issues. **Ask**

- What might limit the research a scientist can do? personal values, guidelines and laws
- How might the work a scientist does raise ethical issues? Students might answer that the knowledge scientists gain in their research creates new ethical issues.

UNIT 1: INTRODUCING BIOLOGY

BIOZINE at CLASSZONE.COM

INTERNET MAGAZINE

Go online for the latest biology news and updates on all BioZine articles.

Expanding the Textbook

News Feeds

Science Daily
CNN
BBC

Careers

Bio Bytes

Opinion Poll

Strange Biology

Scientists can change an organism's genes. Should they?

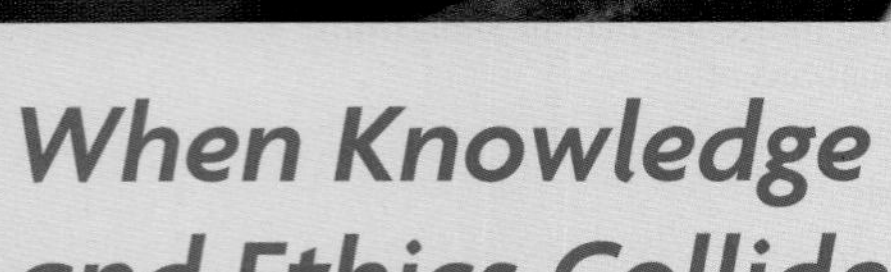

When Knowledge and Ethics Collide

Our ability to change living things grows as we learn more about life. But sometimes biotechnology makes us question whether we should change organisms just because we can. Maybe the technology is dangerous or maybe it challenges our values. Consider the greenish pig above. A gene from a fluorescent jellyfish was added to its genome by genetic engineering. Genetic engineering holds great promise for medicine. But how and when should we alter an organism's genes?

Strange Biology

A fluorescent pig is pretty strange. Have students access BioZine at **ClassZone.com** and check out the feature Strange Biology. Have students relate the information they find there to a concept they learned about in Unit 1.

64 Unit 1: Introducing Biology

What is Bioethics?

A short answer is that bioethics is the study of the moral questions that are raised as a result of biology research and its applications. But what do questions of ethics have to do with biology? It might seem better to leave questions about values in a philosophy or social studies class. However, today's cutting-edge research often prompts discussions about some of our most basic values. In the end, you might find that biology class is the best place to consider any number of ethical questions.

Ethical questions require all of us to make decisions about "the right thing to do." Often, the right thing to do is very clear. The decision benefits ourselves, our families, and our society, and it follows the accepted values of society. However, many times a decision about an ethical issue is not so obvious. It is in these cases when strong feelings on different sides of an ethical question can produce conflicts—in ourselves, our families, and our society. Can we rely upon biology, or any other scientific field, for our decisions?

For better or for worse, science can only provide us with information. The knowledge that comes from scientific research is very useful, and often necessary, in helping people arrive at decisions, but science only provides part of the answer to ethical questions. All of the advances in science have given us the ability to do many wondrous things. But bioethics asks us to question whether we should actually do all of those things.

We can add new genes to an organism's DNA. We can clone animals. We can extend human life expectancies. We can test people for genetic diseases. But should we, as a society, do all of these things? And who should decide whether we use all of our technological advances? Should these decisions be left to researchers? to universities? to corporations? Should the government make laws to cover bioethical issues? In the end, any decision based on a bioethical question will likely come down to a combination of scientific knowledge, personal values, and law.

TECHNOLOGY

Genetic Testing

Genetic testing is used in many ways. We can identify disease-causing genes, determine the guilt or innocence of crime suspects, and reunite families that have been separated. But should genetic testing be used by employers to make decisions about employees?

Suppose that a company secretly obtained and tested DNA samples from some of its employees. Because of rising medical insurance claims, the company wanted to know if the employees had a gene that increased their risk for developing a certain medical condition. Does this seem like a plot for a television show? It isn't. In 2002, a company had to pay more than $2 million in damages for testing the DNA of employees without their knowledge.

Consider another case. In 2005 a basketball player named Eddy Curry missed the end of the season due to a potential heart problem. His team wanted to use a genetic test to find out if he had a life-threatening condition. Curry refused because the test results could have ended his career. The team refused to let him play. Both the team and Curry made choices. Who do you think was right?

Read More >> at CLASSZONE.COM

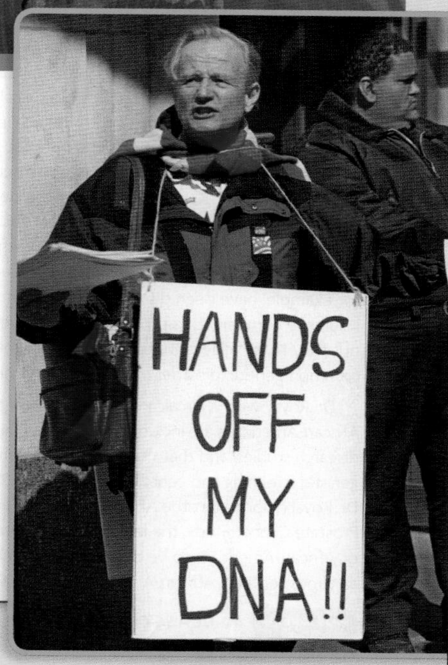

Vocabulary of Ethics

Students may need clarification of some of the terms used to discuss ethical issues.

morals—rules or habits of conduct, with reference to standards of right and wrong.

value—a principle, standard, or quality considered worthwhile or desirable.

ethics—rules or standards governing the conduct of a person or the member of a profession; the study of moral choices.

bioethics—the study of the ethical and moral issues that arise from new biological discoveries and medical advances, often in the field of genetic engineering.

biotechnology—the use and application of living things and biological processes.

genetic engineering—changing the genetic makeup of an organism, often by adding a gene from a different species.

genetic testing—the analysis of an individual's DNA to detect the presence of a gene or genes that are associated with an inherited disorder or an increased risk for a disease, such as cancer; also called genetic screening.

Current News

Using the Current News section of BioZine online, have students look for stories about current biological research. Have students consider these questions:

- What question(s) were scientists trying to answer?
- What experimental procedures and methods did the scientists use?
- What kind of language is being used to describe the research and experimentation?
- Are there any ethical issues that might arise from the research?

UNIT 1

Take It Further

The Equal Employment Opportunity Commission (EEOC) settled the first lawsuit involving genetic discrimination in the workplace in 2001. The lawsuit was filed on behalf of employees of the Burlington Northern Santa Fe Railroad who had submitted claims of work-related carpal tunnel syndrome. Without the employees' knowledge, they were tested for a rare genetic condition, HNPP (Hereditary Neuropathy with liability to Pressure Palsies). It is caused by a deletion on chromosome 17, which may predict some forms of carpal tunnel syndrome. Workers were also screened for alcoholism and diabetes. Because these conditions are not job related, testing for them violates the Americans with Disabilities Act and is illegal. The railroad quickly agreed to a settlement.

Hundreds of cases of genetic discrimination have been documented. These cases include a child's health insurance coverage being dropped after a genetic test found an inherited disorder—Fragile X syndrome, and a woman losing her job after her employer discovered that her mother died from Huntington's disease—a fatal genetic disorder. As our ability to gather and process genetic information grows, society will be faced with questions of how to define legitimate and illegitimate uses for this information.

Bioethics and Society

Many bioethics issues place an individual's right to privacy against the right of a company to conduct business, against the need of a community to have access to health information, or against the need of scientists to share research. In March of 2000, for example, Iceland's government sold the genetic and medical records of its 275,000 citizens to a Swiss drug manufacturer for $200 million. The money helped Iceland's economy, and any medications or tests for genetic diseases that result from the medical records will be provided for free to all Icelanders.

However, the government's actions could also be considered to be very troubling. Even though the citizens were given the option to not be included in the database, were the Icelanders' rights to privacy over their genetic records violated? Does anyone other than the individual have the right to be given access to this very personal information?

As biotechnology continues to advance, you will face new bioethics questions throughout your lifetime. Will you be ready?

CAREERS

Geneticist in Action

DR. CHARMAINE ROYAL

TITLE Professor, Pediatrics, Howard University

EDUCATION Ph. D., Human Genetics, Howard University

Many bioethicists focus on the ethical implications of technology. Dr. Charmaine Royal, however, is concerned with the ethics of experimental design and the applications and implications of biological research. Dr. Royal, who is a geneticist at the Human Genome Center of Howard University, points out that some scientists in the past tried to use genetic research to justify treating non-Caucasians as inferior. She also notes that although there is no biological basis for any meaningful differences among races, many African-Americans are still suspicious of genetic research. Many, for example, have been discriminated against when an insurance company or a prospective employer finds out they have sickle cell anemia, which is a relatively common genetic disorder in African-Americans.

Dr. Royal, who is Jamaican, wants to ensure that African-Americans are included and treated fairly in research studies, and that they receive the benefits of genetic screening and genetic counseling. In 1998 Dr. Royal helped start the African-American Hereditary Prostate Cancer Study, the first large-scale genetic study of African-Americans to be designed and carried out by an almost entirely African-American research team.

Read More >> at CLASSZONE.COM

Health insurance applicants are screened for preexisting conditions, such as HIV. If a condition is found, companies might offer insurance to a person at a higher cost. Should insurance companies be allowed to do genetic screening to detect whether people have genes that might increase their risk of developing cancer or alcoholism? If not, should healthy people have to pay more to make up for higher costs the company has to pay for people who refuse to be screened? From the company's point of view, its responsibility is to make a profit for its shareholders. With genetic testing, the company can protect itself from potentially large costs. As you can see, a company's policy based on its ethics may differ from what others see as ethical.

Science alone cannot answer bioethics questions. When these questions arise, we all need to weigh the issues for ourselves. As biotechnology continues to advance, you will face new bioethics questions throughout your lifetime. Will you be ready?

Questions to Consider

- Should scientists do all of the things that technology has made it possible for them to do?
- Who should decide how biotechnology is used?
- Should scientific knowledge and personal beliefs play equal or unequal roles in decisions about biotechnology?

Read More >> at CLASSZONE.COM

Careers

Have students go to BioZine at **ClassZone.com** to learn about different careers in biology. For each career they read about, have students write a brief paragraph that addresses the following questions:

- What topic(s) does this scientist study?
- What are the benefits and risks associated with this type of research?
- How could this scientist's work affect your life or the environment?
- Are there any controversial or ethical issues related to this type of research?
- How do the ethical issues compare to those in other biology-related careers?

UNIT 2

Cells

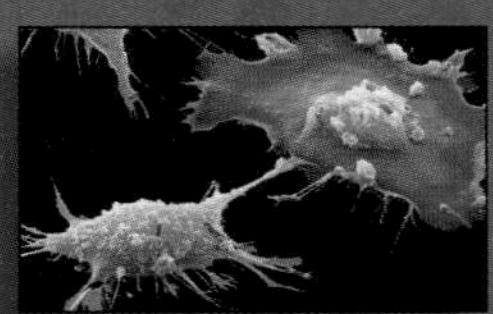

CHAPTER 3
Cell Structure and Function 68

CHAPTER 4
Cells and Energy 98

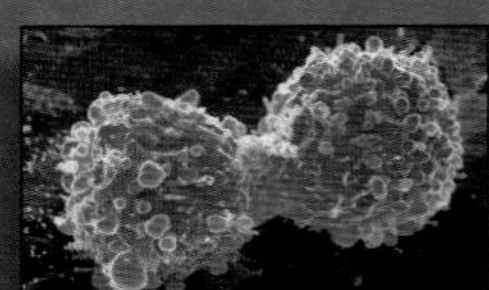

CHAPTER 5
Cell Growth and Division 132

BIOZINE

INTERNET MAGAZINE
Stem Cell Research—Potential Solutions, Practical Challenges 162

TECHNOLOGY Somatic Cell Nuclear Transfer

CAREER Cell Biologist

Unit Project

Purpose **Demonstrate an understanding of the structure and function of cell organelles and the relationships between them.**

Overview Students prepare a blueprint and write a proposal for a miniature golf course that provides a tour of a cell and its organelles. Students will

- incorporate the main cell organelles from either a plant or animal cell
- identify the size, structure, and function of each organelle
- identify and explain the relationships between different organelles

Preparation Make a copy of the project description and rubric for each student (*Unit Resource Book*, pp. 95–96). Tell students that they will be evaluated not just on their knowledge of cell structure but also their design. An optional student handout is available, providing information on cell structures and their size.

Project Management Allow three weeks for the completion of the project. Check on students' progress at the end of each week leading up to the completion date.

Unit Resource Book Unit 2 Project, pp. 95–99

CHAPTER 3

Indiana Resource Preview

Print Resources

Cell Structure and Function

INDIANA STANDARDS		Sections	PAGES and PACING	UNIT RESOURCE BOOK
NOS.8	3.1	**Cell Theory** **KEY CONCEPT** Cells are the basic unit of life.	pp. 70–72 30 minutes	URB pages 1–4
B.2.1, B.2.4	3.2	**Cell Organelles** **KEY CONCEPT** Eukaryotic cells share many similarities.	pp. 73–79 45 minutes	URB pages 5–8
		DATA ANALYSIS: Defining Variables Operational Definitions	p. 80 20 minutes	URB page 21
B.2.2	3.3	**Cell Membrane** **KEY CONCEPT** The cell membrane is a barrier that separates a cell from the external environment.	pp. 81–84 45 minutes	URB pages 9–12
B.2.2	3.4	**Diffusion and Osmosis** **KEY CONCEPT** Materials move across membranes because of concentration differences.	pp. 85–87 30 minutes	URB pages 13–16
B.2.2, NOS.1, NOS.5		**CHAPTER INVESTIGATION: Design Your Own** Diffusion Across a Membrane	p. 88 90 minutes	**Lab Binder** Cells pages 1–3
B.2.2	3.5	**Active Transport, Endocytosis, and Exocytosis** **KEY CONCEPT** Cells use energy to transport materials that cannot diffuse across a membrane.	pp. 89–91 30 minutes	URB pages 17–20
B.2.1, NOS.6		**OPTIONS FOR INQUIRY**	pp. 92–93 45 minutes	**Lab Binder** Cells pages 4–7
		Chapter Review	pp. 94–97	**Assessment Book** Chapter Tests A, B pages 11–18

INDIANA STANDARDS

B.2.1 Describe features common to all cells that are essential for growth and survival, and explain their functions.
B.2.2 Describe the structure of a cell membrane and explain how it regulates the transport of materials into and out of the cell and prevents harmful materials from entering the cell.
B.2.4 Explain that all cells contain ribosomes, the key sites for protein synthesis, where genetic material is decoded in order to form unique proteins.
NOS.1 Develop explanations based on reproducible data and observations gathered during laboratory investigations.
NOS.5 Apply standard techniques in laboratory investigations to measure physical quantities in appropriate units and convert known quantities to other units as necessary.
NOS.6 Use analogies and models (mathematical and physical) to simplify and represent systems that are difficult to understand or directly experience due to their size, time scale, or complexity, and recognize the limitations of analogies and models.
NOS.8 Explain that the body of scientific knowledge is organized into major theories, which are derived from and supported by the results of many experiments, and allow us to make testable predictions.

Labs

PUPIL EDITION LABS	
Modeling the Cell Membrane, Section 3, p. 83 Students model a cell membrane. **Lab Binder** p. 8	**Time:** 15 minutes **Materials:** 50 cotton swabs, rubber band, 2 pipe cleaners, drinking straw
Diffusion Across a Membrane, p. 88 Students investigate osmosis using isotonic, hypertonic, and hypotonic solutions. **Lab Binder** pp. 1–3	**Time:** 90 minutes **Materials:** 2 vinegar-soaked chicken eggs, water, balance, 2 plastic cups, distilled water, 5% and 20% NaCl solutions, 50% glucose solution, masking tape, marker, 500-mL beaker, 20 cm plastic wrap, 2 rubber bands

OPTIONS FOR INQUIRY	
Comparing Cells, p. 92 Students compare and contrast different eukaryotic cells. **Lab Binder** pp. 4–6	**Time:** 45 minutes **Materials:** 3 microscope slides, razor tool, sliced onion, methylene blue, eyedropper, 3 cover slips, microscope, sliced celery, *Elodea*, human cheek cell slides
Modeling the Cell, p. 93 Students model organelles and cell structure. **Lab Binder** p. 7	**Time:** 45 minutes **Materials:** 2 plastic sandwich bags, gelatin jigglers, balloon, marker, coffee stirrers, drinking straws, erasers, sponges, beads

LAB BINDER Unit 2 Cells

Additional Investigation: Cell Motility and the Cytoskeleton, pp. 9–12

Biotechnology Lab: Staining Biological Specimens, pp. 41–44

Real World Lab: Diffusion and Dialysis, pp. 45–48

Challenge Lab: Estimating a Cell Count, pp. 49–53; Cytoplasmic Streaming in *Elodea*, pp. 55–58

Vernier Probeware Lab: Diffusion Through Membranes, pp. 62–67; The Effect of Alcohol on Biological Membranes, pp. 68–72; Biological Membranes, pp. 73–78

LAB GENERATOR

A searchable CD of all labs in the program in editable format, including forensic, probeware, and biotechnology labs.

Presentation Tools

POWER PRESENTATIONS

Presentation Chapter 3
PowerPresentations for each section incorporate images and clips from the Media Gallery. Includes Note Navigator for each section.

MEDIA GALLERY

Contains the following images and video clips, as well as animations, simulations, and forms of visuals from the book.

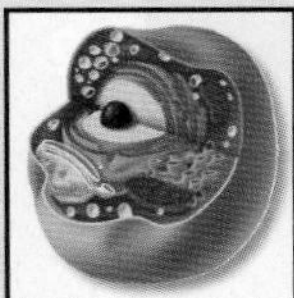
Cell structure

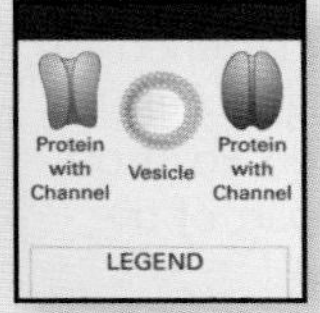

Membrane transport

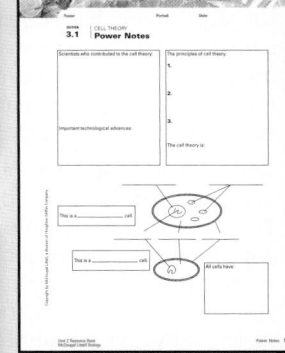

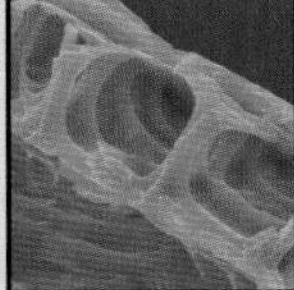
Cell wall

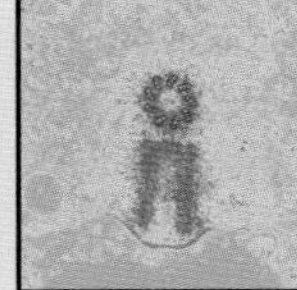
Cell division

Power Notes

VIDEO

Find a set of short video clips on cells, cell theory, and cell communication.

ANIMATED BIOLOGY

Cell Organelles
Get Through a Cell Membrane

TRANSPARENCIES

Plant Cell T9
Animal Cell T10
Cell Organelles T12
Fluid Mosaic Model T13
Selective Permeability T14
Cell Receptors T15
Passive and Active Transport T16
Endocytosis and Exocytosis T17

Online BIOLOGY CLASSZONE.COM

BioZine
Animated Biology
Interactive Review
SciLinks
Resource Centers

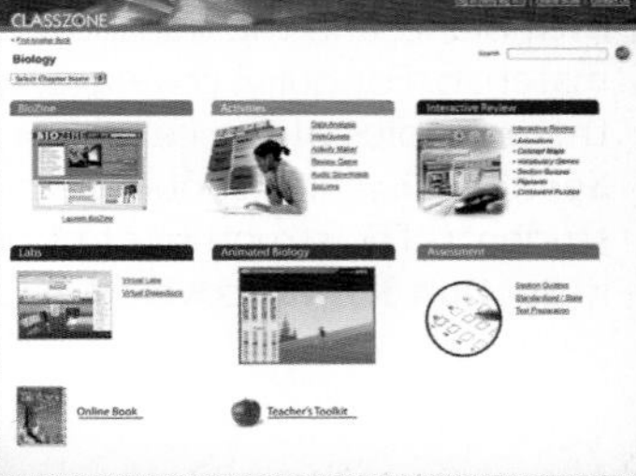

CHAPTER 3

▼ Focus and Motivate

Why do these cells look like fried eggs?

Have students read the caption and Connecting Concepts. Students may suggest the cells have been flattened like a fried egg by the vacuuming process used to prepare the specimen. Point out the still voluminous central part of the cell, analogous to an egg yolk.

Tell students that macrophages, like many other cells in the body, can crawl. They crawl to sites of infection and engulf invading bacterial cells. Cell movement is a complex process that involves the cell membrane and a skeleton-like system of fibers that stretch throughout the cell. Students will learn more about a cell and its inner structure in this chapter.

Ask, What can you learn by looking at cells? get a sense of structure and shape; also a sense of relative size, in this case the size of a macrophage to a bacterium

BIOZINE ClassZone.com

Students can access BioZine at **ClassZone.com** to learn about the variety of careers open to biologists.

In a Hurry?

The critical material of the chapter is found in **Sections 3.2, 3.3, 3.4,** and **3.5,** which cover cell organelles, the cell membrane, and the transport of materials. For quick coverage, review the principles of the cell theory in **Section 3.1,** which should be familiar to students. The structure of phospholipids in **Section 3.3** was covered in Chapter 2.

CHAPTER 3

Cell Structure and Function

KEY CONCEPTS

3.1 Cell Theory
Cells are the basic unit of life.

3.2 Cell Organelles
Eukaryotic cells share many similarities.

3.3 Cell Membrane
The cell membrane is a barrier that separates a cell from the external environment.

3.4 Diffusion and Osmosis
Materials move across membranes because of concentration differences.

3.5 Active Transport, Endocytosis, and Exocytosis
Cells use energy to transport materials that cannot diffuse across a membrane.

Online BIOLOGY CLASSZONE.COM

Animated BIOLOGY
View animated chapter concepts.
- Cell Organelles
- Get Through a Cell Membrane

BIOZINE
Keep current with biology news.
- Featured stories
- News feeds
- Careers

RESOURCE CENTER
Get more information on
- Prokaryotic and Eukaryotic Cells
- Diffusion and Osmosis

Teacher Demo

Eye Opener **Use a bubble frame to explore the properties of a bilayer and how it interacts with polar and nonpolar molecules. A bubble frame can be made from straws and two lengths of string.**

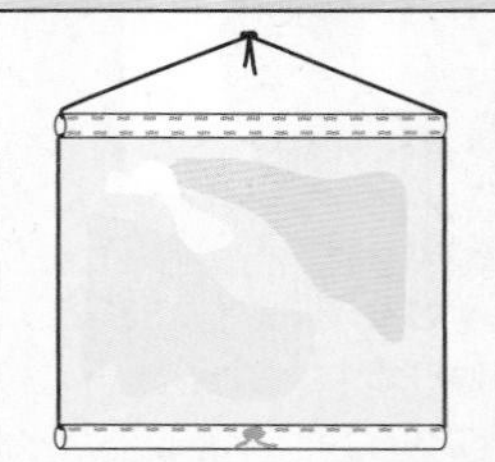

Materials
- bubble solution
- bubble frame or loop
- aluminum pan
- 1-inch flexible PVC pipe
- scissors
- small container of water

If using store-bought solution, add extra detergent or glycerin for a thicker film. To make your own solution, mix 2/3 cup of liquid dish detergent with 3 tablespoons of glycerin per gallon of water; let it sit overnight.

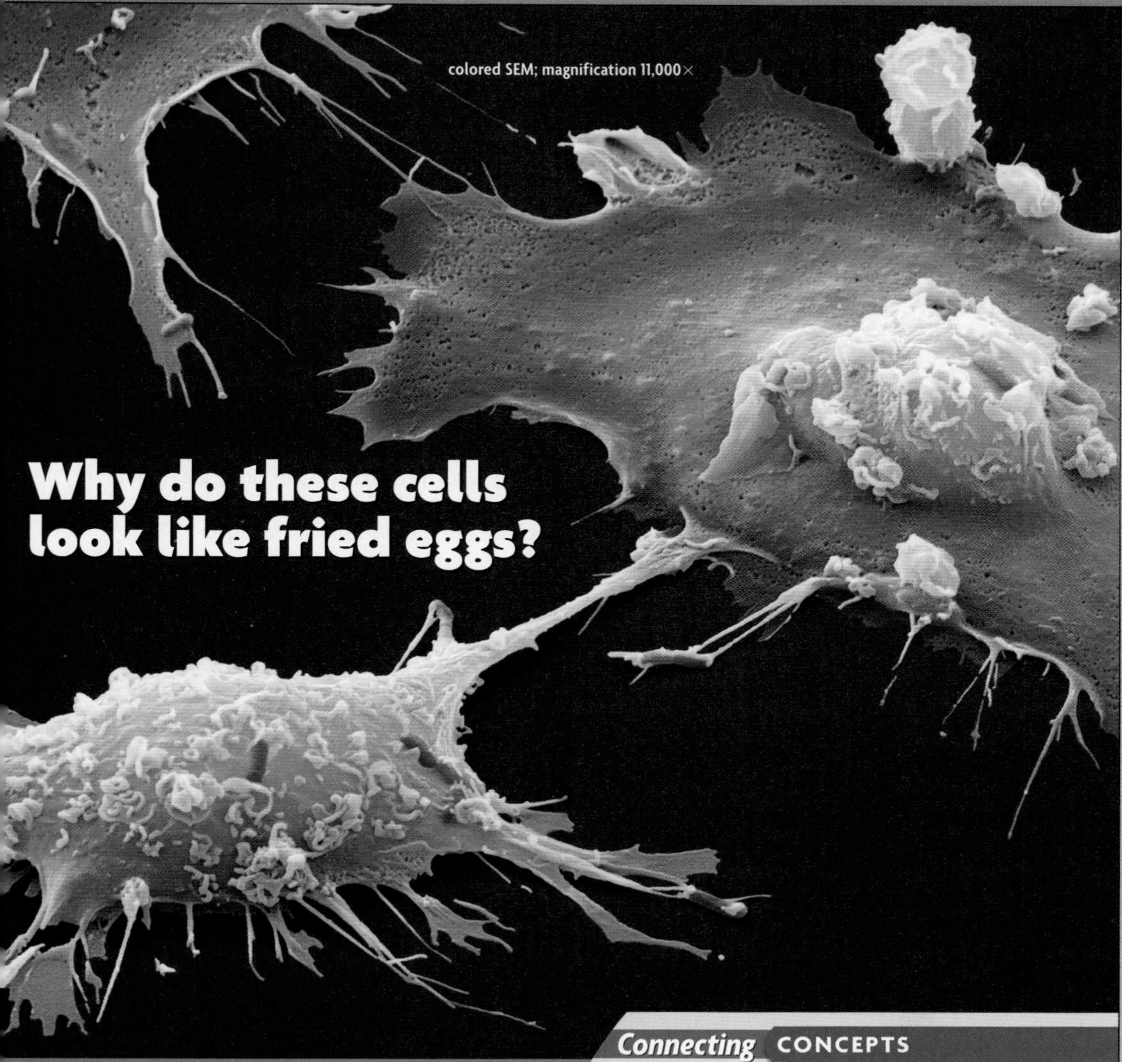

colored SEM; magnification 11,000×

Why do these cells look like fried eggs?

Connecting CONCEPTS

Macrophages (large tan cells) take in and digest foreign material, such as invading bacteria (small red cells). They play an important role in your immune system. Many macrophages travel the body, recognize foreign material, engulf it, and break it down using chemicals. They have an adaptable internal skeleton that helps them move and stretch out their "arms" to capture invading particles.

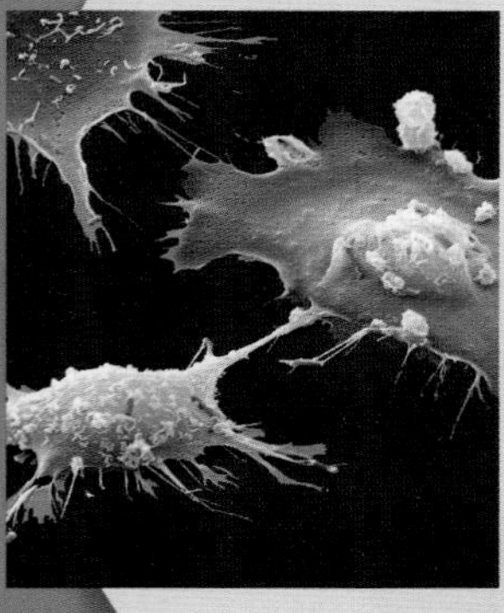

Technology **The scanning electron microscope (SEM) uses electrons to create greatly magnified, three-dimensional images of surface structures. Samples must be carefully prepared to withstand the vacuum and to prevent shriveling. This means that any cell or organism you see in an SEM image is dead. In addition, images are generated in black and white (left). The picture above is artificially colored to highlight specific parts.**

Demonstrate

- Place the bubble frame in the solution, then slowly lift the frame from the solution.
- Wet your finger in the solution and gently press it into the film. Move your finger around within the film.
- Repeat the process with your finger dipped in water and then with your finger dry.
- Cut a short length of PVC pipe and wet it in solution. Pull up the frame and move the pipe into and around the film. Have two students come up to pass a pencil through the pipe, from one side to the other.

Discuss Relate the bubble film to a cell membrane. The solution of soap and water forms a bilayer. Lipid molecules (soap) are positioned on either side of an inner layer of water molecules. Their polar heads point inward, attracted to water molecules; their nonpolar tails point outward. **Ask**

- Why could I move my finger within the film when covered in solution or water? With solution, the bilayer was maintained; water is a polar molecule.
- How might nonpolar or large molecules move across a bilayer? through a channel; in cells, through protein channels

Activate Prior Knowledge

Direct students' attention to the chapter title. **Ask,** Have you ever heard the expression "form follows function"? What does it mean? Students will probably relate physical shape to a job done.

Give the example of a diesel engine and gasoline engine. Both have the same shape, yet they operate in different ways. **Ask,** What's the difference? The engines have different internal structures and use different fuels. Give students another example: motor oil doesn't look much different from maple syrup. **Ask,** What's the difference? chemical make up

Discuss that structure and function can relate to shape, internal structure, or chemical make up.

Preview Vocabulary

Academic Vocabulary The words *structure* and *function* are ones most students are familiar with. Ask students to define them.

structure, the way in which parts are put together to form a whole

function, the action for which something is particularly fitted

Discuss with students that the working parts of cellular structure include atoms, molecules, and organelles. Function relates directly to the properties of a cell's parts.

Greek and Latin Word Origins In this chapter, students will see scientific terms constructed from classical roots. Have students watch for applications of these word parts:

cyto- = cell
endo- = within
iso- = equal
hypo- = below
kary- = kernel
exo- = out of
hyper- = above

English Learners Discuss with English learners that some science terms, such as *cell,* are taken from everyday language and given new meaning. Others, such as *chloroplast,* are created specifically for scientific use. Have students look in the *Multilanguage Glossary* to see how or if these words translate into their home languages. Discuss with students strategies for recalling such terms.

SECTION 3.1

▼ Plan and Prepare

Objectives

- Describe developments that led to the cell theory.
- Differentiate between eukaryotic and prokaryotic cells.

Section Resources

Unit Resource Book Study Guide pp. 1–2 Power Notes p. 3 Reinforcement p. 4
Interactive Reader Chapter 3 **Spanish Study Guide** pp. 21–22
Biology Toolkit pp. C21, C31
Technology Power Presentation 3.1 Media Gallery DVD Online Quiz 3.1

Activate Prior Knowledge Point out that living things come in all sizes. For example, compare a tadpole to a blue whale. **Ask,** How does the size of a cell in a tadpole compare to the size of a cell in a whale? Most cells in a whale are similar in size to those in a tadpole. **Ask,** What makes a whale so much larger than a tadpole? A whale has far more cells than a tadpole or the frog a tadpole grows into. Discuss that most cells are microscopic and that we can't see a whale cell any easier than we can see a tadpole cell.

▼ Teach

Science Trivia

- Hooke's microscope magnified objects only 30 times (30×) even though it had three lenses.
- Leeuwenhoek's microscopes had only one lens, but they magnified objects up to 300 times (300×).
- Many of the cells shown in this book have been magnified thousands of times by an electron microscope.

3.1 Cell Theory

KEY CONCEPT Cells are the basic unit of life.

MAIN IDEAS

- Early studies led to the development of the cell theory.
- Prokaryotic cells lack a nucleus and most internal structures of eukaryotic cells.

VOCABULARY

cell theory, p. 71
cytoplasm, p. 72
organelle, p. 72
prokaryotic cell, p. 72
eukaryotic cell, p. 72

INDIANA STANDARDS

NOS.8 Explain that the body of scientific knowledge is organized into major theories, which are derived from and supported by the results of many experiments, and allow us to make testable predictions.

Connect You and all other organisms are made of cells. As you saw on the previous page, a cell's structure is closely related to its function. Today we know that cells are the smallest unit of living matter that can carry out all processes required for life. But before the 1600s, people had many other ideas about the basis of life. Like many breakthroughs, the discovery of cells was aided by the development of new technology—in this case, the microscope.

MAIN IDEA

Early studies led to the development of the cell theory.

TAKING NOTES

As you read, make an outline using the headings as topics. Summarize details that further explain those ideas.

I. Main Idea
A. Supporting idea
1. Detail
2. Detail
B. Supporting idea

Almost all cells are too small to see without the aid of a microscope. Although glass lenses had been used to magnify images for hundreds of years, the early lenses were not powerful enough to reveal individual cells. The invention of the compound microscope in the late 1500s was an early step toward this discovery. The Dutch eyeglass maker Zacharias Janssen, who was probably assisted by his father, Hans, usually gets credit for this invention.

A compound microscope contains two or more lenses. Total magnification, the product of the magnifying power of each individual lens, is generally much more powerful with a compound microscope than with a single lens.

Discovery of Cells

In 1665, the English scientist Robert Hooke used the three-lens compound microscope shown in **FIGURE 3.1** to examine thin slices of cork. Cork is the tough outer bark of a species of oak tree. He observed that cork is made of tiny, hollow compartments. The compartments reminded Hooke of small rooms found in a monastery, so he gave them the same name: cells. The plant cells he observed, shown in **FIGURE 3.2** (top), were dead. Hooke was looking only at cell walls and empty space.

Around the same time, Anton van Leeuwenhoek, a Dutch tradesman, was studying new methods for making lenses to examine cloth. As a result of his research, his single-lens microscopes were much more powerful than Hooke's crude compound microscope. In 1674, Leeuwenhoek became one of the first people to describe living cells when he observed numerous single-celled organisms swimming in a drop of pond water. Sketches of his "animalcules" are pictured in **FIGURE 3.2** (bottom).

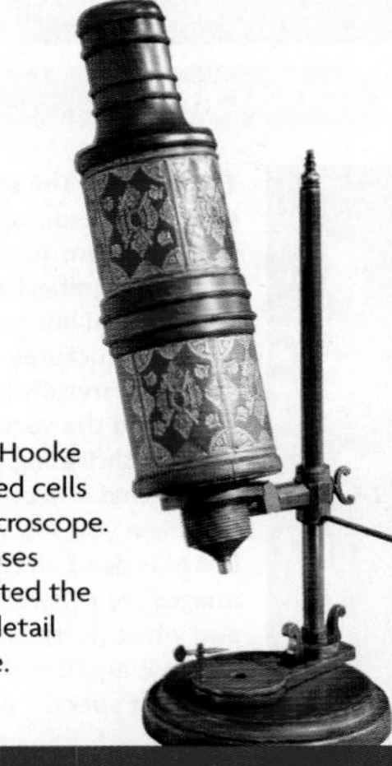

FIGURE 3.1 Hooke first identified cells using this microscope. Its crude lenses severely limited the amount of detail he could see.

Differentiated Instruction

ENGLISH LEARNERS

Remind students to use the tools they find in their book, for example the note-taking strategy shown on page 70. Have them label their outlines with the section title and the key concept shown at the top of the page. Point out that the main ideas are already labeled for them (blue headings). Connect the lettered items in the outline to the black headings in the text. Have students include all key vocabulary within the details of their outlines.

Biology Toolkit, Main Idea/Detail Notes, p. C21

HANDS-ON ACTIVITY

Provide students with a variety of hand magnifiers and a microscope. Have students use soft rulers that can bend along the lens, to determine the magnification of each lens. Students will need to divide the actual size of the object into the magnified size. Printed letters work well as the object. Have students look at the same object under a microscope. **Ask,** What is different about the image in the microscope? bigger, and also inverted

Safety Remind students that any lens that touches the eye must be cleaned after use.

As people continued to improve the microscope over the next century and a half, it became sturdier, easier to use, and capable of greater magnification. This combination of factors led people to examine even more organisms. They observed a wide variety of cell shapes, and they observed cells dividing. Scientists began to ask important questions: Is all living matter made of cells? Where do cells come from?

Cell Theory

The German scientist Matthias Schleiden also used compound microscopes to study plant tissue. In 1838, he proposed that plants are made of cells. Schleiden discussed the results of his work with another German scientist, Theodor Schwann, who was struck by the structural similarities between plant cells and the animal cells he had been studying. Schwann concluded that all animals are made of cells. Shortly thereafter, in 1839, he published the first statement of the cell theory, concluding that all living things are made of cells and cell products. This theory helped lay the groundwork for all biological research that followed. However, it had to be refined over the years as additional data led to new conclusions. For example, Schwann stated in his publication that cells form spontaneously by free-cell formation. As later scientists studied the process of cell division, they realized that this part of Schwann's idea was wrong. In 1855, Rudolf Virchow, another German scientist, reported that all cells come from preexisting cells. These early contributors are shown in **FIGURE 3.3.**

This accumulated research can be summarized in the cell theory, one of the first unifying concepts developed in biology. The major principles of the **cell theory** are the following:

- All organisms are made of cells.
- All existing cells are produced by other living cells.
- The cell is the most basic unit of life.

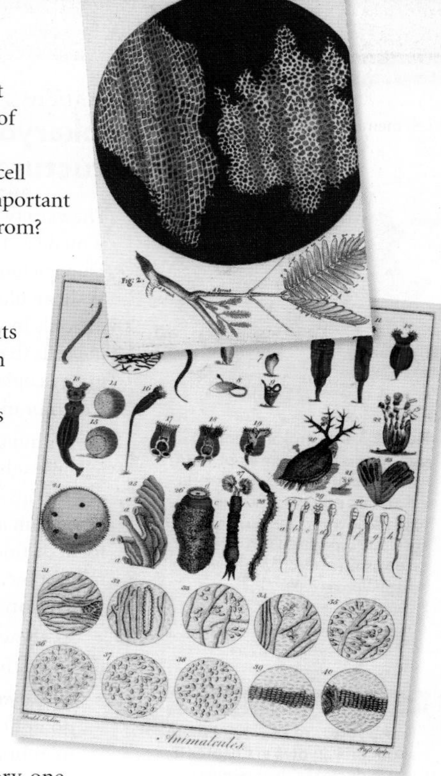

FIGURE 3.2 Hooke observed the cell walls of dead plant cells (top). In contrast, Leeuwenhoek observed and drew microscopic life, which he called animalcules, in pond water (bottom).

A Summarize **Explain the three major principles of cell theory in your own words.**

FIGURE 3.3 Contributors to Cell Theory

HOOKE

1665 Hooke was the first to identify cells, and he named them.

LEEUWENHOEK

1674 Because he made better lenses, Leeuwenhoek observed cells in greater detail.

SCHLEIDEN

1838 Schleiden was the first to note that plants are made of cells.

SCHWANN

1839 Schwann concluded that all living things are made of cells.

VIRCHOW

1855 Virchow proposed that all cells come from other cells.

INCLUSION

You can use length to demonstrate powers of magnification to a student who is visually impaired. Take an object such as a pencil and measure its length with a tape measure. Then extend the tape measure 10 times the length. Have the student walk the extended length. **Ask,** Where would a magnification of 100 put us? outside the classroom A magnification of 1000? maybe outside the school

PRE-AP

Have students draw a timeline that includes the five dates shown in **FIGURE 3.3.** Then have students use library references or the Internet to include dates in a topic area of interest to them. You may want to compile the information that students gather into a single timeline in the classroom.

Biology Toolkit, Timeline, p. C31

History of Science

The observations that led to the development of the cell theory **(FIGURE 3.3)** spanned two centuries. Put this into context. **Ask,** in what year did the following events occur?

- the landing of the *Mayflower* 1620
- Declaration of Independence 1776
- Louisiana Purchase 1803
- Emancipation Proclamation 1863

Ask, Why did it take so long after cells were discovered for the cell theory to be developed? Better and more powerful microscopes were needed to make many different observations that contributed to the cell theory.

The Inside Story

In the early days of biology, many of those we describe as scientists came to science in roundabout ways. For example, among the scientists shown in **FIGURE 3.3,** only **Hooke** started life as a scientist. **Schleiden** originally studied law; **Schwann** and **Virchow** were medical doctors.

Born the son of a basket-maker, **Leeuwenhoek** was trained as a draper, a fabric merchant. He was accustomed to using magnifying lenses to examine threads. At the age of 28, this successful merchant was appointed to a government position that ensured his financial security. Free to train his microscope on the invisible world of living matter, Leeuwenhoek's work earned him the title of the Father of Microbiology. Such was his celebrity that he was visited by several reigning monarchs, including Queen Elizabeth I of England and Czar Peter the Great of Russia.

Answers

A Summarize All organisms are made of cells. All cells are made by other living cells. The cell is the basic unit that can carry out all life functions.

▼ Teach *continued*

ONLINE BIOLOGY Go to the chapter Resource Center at **ClassZone.com** for additional resources and information on prokaryotic and eukaryotic cells.

Vocabulary

Greek and Latin Word Origins The key to understanding the terms **prokaryotic** and **eukaryotic** is the Greek root *karuon,* which means "nut" or "kernel," the center of a seed. Here *kernel* refers to the nucleus. A cell with a true nucleus is *eukaryotic.*

eu- = true *pro-* = before

In contrast, prokaryotic cells belong to an ancient class of cells that appeared on Earth long before eukaryotic cells: "before the nucleus."

Answers

A Summarize Most cells are microscopic in size, composed of similar building blocks, and are enclosed by a membrane that controls the movement of materials into and out of the cell.

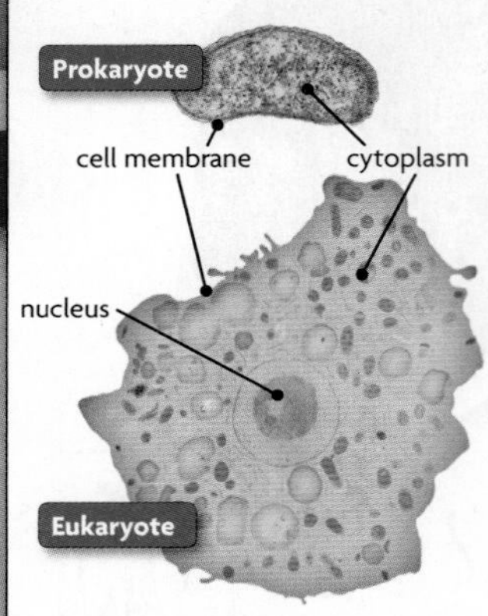

FIGURE 3.4 In prokaryotic cells, such as this bacterium (top), DNA is suspended in the cytoplasm. In eukaryotic cells, such as this protozoan (bottom), the nuclear envelope separates DNA from the cytoplasm. (colored TEMs; magnifications: protozoan 3200×; bacterium 19,000×)

Connecting CONCEPTS

Prokaryotes You will learn more about prokaryotes in **Chapter 18**, which discusses their requirements to sustain life, their role in the ecosystem, and, their role in human disease.

MAIN IDEA

Prokaryotic cells lack a nucleus and most internal structures of eukaryotic cells.

The variety of cell types found in living things is staggering. Your body alone is made of trillions of cells of many different shapes, sizes, and functions. They include long, thin nerve cells that transmit sensory information, as well as short, blocky skin cells that cover and protect the body. Despite this variety, the cells in your body share many characteristics with one another and with the cells that make up every other organism. In general, cells tend to be microscopic in size and have similar building blocks. They are also enclosed by a membrane that controls the movement of materials into and out of the cell.

Within the membrane, a cell is filled with cytoplasm. **Cytoplasm** is a jellylike substance that contains dissolved molecular building blocks—such as proteins, nucleic acids, minerals, and ions. In some types of cells, the cytoplasm also contains **organelles,** which are structures specialized to perform distinct processes within a cell. Most organelles are surrounded by a membrane. In many cells, the largest and most visible organelle is the nucleus, which stores genetic information.

As shown in **FIGURE 3.4**, cells can be separated into two broad categories based on their internal structures: prokaryotic cells and eukaryotic cells.

- **Prokaryotic cells** (pro-KAR-ee-AHT-ihk) do not have a nucleus or other membrane-bound organelles. Instead, the cell's DNA is suspended in the cytoplasm. All prokaryotes are microscopic single-celled organisms.
- **Eukaryotic cells** (yoo-KAR-ee-AHT-ihk) have a nucleus and other membrane-bound organelles. The nucleus, the largest organelle, encloses the genetic information. Eukaryotes may be multicellular or single-celled organisms.

VISUAL VOCAB

Prokaryotic cells do not have a nucleus or other membrane-bound organelles.

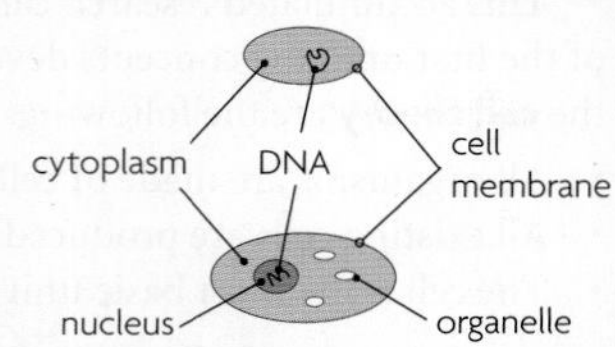

Eukaryotic cells have a nucleus and other membrane-bound organelles.

A Summarize What characteristics are shared by most cells?

3.1 ASSESSMENT

ONLINE QUIZ ClassZone.com

NOS.8

REVIEWING MAIN IDEAS

1. How did improvements in the microscope help scientists form the **cell theory**?
2. How do **prokaryotic** and **eukaryotic cells** differ?

CRITICAL THINKING

3. **Analyze** Today, scientists can study human cells grown in petri dishes. Explain how this technique builds on the work of early scientists.
4. **Compare** In what way are cells similar to atoms?

Connecting CONCEPTS

5. **Medicine** Suppose a certain poison kills human cells by blocking pores in the nuclear membrane. Explain why it would or would not kill bacteria.

▼ Assess and Reteach

Assess Use the Online Quiz or Section Quiz (*Assessment Book,* p. 47).

Reteach Make use of the note-taking strategy presented on page 70 of the pupil's edition to help students summarize the material in this section.

3.1 ASSESSMENT

1. Improvements allowed scientists to see cells in greater and greater detail and enabled them to discover cells in all types of living matter.
2. Eukaryotic cells have a nucleus and membrane-bound organelles; prokaryotic cells do not.
3. Once it was understood that cells were the basic building blocks of living matter, scientists could concentrate on describing different types of cells and discovering the relationship between cell type and cell function. One way to do this is to isolate the cell itself.
4. Both are basic units, or building blocks. The atom is the basic unit of matter; the cell is the basic unit of living organisms.
5. It would not kill bacteria because bacteria do not have a nucleus, so there are no nuclear pores to be blocked.

3.2 Cell Organelles

KEY CONCEPT Eukaryotic cells share many similarities.

MAIN IDEAS

- Cells have an internal structure.
- Several organelles are involved in making and processing proteins.
- Other organelles have various functions.
- Plant cells have cell walls and chloroplasts.

VOCABULARY

cytoskeleton, p. 73
nucleus, p. 75
endoplasmic reticulum, p. 76
ribosome, p. 76
Golgi apparatus, p. 76
vesicle, p. 77
mitochondrion, p. 77
vacuole, p. 77
lysosome, p. 78
centriole, p. 78
cell wall, p. 79
chloroplast, p. 79

INDIANA STANDARDS

B.2.1 Describe features common to all cells that are essential for growth and survival, and explain their functions.

B.2.4 Explain that all cells contain ribosomes, the key sites for protein synthesis, where genetic material is decoded in order to form unique proteins.

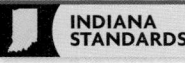

Connect Your body is highly organized. It contains organs that are specialized to perform particular tasks. For example, your skin receives sensory information and helps prevent infection. Your intestines digest food, your kidneys filter wastes, and your bones protect and support other organs. On a much smaller scale, your cells have a similar division of labor. They contain specialized structures that work together to respond to stimuli and efficiently carry out other necessary processes.

MAIN IDEA

Cells have an internal structure.

Like your body, eukaryotic cells are highly organized structures. They are surrounded by a protective membrane that receives messages from other cells. They contain membrane-bound organelles that perform specific cellular processes, divide certain molecules into compartments, and help regulate the timing of key events. But the cell is not a random jumble of suspended organelles and molecules. Rather, certain organelles and molecules are anchored to specific sites, which vary by cell type. If the membrane was removed from a cell, the contents wouldn't collapse and ooze out in a big puddle. How does a cell maintain this framework?

Each eukaryotic cell has a **cytoskeleton,** which is a network of proteins that is constantly changing to meet the needs of a cell. It is made of small protein subunits that form long threads, or fibers, that crisscross the entire cell, as shown in **FIGURE 3.5.** Three main types of fibers make up the cytoskeleton and allow it to serve a wide range of functions.

- Microtubules are long hollow tubes. They give the cell its shape and act as "tracks" for the movement of organelles. When cells divide, microtubules form fibers that pull half of the DNA into each new cell.
- Intermediate filaments, which are somewhat smaller than microtubules, give a cell its strength.
- Microfilaments, the smallest of the three, are tiny threads that enable cells to move and divide. They play an important role in muscle cells, where they help the muscle contract and relax.

FIGURE 3.5 The cytoskeleton supports and shapes the cell. The cytoskeleton includes microtubules (green) and microfilaments (red). (epifluorescence microscopy; magnification 750×)

components of the cytoskeleton

Differentiated Instruction

ENGLISH LEARNERS

Have students work in pairs in their home language to set up a matrix that will enable them to compare the different structures in a cell, as described in the accompanying Pre-AP note. Students should use the *Multilanguage Glossary* because many of the cell structures are included as key terms.

Biology Toolkit, Think-Pair-Share, p. C13

PRE-AP

Have students leaf through the section and then choose a graphic organizer that will help them organize the information. Note the hierarchy of information that is possible:

- type of cell: prokaryotic/eukaryotic
- type of organism: animal/plant
- type of organelle: location/function

Biology Toolkit, Semantic Feature Analysis, p. D7

SECTION 3.2

Plan and Prepare ▼

Objectives

- Describe the internal structure of eukaryotic cells.
- Summarize the functions of organelles in plant and animal cells.

Section Resources

Unit Resource Book
Study Guide pp. 5–6
Power Notes p. 7
Reinforcement p. 8

Interactive Reader Chapter 3
Spanish Study Guide pp. 23–24

Biology Toolkit pp. C13, C23, C38, D7

Technology
Power Presentation 3.2
Media Gallery DVD
Online Quiz 3.2

Activate Prior Knowledge Hold up an "instant" cold pack, the type with two compartments. **Ask,** Have you ever used a cold pack like this? How does it work? Breaking the seal between the compartments causes two substances (water and ammonium nitrate) to mix, producing "instant" cold. Relate this to how having compartments within a eukaryotic cell enables it to carry on different chemical activities at the same time: no mixing.

Teach ▼

Vocabulary

cytoskeleton Tell students that the prefix *cyto-* comes from the Greek *kytos,* meaning "hollow vessel." Remind students that Hooke chose the word *cell* because he thought it was a good description for the empty or hollow compartments he saw. Tell students that the prefix *cyto-* signals something that belongs to a cell. As you go through the section, students will see that cells are anything but empty.

▼ Teach *continued*

TEACH FROM VISUALS

FIGURE 3.6 Explain that the cell diagrams represent idealized versions of each cell type. For example, only a very small portion of the cytoskeleton has been shown in each diagram so that other cell parts can be seen more easily. In reality, the cytoskeleton fills a living cell. Have students compare the diagrams to the micrograph in **FIGURE 3.5.**

Address Misconceptions

Common Misconception Because of the ways cells are portrayed, with only a few representatives of each organelle shown, students may think of a cell as a bag of cytoplasm with a loose assortment of organelles floating about.

Correcting the Misconception Quantitative analysis of cell material shows that the parts of a cell are so numerous that they constantly bump up against one another and against the cell membrane and cytoskeleton.

Answers

A Critical Viewing The plant cell has chloroplasts, a central vacuole, and a cell wall. The animal cell has centrioles and lysosomes.

FIGURE 3.6 Cell Structure

Animated
BIOLOGY
Explore cell organelles at ClassZone.com.

Eukaryotic cells have highly organized structures, including membrane-bound organelles. Plant and animal cells share many of the same types of organelles, but both also have organelles that are unique to their needs.

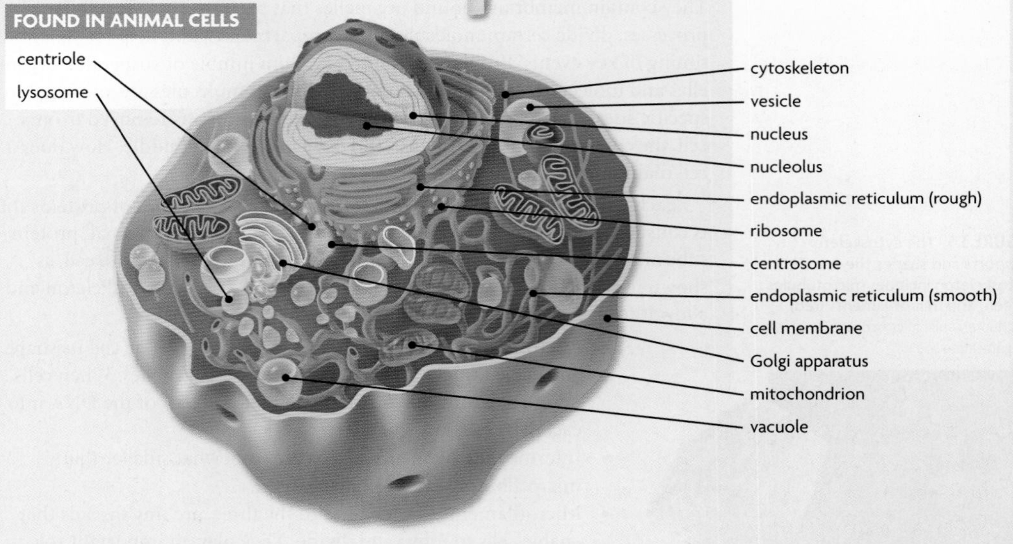

A CRITICAL VIEWING **What differences do you observe between animal and plant cells?**

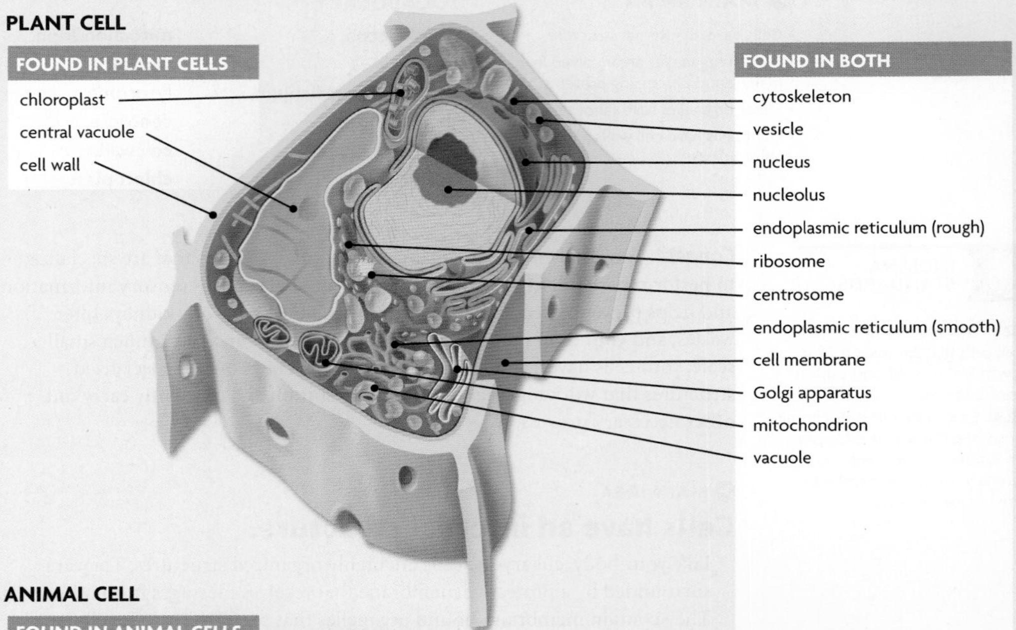

Differentiated Instruction

BELOW LEVEL

Have students copy an outline of the two cells from **FIGURE 3.6** into their science notebooks. As students learn about each organelle, have them draw it into the diagrams, including definitions and notes. Once complete, students will have a good tool for review.

Biology Toolkit, Combination Notes, p. C23

TEACH WITH TECHNOLOGY

Students may be interested in viewing the art of David Goodsell, a molecular biologist and artist whose drawings are meant to depict cellular structures in a realistic way. Go to **ClassZone.com** to link to his Web site and then project some of his work on the board. Compare his work with the idealized models above.

Cytoplasm, which you read about in Section 3.1, is itself an important contributor to cell structure. In eukaryotes, it fills the space between the nucleus and the cell membrane. The fluid portion, excluding the organelles, is called cytosol and consists mostly of water. The makeup of cytoplasm shows that water is necessary for maintaining cell structure. This is only one of many reasons that water is an essential component for life, however. Many chemical reactions occur in the cytoplasm, where water acts as an important solvent.

The remainder of this chapter highlights the structure and function of the organelles found in eukaryotic cells. As **FIGURE 3.6** shows, plant and animal cells use many of the same types of organelles to carry out basic functions. Both cell types also have organelles that are unique to their needs.

A Infer What problems might a cell experience if it had no cytoskeleton?

TAKING NOTES

Make a chart to correlate each organelle with its function.

Organelle	Function
Nucleus	stores DNA
Ribosome	

MAIN IDEA

Several organelles are involved in making and processing proteins.

Much of the cell is devoted to making proteins. Proteins are made of 20 types of amino acids that have unique characteristics of size, polarity, and acidity. They can form very long or very short protein chains that fold into different shapes. And multiple protein chains can interact with each other. This almost limitless variety of shapes and interactions makes proteins very powerful. Proteins carry out many critical functions, so they need to be made correctly.

Connecting CONCEPTS

Biochemistry Recall from **Chapter 2** that certain amino acids within a protein molecule may form hydrogen bonds with other amino acids. These bonds cause the protein to form a specific shape.

Nucleus

The **nucleus** (NOO-klee-uhs) is the storehouse for most of the genetic information, or DNA (deoxyribonucleic acid), in your cells. DNA contains genes that are instructions for making proteins. There are two major demands on the nucleus: (1) DNA must be carefully protected, and (2) DNA must be available for use at the proper times. Molecules that would damage DNA need to be kept out of the nucleus. But many proteins are involved in turning genes on and off, and they need to access the DNA at certain times. The special structure of the nucleus helps it meet both demands.

The nucleus is composed of the cell's DNA enclosed in a double membrane called the nuclear envelope. Each membrane in the nuclear envelope is similar to the membrane surrounding the entire cell. As **FIGURE 3.7** shows, the nuclear envelope is pierced with holes called pores that allow large molecules to pass between the nucleus and cytoplasm.

The nucleus also contains the nucleolus. The nucleolus is a dense region where tiny organelles essential for making proteins are assembled. These organelles, called ribosomes, are a combination of proteins and RNA molecules. They are discussed on the next page, and a more complete description of their structure and function is given in Chapter 8.

FIGURE 3.7 The nucleus stores and protects DNA. (colored SEM; magnification 90,000×)

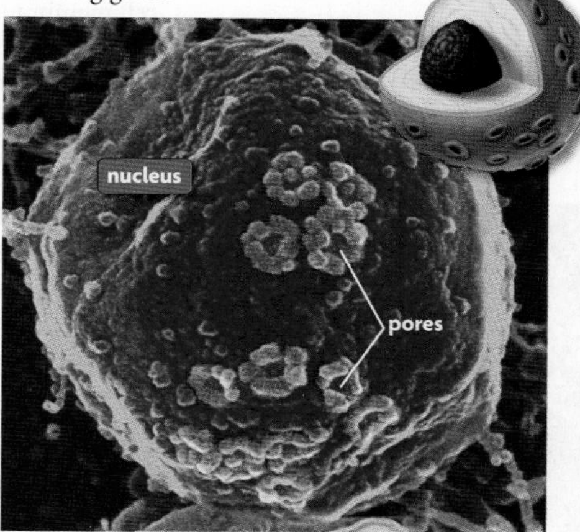

Answers

A Infer The cell would be disorganized. It would be weak and might fall apart. The cell would also be unable to move, divide, and transport organelles.

TEACH FROM VISUALS

FIGURE 3.7 Have students look carefully at the colorized micrograph. The nuclear pores highlighted in pink represent only a tiny portion of pores that are present on this nucleus. If students look closely, they will see pores cover the entire surface of the nucleus. **Ask,** What is distinctive about the nuclear membrane? Why is it described as an envelope? It is a double membrane with a bilipid membrane folded upon itself, creating a space in between, which is the inside of the envelope.

Suggest the analogy of the nucleus as a castle keep, the stronghold of a castle. **Ask,** What are the nuclear envelope and nuclear pores analogous to? The interior space of the double membrane acts almost like a moat, forcing materials to move across a few thousand tiny drawbridges, the nuclear pores.

Take It Further

Being isolated in the nucleus—away from other organelles and enzymes that can inflict damage—protects the genetic information in **eukaryotes.** Students may ask how **prokaryotes** can survive if their DNA is not so well protected. Some scientists think that the movement of organelles within a cell or the movement of the cell itself by the action of the cytoskeleton may create shearing forces that could damage or destroy the DNA. The nucleus may protect DNA from the cytoskeleton. Because prokaryotes have no cytoskeleton, their DNA does not need the protection of a nucleus.

ENGLISH LEARNERS

Point out that the same words can be used to mean different things, depending on context. For example, in Chapter 2, the nucleus was described as being the center of an atom, where protons and neutrons are located. Here the nucleus is an organelle that houses genetic material. Students may find that to be true in their own home language. For example, *el núcleo* is used for both in Spanish.

INCLUSION

Students who are hearing impaired benefit by having visual cues accompany an oral presentation. Project the cell diagrams of **FIGURE 3.6** from the *Media Gallery* and point to each cell part as you discuss it with the class. As with English learners, students who are hearing impaired need plenty of cues from your mouth and facial expressions. When possible, face students as you speak and speak slowly and clearly.

▼ Teach *continued*

TEACH FROM VISUALS

FIGURES 3.8–3.12 Have students look at the micrographs on pages 76 and 77. It should be clear from these images that much of the work of a cell is done in separate compartments. **Ask**

- What do all the organelles shown in the micrographs on pages 76 and 77 have in common? They are not only surrounded by membranes, but many have internal membranes.
- What are these membranes composed of? lipid bilayer
- What does the membrane do? It isolates an organelle's contents from the surrounding cytoplasm and controls the internal environment in which its chemical activities take place.

Mention that the only organelle not bound by a membrane is the ribosome.

The Inside Story

The **Golgi apparatus** was discovered by medical researcher **Camillo Golgi** in 1898, while working with a new staining technique he had developed. In the days before the electron microscope, discoveries of cell structure were limited by the ability of scientists to find stains that would clarify the finer details of cells and tissue using just a light microscope. In 1906, Golgi won a Nobel Prize for his work in detailing structures of the nervous system. Golgi's celebrity today, however, is maintained because an organelle was named after him.

What would it be like to study cell structure if the structures were identified by the people who discovered them? The cell might be called a Hooke and the nucleus a Brown body. The endoplasmic reticulum would be the Claude-Porter apparatus, and the ribosome would be known as a Palade.

FIGURE 3.8 The endoplasmic reticulum aids in the production of proteins and lipids. (colored TEM; magnification about 20,000×)

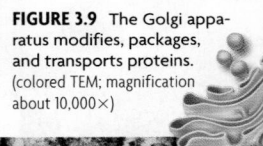

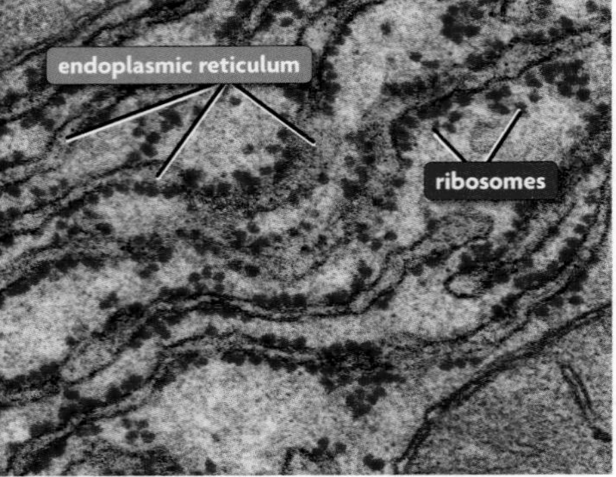

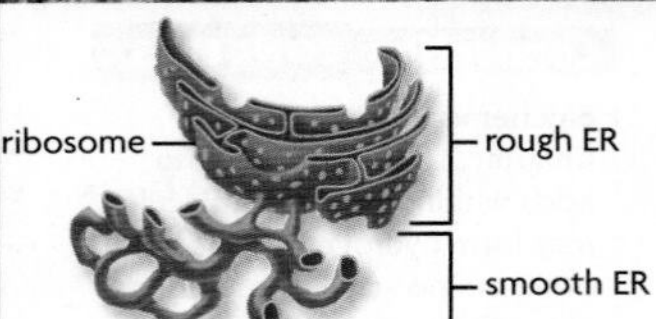

Endoplasmic Reticulum and Ribosomes

A large part of the cytoplasm of most eukaryotic cells is filled by the endoplasmic reticulum, shown in **FIGURE 3.8.** The **endoplasmic reticulum** (EHN-duh-PLAZ-mihk rih-TIHK-yuh-luhm), or the ER, is an interconnected network of thin folded membranes. The composition is very similar to that of the cell membrane and nuclear membranes. The ER membranes form a maze of enclosed spaces. The interior of this maze is called the lumen. Numerous processes, including the production of proteins and lipids, occur both on the surface of the ER and inside the lumen. The ER must be large enough to accommodate all these processes. How does it fit inside a cell?

The ER membrane has many creases and folds. If you have ever gone camping, you probably slept in a sleeping bag that covered you from head to foot. The next morning, you stuffed it back into a tiny little sack. How does the entire sleeping bag fit inside such a small sack? The surface area of the sleeping bag does not change, but the folds allow it to take up less space. Likewise, the ER's many folds enable it to fit within the cell.

In some regions, the ER is studded with **ribosomes** (RY-buh-SOHMZ), tiny organelles that link amino acids together to form proteins. Ribosomes are both the site of protein synthesis and active participants in the process. Ribosomes are themselves made of proteins and RNA. After assembly in the nucleolus, ribosomes pass through the nuclear pores into the cytoplasm, where most protein synthesis occurs.

Surfaces of the ER that are covered with ribosomes are called rough ER because they look bumpy when viewed with an electron microscope. As a protein is being made on these ribosomes, it enters the lumen. Inside the lumen, the protein may be modified by having sugar chains added to it, which can help the protein fold or give it stability.

Not all ribosomes are bound to the ER; some are suspended in the cytoplasm. In general, proteins made on the ER are either incorporated into the cell membrane or secreted. In contrast, proteins made on suspended ribosomes are typically used in chemical reactions occurring within the cytoplasm.

Surfaces of the ER that do not contain ribosomes are called smooth ER. Smooth ER makes lipids and performs a variety of other specialized functions, such as breaking down drugs and alcohol.

FIGURE 3.9 The Golgi apparatus modifies, packages, and transports proteins. (colored TEM; magnification about 10,000×)

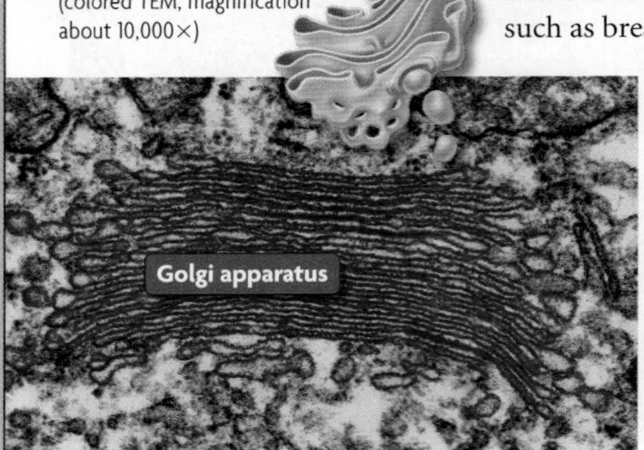

Golgi Apparatus

From the ER, proteins generally move to the Golgi apparatus, shown in **FIGURE 3.9.** The **Golgi apparatus** (GOHL-jee) consists of closely layered stacks of membrane-enclosed spaces that process, sort, and deliver proteins. Its membranes contain enzymes that make additional changes to proteins. The Golgi apparatus also packages proteins. Some of the packaged proteins are stored within the Golgi apparatus for later use. Some are transported to other organelles within the cell. Still others are carried to the membrane and secreted outside the cell.

Differentiated Instruction

BELOW LEVEL

To help students understand how a large surface area can fit into a small space, show them a pocket-sized package of facial tissues. Carefully pull out the tissues, unfold them, and spread them out in a single layer on a desk. Students will see how folding a membrane allows it to fit a large surface area into a small space.

PRE-AP

Have groups of students work out a pathway from the nucleus to the cell membrane that would keep a protein from ever entering the cytoplasm. They can start with information passed from the nucleus to the ER, then on to the Golgi apparatus and lysosomes. Have each group present its ideas to the class. Discuss that some products produced by the cell are exported in this way.

Biology Toolkit, Think-Pair-Share, p. C13

Vesicles

Cells need to separate reactants for various chemical reactions until it is time for them to be used. **Vesicles** (VEHS-ih-kuhlz), shown in **FIGURE 3.10**, are a general name used to describe small membrane-bound sacs that divide some materials from the rest of the cytoplasm and transport these materials from place to place within the cell. Vesicles are generally short-lived and are formed and recycled as needed.

After a protein has been made, part of the ER pinches off to form a vesicle surrounding the protein. Protected by the vesicle, the protein can be safely transported to the Golgi apparatus. There, any necessary modifications are made, and the protein is packaged inside a new vesicle for storage, transport, or secretion.

A Compare and Contrast **How are the nucleus and a vesicle similar and different in structure and function?**

FIGURE 3.10 Vesicles isolate and transport specific molecules. (colored SEM; magnification 20,000×)

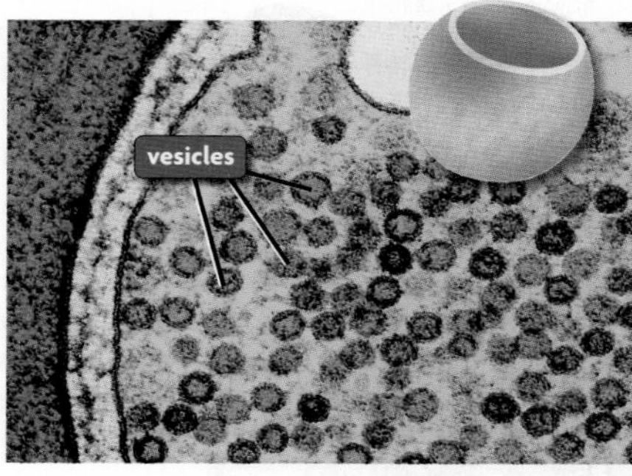

MAIN IDEA

Other organelles have various functions.

Mitochondria

Mitochondria (MY-tuh-KAHN-dree-uh) supply energy to the cell. Mitochondria (singular, *mitochondrion*) are bean shaped and have two membranes, as shown in **FIGURE 3.11**. The inner membrane has many folds that greatly increase its surface area. Within these inner folds and compartments, a series of chemical reactions takes place that converts molecules from the food you eat into usable energy. You will learn more about this process in Chapter 4.

Unlike most organelles, mitochondria have their own ribosomes and DNA. This fact suggests that mitochondria were originally free-living prokaryotes that were taken in by larger cells. The relationship must have helped both organisms to survive.

FIGURE 3.11 Mitochondria generate energy for the cell. (colored TEM; magnification 33,000×)

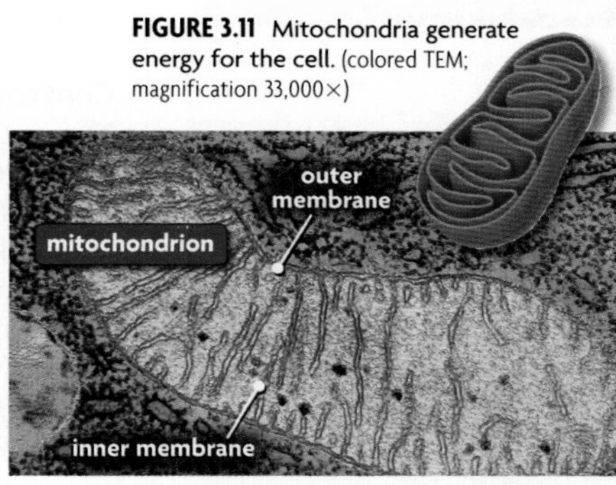

Vacuole

A **vacuole** (VAK-yoo-OHL) is a fluid-filled sac used for the storage of materials needed by a cell. These materials may include water, food molecules, inorganic ions, and enzymes. Most animal cells contain many small vacuoles. The central vacuole, shown in **FIGURE 3.12**, is a structure unique to plant cells. It is a single large vacuole that usually takes up most of the space inside a plant cell. It is filled with a watery fluid that strengthens the cell and helps to support the entire plant. When a plant wilts, its leaves shrivel because there is not enough water in each cell's central vacuole to support the leaf's normal structure. The central vacuole may also contain other substances, including toxins that would harm predators, waste products that would harm the cell itself, and pigments that give color to cells—such as those in the petals of a flower.

FIGURE 3.12 Vacuoles temporarily store materials. (colored TEM; magnification 9000×)

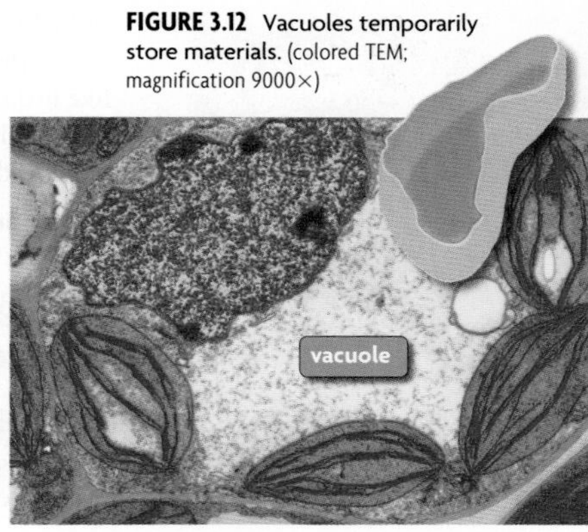

Answers

A **Compare and Contrast** Both are membrane-bound compartments that store and separate certain materials. The nucleus is an almost permanent structure protected by a double membrane bilayer, whereas a vesicle is a temporary organelle.

Vocabulary

Word Origins Words can have diminutive forms, which suggest a smaller version of something large. For example, *duck* becomes *duckling*. A similar thing happens with several of the terms introduced in this section. In each instance, a suffix is added to the original to produce the diminutive.

organ	*organelle*
nucleus	*nucleolus*
vessel	*vesicle*
vacuum	*vacuole*
center	*centriole*

Integrating Anthropology

Anthropologists use **mitochondrial DNA** to trace human ancestry. When cells divide, not only is the genetic material shared between two cells, but so are the organelles. With sexual reproduction, mitochondria are passed to offspring only through the egg—sperm contain little cytoplasm—so a direct female lineage can be traced. Research indicates that modern humans originated in Africa between 100,000 and 200,000 years ago.

ENGLISH LEARNERS

Point out the irregular plural forms of key vocabulary in this section:

nucleus	*nuclei*
mitochondrion	*mitochondria*

You may also want to point out that *endoplasmic reticulum* and *Golgi apparatus* are structures that are referred to only in the singular.

▼ Teach *continued*

ONLINE BIOLOGY To see what happens when an organelle fails to function as it should, have students do the WebQuest in Options for Inquiry on page 93.

Take It Further

Lysosomes, which contain about 40 different digestive enzymes, are the recycling centers of the cell. What the cell is recycling, in large part, is itself. The process is called **autophagy,** meaning to "eat oneself." For example, in a liver cell, a mitochondrion has an average lifespan of 10 days. A lysosome engulfs the organelle, breaks it down, and then releases the recycled materials to the cytoplasm, providing raw material for the manufacture of more organelles. In fact, cells continually break down and rebuild themselves.

Integrating Chemistry

The digestive enzymes in a lysosome, like all enzymes, have an **optimum pH** at which they work best. Enzymes of the lysosome function best in an acidic environment with a pH of 5. The pH of cytoplasm is about 7. **Ask,** How does this difference in pH offer some protection to the cell if a lysosome should leak? The enzymes would not be very active, so they would not cause much damage to the cell's contents.

Answers

A Compare All are membrane-bound organelles that store or separate certain substances.

FIGURE 3.13 Lysosomes digest and recycle foreign materials or worn-out parts. (colored TEM; magnification 21,000×)

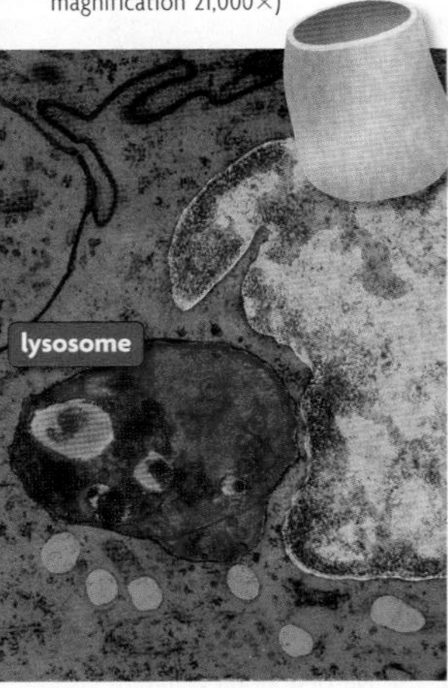

FIGURE 3.14 Centrioles divide DNA during cell division. (colored TEM; magnification 35,000×)

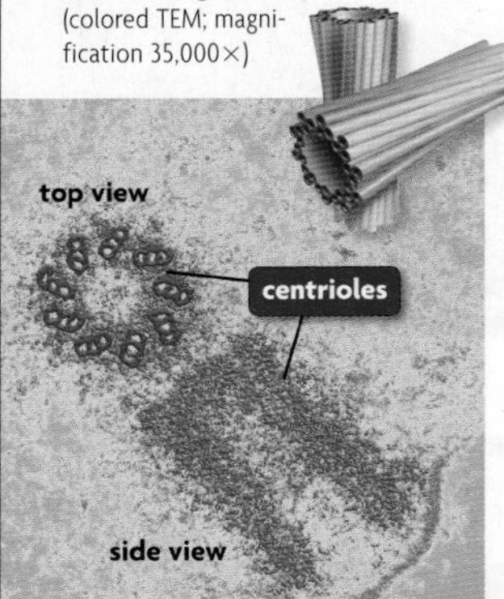

Lysosomes

Lysosomes (LY-suh-SOHMZ), shown in **FIGURE 3.13**, are membrane-bound organelles that contain enzymes. They defend a cell from invading bacteria and viruses. They also break down damaged or worn-out cell parts. Lysosomes tend to be numerous in animal cells. Their presence in plant cells is still questioned by some scientists, but others assert that plant cells do have lysosomes, though fewer than are found in animal cells.

Recall that all enzymes are proteins. Initially, lysosomal enzymes are made in the rough ER in an inactive form. Vesicles pinch off from the ER membrane, carry the enzymes, and then fuse with the Golgi apparatus. There, the enzymes are activated and packaged as lysosomes that pinch off from the Golgi membrane. The lysosomes can then engulf and digest targeted molecules. When a molecule is broken down, the products pass through the lysosomal membrane and into the cytoplasm, where they are used again.

Lysosomes provide an example of the importance of membrane-bound structures in the eukaryotic cell. Because lysosomal enzymes can destroy cell components, they must be surrounded by a membrane that prevents them from destroying necessary structures. However, the cell also uses other methods to protect itself from these destructive enzymes. For example, the enzymes do not work as well in the cytoplasm as they do inside the lysosome.

Centrosome and Centrioles

The centrosome is a small region of cytoplasm that produces microtubules. In animal cells, it contains two small structures called centrioles. **Centrioles** (SEHN-tree-OHLZ) are cylinder-shaped organelles made of short microtubules arranged in a circle. The two centrioles are perpendicular to each other, as shown in **FIGURE 3.14.** Before an animal cell divides, the centrosome, including the centrioles, doubles and the two new centrosomes move to opposite ends of the cell. Microtubules grow from each centrosome, forming spindle fibers. These fibers attach to the DNA and appear to help divide it between the two cells.

Centrioles were once thought to play a critical role in animal cell division. However, experiments have shown that animal cells can divide even if the centrioles are removed, which makes their role more questionable. In addition, although centrioles are found in some algae, they are not found in plants.

Centrioles also organize microtubules to form cilia and flagella. Cilia look like little hairs; flagella look like a whip or a tail. Their motion forces liquids past a cell. For single cells, this movement results in swimming. For cells anchored in tissue, this motion sweeps liquid across the cell surface.

A Compare In what ways are lysosomes, vesicles, and the central vacuole similar?

MAIN IDEA

Plant cells have cell walls and chloroplasts.

Plant cells have two features not shared by animal cells: cell walls and chloroplasts. Cell walls are structures that provide rigid support. Chloroplasts are organelles that help a plant convert solar energy to chemical energy.

Differentiated Instruction

PRE-AP

Have students read through the sequence of events described in the last two paragraphs of the section on lysosomes, where the text describes how lysosomes are formed. Refer to the diagram of the animal cell in **FIGURE 3.6** and the micrographs in **FIGURES 3.9** and **3.10.** Have students diagram the process described. Tell students to think in terms of an assembly line.

Biology Toolkit, Sequence Diagram, p. C38

Cell Walls

In plants, algae, fungi, and most bacteria, the cell membrane is surrounded by a strong **cell wall,** which is a rigid layer that gives protection, support, and shape to the cell. The cell walls of multiple cells, as shown in **FIGURE 3.15,** can adhere to each other to help support an entire organism. For instance, much of the wood in a tree trunk consists of dead cells whose cell walls continue to support the entire tree.

Cell wall composition varies and is related to the different needs of each type of organism. In plants and algae, the cell wall is made of cellulose, a polysaccharide. Because molecules cannot easily diffuse across cellulose, the cell walls of plants and algae have openings, or channels. Water and other molecules small enough to fit through the channels can freely pass through the cell wall. In fungi, cell walls are made of chitin, and in bacteria, they are made of peptidoglycan. The unique characteristics and functions of these materials will be discussed in Chapters 18 and 19.

FIGURE 3.15 Cell walls shape and support individual cells and entire organisms. (LM; magnification 3000×)

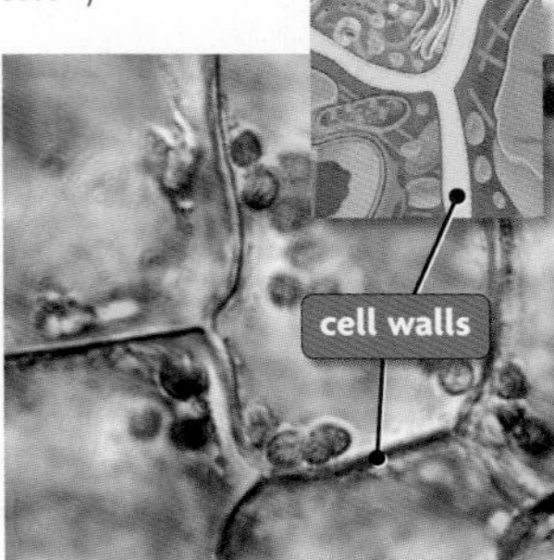

Chloroplasts

Chloroplasts (KLAWR-uh-PLASTS) are organelles that carry out photosynthesis, a series of complex chemical reactions that convert solar energy into energy-rich molecules the cell can use. Photosynthesis will be discussed more fully in Chapter 4. Like mitochondria, chloroplasts are highly compartmentalized. They have both an outer membrane and an inner membrane. They also have stacks of disc-shaped sacs within the inner membrane, shown in **FIGURE 3.16.** These sacs, called thylakoids, contain chlorophyll, a light-absorbing molecule that gives plants their green color and plays a key role in photosynthesis. Like mitochondria, chloroplasts also have their own ribosomes and DNA. Scientists have hypothesized that they, too, were originally free-living prokaryotes that were taken in by larger cells.

Both chloroplasts and mitochondria are present in plant cells, where they work together to capture and convert energy. Chloroplasts are found in the cells of certain other organisms as well, including green algae.

FIGURE 3.16 Chloroplasts convert solar energy into chemical energy through photosynthesis. (colored TEM; magnification 21,000×)

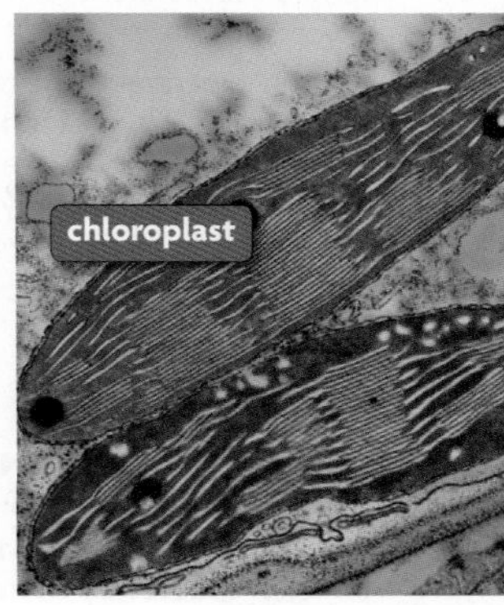

Ⓐ Analyze **Would it be accurate to say that a chloroplast makes energy for a plant cell? Explain your answer.**

3.2 ASSESSMENT

B.2.1, B.2.4

REVIEWING MAIN IDEAS

1. What are the functions of the **cytoskeleton**?
2. Describe the structure of the **nucleus.**
3. Explain the structure and function of the **mitochondrion.**
4. What function does the **cell wall** perform in a plant?

CRITICAL THINKING

5. **Compare** What similarities do mitochondria and **chloroplasts** share?
6. **Compare** Describe how the **endoplasmic reticulum,** mitochondrion, and **Golgi apparatus** are structurally similar.

Connecting CONCEPTS

7. **Health** Medicine, alcohol, and many drugs are detoxified in liver cells. Why do you think the liver cells of some people who abuse alcohol and drugs have an increased amount of smooth ER?

TEACH FROM VISUALS

FIGURES 3.15 AND 3.16 Have students compare the two micrographs. **Ask**

- How are the two images related? Both show plants cells. More of the cell is seen in Figure 3.15, given the lower magnification. Students may recognize that the smaller structures within the cell are the chloroplasts detailed in Figure 3.16.
- How are the two images different? Figure 3.15 is a light micrograph at low resolution; Figure 3.16 is an electron micrograph at high resolution. The second image shows more detail than the first.

Answers

Ⓐ **Analyze** No, energy cannot be made or destroyed. The chloroplast converts energy to a form that a cell can use.

Assess and Reteach ▼

Assess Use the Online Quiz or Section Quiz (*Assessment Book,* p. 48).

Reteach Have students choose an organelle and write an advertisement that explains why a cell needs to "buy" that organelle and why the cell cannot live without one. Make sure every organelle is covered. Then post the ads in the classroom.

3.2 ASSESSMENT

1. The cytoskeleton supports and shapes a cell, helps position and transport organelles, provides strength, assists in cell division, and aids cell movement.
2. The nucleus is surrounded by a double membrane with pores that connect its interior to the cytoplasm. DNA and the nucleolus are located inside the nucleus.
3. A mitochondrion supplies energy to a cell by releasing the energy stored in food molecules. The outer membrane surrounds a highly folded inner membrane where the chemical activity occurs. It has its own ribosomes and DNA.
4. The cell wall protects, supports, and shapes a plant cell, and regulates what moves into the cell. The cell walls of multiple cells can help support the entire plant.
5. Both membrane-bound organelles have their own DNA and help make energy available to the cell.
6. All are composed of membrane-enclosed chambers. The surface area of each is greatly increased by folds and layers.
7. Increased amounts of smooth ER in the liver cells suggests that the cells have responded to increased amounts of toxins by producing more smooth ER to handle the processing.

DATA ANALYSIS

Introduce

Discuss with students how an operational definition differs from a regular definition. In general terms, a definition gives the precise meaning of something or describes it basic qualities. An operational definition provides a way to test for those qualities. **Ask**

- How is an operational definition used in an experiment? It describes a phenomenon in terms of how it is to be measured and so can be used to test for that phenomenon.
- In the example given, what is being measured? number of chloroplasts at different times of year
- What does the relative number of chloroplasts represent to the scientists doing the research? level of photosynthetic activity

Discuss

Talk about the fact that in both examples given, the objects of interest to the scientists—photosynthesis and immunity—are not something that can be observed directly. Yet scientists can use physical evidence—number of chloroplasts or bacteria—to test their hypotheses.

Unit Resource Book, Data Analysis, p. 21

DATA ANALYSIS ClassZone.com

Operational Definitions

The **operational definition** of a dependent variable is a description of what is to be observed and measured in an experiment, and what that measurement represents. It is important for scientists to include in their reports the operational definition of the dependent variable so that different scientists repeating the experiment will collect and record data in exactly the same way.

EXAMPLE

Students wanted to determine if the rate of photosynthesis was greater in summer or fall. They collected leaves from many trees in both summer and fall and counted the number of chloroplasts with chlorophyll.

Chloroplasts are organelles that can have a variety of pigments. Only chloroplasts that contain chlorophyll, a type of pigment, can carry out photosynthesis. The rate of photosynthesis increases as the number of chloroplasts with chlorophyll increases. Students wanted to determine if the rate of photosynthesis was greater in summer or fall. They collected leaves from many trees in both summer and fall and counted the number of chloroplasts with chlorophyll.

In this experiment, the number of chloroplasts with chlorophyll is what is being measured. The operational definition is the number of chloroplasts with chlorophyll in the leaf. This number represents the rate at which a plant can carry out photosynthesis.

TABLE 1. CHLOROPLASTS WITH CHLOROPHYLL

Tree	Leaf Chloroplasts with Chlorophyll (no./cell)	
	Summer	Fall
Birch	192	44
Linden	182	32
Maple	183	28
Weeping willow	177	35

FORM AN OPERATIONAL DEFINITION

Some studies suggest that drinking cranberry juice may help prevent the development of urinary tract infections caused by bacterial cells, which are prokaryotes. Researchers hypothesize that a chemical in cranberry juice may stop the bacteria from attaching to cells in the wall of the urinary bladder. Researchers grew the eukaryotic bladder cells in culture and exposed them to a solution containing bacteria. The cells were then treated with a solution of different juices or water to determine if the juices interfered with bacterial attachment. The results are shown in the graph.

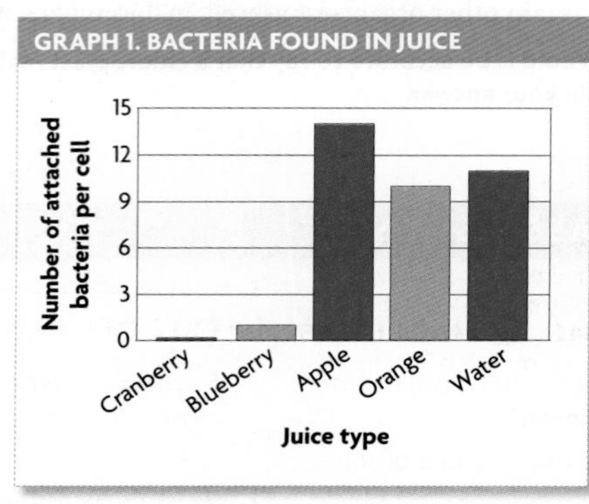

1. **Apply** What is the operational definition of the dependent variable in this experiment?
2. **Conclude** Which juices may be effective in preventing urinary tract infections?

Answers

1. The operational definition is the number of attached bacteria per cell. It indicates whether a particular juice interferes with bacterial attachment.
2. cranberry and blueberry

3.3 Cell Membrane

KEY CONCEPT The cell membrane is a barrier that separates a cell from the external environment.

MAIN IDEAS
- Cell membranes are composed of two phospholipid layers.
- Chemical signals are transmitted across the cell membrane.

VOCABULARY
cell membrane, p. 81
phospholipid, p. 81
fluid mosaic model, p. 82
selective permeability, p. 83
receptor, p. 84

B.2.2 Describe the structure of a cell membrane and explain how it regulates the transport of materials into and out of the cell and prevents harmful materials from entering the cell.

Connect Think about how the products you buy are packaged—a pint of berries, perhaps, or a tube of toothpaste. The berries are probably in a plastic container that has holes to allow air circulation. The toothpaste is in a tube strong enough to be squeezed without ripping. Both containers protect their contents, but they do so in different ways. Like these products, the cell needs protection, but it must also be able to respond to its surroundings. It is constantly taking in and getting rid of various molecules. The structure of the cell membrane allows it to perform all those functions.

MAIN IDEA

Cell membranes are composed of two phospholipid layers.

The **cell membrane,** or the plasma membrane, forms a boundary between a cell and the outside environment and controls the passage of materials into and out of a cell. The cell membrane consists of a double layer of phospholipids interspersed with a variety of other molecules. A **phospholipid** (FAHS-foh-LIHP-ihd) is a molecule composed of three basic parts:

- a charged phosphate group
- glycerol
- two fatty acid chains

VISUAL VOCAB

A **phospholipid** is composed of three basic parts:

charged phosphate group
glycerol
two fatty acid chains

Connecting **CONCEPTS**

Biochemistry Recall from **Chapter 2** that a hydrogen bond is a weak chemical bond that forms between a slightly positive hydrogen atom and a negatively charged region of another molecule.

Together, the glycerol and the phosphate groups form the "head" of a phospholipid; the fatty acids form the "tail." Because the head bears a charge, it is polar. Recall that water molecules are also polar. Therefore, the polar head of the phospholipid forms hydrogen bonds with water molecules. In contrast, the fatty acid tails are nonpolar and cannot form hydrogen bonds with water. As a result, the nonpolar tails are attracted to each other and repelled by water.

Because the membrane touches the cytoplasm inside the cell and the watery fluid outside the cell, the properties of polar heads and nonpolar tails cause the phospholipids to arrange themselves in layers, like a sandwich.

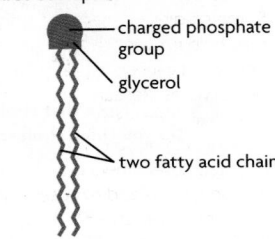

Plan and Prepare

Objectives

- Describe the structure of the cell membrane.
- Summarize how chemical signals are transmitted across the cell membrane.

Section Resources

Unit Resource Book
Study Guide pp. 9–10
Power Notes p. 11
Reinforcement p. 12
Pre-AP Activity pp. 23–24

Interactive Reader Chapter 3
Spanish Study Guide pp. 25–26

Biology Toolkit pp. C23, C27

Technology
Power Presentation 3.3
Media Gallery DVD
Online Quiz 3.3

Activate Prior Knowledge Mention to students that a cell is about 80 percent water by weight. **Ask,** What property do water molecules have? They are polar. Students may associate polarity with magnetic force. **Ask,** What type of force is at work in a water molecule? electrical force Tell students that how other substances react with water is critical to understanding cell structure and activity.

Teach

Vocabulary

Academic Vocabulary The words **compose** and **comprise** are sometimes mistakenly used interchangeably. Use the main idea on this page to help students distinguish between them.

compose, to make up the parts of
comprise, to include or contain

A membrane is *composed* of phospholipids; a membrane *comprises* a double layer of phospholipids. The parts *compose* the whole; the whole *comprises* the parts.

Differentiated Instruction

ENGLISH LEARNERS

Help students structure a main idea web. Model the approach by placing the key concept in a central box: "The cell membrane is a barrier that separates a cell from the external environment." Show students how to connect the main ideas of the section to this key concept. Tell them to break down the main ideas into smaller parts if that works better. For example, the second level of ideas might be structured as "membrane structure," "membrane behavior," and "moving across the membrane."

Biology Toolkit, Main Idea Web, p. C27

INCLUSION

Make a model of a phospholipid for a student who is visually impaired. You could, for example, stick two pipe cleaners into a gumdrop. Use the model to help the student distinguish between its polar and nonpolar regions. Three gumdrops attached by toothpicks can also be used to make a water molecule to demonstrate how a polar water molecule interacts with a phospholipid.

▼ Teach continued

TEACH FROM VISUALS

FIGURE 3.17 Point out the parts of the membrane. **Ask**

- How are cytoskeleton proteins involved in the membrane? They are attached to the inside of the membrane and help support it.
- What is the function of the protein channels? They provide passageways for materials to cross the membrane.
- Which part of the membrane is nonpolar? the inside

Take It Further

The distinctive structure of phospholipid molecules causes them to organize spontaneously into a bilayer in the presence of water. This structure is sometimes described explicitly in terms of their relationship to water. The phospholipid head is **hydrophilic,** or "water-loving." The phospholipid tail is **hydrophobic,** or "water-fearing."

Phospholipids bury their nonpolar tails within the bilayer, leaving their polar heads at the surface. They naturally form into a self-enclosed shape, so no hydrophobic edge of the bilayer is exposed to water. This property makes the bilayer self-healing because phospholipids will quickly rearrange themselves to cover any surface break that exposes the hydrophilic tails to water.

Science Trivia

- A typical human body cell measures 10–30 microns in diameter.
- The cell membrane is a little less than 10 nanometers thick.
- If the cell were the size of a large baseball field (Wrigley), then the membrane surrounding it would measure about 6 centimeters thick.

Answers

A Infer Nonpolar. If cholesterol were polar, it would form hydrogen bonds with the polar heads and water. Instead, cholesterol is located between the fatty acid chains.

The polar heads are like the bread. They form the outer surfaces of the membrane, where they interact with the watery environment both outside and inside a cell. The nonpolar tails are like the filling. They are sandwiched between the layers of polar heads, where they are protected from the watery environment.

FIGURE 3.17 shows other molecules embedded within the phospholipid layers. They give the membrane properties and characteristics it would not otherwise have. These molecules serve diverse functions. Here are a few examples:

- Cholesterol molecules strengthen the cell membrane.
- Some proteins extend through one or both phospholipid layers and help materials cross the membrane. Other proteins are key components of the cytoskeleton. Different cell types have different membrane proteins.
- Carbohydrates attached to membrane proteins serve as identification tags, enabling cells to distinguish one type of cell from another.

FIGURE 3.17 Cell Membrane

The cell membrane is made of two phospholipid layers embedded with other molecules, such as proteins, carbohydrates, and cholesterol.

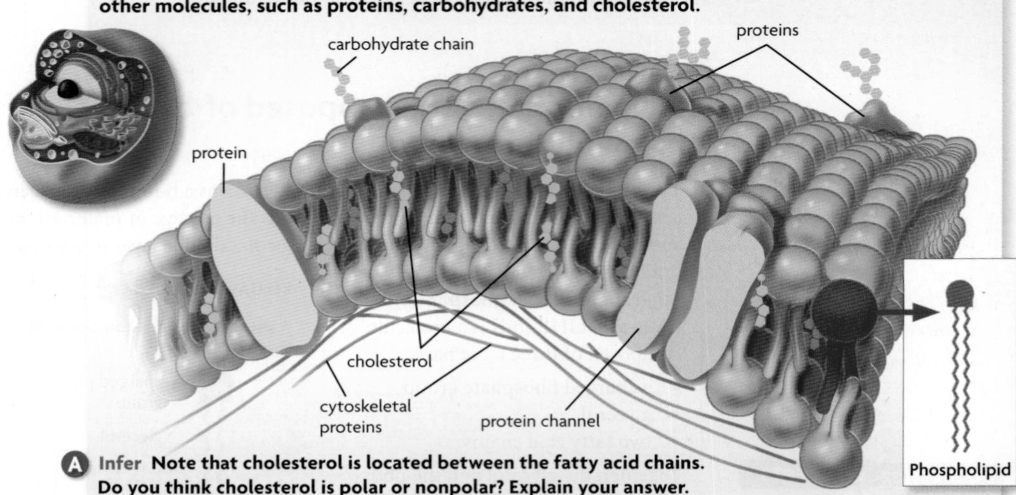

A Infer Note that cholesterol is located between the fatty acid chains. Do you think cholesterol is polar or nonpolar? Explain your answer.

Fluid Mosaic Model

Scientists have developed the **fluid mosaic model,** which describes the arrangement of the molecules that make up a cell membrane. This model of cell membrane structure takes its name from two characteristics. First, the cell membrane is flexible, not rigid. The phospholipids in each layer can move from side to side and slide past each other. As a result, the membrane behaves like a fluid, similar to a film of oil on the surface of water. However, proteins embedded in the membrane do not flip vertically. If one part of a protein is outside the membrane, it will stay outside the membrane. Second, the variety of molecules studding the membrane is similar to the arrangement of colorful tiles with different textures and patterns that make up a dynamic mosaic.

Differentiated Instruction

HANDS-ON ACTIVITY

Bring in a couple of boxes of metal fasteners, the type with a round head and double-pronged shank. Have students form into teams, and give each team 25 fasteners. Allow them five minutes to come up with three possible configurations that lipids might form in the presence of water. The only rule that applies is that the "tails" must be kept separate from water. Allow for the possibility of a second nonpolar substance being present. Sample configurations:

1. A micelle forms if the lipid tails are small enough to pack in tightly toward the center.
2. A monolayer forms if a second nonpolar substance is present, as happens with soap bubbles or when detergent surrounds a drop of oil.
3. A bilayer forms if water surrounds the lipids, inside and out.

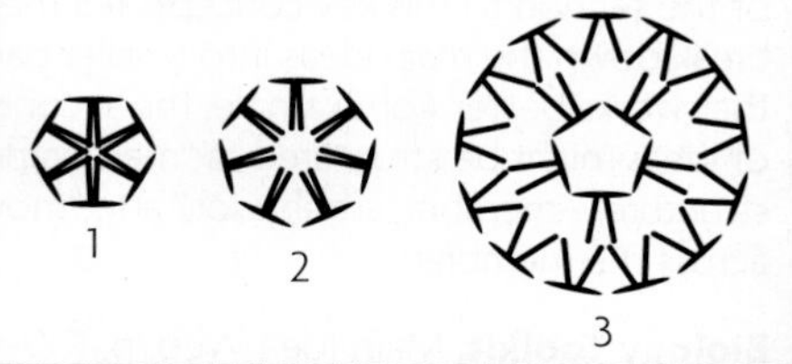

QUICK LAB MODELING

NOS.6

Modeling the Cell Membrane

The cell membrane regulates what moves into and out of the cell.

PROBLEM How does the cell membrane regulate what moves into and out of the cells?

MATERIALS

- 50 cotton swabs
- 1 thick medium-sized rubber band
- 2 pipe cleaners, each a different color
- 1 drinking straw
- scissors

PROCEDURE

1. Bundle the swabs as shown.
2. Make a receptor from one pipe cleaner. It should extend through the bunch of swabs and have a region that would bind to a signal molecule. Use the other pipe cleaner to make a carbohydrate chain. Insert the chain into the "membrane" of the bunch of swabs.
3. Cut the drinking straw in half and insert both halves into the bunch of swabs.

ANALYZE AND CONCLUDE

1. **Explain** How do the swabs represent the polar and nonpolar characteristics of the cell membrane?
2. **Apply** In this model, the swabs and proteins can be moved around. Explain whether this is an accurate representation of actual cell membranes.

Selective Permeability

The cell membrane has the property of **selective permeability,** which means it allows some, but not all, materials to cross. Selective permeability is illustrated in **FIGURE 3.18.** The terms *semipermeable* and *selectively permeable* also refer to this property. As an example, outdoor clothing is often made of semipermeable fabric. The material is waterproof yet breathable. Molecules of water vapor from sweat are small enough to exit the fabric, but water droplets are too large to enter.

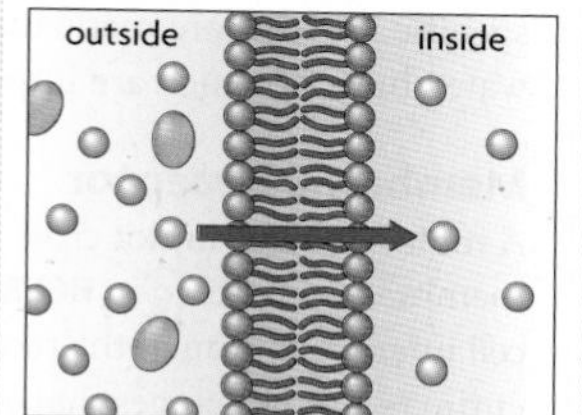

FIGURE 3.18 A selectively permeable membrane allows some, but not all, molecules to cross.

Selective permeability enables a cell to maintain homeostasis in spite of unpredictable, changing conditions outside the cell. Because a cell needs to maintain certain conditions to carry out its functions, it must control the import and export of certain molecules and ions. Thus, even if ion concentrations change drastically outside a cell, these ions won't necessarily interfere with vital chemical reactions inside a cell.

Connecting CONCEPTS

Homeostasis Recall from **Chapter 1** that homeostasis must be maintained in all organisms because vital chemical reactions can take place only within a limited range of conditions.

Molecules cross the membrane in several ways. Some of these methods require the cell to expend energy; others do not. How a particular molecule crosses the membrane depends on the molecule's size, polarity, and concentration inside versus outside the cell. In general, small nonpolar molecules easily pass through the cell membrane, small polar molecules are transported via proteins, and large molecules are moved in vesicles.

A Connect **Describe a semipermeable membrane with which you are already familiar.**

BELOW LEVEL

To demonstrate selective permeability, make a mixture of sand and gravel. Pour the mixture through a piece of screen or sieve. The sand will pass through, but the gravel will not. **Ask,** In what way is the screen or sieve permeable? allows passage of materials **Ask,** In what way is the screen or sieve selective? only small particles pass through Discuss other types of selectivity, such as chemical selectivity.

PRE-AP

Have students compare the diagram in **FIGURE 3.18** with those of **FIGURES 3.19** and **3.20.** Have them redraw the diagrams in their science notebook, noting similarities and differences. Point out that both types of signaling discussed on page 84 fall under the broad category of the effects of a membrane's selective permeability. Students can continue to add to their notes in the next two sections with the discussion of different types of transport.

Biology Toolkit, Combination Notes, p. C23

QUICK LAB

Time 15 minutes	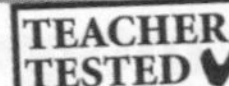 TEACHER TESTED
Lab Binder Cells, p. 8	

Purpose Model the structure of a cell membrane.

LAB MANAGEMENT

- Cotton swabs should be tightly packed so they do not fall out of the rubber band, yet not so tightly packed that students cannot insert the other materials. Vary the number of swabs according to the size of the rubber band used.
- Discuss that the cotton swab is representing two phospholipids, not one. This is a limitation of the model.

Answers

Analyze and Conclude

1. The swab tips represent the polar heads, and the sticks represent the nonpolar tails of the phospholipids making up the interior of the membrane. The spaces between the tips and sticks represent the semipermeable nature of the membrane.
2. This is accurate because the cell membrane is fluid. Proteins and phospholipids slide past each other.

Vocabulary

Academic Vocabulary The words **permeate** and **pervade** have similar roots, meaning to "pass or move through," and are used synonymously in everyday language. *Permeability,* when used in reference to membranes, describes a physical quality. Materials that are able to pass through a cell membrane are penetrating a physical barrier.

Answers

A Connect *Sample Answer:* A strainer is semipermeable because it allows water to pass through but holds back the spaghetti.

▼ Teach *continued*

Integrating Pharmacology

Many drugs used for medical treatment act by binding to **receptors** and inhibiting or enhancing their activity. Drugs that bind to a membrane receptor do not have to enter the cell; they can control intracellular reactions from outside the cell. Researchers can now use computers to design drugs with structures that fit the docking site of the specific receptor they want to inhibit.

Answers

A Contrast Intracellular receptors are located within a cell and bind to molecules that cross directly through the membrane. Membrane receptors are located in the membrane, bind to molecules that cannot cross it, and transmit the signal to the cell interior by changing shape.

▼ Assess and Reteach

Assess Use the Online Quiz or Section Quiz (*Assessment Book*, p. 49).

Reteach Use **FIGURE 3.17** to go over the key points of the section. Have students make a table of the components of the cell membrane, including a description of the functions of each.

MAIN IDEA

Chemical signals are transmitted across the cell membrane.

Recall that cell membranes may secrete molecules and may contain identifying molecules, such as carbohydrates. All these molecules can act as signals to communicate with other cells. How are these signals recognized?

A **receptor** is a protein that detects a signal molecule and performs an action in response. It recognizes and binds to only certain molecules, which ensures that the right cell gets the right signal at the right time. The molecule a receptor binds to is called a ligand. When a receptor and a ligand bind, they change shape. This change is critical because it affects how a receptor interacts with other molecules. Two major types of receptors are present in your cells.

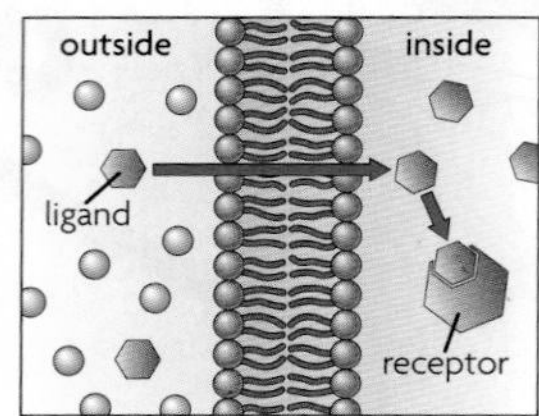

FIGURE 3.19 Intracellular receptors are located inside the cell. They are bound by molecules that can cross the membrane.

Intracellular Receptor

A molecule may cross the cell membrane and bind to an intracellular receptor, as shown in **FIGURE 3.19.** *Intracellular* means "within, or inside, a cell." Molecules that cross the membrane are generally nonpolar and may be relatively small. Many hormones fit within this category. For example, aldosterone can cross most cell membranes. However, it produces an effect only in cells that have the right type of receptor, such as kidney cells. When aldosterone enters a kidney cell, it binds to an intracellular receptor. The receptor-ligand complex enters the nucleus, interacts with the DNA, and turns on certain genes. As a result, specific proteins are made that help the kidneys absorb sodium ions and retain water, both of which are important for maintaining normal blood pressure.

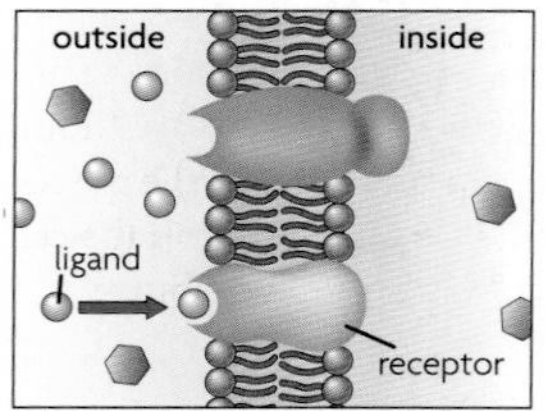

FIGURE 3.20 Membrane receptors bind to molecules that cannot enter the cell. When bound, the receptor transmits the signal inside the cell by changing shape.

Membrane Receptor

A molecule that cannot cross the membrane may bind to a receptor in the cell membrane, as shown in **FIGURE 3.20.** The receptor then sends the message to the cell interior. Although the receptor binds to a signal molecule outside the cell, the entire receptor changes shape—even the part inside the cell. As a result, it causes molecules inside the cell to respond. These molecules, in turn, start a complicated chain of events inside the cell that tells the cell what to do. For instance, band 3 protein is a membrane receptor in red blood cells. When activated, it triggers processes that carry carbon dioxide from body tissues to the lungs.

A Contrast How do intracellular receptors differ from membrane receptors?

3.3 ASSESSMENT

ONLINE QUIZ ClassZone.com

B.2.2

REVIEWING MAIN IDEAS

1. Why do **phospholipids** form a double layer?
2. Explain how membrane **receptors** transmit messages across the **cell membrane.**

CRITICAL THINKING

3. **Compare** Describe the similarities between enzymes and receptors.
4. **Infer** If proteins were rigid, why would they make poor receptors?

Connecting CONCEPTS

5. **Human Biology** Insulin helps cells take up sugar from the blood. Explain the effect on blood sugar levels if insulin receptors stopped working.

3.3 ASSESSMENT

1. Phospholipids form a double layer in response to the presence of polar water molecules surrounding them. The polar heads of phospholipids interact with the water inside and outside the cell, forming transient hydrogen bonds. The nonpolar tails are repelled by water and interact with each other inside the membrane.
2. Membrane receptors bind to a signal molecule on the outside of a cell. Upon binding, the membrane receptor changes shape, which sends a message inside the cell.
3. Both enzymes and receptors are proteins that bind to a specific ligand or substrate, change shape in response to binding, and cause some sort of action or response.
4. If proteins were rigid, they would be unable to change shape. Therefore, they could not effectively transmit a message to the cell interior.
5. The body would no longer receive the message from insulin. Cells would not take up sugar, blood sugar levels would rise, and death would result.

3.4 Diffusion and Osmosis

KEY CONCEPT Materials move across membranes because of concentration differences.

MAIN IDEAS

- Diffusion and osmosis are types of passive transport.
- Some molecules diffuse through transport proteins.

VOCABULARY

passive transport, p. 85
diffusion, p. 85
concentration gradient, p. 85
osmosis, p. 86
isotonic, p. 86
hypertonic, p. 86
hypotonic, p. 87
facilitated diffusion, p. 87

B.2.2 Describe the structure of a cell membrane and explain how it regulates the transport of materials into and out of the cell and prevents harmful materials from entering the cell.

Connect If you have ever been stuck in traffic behind a truck full of pigs, you know that "unpleasant" fails to fully describe the situation. That is because molecules travel from the pigs to receptors in your nose, which your brain interprets as a really bad odor. Or perhaps you have tie-dyed a T-shirt and have seen dye molecules spread throughout the pot of water, turning it neon green or electric blue. Why does that happen? Why don't the molecules stay in one place?

MAIN IDEA

Diffusion and osmosis are types of passive transport.

Cells almost continually import and export substances. If they had to expend energy to move every molecule, cells would require an enormous amount of energy to stay alive. Fortunately, some molecules enter and exit a cell without requiring the cell to work. As **FIGURE 3.21** shows, **passive transport** is the movement of molecules across a cell membrane without energy input from the cell. It may also be described as the diffusion of molecules across a membrane.

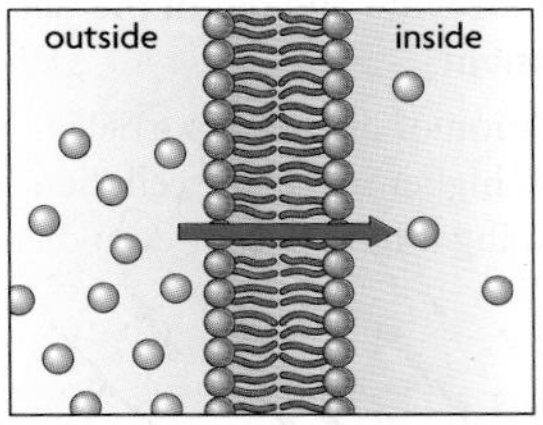

outside
inside

FIGURE 3.21 Passive transport is the movement of molecules across the membrane from areas of higher concentration to areas of lower concentration. It does not require energy input from the cell.

Diffusion

Diffusion is the movement of molecules in a fluid or gas from a region of higher concentration to a region of lower concentration. It results from the natural motion of particles, which causes molecules to collide and scatter. Concentration is the number of molecules of a substance in a given volume, and it can vary from one region to another. A **concentration gradient** is the difference in the concentration of a substance from one location to another. Molecules diffuse down their concentration gradient—that is, from a region of higher concentration to a region of lower concentration.

In the tie-dye example, dye molecules are initially at a high concentration in the area where they are added to the water. Random movements of the dye and water molecules cause them to bump into each other and mix. Thus, the dye molecules move from an area of higher concentration to an area of lower concentration. Eventually, they are evenly spread throughout the solution. This means the molecules have reached a dynamic equilibrium. The concentration of dye molecules is the same throughout the solution (equilibrium), but the molecules continue to move (dynamic).

***Connecting* CONCEPTS**

Human Biology As you will learn in **Chapter 30**, diffusion plays a key role in gas exchange in the lungs and other body tissues.

Differentiated Instruction

ENGLISH LEARNERS

Have students use a 2 × 2 word square for each type of passive diffusion. In the first square, have them write the word and its translation from the *Multilanguage Glossary*. In the second, they should draw a diagram of the process. In the third, have them describe the process in their own words and then write the English Glossary definition. In the fourth, have them write a sentence using the word. Repeat this activity for types of transport in the next section.

Biology Toolkit, Word Squares, p. D4

HANDS-ON ACTIVITY

Demonstrate that diffusion can occur in a solid—not just liquids and gases—though at a slower rate. At the beginning of class, place a drop of potassium permanganate on the surface of solidified agar or gelatin in a jar. Check it periodically. Students will see the purple permanganate diffuse slowly through the solid. Remind students that particles are in motion in all states of matter. Only at absolute zero, −273.15°C, would atoms have no motion or energy—a condition never reached.

Plan and Prepare

Objectives

- Describe passive transport.
- Distinguish between osmosis, diffusion, and facilitated transport.

Section Resources

Unit Resource Book
Study Guide pp. 13–14
Power Notes p. 15
Reinforcement p. 16

Interactive Reader Chapter 3
Spanish Study Guide pp. 27–28

Biology Toolkit pp. C19, D4

Technology
Power Presentation 3.4
Media Gallery DVD
Online Quiz 3.4

Activate Prior Knowledge Have students picture a cup of water and a container of drink mix and then create a solution by mixing the two. **Ask,** Which is the solute? drink mix Which is the solvent? water **Ask,** What happens to the concentration of each if you continue to add the mix? The solute becomes more concentrated and the solvent less concentrated. Tell students that concentration is a factor that affects what happens across a cell membrane.

Teach

TEACH FROM VISUALS

FIGURE 3.21 Point out that the cell membrane determines what particles will pass through it but not the direction of the movement. **Ask**

- Are the particles shown likely to be polar or nonpolar? nonpolar because they are passing freely through the cell membrane
- Do the particles to the right of the membrane also move? If so, in which direction? The particles move back and forth across the membrane.

▼ Teach *continued*

Integrating Physics

In any system, there is a tendency for **entropy,** or disorder, to increase. Diffusion increases as localized concentrations of solute particles move to a state in which the particles are randomly mixed. An input of energy would be required to reverse the process. Diffusion is a spontaneous process that occurs without any input of energy.

TEACH FROM VISUALS

FIGURE 3.23 Describe osmosis as a special case of diffusion in which the solvent moves across a semipermeable membrane. Be sure students recognize that *isotonic, hypertonic,* and *hypotonic* refer to the concentration of the solute, even though it is the solvent, in this case water, that moves in response to the solute's concentration gradient. To help students remember, have them think of the *v* in *sol**v**ent* as an arrow of the solvent's movement or relate it to the *v* in *mo**v**e*.

FIGURE 3.24 Be sure students understand that diffusion describes the net movement of particles in response to concentration. This may or may not happen across a membrane.

Take It Further

Plant cells are less likely than animal cells to burst in a hypotonic solution because they have rigid cell walls. In fact, plant cells are healthiest in a hypotonic environment. A plant cell swells to the point where it exerts a backward pressure, called **turgor pressure,** which prevents further uptake of water. Animal cells do best in an isotonic environment.

Answers

Ⓐ Apply The cell would lose water and shrink.

FIGURE 3.22 Diffusion results from the natural motion of particles.

In cells, diffusion plays an important role in moving substances across the membrane. Small lipids and other nonpolar molecules, such as carbon dioxide and oxygen, easily diffuse across the membrane. For example, most of your cells continually consume oxygen, which means that the oxygen concentration is almost always higher outside a cell than it is inside a cell. As a result, oxygen generally diffuses into a cell, without the cell's expending any energy.

Osmosis

Water molecules, of course, also diffuse. They move across a semipermeable membrane from an area of higher water concentration to an area of lower water concentration. This process is called **osmosis.** It is important to recognize that the higher the concentration of dissolved particles in a solution, the lower the concentration of water molecules in the same solution. So if you put 1 teaspoon of salt in a cup of water and 10 teaspoons of salt in a different cup of water, the first cup would have the higher water concentration.

A solution may be described as isotonic, hypertonic, or hypotonic relative to another solution. Note that these terms are comparisons; they require a point of reference, as shown in **FIGURE 3.23.** For example, you may be taller than your coach or taller than you were two years ago, but you are never just taller. Likewise, a solution may be described as isotonic only in comparison with another solution. To describe it as isotonic by itself would be meaningless.

1. A solution is **isotonic** to a cell if it has the same concentration of dissolved particles as the cell. Water molecules move into and out of the cell at an equal rate, so the cell's size remains constant.
2. A **hypertonic** solution has a higher concentration of dissolved particles than a cell. This means water concentration is higher inside the cell than outside. Thus, water flows out of the cell, causing it to shrivel or even die.

FIGURE 3.23 Effects of Osmosis

Osmosis is the diffusion of water across a semipermeable membrane from an area of higher water concentration to an area of lower water concentration.

1 ISOTONIC SOLUTION

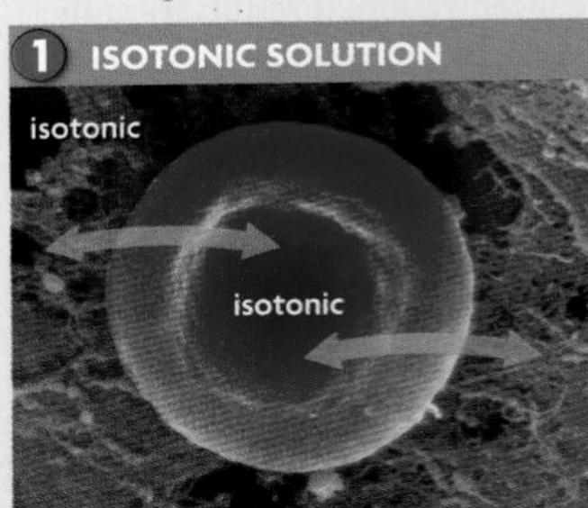

A solution is isotonic to a cell if it has the same concentration of solutes as the cell. Equal amounts of water enter and exit the cell, so its size stays constant.

2 HYPERTONIC SOLUTION

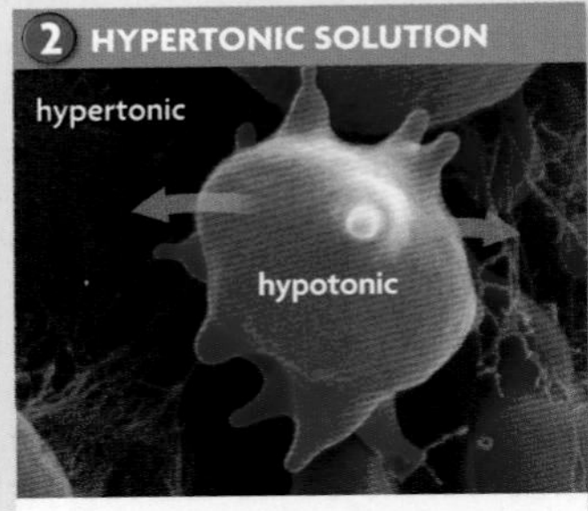

A hypertonic solution has more solutes than a cell. Overall, more water exits a cell in hypertonic solution, causing the cell to shrivel or even die.

3 HYPOTONIC SOLUTION

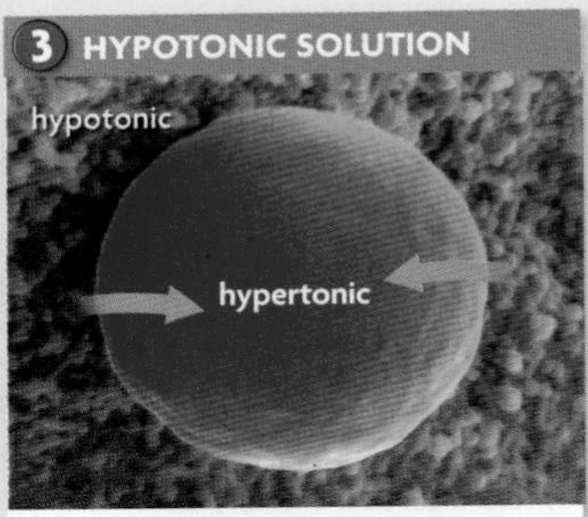

A hypotonic solution has fewer solutes than a cell. Overall, more water enters a cell in hypotonic solution, causing the cell to expand or even burst.

colored SEMs; magnification 4500×

Ⓐ Apply How would adding salt to the isotonic solution above affect the cell?

Differentiated Instruction

PRE-AP

Have students redraw the three cells shown in **FIGURE 3.23** onto a sheet of paper and then draw differently colored dots for both solute and solvent to represent the relative amounts of each. Ask students to write a paragraph explaining how relative concentrations relate to the arrows shown in each part of the figure.

Biology Toolkit, Quick-Write, p. C19

3 A **hypotonic** solution has a lower concentration of dissolved particles than a cell. This means water molecules are more concentrated outside the cell than inside. Water diffuses into the cell. If too much water enters a cell, the cell membrane could potentially expand until it bursts.

Some animals and single-celled organisms can survive in hypotonic environments. Their cells have adaptations for removing excess water. In plants, the rigid cell wall prevents the membrane from expanding too much. Remember from Section 3.2 that pressure exerted on the cell wall by fluid inside the central vacuole provides structural support for each cell and for the plant as a whole.

VOCABULARY

The words *isotonic, hypertonic,* and *hypotonic* share the root word *tonic,* which means "pressure." Their prefixes give them different comparative meanings.
iso- = equal, same
hyper- = over, above
hypo- = under, below

A **Apply** **What will happen to a houseplant if you water it with salt water (a hypertonic solution)?**

MAIN IDEA

Some molecules diffuse through transport proteins.

Some molecules cannot easily diffuse across a membrane. They may cross more easily through transport proteins—openings formed by proteins that pierce the cell membrane. **Facilitated diffusion** is the diffusion of molecules across a membrane through transport proteins. The word *facilitate* means "to make easier." Transport proteins make it easier for molecules to enter or exit a cell. But the process is still a form of passive transport. The molecules move down a concentration gradient, requiring no energy expenditure by the cell.

There are many types of transport proteins. Most types allow only certain ions or molecules to pass. As **FIGURE 3.24** shows, some transport proteins are simple channels, or tunnels, through which particles such as ions can pass. Others act more like enzymes. When bound, the protein changes shape, allowing the molecule to travel the rest of the way into the cell.

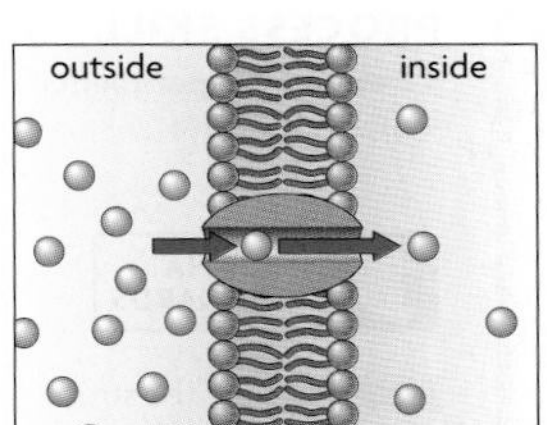

FIGURE 3.24 Facilitated diffusion enables molecules that cannot directly cross the phospholipid bilayer to diffuse through transport proteins in the membrane.

B **Summarize** **Explain why transport proteins are needed in the cell membrane.**

3.4 ASSESSMENT

ONLINE QUIZ ClassZone.com

B.2.2

REVIEWING MAIN IDEAS

1. Explain what a **concentration gradient** is and what it means for a molecule to diffuse down its concentration gradient.
2. Explain why **facilitated diffusion** does not require energy from a cell.

CRITICAL THINKING

3. **Apply** A cell is bathed in fluid. However, you notice that water is flowing out of the cell. In what kind of solution is this cell immersed: **isotonic, hypotonic,** or **hypertonic**?
4. **Compare** How are receptors and transport proteins similar?

***Connecting* CONCEPTS**

5. **Health** When a person becomes dehydrated due to the loss of fluids and solutes, saline solution (water and salts) is infused into the bloodstream by medical personnel. Why is saline solution used instead of pure water?

3.4 ASSESSMENT

1. A concentration gradient is the difference in concentration of a substance from one location to another. A molecule diffuses down its concentration gradient by moving from a region of higher concentration to a region of lower concentration.
2. No energy is needed because the molecules move down a concentration gradient.
3. hypertonic
4. Both are proteins and may work with only specific molecules. In addition, both may require a change in shape to accomplish their function.
5. Pure water would be hypotonic relative to the contents of blood cells, so water would rush into the blood cells and could cause the cells to burst. The saline solution is isotonic relative to the cell contents.

ONLINE BIOLOGY Go to the chapter Resource Center at **ClassZone.com** for additional resources and information about diffusion and osmosis.

History of Science

For many years, cell biologists wondered how polar water molecules were able to diffuse across the lipid cell membrane so rapidly. They suspected that water-channel proteins similar to the one in **FIGURE 3.24** might be at work. In the mid-1980s, **Peter Agre** started to search. In 1992, he found water channels in red blood cells and named them aquaporins.

A single human aquaporin-1 channel facilitates water transport at a rate of roughly 3 billion molecules per second. Aquaporins have also been found in bacteria, plants, and animals. In 2003, Agre won the Nobel Prize for his work.

Answers

A **Apply** Water will diffuse out of the plant cells, and the plant will wilt.

B **Summarize** Some molecules cannot easily diffuse across the membrane. Transport proteins provide a way for some of these molecules to enter cells without having to interact with phospholipids. Some form channels; others act more like enzymes and change shape.

Assess and Reteach

Assess Use the Online Quiz or Section Quiz (*Assessment Book,* p. 50).

Reteach Create a game that models diffusion, osmosis, and facilitated diffusion by using students to represent solute particles (girls) and solvent particles (boys). A row of 10 students can model the cell membrane.

INVESTIGATION

Time 90 minutes	TEACHER TESTED
Teacher Preparation	
Student Difficulty	
Lab Binder Cells, pp. 1–3	

Purpose Investigate osmosis.

Overview Students observe the effects of isotonic, hypertonic, and hypotonic solutions on chicken eggs. They will

- soak eggs in two different solutions
- measure the difference in mass of each egg before and after soaking
- identify solutions as isotonic, hypertonic, or hypotonic relative to the egg

LAB PREPARATION

- Place eggs in vinegar in individual plastic cups, cover with plastic wrap held with a rubber band, and soak for 24–48 hours in a refrigerator. Use about 250 mL vinegar in each cup to ensure consistency.
- Keep eggs refrigerated until about 30 minutes before use. Distribute two cups with eggs per team.
- To prepare 5% NaCl: add 50 g NaCl (table salt) to 1 L of water; 20% NaCl: add 200 g NaCl to 1 L of water; 50% glucose: add 500 g glucose to 1 L of water

LAB MANAGEMENT

- Have students rinse the eggs carefully to remove calcium.
- Provide spoons or glass rods to prevent the eggs from floating.
- Weigh each egg before and after soaking, after draining liquid.

Safety Remind students to wash their hands after handling the eggs.

POST-LAB DISCUSSION

Explain that vinegar dissolves the shell's calcium. **Ask,** What kept the egg intact? selectively permeable membrane

Teacher Note "I like this lab because some students are still surprised to learn that an egg is a cell."

Diffusion Across a Membrane

In this investigation, you will determine whether different solutions are hypotonic, isotonic, or hypertonic relative to the inside of a chicken egg. Your teacher has already soaked the eggs in vinegar, which removes calcium from the shell. This allows the egg to act as a single cell encased in a selectively permeable membrane.

PROBLEM Are the tested solutions hypotonic, isotonic, or hypertonic to the egg?

MATERIALS

- 2 vinegar-soaked chicken eggs
- water
- balance
- 2 disposable plastic cups
- distilled water
- 5% NaCl solution
- 20% NaCl solution
- 50% glucose solution
- 10 cm masking tape
- marker
- 500-mL beaker
- 20 cm piece of plastic wrap
- 2 rubber bands

PROCESS SKILL

- **Designing Experiments**
- **Analyzing Data**

B.2.2 Describe the structure of a cell membrane and explain how it regulates the transport of materials into and out of the cell and prevents harmful materials from entering the cell.

NOS.1 Develop explanations based on reproducible data and observations gathered during laboratory investigations.

NOS.5 Apply standard techniques in laboratory investigations to measure physical quantities in appropriate units and convert known quantities to other units as necessary.

PROCEDURE

1. Choose two solutions you want to test in your experiment to determine whether they are hypotonic, isotonic, or hypertonic relative to the chicken egg. Select from distilled water, 5% NaCl, 20% NaCl, and 50% glucose solutions.
2. Identify the variables you will measure and the constants you will maintain during the investigation. Examples of constants include the amount of solution used for each egg.
3. Design a data table, such as the example shown below, to organize your results.
4. Thoroughly rinse each egg and find its mass. Place each egg in a separate plastic cup.
5. Cover each egg with one of the solutions you are testing. Label the cups with the solution names.
6. Cover each cup with plastic wrap, securing it with a rubber band. Soak the eggs overnight.
7. The next day, find the mass of each egg and note any changes in appearance.

TABLE 1. CHANGES IN EGG MASS

	Name of Solution 1	Name of Solution 2
Initial mass of egg (g)		
Mass of egg after soaking in solution (g)		

ANALYZE AND CONCLUDE

1. **Apply** What is the operational definition of the dependent variable in this lab?
2. **Analyze** How did you conclude whether the solutions you tested were hypotonic, isotonic, or hypertonic?
3. **Identify** What were the independent and dependent variables in your experiment? What was held constant?
4. **Calculate** Calculate the change in the mass of the eggs. Explain how this may relate to your findings.
5. **Predict** What effect would eating too much salt have on the human body?
6. **Experimental Design** List possible reasons for any inconsistent results you may have observed.

Answers

Sample Data

Students in the test group recorded descriptive answers instead of quantitative answers. For a sample of student data, go to page R101.

Analyze and Conclude

1. change in mass of the egg after soaking
2. by observing changes in mass and size
3. independent variable: different solutions; dependent variable: change in mass; constants: amount of solution, temperature, soaking time
4. Eggs soaked in 20% salt and glucose solutions get smaller; eggs soaked in distilled water get larger; eggs soaked in 5% salt solution stay about the same. Students should explain in terms of water moving in or out of each cell.
5. Fluid surrounding cells would be hypertonic. Water would flow out of the cells, causing them to shrink and possibly die.
6. Permeability of egg shells could vary because of different shell thickness or different lengths of exposure to vinegar.

3.5 Active Transport, Endocytosis, and Exocytosis

KEY CONCEPT Cells use energy to transport materials that cannot diffuse across a membrane.

MAIN IDEAS
- Proteins can transport materials against a concentration gradient.
- Endocytosis and exocytosis transport materials across the membrane in vesicles.

VOCABULARY
active transport, p. 89
endocytosis, p. 90
phagocytosis, p. 90
exocytosis, p. 91

B.2.2 Describe the structure of a cell membrane and explain how it regulates the transport of materials into and out of the cell and prevents harmful materials from entering the cell.

Connect You have seen that a cell membrane controls the passive transport of materials into and out of a cell. However, a cell needs many substances that cannot simply diffuse across the membrane. The cell has several ways to take in or get rid of these materials. These processes, such as active transport, endocytosis, and exocytosis, all need energy from the cell.

MAIN IDEA
Proteins can transport materials against a concentration gradient.

You just learned that some transport proteins let materials diffuse into and out of a cell down a concentration gradient. Many other transport proteins, often called pumps, move materials against a concentration gradient. **Active transport** drives molecules across a membrane from a region of lower concentration to a region of higher concentration. This process, shown in **FIGURE 3.25**, uses transport proteins powered by chemical energy. Cells use active transport to get needed molecules regardless of the concentration gradient and to maintain homeostasis.

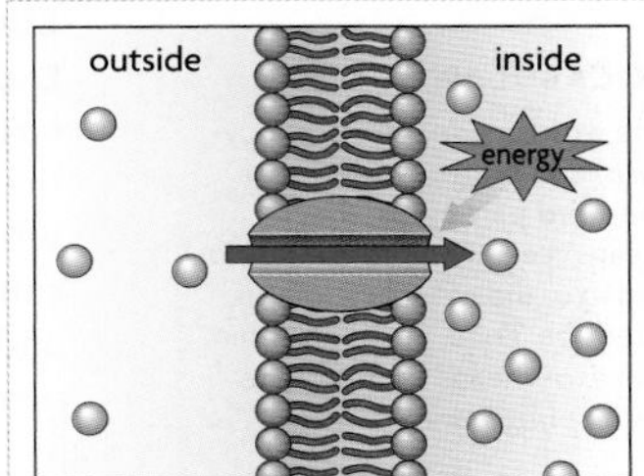

FIGURE 3.25 During active transport, a cell uses energy to move substances against a concentration gradient—that is, from a lower to a higher concentration.

Before we discuss active transport proteins, let's look at transport proteins in general. All transport proteins span the membrane, and most change shape when they bind to a target molecule or molecules. Some transport proteins bind to only one type of molecule. Others bind to two different types. Some proteins that bind to two types of molecules move both types in the same direction. Others move the molecules in opposite directions.

***Connecting* CONCEPTS**

Human Biology As you will learn in **Chapter 32**, active transport is a necessary part of nutrient absorption.

Differentiated Instruction

ENGLISH LEARNERS

If students created word squares for types of transport in Section 3.4 (English Learners note page 85), have them do the same for this section. You can also have students form into groups of three, counting off within the group from one to three. Then assemble all ones, twos, and threes into expert panels, each panel studying a type of transport in this section and preparing a lesson plan for the group. Reconvene the home groups and have each expert teach the group.

Biology Toolkit, Jigsaw Reading, p. C15

BELOW LEVEL

Have students prepare a table to compare different types of cellular transport. Help them choose categories for comparison, such as whether the transport is passive or active, whether it is toward or against a gradient, and whether it involves a channel or pump. Make sure students understand that endocytosis and exocytosis are not types of active transport even though they require energy input.

Biology Toolkit, Semantic Feature Analysis, p. D7

SECTION 3.5

Plan and Prepare

Objectives
- Describe active transport.
- Distinguish among endocytosis, phagocytosis, and exocytosis.

Section Resources

Unit Resource Book
Study Guide pp. 17–18
Power Notes p. 19
Reinforcement p. 20
Pre-AP Activity pp. 25–26

Interactive Reader Chapter 3
Spanish Study Guide pp. 29–30

Biology Toolkit pp. C15, C19, D7

Technology
Power Presentation 3.5
Media Gallery DVD
Online Quiz 3.5

Activate Prior Knowledge Use the analogy of a water pump and waterfall to represent active or passive transport. **Ask,** Which is active transport and which is passive transport and why? The waterfall is passive because no input of energy is required to move water; the pump is active because energy is needed to move water. Explain that cells often need to gather ions and other substances against a gradient. Cellular systems that move materials against a gradient are referred to as pumps.

Teach

TEACH FROM VISUALS

FIGURE 3.25 Have students compare the inside and the outside of the cell in the diagram. **Ask,** What is the result of the process shown? More particles accumulate inside the cell than outside the cell. Have students compare this diagram to **FIGURE 3.24** on page 87 and describe the differences.

▼ Teach continued

Take It Further

Many types of cells have **proton pumps,** which are essential for cellular respiration and photosynthesis. Energy extracted by electron transport chains in these processes is used to pump protons up their concentration gradient. The protons then flow back down their gradient by diffusion, providing energy to transform the molecule ADP into the energy carrier ATP. Students will learn about ATP in **Chapter 4.**

The Inside Story

The biologist **Elie Metchnikoff** originated the theory on which modern cellular immunology is based—that the body is protected by mobile cells (white blood cells) that engulf bacteria and other pathogens. He coined the term **phagocytosis** and won a Nobel Prize for his work in 1908.

The official biography of the Nobel Foundation describes Metchnikoff in this way: "Photographs taken of him when he was working at the Pasteur Institute show him with long hair and an unkempt beard. It is said of him that at this time he usually wore overshoes in all weathers and carried an umbrella, his pockets being overfull with scientific papers, and that he always wore the same hat, and often, when he was excited, sat on it."

Answers

A Synthesize Both are proteins that recognize only specific target molecules and change shape when they bind.

FIGURE 3.26 Just as a cell uses energy in the process of active transport, this boy uses energy to pump air against a concentration gradient.

The key feature of active transport proteins is that they can use chemical energy to move a substance against its concentration gradient. Most use energy from a molecule called ATP, either directly or indirectly. For example, nerve cells, or neurons, need to have a higher concentration of potassium ions and a lower concentration of sodium ions than the fluid outside the cell. The sodium-potassium pump uses energy directly from the breakdown of ATP. It pumps three sodium ions out of the cell for every two potassium ions it pumps in. The proton pump, another transport protein, uses energy from the breakdown of ATP to move hydrogen ions (or protons) out of the cell. This action forms a concentration gradient of hydrogen ions (H^+), which makes the fluid outside the cell more positively charged than the fluid inside. In fact, this gradient is a form of stored energy that is used to power other active transport proteins. In plant cells, this gradient causes yet another protein to transport sucrose into the cell—an example of indirect active transport.

A Synthesize In what ways are active transport proteins similar to enzymes?

MAIN IDEA

Endocytosis and exocytosis transport materials across the membrane in vesicles.

A cell may also use energy to move a large substance or a large amount of a substance in vesicles. Transport in vesicles lets substances enter or exit a cell without crossing through the membrane.

VOCABULARY

The words *endocytosis, exocytosis,* and *phagocytosis* share the word part *cyto-*, which means "cell." The prefixes *endo-* and *exo-* indicate location or direction. *Endo-* means "within," and *exo-* means "out of." The prefix *phago-* means "eating."

Endocytosis

Endocytosis (EN-doh-sy-TOH-sihs) is the process of taking liquids or fairly large molecules into a cell by engulfing them in a membrane. In this process, the cell membrane makes a pocket around a substance. The pocket breaks off inside the cell and forms a vesicle, which then fuses with a lysosome or a similar type of vesicle. Lysosomal enzymes break down the vesicle membrane and its contents (if necessary), which are then released into the cell.

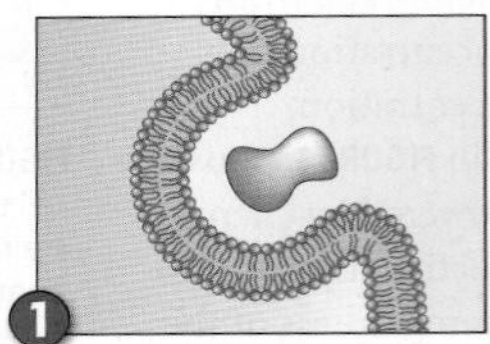

1 During endocytosis, the cell membrane folds inward and fuses together, surrounding the substance in a pocket.

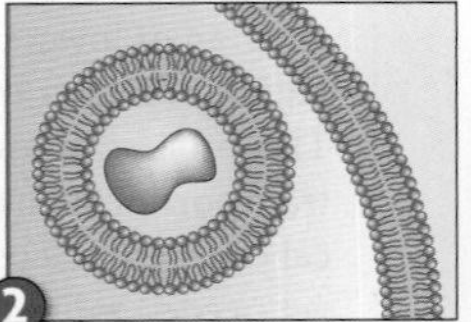

2 The pocket pinches off inside the cell, forming a vesicle.

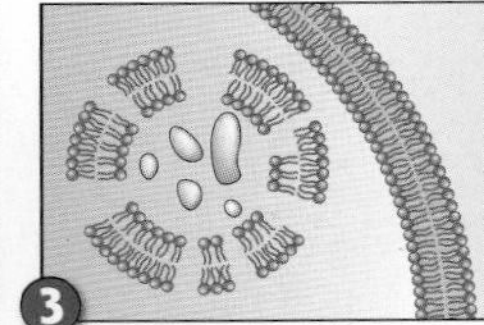

3 The vesicle fuses with a lysosome or a similar vesicle, where enzymes break down the membrane and its contents.

Phagocytosis (FAG-uh-sy-TOH-sihs) is a type of endocytosis in which the cell membrane engulfs large particles. The word literally means "cell eating." Phagocytosis plays a key role in your immune system. Some white blood cells called macrophages help your body fight infection. They find foreign materials, such as bacteria, and engulf and destroy them.

Differentiated Instruction

HANDS-ON ACTIVITY

Help students develop a sense of scale by comparing the size of a small eukaryotic cell and its organelles to an *E. coli* bacterium that measures 500 × 1500 nm. Have students prepare a classroom display that can encompass these measures: cell 20,000 nm; nucleus 7000 nm; chloroplast 2000 × 5000 nm; mitochondrion 500 × 1500 nm; ribosome 25 nm; thickness of cell membrane 10 nm; protein 7 nm; water molecule 0.4 nm. Tell students that cells, organelles, proteins, and bacteria vary in size but that these numbers are within a normal range.

PRE-AP

Some scientists think that mitochondria and chloroplasts are descendants of primitive prokaryotes. Have students write a paragraph that cites evidence from this chapter that supports this conclusion. Students should mention the similar size of those organelles to a prokaryote, that both mitochondria and chloroplasts have their own DNA and double membranes, and that cells demonstrate the ability to engulf bacteria by phagocytosis.

Biology Toolkit, Quick-Write, p. C19

Exocytosis

Exocytosis (EHK-soh-sy-TOH-sihs), the opposite of endocytosis, is the release of substances out of a cell by the fusion of a vesicle with the membrane. During this process, a vesicle forms around materials to be sent out of the cell. The vesicle then moves toward the cell's surface, where it fuses with the membrane and lets go of its contents.

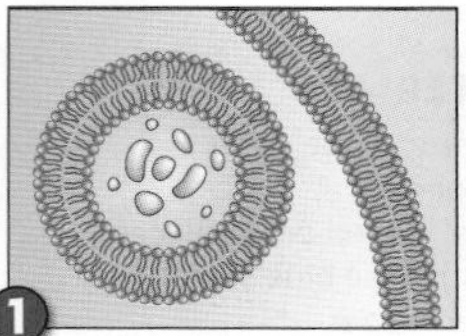

1 The cell forms a vesicle around material that needs to be removed or secreted.

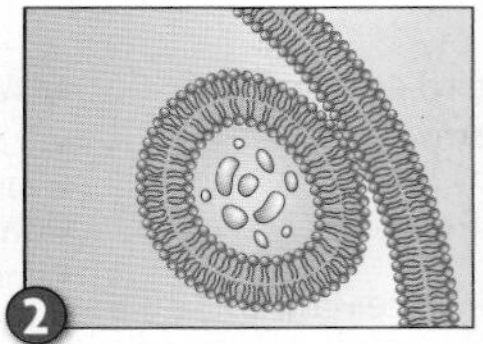

2 The vesicle is transported to the cell membrane.

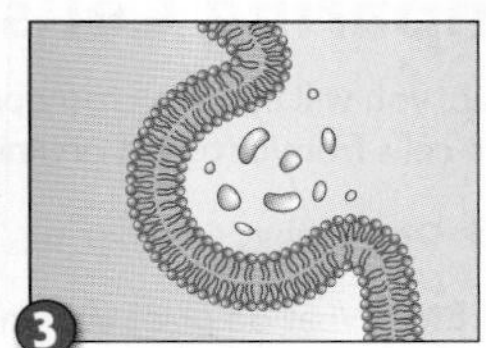

3 The vesicle membrane fuses with the cell membrane and releases the contents.

Connecting **CONCEPTS**

Endocrine System As you will learn in **Chapter 29**, thyroid hormones play an important role in controlling your growth and development. These hormones are released into the blood by exocytosis.

Exocytosis happens all the time in your body. In fact, you couldn't think or move a muscle without it. When you want to move your big toe, for example, your brain sends a message that travels through a series of nerve cells to reach your toe. This message, or nerve impulse, travels along each nerve cell as an electrical signal, but it must be converted to a chemical signal to cross the tiny gap that separates one nerve cell from the next. These chemicals are stored in vesicles within the nerve cells. When a nerve impulse reaches the end of a cell, it causes the vesicles to fuse with the cell membrane and release the chemicals outside the cell. There they attach to the next nerve cell, which triggers a new electrical impulse in that cell.

NSTA SCiLINKS scilinks.org
For more information about active transport, go to scilinks.org.
Keycode: MLB003

A Hypothesize What might happen if vesicles in your neurons were suddenly unable to fuse with the cell membrane?

3.5 ASSESSMENT

ONLINE QUIZ ClassZone.com

B.2.2

REVIEWING MAIN IDEAS

1. How do transport proteins that are pumps differ from those that are channels?
2. How do **endocytosis** and **exocytosis** differ from diffusion?

THINKING CRITICALLY

3. **Apply** Small lipid molecules are in high concentration outside a cell. They slowly cross the membrane into the cell. What term describes this action? Does it require energy?
4. **Apply** Ions are in low concentration outside a cell. They move rapidly into the cell via protein molecules. What term describes this action? Does it require energy?

Connecting **CONCEPTS**

5. **Diffusion** Suppose molecules were unable to diffuse into and out of cells. How might life be different if cells had to use **active transport** to move every substance? Explain your reasoning.

3.5 ASSESSMENT

1. Pumps require energy, transport a molecule against its concentration gradient, and change shape upon binding. A protein channel does not change shape or require energy. It allows certain molecules to diffuse through it, down their concentration gradient.
2. They require energy input; diffusion does not. They also enable larger particles to enter a cell, particles that are too large to diffuse across a cell membrane.
3. diffusion, no
4. active transport, yes
5. Cells would require vast amounts of energy to perform even simple functions. Perhaps organisms would have to take in more food to provide more energy. If food were limited, perhaps only photosynthetic organisms would be able to survive. Perhaps organisms would move and respond more slowly and be more sedentary. Perhaps organisms would be simpler, and highly specialized organs would not have developed.

ONLINE BIOLOGY Have students try different mechanisms for moving materials across a cell membrane. See Animated Biology in Options for Inquiry on page 93.

Take It Further

There are three types of endocytosis. In **phagocytosis,** cells engulf a particle or another cell and enclose it within a sac. In **pinocytosis,** cells gulp droplets of extracellular fluid and any solutes that are dissolved in it. **Receptor-mediated endocytosis** is much more specific. It requires a specific receptor protein, which helps to form the vesicle in which the substance is brought into the cell. Cholesterol enters a cell when a cholesterol-LDL complex binds to an LDL receptor on the cell membrane.

Answers

A Hypothesize The neurons would be unable to transmit signals, so you would be unable to respond to stimuli.

Assess and Reteach

Assess Use the Online Quiz or Section Quiz (*Assessment Book,* p. 51).

Reteach Use the Online Biology animation of transport across cell membranes on page 93 to review the material in this section. Have students prepare or share comparison tables, as suggested on page 89.

OPTIONS FOR INQUIRY

INVESTIGATION

Time 45 minutes	TEACHER TESTED
Teacher Preparation	
Student Difficulty	
Lab Binder Cells, pp. 4–6	

Purpose Directly observe cells.

Overview Students will compare and contrast different eukaryotic cells. They will

- make and stain wet mounts of slices of onion, celery, and *Elodea* leaf
- examine human cheek cells on a prepared slide

LAB PREPARATION

Prepare slices of onion and celery ahead of time, slicing them as thin as possible.

LAB MANAGEMENT

- Demonstrate how to place a cover slip on a slide to avoid trapping air.

Safety If you use glass cover slips, caution students to handle them carefully because of the sharp edges.

- Have students view slides under low power before switching to high power.

Safety Remind students to clean eyepieces with alcohol wipes after using them.

POST-LAB DISCUSSION

Mention to students that animal cells tend to be colorless, whereas some color appears in plant cells that have chloroplasts because of the green pigment chlorophyll. However, not all plant cells have chloroplasts. Stains are needed to make parts of a cell visible.

Teacher Note "Students regularly get bubbles under the cover slip and misidentify the bubbles as 'cells.'"

Use these inquiry-based labs and online activities to deepen your understanding of cell structure.

INVESTIGATION

Comparing Cells

INDIANA STANDARDS

B.2.1 Describe features common to all cells that are essential for growth and survival, and explain their functions.

NOS.6 Use analogies and models (mathematical and physical) to simplify and represent systems that are difficult to understand or directly experience due to their size, time scale, or complexity, and recognize the limitations of analogies and models.

In this lab, you will use a microscope to examine and compare cells from different organisms.

SKILLS Observing, Comparing, Drawing

PROBLEM What do plant and animal cells have in common?

PROCEDURE

1. Refer to page R8 if you need to review instructions on using a microscope and making a wet mount.
2. Construct a table to organize your observations and drawings.
3. Peel a thin slice of onion and place it on the slide.
4. Carefully add a drop of methylene blue to the onion. Avoid getting the stain on your clothes. Place one side of a cover slip against the methylene blue, and gently lower it, being careful not to trap air bubbles.
5. Examine the onion under the microscope at low and high power, and draw what you see. Large structures such as the nucleus, cell membrane, and cell wall should be visible. Label as many cell structures as you can.
6. Repeat steps 2 through 4 for the celery and the elodea.
7. Examine prepared slides of human cheek cells under the microscope at low and high power. Draw what you see, and label as many structures as you can.

ANALYZE AND CONCLUDE

1. **Compare** What characteristics do all of the cells have in common? List as many as you can.
2. **Contrast** Identify the unique characteristics of each cell type.
3. **Connect** What type of cells did you examine, eukaryotic or prokaryotic? Explain your answer.
4. **Infer** Why do you think it was necessary to add methylene blue to the slides?

MATERIALS

- 3 microscope slides
- razor tool
- thinly sliced onion pieces
- methylene blue stain
- eyedropper
- 3 plastic cover slips
- microscope
- thinly sliced celery stalk
- elodea leaf
- prepared slides of human cheek cells

Answers

Expected Results

Students should be able to identify the cell membrane, nucleus, and cytoplasm in cheek cells; the cell wall, nucleus, chloroplasts, and cytoplasm in *Elodea* cells; and the cell wall, nucleus, and cytoplasm in celery and onion cells.

Analyze and Conclude

1. All cells have a nucleus and cytoplasm. All cells have a cell membrane, but the membrane may not be visible in the plant cells because of the presence of the cell wall.
2. Each type of cell has a unique shape. The *Elodea* cells have chloroplasts. The celery cells are long and narrow. The onion cells are rectangular, with cell walls visible. Cheek cells appear flat and round, with nucleus visible.
3. All of the cells are eukaryotic. They all have an enclosed nucleus.
4. Cells are transparent. Stain is needed to make the structures visible.

INVESTIGATION

Modeling the Cell

The diversity of life on Earth is enormous, although all living things are made from the same basic structural unit, the cell. In your body alone, there are trillions of cells. In this activity, you will make a model of a cell.

SKILL Modeling

PROBLEM What components make up a cell?

MATERIALS
- 2 resealable plastic sandwich bags
- gelatin jigglers
- a small round balloon
- a permanent marker
- coffee stirring straws
- drinking straws cut in half
- different sizes of erasers
- slices of two colors of sponges
- tiny beads

PROCEDURE
1. Use the materials to construct a detailed model of a cell.
2. Be sure to include at least the following components in your model: cell membrane, cytoplasm, nucleus, cytoskeleton, ribosomes, mitochondria, Golgi apparatus, and centrioles.
3. Use both sandwich bags in constructing your model.
4. Tightly seal your cell after it has been completed.

ANALYZE AND CONCLUDE
1. **Apply** Make a table to list which materials you chose to represent the various cell structures and to explain your choices.
2. **Analyze** What is the significance of the double bag?
3. **Connect** What substance represents the cytoplasm? Explain why your choice is suitable.

ANIMATED BIOLOGY

Get Through a Cell Membrane

Many substances, including sugars and wastes, cannot diffuse through a cell membrane. Use a set of proteins and vesicles to move materials into and out of a cell to keep it healthy and in balance with the environment.

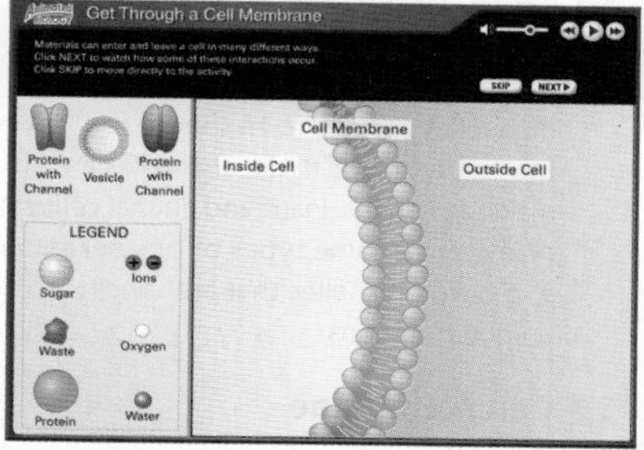

WEBQUEST

Cell organelles interact with many substances to keep cells alive and well. In this WebQuest, you will explore what happens when an organelle does not function as it should. Review a patient's symptoms, research them, and diagnose her illness. Explore how the health of an entire person can depend on just one organelle.

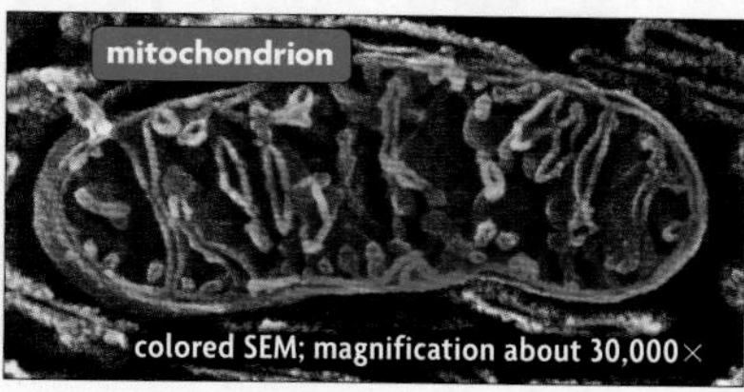

colored SEM; magnification about 30,000×

BIOZINE

Stories about cell biology—such as "Higher CO_2 Levels Increase Productivity In Plants" and "Stem Cells Help Mend Broken Hearts"—are often in the headlines. Catch the latest news about cell biology in the BioZine.

Online Biology ▼

ANIMATED BIOLOGY Students will choose from various types of transport to get materials across a cell membrane. Use with **Section 3.5.**

WEBQUEST The WebQuest takes one full class period. Students complete the activity online and will need access to a printer to print their answers. Sample answers, teacher notes, and alternative assessment ideas are available on **ClassZone.com.** Use with **Section 3.2.**

INVESTIGATION

TEACHER TESTED

Time	45 minutes
Teacher Preparation	(1 flask)
Student Difficulty	(1 flask)
Lab Binder	Cells, p. 7

Purpose Use everyday materials to construct a model of a cell.

LAB MANAGEMENT

- Collect the model cells to keep for future use and to avoid rupture in school lockers or backpacks.
- Provide small green objects (chloroplasts), small plastic bags (central vacuoles), and green cellophane (cell wall) for students who want to make plant cells.

POST-LAB DISCUSSION

Discuss the various materials used to represent the cell organelles. Have students defend their choices of materials. This discussion can serve as a good review of the chapter material.

Answers

Analyze and Conclude

1. Go to page R101 for an example of a student table.
2. It represents the lipid bilayer characteristic of the cell membrane.
3. Students should use gelatin jigglers to represent the cytoplasm. They simulate the thick, yet fluid, nature of cytoplasm and demonstrate how cytoplasm, as well as the cytoskeleton, helps support the cell.

Interactive Review

Encourage students to go to **ClassZone.com** for a detailed review of each section, including visuals and vocabulary practice.

Unit Resource Book, Vocabulary Practice, pp. 27–30

CHAPTER 3 Interactive Review @ CLASSZONE.COM

KEY CONCEPTS | Vocabulary Games | Concept Maps | Animated Biology | Online Quiz

3.1 Cell Theory

Cells are the basic unit of life. The contributions of many scientists led to the discovery of cells and the development of the cell theory. The cell theory states that all organisms are made of cells, all cells are produced by other living cells, and the cell is the most basic unit of life.

3.2 Cell Organelles

Eukaryotic cells share many similarities. They have a nucleus and other membrane-bound organelles that perform specialized tasks within the cell. Many of these organelles are involved in making proteins. Plant and animal cells share many of the same types of organelles, but both also have organelles that are specific to the cells' unique functions.

3.3 Cell Membrane

The cell membrane is a barrier that separates a cell from the external environment. It is made of a double layer of phospholipids and a variety of embedded molecules. Some of these molecules act as signals; others act as receptors. The membrane is selectively permeable, allowing some but not all materials to cross.

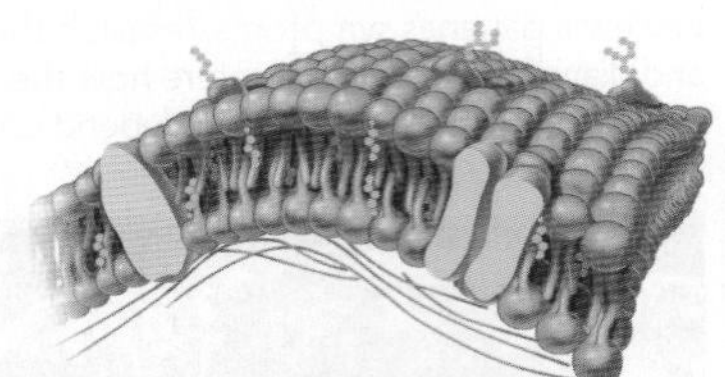

3.4 Diffusion and Osmosis

Materials move across membranes because of concentration differences. Diffusion is the movement of molecules in a fluid or gas from a region of higher concentration to a region of lower concentration. It does not require a cell to expend energy; therefore, it is a form of passive transport. Osmosis is the diffusion of water. Net water movement into or out of a cell depends on the concentration of the surrounding solution.

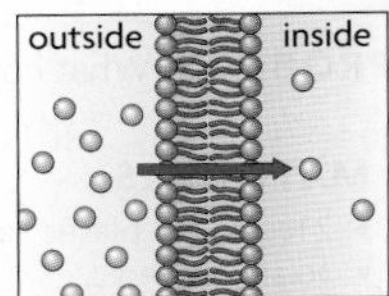

Passive transport

3.5 Active Transport, Endocytosis, and Exocytosis

Cells use energy to transport materials that cannot diffuse across a membrane. Active transport is the movement of molecules across a membrane from a region of lower concentration to a region of higher concentration—against a concentration gradient. The processes of endocytosis and exocytosis move substances in vesicles and also require energy.

Endocytosis

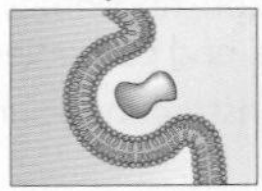
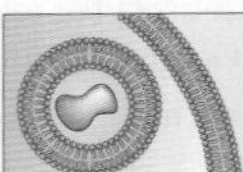
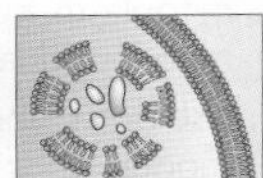

Exocytosis

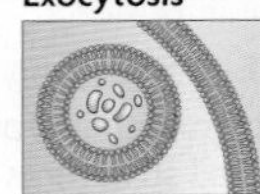
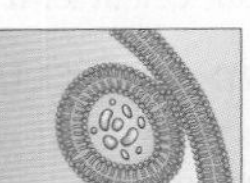
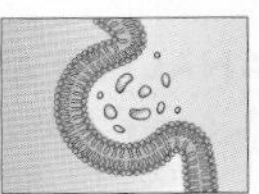

Synthesize Your Notes

Main Idea Web Plant and animal cells, though similar, each have some unique features. Identify how these cell types differ by placing plant cell characteristics on the left side of the main idea web and animal cell characteristics on the right.

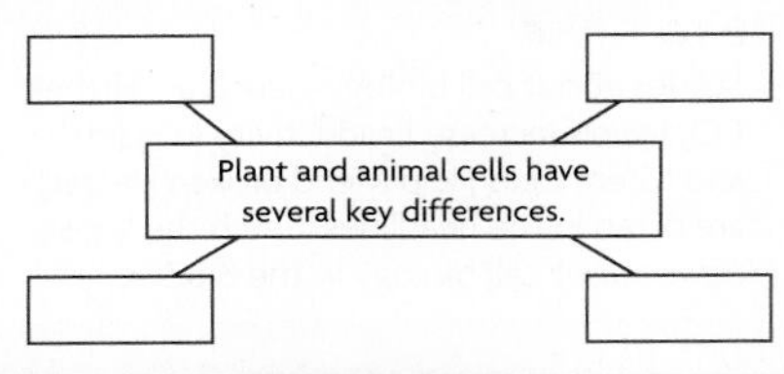

Concept Map Fill in the concept map to summarize what you know about forms of transport.

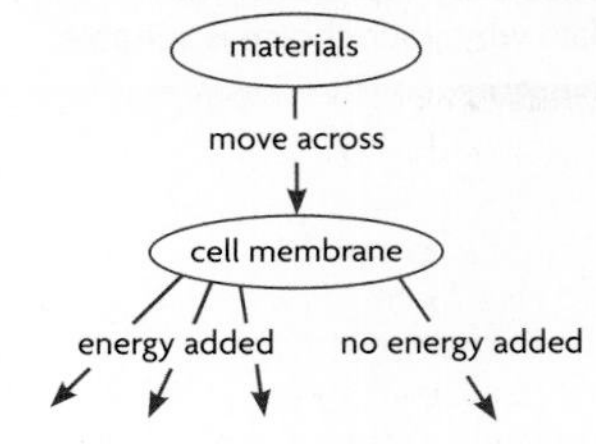

active transport
passive transport
diffusion
endocytosis
materials
exocytosis
osmosis
cell membrane

Reviewing Vocabulary

1. cell membrane
2. rough endoplasmic reticulum (also accept ribosomes)
3. nucleus
4. centriole
5. mitochondrion
6. Golgi apparatus
7. cytoskeleton
8. endoplasmic reticulum (smooth)
9. Eukaryotic and prokaryotic cells are surrounded by a cell membrane. Only eukaryotic cells have a nucleus and membrane-bound organelles.
10. Both the cell wall and cell membrane surround the cell. The cell wall is a rigid structure, while the cell membrane is not.
11. Both diffusion and facilitated diffusion allow materials to cross a semipermeable membrane without the use of energy. In simple diffusion, a molecule capable of crossing the cell membrane will pass through on its own. Facilitated diffusion requires a transport protein and allows only specific types of molecules to pass.
12. An organelle carries out a specific function or set of functions within a cell.
13. Prokaryotes do not have a nucleus, or "nut." Eukaryotes do have a nucleus.

Chapter Assessment

CHAPTER REVIEW

17. The nucleus has the DNA, which codes for proteins, and the nucleolus, which is where ribosomes are made. Ribosomes exit through nuclear pores, and some associate with the ER. Proteins made on the ribosomes may undergo modification in the ER. From the ER, they may be packaged into vesicles and sent to the Golgi apparatus for further modifications. A completed protein can be stored, released into the cell for use, released to the cell membrane for use, or excreted outside of the cell.
18. Mitochondria produce chemical reactions that convert simple food molecules into energy. They are similar to prokaryotes in that they contain their own DNA but no membrane-bound organelles.
19. Look for cell walls and chloroplasts (plant cell features) or centrioles (animal cell features).
20. The polar heads of the phospholipids can form hydrogen bonds with the polar water molecules. The nonpolar tails are sandwiched inside the membrane where they can't react with the water.
21. Membrane receptors allow large ligands to bind to the outside of the cell. The receptor then changes physically, including the part inside the cell, which triggers a response.
22. Transport proteins can form a larger opening or pore that allows them to pass.
23. When the concentration of the molecule is higher on the other side of the membrane.
24. Yes, both are needed to move substances in and out of a cell and to maintain the cell's volume.

Chapter Vocabulary

3.1 cell theory, p. 71
cytoplasm, p. 72
organelle, p. 72
prokaryotic cell, p. 72
eukaryotic cell, p. 72

3.2 cytoskeleton, p. 73
nucleus, p. 75
endoplasmic reticulum, p. 76
ribosome, p. 76
Golgi apparatus, p. 76
vesicle, p. 77
mitochondrion, p. 77
vacuole, p. 77
lysosome, p. 78
centriole, p. 78
cell wall, p. 79
chloroplast, p. 79

3.3 cell membrane, p. 81
phospholipid, p. 81
fluid mosaic model, p. 82
selective permeability, p. 83
receptor, p. 84

3.4 passive transport, p. 85
diffusion, p. 85
concentration gradient, p. 85
osmosis, p. 86
isotonic, p. 86
hypertonic, p. 86
hypotonic, p. 87
facilitated diffusion, p. 87

3.5 active transport, p. 89
endocytosis, p. 90
phagocytosis, p. 90
exocytosis, p. 91

Reviewing Vocabulary

Labeling Diagrams

In your notebook, write the vocabulary term that matches each numbered item below.

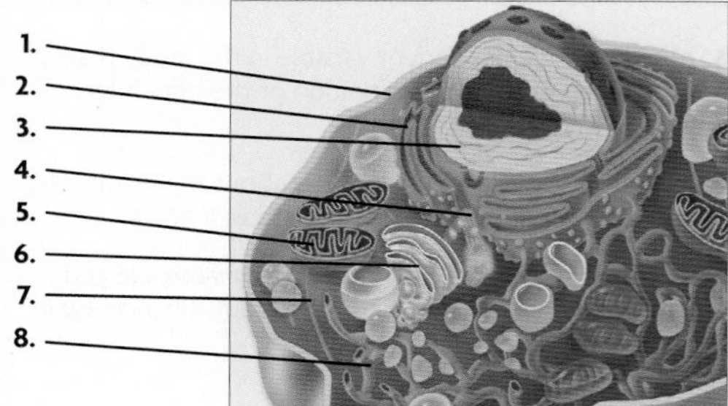

Compare and Contrast

Describe one similarity and one difference between the two terms in each of the following pairs.

9. eukaryotic, prokaryotic
10. cell wall, cell membrane
11. diffusion, facilitated diffusion

Greek and Latin Word Origins

12. The word *organelle* is the diminutive, or "tiny," form of the Latin word for organs of the body. How is an organelle like a tiny organ?

13. The Greek word *karuon* means "nut." The prefix *pro-* means "before," and the prefix *eu-* means "true." Thus, *prokaryote* means "before nut" and *eukaryote* means "true nut." How do these meanings relate to structural differences between these two cell types?

Reviewing MAIN IDEAS

14. According to the cell theory, what is required for an object to be considered alive?

15. What role do membranes play in prokaryotic cells? in eukaryotic cells? **B.2.2**

16. How do the cytoskeleton and the cytoplasm contribute to a cell's shape?

17. You know that many organelles are involved in protein production. Briefly explain where proteins are made, modified, and packaged within a cell. **B.2.4**

18. Explain what mitochondria do and why evidence suggests that they might have descended from free-living prokaryotes in the evolutionary past. **B.2.3**

19. If you were looking through a microscope at an unknown cell, how might you determine whether it was a plant cell or an animal cell? **B.2.2**

20. Cells are surrounded by a watery fluid, and they contain watery cytoplasm. Explain how the structure of the lipid bilayer is related to these two watery environments.

21. How are cells able to respond to signal molecules that are too large to enter the cytoplasm?

22. How do transport proteins make it easier for certain molecules to diffuse across a membrane?

23. Under what conditions would a molecule need to be actively transported across a membrane? **B.2.2**

24. Do you think that endocytosis and exocytosis can occur within the same cell? Explain your reasoning.

Reviewing Main Ideas

14. It must be made of cells that are produced by other living cells and that carry out life functions, such as metabolism and maintaining homeostasis.
15. Both cell types have a cell membrane that forms a protective barrier between the cell and its environment and controls the passage of materials in and out. Eukaryotic cells have membrane-bound organelles; prokaryotic cells do not.
16. The cytoskeleton is made up of a network of proteins that gives the cell a strong structure while constantly changing in response to the cell's changing needs. The cytoplasm fills in the areas around the cytoskeleton, keeping the membrane from collapsing onto the cytoskeleton.

ITEM CORRELATIONS

Standard	Items
B.2.2	15, 19, 23, 31, 34, 38
B.2.3	18
B.2.4	17, 32, 33
NOS.10	25

CHAPTER REVIEW

Critical Thinking

25. The cell theory depended on the invention of microscopes that allowed scientists to see cells.
26. Eukaryotic cells contain everything a prokaryotic cell contains and more, suggesting that these characteristics developed over time. The presence of mitochondria and chloroplasts, which have their own DNA and membranes, suggests that these organelles descended from prokaryotes that were engulfed by a larger cell.
27. The ER manufactures more phospholipid membrane.
28. Vesicles are used for temporary transport and storage. Vacuoles tend to be more permanent features of a cell.
29. Only cells with the proper receptors will respond to a specific ligand.
30. *Sample Answer:* Transporting proteins and removing wastes.
31. Like active transport, facilitated diffusion requires membrane proteins. Like passive transport, facilitated diffusion occurs down a concentration gradient and does not require energy.

Interpreting Visuals

32. Protein synthesis and secretion. We see the vesicle-wrapped proteins leaving the ribosomes and ER, getting processed and repackaged in the Golgi apparatus, and being released by exocytosis.
33. The cell would run out of the amino acids needed for protein synthesis.
34. They must be the same or very similar in order to fuse.

Critical Thinking

25. Summarize How was the development of cell theory closely tied to advancements in technology? **NOS.10**

26. Analyze What structural differences suggest that eukaryotic cells evolved from prokaryotic cells?

27. Synthesize If vesicles are almost constantly pinching off from the ER to carry proteins to the Golgi apparatus, why does the ER not shrink and finally disappear?

28. Compare and Contrast You know that both vesicles and vacuoles are hollow compartments used for storage. How do they differ in function?

29. Infer When cells release ligands, they are sent through the blood stream to every area of the body. Why do you think that only certain types of cells will respond to a particular ligand?

30. Provide Examples What are two ways in which exocytosis might help a cell maintain homeostasis?

31. Compare How is facilitated diffusion similar to both passive transport and active transport? **B.2.2**

Interpreting Visuals

Use the diagram to answer the next three questions.

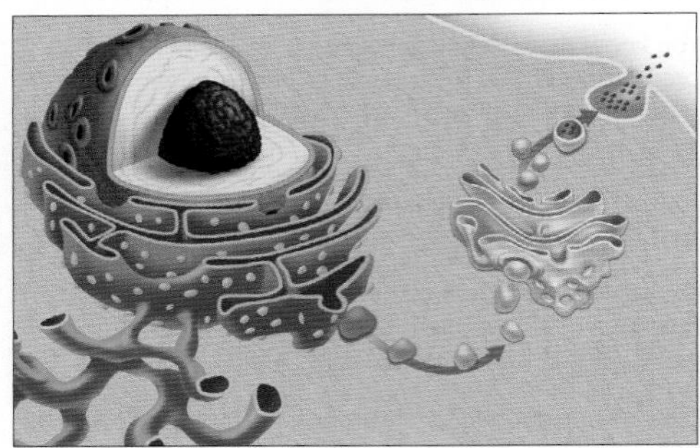

32. Apply What process is occurring in the diagram, and how do you know? **B.2.4**

33. Predict If the transport proteins that carry amino acids into this cell stopped working, how might the process shown be affected? **B.2.4**

34. Infer What might you conclude about the membrane structure of the final vesicle and the cell membrane? **B.2.2**

Analyzing Data

Use the text and table below to answer the next three questions. Reactive oxygen species, or ROS, are clusters of highly reactive oxygen atoms that can damage the body. As people age, the amount of ROS in the body increases, causing a condition called oxidative stress. In one study, researchers studied how the number of mitochondria might be involved in this situation.

- Muscle tissue was obtained from patients.
- Radioactive probes labeled the mitochondria.
- A machine counted the mitochondria per cell.

AGE AND MUSCLE CELL MITOCHONDRIA

Patient	Age	Mitochondria per Muscle Cell
1	47	2026
2	89	2987
3	65	2752
4	38	1989

35. Apply If the independent variable in this study is age, what is the operational definition of the dependent variable?

36. Analyze What do the data show about the relationship between age and number of mitochondria?

37. Infer What might the relationship between age and number of mitochondria indicate about the increase in ROS levels?

Connecting CONCEPTS

38. Write an Analogy The cell membrane regulates what can enter and exit a cell. In eukaryotes, it encloses a complex group of organelles that carry out special jobs. Make an analogy to describe the cell membrane and the variety of organelles and processes that take place inside it. Explain any limitations of your analogy. **B.2.2**

39. Connect On page 69 of this chapter, you saw a picture of macrophages eating up bacteria. Identify the ways in which the cytoskeleton helps the macrophage carry out this job.

Analyzing Data

35. The number of radioactive-labeled mitochondria per muscle cells of different ages, as counted by machine.
36. As people age, the number of mitochondria per muscle cell increases.
37. *Sample Answer:* As people age, ROS levels might increase because there are more mitochondria. It is possible that the mitochondria make ROS as a byproduct.

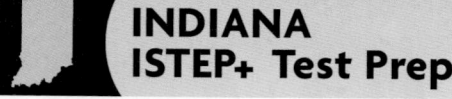

INDIANA ISTEP+ Test Prep

B.2.1; B.2.2; B.2.6; NOS.8

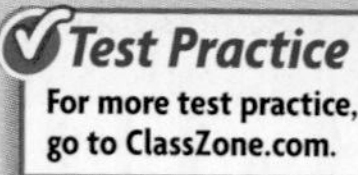

Test Practice
For more test practice, go to ClassZone.com.

1 The cell theory states that the cell is the most basic unit of life, all organisms are made of cells, and all cells come from cells. What makes the cell theory a scientific theory?

A It is based on a scientific publication that is read by scientists worldwide.
B It is based on the work of many scientists and leads to accurate predictions.
C It is based on ideas that have been proven true and that are not subject to revision.
D It is based on preliminary evidence but still needs to be confirmed with experiments.

2

Molecule Concentration Outside and Inside a Cell

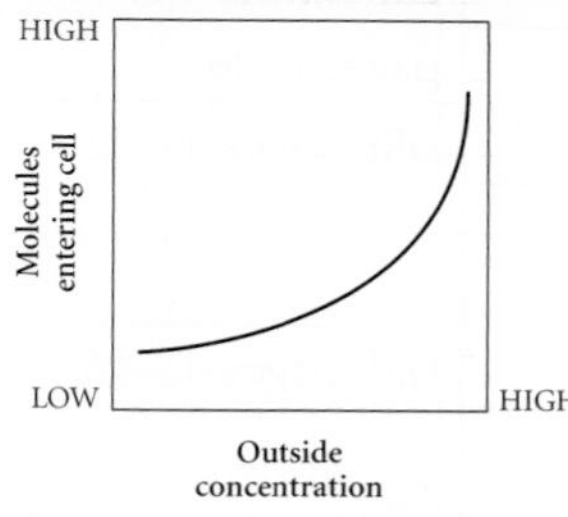

This graph shows that as the concentration of molecules increases outside of a cell, more and more molecules enter the cell. These molecules are able to enter the cell because the

A molecules are polar.
B cytoplasm is warm.
C cell membrane is semipermeable.
D nucleus is regulating movement.

THINK THROUGH THE QUESTION

Which answer choice explains why molecules can enter a cell?

3 Which of the following pairs incorrectly matches a cell structure with its function?

A cell membrane: protein synthesis
B nucleus: information (DNA) storage
C vacuole: storage
D chloroplast: energy conversion

4 Which of the following is a function of the Golgi apparatus?

A storing genetic information
B recycling waste products of the cell
C providing a protective barrier
D processing and storing proteins

5

Number of Mitochondria in Different Cell Types

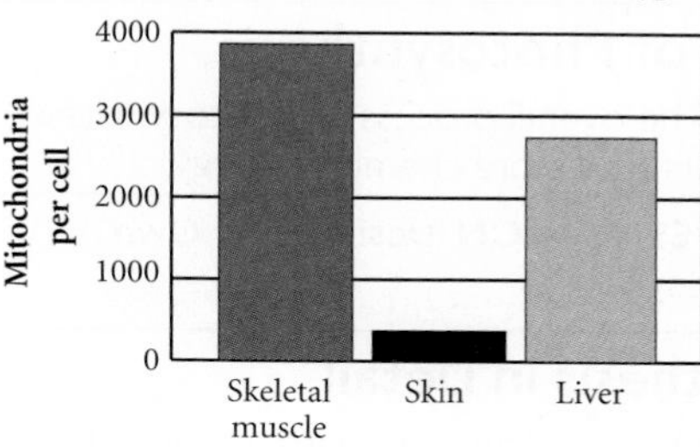

The graph shows the number of mitochondria per cell for different cell types. Which statement ***best*** explains these data?

A The number of mitochondria in the skin will increase if the number in the liver decreases.
B The liver requires the greatest amount of energy per cell.
C The skeletal muscle was taken from a very active athlete.
D The skin requires the least amount of energy per cell.

6 Some viruses attack cells by inserting their own DNA into the host cells' DNA. Why might it be simpler for these viruses to attack prokaryotic cells than eukaryotic cells?

Standards-Based Assessment

1. B	4. D
2. C	5. D
3. A	6. See Below

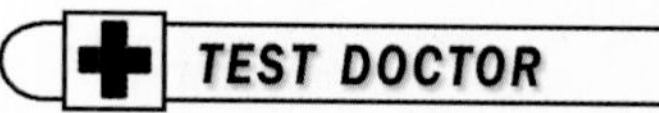

Question 1 Answer B is correct. Answer A is incorrect because a single publication is not sufficient evidence to support a theory. Answer C is incorrect because a theory can change based on new evidence. Answer D is incorrect because preliminary evidence is not sufficient to support a theory; a theory explains a wide range of experimental results.

Question 3 Answer A is correct because protein synthesis occurs on ribosomes, not in the cell membrane. Answers B, C, and D are incorrect because they correctly pair cell structure and function.

Question 6 Prokaryotic cells do not have a nucleus. It is possible that the DNA is more protected in a eukaryotic cell.

Connecting Concepts

38. An analogy that could work in this case would compare a cell to a city that has various industries, modes of transport, and a defined but permeable border. The cell nucleus could be compared to a city government. A limitation of this analogy would be that industries may be able to function or produce their products without instruction or material from the government.

39. The cytoskeleton enables macrophages to move and capture the bacteria.

ITEM CORRELATIONS

Standard	Items
B.2.1	3, 4, 6
B.2.2	2
B.2.6	5
NOS.8	1

CHAPTER 4

Indiana Resource Preview

Print Resources

Cells and Energy

INDIANA STANDARDS		Sections	PAGES and PACING	UNIT RESOURCE BOOK
B.3.2	4.1	**Chemical Energy and ATP** **KEY CONCEPT** All cells need chemical energy.	pp. 100–102 30 minutes	URB pages 31–34
B.3.1	4.2	**Overview of Photosynthesis** **KEY CONCEPT** The overall process of photosynthesis produces sugars that store chemical energy.	pp. 103–105 30 minutes	URB pages 35–38
NOS.1, NOS.3		CHAPTER INVESTIGATION: Design Your Own Rates of Photosynthesis	pp. 106–107 90 minutes	**Lab Binder** Cells pages 13–16
B.3.1	4.3	**Photosynthesis in Detail** **KEY CONCEPT** Photosynthesis requires a series of chemical reactions.	pp. 108–112 30 minutes	URB pages 39–42
B.3.2	4.4	**Overview of Cellular Respiration** **KEY CONCEPT** The overall process of cellular respiration converts sugar into ATP using oxygen.	pp. 113–115 30 minutes	URB pages 43–46
NOS.1		DATA ANALYSIS: Interpreting Graphs Photosynthesis and Plants	p. 116 15 minutes	URB page 55
B.3.2	4.5	**Cellular Respiration in Detail** **KEY CONCEPT** Cellular respiration is an aerobic process with two main stages.	pp. 117–121 30 minutes	URB pages 47–50
B.3.3	4.6	**Fermentation** **KEY CONCEPT** Fermentation allows the production of a small amount of ATP without oxygen	pp. 122–125 45 minutes	URB pages 51–54
NOS.1, NOS.3		OPTIONS FOR INQUIRY	pp. 126–127 45 minutes, 45 minutes	**Lab Binder** Cells pages 17–20
		Chapter Review	pp. 128–131	**Assessment Book** Chapter Tests A, B pages 73–80

INDIANA STANDARDS

B.3.1 Describe how some organisms capture the sun's energy through the process of photosynthesis by converting carbon dioxide and water into high energy compounds and releasing oxygen.

B.3.2 Describe how most organisms can combine and recombine the elements contained in sugar molecules into a variety of biologically essential compounds by utilizing the energy from cellular respiration.

B.3.3 Recognize and describe that metabolism consists of all of the biochemical reactions that occur inside cells, including the production, modification, transport, and exchange of materials that are required for the maintenance of life.

NOS.1 Develop explanations based on reproducible data and observations gathered during laboratory investigations.

NOS.3 Clearly communicate their ideas and results of investigations verbally and in written form using tables, graphs, diagrams, and photographs.

Labs

PUPIL EDITION LABS

Rates of Photosynthesis, pp. 106–107 Students design an experiment to test the effect of different light sources on the rate of photosynthesis. **Lab Binder** pp. 13–16	**Time:** 90 minutes **Materials:** young ivy leaves, hole punch, 2 100-mL beakers, 5-mL sodium bicarbonate/detergent solution, water, plastic 10 cc syringe, forceps, strong light source, other light sources, stopwatch
Fermentation, Section 6, p. 124 Students measure the amount of fermentation in various beverages. **Lab Binder** pp. 21–22	**Time:** 20–30 minutes **Materials:** 2 empty plastic bottles, 1 package of yeast, 2 100-mL graduated cylinders, 2 250-mL beakers, 2 beverages, 2 round balloons, 30 cm string, metric ruler

OPTIONS FOR INQUIRY

Cellular Respiration, p. 126 Students investigate cellular respiration in dormant and germinated seeds. **Lab Binder** pp. 17–19	**Time:** 45 minutes **Materials:** 3 test tubes, marking pen, 6 pre-soaked seeds, 6 dry seeds, 6 cotton plugs, 1.5 teaspoons potassium hydroxide (KOH) powder, rubber band, 100-mL beaker, 25 mL colored water, metric ruler
Investigate Fermentation in Foods, p. 127 Students determine what conditions affect the rate of fermentation. **Lab Binder** p. 20	**Time:** 45 minutes **Materials:** plastic bottles, yeast, foods or beverages containing sugar, warm water, round balloons, balance, spatula, graduated cylinders, paper towels, string, metric ruler

LAB BINDER Unit 2 Cells

Additional Investigation: Designing an Experiment to Test a Hypothesis, pp. 23–28

Vernier Probeware Lab: Photosynthesis and Respiration, pp. 59–61; The Effect of Temperature on Respiration, pp. 79–82

Virtual Lab Worksheet: Carbon Transfer Through Snails and *Elodea,* p. 83

LAB GENERATOR

A searchable CD of all labs in the program in editable format, including forensic, probeware, and biotechnology labs.

Presentation Tools

POWER PRESENTATIONS

Presentation Chapter 4
PowerPresentations for each section incorporate images and clips from the Media Gallery. Includes Note Navigator for each section.

MEDIA GALLERY

Contains the following images and video clips, as well as animations, simulations, and forms of visuals from the book.

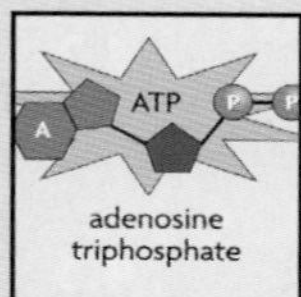

ATP-ADP interaction

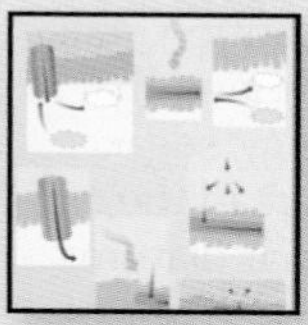
Cellular energy

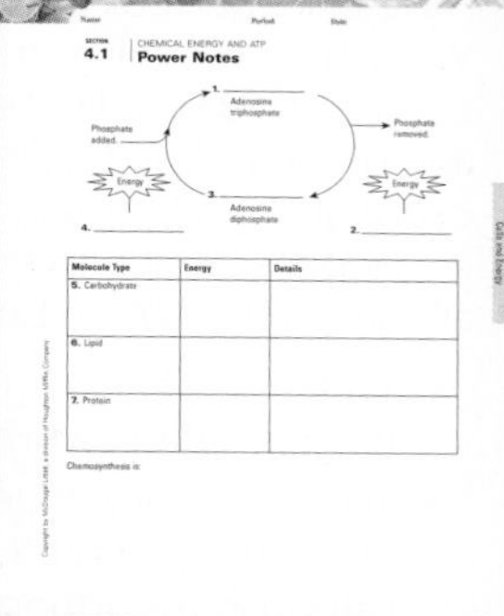

Power Notes

Weightlifter

Volvox

VIDEO

View a short video clip exploring fermentation.

ANIMATED BIOLOGY

Photosynthesis
Cellular Respiration
Mirror Processes

TRANSPARENCIES

ATP and ADP T18
Photosynthesis T19
Light-Dependent Reactions T20
The Calvin Cycle T21
Cellular Respiration T22
The Krebs Cycle T23
The Electron Transport Chain T24
Fermentation T25

Online BIOLOGY CLASSZONE.COM

BioZine
Animated Biology
Interactive Review
SciLinks
Resource Centers

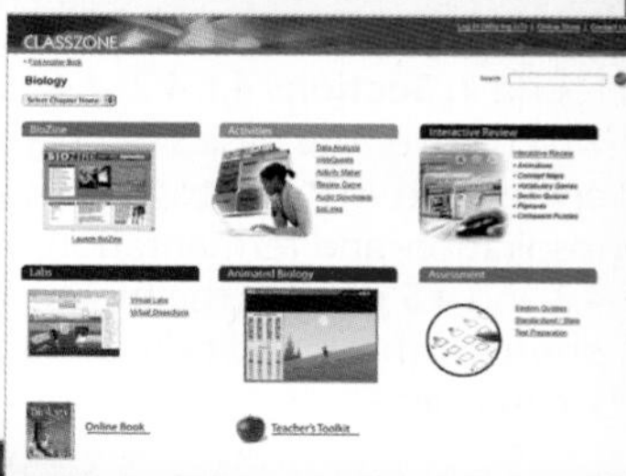

CHAPTER

4

▼ Focus and Motivate

What makes these cells so important to many other organisms?

Have students look at the caption. **Ask,** What are three things mentioned that are critical to your life? energy, sugar, and oxygen Have students read the explanation. Tell students that diatoms are responsible for up to 25 percent of all carbon fixation on Earth. **Ask**

- What is another name for carbon fixation? photosynthesis
- Why does carbon need to be fixed? Organisms cannot use inorganic carbon in the atmosphere until it is "fixed" and incorporated into the organic molecules necessary for life.
- What types of organic molecules are necessary for life? carbohydrates (including sugar), lipids, nucleic acids, and proteins
- How does a whale use the organic molecules it gets from feeding on diatoms? breaks them down for materials and energy needed to maintain life

BIOZINE ClassZone.com

Students can access BioZine at **ClassZone.com** to receive updates to featured topics in the book.

In a Hurry?

The critical material of the chapter is found in **Sections 4.1, 4.2, 4.4,** and **4.6**—which cover the basics of chemical energy and ATP, photosynthesis, cellular respiration, and fermentation. **Sections 4.3** and **4.5** present the biochemistry of photosynthesis and cellular respiration in greater detail.

CHAPTER 4

Cells and Energy

KEY CONCEPTS

4.1 Chemical Energy and ATP
All cells need chemical energy.

4.2 Overview of Photosynthesis
The overall process of photosynthesis produces sugars that store chemical energy.

4.3 Photosynthesis in Detail
Photosynthesis requires a series of chemical reactions.

4.4 Overview of Cellular Respiration
The overall process of cellular respiration converts sugar into ATP using oxygen.

4.5 Cellular Respiration in Detail
Cellular respiration is an aerobic process with two main stages.

4.6 Fermentation
Fermentation allows the production of a small amount of ATP without oxygen.

Online BIOLOGY CLASSZONE.COM

View animated chapter concepts.
- Photosynthesis
- Cellular Respiration
- Carbon Dioxide Transfer Through Snails and Elodea
- Mirror Processes

BIOZINE

Keep current with biology news.
- News feeds
- Careers
- Bio Bytes

RESOURCE CENTER

Get more information on
- Chemosynthesis
- Photosynthesis
- Fermentation

Student Activity

Purpose **Using a drinking straw to exhale into limewater, students will observe that one of the end products of cellular respiration is carbon dioxide.**

Safety Note Warn students to be careful not to inhale through the straw when doing this activity.

Materials (per team)

100 mL limewater

1 drinking straw per student

500-mL (1-pint) jar or glass

Prepare Dissolve one tablespoon of lime (calcium hydroxide, garden lime, or pickling lime) in about 1 L of water. Cover and let stand overnight. Pour off clear liquid (limewater) into a second jar, discard the residue, and cover.

colored SEM; magnification 1000×

What makes these cells so important to many other organisms?

Connecting CONCEPTS

These diatoms are single-celled algae that use the process of photosynthesis to store chemical energy in sugars. Animals eat photosynthetic organisms such as plants and algae to get this chemical energy. Photosynthetic organisms also produce the oxygen that is required to release much of the chemical energy in sugars.

Ecology Microscopic diatoms are absolutely necessary for the survival of other marine organisms, including the humpback whale. Why? Diatoms are eaten by small, shrimplike animals called krill. In turn, humpbacks and several other species of whales feed mainly on krill. In fact, a blue whale's stomach can hold more than a ton of krill.

Introduce Tell students that limewater turns milky white when combined with carbon dioxide. Have them take turns using their straws to blow gently into the limewater. As they do so, ask students to think about what happens every time they take a breath. They should continue blowing into the limewater until it turns a milky white. **Ask,** How is the air you exhale different from the air you inhale? Exhaled breath has much more carbon dioxide than air that is inhaled.

Discuss Point out that limewater turns milky white because it combines with carbon dioxide to form a white compound called calcium carbonate, or limestone, which is insoluble in water. If the white solution is allowed to stand for several hours, the calcium carbonate will settle to the bottom of the jar.

Ask, Where do you think the carbon dioxide comes from? It is given off by cells as a product of cellular respiration, transported to the lungs, and exhaled.

Activate Prior Knowledge

Direct students to the chapter title. **Ask,** What cellular activities require energy? Students may suggest obvious things such as muscle cells contracting, repair of body tissue, transmission of nerve impulses, but practically all cellular activity requires an input of energy. Have students think about the energy drinks and power bars that are widely consumed. **Ask,** Do energy drinks and power bars do something different from any other food that you eat? Explain. They may contain certain types of carbohydrates that can be used more quickly and so supply energy faster. Point out that an energy bar provides no more energy than a bagel or a banana. The human body has enough stored energy in fat and glycogen to allow someone to run several back-to-back marathons.

Preview Vocabulary

Academic Vocabulary Tell students that the processes described in this chapter can be summed up by one word: *metabolism.* Metabolism is the total of all the chemical processes that occur in an organism.

Metabolic processes take one of two directions. Either they are *synthetic* processes that build up material and store energy, or they are *catabolic* processes that break material down, often releasing energy. (The root *cata-* means to "fall or drop down," whereas *meta-* means "change.")

Chemosynthesis and *photosynthesis* are synthetic processes that capture the energy needed for life and store it in sugars. *Cellular respiration* and *fermentation* are catabolic processes that break down sugars and deliver energy to sustain life.

English Learners Tell students that they will be studying processes in this chapter that occur either as a *cycle* or *sequence* of events. **Ask,** What shape would you expect to use if you were drawing a cycle? circle a sequence? straight line Discuss how a cycle repeats, while a sequence has a distinct beginning point and endpoint. Have students point out examples of each in the chapter.

SECTION 4.1

▼ Plan and Prepare

Objectives

- Recognize the importance of ATP as an energy-carrying molecule.
- Identify energy sources used by organisms.

Section Resources

Unit Resource Book Study Guide pp. 31–32 Power Notes p. 33 Reinforcement p. 34 Pre-AP Activity pp. 57–58
Interactive Reader Chapter 4 **Spanish Study Guide** pp. 31–32
Biology Toolkit pp. C26, C28, C39, D9
Technology Power Presentation 4.1 Media Gallery DVD Online Quiz 4.1

Activate Prior Knowledge Ask students to think about how smaller units are sometimes more convenient. **Ask,** Would you rather have fifty $1 bills or one $50 bill? One-dollar bills have more practical use, in vending machines for example; $50 bills are less readily accepted. Tell students that energy in organisms is packaged in small units. These "energy packets" will be introduced in this chapter.

▼ Teach

TEACH FROM VISUALS

VISUAL VOCAB Have students compare the molecular structures of ATP and ADP. **Ask**

- How are ATP and ADP alike? Both contain adenosine and phosphate groups.
- How are they different? ATP has three phosphate groups; ADP two.
- Why is this difference important? The extra bond is a potential source of energy.

4.1 Chemical Energy and ATP

KEY CONCEPT All cells need chemical energy.

MAIN IDEAS

- The chemical energy used for most cell processes is carried by ATP.
- Organisms break down carbon-based molecules to produce ATP.
- A few types of organisms do not need sunlight and photosynthesis as a source of energy.

VOCABULARY

ATP, p. 100
ADP, p. 101
chemosynthesis, p. 102

Review
carbohydrate, lipid, protein

B.3.2 Describe how most organisms can combine and recombine the elements contained in sugar molecules into a variety of biologically essential compounds by utilizing the energy from cellular respiration.

Connect The cells of all organisms—from algae to whales to people—need chemical energy for all of their processes. Some organisms, such as diatoms and plants, absorb energy from sunlight. Some of that energy is stored in sugars. Cells break down sugars to produce usable chemical energy for their functions. Without organisms that make sugars, living things on Earth could not survive.

MAIN IDEA

The chemical energy used for most cell processes is carried by ATP.

Sometimes you may feel that you need energy, so you eat food that contains sugar. Does food, which contains sugar and other carbon-based molecules, give you energy? The answer to this question is yes and no. All of the carbon-based molecules in food store chemical energy in their bonds. Carbohydrates and lipids are the most important energy sources in foods you eat. However, this energy is only usable after these molecules are broken down by a series of chemical reactions. Your energy does come from food, but not directly.

All cells, like that in **FIGURE 4.1**, use chemical energy carried by ATP—adenosine triphosphate. **ATP** is a molecule that transfers energy from the breakdown of food molecules to cell processes. You can think of ATP as a wallet filled with money. Just as a wallet carries money that you can spend, ATP carries chemical energy that cells can use. Cells use ATP for functions such as building molecules and moving materials by active transport.

VISUAL VOCAB

ATP transfers energy to cell processes.

adenosine triphosphate tri=3

ADP is a lower-energy molecule that can be converted into ATP.

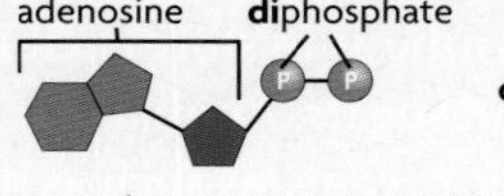

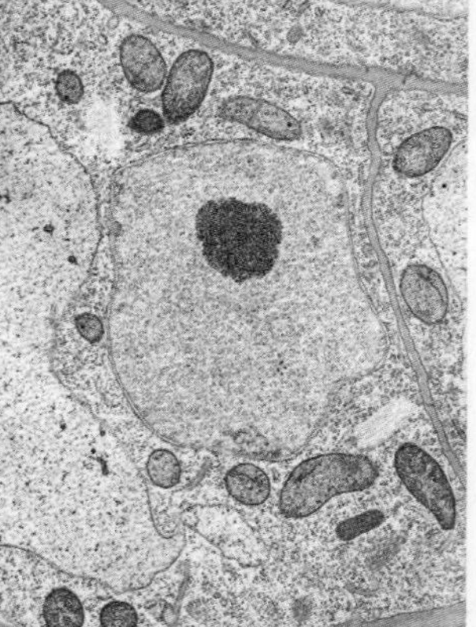

FIGURE 4.1 All cells, including plant cells, use ATP for energy. (colored TEM; magnification 9,000×)

The energy carried by ATP is released when a phosphate group is removed from the molecule. ATP has three phosphate groups, but the bond holding the third phosphate group is unstable and is very easily broken. The removal of the third phosphate group usually involves a reaction that releases energy.

Differentiated Instruction

ENGLISH LEARNERS

Point out the wallet-money analogy used in the text. Have students look at the wording to see how the comparison is made. The word *as* signals the analogy: ". . . think of ATP as a wallet filled with money. Just as a wallet carries money, ATP carries chemical energy."

Prompt students to develop the analogy further. For example, energy and money are resources that can be "spent." They both must be "earned" and "stored." Both have value.

Biology Toolkit, Analogies, p. D9

PRE-AP

The material in this chapter first looks at energy processes in overview and then in detail. Suggest to students that they use Cornell notes to outline this chapter, so they can incorporate drawings into their notes. In their summaries, have students think about how material in one section relates to another.

Biology Toolkit, Cornell Notes, p. C26

FIGURE 4.2 ATP and ADP

Adding a phosphate group to ADP forms ATP.

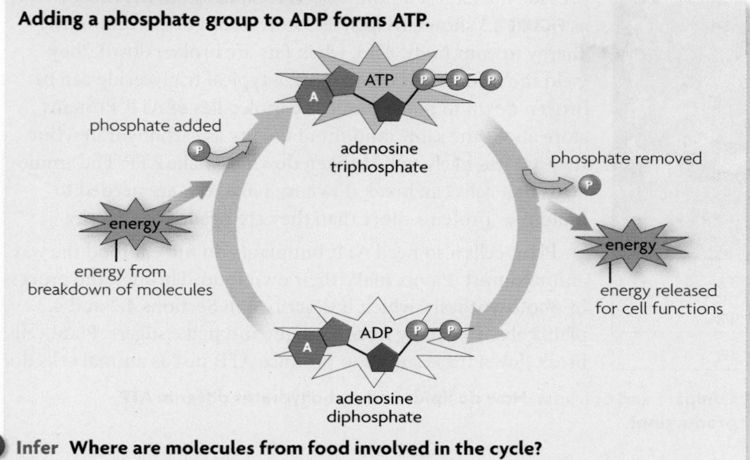

A Infer **Where are molecules from food involved in the cycle?**

When the phosphate is removed, energy is released and ATP becomes ADP—adenosine diphosphate. **ADP** is a lower-energy molecule that can be converted into ATP by the addition of a phosphate group. If ATP is a wallet filled with money, ADP is a nearly empty wallet. The breakdown of ATP to ADP and the production of ATP from ADP can be represented by the cycle shown in **FIGURE 4.2.** However, adding a phosphate group to ADP to make ATP is not a simple process. A large, complex group of proteins is needed to do it. In fact, if just one of these proteins is faulty, ATP is not produced.

B Synthesize **Describe the relationship between energy stored in food and ATP.**

TAKING NOTES

Use a supporting main ideas chart to organize concepts related to chemical energy.

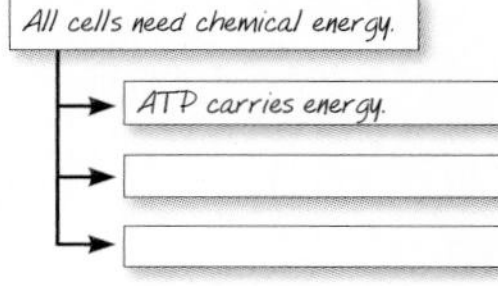

MAIN IDEA

Organisms break down carbon-based molecules to produce ATP.

Foods that you eat do not contain ATP that your cells can use. First, the food must be digested. One function of digestion is to break down food into smaller molecules that can be used to make ATP. You probably know that different foods have different amounts of calories, which are measures of energy. Different foods also provide different amounts of ATP. The number of ATP molecules that are made from the breakdown of food is related to the number of calories in food, but not directly.

The number of ATP molecules produced depends on the type of molecule that is broken down—carbohydrate, lipid, or protein. Carbohydrates are not stored in large amounts in your body, but they are the molecules most commonly broken down to make ATP. The breakdown of the simple sugar glucose yields about 36 molecules of ATP.

***Connecting* CONCEPTS**

Biochemistry As you learned in **Chapter 2**, carbon-based molecules in living things—carbohydrates, lipids, proteins, and nucleic acids—have different structures and functions.

ENGLISH LEARNERS

Show students how a cycle diagram can be a useful tool for understanding what they have read and for summarizing scientific information. Have students list the events in the ADP/ATP cycle. Point out that there are two distinct sets of arrows: blue for phosphate and gold for energy. Have students talk about the diagram, making statements about the cycle of events.

Biology Toolkit, Cycle Diagram, p. C39

BELOW LEVEL

Model using a graphic organizer, such as a mind map, to organize material in this section. Start with ATP in a central circle, then on four diagonal lines branching from the center, have students suggest statements that relate to the ATP. Possible statements: It is an energy carrier; it gets energy from the breakdown of food molecules; it is produced when phosphate is added to ADP; and it releases energy when converted back to ADP. Have students copy the map into their notebooks.

Biology Toolkit, Mind Map, p. C28

TEACH FROM VISUALS

FIGURE 4.2 Have students connect the diagram to **VISUAL VOCAB** and follow the triphosphate-diphosphate cycle. **Ask,** When is energy available for cell processes? after a phosphate is removed from ATP

Integrating Chemistry

Remind students that a phosphate group is a **polyatomic ion,** that is, a charged group of atoms that are held together by covalent bonds. Each phosphate group in ATP is negatively charged. Because the groups are crowded together, yet repel each other due to their like charges, the bonds between phosphate groups are unstable.

ATP can be thought of as a compressed spring that stores potential energy. When the third phosphate group is removed, the "spring" relaxes and energy is released. ADP is analogous to the relaxed spring that has released its potential energy but can be compressed again.

Vocabulary

Calorie A food Calorie (also called a kilocalorie; 1000 calories) is the amount of heat energy required to raise the temperature of one kilogram of water by 1°C. When a mole of ATP is converted to ADP in a cell, about 7.3 Calories (7.3 kilocalories) of energy are released.

Answers

A Infer Food molecules are supplying the energy to add phosphate to ADP (shown to the left) and convert it to ATP.

B Synthesize Food molecules store chemical energy in their bonds. Food is broken down into smaller molecules that are broken down further to transfer this energy to ATP.

▼ Teach *continued*

ONLINE BIOLOGY Go to the chapter Resource Center at **ClassZone.com** for additional resources and information on chemosynthesis.

Integrating Physics

Most **wavelengths of light** are either absorbed or scattered by water. In clear ocean water, visible light decreases about 10-fold with each 75 meters (246 feet) of depth. Only 1 percent of the light at the surface reaches a depth of 150 meters (492 feet). Some photosynthetic organisms, such as red algae, can live at greater depths because they contain light-absorbing molecules that absorb the blue and green wavelengths that penetrate deeper into the water. Below 150 meters (492 feet), producers capture energy from chemical compounds through the process of chemosynthesis.

Answers

A Compare and Contrast Lipids provide more ATP than carbohydrates do.

B Compare Both chemosynthetic organisms and plants make their own food and both are eaten by other organisms that cannot make their own food.

▼ Assess and Reteach

Assess Use the Online Quiz or Section Quiz (*Assessment Book*, p. 67).

Reteach As a class, review **FIGURE 4.2.** Have students close their books and draw and label the diagram from memory.

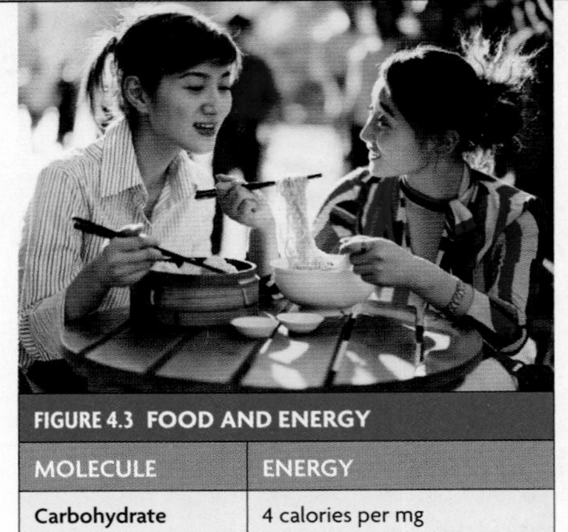

FIGURE 4.3 FOOD AND ENERGY

MOLECULE	ENERGY
Carbohydrate	4 calories per mg
Lipid	9 calories per mg
Protein	4 calories per mg

You might be surprised to learn that carbohydrates do not provide the largest amount of ATP. Lipids store the most energy, as **FIGURE 4.3** shows. In fact, fats store about 80 percent of the energy in your body. And, when fats are broken down, they yield the most ATP. For example, a typical triglyceride can be broken down to make about 146 molecules of ATP. Proteins store about the same amount of energy as carbohydrates, but they are less likely to be broken down to make ATP. The amino acids that cells can break down to make ATP are needed to build new proteins more than they are needed for energy.

Plant cells also need ATP, but plants do not eat food the way animals must. Plants make their own food. Through the process of photosynthesis, which is described in Sections 4.2 and 4.3, plants absorb energy from sunlight and make sugars. Plant cells break down these sugars to produce ATP, just as animal cells do.

A Compare and Contrast How do lipids and carbohydrates differ in ATP production?

MAIN IDEA

A few types of organisms do not need sunlight and photosynthesis as a source of energy.

Most organisms rely directly or indirectly on sunlight and photosynthesis as their source of chemical energy. But some organisms do not need sunlight. In places that never get sunlight, such as in the deep ocean, there are areas with living things. Some organisms live in very hot water near cracks in the ocean floor called hydrothermal vents. These vents release chemical compounds, such as sulfides, that can serve as an energy source. **Chemosynthesis** (KEE-mo-SIHN-thih-sihs) is a process by which some organisms use chemical energy instead of light energy to make energy-storing carbon-based molecules. However, these organisms still need ATP for energy. The processes that make their ATP are very similar to those in other organisms. Like plants, chemosynthetic organisms make their own food. It is the raw materials that differ.

B Compare How are chemosynthetic organisms and plants similar as energy

4.1 ASSESSMENT

ONLINE QUIZ ClassZone.com

B.3.2

REVIEWING MAIN IDEAS

1. How are **ATP** and **ADP** related?
2. What types of molecules are broken down to make ATP? Which are most often broken down to make ATP?
3. How are some organisms able to survive without sunlight and photosynthesis?

CRITICAL THINKING

4. **Apply** Describe how you do not get energy directly from the food that you eat.
5. **Compare and Contrast** How are the energy needs of plant cells similar to those of animal cells? How are they different?

Connecting CONCEPTS

6. **Chemical Reactions** A water molecule is added to an ATP molecule to break down ATP into ADP and a phosphate group. Write the chemical equation that represents this reaction.

4.1 ASSESSMENT

1. High-energy ATP molecules are converted into lower-energy ADP molecules when a phosphate is removed and energy is released. ADP is converted back into ATP by the addition of a phosphate.
2. Carbohydrates, lipids, and proteins; lipids and carbohydrates are the main sources of ATP.
3. Chemosynthetic organisms use chemicals from their environment to make high-energy carbon-based molecules.
4. Food is not directly used for energy, but it is broken down to make ATP, which provides energy.
5. Both plants and animals use ATP to power cell functions. Plants make their own food to be broken down to make ATP; animals must consume other organisms for the food that is broken down to make ATP.
6. $H_2O + ATP \rightarrow ADP + P$

4.2 Overview of Photosynthesis

KEY CONCEPT The overall process of photosynthesis produces sugars that store chemical energy.

MAIN IDEAS

- Photosynthetic organisms are producers.
- Photosynthesis in plants occurs in chloroplasts.

VOCABULARY

photosynthesis, p. 103
chlorophyll, p. 103
thylakoid, p. 104
light-dependent reactions, p. 105
light-independent reactions, p. 105

Review
chemical reaction, carbohydrate, enzyme, chloroplast

B.3.1 Describe how some organisms capture the sun's energy through the process of photosynthesis by converting carbon dioxide and water into high energy compounds and releasing oxygen.

Connect Solar-powered calculators, homes, and cars are just a few things that use energy from sunlight. In a way, you are also solar-powered. Of course, sunlight does not directly give you the energy you need to play a sport or read this page. That energy comes from ATP. Molecules of ATP are often made from the breakdown of sugars, but how are sugars made? Plants capture some of the energy in sunlight and change it into chemical energy stored in sugars.

MAIN IDEA

Photosynthetic organisms are producers.

Some organisms are called producers because they produce the source of chemical energy for themselves and for other organisms. Plants, as well as some bacteria and protists, are the producers that are the main sources of chemical energy for most organisms on Earth. Certainly, animals that eat only plants obtain their chemical energy directly from plants. Animals that eat other animals, and bacteria and fungi that decompose other organisms, get their chemical energy indirectly from plants. When a wolf eats a rabbit, the tissues of the rabbit provide the wolf with a source of chemical energy. The rabbit's tissues are built from its food source—the sugars and other carbon-based molecules in plants. These sugars are made through photosynthesis.

Photosynthesis is a process that captures energy from sunlight to make sugars that store chemical energy. Therefore, directly or indirectly, the energy for almost all organisms begins as sunlight. Sunlight has several types of radiant energy, such as ultraviolet radiation, microwaves, and the visible light that lets you see. Plants absorb visible light for photosynthesis. Visible light appears white, but it is made up of several colors, or wavelengths, of light.

Chlorophyll (KLAWR-uh-fihl) is a molecule in chloroplasts, shown in **FIGURE 4.4,** that absorbs some of the energy in visible light. Plants have two main types of chlorophyll, called chlorophyll *a* and chlorophyll *b*. Together, these two types of chlorophyll absorb mostly red and blue wavelengths of visible light. Neither type absorbs much green light. Plants have other light-absorbing molecules that absorb green light, but there are fewer of these molecules. As a result, the green color of plants comes from the reflection of light's green wavelengths by chlorophyll.

FIGURE 4.4 Chloroplasts in plant cells contain a light-absorbing molecule called chlorophyll. (leaf cell: colored TEM; magnification 4000×)

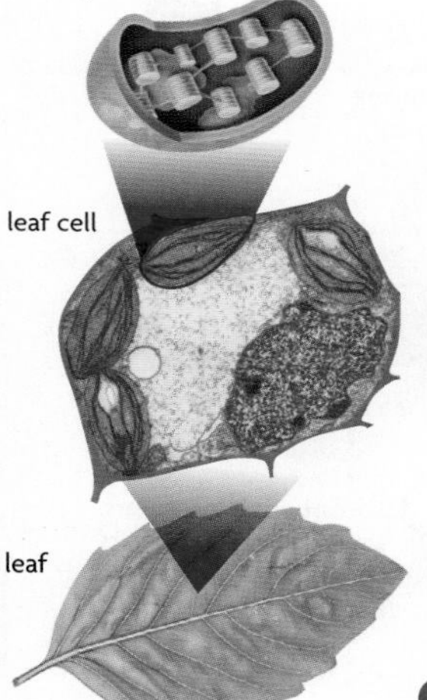

chloroplast

leaf cell

leaf

A Apply Describe the importance of producers and photosynthesis.

Differentiated Instruction

ENGLISH LEARNERS

Effective questioning helps students think more deeply as they read and develop their own questions about language and meaning. List some key questions to ask before, during, and after reading. Before: What do you already know about photosynthesis? What do you need to find out? During: What have you learned so far? What is new to you? After: What was the most important part of the reading? What questions do you still have?

Biology Toolkit, Questions to Guide Reading, p. C4

Plan and Prepare

Objectives

- Relate producers to photosynthesis.
- Describe the process of photosynthesis.

Section Resources

Unit Resource Book
Study Guide pp. 35–36
Power Notes p. 37
Reinforcement p. 38

Interactive Reader Chapter 4
Spanish Study Guide pp. 33–34

Biology Toolkit pp. C4, C19

Technology
Power Presentation 4.2
Media Gallery DVD
Online Quiz 4.2

Activate Prior Knowledge Have students think about the word *producer* in a different context. **Ask,** What do producers do who work in film, radio, television, and music-recording? oversee production of something they do not actually make Relate this to photosynthesis. Plants do not make energy; they capture it, store it, and deliver it. **Ask,** What law says that energy can be transformed but never created or destroyed? first law of thermodynamics

Teach

Vocabulary

chloroplast, chlorophyll Tell students these terms relate to plant color:

chloro- = "green"

The root *-phyll* or *phyllon* means "leaf," and the root *-plast* or *plastos* means "molded," as into an organized body.

Answers

A Apply Photosynthesis enables producers to capture energy from sunlight and make sugars that store chemical energy. The food produced becomes a source of energy for nonproducers.

▼ Teach *continued*

TEACH FROM VISUALS

FIGURE 4.5 Point out that the numbers in the figure correspond to the numbered list on page 105. **Ask**

- Where do the light-dependent and light-independent reactions occur? thylakoid membranes, stroma
- What two reactants are shown entering the chloroplast? water and carbon dioxide
- What two products are shown leaving the chloroplast? oxygen and sugar

Integrating Physics

The sunlight used in photosynthesis is a form of electromagnetic, or radiant, energy. The Sun produces a full spectrum of **electromagnetic radiation,** but Earth's atmosphere filters out much of it. The radiation that the atmosphere does allow in appears toward the middle of the spectrum, and this is what we see as color, or **visible light.**

Within the spectrum of visible light are different wavelengths that we associate with different colors. The wavelengths range from 400 to 700 nanometers (nm) on the electromagnetic spectrum, with blue light being the shortest wavelength at 400 nm and red light being the longest at 700 nm.

Light that comes to Earth may be reflected or absorbed. A substance that absorbs light is called a **pigment.** The colors we see result from reflected light, that is not absorbed by pigments. A leaf appears green because it reflects green light, while absorbing red and blue light.

Answers

A Identify The reactants are water and carbon dioxide. The products are sugar and oxygen.

MAIN IDEA

Photosynthesis in plants occurs in chloroplasts.

Chloroplasts are the membrane-bound organelles where photosynthesis takes place in plants. Most of the chloroplasts are in leaf cells that are specialized for photosynthesis, which has two main stages as shown in **FIGURE 4.5.** The two main parts of chloroplasts needed for photosynthesis are the grana and the stroma. Grana (singular, *granum*) are stacks of coin-shaped, membrane-enclosed compartments called **thylakoids** (THY-luh-KOYDZ). The membranes of the thylakoids contain chlorophyll, other light-absorbing molecules, and proteins. The stroma is the fluid that surrounds the grana inside a chloroplast.

FIGURE 4.5 Photosynthesis Overview

Chloroplasts absorb energy from sunlight and produce sugars through the process of photosynthesis.

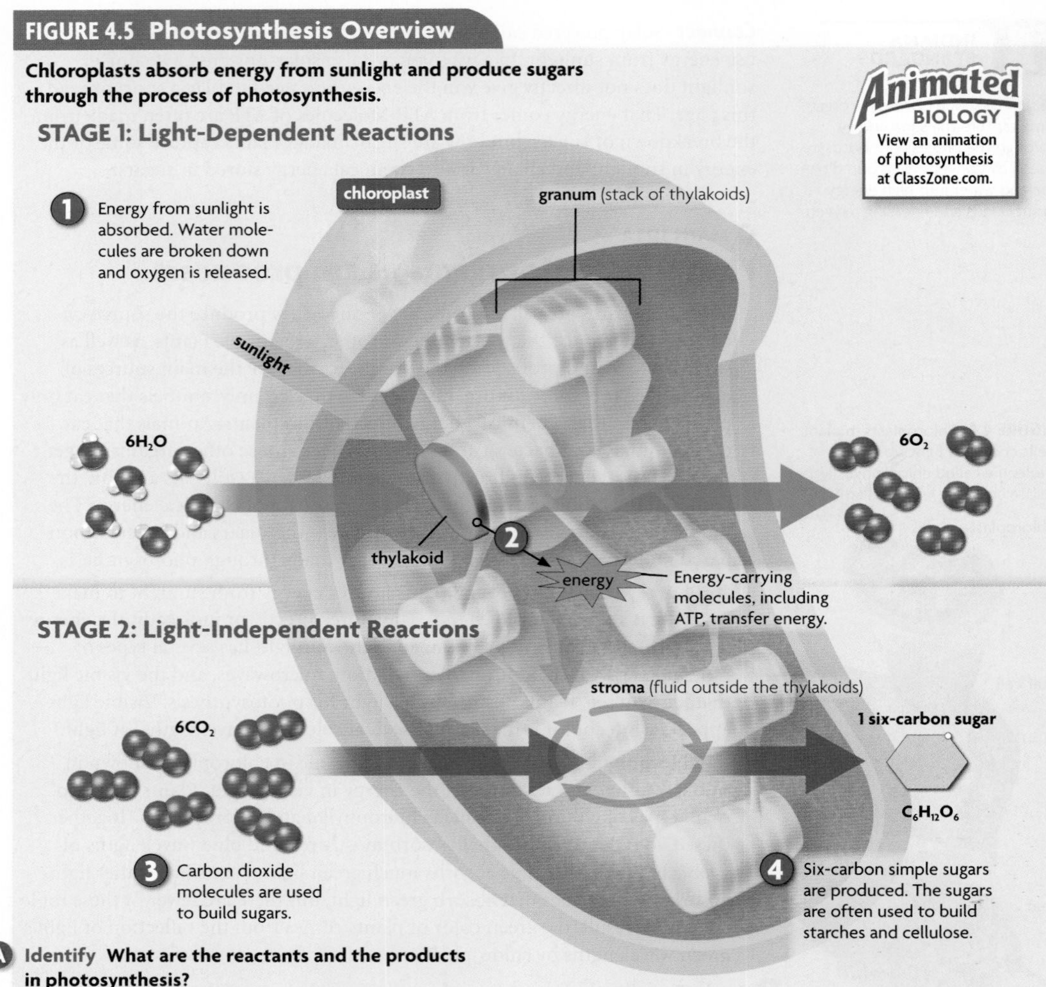

Animated BIOLOGY
View an animation of photosynthesis at ClassZone.com.
STAGE 1: Light-Dependent Reactions
chloroplast
granum (stack of thylakoids)
1 Energy from sunlight is absorbed. Water molecules are broken down and oxygen is released.
sunlight
$6H_2O$
$6O_2$
thylakoid
2
energy
Energy-carrying molecules, including ATP, transfer energy.
STAGE 2: Light-Independent Reactions
stroma (fluid outside the thylakoids)
$6CO_2$
1 six-carbon sugar
$C_6H_{12}O_6$
3 Carbon dioxide molecules are used to build sugars.
4 Six-carbon simple sugars are produced. The sugars are often used to build starches and cellulose.

A Identify What are the reactants and the products in photosynthesis?

Differentiated Instruction

BELOW LEVEL

Have students write about the process of photosynthesis. Ask them to break it down into the *photo-* part (light-dependent reactions that capture energy from sunlight) and the *-synthesis* part (light-independent reactions that produce sugars). Tell students to write continuously for five minutes, even if they simply end up writing the same thing over and over again. Suggest they look at **FIGURE 4.5** as they write.

Biology Toolkit, Quick-Write, p. C19

TEACH WITH TECHNOLOGY

If a PC microscope is available, project a slide of plant leaf cells onto a computer screen. Use a prepared slide or make a wet mount of an *Elodea* leaf. Point out the green chloroplasts. Have students locate the mesophyll cells in the center of the leaf that contain the most chloroplasts and recognize that these cells are where most photosynthesis occurs in a plant. As a comparison, project a slide of a root tip. **Ask,** Why do you think there are no chloroplasts in root cells? Root cells grow underground; they are not exposed to sunlight.

The **light-dependent reactions** capture energy from sunlight. These reactions take place within and across the membrane of the thylakoids. Water (H_2O) and sunlight are needed for this stage of photosynthesis.

1. Chlorophyll absorbs energy from sunlight. The energy is transferred along the thylakoid membrane. H_2O molecules are broken down. Oxygen molecules (O_2) are released.
2. Energy carried along the thylakoid membrane is transferred to molecules that carry energy, such as ATP.

The **light-independent reactions** use energy from the light-dependent reactions to make sugars. These reactions occur in the stroma of chloroplasts. Carbon dioxide molecules (CO_2) are needed during this stage of photosynthesis.

3. CO_2 is added to a cycle of chemical reactions to build larger molecules. Energy from the light-dependent reactions is used in the reactions.
4. A molecule of a simple sugar is formed. The sugar, usually glucose ($C_6H_{12}O_6$), stores some of the energy that was captured from sunlight.

Connecting CONCEPTS

Calvin Cycle The light-independent reactions include a series of chemical reactions called the Calvin cycle. You can read more about the Calvin cycle in **Section 4.3.**

The equation for the whole photosynthesis process is shown below. As you can see, there are many arrows between the reactants—CO_2 and H_2O—and the products—a six-carbon sugar and O_2. Those arrows tell you that photosynthesis has many steps. For example, the light-independent reactions need only one molecule of CO_2 at a time, and the six-carbon sugar comes from a reaction that combines two three-carbon sugars. Also, enzymes and other chemicals are needed, not just light, carbon dioxide, and water.

$$\underset{\text{carbon dioxide}}{6CO_2} + \underset{\text{water}}{6H_2O} \xrightarrow{\quad} \xrightarrow{\quad} \underset{\text{light, enzymes}}{\xrightarrow{\quad} \xrightarrow{\quad}} \xrightarrow{\quad} \xrightarrow{\quad} \underset{\text{a sugar}}{C_6H_{12}O_6} + \underset{\text{oxygen}}{6O_2}$$

Glucose and other simple sugars, such as fructose, are not the only carbohydrates that come from photosynthesis. Plants need the simple sugars to build starch and cellulose molecules. In effect, plants need photosynthesis for their growth and development. You will learn more about the importance of another product of photosynthesis—oxygen—in Sections 4.4 and 4.5.

A Summarize How is energy from sunlight used to make sugar molecules?

4.2 ASSESSMENT

ONLINE QUIZ ClassZone.com

B.3.1

REVIEWING MAIN IDEAS

1. What are the roles of chloroplasts and **chlorophyll** in **photosynthesis**?
2. Describe the stages of photosynthesis. Use the terms **thylakoid, light-dependent reactions,** and **light-independent reactions** in your answer.

CRITICAL THINKING

3. **Apply** Suppose you wanted to develop a light to help increase plant growth. What characteristics should the light have? Why?
4. **Analyze** Explain why photosynthesis is important for building the structure of plant cells.

Connecting CONCEPTS

5. **Chemical Reactions** Overall, do you think photosynthesis is endothermic or exothermic? Explain your answer.

4.2 ASSESSMENT

1. Photosynthesis occurs in chloroplasts, powered by energy captured by chlorophyll. Chlorophyll is a light-absorbing molecule located in chloroplasts.
2. The first stage of photosynthesis is the light-dependent reactions that take place in the thylakoids. Energy is absorbed from sunlight and transferred through the thylakoid membrane. The energy is used in the light-independent reactions to produce sugars.
3. The light should emit the optimal wavelengths, such as blue and red, to be absorbed by the pigments in plants.
4. In plants, the cell wall is responsible for structure and support. Cell walls are made from cellulose, which is a carbohydrate that is built up from sugars produced during photosynthesis.
5. Endothermic; it absorbs energy to produce sugars.

ONLINE BIOLOGY Go to the chapter Resource Center at **ClassZone.com** for additional resources and information on photosynthesis.

Vocabulary

light-dependent, light-independent Explain that these reactions were previously known as light reactions and dark reactions, respectively. These terms are no longer used, but students may still find them in books.

Address Misconceptions

Common Misconception Students often think that photosynthesis is a single reaction in which CO_2 and H_2O combine to form sugar and O_2.

Correcting the Misconception Have students look at **FIGURE 4.5,** then direct their attention to the equation on this page. Explain that the many arrows represent many steps.

Answers

A Summarize Energy from sunlight is absorbed to generate energy-carrying molecules. The energy-carrying molecules are transferred to the reactions that make sugars.

Assess and Reteach

Assess Use the Online Quiz or Section Quiz (*Assessment Book,* p. 68).

Reteach Draw an oval on the board to represent a chloroplast. Tell students to take a quick look at **FIGURE 4.5,** then close their books. Have students provide the details of photosynthesis to be filled in on the diagram.

INVESTIGATION

Time 90 minutes TEACHER TESTED
Teacher Preparation
Student Difficulty
Lab Binder Cells, pp. 13–16

Purpose Design an experiment to test the effect of different light sources on the rate of photosynthesis.

Overview Students will test different light sources on leaf disks. They will

- choose a light source, such as light color or intensity, as an independent variable
- design an experiment to test the effect of the light on photosynthesis in leaf disks
- test disks in water rather than bicarbonate solution as a control
- prepare leaf disks by first infusing them with CO_2 and then using them in the experiment

LAB PREPARATION

- Prepare a solution of sodium bicarbonate and detergent by dissolving 1/8 teaspoon of baking soda and 1 drop of diluted liquid dishwashing detergent in 300 mL water. Too much baking soda will cause CO_2 bubbles to form on the surface of the leaf disks, preventing them from sinking.
- Provide colored cellophane or filters for the light sources to test light color.

Safety Be sure to remove the needles from the syringes.

MATERIALS

- young ivy leaves
- hole punch
- 2 100-mL beakers
- 5 mL sodium bicarbonate/detergent solution
- water
- plastic 10-cc syringe
- forceps
- strong light source
- other light sources
- stopwatch

PROCESS SKILLS

- **Designing Experiments**
- **Analyzing**
- **Calculating**
- **Graphing**
- **Inferring**

NOS.1 Develop explanations based on reproducible data and observations gathered during laboratory investigations.

NOS.3 Clearly communicate their ideas and results of investigations verbally and in written form using tables, graphs, diagrams, and photographs.

Rates of Photosynthesis

Photosynthesis converts some of the energy absorbed from sunlight into the chemical energy of sugars. The process is also the major source of oxygen in Earth's atmosphere. In this lab you will design an experiment to determine the effect of different light sources on the rate of photosynthesis in leaves.

PROBLEM How does a light source affect the rate of photosynthesis?

PROCEDURE

1. Use the hole punch to make five disks from an ivy leaf.
2. Fill one beaker halfway with the sodium bicarbonate/detergent solution. Fill a second beaker with water.
3. Remove the plunger from the syringe and place the ivy leaf disks into the syringe. Insert the plunger and draw 5 cc (5 mL) of the sodium bicarbonate/detergent solution into the syringe as shown in the photograph below (left).
4. Hold the syringe so that the tip is pointing upwards. Push on the plunger to squirt out any air in the syringe.
5. Place your finger on the tip of the syringe, as shown in the photograph below (right). Withdraw the plunger to form a vacuum, but be careful to not pull the plunger all the way out of the syringe. When the vacuum is formed, the gases in the air spaces in the leaf disks move into the syringe and the solution diffuses into the air spaces. Shake the syringe several times while your finger is on the tip.
6. Take your finger off of the tip of the syringe. This causes the leaf disks to sink to the bottom of the syringe because they become more dense from the diffusion of solution into the air spaces.
7. Open the syringe by pulling the plunger almost all the way out. Place your finger over the tip of the syringe and turn it so the tip is pointing down. Carefully remove the plunger and pour the contents of the syringe into the beaker of water. Use the forceps to remove the leaf disks if they stick to the walls of the syringe.
8. Place the beaker with the leaf disks under the light source and immediately start the stopwatch. Record the time it takes for each leaf disk to float to the top of the water. Use the rate at which the disks float as an indirect measurement of the rate of photosynthesis.

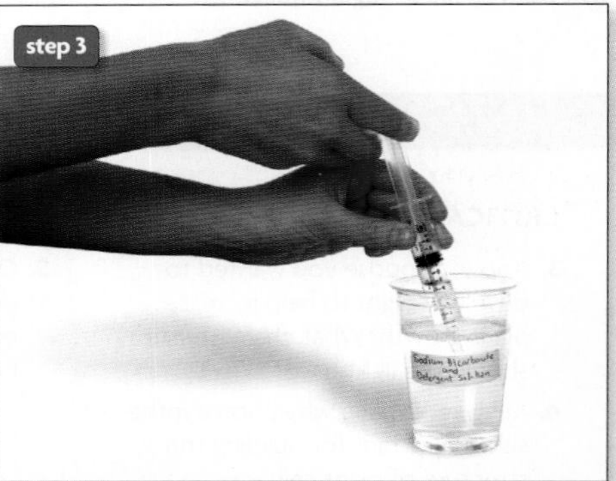

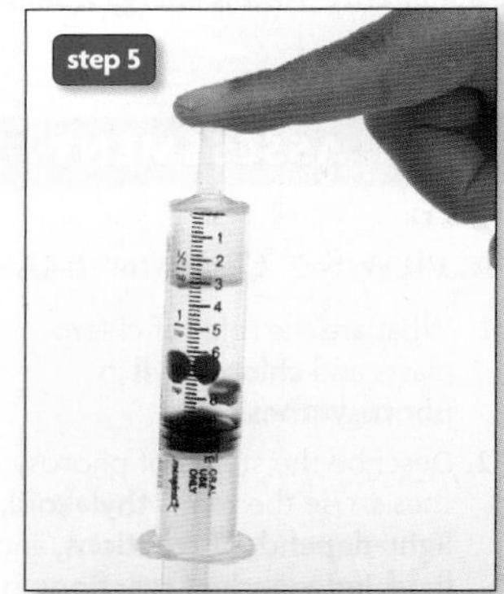

Answers

Sample Data

Students in the test group all tested red, blue, and green light color as the independent variable. Three sets of data are shown.

Sample 1
red light: 5 disks/35 s = 0.14 disks/s
blue light: 5 disks/26 s = 0.19 disks/s
green light: 5 disks/116 s = 0.04 disks/s

Sample 2
red light: 5 disks/32 s = 0.16 disks/s
blue light: 5 disks/20 s = 0.25 disks/s
green light: 5 disks/85 s = 0.06 disks/s

Sample 3
red light: 5 disks/39 s = 0.13 disks/s
blue light: 5 disks/35 s = 0.14 disks/s
green light: 5 disks/95 s = 0.05 disks/s

Analyze and Conclude

1. The independent variable will depend upon how students tested different light sources. The dependent variable is the rate of photosynthesis.

DESIGN

1. Decide how to test different light sources on the rate of photosynthesis. Identify your independent variable. Have your teacher approve your choice.
2. Identify your control condition and the constants in the experiment. Examples of constants are the distance between the light and the beaker, and the temperature of the water.
3. Write the procedure for your experiment.
4. Design a data table, such as the one shown below, to record and organize your results.

TABLE 1. THE EFFECT OF LIGHT SOURCES ON THE RATE OF PHOTOSYNTHESIS

Time (sec)	Type of light _______ (# of disks)	Type of light _______ (# of disks)	Type of light _______ (# of disks)
0	0	0	0

5. Gather the additional materials you need for your experiment.
6. Test the rate of photosynthesis using the procedure on page 106. Be sure not to get any water on the light sources. Record your results. Continue collecting data until all five disks float in each experimental condition. (**Note:** If you test more than one condition at once, record a time and disk count for all of the beakers every time a disk floats in any of the beakers.)
7. If time allows, conduct three trials of your experiment.

ANALYZE AND CONCLUDE

1. **Identify** What are the independent and dependent variables in your experiment?
2. **Calculate** Determine the mean rate of photosynthesis in each condition of your experiment. To calculate the rate of photosynthesis, use the formula below:

$$\frac{\textbf{5 (\# disks floating)}}{\textbf{total time (sec)}} = \underline{\quad\quad} \textbf{ disks/sec}$$

3. **Analyze** Determine the best type of graph to use to represent your data. Explain your choice and construct the graph. Be sure to carefully label the axes of the graph.
4. **Conclude** Based on your data, what can you conclude about how your independent variable affects the rate of photosynthesis?
5. **Infer** Why do you think sodium bicarbonate was used in this investigation? (**Hint:** Think about the equation for the overall process of photosynthesis.)
6. **Experimental Design** What are possible sources of unavoidable error in your design? Explain why they were present.
7. **Experimental Design** Identify possible reasons for inconsistent results.

2. Students should display calculations for all trials and then show an average for each group. For example, red light = 0.35 disks/sec, green light = 0.27 disks/sec
3. The best graph would be a bar graph, with a bar representing the average rate of each group of the independent variable. Students should indicate that a bar graph is best because the groups are independent of one another.
4. Answers should include an explanation about the relationship between students' manipulation of the independent variable and the data collected.
5. Sodium bicarbonate is used as a source of carbon dioxide gas, which is a necessary reactant of photosynthesis.
6. Answers could include change in water temperature, differences between leaf regions, and damage to leaf tissues; they account for random error in experiments.
7. differences in methods between groups, random error, measurement error

INVESTIGATION

LAB MANAGEMENT

- Students may need help designing their experiments. Help them choose their independent variables and decide which factors are to be controlled. Have students write an operational definition for their dependent variable.
- Place leaf disks in the solution so they do not dry out before use.
- Clear plastic cups or petri dishes can be substituted for beakers. If petri dishes are used, the beaker of water in Procedure step 2 is not needed. Add enough bicarbonate solution to the petri dish to cover the disks completely.
- If all the leaf disks do not sink in Procedure step 6, repeat step 5. Tell students to hold the vacuum for about 10 seconds. If disks still do not sink, add a bit more detergent to the solution.
- Tell students to avoid major veins in the leaf when making the disks.

POST-LAB DISCUSSION

Have students evaluate their experimental design. Ask them if they would change their procedure in any way. **Ask**

- What is the operational definition in this lab? number of leaf disks that floated in a measured amount of time
- Why is this a measure of the rate of photosynthesis? Floating is a sign that photosynthesis is occurring.
- What is meant by the mean rate of photosynthesis? the amount of photosynthesis performed by the average leaf disk

Discuss conclusions that can be made from the results. Students who test light color should conclude that plants use red and blue light but little green.

SECTION 4.3

▼ Plan and Prepare

Objectives

- Describe the light-dependent reactions in which energy is captured.
- Describe the light-independent reactions in which sugar is produced.

Section Resources

Unit Resource Book Study Guide pp. 39–40 Power Notes p. 41 Reinforcement p. 42
Interactive Reader Chapter 4 **Spanish Study Guide** pp. 35–36
Biology Toolkit pp. C2, C11, C14, C24, C30
Technology Power Presentation 4.3 Media Gallery DVD Online Quiz 4.3

Activate Prior Knowledge Remind students of atomic structure. **Ask,** Of all the particles that make up an atom, which has the ability to move in or out of an atom? only the electron, assuming no radioactive decay Discuss that energy is associated with the transfer of electrons in the making or breaking of bonds. In photosynthesis, electrons take on a special role in getting energy into a living system.

4.3 Photosynthesis in Detail

KEY CONCEPT Photosynthesis requires a series of chemical reactions.

MAIN IDEAS

- The first stage of photosynthesis captures and transfers energy.
- The second stage of photosynthesis uses energy from the first stage to make sugars.

VOCABULARY

photosystem, p. 108
electron transport chain, p. 109
ATP synthase, p. 110
Calvin cycle, p. 111

Review
chlorophyll, thylakoid, light-dependent reactions, light-independent reactions

B.3.1 Describe how some organisms capture the sun's energy through the process of photosynthesis by converting carbon dioxide and water into high energy compounds and releasing oxygen.

Connect In a way, the sugar-producing cells in leaves are like tiny factories with assembly lines. In a factory, different workers with separate jobs have to work together to put together a finished product. Similarly, in photosynthesis many different chemical reactions, enzymes, and ions work together in a precise order to make the sugars that are the finished product.

MAIN IDEA

The first stage of photosynthesis captures and transfers energy.

In Section 4.2 you read a summary of photosynthesis. However, the process is much more involved than that general description might suggest. For example, during the light-dependent reactions, energy is captured and transferred in the thylakoid membranes by two groups of molecules called **photosystems.** The two photosystems are called photosystem I and photosystem II.

Overview of the Light-Dependent Reactions

The light-dependent reactions are the *photo-* part of photosynthesis. During the light-dependent reactions, chlorophyll and other light-absorbing molecules capture energy from sunlight. Water molecules are broken down into hydrogen ions, electrons, and oxygen gas. The oxygen is given off as a waste product. Sugars are not made during this part of photosynthesis.

FIGURE 4.6 The light-dependent reactions capture energy from sunlight and transfer energy through electrons. The solar cells that power a solar car do the same thing.

The main functions of the light-dependent reactions are to capture and transfer energy. In these reactions, as in the solar car in **FIGURE 4.6,** energy is transferred to electrons. The electrons are only used for energy in a few specific processes. Recall a time you have gone to an amusement park. To go on rides, you needed special tickets that could only be used there. Similarly, the electrons are used for energy during photosynthesis but not for the cell's general energy needs.

Energy from the electrons is used to make molecules that act as energy carriers. These energy carriers are ATP and another molecule called NADPH. The ATP from the light-dependent reactions is usually not used for a cell's general energy needs. In this case, ATP molecules, along with NADPH molecules, go on to later stages of photosynthesis.

▼ Teach

Vocabulary

Academic Vocabulary Two words used in this section are **transport** and **transfer.** They are similar but not synonymous. *Transport* refers to an object being moved or carried, such as electrons in *electron transport* or ions and molecules in *active* or *passive transport.* The word *transfer* refers to a change in location, as in energy being transferred from sunlight to electrons to ATP or NADPH. It may help students to think of a bus transfer, as opposed to a bus as a means of transport.

Differentiated Instruction

ENGLISH LEARNERS

Before beginning this section, have a brainstorming session in which you work with students to produce a graphic organizer, such as a cluster diagram. This will enable you to review what they have learned about photosynthesis so far. A cluster diagram is a fairly unstructured way of generating ideas, as well as getting a lot of student feedback in a short amount of time. This information could later be reformatted into a concept map.

Biology Toolkit, Brainstorming, p. C11; Cluster Diagram, p. C30

BELOW LEVEL

Have students preview the material in this section by creating an outline. Be sure they start with the key concept, then add the headings and numbered items. Point out that the summaries on pages 110 and 112 recapitulate the steps outlined in each part.

Biology Toolkit, Section Preview, p. C2

Photosystem II and Electron Transport

In photosystem II, chlorophyll and other light-absorbing molecules in the thylakoid membrane absorb energy from sunlight. The energy is transferred to electrons. Photosystem II, shown in **FIGURE 4.7**, needs water to function.

1. **Energy absorbed from sunlight** Chlorophyll and other light-absorbing molecules in the thylakoid membrane absorb energy from sunlight. The energy is transferred to electrons (e^-). High-energy electrons leave the chlorophyll and enter an **electron transport chain,** which is a series of proteins in the membrane of the thylakoid.
2. **Water molecules split** Enzymes break down water molecules. Oxygen, hydrogen ions (H^+), and electrons are separated from each other. The oxygen is released as waste. The electrons from water replace those electrons that left chlorophyll when energy from sunlight was absorbed.
3. **Hydrogen ions transported** Electrons move from protein to protein in the electron transport chain. Their energy is used to pump H^+ ions from outside to inside the thylakoid against a concentration gradient. The H^+ ions build up inside the thylakoid. Electrons move on to photosystem I.

Photosystem I and Energy-Carrying Molecules

In photosystem I, chlorophyll and other light-absorbing molecules in the thylakoid membrane also absorb energy from sunlight. The energy is added to electrons, some of which enter photosystem I from photosystem II.

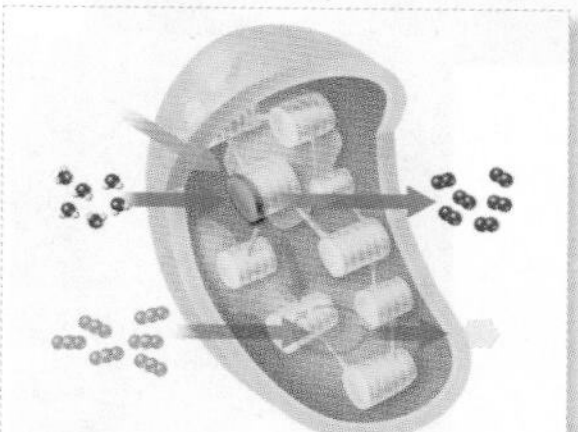

Light-dependent reactions take place in and across the thylakoid membrane.

FIGURE 4.7 Light-Dependent Reactions

Photosystems II and I absorb energy from sunlight and transfer energy to the Calvin cycle.

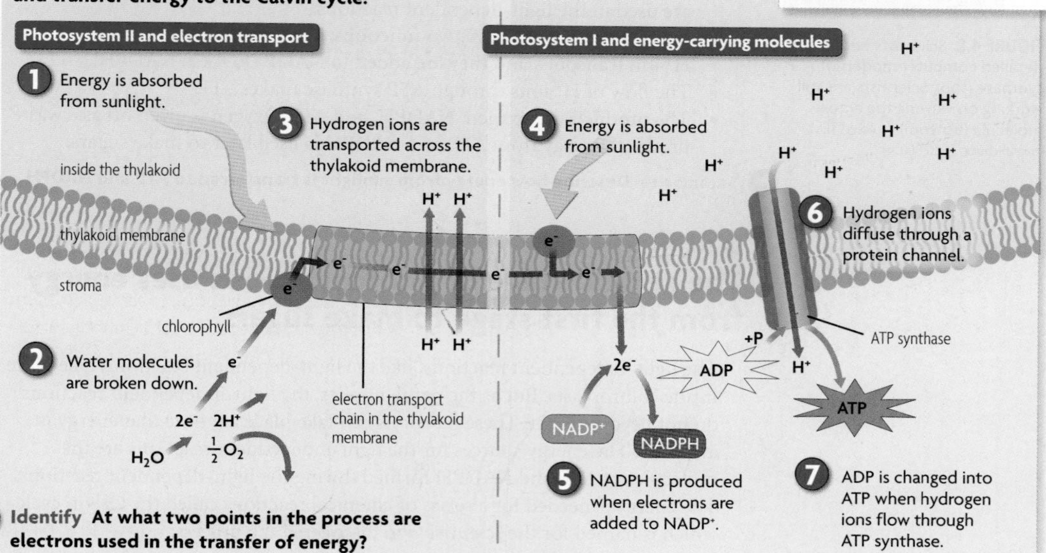

A Identify At what two points in the process are electrons used in the transfer of energy?

TEACH FROM VISUALS

FIGURE 4.7 Use the figure to walk students through the steps of the light-dependent reactions. Point out how the numbered steps in the text on pages 109–110 correspond to the numbered steps in the figure. **Ask**

- Where do the light-dependent reactions occur? thylakoid membrane of chloroplast
- What is the source of the electrons in the electron-transport chain? chlorophyll
- How are the electrons released from the water molecules used? to replace energized electrons that leave the chlorophyll molecules
- What role do these electrons play? provide energy to move hydrogen ions into the thylakoid and to produce molecules of NADPH
- What two energy carriers are produced? NADPH, ATP
- In what step is active transport occurring? step 3 passive transport? step 6

Students may wonder why the photosystems seem to be out of order in the process. Explain that photosystem I was discovered before photosystem II. Both photosystems occur simultaneously, although they are described as happening in a sequence.

Integrating Chemistry

Students may wonder what 1/2 O_2 in **FIGURE 4.7** signifies. Explain that the coefficients in the process, including the chemical equation of photosynthesis, reflect the number of **moles** of the molecules involved (6.02×10^{23}), not the number of molecules.

Answers

A Identify In photosystem II, electrons provide energy to transport hydrogen ions across the thylakoid membrane. In photosystem I, electrons are used to produce NADPH.

ENGLISH LEARNERS

Students must deal with many abbreviated chemical names and acronyms such as ATP, ADP, $NADP^+$, and NADPH. Compare these acronyms to more common linguistic shortcuts such as CDs and DVDs. Point out how the names of these compounds signal important distinctions (for example, *tri-* versus *di-*).

INCLUSION

Help students with short attention spans to organize the material in this section by using index cards. Tell them to work with the summaries on pages 110 and 112. On each card, they should write a step of a reaction in as simple a statement as possible. (Examples: Light is absorbed by chlorophyll molecules in a plant cell. Water molecules break down.) Students should put the cards in order and number them.

Biology Toolkit, Summarizing, p. C24

▼ Teach *continued*

History of Science

Jan Baptista van Helmont was the first to try to scientifically address the question of where plants got their food. His experiment, which was conducted in the 1600s, tested the idea that all of a plant's nutrients came from soil. He planted a willow-tree seedling in a pot of soil, after weighing both the tree and the soil. After five years, the tree had gained 74 kilograms (164 pounds), but the soil had lost only 57 grams (2 ounces). He wrongly concluded that the nutrients were coming from the water he provided.

In the late 1700s, **Joseph Priestley** was able to demonstrate that a plant produces oxygen, or "restores air." Several years after, **Jan Ingenhousz** showed that air was "restored" only when the green parts of the plant were exposed to sunlight. At this point, the assumption was that plants were able to absorb carbon dioxide from the air, and split it to produce carbon, which was then joined to water to form carbohydrates.

It was not until the late 1930s that a complete understanding of photosynthesis was achieved. **C. B. van Niel** realized that it was not carbon dioxide being split, but water. In the presence of sunlight, hydrogen split from water was added to carbon dioxide to produce sugar, with oxygen as a byproduct.

Answers

A Summarize Electrons absorb energy from sunlight. Some of the energy is used to pump hydrogen ions against a concentration gradient, which then flow back through a protein channel to enable ATP synthase to add a phosphate group to ADP to produce ATP. Energized electrons also provide energy to add hydrogen ions to NADP$^+$ to produce NADPH.

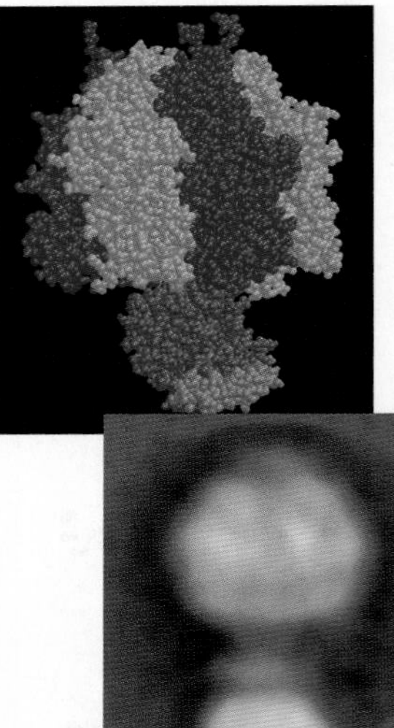

FIGURE 4.8 Scientists have made detailed computer models of ATP synthase (top). Scientists are still working on viewing the actual molecule (bottom). (colored TEM; magnification 1,800,000×)

4 **Energy absorbed from sunlight** As in photosystem II, chlorophyll and other light-absorbing molecules inside the thylakoid membrane absorb energy from sunlight. Electrons are energized and leave the molecules.

5 **NADPH produced** The energized electrons are added to a molecule called NADP$^+$, which functions like ADP. A molecule called NADPH is made. In photosynthesis, NADPH functions like ATP. The molecules of NADPH go to the light-independent reactions.

ATP Production

The final part of the light-dependent reactions makes ATP. The production of ATP depends on the H$^+$ ions that build up inside the thylakoid from photosystem II, and on a complex enzyme in the thylakoid membrane.

6 **Hydrogen ion diffusion** Hydrogen ions flow through a protein channel in the thylakoid membrane. Recall that the concentration of H$^+$ ions is higher inside the thylakoid than it is outside. This difference in H$^+$ ion concentration is called a chemiosmotic gradient, which stores potential energy. Therefore, the ions flow through the channel by diffusion.

7 **ATP produced** The protein channel in step 6 is part of a complex enzyme called **ATP synthase,** shown in **FIGURE 4.8.** As the ions flow through the channel, ATP synthase makes ATP by adding phosphate groups to ADP.

Summary of the Light-Dependent Reactions

- Energy is captured from sunlight by light-absorbing molecules. The energy is transferred to electrons that enter an electron transport chain.
- Water molecules are broken down into H$^+$ ions, electrons, and oxygen molecules. The water molecules provide the H$^+$ ions and electrons that are used in the light-dependent reactions.
- Energized electrons have two functions. They provide energy for H$^+$ ion transport, and they are added to NADP$^+$ to form NADPH.
- The flow of H$^+$ ions through ATP synthase makes ATP.
- The products are oxygen, NADPH, and ATP. Oxygen is given off as a waste product. Energy from ATP and NADPH is used later to make sugars.

A Summarize Describe how energy from sunlight is transferred to ATP and NADPH.

MAIN IDEA

The second stage of photosynthesis uses energy from the first stage to make sugars.

The light-independent reactions, like the light-dependent reactions, take place inside chloroplasts. But as the name implies, the light-independent reactions do not need sunlight. These reactions can take place anytime that energy is available. The energy sources for the light-independent reactions are the molecules of ATP and NADPH formed during the light-dependent reactions. The energy is needed for a series of chemical reactions called the Calvin cycle, which is named for the scientist who discovered the process.

Differentiated Instruction

HANDS-ON ACTIVITY

Have students submerge a freshly-picked leaf in water. They should observe the leaf after about 30 minutes. Students should see bubbles of oxygen forming on the underside of the leaf, demonstrating that the light-dependent reactions continued after the leaf was picked. **Ask,** Where did the oxygen come from? water molecules

The Calvin Cycle

The Calvin cycle cannot take place without the ATP from the light-dependent reactions. The chemical reactions of the **Calvin cycle** use carbon dioxide (CO_2) gas from the atmosphere and the energy carried by ATP and NADPH to make simple sugars. Because the light-independent reactions build sugar molecules, they are the *synthesis* part of photosynthesis. Only one molecule of CO_2 is actually added to the Calvin cycle at a time. The simplified cycle in **FIGURE 4.9** shows three CO_2 molecules added at once.

1. **Carbon dioxide added** CO_2 molecules are added to five-carbon molecules already in the Calvin cycle. Six-carbon molecules are formed.
2. **Three-carbon molecules formed** Energy—ATP and NADPH—from the light-dependent reactions is used by enzymes to split the six-carbon molecules. Three-carbon molecules are formed and rearranged.
3. **Three-carbon molecules exit** Most of the three-carbon molecules stay in the Calvin cycle, but one high-energy three-carbon molecule leaves the cycle. After two three-carbon molecules have left the cycle, they are bonded together to build a six-carbon sugar molecule such as glucose.
4. **Three-carbon molecules recycled** Energy from ATP molecules is used to change the three-carbon molecules back into five-carbon molecules. The five-carbon molecules stay in the Calvin cycle. These molecules are added to new CO_2 molecules that enter the cycle.

VOCABULARY

The light-dependent reactions are the *photo-* part of photosynthesis. The light-independent reactions are the *synthesis* part of photosynthesis.

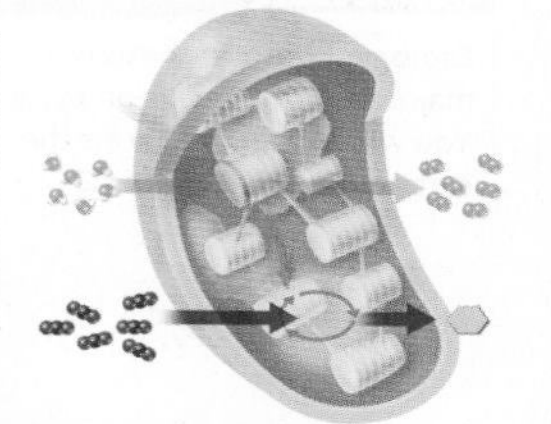

FIGURE 4.9 Light-Independent Reactions (Calvin Cycle)

The Calvin cycle produces sugars.

1 Carbon dioxide (CO_2) molecules enter the cycle and are added to five-carbon molecules. Six-carbon molecules are formed.
3 C from CO_2
3 CCCCCC
6 ATP
6 ADP
6 NADPH
6 NADP+
2 Energy is added. The six-carbon molecules split to form three-carbon molecules. More energy is added and the molecules are rearranged into higher-energy molecules.
6 CCC
CCC
CCC
CCCCCC
3 A high-energy three-carbon molecule exits for every 3 CO_2 molecules that enter. After 2 three-carbon molecules have exited, they bond to form 1 six-carbon sugar.
5 CCC
3 CCCCC
3 ADP
3 ATP
4 Three-carbon molecules are changed back to five-carbon molecules by energy from ATP.

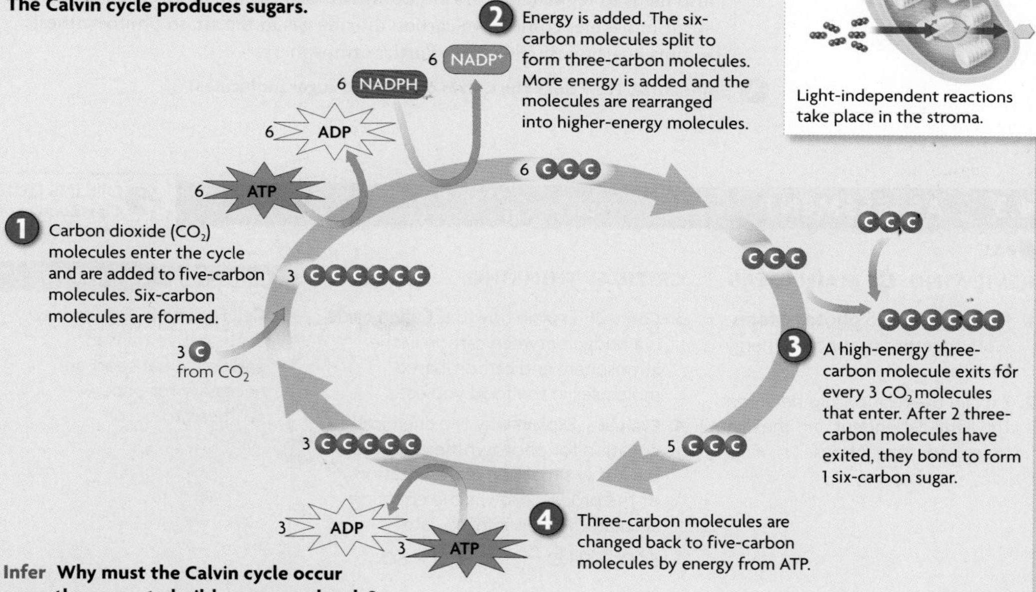

Light-independent reactions take place in the stroma.

A Infer Why must the Calvin cycle occur more than once to build a sugar molecule?

TEACH FROM VISUALS

FIGURE 4.9 Use the figure to teach an overview of the Calvin cycle. Point out how the numbered steps in the text correspond to the numbered steps in the figure. **Ask**

- Where in the chloroplast do light-independent reactions occur? stroma of chloroplast
- Where are the ATP and NADPH coming from? light-dependent reactions
- Why are these reactions called a cycle? The five-carbon molecule of the process is regenerated, so the cycle continues.

Point out that the molecule produced in the Calvin cycle is actually a three-carbon sugar, not a six-carbon glucose. Two molecules of the three-carbon sugar combine to form one molecule of a six-carbon glucose, but this reaction is not part of the Calvin cycle.

Science Trivia

- Rubisco, which is an enzyme that sets up the Calvin cycle, is thought to be the most abundant protein on Earth. It has been estimated that there are 22 pounds of Rubisco for every human on Earth.
- Rubisco is very slow and inefficient. It catalyzes between 2 and 8 molecules of CO_2 per second compared to thousands per second for most enzymes.

Vocabulary

Academic Vocabulary The process that occurs in the Calvin cycle is often referred to as carbon **fixation.** The carbon is *fixed* or "fastened" into an organic compound, which for organisms is its usable form. This expression is also used for nitrogen: nitrogen fixation.

Answers

A Infer As described in the text, only one carbon dioxide molecule, and so just one carbon, is added to the Calvin cycle with each turn.

BELOW LEVEL

Students who have mastered the details of photosynthesis can act as teachers for those who are struggling. Set up student pairs: the teacher reads through the text, encourage the struggling student to ask questions. Set the goal for each pair to make an enlarged drawing of a plant cell, showing light-dependent reactions in thylakoid and light-independent reactions in stroma. Have students use summaries on pages 110 and 112 as points of reference.

Biology Toolkit, Reciprocal Teaching, p. C14

▼ Teach *continued*

History of Science

The details of the Calvin cycle were worked out by **Melvin Calvin** and his colleague **A. A. Benson.** They used radioactive carbon (C-14) and paper chromatography, new scientific tools in the late 1940s, to trace the incorporation of the carbon atom in CO_2 into sugar. The cycle is often called the Calvin-Benson cycle, although only Calvin won a Nobel Prize for the work in 1961.

Answers

A Summarize Carbon dioxide is added to five-carbon molecules in the cycle. Energy from ATP and NADPH is used in a series of chemical reactions that build the three-carbon molecules needed to form a six-carbon sugar.

▼ Assess and Reteach

Assess Use the Online Quiz or Section Quiz (*Assessment Book,* p. 69).

Reteach Work with students to put together a concept map of the photosynthetic process. Start the concept map with the word *sunlight.* Tell students the concept map must end with *glucose.*

Summary of the Light-Independent Reactions

- Carbon dioxide enters the Calvin cycle.
- ATP and NADPH from the light-dependent reactions transfer energy to the Calvin cycle and keep the cycle going.
- One high-energy three-carbon molecule is made for every three molecules of carbon dioxide that enter the cycle.
- Two high-energy three-carbon molecules are bonded together to make a sugar. Therefore, six molecules of carbon dioxide must be added to the Calvin cycle to make one six-carbon sugar.
- The products are a six-carbon sugar such as glucose, $NADP^+$, and ADP. The $NADP^+$ and ADP molecules return to the light-dependent reactions.

Functions of Photosynthesis

Photosynthesis is much more than just a biochemical process. Photosynthesis is important to most organisms on Earth, as well as to Earth's environment. Recall that plants produce food for themselves and for other organisms through photosynthesis. Both plant cells and animal cells release the energy stored in sugars through cellular respiration. Cellular respiration, which uses the oxygen that is a waste product of photosynthesis, is the process that makes most of the ATP used by plant and animal cells.

Photosynthesis does more than make sugars. It also provides materials for plant growth and development. The simple sugars from photosynthesis are bonded together to form complex carbohydrates such as starch and cellulose. Starches store sugars until they are needed for energy. Cellulose is a major part of plant structure—it is the building block of plant cell walls. Photosynthesis also helps to regulate Earth's environment. The carbon atoms used to make sugar molecules come from carbon dioxide gas in the air, so photosynthesis removes carbon dioxide from Earth's atmosphere.

Connecting CONCEPTS

Ecology Photosynthesis is a major part of the carbon cycle. You will learn more about the carbon cycle in **Chapter 13.**

Summarize How does the Calvin cycle build sugar molecules?

4.3 ASSESSMENT

ONLINE QUIZ ClassZone.com

B.3.1

REVIEWING MAIN IDEAS

1. How do the two **photosystems** work together to capture energy from sunlight?
2. Explain the relationship between the light-dependent and the light-independent reactions.

CRITICAL THINKING

3. **Connect** Explain how the **Calvin cycle** is a bridge between carbon in the atmosphere and carbon-based molecules in the food you eat.
4. **Evaluate** Explain why the chemical equation for photosynthesis (below) is a highly simplified representation of the process. How is the equation accurate? How is it inaccurate?

$$6CO_2 + 6H_2O \longrightarrow C_6H_{12}O_6 + 6O_2$$

Connecting CONCEPTS

5. **Cell Functions** Explain how both passive transport and active transport are necessary for photosynthesis to occur.

4.3 ASSESSMENT

1. Photosystem II absorbs energy and energizes electrons. The electrons are passed along to photosystem I, which absorbs more energy and adds it to the electrons.
2. The light-dependent reactions absorb energy from sunlight and transfer the energy to the light-independent reactions that produce sugars.
3. Carbon dioxide is removed from the atmosphere by plants for photosynthesis. The carbon is incorporated into sugars and other carbon-based molecules that are eaten by other organisms.
4. The equation shows the general reactants and products of the process. However, it does not show intermediate steps. For example, carbon dioxide and water do not actually react with each other.
5. Active transport moves hydrogen ions against the concentration gradient in photosystem II. Passive transport occurs when hydrogen ions flow through the channel bound to ATP synthase.

4.4 Overview of Cellular Respiration

KEY CONCEPT The overall process of cellular respiration converts sugar into ATP using oxygen.

MAIN IDEAS

- Cellular respiration makes ATP by breaking down sugars.
- Cellular respiration is like a mirror image of photosynthesis.

VOCABULARY

cellular respiration, p. 113
aerobic, p. 113
glycolysis, p. 113
anaerobic, p. 113
Krebs cycle, p. 115

Review
mitochondria, ATP, electron transport chain

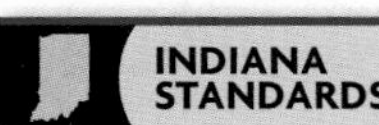

B.3.2 Describe how most organisms can combine and recombine the elements contained in sugar molecules into a variety of biologically essential compounds by utilizing the energy from cellular respiration.

Connect The term *cellular respiration* may lead you to form a mental picture of cells breathing. This image is not correct, but it is useful to remember. Your cells need the oxygen that you take in when you breathe. That oxygen helps your body release the energy in sugars and other carbon-based molecules. Indirectly, your breathing is connected to the ATP that your cells need for everything you do.

MAIN IDEA

Cellular respiration makes ATP by breaking down sugars.

Plants use photosynthesis to make their own food. Animals eat other organisms as food. But food is not a direct source of energy. Instead, plants, animals, and other eukaryotes break down molecules from food to produce ATP. **Cellular respiration** releases chemical energy from sugars and other carbon-based molecules to make ATP when oxygen is present. Cellular respiration is an **aerobic** (air-OH-bihk) process, which means that it needs oxygen to take place. Cellular respiration takes place in mitochondria, which are often called the cell's "powerhouses" because they make most of a cell's ATP.

A mitochondrion, shown in **FIGURE 4.10**, cannot directly make ATP from food. First, foods are broken down into smaller molecules such as glucose. Then glucose is broken down, as shown below. **Glycolysis** (gly-KAHL-uh-sihs) splits glucose into two three-carbon molecules and makes two molecules of ATP. Glycolysis takes place in a cell's cytoplasm and does not need oxygen. Glycolysis is an **anaerobic** process because it does not need oxygen to take place. However, glycolysis is necessary for cellular respiration. The products of glycolysis are broken down in mitochondria to make many more ATP.

mitochondrion

plant cell

FIGURE 4.10 Mitochondria, found in both plant and animal cells, produce ATP through cellular respiration. (colored TEM; magnification 7,000×)

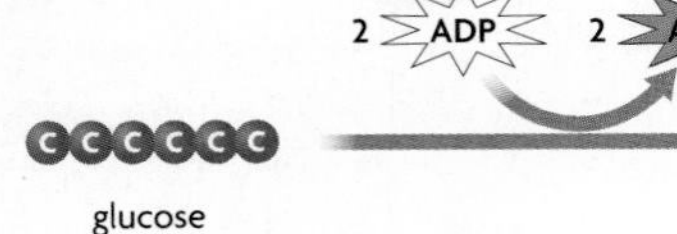

A Explain What is the function of cellular respiration?

Differentiated Instruction

ENGLISH LEARNERS

Have students preview this section by comparing it to **Section 4.2.** Point out the similarities between the two sections: the process diagrams corresponding to numbered text, the same chemical compounds, for example, H_2O, CO_2, O_2, and ATP. Now read the main idea on page 114: "Cellular respiration is like a mirror image of photosynthesis." Discuss what this sentence means in the context of these two sections.

Biology Toolkit, Compare/Contrast Chart, p. C34

TEACH WITH TECHNOLOGY

If you have materials and probeware available, have students observe cellular respiration. They can measure the rate of cellular respiration in germinating seeds and the effect of temperature on rate.

SECTION 4.4

Plan and Prepare

Objectives

- Describe the process of cellular respiration.
- Compare cellular respiration to photosynthesis.

Section Resources

Unit Resource Book
Study Guide pp. 43–44
Power Notes p. 45
Reinforcement p. 46
Pre-AP Activity pp. 59–60

Interactive Reader Chapter 4
Spanish Study Guide pp. 37–38

Biology Toolkit pp. C13, C19, C34

Technology
Power Presentation 4.4
Media Gallery DVD
Online Quiz 4.4

Activate Prior Knowledge Tell students that by the time a person reaches age 16, he or she will have probably taken more than 200 million breaths. **Ask**

- Why is breathing vital to life? supplies oxygen needed for cellular respiration and release of energy
- How is the air you breathe in different from the air you breathe out? more oxygen, less carbon dioxide

Teach

Vocabulary

Greek and Latin Word Origins Tell students that **glycolysis** comes from the Greek *glukus,* meaning "sweet" and *lysis,* meaning "to loosen" or "split." *Glycolysis* literally means "to split the sweet."

Answers

A Explain Cellular respiration breaks down sugars to produce ATP for cell activities.

▼ Teach *continued*

ONLINE BIOLOGY Have students view the interactive animation that compares photosynthesis to respiration. See Options for Inquiry on page 127.

TEACH FROM VISUALS

FIGURE 4.11 Remind students to refer to the numbered list on page 115 when studying the figure. **Ask**

- What process leads to cellular respiration, and where does it take place? glycolysis, which occurs in cytoplasm
- Where does cellular respiration take place? mitochondria
- What two reactants are shown entering the mitochondrion? three-carbon molecules and oxygen
- Where do the three-carbon molecules go when they enter the mitochondrion? into the matrix
- What two products are shown leaving the mitochondrion? carbon dioxide, water

Address Misconceptions

Common Misconception Students often think that cellular respiration takes place only in animal cells.

Correcting the Misconception Cellular respiration takes place in almost all organisms. Note that the cells of all eukaryotes have mitochondria. Cellular respiration takes place in many prokaryotic organisms as well, although they do not have mitochondria. The enzymes and transport proteins are found free in the cytoplasm and attached to the cell membrane.

Answers

A Identify The reactants are three-carbon molecules and oxygen. The products are water and carbon dioxide.

MAIN IDEA

Cellular respiration is like a mirror image of photosynthesis.

Connecting CONCEPTS

Photosynthesis Review the overall process of photosynthesis in Section 4.2 and compare photosynthesis to cellular respiration.

Photosynthesis and cellular respiration are not true opposites, but you can think about them in that way. For example, chloroplasts absorb energy from sunlight and build sugars. Mitochondria release chemical energy to make ATP. The chemical equation of cellular respiration is also basically the reverse of photosynthesis. But the structures of chloroplasts and mitochondria are similar. A mitochondrion is surrounded by a membrane. It has two parts that are involved in cellular respiration: the matrix and the inner mitochondrial membrane. In mitochondria, cellular respiration takes place in two main stages, as shown in **FIGURE 4.11.**

FIGURE 4.11 Cellular Respiration Overview

When oxygen is available, ATP is produced by cellular respiration in mitochondria.

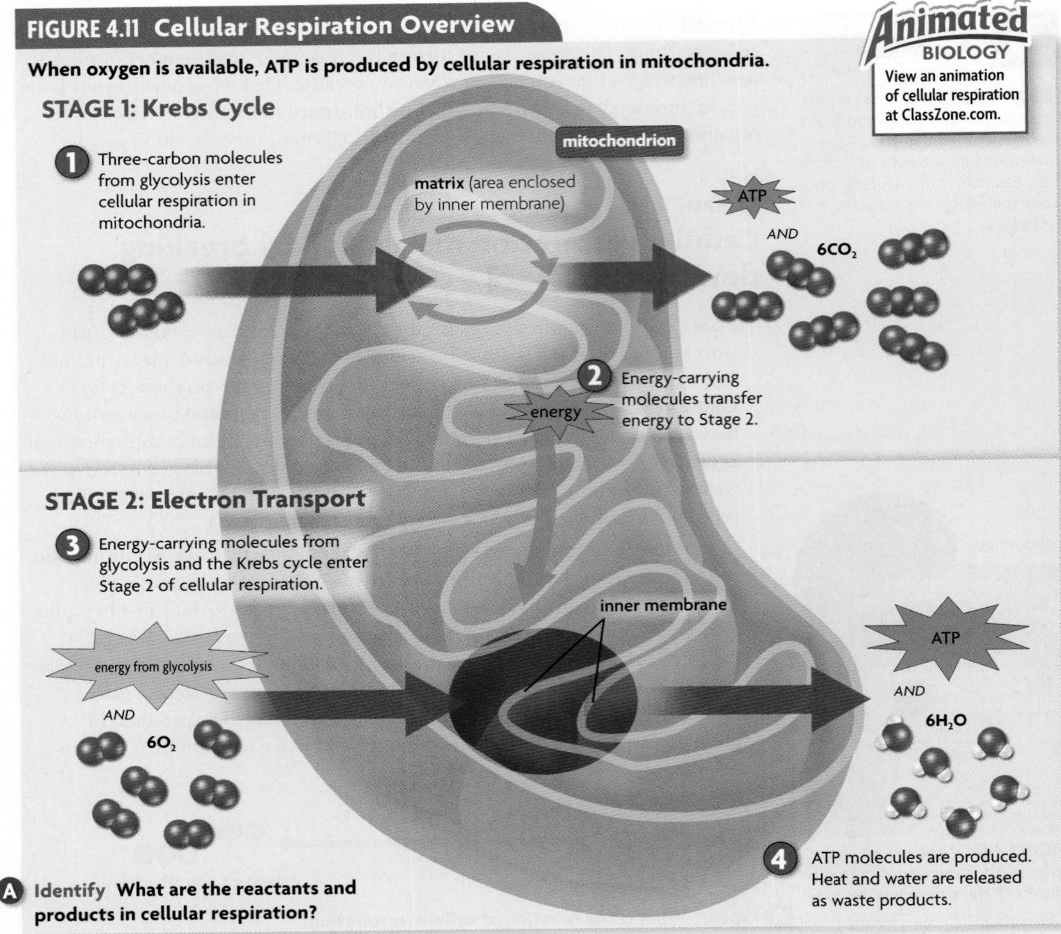

Animated BIOLOGY
View an animation of cellular respiration at ClassZone.com.
STAGE 1: Krebs Cycle
1 Three-carbon molecules from glycolysis enter cellular respiration in mitochondria.
mitochondrion
matrix (area enclosed by inner membrane)
ATP
AND
$6CO_2$
2 Energy-carrying molecules transfer energy to Stage 2.
energy
STAGE 2: Electron Transport
3 Energy-carrying molecules from glycolysis and the Krebs cycle enter Stage 2 of cellular respiration.
inner membrane
energy from glycolysis
AND
$6O_2$
ATP
AND
$6H_2O$
4 ATP molecules are produced. Heat and water are released as waste products.

A Identify What are the reactants and products in cellular respiration?

Differentiated Instruction

PRE-AP

Have students compare the diagrams shown in **FIGURE 4.5** on page 104 with **FIGURE 4.11** on page 114. Ask them to write a few paragraphs on how the membranous structures in chloroplasts (thylahoids) and mitochondria (inner membrane) contribute to the processes that take place in each. Students should mention both separation and increased surface area.

Biology Toolkit, Quick-Write, p. C19

INCLUSION

To help students with visual impairments, have students work in pairs to compare the photosynthesis diagrams shown in **FIGURE 4.5** on page 104 and **FIGURE 4.11** on page 114. Have one student act as a "tour guide" and describe what is happening. The second student may ask questions until he or she has a full picture.

Biology Toolkit, Think-Pair-Share, p. C13

The **Krebs cycle** produces molecules that carry energy to the second part of cellular respiration. The Krebs cycle, named for the scientist who discovered the process, takes place in the interior space, or matrix, of the mitochondrion.

To learn more about ATP and how it is used, go to scilinks.org.
Keycode: MLB004

1. Three-carbon molecules from glycolysis are broken down in a cycle of chemical reactions. A small number of ATP molecules are made. Other types of energy-carrying molecules are also made. Carbon dioxide is given off as a waste product.
2. Energy is transferred to the second stage of cellular respiration.

An electron transport chain made of proteins needs energy-carrying molecules from the Krebs cycle and oxygen to make ATP. This part of the process takes place in and across the inner mitochondrial membrane.

3. Energy is transferred to a chain of proteins in the inner membrane of the mitochondrion.
4. A large number of ATP molecules are made. Oxygen enters the process and is used to make water molecules. Water and heat are given off as waste products.

Up to 38 ATP molecules are made from the breakdown of one glucose molecule—2 from glycolysis and 34 or 36 from cellular respiration. The equation for cellular respiration is shown below, but it actually has many more steps. For example, the cellular respiration equation includes glycolysis. And many enzymes are also part of the process.

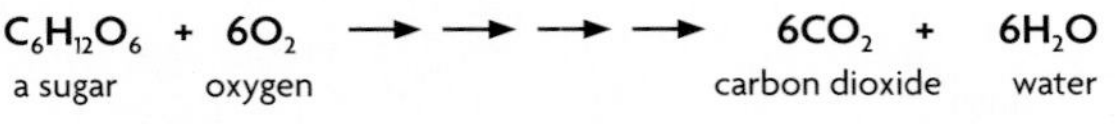

$$C_6H_{12}O_6 + 6O_2 \rightarrow \rightarrow \rightarrow \rightarrow 6CO_2 + 6H_2O$$

a sugar, oxygen, carbon dioxide, water

Use **FIGURE 4.12** to compare cellular respiration with photosynthesis. As you can see, photosynthesis uses the products of cellular respiration. It converts energy from sunlight into sugars. Cellular respiration needs the products of photosynthesis. It releases stored energy from sugars to make ATP that can be used by cells.

FIGURE 4.12 COMPARING PROCESSES

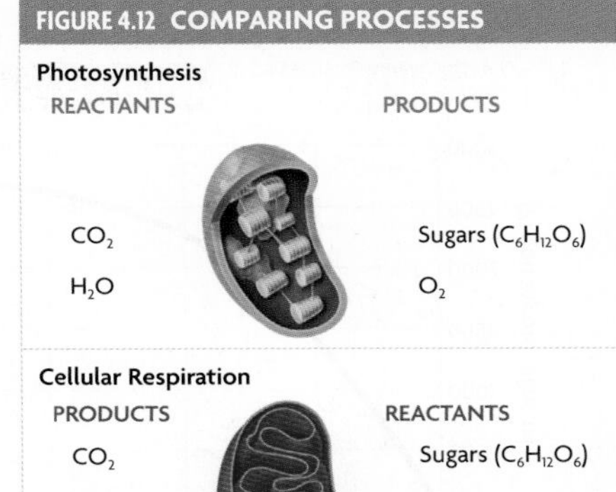

The products of photosynthesis—sugars and O_2—are the reactants in cellular respiration.

A Apply Does glucose actually react with oxygen during cellular respiration? Explain.

Take It Further

Glycolysis was probably among the first biochemical processes to evolve. It is likely that early forms of life produced ATP from glycolysis, because the process takes place in the cytoplasm and does not require oxygen. According to the **endosymbiosis theory,** mitochondria were once prokaryotes that were engulfed by other prokaryotes. This process may have led to the evolution of cellular respiration.

Answers

A Apply No, glucose is split by glycolysis prior to the aerobic parts of cellular respiration, when oxygen enters the process.

Assess and Reteach ▼

Assess Use the Online Quiz or Section Quiz (*Assessment Book,* p. 70).

Reteach Draw an oval on the board to represent a mitochondrion. Tell students to take a quick look at **FIGURE 4.11,** then close their books. Have students provide the details of cellular respiration to be filled in on the diagram.

4.4 ASSESSMENT

ONLINE QUIZ ClassZone.com

B.3.2

REVIEWING MAIN IDEAS

1. How are **cellular respiration** and **glycolysis** related?
2. Summarize the **aerobic** stages of cellular respiration. Be sure to discuss the **Krebs cycle** and the electron transport chain in your answer.

CRITICAL THINKING

3. **Analyze** Describe the relationship between cellular respiration and photosynthesis. Discuss the functions of chloroplasts and mitochondria.
4. **Apply** Is glucose a reactant in the aerobic stages of cellular respiration? Explain.

***Connecting* CONCEPTS**

5. **Chemical Reactions** Is the process of cellular respiration exothermic or endothermic? Explain your answer.

4.4 ASSESSMENT

1. Glycolysis breaks down glucose in the cytoplasm before cellular respiration occurs in the mitochondria. The aerobic processes in mitochondria use the products of glycolysis.
2. Answers should indicate that the products of glycolysis are broken down by the Krebs cycle to make energy-carrying molecules and carbon dioxide. Energy from the Krebs cycle is used by the electron transport chain to make ATP.
3. The reactants and products of the overall processes are essentially the reverse of each other. The chloroplasts and mitochondria also have approximately opposite functions. Chloroplasts absorb energy and build carbon-based molecules, and mitochondria break down carbon-based molecules to release energy.
4. No; glucose is broken down during glycolysis, which is an anaerobic process.
5. Exothermic; energy is released as heat and ATP.

Introduce

Have students compare the two graphs on the page and discuss what general information one can take away from the graph before looking at it in any detail.

Ask

- What do the differences in the appearance of the graphs suggest about the nature of the phenomena that are being measured? Graph 1 suggests a phenomenon that builds over time and then levels off. The phenomenon in Graph 2 appears to be cyclical.
- Looking at Graph 1, why might sugar production peak between 3000 and 4000 mm of precipitation? Answers will vary, but students should suggest that there is a physical limit to how much a plant can produce, as well as a limit to how much water a plant can absorb or use. This can be compared to how much weight a human can gain by eating. At some point it becomes physically impossible for someone to keep eating.

Discuss

Tell students that Biosphere 2 was designed to model the interactions and functions of Earth's different ecosystems, such as forests and oceans, and how they affect the atmosphere. Sunlight was allowed into Biosphere 2, much like it is allowed through the glass of a greenhouse. Have students look at Graph 2. **Ask,** What effect does sunlight have on the fluctuating amount of carbon dioxide? Photosynthesis requires sunlight, so when sunlight is absent or less abundant, less carbon dioxide will be taken up by plants for photosynthesis. Discuss how the graph might appear for the days that follow.

Unit Resource Book, Data Analysis, p. 56

DATA ANALYSIS ClassZone.com

NOS.1

Photosynthesis and Plants

After scientists record their data in tables, they usually make graphs to display the results. Graphs show the relationship between two variables. The pattern of curve or line that is drawn will help you to form conclusions about your data.

EXAMPLE

Scientists study the net amount of sugar production per square meter per year in forest plants. Look at the graph below. Notice that the net amount of sugar produced increases rapidly at first, then levels off after about 2500 mm of precipitation. Scientists can conclude that forests need about 2500 mm of rain annually for maximum net sugar production.

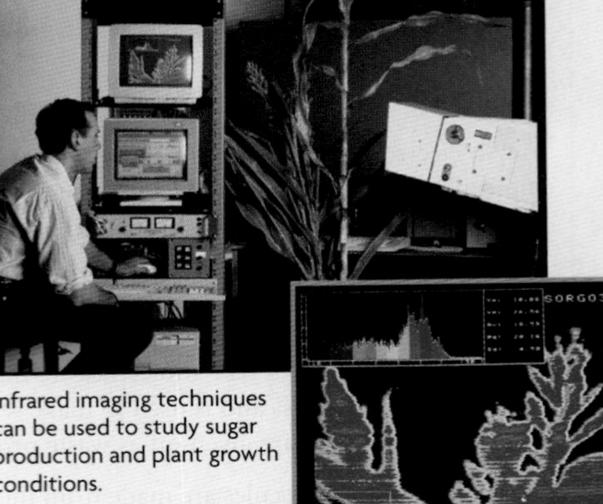

Infrared imaging techniques can be used to study sugar production and plant growth conditions.

GRAPH 1. NET SUGAR PRODUCTION

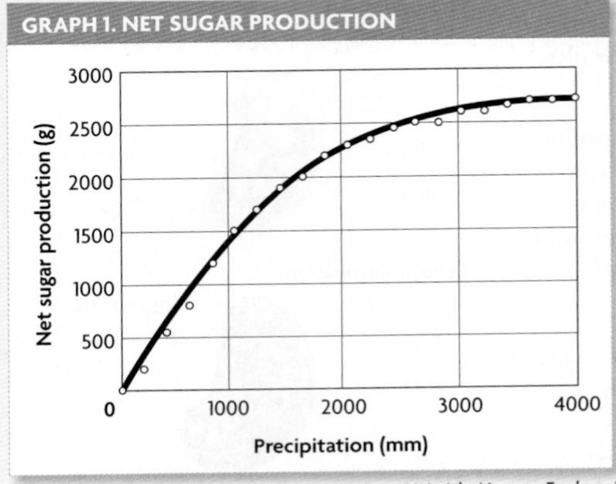

Source: H. Leith, *Human Ecology 1*

INTERPRET A GRAPH

Look at the graph to the right. It shows the amount of carbon dioxide in the air during different times of the day in Biosphere 2, an enclosed research and education center in Arizona.

1. **Interpret** What is the relationship between the time of day and the amount of carbon dioxide in the research facility?
2. **Infer** Using your knowledge of the process of photosynthesis, draw a conclusion about the pattern of the data.

GRAPH 2. CO_2 LEVELS OVER TIME

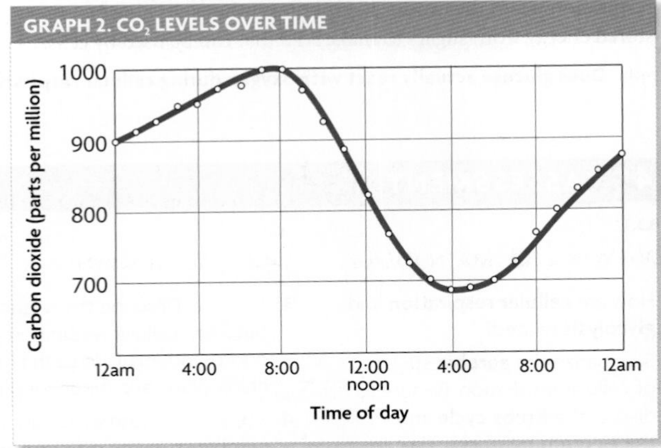

Answers

1. During daylight hours, the concentration of carbon dioxide decreases. During the night, carbon dioxide in the air increases.
2. During daylight hours, plants remove carbon dioxide from the air to be used in photosynthesis. During the night, when there is no sunlight, photosynthesis decreases and less carbon dioxide is removed from the air.

4.5 Cellular Respiration in Detail

KEY CONCEPT Cellular respiration is an aerobic process with two main stages.

MAIN IDEAS
- Glycolysis is needed for cellular respiration.
- The Krebs cycle is the first main part of cellular respiration.
- The electron transport chain is the second main part of cellular respiration.

Review
glycolysis, Krebs cycle, electron transport chain, cellular respiration, aerobic respiration

B.3.2 Describe how most organisms can combine and recombine the elements contained in sugar molecules into a variety of biologically essential compounds by utilizing the energy from cellular respiration.

Connect If chloroplasts are like tiny factories that make products, mitochondria are like power plants that burn fuel to produce electricity. In a power plant, a processed fuel is burned in the presence of oxygen and energy is released as useful electricity. During cellular respiration, oxygen and digested molecules from food are used to produce useful energy in the form of ATP.

MAIN IDEA

Glycolysis is needed for cellular respiration.

In Section 4.4 you read a summary of how cellular respiration produces ATP molecules. But cellular respiration, like photosynthesis, is a very complex process. For example, glucose and oxygen do not react directly with one another, and many chemical reactions, such as glycolysis, must take place.

Glycolysis is an ongoing process in all cells, including yours. It takes place in the cytoplasm before cellular respiration, and it does not require oxygen. Glycolysis makes a small number of ATP molecules, but its other products are much more important. If oxygen is available, the products of glycolysis are used to produce many more ATP molecules through cellular respiration. The process of glycolysis can be summarized as follows.

1. Two ATP molecules are used to energize a glucose molecule. The glucose molecule is split into two three-carbon molecules. A series of enzymes and chemical reactions rearranges the three-carbon molecules.
2. Energized electrons from the three-carbon molecules are transferred to molecules of NAD^+. Molecules of NADH are formed. A series of reactions converts the three-carbon molecules to pyruvate (py-ROO-vayt), which enters cellular respiration. Four ATP molecules are made.

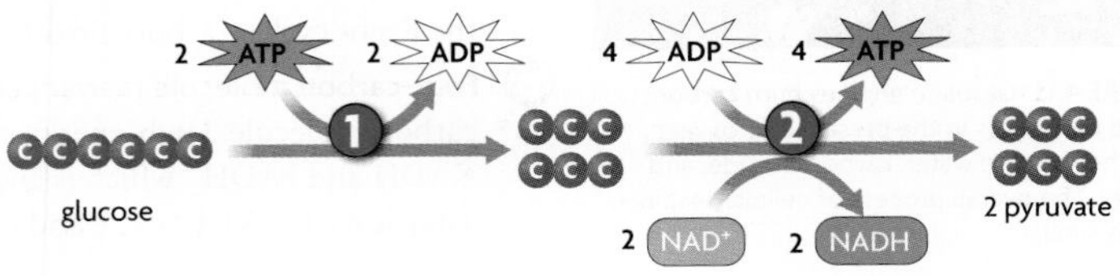

Differentiated Instruction

ENGLISH LEARNERS

Before beginning this section, have a brainstorming session in which you work with students to produce a cluster diagram on cellular respiration. Have them compare this diagram to the one they made for photosynthesis in **Section 4.3,** page 108.

Biology Toolkit, Brainstorming, p. C11; Cluster Diagram, p. C30

BELOW LEVEL

As suggested for **Section 4.3,** page 108, have students preview the section by creating an outline. Have them include the numbered steps as well as the bulleted items detailing the products of glycolysis and cellular respiration.

Biology Toolkit, Section Preview, p. C2

Plan and Prepare

Objectives

- Describe the process of glycolysis.
- Describe the details of the Krebs cycle and the electron transport chain.

Section Resources

Unit Resource Book Study Guide pp. 47–48 Power Notes p. 49 Reinforcement p. 50
Interactive Reader Chapter 4 **Spanish Study Guide** pp. 39–40
Biology Toolkit pp. C2, C11, C19, C24, C30, C38
Technology Power Presentation 4.5 Media Gallery DVD Online Quiz 4.5

Activate Prior Knowledge Have students compare cellular respiration to combustion. **Ask,** How are combustion and cellular respiration alike? How are they different? Both are chemical reactions that use oxygen to release energy; both produce heat. Cellular respiration releases energy slowly, with many reactions, while combustion releases energy as heat and light all at once.

Teach

TEACH FROM VISUALS

Have students look at the equation at the bottom of the page. **Ask,** How do you know that glycolysis releases energy? Two ATP molecules (net) and two NADH molecules are produced.

▼ Teach *continued*

Answers

A Summarize Glycolysis makes four ATP molecules but two ATP are used to split the glucose molecule, yielding a net gain of two ATP.

Integrating Chemistry

Point out that pyruvate does not directly enter the Krebs cycle. As students can see in **FIGURE 4.14,** one carbon is split off from the molecule; a two-carbon molecule, called **acetyl-CoA,** enters the Krebs cycle.

Acetyl-CoA is one of the most important molecules in the body. Almost all nutrients—proteins, lipids, and carbohydrates—generate acetyl-CoA when they are broken down. The large amounts of acetyl-CoA produced are channeled into the Krebs cycle if the body is in need of energy, or into the synthesis of fat to be stored for future energy needs.

History of Science

In the 1930s, biochemists wondered about the nature of the pathway that produced the large amounts of ATP needed by the body. They reasoned that the body's supply of the compound that started the pathway would be used up rapidly.

Hans Krebs solved the mystery in 1937 when he determined that the pathway is cyclic. The four-carbon molecule that starts the cycle when it combines with acetyl-CoA is regenerated to keep the cycle going. The pathway, named for Krebs, is also called the citric acid cycle because citric acid is the first substance formed. Krebs won the Nobel Prize for his work in 1953.

Connecting CONCEPTS

Fermentation When cells do not have a supply of oxygen for the aerobic processes of cellular respiration, the anaerobic processes of fermentation take place. You will learn about fermentation in Section 4.6.

Although glycolysis makes four ATP molecules, recall that two ATP molecules are used to first split the glucose molecule. So the breakdown of one glucose molecule by glycolysis gives a net gain of two ATP molecules. The pyruvate and NADH produced by glycolysis are used for cellular respiration when oxygen is present. NADH is an electron carrier like NADPH, the electron carrier in photosynthesis.

A Summarize How does glycolysis result in a net gain of two ATP molecules?

MAIN IDEA

The Krebs cycle is the first main part of cellular respiration.

Cellular respiration makes many more ATP molecules than does glycolysis. It begins with the breakdown of pyruvate in steps 1 and 2 below. The process continues with the Krebs cycle, shown in **FIGURE 4.14.** Notice that steps 1, 4, and 5 below are very similar. In those steps, a carbon-based molecule is split, a molecule of carbon dioxide is formed, and energy-carrying NADH molecules are made. In fact, the main function of the Krebs cycle is to transfer high-energy electrons to molecules that carry them to the electron transport chain. The Krebs cycle is also sometimes called the citric acid cycle because citric acid is the first molecule formed, as you can see in step 3 below.

FIGURE 4.13 Gasoline engines burn carbon-based molecules in the presence of oxygen, and they release water, carbon dioxide, and energy. The overall process of cellular respiration is similar.

1. **Pyruvate broken down** A pyruvate molecule is split into a two-carbon molecule and a molecule of carbon dioxide, which is given off as a waste product. High-energy electrons are transferred from the two-carbon molecule to NAD^+, forming a molecule of NADH. The NADH moves to the electron transport chain.
2. **Coenzyme A** A molecule called coenzyme A bonds to the two-carbon molecule made from the breakdown of pyruvate. This intermediate molecule goes to the Krebs cycle.
3. **Citric acid formed** The two-carbon part of the intermediate molecule is added to a four-carbon molecule to form a six-carbon molecule called citric acid. Coenzyme A goes back to step 2.
4. **Citric acid broken down** The citric acid molecule is broken down by an enzyme and a five-carbon molecule is formed. A molecule of NADH is made and moves out of the Krebs cycle. A molecule of carbon dioxide is given off as a waste product.
5. **Five-carbon molecule broken down** The five-carbon molecule is broken down by an enzyme. A four-carbon molecule, a molecule of NADH, and a molecule of ATP are formed. The NADH leaves the Krebs cycle. Carbon dioxide is given off as a waste product.
6. **Four-carbon molecule rearranged** Enzymes rearrange the four-carbon molecule. High-energy electrons are released. Molecules of NADH and $FADH_2$, which is another electron carrier, are made. They leave the Krebs cycle and the four-carbon molecule remains.

Differentiated Instruction

INCLUSION

As suggested for **Section 4.3,** have students who have difficulty processing multiple levels of information organize material by using index cards. Tell them to work with the numbered lists on pages 117, 118, and 120 and write the steps in as simple a statement as possible. For example, on cards labeled *glycolysis,* they could write (1) ATP is used to split a molecule of glucose (6C). (2) Pyruvate (3C), ATP, and NADH are produced.

Biology Toolkit, Summarizing, p. C24

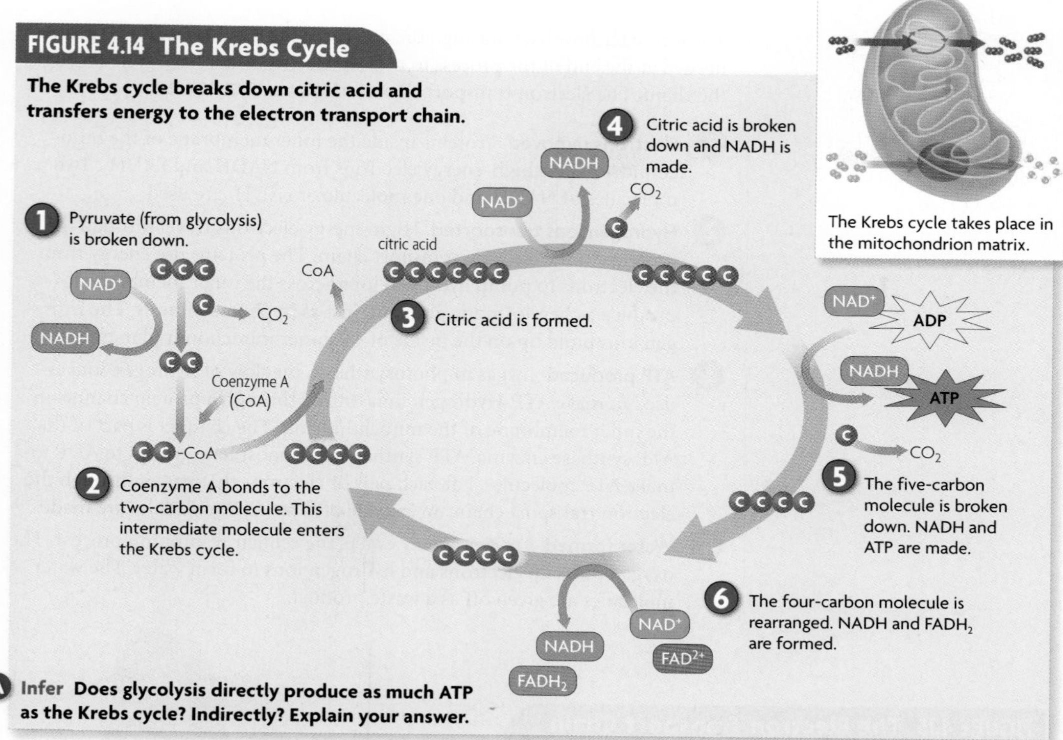
FIGURE 4.14 The Krebs Cycle
The Krebs cycle breaks down citric acid and transfers energy to the electron transport chain.
1 Pyruvate (from glycolysis) is broken down.
NAD+
NADH
CO2
CoA
Coenzyme A (CoA)
-CoA
2 Coenzyme A bonds to the two-carbon molecule. This intermediate molecule enters the Krebs cycle.
citric acid
3 Citric acid is formed.
4 Citric acid is broken down and NADH is made.
NADH
NAD+
CO2
NAD+
ADP
NADH
ATP
CO2
5 The five-carbon molecule is broken down. NADH and ATP are made.
6 The four-carbon molecule is rearranged. NADH and FADH2 are formed.
NAD+
NADH
FAD2+
FADH2
The Krebs cycle takes place in the mitochondrion matrix.

A Infer Does glycolysis directly produce as much ATP as the Krebs cycle? Indirectly? Explain your answer.

The products from the breakdown of one molecule of pyruvate are

- three molecules of carbon dioxide that are given off as a waste product
- one molecule of ATP
- four molecules of NADH to the electron transport chain
- one molecule of $FADH_2$ to the electron transport chain

Remember, glycolysis produces two pyruvate molecules. Therefore, the products above are half of what comes from one glucose molecule. The totals are six carbon dioxide, two ATP, eight NADH, and two $FADH_2$ molecules.

B Analyze In what two ways is the Krebs cycle important for making ATP?

MAIN IDEA

The electron transport chain is the second main part of cellular respiration.

The electron transport chain takes place in and across the inner membrane of a mitochondrion. As with electron transport in photosynthesis, proteins make up the electron transport chain in cellular respiration. The proteins use energy from the electrons supplied by NADH and $FADH_2$ to pump hydrogen ions against a concentration gradient, and across the inner mitochondrial membrane.

BELOW LEVEL

Have students work in small groups to make a summary diagram of glycolysis and cellular respiration. They should draw a mitochondrion, including the folded inner membrane; then start the sequence with a molecule of glucose in the cytoplasm and end it with the production of water and ATP. Tell students to keep the diagram simple, using boxes to represent a reaction. Suggest that they show reactants and products, but not include any numbers of molecules.

Biology Toolkit, Sequence Diagram, p. C38

TEACH FROM VISUALS

FIGURE 4.14 Use the figure to teach the details of the Krebs cycle, using the numbered items in the text to help clarify. Remind students that the diagram has been simplified and is not balanced in terms of electrons and ions.

Ask

- What event starts the Krebs cycle? Pyruvate (from glycolysis) is broken down and a two-carbon molecule bonded to Coenxyme A (acetyl-CoA) enters the Krebs cycle.
- Where does the Krebs cycle take place? mitochondrion matrix
- How many membranes does a pyruvate molecule cross? two: outer and inner membranes of mitochondrion

Take It Further

In glycolysis, most of the chemical energy from glucose remains in the bonds of pyruvate. In the Krebs cycle, the six molecules of carbon dioxide that are formed are much lower in energy. Most of the energy from glucose has been transferred to NADH and $FADH_2$.

Answers

A Infer Glycolysis and the Krebs cycle directly produce equal amounts of ATP. Indirectly, the Krebs cycle is responsible for more ATP production through the transfer of energy to the electron transport chain.

B Analyze The Krebs cycle produces two ATP and energy-carrying molecules that are used to produce more ATP in the electron transport chain.

▼ Teach *continued*

TEACH FROM VISUALS

FIGURE 4.15 Use the figure to teach the electron transport chain. Explain that the ions and electrons in the diagram are not balanced for the sake of simplicity. **Ask**

- Where do hydrogen ions accumulate? on the inside of the inner mitochondrial membrane
- Where does the energy come from that pumps H^+ against their gradient? from electrons removed from NADH and $FADH_2$

Take It Further

Remind students that a hydrogen atom consists of one proton and one electron. When that electron is lost, the hydrogen atom becomes a hydrogen ion. A **hydrogen ion** is simply a naked proton.

Integrating Genetics

The proteins in the electron transport chain, called **cytochromes,** are found in vastly different organisms. Cytochrome c is found in all aerobic organisms, indicating that all aerobic organisms probably descended from a common ancestor that used this molecule for cellular respiration. The amino acid sequence of cytochrome c differs slightly in different species. Closely related species have more similar sequences than distantly related species.

Answers

A Explain Hydrogen ions are transported across the inner membrane and then flow through ATP synthase to produce ATP.

The ions later flow back through the membrane to produce ATP. Oxygen is needed at the end of the process to pick up electrons that have gone through the chain. The electron transport chain is shown in **FIGURE 4.15.**

1. **Electrons removed** Proteins inside the inner membrane of the mitochondrion take high-energy electrons from NADH and $FADH_2$. Two molecules of NADH and one molecule of $FADH_2$ are used.
2. **Hydrogen ions transported** High-energy electrons travel through the proteins in the electron transport chain. The proteins use energy from the electrons to pump hydrogen ions across the inner membrane to produce a chemiosmotic gradient, just as in photosynthesis. The hydrogen ions build up on the inside of the inner mitochondrial membrane.
3. **ATP produced** Just as in photosynthesis, the flow of hydrogen ions is used to make ATP. Hydrogen ions diffuse through a protein channel in the inner membrane of the mitochondrion. The channel is part of the ATP synthase enzyme. ATP synthase adds phosphate groups to ADP to make ATP molecules. For each pair of electrons that passes through the electron transport chain, an average of three ATP molecules are made.
4. **Water formed** Oxygen finally enters the cellular respiration process. The oxygen picks up electrons and hydrogen ions to form water. The water molecules are given off as a waste product.

FIGURE 4.15 The Electron Transport Chain

Energy from the Krebs cycle is used to produce ATP.

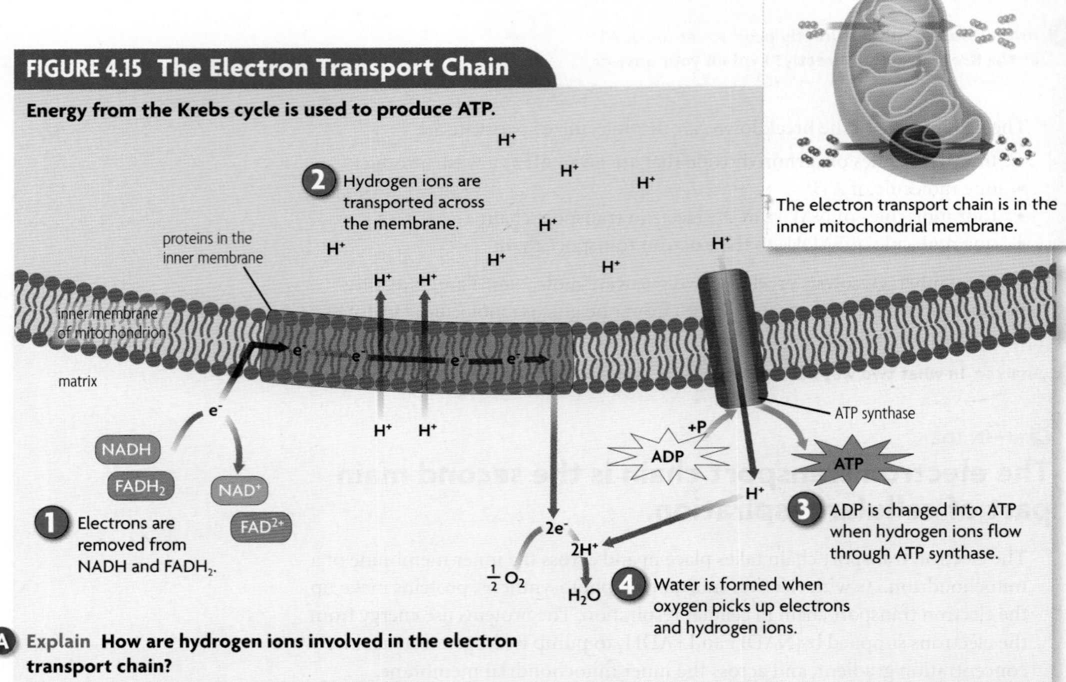

The electron transport chain is in the inner mitochondrial membrane.
2 Hydrogen ions are transported across the membrane.
proteins in the inner membrane
inner membrane of mitochondrion
matrix
H⁺
e⁻
NADH
FADH₂
NAD⁺
FAD²⁺
1 Electrons are removed from NADH and FADH₂.
ATP synthase
+P
ADP
ATP
3 ADP is changed into ATP when hydrogen ions flow through ATP synthase.
2e⁻
2H⁺
½ O₂
H₂O
4 Water is formed when oxygen picks up electrons and hydrogen ions.

A Explain How are hydrogen ions involved in the electron transport chain?

Differentiated Instruction

PRE-AP

Give students five minutes to write on the question of how oxygen functions in providing energy to a cell. They should refer to **FIGURES 4.14** and **4.15.** Ask them also to consider the role of hydrogen. Students should realize that it is the electrons and hydrogen ions that are used to produce ATP. Oxygen is used as an electron acceptor.

Biology Toolkit, Quick-Write, p. C19

The products of cellular respiration—including glycolysis—are

- Carbon dioxide from the Krebs cycle and from the breakdown of pyruvate before the Krebs cycle
- Water from the electron transport chain
- A net gain of up to 38 ATP molecules for every glucose molecule—2 from glycolysis, 2 from the Krebs cycle, and up to 34 from the electron transport chain

Comparing Cellular Respiration and Photosynthesis

Again, think about how photosynthesis and cellular respiration are approximately the reverse of each other. Photosynthesis stores energy from sunlight as chemical energy. In contrast, cellular respiration releases stored energy as ATP and heat. Look at **FIGURE 4.17**, and think about other similarities and differences between the processes.

FIGURE 4.16 Like sandbags passed down a line of people, high-energy electrons are passed along a chain of proteins in the inner mitochondrial membrane.

FIGURE 4.17 PHOTOSYNTHESIS AND CELLULAR RESPIRATION

	PHOTOSYNTHESIS	CELLULAR RESPIRATION
Organelle for process	chloroplast	mitochondrion
Reactants	CO_2 and H_2O	sugars ($C_6H_{12}O_6$) and O_2
Electron transport chain	proteins within thylakoid membrane	proteins within inner mitochondrial membrane
Cycle of chemical reactions	Calvin cycle in stroma of chloroplasts builds sugar molecules	Krebs cycle in matrix of mitochondria breaks down carbon-based molecules
Products	sugars ($C_6H_{12}O_6$) and O_2	CO_2 and H_2O

Recall the roles of electrons, hydrogen ions, and ATP synthase. In both processes, high-energy electrons are transported through proteins. Their energy is used to pump hydrogen ions across a membrane. And the flow of hydrogen ions through ATP synthase produces ATP. As you can see, the parts of the processes are very similar, but their end points are very different.

Ⓐ Analyze **How does the electron transport chain depend on the Krebs cycle?**

4.5 ASSESSMENT

ONLINE QUIZ ClassZone.com

B.3.2

REVIEWING ▶ MAIN IDEAS

1. What is the role of pyruvate in cellular respiration?
2. Describe in your own words the function of the Krebs cycle.
3. Explain the functions of electrons, hydrogen ions, and oxygen in the electron transport chain.

CRITICAL THINKING

4. **Compare and Contrast** Describe the similarities and differences between the Krebs cycle and the Calvin cycle.
5. **Evaluate** Is oxygen necessary for the production of all ATP in your cells? Why or why not?

***Connecting* CONCEPTS**

6. **Common Ancestry** Protein molecules called cytochromes are part of the electron transport chain. They are nearly identical in every known aerobic organism. How do these molecules show the unity of life on Earth?

ONLINE BIOLOGY Students can do a virtual lab involving snails and elodea to see how carbon dioxide cycles through a living system. See Options for Inquiry on page 127.

Integrating Ecology

About 40 percent of the energy in glucose is converted to ATP during cellular respiration. The rest is lost as heat. Much of this heat keeps the body warm. This loss of energy explains why so little energy is available at each **trophic level** and why the length of **food chains** is limited. It also explains why people feel so warm when they exercise.

Answers

Ⓐ **Analyze** Energy from the Krebs cycle is necessary for the electron transport chain to function.

Assess and Reteach ▼

Assess Use the Online Quiz or Section Quiz (*Assessment Book,* p. 71).

Reteach Work with students to put together a concept map of cellular respiration. Start the concept map with the word *glycolysis.* Tell students that the concept map must end with the word *water.*

4.5 ASSESSMENT

1. Pyruvate, produced by the breakdown of glucose, is needed for the Krebs cycle, which is a part of cellular respiration.
2. The Krebs cycle breaks down and extracts energy from carbon-based molecules, transfers it to the electron transport chain, makes a small amount of ATP, and releases carbon dioxide.
3. The electron transport chain pumps hydrogen ions across the inner mitochondrial membrane. Hydrogen ions then flow through a channel that is bound to ATP synthase. Oxygen picks up electrons and hydrogen ions so that the electron transport chain can continue to function.
4. Both occur in the interior space of their respective organelles, and both are cycles of chemical reactions. The Calvin cycle builds larger carbon-based molecules in chloroplasts to store energy. The Krebs cycle breaks down carbon-based molecules in the mitochondria to release energy.
5. No; ATP is also formed during glycolysis, which can continue without oxygen.
6. The similarity of cytochromes in many different organisms suggests a common ancestor.

▼ Plan and Prepare

Objectives

- Describe the process of fermentation.
- Summarize the importance of fermentation.

Section Resources

Unit Resource Book Study Guide pp. 51–52 Power Notes p. 53 Reinforcement p. 54
Interactive Reader Chapter 4 **Spanish Study Guide** pp. 41–42
Biology Toolkit pp. C11, C20, C30, D4
Technology Power Presentation 4.6 Media Gallery DVD Online Quiz 4.6

Activate Prior Knowledge Have students consider a long-distance runner. **Ask**

- How do long-distance runners, such as marathoners, provide the energy their bodies need for a race? by carb-loading, eating carbohydrate-rich foods
- What has happened to a runner who "hits the wall"? The carbohydrates are depleted. The body now burns more fat, which requires more oxygen, energy, and time to burn.

"Hitting the wall" means a runner is making ATP through glycolysis and fermentation.

4.6 Fermentation

KEY CONCEPT Fermentation allows the production of a small amount of ATP without oxygen.

MAIN IDEAS

- Fermentation allows glycolysis to continue.
- Fermentation and its products are important in several ways.

VOCABULARY

fermentation, p. 122
lactic acid, p. 123

Review
ATP, glycolysis, cellular respiration, aerobic, anaerobic

B.3.3 Recognize and describe that metabolism consists of all of the biochemical reactions that occur inside cells, including the production, modification, transport, and exchange of materials that are required for the maintenance of life.

Connect Think about a time that you worked or exercised hard. Maybe you moved heavy boxes or furniture. Maybe, playing basketball, you found yourself repeatedly running up and down the court. Your arms and legs began to feel heavy, and they seemed to lose strength. Your muscles became sore, and even when you rested you kept breathing hard. Your muscles were using fermentation.

MAIN IDEA

Fermentation allows glycolysis to continue.

The cells in your body cannot store large amounts of oxygen for cellular respiration. The amount of oxygen that is provided by breathing is enough for your cells during normal activities. When you are reading or talking to friends, your body can maintain its oxygen levels. When you are doing high levels of activity, as the sprinter is in **FIGURE 4.18**, your body cannot bring in enough oxygen for your cells, even though you breathe faster. How do your cells function without enough oxygen to keep cellular respiration going?

Recall that glycolysis yields two ATP molecules when it splits glucose into two molecules of pyruvate. Glycolysis is always occurring and does not require oxygen. If oxygen is available, the products of glycolysis—pyruvate and the electron carrier NADH—are used in cellular respiration. Then, oxygen picks up electrons at the end of the electron transport chain in cellular respiration. But what happens when oxygen is not there to pick up electrons? The production of ATP without oxygen continues through the anaerobic processes of glycolysis and fermentation.

Fermentation does not make ATP, but it allows glycolysis to continue. Fermentation removes electrons from NADH molecules and recycles NAD^+ molecules for glycolysis. Why is this process important? Because glycolysis, just like cellular respiration, needs a molecule that picks up electrons. It needs molecules of NAD^+.

FIGURE 4.18 Muscle cells use anaerobic processes during hard exercise.

VISUAL VOCAB

Fermentation is an anaerobic process that allows glycolysis to continue.

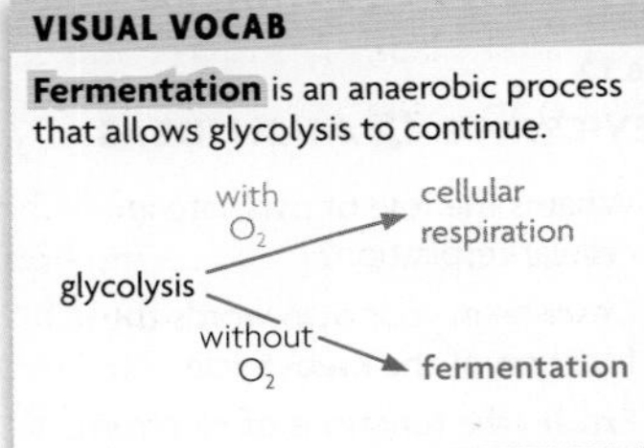

▼ Teach

Vocabulary

Greek and Latin Origins Remind students that the Greek and Latin prefix *an-* means "not." In combination with the Greek root *aer,* meaning "air," **anaerobic** means "not aerobic" or "not in air." Tell students that the *aer-* of **aerobic** is the *air* that they inhale.

Differentiated Instruction

ENGLISH LEARNERS

If you used the strategy of a brainstorming session for students for **Sections 4.3** and **4.5,** continue the practice here. Produce a cluster diagram to organize information about the process of fermentation. Compare this diagram to the ones made earlier. Point out the details that are critical for students to know.

Biology Toolkit, Brainstorming, p. C11; Cluster Diagram, p. C30

BELOW LEVEL

Rather than have students use an outline for this section, suggest they use a two-column graphic organizer to compare lactic acid and alcoholic fermentation. To get them started, have them consider these questions:

- What are the reactants?
- What are the products?
- What consumer products are made from the process?

Biology Toolkit, T-Chart, p. C20

Without NAD^+ to pick up high-energy electrons from the splitting of glucose, glycolysis would stop. When the high-energy electrons are picked up, though, a eukaryotic cell can continue breaking down glucose and other simple sugars to make a small amount of ATP.

Suppose that a molecule of glucose has just been split by glycolysis in one of your muscle cells, but oxygen is unavailable. A process called lactic acid fermentation takes place. Lactic acid fermentation occurs in your muscle cells, the cells of other vertebrates, and in some microorganisms. **Lactic acid,** $C_3H_6O_3$, is what causes your muscles to "burn" during hard exercise.

1. Pyruvate and NADH from glycolysis enter the fermentation process. Two NADH molecules provide energy to convert pyruvate into lactic acid. As the NADH is used, it is converted back into NAD^+.
2. Two molecules of NAD^+ are recycled back to glycolysis. The recycling of NAD^+ allows glycolysis to continue.

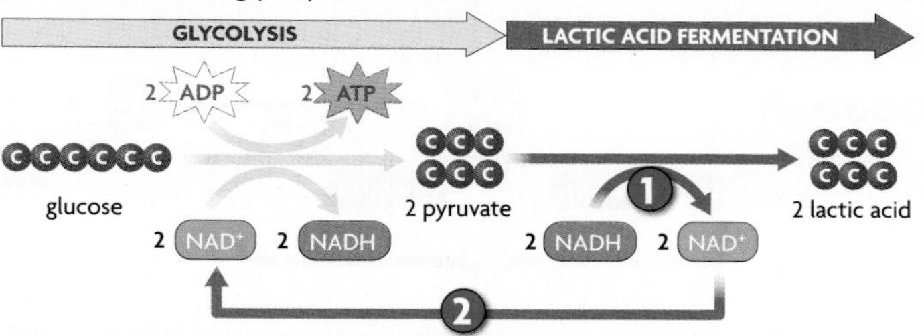

As you can see, the role of fermentation is simply to provide glycolysis with a steady supply of NAD^+. By itself, fermentation does not produce ATP. Instead, it allows glycolysis to continue to produce ATP. However, fermentation does produce the lactic acid waste product that builds up in muscle cells and causes a burning feeling. Once oxygen is available again, your cells return to using cellular respiration. The lactic acid is quickly broken down and removed from the cells. This is why you continue to breathe hard for several minutes after you stop exercising. Your body is making up for the oxygen deficit in your cells, which allows the breakdown of lactic acid in your muscles.

A Sequence **Which process must happen first, fermentation or glycolysis? Explain.**

TAKING NOTES

Use a mind map to take notes on the processes involved in fermentation.

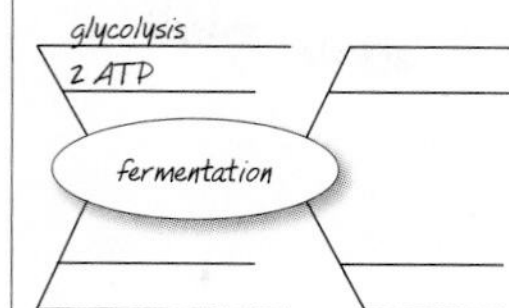

Connecting CONCEPTS

Human Biology Muscle cells need ATP to contract. You will learn how muscles produce your movements in **Chapter 33**.

MAIN IDEA

Fermentation and its products are important in several ways.

How would your diet change without cheese, bread, and yogurt? How would pizza exist without cheese and bread? Without fermentation, a pizza crust would not rise and there would be no mozzarella cheese as a pizza topping. Cheese, bread, and yogurt are just a few of the foods made by fermentation. Milk is changed into different cheeses by fermentation processes carried out by different types of bacteria and molds. Waste products of their fermentation processes give cheeses their different flavors and textures. Additionally, some types of bacteria that use lactic acid fermentation sour the milk in yogurt.

ONLINE BIOLOGY To learn more about how lactic acid fermentation affects muscles, go to the WebQuest in Options for Inquiry on page 127.

Take It Further

Oxygen greatly increases the amount of energy available to an organism. An anaerobic organism gets only two ATP molecules out of a molecule of glucose. By comparison, an aerobic organism can get up to 38 molecules of ATP from one molecule of glucose.

The Inside Story

Ideas about healthy eating and long life have been around for quite a while. So have health-food fads. In 1908, Russian biologist **Elie Metchnikoff** published a book called *The Prolongation of Human Life.* In his book, Metchnikoff suggested that the long life spans associated with Bulgarian people were due to their high consumption of foods cultured with *Lactobacillus* bacteria. More simply put, they ate a lot of **yogurt.**

The production of yogurt by lactic acid fermentation is believed to have been discovered by Balkan tribes as many as 4500 years ago. Until 1908, yogurt was eaten mainly by people in eastern European and Middle Eastern countries. Metchnikoff devoted the last ten years of his life to the study of lactic acid fermentation and longevity. He named the bacterium that produces yogurt *Lactobacillus bulgaricus* in honor of the Bulgarian people.

HANDS-ON ACTIVITY

Students may be interested in making yogurt. There are many recipes available on the Internet. The yogurt can be incubated using a commercial yogurt machine, or it can be heated on a stove or hot plate, following directions in the recipe. A small amount of commercial yogurt that contains living cultures is used as a starter.

Answers

A Sequence Gycolysis must occur first because fermentation requires pyruvate and NADH.

▼ Teach *continued*

TEACH FROM VISUALS

Have students compare the diagram shown on this page with the one shown on page 123. **Ask**

- How are alcoholic fermentation and lactic acid fermentation similar? begin with glycolysis of glucose, produce ATP and NAD^+
- How are they different? Lactic acid fermentation produces lactic acid; alcoholic fermentation produces alcohol and carbon dioxide.

QUICK LAB

Time 20–30 minutes TEACHER TESTED

Lab Binder Cells, pp. 21–22

Purpose Measure the amount of fermentation in various beverages.

LAB MANAGEMENT

- Be sure to use fresh yeast. Check the expiration date.
- Students can use duct tape to seal the balloon onto the bottle neck.
- Students should measure the circumference of the balloon as a measure of fermentation.

Expected Results

Beverages that contain the most sugar will yield the most carbon dioxide.

Analyze and Conclude

1. independent variable: type or temperature of beverage; dependent variable: inflation of balloon indicating the amount of carbon dioxide produced; constants: amount of beverage and yeast, size of balloon
2. The type of beverage affected how much carbon dioxide was produced because different beverages have different amounts of sugar. A higher sugar concentration increases the rate of fermentation.
3. inconsistent methods, poorly controlled constants, random error (for example, different yeast activity, differences in balloons used)

Lactic acid fermentation is not the only anaerobic process. Alcoholic fermentation is used by many yeasts and by some types of plants. Alcoholic fermentation begins at the same point as lactic acid fermentation. That is, glycolysis splits a molecule of glucose and produces two net ATP molecules, two pyruvate molecules, and two NADH molecules. Pyruvate and NADH enter alcoholic fermentation.

1. Pyruvate and NADH from glycolysis enter alcoholic fermentation. Two NADH molecules provide energy to break down pyruvate into an alcohol and carbon dioxide. As the NADH molecules are used, they are converted back into molecules of NAD^+.
2. The molecules of NAD^+ are recycled back to glycolysis. The recycling of NAD^+ allows glycolysis to continue.

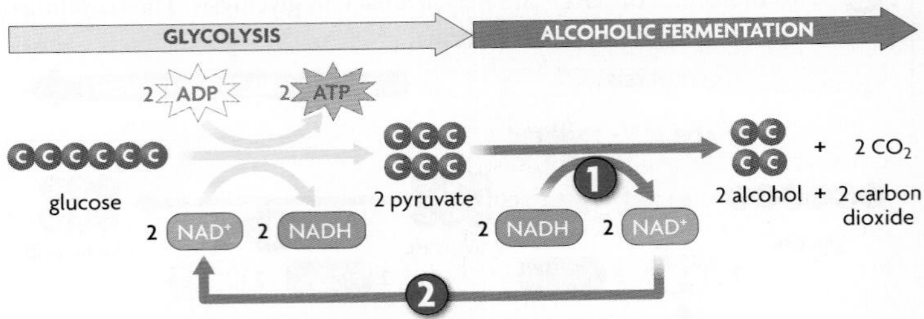

The products of this process are two molecules of an alcohol, often ethyl alcohol, two molecules of carbon dioxide, and two molecules of NAD^+. Just like lactic acid fermentation, alcoholic fermentation recycles NAD^+ and so allows glycolysis to keep making ATP.

QUICK LAB DESIGN YOUR OWN

NOS.1

Fermentation

One waste product of alcoholic fermentation is carbon dioxide. In this lab you will determine which beverage causes yeast to undergo a higher rate of fermentation.

PROBLEM What factors affect the rate of fermentation in yeast?

PROCEDURE

1. Write an operational definition for the dependent variable that you will use to measure the rate of fermentation.
2. Develop a technique using a balloon to measure fermentation rate.
3. Design your experiment. Have your teacher approve your experimental design. Write your experimental procedure and conduct your experiment.
4. Construct a data table to record your data. Construct a graph to display your data.

ANALYZE AND CONCLUDE

1. **Identify** What are the independent variable, dependent variable, and constants?
2. **Analyze** How did the independent variable affect the rate of fermentation? Why?
3. **Experimental Design** Identify possible reasons for any inconsistent results you observed.

MATERIALS

- 2 empty plastic bottles
- 1 package of yeast
- 2 100-mL graduated cylinders
- 2 250-mL beakers
- 2 beverages
- 2 round balloons
- 30 cm string
- metric ruler

Differentiated Instruction

TEACH WITH TECHNOLOGY

If you have access to probeware, have students make a quantitative measure of the carbon dioxide produced by alcoholic fermentation.

ENGLISH LEARNERS

Remember to take extra time early in the year to walk students through the laboratory directions. Students should prepare word squares specifically for terms associated with experimental procedures: *variable, independent variable, dependent variable, constant,* and *operational definition.* Search the Quick Lab instructions for difficult vocabulary or constructions. You might want to read the materials list aloud, holding up each item as you say its name.

Biology Toolkit, Word Squares, p. D4

FIGURE 4.19 Fermentation by molds and bacteria produces the different flavors and textures of various cheeses.

Alcoholic fermentation in yeast is particularly useful. When bread or pizza crust is made, yeast is used to cause the dough to rise. The yeast breaks down sugars in the dough through glycolysis and alcohol fermentation. The carbon dioxide gas produced by alcoholic fermentation causes the dough to puff up and rise. When the dough is baked, the alcohol that is produced during fermentation evaporates into the air. The yeast in dough is killed by the heat of baking.

Bacteria that rely upon fermentation play a very important role in the digestive systems of animals. Microorganisms in the digestive tracts of animals, including humans, must obtain their ATP from anaerobic processes because oxygen is not available. Without them, neither you nor other animals would be able to fully digest food. Why? These bacteria continue the breakdown of molecules by taking in undigested material for their needs. The additional breakdown of materials by digestive bacteria allows the host animal to absorb more nutrients from food.

A **Apply Explain the importance of alcoholic fermentation in the production of bread's light, fluffy texture.**

4.6 ASSESSMENT

ONLINE QUIZ ClassZone.com

B.3.3

REVIEWING MAIN IDEAS

1. What is the relationship between glycolysis and **fermentation**?
2. Summarize the process of alcoholic fermentation in yeast.

CRITICAL THINKING

3. **Compare and Contrast** How are **lactic acid** fermentation and alcoholic fermentation similar? How are they different?
4. **Compare and Contrast** Describe the similarities and differences between cellular respiration and fermentation.

***Connecting* CONCEPTS**

5. **Cellular Respiration** How is the role of oxygen in cellular respiration similar to the role of NAD^+ in fermentation ?

ONLINE BIOLOGY Go to the chapter Resource Center at **ClassZone.com** for additional resources and information on fermentation.

Vocabulary

Word Origins The word **fermentation** and the word **brew** share the same root, *bhreu-*, meaning "boil" or "bubble." This relates to the gas released by yeast during the process of alcoholic fermentation. In German, the root word was reduced to *bher-* and later *bhermen,* which eventually became *ferment.*

Answers

A **Apply** Carbon dioxide produced from alcoholic fermentation creates gas pockets in the bread, which cause the bread to rise.

Assess and Reteach ▼

Assess Use the Online Quiz or Section Quiz (*Assessment Book,* p. 72).

Reteach Have students identify products that are made by fermentation. Choose among the products and ask different students to write the fermentation process associated with the product on the board.

4.6 ASSESSMENT

1. Glycolysis leads to fermentation if no oxygen is available. NAD^+ produced by fermentation allows glycolysis to continue.
2. Sugars are broken down by glycolysis. Pyruvate and NADH enter alcoholic fermentation, producing alcohol and carbon dioxide. NAD^+ is recycled back to glycolysis.
3. Both are anaerobic processes that break down glucose to make ATP and recycle NAD^+ to glycolysis. Lactic acid fermentation produces lactic acid; alcoholic fermentation produces an alcohol and carbon dioxide.
4. Both produce ATP through the breakdown of carbon-based molecules, and both allow glycolysis to continue by recycling electron acceptors. Cellular respiration requires oxygen and produces much more ATP than fermentation.
5. Both oxygen and NAD^+ pick up electrons and allow ATP production to continue.

OPTIONS FOR INQUIRY

INVESTIGATION

Time 45 minutes	TEACHER TESTED
Teacher Preparation	
Student Difficulty	
Lab Binder Cells, pp. 17–19	

Purpose Investigate cellular respiration in dormant and germinated seeds.

Overview Students will compare the volume of oxygen used by dormant and germinated seeds. They will

- prepare test-tube respirometers
- measure water height in response to the partial vacuum created by oxygen consumption

LAB PREPARATION

- Use large, fresh seeds (peas or beans). Soak the seeds for 24–48 hours.

LAB MANAGEMENT

- Remind students that cellular respiration uses O_2 and forms CO_2. The pressure due to CO_2 might cancel out any change due to the uptake of O_2. To solve this problem, potassium hydroxide is added to combine with CO_2 to form insoluble potassium carbonate.
- Be sure that students do not remove the tubes from the beaker while measuring water height.
- Students should measure the height of the water in the tubes after inverting them and repeat the next day. Have students calculate any differences in height if any.
- Store setups at room temperature.

POST-LAB DISCUSSION

Discuss the change in volume of gas in the tubes as indicative of the amount of O_2 consumed. **Ask,** Why did water move up into the tube? Water rises due to the partial vacuum created by oxygen consumption.

Use these inquiry-based labs and online activities to deepen your understanding of photosynthesis and cellular respiration.

INDIANA STANDARDS

NOS.1 Develop explanations based on reproducible data and observations gathered during laboratory investigations.

NOS.3 Clearly communicate their ideas and results of investigations verbally and in written form using tables, graphs, diagrams, and photographs.

INVESTIGATION

Cellular Respiration

Plant cells use cellular respiration to make ATP from the sugars they produce during photosynthesis. In this experiment, you will compare cellular respiration rates in dormant and germinated seeds.

SKILLS Measuring, Collecting Data, Graphing, Analyzing Data

MATERIALS
- 3 test tubes
- marking pen
- 6 pre-soaked seeds
- 6 dry seeds
- 6 cotton plugs
- 1.5 teaspoons potassium hydroxide (KOH) powder
- rubber band
- 100-mL beaker
- 25 mL colored water
- metric ruler

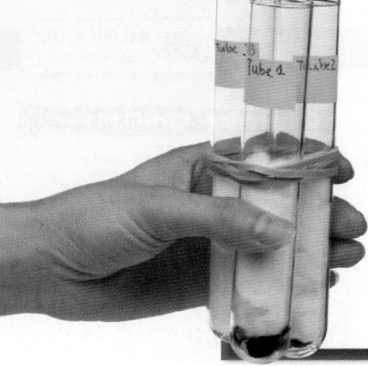

PROBLEM How do respiration rates compare in dormant and germinated seeds?

PROCEDURE

1. Label the three test tubes as follows:
   Tube 1: pre-soaked seeds; Tube 2: dry seeds;
   Tube 3: no seeds
2. Layer into the test tubes the following materials. Be sure that the layers of materials are compact, but not too tight.
   Tube 1: pre-soaked seeds, cotton plug, 1/2 tsp. potassium hydroxide, cotton plug
   Tube 2: dry seeds, cotton plug, 1/2 tsp. potassium hydroxide, cotton plug
   Tube 3: cotton plug, 1/2 tsp. potassium hydroxide, cotton plug

Caution: Potassium hydroxide is a strong base; avoid contact with eyes, skin, and clothing.

3. Use the rubber band to hold the three test tubes together.
4. Pour the 25 mL of colored water into the beaker.
5. Invert the test tubes and place them in the beaker.
6. Construct a data table and record the distance that the colored water travels up each of the three test tubes.

ANALYZE AND CONCLUDE

1. **Analyze** Choose the type of graph that best represents the data. Construct your graph.
2. **Analyze** Describe your observations and measurements of test tubes 1 and 2. What do the data show? Explain why differences between the two tubes might exist.
3. **Evaluate** What is the function of test tube 3 in the experiment? What do the measurements from this test tube demonstrate?
4. **Infer** Potassium hydroxide reacts with, and removes, carbon dioxide from the air. Why might cellular respiration be responsible for water rising into some of the test tubes?
5. **Predict** Suppose this experiment were allowed to run an additional day. What might you expect to encounter? What about after a week?

Answers

Analyze and Conclude

1. A bar graph is best; check students' work.
2. Oxygen consumption was measured by the height of the water in the tubes. Water level in the tube with germinated seeds was greater than that in the tube with dormant seeds. Dormant seeds respire very slowly.
3. Tube 3 is a control. It may show a slight rise in water level due to atmospheric pressure changes.
4. The volume of gas and corresponding air pressure in the test tubes decreased with increasing cellular respiration, that is, with increasing consumption of O_2.
5. Water level would be higher after one day. After one week, the germinated seeds may die because there is no CO_2 in the tube for photosynthesis.

INVESTIGATION

Investigate Fermentation in Foods

Carbon dioxide gas is released as a waste product of fermentation in yeasts. In this experiment you will change an independent variable to change the rate of fermentation.

SKILL Designing Experiments

MATERIALS

- plastic bottles
- yeast
- foods or beverages containing sugar
- warm water
- round balloons
- balance
- spatula
- graduated cylinders
- paper towels
- string
- metric ruler

PROBLEM What conditions affect fermentation?

DESIGN

1. Choose a variable, such as temperature or concentration, to test in the experiment. Use at least two experimental conditions.
2. Design your procedure and get your teacher's approval. List the experimental constants.
3. Design a data table that includes both the independent variable and the dependent variable.
4. Conduct your experiment. Measure carbon dioxide production for 15 minutes during each experimental trial.

ANALYZE AND CONCLUDE

1. **Identify** What is your independent variable? What is the dependent variable? How did you operationally define the dependent variable?
2. **Analyze** Choose the best way to graph your data. Construct your graph.
3. **Analyze** How did your manipulation of the independent variable affect fermentation rate?
4. **Experimental Design** What are possible sources of unavoidable error in your design? Explain why they were present.

Online BIOLOGY CLASSZONE.COM

VIRTUAL LAB

Carbon Dioxide Transfer Through Snails and Elodea

How does CO_2 cycle through a simple biological system? In this interactive lab, you will place snails and elodea in varying conditions and test for the presence of CO_2.

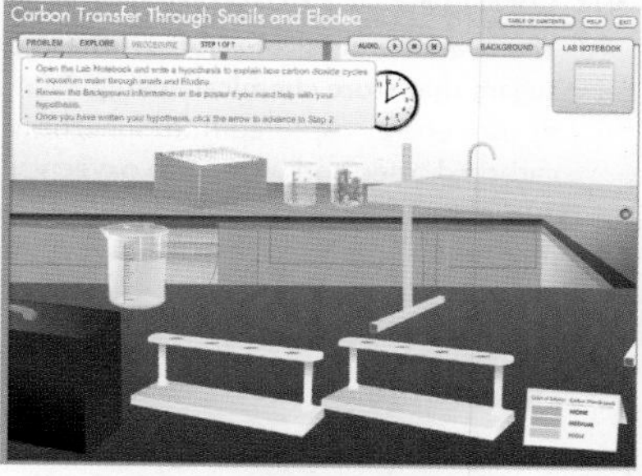

ANIMATED BIOLOGY

Mirror Processes

Are the light-dependent reactions of photosynthesis really a "mirror image" of the electron transport chain in cellular respiration? Build a diagram of each to compare how electrons move through the system.

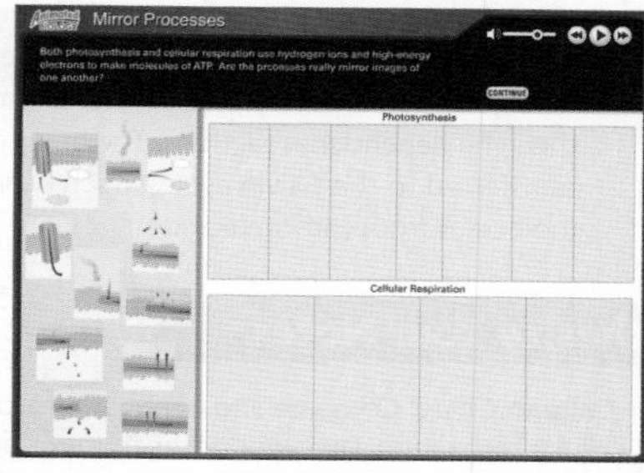

WEBQUEST

An athletic challenge, such as weightlifting, requires a lot of energy and can stress muscles to their limits. Complete this WebQuest to learn how athletes cope with the burn. Review how cells process energy and explore how athletes train.

Answers

Sample Data

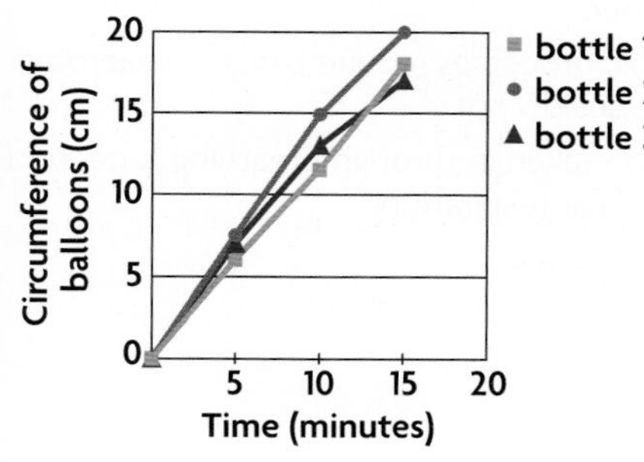

Analyze and Conclude

1. Independent variables will vary; dependent variable is amount of fermentation; operational definition is balloon's circumference.
2. A line graph should be used if repeated measurements are taken, a bar graph if only one measurement is taken.
3. Students should explain their conclusions.
4. *Sample Answer:* If other processes that produce gas were occurring, that gas would cause the balloons to inflate.

Online Biology ▼

VIRTUAL LAB Use this lab after both photosynthesis and cellular respiration have been introduced.

ANIMATED BIOLOGY Use this interactive animation to reinforce the concepts of **Sections 4.2** and **4.4.**

WEBQUEST The WebQuest will take one full class period. Students will need to complete the activity online and then will need access to a printer to print their answers to hand in. Sample answers, teacher notes, and alternative assessment ideas are available on **ClassZone.com.** Use with **Section 4.6.**

INVESTIGATION	
Time 45 minutes	TEACHER TESTED
Teacher Preparation (1 flask)	
Student Difficulty (1 flask)	
Lab Binder Cells, p. 20	

LAB PREPARATION

- Have bottled water and hot and cold tap water available.

LAB MANAGEMENT

- Check for experimental designs that test more than one independent variable at a time.

Teacher Note "I like the fact that students are provided opportunities to develop inquiry skills doing this activity. I allowed my advanced students to choose the variable."

POST-LAB DISCUSSION

Discuss the variables that students tested and the results obtained. **Ask,** Why might fermentation increase with increasing temperature? Chemical reaction rates increase with an increase in temperature.

CHAPTER REVIEW

Interactive Review

Encourage students to go to **ClassZone.com** for a detailed review of each section, including visuals and vocabulary practice.

Unit Resource Book, Vocabulary Practice, pp. 61–64

CHAPTER 4 Interactive Review @ CLASSZONE.COM

KEY CONCEPTS | Vocabulary Games | Concept Maps | Animated Biology | Online Quiz

4.1 Chemical Energy and ATP

All cells need chemical energy. Adenosine triphosphate (ATP) is the primary source of energy in all cells. ATP transfers energy for cell processes such as building new molecules and transporting materials.

4.2 Overview of Photosynthesis

The overall process of photosynthesis produces sugars that store chemical energy. Photosynthesis uses energy captured from sunlight to change carbon dioxide and water into oxygen and sugars. Sunlight is absorbed during the light-dependent reactions, and sugars are made during the light-independent reactions.

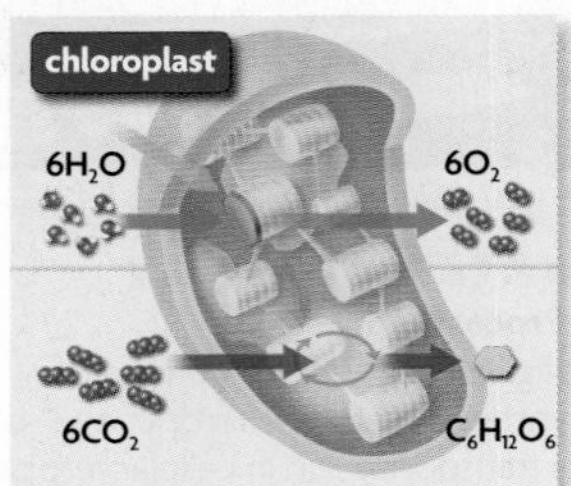

4.3 Photosynthesis in Detail

Photosynthesis requires a series of chemical reactions. Energy from sunlight is absorbed in the thylakoid membrane by photosystems II and I in the light-dependent reactions. The energy is transferred to the Calvin cycle, which builds sugar molecules from carbon dioxide.

4.4 Overview of Cellular Respiration

The overall process of cellular respiration converts sugar into ATP using oxygen. Glycolysis splits glucose and when oxygen is present the products of glycolysis are used in cellular respiration. The Krebs cycle transfers energy to the electron transport chain, which produces most of the ATP in eukaryotic cells.

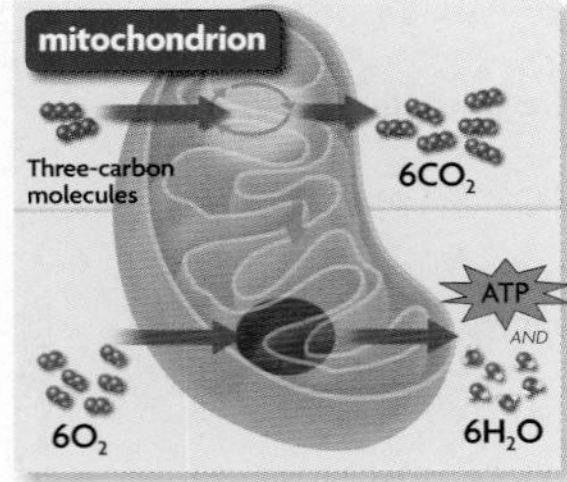

4.5 Cellular Respiration in Detail

Cellular respiration is an aerobic process with two main stages. The Krebs cycle breaks down carbon-based molecules and transfers energy to electron carriers. The electron carriers provide energy to the electron transport chain. ATP is produced by the electron transport chain when hydrogen ions flow through ATP synthase.

4.6 Fermentation

Fermentation allows the production of a small amount of ATP without oxygen. Fermentation allows glycolysis to continue producing ATP when oxygen is unavailable. Lactic acid fermentation occurs in many cells, including human muscle cells.

Synthesize Your Notes

Two-Column Chart Compare and contrast photosynthesis and cellular respiration. Use your notes to make detailed charts that include details about both processes. Highlight important vocabulary and processes.

Photosynthesis	Cellular Respiration
absorbs sunlight occurs in chloroplasts $6CO_2 + 6H_2O \rightarrow C_6H_{12}O_6 + 6O_2$	produces ATP occurs in mitochondria $C_6H_{12}O_6 + 6O_2 \rightarrow 6CO_2 + 6H_2O$

Concept Map Use a concept map like the one below to summarize and organize the processes of photosynthesis, cellular respiration, and fermentation.

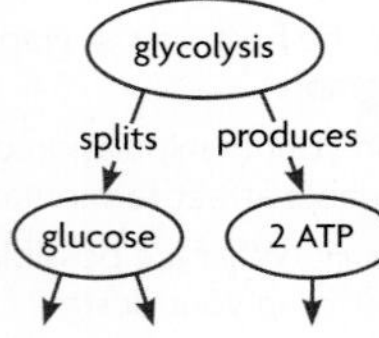

Reviewing Vocabulary

1. builds sugars
2. absorb and transfer energy
3. produces ATP when oxygen is available
4. with oxygen
5. breaks down pyruvate
6. allows glycolysis to continue
7. Photosynthesis uses light to put sugars together.
8. Aerobic processes require oxygen, anaerobic processes do not.
9. Oxygen taken in through breathing is needed for cellular respiration.

Chapter Assessment

Chapter Vocabulary

4.1 ATP, p. 100
ADP, p. 101
chemosynthesis, p. 102

4.2 photosynthesis, p. 103
chlorophyll, p. 103
thylakoid, p. 104
light-dependent reactions, p. 105
light-independent reactions, p. 105

4.3 photosystem, p. 108
electron transport chain, p. 109
ATP synthase, p. 110
Calvin cycle, p. 111

4.4 cellular respiration, p. 113
aerobic, p. 113
glycolysis, p. 113
anaerobic, p. 113
Krebs cycle, p. 115

4.6 fermentation, p. 122
lactic acid, p. 123

Reviewing Vocabulary

Keep It Short

For each vocabulary term below, write a short, precise phrase that describes its meaning. For example, a short phrase to describe *ATP* could be "energy for cells."

1. photosynthesis **B.3.1**
2. light-dependent reactions **B.3.1**
3. cellular respiration **B.3.2**
4. aerobic
5. Krebs cycle **B.3.2**
6. fermentation

Greek and Latin Word Parts

Use the definitions of the word parts to answer the next three questions.

Prefix or Root	Meaning
photo-	light
syn-	together
aero-	air
spirare	to breathe

7. Describe how the meaning of the term *photosynthesis* is a combination of the meanings of the prefixes *photo-* and *syn-*.
8. Explain how the prefix *aero-* is related to the terms *aerobic* and *anaerobic*.
9. Why is the root *spirare* the basis of the term *cellular respiration?* Explain your answer.

Reviewing MAIN IDEAS

10. Describe the roles of ADP and ATP in the transfer and use of energy in cells.
11. What types of carbon-based molecules are most often broken down to make ATP? Explain how ATP production differs depending on the type of carbon-based molecule that is broken down.
12. Describe how and where energy from light is absorbed during photosynthesis. What happens to the energy after it is absorbed? **B.3.1**
13. Write the chemical equation for photosynthesis and explain what it represents. **B.3.1**
14. What roles do electrons and hydrogen ions play in the light-dependent reactions of photosynthesis? **B.3.1**
15. Describe how the light-independent reactions are the *synthesis* part of photosynthesis. **B.3.1**
16. How does glycolysis contribute to the overall process of cellular respiration? **B.3.2**
17. Write the chemical equation for cellular respiration and explain what it represents. **B.3.2**
18. What is the function of the Krebs cycle? In your answer, describe the products of the Krebs cycle and what happens to them. **B.3.2**
19. Explain the function of the electron transport chain in cellular respiration. Why is oxygen needed for the electron transport chain? **B.3.2**
20. Fermentation does not produce ATP. Why is fermentation such an important process in cells?
21. How is alcoholic fermentation similar to lactic acid fermentation? How is it different?

Reviewing Main Ideas

10. ATP, a high-energy molecule, transfers energy to cell processes. ADP, a lower-energy molecule, can be converted into ATP.
11. Carbohydrates; breakdown of lipids produces the most ATP, followed by carbohydrates and proteins.
12. Molecules absorb energy in the chloroplast and transfer the energy to electrons that move through the thylakoid membrane. These are used to produce energy-carrying molecules.
13. $6CO_2 + 6H_2O \rightarrow C_6H_{12}O_6 + 6O_2$; the equation is for the overall process and shows the overall reactants and products.
14. Electrons transfer energy, and hydrogen ions flow through ATP synthase to produce ATP.
15. The light-independent reactions build or "put together" sugars from carbon dioxide.
16. Glycolysis breaks down glucose, the products of which enter cellular respiration when oxygen is present.

17. $C_6H_{12}O_6 + 6O_2 \rightarrow 6CO_2 + 6H_2O$; the equation is for the overall process and shows the overall reactants and products.
18. The Krebs cycle breaks down pyruvate and produces electron carriers (NADH and $FADH_2$) and carbon dioxide waste. The electron carriers are used to provide energized electrons to the electron transport chain.
19. The electron transport chain uses energy from energized electrons to pump H^+ ions across the inner mitochondrial membrane. The H^+ ions flow back across, through ATP synthase, to produce ATP. Oxygen picks up the electrons after they pass through the chain.
20. Fermentation allows glycolysis to continue to produce a small amount of ATP when oxygen is unavailable.
21. Both recycle NAD^+ to glycolysis and both break down pyruvate, but the products of the two fermentation processes differ (lactic acid vs. alcohol and CO_2).

ITEM CORRELATIONS

Standard	Items
B.3.1	1, 2, 12, 13, 14, 15, 32
B.3.2	3, 5, 16, 17, 18, 19

CHAPTER REVIEW

Critical Thinking

22. because the cells will not be able to produce ATP to continue to function
23. Electrons, H^+ ions, electron carriers; examples could include the electron transport chains, the transfer of electron carriers, and the flow of H^+ ions down a concentration (chemiosmotic) gradient.
24. Photosynthesis stores energy in sugars; cellular respiration releases energy (as ATP and heat) from the breakdown of sugars.
25. Both require the products of glycolysis; glycolysis requires either process to pick up the products and supply molecules to pick up electrons.
26. The light-dependent reactions and electron transport chain are nearly identical because both use energized electrons to pump H^+ ions across a membrane and produce ATP and other electron carriers. The Krebs cycle and Calvin cycle are nearly opposite; the Krebs cycle breaks down carbon-based molecules and supplies energy, and the Calvin cycle uses energy to build sugars.

Interpreting Visuals

27. Photosynthesis stores energy because it absorbs sunlight; cellular respiration releases energy as ATP and heat.
28. because photosynthesis produces sugars and oxygen needed for cellular respiration, and cellular respiration produces the carbon dioxide and water needed for photosynthesis
29. photosynthesis, because it produces the sugars and oxygen needed for cellular respiration

Critical Thinking

22. Infer Human brain cells do not use fermentation. Explain why a lack of oxygen for even a short period of time might result in the death of brain cells.

23. Apply Energy is transferred in several different ways during photosynthesis and cellular respiration. Give two examples of how energy is transferred in the processes. Explain both examples.

24. Analyze How do photosynthesis and cellular respiration form a cycle of energy storage and use?

25. Synthesize How do cellular respiration and fermentation depend on glycolysis? How does glycolysis depend on aerobic and anaerobic processes?

26. Analyze Consider the following two groups of processes:
- light-dependent reactions and electron transport chain
- Calvin cycle and Krebs cycle

Which pair is nearly identical? Which is nearly opposite? Explain.

Interpreting Visuals

Use the diagram to answer the next three questions.

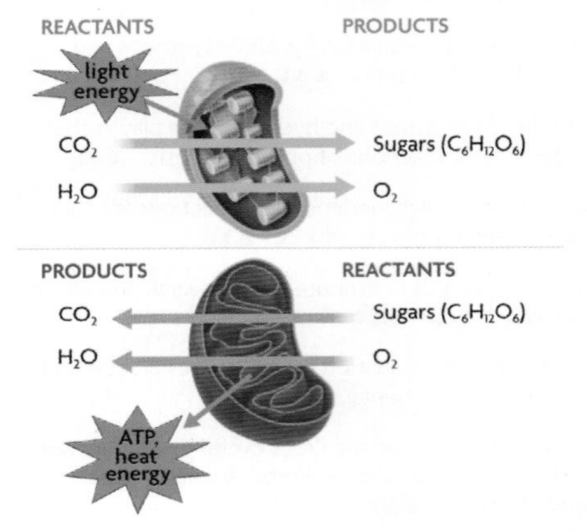

27. Apply Which process stores energy? Which process releases energy? How do you know?

28. Infer Use information in the visual to explain why a plant would be able to survive in a sealed transparent container.

29. Infer Which of the processes in the diagram is necessary for most living things to survive? Explain.

Analyzing Data

Use information in the text and the graph below to answer the next two questions.

Plants have several different molecules that together absorb all of the different wavelengths of visible light. Visible light ranges between the wavelengths of about 400 and 700 nanometers (nm).

ABSORPTION OF LIGHT BY CHLOROPHYLL

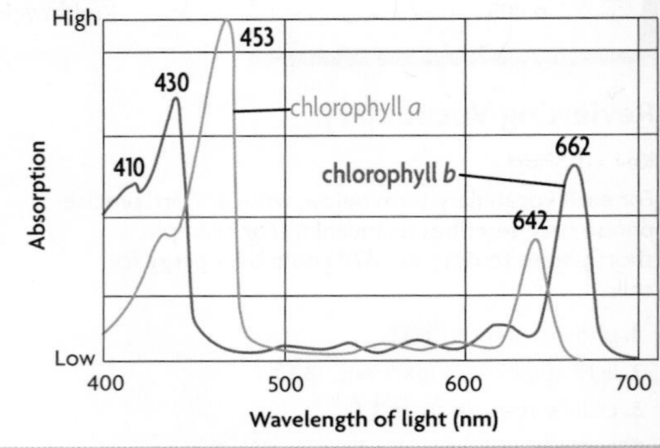

30. Analyze Data What range of wavelengths is absorbed by chlorophyll *a*? chlorophyll *b*?

31. Synthesize Suppose a type of plant has only chlorophylls *a* and *b* and is exposed to different wavelengths of light. At which wavelengths would there be the greatest amounts of carbon dioxide in the air around the plants? The least? Explain your answers.

Connecting CONCEPTS

32. Write an Analogy Suppose that photosynthesis or cellular respiration takes place in a factory. You are a tour guide at the factory, explaining each step of the process to a group of visitors. Use analogies to describe what happens at each step. For example, you could describe the photosystems of photosynthesis as "the green machines next to windows to absorb light." Be sure to include important details of the process you select. B.3.1

33. Analyze Look at the micrograph of diatoms and the photograph of the whale on pages 98–99. Write a paragraph that explains the two ways in which the whale depends on diatoms for the energy that its cells need.

Analyzing Data

30. 400–460 and 620–660; 400–450 and 630–680
31. greatest CO_2, 460–620, because little energy is being absorbed from light and less oxygen is being produced; least CO_2, 400–460 and 620–680, because the chlorophylls absorb energy for photosynthesis at those wavelengths and produce more oxygen

Connecting Concepts

32. Answers should indicate knowledge of the steps of photosynthesis or cellular respiration and where they occur in cells.
33. Answers should indicate that whales require the sugars and the oxygen produced by diatoms.

INDIANA ISTEP+ Test Prep

B.2.3; B.3.1; B.3.2; B.3.4

Test Practice
For more test practice, go to ClassZone.com.

1 Which of the following groups of organisms uses cellular respiration in mitochondria to produce ATP for their energy needs?

A plants only
B eukaryotes
C animals only
D prokaryotes

2

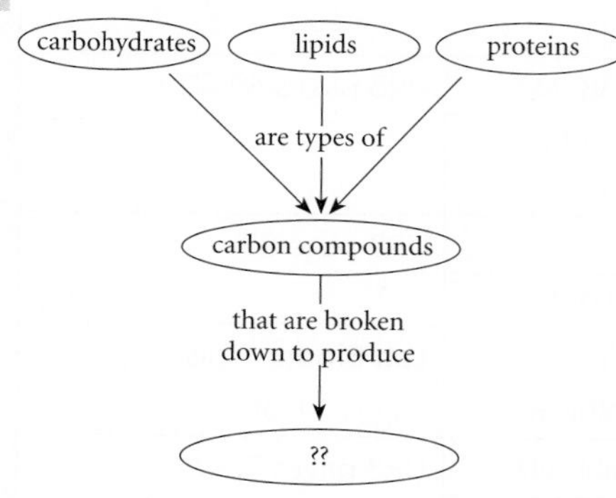

This concept map shows some of the carbon-based molecules in cells. Some of these molecules can be broken down to produce usable chemical energy. Which of the following terms ***best*** completes this concept map?

A electrons
B ATP
C lactic acid
D hydrogen ions

3 Photosynthesis is a part of various cycles that help to move oxygen and carbon through the environment. What form of abiotic carbon do plants remove from the environment?

A glucose
B starch
C carbon dioxide
D ATP

THINK THROUGH THE QUESTION

Some terms in questions, such as biotic or abiotic, may be unfamiliar to you. Often, terms like these are used to present an example but are not necessary to answer the question. Find the important pieces of information in the question and focus on those points.

4

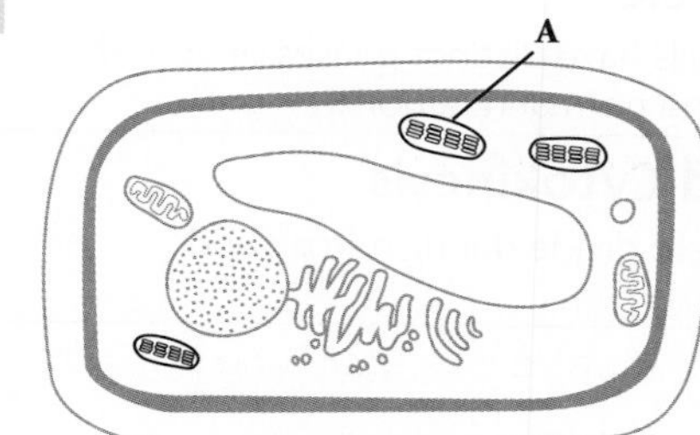

Which of the following ***best*** represent the final products of the chemical reactions that take place inside the organelle labeled A in this diagram?

A sugars, oxygen
B ATP, electrons
C ATP, sugars
D carbon dioxide, water

5 Which process is represented by the following chemical equation?

$6CO_2 + 6H_2O \rightarrow \rightarrow \rightarrow \rightarrow C_6H_{12}O_6 + 6O_2$

A photosynthesis
B fermentation
C glycolysis
D cellular respiration

6 Where do light-dependent reactions take place? Where do light-independent reactions take place?

Standards-Based Assessment

1. B	4. A
2. B	5. A
3. C	6. See Below

TEST DOCTOR

Question 1 Answer B is correct. Answers A and C are incorrect because both plants and animals have mitochondria. Answer D is incorrect because prokaryotes do not have mitochondria.

Question 3 Answer C is correct. Answers A, B, and D are incorrect because they are not removed from the environment by photosynthesis; photosynthesis makes sugars, and mitochondria break down sugars to make ATP.

Question 5 Answer A is correct because photosynthesis uses energy from light to convert carbon dioxide and water into sugars (and oxygen as a byproduct). Answer B is incorrect because fermentation starts with pyruvate and NADH. Answer C is incorrect because glycolysis starts with glucose. Answer D is incorrect because cellular respiration starts with three-carbon molecules.

Question 6 Light-dependent reactions take place at the thylakoid membrane. Light-independent reactions take place at the stroma.

ITEM CORRELATIONS

Standard	Items
B.2.3	4
B.3.1	5, 6
B.3.2	1, 2
B.3.4	3

CHAPTER 5

Indiana Resource Preview

Print Resources

Cell Growth and Division

INDIANA STANDARDS		Sections	PAGES and PACING	UNIT RESOURCE BOOK
B.6.1	5.1	**The Cell Cycle** **KEY CONCEPT** Cells have distinct phases of growth, reproduction, and normal functions.	pp. 134–137 30 minutes	URB pages 65–68
B.6.1	5.2	**Mitosis and Cytokinesis** **KEY CONCEPT** Cells divide during mitosis and cytokinesis.	pp. 138–142 30minutes	URB pages 69–72
NOS.3		DATA ANALYSIS: Constructing Data Tables	p. 142 30 minutes	URB page 85
NOS.3		CHAPTER INVESTIGATION: Mitosis in Onion Root Cells	p. 143 45 minutes	**Lab Binder** Cells pages 29–31
	5.3	**Regulation of the Cell Cycle** **KEY CONCEPT** Cell cycle regulation is necessary for healthy growth.	pp. 144–147 30 minutes	URB pages 73–76
	5.4	**Asexual Reproduction** **KEY CONCEPT** Many organisms reproduce by cell division.	pp. 148–150 30minutes	URB pages 77–80
B.6.2	5.5	**Multicellular Life** **KEY CONCEPT** Cells work together to carry out complex functions.	pp. 151–155 30 minutes	URB pages 81–84
NOS.6		OPTIONS FOR INQUIRY	pp. 156–157 45 minutes, 45 minutes	**Lab Binder** Cells pages 33–35
		Chapter Review	pp. 158–161	**Assessment Book** Chapter Tests A, B pp. 93–100

INDIANA STANDARDS

B.6.1 Describe the process of mitosis and explain that this process ordinarily results in daughter cells with a genetic make-up identical to the parent cells.
B.6.2 Understand that most cells of a multicellular organism contain the same genes, but develop from a single cell (e.g., a fertilized egg) in different ways due to differential gene expression.

NOS.3 Clearly communicate their ideas and results of investigations verbally and in written form using tables, graphs, diagrams, and photographs.
NOS.6 Use analogies and models (mathematical and physical) to simplify and represent systems that are difficult to understand or directly experience due to their size, time scale, or complexity, and recognize the limitations of analogies and models.

Labs

PUPIL EDITION LABS

Mitosis in Onion Root Cells, p. 143 Students observe and identify the different stages of the cell cycle. **Lab Binder** pp. 29–31	**Time:** 45 minutes **Materials:** slides of onion root cells, microscope
Cancer, Section 3, p. 147 Students observe and compare normal cells and cancerous cells. **Lab Binder** p. 36	**Time:** 20 minutes **Materials:** microscope, slides of normal cells, slides of cancerous cells

OPTIONS FOR INQUIRY

Modeling Cell Surface Area-to-Volume Ratio, p. 156 Students model the effect of cell surface area-to-volume ratio on diffusion. **Lab Binder** pp. 33–34	**Time:** 45 minutes **Materials:** plastic knife, phenolphthalein agar, metric ruler, 250-mL beaker, 100-mL graduated cylinder, 100 mL sodium hydroxide solution, timer, plastic spoon, paper towel
Apoptosis, p. 157 Students research the role of apoptosis in a developmental process. **Lab Binder** p. 35	**Time:** 45 minutes **Materials:** Computer with Internet access

LAB BINDER Unit 2 Cells

Additional Investigation: Animating Mitosis, pp. 37–39

Virtual Lab Worksheet: Investigating Bacterial Growth, p. 84

LAB GENERATOR

A searchable CD of all labs in the program in editable format, including forensic, probeware, and biotechnology labs.

Presentation Tools

POWER PRESENTATIONS

Presentation Chapter 5
PowerPresentations for each section incorporate images and clips from the Media Gallery. Includes Note Navigator for each section.

MEDIA GALLERY

Contains the following images and video clips, as well as animations, simulations, and forms of visuals from the book.

Stem cells

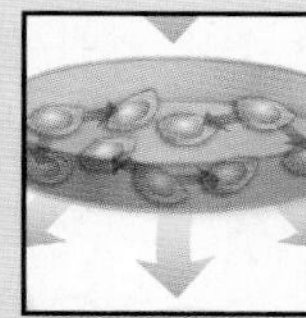

Cell cycle

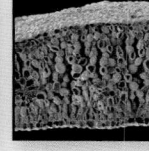

Skin cancer

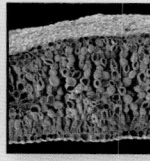

Leaf cross-section

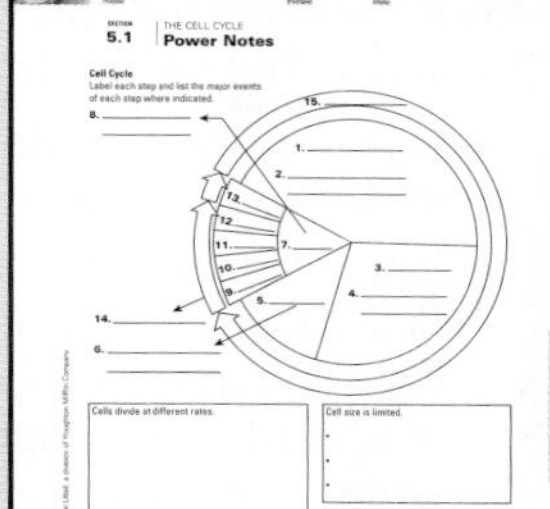

Power Notes

VIDEO

Examine a series of short video clips on stem cells, cell growth, and cell division.

ANIMATED BIOLOGY

Mitosis

Mitosis Stage Matching Game

Binary Fission

TRANSPARENCIES

The Cell Cycle T26

Chromosome Structure T27

Mitosis and Cytokinesis T28

Harvesting Embryonic Stem Cells T29

Online BIOLOGY CLASSZONE.COM

BioZine

Animated Biology

Interactive Review

SciLinks

Resource Centers

CHAPTER 5

▼ Focus and Motivate

What does it mean for a cell to be immortal?

Have students give their definition of *immortal*. Most students will probably say it means to live forever. Then have them read the explanation. **Ask**

- How do scientists define *immortality* for cells? division without limits
- What can you infer about how cell division in a normal cell compares to cell division in a cancer cell? Division in normal cells is limited, or regulated, in some way.

Discuss with students the underlying idea that uncontrolled cell growth can be unhealthy for an organism. The cell divisions of normal cells are controlled by the body. They take place in response to conditions in the body and may relate to injury or infection, developmental changes, or the need for maintenance. Students should understand that it is really the cell line, not a single cell, that is immortal.

BIOZINE ClassZone.com

Students can access BioZine at **ClassZone.com** to learn about some of the latest research in the biological sciences.

In a Hurry?

The critical material of the chapter is found in **Sections 5.1, 5.2,** and **5.4,** which cover the cell cycle, changes to chromosomes during the phases of mitosis, and asexual reproduction by binary fission and mitosis. A quick read of **Section 5.3** will introduce students to the factors that regulate cell division of normal cells and the uncontrolled cell division of cancer cells. **Section 5.5** introduces the levels of organization in multicellular organisms, cell differentiation, and stem cells.

CHAPTER 5

Cell Growth and Division

KEY CONCEPTS

5.1 The Cell Cycle
Cells have distinct phases of growth, reproduction, and normal functions.

5.2 Mitosis and Cytokinesis
Cells divide during mitosis and cytokinesis.

5.3 Regulation of the Cell Cycle
Cell cycle regulation is necessary for healthy growth.

5.4 Asexual Reproduction
Many organisms reproduce by cell division.

5.5 Multicellular Life
Cells work together to carry out complex functions.

Online BIOLOGY CLASSZONE.COM

Animated BIOLOGY
View animated chapter concepts.
- Mitosis
- Binary Fission
- Investigating Bacterial Growth
- Mitosis Stage Matching Game

BIOZINE
Keep current with biology news.
- Featured Stories
- Strange Biology
- Polls

RESOURCE CENTER
Get more information on
- Cell Cycle
- Asexual Reproduction
- Levels of Organization

Student Activity

Purpose **Have students compare a diagram of an interphase cell with one of separating telophase cells and infer the sequence of events needed to connect the two stages.**

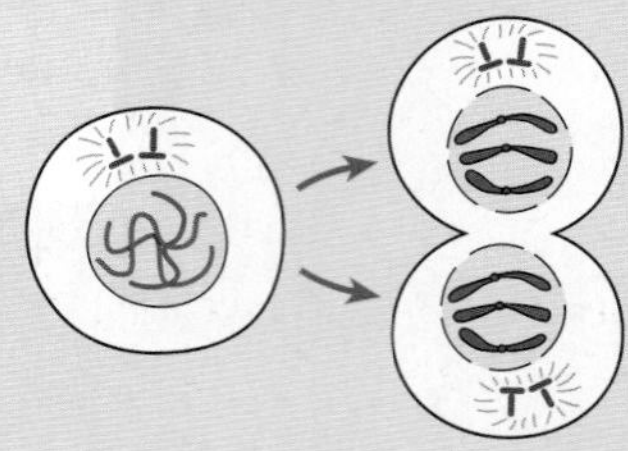

Materials (per team)
- colored pencils
- 6 index cards

Draw on the board the diagrams shown. Label DNA, nuclear envelope, and centrosome.

colored SEM; magnification 5000×

What does it mean for a cell to be immortal?

Connecting CONCEPTS

The photograph above shows a lung cancer cell undergoing cell division. Unlike healthy cells, cancer cells can divide without limit—they are what scientists call *immortal.* This property is useful to scientists who culture cancer cells for research purposes. However, cancer cells are very dangerous in the body, where they may form tumors and invade tissues.

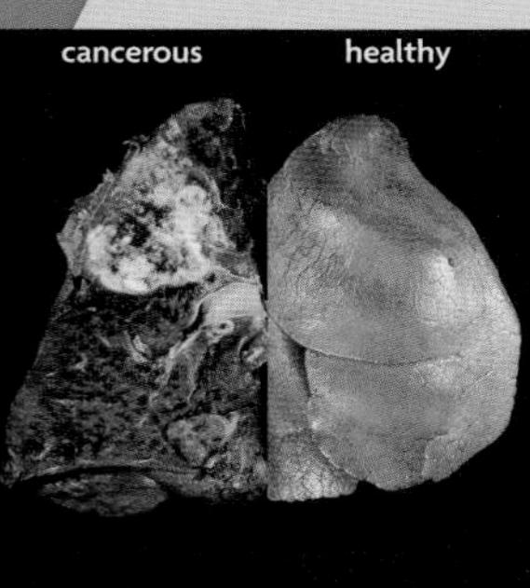

Human Biology These photographs show half of a cancerous lung and half of a healthy lung. Gases diffuse across the surfaces of a healthy lung, so the membrane surfaces must be thin and moist. Exposure to substances such as tobacco smoke can cause changes in the lung cells. Cilia are destroyed, and the lung lining becomes thicker. The lungs can no longer clean themselves, so they are more susceptible to cancer-causing agents.

Introduce Tell students that the diagrams on the board represent the before and after diagrams of a cell dividing. Have students form small groups, and give them five minutes to sort out the steps needed to get from the initial phase to the ending phase. Suggest they use scrap paper to do their problem solving. After five minutes, have one member of each group draw out the steps onto as many of the index cards as needed to complete the picture.

Discuss Have each group describe the steps they outlined. **Ask**

- What changes were critical in getting your cell to divide successfully? doubling of DNA, DNA condensing to form chromosomes, separation of duplicated chromosomes and centrosomes, and the division and re-formation of the nuclear envelope and cell membrane
- What happens to the organelles in the cytoplasm during cell division? Organelles also need to be divided equally between the two new cells.

Activate Prior Knowledge

To get students thinking about doubling and division, have them think about baking cookies. **Ask,** If you want two batches of cookies, not just one, what do you need to do to the recipe? Double it. Discuss that doubling a recipe means doubling all the ingredients in the original recipe.

Have students apply this idea to cell division. **Ask,** For cells to be functional after division, what needs to be present? complete set of DNA, organelles, cytoplasm, cell membrane, cell wall if a plant cell

Preview Vocabulary

Greek and Latin Word Origins Students will be studying *cycles, phases,* and *stages* in this chapter. A cycle is a repeating series of events. It has an obvious relationship to the Latin word *cyclus,* meaning "circle." The word *phase* comes from the Greek *phasis,* meaning "appearance." Remind students of the phases of the moon. Each phase of mitosis has a distinctive appearance. The word *stage* comes from the Latin *status,* or "stand." Students may think in terms of stagecoaches and the stopping points, or stands, along a journey. A cell must move through the stages in the cell cycle to reach the point where it can successfully divide.

Academic Vocabulary In this chapter, students will see some familiar words used together:

divide, to separate
duplicate, an identical copy
double, to increase twofold
copy, a reproduction of an original

Cells *double* their DNA in order to *divide* and create two nearly identical *duplicates,* or *copies.*

English Learners Students may find the use of the familiar terms parent and daughter potentially confusing when applied to cell division. The idea that daughter cells originate from the same parent is straightforward. Point out to students that what is distinctive about this use is that the parent no longer exists once the daughters come into being.

SECTION 5.1

▼ Plan and Prepare

Objectives

- Describe the stages of the cell cycle.
- Compare rates of division in different cell types.
- Identify factors that limit cell size.

Section Resources

Unit Resource Book Study Guide pp. 65–66 Power Notes p. 67 Reinforcement p. 68
Interactive Reader Chapter 5 **Spanish Study Guide** pp. 43–44
Biology Toolkit pp. C17, C19, D1
Technology Power Presentation 5.1 Media Gallery DVD Online Quiz 5.1

Activate Prior Knowledge Link growth to cell division. **Ask,** Why do you always have to cut your hair, your fingernails, and the lawn? growth caused by new cells being made Tell students that in this section, they will learn how new cells are created.

▼ Teach

TEACH FROM VISUALS

FIGURE 5.1 Point out the clockwise arrangement of the diagram. Relate the outer arrows to the inner descriptions. **Ask**

- What are the four main stages of the cell cycle? gap 1, synthesis, gap 2, mitosis
- What can you infer about the relative amount of time a cell spends in each stage? An actively dividing cell spends the least amount of time in the mitosis stage. The length of gap 1 varies the most and is usually the longest.

5.1 The Cell Cycle

KEY CONCEPT Cells have distinct phases of growth, reproduction, and normal functions.

MAIN IDEAS

- The cell cycle has four main stages.
- Cells divide at different rates.
- Cell size is limited.

VOCABULARY

cell cycle, p. 134
mitosis, p. 135
cytokinesis, p. 135

INDIANA STANDARDS

B.6.1 Describe the process of mitosis and explain that this process ordinarily results in daughter cells with a genetic make-up identical to the parent cells.

Connect Many of life's little chores such as sweeping and dusting, are quietly satisfying and rather fun. Washing dishes by hand, however, is never fun, which is why some clever person made the dishwasher. This handy invention soaks, washes, and rinses your dishes to a spot-free, sanitary sparkle. You unload the dishes, and the machine is ready to start the cycle all over again. A cell goes through a cycle, too. This cycle of growth, DNA synthesis, and division is essential for an organism to grow and heal. If it goes out of control, abnormal cell growth may occur, resulting in cancer cells like those shown on the previous page.

MAIN IDEA

The cell cycle has four main stages.

Just as all species have life cycles, from tiny chihuahuas to massive beluga whales, cells also have a life cycle. The **cell cycle** is the regular pattern of growth, DNA duplication, and cell division that occurs in eukaryotic cells. **FIGURE 5.1** shows its four main stages: gap 1, synthesis, gap 2, and mitosis. Gap 1, synthesis, and gap 2 together make up what is called interphase.

The stages of the cell cycle get their names from early studies of cell division. Scientists' observations were limited by the microscopes of the time. When a cell was not actively dividing, they could not see activity in it. Thus, they originally divided the cell cycle into two parts: interphase, when the cell appeared to be at rest, and mitosis, when the cell was dividing. Improved techniques and tools later allowed scientists to detect the copying of DNA (DNA synthesis), and they changed their description of the cell cycle to include the synthesis stage. Since they still could not see anything happening during the other parts of interphase, scientists named the periods between mitosis and synthesis "gap 1" and "gap 2." Eventually, scientists learned that, during interphase, cells carry out their normal functions and undergo critical growth and preparation for cell division.

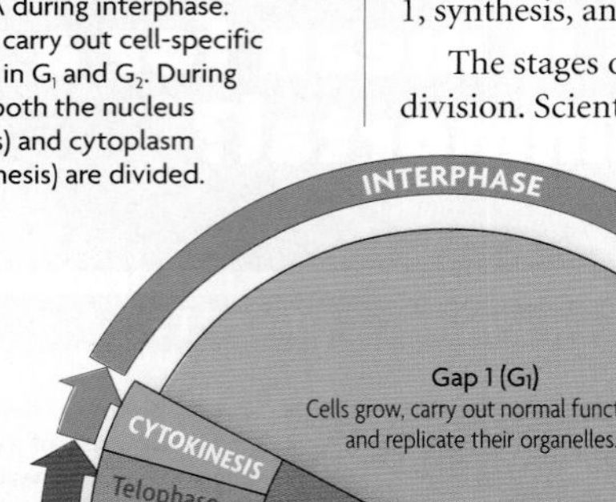

FIGURE 5.1 Cells grow and copy their DNA during interphase. They also carry out cell-specific functions in G_1 and G_2. During M stage, both the nucleus (in mitosis) and cytoplasm (in cytokinesis) are divided.

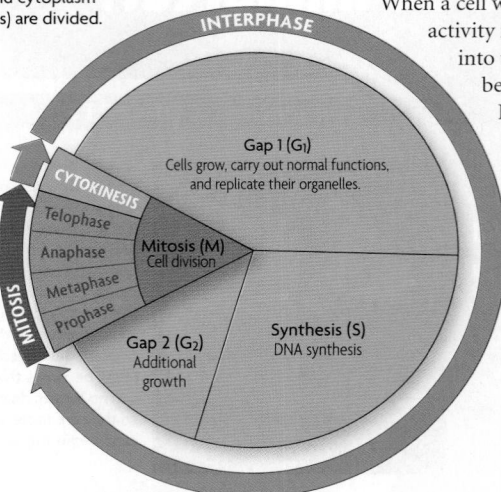

Differentiated Instruction

BELOW LEVEL

Help students understand the vocabulary involved in the cell cycle by using a word-sort activity. Prepare cards with the words *gap 1, synthesis, gap 2,* and *mitosis* on the front and a brief description about that stage on the back. Have students arrange the cards in the correct sequence and discuss what happens during each stage, using the back of the cards if they need a reminder.

Biology Toolkit, Word Sort, p. D1

ENGLISH LEARNERS

Students might find it easier to understand the cell cycle if they think of it as a linear sequence of events. Help them visualize what is occurring at each step, using **FIGURE 3.6** (page 74) to remind them of a eukaryote's cell structure. Have them draw out the sequence in their science notebooks.

Biology Toolkit, Connect to Content through Visuals, p. C17

Gap 1 (G_1)

The first stage of the cell cycle is gap 1 (G_1). During G_1, a cell carries out its normal functions. If it is a skeletal muscle cell, it contracts to move joints. If it is an adrenal cell, it secretes hormones such as adrenaline. If it is an intestinal cell, it absorbs nutrients. During G_1, cells also increase in size, and organelles increase in number. A cell spends most of its time in the G_1 stage, although the length of this stage varies by cell type.

During G_1, the cell must pass a critical checkpoint before it can proceed to the synthesis stage. Just as it would be dangerous for you to run a marathon if you had not slept or eaten for several days, it would also be dangerous for your cells to continue dividing if certain conditions were not met. For instance, most animal cells need enough nutrition, adequate size, and relatively undamaged DNA to divide successfully. They also need specific signals from other cells, telling them whether more cell division is needed.

Synthesis (S)

The second stage of the cell cycle is the synthesis (S) stage. *Synthesis* means "the combining of parts to make a whole." During the S stage, the cell makes a copy of its nuclear DNA. In eukaryotes, DNA is located in the nucleus. During interphase, it is loosely organized and appears grainy in photographs. By the end of the S stage, the cell nucleus contains two complete sets of DNA.

Gap 2 (G_2)

Gap 2 (G_2) is the third stage of the cell cycle. During G_2, cells continue to carry out their normal functions, and additional growth occurs. Like G_1, this stage includes a critical checkpoint. Everything must be in order—adequate cell size, undamaged DNA—before the cell goes through mitosis and division.

Mitosis (M)

Mitosis (M), the fourth stage of the cell cycle, includes two processes: mitosis and cytokinesis. **Mitosis** (my-TOH-sihs) is the division of the cell nucleus and its contents. During mitosis, the nuclear membrane dissolves, the duplicated DNA condenses around proteins and separates, and two new nuclei form. Lastly, **cytokinesis** (SY-toh-kuh-NEE-sihs) is the process that divides the cell cytoplasm. The result is two daughter cells that are genetically identical to the original cell.

VISUAL VOCAB

Mitosis is the division of the cell nucleus and its contents.

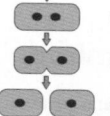

parent cell
mitosis
cytokinesis
daughter cells

Cytokinesis divides the cell cytoplasm.

The stages of the cell cycle and the proteins that control it are similar in all eukaryotes. For example, scientists have demonstrated that some of the molecules that regulate checkpoints in the yeast cell cycle can work in human cells, too. Such similarities suggest that eukaryotes share a common ancestry.

A Predict **What might happen if the G_2 checkpoint stopped working in cells?**

TAKING NOTES

Construct your own cycle diagram to take notes about processes such as the cell cycle.

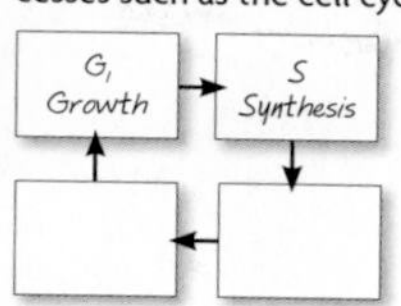

***Connecting* CONCEPTS**

DNA replication As you will learn in **Chapter 8**, DNA synthesis is also called DNA replication. During this process, the DNA molecule unzips and each strand is used as a pattern for a new DNA strand.

PRE-AP

As described on the bottom of page 135, the proteins that control the cell cycle, and therefore the DNA that codes for them, are highly conserved. Similar proteins are found in many organisms, not just in eukaryotes, but also in bacteria. Have students write for five minutes on why a control mechanism that limits growth rather than encourages it would be an advantageous adaptation. Suggest they think about the cancer cells pictured on the chapter opener.

Biology Toolkit, Quick-Write, p. C19

TEACH WITH TECHNOLOGY

To have students become more familiar with the stages of the cell cycle, have them go to the link at **ClassZone.com** to play the game "Cell Division Supervisor." Students must use their knowledge of the cell cycle to successfully replace a cell that has died.

Vocabulary

Academic Vocabulary The word **gap** suggests a break or an interruption. Scientists named the two stages of the cell cycle *gaps* because they did not know the cell was active during these stages.

Take It Further

Three important **checkpoints** in a cell cycle ensure that specific events occur correctly and in the proper order, thus signaling that a cell is ready to divide.

- The first checkpoint begins at the end of gap 1, during which a cell checks the DNA for any damage before copying begins and also makes sure that conditions are right for division.
- By the second checkpoint, at the end of gap 2, both DNA and the centrosome need to have been successfully copied, and those parts of the cytoskeleton that help to pull the two halves apart must be in place.
- The third and final checkpoint occurs halfway through mitosis, to check that the two copies of DNA have been properly attached to the cytoskeleton that will separate them.

Address Misconceptions

Common Misconception Students often think that cytokinesis is part of the process of mitosis, especially given its inclusion as part of the M stage of the cell cycle.

Correcting the Misconception Use the Visual Vocab to reinforce the point that mitosis and cytokinesis are two distinct processes. Mitosis is the division of the cell nucleus and its contents, resulting in two identical nuclei. Cytokinesis is the division of the cell cytoplasm, resulting in two cells, each of which contains one of the nuclei from mitosis. The two processes overlap. The cytoplasm begins to divide during the last phases of mitosis. Together mitosis and cytokinesis make up the mitosis stage of the cell cycle.

Answers

A Predict Cells may be the wrong size, have damaged DNA, and fail to divide.

▼ Teach continued

ONLINE BIOLOGY Go to the chapter Resource Center at **ClassZone.com** for additional resources and information on the cell cycle.

Take It Further

It might be helpful for students to think in terms of a cell population when relating the rate of cell division to the length of cell life spans. For example, from the information supplied in **FIGURE 5.2,** we would expect a population of muscle cells to divide at a much slower rate than a population of skin cells.

Explain to students that specialization in cells sometimes includes cells whose job it is to divide to supply new cells. These are **stem cells,** which are discussed in **Section 5.5.** Many of the cells in the human body that need constant replacement, such as blood cells and surface skin cells, are unable to divide. Stem cells that are part of the cell population provide new cells that, once produced, differentiate into the type of cell needed.

Answers

A Infer A skin cell would probably have a short G_1. Skin cells undergo a lot of wear and tear because they are exposed on the outside of the body. Therefore, they are probably replaced quickly.

Multicellular organisms use cell division for growth and repair.

FIGURE 5.2 CELL LIFE SPAN

CELL TYPE	APPROXIMATE LIFE SPAN
Skin cell	2 weeks
Red blood cell	4 months
Liver cell	300–500 days
Intestine—internal lining	4–5 days
Intestine—muscle and other tissues	16 years

Source: Spaulding et al., *Cell* 122:1.

MAIN IDEA

Cells divide at different rates.

Rates of cell division vary widely, as shown in **FIGURE 5.2.** The prokaryotic cell cycle is similar but not identical to that of eukaryotic cells. Recall that prokaryotes do not have the membrane-bound organelles and cytoskeleton found in eukaryotes. Thus, prokaryotic cells typically divide much faster than do eukaryotic cells.

The rate at which your cells divide is linked to your body's need for those cells. In human cells, the S, G_2, and M stages together usually take about 12 hours. The length of the G_1 stage differs most from cell type to cell type. The rate of cell division is greater in embryos and children than it is in adults. Their cell cycle is shorter, and many of their organs are still developing. But the rate of cell division also varies within different tissues of the adult body. The internal lining of your digestive tract receives a lot of wear and tear. As a result, cells that line your stomach and intestine are replaced every few days. In contrast, cells that make up the rest of your intestine (mainly smooth muscle) and many of your internal organs, such as lungs, kidney, and liver, divide only occasionally, in response to injury or cell death.

Cells that divide only rarely are thought to enter a stage that some scientists call G_0. In G_0, cells are unlikely to divide, although they continue to carry out their normal functions. Some cells, such as neurons, appear to stay permanently in the G_0 stage. However, some data suggest that neurons actually can divide, and this question continues to be actively researched. Other cells, such as lymphocytes, a type of white blood cell, may remain in G_0 for years until they recognize an invader. Once the invader binds to a lymphocyte receptor, the lymphocyte goes through rapid cell divisions to help fight infection.

Connecting **CONCEPTS**

Lymphocytes As you will learn in **Chapter 31,** lymphocytes are a part of your immune system. There are two major types of lymphocytes, B and T cells. Both types recognize specific antigens.

A Infer Do you think a skin cell would have a long or short G_1 stage? Explain why.

MAIN IDEA

Cell size is limited.

Cells have upper and lower size limits. If cells were too small, they could not contain all of the necessary organelles and molecules. For instance, a cell with too few mitochondria would not have enough energy to live. Nor can cells grow beyond a certain size, even if surrounded by plenty of nutrients. The upper limit on cell size is due to the ratio of cell surface area to volume. Recall that oxygen, nutrients, and wastes move across the cell membrane, or the surface of the cell. These materials must be transported in adequate amounts and with adequate speed to keep the inside of the cell functioning. But as a cell increases in size, its volume increases faster than its surface area, as shown in **FIGURE 5.3.** Therefore, a further increase in size could result in a surface area too small for the adequate exchange of materials.

Differentiated Instruction

INCLUSION

Use cubic cell models to help literal thinkers understand the relationship between surface area and volume. Two sizes of cutouts are provided in the Teacher Resources at **ClassZone.com.** Use eight cutouts of the smaller cube (2 cm^3) to fill the interior of the larger cube (4 cm^3). Work with students to calculate the ratio of surface area to volume for each cube. Then have students compare the surface area of eight smaller cubes to that of one large cube. Make sure students understand that the sides represent cell membrane.

Remind students that cells work together. Have students consider the advantages of eight smaller cells of a given volume working together compared to one larger cell of equal volume.

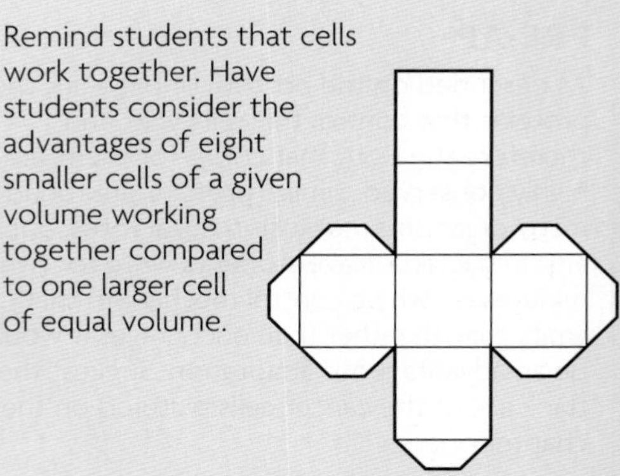

FIGURE 5.3 Ratio of Surface Area to Volume in Cells

As a cell grows, its volume increases more rapidly than its surface area. When the surface area–to–volume ratio is too small, the cell cannot move materials into and out of the cell at a sufficient rate or in sufficient quantities.

Relative size	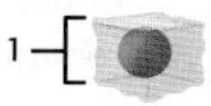 1	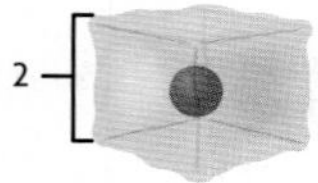 2	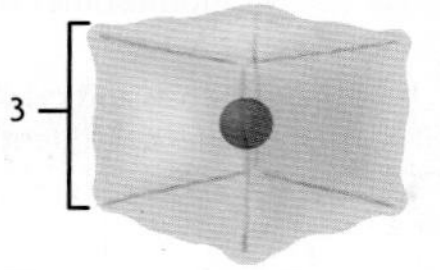 3
Surface area (length × width × number of sides)	6	24	54
Volume (length × width × height)	1	8	27
Ratio of surface area to volume	$\frac{6}{1}$ = 6:1	$\frac{24}{8}$ = 3:1	$\frac{54}{27}$ = 2:1

A Compare Which cell has the largest surface area? Which cell has the largest surface area to volume ratio?

Some cells, however, must be large. A neuron running down a giraffe's neck to its legs may be several meters long, for instance. But it is not shaped like a cube or a sphere. Instead, it is extremely long and thin. This structure gives the neuron a large surface area with a relatively small increase in volume.

To maintain a suitable cell size, growth and division must be coordinated. If a cell more than doubled its size before dividing, the daughter cells would be larger than the original cell. If this happened each generation, cells would quickly become too large to live. Similarly, if a cell did not double its size before dividing, the daughter cells would be smaller than the original cell. If this happened each generation, cells would quickly become too small to live.

For more information about mitosis, go to scilinks.org.
Keycode: MLB005

B Connect Which has the larger ratio of surface area to volume, a tennis ball or a soccer ball? Explain your reasoning.

5.1 ASSESSMENT

ONLINE QUIZ
ClassZone.com

B.6.1

REVIEWING MAIN IDEAS

1. During which stage of the **cell cycle** is the DNA copied?
2. Which stages of the cell cycle generally require about the same amount of time in all human cells?
3. What limits the maximum size of a cell?

CRITICAL THINKING

4. **Infer** Suppose you were to draw a diagram representing the cell cycle of a neuron. Explain where and how you would represent G_0.
5. **Predict** Suppose you treat cells with chemicals that block **cytokinesis.** Describe what you think the cells would look like.

Connecting CONCEPTS

6. **Scientific Process** Predict how the rate of cell division would differ between single-celled algae living in a sunny, nutrient-rich pond versus algae living in a shady, nutrient-poor pond. How could you test your prediction?

TEACH FROM VISUALS

FIGURE 5.3 Go over the math needed to calculate the ratio of surface area to volume of a cell. **Ask,** What formula is used to calculate the surface area of a cell? length × width × number of sides What formula is used to calculate the volume of a cell? length × width × height

Point out that the surface area of a cube increases by the length squared and its volume increases by length cubed. Calculate and list on the board the squares and cubes of the numbers 1 through 9 to show how much more rapidly the cube (volume) increases compared to the square (surface area) of the number.

Answers

A Compare Cell 3 has the largest surface area; Cell 1 has the largest surface-area-to-volume ratio.

B Connect a tennis ball, because volume increases more rapidly than does surface area as a ball gets larger

Assess and Reteach ▼

Assess Use the Online Quiz or Section Quiz (*Assessment Book,* p. 87).

Reteach Randomly write on the board the events of the cell cycle and have students indicate the proper order.

5.1 ASSESSMENT

1. synthesis (S)
2. S, G_2, and M stages
3. the ratio of cell surface area to volume
4. Students should suggest representing G_0 as an offshoot of G_1, because during G_0, a cell carries out normal functions but does not divide. G_1 is the only stage that does not involve DNA synthesis, duplicated DNA, or cell division.
5. The cells would probably look large and have two nuclei located at opposite sides of the cell.
6. It is likely that the algae in the sunny pond would have a faster rate of cell division than the algae in the shady pond. Any feasible way of testing the prediction is acceptable. One example could be to gather algae from the two ponds and evaluate what percentages of the samples were in each stage of the cell cycle. Presumably, a higher percentage of the algae in the shady pond would be in G_1 compared to the algae in the sunny pond.

Chapter 5: Cell Growth and Division 137

SECTION 5.2

▼ Plan and Prepare

Objectives

- Describe the structure of a chromosome.
- Follow chromosomes through the processes of mitosis and cytokinesis.

Section Resources

Unit Resource Book
- Study Guide pp. 69–70
- Power Notes p. 71
- Reinforcement p. 72
- Pre-AP Activity pp. 87–88

Interactive Reader Chapter 5
Spanish Study Guide pp. 45–46

Biology Toolkit pp. C6, C23

Technology
- Power Presentation 5.2
- Media Gallery DVD
- Online Quiz 5.2

Activate Prior Knowledge Have students think about packing for a trip.
Ask

- What would you do if you had to put a lot of clothes into a small suitcase? Compress the clothes.
- If you were sharing the suitcase with your twin brother or sister, what would you need to do? compress the clothes, and later separate them

Tell students that strands of DNA need to be both condensed and separated for a cell to divide.

▼ Teach

Vocabulary

Academic Vocabulary Have students compare these words:

condense, to reduce the volume of
compress, to press together

The words share a prefix that means "together." The root *densare* of *condense* means to "thicken." Tell students that *condense* and *compress* are not synonymous, but the result is an object that is made more **compact.**

5.2 Mitosis and Cytokinesis

KEY CONCEPT Cells divide during mitosis and cytokinesis.

MAIN IDEAS

- Chromosomes condense at the start of mitosis.
- Mitosis and cytokinesis produce two genetically identical daughter cells.

VOCABULARY

chromosome, p. 138
histone, p. 139
chromatin, p. 139
chromatid, p. 139
centromere, p. 139
telomere, p. 139
prophase, p. 140
metaphase, p. 140
anaphase, p. 140
telophase, p. 140

INDIANA STANDARDS

B.6.1 Describe the process of mitosis and explain that this process ordinarily results in daughter cells with a genetic make-up identical to the parent cells.

Connect When you were a child, perhaps you attended a birthday party where goody bags were handed out. Whoever stuffed the bags had to make sure that each bag had exactly the same number of erasers, candies, and stickers. Otherwise, some ill-mannered child (not you, of course) might have raised a fuss if an item was missing. In a similar way, your cells must receive a full set of DNA—no more, no less—to work properly. Dividing DNA is a complicated task because the DNA is so long and stringy. Mitosis is an amazing process that efficiently sorts two sets of DNA and divides them between two nuclei.

MAIN IDEA

Chromosomes condense at the start of mitosis.

DNA is a double-stranded molecule made of four different subunits called nucleotides. A **chromosome** is one long continuous thread of DNA that consists of numerous genes along with regulatory information. Your body cells have 46 chromosomes each. If stretched out straight and laid end to end, the DNA in just one of your cells would be about 3 meters (10 feet) long. How does it fit inside the nucleus of a microscopic cell?

Connecting CONCEPTS

Biochemistry As you will learn in **Chapter 8,** a nucleotide is made of three parts: a sugar, a phosphate group, and a nitrogen-containing molecule called a base. When the sugars and phosphate groups bond, they form the backbones of the long chains called nucleic acids.

phosphate
base
sugar

DNA wraps around proteins that help organize and condense it. During interphase, or when a cell is not dividing, DNA is loosely organized—it looks a bit like spaghetti. During mitosis, however, your chromosomes are tightly condensed, as shown in **FIGURE 5.4**. These changes in DNA's organization allow a cell to carry out its necessary functions. During all of interphase, proteins must access specific genes for a cell to make specific proteins or to copy the entire DNA sequence. During mitosis, the duplicated chromosomes must condense to be divided between two nuclei. If chromosomes remained stringy during mitosis, they could become entangled. Perhaps a cell would get two copies of one chromosome and no copies of a different one. **FIGURE 5.5** shows the process that converts a chromosome from a linear strand of DNA to its highly condensed form. The key to this process is the association between DNA and proteins.

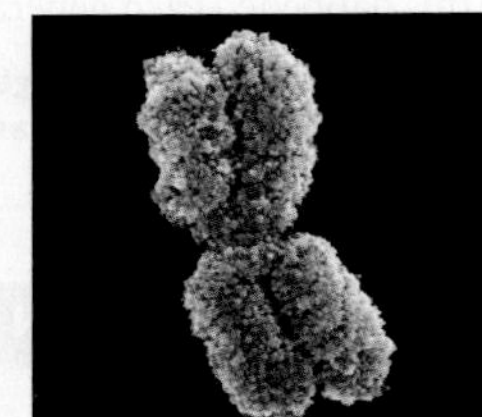

FIGURE 5.4 This duplicated chromosome is tightly condensed. (colored SEM; magnification unknown)

Differentiated Instruction

ENGLISH LEARNERS

Point to the vocabulary list for the section. Tell students that the first six words relate to DNA. Point out that three of the words (*chromosome, chromatin, chromatid*) are various forms of DNA. Tell them that the *-phase* words are the steps of mitosis they were introduced to in **Section 5.1.** Suggest students use diagrams with their notes to work out the relationship between the terms.

Biology Toolkit, Combination Notes, p. C23

BELOW LEVEL

Have students use the technique of directed reading-thinking to preview the section and identify material that is familiar to them. Have them set up a table and fill in the following categories as they preview, read, and review:

- What I know I know
- What I think I know
- What I think I'll learn
- What I learned

Biology Toolkit, DRTA, p. C6

FIGURE 5.5 Chromosome Structure

DNA condenses tightly during the early stages of mitosis.

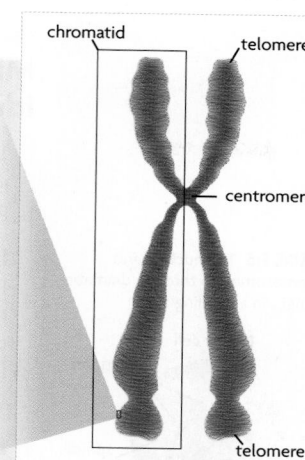

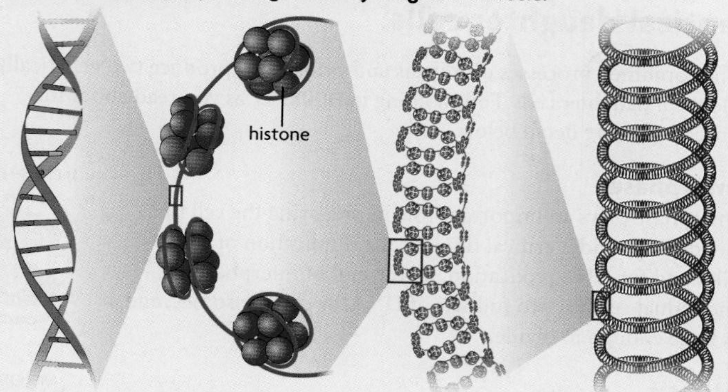

chromatid

telomere

centromere

telomere

DNA double helix Each continuous, double-stranded DNA molecule makes one chromosome.

DNA and histones DNA wraps at regular intervals around proteins called histones, forming chromatin.

Chromatin Interactions between parts of the histones further compact the DNA.

Supercoiled DNA The chromatin coils more and more tightly around organizing proteins.

Condensed, duplicated chromosome The condensed, duplicated chromosomes can be aligned and separated during mitosis.

A Infer Overall, DNA has a negative charge. Look at the histone proteins in the figure. What type of overall charge do you think they have? Explain.

At almost all times during the cell cycle, each of your chromosomes is associated with a group of proteins called **histones.** DNA wraps around histones at regular intervals, similar to beads on a string. Parts of the histones interact with each other, further compacting the DNA. At this stage—the "spaghetti" stage—the loose combination of DNA and proteins is called **chromatin.** The word "loose" describes how much the DNA strand folds back on itself; it does not mean the DNA is loosely wrapped around the histones.

As a cell progresses into mitosis, chromatin further condenses. It continues to coil more and more tightly around organizing proteins, finally forming small thick rods. Recall that each chromosome has already been copied during the previous S stage. Thus, the chromosome looks similar to an "X" in which the left and right halves are two identical DNA double helixes. One half of a duplicated chromosome is called a **chromatid** (KROH-muh-tihd). Together, the two identical chromatids are called sister chromatids. Sister chromatids are held together at the **centromere** (SEHN-truh-MEER), a region of the condensed chromosome that looks pinched.

In addition, the ends of DNA molecules form structures called **telomeres** (TEHL-uh-meers), which are made of repeating nucleotides that do not form genes. They prevent the ends of chromosomes from accidentally attaching to each other, and they help prevent the loss of genes. A short section of nucleotides is lost from a new DNA molecule each time it is copied. It is important that these nucleotides are lost from telomeres, not from the genes themselves.

B Apply What is the relationship between a molecule of DNA and a chromosome?

TAKING NOTES

Use a main idea web to help you study the makeup and organization of chromosomes.

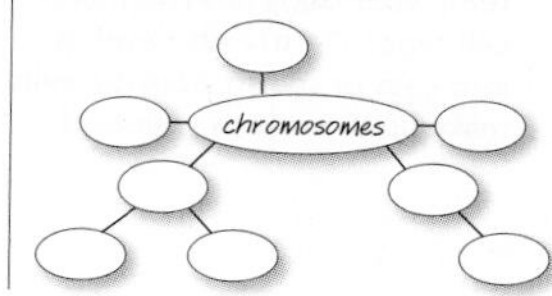

INCLUSION

For students who have difficulty working with layers of information, model for them how you read the text on pages 138–139 for understanding. Relate descriptions in the text to the various parts of **FIGURE 5.5,** demonstrating for students how to connect the two.

TEACH FROM VISUALS

FIGURE 5.5 Have students look carefully at the diagram, starting with the DNA double helix on the left. Discuss how that structure relates to each successive structure. **Ask**

- Starting with the DNA double helix on the left, how does that part of the diagram relate to the next part of the diagram, and how can you tell? The first is a much more detailed version of the DNA strand in the "DNA and histones" diagram. The outline of a square shows which part of the diagram has been magnified.
- Where do you see helixes (spirals) in this figure? There are spiraling shapes in each of the DNA diagrams. Students may perceive spiraling in the chromatids.

Make sure students understand that the two spiraling strands of the DNA double helix represent a single molecule. **Ask,** What happens to DNA by the time it reaches the structure shown on the right? DNA has been copied during interphase. Each copy of the DNA molecule wraps around histones to form a coil that then coils again to form a supercoil.

Vocabulary

Greek and Latin Word Origins Tell students that many of the vocabulary words in this section come from Greek prefixes and suffixes, producing names that are descriptive. **Telomere** and **centromere** refer to parts of a chromosome:

-mere = part or segment
telo- = end
centro- = center

The Greek root *chromo* means "color" and refers to the fact that DNA in its various forms readily attracted the stains that made it visible under the microscope. The rest of the word **chromosome** completes the description:

soma = body

Answers

A Infer Positive; negative and positive charges attract each other. If the histones were negatively charged, they would repel DNA.

B Apply A chromosome is made of one continuous DNA molecule.

▼ Teach *continued*

History of Science

With the **cell theory** established by the mid 1800s, attention turned to the mechanism by which one cell becomes two. Advances in staining techniques and the development of better microscopes were required to get a clear picture of what was happening during **mitosis.** In studying eukaryotic cells, scientists were puzzled because the nucleus seemed to disappear from the parent cell and then reappear in each daughter cell.

In 1882, German scientist **Walther Flemming** published the definitive paper detailing the steps of mitosis in eukaryotic cells. Using a new staining technique and greatly enhanced microscope technology, he put together the sequence by studying the fixed and stained cells from a salamander larva. He saw that as the nucleus disappeared, threadlike structures came to the center of the cell to divide. Fleming coined the term *mitosis* for the process, the Greek word *mitos,* meaning "thread." He went on to observe this process in both living and fixed cells of many different types of organisms. He concluded that it was a universal feature of organisms.

Vocabulary

Greek and Latin Roots The word **phase** comes from the Greek root meaning "appearance."

inter- = between
pro- = before
meta- = after
ana- = back
telo- = end

Ask, What do you think the prefixes used are referring to? appearance of chromosomes

FIGURE 5.6 The nucleus and chromosomes go through dramatic changes in a dividing cell.

Parent cell

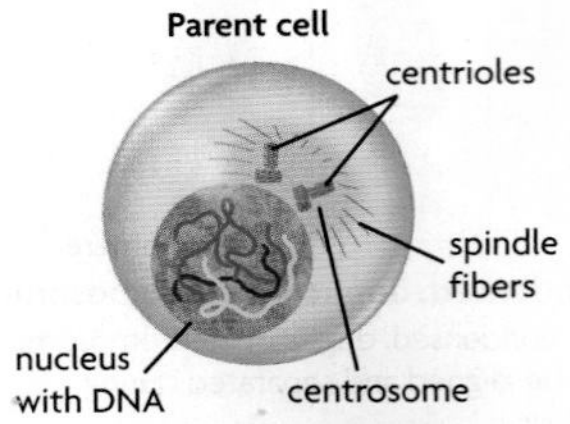

Connecting CONCEPTS

Cells As you will learn in **Chapter 6,** your body has two major cell types. Germ cells develop into eggs or sperm. Somatic cells make up the rest of your body.

MAIN IDEA

Mitosis and cytokinesis produce two genetically identical daughter cells.

The combined processes of mitosis and cytokinesis produce two genetically identical daughter cells. Follow along in **FIGURE 5.7** as you read about the process in more detail below.

Interphase

INTERPHASE

Interphase plays an important role in preparing the cell to divide. It provides critical time for the duplication of organelles and for DNA replication. By the end of interphase, an individual cell has two full sets of DNA, or chromosomes, and is large enough to divide.

Mitosis

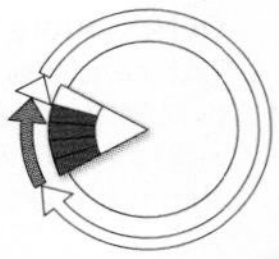

MITOSIS

Mitosis divides a cell's nucleus into two genetically identical nuclei, each with its own single, full set of DNA. This process occurs in all of your body cells—except those that form eggs or sperm—and prepares them for cytokinesis. Although mitosis and cytokinesis are continuous processes, scientists have divided them into phases to make them easier to understand and discuss. The four main phases of mitosis are prophase, metaphase, anaphase, and telophase. Cytokinesis begins during late anaphase or telophase.

1. During **prophase,** chromatin condenses into tightly coiled chromosomes. Each consists of two identical sister chromatids. The nuclear envelope breaks down, the nucleolus disappears, and the centrosomes and centrioles begin to migrate to opposite sides of the cell. Organized microtubules called spindle fibers grow from the centrioles and radiate toward the center of the cell.
2. In **metaphase,** the spindle fibers attach to a protein structure on the centromere of each chromosome and align the chromosomes along the cell equator, around the middle of the cell.
3. During **anaphase,** sister chromatids separate from each other. The spindle fibers begin to shorten, which pulls the sister chromatids away from each other and toward opposite sides of the cell.
4. In **telophase,** a complete set of identical chromosomes is positioned at each pole of the cell. The nuclear membranes start to form, the chromosomes begin to uncoil, and the spindle fibers fall apart.

Cytokinesis

CYTOKINESIS

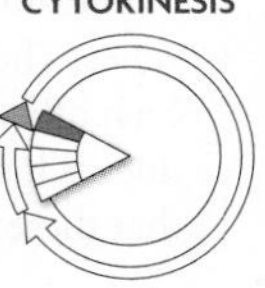

Cytokinesis divides the cytoplasm into two cells and completes a full stage of the cell cycle. Cytokinesis differs in animal and plant cells. In animal cells, the membrane forms a furrow, or trench, that is pulled inward by tiny filaments, like a drawstring. Gradually, the membrane pinches closed, forming a separate cell around each nucleus.

Differentiated Instruction

BELOW LEVEL

Remind students that mnemonic devices, or memory aids, can help with recall. To remember the order of phases in mitosis, ask students to come up with an expression that uses the first letter of each phase. Examples: People may answer telephones or peas make awful tarts.

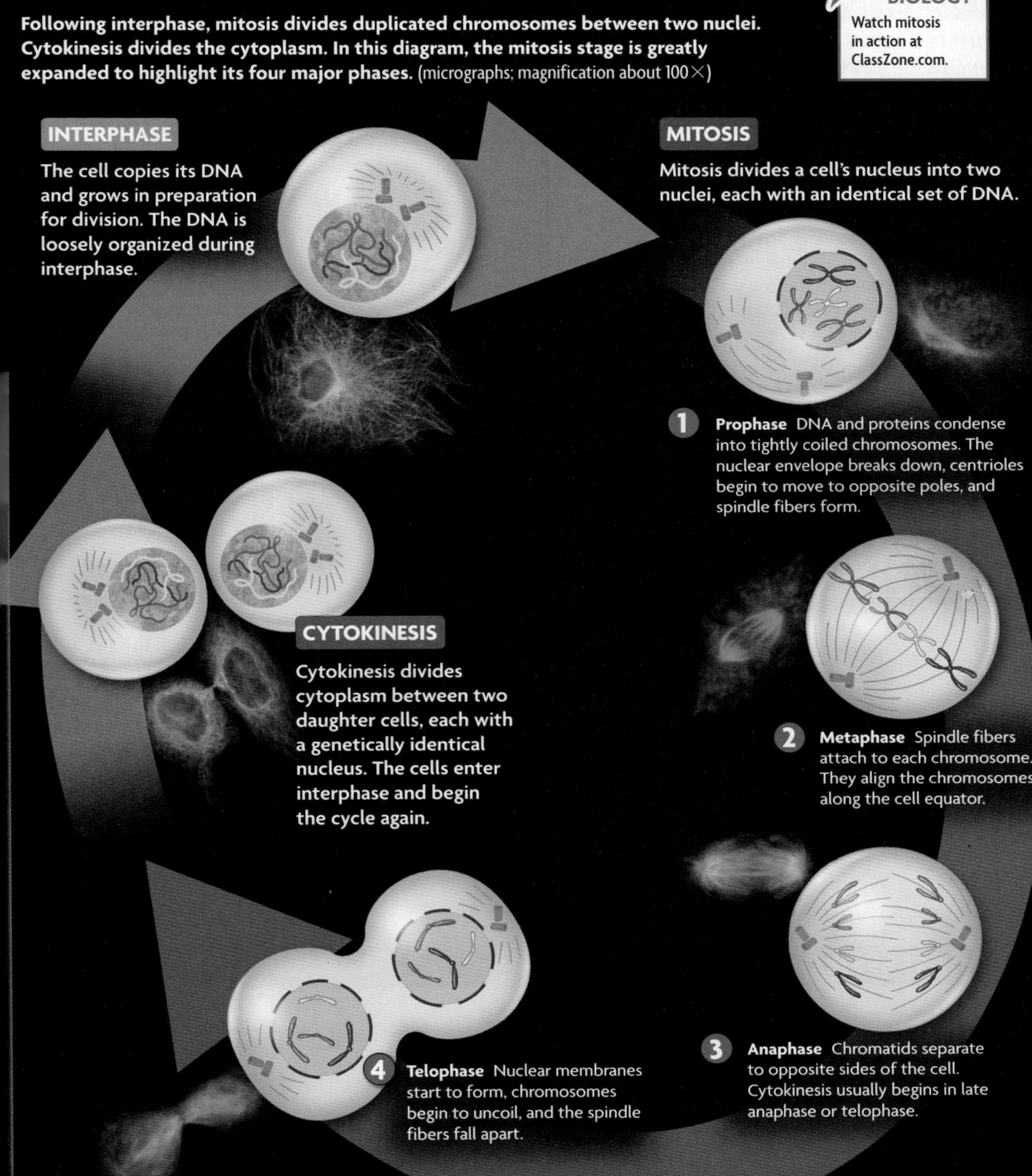

Animated BIOLOGY
Watch mitosis in action at ClassZone.com.
INTERPHASE
The cell copies its DNA and grows in preparation for division. The DNA is loosely organized during interphase.
MITOSIS
Mitosis divides a cell's nucleus into two nuclei, each with an identical set of DNA.
1 Prophase DNA and proteins condense into tightly coiled chromosomes. The nuclear envelope breaks down, centrioles begin to move to opposite poles, and spindle fibers form.
2 Metaphase Spindle fibers attach to each chromosome. They align the chromosomes along the cell equator.
3 Anaphase Chromatids separate to opposite sides of the cell. Cytokinesis usually begins in late anaphase or telophase.
4 Telophase Nuclear membranes start to form, chromosomes begin to uncoil, and the spindle fibers fall apart.
CYTOKINESIS
Cytokinesis divides cytoplasm between two daughter cells, each with a genetically identical nucleus. The cells enter interphase and begin the cycle again.

FIGURE 5.7 The Cell Cycle in Detail

Following interphase, mitosis divides duplicated chromosomes between two nuclei. Cytokinesis divides the cytoplasm. In this diagram, the mitosis stage is greatly expanded to highlight its four major phases. (micrographs; magnification about 100×)

A CRITICAL VIEWING **How many chromosomes does the cell have at the start of mitosis? How many does it have after cytokinesis?**

TEACH WITH TECHNOLOGY

Walther Flemming (History of Science) published many drawings of mitosis. Some are available on the Internet. Go to Teacher Resources at **ClassZone.com** for one such resource. Project the images for students and have them compare the drawings. Discuss the importance of these images as a source of information.

TEACH FROM VISUALS

FIGURE 5.7 Point out that the diagrams have been greatly simplified. They show only 4 chromosomes, whereas the accompanying TEMs show 46. Have students relate the chromosomes in each phase of mitosis with the chromosome structures shown in **FIGURE 5.5** on page 139. Have students identify points where DNA is single and where it is doubled. **Ask**

- How are the chromosomes shown in step 1 (prophase) different from those in step 4 (telophase)? Sister chromatids have separated by step 4. The daughter chromosomes have just one copy of DNA.
- What type of chromosome is pictured in **FIGURE 5.4** on page 138? metaphase chromosome
- What other cellular structure, besides DNA, must double for another round of mitosis to occur? centrosome

Take It Further

The **centrosome** is the organizing center for the microtubules that make up the mitotic spindle. The microtubules are colored bright green in the TEMs shown in **FIGURE 5.7.** The **tubulin** units that make up microtubules can rapidly assemble, as they do during metaphase, or disassemble, as they do during telophase. The **centrioles,** also made up of microtubules, appear to play a role in the duplication of the centrosome in animal cells. Plant cells do not have centrioles.

Answers

A Critical Viewing four (duplicated) chromosomes; four (unduplicated) chromosomes

▼ Teach *continued*

DATA ANALYSIS

Introduce

Remind students that units of measure typically go into the column headings, reserving the cells of a table for numbers alone. All values in a column must be in the same unit of measure.

Answers

1. Students will list the given temperatures in the first column and the number of daily doublings in the second column. An appropriate title would be "Effect of Temperature on Cell Division in Chlorella."
2. The independent variable is temperature, and the dependent variable is the number of daily doublings.

Unit Resource Book, Data Analysis, p. 85

Answers

A Contrast In animal cells, the membrane pinches together to separate the cytoplasm. In plant cells, a cell plate forms and divides the cell, along which the cell membrane and cell wall re-form.

▼ Assess and Reteach

Assess Use the Online Quiz or Section Quiz (*Assessment Book,* p. 88).

Reteach Have students view the animation of mitosis at **ClassZone.com** or use mitosis diagrams from the Media Gallery. Then have students draw and label their own diagrams of the four major phases of mitosis and of cytokinesis. Have them relate chromosome structure to the stages of the cell cycle.

DATA ANALYSIS

NOS.3

CONSTRUCTING DATA TABLES

Scientists use data tables to record their data. Data tables are organized by the independent and dependent variables. Usually the independent variable is listed in the left column, and the other columns list the dependent variables. Each separate observation is listed in its own row. When measurements are taken using units, they are listed in the column headings in parentheses. All tables should have numbers and titles.

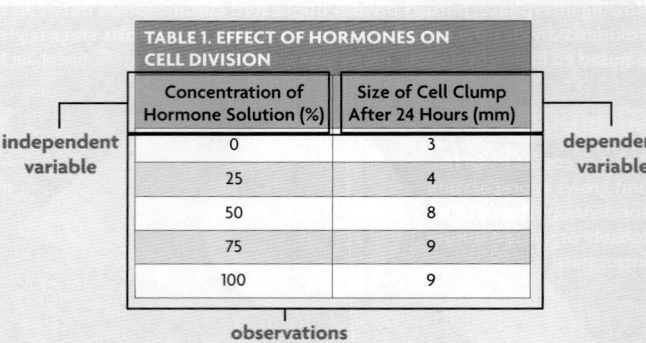

TABLE 1. EFFECT OF HORMONES ON CELL DIVISION

Concentration of Hormone Solution (%)	Size of Cell Clump After 24 Hours (mm)
0	3
25	4
50	8
75	9
100	9

independent variable — dependent variable — observations

Table 1 shows data from a hypothetical experiment in which growth hormones were added to clumps of cells in a laboratory, and the growth of the cell clumps was measured.

1. **Display Data** Suppose a scientist decided to measure the effect of temperature on cell division in *chlorella,* a type of green algae. Set up a table that could be used to record the results for the number of daily doublings of the cells: 20°C, 3 doublings; 30°C, 7 doublings; 40°C, 12 doublings; 50°C, 0 doublings.
2. **Apply** Label the independent and dependent variables on your table.

During cytokinesis in plant cells, the membrane cannot pinch inward because of the cell wall. Instead, a cell plate forms between the two nuclei. It is made by the Golgi apparatus, which supplies the new plasma membrane. A new wall then grows as cellulose and other materials are laid down. Typically, cytoplasm is divided evenly between daughter cells in both plant and animal cells.

The formation of new cells is critical in both multicellular and single-celled organisms. Single-celled organisms use cell division to reproduce, whereas multicellular organisms use it for growth, development, and repair.

A Contrast How does cytokinesis differ in animal and plant cells?

5.2 ASSESSMENT

ONLINE QUIZ ClassZone.com

B.6.1

REVIEWING ▶ MAIN IDEAS

1. Draw what a **chromosome** looks like during **metaphase.** Identify the **chromatids** and the **centromere.**
2. Briefly explain why the daughter cells resulting from mitosis are genetically identical to each other and to the original cell.

CRITICAL THINKING

3. **Contrast** How do **prophase** and **telophase** differ?
4. **Apply** Using a light microscope, you observe a cell that has no nucleus. What features would you look for to determine whether it is a eukaryotic cell undergoing mitosis or a prokaryotic cell?

Connecting CONCEPTS

5. **Protein Synthesis** For a cell to make proteins, enzymes must access its genes. When **histones** are modified with acetyl groups (-$COCH_3$), their positive charge is neutralized, so they wrap DNA less tightly. How might this affect the rate of protein synthesis?

5.2 ASSESSMENT

1. Students will list the given temperatures in the first column and the number of daily doublings in the second. An appropriate title would be "Effect of Temperature on Cell Division in *Chlorella.*"
2. The independent variable is temperature and the dependent variable is the number of daily doublings.
3. Prophase and telophase are opposites. The nuclear envelope fragments, chromosomes condense, and spindle fibers start to assemble in prophase. In telophase, the reverse occurs: the nuclear envelope re-forms, chromosomes uncoil, and spindle fibers disassemble.
4. Other organelles should be visible in a eukaryotic cell along with (condensed) chromosomes and spindle fibers if it were undergoing mitosis.
5. Acetylation (adding an acetyl group) could increase the rate of protein synthesis because the looser DNA wrapping may make it easier for enzymes to access the genes.

Mitosis in Onion Root Cells

MATERIALS
- slides of onion root cells
- microscope

PROCESS SKILLS
- **Observing**
- **Collecting Data**
- **Concluding**

NOS.3 Clearly communicate their ideas and results of investigations verbally and in written form using tables, graphs, diagrams, and photographs.

In this lab, you will examine cells from onion root tissue under the microscope and identify the different stages of cell division. You will also determine how much time is spent in each stage of the cell cycle.

PROBLEM How much time do cells spend in each part of the cell cycle?

PROCEDURE

1. Obtain a slide of onion root cells. Examine the slide under the microscope using the low-power lens.
2. Find examples of cells in each stage of the cell cycle, including interphase and the stages of mitosis—prophase, metaphase, anaphase, and telophase. Draw and label each cell. Label structures within the cell.
3. Select a random area of the slide to study using the high-power lens.
4. Identify and record the stage of each cell in the view. Make a data table, like the one shown below, and record your data.
5. Repeat step 3 two more times.
6. Calculate the percentage of cells in each part of the cell cycle for each sample.

TABLE 1. STAGES OF THE CELL CYCLE

Sample	Total Cells	Interphase		Prophase		Metaphase		Anaphase		Telophase	
	No.	No.	%	No.	%	No.	%	No.	%	No.	%
1											
2											
3											

ANALYZE AND CONCLUDE

1. **Analyze** What patterns exist in your data? In which stage of the cell cycle are most of the cells you examined? How do these data support what you know about the cell cycle?
2. **Calculate** Find the average percentage of cells in each stage of the cell cycle among the three samples. Assume that a cell takes 24 hours to complete one cell cycle. Calculate how much time is spent in each stage of the cell cycle. (**Hint:** Multiply the percentage of cells in each stage, as a decimal, by 24 hours.)
3. **Apply** The cells in the root of an onion are actively dividing. How might the numbers you count here be different than if you had examined cells from a different part of the plant?
4. **Predict** A chemical company is testing a new product that it believes will increase the growth rate of food plants. Suppose you are able to view the slides of onion root tips that have been treated with the product. If the product is successful, how might the slides look different from the slides you viewed in this lab? Draw some examples of what the treated slides might look like.

EXTEND YOUR INVESTIGATION

Design an experiment that would test the product described in question 4. Assume the product is a liquid that can be added to the soil in which the plant is growing.

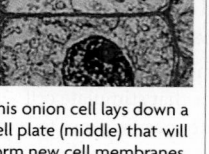

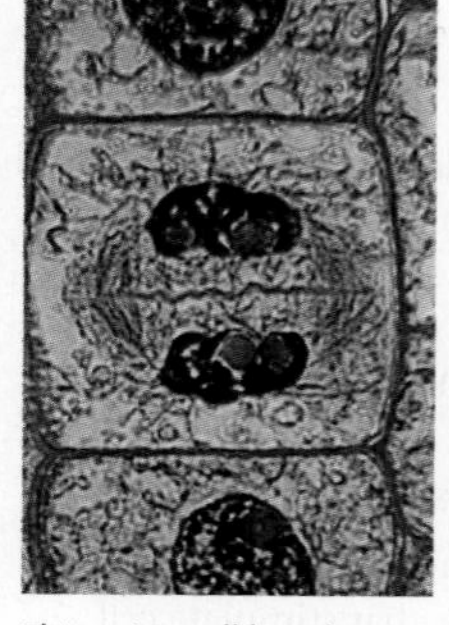

This onion cell lays down a cell plate (middle) that will form new cell membranes and the cell wall. (LM, magnification 570×)

Answers

Sample Data

For a sample of a student table, go to page R102.

Analyze and Conclude

1. Most cells will be in interphase. About 90 percent of the cell cycle is spent in interphase.
2. Students should use the following formula for calculations: percentage of cells in stage × 24 hours. In a 24-hour period, the majority of the time is spent in interphase.
3. More cells will be in interphase in other parts of the plant.
4. Treated root tips should have a higher percentage of cells undergoing mitosis.

Extend Your Investigation

Students should design an experiment in which the effects of the product are the dependent variable. Varying applications of the product (amounts, times) are possible independent variables. A control would be a plant that is not treated with the product.

INVESTIGATION

Time 45 minutes	TEACHER TESTED
Teacher Preparation	
Student Difficulty	
Lab Binder Cells, pp. 29–31	

Purpose Observe and identify the different stages of the cell cycle.

Overview Students will use a microscope to examine cells from onion root tissue. They will

- draw and label the structures at each stage of the cell cycle
- record the stage of each cell in a random area
- calculate the percentage of cells in each stage of the cell cycle

LAB MANAGEMENT

- Be sure students can correctly identify the stages of the cell cycle.
- Remind students that to take a random sample, they move the slide on the microscope stage when it is not being viewed. The random sample should be full of cells and not near the edge of the slide. If the random sample is not full of cells, students should repeat the process.
- Make sure students know how to calculate percentage. Suggest students round percentages so that together they equal 100 percent.

Safety Caution students to be careful when handling the slides. Remind them to wipe down the eyepieces of the microscope with alcohol wipes after use.

Inclusion If equipment is available, project the microscope image for students who are visually impaired.

POST-LAB DISCUSSION

Have students compare results for possible trends.

SECTION 5.3

▼ Plan and Prepare

Objectives

- Identify internal and external factors that regulate cell division.
- Explain cancer in terms of the cell cycle.

Section Resources

Unit Resource Book
Study Guide pp. 73–74
Power Notes p. 75
Reinforcement p. 76
Pre-AP Activity pp. 89–90
Interactive Reader Chapter 5
Spanish Study Guide pp. 47–48
Biology Toolkit pp. C16, C29, C32, C36, D4
Technology
Power Presentation 5.3
Media Gallery DVD
Online Quiz 5.3

Activate Prior Knowledge Determine what students know about cancer. **Ask,** What is cancer? Cancer is uncontrolled cell division. Tell students that cancers are caused by a variety of factors and that most affect the cell cycle.

▼ Teach

TEACH FROM VISUALS

FIGURE 5.8 Point out that the tan colored cells growing in the culture dishes are just a single layer. **Ask**

- What would a cross-sectional view of each dish look like? top dish: one layer of a cell; bottom dish: clump of cells spreading up and across the single layer of normal cells
- What external factor is helping to regulate normal cell division? contact with other cells

5.3 Regulation of the Cell Cycle

KEY CONCEPT Cell cycle regulation is necessary for healthy growth.

MAIN IDEAS

- Internal and external factors regulate cell division.
- Cell division is uncontrolled in cancer.

VOCABULARY

growth factor, p. 144
apoptosis, p. 145
cancer, p. 146
benign, p. 146
malignant, p. 146
metastasize, p. 146
carcinogen, p. 146

Connect Have you ever watched a movie in which people play with the elements of nature? They might bring back dinosaurs or make a newfangled robot. And have you noticed that these movies are always scary? That's because things go out of control. The robots take over, or the dinosaurs start eating humans. If cell growth goes out of control in your body, the result can be even scarier. Cancer is uncontrolled cell growth and results from many factors that affect the cell cycle. So how does your body regulate all the millions of cell divisions happening in your body?

MAIN IDEA

Internal and external factors regulate cell division.

Both external and internal factors regulate the cell cycle in eukaryotic cells. External factors come from outside the cell. They include messages from nearby cells and from distant parts of the organism's body.

Internal factors come from inside the cell and include several types of molecules found in the cytoplasm. Both types of factors work together to help your body control the process of cell division.

FIGURE 5.8 Normal animal cells (top) respond to external factors and stop dividing when they touch each other. Cancer cells (bottom) fail to respond and form clumps.

Normal cell growth

Cancerous cell growth

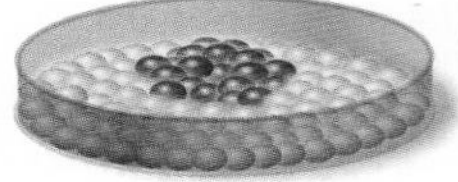

External Factors

External factors that help regulate the cell cycle include physical and chemical signals. One example of a physical signal is cell–cell contact. Most mammal cells grown in the laboratory form a single layer on the bottom of a culture dish, as shown in **FIGURE 5.8.** Once a cell touches other cells, it stops dividing. The exact reason for this phenomenon is unknown. One hypothesis is that receptors on neighboring cells bind to each other and cause the cells' cytoskeletons to form structures that may block the signals that trigger growth.

Many cells also release chemical signals that tell other cells to grow. For example, **growth factors** are a broad group of proteins that stimulate cell division. Growth factors bind to receptors that activate specific genes to trigger cell growth. In general, cells grow and divide in response to a combination of different growth factors, not just one.

Differentiated Instruction

BELOW LEVEL

Have students organize notes around the key concept, placing it in a box. From this, students should draw a vertical line to which they attach the headings and subheadings for this section and show how the material in the text supports the key concept.

Biology Toolkit, Supporting Main Ideas, p. C29

ENGLISH LEARNERS

Divide students into small groups and have students number off. Ask students questions about the factors that regulate the cell cycle and what happens to surrounding cells if a cell starts to divide in an unregulated way. After each question, give the groups time to develop their answer. Then call out a number to identify a spokesperson for the group.

Biology Toolkit, Numbered Heads Together, p. C16

Some growth factors affect many different types of cells. For example, platelets are sticky fragments of bone marrow cells. They form clots that help stop bleeding. Platelets store a type of growth factor that helps your body repair wounds by triggering the growth of many different cell types. Other growth factors have more specific targets. For instance, erythropoietin (ih-RIHTH-roh-poy-EE-tihn) stimulates the production only of cells that will become red blood cells. Red blood cells carry oxygen. If you moved from the coast to the mountains, your blood oxygen levels would be lower because the air pressure is lower at higher altitudes. The decrease in blood oxygen levels would cause your body to produce more erythropoietin. That factor would increase the number of red blood cells and raise your blood oxygen levels.

Various hormones may also stimulate the growth of certain cell types. In particular, growth hormone results in bone growth and also affects your protein and fat metabolism.

Internal Factors

When external factors bind to their receptors, they can trigger internal factors that affect the cell cycle. Two of the most important and well-studied internal factors involved in the eukaryotic cell cycle are kinases and cyclins. A kinase is an enzyme that, when activated, transfers a phosphate group from one molecule to a specific target molecule. This action typically increases the energy of the target molecule or changes its shape. Your cells have many types of kinases, and they are almost always present in the cell. Those kinases that help control the cell cycle are activated by cyclins. Cyclins are a group of proteins that are rapidly made and destroyed at certain points in the cell cycle. These two factors help a cell advance to different stages of the cell cycle when cells bind to each other.

Apoptosis

Just as some cells need to grow and divide, other cells need to die. **Apoptosis** (AP-uhp-TOH-sihs) is programmed cell death. It occurs when internal or external signals activate genes that help produce self-destructive enzymes. Many questions remain about this process. What is known is that the nucleus of an apoptotic cell tends to shrink and break apart, and the cell is recognized by specialized cells in the immune system. These cells very tidily gobble up the apoptotic cell and recycle its chemical parts for use in building other molecules. **FIGURE 5.9** shows a classic example of apoptosis. In the early stages of development, human embryos have webbing between their fingers and toes, or digits. Before a baby is born, those cells typically go through apoptosis. Most babies are born with little unwebbed fingers and toes they love to put in their mouths.

FIGURE 5.9 Human embryos have webbed digits early in their development. The cells between the digits undergo apoptosis during later stages of development. As a result, the baby is born with unwebbed fingers and toes.

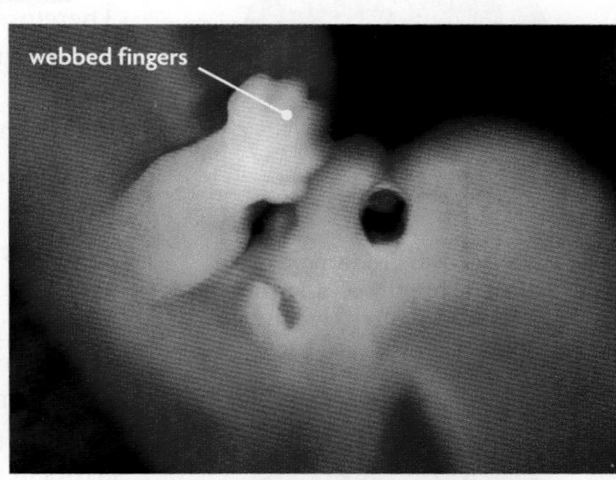

A Predict **Suppose a child was born whose receptors for growth hormone did not work properly. How do you think this would affect the child's development?**

PRE-AP

Tell students that as they are sitting in class, millions of skins cells are dying. Have students speculate as to the series of events that occur when a single cell dies. Have them think of causes and effects, and the internal and external factors involved.

Biology Toolkit, Cause and Effect Chain, p. C36

Vocabulary

kinase One internal factor that regulates the cell cycle are a group of proteins called kinases. Tell students that the word *kinase* is a combination of *kin(etic)* and *-ase. Kinetic* comes from the Greek *kinein,* which means "to move." The suffix *-ase* means "enzyme." Kinase moves a phosphate group from one molecule to a specific target molecule, and thus affects that molecule's activity.

cyclin An internal factor that controls kinases are cyclins. The *cyclic* nature of these proteins is that they can be rapidly made or destroyed, thus controlling the cell cycle.

Take It Further

The process of **apoptosis** is not just a function of embryonic development. In adults, cell death is balanced by cell division, which keeps body tissue from growing or shrinking as cells reach the end of their life span. Cells that die through injury, a process called **cell necrosis,** may swell and burst, damaging surrounding cells. In contrast, during apoptosis, cells collapse inward, without spilling their contents.

Apoptosis also takes place in plants. The leaves of deciduous trees fall off before winter due to apoptosis. *Apoptosis* is a Greek word that means "a falling off."

Answers

A Predict The ability of the child to produce new cells and therefore tissues at the proper rate would be affected, which could affect height and weight, but also developing tissues and organs.

▼ Teach *continued*

ONLINE BIOLOGY Have students do the WebQuest in Options for Inquiry on page 157 to learn more about skin cancer.

Take It Further

According to the American Cancer Society, **skin cancer** is the most common of all cancers. It is very treatable if found early, so people are encouraged to examine their skin every few months to look for changes in moles, freckles, and other marks on the skin. The American Academy of Dermatology suggests using the ABCD rule. These letters can be used as a mnemonic to help people remember what to look for. Asymmetry is irregular shape. Border is an irregular border. Color is for change in color, many colors, or uneven distribution of colors. Dimension is for diameter larger than 6 millimeters (1/4 in.). New growth, changes in growths, or a sore that does not heal are warning signs and need to be checked by a physician. Have students find the ABCD of the cancerous mole in **FIGURE 5.11.**

Vocabulary

Academic Vocabulary The words **benign** and **malignant** are a part of everyday language:

benign, of a kind, gentle disposition
malignant, disposed to do evil

The words **cancerous** and **metastasize** are also used in an everyday language, to suggest "spreading evil." You might want to introduce students to the word **connotation** in this context:

connotation = an idea or meaning suggested by a word or thing

FIGURE 5.10 Cancer cells form tumors that may metastasize to other parts of the body.

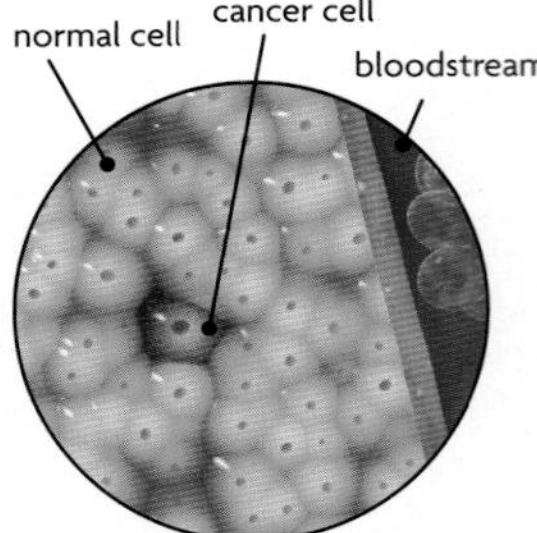

1. A healthy cell may become a cancer cell if certain genes are damaged.

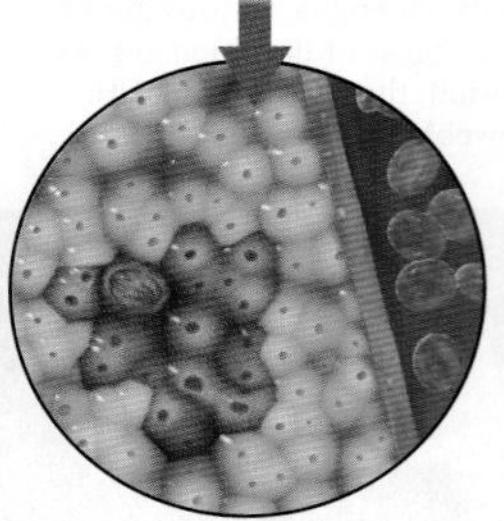

2. Cancer cells divide more often than do healthy cells and may form disorganized clumps called tumors.

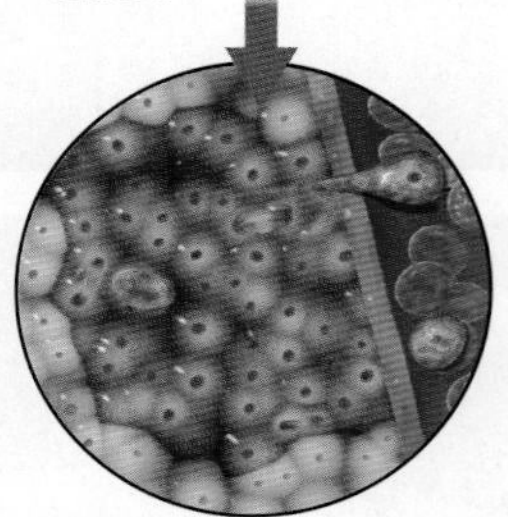

3. Sometimes, cancer cells break away from the tumor. They can be carried in the bloodstream to other parts of the body, where they form new tumors.

MAIN IDEA

Cell division is uncontrolled in cancer.

Cancer is the common name for a class of diseases characterized by uncontrolled cell division. It arises when regulation of the cell cycle breaks down. Unlike healthy cells, cancer cells grown in a culture dish continue to divide, even when surrounded by neighboring cells. Cancer cells can also continue to divide in the absence of many of the growth factors required for division in healthy cells. As a result, they divide much more often than do healthy cells.

Cancer cells form disorganized clumps called tumors. In a **benign** tumor, the cancer cells typically remain clustered together. This means the tumor may be relatively harmless and can probably be cured by removing it. However, if a tumor is **malignant,** some of the cancer cells can break away, or **metastasize** (mih-TAS-tuh-SYZ), from the tumor. These breakaway cells can be carried in the bloodstream or lymph system to other parts of the body, as shown in **FIGURE 5.10,** where they can form more tumors, called metastases. Once a tumor metastasizes, it is much more difficult to entirely rid the body of tumors.

But why are tumors harmful? Cancer cells do not perform the specialized functions needed by the body. In the lung, for example, cancer cells do not exchange oxygen and carbon dioxide. In the brain, they do not transmit the carefully ordered electrical messages needed to interpret information. Therefore, the body has large clumps of rapidly dividing cells that require lots of food and a hearty blood supply but that contribute nothing to the body's function. In addition, a growing tumor can exert great pressure on surrounding organs. For instance, a tumor growing inside the skull will cramp the brain for space, and some regions will be unable to function properly. If cancer cells continue to grow unchecked, they will eventually kill the organism.

Cancer cells come from normal cells that have suffered damage to the genes that help make proteins involved in cell-cycle regulation. Most cancer cells carry mutations, or errors, in two types of genes. One type, called oncogenes, accelerate the cell cycle. The second type act as cell-cycle brakes. Mutations in these genes can be inherited. For instance, some breast cancers appear to be caused by inherited errors in specific genes. Other mutations can be caused by exposure to radiation or chemicals. For example, some skin cancers are due to DNA damage caused by ultraviolet radiation from sunlight. Substances known to produce or promote the development of cancer are called **carcinogens** (kahr-SIHN-uh-juhnz). These include tobacco smoke and certain air pollutants, which are both associated with lung cancer. Some mutated forms of oncogenes are even carried by viruses; one such virus can cause cervical cancer.

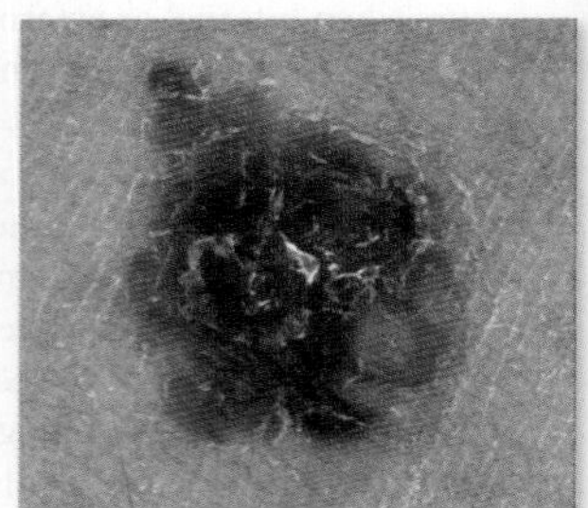

FIGURE 5.11 This cancerous mole is an example of a skin cancer, which may metastasize quickly.

Differentiated Instruction

BELOW LEVEL

Have students create a Y diagram to compare benign and malignant growth. Tell them to write *Benign* at the top the left arm of the Y and *Malignant* at the top of the right. Students should list the characteristics of each type of tumor under each heading. Once they have finished, have them cross out the characteristics shared by both benign and malignant growth, and list those characteristics in the stem.

Biology Toolkit, Y Diagram, p. C32

ENGLISH LEARNERS

Have students prepare two-by-two word squares for the vocabulary on this page. They should include the word and a translation in their own language, a definition in their own words, and their use of it in a sentence. Help them come up with a drawing that will help to recall the word.

Biology Toolkit, Word Squares, p. D4

QUICK LAB OBSERVING

Cancer

In this lab, you will compare normal cells with cancerous cells and observe the differences between them.

MATERIALS

- microscope
- slides of normal cells
- slides of cancerous cells

PROBLEM How do normal and cancerous cells compare?

PROCEDURE

1. Examine the slides of normal cells under the microscope. Draw and describe your observations.
2. Repeat step 1 with slides of cancer cells.

ANALYZE AND CONCLUDE

1. **Compare** How does the structure of the normal cells compare with the structure of the cancerous cells for each of the slides you viewed?
2. **Infer** Cancer cells not only appear different from normal cells but they also divide more rapidly. Why do you think chemotherapy, a common treatment for cancer, results in the loss of hair?

Standard cancer treatment often involves both radiation and chemotherapy. Radiation therapy is the use of radiation to kill cancer cells and shrink tumors. It works by damaging a cell's DNA so much that the cell cannot divide. Radiation is usually localized—that is, its use is targeted to a specific region—because it can also hurt healthy cells. Chemotherapy uses certain drugs, often in combination, to kill actively dividing cells. Like radiation, it kills both cancerous and healthy cells. However, chemotherapy is systemic—drugs travel throughout the entire body.

Medical researchers use laboratory-grown cancer cells in their search for cancer treatments. Much of what is known about the cell cycle has come from studies that use cancer cells. The most famous cancer cells used for research are called HeLa cells. HeLa cells were originally obtained in 1951 from a cervical tumor removed from a woman named Henrietta Lacks. This cell line continues to be grown and studied in laboratories all over the world.

Analyze HeLa cells are also used to study cell signaling processes. What might be a disadvantage of using cancer cells to study processes occurring in healthy cells?

5.3 ASSESSMENT

ONLINE QUIZ ClassZone.com

REVIEWING MAIN IDEAS

1. Describe what a **growth factor** is and how it influences the cell cycle.
2. Explain how **cancer** cells differ from healthy cells.

CRITICAL THINKING

3. **Contrast** How do **benign** and **malignant** tumors differ?
4. **Hypothesize** Suppose chromosomes in a skin cell are damaged by ultraviolet radiation. If the damaged genes do not affect cell cycle regulation, do you think the cell will become cancerous? Explain.

Connecting CONCEPTS

5. **Cell Organelles** Some anticancer drugs prevent microtubules from forming spindle fibers. Why do you think these drugs might be effective treatments for cancer?

5.3 ASSESSMENT

1. A growth factor is an external signal that stimulates growth and division of cells.
2. Cancer cells have uncontrolled division, grow rapidly without many growth factors, can form tumors, can metastasize, and do not contribute to the body's function.
3. Benign tumors—cancer cells clustered together and relatively harmless; Malignant tumors—cancer cells can metastasize and form more tumors.
4. No, if the damage does not affect the cell cycle, the cell will probably continue to divide normally and will not become cancerous.
5. Without microtubules and spindle fibers, mitosis cannot take place.

QUICK LAB

Time 20 minutes

Lab Binder Cells, p. 36

Purpose Observe and compare normal cells and cancerous cells.

LAB MANAGEMENT

- When making comparisons, students should look for the following traits in the cancerous cells or tumors: a large number of dividing cells, changes to the nucleus such as size and shape, and changes in cell size and shape.

Safety Caution students to be careful when handling the slides. Remind them to wipe down the eyepieces of the microscope with alcohol wipes after use.

Teacher Note "I would have students hypothesize consequences for different cell types if mutations occur."

Answers

Analyze and Conclude

1. In general, cancerous cells differ from normal cells in size, shape, color, and in the shape and size of the nucleus.
2. Chemotherapy affects rapidly dividing cells, both cancerous and normal. Cells in the hair follicles probably divide rapidly, so they are killed by chemotherapy.

Answers

A Analyze Cancer cells are mutants and may not have exactly the same processes as a healthy cell. This could lead to errors.

Assess and Reteach ▼

Assess Use the Online Quiz or Section Quiz (*Assessment Book,* p. 89).

Reteach Make a T-chart on the board, one side for cancer cells and one side for normal cells. Have students list the characteristics of cancer cells, then define a normal cell by how it is different from a cancer cell.

SECTION 5.4

▼ Plan and Prepare

Objectives

- Compare and contrast binary fission and mitosis.
- Describe how some eukaryotes reproduce through mitosis.

Section Resources

Unit Resource Book Study Guide pp. 77–78 Power Notes p. 79 Reinforcement p. 80
Interactive Reader Chapter 5 **Spanish Study Guide** pp. 49–50
Biology Toolkit pp. C19, C20, C34
Technology Power Presentation 5.4 Media Gallery DVD Online Quiz 5.4

Activate Prior Knowledge Spider plants are common household plants, which produce plantlets, or "babies," that can be removed, placed in soil, and will grow independently. **Ask,** Why can this form of reproduction be called asexual? The genetic material for the baby comes from only one parent.

▼ Teach

Vocabulary

binary fission Point out that the word *binary* means "consisting of two parts." The word *fission* means "the act or process of splitting into two parts." Point out that despite various forms of asexual reproduction that occur in multicellular organisms, binary fission is a term reserved for single-celled, prokaryotic organisms.

5.4 Asexual Reproduction

KEY CONCEPT Many organisms reproduce by cell division.

MAIN IDEAS

- Binary fission is similar in function to mitosis.
- Some eukaryotes reproduce through mitosis.

VOCABULARY

asexual reproduction, p. 148
binary fission, p. 148

Connect In this flashy world of ours, you may think that the humble bacterium would have little chance of finding a mate. No dazzling smile, no fancy hair products, no shiny car, and—if we are brutally honest—not even a brain. With all of these limitatio\ns, it may seem that our bacteria friends would be destined to die out. And yet, bacteria are found in abundance and live just about everywhere on Earth. How can there be so many bacteria?

MAIN IDEA

Binary fission is similar in function to mitosis.

Reproduction is a process that makes new organisms from one or more parent organisms. It happens in two ways—sexually and asexually. Sexual reproduction involves the joining of two specialized cells called gametes (eggs and sperm cells), one from each of two parents. The offspring that result are genetically unique; they have a mixture of genes from both parents. In contrast, **asexual reproduction** is the creation of offspring from a single parent and does not involve the joining of gametes. The offspring that result are, for the most part, genetically identical to each other and to the single parent.

Connecting CONCEPTS

Cell Structure Recall from **Chapter 3** that many scientists hypothesize that mitochondria and chloroplasts were originally free-living prokaryotes. One piece of evidence that supports this hypothesis is the fact that these two organelles replicate much as bacteria do, through fission.

Binary Fission and Mitosis

Most prokaryotes reproduce through binary fission. **Binary fission** (BY-nuh-ree FIHSH-uhn) is the asexual reproduction of a single-celled organism by division into two roughly equal parts. Binary fission and mitosis have similar results. That is, both processes form two daughter cells that are genetically identical to the parent cell. However, the actual processes are different in several important ways.

VISUAL VOCAB

Binary fission is the asexual reproduction of a single-celled organism by division into two roughly equal parts.

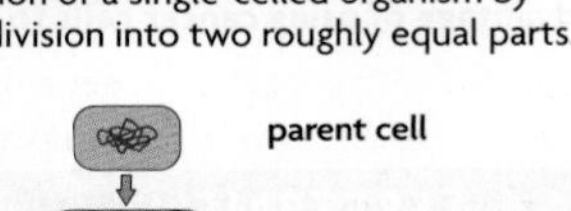

As you already learned, prokaryotes such as bacteria do not have nuclei. And although they do have DNA, they have much less of it than do most eukaryotes. Also, most of a bacterium's DNA is in the form of one circular chromosome, and bacteria have no spindle fibers.

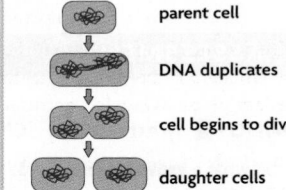

Differentiated Instruction

BELOW LEVEL

Have students make a chart to compare and contrast binary fission and mitosis. Have them place the terms in two boxes with an arrow pointing from each to a single box that describes the shared characteristics. Then have them draw arrows from this box to two separate boxes that detail the differences. Refer students to page 135 to review mitosis if necessary.

Biology Toolkit, Compare/Contrast Chart, p. C34

ENGLISH LEARNERS

Ask students to record in a T-chart the advantages and disadvantages of asexual reproduction. Model finding items for each column. Encourage students to work together to complete the charts. A key principle of language learning is that language develops best when students focus on accomplishing something with others rather than focus on language itself.

Biology Toolkit, T-Chart, p. C20

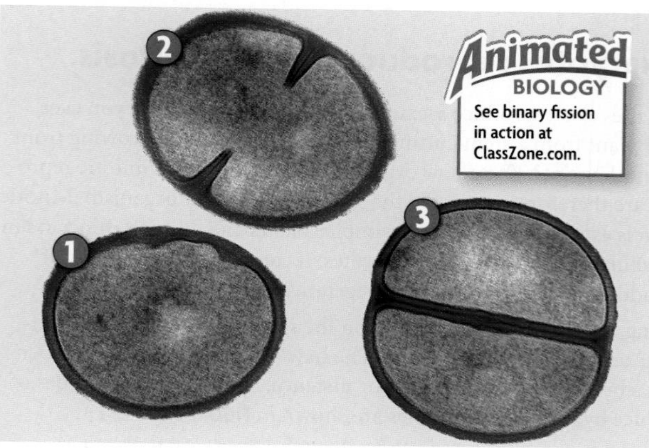
2
Animated
BIOLOGY
See binary fission in action at ClassZone.com.
1
3

FIGURE 5.13 Binary fission is shown in this micrograph of three individual bacteria, each at a different stage of binary fission. First, a cell elongates (1), and the DNA is replicated. Next, the cell membrane pinches inward (2). Finally, the membrane meets, and a new cell wall is laid down, forming two separate cells (3). (colored TEM; magnification 60,000×)

Binary fission, shown in **FIGURE 5.13**, starts when the bacterial chromosome is copied. The two chromosomes are both attached to the cell membrane. As the cell grows and gets longer, the chromosomes move away from each other. When the cell is about twice its original size, it undergoes cytokinesis. The membrane pinches inward, and a new cell wall is laid down between the two chromosomes, which completes the separation into two daughter cells.

FIGURE 5.14 BACTERIA GROWTH

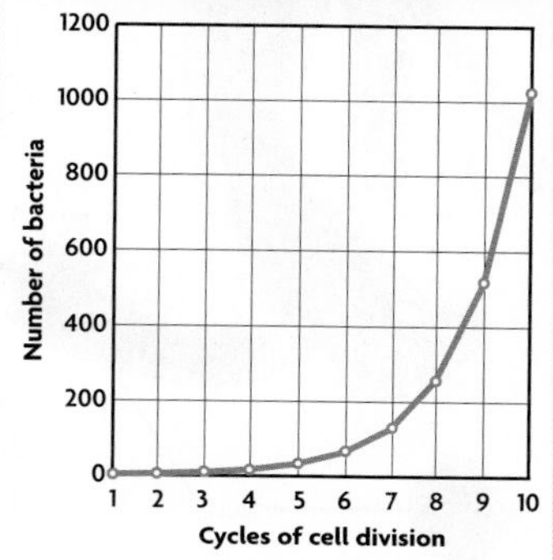

Number of bacteria: 0, 200, 400, 600, 800, 1000, 1200

Cycles of cell division: 1, 2, 3, 4, 5, 6, 7, 8, 9, 10

One bacterium can result in a total of 1024 cells after only 10 rounds of cell division.

Advantages and Disadvantages of Asexual Reproduction

Very often, whether something is helpful or harmful depends on the situation. In favorable environments that do not change much, asexual reproduction can be more efficient than sexual reproduction. Recall that asexual reproduction results in genetically identical offspring. If they are well suited to the environment, genetic variation could be more harmful than helpful. In other words, if it ain't broke, don't fix it.

However, asexual reproduction may be a disadvantage in changing conditions. Genetically identical offspring will respond to the environment in the same way. If population members lack traits that enable them to reproduce, the entire population could die off. In contrast, sexual reproduction increases genetic diversity, which raises the chance that at least a few individuals will survive or even thrive in changing conditions.

Keep in mind, however, that the act of asexual reproduction itself is not more efficient; rather, the associated costs of sexual reproduction are greater. For example, all asexually reproducing organisms can potentially reproduce. Suppose two organisms each have ten offspring. If one organism reproduces asexually, all ten offspring can have offspring of their own. If the other organism reproduces sexually, having five females and five males, only the five females can bear offspring. In addition, sexually reproducing organisms must attract a mate. This effort involves not only the time and energy needed to find a mate but also many structures, signals, and behaviors that have evolved to attract mates. Organisms that reproduce asexually do not have these costs.

Connecting CONCEPTS

Evolution As you will learn in **Chapter 18**, the misuse of antibiotics has resulted in multidrug-resistant bacteria. The bacteria not killed by antibiotics can reproduce quickly, passing the genes for antibiotic resistance on to their offspring.

A Summarize How is asexual reproduction an advantage in some conditions?

ONLINE BIOLOGY Students can do a virtual lab on bacterial growth to explore some of the external factors that affect the rate of reproduction/division for these single-celled organisms. See Options for Inquiry on page 157.

TEACH FROM VISUALS

FIGURE 5.14 Have students compare the units on the axes to see how quickly a population of bacteria can grow by binary fission. With each division, the number of bacteria doubles. Point out that the increase in the total number of bacteria at each successive cycle is exponential:

$$\text{number of bacteria} = 2^x$$

where x is the number of the cycle. Point out that the shape of the graph line is typical of exponential growth—a modest beginning followed by explosive growth.

Take It Further

Because bacterial reproduction is asexual, a population of bacteria is genetically identical. However, once a genetic mutation occurs within a population, it can spread rapidly because of exponential growth.

Genetic diversity can occur by other means within a population of bacteria. For example, a virus that infects one bacterium can transfer genetic material from that bacterium to another, a process called **transduction.** Bacterial cells can also share genetic material directly by the process of **conjugation.** The donor of genetic material is able to attach to a second bacterial cell by way of a tubular structure called a pilus. The "male" transfers DNA by way of the pilus to the "female."

PRE-AP

Have students read the last paragraph on page 149, about the costs associated with sexual reproduction. Ask them to write for five minutes on the question of who (or what) benefits despite the costs associated with sexual reproduction.

Biology Toolkit, Quick-Write, p. C19

HANDS-ON ACTIVITY

Have students model bacterial growth by binary fission, using a pile of beads. Tell students to start with one bead and add a second to represent the two bacteria that result from one cycle of division. Have students continue to add one bead for each bacterium after each cycle of division. Tell students to keep track of the number of cycles of cell division that occur before they run out of beads.

Answers

A Summarize Asexual reproduction produces genetically identical offspring that are well suited to their environment.

▼ Teach *continued*

TEACH FROM VISUALS

FIGURE 5.15 Have students find the bud on the yeast and the hydra. **Ask,** What is distinctive about the cells of the budding hydra compared to those of the budding yeast? In the hydra, there is some differentiation among the cells of the bud, whereas for the yeast, the cells are identical.

Explain that when the hydra bud breaks off, it will continue to grow by mitosis to be the same size as the parent.

Answers

A Synthesize Since asexually reproduced plants are clones, we can theoretically grow a particular plant in abundance under certain conditions. However, if conditions change, a significant portion of our food supply could be adversely affected.

▼ Assess and Reteach

Assess Use the Online Quiz or Section Quiz (*Assessment Book,* p. 90).

Reteach Have students summarize in what ways the asexual reproduction of a bacterial or yeast cell is the same as and different from the mitotic division of cells that occurs in a multicellular organism.

MAIN IDEA

Some eukaryotes reproduce through mitosis.

FIGURE 5.15 Yeast and hydras can reproduce by budding.
(hydra: LM, magnification 12×; yeast: colored SEM, magnification 3,200×)

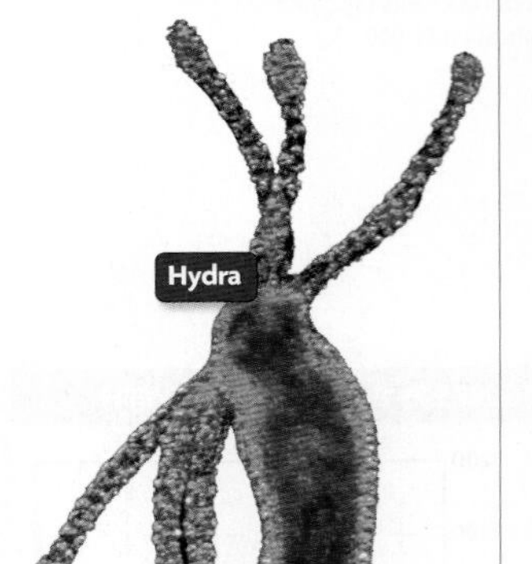

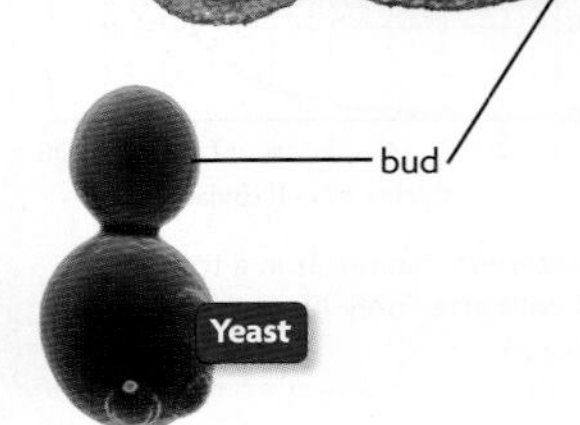

Some eukaryotes also reproduce asexually, through mitosis. Have you ever grown a new plant from a stem cutting? Or seen a new sea star growing from the arm of another one? These new organisms are the result of mitotic reproduction and are therefore genetically the same as the parent organism. Mitotic reproduction is especially common in simpler plants and animals. It occurs in both multicellular and unicellular eukaryotes. It can take several forms, including budding, fragmentation, and vegetative reproduction.

In budding, a small projection grows on the surface of the parent organism, forming a separate new individual. The new organism may live independently or attached as part of a colony. For instance, hydras and some types of yeast reproduce by budding. Examples are shown in **FIGURE 5.15.**

In fragmentation, a parent organism splits into pieces, each of which can grow into a new organism. Flatworms and sea stars both reproduce by fragmentation. Many plants, including strawberries and potatoes, reproduce via vegetative reproduction. In general, vegetative reproduction involves the modification of a stem or underground structures of the parent organism. The offspring often stay connected to the original organism, through structures called runners, for example.

Many organisms can reproduce both asexually and sexually. The form of reproduction may depend on the current conditions. The sea anemone can reproduce in many ways. It can reproduce asexually by dividing in half, by breaking off small pieces from its base, or by budding. It can also reproduce sexually by making eggs and sperm. Some species of anemone have males and females. In other anemone species, the same organism can produce both eggs and sperm cells.

Synthesize How might the asexual reproduction of genetically identical plants be useful to humans? How could it prove harmful to our food supply? A

5.4 ASSESSMENT

ONLINE QUIZ ClassZone.com

REVIEWING MAIN IDEAS

1. Explain how mitosis differs from **binary fission.**
2. Briefly explain why cutting a flatworm into pieces would not kill it.

CRITICAL THINKING

3. **Infer** How does an organism benefit by being able to reproduce both sexually and asexually?
4. **Apply** Yeasts are growing in two dishes. You treat one dish with a chemical that blocks DNA replication but forget to label it. How can you identify the treated dish?

Connecting CONCEPTS

5. **Ecology** Two populations live in the same habitat and compete for food. The first group is larger and uses **asexual reproduction**; the second reproduces sexually. What could happen to cause the second group to outnumber the first?

5.4 ASSESSMENT

1. Mitosis is carried out only in eukaryotes; it involves the division of DNA in the nucleus by way of spindle fibers to ensure that both daughter cells receive a full set of chromosomes. Organisms that undergo binary fission do not have a nucleus; they tend to have a single, circular chromosome, so division of the DNA is simpler.
2. The flatworm can reproduce asexually by fragmentation.
3. Sexual reproduction provides greater genetic diversity and adaptability; asexual reproduction allows for rapid population growth under certain conditions without a mate.
4. Yeast in the untreated dish will be growing and budding; yeast in the treated dish will be unable to bud.
5. Change in environmental conditions could severely limit the growth of the first population. The second population would be more likely to have individuals that could adapt to the change. These individuals would be able to reproduce successfully in the new conditions and increase the population.

5.5 Multicellular Life

KEY CONCEPT Cells work together to carry out complex functions.

MAIN IDEAS
- Multicellular organisms depend on interactions among different cell types.
- Specialized cells perform specific functions.
- Stem cells can develop into different cell types.

VOCABULARY
tissue, p. 151
organ, p. 151
organ system, p. 151
cell differentiation, p. 152
stem cell, p. 153

Review
homeostasis

INDIANA STANDARDS

B.6.2 Understand that most cells of a multicellular organism contain the same genes, but develop from a single cell (e.g., a fertilized egg) in different ways due to differential gene expression.

Connect Each of us enters this world as a screaming infant. At first, the ability to eat solid foods or take a step draws forth great praise. These general skills rapidly lose their wonder, however, and by the time you reach the age of 18, everyone wants to know what you plan to do with yourself. Will you build houses or design clothing or treat patients? What will your specialty be? Cells, too, undergo specialization to carry out the complex functions required by the body.

MAIN IDEA

Multicellular organisms depend on interactions among different cell types.

Within multicellular organisms, cells communicate and work together in groups that form increasingly larger, more complex structures. This arrangement progresses from cells to tissues to organs to organ systems, as shown in **FIGURE 5.16**. **Tissues** are groups of cells that work together to perform a similar function. Groups of tissues that work together to perform a specific function or related functions are called **organs.** For instance, plants have photosynthetic tissues made of chlorophyll-containing cells. Conductive tissues transport sugars, water, and minerals to and from other parts of the plant. Protective tissues help prevent water loss. Together, these and other tissues form a leaf, the plant's food-producing organ.

Organs that carry out similar functions are further grouped into **organ systems.** In plants, the shoot system is above the ground. It includes stems that support the plant, leaves that capture radiant energy, and flowers that aid reproduction. Beneath the ground, the root system has different types of roots and root hairs that anchor the plant and absorb water and minerals.

As organ systems work together, they help an organism maintain homeostasis. For example, plants need to maintain a certain level of water within their cells, or they will wilt and die. They absorb water through their roots and expel it as water vapor through openings in their leaves called stomata. Stomata are controlled by special cells called guard cells, which close the stomata when a plant's water intake cannot keep up with its water loss.

***Connecting* CONCEPTS**

Homeostasis As you learned in **Chapter 1**, homeostasis is the maintenance of a stable internal environment. Both an organism's physiology and its behavior help it achieve homeostasis.

A Apply **Suppose your family goes out of town and forgets to ask your neighbor to water the plants. Do you think the plants' stomata will be open or closed? Explain.**

Differentiated Instruction

BELOW LEVEL

Have students use an outline to organize their notes for this section. Suggest they include definitions of key vocabulary with their outlines. This should help them see the relationship between the vocabulary in each subsection.

Biology Toolkit, Outline, p. C25

Plan and Prepare

Objectives

- Describe the specialization in multicellular organisms.
- Identify different types of stem cells.

Section Resources

Unit Resource Book Study Guide pp. 81–82 Power Notes p. 83 Reinforcement p. 84
Interactive Reader Chapter 5 **Spanish Study Guide** pp. 51–52
Biology Toolkit pp. C13, C18, C25, C38, D9
Technology Power Presentation 5.5 Media Gallery DVD Online Quiz 5.5

Activate Prior Knowledge Have students look at one of their hands. **Ask**

- What are some of the different types of cells in your hand? those making up skin, hair, fingernails, muscle, bone, blood, nerves
- Are the cells in the trunk of your body any different? similar types of cells, but in addition, many more associated with internal organs

Discuss differentiation as how cells are different and how they are allocated.

Teach

Vocabulary

Academic Vocabulary Tell students that there are two views of multicellular organisms:

anatomy, the study of the bodily structures of an organism or its parts

physiology, the study of the functions of organisms or any of its parts

Answers

A Apply Because the plants are not receiving any water, they will need to conserve the water that they have. The stomata will most likely be closed.

▼ Teach *continued*

ONLINE BIOLOGY Go to the chapter Resource Center at **ClassZone.com** for additional resources and information on levels of organization.

Answers

A Apply Roots branch into smaller and smaller structures that increase the surface area, thereby allowing increased absorption of water and nutrients and better anchoring of the plant.

Science Trivia

- A human has about 200 different types of cells.
- At any one time, a human cell might be expressing only 20 percent of its genes.

Vocabulary

apical The words *apical* and *apex* share the same root, and refer to the tip or high point.

basal The words *basal* and *base* share the same root, and refer to the bottom.

migrate *Migrate* means "to change location periodically," which suggests a lack of permanence. For most animals cells, this applies only up to the point when differentiation occurs.

FIGURE 5.16 Levels of Organization

Cells work together in groups that form larger, specialized structures.

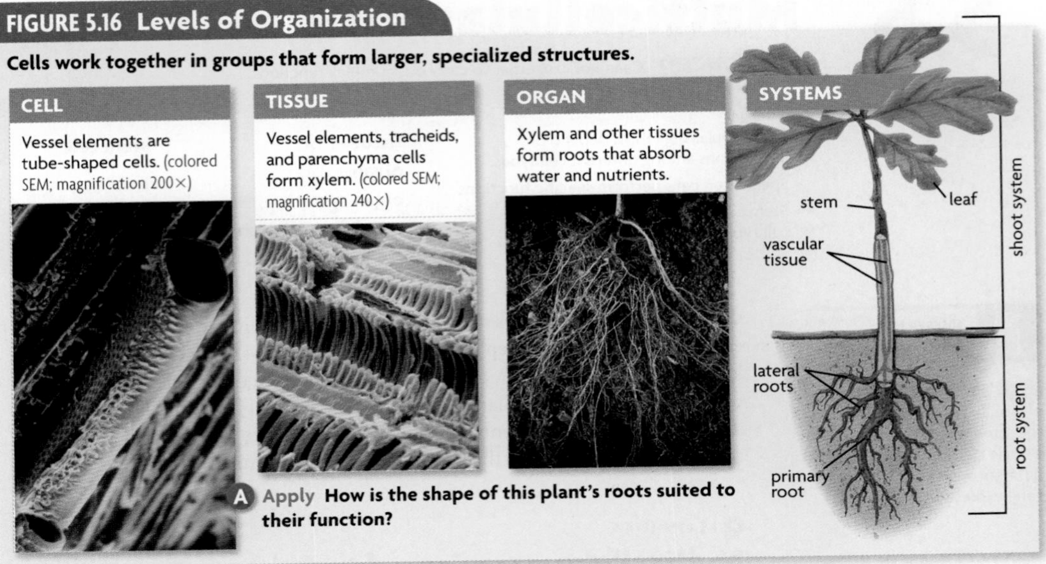

CELL
Vessel elements are tube-shaped cells. (colored SEM; magnification 200×)
TISSUE
Vessel elements, tracheids, and parenchyma cells form xylem. (colored SEM; magnification 240×)
ORGAN
Xylem and other tissues form roots that absorb water and nutrients.
SYSTEMS
stem
leaf
vascular tissue
lateral roots
primary root
shoot system
root system

A Apply How is the shape of this plant's roots suited to their function?

MAIN IDEA

Specialized cells perform specific functions.

Connecting **CONCEPTS**

Gametogenesis As you will learn in **Chapter 6**, the egg is stocked with organelles and molecules necessary for an embryo to grow. Many of these molecules are not evenly distributed throughout the cell; they form gradients.

It is easy to see that a skin cell can divide to make a new skin cell, or that a single bacterium can generate another bacterium. But how does a complex organism like you develop? Your body began as a single fertilized egg. If the egg simply divided to make lots of identical cells, it would not form a baby. To form the intricate structures that make up your body and the bodies of countless organisms around you, cells must specialize.

Cell differentiation is the process by which unspecialized cells develop into their mature forms and functions. While almost every cell in your body has a full set of DNA, each type of cell uses only the specific genes it needs to carry out its function. That is, a cell differentiates among the genes and uses only certain ones. You can think of your DNA as a cookbook. When you want to make a specific dish, you select that recipe and carry out its instructions. If you need to make a dessert, you might bake turtle brownies. If you need to make a main course, you might roast apple-stuffed pork chops or fix a hearty lentil stew. The dishes are very different, but they all come from the same cookbook.

A cell's location within the embryo helps determine how it will differentiate. In plant cells, the first division of a fertilized egg is unequal, or asymmetric, and produces two cells—the apical cell and the basal cell. The apical cell forms most of the embryo, including the growth point for stems and leaves. The major role of the basal cell is to provide nutrients to the embryo; it also creates the growth point for the roots. Plant cells cannot easily migrate because of the cell wall, but they adapt to changing conditions and continue to develop throughout their lifetime. As the plant grows, new cells continue to

Differentiated Instruction

ENGLISH LEARNERS

Point out the analogy on page 152 comparing DNA to a cookbook. Model for students how to make the associations between the different elements of this analogy:

DNA = cookbook

different genes = different ingredients

differentiated cells = different recipes

The analogy is based on the idea that both DNA and a cookbook represent sets of instructions contained in a single place.

Biology Toolkit, Analogies, p. D9

differentiate based on their location. For example, cells on the outer layer of a leaf may become epidermal cells that secrete a waxy substance that helps prevent water loss. Cells on the lower leaf surface may become guard cells that control the exchange of water, air, and carbon dioxide.

In animals, an egg undergoes many rapid divisions after it is fertilized. The resulting cells can migrate to a specific area, and the cells quickly begin to differentiate. The early animal embryo generally takes the shape of a hollow ball. As the embryo develops, part of the ball folds inward, forming an inner layer and creating an opening in the outer cell layer. A middle layer of cells then forms between the other two.

FIGURE 5.17 Cell Differentiation

Cell differentiation in the developing animal embryo is based on location.

Outer Skin cells help prevent infection and dehydration. (colored SEM; magnification 500×)

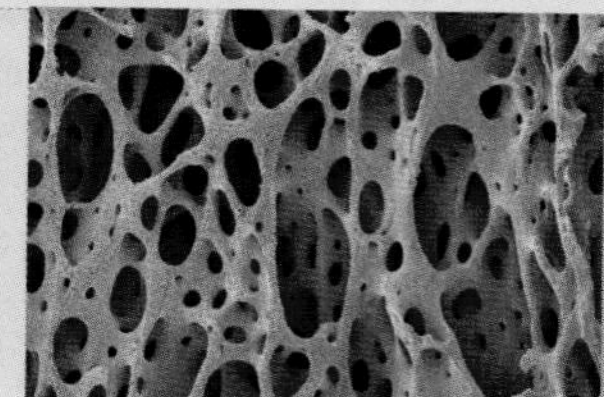

Middle Bone cells form a hard matrix (shown) that supports and protects organs. (colored SEM; magnification 15×)

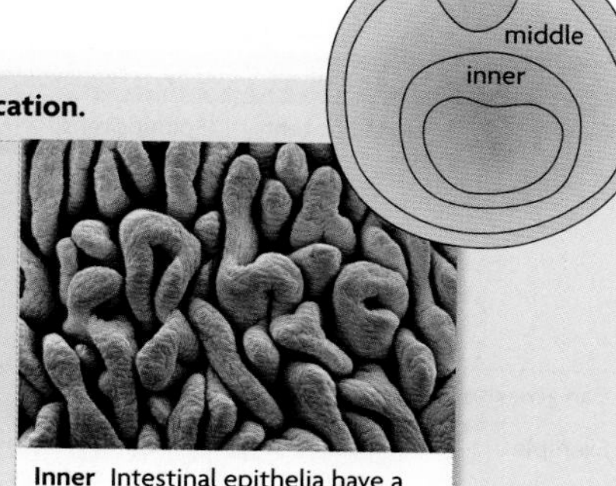

Inner Intestinal epithelia have a large surface area that increases absorption. (colored SEM; magnification 25×)

As shown in **FIGURE 5.17**, in vertebrates, the outer cell layer differentiates to form the outer layer of skin and elements of the nervous system such as the brain and spinal cord. The middle cell layer forms bones, muscles, kidneys, and the inner layer of skin. The inner cell layer forms internal organs such as the pancreas, lungs, and digestive system lining.

A Analyze **Why is regulation of the differentiation process during the early stages of development so critical?**

MAIN IDEA

Stem cells can develop into different cell types.

Stem cells are a unique type of body cell that have the ability to (1) divide and renew themselves for long periods of time, (2) remain undifferentiated in form, and (3) develop into a variety of specialized cell types. When a stem cell divides, it forms either two stem cells or one stem cell and one specialized cell.

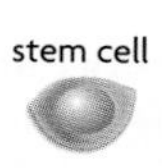

TEACH FROM VISUALS

FIGURE 5.17 Have students find the three layers in the cross-sectional diagram of the animal embryo. **Ask,** What is the shape of the embryo that this cross section represents? a hollow ball

Point out the embryo's outer layer of cells. Have students locate the photograph of cells that came from this layer. **Ask**

- What other type of cell differentiates in the outer layer? nerve cell
- What forms in the middle layer? bones, muscles, kidneys, inner layer of skin
- What forms in the inner layer? pancreas, lungs, digestive system lining

Integrating Embryology

Three processes affect the embryonic development of seed plants and animals. Embryonic development involves cell division, cell differentiation, and **morphogenesis.** Morphogenesis is the process by which cells are organized into tissues and organs that give an organism its shape, determining which end of a plant turns into the shoot system and which end of an animal turns into the head.

In humans, disruption of the process can lead to conditions such as **cleft palate** or **cleft lip.** This occurs during weeks 10–12 of embryonic development if the bones that make up the palate fail to join properly.

Answers

A Analyze The early stages of differentiation lead to the development of progressively more specialized tissues and organs. Distribution of cell differentiation in the early stages could cause severe abnormalities in an organism's body structure.

PRE-AP

Tell students that during development of a human embryo, a portion of the outer layer of cells pushes in to the center to form the endoderm, an inner layer of cells surrounding an inner cavity. This creates a middle layer of cells, the mesoderm, surrounded by the remaining outer layer of cells, the ectoderm. Have students speculate on the fate of each layer's cells and which structures they likely form, based on their location. Have students consider the fate of the central cavity.

Biology Toolkit, Think-Pair-Share, p. C13

BELOW LEVEL

Using the text on pages 151–153, have students draw a sequence diagram that follows the development of an embryo, starting with the fertilized egg. Have students include the highlighted vocabulary of the first two subsections. Go over the diagrams to help students clarify the sequence.

Biology Toolkit, Sequence Diagram, p. C38

▼ Teach *continued*

TEACH FROM VISUALS

FIGURE 5.18 Suggest students view the figure as a timeline. Describe the change from pluripotent to multipotent as a progression. Suggest students think of pluripotent as capable of generating cells of all tissue types and multipotent as capable of generating all cells of a single tissue type.

History of Science

The term *stem cell* was coined by biologist **Gail Martin** in 1981 when she and fellow scientists working at the University of California at San Francisco were able to establish a culture of pluripotent cells from a mouse embryo. She used the term because these are the cells that all other cells "stem" from. In 1988, at the University of Wisconsin-Madison, four embryonic stem cell lines from a species of hamster were established. In 1995, researchers at the university's primate research center established the first embryonic stem cell line from a primate species, the rhesus monkey. Then in 1998, **James Thomson** and his colleagues developed five lines of human embryonic stem cells.

During this time, ethical issues associated with the use of human embryonic stem cells caused President George H. W. Bush to place a ban on using federal funds for such research. President Clinton reversed the ban. Then President George W. Bush reestablished it.

For more on stem cell research, see the Unit 2 BioZine on page 162.

Take It Further

Adult stem cells are necessary for survival. These stem cells replace specialized cells in the body that cannot reproduce themselves. Erythrocytes, leukocytes, platelets, and cells lining the intestines all need frequent replacement. For example, an erythrocyte, or red blood cell, lives only about three or four months. **Ask,** What could cause an immediate need for adult stem cells to make red blood cells? bleeding, blood donation white blood cells? an infection or wound

Stem Cell Classification

Stem cells can be categorized by their ability, or potential, to develop into the differentiated cell types of different tissues, as shown in **FIGURE 5.18.** In general, the more differentiated a stem cell already is, the fewer the types of cells it can form.

- Totipotent stem cells can grow into any other cell type. Only a fertilized egg and the cells produced by the first few divisions of an embryo are totipotent.
- Pluripotent stem cells can grow into any cell type except for totipotent stem cells.
- Multipotent stem cells can only grow into cells of a closely related cell family.

VOCABULARY

Potent comes from a Latin word meaning "to be able." The addition of prefixes defines the level of power or ability.
toti- = all
pluri- = more, several
multi- = many

FIGURE 5.18 STEM CELL CLASSIFICATION

Class	totipotent	pluripotent	multipotent
Type of cell	fertilized egg	embryonic stem cell (inner cell mass)	adult stem cell (example from blood)
Can give rise to	all cells	almost any cell	closely related cells
Example	new organism	neurons, skin, muscle, kidney, cartilage, bone, liver, pancreas	red blood cells, platelets, white blood cells

Stem cells are also classified by their origin, as either adult or embryonic. Adult stem cells have been studied for decades, but the ability to grow human embryonic stem cells was not developed until 1998. Since that time, embryonic stem cells have attracted great attention because of their potential to form almost any cell type. Both adult and embryonic stem cells offer unique advantages and challenges to researchers.

Adult Stem Cells

Adult stem cells are partially undifferentiated cells located among the specialized cells of many organs and tissues. They are found all over the body, in the brain, liver, bone marrow, skeletal muscle, dental pulp, and even fat. These stem cells are also found in children and in umbilical cord blood, so the term *somatic stem cell* is more accurate although less frequently used.

A major advantage of adult stem cells is that they can be taken from a patient, grown in culture, and put back into the patient. Thus, the risk of transplant rejection by a patient's immune system is very low. This method also avoids many ethical issues associated with using embryonic stem cells.

Adult stem cells currently pose many disadvantages as well. They are few in number, difficult to isolate, and sometimes tricky to grow. They may also contain more DNA abnormalities than do embryonic stem cells. For years, much evidence suggested that adult stem cells were multipotent. This would mean that a stem cell from fat would produce only fat cells, never muscle cells. Newer data suggest otherwise. Adult stem cells treated with the right combination of molecules may give rise to a completely different type of tissue. This process, called transdifferentiation, remains an active area of research.

Embryonic Stem Cells

Most embryonic stem cells come from donated embryos grown in a clinic. These embryos are the result of in vitro fertilization, a process by which eggs are fertilized outside a woman's body. The stem cells are taken from a cluster of undifferentiated cells in the three-to-five-day-old embryo.

Differentiated Instruction

ENGLISH LEARNERS

To test students' understanding, question students about cell differentiation and how it relates to different types of stem cells. Have students react to the statements as being true or false using thumbs-up/thumbs-down signals. Or use cards to have students provide their own responses.

Biology Toolkit, Card Responses, p. C18

These cells, called the inner cell mass, do not have the characteristics of any specific cell type. Because they are pluripotent, they can form any of the 200 cell types of the body. They can also be grown indefinitely in culture. These qualities have given many people hope that many now devastating diseases will be treatable or even curable in the future.

Embryonic stem cells also have a downside. If these cells are used in treatment, a patient's body might reject them as foreign material. The stem cells could potentially grow unchecked in a patient's body and form a tumor. The use of embryonic stem cells also raises many ethical questions. The most common method of getting embryonic stem cells, **FIGURE 5.19**, currently involves destruction of the embryo, which some people consider ethically unacceptable.

FIGURE 5.19 HARVESTING EMBRYONIC STEM CELLS

First, an egg is fertilized by a sperm cell in a petri dish. The egg divides, forming an inner cell mass. These cells are then removed and grown with nutrients. Scientists try to control how the cells specialize by adding or removing certain molecules.

Research and Treatment Hope

Stem cells have long been used to treat patients with leukemia and lymphoma, and they offer hope for treating many other diseases as well. For instance, some patients might be cured of diabetes if nonworking cells in the pancreas were replaced with healthy, growing cells. Similarly, damaged organs, such as the heart, might be strengthened by an injection of healthy cells. Research, such as the testing of new drugs, might also benefit. The current research system requires a lot of time and money. Many of the most innovative drugs have little chance of reaching the patient. Potentially, these new compounds could be tested on large numbers of specific cell types grown from stem cells.

A Compare and Contrast List treatment benefits and risks of both types of stem cells.

5.5 ASSESSMENT

ONLINE QUIZ ClassZone.com

B.6.2

REVIEWING MAIN IDEAS

1. How does communication between cells help maintain homeostasis?
2. Explain why **cell differentiation** is an important part of the development of a multicellular organism.
3. What are the defining characteristics of **stem cells**?

CRITICAL THINKING

4. **Compare** Describe how **tissues, organs,** and **organ systems** are similar.
5. **Evaluate** Explain which factor you think is most important in deciding whether stem-cell research should be legal and government-funded.

Connecting CONCEPTS

6. **Animal Behavior** Choose an animal and give an example of how its behavior reflects its need to maintain homeostasis.

5.5 ASSESSMENT

1. Different cells are needed for different functions, and their activities need to be coordinated to maintain the body's internal environment.
2. needed for different functions because one kind of cell cannot perform all the activities required for life
3. Stem cells divide continually, while remaining undifferentiated for long periods of time; yet they can develop into specialized cell types.
4. Tissues are groups of specialized cells that make up organs, and organs work together in organ systems.
5. Answers will vary.
6. *Sample Answer:* Bears store large amounts of energy in fat tissue during warm months, then sleep through much of the winter, conserving energy when food is scarce.

Integrating Medical Science

Although embryonic stem cell research is still in experimental stages, adult stem cells are currently used for some cancer treatments. An **autologous stem cell transplant** is used to treat lymphomas and some other cancers. A person's own stem cells are harvested from bone marrow or blood and frozen and returned to the body after chemotherapy or radiation treatment. An **allogeneic stem cell transplant** is used to treat leukemias and other bone marrow disorders, using stem cells from a donor. In both types of transplants, the stem cells are added to the person's blood and move to the bone marrow, where they begin making blood cells.

Answers

A Compare and Contrast Adult stem cells taken from a patient's body are less likely to be rejected. However, they can be difficult to isolate and grow, and have limited potential as far as what tissue can develop. Embryonic stem cells can develop into almost any cell type. However, they may be rejected by a patient's body.

Assess and Reteach ▼

Assess Use the Online Quiz or Section Quiz (*Assessment Book,* p. 91).

Reteach Have pairs of students quiz each other on key material in this section. Have them write down their questions and answers. Then collect the questions and review as a class.

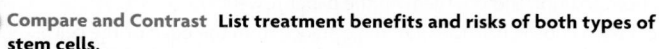

OPTIONS FOR INQUIRY

INVESTIGATION

Time 45 minutes	TEACHER TESTED
Teacher Preparation	
Student Difficulty	
Lab Binder Cells, pp. 33–34	

Purpose Model the effect of cell surface area-to-volume ratio on diffusion.

Overview Students use differently sized phenolphthalein agar cubes soaked in a sodium hydroxide solution to observe diffusion time. They will

- measure and calculate the surface area-to-volume ratio of each cube
- measure how far the sodium hydroxide diffused into each cube

LAB PREPARATION

- Prepare the phenolphthalein agar by mixing 20 g of agar to 1 L of distilled water. Heat to a boil, stir frequently until clear. Cool agar, add a few drops of 1% phenolphthalein solution, and stir. Agar should not turn pink.
- Prepare NaOH solution. Mix 4 g of NaOH to 100 mL of distilled H_2O.

LAB MANAGEMENT

Safety NaOH solution is corrosive; have students handle with care and wash their hands after the investigation. Refer to Material Safety Data Sheets.

POST-LAB DISCUSSION

Explain that warm-blooded animals with a low surface area-to-volume ratio conserve more heat than do animals with a high surface area-to-volume ratio. Animal species living in cold climates have smaller extremities than related species living in warmer climates. Discuss how the results of students' investigations support the value of these adaptations.

Use these inquiry-based labs and online activities to deepen your understanding of cell growth and development.

NOS.6 Use analogies and models (mathematical and physical) to simplify and represent systems that are difficult to understand or directly experience due to their size, time scale, or complexity, and recognize the limitations of analogies and models.

INVESTIGATION

Modeling Cell Surface Area–to–Volume Ratio

A cell's surface area–to–volume ratio affects the amount of material that can diffuse across the membrane and throughout the cell. You will make cell models to determine how this ratio changes as cell size increases.

SKILLS Modeling, Inferring

PROBLEM Which cell has the greatest surface area–to–volume ratio?

MATERIALS

- plastic knife
- phenolphthalein agar
- metric ruler
- 250-mL beaker
- 100-mL graduated cylinder
- 100 mL sodium hydroxide solution
- timer
- plastic spoon
- paper towel

PROCEDURE

1. Make three model cells by using the knife to cut three cubes from the phenolphthalein agar. Cell A should be 3 cm on each side, cell B should be 2 cm on each side, and cell C should be 1 cm on each side. Use the ruler to make exact measurements.
2. Calculate the area of one side of each cell. Calculate the total surface area of each cell. Record your data in Table 1. (**Hint:** Multiply the area of one side by the number of sides.)
3. Calculate the volume of each cell. Record your data in the table. (**Hint:** Multiply the length by the width by the height of the cube.)
4. Calculate the ratio of surface area to volume for each cell. For example, for cell A, the ratio would be 54 cm^2:27 cm^3 = 2:1 = 2. Record your data.
5. Put the model cells in the beaker. Carefully cover them with sodium hydroxide solution, which turns the agar pink. Soak the cells in solution for four minutes. Use a spoon to turn the cells repeatedly throughout that time.
6. Remove the cells from solution and dry them on the paper towel.
7. Use the knife to cut each cube in half. Measure the distance from the edge of the cell to the inner edge of the pink line. This shows how far the sodium hydroxide diffused.

TABLE 1. CALCULATIONS OF CELL SIZE

Cell	Area of One Side (cm^2)	Total Surface Area (cm^2)	Volume of Cell (cm^3)	Surface Area–to–Volume Ratio
A				
B				
C				

ANALYZE AND CONCLUDE

1. **Analyze** How does the surface area–to–volume ratio change as cell size increases? How might this affect the diffusion of materials throughout a cell?
2. **Apply** Identify which cell turned pink in the greatest proportion, and explain how this relates to cell size.
3. **Apply** How does a cell's surface area–to–volume ratio affect its ability to stay alive?

Answers

Expected Results

Sodium hydroxide should diffuse farther with increasing surface area-to-volume ratio. The surface area-to-volume ratio for each cell is as follows:

Cell A = 54:27 = 2:1 = 2
Cell B = 24:8 = 3:1 = 3
Cell C = 6:1 = 6

Analyze and Conclude

1. The surface area-to-volume ratio decreases as cell size increases. The size of the cell membrane is not increasing as much as the volume of the cell. Functions that rely on material diffusing in or out will be adversely affected as cell size increases.
2. Diffusion and osmosis are more efficient in cell C, the smallest cell, with the largest surface area-to-volume ratio.
3. The transport of all materials occurs across the membrane. The surface area of the cell membrane must be large enough for enough materials to enter the cell and waste materials to exit the cell to maintain life.

INVESTIGATION

Apoptosis

In this lab, you will research the role of apoptosis in a developmental process.

SKILL Communicating

PROBLEM What role does apoptosis play as organisms develop?

RESEARCH

1. Use the Internet to research one of the following processes:
   - the development of neural connections in the human brain
   - the development and maintenance of the human immune system
   - the metamorphosis of a tadpole into an adult frog
2. Explain the role of apoptosis in your topic in a typed, one-page summary. In your answer, clearly identify the state of the organism before the apoptotic changes, the state of the organism following apoptosis, and what would be the result if apoptosis failed to occur.

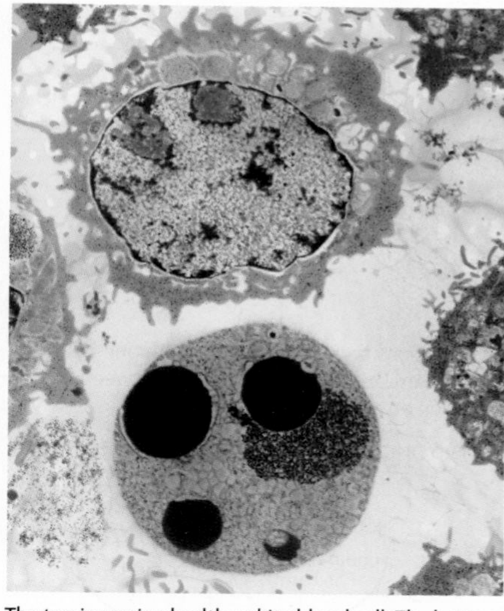

The top image is a healthy white blood cell. The bottom image shows an apoptotic white blood cell with a darkened nucleus. (colored TEM; magnification 4,500×)

Online BIOLOGY CLASSZONE.COM

VIRTUAL LAB
Investigating Bacterial Growth
Not all bacteria thrive in the same environmental conditions. In this interactive lab, you will determine which strains of bacteria grow in an environment with oxygen and which strains grow without oxygen.

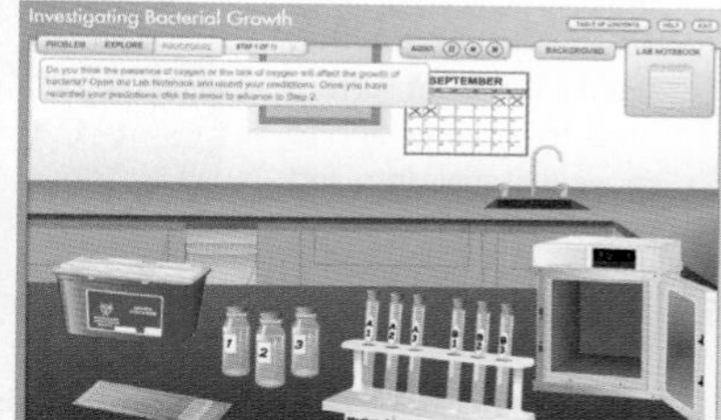

ANIMATED BIOLOGY
Mitosis Stage Matching Game
How well can you recognize the stages of mitosis? Test your skills by categorizing images showing different phases of mitosis.

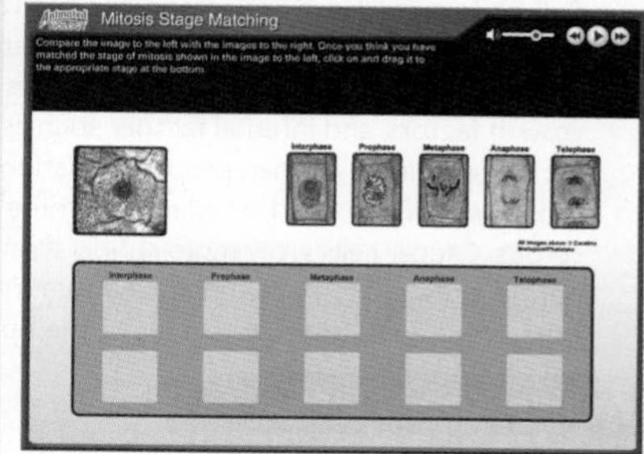

WEBQUEST
Cancer occurs when the cell cycle breaks down. In this WebQuest, you will learn about the most common cancer in the United States—skin cancer. Explore its causes, how cells become cancerous, and why prevention is truly the best medicine.

Answers

1–2. • Brain development: brain cells divide, migrate to new locations, make connections. Apoptosis rids the brain of extra neurons and glial cells. Failure might result in abnormal development.
- Immune system: B cells and T cells are cells that recognize and attack foreign invaders. B cells and T cells proliferate in response to infection. Once the job is finished, extra B cells and T cells are killed by apoptosis. Only a relatively small number of the cells remain in case of another infection.
- Tadpole: As the aquatic tadpole develops into terrestrial adult form, cells in the tail die. Cells in the undifferentiated gut die and are replaced by specialized cells that form tissues and organs, such as lung and limbs.

Online Biology ▼

VIRTUAL LAB Students test the effects of two independent variables (oxygen and temperature) on bacterial growth. Use this lab to reinforce the concepts in **Section 5.4.**

ANIMATED BIOLOGY Students will test their ability to recognize the stages of mitosis by categorizing images showing different phases of mitosis. Use this interactive animation to reinforce the concepts of **Section 5.2.**

WEBQUEST The WebQuest will take one full class period. Students complete the activity online and then will need access to a printer to print their answers. Sample answers, teacher notes, and alternative assessment ideas are available on **ClassZone.com.** Use with **Section 5.3.**

INVESTIGATION TEACHER TESTED ✓

Time	45 minutes
Teacher Preparation	(1 flask)
Student Difficulty	(2 flasks)
Lab Binder	Cells, p. 35

POST-LAB DISCUSSION

Discuss students' summaries for the three processes. Have students summarize the role that apoptosis plays as organisms develop.

CHAPTER REVIEW

Interactive Review

Encourage students to go to **ClassZone.com** for a detailed review of each section, including visuals and vocabulary practice.

Unit Resource Book, Vocabulary Practice, pp. 91–94

ITEM CORRELATIONS	
Standard	**Items**
B.6.1	1-7, 15, 16, 27, 34
B.6.3	21

CHAPTER 5

Interactive Review @ CLASSZONE.COM

KEY CONCEPTS | Vocabulary Games | Concept Maps | Animated Biology | Online Quiz

5.1 The Cell Cycle

Cells have distinct phases of growth, reproduction, and normal functions. The cell cycle has four main stages: G_1, S, G_2, and M. The length of the cell cycle can vary, resulting in different rates of cell division. This variability is based on the body's need for different cell types. Cells also divide because they need a sufficient surface area–to–volume ratio to move materials into and out of the cell.

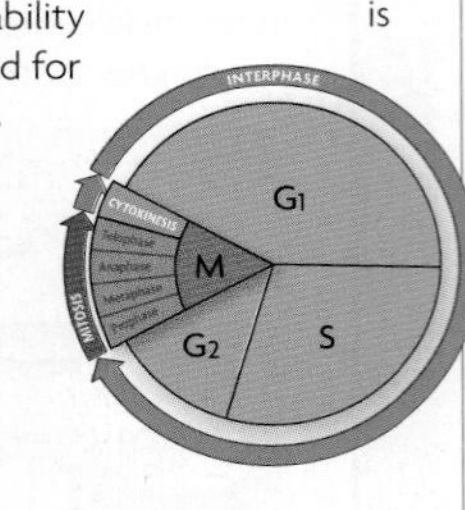

5.2 Mitosis and Cytokinesis

Cells divide during mitosis and cytokinesis. Mitosis divides the nucleus into two genetically identical nuclei in a four-phase process: prophase, metaphase, anaphase, telophase. In prophase, the duplicated chromosomes condense tightly. Cytokinesis actually divides the cell cytoplasm.

5.3 Regulation of the Cell Cycle

Cell cycle regulation is necessary for healthy growth. Cell growth and division are regulated by both external factors, such as hormones and growth factors, and internal factors, such as cyclins and kinases. When proper regulation of cell growth is disrupted, a cell may become cancerous. Cancer cells grow more rapidly than do normal cells and form clumps called tumors that may metastasize to other regions of the body.

5.4 Asexual Reproduction

Many organisms reproduce by cell division. Most prokaryotes reproduce through a process called binary fission, in which a cell divides into two approximately equal parts. Some eukaryotes reproduce through mitosis. The offspring that result from asexual reproduction are genetically identical to the parent organism, except when mutations occur. Whether being identical is an advantage or a disadvantage depends on the environment.

5.5 Multicellular Life

Cells work together to carry out complex functions. Within multicellular organisms, cells form tissues, tissues form organs, and organs form organ systems. The cells differentiate to perform specific functions. Much of this specialization is determined by a cell's location within the developing embryo. Stem cells are a special type of cell that continue to divide and renew themselves for long periods of time.

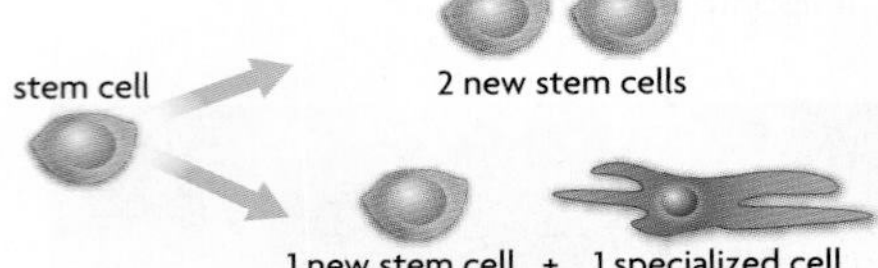

Synthesize Your Notes

Concept Map Use a concept map like the one below to summarize what you know about mitosis.

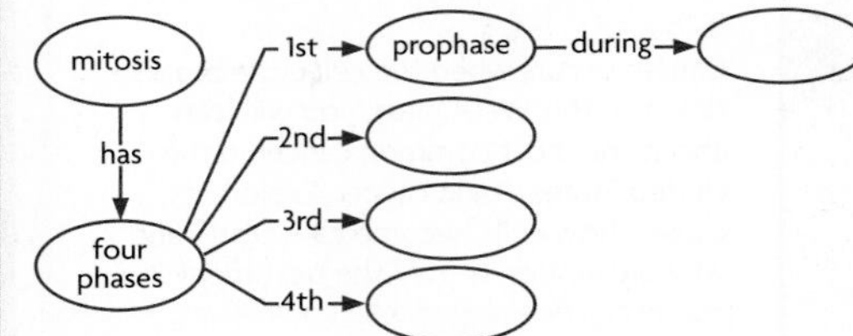

Venn Diagram Draw a Venn diagram like the one below to summarize the similarities and differences between embryonic and adult stem cells.

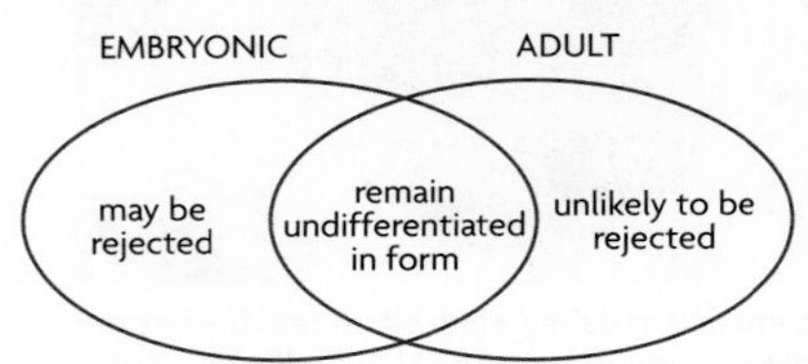

Reviewing Vocabulary

1. sketch of a cell with nucleus starting to disintegrate and chromosomes in condensed, duplicated form
2. sketch of a cell with chromosomes lined up in the middle with one chromatid facing each pole
3. sketch of a cell with chromatid pairs pulled apart by spindle fibers and being pulled toward the poles
4. sketch of a cell forming into two, each with a nucleus forming and with single chromosomes
5. sketch of two separate identical cells, each with intact nucleus
6. sketch of central point in a condensed, duplicated chromosome where sister chromatids are joined
7. sketch of a chromosome with end regions shaded or distinguished and labeled
8. Prophase is the first, and therefore earliest, stage of mitosis, before chromosomes line up at the middle of the cell.
9. Telophase is the last, and therefore ending, phase of mitosis. The telomere is the region of DNA located at each end of a chromosome.
10. The chromosomes themselves appear to be threadlike when viewed through a microscope. Some students may think the spindle fibers look like threads.

Chapter Assessment

Chapter Vocabulary

5.1 cell cycle, p. 134
mitosis, p. 135
cytokinesis, p. 135

5.2 chromosome, p. 138
histone, p. 139
chromatin, p. 139
chromatid, p. 139
centromere, p. 139
telomere, p. 139
prophase, p. 140
metaphase, p. 140
anaphase, p. 140
telophase, p. 140

5.3 growth factor, p. 144
apoptosis, p. 145
cancer, p. 146
benign, p. 146
malignant, p. 146
metastasize, p. 146
carcinogen, p. 146

5.4 asexual reproduction, p. 148
binary fission, p. 148

5.5 tissue, p. 151
organ, p. 151
organ system, p. 151
cell differentiation, p. 152
stem cell, p. 153

Reviewing Vocabulary

Visualize Vocabulary

For each term below, draw a simple picture that represents the meaning of the word. Here is an example for *mitosis.* **B.6.1**

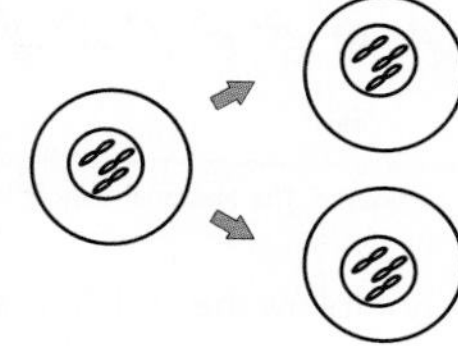

1. prophase
2. metaphase
3. anaphase
4. telophase
5. cytokinesis
6. centromere
7. telomere

Word Origins

8. The prefix *pro-* means "earlier than" or "prior to." Explain how this meaning relates to the word *prophase.*
9. The prefix *telo-* means "distant, far, or end." How does this meaning relate to the words *telophase* and *telomere*?
10. The term *mitosis* comes from the Greek root *mitos,* which means "thread." How does this meaning relate to the process of mitosis?

Reviewing MAIN IDEAS

11. The cell cycle has four main stages—G_1, S, G_2, and M. What occurs in the cell during each stage?
12. Compare the rates of cell division occurring in your neurons and your hair follicles.
13. What is the relationship between a cell's surface area and its volume?
14. You know that a chromosome is a very long, continuous strand of DNA. How do proteins help condense chromosomes?
15. Describe what happens in each main phase of mitosis—prophase, metaphase, anaphase, and telophase. **B.6.1**
16. How does the process of cytokinesis differ from the process of mitosis? **B.6.1**
17. Increased levels of cyclin help trigger a cell to divide. Do you think a growth factor would increase or decrease cyclin levels? Explain.
18. Describe how uncontrolled cell division is dangerous in organisms.
19. List one similarity and one difference between binary fission and mitosis.
20. You pull a leaf from a plant and place it in a cup of water. After a week, roots start to grow from the leaf. What type of reproduction has occurred, and what role does mitosis play in it?
21. Briefly describe how cell differentiation occurs in the developing animal embryo. **B.6.3**
22. List three characteristics of all stem cells.

Reviewing Main Ideas

11. A cell grows and carries out its normal functions in G_1. During the S stage, DNA is copied. The cell continues to grow during G_2. During the four phases of mitosis, the cell's nucleus breaks down, the duplicated chromosomes line up at the cell's center, and then separate. The cell membrane starts to pinch together as the last part of mitosis, known as cytokinesis, brings about the division of one cell into two. Each of those cells return to interphase.
12. Cell division occurs much more rapidly in hair follicles than in neurons.
13. The larger a cell, the smaller is the surface area of cell membrane available to support a given volume of the cell's interior. Assuming a cell shaped like a cube or sphere, surface area increases by the power of 2 compared to an increase in volume by the power of 3.
14. DNA strands are wrapped around proteins called histones, which keep the strands from getting tangled. The tighter the coils, the more condensed the DNA becomes, which enables duplicated DNA to be separated and evenly distributed between two cells during mitosis.
15. Prophase: chromosomes condense, nuclear envelope starts to break down, spindle fibers form. Metaphase: spindle fibers align the chromosomes at the center of the cell. Anaphase: spindle fibers pull the sister chromatids apart and toward opposite sides of the cell. Telophase: chromosomes uncoil, spindle fibers break down, and the nuclear membrane re-forms.
16. Cytokinesis is the division of the cytoplasm, whereas mitosis is the division of the chromosomes. Cytokinesis occurs when the cell membrane closes in to form two new animals cells or when the cell wall closes in to form two new plant cells.
17. A growth factor would likely increase cyclin levels because cyclin helps stimulate the cell division cycle.
18. A body needs a certain number of specific types of cells to function properly and maintain a stable environment and homeostasis. Uncontrolled cell division throws off this balance. More cells means more energy and resources than might be available, possibly depriving other cells of what they need to function.
19. Both mitosis and binary fission are types of cell division that result in identical daughter cells. Binary fission occurs in prokaryotes, where no nucleus is present, and results in two new organisms. Mitosis requires breakdown of the nucleus. It is used for growth and repair in multicellular organisms.
20. It is vegetative reproduction, a form of asexual reproduction. The newly formed plant grows new roots and stems by mitosis.
21. Dividing cells in the developing embryo form into three layers, and cells in those layers develop into specific types of tissues and organs.
22. Stem cells have the ability to divide and renew themselves for long periods, remain undifferentiated in form for long periods, and have the capacity to develop into a variety of specialized cell types.

Critical Thinking

23. Regulatory proteins control cell division by acting as stop or go signals. They can delay cell division if external conditions are not favorable or if new cells are not needed, which reserves resources for other functioning cells. Regulatory proteins can promote cell division if conditions require it. They also ensure that DNA has been properly copied so that the new cells produced function properly.
24. More cells on the dark side of a plant will cause the plant to tilt toward the light. The sunlight itself might act as a trigger to cause dark-side cells to divide more quickly and light-side cells to divide more slowly.
25. This technique would allow faster growth of potatoes because the plants are not grown from seed, and there may be a greater yield. However, because it is an asexual form of reproduction, the entire crop is genetically identical. If the original potato plants are susceptible to a particular disease or pest, then the whole crop is at risk.
26. It provides a source of variation that may help them survive.
27. After the S phase, each pair would have doubled, so there would be 48 chromatids in the cell.
28. If DNA does not attach to the histones in the right way, then DNA might become tangled or damaged. This might prevent the DNA from being copied correctly or prevent the duplicated DNA from dividing equally between the two new cells during mitosis.

Critical Thinking

23. **Synthesize** How do regulatory proteins of the cell cycle help maintain homeostasis?
24. **Hypothesize** Plants often grow in the direction of a sunny window, yet plant cells cannot easily migrate due to their rigid cell walls. How do you think plants grow toward light?
25. **Analyze** A scientist wants to use asexually reproducing vegetables to increase crop yields. He plans to distribute budding potatoes and teach farmers how to separate them into new plants. What are some potential benefits and risks that could result from this situation?
26. **Analyze** The rates of DNA mutations in bacteria are known to increase when they are under stressed environmental conditions. Why do you think this is important for an organism that reproduces asexually?
27. **Apply** Suppose an organism usually has 24 chromosomes in its nucleus. How many chromatids would it have just after the S phase of the cell cycle? **B.6.1**
28. **Predict** If a mutation made histone proteins bind less tightly to DNA, how might the cell cycle be affected?

Interpreting Visuals

Use the picture of onion root cells shown below to answer the next three questions.

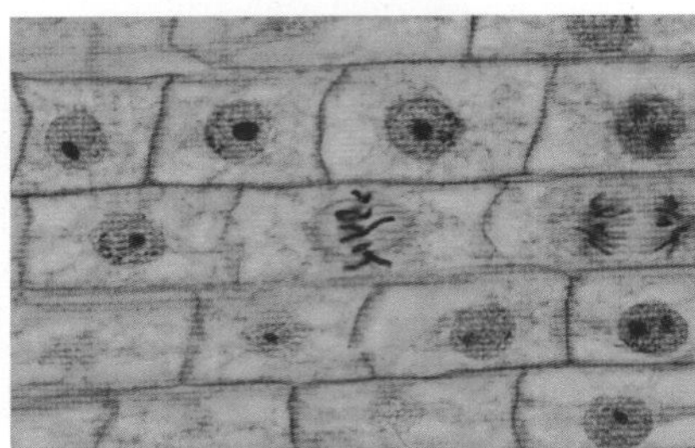

magnification 120×

29. **Apply** In what stage of the cell cycle are most of these cells? Explain.
30. **Apply** How can you visually distinguish between newly formed cells and older cells?
31. **Synthesize** If this onion were immersed in salt water, how would the cells undergoing mitosis be affected? (**Hint:** Think about the process of osmosis.)

Analyzing Data

The graph below shows the five-year survival rate, expressed as percentages, of patients diagnosed with cancer from 1985 through 1997. This data is for all types of invasive cancers and includes males and females of all races. Use the graph to answer the next two questions.

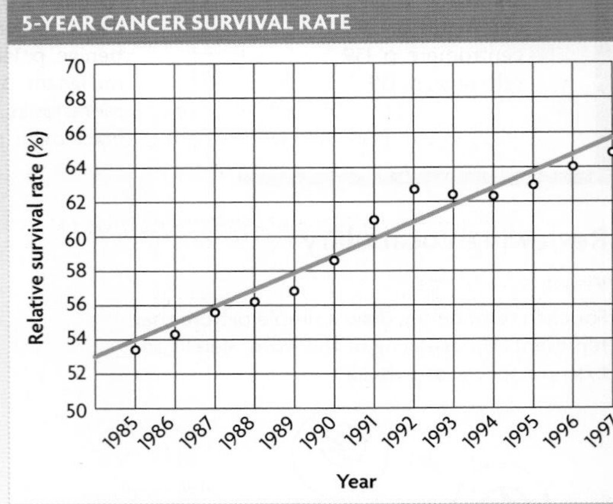

Source: The National Cancer Institute

32. **Analyze** Which points do not follow the best-fit line for the data?
33. **Interpret** What is the trend in the data of cancer survival during the span of time given?

Connecting CONCEPTS

34. **Write a Narrative** Imagine that you are a single chromosome about to undergo replication and mitosis. Describe what will happen to you from the S phase through mitosis. Be creative. Use humor and first-person point of view. Come up with sounds or perspectives that illustrate what is happening. Be sure to include all details of the process and related terms. **B.6.1**
35. **Design an Experiment** Cancer cells, such as those shown on page 133, are frequently grown in labs for research uses. Suppose you wanted to determine whether a certain substance was a carcinogen. Outline an experimental plan to describe what questions you would want to answer, what experiments you would perform, and what the different possible results would suggest.

Interpreting Visuals

29. Most of these cells appear to be in interphase, which is indicated by the presence of the nucleus. Cells spend most of their time in interphase.
30. The newly formed cells are smaller in volume, and the nucleus takes up most of the cytoplasm. Older cells have more cytoplasmic space to nuclear space.
31. If the cells were immersed in salt water, there would be a higher concentration of salt outside the cells than inside, causing the cells to lose water by the process of osmosis. Cells generally do not divide when in adverse conditions.

Analyzing Data

32. Points for years 1989, 1991, and 1992 are well off the line; to a lesser degree, so are years 1986, 1988, 1993, 1995, 1996, and 1997.
33. During the period shown, the number of people who survived cancer for at least five years increased by 15 percent overall.

INDIANA ISTEP+ Test Prep

B.6.1; B.6.2; B.6.3; NOS.1

Test Practice
For more test practice, go to ClassZone.com.

1 Scientists searching for new anticancer drugs treat a cell culture with a certain compound. Following treatment, they notice that the culture has stopped growing. Untreated cells from the same culture, however, have continued to grow. These results could indicate that the compound blocks the normal cell cycle. What else could have caused these results?

A The compound had degraded.
B The compound prevented cells from mutating.
C The compound killed the treated cells.
D The compound had no effect.

THINK THROUGH THE QUESTION

The untreated cells serve as a control in this experiment. Therefore, differences between the treated and untreated cells should be the result of the drug. If the drug has no effect, the two groups of cells should be the same.

2 After being scraped or a cut, the skin is able to heal. What biological process ***best*** accounts for the replacement of skin cells?

A mitosis
B meiosis
C asexual reproduction
D cementation

3

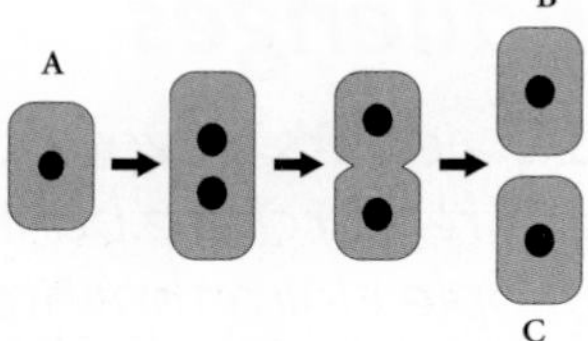

In this diagram, cell A is undergoing mitosis. If cell A has 6 chromosomes, how many chromosomes will the resulting cells B and C have?

A none
B 3 each
C 6 each
D 12 each

4 What is a main function of spindle fibers?

A to condense chromatin into chromosomes
B to separate chromosomes during mitosis
C to replicate the chromosomes before cell division
D to decondense chromosomes following mitosis

5

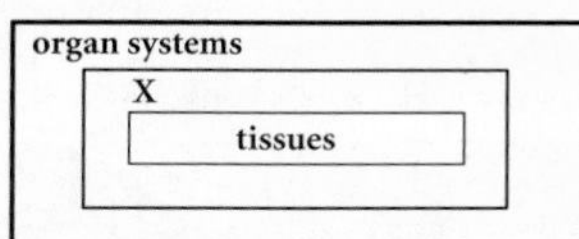

This figure represents some levels of structural and functional organization in multicellular organisms. Which term fits in the box marked "X"?

A cells
B organelles
C organs
D organisms

6 Stem cells can form many kinds of cells. In contrast, most body cells cannot form different types of cells. For example, skin cells can only make skin cells, and nerve cells only make nerve cells. Write a statement explaining why skin cells will never become nerve cells.

Standards-Based Assessment

1. C	4. B
2. A	5. C
3. C	6. See Below

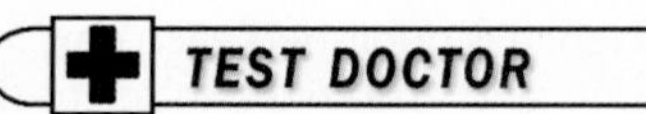

Question 2 Answer A is correct. Answer B is incorrect because meiosis helps form sex cells. Answer C is incorrect because asexual reproduction forms offspring from a single parent. Answer D is incorrect because cementation has nothing to do with the growth or division of cells.

Question 3 Answer C is correct. Answer A is incorrect because mitosis produces genetically identical daughter cells, so the chromosomes do not disappear. Answer B is incorrect because meiosis produces daughter cells with half the original number of chromosomes. Answer D is incorrect because although the chromosomes are doubled before mitosis begins, they are divided into two separate daughter cells during mitosis and cytokinesis.

Question 6 Skin and nerve cells have the same DNA, but each cell uses only part of the DNA message.

Connecting Concepts

34. Answer should describe DNA being duplicated creating a "twin," increased coiling as chromatin takes the form of a chromosome, being pulled to the center as nuclear membrane breaks down, being separated from twin and pulled away and finally separated as new cells form.
35. The point of the experiment would be to discover if the substance caused changes in an organism's DNA and affected the cell cycle. A test animal could be exposed to various levels of the material to see at what level, if any, changes occurred. Tumors would be an obvious sign of cancer; samples of tissues might also show signs of change. The test might show some organs and tissues were more likely to be affected. The DNA of the test animal could be compared to that of a normal animal to look for mutations—how many and to what genes.

ITEM CORRELATIONS

Standard	Items
B.6.1	2, 3, 4
B.6.2	6
B.6.3	5
NOS.1	1

UNIT
2

Introduce

Tell students that a lot of information about science is published each day: in newspapers and magazines, in scientific journals, and on the Internet. When reading science, students should consider the source as well as the information presented. There are generally four types of sources for science information.

Primary sources are the professional print and web journals principally intended for science professionals, for example, *Science* and *Nature* magazines.

Secondary sources are science magazines, books, and websites intended for a science-literate public, for example, *Scientific American* and *Science News*.

General sources include national newspapers and magazines that have science writers on staff who report on science for the general public, for example, *The New York Times, Time*, and *Newsweek*.

Local and mass media offer reports that are limited in scope and often contain information gathered from general sources.

Discuss with students how these different sources vary and the attributes of each. **Ask**

- If you were doing a report for school, which source would you choose? Most students would probably use secondary and general sources.
- Why might it be useful to look at a primary source when evaluating a story you read in a secondary or general source? The primary source gives more information on the research itself, often indicating limitations or reservations the researchers have. Dissenting views could be published in the primary source.

UNIT 2: CELLS

BIOZINE at CLASSZONE.COM

INTERNET MAGAZINE

Go online for the latest biology news and updates on all BioZine articles.

Expanding the Textbook

News Feeds
- Science Daily
- CNN
- BBC

Careers

Bio Bytes

Opinion Poll

Strange Biology

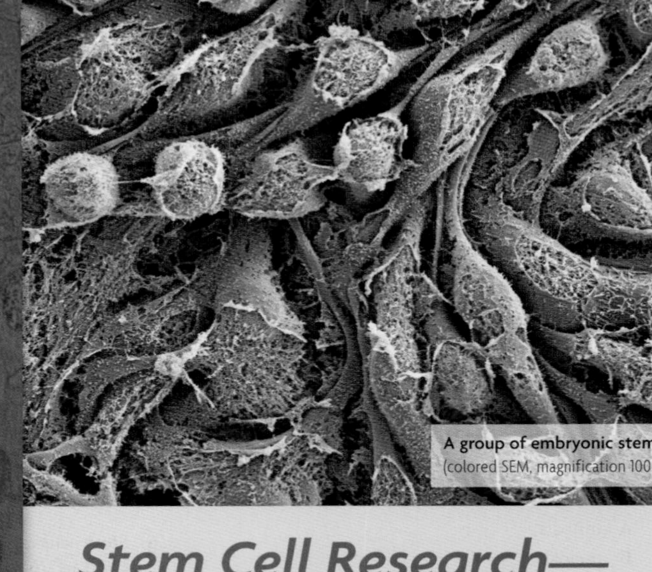

A group of embryonic stem cells (colored SEM, magnification 1000×)

Stem Cell Research—Potential Solutions, Practical Challenges

A news program asks viewers to vote online: "Should stem cell research be banned? Yes or no?" Some people claim that stem cell therapy will revolutionize medicine. Others believe that some types of stem cell research violate ethical standards and are not justified by the potential benefits. Between these two positions exists a wide range of ideas about what is or is not acceptable. Would you know how to vote?

Current News

Using an interactive whiteboard or the computer lab, have students compare the stories being covered by the media sources featured in the Current News section of BioZine online. Have students consider these questions:

- What stories about biology are making headlines at these different news sources?
- How does the coverage of the same story by different news sources compare?
- To whom do reporters go for verification and for commentary?

Opinion Poll

Have students go to BioZine at **ClassZone.com** to take the online poll by a given day. On that day check the results and report the outcome to the class. **Ask**

- Did the poll, as worded, enable you to fully express your opinion? If not, explain.
- How might the way in which a question is worded influence a response? Give some examples.
- Why is it important to know who is conducting a poll?

Using Stem Cells

Stem cells are undifferentiated cells that can regenerate themselves and develop into specialized types of cells. Stem cell research offers the hope of understanding basic cell processes and treating or even curing many dreaded diseases. However, a lot of technical challenges must be overcome before stem cell therapy is a realistic option, and ethical issues continue to surround stem cell research.

Potential Benefits

Stem cell research offers many potential benefits.

- Studying adult stem cells may help scientists better understand how tissues develop and what goes wrong when those tissues become diseased.
- A better understanding of the properties of stem cells may give scientists more information about how cancer cells replace themselves and thus helps scientists develop more targeted cancer therapies.
- Stem cells could be used to grow human tissues to test the effects of drugs and chemicals.
- Stem cells may be used to replace healthy cells that are killed by radiation treatment for cancer.
- Stem cells may be used to replace tissues. For example, chemotherapy kills blood-producing cells in bone marrow. Many chemotherapy patients have marrow taken before treatment that is later reinjected into the patient after treatment. However, the marrow could have cancer cells. The use of blood-producing stem cells in place of bone marrow transplants would remove this danger.

TECHNOLOGY

Somatic Cell Nuclear Transfer

Somatic cell nuclear transfer (SCNT), also called therapeutic cloning, is a method for obtaining stem cells that has been used to clone animals. The process is still under development, however, and it has not yet been used to produce human stem cells. SCNT offers the hope of using a patient's own DNA to produce stem cells that can form many types of specialized cells. The use of stem cells that are genetically identical to a patient would decrease that person's risk of cell rejection and the need for drugs to suppress the immune system. Many SCNT studies have been done in mice; the diagram to the right shows how the SCNT process might be applied in human cells.

1. An unfertilized egg is taken from a female's body, and the nucleus—containing the DNA—is removed. A cell is then taken from a patient's body. The nucleus is removed and inserted into the egg.
2. The egg is given a mild electrical stimulation, which makes it divide. The DNA comes from the patient's nucleus, and the materials needed for division come from the egg.
3. The stem cells could then be cultured and caused to differentiate into any tissue or organ needed by the patient.

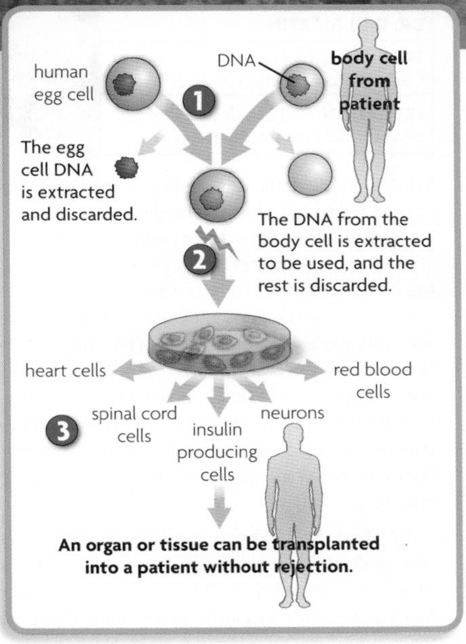

human egg cell
DNA
body cell from patient
1
The egg cell DNA is extracted and discarded.
The DNA from the body cell is extracted to be used, and the rest is discarded.
2
heart cells
red blood cells
3
spinal cord cells
insulin producing cells
neurons
An organ or tissue can be transplanted into a patient without rejection.

Once a stem cell line is established, in theory it can continue to grow indefinitely. Researchers could use these cell lines without having to harvest more stem cells. The cell lines also could be frozen and shipped to other researchers around the world.

Read More >> at CLASSZONE.COM

Vocabulary of Stem Cells

Students may need clarification of some of the terms used in stem cell research.

stem cell—an undifferentiated cell that can divide to produce one or more specialized cells. When a stem cell divides, it can produce more stem cells or differentiate into specialized cells, such as blood or muscle cells. Controlling stem-cell differentiation is one the biggest challenges of stem cell research.

totipotent—quality of a fertilized egg to give rise to all cells in the body and thus form an entire organism.

differentiation—the process by which a cell develops physical characteristics that make it suited to a particular function. The process occurs in response to biochemical signals or environmental conditions.

blastocyst—a hollow ball of undifferentiated cells formed just after fertilization in the embryos of some animals. In humans, the outer layer of cells develops into the placenta and the inner cell mass becomes the fetus.

embryonic stem cell—cells of the inner cell mass of a blastocyst, before they begin to differentiate. In humans, this stage is reached less than a week after fertilization. The blastocyst is made up of 100 to 150 cells.

pluripotent—the quality of an embryonic stem cell that enables it to differentiate into almost any type of cell.

adult stem cell—undifferentiated cells of a certain type of tissue that are used for growth and repair. For example, stem cells in human skin divide and differentiate into the specific skin cells found in different layers of the skin.

multipotent—quality of an adult stem cell that limits its differentiation to cells of a certain tissue type.

cell line—a group of stem cells developed by repeated division of a single cell. Once established, a cell line can be used to produce an unlimited supply of undifferentiated cells. It can also be frozen and kept in a cell bank.

Expanding the Textbook

Have students go the BioZine at **ClassZone.com** to read more about stem cells. Have students take notes on different types of stem cells. Students should come to class prepared to discuss the advantages and disadvantages of each type. Have students identify the conditions or diseases that are most often cited as possibly benefiting from stem cell research or treatment.

You could extend the discussion to include students' understanding of the ethical questions surrounding stem cell research. What do students think is the appropriate role of government in regulating such research? Students can research current state and federal regulations and funding for stem cell research.

Take It Further

According to the National Academies of Science, stem-cell-based therapies have the potential to help some of the millions of people who are treated for the following conditions and diseases:

- cardiovascular disease: roughly 70 million Americans live with this disease.
- autoimmune diseases: approximately 14 to 22 million people are affected.
- diabetes: there are approximately 14.7 million patients.
- osteoporosis: approximately 10 million patients are treated per year.
- Alzheimer's disease: approximately 4.5 million Americans have this disease.
- Parkinson's disease: approximately 1.5 million Americans currently have this disease.
- spinal-cord injuries: approximately 0.25 million patients are treated each year.

Technical Challenges

Adult stem cells have been used therapeutically for years in the form of bone marrow transplants. Nevertheless, many technical challenges must still be overcome before stem cells can be used to treat a wide range of disorders. Examples are highlighted below.

Supply Stem cells can be taken from a variety of sources, including an embryo, a patient, a patient's relative, or an established stem cell line. Each source presents unique challenges. Established cell lines may seem like the obvious choice, but some scientists are concerned that these cells have built up a lot of mutations as they have undergone thousands of divisions.

CAREERS

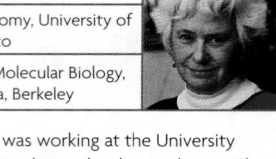

Cell Biologist in Action

DR. GAIL MARTIN
TITLE Professor, Anatomy, University of California, San Francisco
EDUCATION Ph. D., Molecular Biology, University of California, Berkeley

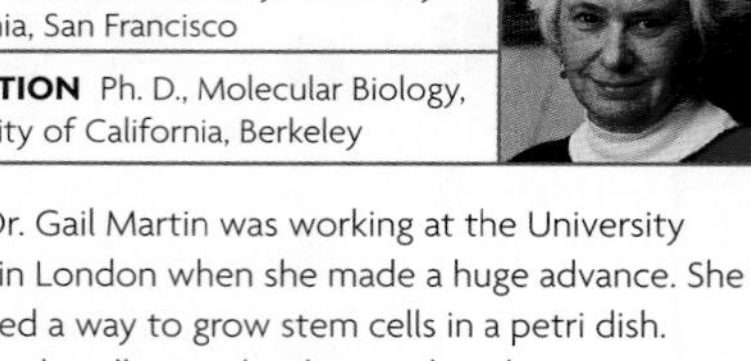

In 1974 Dr. Gail Martin was working at the University College in London when she made a huge advance. She developed a way to grow stem cells in a petri dish. These fragile cells were hard to work with, so Dr. Martin's breakthrough removed a big obstacle to stem cell research. Seven years later, she made another key discovery while working in her own laboratory at the University of California at San Francisco (UCSF) in her native United States—how to harvest stem cells from mouse embryos. Her work has helped other scientists develop ways to harvest stem cells from human embryos and explore their use in treating disorders.

Dr. Martin likes to point out that her work shows how small advances in basic biology can pay off years later in unexpected ways. She states that many people focus on cures for specific diseases, not realizing that these cures "may come from basic research in seemingly unrelated areas. What is really going to be important 20 years from now isn't clear."

Read More >> at CLASSZONE.COM

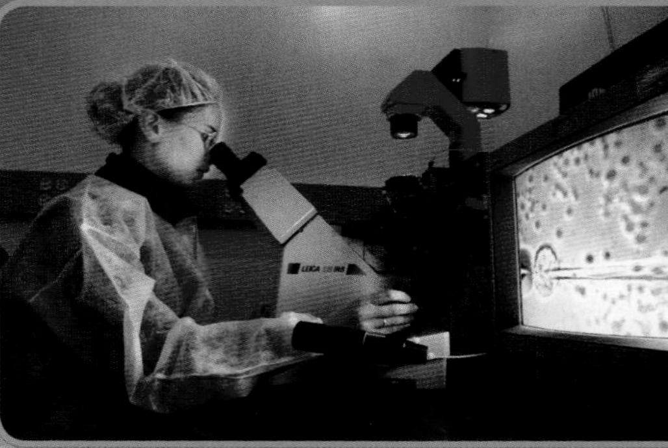

This researcher is micro-injecting mouse stem cells into fertilized mouse eggs to be used in drug research.

Transplantation into the target area The delivery of stem cells to targeted tissues can be complex, especially if the tissues are deep inside the body. And once delivered, stem cells must "learn" to work with other cells. For instance, inserted cardiac cells must beat in unison with a patient's heart cells to be effective.

Prevention of rejection Stem cells may be rejected if a patient's body sees them as foreign. This problem can remain even when certain identifying proteins are removed from the cells' membranes. The development of SCNT technology in humans could help solve this problem so that patients would not have to take drugs to suppress their immune system.

Suppression of tumor formation By their very nature, stem cells remain undifferentiated and continue to divide for long periods of time. When transplanted into an organism, many embryonic stem cells tend to form tumors. This risk must be removed before they can be used therapeutically.

Unanswered Questions

Stem cell research and therapy do not only involve questions of what we can do. They also involve questions about what we should do, who should benefit, and who should pay.

- Should human embryos be a source of stem cells?
- How can scientists protect their work when patent laws vary from country to country?
- How should stem cell research be funded?
- How can the benefits of stem cell research best be shared by all people, regardless of income?
- Should insurance cover costly stem cell procedures?

Read More >> at CLASSZONE.COM

BIOZINE ClassZone.com

Have students use the resources available in the Unit 2 BioZine at **ClassZone.com** to report about a recent discovery in cell biology. In addition to the secondary and general sources available in BioZine, have students work with a librarian to locate the original, primary source. Have students compare the reports. **Ask**

- How well did the secondary and general sources do in describing the discovery or event?
- What was left out of the reports written for the general public?
- How do the different sources vary in describing the potential benefits or applications of the discovery?
- What concerns, if any, are expressed by the people who report on the discovery, and how do those concerns differ among the various reports you read?

UNIT 3

Genetics

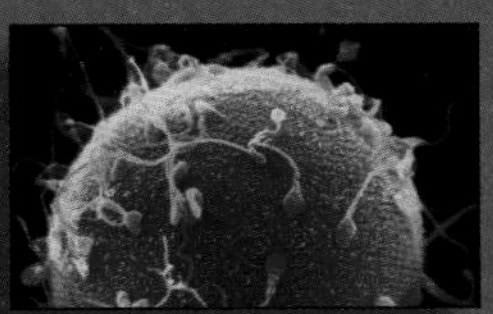

CHAPTER 6
Meiosis and Mendel 166

CHAPTER 7
Extending Mendelian Genetics 198

CHAPTER 8
From DNA to Proteins 224

CHAPTER 9
Frontiers of Biotechnology 262

INTERNET MAGAZINE
Medical Technology—The Genetic Forefront 292

TECHNOLOGY Biochips

CAREER Cancer Geneticist

Unit Project

Purpose **Understand, prepare, and interpret a pedigree, and explain how it can be used as a diagnostic model.**

Overview Students prepare and interpret a model pedigree using appropriate symbols. Students will

- research a specific assigned genetic trait and a provided pedigree
- research how pedigrees are used in genetic counseling
- reproduce the pedigree on a three-panel, freestanding storyboard
- describe and explain the symbols and markers of interest in each generation
- clearly identify the trait and describe its mode of inheritance, using dialog boxes posted on the storyboard

Preparation Make a copy of the project description and rubric for each student (*Unit Resource Book*, pp. 133–134). Tell students that they should be creative in the preparation of their pedigree storyboard, but that all symbols must be correct.

Project Management Allow three weeks for the completion of the project. Check on students' progress at the end of each week leading up to the completion date.

Unit Resource Book Unit 3 Project, pp. 133–135

CHAPTER 6

Indiana Resource Preview

Print Resources

Meiosis and Mendel

INDIANA STANDARDS		Sections	PAGES and PACING	UNIT RESOURCE BOOK
B.6.4	6.1	**Chromosomes and Meiosis** **KEY CONCEPT** Gametes have half the number of chromosomes that body cells have.	pp. 168–171 45 minutes	URB pages 1–4
NOS.1		DATA ANALYSIS: Interpreting Bar Graphs	p. 172, 35 min	URB page 25
B.6.4	6.2	**Process of Meiosis** **KEY CONCEPT** During meiosis, diploid cells undergo two cell divisions that result in haploid cells.	pp. 173–176 45 minutes	URB pages 5–8
B.5.2	6.3	**Mendel and Heredity** **KEY CONCEPT** Mendel's research showed that traits are inherited as discrete units.	pp. 177–179 30 minutes	URB pages 9–12
B.5.2	6.4	**Traits, Genes, and Alleles** **KEY CONCEPT** Genes encode proteins that produce a diverse range of traits.	pp. 180–182 45 minutes	URB pages 13–16
B.7.1, B.7.3	6.5	**Traits and Probability** **KEY CONCEPT** Trait inheritance follows the rules of probability.	pp. 183–187 45 minutes	URB pages 17–20
B.7.1, B.7.3		CHAPTER INVESTIGATION: Allele Combinations and Punnett Squares	p. 188 45 minutes	**Lab Binder** Genetics pages 1–2
B.6.5	6.6	**Meiosis and Genetic Variation** **KEY CONCEPT** Independent assortment and crossing over during meiosis result in genetic diversity.	pp. 189–191 30 minutes	URB 21–24
B.6.4, B.7.1, B.7.3		OPTIONS FOR INQUIRY	pp. 192–193 30 min each	**Lab Binder** Genetics pages 3–6
		Chapter Review	pp. 194–197	**Assessment Book** Chapter Tests A, B pp. 115–122

INDIANA STANDARDS

B.5.2 Describe how hereditary information passed from parents to offspring is encoded in regions of DNA molecules called genes.
B.6.4 Describe and model the process of meiosis and explain the relationship between the genetic make-up of the parent cell and the daughter cells (gametes).
B.6.5 Explain how, in sexual reproduction, crossing over, independent assortment, and random fertilization, result in offspring that are genetically different from the parents.
B.7.1 Distinguish between dominant and recessive alleles and determine the phenotype that would result from the different possible combinations of alleles in an offspring.
B.7.3 Determine the likelihood of the appearance of a specific trait in an offspring given the genetic make-up of the parents.
NOS.1 Develop explanations based on reproducible data and observations gathered during laboratory investigations.

Labs

PUPIL EDITION LABS

Using a Testcross, Section 5, p. 185 Students determine the genotype of a plant by analyzing a testcross. **Lab Binder** pp. 7–8	**Time:** 15 minutes **Materials:** pencil, paper
Allele Combinations and Punnett Squares, p. 188 Students use a Punnett square to predict the inheritance of alleles in a dihybrid cross. **Lab Binder** pp. 1–2	**Time:** 30 minutes **Materials:** paper, pencil, calculator

OPTIONS FOR INQUIRY

Modeling Meiosis, p. 192 Students model the stages of meiosis. **Lab Binder** pp. 3–4	**Time:** 30 minutes **Materials:** 4 white pipe cleaners, 2 2-cm pieces hook-and-loop tabs, colored markers, notebook paper
Probability Practice, p. 193 Students model the distribution of alleles and calculate probabilities of combinations. **Lab Binder** pp. 5–6	**Time:** 30 minutes **Materials:** 2 coins, 4 cm masking tape, marker, one folded 3" × 5" index card with a monohybrid cross on it

LAB BINDER Unit 3 Genetics

Additional Investigation: Modeling Monohybrid and Dihybrid Crosses, pp. 9–14

Virtual Lab Worksheet: Breeding Mutations in Fruit Flies, p. 77

LAB GENERATOR

A searchable CD of all labs in the program in editable format, including forensic, probeware, and biotechnology labs.

Presentation Tools

POWER PRESENTATIONS

Presentation Chapter 6

PowerPresentations for each section incorporate images and clips from the Media Gallery. Includes Note Navigator for each section.

MEDIA GALLERY

Contains the following images and video clips, as well as animations, simulations, and forms of visuals from the book.

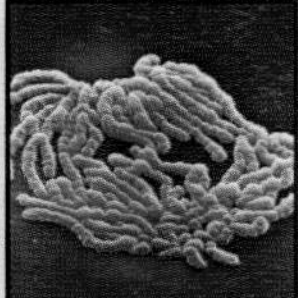

Meiosis

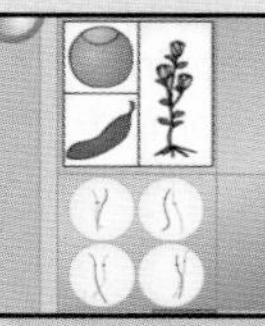
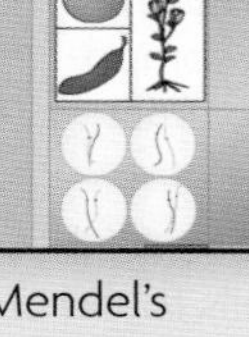

Mendel's experiments

Offspring variation

Gregor Mendel

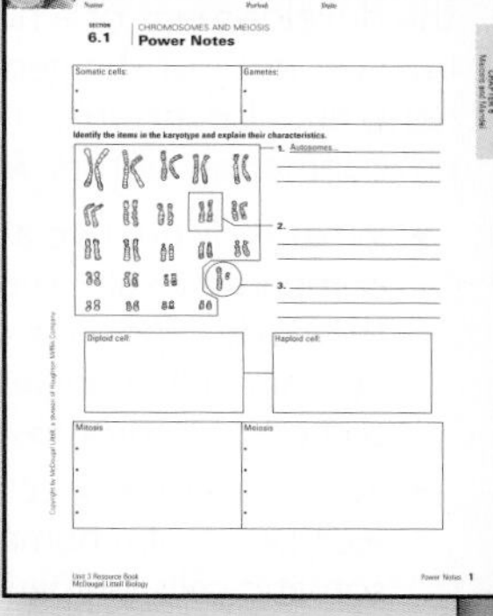

Power Notes

VIDEO

Check out a set of short video clips exploring meiosis and heredity.

ANIMATED BIOLOGY

Meiosis

Genotypes and Phenotypes

Mendel's Experiment

TRANSPARENCIES

Mitosis and Meiosis T30

Meiosis in Detail T31

Punnett Square T32

Dihybrid Cross T33

BioZine

Animated Biology

Interactive Review

SciLinks

Resource Centers

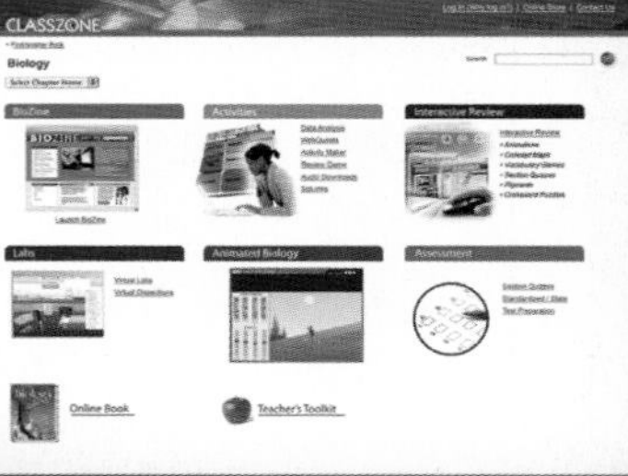

CHAPTER

6

▼ Focus and Motivate

What makes you who you are?

Students should recognize that there is no simple answer to the question posed; the development of a human being involves not just the genetic component, but also internal and external environmental factors. **Ask**

- What is distinctive about sex cells, as compared to all other cells found in the body? Sperm and egg cells contain only a single set of chromosomes, not chromosome pairs.
- What role do sex cells play in the well-being of a human? Unlike somatic cells, human sex cells do not contribute to the general maintenance of the human body. Rather they control sexual determination and development.

BIOZINE ClassZone.com

Students can access BioZine at **ClassZone.com** to receive updates to featured topics in the book.

In a Hurry?

Use **FIGURE 6.2** of **Section 6.1** and **FIGURE 6.5** of **Section 6.2** to cover the details of meiosis. **Section 6.3** deals with Mendel's experiments, while **Sections 6.4** and **6.5** discuss genes and alleles. **Section 6.6** relates sexual reproduction to genetic diversity.

CHAPTER 6

Meiosis and Mendel

KEY CONCEPTS

6.1 Chromosomes and Meiosis
Gametes have half the number of chromosomes that body cells have.

6.2 Process of Meiosis
During meiosis, diploid cells undergo two cell divisions that result in haploid cells.

6.3 Mendel and Heredity
Mendel's research showed that traits are inherited as discrete units.

6.4 Traits, Genes, and Alleles
Genes encode proteins that produce a diverse range of traits.

6.5 Traits and Probability
The inheritance of traits follows the rules of probability.

6.6 Meiosis and Genetic Variation
Independent assortment and crossing over during meiosis result in genetic diversity.

Online BIOLOGY CLASSZONE.COM

Animated BIOLOGY
View animated chapter concepts.
- Meiosis
- Genotypes and Phenotypes
- Breeding Mutations in Fruit Flies
- Mendel's Experiment

BIOZINE
Keep current with biology news.
- Featured stories
- News feeds
- Strange Biology

RESOURCE CENTER
Get more information on
- Chromosomes
- Gregor Mendel
- Sexual Reproduction
- Heredity

Teacher Demo

Modeling Use a simple model of crossing over to preview how different combinations of alleles are formed through crossing over.

Materials

- 4 toothpicks
- 4 red gumdrops
- 4 green gumdrops
- 2 twist ties

Prepare Thread two red gumdrops onto each of two toothpicks. Tie the toothpicks together with a twist tie. Thread two green gumdrops onto each of two toothpicks. Tie the toothpicks together with a twist tie. The gumdrops on each toothpick represent the genetic information supplied by each parent. Each toothpick pair represents one duplicated chromosome (two sister chromatids) of a homologous pair. The twist tie represents the centromere.

colored SEM; magnification 1300×

What makes you who you are?

The human egg and sperm cells (above) are the result of meiosis, a process that reduces chromosome number by half. Millions of sperm could potentially fertilize the egg, but only one actually succeeds. The fusion of egg and sperm triggers a series of events that lead to the development of a healthy new organism who will display features of both the mother and the father.

Connecting CONCEPTS

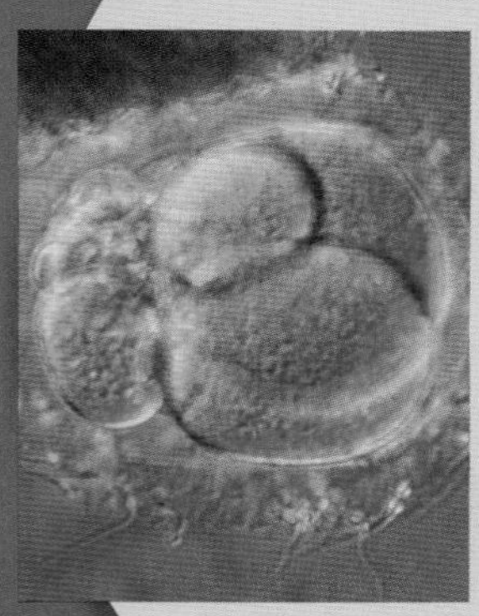

Receptors This micrograph (left) shows a four-cell human embryo surrounded by a matrix of proteins and sugars. This matrix originally surrounded the egg and acted as a receptor for sperm cells from organisms of the same species. For example, a cow sperm cannot bind to a mouse egg. When a sperm passes through the matrix and binds to the egg membrane, the matrix hardens, which blocks other sperm from binding. (colored LM; magnification 450×)

Introduce Bring the pairs of homologous chromosomes together as in prophase I. Line them line up, side by side, as in metaphase I. Describe how in anaphase I, DNA on homologous chromatids can cross over, exchanging one red and green gumdrop located at the same position on two inner chromatids. Separate the pairs, as in telophase I. Then show the separation of the chromatids into individual chromosomes, as in meiosis II.

Discuss Point out that during meiosis, genetic recombination can occur between homologous chromosomes. **Ask,** How is the genetic material that is exchanged during meiosis alike and how is it different? The exchanged DNA is located at the same position on each chromatid, which means it codes for the same cell functions. However genetic material from one parent can differ from that of the other even though it provides for the same cell functions. The exchange introduces genetic diversity into the chromosomes.

Activate Prior Knowledge

The chapter introduces how the genetic material from two parents results in a single offspring, and how this material is physically represented as traits in the offspring. **Ask,** If you were looking at a couple who are expecting a child, what traits could you predict for the child just by observing the parents? Students may say color of hair, eyes, and skin; height and body type; and facial features. Discuss traits that seem to be a combination of the two parents, compared with traits that seem to come directly from one parent and not the other. **Ask,** What affects the traits and development of an offspring after he or she is born? his or her environment

Preview Vocabulary

Greek and Latin Word Origins Students will see a number of words in this chapter that relate to giving birth or bearing offspring. The Latin root *gen,* which means "to give birth to," is the root of these words:

genetics, gene, generation

The Latin root *ferre,* which means "to bear" as in "bear fruit," is the root of the word *fertilize.*

Academic Vocabulary Tell students that one of Mendel's great strengths as a scientist was his skill as a statistician. Have students review these words related to statistics:

probability *predict*
ratio *average*
outcome *event*

English Learners Tell students that they will see many references to pairs forming and separating in this chapter. Have them use the *Multilanguage Glossary* to preview these terms:

meiosis *gamete* *fertilization*
haploid *diploid*

Tell students to be alert for pairs of antonyms that signal a change in number, such as *divide, double; pair, half;* and *separate, join.*

SECTION 6.1

▼ Plan and Prepare

Objectives

- Differentiate between body cells and gametes.
- Compare and contrast autosomes and sex chromosomes.

Section Resources

Unit Resource Book Study Guide pp. 1–2 Power Notes p. 3 Reinforcement p. 4
Interactive Reader Chapter 6 **Spanish Study Guide** pp. 53–54
Biology Toolkit pp. C4, D3
Technology Power Presentation 6.1 Media Gallery DVD Online Quiz 6.1

Activate Prior Knowledge Remind students the human egg and sperm are different from all other human cells. **Ask,** What makes sex cells different from all others, is it because they carry X and Y chromosomes? Explain. No. They carry only a single set of chromosomes, not chromosome pairs. Body cells have some pairing of X and Y chromosomes; eggs have a single X; sperm have a single X or Y.

▼ Teach

Vocabulary

Greek and Latin Word Origins
The word **gamete** comes from the Greek word *gamos,* meaning "marriage." The words that follow share the same root; note the prefix indicating number:

polygamy	*polygamous*
monogamy	*monogamous*
bigamy	*bigamous*

Answers

A Identify somatic, or body, cells

6.1 Chromosomes and Meiosis

KEY CONCEPT Gametes have half the number of chromosomes that body cells have.

MAIN IDEAS

- You have body cells and gametes.
- Your cells have autosomes and sex chromosomes.
- Body cells are diploid; gametes are haploid.

VOCABULARY

somatic cell, p. 168
gamete, p. 168
homologous chromosome, p. 169
autosome, p. 169
sex chromosome, p. 169
sexual reproduction, p. 170
fertilization, p. 170
diploid, p. 170
haploid, p. 170
meiosis, p. 170

INDIANA STANDARDS

B.6.4 Describe and model the process of meiosis and explain the relationship between the genetic make-up of the parent cell and the daughter cells (gametes).

Connect Perhaps you are familiar with the saying, "Everything old is new again." This phrase usually indicates that a past style is again current. However, it applies equally well to you. The fusion of a single egg and sperm cell resulted in the complex creature that is you. There's never been anyone quite like you. And yet the DNA that directs your cells came from your mother and father. And their DNA came from their mother and father, and so on and so on. In this chapter, you will examine the processes that went into making you who you are.

MAIN IDEA

You have body cells and gametes.

You have many types of specialized cells in your body, but they can be divided into two major groups: somatic cells and germ cells. **Somatic cells** (soh-MAT-ihk), also called body cells, make up most of your body tissues and organs. For example, your spleen, kidneys, and eyeballs are all made entirely of body cells. DNA in your body cells is not passed on to your children. Germ cells, in contrast, are cells in your reproductive organs, the ovaries or the testes, that develop into gametes. **Gametes** are sex cells—ova, or eggs, in the female, and spermatozoa, or sperm cells, in the male. DNA in your gametes can be passed on to your children.

Each species has a characteristic number of chromosomes per cell. This number is typically given for body cells, not for gametes. Chromosome number does not seem to be related to the complexity of an organism. For example, yeast have 32 chromosomes, which come in 16 pairs. The fruit flies commonly used in genetic experiments have 8 chromosomes, which come in 4 pairs. A fern holds the record for the most chromosomes—more than 1200. Each of your body cells contains a set of 46 chromosomes, which come in 23 pairs. These cells are genetically identical to each other unless mutations have occurred. As you learned in Chapter 5, cells within an organism differ from each other because different genes are expressed, not because they have different genes.

TAKING NOTES

Make a two-column table to keep track of the vocabulary in this chapter.

Term	*Definition*
somatic cell *gamete*	

A Identify **Which cell type makes up the brain?**

Differentiated Instruction

ENGLISH LEARNERS

Use questions to guide students' reading on major concepts and determine their prior knowledge. **Ask,** How does a gamete differ from a body cell? Ask the question before the section, remind students of it as they read, and after they finish. Model for students how to ask more questions. **Ask,** Why does a gamete have only half the number of chromosomes as a body cell? Encourage students to ask each other questions.

Biology Toolkit, Questions to Guide Reading, p. C4

BELOW LEVEL

Point out that there are many vocabulary terms in this section that work as pairs, for example, haploid and diploid. Suggest students look for logical pairings, writing their own definition, adding a glossary definition, then including a picture to reinforce the meaning. They can use this technique for any unfamiliar terms, not just key vocabulary.

Biology Toolkit, Student Vocabulary, p. D3

MAIN IDEA

Your cells have autosomes and sex chromosomes.

Suppose you had 23 pairs of gloves. You would have a total of 46 gloves that you could divide into two sets, 23 right and 23 left. Similarly, your body cells have 23 pairs of chromosomes for a total of 46 that can be divided into two sets: 23 from your mother and 23 from your father. Just as you use both gloves when it's cold outside, your cells use both sets of chromosomes to function properly.

Together, each pair of chromosomes is referred to as a homologous pair. In this context, *homologous* means "having the same structure." **Homologous chromosomes** are two chromosomes—one inherited from the mother, one from the father—that have the same length and general appearance. More importantly, these chromosomes have copies of the same genes, although the two copies may differ. For example, if you have a gene that influences blood cholesterol levels on chromosome 8, you will have one copy from your mother and one copy from your father. It is possible that one of these copies is associated with high cholesterol levels, while the other is associated with low cholesterol levels. For convenience, scientists have assigned a number to each pair of homologous chromosomes, ordered from largest to smallest. As **FIGURE 6.1** shows, the largest pair of chromosomes is number 1, the next largest pair is number 2, and so forth.

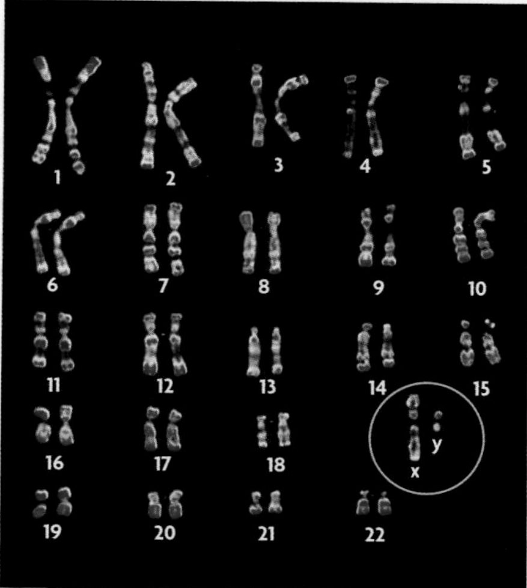

FIGURE 6.1 Human DNA is organized into two sets of 23 chromosomes. Each set contains 22 autosomes and 1 sex chromosome. Females have two X chromosomes. Males have an X and a Y chromosome (circled). (colored LM; magnification 4400×)

Collectively, chromosome pairs 1 through 22 make up your **autosomes,** chromosomes that contain genes for characteristics not directly related to the sex of an organism. But what about the 23rd chromosome pair?

Most sexually reproducing species also have **sex chromosomes** that directly control the development of sexual characteristics. Humans have two very different sex chromosomes, X and Y. How sex is determined varies by species. In all mammals, including humans, an organism's sex is determined by the XY system. An organism with two X chromosomes is female. An organism with one X and one Y chromosome is male. Sex chromosomes make up your 23rd pair of chromosomes. Although the X and Y chromosomes pair with each other, they are not homologous. The X chromosome is the larger sex chromosome and contains numerous genes, including many that are unrelated to sexual characteristics. The Y chromosome is the sex chromosome that contains genes that direct the development of the testes and other male traits. It is the smallest chromosome and carries the fewest genes.

"The parents are both geneticists."

A Summarize Are homologous chromosomes identical to each other? Explain.

ONLINE BIOLOGY Go to the chapter Resource Center at **ClassZone.com** for additional resources and information on chromosomes.

Take It Further

Tell students that in birds, butterflies, and some fish species, the female gamete determines the gender of the individual. In these species, female gametes contain either a **Z chromosome** or a **W chromosome.** Male gametes have only a Z chromosome. A ZW offspring is female; ZZ is male.

While **sex determination** is chromosomal in many species, there are exceptions. The sex of some reptiles, such as the American alligator, is determined by the temperature of the environment surrounding incubating eggs. Temperatures in the low 90s (Fahrenheit) make the young alligators male, while temperatures in the mid-80s yield females.

Vocabulary

Academic Vocabulary The complete set of chromosomes for an organism are sometimes referred to as a *chromosome complement*. The word **complement** has different uses but it typically refers to a **complete** set or pairing. For example, in grammar, the word used after a verb to complete the predicate is its complement. In logic, the complement is a universal set, the set of all elements.

Answers

A Summarize No, they are very similar in size and shape and carry the same type of genes, but the version of the genes may differ.

INCLUSION

For students who have difficulty processing information, you may might want to project **FIGURE 6.3** from the Media Gallery and relate what is discussed in the text on page 169 to the image. Model how you interpret the text as you read and how you relate that information to the photograph. Point out that the chromosomes shown are metaphase chromosomes, which means each is made up of a pair of chromatids. However the term *chromosome pair* refers to both homologous chromosomes, not the chromatid pairs.

▼ Teach *continued*

TEACH FROM VISUALS

VISUAL VOCAB Have students study the figure. **Ask**

- If these cells were human cells, how many chromosomes would the haploid cell have? 23
- How many chromosomes would the diploid cell have? 46

Take It Further

Not all eukaryotic organisms have just two sets of chromosomes. **Polyploidy** is a condition in which an organism has multiple sets of chromosomes. Polyploidy occurs in some species of animals, for example, in species of salmon, goldifsh, and salamanders. It is much more common in certain types of plants. For example, some species of chrysanthemums are **tetraploid** with 36 chromosomes in four sets, **hexaploid** with 54 chromosomes in six sets, **octaploid** with 72 chromosomes in eight sets, and **decaploid** with 90 chromosomes in ten sets. Naturally occurring polyploidy plants almost always have an even number of chromosome sets.

Science Trivia

The haploid cells resulting from meiosis are initially quite small. After processing in the testes or ovaries, they can end up much larger than somatic cells.

- Ostrich eggs are about 180 mm long and 140 mm wide, and weigh 1.2 kg, making them over 2000 times larger than the smallest hummingbird egg.
- The sperm of *Drosophila bifurca*, a fruit fly, can reach up to 6 cm in length.

MAIN IDEA

Body cells are diploid; gametes are haploid.

Sexual reproduction involves the fusion of two gametes that results in offspring that are a genetic mixture of both parents. The actual fusion of an egg and a sperm cell is called **fertilization.** When fertilization occurs, the nuclei of the egg and sperm cell fuse to form one nucleus. This new nucleus must have the correct number of chromosomes for a healthy new organism to develop. Therefore, the egg and sperm cell need only half the usual number of chromosomes—one chromosome from each homologous pair.

Diploid and Haploid Cells

Body cells and gametes have different numbers of chromosomes. Your body cells are diploid. **Diploid** (DIHP-LOYD) means a cell has two copies of each chromosome: one copy from the mother, and one copy from the father. Diploid cells can be represented as $2n$. In humans, the diploid chromosome number is 46.

VOCABULARY

Diploid comes from the Greek word *diplous,* which means "double". *Haploid* comes from the Greek word *haplous,* which means "single."

VISUAL VOCAB

Diploid cells have two copies of each chromosome: one copy from the mother and one from the father.

Body cells are diploid (*2n*).

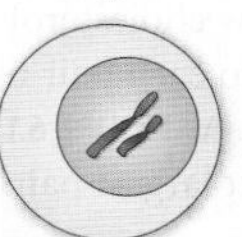

Gametes (sex cells) are haploid (*n*).

Haploid cells have only one copy of each chromosome.

Gametes are not diploid cells; they are haploid cells, represented as n. **Haploid** (HAP-LOYD) means that a cell has only one copy of each chromosome. Each human egg or sperm cell has 22 autosomes and 1 sex chromosome. In the egg, the sex chromosome is always an X chromosome. In the sperm cell, the sex chromosome can be an X chromosome or a Y chromosome. The reason for this difference will be discussed in the following sections.

Maintaining the correct number of chromosomes is important to the survival of all organisms. Typically, a change in chromosome number is harmful. However, increasing the number of sets of chromosomes can, on occasion, give rise to a new species. The fertilization of nonhaploid gametes has played an important role in plant evolution by rapidly making new species with more than two sets of chromosomes. For example, some plants have four copies of each chromosome, a condition called tetraploidy ($4n$). This type of event has occurred in many groups of plants, but it is very rare in animals.

***Connecting* CONCEPTS**

Plant Life Cycles As you will learn in **Chapter 22,** all plants complete their life cycle by alternating between two phases: diploid and haploid. During the diploid phase, plants make spores. During the haploid phase, plants make gametes.

Meiosis

Germ cells in your reproductive organs undergo the process of meiosis to form gametes. **Meiosis** (my-OH-sihs) is a form of nuclear division that divides a diploid cell into haploid cells. This process is essential for sexual reproduction. The details of meiosis will be presented in the next section. But **FIGURE 6.2** highlights some differences between mitosis and meiosis in advance to help you keep these two processes clear in your mind.

Differentiated Instruction

TEACH WITH TECHNOLOGY

If your classroom is equipped with a personal response system, use it to test students on haploid, diploid, and polyploid cells; mitosis and meiosis; and autosomes and sex chromosomes. Test on the number of chromosome sets in each type of cell, where in the body each cell type or process occurs, and what the importance of each cell or chromosome type is.

FIGURE 6.2 Comparing Mitosis and Meiosis

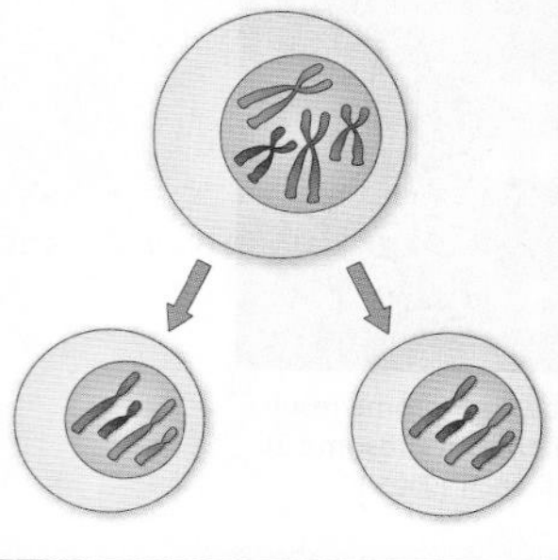

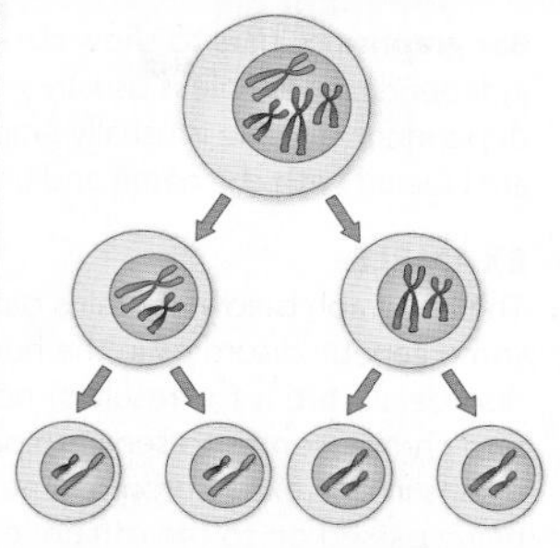

MITOSIS	MEIOSIS
Produces genetically identical cells	Produces genetically unique cells
Results in diploid cells	Results in haploid cells
Takes place throughout an organism's lifetime	Takes place only at certain times in an organism's life cycle
Involved in asexual reproduction	Involved in sexual reproduction

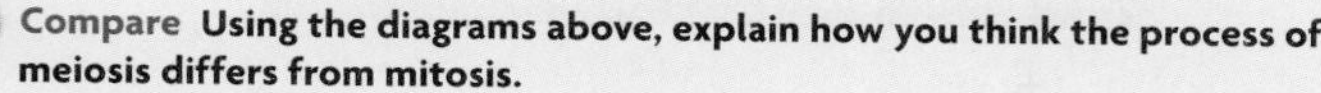

A Compare Using the diagrams above, explain how you think the process of meiosis differs from mitosis.

In Chapter 5 you learned about mitosis, another form of nuclear division. Recall that mitosis is a process that occurs in body cells. It helps produce daughter cells that are genetically identical to the parent cell. In cells undergoing mitosis, DNA is copied once and divided once. Both the parent cell and the daughter cells are diploid. Mitosis is used for development, growth, and repair in all types of organisms. It is also used for reproduction in asexually reproducing eukaryotes.

In contrast, meiosis occurs in germ cells to produce gametes. This process is sometimes called a "reduction division" because it reduces chromosome number by half. In cells undergoing meiosis, DNA is copied once but divided twice. Meiosis makes genetically unique haploid cells from a diploid cell. These haploid cells then undergo more processing in the ovaries or testes, finally forming mature gametes.

B Apply Why is it important that gametes are haploid cells?

6.1 ASSESSMENT

ONLINE QUIZ ClassZone.com

B.6.4

REVIEWING MAIN IDEAS

1. Where are germ cells located in the human body?
2. What is the difference between an **autosome** and a **sex chromosome**?
3. Is the cell that results from **fertilization** a **haploid** or **diploid** cell? Explain.

CRITICAL THINKING

4. **Infer** Does mitosis or **meiosis** occur more frequently in your body? Explain your answer.
5. **Analyze** Do you think the Y chromosome contains genes that are critical for an organism's survival? Explain your reasoning.

Connecting CONCEPTS

6. **Telomeres** The ends of DNA molecules form telomeres that help keep the ends of chromosomes from sticking to each other. Why might this be especially important in germ cells, which go through meiosis and make haploid **gametes**?

6.1 ASSESSMENT

1. in the reproductive organs (ovaries and testes)
2. Autosomes directly affect only body traits, whereas sex chromosomes directly affect the sexual characteristics of an organism.
3. Diploid; the combination of 23 chromosomes from the mother and 23 from the father restores the diploid number of chromosomes (46).
4. Mitosis occurs throughout an organism's lifetime throughout many cells of the entire body, compared to meiosis, which only occurs at certain times and only in the reproductive organs.
5. No, females do not have a Y chromosome, and they are able to survive.
6. If the ends of two chromosomes stick together, the chromosomes will not separate correctly during meiosis. One of the resulting gametes will have an extra chromosome, and the other will be missing a chromosome.

TEACH FROM VISUALS

FIGURE 6.2 Have students study the table, which points out the differences between mitosis and meiosis. **Ask**

- How are mitosis and meiosis alike? Both involve division of the nucleus followed by the formation of new cells.
- What word pairs in the accompanying descriptions of mitosis and meiosis point to the differences between the two types of division? identical/unique, diploid/haploid, asexual/sexual

Vocabulary

Greek and Latin Word Origins The word **meiosis** comes from the Greek *meiōn,* meaning "less." This is the same root of the word **minor.**

Answers

A Compare In meiosis, a cell undergoes two cell divisions and produces four cells, each with half the original number of chromosomes. In mitosis, a cell undergoes only one division and produces two cells that have the same number of chromosomes as the original cell.

B Apply Gametes fuse to form a new organism. Because each gamete has half the chromosomes of the parent cell, fertilization produces a new organism with the correct number of chromosomes.

Assess and Reteach ▼

Assess Use the Online Quiz or Section Quiz (*Assessment Book,* p. 109).

Reteach Work with students to prepare a compare and contrast chart for mitosis and meiosis. Ask them to include all the key vocabulary from this section.

DATA ANALYSIS

Introduce

Bar graphs are used to compare data about different organisms or other things, or to show data that are not continuous. Multiple sets of data can be compared by drawing several bars next to each other, using a scale for the dependent variable that is large enough to account for all data. **Ask**

- Why can't a line graph be used to show the frequency of genetic disorders? They are distinct disorders. The data do not show a continuous process.
- Why can't a line graph be used to show the number of chromosomes in different organisms? The chromosome numbers are independent of each other.

Take It Further

Down, Patau, and Edwards syndromes are all genetic disorders caused by **trisomy,** the presence of an extra chromosome. Down syndrome is caused by trisomy 21, the presence of a third chromosome 21. Edwards syndrome results from trisomy 18, and Patau syndrome from trisomy 13.

Explain to students that a **syndrome** is a group of signs or symptoms that occur together and characterize a disorder. For example, Down syndrome is characterized by mental retardation, congenital heart defects, decreased muscle tone, slanting eyes, and a short stature.

Discuss

Have students focus on Graph 2. **Ask**

- What is the range of chromosome number shown in the graph? about 10 to over 200
- What organisms shown in the graph have a chromosome number most similar to that of humans? bats, porpoises, potatoes

Unit Resource Book, Data Analysis, p. 25

DATA ANALYSIS INTERPRETING BAR GRAPHS

DATA ANALYSIS ClassZone.com

NOS.1

Genetic Data

Bar graphs use bars to show data. In a bar graph, the independent variable is usually graphed on the *x*-axis and the dependent variable is usually graphed on the *y*-axis. Both axes are labeled with the name and unit of the variable.

EXAMPLE

The bar graph below contains data about the frequency of some genetic disorders in the human population. Each of the disorders listed is the result of nondisjunction, the failure of two chromosomes to separate properly during meiosis. This results in one extra chromosome or one less chromosome being passed on to the offspring.

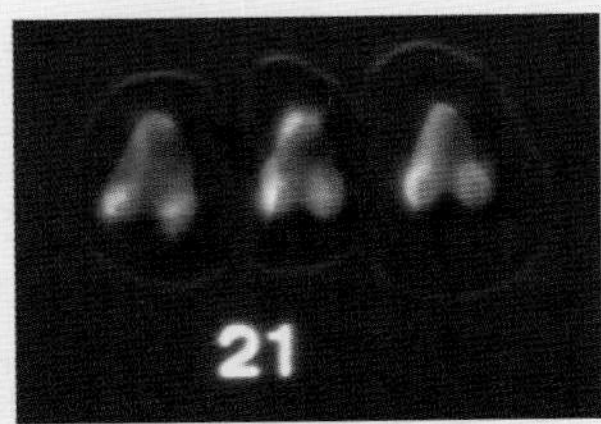

In most cases, Down syndrome results from having an extra chromosome 21. (colored LM; magnification 2000×)

For each syndrome on the *x*-axis, the bar extends vertically on the *y*-axis to represent the incidence per 100,000 births. For example, out of 100,000 births, 111 children are born with Down syndrome.

GRAPH 1. FREQUENCY OF GENETIC DISORDERS

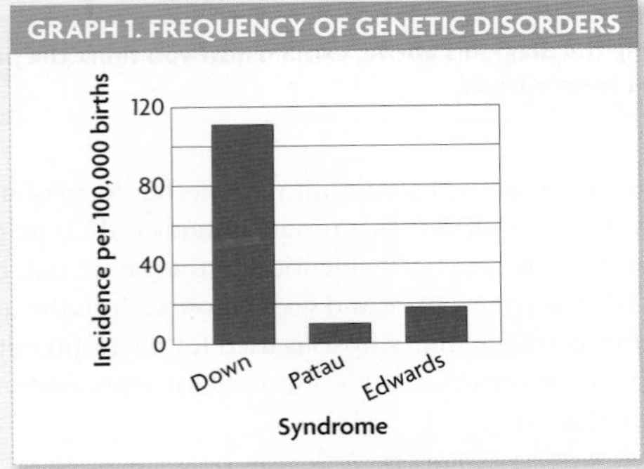

Source: U.S. National Library of Medicine

INTERPRET A BAR GRAPH

The bar graph below contains data about the diploid number of chromosomes in different organisms.

GRAPH 2. DIPLOID NUMBER OF CHROMOSOMES IN VARIOUS ORGANISMS

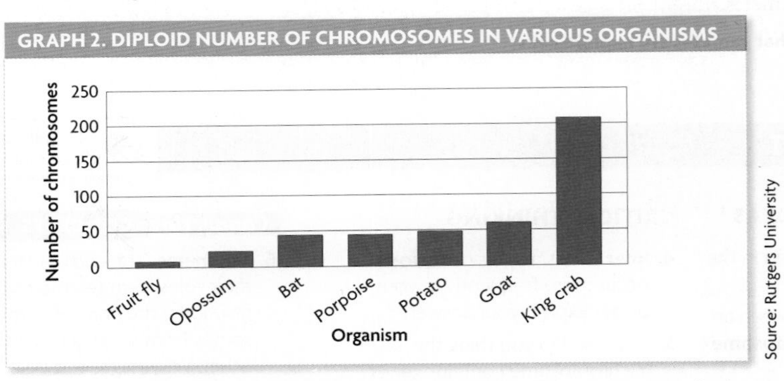

Source: Rutgers University

1. **Analyze** Which organism has the greatest number of chromosomes? The least?
2. **Evaluate** Does chromosome number appear to correlate to the type of organism? Explain.
3. **Hypothesize** Do you think there is an upper limit to chromosome number? Explain.

Answers

1. king crab; fruit fly
2. No, the two arthropods have the greatest difference of chromosome number, and it appears that the potato (a plant) has a number closer to that of the humans than opossums.
3. yes, because the chromosomes need to be able to fit within the nucleus of a cell

6.2 Process of Meiosis

KEY CONCEPT During meiosis, diploid cells undergo two cell divisions that result in haploid cells.

MAIN IDEAS
- Cells go through two rounds of division in meiosis.
- Haploid cells develop into mature gametes.

VOCABULARY
gametogenesis, p. 176
sperm, p. 176
egg, p. 176
polar body, p. 176

B.6.4 Describe and model the process of meiosis and explain the relationship between the genetic make-up of the parent cell and the daughter cells (gametes).

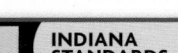

Connect Sometimes division is difficult, such as splitting the bill at a restaurant or dividing people into teams for basketball. Luckily, understanding how meiosis divides chromosomes between cells is not that hard. Meiosis begins with a diploid cell that has already undergone DNA replication. The cell copies the chromosomes once and divides them twice, making four haploid cells.

MAIN IDEA
Cells go through two rounds of division in meiosis.

Meiosis is a form of nuclear division that creates four haploid cells from one diploid cell. This process involves two rounds of cell division—meiosis I and meiosis II. Each round of cell division has four phases, which are similar to those in mitosis. To keep the two processes distinct in your mind, focus on the big picture. Pay attention to how meiosis reduces chromosome number and creates genetic diversity.

Homologous Chromosomes and Sister Chromatids

To understand meiosis, you need to distinguish between homologous chromosomes and sister chromatids. As **FIGURE 6.3** shows, homologous chromosomes are two separate chromosomes: one from your mother, one from your father. Homologous chromosomes are very similar to each other, since they have the same length and carry the same genes. But they are not copies of each other. In contrast, each half of a duplicated chromosome is called a chromatid. Together, the two chromatids are called sister chromatids. Thus, *sister chromatids* refers to the duplicated chromosomes that remain attached (by the centromere). Homologous chromosomes are divided in meiosis I. Sister chromatids are not divided until meiosis II.

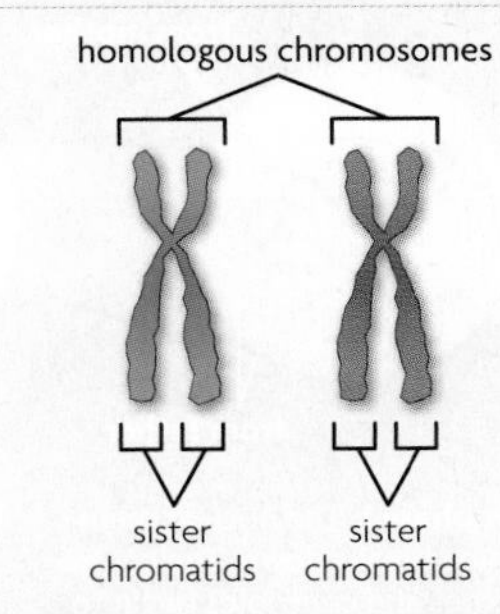

FIGURE 6.3 Homologous chromosomes (shown duplicated) are two separate chromosomes—one inherited from the mother, and one from the father.

***Connecting* CONCEPTS**

Mitosis As you learned in **Chapter 5**, a condensed, duplicated chromosome is made of two chromatids. Sister chromatids separate during anaphase in mitosis.

TAKING NOTES

Draw a Venn diagram like the one below to summarize the similarities and differences between meiosis I and meiosis II.

Meiosis I | Meiosis II
divides homologous chromosomes | chromosomes condense | divides sister chromatids

Differentiated Instruction

ENGLISH LEARNERS

Have students make a sequence diagram for meiosis I and meiosis II with a single pair of homologous chromosomes, like those in **FIGURE 6.3.** Tell them that meiosis is considered a reduction division because the chromosome number is reduced. Have them make a sequence diagram of mitosis, using **FIGURE 5.7** (parts 1–4) on page 141 as a guide. Tell students to compare the two diagrams and describe the differences to you.

Biology Toolkit, Compare/Contrast Chart, p. C34

PRE-AP

Prepare a number of true/false questions on the different phases of meiosis I and II. Having learned the basic phases of division in mitosis, see how well students anticipate how those apply to meiosis. Students should go back after reading the section and correct their answers as needed.

Biology Toolkit, Anticipation Guide, p. C3

Plan and Prepare ▼

Objectives

- Compare and contrast the two rounds of division in meiosis.
- Describe how haploid cells develop into mature gametes.

Section Resources

Unit Resource Book
Study Guide pp. 5–6
Power Notes p. 7
Reinforcement p. 8

Interactive Reader Chapter 6
Spanish Study Guide pp. 55–56

Biology Toolkit pp. C3, C34

Technology
Power Presentation 6.2
Media Gallery DVD
Online Quiz 6.2

Activate Prior Knowledge Discuss meiosis as though it is a simple equation wherein the DNA of two parents combines to form the DNA of one offspring. **Ask,** In order to make 1 + 1 = 1, what needs to happen to the DNA of the parents? needs to be reduced by half

Teach ▼

TEACH FROM VISUALS

FIGURE 6.3 Have students study the homologous chromosomes. **Ask**

- What can you say about the genetic material on two sister chromatids? It is identical.
- What can you say about the genetic material on the homologous chromosomes? The genes they contain code for and control the same features and functions, but they may do so in different ways, yielding variations in traits and functions.

▼ Teach *continued*

Vocabulary

Academic Vocabulary The steps of mitosis and meiosis are referred to as **phases.** A phase is one of a series of gradual changes, such as the phases of the moon.

An **equator** is a line that divides an object into two equal parts. Earth's equator divides Earth into the Northern and Southern Hemispheres. During metaphase of meiosis and mitosis, chromosomes line up along the cell equator. This allows the chromosomes to be divided equally to the two halves of the cell.

Greek and Latin Word Origins The prefixes of the four phases in meiosis I and meiosis II come from Greek word parts:

pro- = before
meta- = beside, after
ana- = up
telo- = end

TEACH FROM VISUALS

FIGURE 6.5 Have students examine steps 1–8. **Ask**

- In what way are the chromosomes in telophase I of meiosis different from those in telophase of mitosis? In telophase I of meiosis, the sister chromatids are not separated. In telophase of mitosis, the sister chromosomes have already separated, forming single chromosomes.
- Tell students that meiosis is often called reduction division. What is reduced in the first division? the number of chromosomes in each cell
- What is reduced in the second division? the amount of DNA in each cell
- In which division do the cells become haploid? in the first division

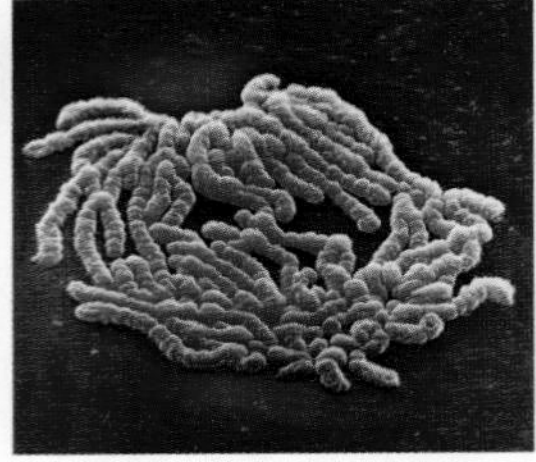

FIGURE 6.4 Homologous chromosomes separate during anaphase I. (colored SEM; magnification 2200×)

Meiosis I

Before meiosis begins, DNA has already been copied. Meiosis I divides homologous chromosomes, producing two haploid cells with duplicated chromosomes. Like mitosis, scientists describe meiosis in terms of phases, illustrated in **FIGURE 6.5** below. The figure is simplified, showing only four chromosomes.

1. **Prophase I** Early in meiosis, the nuclear membrane breaks down, the centrosomes and centrioles move to opposite sides of the cell, and spindle fibers start to assemble. The duplicated chromosomes condense, and homologous chromosomes pair up. They appear to pair up precisely, gene for gene, down their entire length. The sex chromosomes also pair with each other, and some regions of their DNA appear to line up as well.
2. **Metaphase I** The homologous chromosome pairs are randomly lined up along the middle of the cell by spindle fibers. The result is that 23 chromosomes—some from the father, some from the mother—are lined up along each side of the cell equator. This arrangement mixes up the chromosomal combinations and helps create and maintain genetic diversity. Since human cells have 23 pairs of chromosomes, meiosis may result in 2^{23}, or 8,388,608, possible combinations of chromosomes.
3. **Anaphase I** Next, the paired homologous chromosomes separate from each other and move toward opposite sides of the cell. The sister chromatids remain together during this step and throughout meiosis I.
4. **Telophase I** The nuclear membrane forms again in some species, the spindle fibers disassemble, and the cell undergoes cytokinesis. The end result is two cells that each have a unique combination of 23 duplicated chromosomes coming from both parents.

FIGURE 6.5 Meiosis

Meiosis I divides homologous chromosomes.

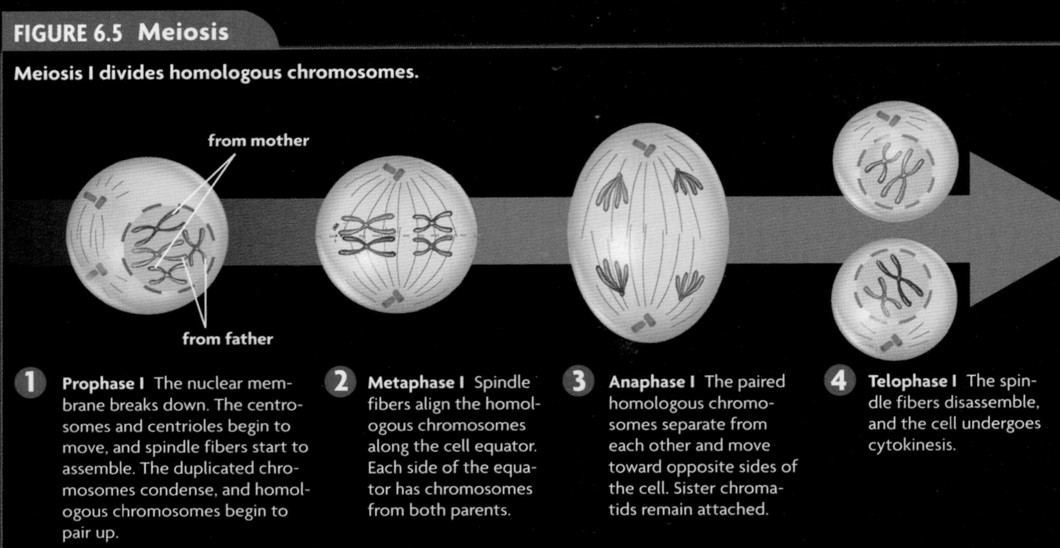

1 **Prophase I** The nuclear membrane breaks down. The centrosomes and centrioles begin to move, and spindle fibers start to assemble. The duplicated chromosomes condense, and homologous chromosomes begin to pair up.

2 **Metaphase I** Spindle fibers align the homologous chromosomes along the cell equator. Each side of the equator has chromosomes from both parents.

3 **Anaphase I** The paired homologous chromosomes separate from each other and move toward opposite sides of the cell. Sister chromatids remain attached.

4 **Telophase I** The spindle fibers disassemble, and the cell undergoes cytokinesis.

Differentiated Instruction

HANDS-ON ACTIVITY

Students can model meiosis I by using four pairs of shoes with laces. For example, students can use two pairs of sneakers and two pairs of leather shoes to represent two pairs of homologous chromosomes. Have students tie each pair of shoes together to represent sister chromatids held together by a centromere. They should place tags on each pair of shoes to indicate whether it came from the mother or the father. Tell students to use two equal lengths of yarn or string to mark a cell's perimeter on the floor. Then have them move the shoes around inside the circle to model the phases of meiosis I. After telophase I, have students form two cells from the two lengths of string. Students should observe that each cell contains a mixture of maternal and paternal chromosomes.

Meiosis II

Meiosis II divides sister chromatids, and results in undoubled chromosomes. The following description of this process applies to both of the cells produced in meiosis I. Note that DNA is not copied again between these two stages.

5 **Prophase II** The nuclear membrane breaks down, centrosomes and centrioles move to opposite sides of the cell, and spindle fibers assemble.

6 **Metaphase II** Spindle fibers align the 23 chromosomes at the cell equator. Each chromosome still has two sister chromatids at this stage.

7 **Anaphase II** Next, the sister chromatids are pulled apart from each other and move to opposite sides of the cell.

8 **Telophase II** Finally, nuclear membranes form around each set of chromosomes at opposite ends of the cell, the spindle fibers break apart, and the cell undergoes cytokinesis. The end result is four haploid cells with a combination of chromosomes from both the mother and father.

Now that you've seen how meiosis works, let's review some key differences between the processes of meiosis and mitosis.

- Meiosis has two cell divisions. Mitosis has only one cell division.
- During meiosis, homologous chromosomes pair up along the cell equator. During mitosis, homologous chromosomes never pair up.
- In anaphase I of meiosis, sister chromatids remain together. In anaphase of mitosis, sister chromatids separate.
- Meiosis results in haploid cells. Mitosis results in diploid cells.

A Contrast What is the major difference between metaphase I and metaphase II?

***Connecting* CONCEPTS**

Cytokinesis As you learned in **Chapter 5,** cytokinesis is the division of the cell cytoplasm. This process is the same in cells undergoing either mitosis or meiosis.

Animated BIOLOGY Watch meiosis in action at ClassZone.com.

Meiosis II divides sister chromatids. The overall process produces haploid cells.

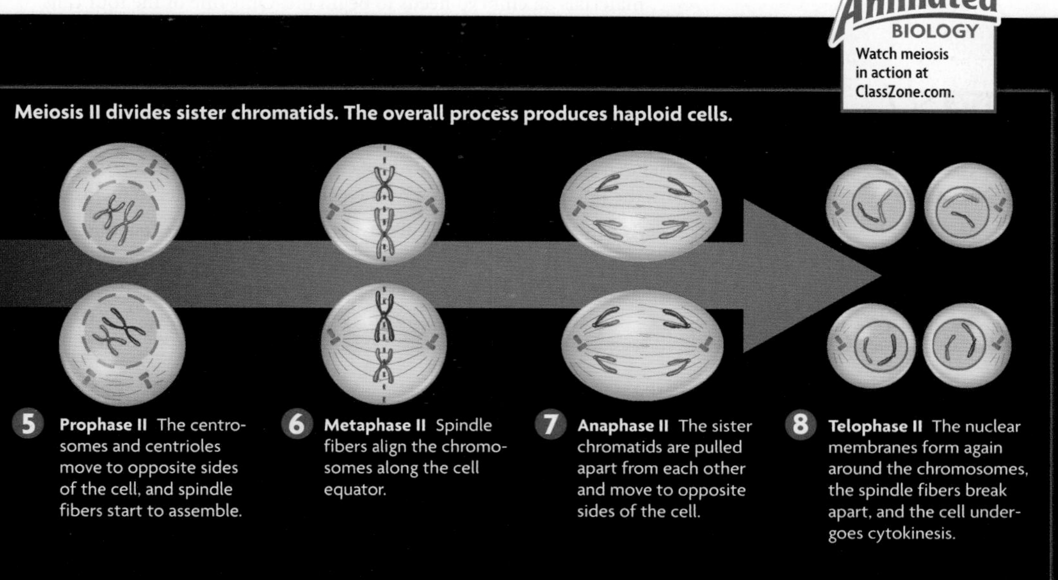

5 **Prophase II** The centrosomes and centrioles move to opposite sides of the cell, and spindle fibers start to assemble.

6 **Metaphase II** Spindle fibers align the chromosomes along the cell equator.

7 **Anaphase II** The sister chromatids are pulled apart from each other and move to opposite sides of the cell.

8 **Telophase II** The nuclear membranes form again around the chromosomes, the spindle fibers break apart, and the cell undergoes cytokinesis.

HANDS-ON ACTIVITY

Students can model meiosis II by continuing the activity from page 174. As prophase II begins, there are two pairs of shoes in each cell, each representing sister chromatids. During metaphase II, the pairs of shoes line up at the equators of the cells. In anaphase II, the shoelaces are untied, and the two shoes in each pair separate and move to opposite sides of the cells. In telophase II (cut strings in half), four cells form, each with two single shoes. **Ask**

- How does the final distribution of the shoes compare with the original distribution? Each cell has one shoe of each type.
- How are the maternal and paternal shoes distributed in the haploid cells? They are mixed up. Most likely, none of the four cells has all maternal or all paternal shoes.

Address Misconceptions

Common Misconception Students may think that only animal reproductive cells undergo meiosis.

Correcting the Misconception Emphasize that if an organism is to reproduce sexually by combining its genetic material with that of another, the number of chromosomes must be halved. The reproductive cells of all organisms that reproduce sexually must undergo meiosis.

Science Trivia

- The duration of meiosis is highly variable in nature.
- In a male mouse, meiosis lasts for about 12 days, most of that time in meiosis I.
- In the male reproductive organs of a lily, meiosis takes about 7 days, 6 of which are in meiosis I.
- Meiosis in a human male takes 24 days; in a female, it takes years and is not completed until fertilization occurs.
- In all sexually reproducing species, prophase I is always much longer than all the other meiotic stages combined.

Answers

A Contrast In metaphase I, pairs of homologous chromosomes line up at the equator. In metaphase II, the chromosomes are not paired.

▼ Teach *continued*

TEACH FROM VISUALS

FIGURE 6.6 Have students compare the processes of sperm production and egg production. **Ask,** In gametogenesis, how does the number of sperm formed in a male compare with the number of eggs formed in a female? For every egg cell produced during gametogenesis, four sperm cells are produced. Tell students that just because a male germ cell becomes four sperm while a female germ cell becomes one egg does not mean the ratio of sperm to egg in a male compared with female is 4:1. In all sexually reproducing animals, the number of sperm in a male is far greater than the number of eggs in a female.

Take It Further

During **embryonic development** in human females, about one million **primary oocytes** are formed by mitosis in each ovary. These cells begin but do not complete prophase I before the female is born. Years later, after puberty, one egg per month undergoes the rest of meiosis I. After metaphase II, the process stops again and will not continue for that egg unless it is fertilized.

Answers

A Apply The sperm cell's primary contribution to an embryo is DNA. By losing cytoplasm and gaining a tail and numerous mitochondria, the sperm cell can swim through the uterus and donate DNA to the egg.

MAIN IDEA

Haploid cells develop into mature gametes.

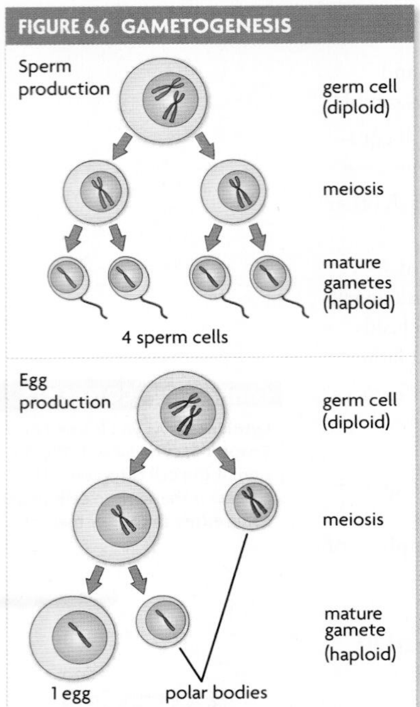

Haploid cells are the end result of meiosis. Yet these cells are incapable of fertilization until they go through more changes to form mature gametes. **Gametogenesis** (guh-MEE-tuh-JEHN-ih-sihs) is the production of gametes. As **FIGURE 6.6** shows, gametogenesis includes both meiosis and other changes that produce a mature cell. The final stages of gametogenesis differ between the sexes.

The **sperm** cell, the male gamete, is much smaller than the **egg,** the female gamete. The sperm cell's main contribution to an embryo is DNA. Yet it must swim to an egg to fertilize it, so the ability to move is critical. Sperm formation starts with a round cell and ends by making a streamlined cell that can move rapidly. During this process, significant changes occur. DNA is tightly packed and much of the cytoplasm is lost, forming a compact head. The sperm cell develops a whiplike flagellum and connecting neck region packed with mitochondria that drive the cell. Other changes also take place, such as the addition of new proteins to the cell membrane.

The formation of an egg is a complicated process, as you will read about in greater detail in Chapter 34. It begins before birth, inside the developing body of a female embryo, and is not finished until that egg is fertilized by a sperm many years later. The process includes periods of active development and long periods of inactivity.

An egg not only gives its share of DNA to an embryo but also contributes the organelles, molecular building blocks, and other materials an embryo needs to begin life. Only one of the four cells produced by each round of meiosis actually makes an egg. One cell—the egg—receives most of the organelles, cytoplasm, and nutrients. Many molecules are not evenly distributed throughout the egg's cytoplasm. This unequal distribution of molecules helps cells in the developing embryo to specialize. The other cells produced by meiosis become **polar bodies,** cells with little more than DNA that are eventually broken down. In many species, including humans, the polar body produced by meiosis I does not undergo meiosis II.

NSTA SCILINKS scilinks.org
For more about meiosis, go to scilinks.org.
Keycode: MLB006

A Apply Briefly explain how a sperm cell's structure is related to its function.

6.2 ASSESSMENT

ONLINE QUIZ ClassZone.com

B.6.4

REVIEWING MAIN IDEAS

1. How do homologous chromosomes differ from sister chromatids?
2. Explain why an **egg** is so much larger than a **sperm** cell.

CRITICAL THINKING

3. **Predict** If, during metaphase I, all 23 maternal chromosomes lined up on one side of the cell, would genetic diversity increase? Explain.
4. **Contrast** List the key differences between meiosis I and II.

***Connecting* CONCEPTS**

5. **Cell Biology** Both mitosis and meiosis are types of nuclear division, but they result in different cell types. Describe how the steps of meiosis I differ from those of mitosis.

▼ Assess and Reteach

Assess Use the Online Quiz or Section Quiz (*Assessment Book,* p. 110).

Reteach Draw the phases of meiosis I and have students provide you with information to label and summarize each phase. Then have volunteers draw the phases of meisosis II, and again have students provide you with information for labeling and summarizing the phases.

6.2 ASSESSMENT

1. homologous chromosomes: same genes but have different versions of them; sister chromatids: copies of each other, produced by DNA replication
2. An egg needs to provide the nutrients and building blocks for life to begin; a sperm needs only to reach the egg and deliver its DNA, so it is streamlined and small.
3. Genetic diversity would not increase because the maternal and paternal chromosomes would not become arranged in new combinations.
4. Meiosis I: begins with diploid cell, homologous chromosomes separate; meiosis II: begins with two haploid cells, sister chromatids separate.
5. Mitosis: chromosomes are duplicated and the copies are separated, one for each cell; meiosis I: duplicated chromosomes remain attached to each other, each new cell gets half of each homologous pair.

6.3 Mendel and Heredity

KEY CONCEPT Mendel's research showed that traits are inherited as discrete units.

MAIN IDEAS
- Mendel laid the groundwork for genetics.
- Mendel's data revealed patterns of inheritance.

VOCABULARY
trait, p. 177
genetics, p. 177
purebred, p. 178
cross, p. 178
law of segregation, p. 179

INDIANA STANDARDS

B.5.2 Describe how hereditary information passed from parents to offspring is encoded in regions of DNA molecules called genes.

Connect When a magician makes a coin disappear, you know the coin has not really vanished. You simply cannot see where it is. Maybe it is up a sleeve or in a pocket. When organisms reproduce, some traits seem to disappear too. For centuries, no one could explain why. Then a careful, observant scientist showed that behind this phenomenon were inherited units, or genes.

MAIN IDEA

Mendel laid the groundwork for genetics.

When we think of how offspring resemble or differ from their parents, we typically refer to specific traits. **Traits** are distinguishing characteristics that are inherited, such as eye color, leaf shape, and tail length. Scientists recognized that traits are hereditary, or passed from one generation to the next, long before they understood how traits are passed on. **Genetics** is the study of biological inheritance patterns and variation in organisms.

The groundwork for much of our understanding of genetics was laid in the middle of the 1800s by an Austrian monk named Gregor Mendel, shown in **FIGURE 6.7.** Scientists of the time commonly thought parents' traits were blended in offspring, like mixing red and white paint to get pink paint. But this idea failed to explain how certain traits remained without being "diluted." Mendel, a shrewd mathematician, bred thousands of plants, carefully counting and recording his results. From his data, Mendel correctly predicted the results of meiosis long before chromosomes were discovered. He recognized that traits are inherited as discrete units from the parental generation, like different colored marbles mixed together that can still be picked out separately. By recognizing that organisms inherit two copies of each discrete unit, what we now call genes, Mendel also described how traits were passed between generations.

A Connect Give two examples of traits not listed above.

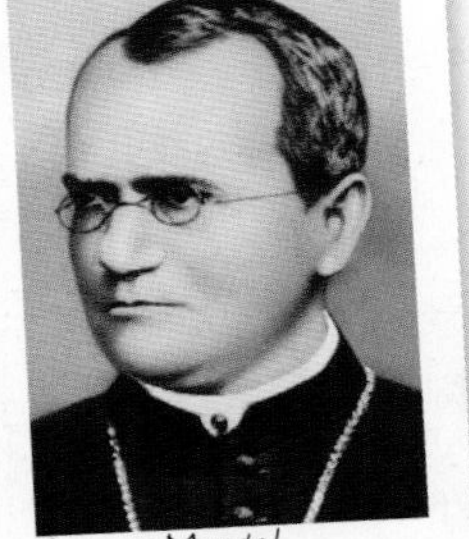

FIGURE 6.7 Gregor Mendel is called "the father of genetics" for discovering hereditary units. The significance of his work went unrecognized for almost 40 years.

MAIN IDEA

Mendel's data revealed patterns of inheritance.

Mendel studied plant variation in a monastery garden. He made three key choices about his experiments that played an important role in the development of his laws of inheritance: control over breeding, use of purebred plants, and observation of "either-or" traits that appeared in only two alternate forms.

Differentiated Instruction

ENGLISH LEARNERS

Let students work in small groups to create a graphic organizer for the second part of the section, "Mendel's Data . . ." Have them write the heading as a main idea in a box, with diverging boxes labeled with key terms and elements of Mendel's experiments.

Biology Toolkit, Supporting Main Ideas, p. C29

PRE-AP

Have students write a short essay evaluating Mendel's experimental design. Students should consider the following questions:

- Why was Mendel's use of pea plants a good choice?
- Why was it necessary for Mendel to use purebred plants in his experiments?

Biology Toolkit, Quick-Write, p. C19

Plan and Prepare

Objectives

- Describe the patterns of inheritance that Mendel's data revealed.
- Summarize Mendel's law of segregation.

Section Resources

Unit Resource Book
Study Guide pp. 9–10
Power Notes p. 11
Reinforcement p. 12
Pre-AP Activity pp. 27–28

Interactive Reader Chapter 6
Spanish Study Guide pp. 57–58

Biology Toolkit pp. C19, C29

Technology
Power Presentation 6.3
Media Gallery DVD
Online Quiz 6.3

Activate Prior Knowledge Students need to realize that genes don't change even though they can produce a range of variation, as in skin color or height. **Ask,** How is it that the same song can sound completely different when played by two different groups? differences in the make up of the band, interpretation of the music Explain that the expression of genes can vary.

Teach

Vocabulary

Academic Vocabulary The words **express** and **expression** are commonly used to describe a quality of communication: how a writer expresses ideas or a painter expresses emotion. In genetics, the words are applied to the effect genes have in the traits an organism exhibits, or *expresses.*

Answers

A Connect Examples include hair color, flower color, height, earlobe type, and blood type.

▼ Teach *continued*

ONLINE BIOLOGY Students can repeat Mendel's experiments online, then do their own virtual crosses with peas. See the interactive animation in Options for Inquiry, page 193. Go to the chapter Resource Center at **ClassZone.com** for additional resources and information on Gregor Mendel.

TEACH FROM VISUALS

FIGURE 6.8 Obtain flowers so students can see the parts of a flower Mendel worked with. **Ask,** Why did Mendel remove the stamens from his plants? to prevent the plant from self-pollinating

FIGURE 6.9 Explain that before Mendel, many scientists thought the traits of parents always became blended in their offspring. **Ask,** If this were true, what flower color would you expect to observe in the F_1 generation? light purple

History of Science

Gregor Mendel and **Charles Darwin** lived at the same time, but it wasn't until after their deaths that the compatibility of their ideas was discovered. Mendel had read Darwin's books and accepted the theory of natural selection; Darwin, on the other hand, was either unaware of Mendel's work or did not grasp its potential relevance to his own.

Because no one understood the significance of his work, Mendel stopped publishing the results of his experiments. He died in 1884, unrecognized for his scientific discoveries. In 1900, Mendel's work was recognized independently by three botanists. By this time, cells and chromosomes were sufficiently understood, providing a physical framework for Mendel's abstract ideas.

FIGURE 6.8 MENDEL'S PROCESS

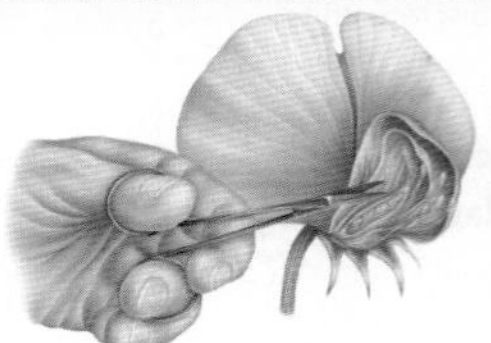

Mendel controlled the fertilization of his pea plants by removing the male parts, or stamens.

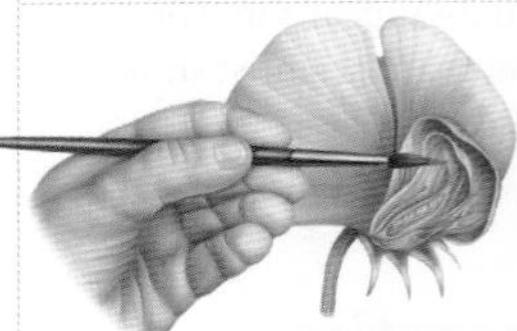

He then fertilized the female part, or pistil, with pollen from a different pea plant.

VOCABULARY
In Latin, the word *filius* means "son" and *filia* means "daughter."

Experimental Design

Mendel chose pea plants for his experiments because they reproduce quickly, and he could easily control how they mate. The sex organs of a plant are in its flowers, and pea flowers contain both male and female reproductive organs. In nature, the pea flower typically self-pollinates; that is, the plant mates with itself. If a line of plants has self-pollinated for long enough, that line becomes genetically uniform, or **purebred.** As a result, the offspring of purebred parents inherit all of the parent organisms' characteristics. Mendel was able to mate plants with specific traits by interrupting the self-pollination process. As you can see in **FIGURE 6.8,** he removed the male parts of flowers and fertilized the female parts with pollen that contained sperm cells from a different plant. Because he started with purebred plants, Mendel knew that any variations in offspring resulted from his experiments.

Mendel chose seven traits to follow: pea shape, pea color, pod shape, pod color, plant height, flower color, and flower position. All of these traits are simple "either-or" characteristics; they do not show intermediate features. The plant is tall or short. Its peas are wrinkled or round. What Mendel did not know was that most of the traits he had selected were controlled by genes on separate chromosomes. The selection of these particular traits played a crucial role in enabling Mendel to identify the patterns he observed.

Results

In genetics, the mating of two organisms is called a **cross.** An example of one of Mendel's crosses is highlighted in **FIGURE 6.9.** In this example, he crossed a purebred white-flowered pea plant with a purebred purple-flowered pea plant. These plants are the parental, or P, generation. The resulting offspring, called the first filial—or F_1—generation, all had purple flowers. The trait for white flowers seemed to disappear. When Mendel allowed the F_1 generation to self-fertilize, the resulting F_2 generation produced both plants with purple flowers and plants with white flowers. Therefore, the trait for white flowers had not disappeared; it had been hidden, or masked.

FIGURE 6.9 Mendel's Experimental Cross

Traits that were hidden when parental purebred flowers were crossed reappeared when the F_1 generation was allowed to self-pollinate.

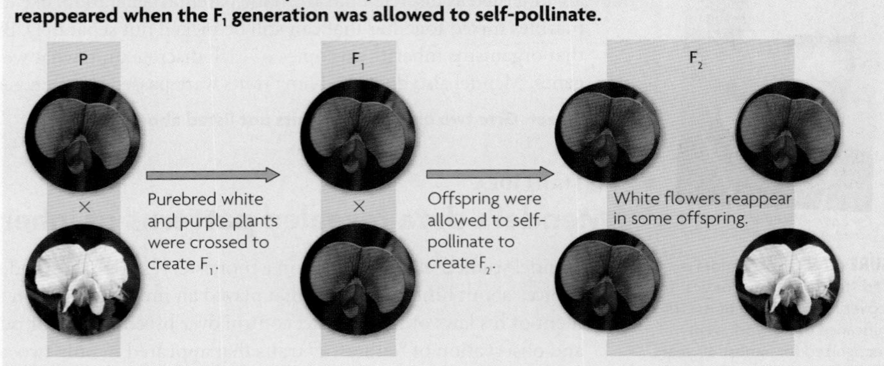
P
F_1
F_2
×
×
Purebred white and purple plants were crossed to create F_1.
Offspring were allowed to self-pollinate to create F_2.
White flowers reappear in some offspring.

Differentiated Instruction

BELOW LEVEL

Ratios and proportions can be difficult for students to understand, even though they are used every day. Begin by reviewing fractions, using a common example such as the number of each color of coated candies in a bag compared to the total number of candies. Then explain that a ratio is a comparison using division of two numbers. Tell students that ratios can be written in three ways, for example, 1:3, 1 to 3, and 1/3.

INCLUSION

Teach Mendelian genetics to students who are visually impaired by making peas of round and wrinkled types using table tennis balls and balls of aluminum foil or crumpled paper. Other traits can be re-created using fabric of different textures or actual flowers that are either terminal or axial.

Mendel did not cross only two plants, however; he crossed many plants. As a result, he was able to observe patterns. He noticed that each cross yielded similar ratios in the F_2 generation: about three-fourths of the plants had purple flowers, and about one-fourth had white flowers. A ratio is a comparison that tells how two or more things relate. This ratio can be expressed as 3:1 (read "three to one") of purple:white flowers. As you can see in **FIGURE 6.10**, Mendel's data show this approximately 3:1 ratio for each of his crosses.

FIGURE 6.10 MENDEL'S MONOHYBRID CROSS RESULTS

F_2 TRAITS	DOMINANT	RECESSIVE	RATIO
Pea shape	5474 round	1850 wrinkled	2.96:1
Pea color	6022 yellow	2001 green	3.01:1
Flower color	705 purple	224 white	3.15:1
Pod shape	882 smooth	299 constricted	2.95:1
Pod color	428 green	152 yellow	2.82:1
Flower position	651 axial	207 terminal	3.14:1
Plant height	787 tall	277 short	2.84:1

Source: Mendel, *Abhandlungen* (1865).

Conclusions

From these observations, Mendel drew three important conclusions. He demonstrated that traits are inherited as discrete units, which explained why individual traits persisted without being blended or diluted over successive generations. Mendel's two other key conclusions are collectively called the **law of segregation**, or Mendel's first law.

- Organisms inherit two copies of each gene, one from each parent.
- Organisms donate only one copy of each gene in their gametes. Thus, the two copies of each gene segregate, or separate, during gamete formation.

Section 6.5 covers Mendel's second law, the law of independent assortment.

Connecting CONCEPTS

Meiosis As you learned in **Section 6.2**, during meiosis, homologous chromosomes pair up in prophase I and are separated in anaphase I. The overall process produces haploid cells that have a random assortment of chromosomes.

A **Infer** **Explain why Mendel's choice of either-or characteristics aided his research.**

6.3 ASSESSMENT

ONLINE QUIZ ClassZone.com

B.5.2

REVIEWING MAIN IDEAS

1. Mendel had no understanding of DNA as the genetic material, yet he was able to correctly predict how **traits** were passed between generations. What does Mendel's work in **genetics** show about the value of scientific observation?
2. Why is it important that Mendel began with **purebred** plants?

CRITICAL THINKING

3. **Analyze** Mendel saw purple flowers in the F_1 generation, but both purple and white flowers in the F_2. How did this help him see that traits are inherited as discrete units?
4. **Evaluate** If Mendel had examined only one trait, do you think he would have developed the **law of segregation**? Explain.

Connecting CONCEPTS

5. **Scientific Process** You have learned that scientific thinking involves observing, forming hypotheses, testing hypotheses, and analyzing data. Use examples from Mendel's scientific process to show how his work fit this pattern.

Vocabulary

Academic Vocabulary The word **segregate** means "to separate" or "to isolate." In genetics, the function of segregation relates to the fact that genes are **discrete** or "separate" units.

Answers

A Infer Mendel could easily observe and quantify the effects of alleles, because there were only two possible outcomes. The application of mathematical analysis helped him see that there were two factors influencing the traits.

Assess and Reteach

Assess Use the Online Quiz or Section Quiz (*Assessment Book*, p. 111).

Reteach Project the image of **FIGURE 6.9** from the Media Gallery. Have students relate the traits exhibited by the offspring of the purebred pea plants to the law of segregation.

6.3 ASSESSMENT

1. Careful observation can lead to conclusions even though the underlying reason or mechanism behind a phenomenon is unknown.
2. Self-pollination of purebred plants always yields the same traits, so Mendel could be sure that any changes he saw were the result of the crosses he made.
3. The units of color (purple and white) were both individually present. They had neither blended together nor vanished.
4. *Sample Answer:* probably not, because by experimenting with multiple traits, he could see that the ratio of dominant to recessive traits in monohybrid crosses was always 3:1
5. Mendel observed the inheritance of certain either-or traits in pea plants and questioned how these traits were inherited over generations without becoming diluted. He hypothesized that he could answer this question by selectively breeding specific types of plants and observing the offspring, which he then did. Quantifying his results helped him develop his law of segregation, which he then tested and demonstrated in other either-or traits of pea plants.

SECTION 6.4

▼ Plan and Prepare

Objectives

- Explain how there can be many versions of one gene.
- Describe how genes influence the development of traits.

Section Resources

Unit Resource Book Study Guide pp. 13–14 Power Notes p. 15 Reinforcement p. 16
Interactive Reader Chapter 6 **Spanish Study Guide** pp. 59–60
Biology Toolkit pp. C20, C30, C40, D1
Technology Power Presentation 6.4 Media Gallery DVD Online Quiz 6.4

Activate Prior Knowledge Discuss the different varieties of specific human physical traits. **Ask,** Why can siblings display such diversity of traits, such as different eye or hair color? They inherited different forms of the genes that code for the development of those traits.

▼ Teach

Vocabulary

Greek and Latin Word Origins The suffix *-zygous* relates to the word **zygote,** which is the cell formed by the union of two gametes. Both come from the Greek word for yoke, the crossbar and halters that harness two farm animals together to work as one. Students can think of *homozygous* or *heterozygous* alleles as two horses side by side: their traits can be identical or very different.

Answers

A Compare and Contrast An allele is an alternative form of a gene, which codes for a different form of the same trait. Alleles are found at the same location, or locus, on homologous chromosomes.

6.4 Traits, Genes, and Alleles

KEY CONCEPT Genes encode proteins that produce a diverse range of traits.

MAIN IDEAS

- The same gene can have many versions.
- Genes influence the development of traits.

VOCABULARY

gene, p. 180
allele, p. 180
homozygous, p. 180
heterozygous, p. 180
genome, p. 181
genotype, p. 181
phenotype, p. 181
dominant, p. 181
recessive, p. 181

B.5.2 Describe how hereditary information passed from parents to offspring is encoded in regions of DNA molecules called genes.

Connect Most things come in many forms. Bread can be wheat, white, or rye. Cars can be two-door, four-door, hatchback, or convertible. Even the variety of potatoes cannot be counted on two hands. Genes, too, come in many forms.

MAIN IDEA

The same gene can have many versions.

As you have learned, Mendel's discrete units of heredity are now called genes. But what are genes? You can think of a **gene** as a piece of DNA that provides a set of instructions to a cell to make a certain protein. This definition is not precise, but it gives you the main idea. Each gene has a locus, a specific position on a pair of homologous chromosomes. Just as a house is a physical structure and an address tells where that house is located, you can think of the locus as the "address" that tells where a gene is located on a chromosome.

Most genes exist in many forms. In Mendel's experiments, the effects of these different forms were easy to see: yellow or green, round or wrinkled. An **allele** (uh-LEEL) is any of the alternative forms of a gene that may occur at a specific locus. Your cells have two alleles for each gene, one on each of the homologous chromosomes on which the locus for that gene is found. Each parent gives one allele. The two alleles may be the same, or they may be different. The term **homozygous** (HOH-moh-ZY-guhs) describes two of the same alleles at a specific locus. For example, both might code for white flowers. The term **heterozygous** (HEHT-uhr-uh-ZY-guhs) describes two different alleles at a specific locus. Thus, one might code for white flowers, the other for purple flowers.

VISUAL VOCAB

Homozygous alleles are identical to each other.

homozygous alleles
wrinkled
wrinkled
heterozygous alleles
wrinkled
round

Heterozygous alleles are different from each other.

A Compare and Contrast Distinguish between the terms *locus* and *allele*.

Differentiated Instruction

ENGLISH LEARNERS

Write the key vocabulary for this section on cards and display them for the class. As you discuss the words in class, point to the terms and arrange them to show how they relate to one another. This arrangement can be used as the foundation for a cluster diagram.

Biology Toolkit, Word Splash, p. D1; Cluster Diagram, p. C30

BELOW LEVEL

To reinforce the difference between a gene and an allele, have students make a chart with two columns labeled *Gene* and *Allele.* Ask them to place the terms in each of the following pairs in the correct column: hair color, brown hair; low cholesterol, cholesterol level; flower color, purple flowers; plant height, tall plant; long tail, tail length.

Biology Toolkit, T-Chart, p. C20

MAIN IDEA

Genes influence the development of traits.

You may have heard about the Human Genome Project. Its goal was to find out the sequence of the 3 billion nucleotide pairs that make up a human's genome. A **genome** is all of an organism's genetic material. Unless you have an identical twin, you have a unique genome that determines all of your traits. Some of your traits can be seen, such as the color of your eyes. Other traits cannot be seen, such as the exact chemical makeup of your eyeball.

In genetics, we often focus on a single trait or set of traits. A genome is all of an organism's genes, but a **genotype** (JEHN-uh-TYP) typically refers to the genetic makeup of a specific set of genes. The genotype of a pea plant includes both of the genes that code for flower color, even if one of these genes is masked. In contrast, the physical characteristics, or traits, of an individual organism make up its **phenotype** (FEE-nuh-TYP). A pea plant with purple flowers has a phenotype for purple flowers. The plant might have a hidden gene for white flowers, but that does not matter to its phenotype.

Dominant and Recessive Alleles

If an organism is heterozygous for a trait, which allele will be expressed? That is, if a plant has one allele for purple flowers and one for white flowers, what color will the flowers be? As Mendel learned, one allele may be dominant over another allele. A **dominant** allele is the allele that is expressed when two different alleles or two dominant alleles are present. A **recessive** allele is the allele that is only expressed when two copies are present. In Mendel's experiments, the allele for purple flowers was dominant to the allele for white flowers. All F_1 plants were purple even though they had only one allele for purple flowers.

VISUAL VOCAB

A **dominant** allele is expressed when two different alleles are present.

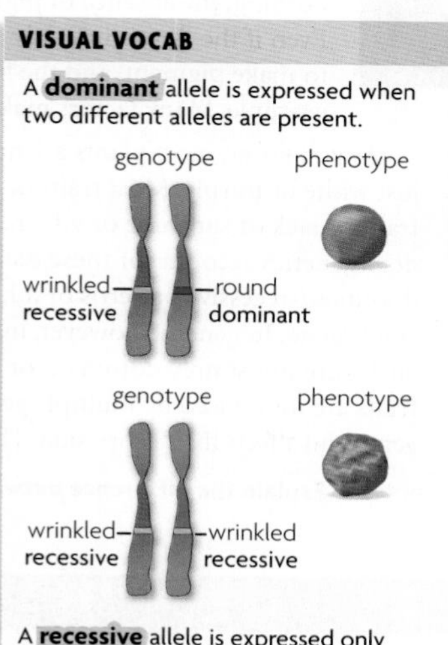

A **recessive** allele is expressed only when two copies are present.

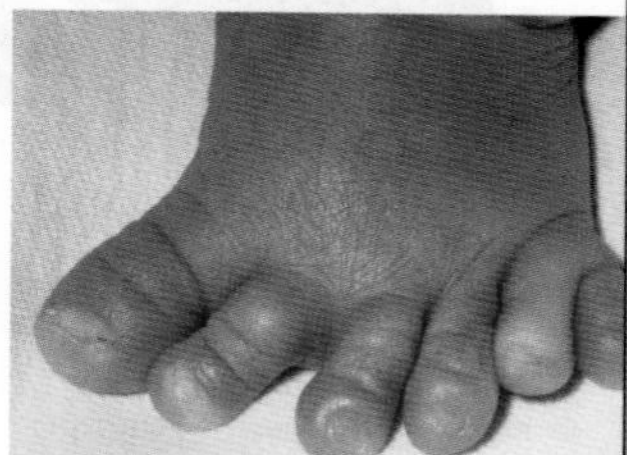

FIGURE 6.11 Polydactyly is the condition of having more than the typical number of fingers or toes. The allele for polydactyly is dominant.

Sometimes the word *dominant* is misunderstood. A dominant allele is not necessarily better or stronger than a recessive allele. It does not necessarily occur most often in the population. An allele is dominant in a heterozygote simply because it is expressed and the other allele is not.

Alleles are often represented on paper with individual letters. An organism's genotype for a trait can be shown with two letters—one per allele. Uppercase letters are used for dominant alleles, and lowercase letters are used for recessive alleles. For example, the dominant allele for height in pea plants is written as *T*, for tall. The recessive allele for short plants is written as *t*.

***Connecting* CONCEPTS**

Exceptions to Mendel's Laws Mendel's theory of inheritance cannot explain all patterns of inheritance. As you will learn in **Chapter 7**, incomplete dominance, codominance, polygenic traits, and environmental influences all provide exceptions.

ONLINE BIOLOGY Go to the chapter Resource Center at **ClassZone.com** for additional resources and information on heredity.

Vocabulary

genotype, phenotype *Genotype* comes from the Greek word *genos,* meaning "race" or "kind." *Phenotype* comes from the Greek word meaning "to show." A genotype indicates the combination of alleles for a select group of traits, whereas the phenotype shows how those alleles are expressed in an individual.

dominant, recessive The word *dominant* comes from the same Latin root as *dominate,* meaning "to rule." The word *recessive* shares the same Latin root as *recede,* meaning "to go back," as in withdraw or retreat.

TEACH FROM VISUALS

FIGURE 6.11 Point out that most people have five fingers and toes on each hand and foot, even though having five digits is recessive. Tell students that this can be explained by the fact that the allele for polydactyly is rarely found in most populations, despite being a dominant allele.

Integrating Agricultural Science

Many agriculturally important crop plants are polyploids, meaning they have multiple sets of chromosomes. These include sugar cane, wheat, oats, bananas, potatoes, coffee, and cotton. The plants tend to be larger or healthier, or have larger flowers than diploid plants. The basic set of chromosomes in a polyploid is the **monoploid** set. A plant breeder can isolate a desirable recessive trait in a monoploid set of chromosomes and then use a chemical called colchicine that interferes with spindle formation. As mitosis begins, the chromosomes are duplicated, but the cell doesn't divide. The result is a homozygous diploid plant with the desired characteristic.

PRE-AP

Have students structure the information in this section in the form of a concept map. Their concept maps should incorporate the Key Concept and Main Ideas of the section, as well as all of the key vocabulary.

Biology Toolkit, Concept Map, p. C40

▼ Teach *continued*

History of Science

The breakthrough that tied genes to the biochemistry of the cell came in 1941 when **George Beadle** and **Edward Tatum** rediscovered the work of **Archibald Garrod** (1909). The relationship between genotype and phenotype became clear when Beadle and Tatum's experimental results led them to the conclusion that each gene is responsible for the production of a single, specific enzyme. This became known as the **one gene/one enzyme** hypothesis. Further research in genetics has shown that not all proteins are enzymes and that some enzymes are made of more than one polypeptide chain. Thus, a more accurate way of expressing this foundation of modern genetics is **one gene/one polypeptide.**

Answers

A Contrast Genotype refers to the actual genes an organism carries. Phenotype typically refers to an organism's physical appearance or the expression of a certain gene.

▼ Assess and Reteach

Assess Use the Online Quiz or Section Quiz (*Assessment Book,* p. 112).

Reteach Work with students to create a concept map that uses as many of the vocabulary terms in this section as possible.

Animated BIOLOGY Explore how genotype affects phenotype at ClassZone.com.

A plant's genotype might be homozygous dominant (*TT*), heterozygous (*Tt*), or homozygous recessive (*tt*).

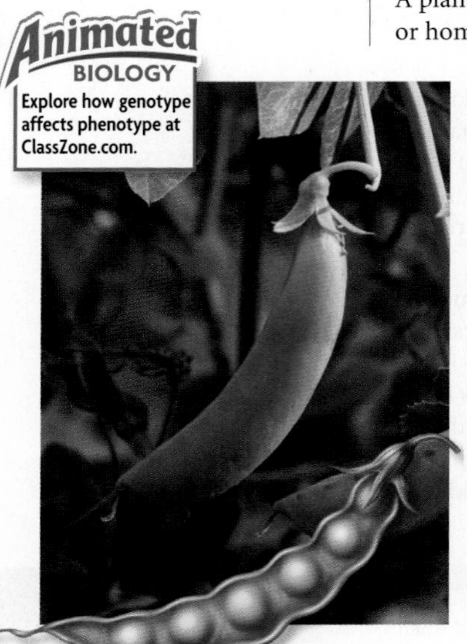

FIGURE 6.12 Both the homozygous dominant and heterozygous genotypes result in smooth, or inflated, pods (top). Only the homozygous recessive genotype results in constricted pods (inset).

Alleles and Phenotype

Because some alleles are dominant over others, two genotypes can produce the dominant phenotype. For example, smooth pods and constricted pods in pea plants, shown in **FIGURE 6.12,** are phenotypes. A plant with smooth pods could have a homozygous dominant (*SS*) or heterozygous (*Ss*) genotype. In contrast, a plant with constricted, or compressed, pods could only have a homozygous recessive (*ss*) genotype.

What actually makes one allele dominant over another? The answer is very complicated. It depends on the nature of the protein that is, or is not, made. Let's look at a fairly simple example. Pigment gives cells color. If *P* directs flower cells to make pigment, the flower may look purple. If *p* directs the cells not to make pigment, the flower looks white. So *P* codes for pigment to be present, but *p* codes for nothing, the absence of pigment. As a result, *P* has to be dominant. Even if the flower has only one *P* allele (*Pp*), that one allele tells its cells to make pigment, and the flower has color. Flower pigment is only one example. Many factors make one allele dominant over another.

As you know, most plants are not simply tall or short. Most flowers are not just white or purple. Most traits occur in a range. Other factors also affect traits. A lack of sunshine or vital nutrients could stunt a plant's growth. How does genetics account for these issues? Mendel studied traits that follow simple dominant-recessive patterns of inheritance, and each trait was the result of a single gene. In general, however, inheritance is much more complex. Most alleles are not simply dominant or recessive; some are codominant. Many traits are influenced by multiple genes. The environment also interacts with genes and affects their expression. These complexities are discussed in Chapter 7.

A Contrast **Explain the difference between genotype and phenotype.**

6.4 ASSESSMENT

ONLINE QUIZ ClassZone.com

B.5.2

REVIEWING ▶ MAIN IDEAS

1. How are the terms **gene,** locus, and **allele** related?
2. Explain why an organism's genotype may be **homozygous** dominant, homozygous recessive, or **heterozygous,** but never heterozygous recessive.

CRITICAL THINKING

3. **Apply** Suppose you are studying a fruit fly's DNA and you discover a gene for antenna length on chromosome 2. What word describes its location, and where would it be found in other fruit flies' DNA?
4. **Predict** If a **recessive** allele helps an organism reproduce, but the **dominant** allele hinders reproduction, which will be more common in a population?

***Connecting* CONCEPTS**

5. **Human Biology** Cystic fibrosis is a recessive disease that causes the production of abnormally thick, life-threatening mucus secretions. What is the **genotype** of a person with cystic fibrosis: *CC*, *Cc*, or *cc*? Explain.

182 Unit 3: Genetics

6.4 ASSESSMENT

1. All have something to do with a particular segment of DNA, or nucleotides. A gene is a region of DNA, a series of nucleotides that codes for a protein. It can come in different forms, called alleles, that code for the same general type of information but the specifics vary. The locus tells where a particular gene or allele is located on a chromosome.
2. The only way a phenotype or genotype can be recessive is if both alleles are recessive.
3. locus; on chromosome 2 at the same locus
4. the recessive allele
5. The person's genotype is *cc*. If a disease or other trait is recessive, a person must have two recessive alleles for the trait to be expressed.

6.5 Traits and Probability

KEY CONCEPT The inheritance of traits follows the rules of probability.

MAIN IDEAS

- Punnett squares illustrate genetic crosses.
- A monohybrid cross involves one trait.
- A dihybrid cross involves two traits.
- Heredity patterns can be calculated with probability.

VOCABULARY

Punnett square, p. 183
monohybrid cross, p. 184
testcross, p. 185
dihybrid cross, p. 186
law of independent assortment, p. 186
probability, p. 187

B.7.1 Distinguish between dominant and recessive alleles and determine the phenotype that would result from the different possible combinations of alleles in an offspring.

B.7.3 Determine the likelihood of the appearance of a specific trait in an offspring given the genetic make-up of the parents.

Connect If you have tried juggling, you know it can be a tricky thing. Keeping three flaming torches or juggling clubs in motion at the same time is a lot to handle. Trying to keep track of what organism has which genotype and which gamete gets which allele can also be a lot to juggle. Fortunately, R. C. Punnett developed a method to graphically keep track of all of the various combinations.

MAIN IDEA

Punnett squares illustrate genetic crosses.

Shortly after Mendel's experiments became widely known among scientists, a poultry geneticist named R. C. Punnett, shown in **FIGURE 6.13,** developed the Punnett square. A **Punnett square** is a grid system for predicting all possible genotypes resulting from a cross. The axes of the grid represent the possible gamete genotypes of each parent. The grid boxes show all of the possible genotypes of offspring from those two parents. Because segregation and fertilization are random events, each combination of alleles is as likely to be produced as any other. By counting the number of squares with each genetic combination, we can find the ratio of genotypes in that generation. If we also know how the genotype corresponds to the phenotype, we can find the ratio of phenotypes in that generation as well.

VISUAL VOCAB

The **Punnett square** is a grid system for predicting possible genotypes of offspring.

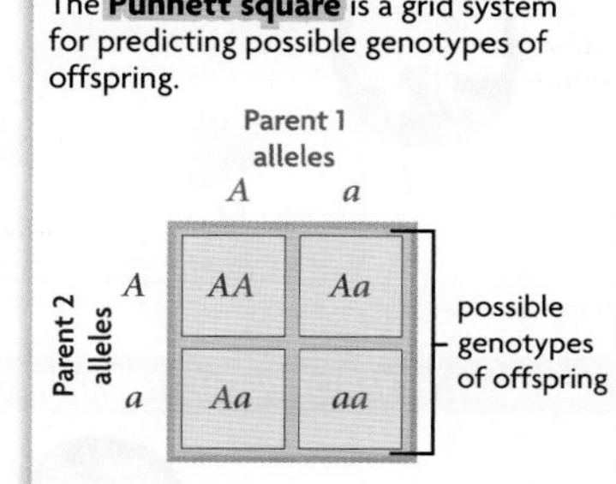

Let's briefly review what you've learned about meiosis and segregation to examine why the Punnett square is effective. Both parents have two alleles for each gene. These alleles are represented on the axes of the Punnett square. During meiosis, the chromosomes—and, therefore, the alleles—are separated.

FIGURE 6.13 R. C. Punnett developed the Punnett square as a way to illustrate genetic crosses.

Differentiated Instruction

ENGLISH LEARNERS

After reading the section, do a jigsaw activity. With students in home groups of four, assign topics by number: (1) Punnett square, (2) monohybrid cross, (3) test cross, (4) dihybrid cross. Have students move into expert groups to prepare a lesson on their topic. Then have the experts return to their home groups to teach their lessons to one another.

Biology Toolkit, Jigsaw Reading, p. C15

BELOW LEVEL

Use an overhead projector to project a blank Punnett square. Lead students through the steps in each of the monohybrid crosses illustrated in this section. Show how to write the possible gamete genotypes of each parent across the top and side of the Punnett square. Draw arrows to show how to record each allele in the appropriate box. Have students determine the genotype and phenotype of each possible offspring.

SECTION 6.5

Plan and Prepare

Objectives

- Describe monohybrid and dihybrid crosses.
- Explain how heredity can be illustrated mathematically.

Section Resources

Unit Resource Book
Study Guide pp. 17–18
Power Notes p. 19
Reinforcement p. 20

Interactive Reader Chapter 6
Spanish Study Guide pp. 61–62

Biology Toolkit pp. C15, C19

Technology
Power Presentation 6.5
Media Gallery DVD
Online Quiz 6.5

Activate Prior Knowledge Discuss probability as it applies to everyday life. **Ask,** In what ways do you apply probability or likelihood in your everyday life? Students may mention card games, answering multiple-choice questions on tests, or sports in which players often guess what the opponent will do next. Discuss how in any of these activities, participants must determine the chance or likelihood of a specific event happening.

Teach

TEACH FROM VISUALS

VISUAL VOCAB Emphasize that it makes no difference which parental genotype is shown on each axis of a Punnett square. On the board, draw two Punnett squares for the cross *Aa* × *aa*. On one, place the *Aa* across the top; on the other, place the *Aa* along the side. Fill in the grids. The results are the same, although the Punnett squares look different.

▼ Teach *continued*

ONLINE BIOLOGY Have students make crosses to determine how certain genes are inherited in fruit flies in the virtual lab in Options for Inquiry on page 193.

TEACH FROM VISUALS

FIGURE 6.14 Point out that this is the cross that Mendel did to produce the F_1 generation. **Ask,** What did Mendel call a homozygous plant such as *FF* or *ff*? a purebred plant

FIGURE 6.15 Point out that this is the cross that Mendel did when he allowed the F_1 plants to self-pollinate to produce the F_2 generation. **Ask,** How did the white flower appear among the off-spring if neither parent had white flowers? Each parent produced some gametes that contained the recessive allele for white flowers. When two such gametes came together, a white-flowered offspring was produced.

The Inside Story

Reginald C. Punnett was an authority on poultry breeding. He developed many new breeds of chickens by transferring genes located on the X chromosome of one breed to the chromosomes of another breed. This work was done in the 1920s and can be thought of as an early method of genetic engineering. His work ended in 1955, when his incubator house was destroyed by fire.

Each gamete gets one of the alleles. Since each parent contributes only one allele to the offspring, only one allele from each parent is written inside each grid box. Fertilization restores the diploid number in the resulting offspring, which is why each grid box has two alleles, one from the mother and one from the father. Since any egg has the same chance of being fertilized by any sperm cell, each possible genetic combination is equally likely to occur.

A Explain What do the letters on the axes of the Punnett square represent?

MAIN IDEA

A monohybrid cross involves one trait.

Thus far, we have studied **monohybrid crosses,** crosses that examine the inheritance of only one specific trait. Three example crosses are used below and on the next page to illustrate how Punnett squares work and to highlight the resulting ratios—for both genotype and phenotype.

FIGURE 6.14 HOMOZYGOUS-HOMOZYGOUS

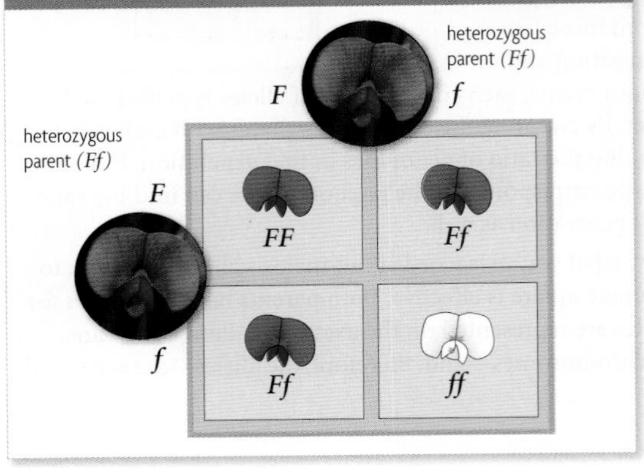

Homozygous-Homozygous

Suppose you cross a pea plant that is homozygous dominant for purple flowers with a pea plant that is homozygous recessive for white flowers. To determine the genotypic and phenotypic ratios of the offspring, first write each parent's genotype on one axis: *FF* for the purple-flowered plant, *ff* for the white-flowered plant. Every gamete from the purple-flowered plant contains the dominant allele, *F*. Every gamete from the white-flowered plant contains the recessive allele, *f*. Therefore, 100 percent of the offspring have the heterozygous genotype, *Ff*. And 100 percent of the offspring have purple flowers, because they all have a copy of the dominant allele, as shown in **FIGURE 6.14.**

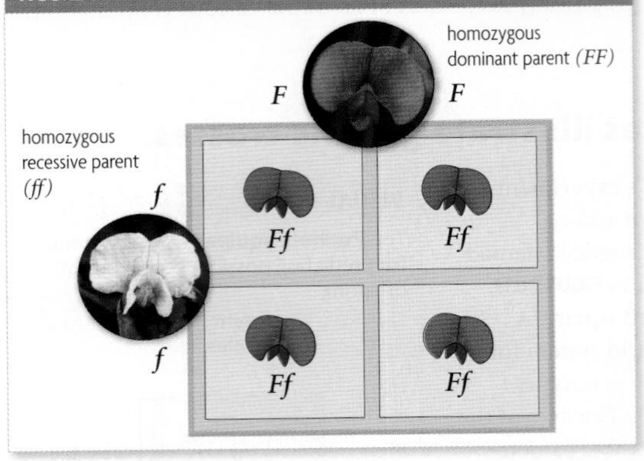

FIGURE 6.15 HETEROZYGOUS-HETEROZYGOUS

Heterozygous-Heterozygous

Next, in **FIGURE 6.15,** you can see a cross between two purple-flowered pea plants that are both heterozygous (*Ff*). From each parent, half the offspring receive a dominant allele, *F*, and half receive a recessive allele, *f*. Therefore, one-fourth of the offspring have a homozygous dominant genotype, *FF*; half have a heterozygous genotype, *Ff*; and one-fourth have a homozygous recessive genotype, *ff*. Both the *FF* and the *Ff* genotypes result in purple flowers. Only the *ff* genotype results in white flowers. Thus, the genotypic ratio is 1:2:1 of homozygous dominant:heterozygous:homozygous recessive. The phenotypic ratio is 3:1 of purple:white flowers.

Answers

A Explain alleles of the parents

Differentiated Instruction

BELOW LEVEL

Be sure students understand that a Punnett square shows the proportions of gamete combinations expected to occur, not the actual numbers of combinations that do occur. As an example, make a Punnett square showing two X chromosome gametes on one axis (from the female parent) and one X chromosome gamete and one Y chromosome gamete on the other axis (from the male parent). Fill in the boxes to show that equal numbers of males and females are to be expected. Compare this with actual ratios of males and females in students' families.

Heterozygous-Homozygous

Finally, suppose you cross a pea plant that is heterozygous for purple flowers (*Ff*) with a pea plant that is homozygous recessive for white flowers (*ff*). As before, each parent's genotype is placed on an axis, as shown in **FIGURE 6.16.** From the homozygous parent with white flowers, the offspring each receive a recessive allele, *f*. From the heterozygous parent, half the offspring receive a dominant allele, *F*, and half receive a recessive allele, *f*. Half the offspring have a heterozygous genotype, *Ff*. Half have a homozygous recessive genotype, *ff*. Thus, half the offspring have purple flowers, and half have white flowers. The resulting genotypic ratio is 1:1 of heterozygous:homozygous recessive. The phenotypic ratio is 1:1 of purple:white.

FIGURE 6.16 HETEROZYGOUS-HOMOZYGOUS

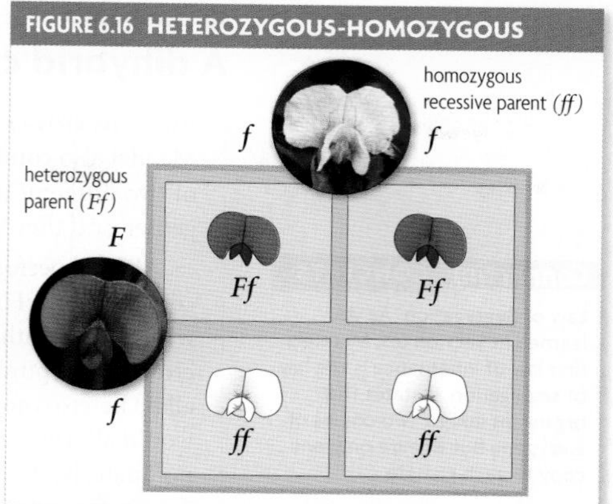

Suppose we did not know the genotype of the purple flower in the cross above. This cross would allow us to determine that the purple flower is heterozygous, not homozygous dominant. A **testcross** is a cross between an organism with an unknown genotype and an organism with the recessive phenotype. The organism with the recessive phenotype must be homozygous recessive. The offspring will show whether the organism with the unknown genotype is heterozygous, as above, or homozygous dominant.

A Apply **From an *FF* × *Ff* cross, what percent of offspring would have purple flowers?**

QUICK LAB **INFERRING** B.7.3

Using a Testcross

Suppose you work for a company that sells plant seeds. You are studying a plant species in which the dominant phenotype is pink flowers (*PP* or *Pp*). The recessive phenotype is white flowers (*pp*). Customers have been requesting more plants with pink flowers. To meet this demand, you need to determine the genotypes of some of the plants you are currently working with.

PROBLEM What is the genotype of each plant?

PROCEDURE

1. Suppose you are presented with Plant A of the species you are studying, which has pink flowers. You want to determine the genotype of the plant.
2. You cross Plant A with Plant B of the same species, which has white flowers and a known genotype of *pp*.
3. The resulting cross yields six plants with pink flowers and six plants with white flowers. Use Punnett squares to determine the genotype of Plant A.

MATERIALS
- pencil
- paper

ANALYZE AND CONCLUDE

1. **Apply** What is the genotype of Plant A? Explain how you arrived at your answer.
2. **Apply** What are the possible genotypes and phenotypes of offspring if Plant A is crossed with a plant that has a genotype of *PP*?
3. **Calculate** What ratio of dominant to recessive phenotypes would exist if Plant A were crossed with a plant that has a genotype of *Pp*?
4. **Evaluate** Is Plant A the best plant, in terms of genotype, that you can work with to produce as many of the requested seeds as possible? Why or why not? Which genotype would be best to work with?

ONLINE BIOLOGY Students can learn how dog breeders use Mendel's principles to enhance certain traits. See the WebQuest in Options for Inquiry, page 193.

Answers

A Apply 100 percent

QUICK LAB

Time 15 minutes — TEACHER TESTED

Lab Binder Genetics, pp. 7–8

Purpose Determine the genotype of a plant by analyzing a testcross.

LAB MANAGEMENT

Tell students that they will need to work backwards from a Punnett square to determine the genotype of one of the parents.

Answers

1. Plant A has a *Pp* genotype. If it were *PP*, there would not have been any white offspring from the testcross.
2. All the offspring would have pink flowers. Half would have the *PP* genotype; the other half would have the *Pp* genotype.
3. 3:1 of pink:white
4. Plant A is not the best plant to work with. A homozygous dominant plant (*PP*) would be better because all crosses would produce only pink-flowered offspring.

PRE-AP

Have students imagine that they will be breeding guinea pigs. Black fur, a recessive trait, is most popular. Have students develop a plan for raising as many black guinea pigs as possible. **Ask,** Which cross will produce the most black guinea pigs? Black × black (both homozygous recessive) will produce all black offspring. **Ask,** Which cross is expected to produce black fur in about half the offspring? a cross between a black guinea pig and a heterozygous guinea pig

Biology Toolkit, Quick-Write, p. C19

▼ Teach continued

The Inside Story

Mendel was either very lucky in his choice of traits to study or he did not report crosses with traits that did not show **independent assortment.** Garden peas have seven pairs of chromosomes. Genes for six of the seven traits Mendel chose are located on separate chromosomes. The gene for the seventh trait shares a chromosome with another gene Mendel studied, but it is so far away from that gene that the two genes sort independently.

TEACH FROM VISUALS

FIGURE 6.17 Have students examine the Punnett square. **Ask,** Would this Punnett square represent the expected results if the genes for the two traits were inherited together? No, if the genes were inherited together, you would not expect to see all the different combinations of alleles.

Vocabulary

Academic Vocabulary The **grid system** of a Punnett square makes it easy to determine all possible combinations of male and female gametes. Many cities have a street grid system, making it easy to find one's way in the city. Maps have a grid system that makes it easy to find specific locations on a map.

Answers

A Analyze Two alleles are shown because two different genes are being observed. Each gamete has one allele for each gene.

MAIN IDEA

A dihybrid cross involves two traits.

All of the crosses discussed so far have involved only a single trait. However, Mendel also conducted **dihybrid crosses,** crosses that examine the inheritance of two different traits. He wondered if both traits would always appear together or if they would be expressed independently of each other.

Connecting CONCEPTS

Law of Segregation As you learned in **Section 6.3,** Mendel's first law of inheritance is the law of segregation. It states that organisms inherit two copies of each gene but donate only one copy to each gamete.

Mendel performed many dihybrid crosses and tested a variety of different combinations. For example, he would cross a plant with yellow round peas with a plant with green wrinkled peas. Remember that Mendel began his crosses with purebred plants. Thus, the first generation offspring (F_1) would all be heterozygous and would all look the same. In this example, the plants would all have yellow round peas. When Mendel allowed the F_1 plants to self-pollinate, he obtained the following results: 9 yellow/round, 3 yellow/wrinkled, 3 green/round, 1 green/wrinkled.

Mendel continued to find this approximately 9:3:3:1 phenotypic ratio in the F_2 generation, regardless of the combination of traits. From these results, he realized that the presence of one trait did not affect the presence of another trait. His second law of genetics, the **law of independent assortment,** states that allele pairs separate independently of each other during gamete formation, or meiosis. That is, different traits appear to be inherited separately.

The results of Mendel's dihybrid crosses can also be illustrated with a Punnett square, like the one in **FIGURE 6.17.** Drawing a Punnett square for a dihybrid cross is the same as drawing one for a monohybrid cross, except that the grid is bigger because two genes, or four alleles, are involved. For example, suppose you cross two plants with yellow, round peas that are heterozygous for both traits (*YyRr*). The four allele combinations possible in each gamete—*YR*, *Yr*, *yR*, and *yr*—are used to label each axis. Each grid box can be filled in using the same method as that used in the monohybrid cross. A total of nine different genotypes may result from the cross in this example. However, these nine genotypes produce only four different phenotypes. These phenotypes are yellow round, yellow wrinkled, green round, and green wrinkled, and they occur in the ratio of 9:3:3:1. Note that the 9:3:3:1 phenotypic ratio results from a cross between organisms that are heterozygous for both traits. The phenotypic ratio of the offspring will differ (from 9:3:3:1) if one or both of the parent organisms are homozygous for one or both traits.

FIGURE 6.17 DIHYBRID CROSS

This dihybrid cross is heterozygous-heterozygous.

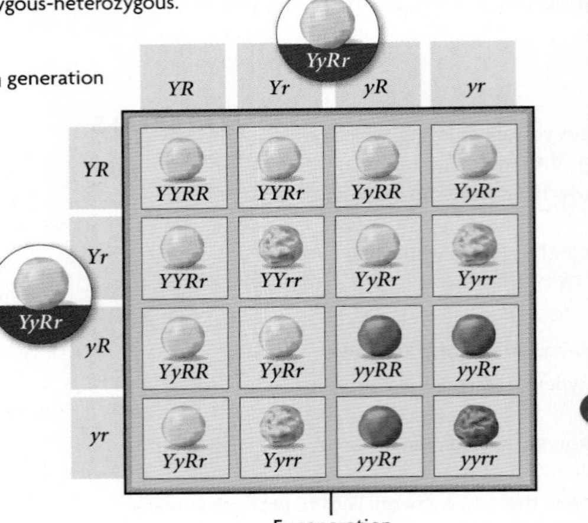

A Analyze In FIGURE 6.17, the boxes on the axes represent the possible gametes made by each parent plant. Why does each box have two alleles?

Differentiated Instruction

BELOW LEVEL

Write the letters *YyRr* on the board to represent a parent's alleles for two traits. Show students how to determine the possible gametes that can form, as follows: Draw an arrow under the letters from the *Y* to the *R* and an arrow from the *Y* to the *r*. Write the gamete genotypes *YR* and *Yr* on the board. Now draw an arrow above the letters from the *y* to the *R* and an arrow from the *y* to the *r*. Write the gamete genotypes *yR* and *yr* on the board. Have students use this method to determine the possible gametes that can form when they make a Punnett square for a dihybrid cross.

HANDS-ON ACTIVITY

Give each student one large paper clip and one small paper clip, one large bean and one small bean. Tell students that the objects represent alleles for a paper-clip gene and a bean gene. Large paper clips and large beans are dominant alleles; small paper clips and small beans are recessive alleles. Have students model independent assortment of their "alleles" into gametes. Students should produce four kinds of "gametes": large paper clip and large bean, large paper clip and small bean, small paper clip and large bean, and small paper clip and small bean.

MAIN IDEA

Heredity patterns can be calculated with probability.

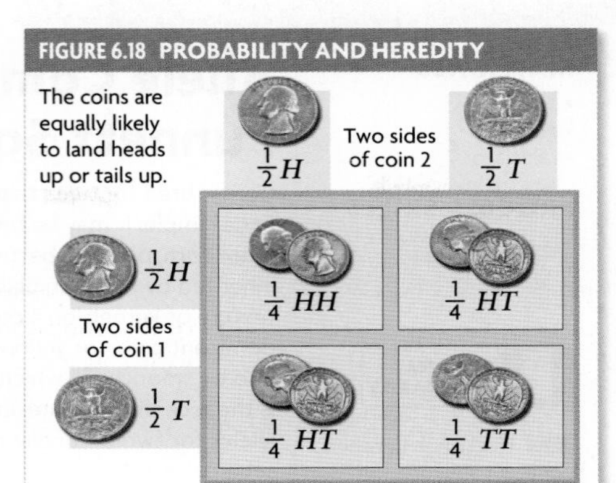

FIGURE 6.18 PROBABILITY AND HEREDITY

Probability is the likelihood that a particular event will happen. It predicts the average number of occurrences, not the exact number of occurrences.

$$\text{Probability} = \frac{\text{number of ways a specific event can occur}}{\text{number of total possible outcomes}}$$

Suppose you flip a coin. The number of total possible outcomes is two: heads up or tails up. The probability that it would land heads up is 1/2, or one out of two. The probability that it would land tails up is also 1/2.

Next, suppose you flip two coins. How one coin lands does not affect how the other coin lands. To calculate the probability that two independent events will happen together, multiply the probability of each individual event. The probability that both coins will land heads up, for example, is $1/2 \times 1/2 = 1/4$.

These probabilities can be applied to meiosis. Suppose a germ cell undergoes meiosis in a plant that is heterozygous for purple flowers. The number of total possible outcomes is two because a gamete could get a dominant or a recessive allele. The probability that a gamete will get a dominant allele is 1/2. The probability that it will get a recessive allele is also 1/2.

If two plants that are heterozygous for purple flowers fertilize each other, the probability that both egg and sperm have a dominant allele is $1/2 \times 1/2 = 1/4$. So, too, the probability that both have a recessive allele is 1/4. There is also a 1/4 chance that a sperm cell with a dominant allele will fertilize an egg with a recessive allele, or that a sperm cell with a recessive allele will fertilize an egg with a dominant allele. These last two combinations are basically the same. In either case, the resulting plant will be heterozygous. Thus, the probability that a pea plant will be heterozygous for this trait is the sum of the probabilities: $1/4 + 1/4 = 1/2$.

Apply **Explain how Mendel's laws relate to probability.**

Integrating Statistics

Have students refer back to Mendel's data in **FIGURE 6.10** on page 179 and look at the ratios in the last column. Students should recognize that Mendel's ratios approximate the expected 3:1 ratio. Tell them that the more observations that are made, the closer the actual ratio will approach the expected ratio. For example, if a coin was tossed 1000 times, we could expect the ratio of heads-to-tails to be closer to 1:1 than if the coin was tossed four times. In statistics, on which science relies heavily, the number of observations or data is referred to as the **sample size.** The larger the sample size, the more reliable is the data.

Compare the coin example with how the ratio of males to females in families is often very different from the expected 1:1 ratio.

Answers

A Apply Mendel's laws of segregation and probability are based on random events. The chance, or probability, that two particular events will occur together during meiosis is determined in the same way as any other set of random events.

6.5 ASSESSMENT

ONLINE QUIZ ClassZone.com

B.7.1, B.7.3

REVIEWING MAIN IDEAS

1. What do the grid boxes in a **Punnett square** represent?
2. Why does the expected genotypic ratio often differ from the expected phenotypic ratio resulting from a **monohybrid cross**?
3. How did Mendel's **dihybrid crosses** help him develop his second law?

CRITICAL THINKING

4. **Calculate** What would be the phenotypic ratios of the offspring resulting from the following cross: *YYRr* × *YyRr*?
5. **Predict** If you are working with two tall pea plants and know that one is *Tt*, how could you determine the genotype of the other plant?

Connecting CONCEPTS

6. **Adaptation** You have seen that one-quarter of offspring resulting from two heterozygous parents are homozygous recessive. Yet for some genes, the recessive allele is more common in the population. Explain why this might be.

Assess and Reteach

Assess Use the Online Quiz or Section Quiz (*Assessment Book*, p. 113).

Reteach Work with students to calculate the probabilities of the genotypes and phenotypes of the offspring shown in the Punnett squares in **FIGURES 6.15** and **6.16.**

6.5 ASSESSMENT

1. all the possible allele combinations of offspring resulting from a cross
2. Multiple genotypes can cause the same phenotype. For example, the homozygous dominant genotype and the heterozygous genotype yield the same phenotype in simple dominant-recessive cases.
3. Mendel was able to observe that the inheritance of one trait did not influence the inheritance of a second trait.
4. all *Y* (yellow); 3:1 *R* : *r* (round:wrinkled)
5. Cross the two plants together. If the offspring are tall:short in a 3:1 ratio, the unknown plant is heterozygous, *Tt*. If all the offspring are tall, the unknown plant is homozygous dominant, *TT*.
6. The recessive condition could be advantageous for survival in some way, or the dominant condition could be disadvantageous.

INVESTIGATION

Time 30 minutes	TEACHER TESTED
Teacher Preparation	
Student Difficulty	
Lab Binder Genetics, pp. 1–2	

Purpose Use a Punnett square to predict the inheritance of alleles in a dihybrid cross.

Overview Students will make a Punnett square to represent a dihybrid cross in corn. They will

- identify the possible genotypes and phenotypes of the offspring
- calculate the expected genotypic and phenotypic ratios among the offspring

LAB PREPARATION

Review with students Mendel's law of independent assortment. Review how to determine the gametes formed in a dihybrid cross.

POST-LAB DISCUSSION

Have students evaluate their Punnett squares. **Ask**

- What gametes did Plant A form? *Rt* and *rt* What gametes did Plant B form? *RT* and *rT*
- Why were no offspring with wrinkled kernels produced? Only one parent (Plant A) had alleles for wrinkled kernels. To express this recessive trait, an offspring would have to inherit a recessive allele from both parents.
- Was it necessary to fill out the entire Punnett square? No, both parents were homozygous for one trait, so there were only two possible genotypes for their gametes. The square could be completed in one-fourth of the space.

Point out that had the parents been homozygous for both alleles, there would be only one possible genotype in the offspring. Had one of the parents been heterozygous for both traits, and the other homozygous for both, only one row or column of the grid would need to be filled out.

Allele Combinations and Punnett Squares

MATERIALS
- paper
- pencil
- calculator

PROCESS SKILLS
- **Calculating**
- **Analyzing**

B.7.1 Distinguish between dominant and recessive alleles and determine the phenotype that would result from the different possible combinations of alleles in an offspring.

B.7.3 Determine the likelihood of the appearance of a specific trait in an offspring given the genetic make-up of the parents.

Corn is bred for traits that improve its usefulness for specific purposes. For example, it may be bred to grow in various climates, to produce more corn, or to be better tasting. These traits depend on the alleles inherited by the corn plant. Suppose that you are studying the color and texture of kernels on a cob. Kernels can be either purple (*R*), which is the dominant color, or yellow (*r*), which is the recessive color. Kernels can also be smooth (*T*), which is the dominant texture, or wrinkled (*t*), which is the recessive texture. In this lab, you will predict the inheritance of alleles for two particular traits in a dihybrid cross by using a Punnett square.

PROBLEM What is the inheritance pattern for a dihybrid cross?

PROCEDURE

1. Suppose you want to cross two corn plants with the following genotypes: Plant A with *Rrtt* and Plant B with *RrTT*.
2. Create a Punnett square like the one below to predict the possible genotypes of the offspring for this dihybrid cross.

3. To fill in the Punnett square, place the four combinations of Plant A's alleles in the narrow boxes at the top.
4. Place the four combinations of Plant B's alleles in the narrow boxes on the left.
5. Complete the Punnett square by crossing the alleles of the two plants.

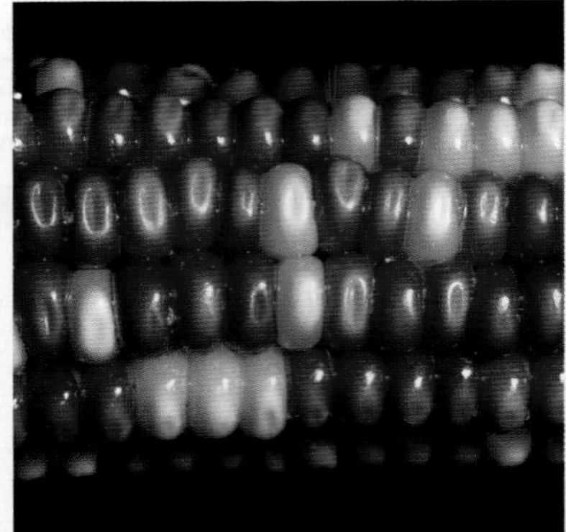

ANALYZE AND CONCLUDE

1. **Apply** List the genotypes and phenotypes produced by this cross.
2. **Calculate** What is the genotypic ratio resulting from this cross? The phenotypic ratio?
3. **Calculate** If the genotypes for kernel texture of two plants are *tt* and *tt*, what is the probability of their having offspring that have smooth kernels? Why?
4. **Predict** Suppose corn plant C has a known genotype of *RRTT*. Could corn plants with cobs that had some yellow and wrinkled kernels be produced by crossing Plant C with a plant with a genotype of your choice? Why or why not?

188 Unit 3: Genetics

Answers

Analyze and Conclude

1. *RRTt, RrTt, rrTt;* purple smooth, yellow smooth
2. genotypic ratio: 1*RRTt* : 2*RrTt* : 1*rrTt* phenotypic ratio: 3:1 of purple-smooth: yellow-smooth
3. Zero; neither parent plant has a dominant allele, *T*, for smooth kernels, so there is no chance of an offspring inheriting a *T* allele and having smooth kernels.
4. Since both yellow and wrinkled kernels are recessive traits, two recessive alleles, one from each parent, are needed for these traits to be expressed in offspring. Plant C has no recessive alleles to contribute to gametes, so no cross involving Plant C can produce offspring with a recessive trait.

6.6 Meiosis and Genetic Variation

KEY CONCEPT Independent assortment and crossing over during meiosis result in genetic diversity.

MAIN IDEAS

- Sexual reproduction creates unique gene combinations.
- Crossing over during meiosis increases genetic diversity.

VOCABULARY

crossing over, p. 190
genetic linkage, p. 191

INDIANA STANDARDS

B.6.5 Explain how, in sexual reproduction, crossing over, independent assortment, and random fertilization, result in offspring that are genetically different from the parents.

Connect A surprising number of people make their living as Elvis impersonators. They wear slicked-up hairdos, large sunglasses, and big white jumpsuits. They mimic his voice, his dancing, and his phrases. They copy every possible detail, but they still do not come close to being the King. For Elvis, like all people, was unique, or one of a kind. And this uniqueness arises more from the events of meiosis—from the tiny shufflings of chromosomes and the crossing over of DNA segments—than from our hairstyles or our clothing.

MAIN IDEA

Sexual reproduction creates unique gene combinations.

FIGURE 6.19 This photograph shows only a small sample of the great genetic potential for variety in the human population.

The major advantage of sexual reproduction is that it gives rise to a great deal of genetic variation within a species, as shown in **FIGURE 6.19.** This variation results largely from (1) the independent assortment of chromosomes during meiosis and (2) the random fertilization of gametes.

Recall that homologous chromosomes pair up randomly along the cell equator during meiosis I. In other words, it's a matter of chance which of the two chromosomes from any homologous pair ends up on a given side of the cell equator. As you've learned, human cells have 23 pairs of chromosomes, and each pair lines up independently. As a result, gametes with 2^{23}, or about 8 million, different combinations of chromosomes can be produced through meiosis from one human cell.

Now, think about the fact that sexual reproduction produces offspring through the random combination of gametes. In humans, for example, a sperm cell with one of 2^{23} (about 8 million) chromosome combinations fertilizes an egg cell, which also has one out of 2^{23} chromosome combinations. Since any sperm cell can fertilize any egg, the total number of possible combinations is the product of $2^{23} \times 2^{23}$, or more than 70 trillion. In other words, any human couple can produce a child with one of about 70 trillion different combinations of chromosomes.

Differentiated Instruction

BELOW LEVEL

Review large numbers, such as millions, billions, and trillions so that students understand why each individual is unique. Write the numerals one million, one billion, and one trillion on the board. Help students to make these numbers more tangible. **Ask,** If the largest passenger plane can hold a thousand people, how many flights would you need to carry the 300 million people in the United States? 300,000

SECTION 6.6

Plan and Prepare

Objectives

- Describe how sexual reproduction creates unique gene combinations.
- Explain how crossing over during meiosis increases genetic diversity.

Section Resources

Unit Resource Book
Study Guide pp. 21–22
Power Notes p. 23
Reinforcement p. 24
Pre-AP Activity pp. 29–30

Interactive Reader Chapter 6
Spanish Study Guide pp. 63–64

Biology Toolkit p. C13

Technology
Power Presentation 6.6
Media Gallery DVD
Online Quiz 6.6

Activate Prior Knowledge Have students think about the kinds of genetic variation that humans show. **FIGURE 6.19** can be used as a starting point. **Ask,** What are some examples of genetic variation in humans? eye color, hair color and texture, baldness, skin color, anatomical differences between the sexes, facial features, height, weight, musculature Point out that humans are able to alter many of their physical traits, but doing so does not alter the genotypes for those traits or the genes that will be passed on to offspring.

Teach

Vocabulary

Academic Vocabulary The everyday usage of the word **random** often simply means "I'm not sure why that happened." In a scientific context, *random* is a word applied to an event in which all possible outcomes are equally likely. In some instances, what seems random to us is not really random at all.

▼ Teach *continued*

ONLINE BIOLOGY Visit the chapter Resource Center at **ClassZone.com** for information and resources on sexual reproduction.

Take It Further

Crossing over is a precise process, with each chromatid usually breaking at the same point. If exchange were not so precise, one chromatid might lose genes and the other chromatid might gain genes. Certain places on the chromatids, called **hotspots,** are more likely to break than other places. Sister chromatids may also exchange chromosome segments. However, these exchanges are not likely to create new gene combinations.

Address Misconceptions

Common Misconception Sister chromatids are always identical.

Correcting the Misconception Point out that this is only true for mitotic division. Emphasize that in meiosis, sister chromatids are identical copies of each other before prophase I, but after this phase, the sister chromatids can differ if crossing over has taken place.

Answers

A Calculate Each egg and sperm has 16 possible chromosome combinations, so the total number of possible combinations would be $16 \times 16 = 256$.

B Synthesize One chromosome will be all purple, one all green; the other two will have a segment of the other color at the base.

***Connecting* CONCEPTS**

Evolution As you will learn in **Chapter 10,** natural selection is a mechanism by which individuals that have inherited beneficial adaptations produce more offspring on average than do other individuals. The rabbit-eared bandicoot (below) has adaptations that enable it to survive and reproduce in regions of Australia.

Independent assortment and fertilization play key roles in creating and maintaining genetic diversity in all sexually reproducing organisms. However, the number of possible chromosome combinations varies by species. The probability that a bald eagle or a rabbit-eared bandicoot will inherit a specific allele is determined in the same way that it is for a pea plant.

Sexual reproduction creates unique combinations of genes. This results in organisms with unique phenotypes. The offspring of sexual reproduction have a mixture of both parents' traits. For example, rabbit-eared bandicoot offspring all share many traits for the things that make them bandicoots, but they may also differ in many ways. Some may be colored more like the mother, others more like the father. Some may dig deeper burrows or hunt more skillfully; others may in time produce more milk for their own offspring or have more litters. Having some of these traits may allow one bandicoot to reproduce in conditions where another bandicoot could not.

A Calculate Fruit fly gametes each have four chromosomes, representing 2^4, or 16, possible chromosome combinations. How many chromosome combinations could result from fertilization between a fruit fly egg and a sperm cell?

MAIN IDEA

Crossing over during meiosis increases genetic diversity.

It is clear that independent assortment creates a lot of variation within a species. Another process, called crossing over, occurs during meiosis and helps create even greater variation. **Crossing over** is the exchange of chromosome segments between homologous chromosomes during prophase I of meiosis I. At this stage, each chromosome has been duplicated, the sister chromatids are still connected to each other, and homologous chromosomes have paired with each other. When homologous chromosomes are in this position, some of the chromatids are very close to each other. Part of one chromatid from each chromosome breaks off and reattaches to the other chromosome, as shown in **FIGURE 6.20.** Crossing over happens any time a germ cell divides. In fact, it can occur many times within the same pair of homologous chromosomes.

FIGURE 6.20 Crossing Over

Crossing over exchanges segments of DNA between homologous chromosomes.

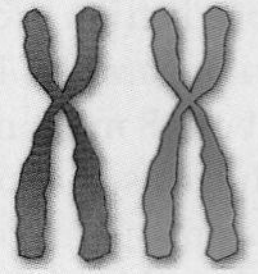

1 Two homologous chromosomes pair up with each other during prophase I in meiosis.

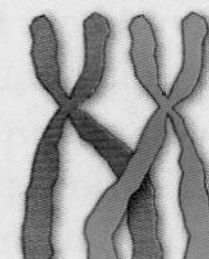

2 In this position, some chromatids are very close to each other and segments cross.

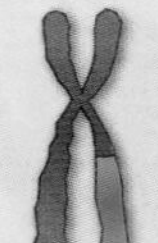

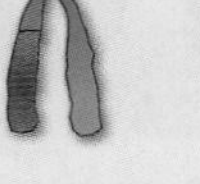

3 Some of these segments break off and reattach to the other homologous chromosome.

B Synthesize Draw the four chromosomes that would result after the above chromosomes go through meiosis.

Differentiated Instruction

ENGLISH LEARNERS

Have students address the question of how crossing over contributes to genetic diversity. Give individual students a chance to think and take notes about the question, telling them to pay special attention to **FIGURE 6.20.** Then have them pair up to compare ideas and prepare a final answer to share with the class.

Biology Toolkit, Think-Pair-Share, p. C13

Because crossing over results in new combinations of genes, it is also called recombination. The term *recombination* generally refers to any mixing of parental alleles, including recombination events, other than crossing over.

Now that you know about crossing over, let's look again at some of Mendel's results and conclusions. As you know from his research, genes located on separate chromosomes assort independently. This independence is caused by the random assortment of chromosomes during meiosis. But you also know that a single chromosome can have hundreds of genes. What happens when two genes are both on the same chromosome? Will they display independent assortment as well? Or will they travel together as a unit?

The answer to these questions is, "It depends." Recall that each gene has its own locus, or place on a chromosome. As **FIGURE 6.21** shows, some genes on the same chromosome are close together; others are far apart. The farther apart two genes are located, the more likely they are to be separated when crossing over happens. Thus, genes located close together tend to be inherited together, which is called **genetic linkage.** Linked genes will be inherited in the same predicted ratios as would a single gene. In contrast, genes that are far apart are more likely to assort independently. For example, the alleles for flower and seed color are located on the same chromosome in pea plants, but they are not near each other. Because they are so far apart, Mendel observed independent assortment for these traits.

FIGURE 6.21 GENETIC LINKAGE

A and B are not linked to C and D because they are so far apart. Crossing over is likely to occur in the space between genes B and C, thereby separating A and B from C and D.

gene A
gene B
A and B are referred to as linked because they would likely be inherited together.
gene C
gene D
C and D are referred to as linked because they would likely be inherited together.

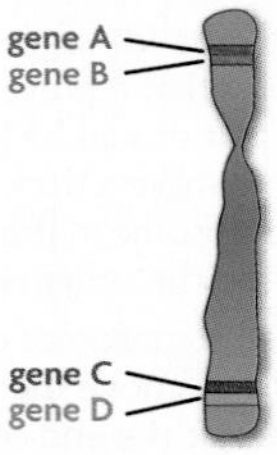

Genetic linkage has let scientists calculate the physical distance between two genes. By exploring relationships between many genes, scientists have been able to build a linkage, or genetic, map of many species. This research tool will be discussed in more detail in Chapter 7.

Predict **Suppose two genes are very close together on a chromosome. Are the genes likely to be separated by crossing over? Explain.**

6.6 ASSESSMENT

ONLINE QUIZ ClassZone.com

B.6.5

REVIEWING MAIN IDEAS

1. Briefly explain how sexual reproduction generates new allele combinations in offspring.
2. How does **crossing over** contribute to genetic diversity?

CRITICAL THINKING

3. **Infer** You know that you get half your DNA from your mom, half from your dad. Does this mean you got one-quarter of your DNA from each of your grandparents? Explain your reasoning.
4. **Synthesize** Suppose you know two genes exist on the same chromosome. How could you determine whether they are located close to each other?

***Connecting* CONCEPTS**

5. **Mitosis** Mitosis creates daughter cells that are genetically identical to the parent cell. If crossing over occurred between sister chromatids during mitosis, would it increase genetic diversity? Explain.

Take It Further

A **linkage map** can be prepared based on recombination frequencies. The distances between genes are called **map units,** with one map unit being defined as a recombination frequency of 1 percent. Creating such a map can help geneticists see and predict how certain genes are linked and passed on together. Students will learn more about this in Chapter 7.

Answers

A Predict The genes are not likely to be separated by crossing over. Genes that are close together tend to be inherited together.

Assess and Reteach ▼

Assess Use the Online Quiz or Section Quiz (*Assessment Book,* p. 114).

Reteach Have students draw a sequence diagram of meiosis, this time incorporating crossing over into the process. Refer them to **FIGURE 6.5** on pages 174–175.

6.6 ASSESSMENT

1. Each egg and sperm already have a mixture of chromosomes from both parents due to the independent assortment of chromosomes. Since any sperm could potentially fertilize any egg, the potential allele combinations are numerous even for simple organisms.
2. Crossing over makes new combinations of maternal and paternal genes. In this way, an egg or a sperm not only receives a unique combination of the maternal and paternal chromosomes, but those chromosomes themselves become a unique patchwork of maternal and paternal genes.
3. Not necessarily. The gametes that you inherited from each of your parents could have contained more chromosomes from one of their parents than the other.
4. Cross two organisms purebred for the two traits coded for by the genes. Then cross the F_1 generation. The more often the traits are inherited together, the closer the genes are on the chromosome.
5. No, sister chromatids are identical to each other, so an exchange of DNA segments would be meaningless.

OPTIONS FOR INQUIRY

INVESTIGATION

Time 30 minutes	TEACHER TESTED
Teacher Preparation	
Student Difficulty	
Lab Binder Genetics, pp. 3–4	

Purpose Model the stages of meiosis.

Overview Students will make a model of meiosis. They will

- make a pair of homologous chromosomes, using pipe cleaners and hook-and-loop tabs
- mark the chromosomes to represent heterozygous alleles at each locus
- model the stages of meiosis and draw the position of the chromosomes at the end of meiosis I and meiosis II

LAB PREPARATION

If beads are available, students can thread them onto the pipe cleaners to represent genes instead of marking the pipe cleaners with markers.

LAB MANAGEMENT

- Review the stages of meiosis before students begin the lab.
- Suggest that students have a mixture of recessive and dominant alleles on each chromosome, rather than having all dominant alleles on one chromosome and all recessive alleles on the other. For example, one chromosome can have alleles *A*, *b*, and *c*; the other can have alleles *a*, *B*, and *C*. Chromosomes should show several genes.

Safety Remind students to handle scissors carefully.

POST-LAB DISCUSSION

Discuss what happened to the chromosomes. **Ask,** Was your starting cell haploid or diploid? diploid Were your final cells haploid or diploid? haploid How many "cells" did you have at the end of meiosis I? 2 at the end of meiosis II? 4 What does each piece of paper at the end of meiosis II represent? a gamete

Use these inquiry-based labs and online activities to deepen your understanding of meiosis.

INDIANA STANDARDS

B.6.4 Describe and model the process of meiosis and explain the relationship between the genetic make-up of the parent cell and the daughter cells (gametes).

B.7.1 Distinguish between dominant and recessive alleles and determine the phenotype that would result from the different possible combinations of alleles in an offspring.

B.7.3 Determine the likelihood of the appearance of a specific trait in an offspring given the genetic make-up of the parents.

INVESTIGATION

Modeling Meiosis

In this lab, you will make a model of meiosis that will be reusable as a study tool.

SKILLS Modeling, Analyzing

PROBLEM How does a diploid cell divide to form haploid cells?

MATERIALS
- 4 white pipe cleaners
- 2 2-cm pieces hook-and-loop tabs
- colored markers
- notebook paper

PROCEDURE

1. Construct a pair of homologous chromosomes. Use pipe cleaners to make the chromosomes and hook-and-loop tabs to represent the centromere that holds the sister chromatids together. The homologous chromosomes should have bands of color that represent the different genes carried on those chromosomes. The pair should be heterozygous for each of the genes. For example, if you choose to make a thick band of dark blue to represent an allele for eye color on one chromosome in the homologous pair, you should make a matching band in light blue on the other chromosome in the pair.
2. Lay out the chromosomes on notebook paper and model the four steps of meiosis I. Then remove the chromosomes and sketch the position of the chromosomes at the end of meiosis I on your paper.
3. Cut the sheet of paper in half to represent cytokinesis. Make sure that each half of the notebook paper, or cell, has one homologous chromosome.
4. Model the four steps of meiosis II in both cells.
5. Remove the chromosomes. Sketch the position of the chromosomes in both cells at the end of meiosis II.
6. Cut the cells in half again to show cytokinesis. Each cell should have one chromosome.

ANALYZE AND CONCLUDE

1. **Predict** Explain how your results would differ if the homologous chromosomes had been homozygous for each of the genes.
2. **Evaluate** Which aspects of meiosis are not represented in your model? What changes could you make to show these processes?
3. **Synthesize** Refer to your model to explain why meiosis is also called "reduction division." Use the words *diploid* and *haploid* in your explanation.

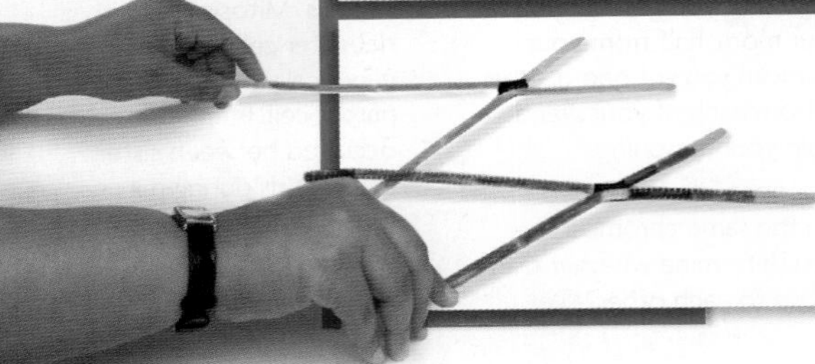

EXTEND YOUR INVESTIGATION

Nondisjunction describes what happens when homologous chromosomes fail to separate during meiosis I or when sister chromatids fail to separate during meiosis II. On chromosome 21, it can lead to Down syndrome. Research the effects of having three copies of chromosome 21.

Answers

Analyze and Conclude

1. Only one kind of gamete would have been produced. The gametes would all have had the same alleles, as Mendel's purebred plants did.
2. Crossing over was not represented. The pipe cleaners could have been cut and then recombined by using tape to hold the pieces together.
3. During meiosis I, the chromosome number is reduced from diploid to haploid as homologous chromosomes separate, but each chromosome is still duplicated. During meiosis II, the amount of genetic material in each chromosome is reduced by half as sister chromatids separate.

Extend Your Investigation

Students should learn that Down syndrome, trisomy 21, is characterized by mental retardation, a flat face, protruding tongue, and other symptoms.

INVESTIGATION

Probability Practice

In this lab, you will model the distribution of alleles, calculate the probabilities of specific allele combinations, and compare them to those that Gregor Mendel found in his work.

SKILL Calculating Probabilities

PROBLEM What is the probability that certain genotypes and phenotypes will occur?

MATERIALS
- 2 coins
- 4 cm masking tape
- marker
- one folded 3" × 5" index card with a monohybrid cross on it (e.g., *Aa* × *aa*, or *AA* × *Aa*)

PROCEDURE
1. Using the coins, tape, and marker, label a set of two coins to simulate the cross listed on your group's index card. Use a capital letter to represent a dominant allele and a lowercase letter to represent a recessive allele. One coin should have the mother's gametes. The other coin should have the father's gametes.
2. Flip the two coins simultaneously. The two coins together make up the genetic material of the zygote. Record the genotype of the offspring.
3. Repeat step 2 for a total of 50 trials. Calculate what percentage of "offspring" had each possible genotype and phenotype. Show your data and calculations to your teacher before moving on.

ANALYZE AND CONCLUDE
1. **Analyze** The crosses below show the predicted phenotypes of the offspring based on Mendel's laws. Compare your genetic cross results (phenotypes) to those of Mendel. Explain possible reasons for any differences you observe in data.
   - *AA* × *aa* : 100% dominant
   - *aa* × *aa* : 100% recessive
   - *Aa* × *aa* : 50% dominant, 50% recessive
2. **Apply** Did the genotype of any one trial depend upon the results of another? Explain.
3. **Synthesize** Explain how meiosis accounts for the distribution of alleles to gametes.

Online BIOLOGY
CLASSZONE.COM

VIRTUAL LAB
Breeding Mutations in Fruit Flies
How are mutations expressed in fruit flies? In this interactive lab, you will cross purebred fruit flies to determine the pattern of inheritance for a set of mutant alleles.

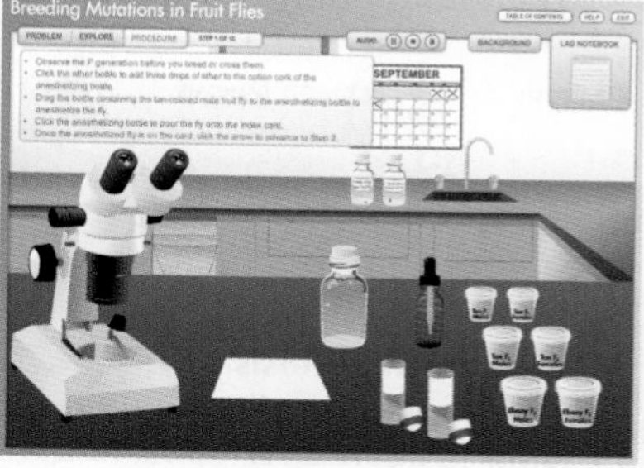

ANIMATED BIOLOGY
Mendel's Experiment
Recreate some of Mendel's experiments with virtual pea plants. Then use your skills to breed a specific type of pea on a tight budget.

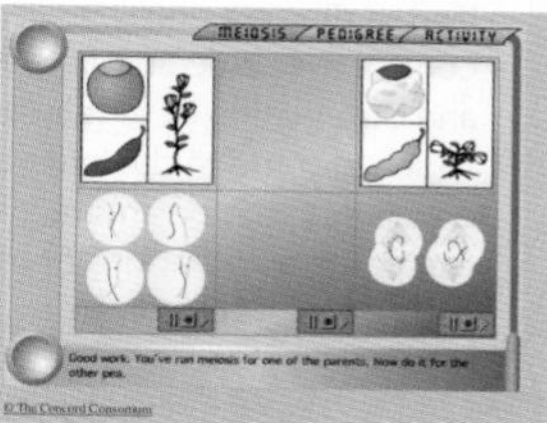

WEBQUEST
Dogs come in many shapes and sizes. How did this variety come about? In this WebQuest you will learn about selective breeding. Find out how dog breeders enhance certain traits, and how breeding can expose genetic disorders. Finally, describe how you might breed dogs to enhance a specific trait.

Answers

Analyze and Conclude

1. This experiment observed only 50 "off-spring"; Mendel observed thousands. The coins may have been weight-biased so that one side landed more often than expected.
2. No, each trial was independent in the same way that chromosomes segregate independently during meiosis.
3. In meiosis I, homologous chromosomes segregate, separating the maternal and paternal alleles into separate cells. In meiosis II, the sister chromatids separate into different cells.

Online Biology ▼

VIRTUAL LAB Use this interactive lab to reinforce the concepts of **Section 6.5.**

ANIMATED BIOLOGY Use this interactive animation to reinforce the concepts of **Section 6.3.**

WEBQUEST The WebQuest takes one full class period. Students complete the activity online and will need access to a printer to print their answers. Sample answers, teacher notes, and alternative assessment ideas are available on **ClassZone.com.** Use with **Section 6.6.**

INVESTIGATION

TEACHER TESTED

Time	30 minutes
Teacher Preparation	1 flask
Student Difficulty	1 flask
Lab Binder	Genetics, pp. 5–6

Purpose Model the distribution of alleles and calculate probabilities of combinations.

LAB MANAGEMENT

- Be sure students understand that they are to label the coins with one allele on each side.
- Have students use equal-sized pieces of tape on both sides of a coin to avoid a weight bias.
- To calculate the percentage of offspring with each genotype, students should multiply the number of flips that yielded each genotype by 2. For example, if 25 out of 50 flips were *Aa*, this genotype would equal 50 percent. Be sure percentages add up to 100 percent.

POST-LAB DISCUSSION

Ask, Do you think the probabilities would have been different if you had flipped the coins 100 times? The probabilities would have been closer to the theoretical values if there had been more trials.

CHAPTER REVIEW

Interactive Review

Encourage students to go to **ClassZone.com** for a detailed review of each section, including visuals and vocabulary practice.

Unit Resource Book, Vocabulary Practice, pp. 31–34

CHAPTER 6

Interactive Review @ CLASSZONE.COM

KEY CONCEPTS | Vocabulary Games | Concept Maps | Animated Biology | Online Quiz

6.1 Chromosomes and Meiosis

Gametes have half the number of chromosomes that body cells have. Your body cells have 23 pairs of homologous chromosomes, making 46 total chromosomes. Gametes have only one chromosome from each homologous pair—23 chromosomes in all.

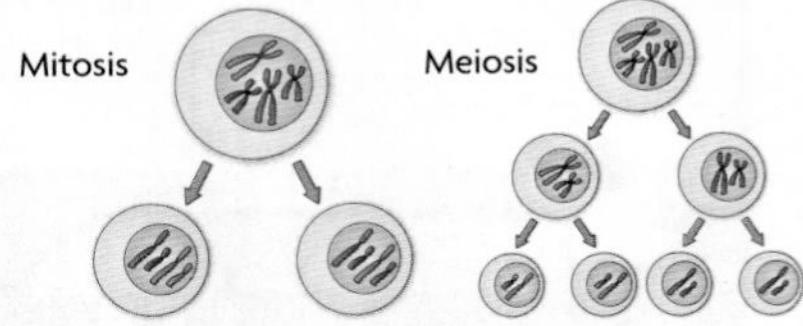

6.2 Process of Meiosis

During meiosis, diploid cells undergo two cell divisions that result in haploid cells. In meiosis I, homologous chromosomes pair up along the cell equator and are divided into separate cells. In meiosis II, sister chromatids are divided into separate cells, making a total of four haploid cells that are genetically unique.

6.3 Mendel and Heredity

Mendel's research showed that traits are inherited as discrete units. His large amount of data, control over breeding, use of purebred plants, and observation of "either-or" traits allowed him to see patterns in the inheritance of traits. He concluded that organisms inherit two copies of each gene and that organisms donate only one copy of each gene in their gametes.

6.4 Traits, Genes, and Alleles

Genes encode proteins that produce a diverse range of traits. Every diploid organism has two alleles for each gene: one from the mother, one from the father. These two alleles may be the same (homozygous) or different (heterozygous). One allele may be dominant over another.

6.5 Traits and Probability

The inheritance of traits follows the rules of probability. Punnett squares are a grid system that help predict all possible genotypes resulting from a cross. When Mendel performed two-trait crosses, he discovered that different traits appear to be inherited separately—the law of independent assortment. The patterns of inheritance that he observed can be predicted using mathematical probabilities.

6.6 Meiosis and Genetic Variation

Independent assortment and crossing over during meiosis result in genetic diversity. Independent assortment produces unique combinations of parental chromosomes. Crossing over between homologous chromosomes creates a patchwork of genes from both parents. Genetic linkage describes genes that are close together and tend to be inherited as a unit.

Synthesize Your Notes

"Y" Diagram Use a "Y" diagram to summarize what you know about meiosis I and II.

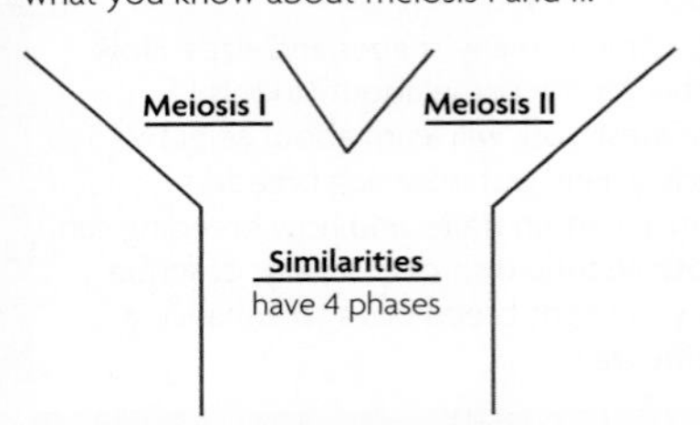

Cycle Diagram Fill in a cycle diagram like the one below to show the relationship between diploid and haploid cells.

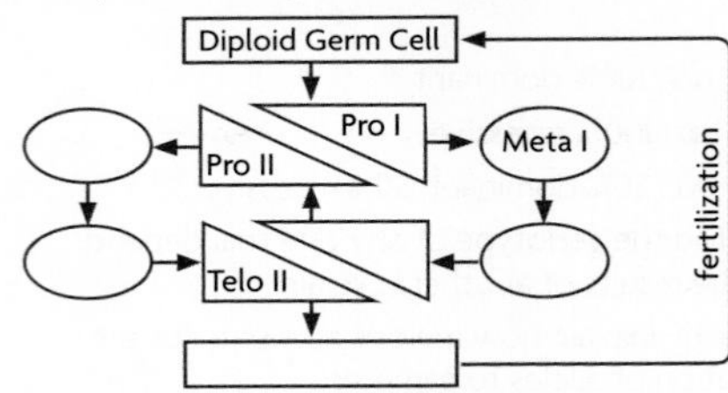

Reviewing Vocabulary

1. gene: could be a drawing of a chromosome, with a small segment indicated
2. fertilization: could be a drawing of a sperm burrowing into an egg
3. crossing over: could be a drawing of a pair of homologous chromosomes that are duplicated, lined up as in metaphase I of meiosis, with parts crossed, as in Figure 6.20.
4. genetic linkage: could be a drawing of a chromosome with two different genes indicated (or the loci for two different genes indicated)
5. haploid: could be a drawing of a gamete cell with only one set of chromosomes (not homologous pairs of chromosomes)
6. Meiosis is a reductive process that diminishes, or reduces, the amount of DNA. It begins with a diploid cell and ends with haploid cells.
7. Haploid cells have a single set of chromosomes, whereas diploid cells have a double set of chromosomes.
8. Homologous chromosomes have the same genes at the each locus. *Homozygous* means that the two alleles at a locus are the same.
9. Both are crosses that Mendel used to study inheritance. A monohybrid cross focuses on only one trait; a dihybrid cross focuses on two traits.
10. Both are kinds of genotypes. Heterozygous genotypes have two different alleles of a gene, one on each chromosome of a homologous pair. Homozygous genotypes have two of the same alleles of a gene, one on each chromosome of a homologous pair.
11. Genotype refers to the underlying alleles, or genetic makeup; phenotype refers to how those alleles are expressed.

Chapter Assessment

Chapter Vocabulary

6.1 somatic cell, p. 168
gamete, p. 168
homologous chromosome, p. 169
autosome, p. 169
sex chromosome, p. 169
sexual reproduction, p. 170
fertilization, p. 170
diploid, p. 170
haploid, p. 170
meiosis, p. 170

6.2 gametogenesis, p. 176
sperm, p. 176
egg, p. 176
polar body, p. 176

6.3 trait, p. 177
genetics, p. 177
purebred, p. 178
cross, p. 178
law of segregation, p. 179

6.4 gene, p. 180
allele, p. 180
homozygous, p. 180
heterozygous, p. 180
genome, p. 181
genotype, p. 181
phenotype, p. 181
dominant, p. 181
recessive, p. 181

6.5 Punnett square, p. 183
monohybrid cross, p. 184
testcross, p. 185
dihybrid cross, p. 186
law of independent assortment, p. 186
probability, p. 187

6.6 crossing over, p. 190
genetic linkage, p. 191

Reviewing Vocabulary

Visualize Vocabulary

For each term below, use simple shapes, lines, or arrows to illustrate its meaning. Below each picture, write a short caption. Here's an example for *diploid:*

1. gene
2. fertilization
3. crossing over
4. genetic linkage
5. haploid

Diploid cells have two copies of each chromosome.

Greek Word Origins

6. The word *meiosis* comes from a Greek word meaning "to diminish," or make less. How does this word's origin relate to its meaning?
7. The word *haploid* comes from the Greek word *haplous*, which means "single." *Diploid* comes from the Greek word *diplous*, which means "double." Explain how these two terms' meanings relate to their origins.
8. The Greek prefix *homo-* means "one and the same." How does this relate to the words *homologous* and *homozygous*?

Compare and Contrast

Describe one similarity and one difference between the two terms in each of the following pairs.

9. monohybrid cross, dihybrid cross
10. heterozygous, homozygous
11. genotype, phenotype

Reviewing MAIN IDEAS

12. Each of your cells has a set of chromosomes, including autosomes and sex chromosomes. Explain the main differences between these two types of chromosomes. **B.5.1**
13. A fruit fly has diploid cells with 8 chromosomes. Explain how many chromosomes are in its haploid gametes. **B.6.4**
14. Meiosis is a continuous process, but we can think of it as taking place in two stages, meiosis I and meiosis II. Describe the products of each stage. How do the products of meiosis I differ from those of meiosis II? **B.6.4**
15. The foundation for our modern study of genetics began with Gregor Mendel, who studied pea plants. What were Mendel's two main conclusions about how traits are passed between generations? **B.5.2**
16. How did Mendel's use of purebred plants—for example, purebred white- and purebred purple-flowered peas—contribute to his understanding of inheritance? **B.5.2**
17. How does the homozygous condition differ from the heterozygous condition? In your answer, use the terms *gene*, *homologous chromosome*, and *allele*. **B.5.2**
18. What does each of the following parts of a Punnett square represent: (a) the entries on each axis of the grid and
(b) the entries in the four squares within the grid?
19. How did the results of Mendel's dihybrid crosses lead him to formulate the law of independent assortment? **B.5.2**
20. How does crossing over during meiosis I increase genetic diversity? **B.6.5**

CHAPTER REVIEW

Reviewing Main Ideas

12. Sex chromosomes directly control the development of sexual characteristics. Autosomes control the development of characteristics that are not directly sex related.
13. four chromosomes, because meiosis results in haploid gamete cells, with only one set of chromosomes
14. Meiosis I separates homologous pairs of chromosomes and results in haploid cells with duplicated chromosomes. Meiosis II separates sister chromatids and results in haploid cells with chromosomes that are not duplicated.
15. Mendel concluded that traits are inherited from parents and that organisms receive two copies of hereditary units, now called genes, one from the mother and one from the father. The two copies segregate during gamete formation.
16. When Mendel crossed two different purebred lines, for example, purple-flowered and white-flowered peas, he saw that there were no white-flowered offspring, but that if F_1 plants were crossed, the white flowers reappeared. This showed that the white flower trait had not disappeared; it was just masked. Additionally, this suggested that offspring received two forms of each gene, one from each parent.
17. The homozygous condition occurs when an organism has two of the same alleles for a particular gene—one on each chromosome of a homologous pair, for example, an allele for white flower color at the locus for the flower color gene on the maternal chromosome, and also an allele for white color at the flower color locus on the paternal chromosome. The heterozygous condition occurs when there are two different alleles of a gene. For example, one chromosome has the purple allele, and its homologous chromosome has the white allele.
18. (a) the possible gamete genotypes for each parent; (b) the possible offspring genotypes
19. Mendel learned from his dihybrid crosses that traits are inherited independently of each other. For example, a white-flowered pea plant could be either short or tall, and a purple-flowered pea plant also could be either short or tall. Flower color and height were not inherited together.
20. Chromatids from homologous chromosomes (maternal and paternal chromosomes) exchange segments during meiosis I, which alters and recombines the genetic makeup of the chromosomes.

ITEM CORRELATIONS

Standard	Items
B.5.1	12
B.5.2	15, 16, 17, 19, 23, 26
B.6.1	22
B.6.4	13, 14, 27, 28
B.6.5	20
B.7.1	25
B.7.3	21

Critical Thinking

21. No, because somatic cells do not turn into gametes. Mutations in germ cells can affect offspring.
22. The chromosome number of the offspring would double each generation. In the first generation, the two gametes with 4 chromosomes would join to make an organism with 8 chromosomes. This organism would make 8-chromosome gametes, which would join to make a 16-chromosome organism, and so on.
23. Before duplication, the pair of homologous chromosomes should be shown as two single chromosomes of the same size and shape. Although the homologous chromosomes carry the same genes, they may have different alleles for those genes. After duplication, each homologous chromosome consists of two identical sister chromatids held together by a centromere.
24. Mendel's law of independent assortment does not apply to two genes that are close together on the same chromosome, because they tend to be linked, or inherited together. Genes that are far apart on a chromosome are more likely to assort independently, because crossing over occurs frequently between them.
25. Smooth petals are likely dominant over wrinkled, and the parents were likely both heterozygous. If smooth = *S* and wrinkled = *s*, the parents were *Ss*.
26. The law of independent assortment does not apply, because the two genes are on the same chromosome. The genes move together, not independently. In other words, the alleles for antenna shape and antenna color are inherited together from the same parent.

Critical Thinking

21. Hypothesize Could a mutation in one of an individual's somatic cells be passed on to the individual's offspring? Explain your answer. **B.7.3**

22. Predict Consider a species with a 2*n*, or diploid, chromosome number of 4. If gametes were formed by mitosis, rather than meiosis, what would happen to the chromosome number of the offspring of these organisms over generations? Explain. **B.6.1**

23. Contrast Draw a pair of homologous chromosomes before and after duplication. Use your drawings to explain how homologous chromosomes and sister chromatids differ. **B.5.2**

24. Synthesize Mendel's law of independent assortment states that allele pairs separate independently of each other during meiosis. How does this law relate to crossing over and genetic linkage?

25. Infer Imagine that you are studying the trait of flower petal shape in a species of plant. Petal shape is determined by a single gene with two alleles. You make a cross of two plants with unknown genotypes, both with smooth petals, and get the following F_1 offspring phenotypes: 23 wrinkled and 77 smooth. What conclusions can you draw about the inheritance of this trait? In your answer, include the probable genotypes of each parent, and which allele is likely dominant. **B.7.1**

26. Analyze In a particular species of butterfly, the genes for two different traits, antenna shape and antenna color, are located on the same chromosome. As a result, crosses between these butterflies do not obey one of Mendel's laws. Which law does not apply, and why? **B.5.2**

Interpreting Visuals

The drawing to the right shows a cell at a certain point during meiosis. Use the drawing to answer the next two questions.

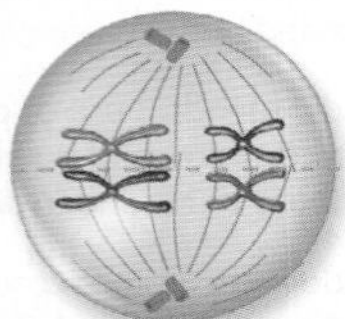

27. Identify What stage of meiosis is shown above? Defend your answer. **B.6.4**

28. Apply Is the above cell diploid or haploid? Explain. **B.6.4**

Analyzing Data

During meiosis, pairs of homologous chromosomes separate independently of the others, and gametes receive one of the two chromosomes from each pair. The number of possible chromosome combinations for a species is 2^n, where *n* = the number of homologous pairs. The graph below shows the number of possible chromosome combinations for a variety of species. Use it to answer the next two questions.

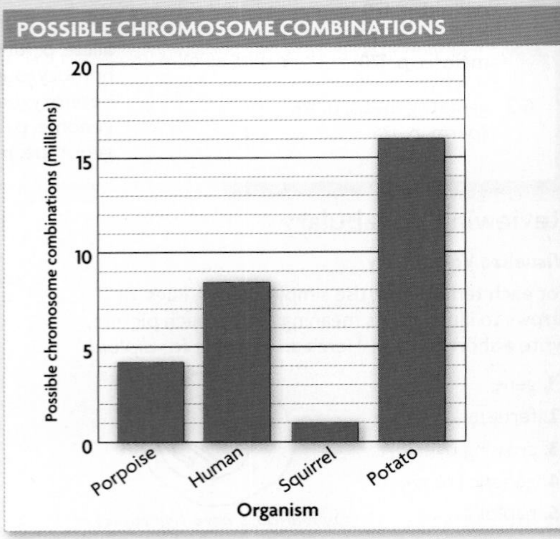

Source: Rutgers University

29. Summarize List the organisms in the above graph, in order, from least to most possible chromosome combinations.

30. Infer What can you infer from the graph about the number of homologous chromosomes in squirrels compared with potatoes?

Connecting CONCEPTS

31. Write a Diary Entry Put yourself in Mendel's shoes. It is the mid-1800s. DNA and genes have not been identified, and the mechanisms of heritability are not understood. Write a diary entry (or letter) about one of Mendel's crosses from his perspective. Describe the results of the cross and ideas that may have come from the results.

32. Synthesize Look again at the picture of the egg and sperm cells on page 167. Each of these sperm cells is genetically unique. What are the sources of variation that make each one different from the others?

196 Unit 3: Genetics

Interpreting Visuals

27. Metaphase I, pairs of homologous chromosomes, each consisting of two sister chromatids, are lined up together at the equator.
28. The cell is still diploid because it has two sets of chromosomes.

Analyzing Data

29. squirrel, porpoise, human, potato
30. Squirrels have fewer homologous chromosomes. (Students may correctly determine that the potato has 24 (2^{24} = ~16 million) and the squirrel has 20 (2^{20} = ~1 million) chromosomes.

INDIANA ISTEP+ Test Prep

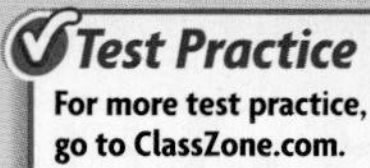

Test Practice For more test practice, go to ClassZone.com.

1 Researchers crossed two types of mice together, type A and type B. In the resulting offspring, half of the DNA comes from type A and half comes from type B. Why?

A X-inactivation occurs with 50/50 chance in each cell.

B The offspring get their DNA from the sperm and their cytoplasm from the egg.

C Each parent contributes one set of chromosomes to each offspring.

D The offspring make binary divisions during development.

2 Two pea plants were both grown from green peas. When these plants are crossed, their offspring produce green, yellow, and white peas. What accounts for the differences between parents and offspring?

A Random mutations are producing more diversity.

B Sexual reproduction has produced new combinations of alleles.

C Environmental factors are affecting the survival of gametes.

D The trait of pea color is not heritable from these parent plants.

3 In peas, the gene for green pod color (*G*) is dominant to the gene for yellow pod color (g). If a heterozygous plant (*Gg*) is crossed with another heterozygous plant (*Gg*), what genotype will likely be the most common among the offspring?

A *GG*

B *Gg*

C *gg*

D *GGgg*

THINK THROUGH THE QUESTION

If necessary, take the time to draw out a Punnett square to answer this question. Remember that the Gg genotype is the same as the gG genotype.

4 Genes that are on two different chromosomes are said to exhibit independent assortment because these chromosomes

A are physically unconnected to the spindle.

B are replicated independently of each other.

C become aligned on opposite poles of the cell.

D end up in the same gamete by random chance.

5

A mutation occurs in a gene on chromosome 3, which is shown here. This mutation could be passed along to offspring if it occurs

A in any cell except sex cells.

B after fertilization but before the zygote develops.

C during development of the zygote.

D in a sex cell that undergoes fertilization.

6 One couple can have children who differ greatly from each other in appearance and other traits. How is this possible?

Standards-Based Assessment

1. C	4. B
2. B	5. D
3. B	6. See Below

Question 1 Answer C is correct. Answer A is incorrect because X-inactivation randomly inactivates only one X chromosome in the cells of females. Answer B is incorrect because offspring get both DNA and cytoplasm from the egg. Answer D is incorrect because binary division is a form of asexual reproduction.

Question 3 Answer B is correct because half the offspring are likely to inherit Gg. Answer A is incorrect because only one-fourth the offspring are likely to inherit GG. Answer C is incorrect because only one-fourth the offspring are likely to inherit gg. Answer D is incorrect because offspring inherit only one chromosome from each parent, not two chromosomes from each parent.

Question 5 Answer D is correct. Answers A, B, and C are incorrect because the mutation has not occurred in a sex cell, therefore it is not passed to offspring.

Question 6 Each egg and sperm has a unique combination of chromosomes from the parents, so each fertilization results in a unique organism. Crossing over between chromosomes during meiosis also creates new combinations of alleles present on the chromosomes, enhancing genetic diversity.

Connecting Concepts

31. Students' responses should summarize the particular monohybrid or dihybrid cross selected. Students should then explain, from Mendel's perspective, what possible conclusions could be made based on the results of the cross.

32. The independent assortment and crossing over of chromosomes during meiosis result in unique gametes, such as sperm.

ITEM CORRELATIONS

Standard	Items
B.5.2	1, 3, 5
B.6.5	2, 4, 6

CHAPTER 7

Indiana Resource Preview

Print Resources

Extending Mendelian Genetics

INDIANA STANDARDS		Sections	PAGES and PACING	UNIT RESOURCE BOOK
B.7.2	7.1	**Chromosomes and Phenotype** **KEY CONCEPT** The chromosomes on which genes are located can affect the expression of traits.	pp. 200–203 30 minutes	URB pages 35–38
B.7.2	7.2	**Complex Patterns of Inheritance** **KEY CONCEPT** Phenotype is affected by many different factors.	pp. 204–207 45 minutes	URB pages 39–42
B.7.2		CHAPTER INVESTIGATION: Codominance	p. 208 30 minutes	**Lab Binder** Genetics pages 15–16
B.5.2	7.3	**Gene Linkage and Mapping** **KEY CONCEPT** Genes can be mapped to specific locations on chromosomes.	pp. 209–211 30 minutes	URB pages 43–46
NOS.3		DATA ANALYSIS: Constructing Bar Graphs	p. 210 30 minutes	URB page 51
B.7.3	7.4	**Human Genetics and Pedigrees** **KEY CONCEPT** A combination of methods is used to study human genetics.	pp. 212–217 45 minutes	URB pages 47–50
B.7.2, B.7.3		OPTIONS FOR INQUIRY	pp. 218–219 30 minutes, 30 minutes	**Lab Binder** Genetics pages 17–22
		Chapter Review	pp. 220–223	**Assessment Book** Chapter Tests A, B pp. 133–140

INDIANA STANDARDS

B.5.2 Describe how hereditary information passed from parents to offspring is encoded in regions of DNA molecules called genes.
B.7.2 Describe dominant, recessive, codominant, sex-linked, incompletely dominant, multiply allelic, and polygenic traits and illustrate their inheritance patterns over multiple generations.
B.7.3 Determine the likelihood of the appearance of a specific trait in an offspring given the genetic make-up of the parents.
NOS.3 Clearly communicate their ideas and results of investigations verbally and in written form using tables, graphs, diagrams, and photographs.

Labs

PUPIL EDITION LABS

Sex-Linked Inheritance, Section 1, p. 202 Students model the inheritance of a sex-linked trait. **Lab Binder** pp. 23–24	**Time:** 20 minutes **Materials:** 2 coins, masking tape, marker, index card with genetic cross
Codominance, p. 208 Students explore codominance by investigating the inheritance of sickle cell disease within a family. **Lab Binder** pp. 15–16	**Time:** 30 minutes **Materials:** paper, pencil

OPTIONS FOR INQUIRY

Pedigree Analysis, p. 218 Students analyze a pedigree. **Lab Binder** pp. 17–19	**Time:** 30 minutes **Materials:** Pedigree Datasheet
Incomplete Dominance, p. 219 Students explore incomplete dominance by examining the human trait of hair texture. **Lab Binder** pp. 21–22	**Time:** 30 minutes **Materials:** paper, pencil

LAB BINDER Unit 3 Genetics

Additional Investigation: Human Heredity, pp. 25–27

Challenge Lab: Examining Banding Patterns in Polytene Chromosomes, pp. 73–76

LAB GENERATOR

A searchable CD of all labs in the program in editable format, including forensic, probeware, and biotechnology labs.

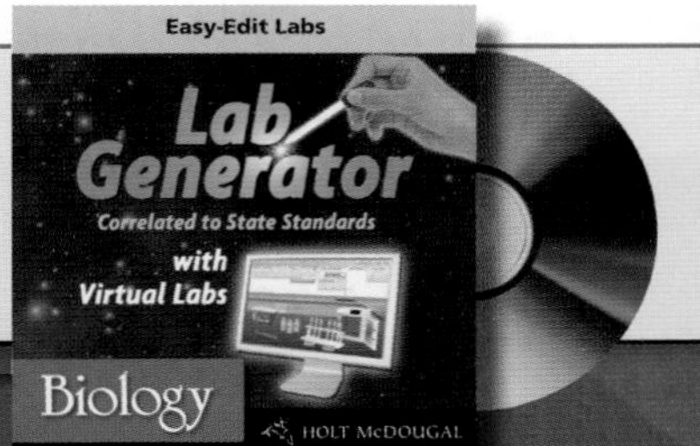

Presentation Tools

POWER PRESENTATIONS

Presentation Chapter 7
PowerPresentations for each section incorporate images and clips from the Media Gallery. Includes Note Navigator for each section.

MEDIA GALLERY

Contains the following images and video clips, as well as animations, simulations, and forms of visuals from the book.

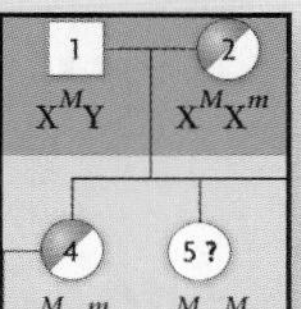
Pedigree

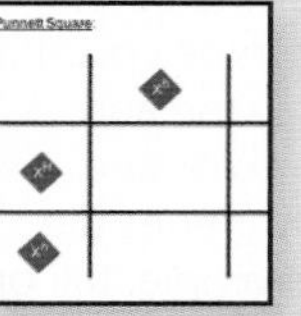
Punnett squares

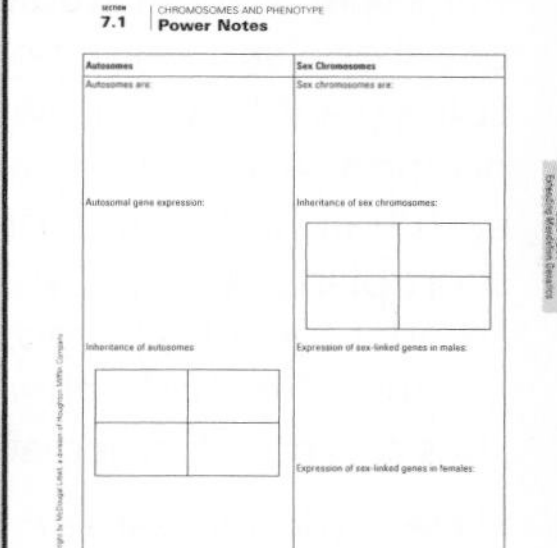

Power Notes

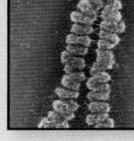

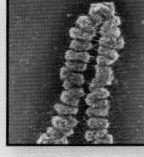

Albino squirrel

Human chromosome

VIDEO

Examine a set of short video clips on sex-linked traits and gene mapping.

ANIMATED BIOLOGY

Human Chromosomes

Tracking Traits

TRANSPARENCIES

Tracing Autosomal Genes T34

Tracing Sex Linked Genes T35

Online BIOLOGY CLASSZONE.COM

- BioZine
- Animated Biology
- Interactive Review
- SciLinks
- Resource Centers

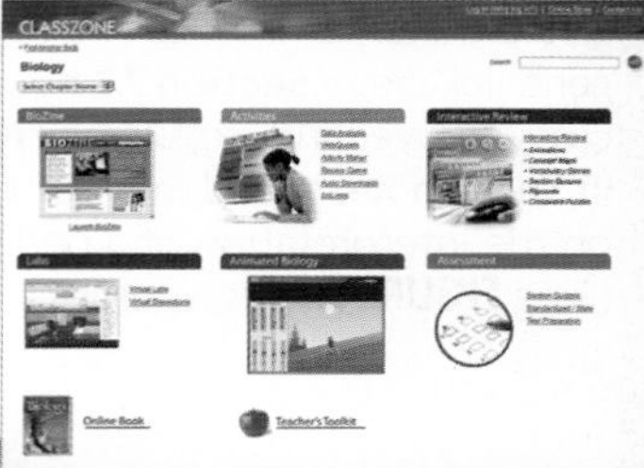

CHAPTER 7

Focus and Motivate

Why are there so many variations among people?

Have students think back to the work of Mendel. **Ask,** What were some of the traits that Mendel studied in pea plants? pea shape and color, pod shape and color, plant height, flower color and position **Ask,** How many varieties did each trait have? two; for example, tall or short plants Remind students that Mendel specifically chose those traits because they had either-or characteristics and no intermediate forms.

Have students examine the people in the photos. **Ask,** Do you think hair color is an either-or characteristic? No, there are more than two hair colors shown. **Ask,** What other observable traits show intermediate forms? skin and eye color Tell students that some traits such as skin, hair, and eye color, are determined by many genes, allowing for greater variation.

BIOZINE ClassZone.com

Students can access BioZine at **ClassZone.com** to learn about the variety of careers open to biologists.

In a Hurry?

The most important material in this chapter—non-Mendelian inheritance—is found in **Section 7.2.** For quick coverage of **Section 7.1,** discuss only sex-linked traits. Summarize the details of gene linkage in **Section 7.3** by reviewing crossing over and explaining **FIGURE 7.10.** In **Section 7.4,** spend most of the time on the interpretation of a pedigree, using **FIGURE 7.14** as a guide.

CHAPTER 7

Extending Mendelian Genetics

KEY CONCEPTS

7.1 Chromosomes and Phenotype
The chromosomes on which genes are located can affect the expression of traits.

7.2 Complex Patterns of Inheritance
Phenotype is affected by many different factors.

7.3 Gene Linkage and Mapping
Genes can be mapped to specific locations on chromosomes.

7.4 Human Genetics and Pedigrees
A combination of methods is used to study human genetics.

Online BIOLOGY CLASSZONE.COM

Animated BIOLOGY
View animated chapter concepts.
- Human Chromosomes
- Tracking Traits

BIOZINE
Keep current with biology news.
- News feeds
- Bio Bytes
- Polls

RESOURCE CENTER
Get more information on
- Phenotype Complexity
- Gene Mapping
- Pedigrees

Teacher Demo

Eye Opener To give students a personal example of non-Mendelian genetics, demonstrate variation in student height.

Prepare Reserve a large open area, such as a gym or hallway, for this demonstration.

Introduce Explain to students that most human phenotypes are not directly observable as following Mendel's principles. One of these traits is height. Tell students that they are going to make a living histogram showing variation in height in the class.

Demonstrate Have students arrange themselves in order according to their height, with the shortest student on the left and the tallest on the right. Each height forms a column, and students of the same height should stand one behind the other in the column. If any students are unable to stand, they can help to arrange the others in the correct order. When all students have been arranged, number the columns or measure the actual heights of students, then record the number of students in each column.

Why are there so many variations among people?

Connecting CONCEPTS

It will come as no surprise to you, but you are not a pea plant. But, Mendel's principles apply to you just as they apply to other organisms. About 99.9 percent of everyone's DNA is identical. So how can a 0.1 percent difference in DNA lead to the wide range of human traits? In many organisms, genetics is more than dominant and recessive alleles.

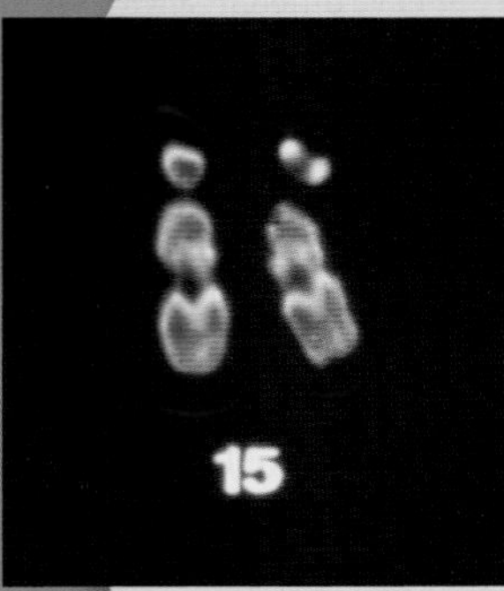

Multiple Gene Traits Two genes for human eye color are located on chromosome 15, shown at the left. One reason for the large variations in phenotype in many species is that most traits are produced by several genes that interact with each other. Eye color in humans is a trait controlled by more than one gene. And the alleles of those genes have different dominant and recessive relationships. (colored LM; magnification 13,000×)

Once back in the classroom, draw a histogram on the board with height or column number labeled on the *x*-axis and number of students on the *y*-axis. The graph will probably be bell shaped.

Discuss Discuss the results. **Ask**

- How is the distribution of height that you observed different from that of Mendelian inheritance? wide range of phenotypes (heights), not just two
- What would the results have been if human height were inherited by an either-or gene according to Mendel's principles? Only two heights would have been observed in the class.

Explain that human height is influenced by several genes that, in turn, can be affected by the environment. **Ask,** What relationship would you expect between the amount of variation in height and the number of genes involved? The more genes involved, the greater the variability. Point out that most human traits are controlled by more than one gene. Students will learn about different kinds of gene interactions in this chapter.

Activate Prior Knowledge

Tell students that Mendel's laws of inheritance don't always apply. For example, cross a red-flowered snapdragon with a white, and the next generation of plants will have pink flowers. Direct students' attention to the chapter title and the photographs. **Ask,** When you look at the photos, why do you think **Mendelian genetics** needs to be extended? It doesn't explain the variation in hair, eye, and skin color.

Preview Vocabulary

Academic Vocabulary Two words commonly used in science are *law* and *principle.* Students may think of them as being synonymous.

law, a statement of what occurs under certain conditions

principle, a basic rule or quality that explains how something works

Use this chapter as a way to help students appreciate the difference. While patterns of inheritance must conform to the principles of genetics, Mendel's laws do not apply in all circumstances, which leads to "non-Mendelian" genetics.

English Learners Students will see the words *map* and *mapping* applied to genes and chromosomes in this chapter. Typically maps involve a two-dimensional coordinate system applied to a surface area. Tell students that chromosome maps are linear and indicate where along a chromosome a gene can be found.

Integrating Chemistry

The color of a baby's eyes at birth does not necessarily represent their true color. Coloration is due to the pigment melanin: the more melanin present, the darker the eyes. Many newborns with blue or gray eyes will develop darker coloration as their bodies begin to produce melanin, usually within the first six months.

SECTION 7.1

▼ Plan and Prepare

Objectives

- Relate dominant-recessive patterns of inheritance in autosomal chromosomes to genetic disorders.
- Describe patterns of inheritance in sex-linked traits.

Section Resources

Unit Resource Book Study Guide pp. 35–36 Power Notes p. 37 Reinforcement p. 38
Interactive Reader Chapter 7 **Spanish Study Guide** pp. 65–66
Biology Toolkit pp. C30, C34, D1
Technology Power Presentation 7.1 Media Gallery DVD Online Quiz 7.1

Activate Prior Knowledge Hold up a pair of dice. **Ask,** If each die only had one number, how many different combinations could you roll? 1 Have students imagine other possible combinations, not counting a number reversal such as 2/1 for 1/2. **Ask,** How many combinations are possible with two different numbers on each die? 3 with 6? 21 Compare the increasing number of combinations to phenotype variations that can occur when multiple alleles are involved in determining traits.

▼ Teach

Take It Further

Mendel did not study sex-linked genes. In fact, pea plants do not have **sex chromosomes.** Only certain plant species that have male and female sex organs on separate plants have sex cells, a characteristic called **dioecious.** Most flowering plants have both male and female parts. Thus, most plants are **hermaphroditic,** or of both sexes.

7.1 Chromosomes and Phenotype

KEY CONCEPT The chromosomes on which genes are located can affect the expression of traits.

MAIN IDEAS

- Two copies of each autosomal gene affect phenotype.
- Males and females can differ in sex-linked traits.

VOCABULARY

carrier, p. 201
sex-linked gene, p. 201
X chromosome inactivation, p. 203

Review
dominant, recessive, phenotype, allele, gene, autosome, sex chromosome, trait

INDIANA STANDARDS

B.7.2 Describe dominant, recessive, codominant, sex-linked, incompletely dominant, multiply allelic, and polygenic traits and illustrate their inheritance patterns over multiple generations.

Connect The next time you are in a crowd of people, take a moment to look at the variety of traits around you. Hair color and texture, eye color and shape, height, and weight are all influenced by genetics. Can dominant and recessive alleles of one gene produce so many subtle differences in any of those traits? In most cases, the answer is no. But the dominant and recessive relationship among alleles is a good place to start when learning about the complexities of genetics.

MAIN IDEA

Two copies of each autosomal gene affect phenotype.

You read in Chapter 6 how some genetic traits depend on dominant and recessive alleles. But many factors affect phenotype, including the specific chromosome upon which a gene is located. Gene expression is often related to whether a gene is located on an autosome or on a sex chromosome. Recall that sex chromosomes determine an organism's sex. Autosomes are all of the other chromosomes, and they do not play a direct role in sex determination.

You also know that sexually reproducing organisms have two of each chromosome. Each pair consists of one chromosome from each of two parents. Both chromosomes have the same genes, but the chromosomes might have different alleles for those genes. And, as Mendel observed, different alleles can produce different phenotypes, such as white flowers or purple flowers.

All of the traits that Mendel studied are determined by genes on autosomes. In fact, most traits in sexually reproducing organisms, including humans, are the result of autosomal genes. Look at **FIGURE 7.1.** Is your hair curly or straight? What about your parents' hair? The genes that affect your hair texture—curly hair or straight hair—are autosomal genes.

Many human genetic disorders are also caused by autosomal genes. The chance of a person having one of these disorders can be predicted, just as Mendel could predict the phenotypes that would appear in his pea plants. Why? Because there are two copies of each gene on autosomes—one on each homologous chromosome—and each copy can influence phenotype.

FIGURE 7.1 Hair texture is just one example of a trait that is controlled by autosomal genes.

Differentiated Instruction

ENGLISH LEARNERS

Before beginning the section, have small groups of students do a word splash activity that includes the new vocabulary, the seven review terms, and the terms *phenotype* and *Punnett square.* Show the words as a cluster on the board. Have students skim the section, work together to arrange the vocabulary in categories, and then explain their choices.

Biology Toolkit, Word Splash, p. D1

BELOW LEVEL

Work with students to prepare a cluster diagram that relates the review vocabulary listed above to the new vocabulary in the section.

Biology Toolkit, Cluster Diagram, p. C30

Disorders Caused by Recessive Alleles

Some human genetic disorders are caused by recessive alleles on autosomes. Two copies of the recessive allele must be present for a person to have the disorder. These disorders often appear in offspring of parents who are both heterozygotes. That is, each parent has one dominant, "normal" allele that masks the one disease-causing recessive allele.

For example, cystic fibrosis is a severe recessive disorder that mainly affects the sweat glands and the mucus glands. A person who is homozygous for the recessive allele will have the disease. Someone who is heterozygous for the alleles will not have the disease, but is a carrier. A **carrier** does not show disease symptoms, but can pass on the disease-causing allele to offspring. In this way, alleles that are lethal, or deadly, in a homozygous recessive individual can remain in a population's gene pool. This inheritance pattern is shown in **FIGURE 7.2.**

FIGURE 7.2 AUTOSOME INHERITANCE

Some genetic disorders, such as cystic fibrosis, are inherited according to Mendel's principles.

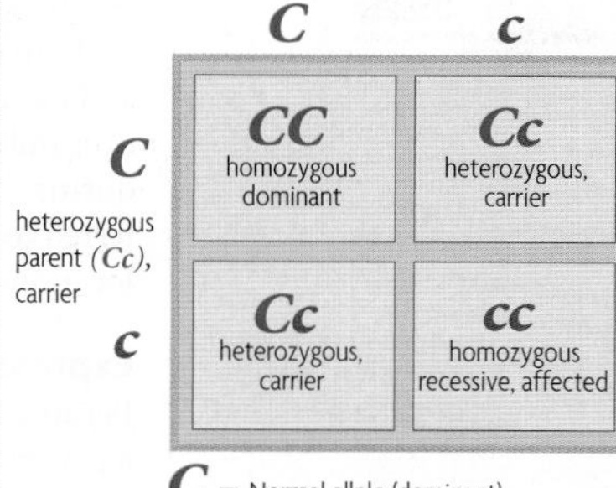

Disorders Caused by Dominant Alleles

Dominant genetic disorders are far less common than recessive disorders. One example is Huntington's disease. Huntington's disease damages the nervous system and usually appears during adulthood. Because the disease is caused by a dominant allele, there is a 50 percent chance that a child will have it even if only one parent has one of the alleles. If both parents are heterozygous for the disease, there is a 75 percent chance that any of their children will inherit the disease. Because Huntington's disease strikes later in life, a person with the allele can have children before the disease appears. In that way, the allele is passed on in the population even though the disease is fatal.

A Connect How are Mendel's observations related to genes on autosomes?

MAIN IDEA

Males and females can differ in sex-linked traits.

Mendel figured out much about heredity, but he did not know about chromosomes. As it turns out, he only studied traits produced by genes on autosomes. Now, we know about sex chromosomes, and we know that the expression of genes on the sex chromosomes differs from the expression of autosomal genes.

Sex-Linked Genes

Genes that are located on the sex chromosomes are called **sex-linked genes.** Recall from Chapter 6 that many species have specialized sex chromosomes called the X and Y chromosomes. In mammals and some other animals, individuals with two X chromosomes—an XX genotype—are female. Individuals with one X and one Y—an XY genotype—are male. As **FIGURE 7.3** shows, a female can pass on only an X chromosome to offspring, but a male can pass on either an X or a Y chromosome.

FIGURE 7.3 SEX CHROMOSOME INHERITANCE

The gametes from an XY male determine the sex of the offspring.

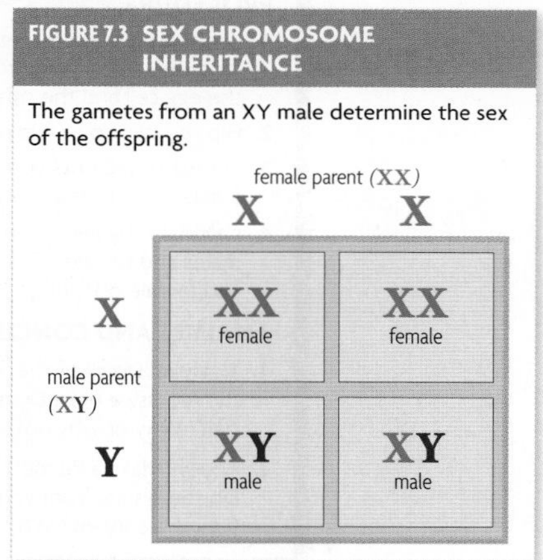

INCLUSION

To help students who are visually impaired work with Punnett squares, glue a yarn outline of a blank Punnett square to a piece of cardboard. Cut out letters from sandpaper to represent alleles or X and Y chromosomes.

TEACH FROM VISUALS

FIGURE 7.2 Have students work through the Punnett square. Review the definitions of *homozygous* and *heterozygous.* **Ask**

- Is a carrier homozygous or heterozygous? heterozygous
- What percentage of the offspring is expected to be a carrier? 50 percent
- Is it possible for a *CC* individual to have offspring with cystic fibrosis? No, offspring must inherit two recessive alleles, one from each parent. A *CC* parent has no recessive allele.

History of Science

George Huntington, an American physician, first documented Huntington's disease in 1872. At the time, he called it Huntington's chorea. This name was taken from the Greek word *chorea,* meaning "dance." Individuals with Huntington's disease often had involuntary, erratic movements suggestive of a dance. After 1963, the disorder became known as **Huntington's disease** in order to represent all forms of the disorder.

The dominant allele that causes Huntington's disease was brought to the United States in 1630 by three men whose families had been persecuted for witchcraft in England because of their strange behavior and mental disturbances. At that time, these symptoms were believed to be caused by consorting with the devil.

Answers

A Connect The traits Mendel studied were due to the expression of two copies of autosomal genes.

▼ Teach *continued*

QUICK LAB

Time 20 minutes	TEACHER TESTED ✓
Lab Binder Genetics, pp. 23–24	

Purpose Model the inheritance of a sex-linked trait.

LAB MANAGEMENT

- Give each group an index card with a different monohybrid cross to model so that all possibilities are covered.
- Explain the notation used for sex-linked genes: sex chromosome is shown as a capital *X* or *Y*; allele is shown as a superscript.
- Students should record both the sex and the genotype of each offspring.

EXPECTED RESULTS

After 50 tosses, calculated frequencies should approach those listed below:

- $X^AX^a \times X^AY$: 25% homozygous dominant females, 25% carrier females, 25% recessive males, 25% males with dominant allele
- $X^AX^A \times X^aY$: 50% carrier females, 50% males with dominant allele
- $X^aX^a \times X^AY$: 50% carrier females, 50% recessive males
- $X^AX^a \times X^aY$: 25% recessive females, 25% carrier females, 25% recessive males, 25% dominant males
- $X^aX^a \times X^aY$: 50% recessive females, 50% recessive males
- $X^AX^A \times X^AY$: 50% homozygous dominant females, 50% males with dominant allele

Answers

Analyze and Conclude

1. Answers will depend on the cross, but should follow the expected results. Females are recessive only if they inherit two recessive alleles; males are recessive if they inherit one.
2. Results should be close to those predicted by the Punnett squares.

TAKING NOTES

Use a two-column chart to compare and contrast the expression of autosomal and sex-linked genes.

autosomes	sex chromosomes

Genes on the Y chromosome are responsible for the development of male offspring, but the X chromosome actually has much more influence over phenotype. The X chromosome has many genes that affect many traits. Scientists hypothesize that the Y chromosome may have genes for more than sex determination, but there is little evidence to support this idea.

In many organisms, including humans, the Y chromosome is much smaller and has many fewer genes than the X chromosome. Evidence suggests that over millions of years of evolution, the joining of the X and Y chromosomes during meiosis has resulted in segments of the Y chromosome being transferred to the X. You will read more about specific sex-linked genes and their locations on the human X and Y chromosomes in Section 7.4.

Expression of Sex-Linked Genes

Because the X and Y chromosomes have different genes, sex-linked genes have a pattern of expression that is different from autosomal genes. Remember, two copies of an autosomal gene affect a trait. What happens when there is only one copy of a gene, as is the case in an XY male? Because males have only one copy of each type of sex chromosome, they express all of the alleles on both chromosomes. In males, there are no second copies of sex-linked genes to mask the effects of another allele. This means that even if all of the alleles of sex-linked genes in a male are recessive, they will be expressed.

QUICK LAB **PREDICTING** B.7.2

Sex-Linked Inheritance

The relationship between genotype and phenotype in sex-linked genes differs from that in autosomal genes. A female must have two recessive alleles of a sex-linked gene to express a recessive sex-linked trait. Just one recessive allele is needed for the same trait to be expressed in a male. In this lab, you will model the inheritance pattern of sex-linked genes.

PROBLEM How does probability explain sex-linked inheritance?

PROCEDURE

1. Use the tape and marker to label two coins with the genetic cross shown on your group's index card. One coin represents the egg cell and the other coin represents the sperm cell.
2. Flip the two coins and record the genotype of the "offspring."
3. Repeat step 2 until you have modeled 50 genetic crosses. Make a data table to record each genetic cross that you model.
4. Calculate the genotype and phenotype probabilities for both males and females. Calculate the frequency of male offspring and female offspring.

MATERIALS

- 2 coins
- masking tape
- marker
- index card with genetic cross

ANALYZE AND CONCLUDE

1. **Analyze** Do all of the females from the genetic cross show the recessive trait? Do all of the males show the recessive trait? Why or why not?
2. **Apply** Make a Punnett square that shows the genetic cross. Do the results from your Punnett square agree with those from your experiment? Why or why not?

Differentiated Instruction

PRE-AP

Have students compare the inheritance of a gene on an autosome with the inheritance of a gene on each kind of sex chromosome. Have them consider these questions:

- How is a male offspring's phenotype affected if he inherits a recessive autosomal allele? a recessive sex-linked allele?
- How is autosomal and sex-linked inheritance similar in heterozygous female offspring?

Biology Toolkit, Compare/Contrast Chart, p. C34

TEACH WITH TECHNOLOGY

If students have access to a spreadsheet program, they can use it to record and organize their coin-toss data and do their calculations for the Quick Lab. Students can also make a bar graph using different colors to show male and female offspring of each genotype.

FIGURE 7.4 The female calico cats have two X chromosomes with different alleles for fur color. Both alleles are expressed in a random pattern. The male cat has only one X chromosome, and its allele for fur color is expressed across the entire body.

X^O = Orange fur allele
X^o = Black fur allele

In mammals, the expression of sex-linked genes in females is also different from the way in which genes on other chromosomes are expressed. In each cell of female mammals, one of the two X chromosomes is randomly "turned off" by a process called **X chromosome inactivation.** Because of X chromosome inactivation, females are a patchwork of two types of cells—one type with an active X chromosome that came from the mother, and a second type with an active X chromosome that came from the father.

Colorful examples of X chromosome inactivation are seen in female tortoiseshell cats and female calico cats. The female calico cats shown in **FIGURE 7.4** have white fur, as well as alleles for black or orange fur on their X chromosomes. Those alleles are expressed randomly in cells across the cat's body. As a result, its coat is a mixture of color splotches. It is truly a patchwork of cells. Because the male cats only have one X chromosome, they have white fur and one sex-linked gene for either orange or black fur.

A Infer Why are males more likely than females to have sex-linked genetic disorders?

Connecting CONCEPTS

Mitosis Recall from **Chapter 5** that DNA coils to form chromosomes. In XX females, one of the two X chromosomes in each cell is "inactivated" by becoming even more tightly coiled.

7.1 ASSESSMENT

ONLINE QUIZ ClassZone.com

B.7.2

REVIEWING MAIN IDEAS

1. How are autosomal traits, including recessive genetic disorders that are carried in a population, related to Mendel's observations of heredity?
2. Describe how **sex-linked genes** are expressed differently in males and in females.

CRITICAL THINKING

3. **Apply** How might a scientist determine whether a trait is sex-linked by observing the offspring of several genetic crosses?
4. **Compare and Contrast** How is the expression of sex-linked genes both similar to and different from the expression of autosomal genes?

Connecting CONCEPTS

5. **Meiosis** Scientists hypothesize that over millions of years, the Y chromosome has lost genes to the X chromosome. During what stages of meiosis might the Y chromosome have transferred genes to the X chromosome? Explain.

7.1 ASSESSMENT

1. Two copies of autosomal genes affect phenotype, as observed in all of Mendel's crosses.
2. In males, all sex-linked genes are expressed. In females, two copies of genes on the X chromosomes affect phenotype, although one X in each cell is randomly inactivated.
3. If more males than females have a particular phenotype, the trait is probably sex-linked.
4. In males, all sex-linked genes are expressed because there is only one copy of each sex-linked gene. In females, sex-linked genes are expressed similarly to autosomal genes in terms of dominance and recessiveness.
5. prophase of meiosis I, because that is when homologous chromosomes pair and crossovers occur

Take It Further

Tell students that the size of the colored splotches in female **calico cats** is determined by the period of time in embryonic development that the X chromosome is inactivated. If inactivation occurs early in development, more skin cells with the expressed color will be formed, and the splotch will be large. If inactivation occurs later in development, most of the skin cells will have already been formed with white fur, and the colored splotch will be small.

Science Trivia

- The human X chromosome carries more than 1000 known genes.
- The human Y chromosome was once thought to hold only a few genes, but it is now known to hold many more. Estimates vary on the number of genes on the Y chromosome, ranging from about 70 to almost 400. Of the known 78 genes, 27 are shared with the X chromosome.
- The X and Y chromosomes are thought to have been the same size at one time. Scientists have calculated that the Y chromosome has lost an average of five genes every million years.

Answers

A Infer because all sex-linked genes, even recessive alleles, are expressed in males

Assess and Reteach ▼

Assess Use the Online Quiz or Section Quiz (*Assessment Book,* p. 129).

Reteach Have students make a Punnett square showing the offspring that would be expected from a cross between an X^RX^r female and an X^RY male, where *R* is a dominant allele for round eyes, and *r* is a recessive allele for oval eyes. Have students list the genotypes and phenotypes for both male and female offspring. Check them for accuracy.

SECTION 7.2

▼ Plan and Prepare

Objectives

- Describe different types of allele interactions.
- Describe polygenic traits and the effect of environmental factors on phenotype.

Section Resources

Unit Resource Book
Study Guide pp. 39–40
Power Notes p. 41
Reinforcement p. 42
Pre-AP Activity pp. 53–54

Interactive Reader Chapter 7
Spanish Study Guide pp. 67–68

Biology Toolkit pp. C34, D7

Technology
Power Presentation 7.2
Media Gallery DVD
Online Quiz 7.2

Activate Prior Knowledge Have students think of a human trait, such as eye color or height, that has many phenotypes. **Ask,** How might this trait be inherited so that more than two phenotypes are possible? More than two alleles of a gene or more than one gene may be involved. **Ask,** Is this pattern of inheritance Mendelian? It is not Mendelian, because Mendel's traits were either-or traits; that is, each trait had only two possible phenotypes.

▼ Teach

Vocabulary

Academic Vocabulary Mendel realized that genes are inherited as **discrete** units, separate and self-contained. However, the phenotype produced can sometimes show **continuous** variation, especially when multiple genes are involved. The word *continuous* suggests an uninterrupted range of expression.

7.2 Complex Patterns of Inheritance

KEY CONCEPT Phenotype is affected by many different factors.

MAIN IDEAS
- Phenotype can depend on interactions of alleles.
- Many genes may interact to produce one trait.
- The environment interacts with genotype.

VOCABULARY
incomplete dominance, p. 204
codominance, p. 205
polygenic trait, p. 206

Review
allele, phenotype, genotype

B.7.2 Describe dominant, recessive, codominant, sex-linked, incompletely dominant, multiply allelic, and polygenic traits and illustrate their inheritance patterns over multiple generations.

Connect Suppose you have blue and yellow paints to paint a room. You paint the walls yellow, let them dry, then paint the walls blue. The blue paint masks the yellow paint, so you could say that the blue paint is "dominant." You could also combine the paints in other ways. You could paint the room in blue and yellow stripes, or you could mix the colors and paint the room green. You can think of different alleles as different paint colors, but in genetics there are many more paint colors—alleles—and many more ways that they are combined.

MAIN IDEA

Phenotype can depend on interactions of alleles.

Although Mendel's basic theory of heredity was correct, his research could not have explained all of the continuous variations for many traits. For example, many traits result from alleles with a range of dominance, rather than a strict dominant and recessive relationship.

The pea flowers that Mendel observed were either white or purple. One allele was dominant, but dominance does not mean that one allele "defeats" the other. Usually, it means that the dominant allele codes for a certain protein and the recessive allele codes for a variation of the protein that has little or no effect. In Mendel's pea flowers, a heterozygous plant makes enough of the purple color that only one dominant allele is needed to give the flowers a purple color. But in many cases, a phenotype comes from more than just one gene, and many genes in a population have more than just two alleles.

***Connecting* CONCEPTS**

Principles of Genetics Recall from **Chapter 6** that a homozygote has two identical alleles of a gene, and a heterozygote has two different alleles of a gene.

Incomplete Dominance

Sometimes, alleles show **incomplete dominance,** in which a heterozygous phenotype is somewhere between the two homozygous phenotypes. Neither allele is completely dominant nor completely recessive. One example of incomplete dominance is the four-o'clock plant. When plants that are homozygous for red flowers are crossed with plants that are homozygous for white flowers, the offspring have pink flowers. The pink color is a third, distinct phenotype. Neither of the original phenotypes of the plants in the parent's generation can be seen separately in the F_1 generation offspring.

Differentiated Instruction

ENGLISH LEARNERS

After reading the section, show students how to create a compare/contrast chart to study incomplete dominance and codominance. Write the terms in two large boxes at the top. Draw arrows down from these to a single box for shared characteristics. Draw arrows from this box down again to a series of smaller boxes that align with one of the two at the top and detail how the two types of interactions are different.

Biology Toolkit, Compare/Contrast Chart, p. C34

FIGURE 7.5 Incomplete Dominance

PHENOTYPE	GENOTYPE	PHENOTYPE	GENOTYPE	PHENOTYPE	GENOTYPE
green	B_1B_1	steel blue	B_2B_2	royal blue	B_1B_2
The green betta fish is homozygous for the green color allele.		The steel blue betta fish is homozygous for the blue color allele.		The royal blue betta fish is heterozygous for the two color alleles.	

Another example of incomplete dominance is the color of betta fish shown in **FIGURE 7.5.** When a green fish (B_1B_1) is crossed with a steel blue fish (B_2B_2), all of the offspring have the heterozygous genotype (B_1B_2). These offspring will be a royal blue color that comes from the phenotypes from both alleles. The alleles of this gene follow a pattern of incomplete dominance. What happens when two royal blue betta fish are crossed? Some offspring (25 percent) will be green (B_1B_1), some (50 percent) will be royal blue (B_1B_2), and some (25 percent) will be steel blue (B_2B_2).

VOCABULARY

When alleles are neither dominant nor recessive, such as with incomplete dominance, uppercase letters with either subscripts or superscripts are used to represent the different alleles.

Codominance

Sometimes, both alleles of a gene are expressed completely—neither allele is dominant nor recessive. In this case, alleles show **codominance,** in which both traits are fully and separately expressed. Suppose a plant that is homozygous for red flowers is crossed with a plant that is homozygous for white flowers. In incomplete dominance, the offspring have pink flowers. Codominant alleles are different. Instead of what looks like an intermediate phenotype, both traits are expressed. The flowers will have some red areas and some white areas.

One trait that you likely know about—human ABO blood types—is an example of codominance. And, because the blood types come from three different alleles in the human population, this trait is also considered a multiple-allele trait. The multiple alleles, shown in **FIGURE 7.6,** are called I^A, I^B, and i. Both I^A and I^B result in a protein, called an antigen, on the surface of red blood cells. Allele i is recessive and does not result in an antigen. Someone with a genotype of I^Ai will have type A blood, and someone with a genotype of I^Bi will have type B blood. But remember that the I^A and I^B alleles are codominant.

FIGURE 7.6 CODOMINANCE

PHENOTYPE (BLOOD TYPE)		GENOTYPES
A	antigen A 	I^AI^A or I^Ai
B	 antigen B	I^BI^B or I^Bi
AB	both antigens 	I^AI^B
O	no antigens 	ii

ONLINE BIOLOGY Go to the chapter Resource Center at **ClassZone.com** for additional resources and information on phenotype complexity.

TEACH FROM VISUALS

FIGURE 7.5 Have students study the phenotypes and genotypes of the betta fish. **Ask,** How can you tell that the two color alleles show incomplete dominance? The color of the heterozygote (royal blue) is a combination of blue and green.

History of Science

Experiments involving **blood transfusions** took place as early as the 1600s; however the first documented instance of human-to-human blood transfusion didn't occur until the early 1800s. While transfusing blood was seen as a great medical advance, mixing blood could lead to blood clumping or other toxic reactions that were fatal. A physician, **Karl Landsteiner,** recognized the adverse reaction as an immune response. His work led to the development of the **ABO system** of blood typing in 1901, for which he was awarded a Nobel Prize in 1930.

Integrating Chemistry

The **antigens** that determine human blood groups are complex molecules found on the surface of red blood cells. The protein base of each molecule is embedded in the cell membrane. Attached to the base is a chain of sugar molecules, called antigen H, which sticks out from the membrane. The alleles for the A and B blood groups do not actually code for A and B antigens. Instead, they code for different enzymes that complete the A and B antigens by attaching a specific molecule to the sugar chain to make it functional.

PRE-AP

Have students create their own example of a trait to compare Mendelian inheritance patterns to patterns of codominance and incomplete dominance. Suggest they format this as a table that compares patterns of inheritance in ratio form, across several generations.

Biology Toolkit, Semantic Feature Analysis, p. D7

ENGLISH LEARNERS

Students may have a difficult time differentiating between incomplete dominance and codominance. Explain that *in-* can mean "into." Tell students that when red four o'clock flowers are crossed with white four o'clock flowers, the red "goes into" the white, forming pink. Tell students that *co-* means "together." If type A blood is crossed with type B blood, they are expressed together as type AB.

▼ Teach *continued*

Vocabulary

epistasis The prefix *epi-* can mean "at," and *stasis* means "a standstill." Because an epistatic gene can prevent the expression of other genes, it could be said that epistasis causes the expression of other genes to be at a standstill. Students may also be familiar with the word **epicenter,** referring to the center of an earthquake or sometimes the center of a controversy.

Take It Further

There are three known genes in humans that affect **eye color.** The GEY gene is located on chromosome 19 and has a green and a blue allele. The green allele is dominant. The BEY1 gene is on chromosome 15 and is the central brown eye color gene. The BEY2 gene is also on chromosome 15 and has a brown and a blue allele. The brown allele is dominant. Geneticists have designed a model using the BEY2 and GEY gene pairs to explain the inheritance of blue, green, and brown eyes. However, the model cannot explain other eye colors such as hazel and gray, nor can it explain why eye color can change over time. This suggests to geneticists that all of the genes responsible for eye color have yet to be discovered.

Answers

A Apply If two people are heterozygotes (I^Bi), they can each pass the recessive allele (i) to their offspring.

People with both codominant alleles (I^AI^B) have both antigens, so they have type AB blood. People with an *ii* genotype have red blood cells without either antigen, and they have type O blood. Two heterozygous people, one with type A blood (I^Ai) and one with type B blood (I^Bi), can have offspring with any of the four blood types, depending on the alleles that are passed on.

A Apply How can two people with type B blood have a child with type O blood?

MAIN IDEA

Many genes may interact to produce one trait.

As you have seen, some variations in phenotype are related to incomplete dominance, codominance, and multiple alleles. But most traits in plants and animals, including humans, are the result of several genes that interact.

Polygenic Traits

Traits produced by two or more genes are called **polygenic traits.** Human skin color, for example, is the result of four genes that interact to produce a continuous range of colors. Similarly, human eye color, which is often thought of as a single gene trait, is polygenic. As **FIGURE 7.7** shows, at least three genes with complicated patterns of expression play roles in determining eye color. For example, the green allele is dominant to blue alleles, but it is recessive to all brown alleles. These genes do not account for all eye color variations, such as changes in eye color over time, the continuous range of eye colors, and patterns of colors in eyes. As a result, scientists hypothesize that still undiscovered genes affect eye color.

VISUAL VOCAB

Traits that are produced by two or more genes are called **polygenic traits.**

many — **poly**; genes — **genic**

Epistasis

Another polygenic trait is fur color in mice and in other mammals. In mice, at least five different genes interact to produce the phenotype. Two genes give the mouse its general color, one gene affects the shading of the color, and one gene determines whether the mouse will have spots. But the fifth gene involved in mouse fur color can overshadow all of the others. In cases such as this, one gene, called an epistatic gene, can interfere with the expression of other genes.

FIGURE 7.7 Eye Color

At least three different genes interact to produce the range of human eye colors, such as in the examples on the right.

GENE NAME	DOMINANT ALLELE	RECESSIVE ALLELE
BEY1	brown	blue
BEY2	brown	blue
GEY	green	blue

Order of dominance: brown > green > blue.

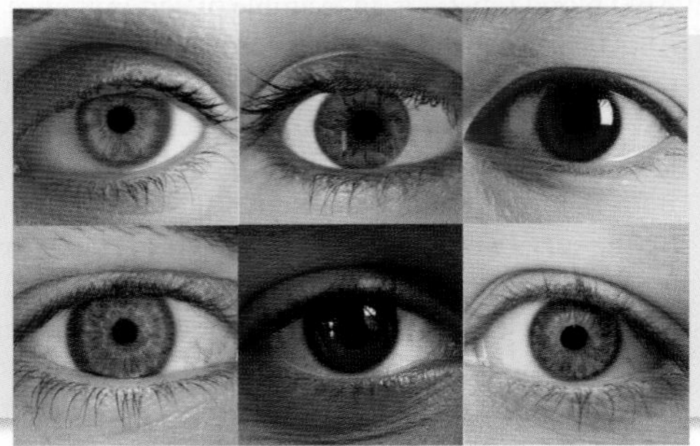

Differentiated Instruction

BELOW LEVEL

The ABO blood group system is a difficult example of codominance because multiple alleles complicate the picture. For a simpler example, describe to students the inheritance of hair color in shorthorn cattle. If a red-haired cow is bred with a white-haired bull, all the offspring are roan, a light red. Examination of the offspring's hairs with a hand lens reveals that some hairs are red and some are white. The allele for red hair and the allele for white hair are expressed equally in codominance.

TEACH WITH TECHNOLOGY

If students have access to graphing calculators, have them enter the data from the Eye Opener Demonstration on pages 198–199 to produce a graph. The graph will show a bell-shaped distribution of phenotypes. Explain to students that polygenic inheritance is quantitative; each dominant allele adds a certain amount of height to the phenotype.

In albinism, a single epistatic gene interferes with the expression of other genes. Albinism, as you can see in **FIGURE 7.8**, is characterized by a lack of pigment in skin, hair, and eyes. A mouse that is homozygous for the alleles that prevent the coloration of fur will be white, regardless of the phenotypes that would normally come from the other four genes. A person with the alleles for albinism will have very light skin, hair, and eyes, regardless of the other genes he or she has inherited.

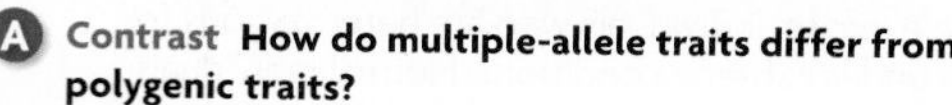

A Contrast **How do multiple-allele traits differ from polygenic traits?**

FIGURE 7.8 Albinism in mammals, such as this hedgehog, is caused by an epistatic gene that blocks the production of pigments.

MAIN IDEA

The environment interacts with genotype.

Phenotype is more than the sum of gene expression. For example, the sex of sea turtles depends both on genes and on environment. Female turtles make nests on beaches and bury their eggs in the sand. Eggs that mature in warmer temperatures develop into female turtles. Eggs that mature in cooler temperatures develop into male turtles.

Genes and environment also interact to determine human traits. Think about height. Genes give someone a tendency to be either short or tall, but they do not control everything. An interesting question for the interaction between genes and environment is "Are identical twins always identical?" Studies of identical twins have shown that the environment during early development can have long-lasting effects. One twin might get more nutrients than the other because of its position in the mother's uterus. This difference can result in height and size differences that last throughout the twins' lives. Also, twins raised in environments with different nutrition and health care often differ in height and other physical traits. In the end, phenotype is usually a mixture of genes and environment.

B Connect **Sunlight can cause a person's hair to become lighter in color. Is this an example of an interaction between genes and the environment? Why or why not?**

Find out more about dominant and recessive traits at scilinks.org.
Keycode: MLB007

7.2 ASSESSMENT

ONLINE QUIZ ClassZone.com

B.7.2

REVIEWING MAIN IDEAS

1. How is **incomplete dominance** expressed in a phenotype?
2. Why might **polygenic traits** vary more in phenotype than do single-gene traits?
3. Explain how interactions between genes and the environment can affect phenotype.

CRITICAL THINKING

4. **Synthesize** How is **codominance** the same as having no dominant and recessive relationship at all between two alleles?
5. **Compare and Contrast** How are codominant alleles and incompletely dominant alleles similar? How are they different?

Connecting CONCEPTS

6. **Principles of Genetics** Why can parents who are heterozygous for type A and type B blood have children with any of the four human blood types? Use a Punnett square to support your answer.

7.2 ASSESSMENT

1. Neither parental phenotype is expressed. Instead, a third, intermediate phenotype is expressed.
2. because many genes are interacting
3. Genes provide a tendency toward a phenotype that the environment can alter.
4. Both alleles are completely expressed in the phenotype; neither is masked.
5. Both are neither completely dominant nor completely recessive. Incomplete dominance produces an intermediate phenotype; codominance produces both traits in a phenotype.
6. A Punnett square will demonstrate that there is a 25 percent chance of any of the four phenotypes because each parent has an allele for either A or B blood as well as the recessive *i* allele.

ONLINE BIOLOGY Students can study the height distribution of men and women in the United States over the past 150 years. Go to Data Analysis Online in Options for Inquiry on page 219.

Take It Further

The distinctive patterns of an individual's **fingerprints** are controlled by polygenic inheritance, but they are also influenced by the fetal environment. The ridge pattern of a fingerprint can be altered during weeks 6 through 13 of fetal development, as the fetus touches the wall of the amniotic sac with its finger pads. This explains why identical twins, who have identical genes, have slightly different fingerprints.

Answers

A **Contrast** Multiple allele traits are influenced by several different versions of one gene; polygenic traits are influenced by multiple genes.

B **Connect** yes, because phenotype is altered by environment

Assess and Reteach ▼

Assess Use the Online Quiz or Section Quiz (*Assessment Book*, p. 130).

Reteach Have students make two Punnett squares showing crosses between two homozygotes that have different alleles of a gene. One Punnett square should show an incomplete dominance pattern and the other a codominance pattern. The traits shown in the Punnett squares can be fictitious, but the inheritance pattern should be accurately shown. Make sure students label the phenotypes and genotypes.

INVESTIGATION

Time 30 minutes	TEACHER TESTED
Teacher Preparation	
Student Difficulty	
Lab Binder Genetics, pp. 15–16	

Purpose Explore codominance by investigating the inheritance of sickle cell disease within a family.

Overview Students will analyze the test results for several members of a family in which the sickle cell trait appears. They will

- infer the genotypes of several family members from the type(s) of hemoglobin in their blood
- make a Punnett square to determine the possible genotypes and phenotypes of offspring of a family member

LAB MANAGEMENT

- Review codominance and the use of superscripts to represent codominant alleles.
- Use a different letter to identify alleles if students have a difficult time distinguishing between *S* and *s*.

Inclusion For students who have a hard time processing data, make a blank Punnett square with the possible gametes produced by each parent marked on it.

POST-LAB DISCUSSION

Have students evaluate their Punnett squares. **Ask**

- What gametes would Jerry form? Would they be produced in equal numbers? *Hb^S and Hb^s gametes, in equal numbers*
- What gametes would Jerry's wife form? Would they be produced in equal numbers? *Hb^S and Hb^s gametes, in equal numbers*
- What is the probability of Jerry and his wife having a child who has only normal hemoglobin? *25%*

Codominance

MATERIALS
- paper
- pencil

PROCESS SKILLS
- **Inferring**
- **Predicting**

B.7.2 Describe dominant, recessive, codominant, sex-linked, incompletely dominant, multiply allelic, and polygenic traits and illustrate their inheritance patterns over multiple generations.

Codominant alleles are both expressed in a person's phenotype. A heterozygote will have the traits associated with both alleles. In this lab, you will explore codominance by analyzing the results of tests for sickle cell disease within a family.

BACKGROUND

Sickle cell disease is caused by a change in the gene for hemoglobin, which is the oxygen-carrying protein in red blood cells. Individuals who are homozygous for the sickle cell allele often cannot endure exercise. Individuals who are heterozygous for the allele can have sickle cell attacks under extreme conditions. Normal individuals (Hb^S Hb^S) have only normal hemoglobin. Homozygous sickle cell individuals (Hb^s Hb^s) have only sickle cell hemoglobin. Heterozygous individuals (Hb^S Hb^s) have both normal hemoglobin and sickle cell hemoglobin.

Jerry Smith collapsed while running a race for his track team. A doctor said that he had a sickle cell attack. Genetic tests were run on several family members. The test results are shown below. An X indicates that form of hemoglobin in red blood cells.

PROBLEM How can you determine the genotypes of people in a family?

TABLE 1. FAMILY PHENOTYPES

Subject	Normal Hemoglobin	Sickle Cell Hemoglobin
Jerry Smith	X	X
Jerry's brother	X	
Jerry's younger sister	X	X
Jerry's youngest sister	X	
Jerry's father	X	
Jerry's grandfather	X	
Jerry's grandmother	X	X

PROCEDURE

1. Use the background information and the genetic test results to answer questions 1–4.
2. Use the background information and a Punnett square to help you answer question 5.

ANALYZE AND CONCLUDE

1. **Analyze** Are any of Jerry's siblings homozygous for the sickle cell allele? Are any of Jerry's siblings heterozygous for sickle cell disease?
2. **Analyze** What genotype is Jerry's father?
3. **Analyze** What genotypes are Jerry's grandparents?
4. **Infer** What is the genotype of Jerry's mother? Explain.
5. **Predict** If Jerry marries a female who is heterozygous for the sickle cell allele, what would be the possible genotypes and phenotypes of their children, according to your Punnett square?

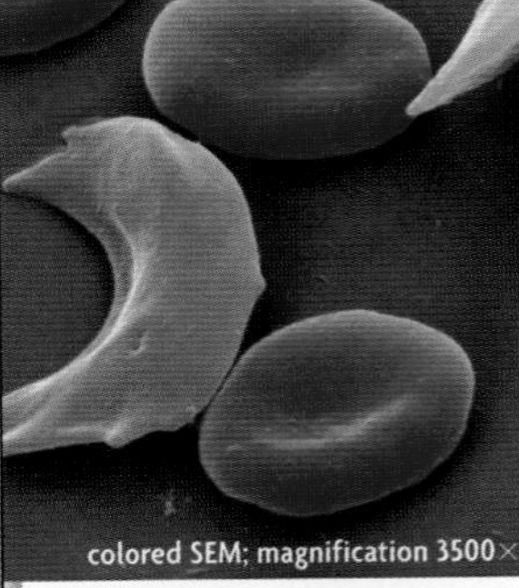
colored SEM; magnification 3500×

Answers

Analyze and Conclude

1. no; younger sister is heterozygous
2. father is Hb^SHb^S
3. grandfather is Hb^SHb^S, grandmother is Hb^SHb^s
4. Jerry's parents produced 50% normal offspring and 50% heterozygous offspring for sickle cell trait, so the mother is Hb^SHb^s.
5. The children would have the following possible genotypes and phenotypes:
   - normal hemoglobin (Hb^SHb^S)—25%
   - normal hemoglobin and sickle cell hemoglobin (Hb^SHb^s)—50%
   - sickle cell hemoglobin (Hb^sHb^s)—25%

7.3 Gene Linkage and Mapping

KEY CONCEPT Genes can be mapped to specific locations on chromosomes.

MAIN IDEAS

- Gene linkage was explained through fruit flies.
- Linkage maps estimate distances between genes.

VOCABULARY

linkage map, p. 210

Review
chromosome, crossing over

INDIANA STANDARDS

B.5.2 Describe how hereditary information passed from parents to offspring is encoded in regions of DNA molecules called genes.

Connect If you leave a banana out on a table until it is very ripe, you might see some of the most useful organisms for genetic research—fruit flies—buzzing around it. In your kitchen, fruit flies are pests. In the laboratory, early experiments with fruit flies showed not only that genes are on chromosomes but also that genes are found at specific places on chromosomes.

MAIN IDEA

Gene linkage was explained through fruit flies.

Gene linkage, which you read about in Chapter 6, was first described by William Bateson and R. C. Punnett, who invented the Punnett square. Punnett and Bateson, like Mendel, studied dihybrid crosses of pea plants. But their results differed from the 9:3:3:1 phenotype ratios that Mendel observed. The results suggested that some genes were linked together. But how could genes be linked and still follow Mendel's law of independent assortment?

American scientist Thomas Hunt Morgan, who worked with fruit flies (*Drosophila melanogaster*), found the answer. At first, Morgan was just looking for an organism to use in genetic research. He found fruit flies very useful because he could quickly and cheaply grow new generations of flies. He observed among fruit flies easily identifiable variations in eye color, body color, and wing shape. Knowing these variations, Morgan and his students set up experiments similar to Mendel's dihybrid crosses. They chose one type of fly with traits associated with the wild type, or most common phenotype. They crossed the wild type flies with mutant flies, or flies with a different, less common phenotype. You can see examples of fruit flies in **FIGURE 7.9.**

Wild type

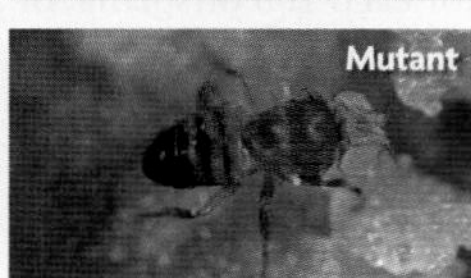

FIGURE 7.9 The wild type fruit fly (top) shows the most common phenotype. The mutant fruit fly (bottom) has no wings, white eyes, and a different body color.

Morgan's results, like those of Punnett and Bateson, did not always follow the 9:3:3:1 ratio predicted by Mendel. But the results did differ in a noticeable pattern. Some traits appeared to be inherited together. Morgan called these traits linked traits, and they appeared to fall into four groups. As it turns out, fruit flies have four pairs of chromosomes. Each of the four groups of linked traits identified by Morgan matches one of the chromosome pairs. Morgan concluded that linked genes were on the same chromosome. The chromosomes, not the genes, assort independently during meiosis. Because the linked genes were not inherited together every time, Morgan also concluded that chromosomes must exchange homologous genes during meiosis.

A Synthesize **How did Morgan's research build upon Mendel's observations?**

Differentiated Instruction

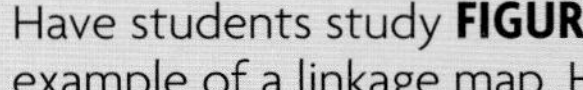

ENGLISH LEARNERS

Have students study **FIGURE 7.10** as an example of a linkage map. Have students describe what they see in the picture. Keep asking questions as you help them see the details of the fly. Use words such as *size, color, shape,* and *texture* in your questions and clarify the meanings of these words as needed.

Biology Toolkit, Connect to Content through Visuals, p. C17

BELOW LEVEL

Have students work in pairs to develop a model of gene linkage, using differently colored beads to represent alleles and doubled-up pipe cleaners to represent chromosomes. They should model how linkage of two traits to a particular chromosome can cause the genes to sort out together during meiosis. Have them address the question of why Mendel did not discover this in his work with garden peas.

Biology Toolkit, Think-Pair-Share, p. C13

Plan and Prepare

Objectives

- Describe the discovery of gene linkage.
- Explain how linkage maps can be used to estimate distances between genes.

Section Resources

Unit Resource Book
Study Guide pp. 43–44
Power Notes p. 45
Reinforcement p. 46

Interactive Reader Chapter 7
Spanish Study Guide pp. 69–70

Biology Toolkit pp. C13, C17, C19

Technology
Power Presentation 7.3
Media Gallery DVD
Online Quiz 7.3

Activate Prior Knowledge Ask students if they have ever waited in line with a group of friends to see a movie or get on an amusement park ride. **Ask,** When it came time to be seated, who did you sit next to—the friend who was standing next to you or the friend at the front of the line? friend next to you Describe how this is similar to gene linkage.

Teach

Take It Further

In *Drosophila,* the allele most frequent in a natural population is designated the **wild type.** All other alleles are considered **mutant** by default. Typically, the symbol for an allele comes from the mutant form, not the wild type.

Answers

A Synthesize Morgan used dihybrid crosses in fruit flies to study a new pattern of inheritance that revealed gene linkage in phenotypes.

Chapter 7: Extending Mendelian Genetics 209

▼ Teach *continued*

DATA ANALYSIS

Discuss

Bar graphs can be used to compare data that are not related. Multiple sets of data can be compared by drawing several bars next to each other.

Answers

1.

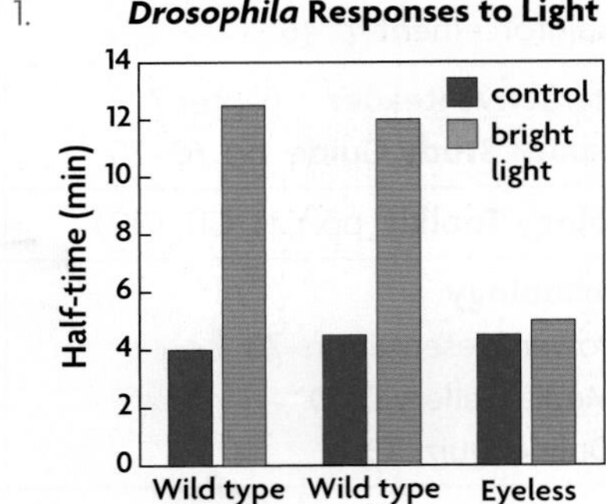

2. The eyeless strain was unaffected due to the mutation, but the other two strains reacted by increasing the amount of time it took half the flies to reach food.

Unit Resource Book, Data Analysis, p. 51

History of Science

A white-eyed male in the wild population of fruit flies in **Thomas Hunt Morgan's** "fly room" led to his **chromosomal theory of heredity.** He discovered that chromosomes are cellular structures that house small units of heredity called genes and that each gene has a specific location on a specific chromosome. In 1933, Morgan was awarded a Nobel Prize for his work.

DATA ANALYSIS

NOS.3

CONSTRUCTING BAR GRAPHS

Scientists tested the reaction of fruit flies to stress by exposing them to bright light—a source of stress for *Drosophila.* The scientists timed how long it took for half of the flies in each group to reach food, which they called a "half-time." Three strains of flies were tested—wild type 1, wild type 2, and a mutant eyeless type—under control conditions and with bright light. The data are shown in Table 1.

1. **Graph Data** Construct a bar graph that shows the data in the table. Recall that the independent variable is on the *x*-axis and the dependent variable is on the *y*-axis.
2. **Analyze** How did the condition of bright light affect the flies? Were all strains affected to the same degree? Why or why not?

TABLE 1. *DROSOPHILA* RESPONSES TO LIGHT

Strain	Condition	Half-Time (min)
Wild type 1	control	4.0
Wild type 1	bright light	12.5
Wild type 2	control	4.5
Wild type 2	bright light	12.0
Eyeless	control	4.5
Eyeless	bright light	5.0

Source: V. Min, B. Condron, Journal of Neuroscience Methods, 145.

MAIN IDEA

Linkage maps estimate distances between genes.

The probability that two genes on a chromosome will be inherited together is related to the distance between them. The closer together two genes are, the more likely it is that they will be inherited together. The farther apart two genes are, the more likely it is that they will be separated during meiosis.

One of Morgan's students, Alfred Sturtevant, hypothesized that the frequency of cross-overs during meiosis was related to the distance between genes. This meant that the closer together two genes were, the more likely they were to stay together when cross-overs took place. Sturtevant identified three linked traits in fruit flies—body color, eye color, and wing size—and then crossed the fruit flies. He recorded the percentage of times that the phenotypes did not appear together in the offspring. This percentage represented the frequency of cross-overs between chromosomes.

Connecting CONCEPTS

Crossing Over Recall from **Chapter 6** that segments of non-sister chromatids can be exchanged during meiosis.

From the cross-over frequencies, Sturtevant made **linkage maps,** which are maps of the relative locations, or loci, of genes on a chromosome. On a linkage map, one map unit is equal to one cross-over for each 100 offspring, or one percentage point. You can see an example of a linkage map in **FIGURE 7.10.**

Making a linkage map is fairly easy if all of the cross-over frequencies for the genes being studied are known. Suppose the following data were collected.

- Gene A and gene B cross over 6.0 percent of the time.
- Gene B and gene C cross over 12.5 percent of the time.
- Gene A and gene C cross over 18.5 percent of the time.

According to Sturtevant's conclusions, genes A and B are 6 map units apart because they cross over 6 percent of the time. Similarly, genes B and C are 12.5 map units apart because they cross over 12.5 percent of the time. But where are the genes located in relation to each other on the chromosome?

Differentiated Instruction

PRE-AP

Tell students that the crossover frequencies between linked genes A and B is 40%; between B and C, 20%; between C and D, 10%; between C and A, 20%; and between D and B, 10%. Have students determine the sequence of the genes on the chromosome. A–C–D–B Upon completion, have students write a brief paragraph explaining how they can determine which genes are more likely to be inherited together.

Biology Toolkit, Quick-Write, p. C19

FIGURE 7.10 Gene Linkage in *Drosophila*

Linkage maps show the relative locations of genes.

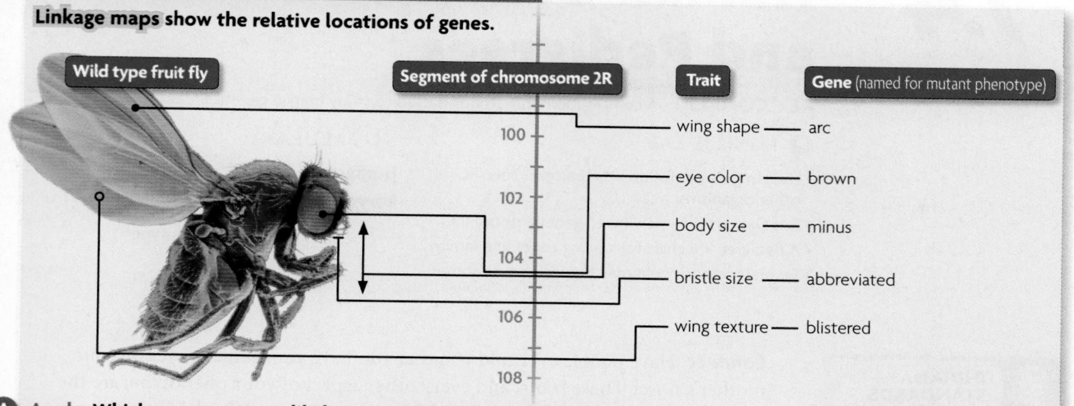

Wild type fruit fly	Segment of chromosome 2R	Trait	Gene (named for mutant phenotype)
	100	wing shape	arc
	102	eye color	brown
		body size	minus
	104	bristle size	abbreviated
	106	wing texture	blistered
	108		

A Apply Which genes are most likely to cross over? Least likely? Why?

(colored SEM; magnification 20×)

Think about gene A as a point on a line. Gene B is either to the left or to the right of gene A. The same is true of the relationship between genes B and C. But if you only know the distances between genes A and B, and between genes B and C, you cannot determine the order of all three genes. You must also know the distance between genes A and C. As shown in **FIGURE 7.11**, the map distances between genes A and B and between genes B and C equal the map distance between genes A and C. Therefore, gene B must be located between genes A and C. If the map distance between genes A and C were 6.5 map units instead of 18.5 map units, then gene A would be between genes B and C.

Although linkage maps show the relative locations of linked genes, the maps do not show actual physical distances between genes. Linkage maps can give you a general idea about distances between genes, but many factors affect gene linkage. As a result, two pairs of genes may be the same number of map units apart, but they may not have the same physical distance between them.

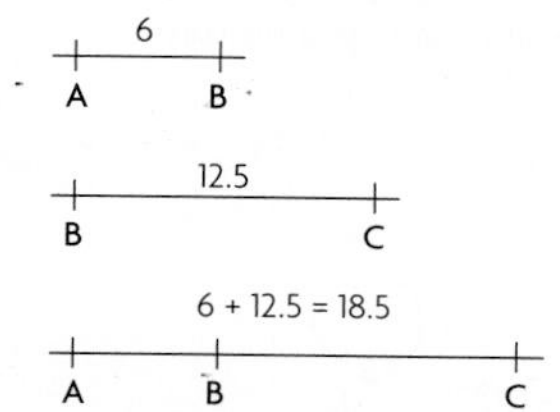

FIGURE 7.11 The order of genes on a chromosome can be determined if all of their cross-over frequencies are known.

B Summarize How can a linkage map be made from observations of traits?

7.3 ASSESSMENT

ONLINE QUIZ ClassZone.com

B.5.2

REVIEWING MAIN IDEAS

1. Summarize the importance of comparing wild type and mutant fruit flies in genetic research.
2. How is a **linkage map** related to cross-overs that take place during meiosis?

CRITICAL THINKING

3. **Compare and Contrast** How are linked genes similar to sex-linked genes? How are they different?
4. **Apply** Draw a linkage map based on the following cross-over percentages for three gene pairs: A – B = 8%, B – C = 10%, and A – C = 2%.

Connecting CONCEPTS

5. **Scientific Process** Punnett, Bateson, and Morgan found phenotype ratios that differed from Mendel's results. Explain how these differences led to new hypotheses and new investigations in genetics.

ONLINE BIOLOGY Go to the chapter Resource Center at **ClassZone.com** for additional resources and information on gene mapping.

Science Trivia

The common fruit fly, *Drosophila melanogaster,* is one of about 900 fruit fly species. It is the favorite of geneticists because it lives and breeds so quickly. It takes about 11 days for eggs to hatch and develop into a new generation of adults capable of laying more eggs or contributing sperm. The speed with which geneticists can produce new generations of fruit flies has allowed them to catalogue—and, in some cases, manipulate—as many as 3000 different mutations, including:

- hairy and bald exoskeletons
- red, pink, purple, and maroon eye colors
- antennae with functional eyes
- two sets of wings

Answers

A Apply blistered and arc, farthest apart; brown and minus, closest together

B Summarize by calculating the percentage of times phenotypes do not appear together in offspring of parents with known genotypes

7.3 ASSESSMENT

1. The different types of flies were important in determining gene linkage because the different phenotypes were easily observed.
2. The higher the frequency of two genes crossing over separately, the farther they are from each other on a chromosome.
3. similar because both show a pattern of linkage in inheritance; different because linked genes are linked to each other on the same chromosome whereas sex-linked genes are linked to either the X or Y chromosome
4. 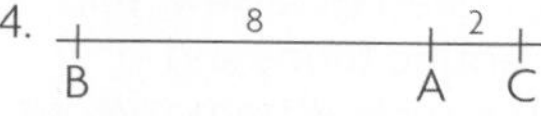

5. In order to explain the differences in results, the scientists proposed an explanation and then tested it.

Assess and Reteach ▼

Assess Use the Online Quiz or Section Quiz (*Assessment Book,* p. 131).

Reteach Project on the board the images of **FIGURES 7.10** and **6.21** from the Media Gallery. Relate the numbers on the gene map to genes shown as bands on the chromosome. Gene B could be the wing shape, with C and D being the genes for eye color and body size, respectively. Have students describe how phenotype and gene linkage could enable these traits to be mapped to the chromosome.

▼ Plan and Prepare

Objectives

- Examine patterns of inheritance in humans.
- Describe how a pedigree is used.
- Identify several methods for mapping human chromosomes.

Section Resources

Unit Resource Book Study Guide pp. 47–48 Power Notes p. 49 Reinforcement p. 50 Pre-AP Activity pp. 55–56
Interactive Reader Chapter 7 **Spanish Study Guide** pp. 71–72
Biology Toolkit pp. C13, C22, C33, D3
Technology Power Presentation 7.4 Media Gallery DVD Online Quiz 7.4

Activate Prior Knowledge Discuss with students the general nature of a genealogy. **Ask,** Have you ever seen a genealogy of your family? How could it be used to trace patterns of inheritance? Students should recognize that a genealogy just traces descendants through a family tree. To be useful for discerning patterns of inheritance, one would need to know about traits of the individuals.

▼ Teach

Vocabulary

Academic Vocabulary Tell students that the words **genealogy** and **pedigree** are defined in the same way: a record of ancestors, a family tree. However, a pedigree chart is typically associated with establishing a blood line or tracing particular traits through descendants.

Answers

A Apply Mendel's principles rely on independent assortment during meiosis, which is a process that occurs in all sexually reproducing organisms.

7.4 Human Genetics and Pedigrees

KEY CONCEPT A combination of methods is used to study human genetics.

MAIN IDEAS

- Human genetics follows the patterns seen in other organisms.
- Females can carry sex-linked genetic disorders.
- A pedigree is a chart for tracing genes in a family.
- Several methods help map human chromosomes.

VOCABULARY

pedigree, p. 214
karyotype, p. 217

Review
phenotype, allele, sex-linked gene, genotype

B.7.3 Determine the likelihood of the appearance of a specific trait in an offspring given the genetic make-up of the parents.

Connect Have people ever told you that you have your father's eyes or your mother's nose? These traits, and every other aspect of your phenotype, are the result of the genes that you inherited from your parents. Which parts of your phenotype come from which parent? In some cases, such as hair color or eye color, it may be very easy to tell. Often, however, it is not so obvious.

MAIN IDEA

Human genetics follows the patterns seen in other organisms.

Fruit flies and pea plants may seem boring and simple, but the basic principles of genetics were worked out using those organisms. Humans follow the same patterns of heredity. First, meiosis independently assorts chromosomes when gametes are made for sexual reproduction. Second, human heredity involves the same relationships between alleles—dominant and recessive interactions, polygenic traits, and sex-linked genes, among others.

The inheritance of many traits is very complex. A single trait may be controlled by several genes that interact. As you read in Section 7.2, eye color is controlled by at least three different genes. And, although several genes affect height, a person's environment during growth and development plays a large role in his or her adult height. What might seem like an obvious phenotype is rarely as simple as it looks.

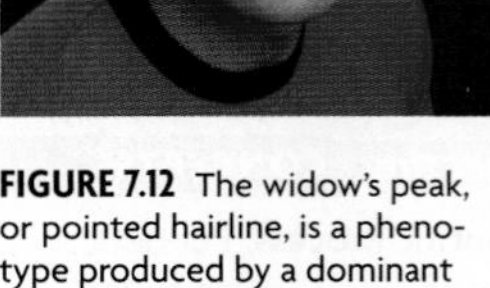

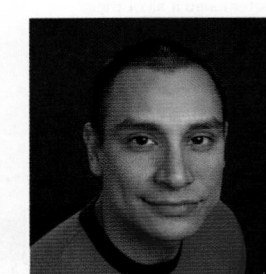

FIGURE 7.12 The widow's peak, or pointed hairline, is a phenotype produced by a dominant autosomal gene.

Nonetheless, single-gene traits are very helpful in understanding human genetics. One such trait is the shape of a person's hairline. A hairline with a downward point, such as a widow's peak shown in **FIGURE 7.12**, is a dominant trait. A straight hairline is a recessive trait. The inheritance of this trait follows the same dominant and recessive pattern as the traits in Mendel's pea plants. Many genetic disorders, such as Huntington's disease, hemophilia, and Duchenne's muscular dystrophy, are also caused by single genes that follow a dominant and recessive pattern. In fact, much of what is known about human genetics comes from studying genetic disorders.

A Apply Why can the genetics of pea plants and fruit flies be applied to humans?

Differentiated Instruction

ENGLISH LEARNERS

Have students scan the pages for terms they may not know or may need to review. Tell them to focus on scientific terms and combinations of terms, such as *homozygous recessive genotype,* but allow them to include unfamiliar general terms as well. Encourage students to use context to create their own definitions, consult the dictionary for expert definitions, and draw visuals to reinforce meaning.

Biology Toolkit, Student Vocabulary, p. D3

MAIN IDEA

Females can carry sex-linked genetic disorders.

Recall from Section 7.1 that some genetic disorders are caused by autosomal genes. A carrier of an autosomal disorder does not show the disease but can pass on the disease-causing allele. Both males and females can be carriers of an autosomal disorder.

In contrast, only females can be carriers of sex-linked disorders. Several genetic disorders are caused by genes on the X chromosome, as you can see in **FIGURE 7.13.** Recall that males have an XY genotype. A male who has a gene for a disorder located on the X chromosome will not have a second, normal allele to mask it. One copy of the allele is enough for males to have the disorder. There are no male carriers of sex-linked disorders, because any male who has the gene displays the phenotype. Females can be carriers, because they may have a normal allele that gives them a normal phenotype. The likelihood of inheriting a sex-linked disorder depends both on the sex of the child and on which parent carries the disorder-causing allele. If only the mother has the allele and is a carrier, a child has a 50 percent chance of inheriting the allele. A daughter who inherits it will not show the phenotype, but a son will.

The British royal family provides a historical example of a sex-linked disorder. Queen Victoria (1819–1901) was a carrier of a recessive sex-linked allele for a disorder called hemophilia, which is a lack of proteins needed for blood to clot. People with hemophilia do not stop bleeding easily. Queen Victoria passed the allele to her son, who had hemophilia. He passed it to his daughter, who was a carrier, and so on. Members of royal families tended to marry into royal families in other countries, and by the early 1900s the royal families of several countries, including Russia and Spain, also had the allele for hemophilia. The allele in all of these people is traced back to Queen Victoria.

VOCABULARY

The term *carrier* means "a person who transports something." In genetics, a carrier is a person who "transports" a recessive allele but does not express the recessive phenotype.

A Contrast How can carriers differ between autosomal and sex-linked disorders?

FIGURE 7.13 Comparing the X and Y Chromosomes

The X chromosome has about 1100 known genes, including many that cause genetic disorders. The Y chromosome is about one-third the size of the X and has only about 250 known genes.

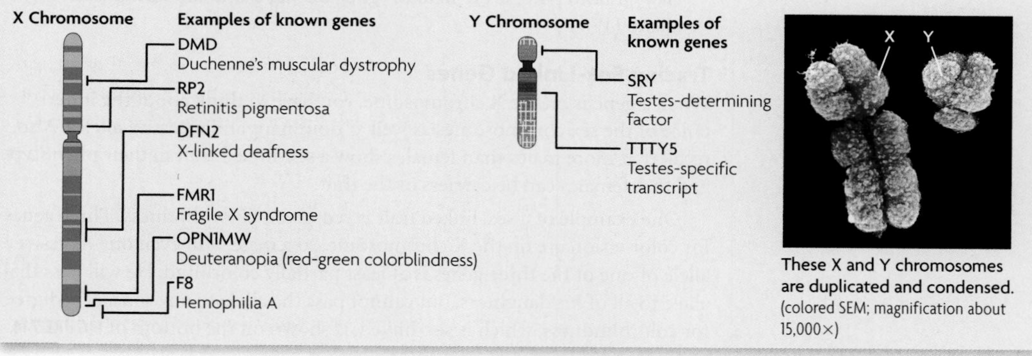

These X and Y chromosomes are duplicated and condensed. (colored SEM; magnification about 15,000×)

ONLINE BIOLOGY Have students trace family history, using DNA from mitochondria and the Y chromosome. Go to the WebQuest in Options for Inquiry on page 219.

Vocabulary

Academic Vocabulary Tell students that they may see the words **disease** and **disorder** used to describe the same medical condition.

disease, a pathological condition resulting from various causes, including infection, genetic defect, or environmental stress

disorder, an ailment that affects the function of the body or mind

Today, many researchers apply the word *disorder* specifically to those conditions that are caused by genes.

Take It Further

Very few genes have been linked to the **human Y chromosome** through pedigree analysis. A mutation on the Y chromosome should be easy to track because the gene would have an immediate effect on the male who possesses it and would be passed on to all of his sons and none of his daughters. Instead, understanding the male-specific genes of the Y chromosome has become the goal of genomic researchers. The Y chromosome was fully sequenced in 2003, but researchers currently have an incomplete picture of the functions it controls. Students will learn more about genomic research in Chapter 9.

Answers

A Contrast Only females can be carriers of sex-linked disorders.

BELOW LEVEL

To have students become more familiar with the patterns of inheritance, have students make an ongoing chart of human traits and genetic disorders as they read this section. They should write the name of each trait or disorder and its pattern of inheritance. At the end of the section, they should briefly summarize the key differences among the different patterns of inheritance. Students can also add information on other human traits or disorders from earlier sections.

Biology Toolkit, Content Frame, p. C22

▼ Teach *continued*

ONLINE BIOLOGY Go to the chapter Resource Center at **ClassZone.com** for additional resources and information on pedigrees.

***Connecting* CONCEPTS**

Genetic Screening Although genetic tests are available for many disorders, people who might be at risk do not always want to be tested. When a test for Huntington's disease became available, many at-risk people refused to be tested. They did not want to live with the knowledge that they would develop a debilitating, fatal disorder later in their lives.

The Inside Story

Huntington's disease (HD) has been described as a genetic time bomb. The allele for the disorder is dominant, so the child of a carrier has a 50-50 chance of inheriting the gene. But since the disorder does not present itself until well into adulthood—between the ages of 30 and 50—a parent may unwittingly pass the gene onto a child long before the parent's symptoms appear.

As a young woman, **Nancy Wexler** watched as HD slowly and painfully claimed her mother's life. In 1978, at risk for the disorder herself, she began a search for the underlying cause. That search took her to a small village in Venezuela, where a relatively large number of the villagers were afflicted with HD. Wexler eventually compiled a massive pedigree of the villagers, which included almost 10,000 people. She also took 2000 blood samples that enabled her to locate the HD gene in 1993, at the tip of chromosome 4. Wexler is today still active in HD research and free of the disorder.

***Connecting* CONCEPTS**

Genetic Screening DNA testing is a direct method of studying genetic disorders. You will learn more about DNA tests and genetic screening in **Chapter 9**.

MAIN IDEA

A pedigree is a chart for tracing genes in a family.

If two people want to know their child's chances of having a certain genetic disorder, they cannot rely upon their phenotypes. The parents also need to know their genotypes. A **pedigree** chart can help trace the phenotypes and genotypes in a family to determine whether people carry recessive alleles. When enough family phenotypes are known, genotypes can often be inferred.

A human pedigree shows several types of information. Boxes represent males and circles represent females. A shaded shape means that a person shows the trait, a white shape means that the person does not, and a shape that is half-shaded and half-white means that a person is a carrier. Lines connect a person to his or her mate, and to their children.

Using phenotypes to figure out the possible genotypes in a family is like putting pieces of a puzzle together. You have to use clues and logic to narrow the possibilities for each person's genotype. One particular clue, for example, can tell you whether the gene is on an autosome or on a sex chromosome. If approximately the same number of males and females have the phenotype, then the gene is most likely on an autosome. If, however, the phenotype is much more common in males, then the gene is likely on the X chromosome.

Tracing Autosomal Genes

It is fairly easy to trace genotypes through a pedigree when you know that you are dealing with a trait controlled by an autosomal gene. Why? A person who does not show the phenotype must have a homozygous recessive genotype. Any other genotype—either heterozygous or homozygous dominant—would produce the phenotype. Use the following steps to work your way through a pedigree for a gene on an autosome. The inheritance of an autosomal trait, such as the widow's peak described earlier, is shown on the top of **FIGURE 7.14.**

- People with a widow's peak have either homozygous dominant (*WW*) or heterozygous (*Ww*) genotypes.
- Two parents without a widow's peak are both homozygous recessive (*ww*), and cannot have children who have a widow's peak.
- Two parents who both have a widow's peak can have a child who does not (*ww*) if both parents are heterozygous for the dominant and recessive alleles (*Ww*).

Tracing Sex-Linked Genes

When a gene is on the X chromosome, you have to think about the inheritance of the sex chromosomes as well as dominant and recessive alleles. Also, recall that more males than females show a sex-linked trait in their phenotype, and that females can be carriers of the trait.

One example of a sex-linked trait is red-green colorblindness. Three genes for color vision are on the X chromosome, so a male with even one recessive allele of one of the three genes is at least partially colorblind. He will pass that allele to all of his daughters, but cannot pass the allele to any sons. A pedigree for colorblindness, which is sex-linked, is shown on the bottom of **FIGURE 7.14.**

Differentiated Instruction

PRE-AP

Have students make a Venn diagram with two overlapping circles to compare and contrast the inheritance pattern of autosomal genes and sex-linked genes. Students should note that autosomal genes are expressed equally in males and females and that sex-linked genes are expressed mostly in males. Heterozygotes can be carriers only if the trait is autosomal and recessive. Only females can be carriers for a sex-linked recessive trait.

Biology Toolkit, Venn Diagram, p. C33

FIGURE 7.14 Interpreting Pedigree Charts

Figuring out genotypes from phenotypes requires you to use a process of elimination. You can often determine which genotypes are possible, and which ones are not.

- Male without phenotype
- Male with phenotype
- Male carrier
- Female without phenotype
- Female with phenotype
- Female carrier

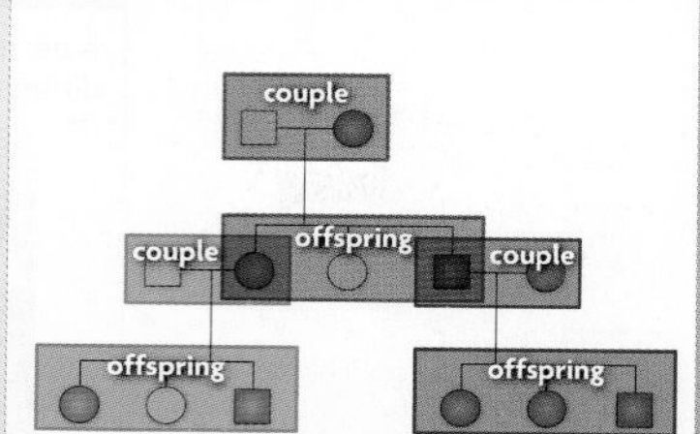

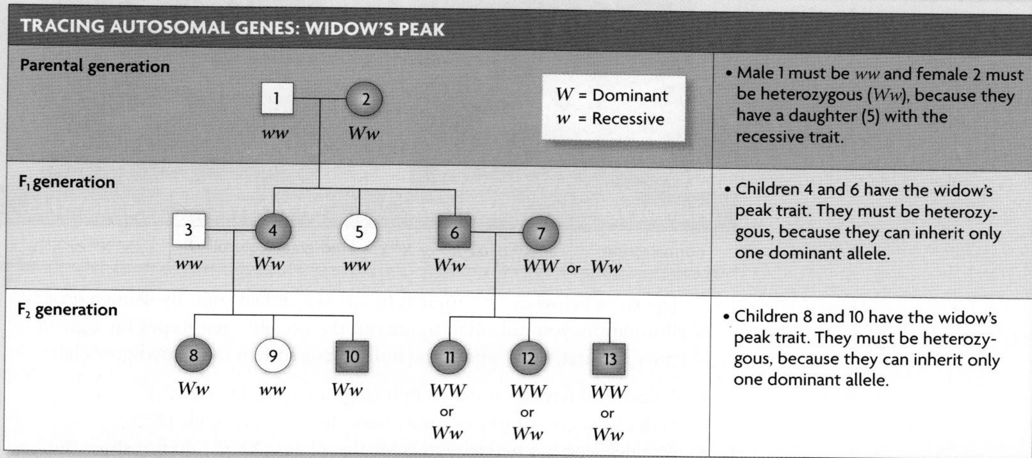

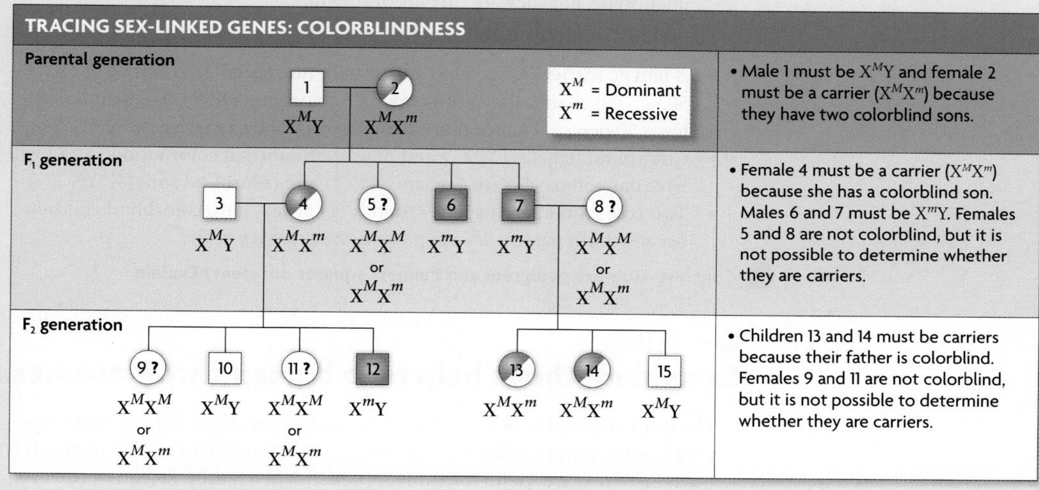

A CRITICAL VIEWING **Explain why it is not possible to identify all of the genotypes in the pedigree charts above. What information would you need to identify the genotypes of those people?**

ONLINE BIOLOGY Have students make Punnett squares and pedigree charts to determine how certain genes are inherited in families. Go to Animated Biology in Options for Inquiry on page 219.

TEACH FROM VISUALS

FIGURE 7.14 Have students examine the widow's peak pedigree chart. **Ask**

- Why can't you tell the genotype of individual 7? You do not know her family history, so all you know for sure is that she has at least one dominant W allele, because she has a widow's peak.
- What is individual 7's most likely genotype? There is a good chance that she is *WW*, because all her children have a widow's peak.
- Have students study the colorblindness pedigree chart. What predictions could you make about future daughters of individuals 7 and 8 if individual 8 were X^MX^m? There is a 50 percent chance that the daughters will be colorblind.

Vocabulary

Word Origins The word **pedigree** is based on the Old French phrase, *pied de gru*, which means "foot of a crane." When family members were placed on a genealogical chart, the branching lines that connected them resembled the imprint of a crane's foot.

The term **widow's peak** comes from English folklore. The word *peak* refers to the appearance of a widow's mourning cap, which had a point extending down at the center of the forehead. The story was that a woman with such a hairline would outlive her husband.

BELOW LEVEL

Tell students that when they analyze a pedigree chart, they should start by asking two questions: Are there patterns in the pedigree that are consistent with a particular type of inheritance? Are there patterns in the pedigree that are inconsistent with a particular pattern of inheritance? Working in pairs, have students analyze the pedigree charts in **FIGURE 7.14.**

Biology Toolkit, Think-Pair-Share, p. C13

Answers

A Critical Viewing Additional family information is necessary when there is more than one possible genotype.

▼ Teach *continued*

Address Misconceptions

Common Misconception Students may think that someone who is colorblind only sees black and white.

Correcting the Misconception With the exception of monochromasy (a form of colorblindness with complete absence of color detection), people who are colorblind see some degree of color.

Take It Further

Three types of **cone cells** in the retina of the eye determine **color vision.** Each type contains a different photopigment that captures a particular range of wavelengths of light. A photopigment molecule consists of a vitamin A-derived portion called retinal and a protein portion called opsin. Production of three types of opsins is controlled by three genes.

The gene for short-wavelength opsin, which determines blue vision, is located on chromosome 7. Blue colorblindness is called **tritanopia.** The genes for middle-wavelength (yellow-green vision) and long-wavelength (yellow-red vision) opsins are on the X chromosome. Yellow-green colorblindness is called **deuteranopia;** yellow-red colorblindness is called **protanopia.** Both deuteranopia and protanopia are commonly referred to as red-green colorblindness.

Answers

A Contrast Punnett squares predict offspring phenotypes from known genotypes; pedigrees predict genotypes from phenotypes. Punnett squares show predicted outcomes, whereas a pedigree shows actual outcomes.

FIGURE 7.15 RED-GREEN COLORBLINDNESS

A person with normal color vision can easily distinguish between different colors. A person who is red-green colorblind cannot.

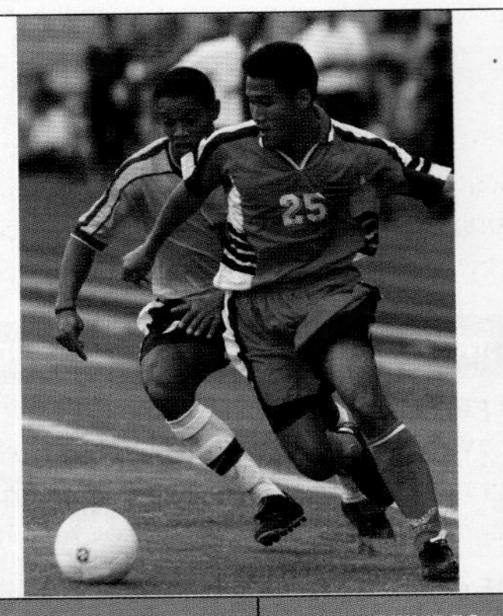

PHENOTYPE	GENOTYPES	PHENOTYPE	GENOTYPES
normal vision	X^MX^m *or* X^MX^M *or* X^MY	red-green colorblind	X^mX^m *or* X^mY

The steps below can be applied to any sex-linked trait. By using a process of elimination, you can often figure out the possible genotypes for a given phenotype. First, think about the individuals shown in the pedigree chart.

- Colorblind females must be homozygous recessive (X^mX^m).
- Males who are colorblind must have the recessive allele (X^mY).
- Females who are heterozygous for the alleles (X^MX^m) do not show the phenotype, but they are carriers of the trait.

Then think about the possible offspring of the people shown in the pedigree.

- A female carrier (X^MX^m) and a male with normal color vision (X^MY) have a 50 percent chance that a son would be colorblind (X^mY). The same couple has a 50 percent chance that a daughter would be a carrier (X^MX^m).
- Colorblind females (X^mX^m) and males with normal color vision (X^MY) will have daughters who are carriers (X^MX^m) and colorblind sons (X^mY).
- Two colorblind parents (X^mX^m and X^mY) always have colorblind children because both parents always pass on the recessive allele.

A Contrast **How are pedigrees and Punnett squares different? Explain.**

MAIN IDEA

Several methods help map human chromosomes.

The human genome, or all of the DNA in a human cell, is so large that mapping human genes is difficult. As a result, a combination of several methods is used. Pedigrees are useful for studying genetics in a family. Scientists can even gather a large number of pedigrees from people who are not related to look for inheritance patterns.

Differentiated Instruction

HANDS-ON ACTIVITY

Provide students with charts that are used to test for various color-vision defects. Many of them can be found in textbooks and on the Internet. Have students examine the charts to determine what colors a person must be able to see if he or she is to interpret each chart correctly.

TEACH WITH TECHNOLOGY

Have students use Internet resources to test their vision for colorblindness. Resources are available in the chapter resources at **ClassZone.com.**

Other methods more directly study human chromosomes. A **karyotype** (KAR-ee-uh-TYP), for example, is a picture of all of the chromosomes in a cell. In order to study the chromosomes, chemicals are used to stain them. The chemical stains produce a pattern of bands on the chromosomes, as shown in **FIGURE 7.16.** The sizes and locations of the bands are very consistent for each chromosome, but the bands differ greatly among different chromosomes. Therefore, different chromosomes can be easily identified in a karyotype.

Karyotypes can show changes in chromosomes. Chromosome changes can be dramatic, such as when a person has too many chromosomes. In Down syndrome, for example, a person has an extra copy of at least part of chromosome 21. In XYY syndrome, a male has an extra Y chromosome. Other times, a karyotype reveals the loss of part of a chromosome. In the figure, you can see a deletion of a large part of chromosome 1. Scientists also use karyotypes to estimate the distances between genes on a chromosome. A karyotype can help show the possible location of a gene on a chromosome.

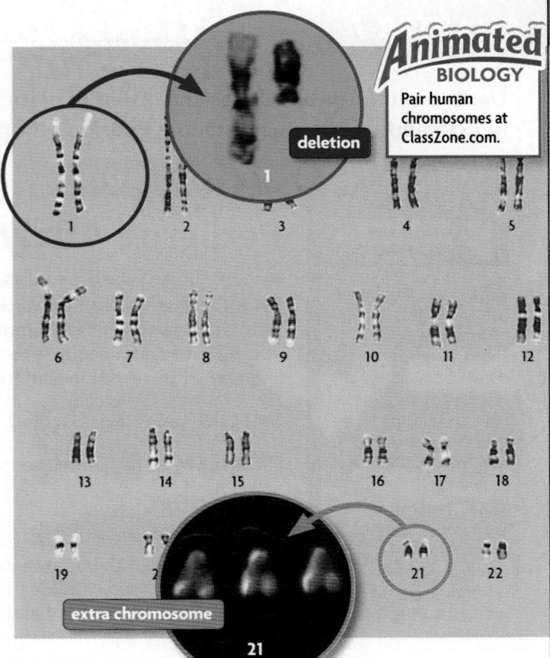

FIGURE 7.16 A karyotype can help show chromosomal disorders, such as the deletion in chromosome 1 (top inset) and the extra chromosome 21 in Down syndrome (bottom inset). (LM; magnifications: deletion 8000×; colored LM, extra chromosome 11,000×)

Chromosome mapping can be done directly by searching for a particular gene. All of the chromosomes are cut apart into smaller pieces. Then this library of chromosome parts is searched to find the gene. Although many genes and their locations have been identified through this process, it is a slow and inefficient method. The large-scale mapping of all of the genes on human chromosomes truly began with the Human Genome Project, which you will read more about in Chapter 9.

Apply Why must a combination of methods be used to study human genetics?

Take It Further

About 95 percent of **Down syndrome** results from **trisomy 21,** having an extra copy of chromosome 21. However, Down syndrome can also result when an individual has a portion of chromosome 21 in triplicate. In this case, the total number of chromosomes is normal, but there are three copies of critical genes on chromosome 21. This occurs when a piece of chromosome 21 gets stuck onto another chromosome (usually chromosome 14) in the egg or sperm. When such an egg or sperm is involved in fertilization, the resulting individual has **translocation trisomy 21.** This form of Down syndrome is the only form that can be inherited from a parent.

Answers

A Apply because of the size of the human genome

7.4 ASSESSMENT

ONLINE QUIZ ClassZone.com

B.7.3

REVIEWING MAIN IDEAS

1. How can Mendel's principles be used to study human traits?
2. Is a person who is homozygous recessive for a recessive genetic disease a carrier? Explain.
3. Describe how phenotypes can be used to predict genotypes in a **pedigree.**
4. What is a **karyotype,** and how can it be used to study human chromosomes?

CRITICAL THINKING

5. **Apply** Suppose a colorblind male and a female with no recessive alleles for colorblindness have children. What is the probability they will have a colorblind son? a colorblind daughter?
6. **Contrast** How do pedigrees for autosomal genes differ from pedigrees for sex-linked genes?

Connecting CONCEPTS

7. **Principles of Genetics** Explain why Mendel's principles of inheritance can be applied to all sexually reproducing species.

Assess and Reteach

Assess Use the Online Quiz or Section Quiz (*Assessment Book,* p. 132).

Reteach Have students make a pedigree chart of a fictitious family in which cystic fibrosis occurs. The chart should show four generations and include some family members who are carriers and others who have the disease. Check the pedigree charts to be sure students have shown the inheritance pattern correctly.

7.4 ASSESSMENT

1. They apply to autosomal single-gene traits with dominant and recessive patterns in all sexually reproducing organisms.
2. No, a carrier is someone who has a gene for the disorder but does not display the phenotype.
3. From a known phenotype, possible genotypes can be inferred.
4. A karyotype is an arrangement of pictures of all chromosomes in a cell that can be used to study their structure.
5. Zero; any son will inherit the normal allele from his mother. Any daughter will have a normal phenotype but will be a carrier.
6. Pedigrees for sex-linked genes will show more males with a recessive trait.
7. because offspring receive one copy of each gene from each parent

OPTIONS FOR INQUIRY

INVESTIGATION

Time 30 minutes	TEACHER TESTED
Teacher Preparation	
Student Difficulty	
Lab Binder Genetics, pp. 17–19	

Purpose Analyze a pedigree.

Overview Students will analyze a pedigree chart for the ability to taste a bitter chemical, PROP. They will

- determine each person's genotype
- identify the medium tasters
- predict the genotypes of two offspring
- conclude whether the gene for tasting PROP is autosomal or sex-linked

LAB MANAGEMENT

- Make copies of the datasheet for students, *Lab Binder,* p. 19.
- Suggest that students number each individual from 1 to 36, from the top.
- Suggest that students look first at the shaded shapes (the supertasters) and determine the parents' genotypes.
- Have students make Punnett squares to determine possible genotypes.

POST-LAB DISCUSSION

Discuss student results. **Ask**

- Were you able to determine the genotypes of any individuals with certainty? If so, which individuals? Parents of all supertasters must be both heterozygous T_1T_2, or medium tasters.
- What makes it difficult to determine the genotypes of individuals marked with unshaded circles and squares? You do not know whether the spouses in this pedigree are T_1T_2 or T_2T_2.
- What do you think is the inheritance pattern for this pedigree? It is probably incomplete dominance, although it could be codominance.

Use these inquiry-based labs and online activities to deepen your understanding of human genetics and complex patterns of inheritance.

INDIANA STANDARDS

B.7.2 Describe dominant, recessive, codominant, sex-linked, incompletely dominant, multiply allelic, and polygenic traits and illustrate their inheritance patterns over multiple generations.

B.7.3 Determine the likelihood of the appearance of a specific trait in an offspring given the genetic make-up of the parents.

INVESTIGATION

Pedigree Analysis

In most human genetics studies, scientists do not know the genotypes of people involved, so possible genotypes must be inferred from pedigrees. In this lab, you will interpret a pedigree to determine genotypes and predict the genotypes of future offspring.

MATERIALS

Pedigree Datasheet

SKILLS Inferring, Calculating Probabilities

PROBLEM What are the genotypes of the people in the pedigree?

PROCEDURE

1. Read the following background information and pedigree.

   People fall into three categories for the ability to taste a bitter chemical called 6-n-propylthiouracil (PROP). People who can taste PROP find it very unpleasant. Scientists hypothesize that these people, called supertasters, are homozygous for the trait ($T_1 T_1$). People who are heterozygous ($T_1 T_2$), called medium tasters, taste PROP as being somewhat bitter. Nontasters ($T_2 T_2$) do not taste the bitterness at all.
2. On your datasheet, fill in the possible genotypes for each person, including the phenotypes for those people who are medium tasters.

ANALYZE AND CONCLUDE

1. **Calculate** What is the probability that Jack will be a supertaster? What is the probability that Jill will be a supertaster? Explain your answers.
2. **Analyze** Is the gene for being a supertaster autosomal or sex-linked? Explain your answer based on the pedigree chart.

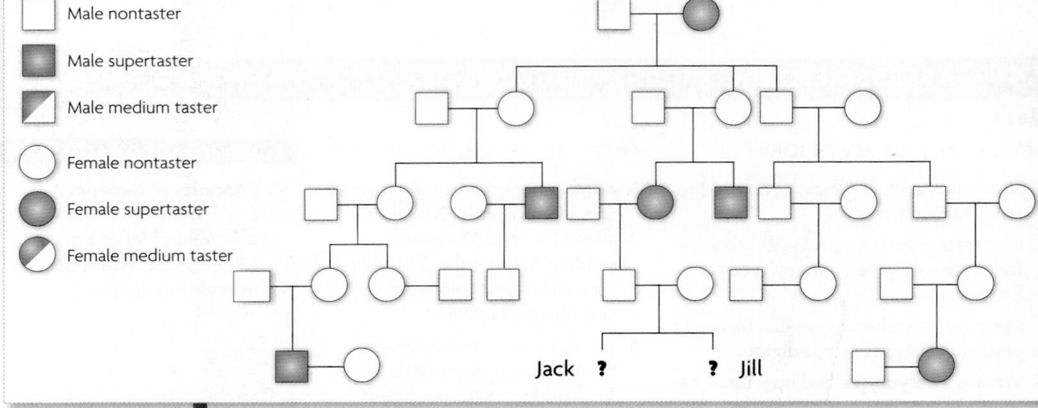

Answers

Student Data

Genotypes: **Row 1** 1. T_1T_2 or T_2T_2; 2. T_1T_1; **Row 2** 3. T_1T_2; 4. T_1T_2; 5. T_1T_2; 6. T_1T_2; 7. T_1T_2; 8. T_1T_2 or T_2T_2; **Row 3** 9. T_1T_2 or T_2T_2; 10. T_1T_2 or T_2T_2; 11. T_1T_2 or T_2T_2; 12. T_1T_1; 13. T_1T_2 or T_2T_2; 14. T_1T_1; 15. T_1T_1; 16. T_1T_2 or T_2T_2; 17. T_1T_2 or T_2T_2; 18. T_1T_2 or T_2T_2; 19. T_1T_2 or T_2T_2; **Row 4** 20. T_1T_2; 21. T_1T_2; 22. T_1T_2 or T_2T_2; 23. T_1T_2 or T_2T_2; 24. T_1T_2; 25. T_1T_2; 26. T_1T_2 or T_2T_2; 27. T_1T_2 or T_2T_2; 28. T_1T_2 or T_2T_2; 29. T_1T_2; 30. T_1T_2; **Row 5** 31. T_1T_1; 32. T_1T_2 or T_2T_2; 33. (Jack) T_1T_2 or T_2T_2; 34. (Jill) T_1T_2 or T_2T_2; 35. T_1T_2 or T_2T_2; 36. T_1T_1

Analyze and Conclude

1. By using a Punnett square, if their mother is heterozygous (T_1T_2), both Jack and Jill will have a 25 percent chance of being supertasters.
2. The trait is autosomal because approximately equal numbers of males and females are supertasters.

INVESTIGATION

Incomplete Dominance

When alleles are incompletely dominant, neither allele is completely dominant nor completely recessive. A heterozygous individual has an intermediate phenotype. In this lab, you will explore incomplete dominance by examining the human trait of hair texture.

SKILL Predicting

PROBLEM What is the genotype of each family member?

MATERIALS
- paper
- pencil

PROCEDURE

Use the information below to answer the questions that follow.

TABLE 1. FAMILY PHENOTYPES

Individual	Hair Texture
Kathy's father	straight
Kathy's mother	curly
Kathy	wavy
Kathy's brother	wavy

ANALYZE AND CONCLUDE

1. **Apply** If I^S is the allele for straight hair and I^C is the allele for curly hair, then what are the genotypes of each individual in Kathy's family? Explain your answer using Punnett squares.
2. **Predict** If Kathy married a man with straight hair and they had children, what type of hair texture (straight, curly, wavy) might their children have? Explain your answer using Punnett squares.
3. **Predict** If Kathy married a man with curly hair and they had children, what type of hair texture might their children have? Explain your answer using Punnett squares.
4. **Predict** If Kathy married a man with wavy hair and they had children, what type of hair texture might their children have? Explain your answer using Punnett squares.

Online BIOLOGY CLASSZONE.COM

ANIMATED BIOLOGY

Tracking Traits

Make Punnett squares and a pedigree chart to track genotypes and phenotypes from one generation to the next. Then determine the probability of trait expression in the offspring.

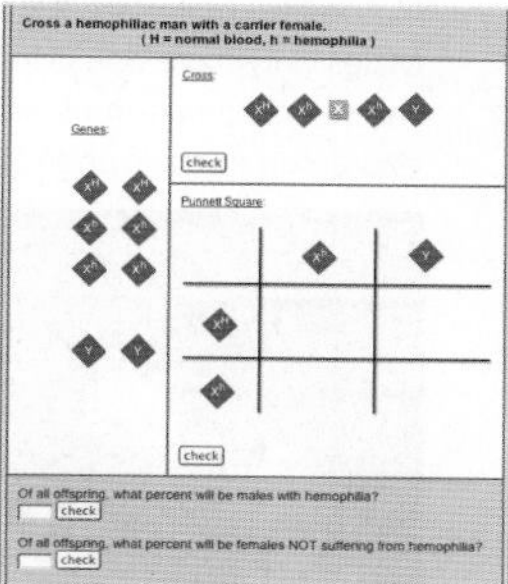

WEBQUEST

How can you track your ancestry when your family history is lost? Complete this WebQuest to find out. Learn how mitochondrial DNA and the DNA on the Y chromosome hold clues about someone's heritage. Find out how far back scientists can track a person's—or a whole population's—ancestry.

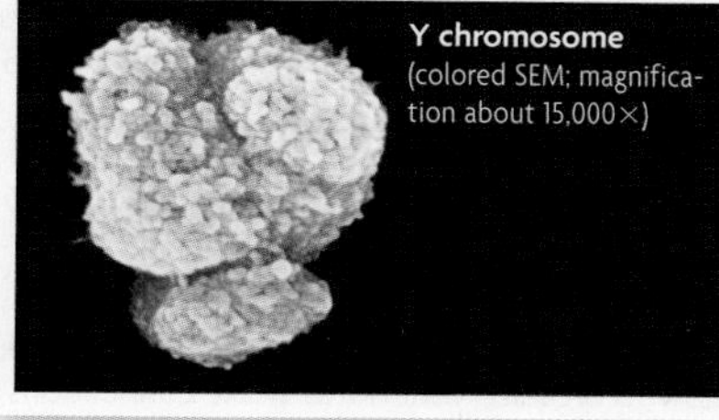

Y chromosome (colored SEM; magnification about 15,000×)

DATA ANALYSIS ONLINE

Height is strongly influenced by genetics. However, the average height of men and women in the United States has increased over the past 150 years. Graph average heights over time and hypothesize why we are getting taller.

Answers

Analyze and Conclude

1. Kathy's father: I^SI^S; Kathy's mother: I^CI^C; Kathy: I^SI^C; Kathy's brother: I^SI^C
2. If Kathy marries a man with straight hair (I^SI^S), their children will have either straight hair (50% I^SI^S) or wavy hair (50% I^SI^C).
3. If Kathy marries a man with curly hair (I^CI^C), their children will have either curly hair (50% I^CI^C) or wavy hair (50% I^SI^C).
4. If Kathy marries a man with wavy hair (I^SI^C), their children will have straight hair (25% I^SI^S), curly hair (25% I^CI^C), or wavy hair (50% I^SI^C).

Online Biology ▼

ANIMATED BIOLOGY Use this interactive animation to reinforce the concepts in **Section 7.4.**

WEBQUEST The WebQuest takes one full class period. Students complete the activity online and will need access to a printer to print their answers. Sample answers, teacher notes, and alternative assessment ideas are available on **ClassZone.com.** Use with **Section 7.4.**

DATA ANALYSIS ONLINE Students will probably choose to make a line graph. They should hypothesize that people are getting taller because of better nutrition. Use with **Section 7.2.**

INVESTIGATION

Time 30 minutes	TEACHER TESTED
Teacher Preparation	
Student Difficulty	
Lab Binder Genetics, pp. 21–22	

LAB MANAGEMENT

- Review incomplete dominance with students before this investigation.

POST-LAB DISCUSSION

Discuss student results. **Ask**

- How can you tell that hair texture is an example of incomplete dominance? The heterozygote shows an intermediate phenotype.
- How would the phenotypes differ if the alleles showed codominance? A person heterozygous for the alleles would have some straight hair and some curly hair.

Chapter 7: Extending Mendelian Genetics 219

CHAPTER REVIEW

Interactive Review

Encourage students to go to **ClassZone.com** for a detailed review of each section, including visuals and vocabulary practice.

Unit Resource Book, Vocabulary Practice, pp. 57–60

CHAPTER 7 Interactive Review @ CLASSZONE.COM

KEY CONCEPTS | Vocabulary Games | Concept Maps | Animated Biology | Online Quiz

7.1 Chromosomes and Phenotype

The chromosomes on which genes are located can affect the expression of traits. Two alleles of autosomal genes interact to produce phenotype. Genes on the sex chromosomes are expressed differently in males and females of many species. In humans, males are XY and females are XX. Males only have one copy of each gene found on the sex chromosomes, so all of those genes are expressed in their phenotype.

7.2 Complex Patterns of Inheritance

Phenotype is affected by many different factors. Phenotype is rarely the result of a simple dominant and recessive relationship between two alleles of a gene. Often, there are more than two possible alleles of a gene. Incomplete dominance produces an intermediate phenotype. Codominance results in both alleles being fully and separately expressed. Many traits are polygenic, or controlled by several genes. Interactions between genes and the environment also affect phenotype.

7.3 Gene Linkage and Mapping

Genes can be mapped to specific locations on chromosomes. Studies of wild type and mutant fruit flies led to a new understanding of genetics. Linked genes are often inherited together. During meiosis, linked genes can be separated from each other when parts of chromosomes are exchanged. By studying the frequency of cross-overs between chromosomes, a linkage map can be made that shows the relative order of genes on a chromosome.

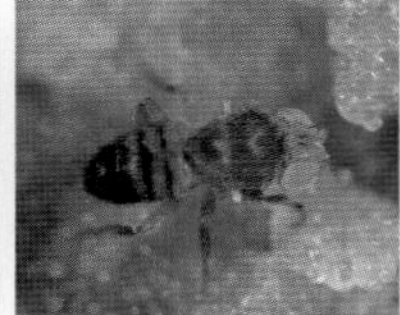

7.4 Human Genetics and Pedigrees

A combination of methods is used to study human genetics. Although most traits do not follow a simple dominant and recessive pattern, single-gene traits are important in the study of human genetics. Several genetic disorders are caused by a single gene with dominant and recessive alleles. Carriers are people who have an allele for a genetic disorder but do not express the allele in their phenotype. The patterns of genetic inheritance can be studied in families by pedigree analysis. Pedigree analysis is an indirect method of investigating human genotypes. Karyotypes can show large changes in chromosomes.

Synthesize Your Notes

Main Idea Web Use a main idea web like the one shown below to organize your notes. Make connections among the genetics concepts in the chapter, such as chromosomes and gene expression.

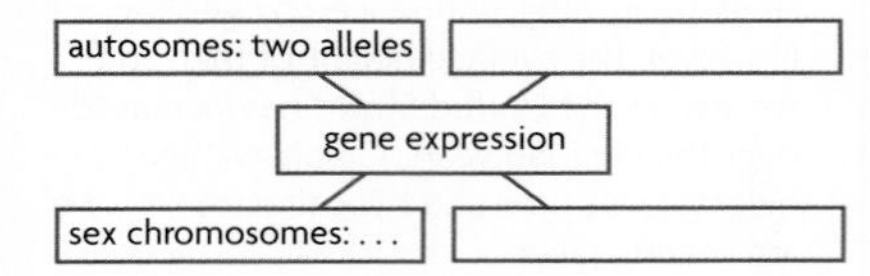

Concept Map Make a concept map like the one shown below to synthesize your knowledge of Mendelian genetics with more complex patterns of inheritance.

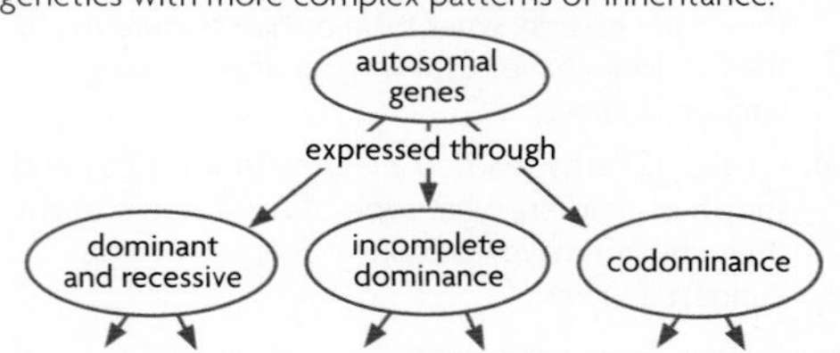

Reviewing Vocabulary

1. Both can be related to genes on the X chromosome. A sex-linked gene is a gene on a sex chromosome. A carrier has one gene for a disorder but does not show the disorder, and many disorders are sex-linked.
2. Both are types of gene expression in which the phenotype of the heterozygote is different from either homozygote. In incomplete dominance, neither allele is completely dominant nor completely recessive. In codominance, both alleles are fully and equally expressed.
3. Both are maps of chromosomes. A linkage map shows the relative order of genes on a chromosome, based on observations of phenotypes. A karyotype is a picture that shows overall chromosome structure.
4. Polygenic trait: answers should indicate a trait produced by two or more genes.
5. Pedigree: answers could show an example of a pedigree chart.
6. X chromosome inactivation: answers could show two XX cells, one cell with one X chromosome active and the other cell with the other X chromosome active.
7. A polygenic trait is the result of the interaction of many (*poly-*) genes (*genic*).
8. Codominant alleles each express "the same amount" of dominance.

Chapter Assessment

Chapter Vocabulary

7.1	7.2	7.3 / 7.4
carrier, p. 201 sex-linked gene, p. 201 X chromosome inactivation, p. 203	incomplete dominance, p. 204 codominance, p. 205 polygenic trait, p. 206	7.3 linkage map, p. 210 7.4 pedigree, p. 214 karyotype, p. 217

Reviewing Vocabulary

Compare and Contrast

Describe one similarity and one difference between the two terms in each of the following pairs.

1. sex-linked gene, carrier
2. incomplete dominance, codominance
3. linkage map, karyotype

Visualize Vocabulary

For each term below, use simple shapes, lines, or arrows to illustrate the meaning. Below each picture, write a short caption. Here's an example for *linkage map.*

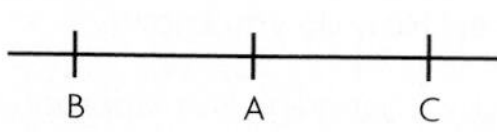

A linkage map shows the order of genes on a chromosome.

4. polygenic trait
5. pedigree
6. X chromosome inactivation

Word Origins

Use the definitions of the word parts to answer the next two questions.

Word Part	Meaning
poly-	many
co-	together; the same amount
genic	produced by genes

7. How are the word parts *poly-* and *genic* related to the meaning of the term *polygenic trait*?
8. How is the prefix *co-* related to the meaning of the term *codominant*?

Reviewing MAIN IDEAS

9. Explain why disorders caused by dominant alleles on autosomes are less common than those caused by recessive alleles on autosomes.

10. Describe how the expression of sex-linked genes can differ between males and females. **B.7.2**

11. How do codominance and incomplete dominance differ from a simple dominant and recessive relationship between alleles? **B.7.2**

12. Humans have a tremendous range of hair, eye, and skin colors. How does the polygenic nature of these traits explain the wide range of phenotypes? **B.7.2**

13. Give two examples that demonstrate how the environment can interact with genotype to affect an organism's phenotype.

14. How did Morgan's research with fruit flies explain Punnett's and Bateson's observations of pea plants?

15. Explain how linked genes and cross-over frequencies are used to make linkage maps.

16. What are two main ways in which human genetics follows the genetic patterns seen in other organisms?

17. Under what circumstances could two individuals with no symptoms of a recessive genetic disease have children that do have the disease? **B.7.3**

18. What are one similarity and one difference between patterns for autosomal and sex-linked genes on a pedigree chart?

19. What is a karyotype, and how can it be used to study human chromosomes and to map human genes?

CHAPTER REVIEW

Reviewing Main Ideas

9. because dominant disorders are frequently fatal, with no offspring produced
10. A female must have two recessive alleles to show a recessive phenotype, whereas a male needs only one recessive allele.
11. A dominant trait is one that is fully expressed in heterozygotes, so there are only two possible phenotypes. In codominance and incomplete dominance, both alleles are expressed in heterozygotes and interact to make a third phenotype, different from either homozygote.
12. These phenotypes are the result of the interaction of more than two genes, so there is a great variety of genetic expression of alleles, and hence phenotypes.
13. Environmental factors such as nutrition and fetal development can affect height and size. Temperature can affect the sex of offspring in some animals, such as turtles.
14. Morgan's results showed that linked genes are on the same chromosome.
15. Genes on the same chromosome tend to be inherited together, but they can be separated by crossing over during meiosis. The frequency of crossing over can be used to determine how far apart genes are and the relative locations of genes on a chromosome. Crossover frequencies are directly proportional to the distance between genes (in map units).
16. (1) Chromosomes independently assort during meiosis in all sexually reproducing organisms and (2) the interaction of alleles (such as dominance and codominance) is the same across sexually reproducing species.
17. If the disorder is autosomal, both parents must be carriers (heterozygotes). If the disorder is sex-linked, the mother must be a carrier.
18. In both cases, the symbols represent the same thing. If the gene is autosomal, both males and females will show the phenotype with equal frequency. If the gene is sex-linked, mostly males will be affected.
19. A karyotype is a picture of stained chromosomes that shows differences between chromosomes, which can be used to detect chromosomal mutations.

ITEM CORRELATIONS

Standard	Items
B.7.2	10, 11, 12, 20, 21, 22, 24
B.7.3	17

Chapter 7: Extending Mendelian Genetics 221

Critical Thinking

20. No, if a person has just one allele for a dominant trait, that trait will be expressed. A carrier is someone who has an allele for a trait that is not expressed (recessive).
21. If a male has a recessive allele of a sex-linked gene, such as for color-blindness, the allele is always expressed because males have only one X chromosome. In contrast, females have two X chromosomes and therefore must have two copies of a recessive allele to express the trait.
22. Both codominance and incomplete dominance can explain these results. White-flowered and purple-flowered plants would be homozygotes, and the lavender-flowered plants would be heterozygotes. This fits with the 1:2:1 ratio of offspring. We cannot necessarily distinguish whether the lavender color is a result of codominance or incomplete dominance. Multiple alleles is not a good explanation, because it does not fit with the 1:2:1 ratio. With multiple alleles, there would likely be more than just the three phenotypes.
23. Alleles: / Possible genotypes:

Alleles	Possible genotypes
3 (A, B, C)	6 (AA, AB, AC, BB, BC, CC)
4 (A, B, C, D)	10 (AA, AB, AC, AD, BB, BC, BD, CC, CD, DD)

24. David and his unaffected siblings are either heterozygotes (*Dd*) or homozygous dominant (*DD*). David's parents are heterozygotes (*Dd*), because they are both unaffected but have an affected offspring. The affected grandparents and David's affected sister are homozygous recessive (*dd*). The unspecified grandparents are either homozygous dominant (*DD*) or heterozygous (*Dd*).
25. Because identical twins have the same genotypes, phenotype differences between them can be studied in connection with environmental differences.

Critical Thinking

20. Analyze Can a person be a carrier for a dominant genetic disorder? Explain. **B.7.2**

21. Apply Both men and women can be colorblind, but there are approximately 100 times more colorblind men than women in the world. Explain why men are more likely to be colorblind than women. **B.7.2**

22. Apply Suppose two plants with light purple, or lavender, flowers are crossed. About 25 percent of the offspring have white flowers, 25 percent have purple flowers, and 50 percent have lavender flowers. Which of the following could explain these results: codominance, incomplete dominance, or multiple alleles? Explain. **B.7.2**

23. Apply Copy the chart below into your notebook. Following the provided example, fill in the chart to show the number of possible genotypes given 2, 3, or 4 alleles.

Number of Alleles	Number of Possible Genotypes
2 (A, B)	3 (AA, AB, BB)
3 (A, B, C)	
4 (A, B, C, D)	

24. Apply Some members of David's family have an autosomal recessive disease. David does not have the disease; neither do his parents, nor his two brothers. His maternal grandfather has the disease, his paternal grandmother has the disease, and his sister has the disease. Draw a pedigree chart to represent the genotypes of all grandparents, parents, and children. Next to each person, write his or her possible genotype. **B.7.2**

25. Synthesize Why are studies of identical twins important in helping understand interactions between environment and genotype? Explain.

Interpreting Visuals

Copy into your notebook the pedigree chart to the right to answer the next two questions. Use *A* as the dominant allele, and use *a* as the recessive allele.

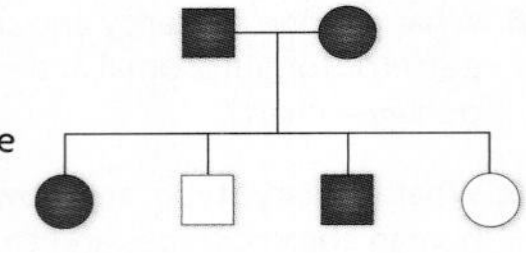

26. Analyze Is this trait most likely recessive or dominant? Explain.

27. Analyze What is the genotype of each individual in the pedigree chart? Explain your answers.

Analyzing Data

A scientist studies four linked traits in fruit flies and observes the frequency with which the traits cross over. The bar graph below shows the cross-over frequencies among genes A, B, C, and D. Use the graph to answer the next three questions.

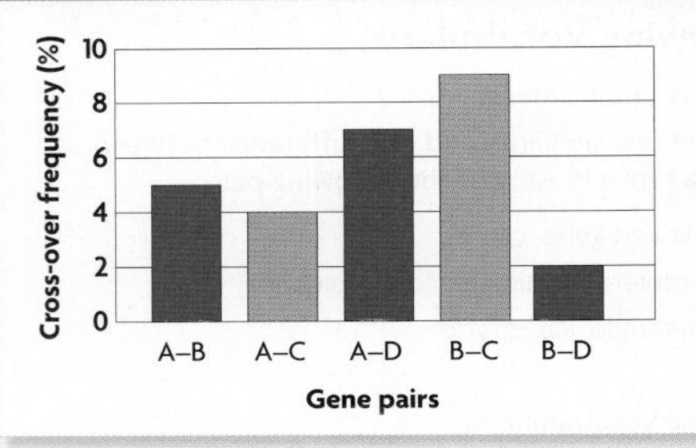

28. Evaluate Which two genes are least likely to be inherited together? How do you know?

29. Evaluate Which two genes are most likely to be inherited together? How do you know?

30. Apply Explain why a bar graph is an appropriate type of graph to use to display these data.

Connecting CONCEPTS

31. Write Ad Copy Imagine that you are starting a business that will make pedigree charts for people who want to map particular family traits. Your ad should be written in simple language that all readers will understand. Your ad should also demonstrate that you possess the necessary understanding of human genetics for a successful pedigree chart-making business.

32. Synthesize Look again at the tremendous range of human phenotypes in the photographs on pages 198–199. How is human genetics similar to and different from the genetics of Mendel's pea plants?

Interpreting Visuals

26. The trait is probably dominant because it is relatively common.
27. The parents must both be heterozygous for the dominant allele; the offspring without the trait must be homozygous recessive. The offspring with the trait can be either homozygous dominant or heterozygous.

Analyzing Data

28. B and C, because they are the farthest apart; they could be separated by crossovers that occur anywhere between them.
29. B and D, because they are so close together; for them to be separated, a crossover would have to occur in the very short distance between them.
30. because the percentages are not dependent on each other

INDIANA ISTEP+ Test Prep

B.6.5; B.7.1; B.7.2

Test Practice For more test practice, go to ClassZone.com.

1 A genotyped pedigree of 239 people shows evidence of an inheritable recessive disease. One female, however, doesn't fit the pattern of inheritance demonstrated by all of the other family members. What is ***most*** likely true of this individual?

A She had been treated for the disease.
B She accumulated additional mutations.
C She is immune to the disorder.
D She was genotyped incorrectly.

THINK THROUGH THE QUESTION

Consider both what a pedigree chart shows and what it doesn't show. Phenotypes are shown on a pedigree, but genotypes are inferred from the phenotypes.

2 Many animals, including humans, have sex chromosomes called the X and Y chromosomes. Which of the following shows the genotype for a normal human male?

A XX
B YY
C XY
D Y

3

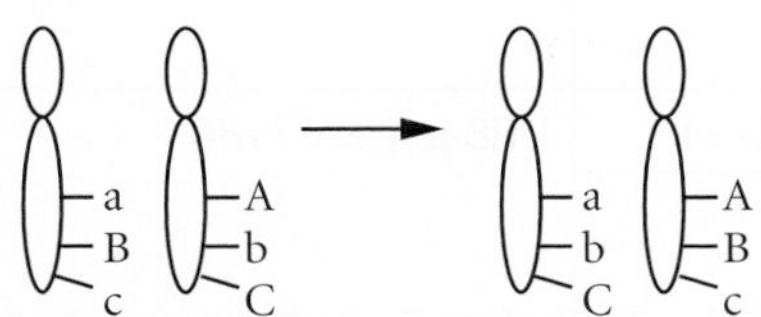

Genes on a pair of chromosomes often cross over during meiosis, as shown in the diagram. The discovery of crossing over added to Mendel's law of independent assortment, which stated that genes assort independently of one another. What did cross-overs indicate?

A Crossing over allows for more than two alleles of a gene.
B Chromosomes assort independently, not genes.
C Mendel's principles could be applied to asexual reproduction.
D Crossing over explains incomplete dominance.

4 A scientist studying two traits in mice knows that each trait is determined by one gene and that both genes are on the same chromosome. If the two traits are not always inherited together by the offspring of the mice, what must be true?

A The genes are not near the centromere.
B The genes are far enough apart to allow crossing over.
C The sister chromatids are unlinked.
D The genes must be on different arms of the chromosome.

5

Fruit Fly Dihybrid Cross

Eeww\eeWw	*eW*	*ew*	*eW*	*ew*
Ew				
Ew				
ew				
ew				

Red eyes is dominant (E); white eyes is recessive (e).
Normal wings is dominant (W); short wings is recessive (w).

A fruit fly with red eyes and short wings is crossed with a fruit fly with white eyes and normal wings. According to the cross shown in the diagram, what is the expected phenotype of fruit flies in the shaded box?

A white eyes and normal wings
B white eyes and clipped wings
C red eyes and normal wings
D red eyes and clipped wings

6 The allele that causes Duchenne's muscular dystrophy is X-linked recessive. The symbol for the dominant allele is X_f. Explain why none of the male offspring would be expected to have Duchenne's muscular dystrophy if an X_fX_f female and an X_fY male have children.

CHAPTER REVIEW

Standards-Based Assessment

1. D	4. B
2. C	5. A
3. B	6. See Below

Question 2 Answer C is correct. Answer A is incorrect because it is the genotype of a female. Answer B is incorrect because an organism with two Y chromosomes cannot live. Answer D is incorrect because an organism with only one Y chromosome cannot live.

Question 4 Answer B is correct. Answer A is incorrect because crossing over is not related to the position of genes relative to the centromere. Answer C is incorrect because crossing over occurs between homologous chromosomes, not between sister chromatids, which are identical copies of each other. Answer D is incorrect because crossing over is not related to the position of genes on a particular arm of a chromosome.

Question 5 Answer A is correct because the genotype (eeWw) produces white eyes and normal wings. Answer B is incorrect because the offspring have a dominant allele, W. Answer C is incorrect because the offspring have two recessive alleles, ee. Answer D is incorrect because the offspring have two recessive alleles for eyecolor, ee, and a dominant allele for wing type, W.

Question 6 The male offspring would inherit only one X chromosome, X_f from the mother. This allele would be expressed. It is dominant so the males would be unaffected.

Connecting Concepts

31. Responses should define sex-linked and autosomal genes and explain how chromosomes are inherited, including a comparison between sex-linked and autosomal inheritance.

32. Both are the result of the same processes: gamete formation by way of meiosis, and interaction of alleles. However, all of the traits Mendel studied were autosomal, dominant/recessive, two-allele traits. The human phenotypes on pp. 198–199 are the result of both autosomal and sex-linked genes, multiple alleles and genes, and many types of allelic interactions, in addition to simple dominant/recessive genetics.

ITEM CORRELATIONS

Standard	Items
B.6.5	3, 4
B.7.1	5, 6
B.7.2	1, 2

CHAPTER 8

Indiana Resource Preview

Print Resources

From DNA to Proteins

INDIANA STANDARDS		Sections	PAGES and PACING	UNIT RESOURCE BOOK
NOS.9	8.1	**Identifying DNA as the Genetic Material** **KEY CONCEPT** DNA was identified as the genetic material through a series of experiments.	pp. 226–228 30 minutes	URB pages 61–64
NOS.1		CHAPTER INVESTIGATION: Extracting DNA	p. 229, 30 min.	**Lab Binder** Genetics pages 29–31
B.5.1	8.2	**Structure of DNA** **KEY CONCEPT** DNA structure is the same in all organisms.	pp. 230–233 30 minutes	URB pages 65–68
NOS.1		DATA ANALYSIS: Interpreting Histograms	p. 234 , 30 min.	URB page 89
B.7.4	8.3	**DNA Replication** **KEY CONCEPT** DNA replication copies the genetic information of a cell.	pp. 235–238 45 minutes	URB pages 69–72
B.5.3	8.4	**Transcription** **KEY CONCEPT** Transcription converts a gene into a single-stranded RNA molecule.	pp. 239–242 45 minutes	URB pages 73–76
B.5.3	8.5	**Translation** **KEY CONCEPT** Translation converts an mRNA message into a polypeptide, or protein.	pp. 243–247 45 minutes	URB pages 77–80
B.6.2	8.6	**Gene Expression and Regulation** **KEY CONCEPT** Gene expression is carefully regulated in both prokaryotic and eukaryotic cells.	pp. 248–251 45 minutes	URB pages 81–84
B.7.5	8.7	**Mutations** **KEY CONCEPT** Mutations are changes in DNA that may or may not affect phenotype.	pp. 252–255 45 minutes	URB pages 85–88
B.5.3, B.7.4, NOS.6		OPTIONS FOR INQUIRY	pp. 256–257 45, 30 min.	**Lab Binder** Genetics pages 32–36
		Chapter Review	pp. 258–261	**Assessment Book** Tests A, B pp. 155–162

INDIANA STANDARDS

B.5.1 Describe the relationship between chromosomes and DNA along with their basic structure and function.
B.5.3 Describe the process by which DNA directs the production of protein within a cell.
B.6.2 Understand that most cells of a multicellular organism contain the same genes, but develop from a single cell (e.g., a fertilized egg) in different ways due to differential gene expression.
B.7.4 Explain the process by which a cell copies its DNA and identify factors that can damage DNA and cause changes in its nucleotide sequence.
B.7.5 Explain and demonstrate how inserting, substituting or deleting segments of a DNA molecule can alter a gene, which is then passed to every cell that develops from it and that the results may be beneficial, harmful or have little or no effect on the organism.
NOS.1 Develop explanations based on reproducible data and observations gathered during laboratory investigations.
NOS.6 Use analogies and models....
NOS.9 Recognize that new scientific discoveries often lead to a re-evaluation of previously accepted scientific knowledge and of commonly held ideas.

Labs

PUPIL EDITION LABS

Extracting DNA, p. 229 Students extract and observe DNA. **Lab Binder** pp. 29–31	**Time:** 30 minutes **Materials:** 10 g raw wheat germ, laboratory spatula, test tube, test tube rack, 10 mL warm distilled water, 2 eyedroppers, 20 mL detergent solution, 3 g meat tenderizer, 20 mL salt solution, 10 mL cold isopropyl alcohol, glass stirring rod
Replication, Section 3, p. 238 Students model the replication of DNA. **Lab Binder** p. 37	**Time:** 5 minutes **Materials:** 2 zipping bags, scissors

OPTIONS FOR INQUIRY

UV Light and Skin Cancer, p. 256 Students test various sunscreens for their ability to block UV rays. **Lab Binder** pp. 32–34	**Time:** 45 minutes **Materials:** 3 different kinds of sunscreen, sunlight or UV light box, 12 UV beads
Modeling Transcription, p. 257 Students make a model of a template strand of DNA and transcribe it onto mRNA having 12 nucleotides that are complementary to the DNA sequence. **Lab Binder** pp. 35–36	**Time:** 30 minutes **Materials:** metric ruler, 60 cm piece of ribbon, scissors, construction paper of 5 colors, marker, stapler

LAB BINDER Unit 3 Genetics

Additional Investigation: Observing *Drosophilia* Mutations, pp. 38–40

Challenge Lab: Exploring Protein Crystallization, pp. 68–72

LAB GENERATOR

A searchable CD of all labs in the program in editable format, including forensic, probeware, and biotechnology labs.

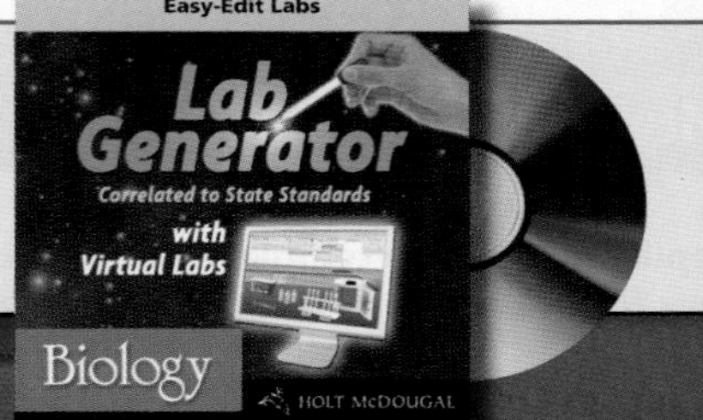

Presentation Tools

POWER PRESENTATIONS

Presentation Chapter 8
PowerPresentations for each section incorporate images and clips from the Media Gallery. Includes Note Navigator for each section.

MEDIA GALLERY

Contains the following images and video clips, as well as animations, simulations, and forms of visuals from the book.

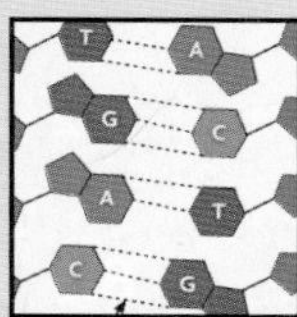
DNA structure

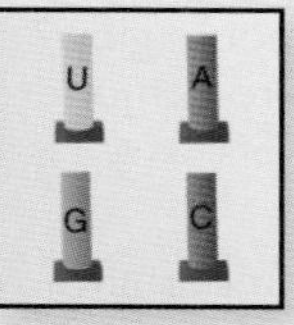
Protein synthesis

Power Notes

mRNA

DNA structure

VIDEO

Find a set of short video clips exploring DNA discoveries and protein synthesis.

ANIMATED BIOLOGY

DNA Replication

Build a Protein

TRANSPARENCIES

DNA Structure T36

Replication T37

Transcription T38

Translation T39

Types of Mutations T40

Online BIOLOGY CLASSZONE.COM

BioZine

Animated Biology

Interactive Review

SciLinks

Resource Centers

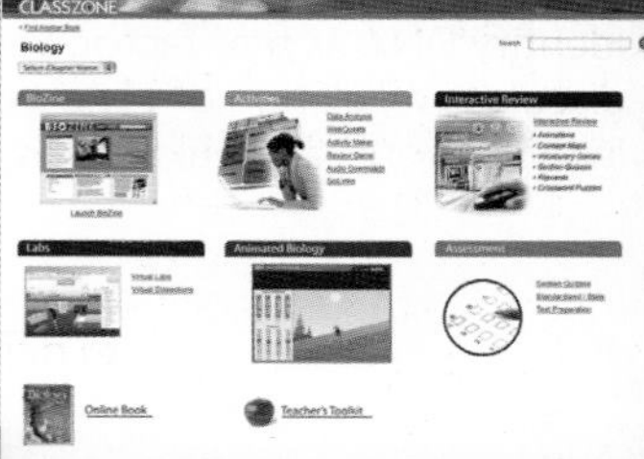

CHAPTER

8

▼ Focus and Motivate

Why is this mouse glowing?

Have students read the explanation that explains that the mouse has been genetically modified. **Ask,** Why would someone want to make a mouse glow? The researchers' purpose is to demonstrate the effectiveness of GFP as a marker.

Tell students that mice are important test subjects because they have many of the same or similar genes as humans have. Researchers can now use GFP to track cancer cells or map the activity of neurons in the brain. This technology may even help in the fight against terrorism. Biologists have developed bacteria with the GFP gene that will glow in the presence of anthrax spores, chemical warfare agents, and explosives from land mines.

BIOZINE ClassZone.com

Students can access BioZine at **ClassZone.com** to take a poll about current issues in biology.

In a Hurry?

The critical material of the chapter is found in **Sections 8.2, 8.3, 8.4, 8.5,** and **8.7,** which cover the structure, replication, and transcription of DNA; protein synthesis; and mutation. A quick reading of the heads in **Section 8.1** will introduce students to the idea of a transforming factor and the researchers who helped identify DNA as that factor. **Section 8.6** discusses regulation of gene expression in prokaryotes and eukaryotes.

CHAPTER

8 From DNA to Proteins

KEY CONCEPTS

8.1 Identifying DNA as the Genetic Material
DNA was identified as the genetic material through a series of experiments.

8.2 Structure of DNA
DNA structure is the same in all organisms.

8.3 DNA Replication
DNA replication copies the genetic information of a cell.

8.4 Transcription
Transcription converts a gene into a single-stranded RNA molecule.

8.5 Translation
Translation converts an mRNA message into a polypeptide, or protein.

8.6 Gene Expression and Regulation
Gene expression is carefully regulated in both prokaryotic and eukaryotic cells.

8.7 Mutations
Mutations are changes in DNA that may or may not affect phenotype.

Online BIOLOGY CLASSZONE.COM

Animated BIOLOGY
View animated chapter concepts.
- DNA Replication
- Build a Protein

BIOZINE
Keep current with biology news.
- Featured stories
- News feeds
- Strange Biology

RESOURCE CENTER
Get more information on
- DNA
- RNA
- Mutations

Student Activity

Purpose **Model replication using a template and complementary forms.**

Prepare Draw two complementary strands on the board, using two sets of paired symbols, for example +/− and ○/□. Then redraw each strand to the right of the original, separated and labeled *Template 1* and *Template 2.*

Note: A student worksheet for this activity is provided in Teacher Resources at **ClassZone.com.** If you choose to use the Replication worksheet, you will need a copy and a pair of scissors for each group of three students.

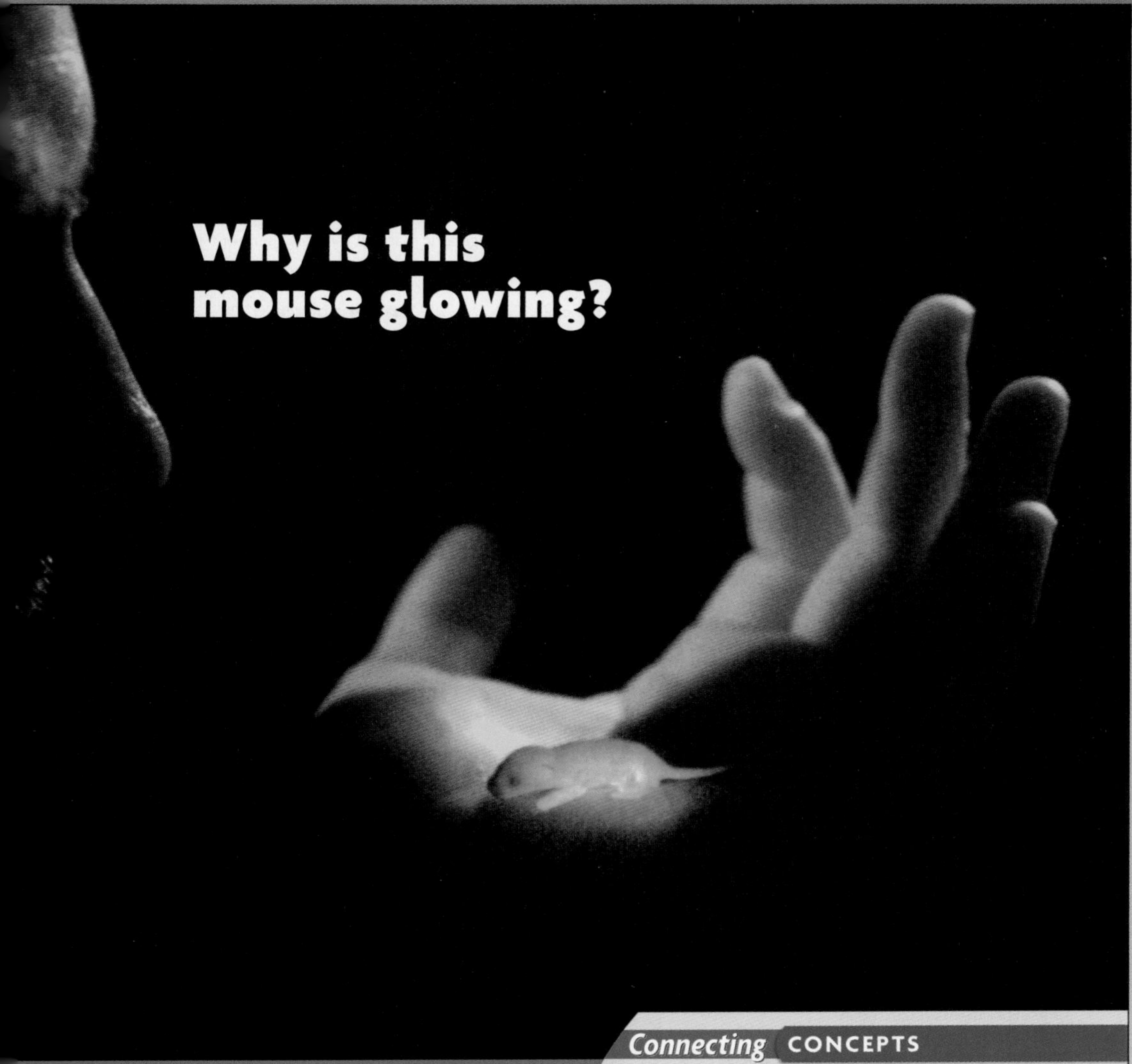

Why is this mouse glowing?

Connecting CONCEPTS

This mouse's eerie green glow comes from green fluorescent protein (GFP), which glows under ultraviolet light. Scientists put a gene from a glowing jellyfish into a virus that was allowed to infect a mouse egg. The jellyfish gene became part of the mouse's genes. As a result, the mouse cells produce the same protein. Researchers hope to track cancer cells using GFP.

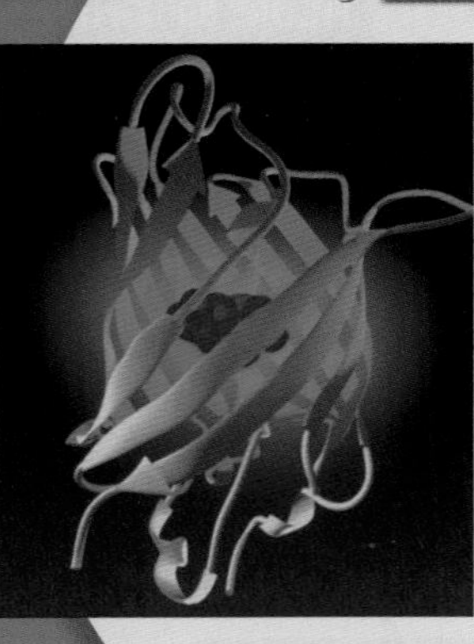

Translation This computer model of GFP shows the amino acids (purple) in the center of the protein that make the protein glow. The genetic code is universal, which means that a gene from one organism can be correctly translated into a protein in another organism. Although the gene for GFP comes from a jellyfish, GFP has been made in bacteria, yeast, slime mold, plants, fruit flies, zebrafish, and mammals.

Introduce Point out that *replication* is the term used for DNA synthesis, which occurs before mitosis. Each strand of the DNA molecule acts as a template, or pattern, for making a complementary strand. The word *complement* refers to a corresponding form that completes a whole, for example, DNA base pairs.

Have two volunteers complete the single strands on the board. Point out that the complementary strand for Template 1 goes below the original and the strand for Template 2 goes above.

Discuss Have students compare the replicated strands with the original. **Ask**

- How does a template work? It serves as a pattern or gauge for that which is to be made.
- Is the resulting strand a mirror image? No, the complementary strand is made up of different shapes.
- What has happened to the original DNA molecule? It has been divided between the two new strands. You may want to discuss this in terms of being conserved.

Activate Prior Knowledge

Direct students' attention to the chapter title. **Ask**

- What is the relationship between DNA and proteins? DNA contains the information a cell needs to make proteins.
- Why are proteins important? Proteins make up the structural components of a cell and direct most of its chemical activity.
- How do Mendel's experiments with pea plants compare to the experiment with the glowing mouse? Both examine the effects of DNA. Mendel crossbred plants of the same species; the mouse experiment used biotechnology to transfer DNA between species.

Preview Vocabulary

Academic Vocabulary Tell students that understanding that DNA is a code is critical to this chapter. The word *code* has different applications:

- a systematic collection of laws or regulations
- a system of signals or symbols used to transmit a message
- a system of symbols and rules used to program a computer

Ask, What idea is central to each definition? that information is transmitted in a systematic way

English Learners Ask students if they are familiar with the word *code.* Lead them to the idea that a code carries a message and that DNA is a code. Point out the titles in **Sections 8.4** and **8.5.** Discuss that *transcription* involves copying the code and *translation* involves converting it into its final form.

Integrating Physics

Green fluorescent protein (GFP) was originally found in the jellyfish *Aequorea victoria.* The jellyfish does not produce its own light but absorbs UV light that filters into the ocean. The shorter wavelengths of UV light are absorbed by GFP, which in turn releases light of a longer wavelength—green. UV light is not visible in the presence of white light. In the photo, a darkened room shows the green light produced by the GFP mouse.

▼ Plan and Prepare

Objectives

- Describe Griffith's discovery of a transforming principle.
- Explain how Avery identified DNA as the transforming principle.
- Summarize the experiments of Hershey and Chase that confirmed DNA as the genetic material.

Section Resources

Unit Resource Book Study Guide pp. 61–62 Power Notes p. 63 Reinforcement p. 64
Interactive Reader Chapter 8 **Spanish Study Guide** pp. 73–74
Biology Toolkit pp. C7, C12, C38
Technology Power Presentation 8.1 Media Gallery DVD Online Quiz 8.1

Activate Prior Knowledge In 1866, Mendel reported transferring pollen between different types of true-breeding pea plants, causing a noticeable transformation in some of the offspring. **Ask,** What do you think Mendel's observations have to do with the transforming principle mentioned in this section? Mendel studied specific traits related to genes that are made up of DNA, the transforming principle.

▼ Teach

TEACH FROM VISUALS

FIGURE 8.1 Review Griffith's experiments. **Ask**

- What were the variables in Griffith's experiment? dead and alive S bacteria, and live R bacteria
- Based on the first three results, what should have happened in the fourth experiment? The mouse should have lived because the S bacteria were dead, along with whatever caused the bacteria to be deadly.

8.1 Identifying DNA as the Genetic Material

KEY CONCEPT DNA was identified as the genetic material through a series of experiments.

MAIN IDEAS

- Griffith finds a "transforming principle."
- Avery identifies DNA as the transforming principle.
- Hershey and Chase confirm that DNA is the genetic material.

VOCABULARY

bacteriophage, p. 228

Review

deoxyribonucleic acid (DNA), gene, enzyme

INDIANA STANDARDS

NOS.9 Recognize that new scientific discoveries often lead to a re-evaluation of previously accepted scientific knowledge and of commonly held ideas.

Connect Some people think a complicated answer is better than a simple one. If they have a head cold, for instance, they may use all sorts of pills, syrups, and sprays, when they simply need rest, water, and warm chicken soup. In the early 1900s, most scientists thought DNA's structure was too repetitive for it to be the genetic material. Proteins, which are more variable in structure, appeared to be a better candidate. Starting in the 1920s, experiments provided data that did not support this idea. By the 1950s, sufficient evidence showed that DNA—the same molecule that codes for GFP in the glowing mouse—carries genetic information.

MAIN IDEA

Griffith finds a "transforming principle."

In 1928 the British microbiologist Frederick Griffith was investigating two forms of the bacterium that causes pneumonia. One form is surrounded by a coating made of sugar molecules. Griffith called these bacteria the S form because colonies of them look smooth. The second form of bacteria do not have a smooth coating and are called the R, or rough, form. As you can see in **FIGURE 8.1,** when Griffith injected the two types of bacteria into mice, only the S type killed the mice. When the S bacteria were killed with heat, the mice were unaffected. Therefore, only live S bacteria would cause the mice to die.

TAKING NOTES

Make a table to keep track of the experiments discussed in this section and how they contributed to our understanding of DNA.

Experiment	Results
Griffith's mice	A transferable material changed harmless bacteria into disease-causing bacteria

FIGURE 8.1 Griffith's Experiments

The S form of the bacterium is deadly; the R form is not.

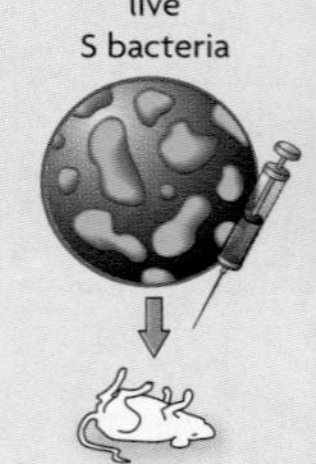
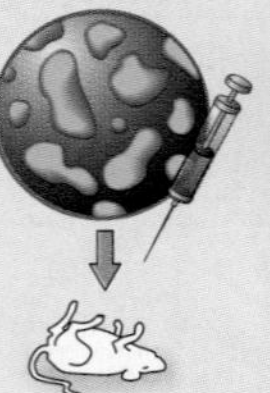

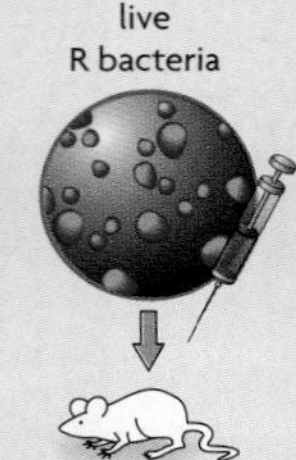

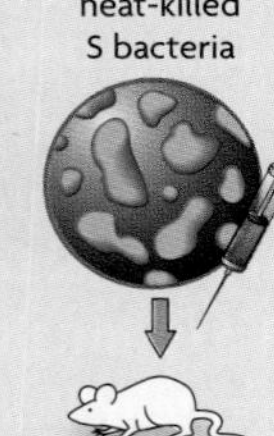

Differentiated Instruction

BELOW LEVEL

Suggest students use the PLAN strategy to work through the sections of this chapter:

Predict what a section is about using the key concept and main ideas.

Locate key vocabulary and important concepts.

Add definitions and details to their notes while reading.

Note in a paragraph or two a summary of the section.

Biology Toolkit, PLAN, p. C7

PRE-AP

Explain to students that Griffith was working on a vaccine for pneumonia when he noticed the transformation bacteria. He was hoping to use heat-killed S bacteria to stimulate an immune response. Have students prepare a sequence diagram of the experiments shown in **FIGURE 8.1,** indicating what each demonstrated. Have students change the result of the fourth experiment to reflect a healthy mouse. Ask them to speculate what Griffith's next steps would have been in testing for a vaccine.

Biology Toolkit, Sequence Diagram, p. C38

Griffith next injected mice with a combination of heat-killed S bacteria and live R bacteria. To his surprise, the mice died. Even more surprising, he found live S bacteria in blood samples from the dead mice. Griffith concluded that some material must have been transferred from the heat-killed S bacteria to the live R bacteria. Whatever that material was, it contained information that changed harmless R bacteria into disease-causing S bacteria. Griffith called this mystery material the "transforming principle."

Connecting CONCEPTS

Microbiology Much of our knowledge of the chemical basis of genetics has come from the study of bacteria. You will learn much more about bacteria in **Chapter 18.**

A Infer What evidence suggested that there was a transforming principle?

MAIN IDEA

Avery identifies DNA as the transforming principle.

What exactly is the transforming principle that Griffith discovered? That question puzzled Oswald Avery and his fellow biologists. They worked for more than ten years to find the answer. Avery's team began by combining living R bacteria with an extract made from S bacteria. This procedure allowed them to directly observe the transformation of R bacteria into S bacteria in a petri dish.

Avery's group next developed a process to purify their extract. They then performed a series of tests to find out if the transforming principle was DNA or protein.

- **Qualitative tests** Standard chemical tests showed that no protein was present. In contrast, tests revealed that DNA was present.
- **Chemical analysis** As you can see in **FIGURE 8.2**, the proportions of elements in the extract closely matched those found in DNA. Proteins contain almost no phosphorus.
- **Enzyme tests** When the team added to the extract enzymes known to break down proteins, the extract still transformed the R bacteria to the S form. Also, transformation occurred when researchers added an enzyme that breaks down RNA (another nucleic acid). Transformation failed to occur only when an enzyme was added to destroy DNA.

FIGURE 8.2 Avery's Discoveries

CHEMICAL ANALYSIS OF TRANSFORMING PRINCIPLE

	% Nitrogen (N)	% Phosphorus (P)	Ratio of N to P
Sample A	14.21	8.57	1.66
Sample B	15.93	9.09	1.75
Sample C	15.36	9.04	1.69
Sample D	13.40	8.45	1.58
Known value for DNA	15.32	9.05	1.69

Source: Avery, O. T. et al., *The Journal of Experimental Medicine* 79:2.

Oswald Avery

B Analyze How do the data support the hypothesis that DNA, not protein, is the transforming principle?

In 1944 Avery and his group presented this and other evidence to support their conclusion that DNA must be the transforming principle, or genetic material. The results created great interest. However, some scientists questioned whether the genetic material in bacteria was the same as that in other organisms. Despite Avery's evidence, some scientists insisted that his extract must have contained protein.

C Summarize List the key steps in the process that Avery's team used to identify the transforming principle.

ENGLISH LEARNERS

After students read the section, have them form three groups. Set up three pieces of chart paper, one each for the experiments of Griffith, Avery, and Hershey and Chase. Label the charts and include this question on each: "What did the experiments show and how did they show it?" Assign a group to each chart and have students answer the question, adding as much information as they can. Then rotate the groups. Discuss the answers with the class.

Biology Toolkit, Carousel Review, p. C12

The Inside Story

Following World War I, **Frederick Griffith** and **Oswald Avery** were both engaged in the effort to stop a global epidemic of **influenza.** Griffith was in London, working on a vaccine to protect against bacterial infection. Avery was in New York, developing serums to control bacterial growth. Neither was thinking about DNA.

Vaccines use either dead or weakened bacteria to stimulate an immune response. In setting up a negative control for his experiments, Griffith accidentally discovered the transforming principle that could change a population of bacteria from one type to another. When Avery first learned of Griffith's discovery, he refused to accept the results. This was no small issue for Avery. He was working on developing **serums** specific to known types of bacteria. What good would a serum be if bacteria could change from one type to another?

Ironically it was Avery, not Griffith, who eventually isolated and identified DNA as the transforming principle. And, equally ironic, Avery's results would also be met with skepticism—until Hershey and Chase came along.

Integrating Microbiology

Heating bacteria to 60°C (140°F) can kill the bacteria without denaturing their DNA. DNA can remain unchanged up to 90°C (194°F). Therefore, the S bacteria in Griffith's experiment died, but their DNA remained intact.

Answers

A Infer R bacteria in the presence of dead S bacteria became pathogenic.

B Analyze The transforming principle contained about the same relative amount of phosphorus as DNA. Proteins contain almost no phosphorus.

C Summarize Avery and his team purified transforming factor and then performed three tests: for the presence of DNA versus protein, for the relative proportion of nitrogen to phosphorus, and for interaction with specific enzymes.

▼ Teach *continued*

TEACH FROM VISUALS

FIGURE 8.3 Point out that the phage functions almost like a hypodermic syringe. The DNA stored in the head is injected through the tail into the bacterium. **Ask,** What happens to the phage after it injects its DNA? It is just an empty shell and can no longer cause disease.

Answers

A Apply Avery's data strongly suggested that DNA was the transforming principle. Hershey and Chase confirmed this by directly labeling the DNA and proteins of bacteriophages growing in culture. The presence of radioactive phosphorus inside the bacteria clearly showed that it was the DNA, not protein, that was transmitted between the viruses and the bacteria.

▼ Assess and Reteach

Assess Use the Online Quiz or Section Quiz (*Assessment Book,* p. 147).

Reteach Have students connect Griffith's experiments to those of Hershey and Chase. Have students speculate what was happening within the bacterial population in Griffith's fourth experiment.

MAIN IDEA

Hershey and Chase confirm that DNA is the genetic material.

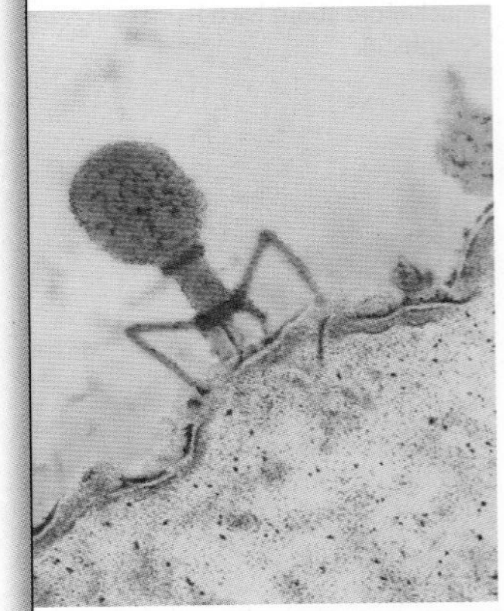

FIGURE 8.3 This micrograph shows the protein coat of a bacteriophage (orange) after it has injected its DNA into an *E. coli* bacterium (blue). (colored TEM; magnification 115,000×)

Conclusive evidence for DNA as the genetic material came in 1952 from two American biologists, Alfred Hershey and Martha Chase. Hershey and Chase were studying viruses that infect bacteria. This type of virus, called a **bacteriophage** (bak-TEER-ee-uh-FAYJ), or "phage" for short, takes over a bacterium's genetic machinery and directs it to make more viruses.

Phages like the ones Hershey and Chase studied are relatively simple—little more than a DNA molecule surrounded by a protein coat. This two-part structure of phages offered a perfect opportunity to answer the question, Is the genetic material made of DNA or protein? By discovering which part of a phage (DNA or protein) actually entered a bacterium, as shown in **FIGURE 8.3,** they could answer this question once and for all.

Hershey and Chase thought up a clever procedure that made use of the chemical elements found in protein and DNA. Protein contains sulfur but very little phosphorus, while DNA contains phosphorus but no sulfur. The researchers grew phages in cultures that contained radioactive isotopes of sulfur or phosphorus. Hershey and Chase then used these radioactively tagged phages in two experiments.

- **Experiment 1** In the first experiment, bacteria were infected with phages that had radioactive sulfur atoms in their protein molecules. Hershey and Chase then used an ordinary kitchen blender to separate the bacteria from the parts of the phages that remained outside the bacteria. When they examined the bacteria, they found no significant radioactivity.
- **Experiment 2** Next, Hershey and Chase repeated the procedure with phages that had DNA tagged with radioactive phosphorus. This time, radioactivity was clearly present inside the bacteria.

From their results, Hershey and Chase concluded that the phages' DNA had entered the bacteria, but the protein had not. Their findings finally convinced scientists that the genetic material is DNA and not protein.

A Apply How did Hershey and Chase build upon Avery's chemical analysis results?

8.1 ASSESSMENT

ONLINE QUIZ ClassZone.com

NOS.9

REVIEWING MAIN IDEAS

1. What was "transformed" in Griffith's experiment?
2. How did Avery and his group identify the transforming principle?
3. Summarize how Hershey and Chase confirmed that DNA is the genetic material.

CRITICAL THINKING

4. **Summarize** Why was the **bacteriophage** an excellent choice for research to determine whether genes are made of DNA or proteins?
5. **Analyze** Choose one experiment from this section and explain how the results support the conclusion.

***Connecting* CONCEPTS**

6. **Mendelian Genetics** Describe how Mendel's studies relate to the experiments discussed in this section.

8.1 ASSESSMENT

1. Harmless R bacteria were transformed into pathogenic S bacteria.
2. They purified the component of S bacteria that caused R bacteria to transform into S bacteria. This extract was tested for the presence of DNA or protein, its chemical composition, and its reaction to enzymes.
3. They labeled the protein of bacteriophages with radioactive sulfur and their DNA with radioactive phosphorus. The bacteriophages were allowed to infect bacteria. Hershey and Chase separated the phages from the infected bacteria and showed that phosphorus, a component of DNA, not sulfur, had entered the bacteria.
4. A bacteriophage consists of little more than a protein coat surrounding DNA. The protein coat is left behind when the viral DNA enters a bacterium.
5. Answers will vary depending on the experiment chosen.
6. Both Mendel's experiments and this series of experiments demonstrate how ideas build on each other, how data from one experiment can raise new questions and lead to more experiments and data. Mendel's observations and ideas about heredity helped lead to questions about the physical nature of what was being transmitted from parent to offspring.

FIGURE 8.4 The Four Nitrogen-Containing Bases of DNA

PYRIMIDINES = SINGLE RING			PURINES = DOUBLE RING		
Name of Base	**Structural Formula**	**Model**	**Name of Base**	**Structural Formula**	**Model**
thymine	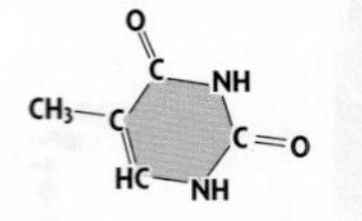	 T	adenine	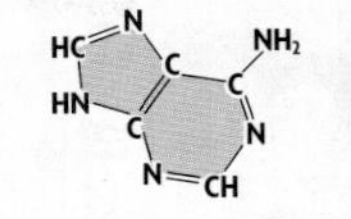	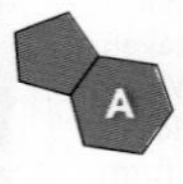 A
cytosine	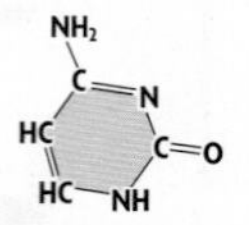	 C	guanine	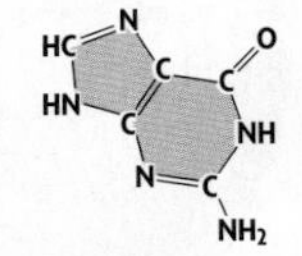	 G

A Compare Which base is most similar in structure to thymine?

By 1950 Erwin Chargaff changed the thinking about DNA by analyzing the DNA of several different organisms. Chargaff found that the same four bases are found in the DNA of all organisms, but the proportion of the four bases differs somewhat from organism to organism. In the DNA of each organism, the amount of adenine approximately equals the amount of thymine. Similarly, the amount of cytosine roughly equals the amount of guanine. These A = T and C = G relationships became known as Chargaff's rules.

VOCABULARY

An amine is a molecule that contains nitrogen. Notice that the four DNA bases end in *-ine* and all contain nitrogen.

B Summarize What is the only difference among the four DNA nucleotides?

MAIN IDEA

Watson and Crick developed an accurate model of DNA's three-dimensional structure.

The breakthrough in understanding the structure of DNA came in the early 1950s through the teamwork of American geneticist James Watson and British physicist Francis Crick. Watson and Crick were supposed to be studying the structure of proteins. Both men, however, were more fascinated by the challenge of figuring out DNA's structure. Their interest was sparked not only by the findings of Hershey, Chase, and Chargaff but also by the work of the biochemist Linus Pauling. Pauling had found that the structure of some proteins was a helix, or spiral. Watson and Crick hypothesized that DNA might also be a helix.

FIGURE 8.5 Rosalind Franklin (above) produced x-ray photographs of DNA that indicated it was a helix. Her coworker, Maurice Wilkins, showed the data without Franklin's consent to Watson and Crick, which helped them discover DNA's structure.

X-Ray Evidence

At the same time, Rosalind Franklin, shown in **FIGURE 8.5**, and Maurice Wilkins were studying DNA using a technique called x-ray crystallography. When DNA is bombarded with x-rays, the atoms in DNA diffract the x-rays in a pattern that can be captured on film. Franklin's x-ray photographs of DNA showed an X surrounded by a circle. Franklin's data gave Watson and Crick the clues they needed. The patterns and angle of the X suggested that

ONLINE BIOLOGY Have students evaluate the genomes of four different species in terms of Chargaff's rules. Go to Data Analysis Online in Options for Inquiry on page 257.

The Inside Story

In 1951, **Rosalind Franklin** was invited to King's College London to be part of a team working on DNA analysis. Franklin used x-rays to study DNA's crystalline structure. Meanwhile, at Cambridge University, **James Watson** and **Francis Crick** were feverishly working to be the first to accurately describe DNA's structure. They knew DNA's components, as did many others, but no one could figure out how the pieces fit together.

In 1953, **Maurice Wilkins,** Franklin's coworker, showed Watson one of Franklin's x-rays, which provided an all-important clue—a DNA molecule was a two-stranded helix of a constant width. Within weeks, Watson and Crick had figured out the structure of DNA.

In 1962, Watson, Crick, and Wilkins shared the Nobel Prize for Physiology or Medicine for this work. Franklin had died of cancer four years earlier, at the age of 37. Some attribute her cancer to exposure to x-rays. While the Nobel Prize is never awarded posthumously, no mention of Franklin's contribution was made at that time. Her work and its oversight have now ensured her a place in history.

Answers

A Compare cytosine, because it has a single ring

B Summarize Their nitrogen-containing bases differ from each other.

INCLUSION

For students who have difficulty sorting out the relationship between different aspects of the text, use DNA's base pairs as a point of reference. Show students where the base pairs are found in various diagrams and photos in the section. Suggest a mnemonic to help students remember the pairs: C-G: Cars need gas; A-T: Acorns grow on trees. Or point out that the letters *C* and *G* are both round, whereas the letters *A* and *T* are made of straight lines.

▼ Teach *continued*

ONLINE BIOLOGY Go to the chapter Resource Center at **ClassZone.com** for additional resources and information on DNA.

Vocabulary

Greek and Latin Word Origins The words **spiral** and **helix** are synonymous. The word spiral comes from a Latin root meaning "coil." The word *helix* comes from a Greek root meaning "to wrap around." A single molecule of DNA molecule has two helixes, or strands, making it a double helix.

Science Trivia

Interpretation of Rosalind Franklin's x-ray image showed the following:

- DNA has a width of about 2 nanometers (10^{-9} m).
- One complete turn of the helix occurs every 3.4 nanometers.
- There are ten base pairs in each turn of the helix, so the base pairs are stacked 0.34 nanometers apart.
- There are approximately 3 billion base pairs in human DNA.

Connecting CONCEPTS

Chemical Bonds Helping students understand the relative strengths of covalent bonds and hydrogen bonds lays the groundwork for understanding DNA replication in **Section 8.3.** Because hydrogen bonds between the bases are easily broken, the two strands of DNA can be readily separated, while the strong covalent bonds between tides keep the individual strands

Answers

A Apply Because A pairs only w and C pairs only with G, DNA wil have approximately the same prc of A and T and the same proport C and G.

James Watson and Francis Crick

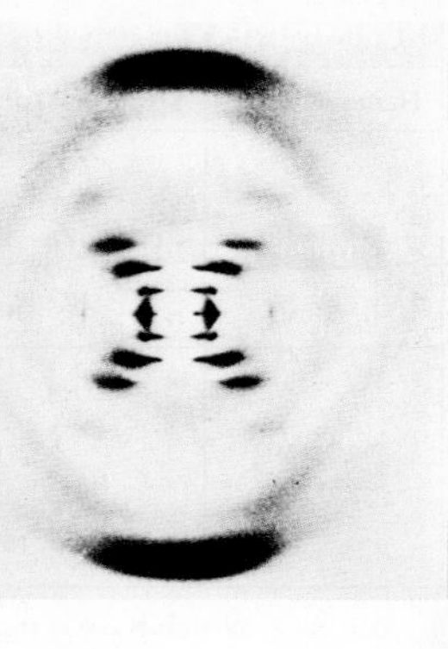

FIGURE 8.6 James Watson (left) and Francis Crick (right) used a model to figure out DNA's structure. Their model was influenced by data from other researchers, including an x-ray image (far right) taken by Rosalind Franklin. When x-rays bounce off vertically suspended DNA, they form this characteristic x-shaped pattern.

The Double Helix

Back in their own laboratory, Watson and Crick made models of metal and wood to figure out the structure of DNA. Their models placed the sugar-phosphate backbones on the outside and the bases on the inside. At first, Watson reasoned that A might pair with A, T with T, and so on. But the bases A and G are about twice as wide as C and T, so this produced a helix that varied in width. Finally, Watson and Crick found that if they paired double-ringed nucleotides with single-ringed nucleotides, the bases fit like a puzzle.

In April 1953 Watson and Crick published their DNA model in a paper in the journal *Nature*. **FIGURE 8.6** shows their **double helix** (HEE-lihks) model, in which two strands of DNA wind around each other like a twisted ladder. The strands are complementary—they fit together and are the opposite of each other. That is, if one strand is ACACAC, the other strand is TGTGTG. The pairing of bases in their model finally explained Chargaff's rules.

A Apply How did the Watson and Crick model explain Chargaff's rules?

MAIN IDEA

Nucleotides always pair in the same way.

Connecting CONCEPTS

Chemical Bonds Recall from **Chapter 2** that a covalent bond is a strong bond in which two atoms share one or more pairs of electrons. Hydrogen bonds are much weaker than covalent bonds and can easily be broken.

The DNA nucleotides of a single strand are joined together by covalent bonds that connect the sugar of one nucleotide to the phosphate of the next nucleotide. The alternating sugars and phosphates form the sides of a double helix, sort of like a twisted ladder. The DNA double helix is held together by hydrogen bonds between the bases in the middle. Individually, each hydrogen bond is weak, but together, they maintain DNA structure.

As shown in **FIGURE 8.7**, the bases of the two DNA strands always pair up in the same way. This is summarized in the **base pairing rules:** thymine (T) always pairs with adenine (A), and cytosine (C) always pairs with guanine (G). These pairings occur because of the sizes of the bases and the ability of the

Differentiated Instruction

sec
hip
sw
ec
eg
ns
es
nt
n

Extracting DNA

MATERIALS
- balance
- 10 g raw wheat germ
- laboratory spatula
- test tube
- test tube rack
- 10 mL warm distilled water
- 2 eyedroppers
- 4 10-mL graduated cylinders
- 20 mL detergent solution
- 3 g meat tenderizer
- 20 mL salt solution
- 10 mL cold isopropyl alcohol
- glass stirring rod

PROCESS SKILLS
- **Observing**
- **Analyzing**

NOS.1 Develop explanations based on reproducible data and observations gathered during laboratory investigations.

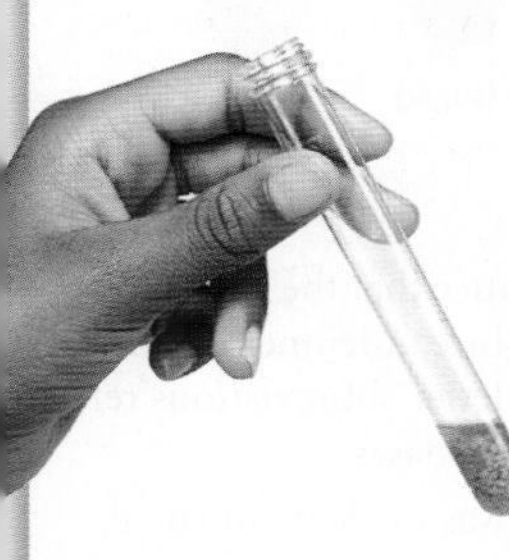

Oswald Avery wrote in a scientific article, "At a critical concentration . . . of alcohol the active material separates out in the form of fibrous strands that wind themselves around the stirring rod." In this lab, you can observe the same thing Avery observed as you extract DNA from wheat germ. This procedure is a simplified version of the one scientists commonly use to extract DNA today.

PROBLEM How do you extract the DNA from plant cells?

PROCEDURE
1. Place a small amount of wheat germ in a test tube. The wheat germ should be about 1 cm high in the test tube.
2. Add enough distilled water to wet and cover all of the wheat germ.
3. Add 25–30 drops of detergent solution to the test tube. For 3 minutes, gently swirl the test-tube contents. Avoid making bubbles.
4. Add 3 g of meat tenderizer.
5. Add 25–30 drops of salt solution to the test tube. Swirl for 1 minute.
6. Tilt the test tube at an angle as shown. Slowly add alcohol so that it runs down the inside of the test tube to form a separate layer on top of the mixture in the tube. Add enough alcohol to double the total volume in the tube. Let the test tube stand for 2 minutes.
7. Watch for stringy, cloudy material to rise from the bottom layer into the alcohol layer. This is the DNA.
8. Use the glass stirring rod to remove some DNA. Be careful to probe only the alcohol layer.
9. Draw in your lab report what the mixture and DNA looked like in steps 2–7. Be sure to include color, texture, and what happened after a new solution was added.

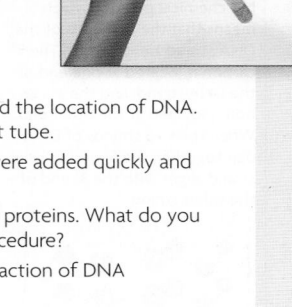

step 6

step 8

ANALYZE AND CONCLUDE
1. **Connect** Consider what you know about cell structure and the location of DNA. Suggest a reason for adding detergent solution to the test tube.
2. **Predict** What do you think might happen if the alcohol were added quickly and the two layers mixed?
3. **Infer** Meat tenderizer contains enzymes that break down proteins. What do you think is the purpose of adding meat tenderizer in this procedure?
4. **Connect** In what type of real-life situation would the extraction of DNA be useful?

EXTEND YOUR INVESTIGATION
Determine a method to calculate what percentage of the wheat germ consists of DNA.

Answers

Expected Results
Students should be able to remove large amounts of DNA from between the two layers.

Analyze and Conclude
1. Detergent breaks up the phospholipid membranes of the cell and its nucleus.
2. Alcohol causes the DNA strands to unfold and clump together. If the alcohol is added quickly, it will mix with the water and become diluted. If DNA does not unfold and clump together, it will not be seen.
3. In the cell, DNA is wrapped around proteins. The enzymes break down these proteins to unwrap the DNA.
4. *Sample Answers:* determine the paternity of a child, identify a crime suspect or victim, identify genetic disorders or susceptibilities

Extend Your Investigation
Find the mass of the wheat germ. Extract the DNA, remove it and find its mass, then calculate its percent mass relative to the wheat germ.

INVESTIGATION

Time 30 minutes TEACHER TESTED
Teacher Preparation
Student Difficulty
Lab Binder Genetics, pp. 29–31

Purpose Extract and observe DNA.

Overview Students extract DNA from wheat germ cells. They will then
- observe properties of the extracted DNA
- analyze the procedure for extracting DNA

LAB PREPARATION
- For detergent solution, mix one part of liquid dishwashing detergent to three parts of distilled water.
- To make 8% salt solution, dissolve 8 g of table salt (NaCl) in 100 mL of distilled water.

LAB MANAGEMENT
- Provide droppers for the detergent and salt solutions.
- Provide small beakers of alcohol for students to pour into the test tubes. For best results, keep the alcohol in an ice bath until it is distributed to students.
- You may wish to distribute hand lenses to students for closer examination of the DNA.
- Arrange for proper disposal of the DNA extractions.

Safety Caution students to wear safety goggles, not rub their faces with their hands, not inhale or sniff alcohol fumes, and wash their hands thoroughly after completing the lab.

POST-LAB DISCUSSION
Have students share any questions raised by their observations. Ask if their questions suggest any further investigation. **Ask,** Why was there so much DNA? Each granule of wheat germ has many individual cells, all of which release their DNA.

▼ Plan and Prepare

Objectives

- Describe the interaction of the four nucleotides that make up DNA.
- Describe the three-dimensional structure of DNA.

Section Resources

Unit Resource Book Study Guide pp. 65–66 Power Notes p. 67 Reinforcement p. 68 Pre-AP Activity pp. 91–92
Interactive Reader Chapter 8 **Spanish Study Guide** pp. 75–76
Biology Toolkit pp. C3, C9, C31
Technology Power Presentation 8.2 Media Gallery DVD Online Quiz 8.2

Activate Prior Knowledge Tell students that scientists found it hard to accept DNA as the genetic material because of its structural simplicity. **Ask**

- What are some examples of simple units that can be used to produce great complexity? letters of an alphabet, 0s and 1s of computer code, building blocks
- Which of these examples offer the best analogy to DNA? alphabet and computer code because both are informational units

▼ Teach

TEACH FROM VISUALS

Have students compare the structure of the nucleotide monomer in **VISUAL VOCAB** to the DNA polymer shown in Connecting Concepts. **Ask**

- What part of the monomer serves to connect the two DNA strands? connection between bases
- What is the pattern of that connection? Single ring bonds to double ring.

8.2 Structure of DNA

KEY CONCEPT DNA structure is the same in all organisms.

MAIN IDEAS

- DNA is composed of four types of nucleotides.
- Watson and Crick developed an accurate model of DNA's three-dimensional structure.
- Nucleotides always pair in the same way.

VOCABULARY

nucleotide, p. 230
double helix, p. 232
base pairing rules, p. 232

Review
covalent bond, hydrogen bond

INDIANA STANDARDS

B.5.1 Describe the relationship between chromosomes and DNA along with their basic structure and function.

Connect The experiments of Hershey and Chase confirmed that DNA carries the genetic information, but they left other big questions unanswered: What exactly is this genetic information? How does DNA store this information? Scientists in the early 1950s still had a limited knowledge of the structure of DNA, but that was about to change dramatically.

MAIN IDEA

DNA is composed of four types of nucleotides.

Since the 1920s, scientists have known that the DNA molecule is a very long polymer, or chain of repeating units. The small units, or monomers, that make up DNA are called **nucleotides** (NOO-klee-oh-TYDZ). Each nucleotide has three parts.

- A phosphate group (one phosphorus with four oxygens)
- A ring-shaped sugar called deoxyribose
- A nitrogen-containing base (a single or double ring built around nitrogen and carbon atoms)

One molecule of human DNA contains billions of nucleotides, but there are only four types of nucleotides in DNA. These nucleotides differ only in their nitrogen-containing bases.

VISUAL VOCAB

The small units, or monomers, that make up a strand of DNA are called **nucleotides.** Nucleotides have three parts.

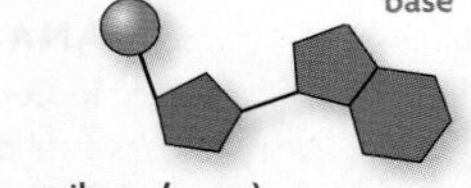

***Connecting* CONCEPTS**

Biochemistry The nucleotides in a strand of DNA all line up in the same direction. As a result, DNA has chemical polarity, which means that the two ends of the DNA strand are different. The 5′ carbon is located at one end of the DNA strand, and the 3′ carbon is located at the other end. When the two strands of DNA pair together, the 5′ end of one strand aligns with the 3′ end of the other strand.

The four bases in DNA are shown in **FIGURE 8.4.** Notice that the bases cytosine (C) and thymine (T) have a single-ring structure. Adenine (A) and guanine (G) have a larger, double-ring structure. The letter abbreviations refer both to the bases and to the nucleotides that contain the bases.

For a long time, scientists hypothesized that DNA was made up of equal amounts of the four nucleotides, and so the DNA in all organisms was exactly the same. That hypothesis was a key reason that it was so hard to convince scientists that DNA was the genetic material. They reasoned that identical molecules could not carry different instructions across all organisms.

Differentiated Instruction

BELOW LEVEL

Prepare a series of short-answer questions or true/false statements to check students knowledge of DNA structure. This will help students focus on the critical information in the section. Students should answer the questions before reading and then check and correct their responses as they read.

Biology Toolkit, Anticipation Guide, p. C3

PRE-AP

Have students prepare a timeline of the discoveries detailed in **Sections 8.2** and **8.3.** Have them identify what piece of information about the genetic material of a cell was revealed at each point in time and who contributed to the discovery.

Biology Toolkit, Timeline, p. C31

FIGURE 8.7 Base Pairing Rules

The base pairing rules describe how nucleotides form pairs in DNA. T always pairs with A, and G always pairs with C.

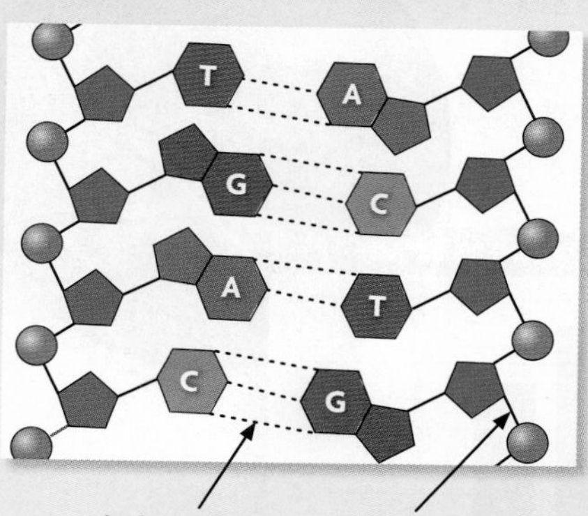

T
A
G
C
A
T
C
G
This ribbonlike part represents the phosphate groups and deoxyribose sugar molecules that make up DNA's "backbone."
The nitrogen-containing bases bond in the middle to form the rungs of the DNA ladder.

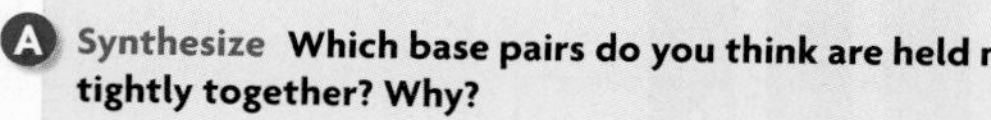

hydrogen bond
covalent bond

A Synthesize **Which base pairs do you think are held more tightly together? Why?**

bases to form hydrogen bonds with each other. Due to the arrangement of their molecules, A can form unique hydrogen bonds with T, and C with G. Notice that A and T form two hydrogen bonds, whereas C and G form three.

You can remember the rules of base pairing by noticing that the letters C and G have a similar shape. Once you know that C and G pair together, you know that A and T pair together by default. If a sequence of bases on one strand of DNA is CTGCTA, you know the other DNA strand will be GACGAT.

B Apply **What sequence of bases would pair with the sequence TGACTA?**

8.2 ASSESSMENT

ONLINE QUIZ ClassZone.com

B.5.1

REVIEWING ▶ MAIN IDEAS

1. How many types of **nucleotides** are in DNA, and how do they differ?
2. How are the **base pairing rules** related to Chargaff's research on DNA?
3. Explain how the **double helix** model of DNA built on the research of Rosalind Franklin.

CRITICAL THINKING

4. **Infer** Which part of a DNA molecule carries the genetic instructions that are unique for each individual: the sugar-phosphate backbone or the nitrogen-containing bases? Explain.
5. **Predict** In a sample of yeast DNA, 31.5% of the bases are adenine (A). Predict the approximate percentages of C, G, and T. Explain.

Connecting CONCEPTS

6. **Evolution** The DNA of all organisms contains the same four bases (adenine, thymine, cytosine, and guanine). What might this similarity indicate about the origins of life on Earth?

TEACH FROM VISUALS

FIGURE 8.7 Help students decode the figure. **Ask**

- How many rings are there in each base pair? three
- Why is DNA's shape called a double helix? It is made of two spirals that are twisted around each other.
- How are the two diagrams related to each other? The left diagram can be superimposed onto the right diagram, with the sugar-phosphate backbones on the spiral strands and the bases on the rungs connecting the strands.

Answers

A Synthesize C and G, because they are connected by three hydrogen bonds, whereas A and T are held by only two

B Apply ACTGAT

Assess and Reteach ▼

Assess Use the Online Quiz or Section Quiz (*Assessment Book*, p. 148).

Reteach Have students make models of DNA by cutting out and arranging cardboard shapes representing deoxyribose, phosphate groups, and the four bases. Encourage students to make their model at least four nucleotides long.

8.2 ASSESSMENT

1. Four; their nitrogen-containing bases differ.
2. Because A pairs only with T, and C pairs only with G, DNA will always have approximately the same proportion of A and T and the same proportion of C and G.
3. Franklin's data suggested that DNA was a helix made of two strands an even width apart. From this, Watson and Crick realized that a base with one ring would bond with a base with two rings.
4. The backbone is the same in all DNA. The nitrogen-containing bases provide the unique instructions.
5. Matching A, T is approximately 31.5 percent. Thus, C and G together make up 37 percent of the bases, so each makes up approximately 18.5 percent of the bases.
6. It suggests that the wide diversity of life that we see might have stemmed from a common ancestor.

Introduce

Histograms differ from bar graphs in that a histogram shows data intervals that are continuous. **Ask**

- How are the data intervals continuous in Graph 1? The ages are divided into continuous 10-year intervals from age 30 to age 89.
- What trend is shown in Graph 1? The most common age of the Nobel laureates is 50–59. Very young and very old winners are less common.

Unit Resource Book, Data Analysis, p. 89

Science Trivia

- The youngest person to receive a Nobel Prize was Sir William Lawrence Bragg, at age 25. He won the prize in physics jointly with his father in 1915 for work in x-ray diffraction, which later paved the way for Rosalind Franklin's work with DNA.
- Raymond Davis, Jr., was the oldest Nobel Prize laureate. He was almost 88 years old when he won the Nobel Prize for Physics in 2002.

Discuss

It is estimated that humans have between 20,000 and 25,000 genes. **Ask,** In which bar in Graph 2 would humans be included? the sixth bar, on the far right

Unit Resource Book, Data Analysis, p. 89

DATA ANALYSIS ClassZone.com

NOS.1

Frequency Distributions

A **histogram** is a graph that shows the frequency distribution of a data set. First, a scientist collects data. Then, she groups the data values into equal intervals. The number of data values in each interval is the frequency of the interval. The intervals are shown along the x-axis of the histogram, and the frequencies are shown on the y-axis.

EXAMPLE

The histogram at right shows the frequency distribution of the ages of winners of the Nobel Prize in Medicine at the time of winning. Francis Crick was 46 and James Watson was 34 when they were jointly awarded a Nobel Prize in Medicine in 1962.

According to the histogram, the most winners have been between 50 and 59 years old at the time of winning. Only five scientists have been between the ages of 80 and 89 at the time of winning a Nobel Prize in Medicine.

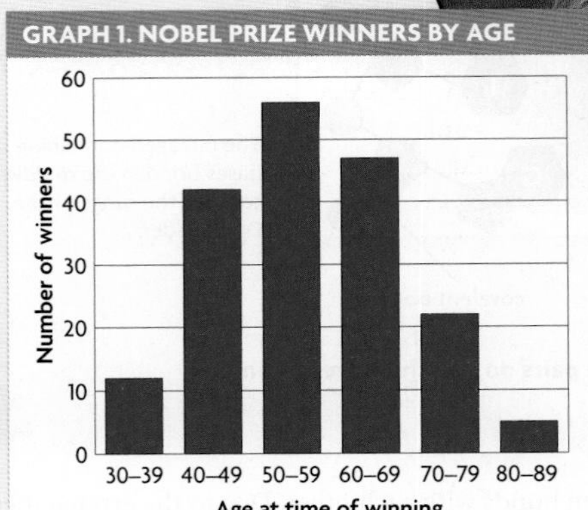

ANALYZE A HISTOGRAM

The histogram below categorizes data collected based on the number of genes in 11 species.

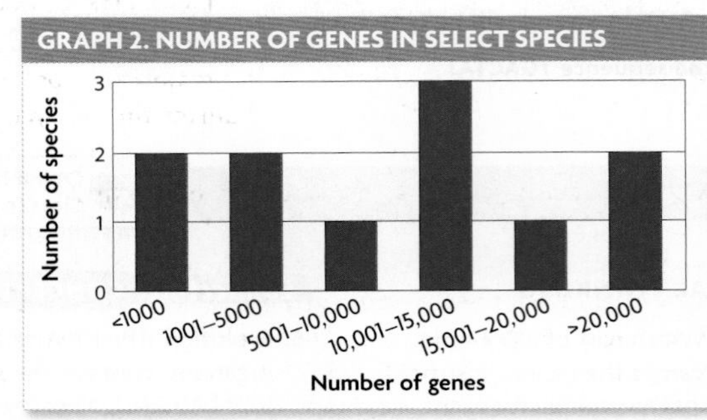

1. **Identify** How many species had between 10,001 and 15,000 genes?
2. **Analyze** Are the data in graph 2 sufficient to reveal a trend in the number of genes per species? Explain your reasoning.

Answers

1. three
2. No, there is no obvious correlation. The highest number of species (3) and the lowest number of species (1) differ by only two. This difference is not significant. Data from 11 species are inadequate to reveal a trend for species in general.

234 Unit 3: Genetics

FIGURE 8.8 Replication

Animated
BIOLOGY
See DNA replication in action at ClassZone.com.

When a cell's DNA is copied, or replicated, two complete and identical sets of genetic information are produced. Then cell division can occur.

1 A DNA molecule unzips as nucleotide base pairs separate. Replication begins on both strands of the molecule at the same time.

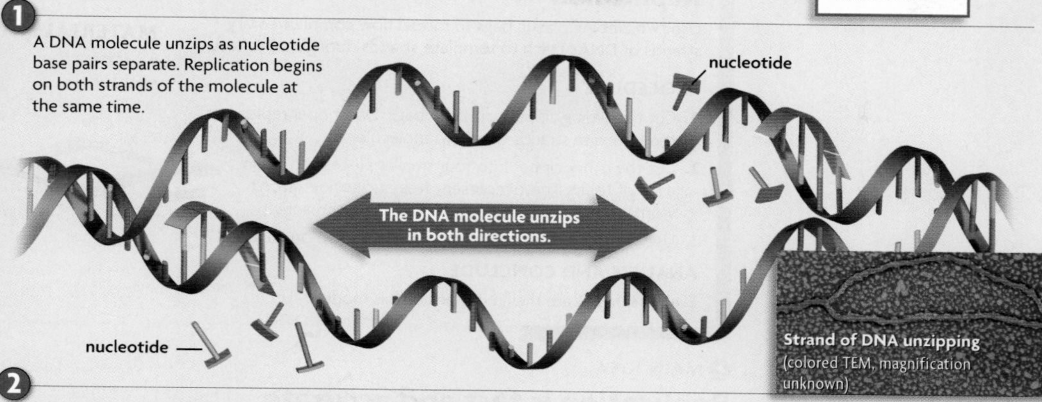

Strand of DNA unzipping (colored TEM; magnification unknown)

2 Each existing strand of the DNA molecule is a template for a new strand. Free-floating nucleotides pair up with the exposed bases on each template strand. DNA polymerases bond these nucleotides together to form the new strands. The arrows show the directions in which new strands form.

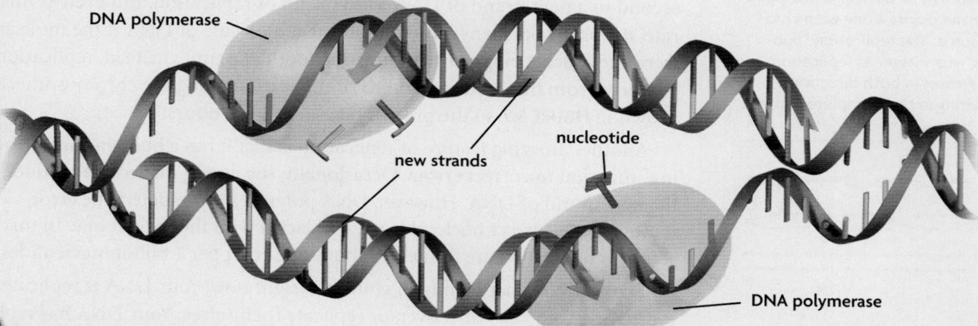

3 Two identical double-stranded DNA molecules result from replication. DNA replication is semiconservative. That is, each DNA molecule contains an original strand and one new strand.

original strand

new strand

Two molecules of DNA

A CRITICAL VIEWING **How is each new molecule of DNA related to the original molecule?**

TEACH FROM VISUALS

FIGURE 8.8 Discuss each step in the figure separately. **Ask**

- In step 1, how does the DNA unzip? The hydrogen bonds between the base pairs break.
- In step 2, how do the new strands compare with the template strands? Each new strand is the complement of its template strand.
- What enzyme is important in step 2? DNA polymerase
- What is the result of DNA replication? two identical DNA molecules
- Why is it important for the cell to correct any errors that occur during replication? If errors were not corrected, one of the new cells that form during cell division would have DNA with incorrect genetic information.

History of Science

The Watson-Crick model of DNA predicted that **DNA replication** is **semiconservative;** that is, each new molecule contains one original strand and one new strand. However, there were two other possible hypotheses. In the **conservative model,** the template molecule remained intact and a new molecule, consisting of two new strands, formed. In the **dispersive model,** the two original strands broke up and dispersed throughout the two new molecules that formed.

Matthew Meselson and **Franklin Stahl** demonstrated that the semiconservative model is correct. They used radioactive nitrogen to label the bases in bacterial DNA and then followed the path of the label through several generations of growth in an unlabeled medium. Their data showed that at first, the radioactivity was all in the parent DNA. After the first generation, all the cells had DNA that was half-labeled. After two generations, half the cells had DNA that was half-labeled, and half the cells had DNA that had no label.

Answers

A Critical Viewing It is identical to the original DNA molecule.

HANDS-ON ACTIVITY

Give students two strands of red yarn and six strands of blue yarn—all of similar length. Have them make a model of DNA from the two red strands. Then have students go through two generations of replication, using the red yarn as template strands and the blue yarn as new strands.

Describe for students the conservative, dispersive, and semiconservative models of replication. (See History of Science.) **Ask**

- If the conservative model were correct, what would the model DNA look like after one generation? One molecule would be all red, and the other would be all blue.
- If the dispersive model were correct, what would the model DNA look like after one generation? Each molecule would consist of segments of red and blue.
- After two divisions, how many molecules have a strand from the original DNA? only two of four

▼ Teach *continued*

QUICK LAB

Time 5 minutes — TEACHER TESTED

Lab Binder Genetics, p. 37

Purpose Model the replication of DNA.

LAB MANAGEMENT

- Have students compare what they are doing to **FIGURE 8.8.**
- The lab can be extended to model complementary base pairing by drawing dots of four different colors on the template strands and dots of matching colors on the pieces representing free nucleotides.

Answers

Analyze and Conclude

The pairing of the free nucleotides in the model is not specific. Pieces of zipper can pair anywhere on the template strand, whereas free nucleotides can pair only with specific bases in DNA replication.

Take It Further

DNA replication takes about eight hours in human cells. If there were only one origin, the process would take about a hundred times longer.

Answers

A Infer Our cells have a large amount of DNA. It must be copied quickly enough to keep up with the demand for cell division and to enable the cell to carry out its normal functions.

▼ Assess and Reteach

Assess Use the Online Quiz or Section Quiz (*Assessment Book*, p. 149).

Reteach Have students review **FIGURE 8.8** and make a flow chart that lists the steps in the process of DNA replication.

QUICK LAB **MODELING** NOS.6

Replication

Use two zipping plastic bags to model how complementary strands of DNA attach to template strands during replication.

MATERIALS
- 2 zipping bags
- scissors

PROCEDURE

1. Cut the sliding zippers off both bags. One zipper represents the template strands of a DNA molecule.
2. Cut the other zipper into four smaller pieces and unzip each of them. These represent free nucleotides. Don't worry about which nucleotide is which in this activity.
3. Use the pieces to model replication as shown on page 237.

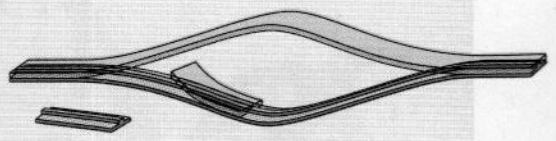

ANALYZE AND CONCLUDE

Evaluate What are the limitations of this model?

MAIN IDEA

Replication is fast and accurate.

FIGURE 8.9 Eukaryotic chromosomes have many origins of replication. The DNA helix is unzipped at many points along each chromosome. The replication "bubbles" grow larger as replication progresses in both directions, resulting in two complete copies.

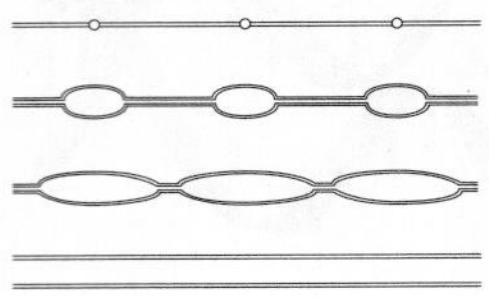

In every living thing, DNA replication happens over and over again, and it happens remarkably fast. In human cells, about 50 nucleotides are added every second to a new strand of DNA at an origin of replication. But even at this rate, it would take many days to replicate a molecule of DNA if the molecule were like a jacket zipper, unzipping one tooth at a time. Instead, replication proceeds from hundreds of origins of replication along the chromosome, as shown in **FIGURE 8.9,** so the process takes just a few hours.

Another amazing feature of replication is that it has a built-in "proofreading" function to correct errors. Occasionally, the wrong nucleotide is added to the new strand of DNA. However, DNA polymerase can detect the error, remove the incorrect nucleotide, and replace it with the correct one. In this way, errors in replication are limited to about one error per 1 billion nucleotides.

Replication is happening in your cells right now. Your DNA is replicated every time your cells turn over, or replicate themselves. Your DNA has replicated trillions of times since you grew from a single cell.

Infer Why does a cell need to replicate its DNA quickly?

8.3 ASSESSMENT

ONLINE QUIZ ClassZone.com

B.7.4

REVIEWING MAIN IDEAS

1. Explain the function of **replication.**
2. Explain how DNA serves as its own template during replication.
3. How do cells help ensure that DNA replication is accurate?

CRITICAL THINKING

4. **Summarize** Describe two major functions of **DNA polymerases.**
5. **Infer** Why is it important that human chromosomes have many origins of replication?

***Connecting* CONCEPTS**

6. **Cell Biology** DNA is replicated before both mitosis and meiosis. How does the amount of DNA produced in a cell during mitosis compare with that produced during meiosis?

8.3 ASSESSMENT

1. to make a copy of all the DNA in a cell so that it can be passed on to a new cell
2. Both strands act as a template. Because base pairing is specific, the sequence of one strand dictates what the sequence of the other strand has to be.
3. Certain types of DNA polymerase have a built-in proofreading function that corrects most mispaired nucleotides.
4. DNA polymerases bond nucleotides together and proofread to ensure accuracy.
5. Each chromosome in a eukaryotic cell is very long. If replication started at only one place, it would take a very long time to finish. Multiple origins of replication let the process happen more quickly.
6. Cells produced by mitosis typically have twice the amount of DNA as cells produced by meiosis.

8.4 Transcription

KEY CONCEPT Transcription converts a gene into a single-stranded RNA molecule.

MAIN IDEAS

- RNA carries DNA's instructions.
- Transcription makes three types of RNA.
- The transcription process is similar to replication.

VOCABULARY

central dogma, p. 239
RNA, p. 239
transcription, p. 240
RNA polymerase, p. 240
messenger RNA (mRNA), p. 240
ribosomal RNA (rRNA), p. 240
transfer RNA (tRNA), p. 240

INDIANA STANDARDS

B.5.3 Describe the process by which DNA directs the production of protein within a cell.

Connect Suppose you want to play skeeball at a game center, but the skeeball lane only takes tokens. You only have quarters. Do you go home in defeat? Stand idly by as someone else becomes high scorer? No, you exchange your quarters for tokens and then proceed to show the other players how it's done. In a similar way, your cells cannot make proteins directly from DNA. They must convert the DNA into an intermediate molecule called RNA, or ribonucleic acid. That conversion process, called transcription, is the focus of this section.

MAIN IDEA

RNA carries DNA's instructions.

Soon after his discovery of DNA structure, Francis Crick defined the **central dogma** of molecular biology, which states that information flows in one direction, from DNA to RNA to proteins. The central dogma involves three processes, as shown in **FIGURE 8.10.**

- Replication, as you just learned, copies DNA (blue arrow).
- Transcription converts a DNA message into an intermediate molecule, called RNA (red arrow).
- Translation interprets an RNA message into a string of amino acids, called a polypeptide. Either a single polypeptide or many polypeptides working together make up a protein (green arrow).

In prokaryotic cells, replication, transcription, and translation all occur in the cytoplasm at approximately the same time. In eukaryotic cells, where DNA is located inside the nuclear membrane, these processes are separated both in location and time. Replication and transcription occur in the nucleus, while translation occurs in the cytoplasm. In addition, the RNA in eukaryotic cells goes through a processing step before it can be transported out of the nucleus. Unless otherwise stated, the rest of this chapter describes how these processes work in eukaryotic cells.

RNA acts as an intermediate link between DNA in the nucleus and protein synthesis in the cytoplasm. Like DNA, **RNA,** or ribonucleic acid, is a chain of nucleotides, each made of a sugar, a phosphate group, and a nitrogen-containing base. You can think of RNA as a temporary copy of DNA that is used and then destroyed.

FIGURE 8.10 The central dogma describes the flow of information from DNA to RNA to proteins. It involves three major processes, shown in a eukaryotic cell below.

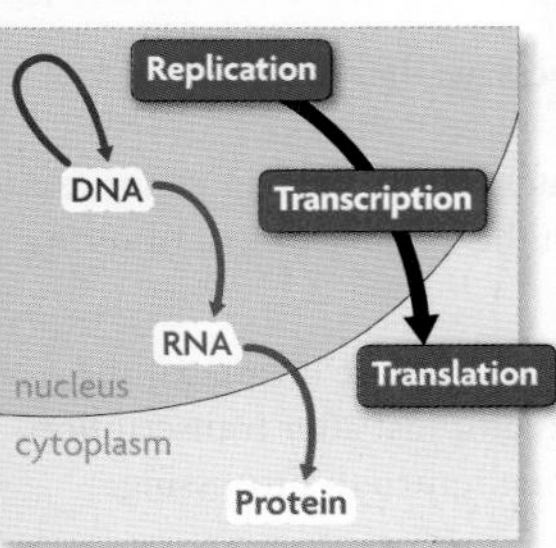

Differentiated Instruction

BELOW LEVEL

Tell students that after reading the section, they will pair up to compare the process of DNA replication with DNA transcription. Have students answer the following questions: How are the processes alike? How are they different?

Biology Toolkit, Think-Pair-Share, p. C13

SECTION 8.4

Plan and Prepare

Objectives

- Describe the relationship between RNA and DNA.
- Identify the three kinds of RNA and their functions.
- Compare transcription to replication.

Section Resources

Unit Resource Book Study Guide pp. 73–74 Power Notes p. 75 Reinforcement p. 76
Interactive Reader Chapter 8 **Spanish Study Guide** pp. 79–80
Biology Toolkit pp. C13, C38
Technology Power Presentation 8.4 Media Gallery DVD Online Quiz 8.4

Activate Prior Knowledge Tell students there are many types of transcriptions. **Ask,** How is the word *transcription* used in music? Typically a piece of music written for one instrument or group is reworked for another. Point out that the music, or message, is the same, but that the medium has changed. Tell students that a similar process happens when DNA is transcribed.

Teach

Take It Further

The central dogma is true for all organisms, from bacteria to humans. However, the dogma does not hold for a type of virus known as a **retrovirus.** In a retrovirus, RNA is the genetic material. When a retrovirus enters a host cell, a single-stranded DNA copy of the RNA is made. The host then adds a complementary strand of DNA to make double-stranded DNA, which directs protein synthesis. HIV is a retrovirus.

▼ Teach *continued*

ONLINE BIOLOGY Go to the chapter Resource Center at **ClassZone.com** for additional resources and information on RNA.

The Inside Story

According to **Francis Crick,** in his book *What Mad Pursuit,* it was he who came up with the term **central dogma** to describe the sequence DNA-to-RNA-to-protein. He thought that *dogma,* rather than *hypothesis,* was more appropriate for a powerful new idea that could act as a guide in directing further research. Not everyone was happy with his choice of terminology, because a dogma is a belief that cannot be doubted. It is in the nature of science to foster doubt, not suppress it. From Crick's point of view, he was thinking of the central dogma as an organizing principle, which if demonstrated to be false, could be replaced by another.

Vocabulary

Academic Vocabulary The word **dogma** is not really a comfortable fit for the world of science.

dogma, an authoritative principle, belief, or statement of ideas or opinion, especially one considered to be absolutely true

theory, a set of statements or principles devised to explain a group of facts or phenomena, especially one that has been repeatedly tested or is widely accepted and can be used to make predictions about natural phenomena

Answers

A Contrast DNA and RNA have different sugar molecules. Also, DNA is typically double-stranded and is made up of nucleotides with bases C, G, A, and T. RNA is single-stranded and is made up of nucleotides with bases C, G, A, and U.

B Analyze DNA is located in the nucleus of eukaryotes, so processes involving DNA, such as transcription, must occur there as well.

***Connecting* CONCEPTS**

DNA Structure As you learned in **Section 8.2**, nucleotides are made of a phosphate group, a sugar, and a nitrogen-containing base. In DNA, the four bases are adenine, cytosine, guanine, and thymine. In RNA, uracil (below) replaces thymine and pairs with adenine.

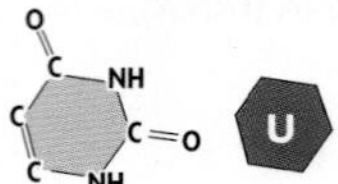

RNA differs from DNA in three significant ways. First, the sugar in RNA is ribose, which has one additional oxygen atom not present in DNA's sugar (deoxyribose). Second, RNA has the base uracil in place of thymine. Uracil, like thymine, forms base pairs with adenine. Third, RNA is a single strand of nucleotides, in contrast to the double-stranded structure of DNA. This single-stranded structure allows some types of RNA to form complex three-dimensional shapes. As a result, some RNA molecules can catalyze reactions much as enzymes do.

A Contrast **How do DNA and RNA differ?**

MAIN IDEA

Transcription makes three types of RNA.

Transcription is the process of copying a sequence of DNA to produce a complementary strand of RNA. During the process of transcription, a gene—not an entire chromosome—is transferred into an RNA message. Just as replication is catalyzed by DNA polymerase, transcription is catalyzed by **RNA polymerases,** enzymes that bond nucleotides together in a chain to make a new RNA molecule. RNA polymerases are very large enzymes composed of many proteins that play a variety of roles in the transcription process. **FIGURE 8.11** shows the basic steps of transcription in eukaryotic cells.

VOCABULARY

The word *transcribe* means "to make a written copy of." *Transcription* is the process of transcribing. A *transcript* is the copy produced by transcription.

1. With the help of other proteins and DNA sequences, RNA polymerase recognizes the transcription start site of a gene. A large transcription complex consisting of RNA polymerase and other proteins assembles on the DNA strand and begins to unwind a segment of the DNA molecule, until the two strands separate from each other.
2. RNA polymerase, using only one strand of DNA as a template, strings together a complementary strand of RNA nucleotides. RNA base pairing follows the same rules as DNA base pairing, except that uracil, not thymine, pairs with adenine. The growing RNA strand hangs freely as it is transcribed, and the DNA helix zips back together.
3. Once the entire gene has been transcribed, the RNA strand detaches completely from the DNA. Exactly how RNA polymerase recognizes the end of a transcription unit is complicated. It varies with the type of RNA.

Transcription produces three major types of RNA molecules. Not all RNA molecules code for proteins, but most play a role in the translation process. Each type of RNA molecule has a unique function.

- **Messenger RNA (mRNA)** is an intermediate message that is translated to form a protein.
- **Ribosomal RNA (rRNA)** forms part of ribosomes, a cell's protein factories.
- **Transfer RNA (tRNA)** brings amino acids from the cytoplasm to a ribosome to help make the growing protein.

Remember that the RNA strand must be processed before it can exit the nucleus of a eukaryotic cell. This step occurs during or just after transcription. However, we will next examine translation and then return to processing.

B Analyze **Explain why transcription occurs in the nucleus of eukaryotes.**

Differentiated Instruction

ENGLISH LEARNERS

To understand the process of transcription, have students use a sequence diagram to detail the information provided on page 240 and in **FIGURE 8.11** on page 241. Help students use the information in the diagram to make statements about the relationships between the different parts of the process.

Biology Toolkit, Sequence Diagram, p. C38

PRE-AP

Have students read through the steps of transcription described on this page and shown in **FIGURE 8.11.** With their books closed, have them create a comic strip recounting the process. Suggest that students think of transcription as an assembly line in which molecules of RNA are manufactured by large transcription complexes. Suggest they use the dialogue balloon typically found in a comic strip to provide short summaries.

8.3 DNA Replication

KEY CONCEPT DNA replication copies the genetic information of a cell.

MAIN IDEAS
- Replication copies the genetic information.
- Proteins carry out the process of replication.
- Replication is fast and accurate.

VOCABULARY
replication, p. 235
DNA polymerase, p. 236

Review
base pairing rules, S phase

B.7.4 Explain the process by which a cell copies its DNA and identify factors that can damage DNA and cause changes in its nucleotide sequence.

Connect Do you know that some of your cells are dying right now? You may live to the ripe old age of 100, but most of your cells will have been replaced thousands of times before you blow out the candles on that birthday cake. Every time that cells divide to produce new cells, DNA must first be copied in a remarkable process of unzipping and zipping by enzymes and other proteins. The next few pages will take you through that process.

MAIN IDEA

Replication copies the genetic information.

One of the powerful features of the Watson and Crick model was that it suggested a way that DNA could be copied. In fact, Watson and Crick ended the journal article announcing their discovery with this sentence: "It has not escaped our notice that the specific pairing we have postulated immediately suggests a possible copying mechanism for the genetic material."

Recall that the bases that connect the strands of DNA will pair only in one way, according to the rules of base pairing. An A must bind with a T, and a C must bind with a G. If the base sequence of one strand of the DNA double helix is known, the sequence of the other strand is also known. Watson and Crick realized that a single DNA strand can serve as a template, or pattern, for a new strand. This process by which DNA is copied during the cell cycle is called **replication.**

Suppose all of your classmates took off their shoes, placed their left shoe in a line, and tossed their right shoe into a pile. You could easily pick out the right shoes from the pile and place them with the matching left shoes. The order of the shoes would be preserved. Similarly, a new strand of DNA can be synthesized when the other strand is a template to guide the process. Every time, the order of the bases is preserved, and DNA can be accurately replicated over and over again.

Replication assures that every cell has a complete set of identical genetic information. Recall that your DNA is divided into 46 chromosomes that are replicated during the S phase of the cell cycle. So your DNA is copied once in each round of the cell cycle. As a result, every cell has a complete set of DNA.

***Connecting* CONCEPTS**

Cell Biology In **Chapter 5** you learned that the cell cycle has four main stages. DNA is replicated during the S (synthesis) stage.

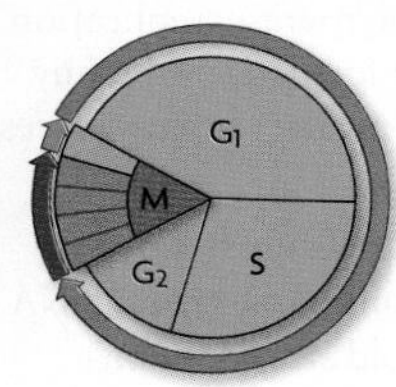

Plan and Prepare

Objectives
- Summarize the process of DNA replication.
- Describe the role of enzymes in DNA replication.

Section Resources

Unit Resource Book Study Guide pp. 69–70 Power Notes p. 71 Reinforcement p. 72
Interactive Reader Chapter 8 **Spanish Study Guide** pp. 77–78
Biology Toolkit pp. C17, C19, C24
Technology Power Presentation 8.3 Media Gallery DVD Online Quiz 8.3

Activate Prior Knowledge Make sure students understand the complementary nature of a template and what it produces. **Ask,** What are some everyday uses of a template? Word-processing templates give text a particular format; carpenters use templates to reproduce shapes; stencils provide openings to create specific shapes.

Teach

Vocabulary

Academic Vocabulary A **copy** is a **duplicate** of what already exists. A **template** forms a pattern that enables someone to make a copy; it is not the same as a copy. **Ask,** How is a DNA sequence used as a template? The sequence of bases in one strand is a template that reproduces the sequence of bases in the other strand. Point out that the sequence of bases makes a copy of the second strand.

Differentiated Instruction

ENGLISH LEARNERS

Have students divide into groups of three. Ask each group to summarize one of the three parts of the section. Encourage students to identify the main points and restate them in concise language. Then one or more students from each group can present the group summary to the class. You may wish to have each of the other groups write questions as they listen to the summaries and ask their questions following the presentations.

Biology Toolkit, Summarizing, p. C24

▼ Teach *continued*

Vocabulary

Academic Vocabulary Help students distinguish between the words **complement** and **compliment.**

complement = either of two parts that completes a whole

compliment = expression of praise

Point out that the word *complement* has as its root the word *complete.* To remember the meaning of *compliment,* students can use the mnemonic that both *praise* and *compliment* have the letter *i.* Tell students that the word *complimentary* can also refer to something freely given, as in a gift.

Take It Further

DNA polymerase adds nucleotides only to the 3′ end of a strand, so a new DNA strand can elongate only in a 5′ to 3′ direction. Along one template strand, a new strand is made in one continuous piece toward the Y-shaped junction of the strands. This new strand is called the **leading strand.** To make the second new strand, DNA polymerase must work along the other template strand in the direction away from the Y-shaped junction of the strands. This new strand of DNA is called the **lagging strand.** The process is similar to backstitching in sewing, and the new strand is made in short fragments. Another enzyme bonds these fragments together to form a continuous strand.

Answers

A Apply It doubles the amount of DNA so that both of the daughter cells resulting from mitosis have their own complete set of DNA.

B Infer Each strand of the DNA molecule dictates what the other strand must be according to the rules of base pairing. That is, because A bonds with T, and C with G, the nucleotides arrange themselves in a complementary pattern. Each replicated molecule consists of one original (template) strand and one new strand.

The fact that cells throughout the body have complete sets of DNA is very useful for forensic scientists. They can identify someone from nearly any cell in the body. A few cells from a drop of blood or from saliva on a cigarette butt are all detectives need to produce a DNA "fingerprint" of a criminal suspect.

A Apply How does replication ensure that cells have complete sets of DNA?

MAIN IDEA

Proteins carry out the process of replication.

Connecting CONCEPTS

Biochemistry You read in **Chapter 2** that many proteins are enzymes that function as catalysts. Enzymes decrease the activation energy and increase the rate of chemical reactions. DNA polymerase catalyzes the reaction that bonds two nucleotides together.

Although people may say that DNA copies itself, the DNA itself does nothing more than store information. Enzymes and other proteins do the actual work of replication. For example, some enzymes start the process by unzipping the double helix to separate the strands of DNA. Other proteins hold the strands apart while the strands serve as templates. Nucleotides that are floating free in the nucleus can then pair up with the nucleotides of the existing DNA strands. A group of enzymes called **DNA polymerases** (PAHL-uh-muh-rays) bond the new nucleotides together. When the process is finished, the result is two complete molecules of DNA, each exactly like the original double strand.

VISUAL VOCAB

DNA polymerases are enzymes that form bonds between nucleotides during replication.

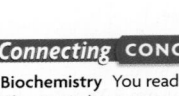

The ending *-ase* signals that this is an enzyme.

DNA polymer ase

This part of the name tells what the enzyme does—makes DNA polymers.

The Replication Process

The following information describes the process of DNA replication in eukaryotes, which is similar in prokaryotes. As you read, follow along with each step illustrated in **FIGURE 8.8.**

1. Enzymes begin to unzip the double helix at numerous places along the chromosome, called origins of replication. That is, the hydrogen bonds connecting base pairs are broken, the original molecule separates, and the bases on each strand are exposed. Unlike unzipping a jacket, this process proceeds in two directions at the same time.
2. Free-floating nucleotides pair, one by one, with the bases on the template strands as they are exposed. DNA polymerases bond the nucleotides together to form new strands that are complementary to each template strand. DNA replication occurs in a smooth, continuous way on one of the strands. Due to the chemical nature of DNA polymerase, replication of the other strand is more complex. It involves the formation of many small DNA segments that are joined together. This more complex process is not shown or described in detail here.
3. Two identical molecules of DNA result. Each new molecule has one strand from the original molecule and one new strand. As a result, DNA replication is called semiconservative because one old strand is conserved, and one complementary new strand is made.

TAKING NOTES

Use a cycle diagram to take notes about processes such as replication.

existing molecule → unzipping → nucleotides added → two DNA molecules formed → existing molecule

B Infer How does step 3 of replication show that DNA acts as a template?

Differentiated Instruction

BELOW LEVEL

Have students relate what they see in **FIGURE 8.8** on page 237 to **FIGURE 8.7** on page 233. Have them visualize the replication process. Tell students they can be creative and describe not just what they see but also what they hear and feel. Have them write continuously for five minutes.

Biology Toolkit, Connect to Content through Visuals and Quick-Write, pp. C17, C19

INCLUSION

Have students practice base pairing to reinforce the concept of complementary strands. Write base sequences on the board and have students produce the complementary strand. For students who are visually impaired, make a cardboard cutout of a single-stranded base sequence, using different-shaped notches for the bases. For example, A could have a V-shaped notch. T would then have a pointed tab that would fit into the notch to base pair. The nucleotides should be T-shaped, including a fragment of backbone as well as the base.

FIGURE 8.11 Transcription

Transcription produces an RNA molecule from a DNA template. Like DNA replication, this process takes place in the nucleus in eukaryotic cells and involves both DNA unwinding and nucleotide base pairing.

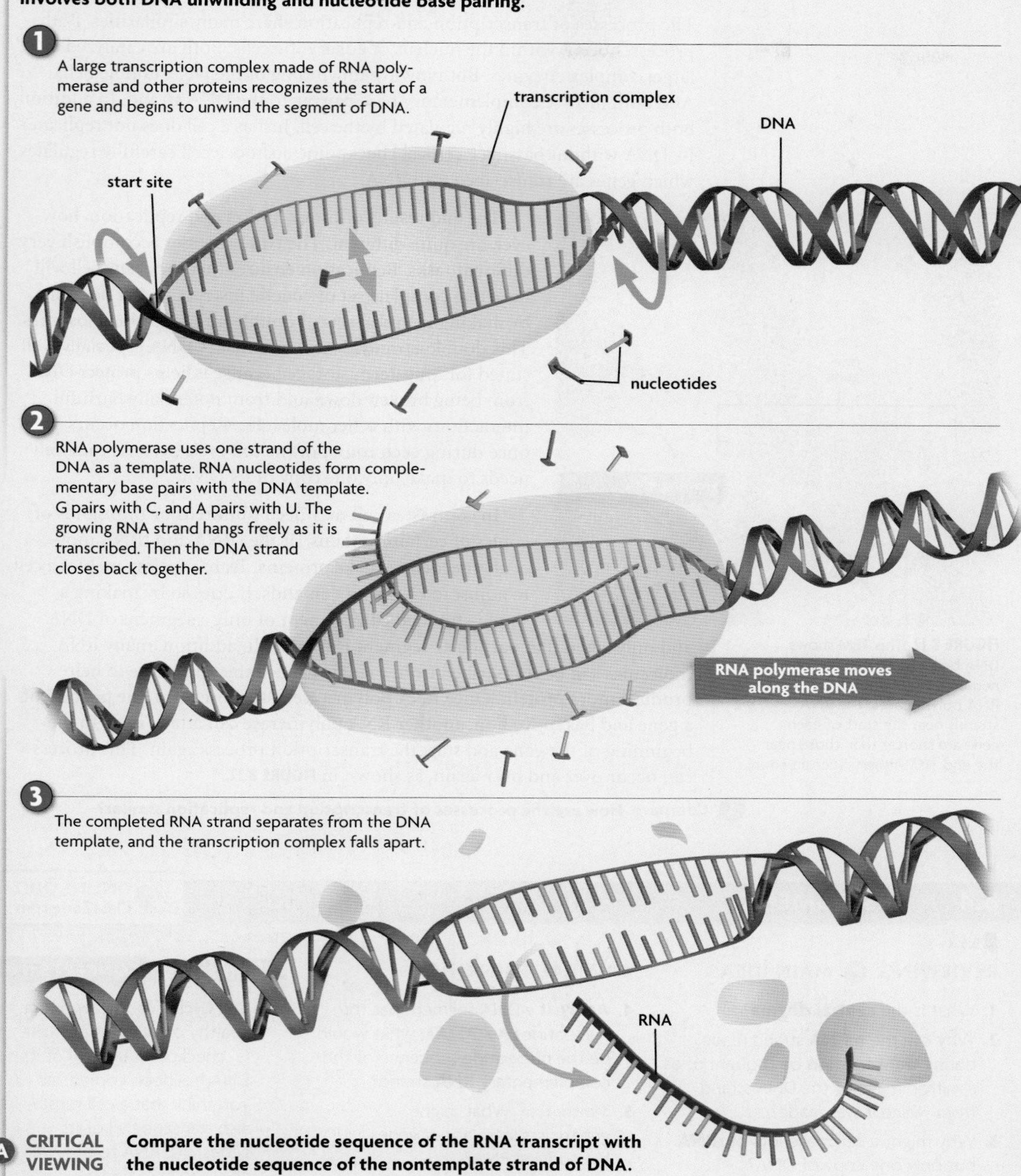

1
A large transcription complex made of RNA polymerase and other proteins recognizes the start of a gene and begins to unwind the segment of DNA.
transcription complex
DNA
start site
nucleotides
2
RNA polymerase uses one strand of the DNA as a template. RNA nucleotides form complementary base pairs with the DNA template. G pairs with C, and A pairs with U. The growing RNA strand hangs freely as it is transcribed. Then the DNA strand closes back together.
RNA polymerase moves along the DNA
3
The completed RNA strand separates from the DNA template, and the transcription complex falls apart.
RNA

A **CRITICAL VIEWING** **Compare the nucleotide sequence of the RNA transcript with the nucleotide sequence of the nontemplate strand of DNA.**

TEACH FROM VISUALS

FIGURE 8.11 Discuss each step in the figure separately. **Ask**

- Why must the DNA strands unwind and separate before transcription can take place? The bases must be exposed so that free nucleotides can pair with them.
- In step 2, how does the base sequence of the RNA transcript being formed compare with the sequence on the template strand? It is complementary.
- What happens to the double-stranded DNA as the RNA polymerase moves to the right, following the arrow? The DNA unwinds to expose more of the gene.
- What happens to the RNA transcript after it separates from the DNA in step 3? It is processed and leaves the nucleus.

Take It Further

Unlike DNA polymerase, **RNA polymerase** cannot proofread the transcript being formed. Consequently, transcription produces more errors than replication does. Because most genes are transcribed many times, a few defective copies of mRNA, and thus protein, usually cause no harmful effects. These errors are not transmitted to the next generation because they affect only the mRNA and protein sequences, not the DNA.

Answers

A Critical Viewing It is the same except that T is replaced by U.

HANDS-ON ACTIVITY

Use a video camera or digital camera to record the steps of transcription. Assign students to come to the front of the room, holding cards labeled with a base. Students should arrange themselves into double-stranded DNA with the correct base pairing. Assign other students holding cards to represent free RNA nucleotides. When the DNA strands unwind, the RNA nucleotides can base pair with the template strand of the DNA.

INCLUSION

Have students extend the mnemonic suggested on page 231. For example, "Don't you know, Acorns grow on Trees, but to Reproduce, Acorns must go Underground."

▼ Teach *continued*

TEACH FROM VISUALS

FIGURE 8.12 Have students notice the different sizes of the growing RNA transcripts. **Ask,** How can you tell where transcription of the genes begins? It will be that point where the mRNA strands are the shortest.

Answers

A Compare Both processes occur within the nucleus of eukaryotic cells, are catalyzed by complex enzymes, involve unwinding of the double helix, involve complementary base pairing to the DNA strand, and are highly regulated by the cell.

▼ Assess and Reteach

Assess Use the Online Quiz or Section Quiz (*Assessment Book,* p. 150).

Reteach Group students into pairs. Have one student in each pair write a ten-base-long DNA sequence and identify the template strand. Have the other student in the pair then write the RNA transcript that will be formed during transcription from that template.

MAIN IDEA

The transcription process is similar to replication.

The processes of transcription and replication share many similarities. Both processes occur within the nucleus of eukaryotic cells. Both are catalyzed by large, complex enzymes. Both involve unwinding of the DNA double helix. And both involve complementary base pairing to the DNA strand. In addition, both processes are highly regulated by the cell. Just as a cell does not replicate its DNA without passing a critical checkpoint, so, too, a cell carefully regulates which genes are transcribed into RNA.

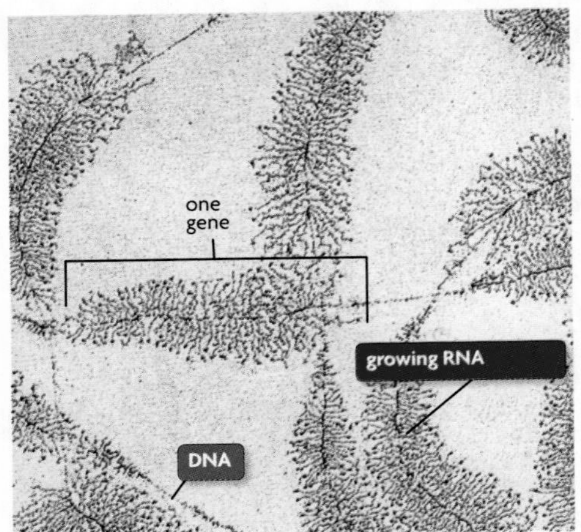

FIGURE 8.12 This TEM shows DNA being transcribed into numerous RNA strands by many RNA polymerases. The RNA strands near the start of each gene are shorter than those near the end. (TEM; magnification unknown)

The end results of transcription and replication, however, are quite different. The two processes accomplish very different tasks. Replication ensures that each new cell will have one complete set of genetic instructions. It does this by making identical sets of double-stranded chromosomes. This double-stranded structure makes DNA especially well suited for long-term storage because it helps protect DNA from being broken down and from potentially harmful interactions with other molecules. Replication occurs only once during each round of the cell cycle because each cell needs to make only one copy of its DNA.

In contrast, a cell may need hundreds or thousands of copies of certain proteins, or the rRNA and tRNA molecules needed to make proteins. Transcription enables a cell to adjust to changing demands. It does so by making a single-stranded complement of only a segment of DNA and only when that particular segment is needed. In addition, many RNA molecules can be transcribed from a single gene at the same time to help produce more protein. Once RNA polymerase has transcribed one portion of a gene and has moved on, another RNA polymerase can attach itself to the beginning of the gene and start the transcription process again. This process can occur over and over again, as shown in **FIGURE 8.12.**

A Compare How are the processes of transcription and replication similar?

8.4 ASSESSMENT

ONLINE QUIZ ClassZone.com

B.5.3

REVIEWING MAIN IDEAS

1. What is the **central dogma**?
2. Why can the **mRNA** strand made during **transcription** be thought of as a mirror image of the DNA strand from which it was made?
3. Why might a cell make lots of **rRNA** but only one copy of DNA?

CRITICAL THINKING

4. **Apply** If a DNA segment has the nucleotides AGCCTAA, what would be the nucleotide sequence of the complementary **RNA** strand?
5. **Synthesize** What might geneticists learn about genes by studying RNA?

***Connecting* CONCEPTS**

6. **Cell Cycle** You know that a healthy cell cannot pass the G_2 checkpoint until all of its DNA has been copied. Do you think that a cell must also transcribe all of its genes into RNA to pass this checkpoint? Explain.

8.4 ASSESSMENT

1. It is a statement that summarizes how information flows in one direction from DNA to RNA to proteins.
2. The mRNA chain is complementary to the DNA molecule. Like a mirror image, the mRNA chain has a distinct relationship to the DNA molecule, but is not identical to it.
3. rRNA is a component of ribosomes, and many ribosomes are needed to keep up with the level of protein synthesis needed by a cell. In contrast, each cell needs only one set of DNA, so it is copied only in preparation for cell division.
4. UCGGAUU
5. Because mRNA encode for only a single gene, studying mRNA can help researchers learn where genes begin and end on a chromosome. It could also indicate what genes are active in specific types of cells.
6. No, every cell has a complete set of DNA, but every cell does not need to use every gene. Therefore, only those genes that are needed by a cell are expressed, and the cell can still pass G_2.

8.5 Translation

KEY CONCEPT Translation converts an mRNA message into a polypeptide, or protein.

MAIN IDEAS
- Amino acids are coded by mRNA base sequences.
- Amino acids are linked to become a protein.

VOCABULARY
translation, p. 243
codon, p. 243
stop codon, p. 244
start codon, p. 244
anticodon, p. 245

Review
peptide bond

INDIANA STANDARDS

B.5.3 Describe the process by which DNA directs the production of protein within a cell.

Connect As you know, translation is a process that converts a message from one language into another. For example, English words can be translated into Spanish words, into Chinese characters, or into the hand shapes and gestures of sign language. Translation occurs in cells too. Cells translate an RNA message into amino acids, the building blocks of proteins. But unlike people who use many different languages, all cells use the same genetic code.

MAIN IDEA

Amino acids are coded by mRNA base sequences.

Translation is the process that converts, or translates, an mRNA message into a polypeptide. One or more polypeptides make up a protein. The "language" of nucleic acids uses four nucleotides—A, G, C, and T in DNA; or A, G, C, and U in RNA. The "language" of proteins, on the other hand, uses 20 amino acids. How can four nucleotides code for 20 amino acids? Just as letters are strung together in the English language to make words, nucleotides are strung together to code for amino acids.

***Connecting* CONCEPTS**

Biochemistry Recall from **Chapter 2** that amino acids are the building blocks of proteins. Although there are many types of amino acids, only the same 20 types make up the proteins of almost all organisms.

Triplet Code

Different words have different numbers of letters. In the genetic code, however, all of the "words," called codons, are made up of three letters. A **codon** is a three-nucleotide sequence that codes for an amino acid. Why is the genetic code read in units of three nucleotides? Well, we can't entirely answer that question, but consider the possibilities. If one nucleotide coded for one amino acid, RNA could code for only four amino acids. If two nucleotides coded for one amino acid, RNA could code for 16 (4^2) amino acids—still not enough. But if three nucleotides coded for one amino acid, RNA could code for 64 (4^3) amino acids, plenty to cover the 20 amino acids used to build proteins in the human body and most other organisms.

VISUAL VOCAB

A **codon** is a sequence of three nucleotides that codes for an amino acid.

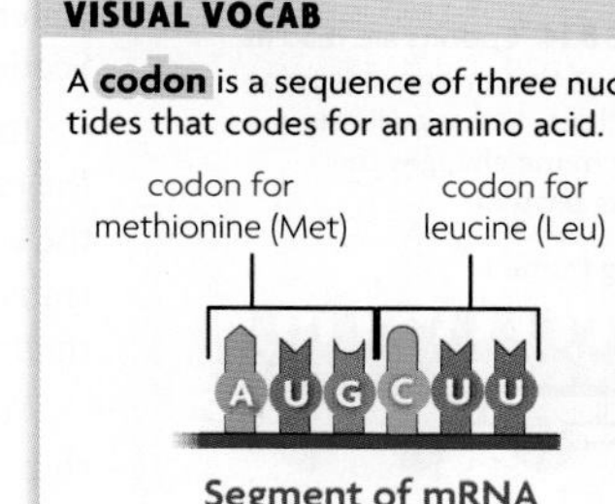

Differentiated Instruction

ENGLISH LEARNERS

Have students create a concept definition map for some key vocabulary from **Sections 8.3–8.5:** *replication, transcription,* and *translation.* Students should prepare a graphic organizer that starts with the word and its Category (what type of thing is it). From this, students should branch out boxes for its *Properties* (what is it like, what it does) and *Examples.* You may wish to include *Comparisons* (some other things like it).

Biology Toolkit, Concept Definition Map, p. D8

SECTION 8.5

Plan and Prepare

Objectives

- Describe how mRNA codons are translated into amino acids.
- Summarize the process of protein synthesis.

Section Resources

Unit Resource Book	
Study Guide	pp. 77–78
Power Notes	p. 79
Reinforcement	p. 80
Interactive Reader	Chapter 8
Spanish Study Guide	pp. 81–82
Biology Toolkit	pp. C19, C22, C38, D4, D8
Technology	
Power Presentation	8.5
Media Gallery DVD	
Online Quiz	8.5

Activate Prior Knowledge Discuss with students the nature of a code. Have them compare a coded message to a computer code. **Ask,** How are these codes the same, and how are they different? Both require translation of information. However, the coded message reproduces the same information, whereas computer code produces actions—operational commands. Tell students that the translation of RNA into protein is more like what happens with a computer code. The information encoded in nucleic acids becomes functioning proteins.

Teach

Vocabulary

Word Origins Tell students that **transcription** is not synonymous with **translation.** The root of *transcribe* is "to write," whereas the root of *translate* is "to transfer."

▼ Teach *continued*

TEACH FROM VISUALS

FIGURE 8.13 Go over the steps for reading the code. **Ask**

- What amino acid is coded by GGA? glycine by UGG? tryptophan by ACU, ACC, ACA, ACG? threonine
- What happens when a ribosome reads the codon AUG? produces methionine (which is also the start codon) UGA? Translation stops.

Addressing Misconceptions

Common Misconception Students may think there are only 20 different amino acids.

Correcting the Misconception Remind students that the structure of an amino acid consists of a central carbon atom bonded to an amino group (–NH_2), a carboxyl group (–COOH), a hydrogen atom (–H), and a side group. Draw the structure on the board. Tell students that an infinite number of side groups are possible, so there is an infinite number of amino acids. Only 20 are commonly found in proteins, however.

History of Science

In 1961, **Francis Crick** and a group of colleagues performed an ingenious series of experiments to demonstrate that the **genetic code** was a **triplet code,** consisting of three consecutive nucleotides. They used a chemical to delete one, two, and three nucleotides from the DNA of a bacteriophage and then looked at a gene "downstream" from the deletions to see if it was transcribed correctly. They found that when one or two nucleotides were deleted, the reading frame of the gene was shifted, and the downstream gene was misread. When three nucleotides were deleted, the downstream gene was read correctly. This also suggested that the reading of the code was continuous, without "punctuation" interrupting the reading.

Answers

Ⓐ **Apply** arginine (Arg)

FIGURE 8.13 Genetic Code: mRNA Codons

The genetic code matches each mRNA codon with its amino acid or function.

Suppose you want to determine which amino acid is encoded by the CAU codon.

1. Find the first base, C, in the left column.
2. Find the second base, A, in the top row. Find the box where these two intersect.
3. Find the third base, U, in the right column. CAU codes for histidine, abbreviated as His.

First base	Second base: U		Second base: C		Second base: A		Second base: G		Third base
U	UUU	phenylalanine (Phe)	UCU	serine (Ser)	UAU	tyrosine (Tyr)	UGU	cysteine (Cys)	U
U	UUC		UCC		UAC		UGC		C
U	UUA	leucine (Leu)	UCA		UAA	STOP	UGA	STOP	A
U	UUG		UCG		UAG	STOP	UGG	tryptophan (Trp)	G
C	CUU	leucine (Leu)	CCU	proline (Pro)	CAU	histidine (His)	CGU	arginine (Arg)	U
C	CUC		CCC		CAC		CGC		C
C	CUA		CCA		CAA	glutamine (Gln)	CGA		A
C	CUG		CCG		CAG		CGG		G
A	AUU	isoleucine (Ile)	ACU	threonine (Thr)	AAU	asparagine (Asn)	AGU	serine (Ser)	U
A	AUC		ACC		AAC		AGC		C
A	AUA		ACA		AAA	lysine (Lys)	AGA	arginine (Arg)	A
A	AUG	methionine (Met)	ACG		AAG		AGG		G
G	GUU	valine (Val)	GCU	alanine (Ala)	GAU	aspartic acid (Asp)	GGU	glycine (Gly)	U
G	GUC		GCC		GAC		GGC		C
G	GUA		GCA		GAA	glutamic acid (Glu)	GGA		A
G	GUG		GCG		GAG		GGG		G

Ⓐ **Apply** **Which amino acid would be encoded by the mRNA codon CGA?**

FIGURE 8.14 Codons are read as a series of three nonoverlapping nucleotides. A change in the reading frame changes the resulting protein.

Reading frame 1

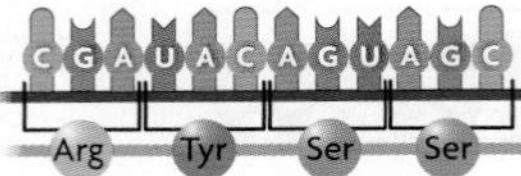

Reading frame 2

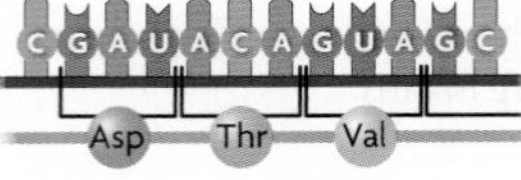

As you can see in **FIGURE 8.13,** many amino acids are coded for by more than one codon. The amino acid leucine, for example, is represented by six different codons: CUU, CUC, CUA, CUG, UUA, and UUG. There is a pattern to the codons. In most cases, codons that represent the same amino acid share the same first two nucleotides. For example, the four codons that code for alanine each begin with the nucleotides GC. Therefore, the first two nucleotides are generally the most important in coding for an amino acid. As you will learn in Section 8.7, this feature makes DNA more tolerant of many point mutations.

In addition to codons that code for amino acids, three **stop codons** signal the end of the amino acid chain. There is also one **start codon,** which signals the start of translation and the amino acid methionine. This means that translation always begins with methionine. However, in many cases, this methionine is removed later in the process.

For the mRNA code to be translated correctly, codons must be read in the right order. Codons are read, without spaces, as a series of three nonoverlapping nucleotides. This order is called the reading frame. Changing the reading frame completely changes the resulting protein. It may even keep a protein from being made if a stop codon turns up early in the translation process. Therefore, punctuation—such as a clear start codon—plays an important role in the genetic code. **FIGURE 8.14** shows how a change in reading frame changes

Differentiated Instruction

BELOW LEVEL

Group students into pairs to practice translating codons. One member of each pair should write a 15-base mRNA sequence starting with AUG. Remind students that RNA sequences do not contain T. The other member of each pair should use **FIGURE 8.13** to translate the sequence into amino acids.

PRE-AP

As mentioned in the text on page 244, most amino acids are coded by more than one codon, a feature called redundancy. Have students write for five minutes on this question: Why might redundancy in the genetic code be an advantage to a cell?

Biology Toolkit, Quick-Write, p. C19

the resulting protein. When the mRNA strand is read starting from the first nucleotide, the resulting protein includes the amino acids arginine, tyrosine, and two serines. When the strand is read starting from the second nucleotide, the resulting protein includes aspartic acid, threonine, and valine.

Common Language

The genetic code is shared by almost all organisms—and even viruses. That means, for example, that the codon UUU codes for phenylalanine when that codon occurs in an armadillo, a cactus, a yeast, or a human. With a few minor exceptions, almost all organisms follow this genetic code. As a result, the code is often called universal. The common nature of the genetic code suggests that almost all organisms arose from a common ancestor. It also means that scientists can insert a gene from one organism into another organism to make a functional protein.

A Calculate Suppose an mRNA molecule in the cytoplasm had 300 nucleotides. How many amino acids would be in the resulting protein?

MAIN IDEA

Amino acids are linked to become a protein.

Let's take a step back to look at where we are in the process of making proteins. You know mRNA is a short-lived molecule that carries instructions from DNA in the nucleus to the cytoplasm. And you know that this mRNA message is read in sets of three nucleotides, or codons. But how does a cell actually translate a codon into an amino acid? It uses two important tools: ribosomes and tRNA molecules, as illustrated in **FIGURE 8.15.**

Recall from Chapter 3 that ribosomes are the site of protein synthesis. Ribosomes are made of a combination of rRNA and proteins, and they catalyze the reaction that forms the bonds between amino acids. Ribosomes have a large and small subunit that fit together and pull the mRNA strand through. The small subunit holds onto the mRNA strand, and the large subunit holds onto the growing protein.

The tRNA acts as a sort of adaptor between mRNA and amino acids. You would need an adaptor to plug an appliance with a three-prong plug into an outlet with only two-prong openings. Similarly, cells need tRNA to carry free-floating amino acids from the cytoplasm to the ribosome. The tRNA molecules fold up in a characteristic L shape. One end of the L is attached to a specific amino acid. The other end of the L, called the anticodon, recognizes a specific codon. An **anticodon** is a set of three nucleotides that is complementary to an mRNA codon. For example, the anticodon CCC pairs with the mRNA codon GGG.

FIGURE 8.15 TRANSLATION MACHINERY

Ribosomes The large and small ribosomal subunits pull mRNA through the ribosome, reading it one codon at a time.

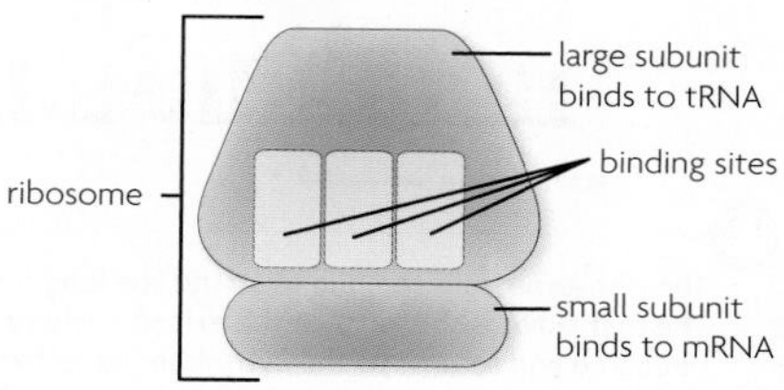

tRNA In cells, tRNA forms a characteristic L shape. One end of the L has an anticodon that recognizes an mRNA codon. The other end is attached to an amino acid.

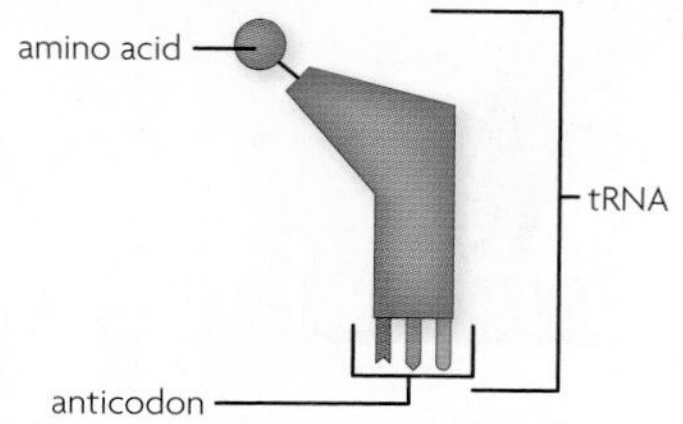

ENGLISH LEARNERS

Have students prepare word squares for *codon, stop codon, start codon,* and *anticodon.* Students' word squares should include the word and its translation, a symbol or picture, their own definition plus the Glossary definition, and a sentence using the word.

Biology Toolkit, Word Squares, p. D4

Vocabulary

Academic Vocabulary Students may find it odd to describe the genetic code as having the **punctuation** of stop and start codes. The Latin word *puctum* means "point," and is derived from an older form meaning "to pierce" or "puncture." Punctuation, in a general sense, signifies an interruption. The word *punctuate* can also be used to describe the act of placing stress or emphasis on a point.

Take It Further

Although most DNA is found in the nucleus, a small amount is located in mitochondria and chloroplasts. Scientists were shocked in the early 1980s when they determined the base sequences of **mitochondrial DNA** and found a somewhat different genetic code than in nuclear DNA. Since then, the genetic code of some protists, such as *Paramecium,* has been found to differ. Thus, the genetic code is not quite universal.

TEACH FROM VISUALS

FIGURE 8.15 Point out that the process of translation requires the transfer of information from one chemical form (nitrogen-containing bases) to another (amino acids); that is, from the language of nucleic acids to the language of proteins. The transition is facilitated by an intermediate—tRNA. In contrast, the language of complementary base pairing of nucleotides used to copy information in both replication (DNA to DNA) and transcription (DNA to RNA) occurs directly. The language does not change.

Answers

A Calculate 100

▼ Teach continued

ONLINE BIOLOGY Have students use a simulation to build a protein, starting with DNA. See Animated Biology in Options for Inquiry on page 257.

TEACH FROM VISUALS

FIGURE 8.16 Use the figure with the text on the following page to summarize the section. Point out the three binding sites in the ribosome and the complementarity of the codon and anticodon. **Ask**

- What is the function of mRNA? provides a copy of the genetic code
- What is the function of tRNA? brings amino acids to the ribosome, in the proper order
- What is the function of ribosomes? The ribosome positions mRNA so that it can be read by tRNA. It breaks the bonds between the tRNAs and their attached amino acids, and forms peptide bonds between amino acids, assembling the protein coded for in a gene.

Integrating Biochemistry

The end of a tRNA molecule opposite the anticodon binds to a specific amino acid with the help of the enzyme **aminoacyl tRNA synthetase.** There are 20 kinds of these enzymes in a cell, one for each kind of amino acid. Each enzyme ensures that the correct amino acid is attached to a tRNA having the anticodon corresponding to that amino acid. The enzymes have two specific binding sites, one for a particular amino acid and the other for a particular tRNA. This specificity is sometimes referred to as the second DNA code.

Answers

Ⓐ Critical Viewing Students' sketches should look very similar to panels 1–3 in Figure 8.16. Amino acid 3 should be bonded to amino acid 2, and the bond between amino acid 2 and tRNA 2 broken. Then tRNA 2 will move to the next position, where it exits. This places tRNA 3 in the middle position and leaves the first position open for tRNA 4 to come in and bond. Amino acid 4 should be bonded to amino acid 3.

FIGURE 8.16 Translation

Translation converts an mRNA transcript into a polypeptide. The process consists of three repeating steps.

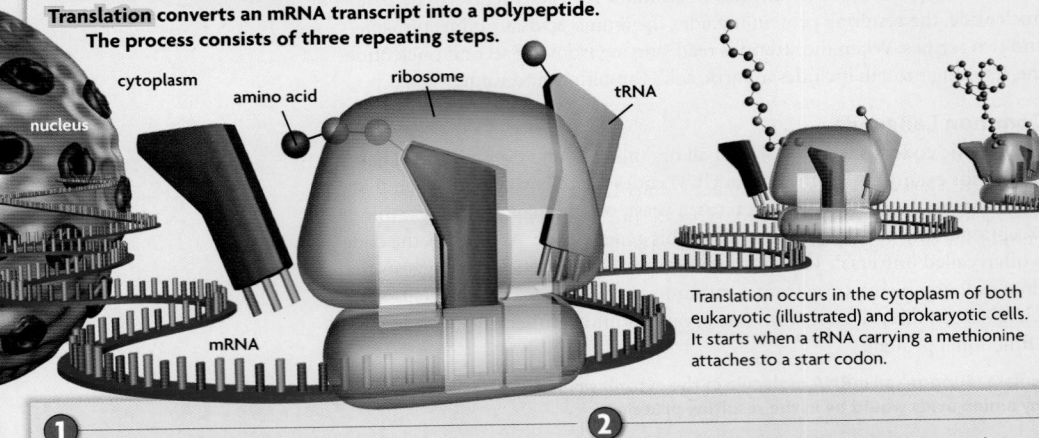

Translation occurs in the cytoplasm of both eukaryotic (illustrated) and prokaryotic cells. It starts when a tRNA carrying a methionine attaches to a start codon.

1 The exposed codon in the first site attracts a complementary tRNA bearing an amino acid. The tRNA anticodon pairs with the mRNA codon, bringing it very close to the other tRNA molecule.

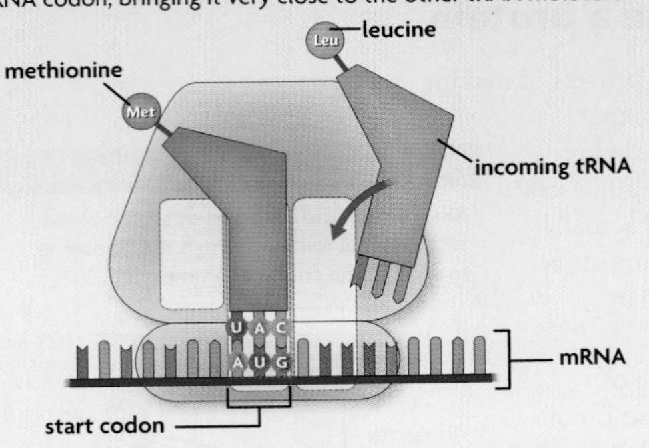

2 The ribosome forms a peptide bond between the two amino acids and breaks the bond between the first tRNA and its amino acid.

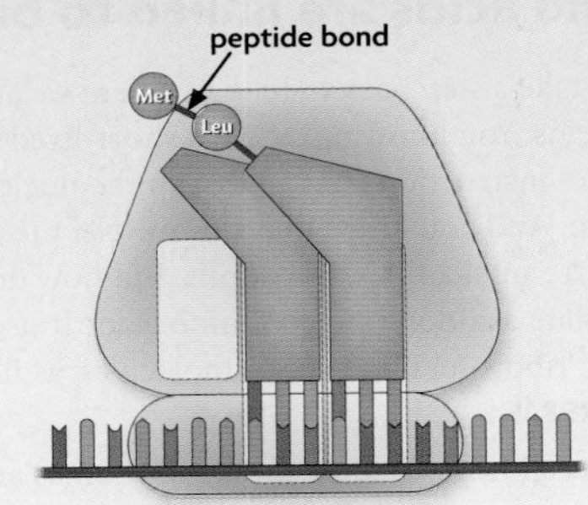

3 The ribosome pulls the mRNA strand the length of one codon. The first tRNA is shifted into the exit site, where it leaves the ribosome and returns to the cytoplasm to recharge. The first site is again empty, exposing the next mRNA codon.

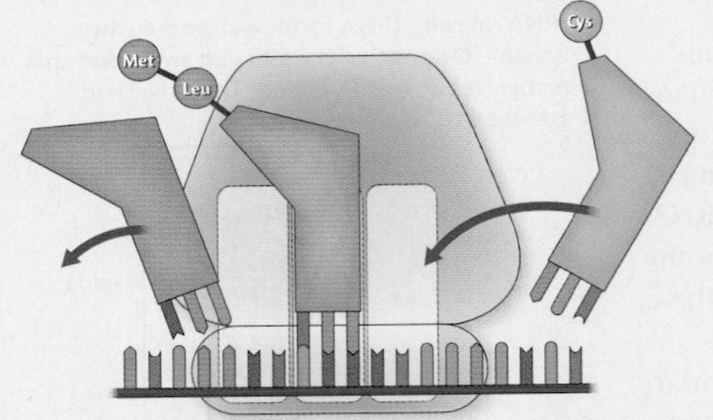

The ribosome continues to translate the mRNA strand until it reaches a stop codon. Then it releases the new protein and disassembles.

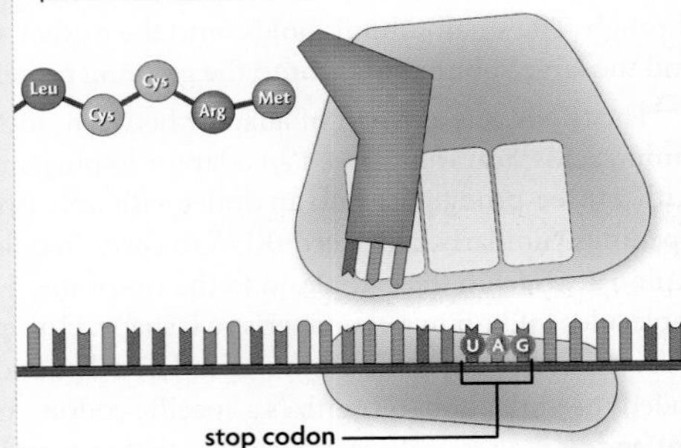

Ⓐ **CRITICAL VIEWING** **The figure above shows how the first two amino acids are added to a growing protein. Draw a series of sketches to show how the next two amino acids are added.**

Differentiated Instruction

BELOW LEVEL

Have students make a flow chart sequencing the events of translation. Suggest that they include drawings.

Biology Toolkit, Sequence Diagram, p. C38

PRE-AP

Have students make a four-column table comparing mRNA, rRNA, and tRNA. They should list the three kinds of RNA in the first column. The second column should indicate where each is found during translation. The third column should give the function of each. Finally, students should write in the fourth column how the molecule's structure makes it suitable for its function.

Biology Toolkit, Content Frame, p. C22

Translation, shown in **FIGURE 8.16**, has many steps and takes a lot of energy from a cell. It happens in the cytoplasm of both prokaryotic and eukaryotic cells. Before translation can begin, a small ribosomal subunit must bind to an mRNA strand in the cytoplasm. Next, a tRNA with methionine attached binds to the AUG start codon. This binding signals a large ribosomal subunit—which has three binding sites for tRNA molecules—to join. The ribosome pulls the mRNA strand through itself one codon at a time. As the strand moves, the start codon and its complementary tRNA molecule shift into the second site inside the large subunit. This shift leaves the first site empty, which exposes the next mRNA codon. The illustration shows the process in one ribosome, but in a cell many ribosomes may translate the same gene at the same time.

1. The exposed codon attracts a complementary tRNA molecule bearing an amino acid. The tRNA anticodon pairs with the mRNA codon. This action brings the new tRNA molecule very close to the tRNA molecule occupying the second site.
2. Next, the ribosome helps form a peptide bond between the two amino acids. The ribosome then breaks the bond between the tRNA molecule in the second site and its amino acid.
3. The ribosome pulls the mRNA strand the length of one codon. The tRNA molecule in the second site is shifted into the third site, which is the exit site. The tRNA leaves the ribosome and returns to the cytoplasm to be charged with another amino acid. The tRNA molecule that was in the first site shifts into the second site. The first site is again empty, exposing the next mRNA codon.

Another complementary tRNA molecule is attracted to the exposed mRNA codon, and the process continues. The ribosome moves down the mRNA strand, attaching new amino acids to the growing protein, until it reaches a stop codon. Then it lets go of the new protein and falls apart.

NSTA SCILINKS scilinks.org
To learn more about protein synthesis, visit scilink.org.
Keycode: MLB008

A Summarize **Explain the different roles of the large and small ribosomal subunits.**

Integrating Biochemistry

An rRNA molecule in the large subunit of the ribosome catalyzes the formation of peptide bonds between amino acids. In this role, it acts as an enzyme. This type of molecule is called a ribozyme.

Answers

A Summarize The small subunit holds onto the mRNA transcript. The large subunit has three sites where the tRNA molecules can dock; it helps form the peptide bond between the amino acids and helps break the bond between the amino acid and its carrier tRNA molecule.

8.5 ASSESSMENT

ONLINE QUIZ ClassZone.com

B.5.3

REVIEWING MAIN IDEAS

1. Explain the connection between a **codon** and an amino acid.
2. Briefly describe how the process of **translation** is started.

CRITICAL THINKING

3. **Synthesize** Suppose a tRNA molecule had the **anticodon** AGU. What amino acid would it carry?
4. **Hypothesize** The DNA of eukaryotic cells has many copies of genes that code for rRNA molecules. Suggest a hypothesis to explain why a cell needs so many copies of these genes.

Connecting CONCEPTS

5. **Biochemical Reactions** Enzymes have shapes that allow them to bind to a substrate. Some types of RNA also form specific three-dimensional shapes. Why do you think RNA, but not DNA, catalyzes biochemical reactions?

Assess and Reteach

Assess Use the Online Quiz or Section Quiz (*Assessment Book,* p. 151).

Reteach Write on the board a DNA sequence three bases long and tell students that it comes from the template strand. (Make sure not to write ATT, ATC, or ACT, as they all code for stop codons.) Have students determine the mRNA codon transcribed from this triplet, the sequence of the tRNA anticodon, and the amino acid that is translated.

8.5 ASSESSMENT

1. A codon is a sequence of three nucleotides that specifies a particular amino acid. Students may describe the physical connection between these two as the tRNA molecule. Each tRNA molecule binds to a specific amino acid and has an anticodon that binds to a specific codon.
2. The small ribosomal subunit binds to the mRNA strand at the start codon, which binds the first tRNA molecule. This complex signals the large ribosomal subunit to bind, forming a functional ribosome, which can then continue accepting tRNA molecules and forming bonds between amino acids.
3. That tRNA molecule would recognize the mRNA codon UCA, so it would carry the amino acid serine.
4. rRNA is critical for making ribosomes to carry out protein synthesis. rRNA must be made in sufficient quantities to keep up with a cell's demands for various proteins.
5. DNA is usually in double-stranded form, wrapped up and condensed to make it compact, not in a catalytic form. In contrast, hydrogen bonds can form between the nucleotides of a single strand of RNA, causing it to form a catalytic structure.

SECTION 8.6

▼ Plan and Prepare

Objectives

- Describe how prokaryotes turn genes on and off.
- Explain how gene expression is regulated in eukaryotic cells.

Section Resources

Unit Resource Book
Study Guide pp. 81–82
Power Notes p. 83
Reinforcement p. 84

Interactive Reader Chapter 8
Spanish Study Guide pp. 83–84

Biology Toolkit pp. C13, C19, C32

Technology
Power Presentation 8.6
Media Gallery DVD
Online Quiz 8.6

Activate Prior Knowledge Tell students that humans have an estimated 20,000 to 25,000 genes. **Ask,** Why wouldn't you expect all these genes to be transcribed and translated at the same time? The cell would run out of energy and raw materials (amino acids and nucleotides). Proteins would accumulate in the cell if they were not needed. **Ask,** What might be an analogy to this in your own life? eating all the food in the house at one time, everyone in class speaking at once, spending savings all at once

8.6 Gene Expression and Regulation

KEY CONCEPT Gene expression is carefully regulated in both prokaryotic and eukaryotic cells.

MAIN IDEAS
- Prokaryotic cells turn genes on and off by controlling transcription.
- Eukaryotic cells regulate gene expression at many points.

VOCABULARY
promoter, p. 248
operon, p. 248
exon, p. 251
intron, p. 251

B.6.2 Understand that most cells of a multicellular organism contain the same genes, but develop from a single cell (e.g., a fertilized egg) in different ways due to differential gene expression.

Connect Ours is a world of marvels. So many, in fact, that we may overlook what seem like little ones, such as plumbing. The turn of a handle sends clean water to your sink or shower. One twist and the water trickles out; two twists and it gushes forth. Another turn of the handle and the water is off again. But think about the mess and waste that would result if you couldn't control its flow. In a similar way, your cells have ways to control gene expression. Depending on an organism's needs, a gene can make a lot of protein, a little protein, or none at all.

MAIN IDEA

Prokaryotic cells turn genes on and off by controlling transcription.

The regulation of gene expression allows prokaryotic cells, such as bacteria, to better respond to stimuli and to conserve energy and materials. In general, this regulation is simpler in prokaryotic cells than in eukaryotic cells, such as those that make up your body. DNA in a prokaryotic cell is in the cytoplasm. Transcription and translation can happen at the same time. As a result, gene expression in prokaryotic cells is mainly regulated at the start of transcription.

A gene includes more than just a protein-coding sequence. It may have many other nucleotide sequences that play a part in controlling its expression. The start of transcription is largely controlled by these sequences, including promoters and operators. A **promoter** is a DNA segment that allows a gene to be transcribed. It helps RNA polymerase find where a gene starts. An operator is a DNA segment that turns a gene "on" or "off." It interacts with proteins that increase the rate of transcription or block transcription from occurring.

VOCABULARY
The word *promote* comes from the Latin prefix *pro-*, meaning "forward," and the Latin word *movere,* meaning "to move."

Bacteria have much less DNA than do eukaryotes, and their genes tend to be organized into operons. An **operon** is a region of DNA that includes a promoter, an operator, and one or more structural genes that code for all the proteins needed to do a specific task. Typically, operons are found only in prokaryotes and roundworms. The *lac* operon was one of the earliest examples of gene regulation discovered in bacteria. It will serve as our example. The *lac* operon has three genes, which all code for enzymes that play a role in breaking down the sugar lactose. These genes are transcribed as a single mRNA transcript and are all under the control of a single promoter and

▼ Teach

Vocabulary

Academic Vocabulary The word **expression** has different applications, but most involve conveying a message or an idea in some form. In genetics, a gene that is expressed is one that is or has been transcribed and translated and thus produces an effect on an organism's phenotype.

Differentiated Instruction

ENGLISH LEARNERS

Have students use a Y diagram to compare and contrast gene expression and regulation in prokaryotic and eukaryotic cells. At the top of each arm of the Y, they should list the characteristics of each as they read. Once students have finished the section, they should move down to the stem of the Y and list all those characteristics shared by both types of cells.

Biology Toolkit, Y Diagram, p. C32

INCLUSION

Have students who are visually impaired work with a partner to go through the process of gene regulation and expression in prokaryotic and eukaryotic cells. Provide yarn, scissors, and construction paper so students can make physical representations of all the components. Have students consider this question: How will the DNA strand containing the genes differ from the RNA transcript?

Biology Toolkit, Think-Pair-Share, p. C13

operator. This means that although we're dealing with several genes, they act together as a unit.

The *lac* operon is turned on and off like a switch. When lactose is absent from the environment, the *lac* operon is switched off to prevent transcription of the *lac* genes and save the cell's resources. When lactose is present, the *lac* operon is switched on to allow transcription. How does this happen?

Bacteria have a protein that can bind specifically to the operator. When lactose is absent, this protein binds to the operator, which blocks RNA polymerase from transcribing the genes. Because the protein blocks—or represses—transcription, it is called a repressor protein.

Without lactose (switched off)

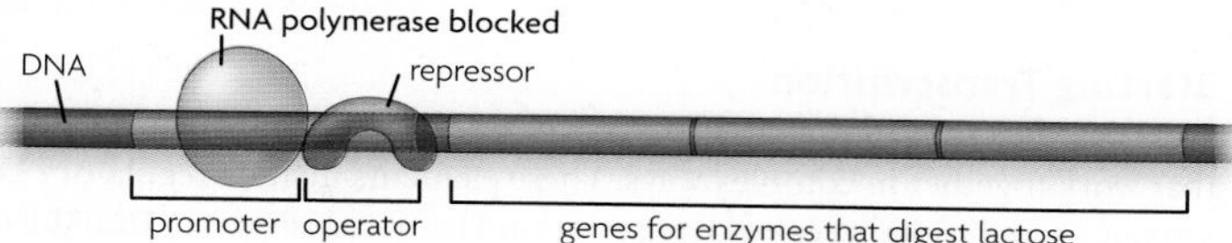

When lactose is present it binds to the repressor, which makes the repressor change shape and fall off the *lac* operon. RNA polymerase can then transcribe the genes in the *lac* operon. The resulting transcript is translated and forms three enzymes that work together to break down the lactose.

With lactose (switched on)

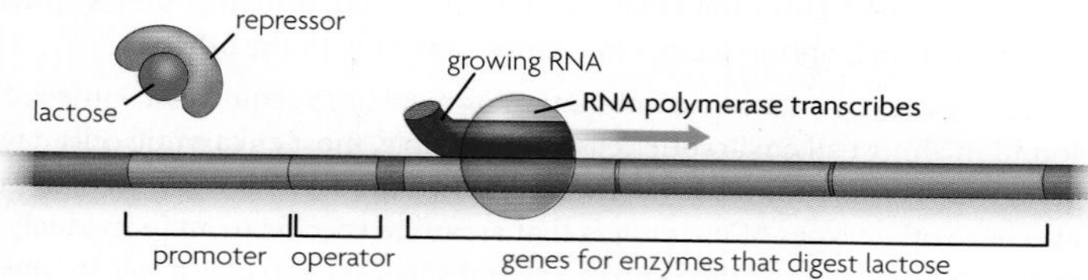

A Analyze Explain how the *lac* operon is turned on or off like a switch.

MAIN IDEA

Eukaryotic cells regulate gene expression at many points.

You have already learned that every body cell in an organism has the same set of DNA. But your cells are not all the same. Cells differ from each other because different sets of genes are expressed in different types of cells. Eukaryotic cells can control the process of gene expression at many different points because of their internal compartments and chromosomal organization. As in prokaryotic cells, however, one of the most highly regulated steps is the start of transcription. In both cell types, RNA processing is a part of the transcription process. In eukaryotic cells, however, RNA processing also includes the removal of extra nucleotide segments from an mRNA transcript.

PRE-AP

Have students write an operational definition of a prokaryotic operon. They should include all the parts that make up a switched-off operon in their definitions, such as promoter, operator, genes, and repressor.

Biology Toolkit, Quick-Write, p. C19

TEACH FROM VISUALS

Have students look at **FIGURE 8.11** on page 241 and compare it to the diagrams on page 249. Point out that the DNA strand is much simplified here; the bases are no longer shown. Point out that the color-coding for DNA (blue) and RNA (brown) has been carried over. **Ask**

- In the diagrams on this page, are you ... two? ... ies ... es that ... DNA ... vantage ... oes not ... es to ... is not

... sent, a ... peron ... m ... lactose is present, it binds to the repressor protein, which blocks the repressor from binding to the operon. RNA polymerase can then transcribe the genes ("on").

lactose binds to repressor to activate lac operon

Take It Further

Eukaryotic cells have several different ways to control **gene expression.** In addition to RNA processing, other points of regulation include the following:

- relative tightness or looseness of the chromatin structure
- RNA transport out of the nucleus
- stability of mRNA molecule
- initiation of translation
- protein processing, stability, and transport

For example, some mRNA molecules have sequences that label them for rapid breakdown; others remain in the cytoplasm much longer. Similarly, some proteins are rapidly degraded or are not fully active until they reach their site of action.

▼ Teach *continued*

ONLINE BIOLOGY The universal nature of the genetic code and its mechanisms of expression have made it possible for scientists to move a gene from one organism to another. Have students use the WebQuest to learn about transgenic organisms. See Options for Inquiry on page 257.

TEACH FROM VISUALS

FIGURE 8.17 Tell students that several regulatory sequences are clustered together in the DNA and that protein transcription factors bind to them. **Ask**

- What regulatory sequences are shown in the figure? TATA box, enhancer, promoter
- How do transcription factors function? They guide the RNA polymerase to the start of the gene.

Addressing Misconceptions

Common Misconception Students often think that every gene in a eukaryotic genome is expressed in every cell. Alternatively, they may think that a cell has only the genes that are needed for that type of cell.

Correcting the Misconception Explain that almost all cells in multicellular organisms contain the same full set of genes. Because the cells are specialized for particular functions, however, they have no use for most of the proteins coded by the genome. Thus, most of the genes they carry are not expressed. For example, a white blood cell has no use for digestive enzymes. If it made them, it would have wasted energy and raw materials in the process. Tell students that some genes code for proteins that are so specialized that those genes have never been expressed in most cells.

Answers

A Predict No, the DNA can bend, bringing an enhancer that is far away close to the start site of a gene.

FIGURE 8.17 Starting Transcription

Transcription factors that bind to promoters and other DNA sequences help RNA polymerase recognize the start of a gene in a eukaryotic cell.

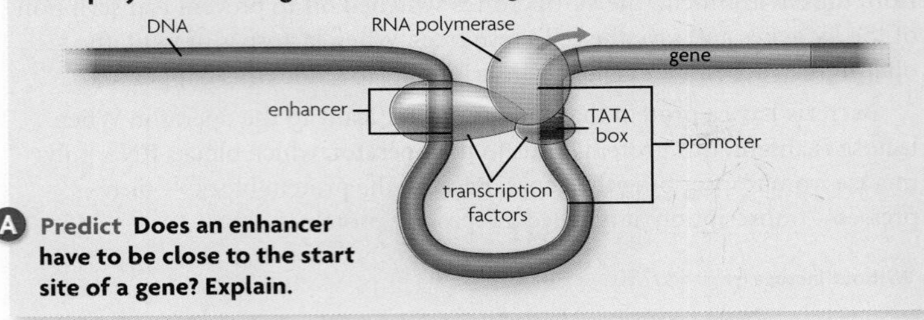

A Predict Does an enhancer have to be close to the start site of a gene? Explain.

Starting Transcription

The start of transcription in eukaryotic cells is controlled by many elements that work together in complex ways. These elements include regulatory DNA sequences and proteins called transcription factors, as shown in **FIGURE 8.17.** They occur in different combinations in different types of cells. The interplay between these elements results in specialized cells and cell responses.

Eukaryotes have many types of regulatory DNA sequences. These sequences are recognized by transcription factors that bind to the DNA strand and help RNA polymerase know where a gene starts. Some DNA sequences, such as promoters, are close to the start of a gene. Others are far away from the genes they affect. However, DNA can loop and bend, bringing these sequences with their transcription factors into close contact with the others.

Each gene has a unique combination of regulatory sequences. Some are found in almost all eukaryotic cells. For example, most eukaryotic cells have a seven-nucleotide promoter (TATAAAA) called the TATA box. Eukaryotic cells also have other types of promoters that are more specific to an individual gene. DNA sequences called enhancers and silencers also play a role by speeding up or slowing down, respectively, the rate of transcription of a gene.

Some genes control the expression of many other genes. Regulation of these genes is very important because they can have a large effect on development. One such gene codes for a protein called sonic hedgehog. This protein was first found in fruit flies, but many other organisms have very similar proteins that serve a similar function. Sonic hedgehog helps establish body pattern. When missing in fruit flies, the embryos are covered with little prickles and fail to form normal body segments.

Connecting CONCEPTS

Animals As you will learn in **Chapter 23**, most animals have homeobox genes. These genes are among the earliest that are expressed and play a key role in development. The illustration below shows the expression of homeobox genes in a fruitfly embryo.

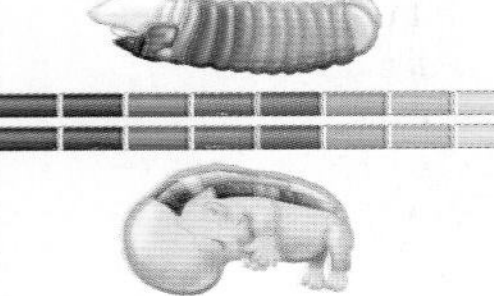

mRNA Processing

Another important part of gene regulation in eukaryotic cells is RNA processing, which is shown in **FIGURE 8.18.** The mRNA produced by transcription is similar to a rough cut of a film that needs a bit of editing. A specialized nucleotide is added to the beginning of each mRNA molecule, which forms a cap. It helps the mRNA strand bind to a ribosome and prevents the strand from being broken down too fast. The end of the mRNA molecule gets a string of A nucleotides, called the tail, that helps the mRNA molecule exit the nucleus.

Differentiated Instruction

BELOW LEVEL

Have students compare gene regulation in prokaryotes to gene regulation in eukaryotes. Ask students to write for five minutes on the question of what the advantage might be for a eukaryotic organism to have such a complicated system of gene regulation. Have them think in terms of a unicellular organism versus a multicellular one, as well as the relative number of genes in each.

Biology Toolkit, Quick-Write, p. C19

FIGURE 8.18 mRNA Processing

An mRNA molecule typically undergoes processing during or immediately after DNA transcription.

In eukaryotic cells, DNA contains noncoding stretches called introns and coding stretches called exons.

DNA
intron exon intron exon intron exon
gene

Protein-coding DNA is transcribed into mRNA.

mRNA
exon intron exon intron exon

mRNA goes through three major processing steps: the removal of introns and the addition of a cap and tail.

mRNA
cap
tail

The exons are spliced together, and the mRNA molecule enters the cytoplasm, where it can be translated.

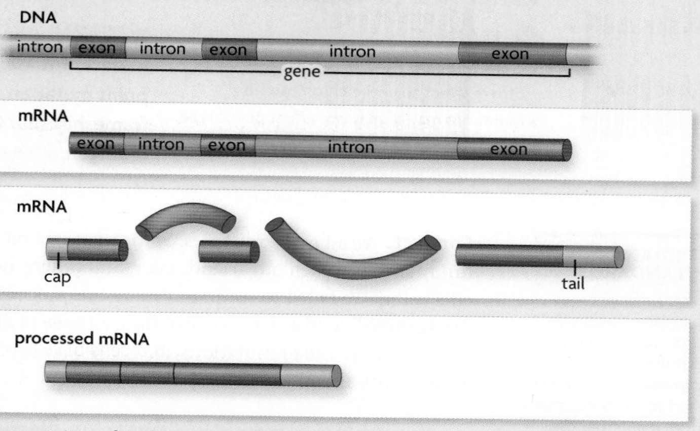

processed mRNA

A Connect Where does mRNA processing take place in a eukaryotic cell?

The "extra footage" takes the form of nucleotide segments that are not included in the final protein. In eukaryotes, **exons** are nucleotide segments that code for parts of the protein. **Introns** are nucleotide segments that intervene, or occur, between exons. Almost no prokaryotes have introns. Introns are removed from mRNA before it leaves the nucleus. The cut ends of the exons are then joined together by a variety of molecular mechanisms.

The role of introns is not clear. They may regulate gene expression. Or they may protect DNA against harmful mutations. That is, if large regions of DNA are noncoding "junk," then mutations occurring in those regions will have no effect. Some mRNA strands can be cut at various points, resulting in different proteins. As a result, introns increase genetic diversity without increasing the size of the genome.

B Apply Which parts of a gene are expressed as protein: introns or exons?

8.6 ASSESSMENT

B.6.2

REVIEWING MAIN IDEAS

1. What is a **promoter**?
2. In eukaryotic cells, genes each have a specific combination of regulatory DNA sequences. How do these combinations help cells carry out specialized jobs?

CRITICAL THINKING

3. **Predict** Suppose a bacterium had a mutated repressor protein that could not bind to the *lac* operator. How might this affect regulation of the **operon**?
4. **Summarize** What are the three major steps involved in mRNA processing?

Connecti

5. **DNA** DNA is loosely organized in areas where RNA polymerase is transcribing genes. What might you infer about a region of DNA that was loosely organized in muscle cells but tightly coiled in lung cells?

Vocabulary

intron, exon Given the prefixes *in-* and *ex-*, students may automatically think of introns as those portions of the genetic code left in and extrons as those portions taken out. Tell students that geneticists think of genes with extra noncoding nucleotides as **interrupted genes.** Thus, the segments that do the interrupting are referred to as introns. Tell students to think of them as sequences that interrupt or interfere with the genetic message. Exons are sequences that exit the nucleus and are expressed.

s in the
tide
is and cut
are
roteins

h ▼

Assess Use the Online Quiz or Section Quiz (*Assessment Book*, p. 152).

Reteach Work with the class to prepare a concept map that details gene regulation in both prokaryotic and eukaryotic cells.

8.6 ASSESSMENT

1. a DNA sequence that allows a gene to be transcribed by helping RNA polymerase recognize the start of a gene
2. These combinations help a cell turn on only specific genes. Based on the different genes that are turned on or off, a cell has a unique set of proteins that enables it to carry out certain functions.
3. The operon could never be turned off. The genes would be continually transcribed.
4. addition of the cap, addition of the tail, and removal of introns with the splicing together of exons
5. The genes in that region of DNA must be used by muscle cells but not by lung cells.

SECTION 8.7

▼ Plan and Prepare

Objectives

- Distinguish between different types of mutations.
- Explain why mutations may or may not affect phenotype.
- List some factors that cause mutations.

Section Resources

Unit Resource Book Study Guide pp. 85–86 Power Notes p. 87 Reinforcement p. 88 Pre-AP Activity pp. 93–94
Interactive Reader Chapter 8 **Spanish Study Guide** pp. 85–86
Biology Toolkit pp. C13, C25
Technology Power Presentation 8.7 Media Gallery DVD Online Quiz 8.7

Activate Prior Knowledge Tell students that sometimes a small mistake can have a big effect. **Ask,** What happens if, in recording your grade, a teacher transposes the numbers of your 3.1 GPA? My B grade becomes an F. Tell students that in this section, they will learn about the effects of mistakes incorporated into the genetic code.

▼ Teach

Take It Further

Cystic fibrosis is caused by a defective CFTR protein, a channel protein in the cell membrane that transports chloride ions in and out of the cell. Although more than 1000 mutations have been found in the gene that encodes this protein, the most common one is a DNA deletion of a TTT sequence. When the defective DNA is transcribed, the mRNA lacks a UUU codon, and thus a phenylalanine is missing from position 508 of the 1480-amino-acid protein. Loss of this single amino acid causes the protein to fold incorrectly, and as a result, it cannot function.

8.7 Mutations

KEY CONCEPTS Mutations are changes in DNA that may or may not affect phenotype.

MAIN IDEAS

- Some mutations affect a single gene, while others affect an entire chromosome.
- Mutations may or may not affect phenotype.
- Mutations can be caused by several factors.

VOCABULARY

mutation, p. 252
point mutation, p. 252
frameshift mutation, p. 252
mutagen, p. 255

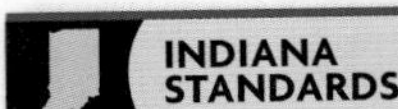

B.7.5 Explain and demonstrate how inserting, substituting or deleting segments of a DNA molecule can alter a gene, which is then passed to every cell that develops from it and that the results may be beneficial, harmful or have little or no effect on the organism.

Connect We all make mistakes. Some may be a bit embarrassing. Others become funny stories we tell our friends later. Still others, however, have far-reaching effects that we failed to see in our moment of decision. Cells make mistakes too. These mistakes, like our own, can have a range of effects. When they occur in DNA, they are called mutations, and cells have evolved a variety of methods for dealing with them.

MAIN IDEA

Some mutations affect a single gene, while others affect an entire chromosome.

You may already know the term *mutation* from popular culture, but it has a specific meaning in biology. A **mutation** is a change in the an organism's DNA. Many types of mutations can occur, as shown in **FIGURE 8.20.** Typically, mutations that affect a single gene happen during replication, whereas mutations that affect a group of genes or an entire chromosome happen during meiosis.

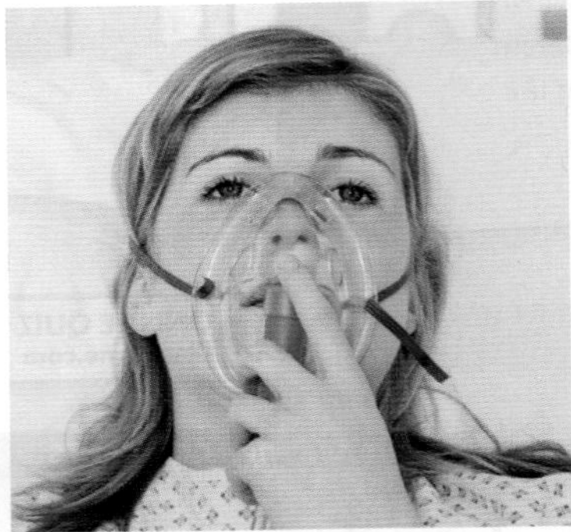

FIGURE 8.19 Cystic fibrosis (CF) is a genetic disease that is most commonly caused by a specific deletion. It causes the overproduction of thick, sticky mucus. Although CF cannot be cured, it is treated in a number of ways, including oxygen therapy (above).

Gene Mutations

A **point mutation** is a mutation in which one nucleotide is substituted for another. That is, an incorrect nucleotide is put in the place of the correct nucleotide. Very often, such a mistake is caught and fixed by DNA polymerase. If it is not, the substitution may permanently change an organism's DNA.

A **frameshift mutation** involves the insertion or deletion of a nucleotide in the DNA sequence. It usually affects a polypeptide much more than does a substitution. Frameshift mutations are so named because they shift the entire sequence following them by one or more nucleotides. To understand how this affects an mRNA strand, imagine a short sentence of three-letter "codons":

THE CAT ATE THE RAT

If the letter *E* is removed, or deleted, from the first "THE," all the letters that follow shift to the left. The sentence now reads:

THC ATA TET HER AT . . .

Differentiated Instruction

ENGLISH LEARNERS

Point out to students that an outline would be a good way to preview and summarize this section. Have students use the standard format: Roman numerals, capital letters, Arabic numerals, and lowercase letters organized under the section title. Remind students to use the same grammatical form for each level, for example, single words or sentences, and present tense verbs or infinitives. You may want to go over different students' outlines to discuss the decisions they made.

Biology Toolkit, Outline, p. C25

PRE-AP

Challenge students to answer and explain the following question: When does a deletion or an insertion not result in a frame shift? If three nucleotides—an entire codon—are either deleted or inserted, one amino acid will be affected, but a frame shift will not occur. Have students write the answer to the question, exchange papers with a partner, and discuss their responses.

Biology Toolkit, Think-Pair-Share, p. C13

FIGURE 8.20 Types of Mutations

A mutation is a change in an organism's DNA.

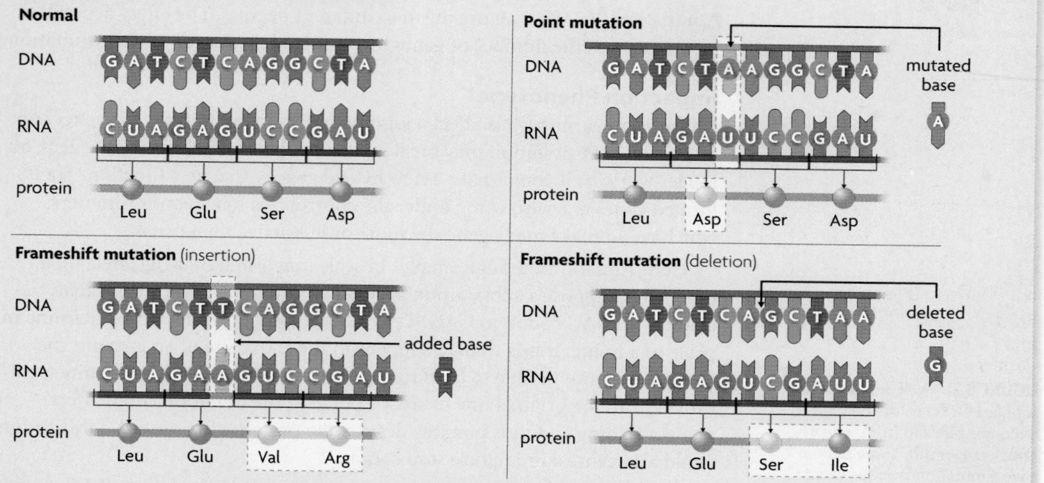

Normal

DNA GATCTCAGGCTA

RNA CUAGAGUCCGAU

protein Leu Glu Ser Asp

Point mutation

DNA GATCTAAGGCTA

RNA CUAGAUUCCGAU

protein Leu Asp Ser Asp

mutated base A

Frameshift mutation (insertion)

DNA GATCTTCAGGCTA

RNA CUAGAAGUCCGAU

added base T

protein Leu Glu Val Arg

Frameshift mutation (deletion)

DNA GATCTCAGCTAA

RNA CUAGAGUCGAUU

deleted base G

protein Leu Glu Ser Ile

A Evaluate Explain which mutation you think would have the greatest effect.

The sentence no longer makes sense. The same would be true if a nucleotide was added, or inserted, and all the letters shifted to the right. In the same way, a nucleotide sequence loses its meaning when an insertion or deletion shifts all the codons by one nucleotide. This change throws off the reading frame, which results in codons that code for different amino acids.

Chromosomal Mutations

Recall that during meiosis, homologous chromosomes exchange DNA segments through crossing over. If the chromosomes do not align with each other, these segments may be different in size. As a result, one chromosome may have two copies of a gene or genes, called gene duplication. The other chromosome may have no copy of the gene or genes. Gene duplication has happened again and again throughout eukaryotic evolution.

Translocation is another type of chromosomal mutation. In translocation, a piece of one chromosome moves to a nonhomologous chromosome. Translocations are often reciprocal, which means that the two nonhomologous chromosomes exchange segments with each other.

Gene duplication

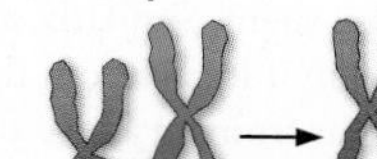

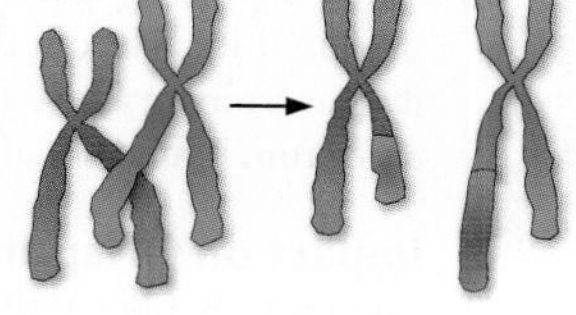

Gene translocation

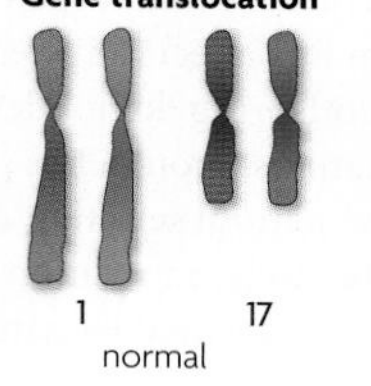

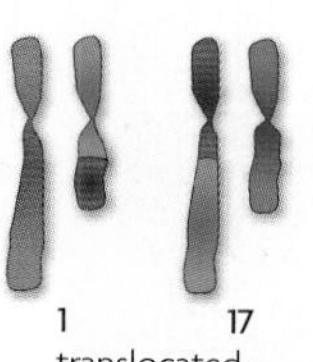

B Explain How does a frameshift mutation affect reading frame?

Vocabulary

Academic Vocabulary The word **frame** originates from a word in Old English that means "forward" or "to further." A **reading frame** is a point of departure, a **frame of reference.** The DNA code is a triplet code; the frame establishes which triplets are created. Have students consider three ways to frame this repeating sequence: CGACGACGA . . .

CGA CGA CGA CGA

GAC GAC GAC GAC

ACG ACG ACG ACG

TEACH FROM VISUALS

FIGURE 8.20 Have students study the details of each diagram. **Ask**

- Would a frameshift mutation have a greater effect if it occurred near the promoter or near the end of the gene? The promoter is located at the very beginning of the gene, so a frameshift mutation occurring there would affect the entire polypeptide. The same mutation occurring at the end of the gene would affect only the final few amino acids.
- Does a point mutation always change the amino acid sequence of the encoded polypeptide? No, if the codon with the substituted nucleotide coded for the same amino acid as the original codon, the amino acid sequence would not change.

Take It Further

Point out that **gene duplications** and **translocations** usually occur in germ cells during prophase I of meiosis. This is when homologous chromosomes pair tightly and cross over.

BELOW LEVEL

Refer students to **FIGURE 8.20.** Have them write a caption for each type of mutation shown, describing the mutation and its consequence.

HANDS-ON ACTIVITY

Provide plastic snap-together beads so students can make models of a pair of homologous chromosomes. The chromosomes should be of different colors if possible. If not, mark the beads on one chromosome with stickers or pieces of masking tape. Have students exchange segments between chromosomes to model gene duplication and translocation. After students have demonstrated these mutations, have them summarize how each kind of mutation occurs.

Answers

A Evaluate Many students may select one of the frameshift mutations as having the greatest effect because they are more likely to affect a greater number of codons.

B Explain The insertion or deletion of a nucleotide throws off the reading frame because genes are read as a series of three nonoverlapping nucleotides.

▼ Teach *continued*

ONLINE BIOLOGY Go to the chapter Resource Center at **ClassZone.com** for additional resources and information on mutations.

Integrating Evolution

Mutant alleles are not always removed from a population by **natural selection.** In the case of **heterozygote superiority,** a mutant allele persists because the heterozygote has an adaptive advantage. Neither of the alleles involved can be eliminated from a population because, in each generation, heterozygotes produce more offspring than homozygotes do.

For example, many p
sickle cell disease (ho
recessive) die before
duce, so they do not
recessive allele to the
However, people wh
for the gene have an
are less likely to cont
possibly because the
reproduce in their sic
cells. These people, w
the sickle cell trait, d
and they do not die
disease. When they r
50 percent chance th
transmit the recessiv
offspring.

Many gene mutations do not affect
Many codons code for same A.A.

Answers

A Apply because body cells are not passed from one generation to another

MAIN IDEA

Mutations may or may not affect phenotype.

A mutation can affect an organism to different degrees. The effect depends on factors such as the number of genes involved and the location of the mutation.

Impact on Phenotype

Chromosomal mutations affect a lot of genes and tend to have a big effect on an organism. A mutation may break up a gene, which could make the gene no longer work, or it could make a new hybrid gene with a new function. Translocated genes may also come under the control of a new set of promoters, which could make many genes be more or less active than usual.

Gene mutations, though smaller in scale, can also have a big effect on an organism. Suppose a substitution occurs in a coding region of DNA that changes an AAG codon to CAG. The resulting protein will have a glutamine in place of a lysine. If this change happens in the active site of an enzyme, the enzyme may not be able to bind to its substrate. If the substituted amino acid differs from the original one in size or polarity, the mutation could affect protein folding and thus possibly destroy the protein's function. A substitution could also cause a premature stop codon.

Even a mutation that occurs in a noncoding region can cause problems. For example, such a mutation could disrupt an mRNA splice site and prevent an intron from being removed. A mutation in a noncoding region could also interfere with the regulation of gene expression, keeping a protein from being produced or causing it to be produced all the time.

Many gene mutations, however, do not affect an organism's phenotype. Remember that many codons code for the same amino acid. Therefore, some substitutions have no effect, especially those occurring in the third nucleotide of a codon. If AAG changes to AAA, the resulting protein still has the correct amino acid, lysine. A mutation that does not affect the resulting protein is called silent. Similarly, an incorrect amino acid might have little effect on a protein if it has about the same size or polarity as the original amino acid or if it is far from an active site. If a mutation occurs in a noncoding region, such as an intron, it may not affect the encoded protein at all.

FIGURE 8.21 The coronary artery supplies blood to the heart. If it becomes blocked (top), a heart attack may result. Some people have a mutation that appears to help protect against coronary artery disease (bottom) by

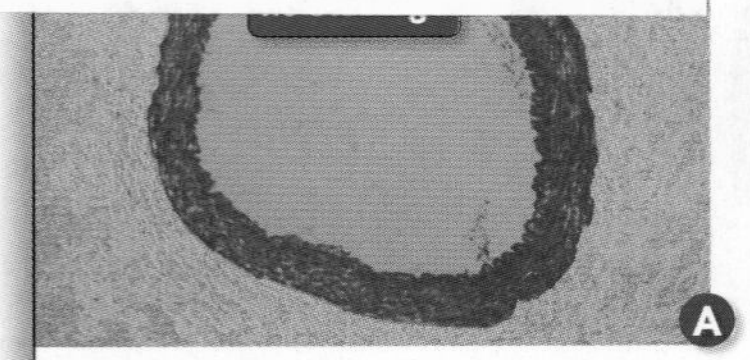

Impact on Offspring

Mutations happen both in body cells and in germ cells. Mutations in body cells affect only the organism in which they occur. In contrast, mutations in germ cells may be passed to offspring. They are the underlying source of genetic variation, which is the basis of natural selection. Mutations in the germ line affect the phenotype of offspring. Often, this effect is so harmful that offspring do not develop properly or die before they can reproduce. Other mutations, though less severe, still result in less adaptive phenotypes. In such cases, natural selection removes these mutant alleles from the population. More rarely, a mutation results in a more beneficial phenotype. These mutations are favored by natural selection and increase in a population.

A Apply **Why aren't mutations in body cells passed on to offspring?**

Differentiated Instruction

TEACH WITH TECHNOLOGY

Some biological supply companies sell kits containing root tips of onion plants that have been exposed to gamma radiation. The root tips are not radioactive and are safe for classroom use. Students can stain the root tips, prepare squashes, and observe mitosis. Chromosome breakage and rearrangements can be observed. In addition, a PC microscope can be used to transfer the images from the microscope to class computers.

MAIN IDEA

Mutations can be caused by several factors.

Mutations are not uncommon, and organisms have many tools to repair them. However, events and substances can make mutations happen faster than the body's repair system can handle.

Replication Errors

As you have learned, DNA polymerase has a built-in proofreading function. Nevertheless, a small number of replication errors are not fixed. They build up over time, and eventually affect how the cell works. For example, many studies suggest that mutations are a significant cause of aging.

Mutagens

Mutagens are agents in the environment that can change DNA. They speed up the rate of replication errors and, in some cases, even break DNA strands. Some mutagens occur naturally, such as ultraviolet (UV) rays in sunshine. Many others are industrial chemicals. Ecologists such as Rachel Carson, shown in **FIGURE 8.22**, warned the public about mutagens.

The human body has DNA repair enzymes that help find and fix mutations. For instance, UV light can cause neighboring thymine nucleotides to break their hydrogen bonds to adenine and bond with each other instead. Typically, one enzyme removes the bonded thymines, another replaces the damaged section, and a third bonds the new segment in place. Sometimes, these enzymes do not work. If these mistakes interfere with regulatory sites and control mechanisms, they may result in cancer. In rare cases, people inherit mutations that make their DNA repair systems less active, which makes these people very vulnerable to the damaging effects of sunlight.

Some cancer drugs take advantage of mutagenic properties by causing similar damage to cancer cells. One type wedges its way between nucleotides, causing so many mutations that cancer cells can no longer function.

FIGURE 8.22 Rachel Carson was one of the first ecologists to warn against the widespread use of pesticides and other potential mutagens and toxins.

(A) Summarize **Explain why mutagens can damage DNA in spite of repair enzymes.**

8.7 ASSESSMENT

ONLINE QUIZ ClassZone.com

B.7.5

REVIEWING MAIN IDEAS

1. Explain why **frameshift mutations** have a greater effect than do **point mutations.**
2. If GUA is changed to GUU, will the resulting protein be affected? Explain.
3. Explain how **mutagens** can cause genetic **mutations** in spite of your body's DNA repair enzymes.

CRITICAL THINKING

4. **Connect** Some genetic mutations are associated with increased risk for a particular disease. Tests exist for some of these genes. What might be the advantages and disadvantages of being tested?
5. **Infer** How could a mutated gene produce a shorter protein than that produced by the normal gene?

Connecting CONCEPTS

6. **Ecology** How might the presence of a chemical mutagen in the environment affect the genetic makeup and size of a population over time?

Vocabulary

Academic Vocabulary Point out the similarity in the words **mutagen, carcinogen,** and **allergen.** The root *gen* means "to give birth to." The word **agent** can be applied in the definition of each, as in the agent that causes mutation, cancer, or allergic reactions. The root for agent is not the same, however. *Agere* means "to do."

Answers

(A) **Summarize** The mutagens can induce more mutations than the repair enzymes can fix.

Assess and Reteach ▼

Assess Use the Online Quiz or Section Quiz (*Assessment Book,* p. 153).

Reteach Work with students to make a concept map summarizing the material in this section. Have them include the four vocabulary terms *mutation, point mutation, frameshift mutation,* and *mutagen,* as well as the terms *gene mutations, chromosomal mutations, gene duplication,* and *gene translocation.*

8.7 ASSESSMENT

1. Point mutations typically affect only one codon (unless they create a premature stop codon). A frameshift mutation affects all the codons in a gene that follow it.
2. No, both GUA and GUU code for the amino acid valine.
3. Mutagens may produce so much damage that the repair enzymes cannot keep up with the repairs.
4. *Sample Answer:* Advantage: would know to look for symptoms, would be able to prepare for possible treatment. Disadvantage: there may be no cure for the disease, or simply having the gene may not mean that getting the disease is inevitable.
5. A frameshift or a point mutation may have changed one of the codons to a stop codon.
6. Initially, the population would likely decrease due to disease. But over time, individuals that had a resistance to the mutagenic effect would be more likely to pass on that trait, and it would become more common in the population. Or, if the trait were advantageous to some, then the mutation might potentially become more prevalent than the original allele.

OPTIONS FOR INQUIRY

INVESTIGATION

Time 45 minutes	TEACHER TESTED
Teacher Preparation	
Student Difficulty	
Lab Binder Genetics, pp. 32–34	

Purpose Test various sunscreens for their ability to block UV rays.

Overview Students will design an experiment to test three sunscreens. They will

- use UV beads to test the effectiveness of three sunscreens
- identify variables and constants in their experiment
- identify sources of avoidable and unavoidable error

LAB MANAGEMENT

- Explain that UV beads have a solar-active pigment embedded in the plastic that changes color when exposed to UV radiation from the sun. They are not affected by artificial light.
- The solar-active pigment keeps the beads from discoloring permanently, so they can be reused after they change back to their original white color.
- Students can test each kind of sunscreen by coating a few beads with each sunscreen or placing beads in a self-sealing plastic bag and coating the bag with sunscreen.

POST-LAB DISCUSSION

Identify the independent and dependent variables in students' experiments. **Ask,** What other factors can you test by using UV beads? Students may suggest testing the effectiveness of sunglasses against UV or comparing the strength of UV rays at different altitudes.

Use these inquiry-based labs and online activities to deepen your understanding of DNA.

INDIANA STANDARDS

B.5.3 Describe the process by which DNA directs the production of protein within a cell.

B.7.4 Explain the process by which a cell copies its DNA and identify factors that can damage DNA and cause changes in its nucleotide sequence.

NOS.6 Use analogies and models (mathematical and physical) to simplify and represent systems that are difficult to understand or directly experience due to their size, time scale, or complexity, and recognize the limitations of analogies and models.

DESIGN YOUR OWN INVESTIGATION

UV Light and Skin Cancer

Exposure to the ultraviolet (UV) radiation in sunlight can lead to skin cancer caused by mutations in the DNA of skin cells. The most common type of damage from UV light is the formation of thymine dimers, or pairs of thymine bases bonded together. These mutations interfere with both replication and transcription. Sunscreens receive ratings based on the amount of protection from UV radiation they provide. The higher the sun protection factor (SPF), the more radiation the lotion blocks.

MATERIALS

- 3 different kinds of sunscreen
- sunlight or UV light box
- 12 UV beads

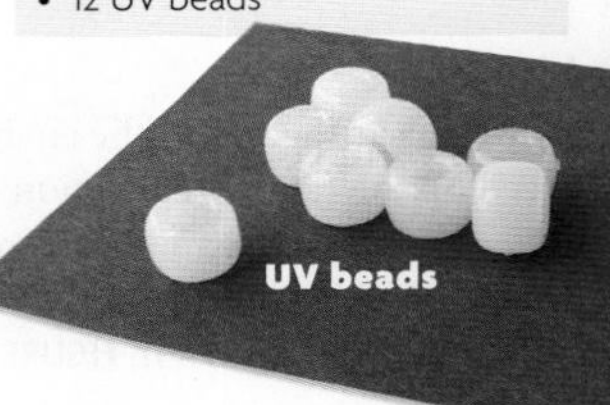

SKILLS Collecting Data, Defining Operational Variables

PROBLEM Which sunscreen blocks more UV rays?

PROCEDURE

1. Choose either three different brands of sunscreen or three samples of the same brand with different SPFs.
2. Design an experiment using the UV beads to test the effectiveness of each of the sunscreens. Remember to include a control group and multiple trials.
3. Identify the independent and dependent variables and any constants in your procedure.
4. Once your teacher has approved your experimental design, carry out your procedure. Record your results in a data table.

ANALYZE AND CONCLUDE

1. **Analyze** What can you conclude about the effectiveness of the sunscreens?
2. **Apply** Identify the operational definition of your variable in this experiment.
3. **Evaluate** What was the importance of having a control in this procedure?
4. **Experimental Design** Identify sources of unavoidable error and reasons for inconsistent results.

EXTEND YOUR INVESTIGATION

Exposure to high levels of UV radiation during the teenage years is a major risk factor for skin cancer, but the cancer itself generally does not develop until many years later. Use what you have learned about mutations to propose a reasonable explanation for why skin cancer usually appears later in life.

Answers

Sample Data

Go to page R102 for an example of student data.

Analyze and Conclude

1. Students may find that one brand is more effective than another or that a higher SPF rating provides more protection.
2. The operational definition of the dependent variable is the number of minutes needed for the UV beads to turn color in sunlight.
3. *Sample Answer:* establish that sunscreen itself does not affect the beads' color
4. A source of unavoidable error could be defective beads. Inconsistent results could be caused by outdated sunscreen, insufficient coating of beads with sunscreen, or some beads being shaded from direct sunlight.

Extend Your Investigation

Students may suggest that a cell must accumulate several mutations before cancer develops or that it takes many years for cancer cells to grow large enough to be detected.

INVESTIGATION

Modeling Transcription

During the process of transcription, a strand of mRNA that complements the base sequence on a strand of DNA is made.

SKILL Modeling

MATERIALS

- metric ruler
- 60 cm piece of wide ribbon
- scissors
- construction paper of 5 colors
- marker
- stapler

PROBLEM How can you model transcription?

PROCEDURE

1. Cut two pieces of ribbon, each about 30 cm long.
2. Choose five colors of construction paper to represent each of the bases in DNA and RNA.
3. Write out a sequence of 12 bases on a strand of DNA. Cut out corresponding squares of construction paper for each base. Use the marker to label each base.
4. Staple each base along the edge of one piece of ribbon so that they are an equal distance apart. This piece represents a single strand of DNA in the nucleus.
5. Write out the set of complementary bases that will make up the strand of mRNA. Cut out corresponding squares of construction paper for each base. Use the marker to label each base.
6. Staple each base in the correct order along the edge of the second piece of ribbon.

ANALYZE AND CONCLUDE

1. **Compare** How is your model similar to the process of transcription?
2. **Apply** Explain what happens when mRNA leaves the nucleus of a eukaryotic cell.
3. **Evaluate** How would you continue to model translation using the materials in this lab?
4. **Experimental Design** What are some limitations of the model you used in this lab?

Online BIOLOGY
CLASSZONE.COM

ANIMATED BIOLOGY
Build a Protein
Can you build a protein from a DNA code? Use enzymes, nucleotides, ribosomes, and transfer RNA to synthesize protein.

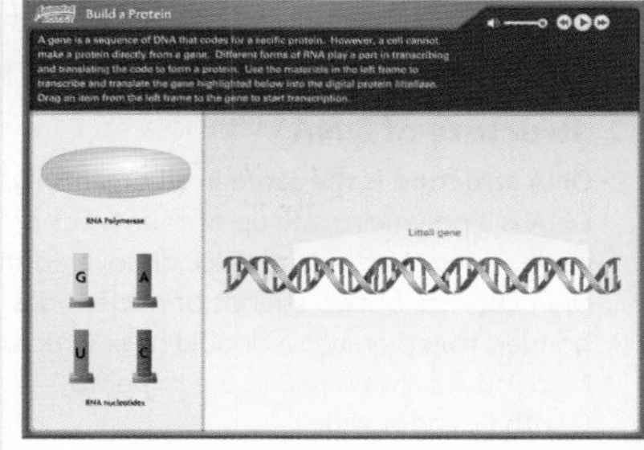

WEBQUEST
What do *Bt* corn and a fluorescent mouse have in common? They both produce proteins with genes from other organisms. In this WebQuest, you will learn more about transgenic organisms. Explore the potential benefits and risks involved when one organism is engineered to produce a protein from another organism.

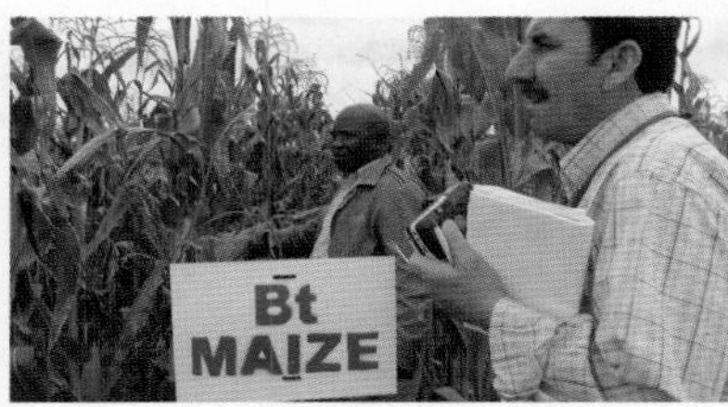

DATA ANALYSIS ONLINE
Erwin Chargaff showed that the proportion of certain base pairs always had a consistent relationship, although the amount of each might vary across species. This idea that A = T and C = G is known as Chargaff's rules. Graph the percentage of bases in four different species to put Chargaff's rules to the test.

Answers

Analyze and Conclude

1. The mRNA sequence is complementary to the DNA sequence.
2. After the mRNA is processed and leaves the nucleus, it moves to a ribosome. It is attached to rRNA and, with the help of tRNAs, is used to make a strand of polypeptide.
3. You could use construction paper to make models of amino acids. Using the genetic code, you could translate the mRNA into a polypeptide.
4. Replication usually takes place at many sites on the DNA. The model shows only one site. Also, regulatory genes and promoters are not shown in the model.

Online Biology ▼

ANIMATED BIOLOGY Use this interactive animation to reinforce the concepts of **Section 8.6.**

WEBQUEST The WebQuest takes one full class period. Students complete the activity online and will need access to a printer to print out their answers. Sample answers, teacher notes, and alternative assessment ideas are available on **ClassZone.com.** Use with **Section 8.1.**

DATA ANALYSIS ONLINE
Students will find that the percentages of bases in the DNA of the four species conform to Chargaff's rules: the same percentage of A as T; the same percentage of C as G. Use with **Section 8.2.**

INVESTIGATION TEACHER TESTED

Time	30 minutes
Teacher Preparation	1
Student Difficulty	1
Lab Binder	Genetics, pp. 35–36

Overview Students will make a model of a template strand of DNA and transcribe it onto mRNA having 12 nucleotides that are complementary to the DNA sequence.

POST-LAB DISCUSSION

Ask, Why did you need five colors of construction paper if DNA has four bases? A fifth base, uracil, takes the place of thymine in RNA.

CHAPTER REVIEW

Interactive Review

Encourage students to go to **ClassZone.com** for a detailed review of each section, including visuals and vocabulary practice.

Unit Resource Book, Vocabulary Practice, pp. 95–98

ITEM CORRELATIONS	
Standard	**Items**
B.2.4	18
B.5.1	10, 11, 30
B.5.3	15, 16, 26
B.7.4	12, 13, 14, 22, 31-33

CHAPTER 8 Interactive Review @ CLASSZONE.COM

KEY CONCEPTS | Vocabulary Games | Concept Maps | Animated Biology | Online Quiz

8.1 Identifying DNA as the Genetic Material

DNA was identified as the genetic material through a series of experiments. Griffith discovered a "transforming principle," which Avery later identified as DNA. Hershey and Chase's experiments with bacteriophages conclusively demonstrated that DNA is the genetic material.

8.2 Structure of DNA

DNA structure is the same in all organisms. DNA is a polymer made up of four types of nucleotides. Watson and Crick discovered that DNA consists of two strands of nucleotides bonded together into a double helix structure. Nucleotides always pair in the same way—C with G, and A with T.

8.3 DNA Replication

DNA replication copies the genetic information of a cell. During replication, a DNA molecule separates into two strands. Each strand serves as a template for building a new complementary strand through a rapid, accurate process involving DNA polymerase and other enzymes.

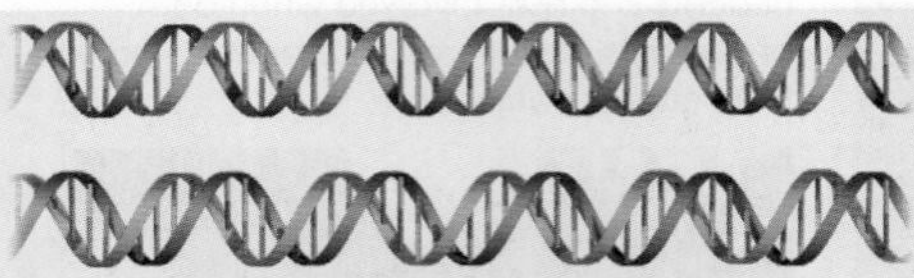

Two identical double-stranded DNA molecules result from replication.

8.4 Transcription

Transcription converts a gene into a single-stranded RNA molecule. The transcription process is similar to DNA replication and makes three types of RNA. Messenger RNA is an intermediate molecule that carries DNA's instructions to be translated.

8.5 Translation

Translation converts an mRNA message into a polypeptide, or protein. This process occurs on ribosomes, which are made of rRNA and proteins. Transfer RNA molecules bring amino acids to the growing protein by selectively pairing with mRNA codons.

8.6 Gene Expression and Regulation

Gene expression is carefully regulated in both prokaryotic and eukaryotic cells. In prokaryotes, transcription is the primary point of control. In eukaryotes, gene expression is controlled at many points, including RNA processing.

8.7 Mutations

Mutations are changes in DNA that may or may not affect phenotype. Some affect a single gene, and others affect an entire chromosome. Mutations may occur naturally, or they may be caused by mutagens. A mutation that does not affect phenotype is called silent. Mutations in sperm or egg cells can be passed to offspring.

Synthesize Your Notes

Summarize How can you summarize the process by which proteins are made? Use your notes to make a detailed version of the graphic organizer below. Include important details about the processes of transcription and translation. Mark important vocabulary terms.

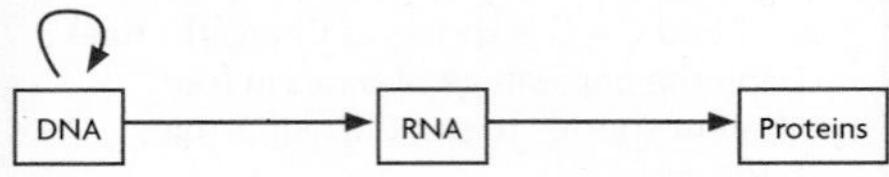

Concept Map Use a concept map like the one below to summarize what you know about mutations.

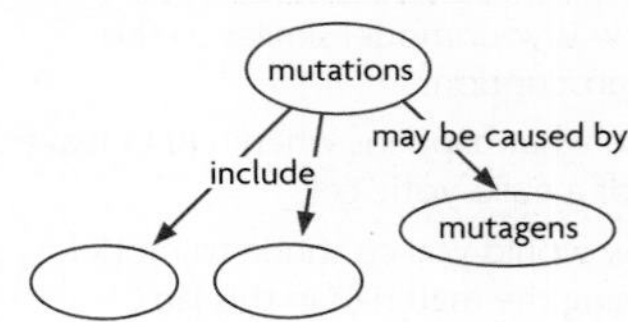

Reviewing Vocabulary

1. Both processes involve the conversion of one type of message into another type of message. Translation reads RNA to make proteins, whereas transcription reads DNA to make RNA.
2. Both types of mutations are changes in the DNA nucleotide sequence. A point mutation involves a change in only one nucleotide. A frameshift mutation involves the insertion or deletion of a nucleotide and throws off the entire reading frame.
3. Both types of RNA are involved in the making of proteins. mRNA makes a template of the code for the protein from DNA. tRNA is a carrier molecule that transfers amino acids to the ribosome.
4. Both are three-nucleotide sequences. A codon is on an mRNA molecule and indicates which amino acid is needed. The anticodon on a tRNA molecule is complementary to the mRNA codon and brings in the needed amino acid.
5. A codon is a three-nucleotide "unit" that "codes" for an amino acid. The nucleotide codons in DNA provide the information that cells need to develop and function and are passed on from one generation to the next.
6. mutagen: a chemical that causes, or gives birth to, a change in DNA; bacteriophage: a virus that infects, or "eats" into bacteria; polypeptide: a molecule that is constructed with many peptide bonds
7. polygenic: something that involves many genes; phagocyte: a cell that eats other cells

Chapter Assessment

Chapter Vocabulary

8.1 bacteriophage, p. 228

8.2 nucleotide, p. 230
double helix, p. 232
base pairing rules, p. 232

8.3 replication, p. 235
DNA polymerase, p. 236

8.4 central dogma, p. 239
RNA, p. 239
transcription, p. 240
RNA polymerase, p. 240
messenger RNA (mRNA), p. 240
ribosomal RNA (rRNA), p. 240
transfer RNA (tRNA), p. 240

8.5 translation, p. 243
codon, p. 243
stop codon, p. 244
start codon, p. 244
anticodon, p. 245

8.6 promoter, p. 248
operon, p. 248
exon, p. 251
intron, p. 251

8.7 mutation, p. 252
point mutation, p. 252
frameshift mutation, p. 252
mutagen, p. 255

Reviewing Vocabulary

Compare and Contrast

Describe one similarity and one difference between the two terms in each of the following pairs.

1. translation, transcription
2. point mutation, frameshift mutation
3. messenger RNA (mRNA), transfer RNA (tRNA)
4. codon, anticodon

Word Origins

5. The word *codon* was coined in 1962 by putting together the word *code* with the suffix *-on*, which means "a hereditary unit." How do these word parts relate to the meaning of the term *codon*?

Use the word parts in this table to answer the next two questions.

Part	Meaning
-gen	to give birth
muta-	to change
phago-	eating
poly-	many

6. Use the meaning of the word parts to write your own definitions for the following terms: *mutagen, bacteriophage, polypeptide.*

7. Suggest a likely definition for these biology terms: *polygenic, phagocyte.*

Reviewing MAIN IDEAS

8. How did qualitative, chemical, and enzyme tests help Avery identify DNA as the transforming principle?

9. Hershey and Chase confirmed that DNA, not protein, was the genetic material. How do the results of their two experiments support this conclusion?

10. Describe Watson and Crick's double helix model of DNA. Include a labeled drawing of the model. B.5.1

11. One DNA strand has the nucleotide sequence AACGTA. What is the sequence of the other strand? B.5.1

12. How do the base pairing rules explain how a strand of DNA acts as a template during DNA replication? B.7.4

13. What are three main steps in DNA replication? B.7.4

14. What does it mean to say that there is a "proofreading" function in DNA replication? B.7.4

15. Describe two differences between DNA and RNA. B.5.3

16. List the main types of RNA and their functions. B.5.3

17. Explain how the interaction between mRNA codons and tRNA anticodons codes for a specific amino acid.

18. What role do ribosomes play in translation? B.2.4

19. Where in the eukaryotic cell do replication, transcription, RNA processing, and translation each occur?

20. How do the promoter and operator work together to control gene expression?

21. Describe mRNA processing in eukaryotic cells.

22. Describe three ways mutations can occur. B.7.4

CHAPTER REVIEW

Reviewing Main Ideas

8. Qualitative tests identified DNA, not protein; chemical analyses identified elements found in DNA, but not in protein; and enzyme tests showed that when proteins were destroyed, the genetic information was still active.
9. When phage proteins were labeled, no radioactivity was found in the bacteria, but when DNA was tagged, radioactivity was found in the bacteria.
10. The double helix is two twisted strands of DNA, with sugar-phosphate backbones on the outside and base pairs matching up on the inside. A paired with T, and C with G.
11. TTGCAT
12. During DNA replication, nucleotide T always pairs with A, and C with G. The nucleotides on one strand are complementary to those on the other.
13. (1) The double helix unzips. (2) DNA polymerase bonds complementary nucleotides in the growing strands. (3) The final product is two double helixes, each with one old strand and one new strand.
14. DNA polymerases identify mis-matched nucleotides and replace them during replication so that the genetic codes "reads" correctly.
15. *Sample Answer:* DNA is double-stranded, whereas RNA is single-stranded. DNA is made up of A, T, C, and G, whereas RNA is made up of A, U, C, and G.
16. mRNA: transcribes genes in DNA into a complementary code; rRNA: part of a ribosome and active in putting together amino acids to form protein; tRNA: translates mRNA so that necessary amino acids brought in from cytoplasm add to a growing polypeptide
17. mRNA codons are the three-nucleotide sequences that code for specific amino acids. Anticodons are tRNA sequences complementary to the mRNA codons that bring the specific amino acid into the growing polypeptide.
18. The ribosome binds to the mRNA that is being translated and also binds to tRNA molecules, which bring in amino acids that attach to the growing polypeptide in the proper sequence.
19. Replication, transcription, and RNA processing occur in the nucleus. Translation occurs in the cytoplasm.
20. The promoter helps RNA polymerase recognize the start of a gene so that an mRNA strand can be made. The operator interacts with other proteins that either block RNA polymerase or allow the gene to be transcribed by mRNA, depending on conditions in the cell.
21. removal of introns, addition of the cap and tail, splicing together of exons
22. Mutations can occur from mutagens, replication errors, or errors in the exchange of chromosome segments during meiosis.

Critical Thinking

23. A mutation may result in a premature stop codon and prevent a protein from being made. A different mutation may result in a codon still coding for the same amino acid, so there would be no change.
24. The nucleotides and amino acids are used as building blocks for DNA synthesis, transcription, and translation.
25. The rate of protein synthesis might be slowed because fewer RNA molecules could exit the nucleus.
26. AUGGUUCACUUUUAA; methionine, valine, histidine, phenylalanine, stop
27. No, because the gene has other sets of regulatory sequences and its own promoter; the presence of lactose and the operator would probably be insufficient to trigger RNA polymerase to begin transcribing.
28. Watson and Crick already knew DNA's composition, based on the accumulated work of other researchers. They applied this knowledge to piece together the three-dimensional structure of DNA. Griffith, Avery, and Hershey and Chase worked with living organisms. They systematically manipulated the possible components of DNA in ways that would enable them to identify DNA as the genetic material based on experimental results.
29. The remaining skin cells may still have mutations in their DNA.
30. They recognized that if a base with one ring paired with a base with two rings, the DNA molecule would have a uniform width. In conjunction with their understanding of Chargaff's rules, this information led Watson and Crick to conclude that A pairs with T, and C pairs with G.

Critical Thinking

23. Apply Give one example of how a mutation may affect an organism's traits, and one example of how a mutation may not affect an organism's traits.

24. Synthesize When you eat a serving of black beans, your body breaks down the beans into smaller subunits. How do you think your body uses the nucleotides and amino acids that are found in black beans?

25. Hypothesize If the nucleus was surrounded by a membrane that had fewer pores, how might the rate of protein synthesis be affected, and why?

26. Apply For the DNA sequence TACCAAGTGAAAATT, write the sequence of its RNA transcript and the sequence of amino acids for which it codes. **B.5.3**

27. Predict Suppose you genetically altered a gene in a line of eukaryotic cells by inserting only the operator from the bacterial *lac* operon. Do you think that adding lactose to the cell culture would cause the cells to start transcribing the altered gene? Explain your reasoning.

28. Contrast What process did Watson and Crick use to develop their model of DNA, and how did it differ from the controlled experiments used by Griffith, Avery, and Hershey and Chase?

29. Infer Having spent much time in sunlight during youth, an older person develops skin cancer and has the growths removed. Why might the growths keep coming back?

30. Synthesize Watson and Crick learned from Franklin's x-ray crystallography that the distance between the backbones of the DNA molecule was the same for the entire length of the molecule. How did this information, combined with what they knew about the sizes of the four bases, lead to their model of DNA structure? **B.5.1**

Interpreting Visuals

Use the diagram to answer the next three questions.

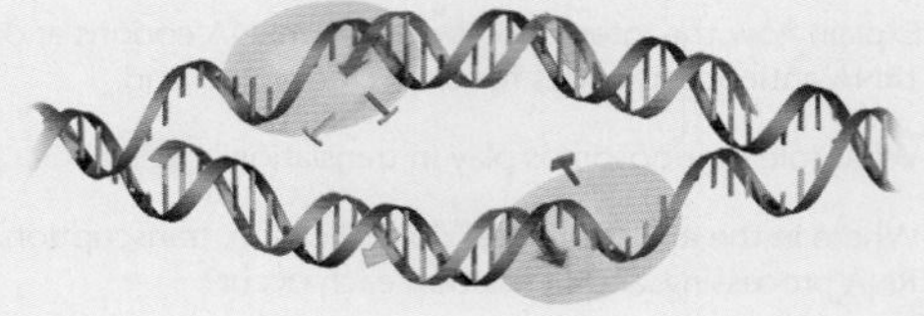

31. Apply What process is taking place in this diagram? **B.7.4**

32. Apply What do the arrows on the yellow strands indicate? **B.7.4**

33. Predict If you were to extend the diagram in both directions, what would you expect to see? **B.7.4**

Analyzing Data

Many factors contribute to breast cancer, including some that are genetic. For example, women with a mutation in the BRCA1 gene have an especially high risk of developing breast cancer. The histogram below shows the total estimated number of new breast cancer cases for women in the United States for 2003. Use the data in the histogram to answer the next two questions.

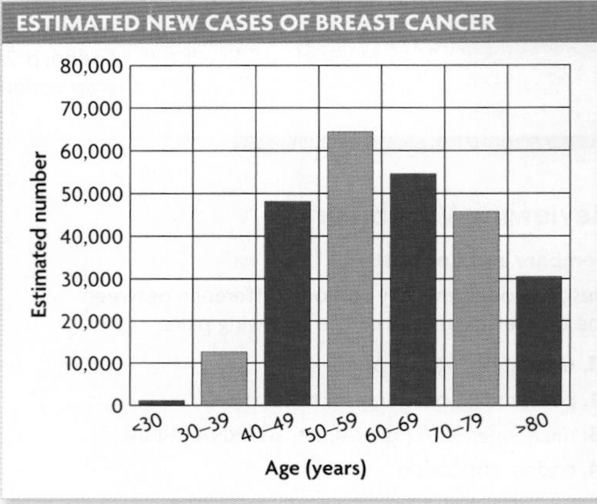

Source: American Cancer Society

34. Analyze In which age group was the incidence of new cases the lowest? the highest?

35. Hypothesize Using the data in this histogram, develop a hypothesis to explain why breast cancer genes are still present in the population.

Connecting CONCEPTS

36. Write an Analogy This chapter used an analogy about exchanging quarters for tokens at a game center to represent the process of transcription. Think of your own analogy for one of the processes you learned about in this chapter. Write a paragraph using that analogy to explain the process. Also, note any limitations of your analogy. (That is, in what ways does it not "fit" the process you're explaining?)

37. Synthesize Look again at the picture of the glowing mouse on page 225. The gene for the protein GFP was inserted into a mouse egg, and then expressed in the mouse. What genetic processes are involved in the expression of this gene?

Interpreting Visuals

31. DNA replication
32. the direction of replication
33. more replication "bubbles" where DNA is unzipping at numerous origins of replication

Analyzing Data

34. under 30; 50–59
35. Breast cancer typically develops at a later age, after most women have had children.

INDIANA ISTEP+ Test Prep

B.5.3; B.5.4; NOS.2

Test Practice For more test practice, go to ClassZone.com.

1 Before the genetic code could be understood, scientists needed to know that a codon is composed of three nucleotides. This situation is an example of the

A fact that codons are the building block of life.
B cumulative nature of scientific evidence.
C way that theories can lead to scientific laws.
D ability of scientists to make hypotheses.

2

AAACACUAU

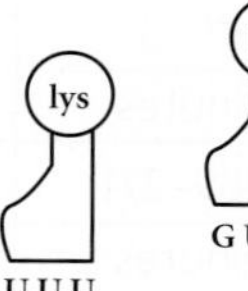

This illustration shows a strand of mRNA and the complementary tRNA molecules that can base pair with the mRNA codons. What is the correct sequence of amino acids?

A lys-his-tyr
B his-tyr-lys
C tyr-lys-his
D lys-tyr-his

3 Less than 60% of the DNA sequence of the human GM-CSF gene and the mouse GM-CSF gene is the same. When scientists put the human gene into mice, however, it functions properly. Which statement ***best*** explains why this happens?

A The resulting proteins are similar enough.
B Mice can make any human protein.
C The DNA is mutated in the mouse.
D The differences are at the ends of the protein.

THINK THROUGH THE QUESTION

The name of the gene is not important in answering this question. All you need to learn from the names is that the question involves only one type of gene. Don't let a complicated name distract you from answering the real question.

4 A mutant protein that has a proline in place of a histidine generally has different chemical properties from the normal protein. Which statement ***best*** explains this difference?

A Proline and histidine cannot exist in the same protein sequence.
B Proline and histidine are both rare amino acids.
C Proline and histidine cannot both be made by the same cell.
D Proline and histidine interact differently with other amino acids.

5

DNA → RNA → X

The diagram above represents the cellular processes of transcription and translation. What word ***best*** replaces X in the last box?

A replication
B protein
C glucose
D molecule

6 What are the three types of RNA and how do they differ?

CHAPTER REVIEW

Standards-Based Assessment

1. B	4. D
2. A	5. B
3. A	6. See Below

Question 2 Answer A is correct. Answer B is incorrect because histidine's anticodon, GUG, does not base pair with the first codon, AAA. Answer C is incorrect because tyrosine's anticodon, AUA, does not base pair with the first codon, AAA. Answer D is incorrect because tyrosine's anticodon, AUA, does not base pair with the second codon, CAC.

Question 4 Answer D is correct. Answers A, B, and C are incorrect because the statements are irrelevant to the protein's function, and they are false statements.

Question 5 Answer B is correct because translation converts an RNA message into a protein. Answer A is incorrect because replication is the process of copying DNA. Answer C is incorrect because glucose is not produced as a direct result of translation. Answer D is incorrect because molecule is a more generic answer than the correct answer, protein.

Question 6 Messenger RNA, or mRNA, is an intermediate message that is translated to make a protein. Ribosomal RNA, or rRNA, forms part of ribosomes. Transfer RNA, or tRNA, brings amino acids from the cytoplasm to a ribosome to help construct proteins.

Connecting Concepts

36. *Sample Answer:* comparing DNA replication to making a photocopy, or comparing translation to translating a book from one language to another

37. The gene is on a chromosome that had to be replicated with each cell division. The gene is then expressed by way of transcription, RNA processing, and translation.

ITEM CORRELATIONS

Standard	Items
B.5.3	5, 6
B.5.4	2, 3, 4
NOS.2	1

CHAPTER 9

Indiana Resource Preview

Print Resources

Frontiers of Biotechnology

INDIANA STANDARDS		Sections	PAGES and PACING	UNIT RESOURCE BOOK
	9.1	**Manipulating DNA** **KEY CONCEPT** Biotechnology relies on cutting DNA at specific places.	pp. 264–267 45 minutes	URB pages 99–102
NOS.6		CHAPTER INVESTIGATION: Modeling Forensics	p. 268 30 minutes	**Lab Binder** Genetics pages 41–46
	9.2	**Copying DNA** **KEY CONCEPT** The polymerase chain reaction rapidly copies segments of DNA.	pp. 269–271 30 minutes	URB pages 103–106
	9.3	**DNA Fingerprinting** **KEY CONCEPT** DNA fingerprints identify people at the molecular level.	pp. 272–274 30 minutes	URB pages 107–110
B.7.5	9.4	**Genetic Engineering** **KEY CONCEPT** DNA sequences of organisms can be changed.	pp. 275–279 45 minutes	URB pages 111–114
NOS.10	9.5	**Genomics and Bioinformatics** **KEY CONCEPT** Entire genomes are sequenced, studied, and compared.	pp. 280–283 45 minutes	URB pages 115–118
NOS.3		DATA ANALYSIS: Constructing Histograms	p. 282, 45 min	URB page 123
	9.6	**Genetic Screening and Gene Therapy** **KEY CONCEPT** Genetics provides a basis for new medical treatments.	pp. 284–285 30 minutes	URB pages 119–122
B.7.3, B.7.5		OPTIONS FOR INQUIRY	pp. 286–287 20 min. each	**Lab Binder** Genetics pages 47–52
		Chapter Review	pp. 288–291	**Assessment Book** Chapter Tests A, B pp. 175–182

INDIANA STANDARDS

B.7.3 Determine the likelihood of the appearance of a specific trait in an offspring given the genetic make-up of the parents.
B.7.5 Explain and demonstrate how inserting, substituting or deleting segments of a DNA molecule can alter a gene, which is then passed to every cell that develops from it and that the results may be beneficial, harmful or have little or no effect on the organism.
NOS.3 Clearly communicate their ideas and results of investigations verbally and in written form using tables, graphs, diagrams, and photographs.
NOS.6 Use analogies and models (mathematical and physical) to simplify and represent systems that are difficult to understand or directly experience due to their size, time scale, or complexity, and recognize the limitations of analogies and models.
NOS.10 Describe how scientific discoveries lead to the development of new technologies, and conversely how technological advances can lead to scientific discoveries through new experimental methods and equipment.

Labs

PUPIL EDITION LABS

Modeling Forensics, p. 268 Students compare simulated DNA samples to identify a crime suspect. **Lab Binder** pp. 41–46	**Time:** 60 minutes **Materials:** Gel Electrophoresis Datasheet, scissors, foam tray, metric ruler, soap dish, 2 100-mL graduated cylinders, 60 mL 1% agarose solution, aluminum foil, 2 wires with alligator clips, 50 mL 3% baking soda solution, 5 small test tubes with rack, 5 pipettes, food coloring, 10 mL graduated cylinder, 10 mL glycerol, 5 9-volt batteries
Modeling Plasmids and Restriction Enzymes, Section 4, p. 278 Students model the formation of recombinant DNA. **Lab Binder** pp. 53–54	**Time:** 15 minutes **Materials:** 3 copies of Plasmid Sequence Datasheet, scissors, 10 cm clear tape, 3 sets of 5 5-cm yarn pieces

OPTIONS FOR INQUIRY

Modeling Genetic Engineering, p. 286 Students model genetic engineering. **Lab Binder** pp. 47–49	**Time:** 20 minutes **Materials:** DNA Sequence Datasheet, scissors, 20 cm clear tape, 5-cm red, green, blue, and yellow yarn pieces
Genetic Screening, p. 287 Students use a pedigree and restriction map to determine the carrier of a genetic disorder. **Lab Binder** pp. 51–52	**Time:** 20 minutes **Materials:** paper, pencil

LAB BINDER Unit 3 Genetics

Additional Investigation: Genetic Engineering, pp. 55–59

Forensics Lab: DNA Fingerprinting, pp. 60–63

Biotechnology Lab: Analysis of DNA Restriction Fragment Size, pp. 64–67

Virtual Lab Worksheet: Gel Electrophoresis, p. 78; Bacterial Transformation, p. 79

LAB GENERATOR

A searchable CD of all labs in the program in editable format, including forensic, probeware, and biotechnology labs.

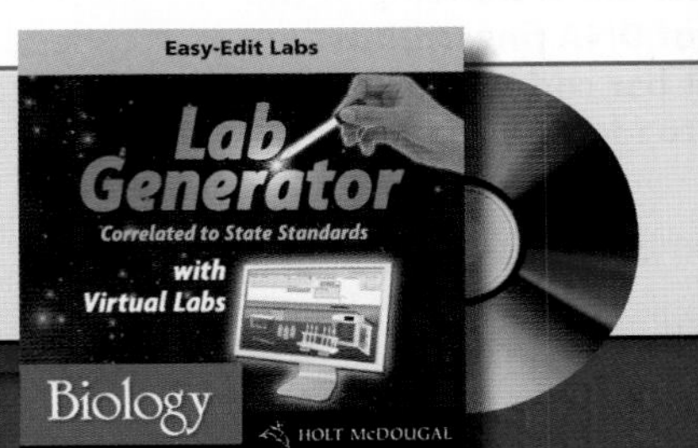

Presentation Tools

POWER PRESENTATIONS

Presentation Chapter 9
PowerPresentations for each section incorporate images and clips from the Media Gallery. Includes Note Navigator for each section.

MEDIA GALLERY

Contains the following images and video clips, as well as animations, simulations, and forms of visuals from the book.

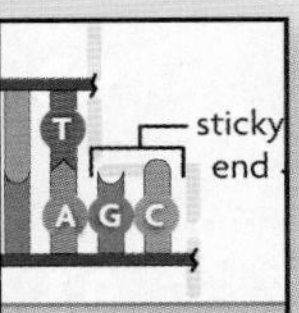

Restriction enzyme

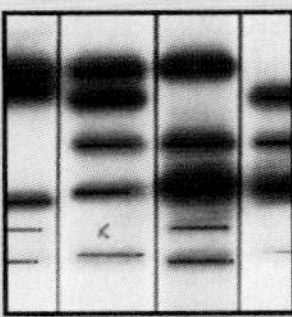
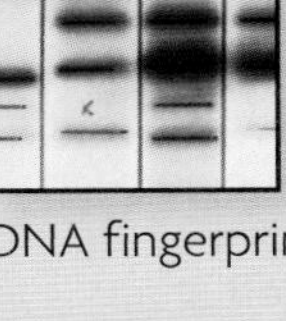
DNA fingerprint

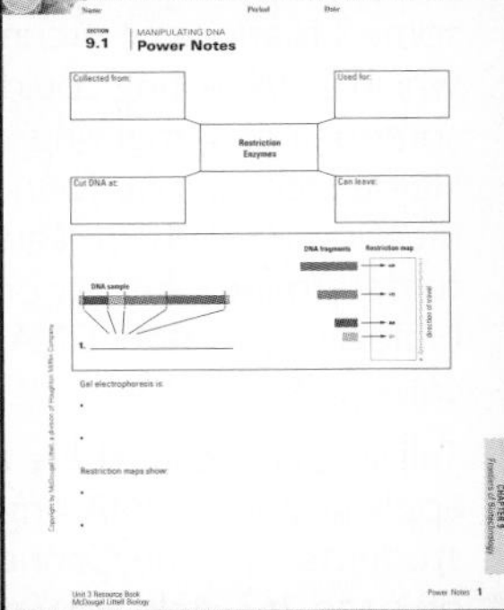

Power Notes

Genetically modified rooster

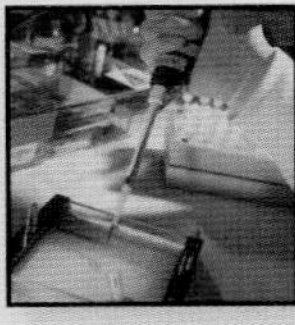
Gel electrophoresis

VIDEO

Examine a set of short video clips on genetic technology and transgenic plants.

ANIMATED BIOLOGY

Restriction Enzymes
Polymerase Chain Reaction

TRANSPARENCIES

Restriction Map T41
Polymerase Chain Reaction T42

Online BIOLOGY CLASSZONE.COM

BioZine
Animated Biology
Interactive Review
SciLinks
Resource Centers

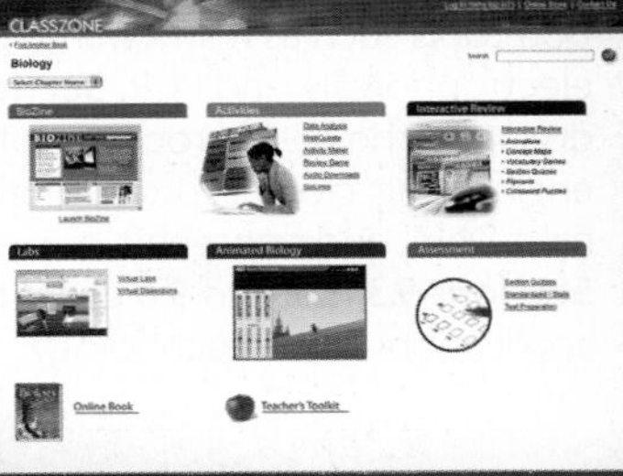

CHAPTER 9

▼ Focus and Motivate

How can biotechnology reunite families?

Discuss the questions that can be answered by DNA testing. **Ask,** What are some situations or circumstances in which DNA testing could help identify someone or something? *Sample Answer:* Human remains are found that cannot be identified by other means. People need to determine whether or not they are biologically related. DNA is left at a crime scene.

Tell students that there are many applications of DNA fingerprinting. Have students read the Connecting Concepts on page 263. **Ask,** How might biotechnology help to repopulate the Galápagos Islands with native tortoise species? Scientists could identify members of the tortoise species that are native to the islands by using DNA fingerprinting and then selectively breed those tortoises. DNA testing can also be used to identify close family relationships between tortoises so that family members are not used as breeding pairs.

BIOZINE ClassZone.com

Students can access BioZine at **ClassZone.com** to learn about some of the latest research in the biological sciences.

In a Hurry?

Sections 9.1 and **9.2** detail DNA manipulation tools such as restriction enzymes, gel electrophoresis, and PCR. **Section 9.4** discusses the basic processes of genetic engineering: cloning, producing recombinant DNA, and transgenic organisms. **Sections 9.3, 9.5,** and **9.6** cover different applications of biotechnology.

CHAPTER 9

Frontiers of Biotechnology

KEY CONCEPTS

9.1 Manipulating DNA
Biotechnology relies on cutting DNA at specific places.

9.2 Copying DNA
The polymerase chain reaction rapidly copies segments of DNA.

9.3 DNA Fingerprinting
DNA fingerprints identify people at the molecular level.

9.4 Genetic Engineering
DNA sequences of organisms can be changed.

9.5 Genomics and Bioinformatics
Entire genomes are sequenced, studied, and compared.

9.6 Genetic Screening and Gene Therapy
Genetics provides a basis for new medical treatments.

Online BIOLOGY CLASSZONE.COM

Animated BIOLOGY
View animated chapter concepts.
- Restriction Enzymes
- Polymerase Chain Reaction
- Gel Electrophoresis
- Bacterial Transformation

BIOZINE
Keep current with biology news.
- Featured stories
- News feeds
- Careers

RESOURCE CENTER
Get more information on
- DNA Manipulation Tools
- Genetic Engineering
- Genomics

Student Activity

Purpose Have students examine bar codes to develop a greater understanding of the banding patterns of DNA fingerprints. Students will treat bar code patterns as DNA fingerprints to identify a crime suspect.

Materials (per team)

- enlarged photocopies of commercial bar codes: 5 unique and 2 identical
- envelope

Prepare To prepare bar codes, cut out or black out the numbers from commercial bar codes. Use an enlargement option, such as 220 percent, to create easy-to-read photocopies of each bar code. Remember to make double the number of copies of the bar code that will serve as the match between the DNA from the crime scene and that of a guilty suspect, but to put only one copy of this code in each "suspect" envelope.

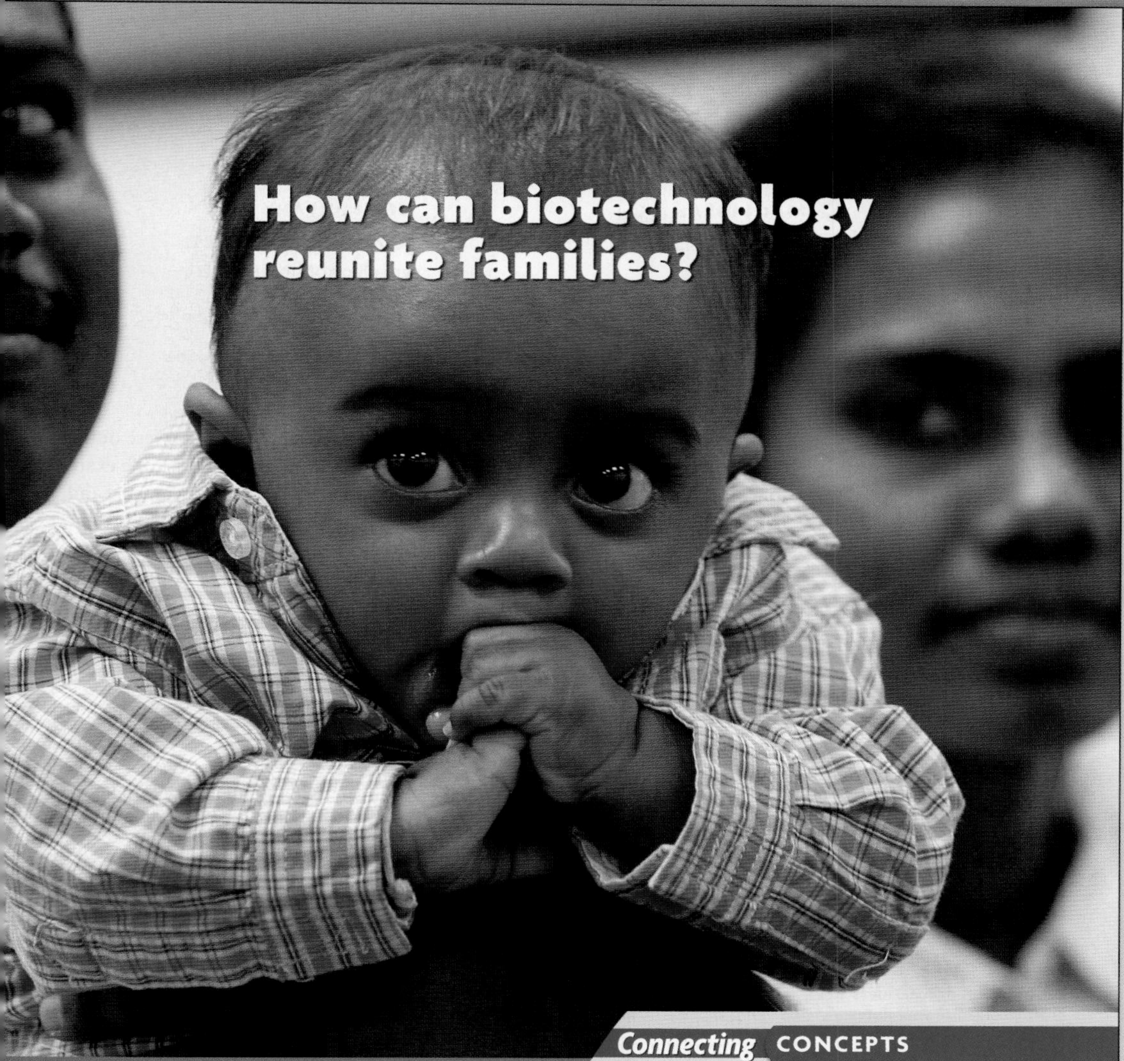

How can biotechnology reunite families?

A natural disaster strikes. Families are separated. One application of biotechnology can help bring the families back together. DNA fingerprinting can identify people at the genetic level. And it allowed the child above, called Baby 81 by rescue workers, to be reunited with his parents months after a tsunami, or tidal wave, devastated many parts of Southeast Asia.

***Connecting* CONCEPTS**

Ecology DNA fingerprinting is not just used to identify people and to help fight crime. It can also be used to identify different species. Scientists at the San Diego Zoo use DNA fingerprinting to identify different tortoise species from the Galapagos Islands. Through the help of DNA fingerprinting, the scientists hope to repopulate the islands with native tortoise species.

Introduce Explain that because it is very unlikely that two people have the same DNA fingerprint, DNA fingerprints can be used to identify a specific person. Bar codes are analogous to DNA fingerprints. Give each team an envelope labeled "suspects' DNA" that contains six different bar codes labeled *A–F*. Tell students that these represent the DNA fingerprints of six suspects. Pass out one more bar code that represents DNA found at the crime scene. Have students compare the "samples" to determine who should be charged with the crime.

Discuss Have students discuss how DNA fingerprinting assists in solving crimes and how it can influence a trial. Tell them that some people in prison who were convicted were later exonerated by DNA evidence.

Ask, How would an investigation be affected if the suspect whose DNA matched the evidence had an identical twin who was also in the area at the time of the crime? Because twins' DNA is identical, DNA fingerprinting alone would not be enough to prove beyond a reasonable doubt which of the twins committed the crime.

Activate Prior Knowledge

Remind students of the role of **meiosis** in sexual reproduction. **Ask**

- How does a child's DNA compare with the DNA of his or her parents? A child inherits half of his or her chromosomes from each parent, so half of the child's DNA will match to the mother's DNA, and half will match the father's DNA.
- How is biotechnology involved in the story on this page? Students may suggest that molecular analysis of the child's DNA and parents' DNA was used to prove that they were related, and that these techniques are the product of advances in biotechnology.

Preview Vocabulary

Greek and Latin Word Origins Tell students that they will see the words *manipulation* and *technique* used to describe DNA technology. Tell students they can think of *manipulation* as "what is being done" and *technique* as "how it is being done." The Latin root *manus* means "hand": *manipulation* is the product of "moving, arranging, or operating, often by hand." The Greek root *teknikos* refers to the "art" of doing something: *technique* means "the systematic procedure for accomplishing a complex task."

Academic Vocabulary Remind students that *technology* is the application of science to solving practical problems. Explain that *biotechnology* involves not only the application of scientific understanding of biological systems and processes to solve problems, but also uses living organisms to achieve the desired effect.

English Learners Have students review their notes on *base-pairing* rules and *replication* from Chapter 8 and the idea of *mapping* as applied to genes and chromosomes in Chapter 7. Tell students that this scientific knowledge is used in the manipulation of DNA in biotechnology. *Manipulation* in this context means changing or rearranging DNA for some particular use.

SECTION 9.1

▼ Plan and Prepare

Objectives

- Summarize how restriction enzymes cut DNA.
- Explain how restriction maps show the lengths of DNA fragments.

Section Resources

Unit Resource Book
Study Guide pp. 99–100
Power Notes p. 101
Reinforcement p. 102

Interactive Reader Chapter 9
Spanish Study Guide pp. 87–88

Biology Toolkit pp. C9, C25

Technology
Power Presentation 9.1
Media Gallery DVD
Online Quiz 9.1

Activating Prior Knowledge Discuss how the ability to collect and interpret DNA has changed crime investigation—and television programming. **Ask,** How many of you watch a television show with the abbreviation *CSI* in its title? What does CSI stand for? Crime Scene Investigation Discuss how DNA figures into a crime investigation. Remind students that human DNA has about 3 billion base pairs, so it is difficult to isolate any one pair or sequence. Tell students that scientists have devised ways to cut DNA and differentiate various sequences from one another, so just a small portion of DNA is needed to make an identification.

9.1 Manipulating DNA

KEY CONCEPT Biotechnology relies on cutting DNA at specific places.

MAIN IDEAS
- Scientists use several techniques to manipulate DNA.
- Restriction enzymes cut DNA.
- Restriction maps show the lengths of DNA fragments.

VOCABULARY
restriction enzyme, p. 265
gel electrophoresis, p. 266
restriction map, p. 267

Review
DNA, enzyme, allele, nucleotide

Connect Many applications of genetics that are widely used today were unimaginable just 30 years ago. Our use of genetics to identify people is just one example. Biotechnology and genetics are used to produce transgenic organisms and clones. They are used to study diseases and evolution. They are used to produce medical treatments for people with life-threatening illnesses. Through many years of research and a combination of many different methods, advances in biotechnology seem to happen on a daily basis.

MAIN IDEA

Scientists use several techniques to manipulate DNA.

By the middle of the 1950s, scientists had concluded that DNA was the genetic material. Watson and Crick had determined the structure of DNA. Yet the field of genetics as we know it today was just beginning. For example, even the genetic code that you learned about in Chapter 8 was not fully understood until the early 1960s. Since that time, scientists have developed a combination of methods to study DNA and genes.

DNA is a very large molecule, but it is still just a molecule. It is far too small to see, and you cannot pick it up or rearrange it with your hands. Therefore, scientists must be able to work with DNA without being able to see or handle it directly. Chemicals, computers, and bacteria are just a few of the tools that have allowed advances in genetics research.

Artificial nucleotides are used to sequence genes. Artificial copies of genes are used to study gene expression. Chemical mutagens are used to change DNA sequences. Computers analyze and organize the vast amounts of data from genetics research. Enzymes, often from bacteria, are used to cut and copy DNA. Bacteria also provide one of the ways in which genes are transferred between different organisms. Throughout this chapter, you will learn about some of the techniques used in biotechnology, as well as some of its applications. You likely have heard of genetic engineering, DNA fingerprinting, and cloning, but how are they done? In many cases, one of the first steps in biotechnology and genetics research is to precisely cut DNA.

TAKING NOTES
Use a supporting main ideas chart to organize your notes on ways in which DNA is manipulated.

Cutting DNA
→ Restriction enzymes cut DNA
→ Gel electrophoresis ...
→

(A) Infer **Why might so many different methods be needed to study DNA and genes?**

▼ Teach

Answer

(A) **Infer** because DNA is microscopic, very long and complex, and difficult to handle or manipulate

Differentiated Instruction

ENGLISH LEARNERS

To help students focus on "right there" questions whose answers can be found in the text, demonstrate the QAR (Question-Answer Relationships) strategy for the section headed "Restriction enzymes cut DNA." **Ask**

- How do bacteria protect themselves against viruses? They produce enzymes that cut up viral DNA.
- Where do restriction enzymes cut DNA molecules? at specific nucleotide sequences called restriction sites
- How do different restriction enzymes cut DNA differently? Some make cuts leaving blunt ends; some leave sticky ends.
- Which is more useful to scientists—DNA with blunt ends or DNA with sticky ends? sticky

Have students write more questions. Then, in small groups, have them prepare "right there" questions about restriction maps.

Biology Toolkit, QAR, p. C9

MAIN IDEA

Restriction enzymes cut DNA.

Why would scientists want to cut DNA? To answer that question, you have to remember that a gene is a sequence of DNA nucleotides, and that a chromosome is one long DNA molecule. A whole chromosome is too large for scientists to study a particular gene easily, so they had to find a way to get much smaller pieces of DNA. Of course, slicing a chromosome into pieces is not as simple as picking up the molecule and cutting it with a pair of scissors. Instead, scientists use enzymes that act as molecular "scissors." These enzymes, which slice apart DNA, come from many different types of bacteria.

Bacterial cells, like your cells, can be infected by viruses. As protection against these invaders, bacteria produce enzymes that cut up the DNA of the viruses. As **FIGURE 9.1** shows, a DNA molecule can be cut apart in several places at once by several molecules of a restriction enzyme, or endonuclease. **Restriction enzymes** are enzymes that cut DNA molecules at specific nucleotide sequences. In fact, any time the enzyme finds that exact DNA sequence, it cuts the DNA molecule. The sequence of nucleotides that is identified and cut by a restriction enzyme is called a restriction site. These enzymes are called restriction enzymes because they restrict, or decrease, the effect of the virus on the bacterial cell.

FIGURE 9.1 A restriction enzyme (blue peaks) from an *E. coli* bacterium helps protect against viruses by cutting DNA (red). This cutting "restricts" the effect of a virus on a bacterium. (colored 3D atomic force micrograph; magnification 63,000×)

Each of the hundreds of known restriction enzymes has a different restriction site. Different restriction enzymes will cut the same DNA molecule in different ways. For example, one restriction enzyme may find three of its restriction sites in a segment of DNA. Another restriction enzyme might find six of its restriction sites in the same segment. Different numbers of fragments with different lengths result. As you can see below, two different restriction enzymes can cut the same strand of DNA in very different ways.

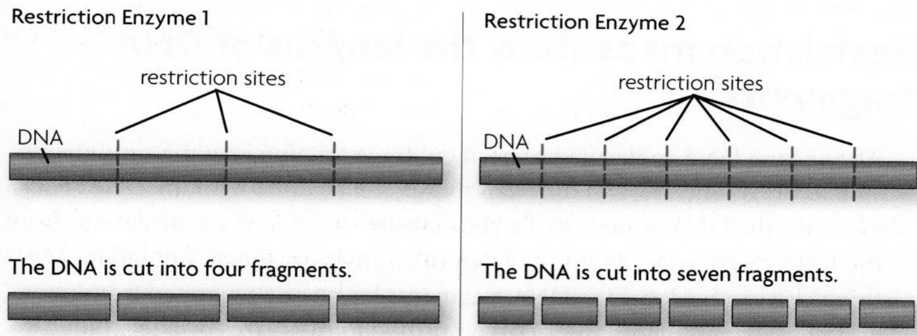
Restriction Enzyme 1
restriction sites
DNA
The DNA is cut into four fragments.
Restriction Enzyme 2
restriction sites
DNA
The DNA is cut into seven fragments.

Restriction enzymes recognize nucleotide sequences that are between four and eight base pairs long, and then cut the DNA within that area. Some enzymes make cuts straight across the two strands of a DNA molecule. These cuts leave behind fragments of DNA that end in what are called "blunt ends."

ONLINE BIOLOGY Go to the chapter Resource Center at **ClassZone.com** for additional resources and information on DNA manipulation.

Integrating Chemistry

Restriction enzymes are a bacterial defense mechanism that destroys the DNA of invading viruses. Students may wonder why the DNA of the host bacterium in **FIGURE 9.1** is not destroyed in the process, or how the bacterium's defensive enzymes recognize friend from foe. Explain that bacterial DNA is highly methylated, meaning methyl groups ($-CH_3$) are attached to some of the bases. The methyl groups protect the bacterium's DNA from the cutting effects of its restriction enzymes.

Take It Further

Restriction enzymes are named using a kind of code. The first letter of the name represents the genus of the bacterium from which the enzyme was isolated. The second two letters come from the first two letters of the bacterium's species descriptor. The first three letters are italicized because they are part of the bacterium's scientific name. If there is a fourth letter, it represents the particular strain of bacteria. A Roman numeral reveals the order in which an enzyme was discovered in the bacterium. So, *Taq*I, seen in **FIGURE 9.2,** was the first restriction enzyme isolated from the bacterium *Thermus aquaticus.* Two other commonly used restriction enzymes are *Eco*RI, isolated from *E. coli* strain RY13, and *Bam*HI, isolated from *Bacillus amyloliquefaciens* strain H.

BELOW LEVEL

Have students outline the section "Restriction enzymes cut DNA" on pages 265 and 266. Remind them to use a system of Roman numerals, Arabic numerals, capital letters, and lowercase letters. Have students include information from **FIGURE 9.2** in their outlines as an example of how a restriction enzyme cuts DNA at a specific site.

Biology Toolkit, Outline, p. C25

▼ Teach *continued*

ONLINE BIOLOGY Students can complete a virtual lab in which gel electrophoresis is used to make a DNA fingerprint of someone who committed a crime. See Options For Inquiry on page 287.

Take It Further

A **palindrome** is a word or phrase that reads the same backward or forward. *Radar, racecar,* and *Madam, I'm Adam* are palindromes. Palindromes in nucleic acids read the same backward or forward across the double strand. For example, the sequence GATC forms a palindrome with the complementary CTAG on the opposite strand; GACT does not make a palindrome with its complementary sequence, CTGA. Restriction enzymes usually recognize palindromic sequences and cut the DNA between the same two bases on the opposite strands at these locations. A restriction site must be a palindrome if sticky ends are to be produced. If the restriction site is not a palindrome, blunt ends form.

Answers

A Infer The ends of the segments would not have nucleotide tails available to bind to complementary base pairs.

B Summarize They recognize and cut different nucleotide sequences, or restriction sites, resulting in different fragments.

Animated
BIOLOGY
Use virtual restriction enzymes at ClassZone.com.

FIGURE 9.2 Restriction Enzymes Cut DNA

Some restriction enzymes leave behind nucleotide tails, or "sticky ends," when they cut DNA.

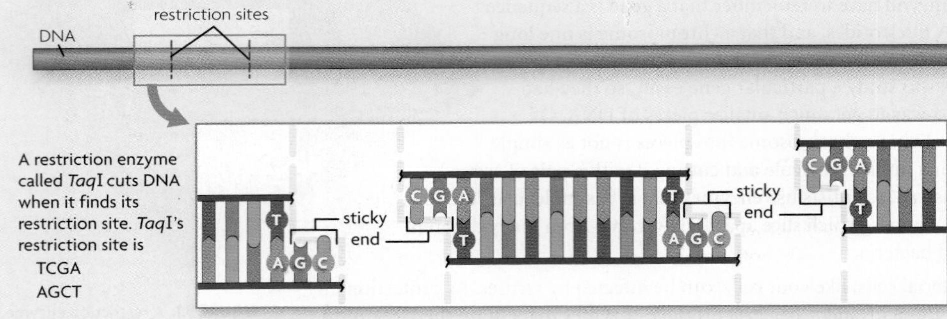
restriction sites
DNA
A restriction enzyme called *Taq*I cuts DNA when it finds its restriction site. *Taq*I's restriction site is
TCGA
AGCT
sticky end
sticky end
T
AGC
CGA
T
T
AGC
CGA
T

A Infer How would the above illustration change if *Taq*I left behind blunt ends rather than sticky ends when it cuts DNA?

Connecting CONCEPTS

DNA Base Pairs Recall from **Chapter 8** that DNA nucleotides match up by complementary base pairing. A always pairs with T, and C always pairs with G.

Other restriction enzymes, as shown in **FIGURE 9.2**, make staggered cuts that leave tails of free DNA bases on each side of the cut. These nucleotide tails of the cut DNA strands are called "sticky ends." Sticky ends are like tiny pieces of Velcro that are ready to hook on to their opposite sides. If two pieces of DNA with sticky ends and complementary base pairs come close to each other, the two segments of DNA will join by hydrogen bonding. Because of this characteristic of DNA, restriction enzymes that leave sticky ends when they cut DNA are often used in biotechnology, as you will learn in Section 9.4.

B Summarize How do different restriction enzymes produce different DNA fragments from the same DNA molecule?

MAIN IDEA

Restriction maps show the lengths of DNA fragments.

After a long DNA molecule has been cut by restriction enzymes into many smaller fragments, several different things can be done with the DNA. For example, the DNA sequence of a gene can be studied, or a gene cut out from the DNA can be placed into the DNA of another organism. But before anything else can be done, the DNA fragments have to be separated from one another. The fragments are sorted according to their sizes by a technique called gel electrophoresis (ih-LEHK-troh-fuh-REE-sihs).

In **gel electrophoresis,** an electrical current is used to separate a mixture of DNA fragments from each other. A sample of DNA is loaded into a gel, which is like a thin slab of hard gelatin. A positive electrode is at one end of the gel. At the other end is a negative electrode. Because DNA has a negative charge,

Differentiated Instruction

PRE-AP

Write the following sequence of numbers on the board:

2 9 5 8 2 7 2 1 0 3 9 7 8 2 2 5 4 1 8 2 2 6

Tell students that a certain restriction enzyme makes a cut between an 8 and a 2. Have students copy the sequence and mark the places where the enzyme would cut. **Ask,** How many fragments are produced? four **Ask,** Are all the fragments the same length? no **Ask,** Can you think of a basis or measure by which you could organize the fragments? size or mass (weight) the fragments move toward the positive electrode, or the positively charged pole. The gel also has tiny pores running through it. The pores allow small molecules to move quickly. Larger molecules cannot easily move through the gel and they travel more slowly. Therefore, the length of a DNA fragment can be estimated from the distance it travels through a gel in a certain period of time. As shown in **FIGURE 9.3**, DNA fragments of different sizes appear as different bands, or lines, on a gel. The pattern of bands on the gel can be thought of as a map of the original strand of DNA. **Restriction maps** show the lengths of DNA fragments between restriction sites in a strand of DNA.

The bands on a gel indicate only the lengths of DNA fragments. Alone, they do not give any information about the DNA sequences of the fragments. Even though restriction maps do not directly show the makeup of a fragment of DNA, the maps are very useful in genetic engineering, which you will read about in Section 9.4. They can also be used to study gene mutations. How? First, a mutation may add or delete bases between restriction sites, which would change the lengths of DNA fragments on a gel. Second, a mutation may change a restriction site, and the DNA would not be cut in the same places.

Suppose, for example, that when a normal allele of a gene is cut by a restriction enzyme, five DNA fragments appear as five different bands on a gel. Then, when a mutant allele of the same gene is cut with the same enzyme, only three bands appear. Comparisons of restriction maps can help diagnose genetic diseases, as you will see in Section 9.6. A restriction map from a person's DNA can be compared with a restriction map from DNA that is known to be normal. If the restriction maps differ, it is an indication that the person has inherited a disease-causing allele of the gene.

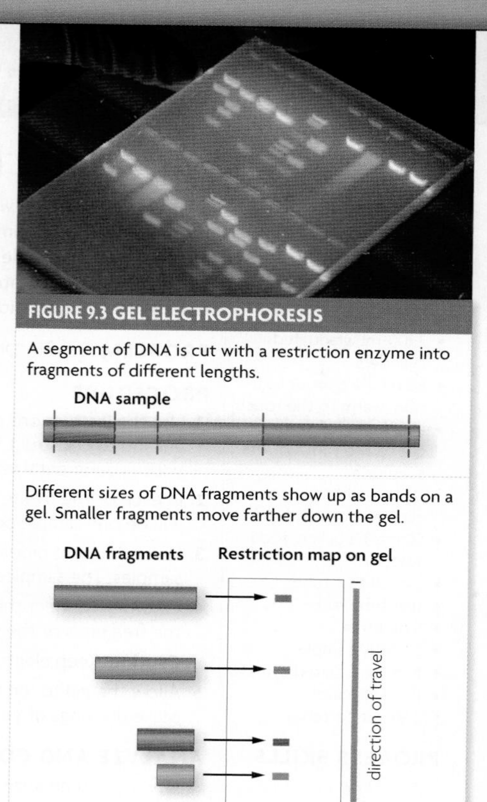

FIGURE 9.3 GEL ELECTROPHORESIS

A segment of DNA is cut with a restriction enzyme into fragments of different lengths.

Different sizes of DNA fragments show up as bands on a gel. Smaller fragments move farther down the gel.

A **Synthesize** **How are restriction enzymes used in making restriction maps?**

9.1 ASSESSMENT

ONLINE QUIZ
ClassZone.com

REVIEWING ▶ MAIN IDEAS

1. List four different ways in which scientists can manipulate DNA.
2. What determines how DNA will be cut by a **restriction enzyme**?
3. How does **gel electrophoresis** separate DNA fragments from each other?

CRITICAL THINKING

4. **Apply** Suppose you cut DNA. You know that you should find four DNA fragments on a gel, but only three appear, and one fragment is very large. Explain what happened.
5. **Synthesize** What is the relationship between restriction sites and a **restriction map**?

Connecting CONCEPTS

6. **Mutations** Would a mutation in a gene always be detectable by using restriction maps? Why or why not?

TEACH FROM VISUALS

FIGURE 9.3 Students may find it difficult to understand that the length of a DNA fragment is represented on the gel by how far it moves from the negative electrode to the positive electrode. **Ask,** If the purple fragment is farthest from the green in the original DNA strand, why is the yellow fragment farthest away from the green in the gel? because the yellow fragment is smaller, it traveled faster toward the positive electrode

History of Science

The 1978 the Nobel Prize in Physiology or Medicine was awarded to **Werner Arber, Hamilton Smith,** and **Daniel Nathans** for their collaborative work on restriction enzymes. Arber discovered the first restriction enzyme and hypothesized that it bonded to DNA at specific sites. Smith verified this and showed how it cut DNA at a specific base sequence. Nathans used the enzyme to develop a genetic-mapping method, an application of restriction enzymes to genetics.

Answers

A **Synthesize** A restriction map is based on the sizes of the DNA fragments produced when restriction enzymes cut a strand of DNA.

9.1 ASSESSMENT

1. DNA can be cut, copied, sequenced, and changed (mutated).
2. the number and location of restriction sites recognized by the restriction enzyme
3. The DNA sample is loaded into a gel through which an electrical current flows. The negatively charged DNA fragments are pulled toward the positive electrode. The largest molecules move slowest, and the smallest move quickest.
4. This might indicate a mutation. One of the restriction sites may have been deleted or changed by the mutation, resulting in one very large fragment where there should have been two fragments.
5. A restriction map reveals the lengths of DNA fragments between restriction sites. The more restriction sites there are, the more fragments there will be on the map.
6. No, a very small change in DNA would not be large enough to detect, even though a mutation occurred.

Assess and Reteach ▼

Assess Use the Online Quiz or Section Quiz (*Assessment Book,* p. 169).

Reteach Write a sequence diagram for the steps a scientist would take to make a restriction map from a sample of DNA.

INVESTIGATION

Time 60 minutes	TEACHER TESTED
Teacher Preparation	
Student Difficulty	
Lab Binder Genetics, pp. 41–46	

Purpose Compare simulated DNA samples to identify a crime suspect.

Overview Students will model a crime investigation by examining DNA evidence. They will

- make and load an agarose gel
- separate simulated DNA samples by gel electrophoresis
- match two simulated DNA samples to identify a criminal

LAB PREPARATION

- Distribute copies of the Gel Electrophoresis datasheet, *Lab Binder,* pp. 45–46.
- Aiming for samples adequate to provide six drops to each group, prepare five DNA samples (food coloring) in small labeled beakers:

  A—1 part purple: 1 part green

  B—purple

  C—same as sample A

  D—green

  E—orange

  Place a pipette in each sample beaker and tell students not to mix up the pipettes.
- To make 3% baking soda solution, dissolve 30 g of baking soda in 1 L of distilled water.
- To make 1% agarose solution, slowly dissolve 10 g of agarose in 1 L of hot (near boiling) 3% baking soda solution on a magnetic stirrer. Keep the agarose solution warm (>37°C or 98.6°F) until needed. When pouring the gels, the solution should be warm to the touch. If too hot, it may warp the foam comb or plastic dish.

LAB MANAGEMENT

- Tell student groups to label their test tubes *A–E* to correspond to the prepared DNA samples. Tell them that sample A was found at the crime scene; B–E are from four suspects.

MATERIALS

- Gel Electrophoresis Datasheet
- scissors
- foam tray
- metric ruler
- plastic soap dish (rectangular)
- 2 100-mL graduated cylinders
- 60 mL 1% agarose solution (warm to the touch)
- aluminum foil strips cut to the width of the soap dish
- 2 wires with alligator clips on both ends
- 50 mL 3% baking soda solution
- 5 small test tubes
- test tube rack
- 5 pipettes
- 5 "DNA" samples
- 10 mL graduated cylinder
- 10 mL glycerol
- 5 9-volt batteries

PROCESS SKILLS

- **Modeling**
- **Analyzing**
- **Concluding**
- **Predicting**

NOS.6 Use analogies and models (mathematical and physical) to simplify and represent systems that are difficult to understand or directly experience due to their size, time scale, or complexity, and recognize the limitations of analogies and models.

Modeling Forensics

In newspapers, on television, and in movies, you often hear about DNA evidence being used to solve crimes. Scientists use a method called gel electrophoresis to separate DNA molecules on the basis of their size. In this lab, you will build a gel electrophoresis apparatus and use it to separate simulated DNA samples to determine a suspect's identity.

PROBLEM Which "DNA" sample matches DNA found at a crime scene?

PROCEDURE

1. Use the instructions on the Gel Electrophoresis Datasheet to make the agarose gel and to construct your gel electrophoresis apparatus. Have your teacher check your experimental set-up before you continue.
2. In each of the five test tubes, add 6 drops of one of the "DNA" samples. There will be one sample per tube. Add 2 drops of glycerol to each tube and gently mix.
3. Use a different pipette to fill each well of the gel with a few drops of one of the samples. The samples should sink into the wells. Do not overfill the wells.
4. Carefully connect the five batteries in a series, as shown on the datasheet. Attach the free ends of the wires to the positive and negative ends of the battery series.

   Caution: Keep electrical equipment from getting wet.
5. Allow the gel to run for at least 30 minutes. Observe and record what happens. Make drawings of your observations.

ANALYZE AND CONCLUDE

1. **Observe** Summarize your observations of what happened to the samples that you ran through the gel.
2. **Analyze** Which samples matched? How do you know?
3. **Apply** How is the analysis of DNA useful for identification of a crime suspect?
4. **Conclude** Gel electrophoresis sorts DNA by the sizes of different fragments. Does the method tell you anything about genes in the DNA? Explain.
5. **Predict** Suppose that you place a mixture of DNA fragments in a single gel electrophoresis well. The fragments have base pair lengths of 300, 5000, 700, 1000, and 500. Make a sketch of how the fragments would appear in the gel after they have been separated by gel electrophoresis. Explain your answer.

EXTEND YOUR INVESTIGATION

How might the separation of the samples be affected by changing the concentration of agarose? Design an experiment to test your hypothesis.

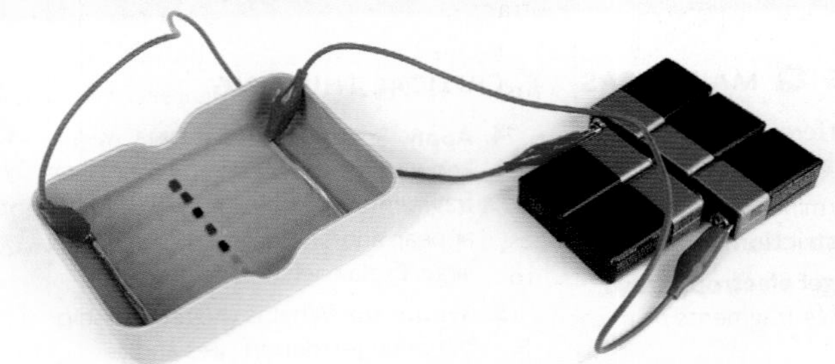

Answers

Analyze And Conclude

1. Lanes A and C: identical patterns (bands of blue, red, and yellow); Lane B: bands of blue and red; Lane D: bands of blue and yellow, and possibly red; Lane E: bands of red and yellow.
2. A and C matched; the bands were identical.
3. Different suspects' DNA can be compared with DNA found at a crime scene.
4. No, the size of DNA fragments cannot alone tell you anything about the genes.
5. 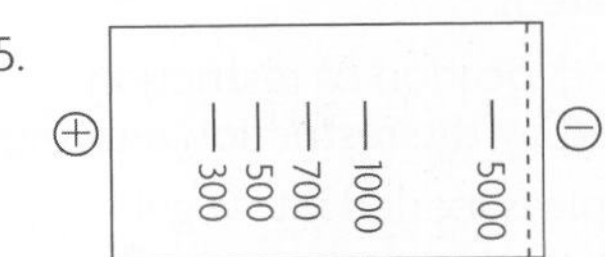

   Large fragments move toward the positive more slowly than smaller ones.

Extend Your Investigation

DNA fragments could move faster or slower depending on agarose concentration.

9.2 Copying DNA

KEY CONCEPT The polymerase chain reaction rapidly copies segments of DNA.

MAIN IDEAS
- PCR uses polymerases to copy DNA segments.
- PCR is a three-step process.

VOCABULARY
polymerase chain reaction (PCR), p. 269
primer, p. 271

Review
DNA polymerase, replication

Connect Forensic scientists use DNA from cells in a single hair at a crime scene to identify a criminal. Doctors test a patient's blood to quickly detect the presence of bacteria that cause Lyme disease. Scientists compare DNA from different species to determine how closely the species are related. However, the original amount of DNA from any of these sources is far too small to accurately study. Samples of DNA must be increased, or amplified, so that they can be analyzed.

MAIN IDEA

PCR uses polymerases to copy DNA segments.

How do scientists get an amount of DNA that is large enough to be studied and manipulated? They copy the same segment of DNA over and over again. **Polymerase chain reaction (PCR)** is a technique that produces millions—or even billions—of copies of a specific DNA sequence in just a few hours. As the name indicates, the DNA polymerase enzymes that you learned about in Chapter 8 play key roles in this process.

Kary Mullis, who invented PCR, is shown in **FIGURE 9.4.** While working for a California biotechnology company in 1983, Mullis had an insight about how to copy DNA segments. He adapted the process of DNA replication that occurs in every living cell into a method for copying DNA in a test tube. Under the right set of conditions, DNA polymerases copy DNA in a test tube just as they do inside cells. However, in cells several other enzymes are needed before the polymerases can do their job. For example, before a cell can begin to copy its DNA, enzymes called helicases unwind and separate DNA molecules. Instead of using these enzymes, Mullis used heat to separate the DNA strands.

FIGURE 9.4 Kary Mullis came up with the idea for PCR while on a surfing trip in 1983. He won the Nobel Prize in chemistry in 1993.

Unfortunately, heat also broke down the *E. coli* polymerases that Mullis first used. Then came Mullis's second stroke of genius: Why not use polymerases from a bacterium that lives in temperatures above 80°C (176°F)? By using this enzyme, Mullis was able to raise the temperature of the DNA to separate the strands without destroying the DNA polymerases. Here again, just as with restriction enzymes that you read about in Section 9.1, a major advance came from applying an adaptation found in nature to biotechnology. Mullis introduced PCR to the world in 1985, and in 1993 he won the Nobel Prize in chemistry for his revolutionary technique.

A Compare and Contrast **How are replication and PCR similar? different? Explain.**

Differentiated Instruction

ENGLISH LEARNERS

After students read the section, have them do a carousel review. On chart paper posted in different parts of the room, write questions such as "How do scientists get a large enough sample of DNA to manipulate?" and "What is PCR?" Assign a small group to each chart, and give each a different colored marker. Groups should review the question, discuss an answer, and write a response. Every three minutes, have groups rotate, put a check mark by answers they agree with, comment on answers they do not agree with, and add their own answers.

Biology Toolkit, Carousel Review, p. C12

Plan and Prepare

Objectives

- Describe the role of polymerases in copying DNA segments.
- Outline the three-step PCR process.

Section Resources

Unit Resource Book
Study Guide pp. 103–104
Power Notes p. 105
Reinforcement p. 106

Interactive Reader Chapter 9
Spanish Study Guide pp. 89–90

Biology Toolkit pp. C12, C18, C34

Technology
Power Presentation 9.2
Media Gallery DVD
Online Quiz 9.2

Activating Prior Knowledge Remind students of the Copy and Paste functions common to word-processing programs. **Ask,** How do you use these functions? Students will probably mention isolating and moving material from one place to another. Explain that copying DNA through PCR is a somewhat analogous process.

Teach

The Inside Story

Heat-stable bacteria used in PCR were isolated in 1967 from a hot spring in Yellowstone National Park. Federal law holds that the National Park Service owns the organisms, but **Kary Mullis** used them without permission. The patent for PCR was sold for $300 million, but the NPS never received royalties.

Answers

A Compare and Contrast Both use polymerases to make copies of DNA. Replication occurs in cells, where other enzymes separate strands of DNA to be copied. PCR is the artificial copying of DNA in a laboratory, with heat used to separate the strands.

▼ Teach *continued*

TEACH FROM VISUALS

FIGURE 9.5 Discuss the information in this figure. **Ask**

- Why is a heat-stable polymerase needed? It must be able to withstand the high temperature needed to separate the DNA strands at the beginning of each cycle.
- Why are two primers needed for each DNA molecule? There must be a primer on each strand of DNA. DNA polymerase cannot make double-stranded DNA unless a primer starts the process.
- How do free nucleotides attach to the existing strand? hydrogen bonding Tell students that it is not until the third cycle of PCR that copies of DNA being produced by PCR actually match the target sequence that the original DNA strand contained.

Integrating Chemistry

Enzymes work best at an **optimum temperature,** usually one that is similar to the temperature of the environment of a cell or an organism. Up to the optimum temperature, the reaction rate increases geometrically because both the enzyme and the substrate have more kinetic energy, so they collide more often. Also, more molecules can overcome the activation energy. Above the optimum temperature, the reaction rate decreases as the thermal energy breaks hydrogen bonds holding the enzyme together. The enzyme's shape changes, and the substrate can no longer bind to the active site.

Answers

Ⓐ **Critical Viewing** 16; 64

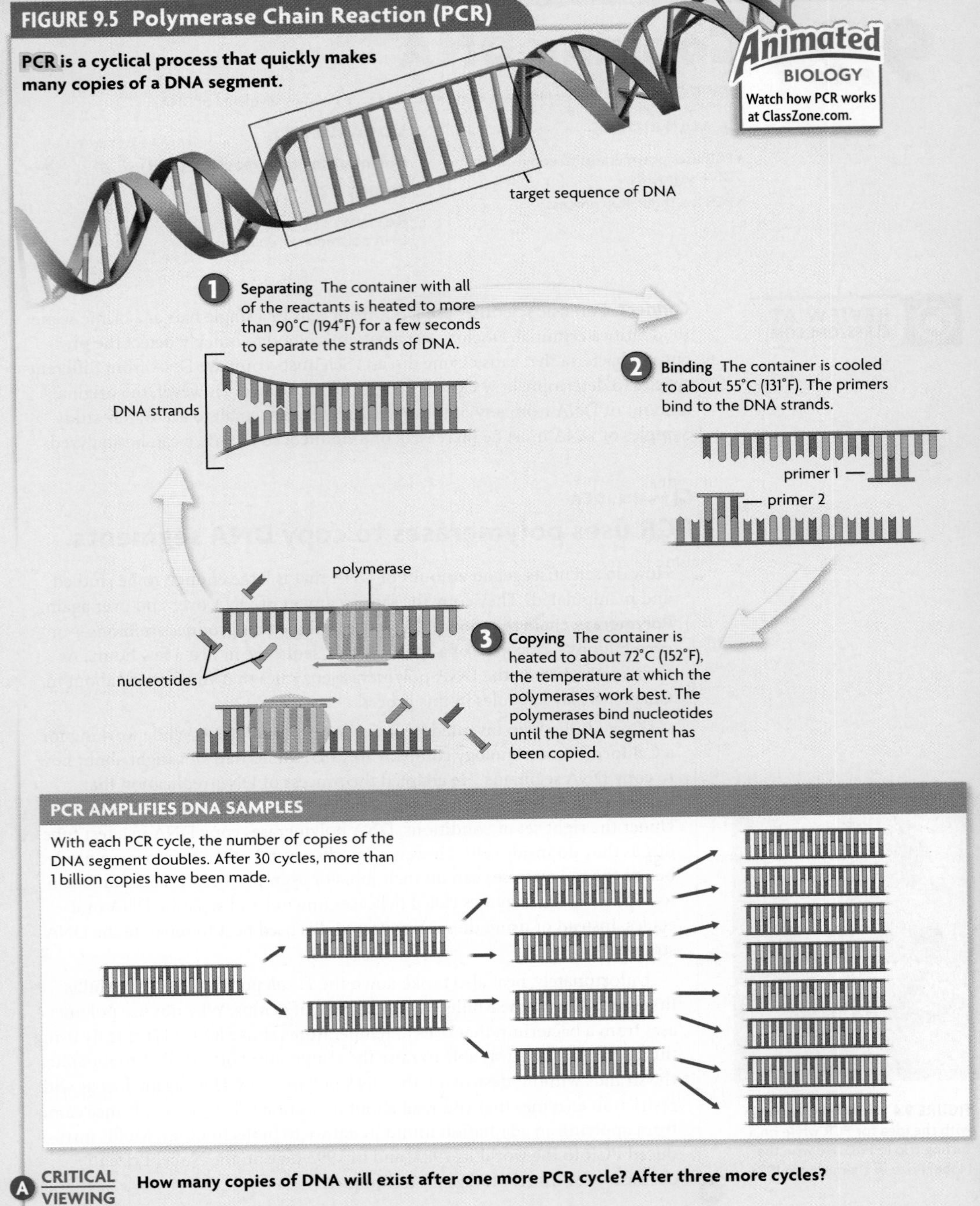

FIGURE 9.5 Polymerase Chain Reaction (PCR)
PCR is a cyclical process that quickly makes many copies of a DNA segment.
Animated BIOLOGY
Watch how PCR works at ClassZone.com.
target sequence of DNA
1 Separating The container with all of the reactants is heated to more than 90°C (194°F) for a few seconds to separate the strands of DNA.
DNA strands
2 Binding The container is cooled to about 55°C (131°F). The primers bind to the DNA strands.
primer 1
primer 2
polymerase
nucleotides
3 Copying The container is heated to about 72°C (152°F), the temperature at which the polymerases work best. The polymerases bind nucleotides until the DNA segment has been copied.
PCR AMPLIFIES DNA SAMPLES
With each PCR cycle, the number of copies of the DNA segment doubles. After 30 cycles, more than 1 billion copies have been made.

Ⓐ **CRITICAL VIEWING** **How many copies of DNA will exist after one more PCR cycle? After three more cycles?**

Differentiated Instruction

PRE-AP

Tell students that primers are needed in both PCR and DNA replication. Have students compare **FIGURE 9.5** to **FIGURE 8.11** on page 241. Have students compare and contrast the process of PCR with that of DNA transcription, including the role of primers and enzymes.

Biology Toolkit, Compare/Contrast Chart, p. C34

INCLUSION

If you plan to go through the steps of PCR in detail, project **FIGURE 9.5** from the Media Gallery. Have hearing-impaired students use a set of signals, such as thumbs-up/thumbs-down, to indicate whether they are following your explanation or whether they need you to repeat information. Remember to face the students when speaking, so they can watch your lips.

Biology Toolkit, Signals, p. C18

MAIN IDEA

PCR is a three-step process.

PCR is a surprisingly simple process. It uses just four materials: the DNA to be copied, DNA polymerases, large amounts of each of the four DNA nucleotides (A, T, C, and G), and two primers. A **primer** is a short segment of DNA that acts as the starting point for a new strand. If DNA polymerases build new DNA strands, why are primers needed for PCR? DNA polymerases can add nucleotides to strands that have already been started, but they cannot start the strands. In PCR, two primers are used to start the copying of DNA close to the desired segment. The two primers are like bookends for the DNA strand. They limit the length of the copied DNA to one small segment of the strand.

PCR has three main steps, as shown in **FIGURE 9.5.** All of the steps of the cycle take place in the same container but at different temperatures. The main function of the first two PCR cycles is to produce the small segment of DNA that is desired. By making a copy of the desired segment, many copies of that tiny piece of DNA can be made, rather than copying an entire chromosome.

1. **Separating** The container with all of the reactants is heated to separate the double-stranded DNA into single strands.
2. **Binding** The container is cooled and the primers bind to their complementary DNA sequences. One primer binds to each DNA strand. The primers bind on opposite ends of the DNA segment being copied.
3. **Copying** The container is heated again and the polymerases begin to build new strands of DNA. Added nucleotides bind to the original DNA strands by complementary base pairing. The polymerases continue attaching nucleotides until the entire DNA segment has been copied.

Each PCR cycle doubles the number of DNA copies. The original piece of DNA becomes two copies. Those two copies become four copies. And the cycle is repeated over and over to quickly copy enough DNA for study. After only 30 cycles of PCR, for example, the original DNA sequence is copied more than 1 billion times. This doubling is why the process is called a chain reaction.

A **Infer** **Why is it necessary to keep changing the temperature in the PCR process?**

VOCABULARY

The term *primer* comes from a Latin word that means "first." In PCR, a primer is the starting point for the DNA copying process.

***Connecting* CONCEPTS**

Replication Look back at the process of DNA replication in **Chapter 8** to compare PCR with replication.

9.2 ASSESSMENT

ONLINE QUIZ
ClassZone.com

REVIEWING MAIN IDEAS

1. Briefly describe the function of **polymerase chain reaction (PCR).**
2. Summarize the cycle involved in the PCR process.

CRITICAL THINKING

3. **Synthesize** Describe how heating double-stranded DNA separates the strands. Why does heating also inactivate DNA polymerases from many organisms?
4. **Analyze** Explain two reasons why **primers** are important in PCR.

***Connecting* CONCEPTS**

5. **Human Genetics** Many human genetic diseases are caused by recessive alleles of genes. How might PCR be important in the diagnosis of these illnesses?

9.2 ASSESSMENT

1. PCR is used to make many copies of a specific segment of DNA.
2. Heat separates strands; primers bind; polymerase builds new strands.
3. Heating breaks the hydrogen bonds between bases, causing the strands to separate. Heat also causes hydrogen bonds in proteins (enzymes) to break apart, which inactivates the enzymes.
4. Primers allow DNA polymerases to add nucleotides, and they limit the size of the DNA segment being copied.
5. PCR can be used to make many copies of different alleles so that they can be analyzed and isolated.

Take It Further

In each **PCR cycle,** the primers bind to their target binding site and allow polymerases to add nucleotides from that point on—in one direction only. This means that the portion of a DNA strand that is downstream from where the primer binds is left out of the PCR process. The same thing is true on the other strand, but on that one, the primer and polymerases are working in the opposite direction, and what was skipped on the other strand is copied. The DNA copies based on each strand are therefore a little bit closer to containing only the target segment than the original DNA. Once the DNA being produced is an exact match of the target sequence, the primers that bind to the separated strands are doing so right at the ends. From that point on, almost all of the DNA copies match the target DNA segment.

Vocabulary

Academic Vocabulary Tell students that the word **prime** is often used as a verb, meaning "to make ready" or "prepare." Walls are primed before painting and wells are primed by pouring water into the pump.

Answers

A **Infer** High temperatures are needed to separate DNA strands, and both enzymes and primers function best at different specific temperatures.

Assess and Reteach ▼

Assess Use the Online Quiz or Section Quiz (*Assessment Book,* p. 170).

Reteach Have students close their books, then ask them to put the steps of PCR into a sequence diagram. They should include the words *primer, separate, bind,* and *copy.*

▼ Plan and Prepare

Objectives

- Describe what a DNA fingerprint represents.
- Summarize how DNA fingerprints are used for identification.

Section Resources

Unit Resource Book
- **Study Guide** pp. 107–108
- **Power Notes** p. 109
- **Reinforcement** p. 110
- **Pre-AP Activity** pp. 125–126

Interactive Reader Chapter 9
Spanish Study Guide pp. 91–92

Biology Toolkit pp. C13, C28

Technology
- Power Presentation 9.3
- Media Gallery DVD
- Online Quiz 9.3

Activate Prior Knowledge Show students a blowup photo of a fingerprint, or have them look at their own. **Ask**

- What characteristics of a fingerprint make it useful for identification? the unique pattern of whorls and ridges in the skin
- What characteristic of DNA might make it useful for identification? the unique sequence of nucleotides

▼ Teach

TEACH FROM VISUALS

FIGURE 9.6 Have students compare the bands of the children with the bands of each parent. **Ask,** What is it about the DNA fingerprints that indicates each child is related to these parents? Each DNA band, or absence of a band, in a child's fingerprint matches that of one of the parent's fingerprints.

Answers

A Synthesize No, it just indicates the number of repeat sequences. Most DNA fingerprinting uses DNA sequences outside of genes.

9.3 DNA Fingerprinting

KEY CONCEPT DNA fingerprints identify people at the molecular level.

MAIN IDEAS
- A DNA fingerprint is a type of restriction map.
- DNA fingerprinting is used for identification.

VOCABULARY
DNA fingerprint, p. 272

Review
restriction enzyme, gel electrophoresis, restriction map

Connect You hear about it in the news all the time. DNA evidence is used to convict a criminal, release an innocent person from prison, or solve a mystery. A couple of decades ago, the lines and swirls of someone's fingertip were a detective's best hope for identifying someone. Now, investigators gather biological samples and analyze DNA for another kind of evidence: a DNA fingerprint.

MAIN IDEA
A DNA fingerprint is a type of restriction map.

Unless you have an identical twin, your complete set of DNA, or your genome, is unique. This variation in DNA among people is the basis of DNA fingerprinting. A **DNA fingerprint** is a representation of parts of an individual's DNA that can be used to identify a person at the molecular level.

A DNA fingerprint is a specific type of restriction map, which you learned about in Section 9.1. First, a DNA sample is cut with a restriction enzyme. Then the DNA fragments are run through a gel and the pattern of bands on the gel is analyzed. As you can see in **FIGURE 9.6**, a DNA fingerprint can show relationships among family members. The children (C) have similar DNA fingerprints to one another, but they are not identical. Also, their DNA fingerprints are combinations of the DNA fingerprints of the parents (M and F).

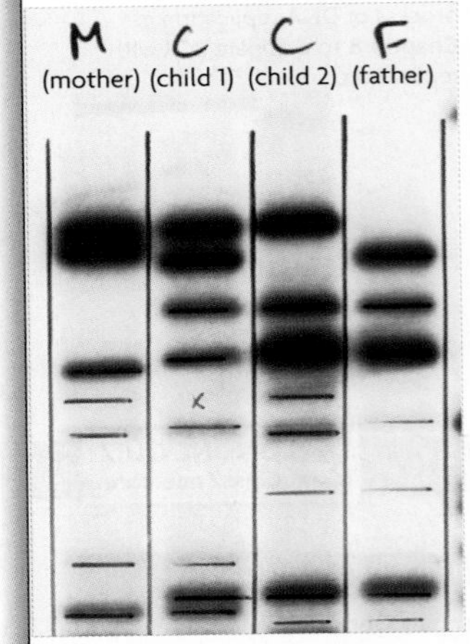

The greatest differences in DNA among people are found in regions of the genome that are not parts of genes. As a result, DNA fingerprinting focuses on noncoding regions of DNA, or DNA sequences outside genes. Noncoding DNA sequences often include stretches of nucleotides that repeat several times, one after another, as shown in **FIGURE 9.7.** Each person's DNA differs in the numbers of copies of the repeats. For example, one person may have seven repeats in one location, and another person may have three in the same place. To get to the specific regions of DNA that can be identified through DNA fingerprinting, the DNA is cut in known locations with restriction enzymes.

The differences in the number of repeats are found by separating the DNA fragments with gel electrophoresis. When there are more repeats, a DNA fragment is larger. The pattern of DNA fragments on a gel represents the uniqueness of a person's DNA. Individuals might have some of the fragments in common, but it is very unlikely that all of them would be the same.

FIGURE 9.6 DNA fingerprints can be compared to identify people. Both children share some bands with each parent.

A Synthesize Does a DNA fingerprint show a person's genotype? Why or why not?

Differentiated Instruction

ENGLISH LEARNERS

Have students create a mind map, starting with the sentence "DNA fingerprinting is used for identification" in a large oval. On diagonals extending from the oval, they can write all of the uses described in the section. Review and assess their work by creating a mind map on the board and completing it with answers that students call out.

Biology Toolkit, Mind Map, p. C28

FIGURE 9.7 DNA Fingerprinting

A DNA fingerprint shows differences in the number of repeats of certain DNA sequences.

This DNA sequence of 33 bases can be repeated many times in a sample of a person's DNA.

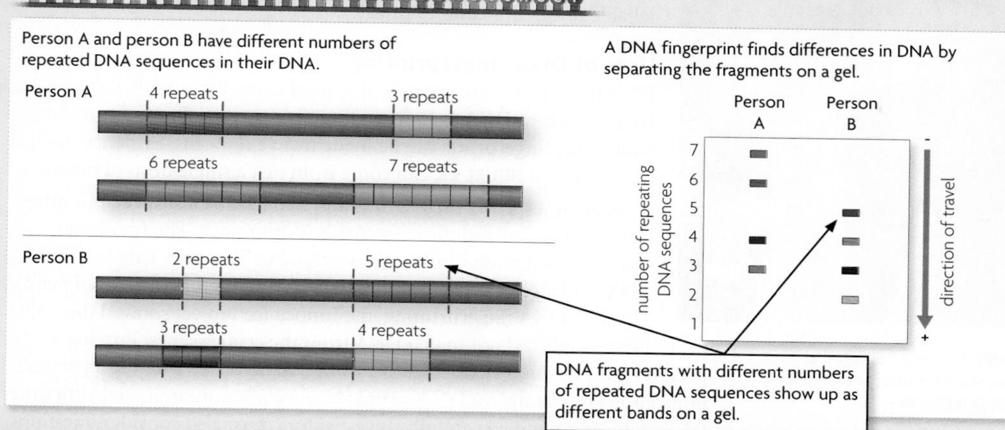

CTAAAGCTGGAGGTGGGCAGGAAGGACCGAGGT
Person A and person B have different numbers of repeated DNA sequences in their DNA.
Person A
4 repeats
3 repeats
6 repeats
7 repeats
Person B
2 repeats
5 repeats
3 repeats
4 repeats
A DNA fingerprint finds differences in DNA by separating the fragments on a gel.
Person A
Person B
number of repeating DNA sequences
7
6
5
4
3
2
1
direction of travel
-
+
DNA fragments with different numbers of repeated DNA sequences show up as different bands on a gel.

A Infer **How would the DNA fingerprints change if a different restriction enzyme cut the DNA in the middle of one of the repeated DNA sequences?**

MAIN IDEA

DNA fingerprinting is used for identification.

DNA fingerprinting to identify people has become a reliable and widely used process since the 1990s. Why? The specific nucleotide sequences that are repeated can be found in everyone. More importantly, from one person to another, the number of repeat sequences can differ greatly, even among brothers and sisters.

DNA Fingerprints and Probability

Identification with DNA fingerprinting depends on probability. Suppose that 1 in every 500 people has three copies of the repeat at location A. This means any person has a 1-in-500 chance of having a matching DNA fingerprint for that region of a chromosome. By itself, the number of repeats in one location cannot be used for identification, because too many people would match.

But then suppose that 1 in every 90 people has six copies of the repeat sequence at location B, and 1 in every 120 people has ten copies of the repeat sequence at location C. Individual probabilities are multiplied by each other to find the total probability. Therefore, when the three separate probabilities are multiplied, suddenly the chance that two people have the same DNA fingerprint is very small.

$$\frac{1}{500} \times \frac{1}{90} \times \frac{1}{120} = \frac{1}{5{,}400{,}000} = \text{1 chance in 5.4 million people}$$

***Connecting* CONCEPTS**

Genome Recall from **Chapter 6** that a genome is the entire set of DNA in a cell. You will learn more about genome research in **Section 9.5.**

TEACH FROM VISUALS

FIGURE 9.7 Discuss the information in this figure. **Ask**

- Where were the DNA samples placed in the gel? at the end nearest to the negative electrode
- Why are the fragments with the fewest number of repeats at the bottom of the fingerprint? Fragments with the fewest number of repeats are smaller and move farther than fragments with more repeats.

The Inside Story

After DNA fragments are separated by gel electrophoresis, the bands are blotted onto a membrane and analyzed with dyes or radioactive probes to make them visible. This technique, the **Southern blot,** has nothing to do with direction. It was developed by **Edwin Southern,** a British biologist. As a play on his name, other blot methods have been named the Western blot, Northern blot, Southwestern blot, and Hawaiian blot. Who says scientists don't have a sense of humor?

Science Trivia

- In most forensic cases, at least five regions of DNA are analyzed.
- Depending on ethnic group, the probability of two people having identical DNA fingerprints ranges from 1 in 100,000 to 1 in 1 billion. The world population is about 6.5 billion.

BELOW LEVEL

Explain to students that probabilities are often written as fractions. A one-in-two chance of flipping the head side of a coin is written as 1/2. One chance in 5.4 million people is written as 1/5,400,000. Give students some probabilities of inheriting genetic disorders, such as cystic fibrosis (1 in 2500 Caucasians) and sickle cell disease (1 in 400 African Americans). Have students write the probabilities as fractions, and then pair up to compare answers.

Biology Toolkit, Think-Pair-Share, p. C13

Answers

A Infer A different pattern would appear in the gel because one of the larger fragments would be split in two.

▼ Teach *continued*

Take It Further

There is now at least one **Innocence Project** in every state except Hawaii, North Dakota, and South Dakota. Most projects rely on volunteer attorneys and law students who review cases of prisoners who claim they were falsely convicted of violent crimes. Although the Cardozo project alone receives up to 200 requests a month, it accepts only those cases in which DNA testing of evidence is possible.

The Inside Story

DNA fingerprinting is helpful in identifying human remains that are otherwise unidentifiable. **The Tomb of the Unknowns** in Arlington National Cemetery contained the remains of one unidentified soldier each from World War I, World War II, the Korean War, and the Vietnam War. In 1998, DNA fingerprinting was used to identify the remains of the Vietnam War soldier. They were returned to his family and reburied in Missouri.

Answers

A Summarize The more sites that are compared, the lower the probability that two people's DNA would share all of them.

▼ Assess and Reteach

Assess Use the Online Quiz or Section Quiz (*Assessment Book*, p. 171).

Reteach Review DNA fingerprinting by projecting **FIGURE 9.6** from the Media Gallery and asking students to point out how the band patterns of the children reflect their relatedness to the parents. Review why bands appear as they do.

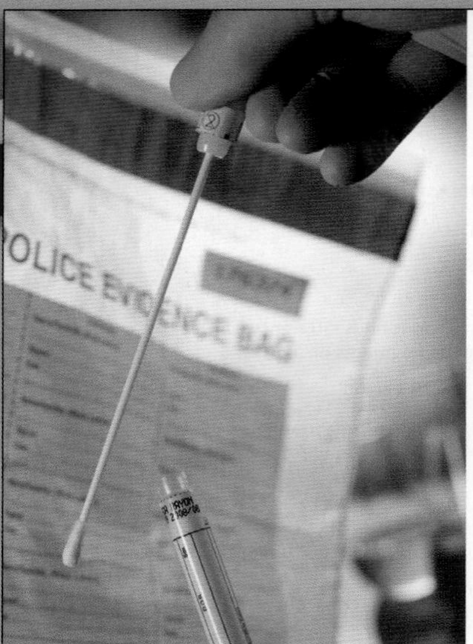

FIGURE 9.8 DNA collected at crime scenes is used as evidence in many legal cases.

Usually, DNA fingerprinting compares at least five regions of the genome. That way it is more certain that the pattern of DNA fragments in the fingerprint is unique. The more regions of DNA that are studied, the less likely it becomes that another person would have the same DNA fingerprint. For this reason, DNA fingerprinting is considered very reliable for identification purposes.

Uses of DNA Fingerprinting

DNA fingerprints are often used in legal cases. Because PCR can make a large sample of DNA even when there is a very small sample to start with, DNA fingerprints can be made from a few cells. Evidence, such as that shown in **FIGURE 9.8**, can come from just a single drop of blood.

Sometimes, DNA fingerprints are used against a suspect, but other times they are used to prove someone's innocence. The Innocence Project at Benjamin Cardozo Law School in New York City has used DNA evidence to help free more than 170 wrongfully convicted people. Through DNA fingerprinting, the Innocence Project showed that DNA from those people did not match DNA from the crime scenes. Proving a person's guilt through DNA fingerprinting is harder than proving a person's innocence. For example, a DNA sample can become contaminated with other DNA if it is not handled carefully. Investigators must also consider questions such as "What is the chance that another person has the same DNA fingerprint?" and "What probability is low enough to be acceptable?" Are chances of 1 in 100,000 low enough? One in 1 million? In fact, there is no legal standard for this probability of a random DNA fingerprint match.

The same DNA fingerprinting methods are also used for identification purposes outside of the courtroom. DNA fingerprints can prove family relationships, such as paternity and the kinship necessary for immigration requests. But DNA fingerprinting is not limited to human identification. Genetic comparisons through DNA fingerprinting are used to study biodiversity and to locate genetically engineered crops. And, as you saw at the beginning of the chapter, researchers are using DNA fingerprinting to identify tortoises native to the Galapagos Islands.

NSTA SCILINKS scilinks.org
To find out more about DNA fingerprinting, go to scilinks.org.
Keycode: MLB009

A Summarize How does identification by DNA fingerprinting depend on probability?

9.3 ASSESSMENT

ONLINE QUIZ ClassZone.com

REVIEWING MAIN IDEAS

1. On what, in a person's DNA, is a **DNA fingerprint** based?
2. Describe two ways in which DNA fingerprinting is used.

CRITICAL THINKING

3. **Compare and Contrast** How are DNA fingerprints and restriction maps similar? different? Explain.
4. **Synthesize** Briefly describe how restriction enzymes, gel electrophoresis, and PCR are used in DNA fingerprinting.

***Connecting* CONCEPTS**

5. **Mutations** Why might noncoding regions of DNA outside of genes be more variable than coding regions of DNA?

9.3 ASSESSMENT

1. the number of repeats of certain DNA sequences
2. *Sample Answer:* establishing genetic relationships between people, tracking genetically modified crops, identifying different species, identifying specific people.
3. Both are based on the lengths of fragments produced by the restriction enzymes. A DNA fingerprint is a restriction map of specific noncoding regions of an individual's DNA.
4. PCR produces multiple copies of a DNA sample, restriction enzymes cut the DNA into fragments to be analyzed, and gel electrophoresis separates the fragments so that their lengths can be compared.
5. Changes in DNA outside genes are less likely to be harmful to an organism or its chances of reproducing successfully. Therefore, mutations in these parts of DNA are more likely to accumulate over generations than are mutations of genes.

9.4 Genetic Engineering

KEY CONCEPT DNA sequences of organisms can be changed.

MAIN IDEAS
- Entire organisms can be cloned.
- New genes can be added to an organism's DNA.
- Genetic engineering produces organisms with new traits.

VOCABULARY
clone, p. 275
genetic engineering, p. 276
recombinant DNA, p. 276
plasmid, p. 276
transgenic, p. 277
gene knockout, p. 279

Review
restriction enzyme

INDIANA STANDARDS

B.7.5 Explain and demonstrate how inserting, substituting or deleting segments of a DNA molecule can alter a gene, which is then passed to every cell that develops from it and that the results may be beneficial, harmful or have little or no effect on the organism.

Connect Glowing mice are used in cancer research. Glowing plants are used to track genetically modified crops. And, in 1999, British researchers introduced glowing yeast cells that locate water pollution. The scientists put a gene for a fluorescent protein into yeast. Under normal conditions, the yeast cells do not glow. But they do glow when certain chemicals are present. The glow identifies areas that need to be cleaned. New biotechnology applications seem to be developed on a daily basis. What advances will you see during your lifetime?

MAIN IDEA

Entire organisms can be cloned.

The term *cloning* might make you think of science fiction and horror movies, but the process is quite common in nature. A **clone** is a genetically identical copy of a gene or of an organism. For example, some plants clone themselves from their roots. Bacteria produce identical genetic copies of themselves through binary fission. And human identical twins are clones of each other.

People have cloned plants for centuries. The process is fairly easy because many plants naturally clone themselves and because plants have stem cell tissues that can develop into many types of cells. Some simple animals, such as sea stars, can essentially clone themselves through a process called regeneration. Mammals, however, cannot clone themselves.

FIGURE 9.9 The cat named CC—for Copy Cat or Carbon Copy—is the first successful clone of a cat (right). The original cat is on the left.

To clone a mammal, scientists swap DNA between cells with a technique called nuclear transfer. First, an unfertilized egg is taken from an animal, and the egg's nucleus is removed. Then the nucleus of a cell from the animal to be cloned is implanted into the egg. The egg is stimulated and, if the procedure is successful, the egg will begin dividing. After the embryo grows for a few days, it is transplanted into a female. In 1997 a sheep named Dolly became the first clone of an adult mammal. The success of Dolly led to the cloning of adult cows, pigs, and mice. Now, a biotechnology company has even said that it can clone people's pets.

But pet owners who expect cloning to produce an exact copy of their furry friend will likely be disappointed. As you can see from the cat called CC in **FIGURE 9.9**, a clone may not look like the original, and it will probably not behave like the original, either. Why? Because, as you have learned, many factors, including environment, affect the expression of genes.

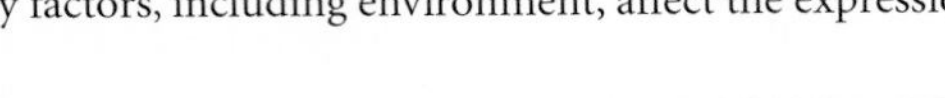

Differentiated Instruction

ENGLISH LEARNERS

Have students answer questions on slates so you can check their comprehension of genetic engineering. As you present the lesson, ask questions such as "Does cloning increase biodiversity?" (no) and "What do some bacteria have that allows for the production of recombinant DNA?" (plasmids). Students write their answers and hold up their slates. Scan the answers and use them to clarify.

Biology Toolkit, Slates, p. C18

SECTION 9.4

Plan and Prepare

Objectives

- Describe how organisms are cloned.
- Explain how new genes can be added to an organism's DNA.

Section Resources

Unit Resource Book
Study Guide pp. 111–112
Power Notes p. 113
Reinforcement p. 114

Interactive Reader Chapter 9
Spanish Study Guide pp. 93–94

Biology Toolkit pp. C5, C18, C19

Technology
Power Presentation 9.4
Media Gallery DVD
Online Quiz 9.4

Activating Prior Knowledge Have students think about whether there are traits they would change in themselves if they could. Tell them that in the near future it may be possible to modify DNA so that children have alleles not found in either parent's DNA. **Ask,** Do you think it is ethical to manipulate the DNA of a human being? Answers will vary, but most students may agree it is beneficial to correct genetic disorders.

Teach

Vocabulary

Greek and Latin Word Origins The word **clone** comes from the Greek *klōn,* meaning "twig," which conveys the idea of branching off. Cloning is a practice commonly used to produce new plants from old.

▼ Teach *continued*

ONLINE BIOLOGY Students can perform a virtual lab on bacterial transformation in Options For Inquiry on page 287.

History of Science

In 1902, German embryologist **Hans Spemann** used a noose made of a hair from his baby boy's head to divide a two-celled salamander embryo. Each cell developed into a salamander. Spemann repeated his experiments with more-developed embryos, but found that cells teased apart from one another in these later stages of development did not develop into salamanders. He concluded that at a certain stage in development, the cells differentiate.

Later, in the late 1920s, Spemann transferred a nucleus from a 16-cell embryo to a single salamander embryo cell that had no nucleus. The cell developed normally, proving that nuclear transfer was possible. Spemann proposed that adult cell nuclei could be used to create clones. Spemann was awarded the Nobel Prize in 1935.

Integrating Microbiology

Plasmids carry only a small number of genes. These genes are not required for the survival and reproduction of the bacterium, but they often provide a benefit to the cell, such as antibiotic resistance. A single plasmid may have as many as ten genes for resistance to various antibiotics. Plasmids can be transferred from cell to cell by a process called **conjugation.**

Answers

A Apply Answers should address the risk of producing an unhealthy clone and the effort that would be needed to produce even one clone.

***Connecting* CONCEPTS**

Biodiversity In **Chapter 1**, you learned that biodiversity can be defined as the number of different species in an area. You will learn more about genetic diversity within a species in **Unit 4.**

Cloning brings with it some extraordinary opportunities. For example, scientists are studying how to use organs from cloned mammals for transplant into humans. This use of cloning could save an enormous number of lives each year. Cloning could even help save endangered species. Cells from endangered species could be taken and used to produce clones that would increase the population of the species.

Cloning is also controversial for a few reasons. The success rate in cloning mammals is very low. It takes hundreds of tries to produce one clone, and sometimes the clone is not as healthy as the original. For example, Dolly seemed to develop and grow normally, but she also had health problems. She seemed to age quickly and did not live as long as a typical sheep, possibly because she was cloned from an adult sheep and had "old DNA." There are also ecological concerns about cloning. Cloned animals in a wild population would reduce biodiversity because the clones would be genetically identical.

A Apply **Given the opportunity, would you have a pet cloned? Explain your answer based on your knowledge of genetics, biotechnology, and cloning.**

MAIN IDEA

New genes can be added to an organism's DNA.

Genetic research relies on cloning, but not the cloning of organisms. Instead, it is the cloning of individual genes. A clone of a gene is a copy of that one segment of DNA. In some cases, scientists insert cloned genes from one organism into a different organism. This changing of an organism's DNA to give the organism new traits is called **genetic engineering.** Genetic engineering is possible because the genetic code is shared by all organisms.

Genetic engineering is based on the use of recombinant DNA technology. **Recombinant DNA** (ree-KAHM-buh-nuhnt) is DNA that contains genes from more than one organism. Scientists are trying to use recombinant DNA in several different ways. For example, recombinant DNA could be used to produce crop plants that make medicines and vitamins. Scientists hope that large amounts of medicines will one day be made through this process, which has been called "pharming." Scientists are also studying ways of using recombinant DNA to make vaccines to protect against HIV, the virus that causes AIDS.

Bacteria are commonly used in genetic engineering. One reason is because bacteria have tiny rings of DNA called plasmids. **Plasmids,** as shown in **FIGURE 9.10,** are closed loops of DNA that are separate from the bacterial chromosome and that replicate on their own within the cell.

FIGURE 9.10 A plasmid is a closed loop of DNA in a bacterium that is separate from the bacterial chromosome. (colored TEM; magnification 48,000×)

VISUAL VOCAB

Recombinant DNA is DNA that combines genes from more than one organism.

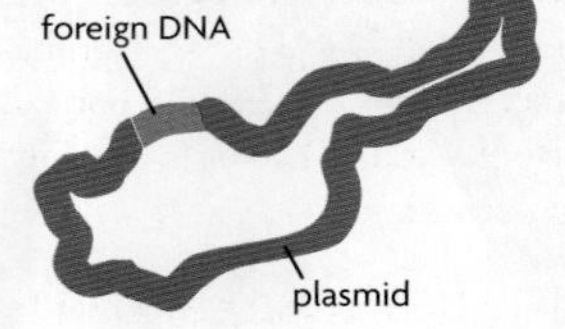

Foreign DNA is inserted into plasmids to make recombinant DNA.

Differentiated Instruction

BELOW LEVEL

Have students make a three-column chart and label the columns *Know, Want to Know,* and *Learned.* Have them list in the first column several things they already know about genetic engineering, such as the use of PCR to clone segments of DNA. Have them list in the second column several things they want to know. Then have students read the section and list several things they have learned about genetic engineering.

Biology Toolkit, KWL, p. C5

FIGURE 9.11 Making Recombinant DNA

Foreign DNA can be inserted into a plasmid to make recombinant DNA.

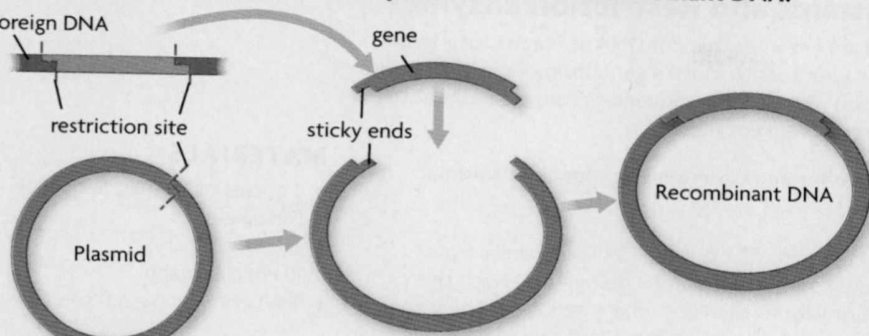

A plasmid and the foreign DNA with the gene are cut with the same restriction enzyme.

The sticky ends of the plasmid and the foreign gene match.

The plasmid and the foreign gene are bonded together to form recombinant DNA.

A Apply Why are sticky ends important for making recombinant DNA?

Plasmids are small rings of DNA used in genetic engineering. Foreign genes (blue, light blue, magenta, green) have been inserted into these plasmids (red). (colored TEM, magnification 29,000×)

Recombinant DNA is found naturally in bacteria that take in exogenous DNA (or DNA from a different organism) and add it to their own. Scientists adapted what happens in nature to make artificial recombinant DNA. First, a restriction enzyme is used to cut out the desired gene from a strand of DNA. Then plasmids are cut with the same enzyme. The plasmid opens, and when the gene is added to the plasmid, their complementary sticky ends are bonded together by a process called ligation. The resulting plasmid contains recombinant DNA, as shown in **FIGURE 9.11.**

B Summarize How does genetic engineering rely on a shared genetic code?

MAIN IDEA

Genetic engineering produces organisms with new traits.

After a gene is added to a plasmid, the genetically engineered plasmids can be put into bacteria. In a way, bacteria are turned into tiny gene factories that make copy after copy of the plasmid. As a result, the transformed bacteria make many copies of the new gene. The bacteria will express the new gene and make that gene's product. The bacteria with the recombinant plasmid are called transgenic. A **transgenic** organism has one or more genes from another organism inserted into its genome. For example, the gene for human insulin can be put into plasmids. The plasmids are inserted into bacteria. The transgenic bacteria make human insulin that is collected and used to treat people with diabetes.

VOCABULARY

The prefix *trans-* means "across," and the root *genic* means "referring to genes." When genes are transferred across different organisms, transgenic organisms are produced.

Genetic Engineering in Plants

Genetic engineering of plants is directly related to genetic engineering of bacteria. To change a plant's DNA, a gene is inserted into a plasmid and the plasmid is inserted into bacteria. After the bacteria infect the plant, the new gene becomes a part of the plant's DNA and is expressed like any other gene.

PRE-AP

After reading the section, tell students to think about a kind of plant that they would like to genetically modify. Give them five minutes to write how they would use restriction enzymes and bacteria plasmids to insert a gene from another species into the DNA of the plant they would like to modify.

Biology Toolkit, Quick-Write, p. C19

ONLINE BIOLOGY Have students complete the WebQuest in Options for Inquiry on page 287 to learn how scientists clone animals and weigh the risks and benefits.

Take It Further

In biotechnology, a cell is **transformed** when foreign DNA is incorporated into its genome and it expresses the product of the new gene. Producing a **transgenic bacterium,** such as the one that makes human insulin, involves many more steps than those that are presented in the text. In addition to inserting a gene into a plasmid, an appropriate promoter must be present, the gene itself might have to be altered so that the protein can be made, and the protein has to be purified so that it can be used.

Answers

A Apply A desired gene can bind to a plasmid's DNA through complementary base pairing.

B Summarize A gene's DNA sequence is translated into the same amino acid sequence across different organisms.

Chapter 9: Frontiers of Biotechnology 277

▼ Teach *continued*

ONLINE BIOLOGY Go to the chapter Resource Center at **ClassZone.com** for additional resources and information on genetic engineering.

QUICK LAB

Time 15 minutes	TEACHER TESTED
Lab Binder Genetics, pp. 53–54	

Purpose Model the formation of recombinant DNA using three restriction enzymes.

LAB PREPARATION

- Make and distribute three copies of the Plasmid Sequence datasheet, *Lab Binder,* p. 54.

LAB MANAGEMENT

- Explain to students that the vehicle that carries a gene from one organism into another is called a vector. Plasmids are one type of vector. Other vectors are viruses and tiny "bullets" containing the gene that are shot into cells.

Answers

Analyze and Conclude

1. You would get four fragments (4-inch, 6-inch, 12-inch, and 18-inch).
2. Because restriction enzymes act at different restriction sites, one restriction enzyme that removes one gene could be cutting into another.

Vocabulary

Academic Vocabulary The word **vector** is used in a number of applications.

- In *physics,* it is a quantity, such as velocity, that has both magnitude and a direction.
- In *microbiology,* it refers to an organism, such as a mosquito or tick, that carries disease-causing micro-organisms from one host to another.
- In *genetics,* it refers to a bacteriophage, plasmid, or other agent that transfers genetic material from one cell to another.

QUICK LAB MODELING NOS.6

Modeling Plasmids and Restriction Enzymes

Restriction enzymes are enzymes that cut DNA at precise locations. These enzymes allow scientists to move a gene from one organism into another. In this lab, you will use DNA sequences from a datasheet to simulate the use of restriction enzymes.

PROBLEM How do different restriction enzymes cut a plasmid?

PROCEDURE

1. Make models of 3 plasmids. Cut out the DNA sequences from the copies of Figure 1 on the datasheet. Use tape to attach the appropriate piece of yarn to each end where indicated. The yarn represents the entire plasmid. The finished plasmid should be a circle.
2. Use the scissors to cut a plasmid at the correct sites for *Eco*RI.
3. Use the sequences for sites of *Hind*III and *Sma*I to repeat step 3 with the other two plasmids.

ANALYZE AND CONCLUDE

1. **Apply** How many DNA fragments would you get if you cut the same plasmid with both *Eco*RI and *Sma*I ?
2. **Infer** Why might scientists use different restrictions enzymes to cut out different genes from a strand of DNA?

MATERIALS

- 3 copies of Plasmid Sequence Datasheet
- scissors
- 10 cm clear tape
- 3 sets of 5 5-cm yarn pieces

This technique has allowed scientists to give plants new traits, such as resistance to frost, diseases, and insects. For instance, a gene known as *Bt* makes a natural pesticide in some organisms. After *Bt* is added to crop plants, smaller amounts of chemical pesticides are needed to protect the crop from insects. Some genetically engineered crops, which are also called genetically modified (GM), are now common in the United States. These crops include *Bt* potatoes and corn, and they are even more important in developing countries. By increasing crop yields, more food is produced more quickly and cheaply.

Genetic Engineering in Animals

In general, transgenic animals are much harder to produce than GM plants because animals are more resistant to genetic manipulation. To produce a transgenic animal, a researcher must first get a fertilized egg cell. Then the foreign DNA is inserted into the nucleus and the egg is implanted back into a female. However, only a small percentage of the genetically manipulated eggs mature normally. And only a portion of those that develop will be transgenic. That is, only a small number will have the foreign gene as a part of their DNA. But those animals that are transgenic will have the gene in all of their cells—including reproductive cells—and the transgenic trait will be passed on to their offspring.

Transgenic mice are often used as models of human development and disease. The first such animal was called the oncomouse. This mouse always develops cancer, because a gene that controls cell growth and differentiation

Differentiated Instruction

TEACH WITH TECHNOLOGY

Assemble a digital slide show of images of cloned animals such as the domestic cat, pig, cattle, frog, carp, sheep, horse, mule, and deer, and transgenic animals such as fluorescent green pigs. Go to **ClassZone.com** for links to Internet sources of images and information on the animals that have been cloned.

was mutated. Researchers use the oncomouse to study both cancer and anti-cancer drugs. Other types of transgenic mice are used to study diabetes, brain function and development, and sex determination.

In another type of genetic manipulation, some mice have genes that have been purposely "turned off." These mice, called **gene knockout** mice, are made by disrupting the function of a gene. Knockout mice are very useful for studying gene function and genetic diseases because a researcher can observe specific changes in gene expression and traits. For example, scientists are using a gene knockout mouse to study obesity, as you can see in **FIGURE 9.12**.

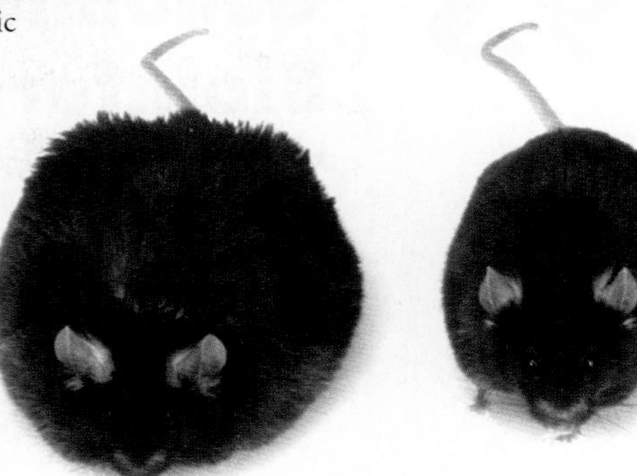

FIGURE 9.12 The knockout mouse (left) does not have a functional gene for a protein called leptin, which helps to control food intake. Researchers are using this type of mouse to study obesity.

Concerns About Genetic Engineering

Scientists have genetically engineered many useful organisms by transferring genes between species to give individuals new traits. At the same time, there are concerns about possible effects of genetically engineered organisms on both human health and the environment. And at an even more basic level, some people wonder whether genetic engineering is ethical in the first place.

Questions have been raised about GM crops, even though scientists have not yet found negative health effects of GM foods. Critics say that not enough research has been done, and that some added genes might cause allergic reactions or have other unknown side effects. Scientists also have concerns about the possible effects of GM plants on the environment and on biodiversity. For example, what would happen if genetically engineered *Bt* plants killed insects that pollinate plants, such as bees and butterflies? In some instances, transgenic plants have cross-pollinated with wild type plants in farming regions. Scientists do not yet know what long-term effect this interbreeding might have on the natural plants. In addition, all organisms in a transgenic population have the same genome. As a result, some scientists worry that a decrease in genetic diversity could leave crops vulnerable to new diseases or pests.

Infer Why is it important that a transgenic trait is passed on to the transgenic organism's offspring?

Take It Further

Genetic engineering raises serious safety and ethical issues:

- New pathogens might be created and released into the environment. Can safety measures that disable the microbes ensure that they cannot survive outside the lab?
- Engineered organisms in our food supply might be harmful. Genetically modified animals are not used for food, but GM plants are. Do we know that they are safe? Should we label all foods that contain GM plants?
- Will a person with an allergy to the plant that donated the foreign gene be allergic to the transgenic plant product? Food labels will have to be very specific.

Currently, many countries, particularly in Europe, are unofficially boycotting all GM foods because of concern over some of these issues.

Answers

A Infer so that additional generations can be studied, and complex genetic engineering will not be needed to produce every transgenic organism

9.4 ASSESSMENT

ONLINE QUIZ ClassZone.com

B.7.5

REVIEWING MAIN IDEAS

1. Why is the offspring of asexual reproduction a **clone**?
2. What are **plasmids**, and how are they used in **genetic engineering**?
3. Describe two applications of **transgenic** organisms.

CRITICAL THINKING

4. **Compare and Contrast** How is the cloning of genes different from the cloning of mammals?
5. **Summarize** How are restriction enzymes used to make both **recombinant DNA** and transgenic organisms?

***Connecting* CONCEPTS**

6. **Ecology** Do you think cloning endangered species is a good idea? What effect might this have on an ecosystem?

Assess and Reteach

Assess Use the Online Quiz or Section Quiz (*Assessment Book,* p. 172).

Reteach Have students make a chart that gives at least one example each of a bacterium, a plant, and an animal that has been genetically engineered. Charts should also list the gene that was inserted into the host cell (if applicable) and the product that was produced or the trait that was changed.

9.4 ASSESSMENT

1. because offspring of asexual reproduction are genetically identical to the parent
2. Plasmids are closed loops of bacterial DNA. New genes can be incorporated into plasmids, and the bacteria will produce the proteins coded for by the genes.
3. Answers could include genetically modified crops, such as *Bt* corn; medical treatments, such as the production of insulin for people who have diabetes; and medical research, such as the use of the oncomouse to study cancer.
4. Cloned genes are the duplication of a small segment of DNA; the cloning of mammals involves the implantation of an entire genome into an egg that can develop into an entire organism.
5. Restriction enzymes are needed to cut DNA around a gene of interest so that it can be inserted into a plasmid to make recombinant DNA, or into a developing embryo to make a transgenic organism.
6. Cloning could be the only means of saving an endangered species, but the ultimate effects on an ecosystem are difficult to predict. Also, clones will be genetically identical, so the gene pool would be so small that the population would never rebound without the help of humans.

SECTION 9.5

▼ Plan and Prepare

Objectives

- Describe genomics.
- Identify how technology helps compare and study genes and proteins.

Section Resources

Unit Resource Book
Study Guide pp. 115–116
Power Notes p. 117
Reinforcement p. 118
Pre-AP Activity pp. 127–128

Interactive Reader Chapter 9
Spanish Study Guide pp. 95–96

Biology Toolkit pp. C19, C25, C33

Technology
Power Presentation 9.5
Media Gallery DVD
Online Quiz 9.5

Activate Prior Knowledge Students may have heard of the Human Genome Project or related studies of human genetic code. **Ask,** What could scientists do with the knowledge of the base sequence of an entire gene or chromosome? Genetic disorders and other medical problems could be addressed or corrected if the gene that codes for them is identifiable.

▼ Teach

Integrating Chemistry

The **Sanger method** is based on the incorporation at random of chemically modified nucleotides, called dideoxynucleotides, into the newly formed strands of DNA. These modified nucleotides cause synthesis of the strand to stop, which forms DNA fragments of specific lengths.

9.5 Genomics and Bioinformatics

KEY CONCEPT Entire genomes are sequenced, studied, and compared.

MAIN IDEAS
- Genomics involves the study of genes, gene functions, and entire genomes.
- Technology allows the study and comparison of both genes and proteins.

VOCABULARY
genomics, p. 280
gene sequencing, p. 280
Human Genome Project, p. 281
bioinformatics, p. 282
DNA microarray, p. 282
proteomics, p. 283

Review
genome, mRNA

NOS.10 Describe how scientific discoveries lead to the development of new technologies, and conversely how technological advances can lead to scientific discoveries through new experimental methods and equipment.

Connect Humans and chimpanzees are identical in 98 to 99 percent of their DNA. How do scientists know this? They have sequenced all of the DNA in both species. Recent technologies are allowing scientists to look at huge amounts of genetic information at once. What might tomorrow's discoveries tell us about evolution, gene expression, and medical treatments?

MAIN IDEA

Genomics involves the study of genes, gene functions, and entire genomes.

A gene, as you know, is a single stretch of DNA that codes for one or more polypeptides or RNA molecules. A genome is all of an organism's genetic information. **Genomics** is the study of genomes, which can include the sequencing of all of an organism's DNA. Scientists compare genomes both within and across species to find similarities and differences among DNA sequences. Comparing DNA from many people at one time helps researchers to find genes that cause disease and to understand how medications work. Biologists who study evolution can learn when closely related species diverged from each other. Scientists can also learn about interactions among genes and find out how an organism's genome makes the organism unique.

TAKING NOTES
Use a mind map to organize your notes on genomics.

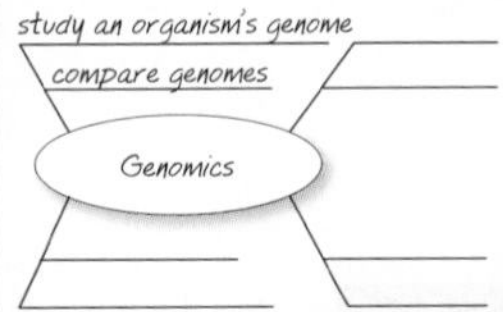

DNA Sequencing

All studies of genomics begin with **gene sequencing,** or determining the order of DNA nucleotides in genes or in genomes. An early sequencing method was developed in the 1970s by British scientist Frederick Sanger. The Sanger method is somewhat similar to PCR, which you read about in Section 9.2.

A radioactive primer is added to a single strand of DNA. Polymerase then builds a short segment of a new DNA strand. The lengths of the new strands are controlled so that they can be separated by gel electrophoresis. Based on the pattern of DNA fragments on the gel, the DNA sequence of the original strand can be put together like the pieces of a puzzle.

Differentiated Instruction

ENGLISH LEARNERS
After reading the section, have students use a Venn diagram to compare genomics with proteomics. Support students as they brainstorm a few items that might go into each section of the diagram. When they finish, help them use the information to make compare-and-contrast statements.

Biology Toolkit, Venn Diagram, p. C33

BELOW LEVEL
Have students construct a standard outline of this section. They should start with the section title, then use large Roman numerals for the main ideas.

Biology Toolkit, Outline, p. C25

You might be surprised to learn that humans do not have the largest genome—the most DNA—among organisms. Scientists have determined the DNA sequences for the genomes of several species, including the ones listed in **FIGURE 9.13.** In some cases, the genomes are used to study basic questions about genes and genetics. In other cases, a genome is sequenced because that organism is used as a model in medical research. In all cases, the genomes of organisms that have been sequenced, including bacteria, insects, plants, and mammals, give us important clues toward finding out how genes function.

Yeast, for example, are very useful for scientists who study gene regulation. Genes that control development in the fruit fly are very similar to those genes in humans. The genomes of several plants have been sequenced so that scientists can learn ways to improve crop yields and to increase the resistance of those crops to disease and weather. The genomes of rats and mice are quite similar to the human genome. As a result, both of these species are used as models for human diseases and gene function.

FIGURE 9.13 COMPARING GENOME SIZES

Organism	Approximate Total DNA (millions of base pairs)
E. coli	4.6
Yeast	12.1
Fruit fly	165
Banana	873
Chicken	1200
Human	3000
Vanilla	7672
Crested newt	18,600
Lungfish	139,000

Source: University of Nebraska

The Human Genome Project

The genomes of yeast and fruit flies are easier to sequence than the human genome. This difficulty is not due to the number of genes that humans have. In fact, while there is still a debate about the exact number of human genes, scientists agree it is surprisingly small. It is estimated that there are somewhere between 30,000 and 40,000 genes in the human genome. But think about the amount of DNA that each of us has in our cells. The human genome has at least 3 billion base pairs. This means that there is an average of about one gene in each sequence of 100,000 bases. Now just try to imagine the huge task of finding out the exact order of all of those DNA bases. In 1990 an international effort began to do exactly that.

The two main goals of the **Human Genome Project** are (1) to map and sequence all of the DNA base pairs of the human chromosomes and (2) to identify all of the genes within the sequence. The first goal was accomplished in 2003 when scientists announced that they had sequenced the human genome. However, the Human Genome Project only analyzed the DNA from a few people. Knowing those few complete DNA sequences is only the first step in understanding the human genome.

FIGURE 9.14 Computer analysis of DNA was necessary in sequencing the human genome.

Today, scientists continue to work on identifying genes, finding the locations of genes, and determining the functions of genes. The complete sequencing of a human genome was a giant step, but much more work still needs to be done. For example, some scientists are working on a project called the HapMap to study how DNA sequences vary among people. The goal of the HapMap is to develop a method that will quickly identify genetic differences that may play a part in human diseases.

A Synthesize How is genomics related to genes and DNA?

ONLINE BIOLOGY Go to the chapter Resource Center at **ClassZone.com** for additional resources and information on genomics.

Take It Further

Any two humans have DNA sequences that are 99.9 percent identical. The variations, however, are important in determining an individual's risk for genetic disorders. These variations are single-base changes called **SNPs** (pronounced *snips*) that occur every few thousand bases. SNPs tend to be inherited together as blocks known as **haplotype blocks.** The goal of the HapMap project is to determine how the haplotype blocks, which are shared by many people, are arranged in the human genome. Once the haplotype blocks are mapped, the specific sequences can be linked to disorders such as diabetes and diseases such as heart disease.

Vocabulary

Word Origins The term **haplotype** is a contraction of the phrase *haploid genotype,* which is the genotype of a single chromosome or single set of chromosomes. For example, if an organism has a genotype of *AaBb,* two haplotypes are possible, depending on which alleles are found on each chromosome. One chromosome in a homologous pair may have the alleles *AB* and the other *ab,* or the homologs may have the alleles *Ab* and *aB.*

Answers

A Synthesize Genomics is the study and comparison of genes and genomes within and across species.

PRE-AP

Ask students how the genomes of a human and a mouse can be so similar when the two organisms are so different. Give students five minutes to write everything they know that might answer this question. Students should recognize that both a mouse and a human have similar tissues, organs, and metabolic reactions. Both organisms need similar enzymes and structural proteins to perform biochemical reactions and build tissues.

Biology Toolkit, Quick-Write, p. C19

▼ Teach continued

DATA ANALYSIS

Introduce

When a scientist makes a **histogram,** he or she sorts data into categories that are related, such as variations in size or height. Histograms are often used to show frequency. In a bar graph, the categories show comparisons of data that are not related or interdependent.

Discuss

Construct a histogram of students' heights. Write all heights on the board, then construct a histogram. To show how histograms can change based on the ranges within categories, compare a histogram based on 6-inch height intervals with one based on 3-inch intervals. **Ask,** In general, what trend do we see in our histograms of students' heights? More students should be of intermediate height. **Ask,** What kind of height data would be better illustrated by a line graph? the growth (annual height) of a student over a period of time

Answers

1. For a sample graph, go to page R102.
2. 101–150 million base pairs
3. Most chromosomes are of intermediate size.

Unit Resource Book, Data Analysis, p. 123

Take It Further

Two approaches were used to map the human genome. Some scientists first made **linkage maps** of known markers. They used the location of the markers to map the sequences between the markers. Finally, they assembled an overall sequence. Another method called the **shotgun approach** sequenced random fragments of DNA. Then powerful computer programs were used to find overlapping sequences that could be arranged relative to each other to produce a longer sequence.

DATA ANALYSIS

NOS.3

CONSTRUCTING HISTOGRAMS

To construct a histogram a scientist will count the number of data points in each category and then graph the number of times that category occurs. The categories are shown on the *x*-axis and the frequencies are shown on the *y*-axis. The data table to the right shows the ranges of base pair lengths for the 24 human chromosomes (chromosomes 1–22, the X chromosome, and the Y chromosome). The data are organized by these ranges.

TABLE 1. HUMAN CHROMOSOME SIZES

Millions of Base Pairs	Number of Human Chromosomes
0–50	2
51–100	6
101–150	8
151–200	6
201–250	2

Source: U.S. Department of Energy Office of Science

1. **Graph Data** Construct a histogram that shows the frequency of base pair lengths for the 24 human chromosomes.
2. **Interpret** Which range of base pair length is most common for human chromosomes?
3. **Analyze** Summarize the overall trend for human chromosome length shown in the histogram.

MAIN IDEA

Technology allows the study and comparison of both genes and proteins.

You have learned about specific genes that produce specific traits. But you also know that genes act as more than simple, separate units. They interact and affect each other's expression. Most biological processes and physical traits are the result of the interactions among many different genes.

Bioinformatics

Genes are sequenced, genomes are compared, and proteins are analyzed. What happens to the huge amounts of data that are produced? These data can be analyzed only if they are organized and searchable. **Bioinformatics** is the use of computer databases to organize and analyze biological data. Powerful computer programs are needed to compare genomes that are billions of base pairs in length, especially if the genomes differ by only a small amount.

Bioinformatics gives scientists a way to store, share, and find data. It also lets researchers predict and model the functions of genes and proteins. Because bioinformatics links different areas of research, it has become vital to the study of genes and proteins. For example, a scientist can now search databases to find the gene that is the code for a known protein.

Connecting CONCEPTS

Computer Models Recall from **Chapter 1** how computer models are used to investigate biological systems that cannot be studied directly. Computer models are often used in genetics and genomics.

DNA Microarrays

DNA microarrays are tools that allow scientists to study many genes, and their expression, at once. A microarray is a small chip that is dotted with all of the genes being studied. The genes are laid out in a grid pattern. Each block of the grid is so small that a one-square-inch chip can hold thousands of genes.

Differentiated Instruction

BELOW LEVEL

Use the following activity to show how short sequences can be overlapped to make a long sequence. Have students copy the following mixed-up word fragments onto a sheet of paper. Then have students arrange them to make a sentence:

seq tand how ce D I un dersta
quen nder e DNA ow to se
quence NA

Have students rewrite the fragments one under the other, overlapping common letters. The final sentence should read "I understand how to sequence DNA."

Complementary DNA (cDNA) labeled with a fluorescent dye is added to the microarray. A cDNA molecule is a single-stranded DNA molecule that is made from an mRNA molecule. The mRNA acts as a template for the cDNA. Therefore, a cDNA molecule is complementary to an mRNA molecule and is identical to a gene's DNA sequence. The cDNA binds to its complementary DNA strand in the microarray by the same base pairing that you learned about in Chapter 8.

Anywhere cDNA binds to DNA in the microarray shows up as a glowing dot because of the dye. A glowing dot in the microarray is a match between a cDNA molecule and the DNA on the chip. Therefore, a glowing dot shows which genes are expressed and how much they are expressed. Microarrays, as shown in **FIGURE 9.15**, help researchers find which genes are expressed in which tissues, and under what conditions. For example, DNA microarrays can compare gene expression in cancer cells with gene expression in healthy cells. Scientists hope that this method will lead to cancer treatments that target the faulty genes.

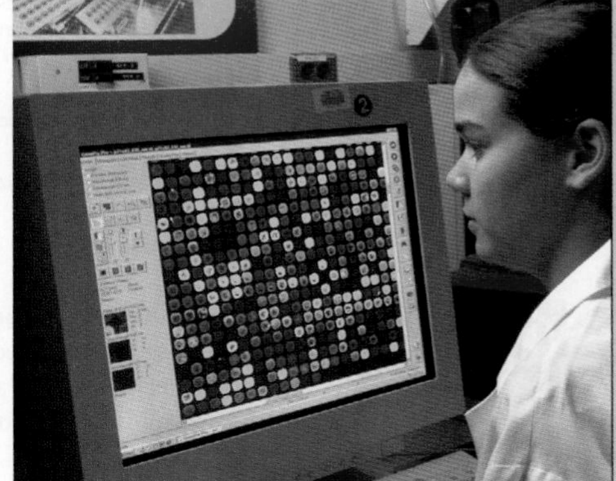

FIGURE 9.15 Gene expression can be studied with microarrays. The red dots show genes that are expressed after exposure to a toxic chemical.

Proteomics

You have read how genomics is the study of genomes. **Proteomics** (PROH-tee-AH-mihks) is the study and comparison of all the proteins that result from an organism's genome. Proteomics also includes the study of the functions and interactions of proteins. Identifying and studying proteins is more difficult than identifying and studying genes. A single gene, depending on how its mRNA is edited, can code for more than one polypeptide. Different proteins are found in different tissues, depending on gene expression. And, often, the functions of proteins have to be studied within a biological system.

Proteomics has potential benefits for many areas of biology. Shared evolutionary histories among organisms are studied by comparing proteins across species. Proteomics allows scientists to learn about proteins involved in human diseases. By better understanding the proteins that might play a part in cancer, arthritis, or heart disease, scientists might be able to develop new treatments that target the proteins. Proteomics even has the potential to help doctors match medical treatments to a patient's unique body chemistry.

Apply **How is bioinformatics a form of data analysis?**

9.5 ASSESSMENT

ONLINE QUIZ ClassZone.com

NOS.10

REVIEWING MAIN IDEAS

1. Describe the goals of the **Human Genome Project.**
2. Why is **bioinformatics** important in genetic research?

CRITICAL THINKING

3. **Apply** Describe the difference between **gene sequencing** and DNA fingerprinting.
4. **Compare and Contrast** How is the study of specific genes different from the study of a genome?

Connecting CONCEPTS

5. **Cell Biology** How might **genomics** and **proteomics** help researchers predict how a medical treatment might affect cells in different tissues?

9.5 ASSESSMENT

1. to sequence the human genome and to map the genes within it
2. Genetic information consists of a very large, complex volume of data. Computer databases store and organize the data.
3. Gene sequencing finds the DNA sequence; a DNA fingerprint shows a number of repeated DNA sequences.
4. Genomics studies all genes.
5. By knowing about how genes and their products interact, researchers could be able to predict how one drug will affect many different areas of the body. They could tailor a treatment to target a specific gene or protein in order to avoid damaging others.

Take It Further

The mRNA molecule used to make complementary DNA (cDNA) for a **microarray** is isolated from the cells in a tissue sample. Single strands of cDNA, which bind to the mRNA, are made using fluorescently labeled nucleotides. The enzyme **reverse transcriptase** catalyzes the formation of the cDNA from the mRNA. The labeled mRNA–cDNA hybrid is applied to a microarray that contains spots of short, single-stranded DNA from each gene being tested. The excess cDNA is rinsed off the array, and the array is scanned for fluorescence. Each fluorescent spot represents a gene that is expressed in the original tissue sample.

Integrating Evolutionary Biology

Most proteins are identified by their functional sites, such as the active site of an enzyme. Nine out of ten functional sites found in human proteins have counterparts in enzymes of fruit flies and nematodes, and 60 percent of human proteins are similar to the proteins of fruit flies and worms. These data suggest that many metabolic processes were established early in evolutionary history.

Answers

A Apply It is the organization and analysis of large amounts of data.

Assess and Reteach

Assess Use the Online Quiz or Section Quiz (*Assessment Book*, p. 173).

Reteach Work with students to create a cluster diagram that includes bioinformatics, proteomics, DNA microarrays, the Human Genome Project, and DNA sequencing.

SECTION 9.6

▼ Plan and Prepare

Objectives

- Explain how genetic screening can detect genetic disorders.
- Describe how gene therapy research seeks to replace faulty genes.

Section Resources

Unit Resource Book Study Guide pp. 119–120 Power Notes p. 121 Reinforcement p. 122
Interactive Reader Chapter 9 **Spanish Study Guide** pp. 97–98
Biology Toolkit p. D8
Technology Power Presentation 9.6 Media Gallery DVD Online Quiz 9.6

Activate Prior Knowledge Tell students that 11 cousins chose to have their stomachs surgically removed after genetic screening revealed that they had inherited the rare CDH1 allele, giving them a 70 percent chance of developing a stomach cancer that had killed their relatives. **Ask,** Do you think some knowledge is not worth having? How would you react in such a situation? Answers will vary.

▼ Teach

TEACH FROM VISUALS

FIGURE 9.16 Tell students that the screening test for DMD is designed to detect deletions or duplications of a particular gene. **Ask,** Do deletions or duplications cause the disease in the three people tested? deletions How do you know? People with the disease have four, five, or six bands; people without it have seven.

Answers

A Infer Answers will vary but could include a discussion of genetic information being used to discriminate against a person in some way.

9.6 Genetic Screening and Gene Therapy

KEY CONCEPT Genetics provides a basis for new medical treatments.

MAIN IDEAS

- Genetic screening can detect genetic disorders.
- Gene therapy is the replacement of faulty genes.

VOCABULARY

genetic screening, p. 284
gene therapy, p. 285

Review
pedigree, genetic engineering

Connect Anyone could be a carrier of a genetic disorder. Genetic screening is used to help people figure out whether they are at risk for passing on that disorder. If they are at risk, what do they do? Do they not have children? Do they have children and hope that a child does not get the disorder? What would you do?

MAIN IDEA

Genetic screening can detect genetic disorders.

Every one of us carries alleles that produce defective proteins. Usually, these genes do not affect us in a significant way because we have other alleles that make up for the deficiency. But about 10 percent of people will find themselves dealing with an illness related to their genes at some point in their lives.

Genetic screening is the process of testing DNA to determine a person's risk of having or passing on a genetic disorder. Genetic screening often involves both pedigree analysis, which you read about in Chapter 7, and DNA tests. Because our knowledge of the human genome is still limited, it is not yet possible to test for every possible defect. Often, genetic screening is used to look for specific genes or proteins that indicate a particular disorder. Some tests can detect genes that are related to an increased risk of developing a disease, such as a gene called BRCA1 that has been linked to breast cancer. There are also tests for about 900 genetic disorders, including cystic fibrosis and Duchenne's muscular dystrophy (DMD). In DMD, it is quite easy to see differences in DNA tests between people with and without the disorder, as shown in **FIGURE 9.16**.

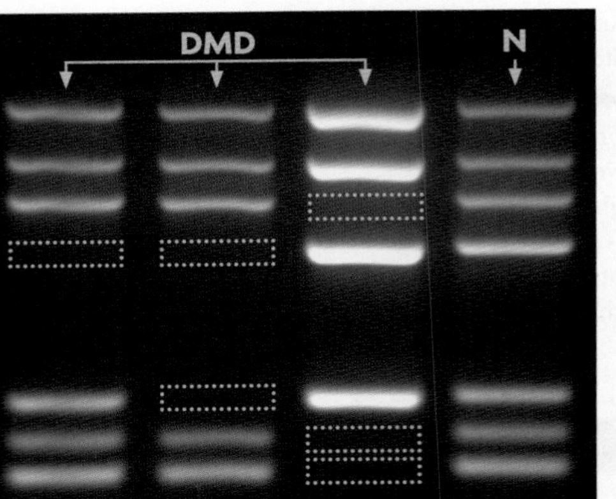

FIGURE 9.16 Genetic screening can be used to detect Duchenne's muscular dystrophy (DMD). Notice the missing bands on the gel (boxes) for three people with DMD as compared with a person without the disorder (N).

Genetic screening can help save lives. It can also lead to some difficult choices. Suppose a person has a family history of cancer and is tested for a gene that may lead to an increased risk of cancer. Is that information helpful or harmful? If a person has a chance of being a carrier of a genetic disorder, should screening be required? As genetic screening becomes more common, more questions like these will need to be answered.

A Infer Why might genetic screening raise ethical concerns about privacy?

Differentiated Instruction

ENGLISH LEARNERS

Have students complete a concept definition map. Write the terms *genetic screening* and *gene therapy* down the left side of a table. Write the words *Category, Characteristics, Examples,* and *Comparison* across the top as column heads. Then have pairs of students complete the map. Under *Category,* for example, students might write *testing* for *genetic screening* and *treatment* for *gene therapy.*

Biology Toolkit, Concept Definition Map, p. D8

MAIN IDEA

Gene therapy is the replacement of faulty genes.

A defective part in a car or in a computer can be easily replaced. If someone has a faulty gene that causes a disorder, is it possible to replace the gene? The goal of gene therapy is to do exactly that. **Gene therapy** is the replacement of a defective or missing gene, or the addition of a new gene, into a person's genome to treat a disease.

For any type of gene therapy to work, researchers such as Dr. Betty Pace, shown in **FIGURE 9.17**, must first get the new gene into the correct cells of a patient's body. Once in the body, the gene has to become a part of the cells' DNA. One method of gene therapy that scientists have tried is to take a sample of bone marrow stem cells and "infect" them with a virus that has been genetically engineered with the new gene. Then the stem cells are put back into the patient's bone marrow. Because they are stem cells, they divide and make more blood cells with the gene.

FIGURE 9.17 Dr. Betty Pace, director of the Sickle Cell Disease Research Center at the University of Texas at Dallas, is studying potential gene therapy treatments for sickle cell disease.

The first successful trial of gene therapy took place in 1990. The treatment was used on two children with a genetic autoimmune disorder, and the children are now adults leading normal lives. However, much of gene therapy is still experimental. For example, researchers are studying several different methods to treat cancer with gene therapy. One experimental approach involves inserting a gene that stimulates a person's immune system to attack cancer cells. Another method is to insert "suicide" genes into cancer cells. These genes activate a drug inside those cells so that only the cancer cells are killed.

Gene therapy has many technical challenges. First, the correct gene has to be added to the correct cells. And even after researchers have figured out how to transfer the desired gene, the gene's expression has to be regulated so that it does not make too much or too little protein. Scientists must also determine if the new gene will affect other genes. The many trials have produced few long-lasting positive results. But because of its great potential, research on gene therapy continues.

Synthesize How does gene therapy rely on genetic screening?

9.6 ASSESSMENT

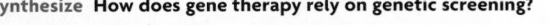

ONLINE QUIZ ClassZone.com

REVIEWING MAIN IDEAS

1. How does **genetic screening** use both old and new methods of studying human genetics?
2. Briefly describe the goals and methods of **gene therapy.**

CRITICAL THINKING

3. **Compare and Contrast** How is gene therapy similar to, and different from, making a transgenic organism?
4. **Synthesize** How are restriction enzymes and recombinant DNA important for gene therapy?

Connecting CONCEPTS

5. **Cell Specialization** How is the type of cell into which a new gene is inserted important in gene therapy?

9.6 ASSESSMENT

1. Genetic screening uses pedigrees and family histories as well as DNA testing.
2. The goal of gene therapy is to replace faulty or missing genes. In some cases, genetically engineered viruses are inserted into the patient's body to deliver functional genes. Another method is to insert genes into cancer cells that will render them vulnerable to specific drugs.
3. They both involve inserting a new gene into an organism, but gene therapy replaces a defective gene with a normal gene in an adult organism; a transgenic organism has genes from more than one species.
4. Restriction enzymes cut DNA to insert a gene into a virus, producing recombinant DNA.
5. Gene expression can depend on promoters, as well as on the particular cell type.

Integrating Medical Science

Many people worry that genetic screening will dramatically alter the way health care is given. One major concern is that **health insurance** companies will either deny coverage or raise health-care costs for people who have genes that cause disorders or other medical problems. Another concern is over who gets to decide what genetic screening tests are appropriate and who pays for them.

Answers

A Synthesize Screening to identify which gene is faulty must be completed before gene therapy can be attempted.

Assess and Reteach ▼

Assess Use the Online Quiz or Section Quiz (*Assessment Book,* p. 174).

Reteach Tell students that scientists now have the tools to test individuals for possible risks of developing illnesses in the future. Have students write a short essay in which they discuss some of the ethical problems that might arise from this technology, such as the possibility of genomic discrimination and loss of personal privacy.

OPTIONS FOR INQUIRY

INVESTIGATION

Time 20 minutes	TEACHER TESTED
Teacher Preparation	
Student Difficulty	
Lab Binder Genetics, pp. 47–49	

Purpose Model genetic engineering.

Overview Students will model the formation of recombinant DNA. They will

- make plasmid models using DNA sequences and tape
- choose an appropriate restriction enzyme that will cut the DNA of the plasmids and the foreign gene
- make recombinant DNA by combining genes from plasmids and foreign DNA

LAB PREPARATION

- Make and distribute copies of the DNA Sequence datasheet, *Lab Binder*, p. 49.

LAB MANAGEMENT

- Review the action of several restriction enzymes to enable students to choose the appropriate enzyme for the sequences in the plasmids and human factor VIII gene.

POST-LAB DISCUSSION

Have students discuss the results. **Ask**

- Which restriction enzyme did you use to cut the DNA? Why did you choose this restriction enzyme? Students should have chosen *Bam*HI because both *Eco*RI and *Hind*III would cut two of the genes and *Sma*I leaves blunt ends.
- Could you have made recombinant DNA if the restriction enzyme produced blunt ends? No, DNA fragments with blunt ends cannot combine to form recombinant DNA.

Use these inquiry-based labs and online activities to deepen your understanding of biotechnology and genetic engineering.

INDIANA STANDARDS

B.7.3 Determine the likelihood of the appearance of a specific trait in an offspring given the genetic make-up of the parents.

B.7.5 Explain and demonstrate how inserting, substituting or deleting segments of a DNA molecule can alter a gene, which is then passed to every cell that develops from it and that the results may be beneficial, harmful or have little or no effect on the organism.

INVESTIGATION

Modeling Genetic Engineering

Scientists use restriction enzymes to make recombinant DNA. Genes are placed into plasmids that are put into bacteria. The plasmids transform the bacteria to produce the new gene product. In this lab, you will model a genetic engineering process. You will insert the human factor VIII gene into a plasmid. This gene produces a protein that causes blood to coagulate. People with mutations in this gene can suffer from hemophilia, a bleeding disease.

MATERIALS

- DNA Sequence Datasheet
- scissors
- 20 cm clear tape
- red and yellow colored pencils

SKILL Modeling

PROBLEM How can a plasmid's DNA be changed?

PROCEDURE

1. Cut out the plasmid DNA sequences from the datasheet. Color the DNA sequences yellow.
2. Use tape to attach the sequences to each end where indicated. The completed plasmid should be circular in shape.
3. Make a human factor VIII gene using the DNA sequences from the datasheet. The gene should be a straight fragment. Color the sequence red.
4. Use the datasheet to choose the appropriate restriction enzymes to cut the plasmid and the human factor VIII gene. Cut the plasmids and the gene with the scissors at the proper places.
5. Construct a new plasmid that contains the human factor VIII gene. Use tape to hold the completed plasmid together.

ANALYZE AND CONCLUDE

1. **Analyze** What characteristic would bacteria implanted with the new plasmid have? Explain.
2. **Apply** What might be the purpose of inserting the human factor VIII gene into a plasmid?

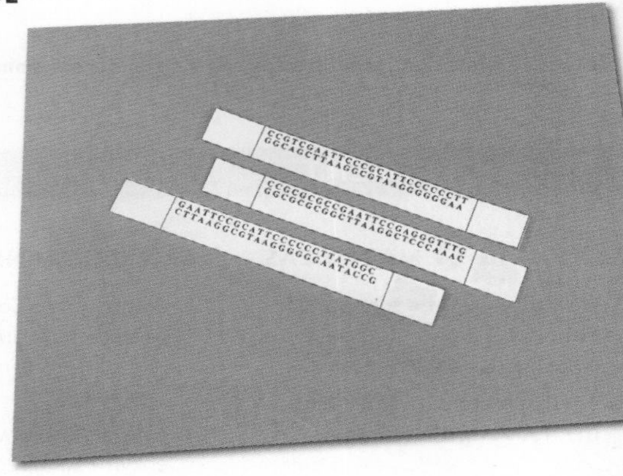

Answers

Expected Results

Students should form a large plasmid that contains genes for gentamycin resistance, ampicillin resistance, and human factor VIII.

Analyze and Conclude

1. The bacteria would be resistant to both ampicillin and gentamycin and be able to produce human factor VIII.
2. The bacteria, now resistant to antibiotics, will reproduce and create a supply of a blood clotting factor that will prevent symptoms of hemophilia.

INVESTIGATION

Genetic Screening

A combination of pedigree analysis and DNA testing is used to screen for genetic diseases. In this investigation, you will use a pedigree and a restriction map to determine who in a family is a carrier of a genetic disorder.

SKILL Analyzing

PROBLEM Which members of the family are carriers of the genetic disorder?

MATERIALS

- paper
- pencil

PROCEDURE

1. Copy the pedigree into your notebook.
2. Look at the gel below. The letters on the gel correspond to the letters of people on the pedigree. Write on your pedigree the alleles that each person has, as shown by the lengths of DNA fragments on the gel. (**Hint:** Person E has two copies of one allele.)
3. Person E's phenotype is given. Determine the phenotypes of the other people—non-carrier or carrier—and show them on the pedigree with the shading conventions you learned in Chapter 7.

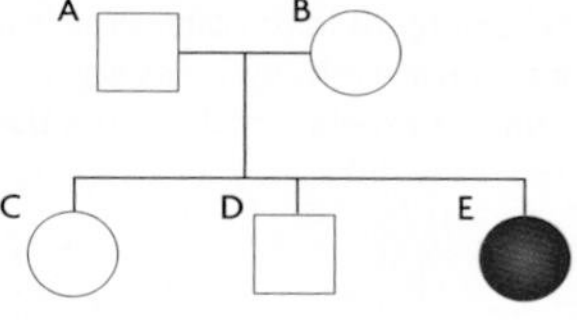

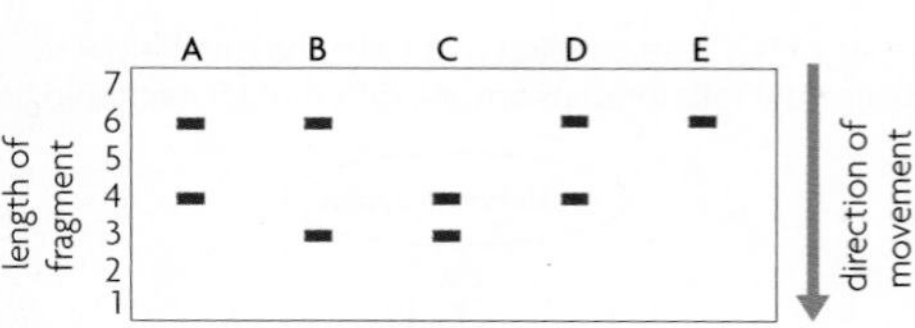

ANALYZE AND CONCLUDE

1. **Analyze** How many people are carriers?
2. **Infer** Is the disorder sex-linked or is it related to a gene on an autosome? Explain.

Online BIOLOGY
CLASSZONE.COM

VIRTUAL LAB
Gel Electrophoresis
How do you use DNA to identify a person? In this virtual lab, you will use gel electrophoresis to make the DNA fingerprint of a person who committed a crime.

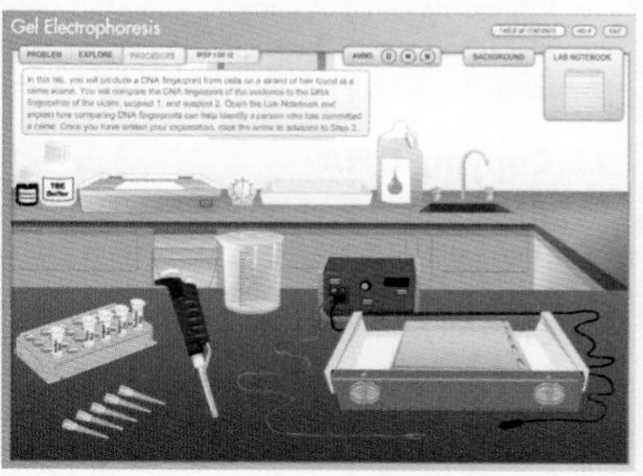

VIRTUAL LAB
Bacterial Transformation
How do genetic engineers make recombinant DNA? In this interactive lab, you will put a new gene into the DNA of a bacterium.

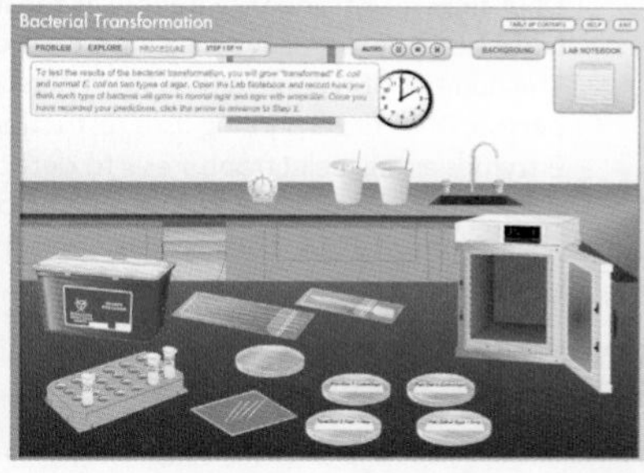

WEBQUEST
Should animal cloning projects be funded? Complete this WebQuest to learn how scientists clone animals, and review the risks and benefits of making animal clones. Then make a recommendation regarding the best use of funds for animal cloning projects.

Online Biology ▼

VIRTUAL LAB Use the Gel Electrophoresis lab to reinforce the concepts of **Section 9.1.** It can also be used with **Section 9.3.**

VIRTUAL LAB Use this Bacterial Transformation lab to reinforce the concepts of **Section 9.4.** This lab provides students with an opportunity to work with bacteria and still adhere to the strict rule of no bacteria labs in the classroom.

WEBQUEST The WebQuest takes one full class period. Students complete the activity online and will need access to a printer to print their answers. Sample answers, teacher notes, and alternative assessment ideas are available on **ClassZone.com.** Use with **Section 9.4.**

INVESTIGATION

Time 20 minutes	TEACHER TESTED ✓
Teacher Preparation 🧪	
Student Difficulty 🧪🧪	
Lab Binder Genetics, pp. 51–52	

LAB MANAGEMENT

- Review the symbols used in a pedigree and some of the ways pedigrees are analyzed.

POST-LAB DISCUSSION

Discuss the results. **Ask,** How did you determine the phenotypes of individuals A and B? Both A and B have to be carriers, because E inherited two copies of the allele for the disorder. **Ask,** How did you determine individual D's phenotype? D has the same two bands as A, with fragment lengths of 6 and 4. If A is a carrier, D must also be a carrier. **Ask,** How did you determine individual C's phenotype? C does not have a fragment of length 6, so he must be homozygous normal (non-carrier).

Answers

Expected Results

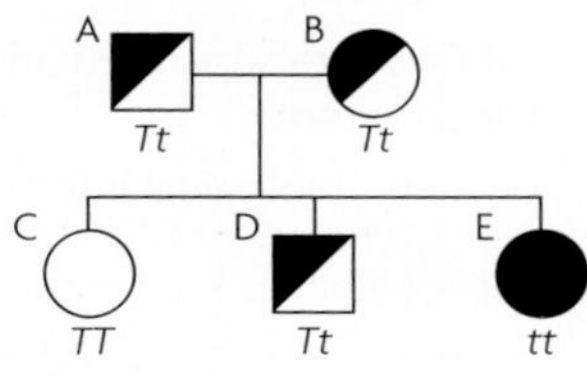

A, B, and D are heterozygous carriers for the genetic disorder; C is homozygous normal; E is homozygous for the defective allele and has the disorder.

Analyze and Conclude

1. Three people (A, B, and D) are carriers.
2. The gene for the disorder is on an autosome. If it was on the X chromosome, individuals A and D would have the disorder rather than be carriers. If the gene was on the Y chromosome, E, a female, could not have the disorder.

Interactive Review

Encourage students to go to **ClassZone.com** for a detailed review of each section, including visuals and vocabulary practice.

Unit Resource Book, Vocabulary Practice, pp. 129–132

CHAPTER 9

Interactive Review @ CLASSZONE.COM

KEY CONCEPTS | Vocabulary Games | Concept Maps | Animated Biology | Online Quiz

9.1 Manipulating DNA

Biotechnology relies on cutting DNA at specific places. Bacterial enzymes called restriction enzymes are used to cut DNA. Each restriction enzyme cuts DNA at a specific DNA sequence. After DNA is cut with a restriction enzyme, the fragments of DNA can be separated using gel electrophoresis. A restriction map of the DNA is made based on the lengths of the fragments.

9.2 Copying DNA

The polymerase chain reaction rapidly copies segments of DNA. The polymerase chain reaction (PCR) is based on the process of DNA replication. By combining the DNA to be copied, DNA nucleotides, primers, and specific polymerase enzymes, a desired segment of DNA can be copied in the laboratory.

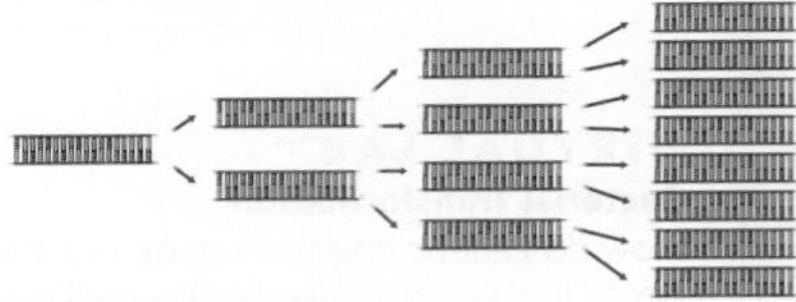

9.3 DNA Fingerprinting

DNA fingerprints identify people at the molecular level. DNA has many repeating base sequences. The number of repeats differs from person to person. DNA fingerprinting uses restriction enzymes and gel electrophoresis to detect these differences. By using DNA fingerprinting on several regions of DNA, one particular person can be identified.

9.4 Genetic Engineering

DNA sequences of organisms can be changed. Clones, or identical genetic copies, of many organisms can be made. Organisms can also be implanted with genes that give them new traits. Often, genes are inserted into plasmids to make recombinant DNA. Genetically engineered plasmids are inserted into bacteria, producing a transgenic organism. Transgenic bacteria, plants, and animals are used in several different ways.

Recombinant DNA

9.5 Genomics and Bioinformatics

Entire genomes are sequenced, studied, and compared. Through DNA sequencing, the genomes of several organisms, including humans, have been found and studied. Genomic data are organized and analyzed through bioinformatics. DNA microarrays are used to study interactions among genes in a genome. In addition, genomics has led to the study and comparison of proteins through proteomics.

9.6 Genetic Screening and Gene Therapy

Genetics provides a basis for new medical treatments. Genetic screening is used to test people for genes that are linked to genetic disorders. One method to correct these faulty genes or to replace missing genes is gene therapy. Gene therapy is experimental, but has the potential to cure many diseases.

Synthesize Your Notes

Two-Column Chart Use your notes to make two-column charts for the processes described in the chapter. On one side of the chart, define and explain the process. On the other side, draw a sketch of the process.

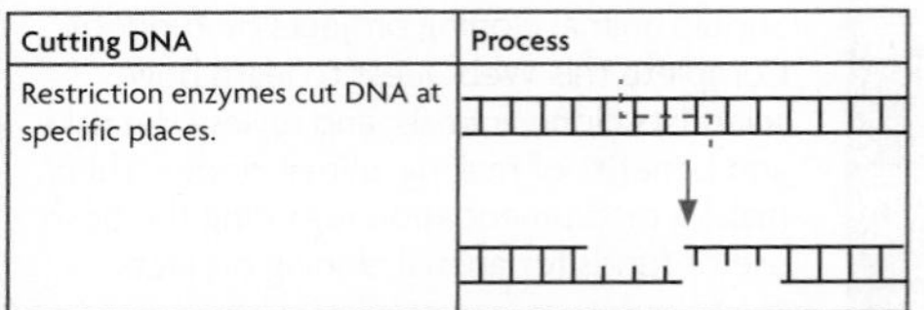

Cutting DNA	Process
Restriction enzymes cut DNA at specific places.	

Concept Map Use concept maps like the one below to visualize the relationships among different biotechnologies.

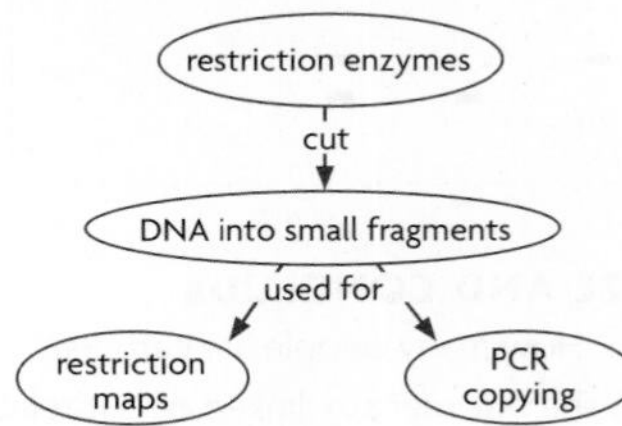

Reviewing Vocabulary

1. plasmid
2. recombinant DNA
3. transgenic organism
4. DNA testing for disorders
5. studying and comparing genomes
6. unique DNA pattern
7. identical genetic copy
8. Fragments of DNA are separated and carried by an electrical current.
9. genomes; proteins; biological information

Chapter Assessment

Chapter Vocabulary

9.1 restriction enzyme, p. 265
gel electrophoresis, p. 266
restriction map, p. 267

9.2 polymerase chain reaction (PCR), p. 269
primer, p. 271

9.3 DNA fingerprint, p. 272

9.4 clone, p. 275
genetic engineering, p. 276
recombinant DNA, p. 276
plasmid, p. 276
transgenic, p. 277
gene knockout, p. 279

9.5 genomics, p. 280
gene sequencing, p. 280
Human Genome Project, p. 281
bioinformatics, p. 282
DNA microarray, p. 282
proteomics, p. 283

9.6 genetic screening, p. 284
gene therapy, p. 285

Reviewing Vocabulary

Label Diagrams

In your notebook, write the vocabulary term that matches each item that is pointed out below.

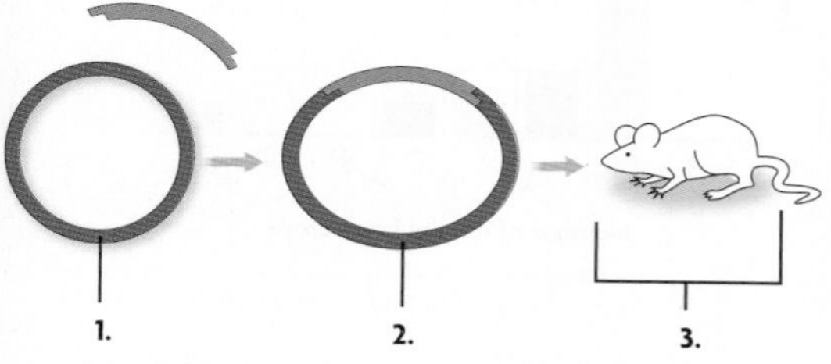

Keep It Short

For each vocabulary term below, write a short, precise phrase that describes its meaning. For example, a short phrase to describe *PCR* could be "DNA copying tool."

4. genetic screening
5. genomics
6. DNA fingerprint
7. clone

Word Origins

8. The prefix *electro-* means "electricity." The suffix *-phoresis* means "transmission" or "carrying." How do these meanings relate to the meaning of the term *electrophoresis*?

9. The suffix *-ics* means "science or study of." What is studied in *genomics?* in *proteomics?* in *bioinformatics?*

Reviewing MAIN IDEAS

10. Why can restriction enzymes be thought of as molecular "scissors"?

11. Explain what gel electrophoresis shows about DNA, and how it is used to separate DNA.

12. PCR requires DNA polymerase from bacteria that live in hot springs. Why can't DNA polymerase from organisms that live in cooler temperatures be used in PCR?

13. Briefly describe the three main steps of PCR.

14. What parts of DNA molecules are the basis of the differences detected by DNA fingerprinting?

15. Why is probability important in DNA fingerprinting?

16. What is the role of nuclear transfer in the process of cloning an animal? **B.7.5**

17. Describe the general process used to make bacteria that have recombinant DNA. Include the terms *restriction enzyme* and *plasmid* in your answer. **B.7.5**

18. How are gene knockout mice useful in determining the function of genes? **B.7.5**

19. How does genomics rely on DNA sequencing?

20. Explain why computer databases are important in genomics and proteomics.

21. How are pedigree analysis and DNA testing used together in genetic screening?

22. What is gene therapy, and how might it be used as a treatment for cancer or for genetic disorders? **B.7.5**

CHAPTER REVIEW

14. noncoding regions of DNA that contain repeated base sequences
15. The more regions that are compared, the less likely it is that two individuals will have the same DNA fingerprint.
16. The nucleus from a cell of the animal to be cloned is transferred to an egg cell.
17. A restriction enzyme is used to cut a desired gene from a DNA molecule. The same enzyme is used to cut open a plasmid. The gene is inserted into the plasmid to form recombinant DNA. The plasmid is then inserted into a bacterium.
18. They allow scientists to study how a gene affects a living organism.
19. In order to find genes and their locations, and to compare genomes across species, the sequence of DNA nucleotides must be determined.
20. Computer databases store a large amount of information that can be quickly and easily searched.
21. A pedigree analysis can indicate a family history of a genetic disorder, and DNA testing can determine whether a person has the disorder or is a carrier of the disorder.
22. Gene therapy is the replacement of a faulty gene or adding a missing gene to treat a disease. In genetic disorders, gene therapy can give the body a means of performing certain functions that its original genes do not code for. With cancer, gene therapy can make cancer cells vulnerable to drugs.

Reviewing Main Ideas

10. Restriction enzymes cut DNA molecules.
11. Gel electrophoresis reveals the sizes of different DNA fragments. Fragments that are smaller are more easily pulled toward the positive electrode, while larger fragments are slower and remain closer to the negative electrode.
12. Heat is used to separate DNA strands in PCR. Enzymes from organisms that live in cooler temperatures would break down at these high temperatures.
13. Complementary strands of DNA are separated, primers bind to each strand, and DNA polymerase binds nucleotides together to form new copies of the DNA.

ITEM CORRELATIONS

Standard	Items
B.7.5	16, 17, 18, 22, 28

Critical Thinking

23. Microarrays allow gene expression and gene interactions to be studied.
24. Both use patterns of bands in a gel. A restriction map shows the sizes of DNA fragments between random restriction sites; DNA fingerprinting shows the sizes of fragments in known locations.
25. A clone of an animal is a genetically identical copy, but cloning is done artificially by implanting a cell's nucleus into an egg and then forcing the egg to develop.
26. The manipulations needed to produce transgenic organisms transfer only selected genes, whereas crossbreeding is a combination of two entire genomes. Both techniques involve two species.
27. Gene expression is affected by many different factors, including the environment both inside and outside the womb, and different mutations within the DNA of each twin.
28. The gene for insulin is added to a plasmid, which is then put into a bacterium. Because the genetic code is the same in all organisms, the transgenic bacteria will express the gene and produce the protein.

Critical Thinking

23. **Analyze** How are DNA microarrays related to genomics?

24. **Compare and Contrast** How are restriction maps and DNA fingerprints similar? How are they different? Explain your answers.

25. **Compare and Contrast** A plant can send out a runner that will sprout a new plant that is a clone of the "parent." Single-celled organisms divide in two, forming two clones. How is the cloning of an animal similar to and different from the cloning that happens in nature?

26. **Synthesize** Some fruits and vegetables are the result of crossing different species. A tangelo, for example, results from crossing a tangerine with a grapefruit. How are the genetic engineering processes of making transgenic organisms similar to and different from crossbreeding?

27. **Apply** Identical twins are technically clones of each other but can differ in both appearance and behavior. How is it possible that two people with the same genome could be different?

28. **Synthesize** Transgenic bacteria can be used to make human insulin. Explain how bacteria can produce a human protein. **B.7.5**

Interpreting Visuals

The gel below shows two different restriction maps for the same segment of DNA. One of the maps is for a normal gene (N) and the other is for a disease gene (D). Use the information in the gel to answer the next two questions.

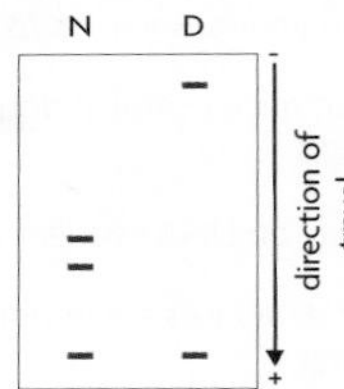

29. **Analyze** Which restriction map (N or D) has the smallest fragment of DNA? Which has the largest fragment? Explain your answers.

30. **Interpret** What do the restriction maps tell you about differences between a normal allele (N) and a disease (D) allele? Explain.

Analyzing Data

Ten of the most commonly modified crops include rice, potatoes, maize, papayas, tomatoes, corn, soybeans, wheat, alfalfa, and sugar cane. The histogram below shows how many times these crops have been modified. Among the 15 countries studied from 2001 through 2003, for example, different researchers modified rice a total of 37 times. Use the data to answer the next two questions.

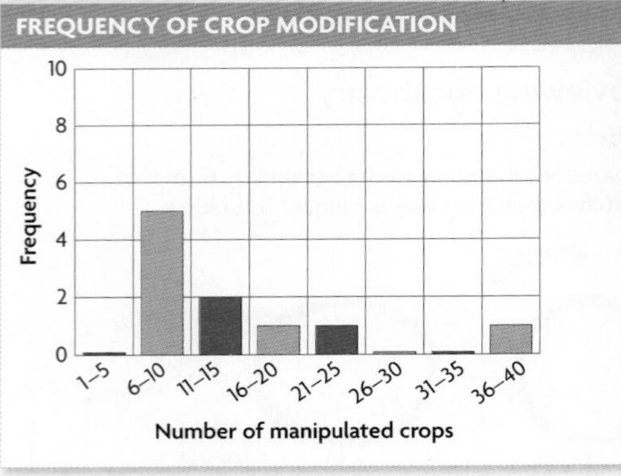

Source: Cohen, *Nature Biotechnology*, 23:1.

31. **Analyze** What is the most common range of genetic modifications for crop plants? The least common?

32. **Calculate** What percentage of crop types fall in the range of 11–15 genetic modifications?

Connecting CONCEPTS

33. **Write an Informational Pamphlet** Suppose that you work for a biotechnology company that specializes in DNA fingerprinting to help reunite families that have been separated. Write a pamphlet that describes how DNA fingerprinting works. Explain why the results of DNA fingerprinting can be trusted.

34. **Synthesize** Look again at the picture of Baby 81 on page 263. After reading this chapter, you know that DNA fingerprinting is just one part of biotechnology. Choose a topic from the chapter, such as genetic engineering or PCR. Discuss how that topic is related to Mendel's work on heredity, and how it is related to the structure and function of DNA.

Interpreting Visuals

29. Both have the smallest fragment; D has the largest fragment. The fragment sizes are shown by the distance they travel through the gel.
30. The disease-causing allele has a mutation that changes a restriction site, so the disease-causing allele is cut only once, not twice.

Analyzing Data

31. 6–10: most common; 1–5, 26–30, 31–35: least common
32. 20 percent

INDIANA ISTEP+ Test Prep

B.5.2; B.7.2; B.7.5; NOS.1

Test Practice For more test practice, go to ClassZone.com.

1

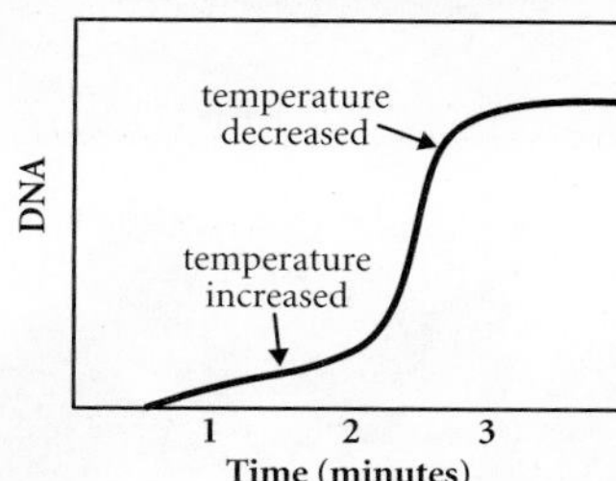

This graph shows the amount of DNA over time during a polymerase chain reaction (PCR). Changes that take place during PCR are shown with arrows. Based upon the graph, it can be inferred that

A one PCR cycle takes about three minutes.
B polymerase doesn't function at high temperatures.
C polymerase needs one minute to begin working well.
D temperature is not an important factor.

2 Some genetic diseases can be treated with medication or lifestyle changes. But the only way to cure genetic diseases is to

A transplant the affected tissue.
B change the affected DNA sequence.
C induce mutations in the affected gene.
D remove the affected gene.

3 Some scientists want to genetically engineer apples to produce the insecticide ***pyrethrin.*** In order to ensure that all offspring from the original tree also produce apples with the chemical, they must be sure that the gene that produces pyrethrin is in the cells of what tissue?

A root
B leaf
C stem
D seed

THINK THROUGH THE QUESTION

To answer this question you don't need to know the details used in the example, such as insecticides and the names of chemicals. Instead, focus on the main point of the question, which addresses genetic engineering and reproduction.

4 A scientist wants to insert a gene into a plasmid as shown in this diagram. In order to open the plasmid to insert the gene, the scientist must use

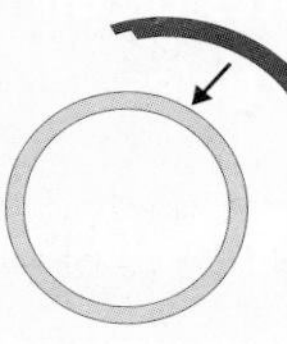

A restriction mapping.
B PCR.
C restriction enzymes.
D restriction sites.

5 *Bt* soybeans are transgenic. These soybean plants express a bacterial gene that codes for a natural pesticide. This is an example of

A mutation.
B gene sequencing.
C proteomics.
D genetic engineering.

6 Alleles that are lethal when present in only one copy are less common in populations than alleles that are lethal when present in two copies. How is this so?

Standards-Based Assessment

1. A	4. C
2. B	5. D
3. D	6. See Below

Question 3 Answer D is correct. Answers A, B, and C are incorrect because roots, leaves, and stems do not contain sex cells; only sex cells pass genes to offspring.

Question 4 Answer C is correct. Answer A is incorrect because restriction mapping shows the lengths of DNA fragments that have been cut between restriction sites in a strand of DNA. Answer B is incorrect because PCR is a technique that produces numerous copies of a specific DNA sequence. Answer D is incorrect because restriction sites are sequences of DNA recognized and cut by restriction enzymes.

Question 6 Organisms that have one copy of the lethal allele are not likely to survive to reproduce, so they do not pass this allele to offspring.

Connecting Concepts

33. Students should explain the basis of DNA fingerprinting, the role of probability in DNA fingerprinting, and how DNA fingerprints are interpreted.

34. Students should synthesize information from the entire unit. Answers should include information on genes, alleles, gene expression, and DNA sequences and may include information on transcription and translation.

ITEM CORRELATIONS

Standard	Items
B.5.2	3
B.7.2	6
B.7.5	2, 4, 5
NOS.1	1

UNIT

3

Introduce

Tell students that technology includes the tools, machines, and processes that increase our ability to control or learn about our environment. Technology is often the application of science knowledge.

Technology began in the Stone Age with the use of hand axes that were used as tools for work or to make other tools. By the Bronze Age, tens of thousands of years later, people had learned to control fire and use it to work with metals.

In the 1800s and 1900s, technology increased rapidly and made huge changes in daily life. Homes and businesses now had indoor plumbing, electricity, and heating and cooling. Means of transportation went from horses to railroads, automobiles, and airplanes. Have students think about changes to modes of communication. Today, information can be communicated instantaneously, via television and radio, cellular phones, text messaging, and the Internet.

Medical technology also has advanced rapidly. New microscopes, diagnostic equipment, and medicines have improved the quality of life and increased the average life span. Many people who would have died from illnesses a century ago now survive.

Discuss with students technology in their lives. **Ask**

- What technology is used in your school that would not have been in a school 150 years ago? *Sample Answers:* electrical lights, heating and cooling systems, computers, telephones, and running water
- What technology allows you to learn about advances in medical technology? Students might mention journals, magazines, newspapers, television news programs, radio broadcasts, and the Internet.

UNIT 3: GENETICS

BIOZINE at CLASSZONE.COM

INTERNET MAGAZINE

Go online for the latest biology news and updates on all BioZine articles.

Expanding the Textbook

News Feeds

Science Daily

CNN

BBC

Careers

Bio Bytes

Opinion Poll

Strange Biology

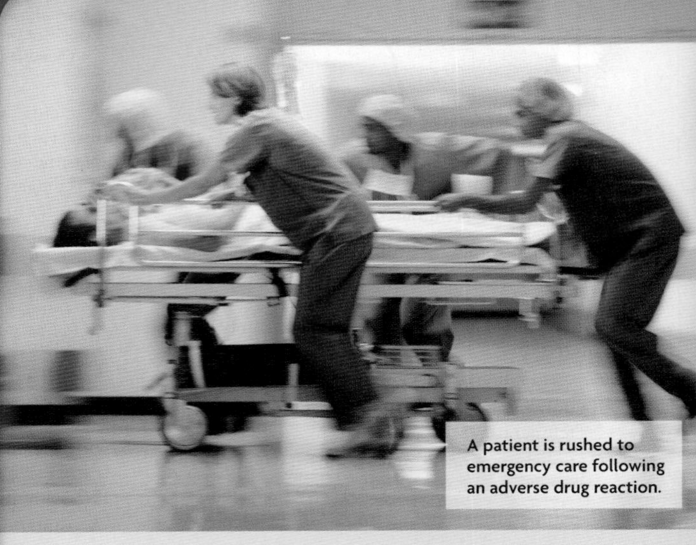

A patient is rushed to emergency care following an adverse drug reaction.

Medical Technology— The Genetic Forefront

A college student comes down with the flu. Worried about missing class, he goes to an emergency clinic and is given a prescription for an antiviral flu drug. Thirty minutes after taking the first pill, he is gasping for breath and his heart is racing. He is rushed to the hospital, where doctors tell him he has had an adverse reaction to his antiviral medication.

Current News

Using the Current News section of BioZine at **ClassZone.com,** have students look for stories about medical technology. **Ask**

- What medical technology is making headlines in the news?
- What effect will the technology have on genetics research?
- How is the technology changing testing, drugs, or other treatments people receive?
- How are people being affected by changes in medical technology?

Opinion Poll

Have students participate in the BioZine online poll. **Ask**

- Should polls be used to evaluate the public's level of acceptance of medical advances?
- Do you think being aware of advances in medical research makes a person more willing to engage in risky behavior, such as smoking?
- Do advances in technology also bring with them the potential for new risks?

A Cure Worse than the Disease

Usually, medications cause only mild side effects, such as drowsiness, headaches, or nausea. Occasionally, patients are allergic to medicines and break out in hives or go into shock. But sometimes reactions to drugs are more serious. In the United States, about 2.2 million patients per year are hospitalized because of adverse drug reactions, and 100,000 die. Of course, no doctor intends for a drug's side effects to be worse than the disease it is meant to cure. Nonetheless, the current process of prescribing drugs based on medical and family history is one of trial and error.

Customized Drugs

An emerging field called pharmacogenomics is about to revolutionize the prescription process. Pharmacogenomics is the study of how genetic variations can cause different people to react in different ways to the same drugs. In most cases, for example, genetics determines the way in which—and the speed at which—a person's body breaks down a medication. If a person's body metabolizes a drug too quickly, the drug may not be effective. If the drug is metabolized too slowly, a standard dose may be too much.

In the future, a patient in need of a prescription could have a blood test, and health care workers could run the blood test results through a computer using biochip, or microarray, technology. In hours, a patient's doctor could have enough information about the person's genetic background to predict how the patient would respond to a certain drug and decide whether the dose should be changed. Individuals may even be able to have their genomes mapped and put onto cards that they can take to every doctor visit. Biochip technology is not yet available in most doctors' offices, but some oncologists (cancer specialists) are already screening patients for particular genotypes before prescribing medications.

Gene Therapy

While pharmacogenomics can provide doctors with more information about their patients, gene therapy may someday provide them with another tool. Some diseases, such as Alzheimer's disease and hemophilia, have a strong genetic basis. Researchers hope to replace disease-causing alleles with normal ones.

TECHNOLOGY

Biochips

To provide truly individualized medicine, doctors would have to analyze a patient's DNA using biochip technology. A biochip is a solid surface to which tiny strands of DNA are attached. It allows thousands of biological reactions to occur within a few seconds. When this type of screening becomes clinically feasible, it will take several steps.

1. DNA will be extracted from the patient's blood.
2. A biochip will be used to map the patient's genome. Computer software could scan the genome looking for single nucleotide polymorphisms (called SNPs, or "snips"), places where human DNA is more variable.
3. A doctor will then compare the patient's genomic results with the latest available medical research.

Ideally, the resulting prescription should be customized to the patient. If a patient has a variation that is found in a small percentage of the population, however, the doctor is unlikely to have enough data about possible reactions.

Read More >> at CLASSZONE.COM

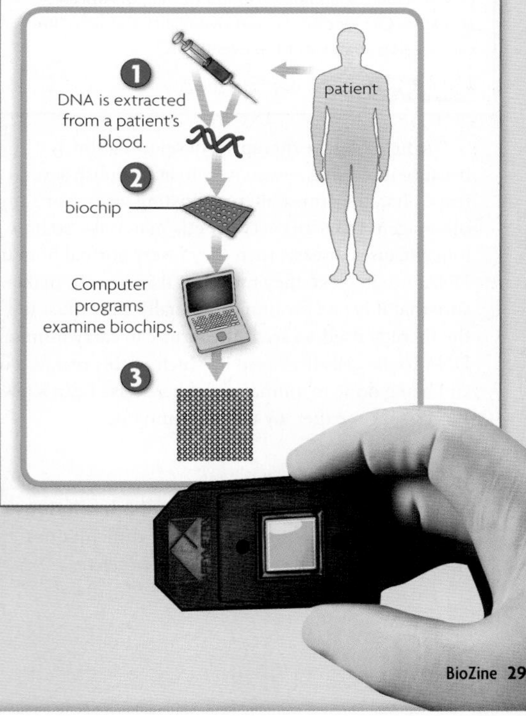

Vocabulary of Medical Technology

Students may need clarification of some of the terms used in medical technology.

pharmacology—the science of drugs, including their origin, composition, and uses. A pharmacologist searches for and develops new medicine.

adverse drug reaction—abnormal, undesired, and potentially harmful effects of a medicine that can range from mild to life threatening.

genomics—the study of all the nucleotide sequences in the chromosomes of an organism. The Human Genome Project is the genomics of human DNA. Genomic sequencing of pathogens may produce better targeted vaccines or drugs.

pharmacogenomics—the study of how an individual's genetic makeup affects a drug's effects on the body. Depending on an individual's genes, a drug can be therapeutic or toxic or ineffective.

therapeutic—exhibiting healing powers.

toxic—capable of causing injury or death, especially by chemical means.

genetic biochip—an orderly arrangement of genomic DNA on a small solid surface. Genetic biochips, also known as DNA microarrays, enable researchers to identify specific genes and their level of activity.

gene therapy—a technique for correcting defective genes responsible for the development of diseases or disorders. The most common research in gene therapy involves replacing the defective gene with a normal gene.

transgenic animal—an animal whose genome has been altered to contain genes of another organism or species. Such animals can be used to produce protein-based drugs such as insulin.

Expanding the Textbook

Have students go to BioZine at **ClassZone.com** to read more about the role of genetics in modern medicine. Have them take notes on different types of medical technologies, such as customized drugs and gene therapy. Suggest they use a matrix to compare different technologies, including potential risks and benefits. Students should come to class prepared to discuss what they have learned.

You could extend the discussion to include students' understanding of the challenges or ethical issues surrounding technology.

- What are some ethical questions that can arise from technology?
- Who should fund medical research, and how does that affect who has access to its benefits?
- How can society ensure everyone benefits from basic medical research?

Take It Further

Genetic disorders result when a gene that contains the instructions for making a specific protein is defective. The goal of gene therapy is to correct the defective gene. In most research, scientists try to replace the defective gene with a normal gene. But how can a gene, which is present in every cell in the body, be replaced? It doesn't have to be replaced in every cell. The gene only needs to be replaced in cells that will produce the needed protein. These cells are called target cells.

A vector, or molecule that carries the normal gene, is used to deliver the normal gene to the target cells. The most commonly used vector is a virus. Viruses can be used because they enter human cells and cause the cells to reproduce the DNA they contain. When viruses are modified to carry a normal human gene, they enter human cells, deliver the normal human gene, and cause the cells to produce the normal gene.

CAREERS

Cancer Geneticist in Action

DR. OLUFUNMILAYO OLOPADE

TITLE Director, Center for Clinical Cancer Genetics, University of Chicago

EDUCATION M.D., University of Ibadan, Nigeria

Breast cancer occurs in many different forms. It has been most widely studied in Caucasian women but takes a very different form in women of African ancestry. Breast cancer hits women of African ancestry earlier and more aggressively than it does Caucasian women. Dr. Olufunmilayo Olopade wants to learn why. Working with scientists in her native Nigeria, Dr. Olopade compared gene expression in samples of cancer tissue from African women with samples of cancer tissue from Canadian women. She found that cancer cells from the African women often lacked estrogen receptors. This finding means that many of the standard treatments are not effective for this group of women.

Dr. Olopade's work will have a huge impact on breast cancer screening and treatment in women of African ancestry. "Cancer doesn't start overnight," she says. "We can develop strategies for preventing it."

Read More >> at CLASSZONE.COM

The field of gene therapy is developing slowly because it requires researchers to accomplish several feats. First, they must alter an existing virus—or some other agent that can carry genetic material—so it no longer causes disease; then they insert normal human DNA into it. Next, they must test this virus to make sure that it is safe for humans. Finally, they must test the therapy itself, to see if the virus can carry human DNA to the cells that need it. Much of this research is still being done in animals, but there have been a few successful gene therapy trials in humans.

Other Uses

New uses for DNA technology offer both solutions and hard choices. Some of the more difficult questions involve the following kinds of projects:

- Researchers can alter the DNA of viruses to make them harmless and then use the harmless version of the virus as a vaccine.
- Scientists are developing transgenic animals that can be used as medical supply factories. For example, researchers hope to breed pigs that have organs that could be used for human transplants.
- Researchers are engineering crops that contain vaccines that could be administered orally. These vaccines would be easier to grow and distribute in developing countries than are current vaccines.

A scientist examines different types of genetically modified rice plants.

Unanswered Questions

The Human Genome Project has generated a lot of excitement about its potential use for pharmacogenomic applications. However, many challenges must be addressed before pharmacogenomics can have widespread clinical application.

- Many of the current studies of patients' responses to different drugs have conflicting results, probably due to small sample sizes, different criteria for measuring a good response, and different population groups.
- Patients' responses to a drug may be caused by many genes. Scientists will need to study the effect of multiple genes to determine response.
- Genotype testing may increase short-term health-care costs, which raises questions about who will pay and who will have access to the technology.

Read More >> at CLASSZONE.COM

Careers

Have students go to BioZine at **ClassZone.com** to learn about careers in biology. Have students check out job listings of a metropolitan newspaper. **Ask**

- How has technology changed this job market?
- What careers did not exist 30 years ago?
- Do you think education must change to meet the needs of the current job market? Explain your thinking.

UNIT 4

Evolution

CHAPTER 10
Principles of Evolution 296

CHAPTER 11
The Evolution of Populations 326

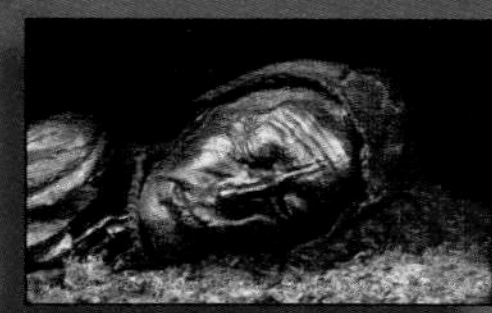

CHAPTER 12
The History of Life 358

INTERNET MAGAZINE
Drug-Resistant Bacteria—A Global Health Issue 390

TECHNOLOGY New Drug Delivery System

CAREER Evolutionary Biologist

Unit Project

Purpose **Understand, compare and contrast the historical achievements, lives, and time of Charles Darwin and Gregor Mendel.**

Overview Students research the lives of Charles Darwin and Gregor Mendel, comparing their lives and work. Students will

- research and take notes of the biographies of Darwin and Mendel
- prepare a timeline showing the significant dates in the lives of each scientist
- write a booklet that describes significant events on the timeline of each scientist and compares and contrasts their lives and work

Preparation Make a copy of the project description and rubric for each student (*Unit Resource Book*, pp. 99–100). Encourage students to be innovative and creative in the preparation of the timelines and booklet.

Project Management Allow three weeks for the completion of the project. Check students' progress at the end of each week leading up to the completion date.

Unit Resource Book Unit 4 Project, pp. 99–101

CHAPTER 10

Indiana Resource Preview

Print Resources

Principles of Evolution

INDIANA STANDARDS		Sections	PAGES and PACING	UNIT RESOURCE BOOK
NOS.9	10.1	**Early Ideas About Evolution** **KEY CONCEPT** There were theories of biological and geologic change before Darwin.	pp. 298–301 30 minutes	URB pages 1–4
B.8.5	10.2	**Darwin's Observation** **KEY CONCEPT** Darwin's voyage provided insights into evolution.	pp. 302–303 45 minutes	URB pages 5–8
B.8.5	10.3	**Theory of Natural Selection** **KEY CONCEPT** Darwin proposed natural selection as a mechanism for evolution.	pp. 304–309 45 minutes	URB pages 9–12
NOS.1		DATA ANALYSIS: Interpreting Line Graphs	p. 308 30 minutes	URB page 21
B.8.7	10.4	**Evidence of Evolution** **KEY CONCEPT** Evidence of common ancestry among species comes from many sources.	pp. 310–314 45 minutes	URB pages 13–16
B.8.5, NOS.6		CHAPTER INVESTIGATION: Predator-Prey Pursuit	p. 315 30 minutes	**Lab Binder** Evolution pages 1–2
B.8.7	10.5	**Evolutionary Biology Today** **KEY CONCEPT** New technology is furthering our understanding of evolution.	pp. 316–319 30 minutes	URB pages 17–20
B.8.5, NOS.1		OPTIONS FOR INQUIRY	pp. 320–321 45 minutes, 45 minutes	**Lab Binder** Evolution pages 3–8
		Chapter Review	pp. 322–325	**Assessment Book** Chapter Tests A, B pp. 197–204

INDIANA STANDARDS

B.8.5 Describe how due to genetic variations, environmental forces, and reproductive pressures, organisms with beneficial traits are more likely to survive, reproduce, and pass on their genetic information.

B.8.7 Describe the modern scientific theory of the origins and history of life on earth, and evaluate the evidence that supports it.

NOS.1 Develop explanations based on reproducible data and observations gathered during laboratory investigations.

NOS.6 Use analogies and models (mathematical and physical) to simplify and represent systems that are difficult to understand or directly experience due to their size, time scale, or complexity, and recognize the limitations of analogies and models.

NOS.9 Recognize that new scientific discoveries often lead to a re-evaluation of previously accepted scientific knowledge and of commonly held ideas.

Labs

PUPIL EDITION LABS

Piecing Together Evidence, Section 4, p. 313 Students form inferences and make predictions from incomplete evidence. **Lab Binder** p. 9	**Time:** 10 minutes **Materials:** picture cut into strips
Predator-Prey Pursuit, p. 315 Students observe the effect of natural selection on a population. **Lab Binder** pp. 1–2	**Time:** 45 minutes **Materials:** piece of fabric, bag of paper pieces

OPTIONS FOR INQUIRY

Using Patterns to Make Predictions, p. 320 Students make inferences based on observations of patterns. **Lab Binder** pp. 3–6	**Time:** 45 minutes **Materials:** cube for each group
Adaptations in Beaks, p. 321 Students infer how beak variations in birds affect natural selection. **Lab Binder** pp. 7–8	**Time:** 45 minutes **Materials:** aluminum pie plate, Petri dishes, sunflower seeds, forceps, clothespins, tongs, chopsticks, stopwatch

LAB BINDER Unit 4 Evolution

Additional Investigation: Biochemical Evidence for Evolution, pp. 11–15

LAB GENERATOR

A searchable CD of all labs in the program in editable format, including forensic, probeware, and biotechnology labs.

Presentation Tools

POWER PRESENTATIONS

Presentation Chapter 10
PowerPresentations for each section incorporate images and clips from the Media Gallery. Includes Note Navigator for each section.

MEDIA GALLERY

Contains the following images and video clips, as well as animations, simulations, and forms of visuals from the book.

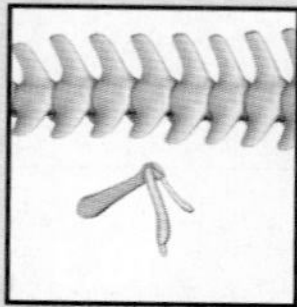
Vestigial structures

Natural selection

Darwin finch

Charles Darwin

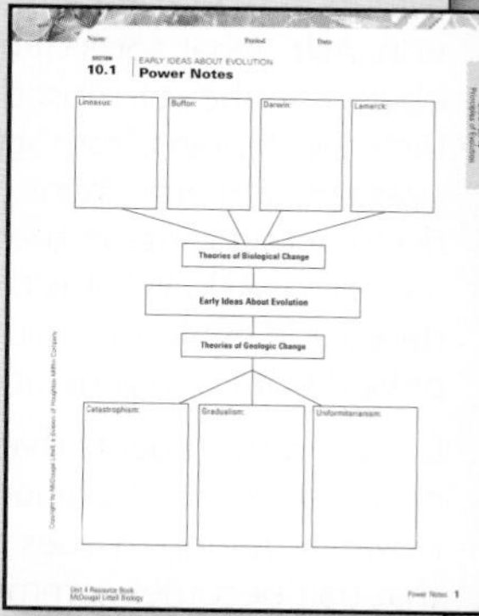

Power Notes

VIDEO

View a set of short video clips examining the study of and evidence for evolution.

ANIMATED BIOLOGY

Natural Selection Principles

Simulate Natural Selection

Online BIOLOGY CLASSZONE.COM

BioZine

Animated Biology

Interactive Review

SciLinks

Resource Centers

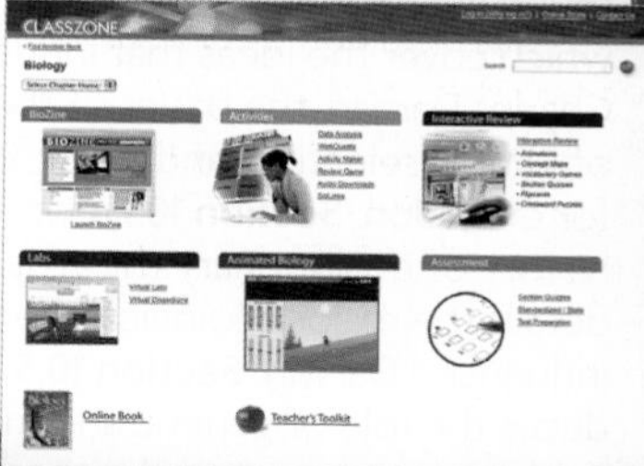

CHAPTER 10

▼ Focus and Motivate

How could evolution lead to this?

Tell students there are two parts to the evolution story: descent and modification. **Ask,** What sorts of modifications are obvious in the star-nosed mole? raylike feelers extending from snout, poor eyesight, and prominent claws **Ask,** How do such traits arise in the first place? mutation **Ask,** What is the role of descent in evolution? Mutations can be passed from one generation to the next.

Discuss with students that mutation must occur for new or modified traits to appear. However, mutation does not explain how that trait becomes common in a species or why some traits disappear altogether. **Ask,** What other factor has been at work in generations of star-nosed moles that has caused these moles to have the features they do? its environment, including other organisms they might be competing with for food or have as prey Discuss how the mole's features can be regarded as a form of specialization that enables the mole to survive.

BIOZINE ClassZone.com

Students can access BioZine at **ClassZone.com** to check out articles featured in "Strange Biology."

In a Hurry?

The critical material of the chapter is found in **Sections 10.2, 10.3,** and **10.4,** which cover the ideas that influenced Charles Darwin, the basics of the theory of natural selection, and classic evidence for evolution. **Section 10.1** reviews the history of evolutionary thought and details the major geological theories that influenced Darwin. **Section 10.5** introduces the role of genetic and molecular evidence in supporting the theories of evolution and natural selection.

CHAPTER

10 Principles of Evolution

KEY CONCEPTS

10.1 Early Ideas About Evolution
There were theories of biological and geologic change before Darwin.

10.2 Darwin's Observations
Darwin's voyage provided insights into evolution.

10.3 Theory of Natural Selection
Darwin proposed natural selection as a mechanism for evolution.

10.4 Evidence of Evolution
Evidence of common ancestry among species comes from many sources.

10.5 Evolutionary Biology Today
New technology is furthering our understanding of evolution.

Online BIOLOGY CLASSZONE.COM

Animated BIOLOGY
View animated chapter concepts.
- Natural Selection Principles
- Simulate Natural Selection

BIOZINE
Keep current with biology news.
- Featured stories
- Strange Biology
- Careers

RESOURCE CENTER
Get more information on
- Charles Darwin
- Artificial Selection
- Genetic Tools to Study Evolution

Student Activity

Purpose **Have teams of students use photographs to group different organisms according to shared traits. Students should recognize that not only closely related species can share traits. Similar features can arise in distantly related organisms in response to similar environmental factors.**

Materials (per team)

Provide each group of students with the same images. Look for pictures of animals that share physical features (for example, wings, horns, claws) but are not necessarily closely related. For example:

cockatoo	hummingbird	ant
sparrow	bee	marlin
toucan	crab	lobster

How could evolution lead to this?

The star-nosed mole has a pink snout that is especially good at finding food. The snout's 22 fingerlike rays can touch up to 12 objects in just one second. The mole also uses strong paddle-shaped feet for burrowing, and its large ear openings give it excellent hearing. These special traits make up for its poor vision—which it doesn't really need underground.

Connecting CONCEPTS

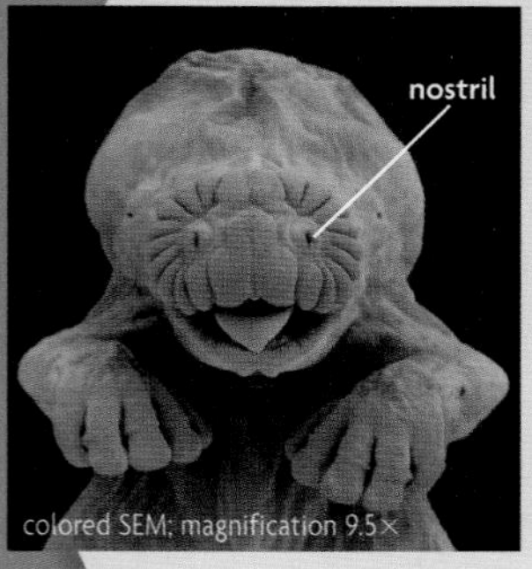

colored SEM; magnification 9.5×

Genetics The pink rays that sprout around the star-nosed mole's nostrils develop differently from the body parts of any other animal. After the mole is born, the rays spring forward to form their "star." Scientists are researching whether the mole has a unique set of genes for development. In this chapter, you will learn how genes are involved in evolution.

Introduce Tell students to group the organisms according to shared traits. Discuss different options for grouping. For example, crabs, lobsters, and fish are all aquatic; however, crabs and lobsters are invertebrates, whereas fish are vertebrates. The goal is to establish groups of animals that are likely to be closely related. Have students look at the physical characteristics of organisms just as Darwin did. Then have each group present its results to the class and give the reasons for the choices made.

Discuss Explain that similarities and differences in traits reflect evolutionary relationships. Talk about any differences in the choices made and point out shared traits students may have overlooked. For example, although ants, bees, crabs, and lobsters live in different habitats, they are all invertebrates.

Ask, What is the source of the shared characteristics in closely related species? shared genes **Ask,** Why do distantly related species share similar traits? They occupy similar environments and therefore may need similar features to move, feed, find shelter, and survive.

Activate Prior Knowledge

Direct students' attention to the chapter title. **Ask,** What does the word *evolution* mean to you in an everyday sense? Answers will tend to be about evolution of character, physical development, personal growth, and changes in thinking or attitude. Tell students that in science, *evolution* refers not to change in individuals but rather to change in species over generations.

Preview Vocabulary

Greek and Latin Word Origins The words **evolve** and **evolution** come from the Latin *evolvere,* which means "to unroll." Students may have heard the word **devolve** (Latin, "to roll down, fall to") in a way that suggests that it is the opposite of *evolve.* While *devolve* does mean "to degenerate or deteriorate gradually," this word is not used in biology as an antonym of *evolve.*

Academic Vocabulary Evolution is typically defined as "descent with modification." Tell students the focus is upon changes that occur across generations, therefore the relationship can be described in terms of descendants and ancestors:

descendant, an individual who can be traced back to a particular familial group

ancestor, an individual or group from whom one is descended

English Learners Students will see a number of common words transformed into "*-isms.*" Explain that the suffix can refer to an action, as in *terrorism,* or a quality, as in *heroism.* In this chapter, *-ism* refers to a theory or set of principles, as in *gradualism.* Point out that the term *Darwinism* is not a scientific term. Darwin is known for the theory of natural selection.

Integrating Zoology

The rays on the star-nosed mole's snout enable it to forage at speeds so fast that the human eye can barely register them. Using high-speed video cameras, scientists have clocked moles detecting and engulfing prey—a worm or an insect larva—in one-fourth of a second. One hypothesis for why this animal eats so fast is that because the prey is so tiny, the mole must eat twice as fast as animals that eat larger prey.

SECTION 10.1

▼ Plan and Prepare

Objectives

- Examine early ideas about evolution.
- Identify three geological theories that influenced scientific debate over evolution.

Section Resources

Unit Resource Book Study Guide pp. 1–2 Power Notes p. 3 Reinforcement p. 4
Interactive Reader Chapter 10 **Spanish Study Guide** pp. 99–100
Biology Toolkit pp. C22, C31
Technology Power Presentation 10.1 Media Gallery DVD Online Quiz 10.1

Activate Prior Knowledge Find out what misconceptions students may have about Darwin and the theory of natural selection. **Ask,** Have you ever heard the expression "survival of the fittest"? What does it suggest to you? Answers will probably focus on the idea that only the strong survive, associating fitness with physical strength. Point out that many of the most successful species—cockroaches and bacteria, for example—are small and have little physical strength. **Ask,** With evolution, what is it that survives? genes associated with specific traits

▼ Teach

Vocabulary

Greek and Latin Word Origins The word **species** comes from the Latin root meaning "kind" or "form." As with the word *series,* the spelling of *species* is the same for both its singular and plural forms. Point to the definition in the text. **Ask,** Why is the ability to produce fertile offspring important to the concept of species? Traits must be passed on.

10.1 Early Ideas About Evolution

KEY CONCEPT There were theories of biological and geologic change before Darwin.

MAIN IDEAS

- Early scientists proposed ideas about evolution.
- Theories of geologic change set the stage for Darwin's theory.

VOCABULARY

evolution, p. 298
species, p. 298
fossil, p. 300
catastrophism, p. 301
gradualism, p. 301
uniformitarianism, p. 301

Review
hybridization

INDIANA STANDARDS

NOS.9 Recognize that new scientific discoveries often lead to a re-evaluation of previously accepted scientific knowledge and of commonly held ideas.

Connect Why are there so many kinds of living things, such as the strange looking star-nosed mole? Earth is home to millions of species, from bacteria to plants to ocean organisms, that look like something from science fiction. The search for reasons for Earth's great biological diversity was aided in the 1800s, when Charles Darwin proposed his theory of evolution by natural selection. But long before Darwin, evolution had been the focus of talk among scholars.

MAIN IDEA

Early scientists proposed ideas about evolution.

Although Darwin rightly deserves much of the credit for evolutionary theory as we know it today, he was not the first person to come up with the idea. **Evolution** is the process of biological change by which descendants come to differ from their ancestors. This concept had been discussed for more than 100 years when Darwin proposed his theory of how evolution works. Today, evolution is a central theme in all fields of biology.

The 1700s were a time of great advances in intellectual thought. Many fields of science came out with new ways of looking at the world. Four scientists in particular are important. They not only made valuable contributions to biology in general but they also laid the foundations upon which Darwin would later build his ideas. **FIGURE 10.1** highlights the work of some of these early scientists.

TAKING NOTES

Create a chart with a column for each scientist mentioned in this section and a second column for his contribution to evolutionary theory.

Scientist	Contribution
Linnaeus	
Buffon	

Carolus Linnaeus In the 1700s, the Swedish botanist Carolus Linnaeus developed a classification system for all types of organisms known at the time. Although Linnaeus used his system to group organisms by their similarities, the system also reflects evolutionary relationships. This system is still in use by scientists today. Years into his career, Linnaeus abandoned the common belief of the time that organisms were fixed and did not change. He proposed instead that some might have arisen through hybridization—a crossing that he could observe through experiments with varieties, or species, of plants. A **species** is a group of organisms so similar to one another that they can reproduce and have fertile offspring.

Differentiated Instruction

ENGLISH LEARNERS

Help students set up a table to categorize the content in this section. Suggest an eight-row, five-column matrix. Explain that they may not need to use every column or row. For example, column 1 might identify early scientists and where they came from, column 2 the dates for their writing or research, column 3 their research, and column 4 their theories or findings.

Biology Toolkit, Content Frame, p. C22

BELOW LEVEL

Have students sort a stack of baseball cards by several criteria, such as league, teams, and positions. Help students understand that Linnaeus used a similar method to group species into categories based on trait similarities. Encourage students to come up with other categories. As a simpler alternative, you can do the same with a deck of playing cards, sorting by suit and number.

Georges Louis Leclerc de Buffon Buffon, a French naturalist of the 1700s, challenged many of the accepted ideas of the day. Based on evidence of past life on Earth, he proposed that species shared ancestors instead of arising separately. Buffon also rejected the common idea of the time that Earth was only 6000 years old. He suggested that it was much older. This argument was similar to that of Charles Lyell, a geologist whose work helped inspire Darwin's writings. You will read more about Lyell later in this section.

Erasmus Darwin Born in 1731, Charles Darwin's grandfather was a respected English doctor and a poet. He proposed that all living things were descended from a common ancestor and that more-complex forms of life arose from less-complex forms. This idea was expanded upon 65 years later by his grandson.

Jean-Baptiste Lamarck In 1809, the year of Darwin's birth, a French naturalist named Lamarck proposed that all organisms evolved toward perfection and complexity. Like other scientists of the time, he did not think that species became extinct. Instead, he reasoned that they must have evolved into different forms.

Lamarck proposed that changes in an environment caused an organism's behavior to change, leading to greater use or disuse of a structure or organ. The structure would become larger or smaller as a result. The organism would pass on these changes to its offspring. For example, Lamarck thought that the long necks of giraffes evolved as generations of giraffes reached for leaves higher in the trees. Lamarck's idea is known as the inheritance of acquired characteristics.

***Connecting* CONCEPTS**

Scientific Process Recall from **Chapter 1** that in every scientific field, knowledge is built upon evidence gathered by earlier scientists.

FIGURE 10.1 Early Naturalists

Evolutionary thought, like all scientific inquiry, draws heavily upon its history. The published works of these scientists contributed important ideas prior to Darwin's theory.

1735 *Systema Naturae*	1749 *Histoire Naturelle*	1794–1796 *Zoonomia*	1809 *Philosophie Zoologique*
Carolus Linnaeus proposed a new system of organization for plants, animals, and minerals, based upon their similarities. 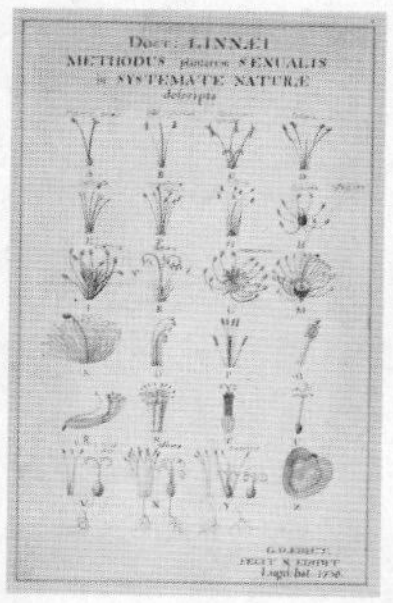	**Georges Buffon** discussed important ideas about relationships among organisms, sources of biological variation, and the possibility of evolution. 	**Erasmus Darwin** considered how organisms could evolve through mechanisms such as competition. 	**Jean-Baptiste Lamarck** presented evolution as occurring due to environmental change over long periods of time. 

A Summarize **Explain why Darwin cannot be considered the first scientist to consider evolution.**

History of Science

The ideas that Earth was ancient and that species could change over time represented radical thinking in the 1700s. The scientific community had for a long time accepted that life forms were ordered in a **Great Chain of Being**. This concept described a system in which species were positioned in a hierarchy of complexity or "perfection"—from lower organisms such as insects and worms to higher, more "perfect" beings such as mammals. The concept was founded on the idea that all species were created in their present form and, therefore, could not change.

Take It Further

Lamarck's idea of the inheritance of **acquired traits** is often presented as the flawed standard by which Darwin's theories are measured. What is sometimes overlooked is that Lamarck understood two things that are key to evolutionary theory—that new physical forms and traits have emerged in response to environmental changes and that these traits appear in subsequent generations. Because he did not know the mechanism by which traits were passed on, Lamarck made the reasonable but incorrect conclusion that traits were arising in individual animals in direct response to environmental changes.

Science Trivia

Many of the great naturalists involved in the early debates on evolution were famous in their day for other achievements.

- Cuvier served as the inspector general of public education for Napoleon.
- Erasmus Darwin was a well-known poet.
- Lamarck was the first naturalist to study insects and worms in depth. He coined the term *invertebrates* and thus established an entire branch of zoology.

PRE-AP

Tell students that the 18th and 19th centuries were periods of great social, political, and scientific change. Have students create a timeline of this period, incorporating information from the text as well as other important dates such as these:

1776—Declaration of Independence (war over)

1789—French Revolution

1798—Malthus: massive human population growth

1848—Karl Marx and Freidrich Engels publish *Communist Manifesto.*

1859—Darwin publishes *On the Origin of Species.*

1866—Mendel publishes research on pea plants.

Biology Toolkit, Timeline, p. C31

Answers

A Summarize Naturalists before Darwin considered evolution. Darwin built upon their ideas.

▼ Teach *continued*

Science Trivia

In 1822, the tiger shark, one of the ocean's largest predatory fish and one of its most dangerous, was given the scientific name *Galeocerdo cuvier* in honor of French zoologist Georges Cuvier, who introduced many marine fish species—such as the ruby snapper, black marlin, and wahoo—to science.

TEACH FROM VISUALS

FIGURE 10.2 Point out to students that the **VISUAL VOCAB** on the next page is based on the right-hand photograph on this page. **Ask**

- What were the rock layers originally? layers of sediment that were buried over time
- Make the comparison to an archaeological dig or an excavation at a building site. How would the cultural artifacts you find change the lower you go? They would reflect older technology or practices.

Answers

A Compare that organisms can change from one generation to the next

B Compare and Contrast All the theories propose how landforms were created. Gradualism and uniformitarianism are based on the idea of slow change and an ancient Earth, with uniformitarianism adding the concept of uniform change. Catastrophism suggested that all extinctions and formations of landforms were caused by extreme, sudden events.

Lamarck did not propose how traits were passed on to offspring, and his explanation of how organisms evolve was flawed. However, Darwin was influenced by Lamarck's idea that changes in physical characteristics could be inherited and were driven by environmental changes over time.

A Compare What common idea about organisms did these scientists share?

MAIN IDEA

Theories of geologic change set the stage for Darwin's theory.

The age of Earth was a key issue in the early debates over evolution. The common view was that Earth was created about 6000 years earlier, and that since that time, neither Earth nor the species that lived on it had changed.

French zoologist Georges Cuvier did not think that species could change. However, he did think that they could become extinct, an idea considered radical by many of his peers. Cuvier had observed that each stratum, or rock layer, held its own specific type of fossils. **Fossils** are traces of organisms that existed in the past. He found that the fossils in the deepest layers were quite different from those in the upper layers, which were formed by more recent deposits of sediment. Cuvier explained his observations in the early 1800s with the theory now known as catastrophism, shown in **FIGURE 10.2.**

***Connecting* CONCEPTS**

Earth Science Cuvier based his thinking on what we know as the Law of Superposition. It states that in a sequence of layered rocks, a given layer was deposited before any layer above it.

FIGURE 10.2 Principles of Geologic Change

Ideas from geology played a role in Darwin's developing theory.

CATASTROPHISM	GRADUALISM	UNIFORMITARIANISM
Volcanoes, floods, and earthquakes are examples of catastrophic events that were once believed responsible for mass extinctions and the formation of all landforms.	Canyons carved by rivers show gradual change. Gradualism is the idea that changes on Earth occurred by small steps over long periods of time.	Rock strata demonstrate that geologic processes, which are still occurring today, add up over long periods of time to cause great change.

B Compare and Contrast How are these three theories similar, and what are their differences?

Differentiated Instruction

INCLUSION

To demonstrate the Law of Superposition, have students who are visually impaired create their own "rock" sequence, using layers sliced from a block of clay. Have students make the first layer the longest, with each subsequent layer trimmed to be slightly shorter at one end. This will produce a step effect. Have students use these "steps" to walk up the layers and indicate relative age as they do.

The theory of **catastrophism** (kuh-TAS-truh-FIHZ-uhm) states that natural disasters such as floods and volcanic eruptions have happened often during Earth's long history. These events shaped landforms and caused species to become extinct in the process. Cuvier argued that the appearance of new species in each rock layer resulted from other species' moving into the area from elsewhere after each catastrophic event.

In the late 1700s, the Scottish geologist James Hutton proposed that the changes he observed in landforms resulted from slow changes over a long period of time, a principle that became known as **gradualism** (GRAJ-oo-uh-LIHZ-uhm). He argued that the laying down of soil or the creation of canyons by rivers cutting through rock were not the result of large-scale events. Rather, they resulted from slow processes that had happened in the past. This idea has become so important to evolution that today the term *gradualism* is often used to mean the gradual change of a species through evolution.

One of the leading supporters of the argument for an ancient Earth was the English geologist Charles Lyell. In *Principles of Geology,* published in the 1830s, Lyell expanded Hutton's theory of gradualism into the theory of **uniformitarianism** (YOO-nuh-FAWR-mih-TAIR-ee-uh-NIHZ-uhm). This theory states that the geologic processes that shape Earth are uniform through time. Lyell observed processes that made small changes in Earth's features. He inferred that similar changes had happened in the past. Uniformitarianism combines Hutton's idea of gradual change over time with Lyell's observations that such changes have occurred at a constant rate and are ongoing. Uniformitarianism soon replaced catastrophism as the favored theory of geologic change. Lyell's theory greatly affected the scientific community—particularly a young English naturalist named Charles Darwin.

VISUAL VOCAB

Uniformitarianism proposes that present geologic processes are the key to the past.

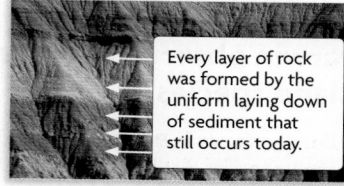

Every layer of rock was formed by the uniform laying down of sediment that still occurs today.

VOCABULARY

The names of these geologic theories can be broken down into familiar words.

- *Catastrophe* means "sudden disaster."
- *Gradual* means "moving or changing slowly."
- *Uniform* means "always staying the same."

***Connecting* CONCEPTS**

Scientific Process Recall from **Chapter 1** that in science, the term *theory* describes a well-supported explanation that incorporates observations, inferences, and tested hypotheses.

A Compare **What important concepts about Earth did Hutton and Lyell agree upon?**

The Inside Story

Before we had the means and understanding to accurately date the age of Earth, many scholars turned to the Bible as one the earliest accounts of Earth's history. **Isaac Newton** tried to scientifically interpret the Bible, using the Book of Genesis as an accurate, historical account of Earth's creation. **James Ussher,** an archbishop of Ireland and noted religious scholar, went one step further. In 1650, he painstakingly added the ages of Adam and his descendants, as written in the Bible. From this, Ussher deduced the date and time of the day Earth was created—the evening of October 22, 4004 B.C. The result of this calculation is an Earth just a little over 6000 years young.

Answers

A Compare that changes to Earth's surface occur slowly and gradually over time

10.1 ASSESSMENT

ONLINE QUIZ ClassZone.com

NOS.9

REVIEWING MAIN IDEAS

1. Briefly describe two ideas about **evolution** that were proposed by scientists in the 18th century.
2. What ideas in Lyell's theory of **uniformitarianism** were important for evolutionary theory?

CRITICAL THINKING

3. **Contrast** What are the key differences between the theories of **gradualism** and **catastrophism**?
4. **Apply** Why are the ideas that Earth undergoes change and is billions of years old important for evolutionary theory?

***Connecting* CONCEPTS**

5. **Genetics** How can you use the concept of genetic inheritance to disprove Lamarck's idea of the inheritance of acquired characteristics?

Assess and Reteach

Assess Use the Online Quiz or Section Quiz (*Assessment Book,* p. 191).

Reteach Have students present an oral summary that compares the three theories of geologic change with changes in thinking about evolution. Students can present this as a timeline that compares ideas about life changing over time with the idea that Earth has also changed.

10.1 ASSESSMENT

1. They proposed that species could change and may have come from a common ancestor.
2. Lyell stated that observable geologic processes, such as the deposition of soil, occur over a long period of time at a uniform rate.
3. Gradualism emphasizes slow changes on Earth over long periods of time, while catastrophism emphasizes change through natural disasters.
4. Evolution often happens over long periods of time. The fact that Earth can change over time inspired the idea that organisms can also change. Earth's great age makes it possible for significant changes to have occurred.
5. For a trait to be passed on to offspring, it must be encoded in the genes. The genes must first be passed on for the trait to appear.

▼ Plan and Prepare

Objectives

- Describe how Darwin arrived at his idea about species variation.
- Recognize how Darwin's discoveries supported Lyell's ancient-Earth theory.

Section Resources

Unit Resource Book Study Guide pp. 5–6 Power Notes p. 7 Reinforcement p. 8
Interactive Reader Chapter 10 **Spanish Study Guide** pp. 101–102
Biology Toolkit p. C36
Technology Power Presentation 10.2 Media Gallery DVD Online Quiz 10.2

Activate Prior Knowledge Tell students that Darwin's thoughts began to take shape while visiting the Galápagos Islands. **Ask,** Thinking in terms of genetics, what is it about a cluster of islands that makes it a good laboratory for studying variation? physical separation **Ask,** What is it that the islands keep separate? genes, meaning that the gene pool is isolated

▼ Teach

Vocabulary

Academic Vocabulary Discuss how the everyday meaning of **adaptation** differs from its scientific meaning. For example, a new student may adapt to an unfamiliar school by joining clubs. In that sense, *adapt* is something one does knowingly and with purpose. In nature, adaptations are traits or behaviors that are genetically determined. No finch can choose to grow its beak bigger.

Answers

A Connect The birds had beaks of different sizes and shapes that were suited to the available food.

10.2 Darwin's Observations

KEY CONCEPT Darwin's voyage provided insights into evolution.

MAIN IDEAS
- Darwin observed differences among island species.
- Darwin observed fossil and geologic evidence supporting an ancient Earth.

VOCABULARY
variation, p. 302
adaptation, p. 302

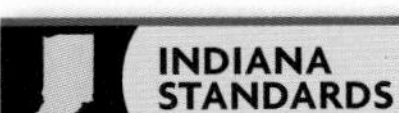

INDIANA STANDARDS

B.8.5 Describe how due to genetic variations, environmental forces, and reproductive pressures, organisms with beneficial traits are more likely to survive, reproduce, and pass on their genetic information.

Connect Lyell's views of gradual geologic change greatly influenced Darwin's thinking. In 1831, the ship HMS *Beagle* set sail from England to map the coast of South America and the Pacific islands. Hired at first to keep the captain company, Darwin was interested in observing the land and its inhabitants. During the voyage, he read Lyell's *Principles of Geology.* When the ship reached South America, Darwin spent most of his time ashore, where he found much evidence supporting Lyell's views.

MAIN IDEA

Darwin observed differences among island species.

Darwin, shown in **FIGURE 10.3**, was struck by the variation of traits among similar species that he observed in all his travels. In biology, **variation** is the difference in the physical traits of an individual from those of other individuals in the group to which it belongs. Variation can occur either among members of different species (*inter*specific variation) or among individuals of the same species (*intra*specific variation). Darwin noted that the species found on one island looked different from those on nearby islands and that many of the islands' species looked different from those on the nearest mainland.

The differences between species on different islands was especially noticeable in the Galápagos Islands, an island chain off the coast of Ecuador in South America. Some differences seemed well suited to the animals' environments and diets, as shown in **FIGURE 10.4**. For example, saddle-backed tortoises, which have long necks and legs, lived in areas with a lot of tall plants. Domed tortoises, with their shorter necks and legs, lived in wet areas rich in mosses and short plants. Similarly, finches with strong, thick beaks lived in areas with a lot of large, hard-shelled nuts, while those species of finch with more delicate beaks were found where insects or fruits were widely available.

FIGURE 10.3 Darwin spent more than 20 years compiling evidence before publishing in 1859 his ideas on how evolution works.

These observations led Darwin to realize that species may somehow be able to adapt to their surroundings. An **adaptation** is a feature that allows an organism to better survive in its environment. Adaptations can lead to genetic change in a population over time.

A Connect What adaptations did Darwin see in the finches of the Galápagos Islands?

Differentiated Instruction

PRE-AP

Describe to students a scenario in which sea lions living in the Galápagos suddenly lose their main food source when changes in currents and sea temperature keep anchovy away from the islands. The only other food available is a small species of crab that lives on the seafloor 100 feet below the surface. Discuss the traits in the sea lion population that might be adaptive and how the population could change. Have students write a description of one possible outcome.

Biology Toolkit, Cause and Effect Chain, p. C36

TEACH WITH TECHNOLOGY

Have students use the Internet to put together a virtual tour of the Galápagos Islands as a digital slideshow. Some good starting points to gather information and photographs can be found in the chapter resources at **ClassZone.com.**

FIGURE 10.4 Adaptations Within Species

Galápagos tortoises (*Geochelone elephantopus*) are evidence that species can adapt to their environments.

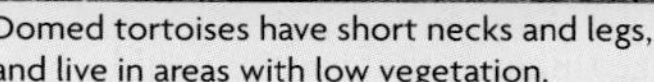

Domed tortoises have short necks and legs, and live in areas with low vegetation.

Saddle-backed tortoises have a high shell edge, allowing them to stretch their long necks.

Galápagos Islands

A Explain Why do these tortoises of the same species look different?

MAIN IDEA

Darwin observed fossil and geologic evidence supporting an ancient Earth.

On his voyage, Darwin found fossil evidence of species changing over time. In Argentina, he found fossils of huge animals, such as *Glyptodon,* a giant armadillo. The fact that these fossils looked like living species suggested that modern animals might have some relationship to fossil forms. These fossils suggested that, in order for such changes to occur, Earth must be much more than 6000 years old.

During his voyage, Darwin also found fossil shells of marine organisms high up in the Andes mountains. Darwin later experienced an earthquake during his voyage and saw firsthand the result: land that had been underwater was moved above sea level. This experience explained what he saw in the Andes. Darwin's observations on his voyage supported Lyell's theory that daily geologic processes can add up to great change over a long period of time. Darwin later extended the ideas of an old Earth and slow, gradual change to the evolution of organisms.

B Infer What could account for fossils of marine organisms being found on top of modern-day mountain ranges?

10.2 ASSESSMENT

ONLINE QUIZ ClassZone.com

B.8.5

REVIEWING MAIN IDEAS

1. What accounts for the **variation** Darwin observed among island species?
2. What did Darwin learn from the fossils that he observed on his voyage?

CRITICAL THINKING

3. **Apply** Explain how wings are an **adaptation** for birds.
4. **Synthesize** How did Darwin's observations support Lyell's theory of an ancient Earth undergoing continual geologic change?

***Connecting* CONCEPTS**

5. **Ecology** Some birds in the Galápagos Islands build nests in trees, while others hide eggs in rock crevices. What could account for this difference in nesting behaviors?

10.2 ASSESSMENT

1. The islands had different environments, and the organisms had adaptations (such as distinctively shaped beaks) that enabled the organisms to live in those environments.
2. Modern animals might be related to fossil forms; Earth is older than was thought at the time; and geologic processes can add up to great change.
3. *Sample Answer:* Wings enable birds to escape prey and hunt for food, so the birds survive and reproduce.
4. Darwin observed marine fossils in the mountains and the uplift of land due to an earthquake.
5. One can speculate that the birds nesting in rock crevices may have predators that can climb trees or cannot reach into a crevice. Similarly, birds nesting in trees suggests that the eggs are safer aboveground.

ONLINE BIOLOGY Go to the chapter Resource Center at **ClassZone.com** for additional resources and information about Charles Darwin.

The Inside Story

The world's oldest living animal—Harriet, a **Galápagos tortoise**—was once Charles Darwin's shipmate. She was one of three Galápagos tortoises captured by Darwin during his expedition. Darwin took the animals back to England and, thinking all three were males, named them Tom, Dick, and Harry. Poorly adapted to the cool English climate, the animals were moved to Australia around 1840. In the 1960s, scientists realized that Harry, the last remaining member of the trio, was actually female. In 1992, DNA testing confirmed that Harriet was born around 1830. Today, Harriet lives at the Australia Zoo outside Brisbane.

Answers

A Explain Genetic variation within the population enabled particular variations in traits to be expressed. Some of these variations proved beneficial within certain environments or conditions.

B Infer Land that was once a marine environment could be uplifted by Earth processes and become terrestrial.

Assess and Reteach ▼

Assess Use the Online Quiz or Section Quiz (*Assessment Book,* p. 192).

Reteach Have students write a news bulletin on the remarkable voyage of the *Beagle* and the amazing things Charles Darwin saw on his trip. Students should incorporate the terms *variation* and *adaptation* into their report.

SECTION 10.3

▼ Plan and Prepare

Objectives

- Compare artificial selection to natural selection.
- Examine the factors Darwin considered in forming his theory of natural selection.
- Summarize the four principles of natural selection.

Section Resources

Unit Resource Book
Study Guide pp. 9–10
Power Notes p. 11
Reinforcement p. 12
Pre-AP Activity pp. 23–24

Interactive Reader Chapter 10
Spanish Study Guide pp. 103–104

Biology Toolkit pp. C13, C19, C26, C33

Technology
Power Presentation 10.3
Media Gallery DVD
Online Quiz 10.3

Activate Prior Knowledge Tell students that one idea that Darwin brought home from his voyage on the *Beagle* was that life forms were infinitely variable. He wanted to study species variation in real time. **Ask,** Why would Darwin turn to animal and plant breeders as a source of information in studying variation? Breeders actively manipulate traits—a form of variation—by pairing mates rather than by letting reproduction occur naturally.

▼ Teach

Science Trivia

- The archeological record suggests that humans began to domesticate dogs, probably from wolves, about 15,000 years ago.
- There are more than 400 breeds of domestic dogs in the world today, but all of them are the same species *(Canis familiaris)*.

10.3 Theory of Natural Selection

KEY CONCEPT Darwin proposed natural selection as a mechanism for evolution.

MAIN IDEAS
- Several key insights led to Darwin's idea for natural selection.
- Natural selection explains how evolution can occur.
- Natural selection acts on existing variation.

VOCABULARY
artificial selection, p. 304
heritability, p. 304
natural selection, p. 305
population, p. 306
fitness, p. 307

Review
phenotype, competition

B.8.5 Describe how due to genetic variations, environmental forces, and reproductive pressures, organisms with beneficial traits are more likely to survive, reproduce, and pass on their genetic information.

Connect Although Darwin began his voyage thinking that species could not change, his experiences during the five-year journey altered his thinking. Variation of similar species among islands, fossil evidence, and geologic events convinced him that evolution occurs. But he had yet to determine *how* evolution could happen.

MAIN IDEA

Several key insights led to Darwin's idea for natural selection.

After his voyage, Darwin spent more than 20 years conducting research while thinking about how evolution occurs. Although he had traveled the world, Darwin also found great insight in his home country of England. One important influence of Darwin's was the work of farmers and breeders.

Artificial Selection

Darwin noticed a lot of variation in domesticated plants and animals. The populations of domesticated species seemed to show variation in traits that were not shown in their wild relatives. Through selection of certain traits, breeders could produce a great amount of diversity. The process by which humans change a species by breeding it for certain traits is called **artificial selection.** In this process, humans make use of the genetic variation in plants and animals by acting as the selective agent. That is, humans determine which traits are favorable and then breed individuals that show those traits.

To explore this idea, Darwin turned to the hobby of breeding pigeons. Although Darwin had no knowledge of genetics, he had noticed certain traits being selected in animals such as livestock and pets. Humans had been breeding pigeons for thousands of years, producing pigeons, such as those in **FIGURE 10.5**, that showed many different traits. In order for artificial—or natural—selection to occur, the trait must be heritable. **Heritability** (HER-ih-tuh-BIHL-uh-tee) is the ability of a trait to be passed down from one generation to the next.

Differentiated Instruction

ENGLISH LEARNERS

Have students use Cornell Notes to outline this lesson. They can record key terms and their definitions in a left column across from the appropriate point in the outline. Then they can add a summary in the bottom section. Encourage students to be concise but still try to include all key information.

Biology Toolkit, Cornell Notes, p. C26

TEACH WITH TECHNOLOGY

There are many organizations associated with domesticated breeding of ornamental plants and animals. Others are involved with heirloom breeds. Choose a selection of images from the Internet to project in class. Discuss how, in seeking to amplify a particular trait, breeders can, in the process, amplify others as well. Go to **ClassZone.com** for some possible sources.

Darwin compared what he learned about breeding to his ideas on adaptation. In artificial selection, features such as reversed neck feathers, large crops, or extra tail feathers are favored over generations only if these traits are liked by breeders. However, if a feature is not desirable or "useful," it might be selected against. During artificial selection humans act as the selective agent. In nature, however, the environment creates the selective pressure that determines if a trait is passed on or not.

Darwin used this line of thinking for his theory of natural selection. **Natural selection** is a mechanism by which individuals that have inherited beneficial adaptations produce more offspring on average than do other individuals. In nature, the environment is the selective agent. Therefore, in nature, characteristics are selected only if they give advantages to individuals in the environment as it is right now. Furthermore, Darwin reasoned, breeds are not produced perfectly all at once. He knew it sometimes took many generations for breeders to produce the varieties he had observed.

Struggle for Survival

Another important idea came from English economist Thomas Malthus. Malthus had proposed that resources such as food, water, and shelter were natural limits to population growth. That is, human populations would grow geometrically if resources were unlimited. Instead, disease and a limited food supply kept the population smaller.

FIGURE 10.5 Artificial Selection of Pigeon Traits

For thousands of years, new varieties of organisms, such as pigeons, have resulted from selective breeding for particular traits.

neck feathers
crop
tail feathers
SELECTIVELY BRED PIGEONS
Jacobins are bred for their reversed neck feathers.
Croppers are bred for their inflatable crop.
Fantails are bred to have many tail feathers.

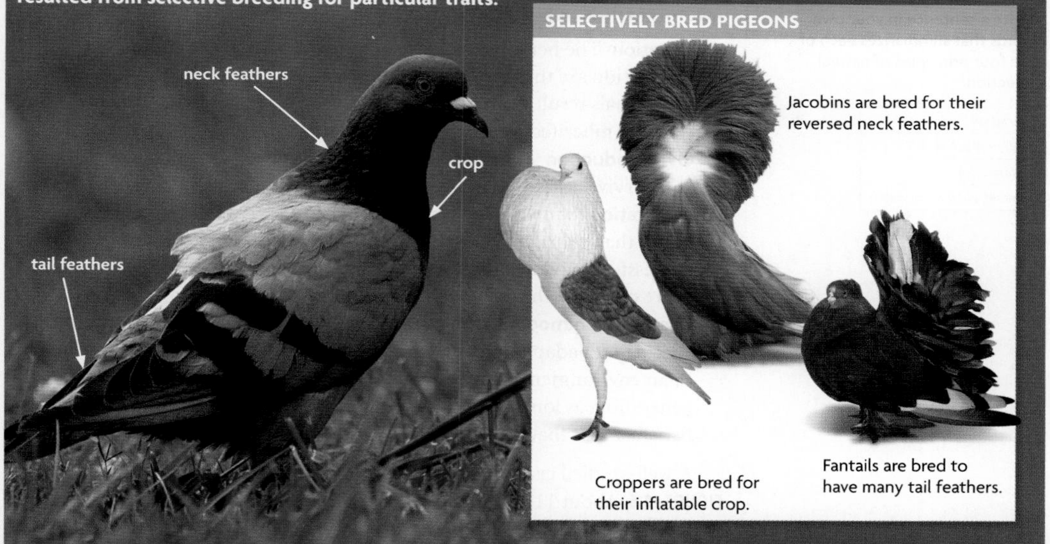

A Connect What other species of organisms are often subjects of artificial selection?

BELOW LEVEL

Have students use a Venn diagram to compare artificial selection to natural selection. Have them consider the selective agent and whether species or breeds are involved. Also, have students consider what benefit is derived from the process.

Biology Toolkit, Venn Diagram, p. C33

ONLINE BIOLOGY Go to the chapter Resource Center at **ClassZone.com** for additional resources and information about artificial selection.

Vocabulary

Academic Vocabulary As students learn about natural **selection** and see the word **select** used in an evolutionary context, it is important that they do not confuse these words with *choice* or *choose,* or ascribe to them any kind of deliberate, goal-oriented sense of purpose. Students will benefit if they think of *selection* as something that occurs for very specific reasons yet isn't chosen or planned.

Integrating Agricultural Science

Using traditional methods, scientists could crossbreed only closely related species or individual plants of the same species. Today, many scientists take advantage of **genetic engineering** techniques to produce plants that incorporate genes from widely different species. For example, **golden rice** is a genetically engineered rice that contains a large amount of beta carotene, a precursor of vitamin A.

Vitamin A deficiency is a leading cause of blindness in the developing world. Golden rice was developed by taking genes that code for beta carotene in daffodils and inserting them into rice. This type of artificial selection would have been almost impossible to accomplish with traditional breeding methods.

See the Unit 7 Biozine, p. 691, for more on golden rice and genetically modified crops.

Answers

A Connect Answers will vary but may include plants, pets, or livestock.

▼ Teach *continued*

Vocabulary

Greek and Latin Word Origins The root *popu* in the word **population** comes from the Latin word *populus*, meaning "people." Other words or expressions that use this root include *popular* and *populist*. The important distinction made about members of a population in science is that they are part of the same gene pool.

Answers

A Explain The competition for resources that Malthus saw among humans was applied by Darwin to all living organisms.

The Inside Story

In 1858, after years of quietly tinkering with his ideas about evolution, **Charles Darwin** received in the mail an unpublished paper from **Alfred Russel Wallace** (1823–1913). Wallace was a naturalist who, like Darwin, sought the mechanism for evolution. He had also spent a lot of time in the tropics, observing interactions between environments and species. Wallace was going to publish his paper *(On the Tendency of Varieties to Depart Indefinitely from the Original Type)*, but he first wanted feedback from Darwin, who was a well-respected member of the scientific community.

As Darwin read Wallace's paper, he realized that this stranger had somehow come to conclusions about evolution that were nearly identical to his own. Fearing that his life's work was about to be preempted, Darwin sought advice from **Charles Lyell,** who arranged for the two naturalists' ideas to be featured concurrently at a meeting of the Linnean Society of London. A year later, in 1859, Darwin's book *On the Origin of Species* was published. It had been 28 years since he first set sail on the *Beagle*.

VOCABULARY

The term *descent* is used in evolution to mean the passing of genetic information from generation to generation.

Darwin reasoned that a similar struggle took place in nature. Resources were limited, and organisms had more offspring than could ever survive. Why did some individuals, and not others, survive?

Darwin found his answer in the variation he had seen within populations. A  **population** is all the individuals of a species that live in an area. Darwin had noticed in the Galápagos Islands that in any population, such as the tortoises or the finches, some individuals had variations that were particularly well-suited to their environment. He proposed that these adaptations arose over many generations. Darwin called this process of evolution "descent with modification."

A Explain How did Malthus's economic theory influence Darwin?

MAIN IDEA

Natural selection explains how evolution can occur.

Charles Darwin was not the only person to develop a theory to explain how evolution may take place. An English naturalist named Alfred Russel Wallace independently developed a theory very similar to Darwin's. Both Darwin and Wallace had studied the huge diversity of plants and animals in the tropics, and both studied the fossil record. In 1858, the ideas of Darwin and Wallace were presented to an important group of scientists in London. The next year, Darwin published his ideas in the book *On the Origin of Species by Means of Natural Selection*.

TAKING NOTES

Write a sentence in your own words that summarizes each of the four principles of natural selection.

variation
overproduction
adaptation
descent with modification

There are four main principles to the theory of natural selection: variation, overproduction, adaptation, and descent with modification.

- **Variation** The heritable differences, or variations, that exist in every population are the basis for natural selection. The differences among individuals result from differences in the genetic material of the organisms, whether inherited from a parent or resulting from a genetic mutation.
- **Overproduction** While having many offspring raises the chance that some will survive, it also results in competition between offspring for resources.
- **Adaptation** Sometimes a certain variation allows an individual to survive better than other individuals it competes against in its environment. More successful individuals are "naturally selected" to live longer and to produce more offspring that share those adaptations for their environment.
- **Descent with modification** Over time, natural selection will result in species with adaptations that are well suited for survival and reproduction in an environment. More individuals will have the trait in every following generation, as long as the environmental conditions continue to remain beneficial for that trait.

A well-studied example of natural selection in jaguars is shown in **FIGURE 10.6.** About 11,000 years ago, many species faced extinction. Large cats, including jaguars, faced a shortage of food due to the changing climate of that time. There were fewer mammals to eat, so the jaguars had to eat reptiles. In the jaguar population, there were variations of jaw and tooth size that became

Differentiated Instruction

PRE-AP

Tell students that the influence of Darwin's evolutionary theories have extended beyond science. His concept of "fitness" was transformed into the idea of "survival of the fittest," which has been incorporated into literature, philosophy, psychology, religion, politics, and economics. Have students write for five minutes on a particular way in which the concept of "survival of the fittest" has been used in popular culture. Have them compare their example to what Darwin meant by "fitness."

Biology Toolkit, Quick-Write, p. C19

important for survival. Like many other species, jaguars can produce more offspring than can be supported by the environment. Jaguars with the biggest jaws and teeth could prey more easily on the shelled reptiles. Because jaw size and tooth size are heritable traits and were beneficial, large jaws and teeth became adaptations for this population. The jaguars' descendants showed modifications, or changes, over time.

In biology, the term **fitness** is a measure of the ability to survive and produce more offspring relative to other members of the population in a given environment. After the change in climate, jaguars that had larger teeth and jaws had a higher fitness than other jaguars in the population. Jaguars that ate less didn't necessarily all die or stop producing altogether; they just reproduced a little less. Today, large teeth and jaws are considered typical traits of jaguars.

VOCABULARY

In everyday language, *fitness* means "physically fit." In biology, however, fitness is related to reproductive success.

A Compare and Contrast **What are the similarities and differences between natural selection and artificial selection?**

Animated BIOLOGY Watch the principles of natural selection in action at ClassZone.com.

FIGURE 10.6 The Principles of Natural Selection

Certain traits become more common in a population through the process of natural selection.

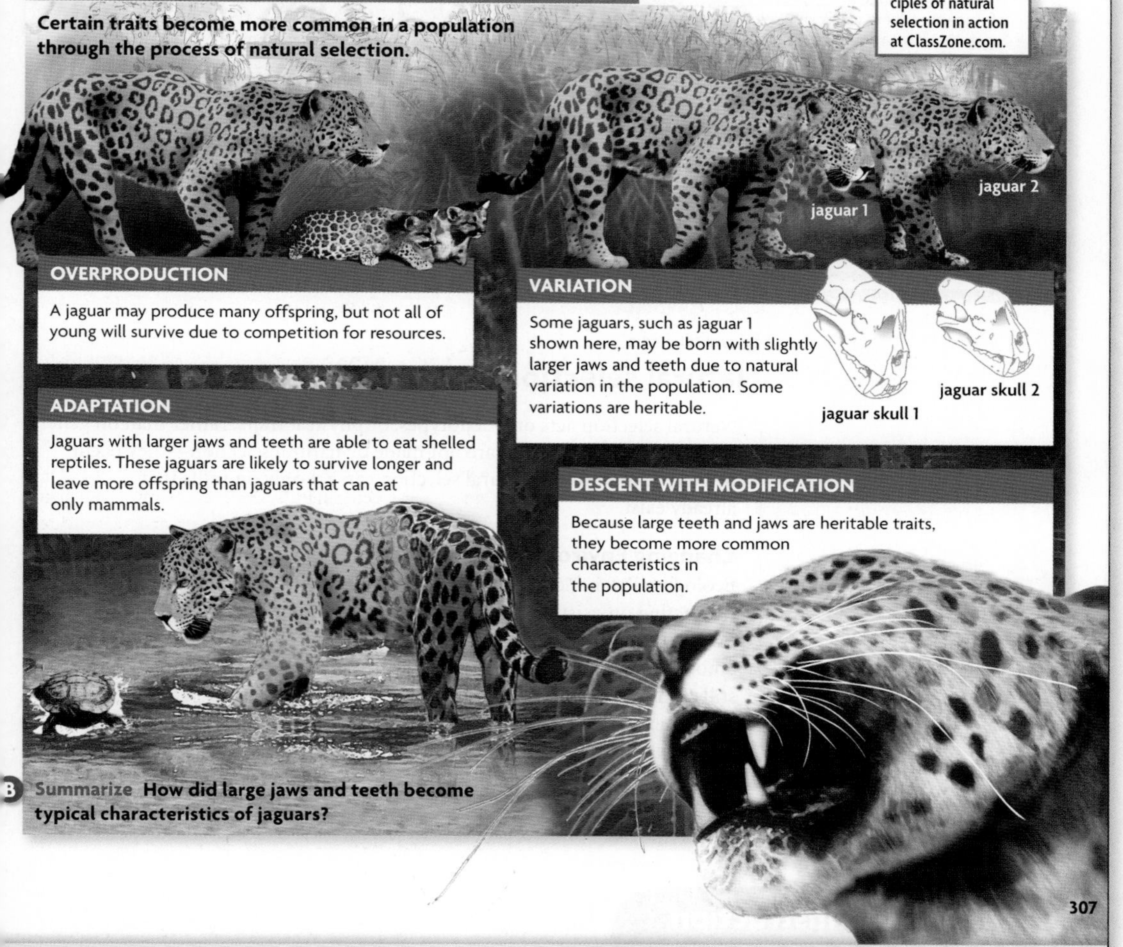

OVERPRODUCTION

A jaguar may produce many offspring, but not all of young will survive due to competition for resources.

VARIATION

Some jaguars, such as jaguar 1 shown here, may be born with slightly larger jaws and teeth due to natural variation in the population. Some variations are heritable.

ADAPTATION

Jaguars with larger jaws and teeth are able to eat shelled reptiles. These jaguars are likely to survive longer and leave more offspring than jaguars that can eat only mammals.

DESCENT WITH MODIFICATION

Because large teeth and jaws are heritable traits, they become more common characteristics in the population.

B Summarize **How did large jaws and teeth become typical characteristics of jaguars?**

307

ONLINE BIOLOGY To see natural selection in action, have students use the simulation in Options for Inquiry on page 321.

TEACH FROM VISUALS

FIGURE 10.6 Use the figure to discuss the four principles of natural selection. **Ask,** What traits are being selected for in this figure? jaw size and teeth size

Relate the diagram to the bulleted list on page 306. Explain that the figure can be read as a cycle diagram, an ongoing series of events that cause the traits in a population to change over time. **Ask,** How might changes in the jaguar population affect the population of reptiles? It's possible a certain defensive mechanism might develop within a prey population to counter the jaguar's adaptation, such as a stronger shell or perhaps a toxin in the skin.

Answers

A Compare and Contrast In natural selection, the environment determines which traits will be favored; in artificial selection, however, humans do the selecting.

B Summarize Natural variation in the population meant that some jaguars had larger jaws and teeth, and these jaguars were better able to survive in the environment long enough to reproduce. Over many generations, these heritable traits became common in the jaguar population.

INCLUSION

Students who have difficulty focusing on details will need to decode **FIGURE 10.6.** Have students work in pairs to isolate each principle depicted. Then ask them to consider how the phenomenon described affects the population as a whole. Have students put the parts back together to describe the cycle of change that causes populations to change.

Biology Toolkit, Think-Pair-Share, p. C13

▼ Teach *continued*

DATA ANALYSIS

Discussion

Ask, What does the variation in the trend line for the experimental group suggest? Wheel-running ability generally increases but still varies until Generation 8. By Generation 9, alleles for the ability have a much higher frequency in the experimental group than in the control group. The researchers hypothesized a recessive allele for the trait. Discuss that the trend for improved wheel-running ability cannot continue indefinitely. There are limitations to the physical capabilities of all living things.

Address Misconceptions

Common Misconception Once a pattern in a graph line is established, the pattern will continue indefinitely.

Correcting the Misconception Have students look at the trend line for the experimental group. **Ask,** What do you think the line will look line by Generation 15? flatter as the mice near their physical limitations Discuss that data must be considered in the context of the animals themselves. **Ask,** Could continued breeding produce a race of supermice? Answers will vary, but look for recognition of the physical limitations of the animal and its capabilities.

Answers

1. The mice in the experimental group show an increase in wheel-running ability as the generation number increases. The mice in the control group show little change in wheel-running ability.
2. The trend suggests that the number of revolutions may be even greater in Generation 10.

Unit Resource Book, Data Analysis, p. 21

DATA ANALYSIS

NOS.1

INTERPRETING LINE GRAPHS

Scientists used mice to study whether exercise ability can improve in animals over several generations. In this experiment, mice were artificially selected for increased wheel-running behavior. The mice that were able to do the most wheel running were selected to breed the next generation. The control group represents generations of mice that were allowed to breed randomly.

- The *x*-axis shows the different generations of mice from Generation 1 to Generation 9.
- The *y*-axis shows the number of revolutions the mice ran on the wheel per day.
- The solid blue line represents the control group, in which generations of mice were allowed to breed randomly.
- The dotted orange line represents the generations of mice that were artificially selected based on their wheel-running activity. This is the experimental group.

GRAPH 1. SELECTION OF EXERCISE ABILITY

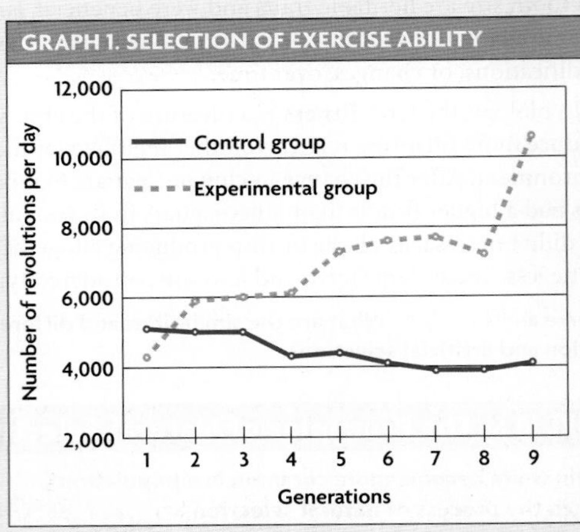

Source: Swallow et. al, *Behavior Genetics* 28:3.

1. **Interpret** What is the difference in results between the mice in the control group and the mice in the experimental group?
2. **Predict** Use the trend in the data to make a general prediction about the number of revolutions on the wheel per day for mice in Generation 10 of the experimental group.

MAIN IDEA

Natural selection acts on existing variation.

Natural selection acts on phenotypes, or physical traits, rather than on genetic material itself. New alleles are not made by natural selection—they occur by genetic mutations. Natural selection can act only on traits that already exist.

Changing Environments

Ecologists Peter and Rosemary Grant observed an example of natural selection acting on existing traits within a population of medium ground finches on one of the Galápagos Islands. A drought in 1977 suddenly reduced the amount of small, soft seeds that the finches preferred. However, there were still plenty of large, tough-shelled seeds. Because the large-beaked finches in the population were able to crack the large, tough seeds, they did not starve. The next year, the Grants noted a big increase of large-beaked hatchlings. In contrast, most of the finches with small beaks had died.

Differentiated Instruction

INCLUSION

Photocopy the graph above at twice its size for students who are visually impaired, so they can follow the graph lines in the Data Analysis example. Or, using a copy made at the same size, push a pin through the data points to enable students to better distinguish the trend in each graph line. Have students describe the trend as they move their fingers across the graph.

Darwin's theory predicted exactly what the Grants observed. A trait that was already in the population became favorable for survival because of a change in the environment, and thus was passed on to future generations.

As an environment changes, different traits will become beneficial. The numbers of large-beaked finches on this Galápagos Island kept rising until 1984, when the supply of large seeds went down after an unusually wet period. These conditions favored production of small, soft seeds and small-beaked birds. With evolution, a trait that is an advantage today may be a disadvantage in the future.

FIGURE 10.7 A panda's wrist bone also functions like a thumb.

Adaptations as Compromises

One mistake people make about natural selection is to think that adaptive characteristics passed down over a long time result in individuals that are perfectly suited to their surroundings. This is not the case. For example, some structures may take on new functions. Pandas have a structure in their wrist that acts like a thumb. As pandas eat bamboo shoots, they hold the shoots as you would hold a carrot. However, a close look at the paw reveals that it has six digits: five digits that resemble your fingers, plus a small thumblike structure. The panda's "thumb," shown in **FIGURE 10.7**, is actually an enlarged wrist bone. The ancestors of today's pandas had five full digits like today's bears, but those early pandas with bigger wrist bones had an advantage in eating bamboo. Because of its size and position, this bone functions like a human thumb. It is not considered a true thumb, because it does not have separate bones and joints as a human thumb does. It is also not a typical wrist bone, as the bone is clearly longer than needed to function for the wrist. Instead, it functions both as a wrist bone and a thumb.

A Explain **Why is the panda's "thumb" considered an adaptive compromise?**

To learn more about natural selection, visit scilinks.org. Keycode: MLB010

ONLINE BIOLOGY Have students do the data analysis in Options for Inquiry on page 321 to work with some of the Grants' data on Galápagos finches.

Integrating Anatomy

The enlarged wrist bone that is often mistaken as the **panda's thumb** is technically a sesamoid bone. Sesamoids are small, round bones that grow in connective tissue, specifically, in the tendons that cross joints. The kneecap, or patella, also is a sesamoid. In the joint, sesamoids act like pulleys, increasing the leverage of the tendon as it moves across the joint. This modifies the pressure on the tissue as it moves, decreasing the incidence of tissue tears.

Answers

A Explain It was originally adapted for a different function, but the animals can use it like humans use their thumbs.

10.3 ASSESSMENT

ONLINE QUIZ ClassZone.com

B.8.5

REVIEWING MAIN IDEAS

1. What did Darwin hope to learn about **artificial selection** by studying pigeons?
2. What are the four principles of **natural selection**?
3. Why must there be variation in the **population** in order for natural selection to occur?

CRITICAL THINKING

4. **Evaluate** Explain why the phrase "survival of the fittest" does not accurately reflect Darwin's concept of evolutionary **fitness.**
5. **Synthesize** Why is it said that natural selection acts on phenotypes rather than on the genetic material of organisms?

Connecting CONCEPTS

6. **Ecology** You have learned that the environment affects how organisms change over generations. How would you explain a species that remains the same for millions of years?

Assess and Reteach ▼

Assess Use the Online Quiz or Section Quiz (*Assessment Book*, p. 193).

Reteach Work with students to create a concept map that describes the four principles of natural selection.

10.3 ASSESSMENT

1. how certain traits can be selected and emphasized
2. The four principles of natural selection are overproduction, variation, adaptation, and descent with modification.
3. Because natural selection acts on phenotypes, there must be variations so that one phenotype offers a better chance of survival than another.
4. In common usage, the phrase is used to suggest that physically stronger individuals survive against weaker individuals. In biology, evolutionary fitness refers to the differential success in the reproduction and survival of offspring.
5. The environment selects the expression of traits, or phenotypes, that are best suited for survival and reproductive fitness. These traits may be coded for by the organism's genotype, but the environment does not affect or change the genes themselves.
6. The environment may not have changed enough to favor new variations in the population, or the organism may not be very sensitive to changes.

SECTION 10.4

▼ Plan and Prepare

Objectives

- Recognize the major sources of evidence for evolution.
- Examine the pattern of features that reveal the history of a species.

Section Resources

Unit Resource Book Study Guide pp. 13–14 Power Notes p. 15 Reinforcement p. 16
Interactive Reader Chapter 10 **Spanish Study Guide** pp. 105–106
Biology Toolkit pp. C15, C28, D10
Technology Power Presentation 10.4 Media Gallery DVD Online Quiz 10.4

Activate Prior Knowledge Most students have probably seen fossil displays in museums. **Ask,** Why are the larger fossil organisms so different from the animals on Earth today? Fossils take millions of years to form, and Earth's surface has changed significantly over time. In that time, evolution has been introducing new species and rendering some extinct.

▼ Teach

Take It Further

Trilobites, shown in **FIGURE 10.8** in fossilized form, were once among the most numerous marine invertebrates in the world. By the end of the Permian period, about 248 million years ago, all trilobite species were extinct, possibly due to a change in the depths of its coastal habitats. Another hypothesis suggests that the way in which the trilobites molted (shed their exoskeletons as a new one grew) may have contributed to their extinction.

10.4 Evidence of Evolution

KEY CONCEPT Evidence of common ancestry among species comes from many sources.

MAIN IDEAS

- Evidence for evolution in Darwin's time came from several sources.
- Structural patterns are clues to the history of a species.

VOCABULARY

biogeography, p. 311
homologous structure, p. 312
analogous structure, p. 313
vestigial structure, p. 314

B.8.7 Describe the modern scientific theory of the origins and history of life on earth, and evaluate the evidence that supports it.

Connect How genetic inheritance works was not known while Darwin was working on his theory of natural selection. However, Darwin documented natural selection from every angle available at the time. His thoroughness was important. It left no doubt in the minds of scientists that all organisms have a past history. Today, the concept of evolution ties together all fields of biology.

MAIN IDEA

Evidence for evolution in Darwin's time came from several sources.

Darwin found evidence from a wide range of sources to support his argument for evolution. The most important and convincing support came from fossils, geography, embryology, and anatomy.

Fossils

Even before Darwin, scholars studying fossils knew that organisms changed over time. Scientists who study fossils study more than just the fossil itself. They also think about its age, its location, and what the environment was like when the organism it came from was alive.

In the late 1700s, geologists wondered why certain types of fossils were found in some layers of rock and not others. Later studies suggested that the fossil organisms in the bottom, or older, layers were more primitive than those in the upper, or newer, layers. Geologists were interested in fossil sequences as a record of events such as earthquakes that disturb rock strata, not as proof of evolution. However, these and other findings in the fossil record supported Darwin's concept of descent with modification.

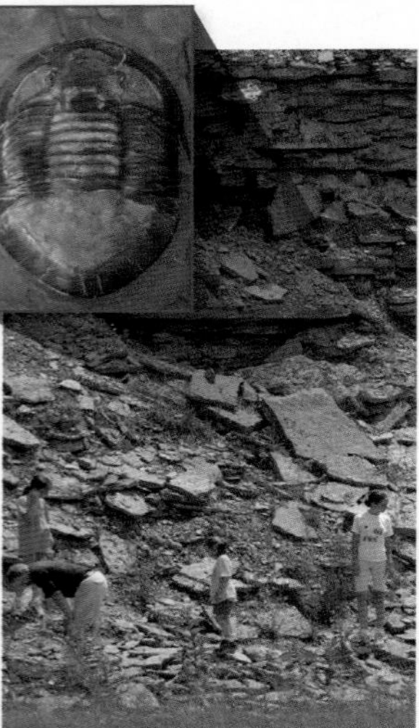

FIGURE 10.8 This trilobite, an early marine invertebrate that is now extinct, was found in this loose rock bed in Ohio. Although far from modern-day oceans, this site is actually the floor of an ancient sea.

Geography

Recall that during the *Beagle* expedition Darwin saw that island plants and animals looked like, but were not identical to, species on the South American continent. He extended this observation, proposing that island species most closely resemble species on the nearest mainland. He hypothesized that at some point in the past, some individuals from the South American mainland had migrated to the islands.

Differentiated Instruction

ENGLISH LEARNERS

Have students form into home groups of four, having each group count off from 1 to 4. Assign to a specific number one of the four categories of evidence for evolution discussed in this section. Then have students regroup according to number to prepare a lesson plan for their home group. Reconvene the home groups and have each student present the evidence to the group.

Biology Toolkit, Jigsaw Reading, p. C15

PRE-AP

Have students state the theory of evolution as a hypothesis, writing it as an if-then statement about life forms having changed over time. Have students write the hypothesis at the center of a circle. Then, in lines extending from the central circle, have students record the evidence that supports the hypothesis.

Biology Toolkit, Mind Map, p. C28

FIGURE 10.9 Variation in Galápagos Finches

Finches on certain Galápagos Islands live in different environments and have beaks of different sizes and shapes.

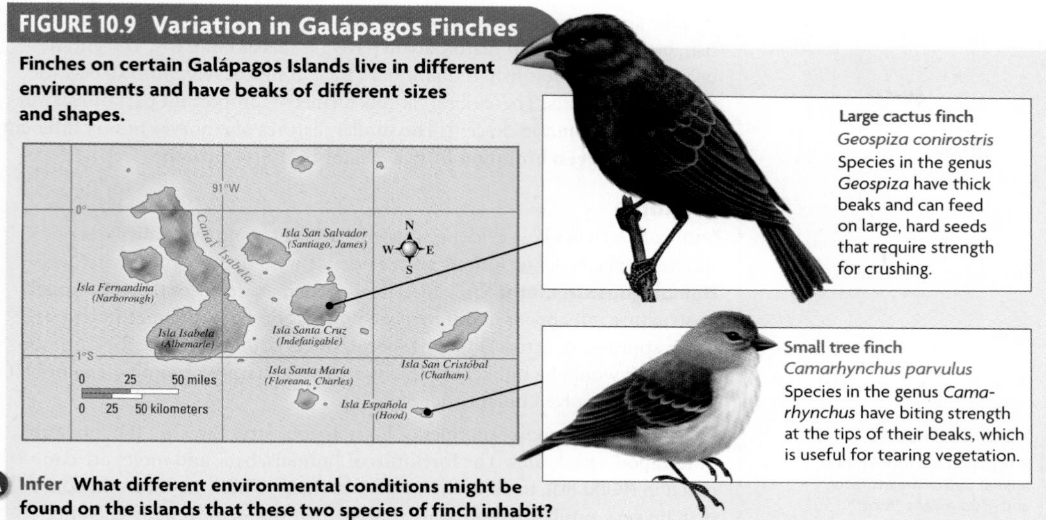

A Infer What different environmental conditions might be found on the islands that these two species of finch inhabit?

Different ecosystems on each island—with different plants, climates, and predators—had favored different traits in these migrants. Over time, these new traits became well established in the separate island populations, since the islands were too far apart for mating to occur.

One clear example of local adaptation is found in what are now known as Darwin's finches. The finches from the Galápagos Islands, shown in **FIGURE 10.9**, have distinct-looking beaks, as well as different habits, diets, and behaviors that evolved after generations of adaptation to specific island habitats. However, they all share a common ancestor from the South American mainland.

Since Darwin's time, the same pattern of evolution on islands has been studied in many living things, such as fruit flies and honeycreepers on the Hawaiian Islands. Darwin was the first scientist to establish this relationship between island and mainland species. Today this is an important principle of **biogeography**, the study of the distribution of organisms around the world.

Embryology

A study proposing a relationship between crabs, which can walk, and barnacles, which are fixed in one place as adults, fascinated Darwin. He had collected barnacles for many years and had noted that immature crabs and barnacles, called larvae, were similar. As **FIGURE 10.10** shows, barnacle and crab larvae both swim and look alike, but the adult animals look and behave very differently.

FIGURE 10.10 Although adult crabs and barnacles look and behave very differently, they can look identical as larvae. This suggested to Darwin that they share a common ancestor.

BELOW LEVEL

Have students use context clues to help understand the meaning of key vocabulary in this section. Students should look for examples that help reinforce meaning.

Biology Toolkit, Context Clues, p. D10

Answers

A Infer The large cactus finch may be found in drier areas in which seeds are hard; the small tree finch in areas with more moisture and softer foods such as fruit.

Integrating Earth Science

The islands of Hawaii formed over the course of a few million years as the Pacific plate moved over a volcanic **hotspot** in Earth's crust. The islands are currently home to over 20 species of **Hawaiian honeycreeper,** a small finchlike bird, although many are now endangered. All these species are descended from an ancestral species 3–4 million years ago. At that time, most of the archipelago had not yet formed. Over millions of years, the number of honeycreeper species grew as more islands formed in the chain. At one time, there were as many as 50 species. **Ask,** What factors might have led to the dramatic spread of the honeycreepers? lack of competition; new niches as new islands formed

The Inside Story

Ernst Haeckel was an influential scientist of the late 19th and early 20th centuries who was a staunch advocate for the theory of evolution. However, Haeckel willfully overstated evidence for his own idea that an organism, as a developing embryo, repeats it own evolutionary history.

For example, if an organism evolved from a reptile that had evolved from a fish, then each of those stages would be repeated in embryonic form before the organism developed its final form. Haeckel knowingly produced exaggerated comparative drawings of embryos that made the outward similarities more pronounced than they actually were.

Haeckel made many valuable contributions in other areas of science, such as ecology. However, he may well be remembered most for muddying the theory he sought to support.

Chapter 10: Principles of Evolution 311

▼ Teach *continued*

Vocabulary

Greek and Latin Word Origins Some students find it difficult to keep the definitions of **homologous** and **analogous** straight. The difference suggested by each prefix is subtle.

homo- = same, like
ana- = proportionate

Here are two mnemonics that may help students distinguish these terms:

- H**o**mologous structures share a common **o**rigin but may not be adapted for similar functions.
- **A**nalogous structures are **a**dapted for similar functions but do not have a common origin.

Take It Further

Although the hind limbs of horses, humans, and dogs are homologous structures, the relative sizes of the bones are quite different in each group. As a result, these organisms walk differently.

- Humans, bears, raccoons, and many other animals are **plantigrades.** They walk on the whole foot, from toes to heel.
- Dogs and cats are **digitigrades.** They walk only on their toes.
- Most hoofed animals, including horses, cows, and deer, are **unguligrades.** They walk on the very tips of their toes.

The bone of a horse's lower leg that seems equivalent to the human shin is actually made up of a metatarsal—a foot bone that usually makes up the lower half of a vertebrate's ankle. The hoof, which bears so much of the great weight of these animals, is equivalent to a fingernail.

Answers

A Apply A dolphin's flipper is homologous to the forelimbs of other mammals.

Like larvae, embryos of vertebrates can be hard to tell apart. For example, fish, birds, reptiles, and mammals all have gill slits as embryos. The gill slits become gills in adult fish. In mammals, the gill slits develop into structures of ears and throats. These observations formed an important part of Darwin's evidence for common descent. The similar features of embryos in very different organisms suggest evolution from a distant common ancestor.

Anatomy

Some of Darwin's best evidence came from comparing the body parts of different species. Chief among such evidence were homologous structures. **Homologous structures** (huh-MAHL-uh-guhs) are features that are similar in structure but appear in different organisms and have different functions. Their appearance across different species offers strong evidence for common descent. It would be unlikely for many species to have such similar anatomy if each species evolved independently.

VOCABULARY
A tetrapod is a four-limbed animal. *Tetra-* means "four," and *-pod* means "foot."

The most common examples of homologous structures are the forelimbs of tetrapod vertebrates. The forelimbs of humans, bats, and moles are compared in **FIGURE 10.11.** In all of these animals, the forelimbs have several bones that are very similar to each other despite their different functions. Notice also how the same bones vary in different animals. Homologous structures are different in detail but similar in structure and relation to each other.

In using homologous structures as evidence of evolution, Darwin posed a logical question: If each of these groups descended from a different ancestor, why would they share these homologous structures? A simple answer is that they share a common ancestor.

FIGURE 10.11 Homologous Structures

Homologous structures, though they often have differing functions, are the result of a common ancestor.

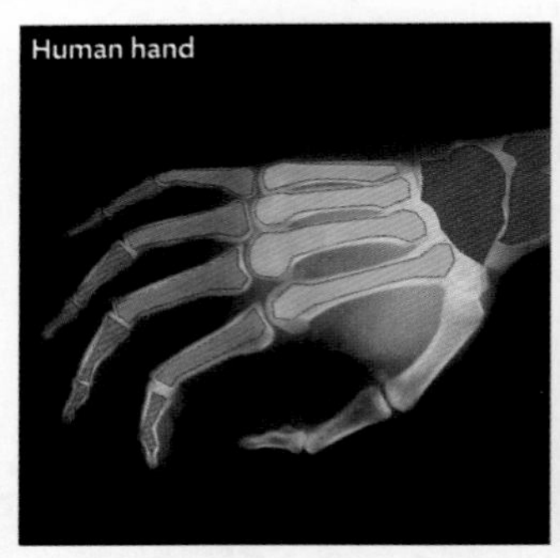

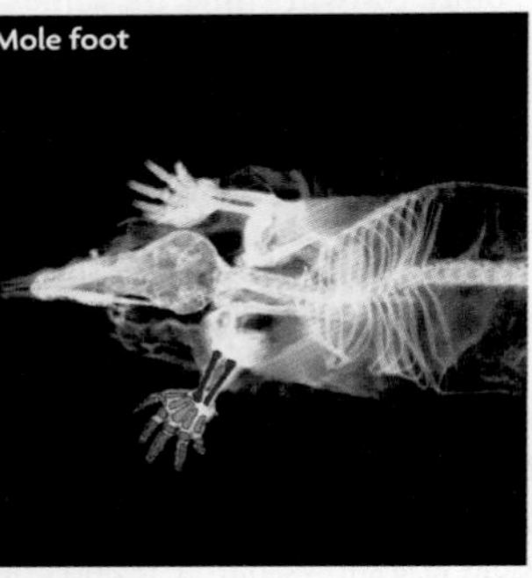

Notice that each of these homologous structures uses the same bones in relation to the others.

A Apply What body part of a dolphin is homologous to the structures shown above?

Differentiated Instruction

HANDS-ON ACTIVITY

Magnify the drawings included here to have students compare homologous structures in the human forearm and the flipper of a whale. Even though the vertebrates evolved in different ways, the limbs are formed from similar bone elements. (The diagrams are included in Teacher Resources at **ClassZone.com.**)

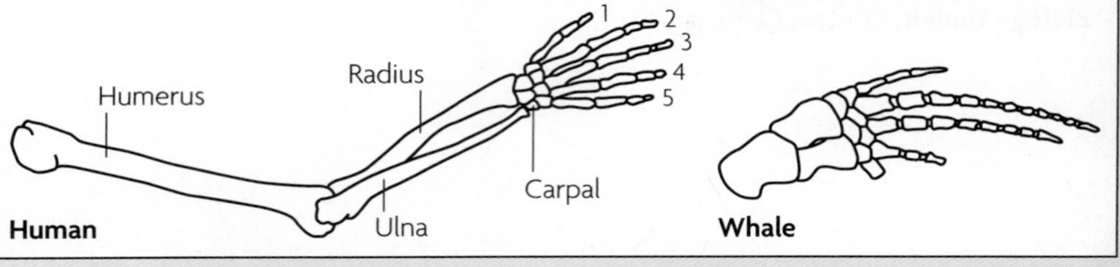

The idea of common descent provides a logical explanation for how homologous structures appeared in diverse groups. Having similar structures doesn't always mean two species are closely related, however. Some structures found in different species have the same functions but did not evolve from a common ancestor.

Suppose two organisms have similar needs caused by the environment. For example, two different organisms need to be able to fly. Both can develop similar adaptations using different body parts. Think about the wings of bats and the wings of flying insects. Clearly these organisms differ in more ways than they are similar. Insects are arthropods, while bats are mammals. The wings of bats and insects are called analogous structures, as shown in **FIGURE 10.12**. **Analogous structures** (uh-NAL-uh-guhs) are structures that perform a similar function—in this case, flight—but are not similar in origin. Bat wings have bones. In contrast, insect wings do not have bones, only membranes. The similar function of wings in bats and flying insects evolved separately. Their ancestors faced similar environmental challenges and came upon similar solutions.

FIGURE 10.12 ANALOGOUS STRUCTURES

Analogous structures evolved separately and are not evidence of a common ancestor. A bat's wing has bones, whereas insect wings do not.

A Analyze **Using the terms *homologous* and *analogous*, identify which group of structures provides evidence for a common ancestor. Explain.**

QUICK LAB **INFERRING**

Piecing Together Evidence

Evolutionary biologists and paleontologists rarely get all of the pieces of what they are studying. In this activity, you will receive pieces of "evidence" about a picture in order to make observations, inferences, and predictions about it.

PROBLEM How are inferences modified when new information is obtained?

MATERIALS
picture cut into strips

PROCEDURE

1. Using the three strips that your teacher has provided, write down all observations and inferences that you can make about this picture.
2. Make a prediction about the picture's topic, using your observations as supporting evidence for your prediction.
3. Record observations, inferences, and a prediction for each remaining strip of "evidence" that you receive from your teacher.

ANALYZE AND CONCLUDE

1. **Analyze** What inferences did you modify as you gathered more evidence from your teacher?
2. **Provide Examples** What type of evidence might paleontologists find that would allow them to see the big picture of a species' evolutionary past?

ENGLISH LEARNERS

Have students practice saying the vocabulary terms *homologous, analogous,* and *vestigial* by offering examples of each and asking students to call out an answer. While English learners may be reluctant to speak in class, these are words that will be a challenge for most students.

ONLINE BIOLOGY Explore evidence that suggests that *T. rex* may have ancestors living on Earth today. Go to the WebQuest in Options for Inquiry on page 321.

Answers

A **Analyze** Homologous structures provide evidence for a common ancestor because, despite differing in appearance or function, they are composed of the same structures, for example, bones. The two species probably had an ancestor in common. Analogous structures are structurally different and therefore do not suggest common ancestry.

QUICK LAB

Time 10 minutes	TEACHER TESTED
Lab Binder Evolution, p. 9	

Purpose Form inferences and make predictions from incomplete evidence.

LAB MANAGEMENT

- Choose a picture that fills the entire frame, rather than one with a lot of background.
- Cut the picture into strips no wider than an inch for a 13 cm × 18 cm (5 in. × 7 in.) sized picture. Give each student three non-adjoining strips to start with, then one strip at a time until they have determined the subject of the picture.

Answers

Analyze and Conclude

1. Answers will vary.
2. Answers might include a complete skeleton or fossil remains that give information about the environment or other species existing at the same time.

▼ Teach continued

Science Trivia

- The ostrich *(Struthio camelus)* is the largest living bird species. Males can approach 3 meters (9 ft) in height and weigh 155 kilograms (340 lbs).
- Female ostriches lay the largest eggs on Earth. At 15 centimeters (6 in.) long and nearly 13 centimeters (5 in.) wide, the ostrich egg is equivalent in volume to two dozen chicken eggs.
- Although its vestigial wings make it flightless, an ostrich can reach running speeds of 72 kilometers per hour (45 mph), making it the fastest-moving land bird in the world.

Answers

A Summarize Vestigial structures are remnants of an organ or a structure that functioned in an ancestor. Because a vestigial structure serves no purpose yet still exists, we can infer that the organism is a descendent of a species for which the structure was functional.

FIGURE 10.13 Vestigial structures, such as the wings of an ostrich, are organs or structures that are greatly reduced from the original ancestral form and have little or no current use.

MAIN IDEA

Structural patterns are clues to the history of a species.

Some organisms have structures or organs that seem to lack any useful function, or at least are no longer used for their original purpose. For example, snakes have tiny pelvic bones and stumplike limbs, even though snakes don't walk. Underdeveloped or unused features are called vestigial structures. **Vestigial structures** (veh-STIHJ-ee-uhl) are remnants of organs or structures that had a function in an early ancestor. As vertebrates, snakes share a common ancestor with tetrapods such as lizards and dogs. The tiny pelvic bones and hind limbs in many snakes are homologous to the pelvic bones of tetrapods.

The wings of ostriches are another example of vestigial structures. Ostriches have wings that they use for balance but not to fly, as shown in **FIGURE 10.13.** Over generations, their increasingly large bodies and powerful long legs may have been enough to avoid predators. If ostriches that lived long ago could escape by running or by kicking viciously, their large wings would no longer have been useful. Thus, the genes coding for large wings were not preserved over generations.

Examples of vestigial structures are found in many organisms. In humans, the appendix is an example of a vestigial structure. The appendix is a remnant of the cecum, which makes up a large part of the large intestine in plant-eating mammals. It helps to digest the cellulose in plants. As omnivores, humans do not eat much cellulose. The human appendix does not have the ability to digest cellulose. In fact, it performs no known function at all.

Vestigial structures did not get smaller in one individual organism. It took many generations for those organs to shrink. Today, biologists consider vestigial structures among the most important examples demonstrating how evolution works.

A Summarize What are vestigial structures, and how do they demonstrate common ancestry?

▼ Assess and Reteach

Assess Use the Online Quiz or Section Quiz (*Assessment Book*, p. 194).

Reteach Have students summarize the evidence for evolution (fossil, developmental, anatomical). Ask them to explain what homologous, analogous, and vestigial structures indicate about evolutionary relationships.

10.4 ASSESSMENT

ONLINE QUIZ ClassZone.com

B.8.7

REVIEWING MAIN IDEAS

1. Describe the four sources of evidence for evolution upon which Darwin based his ideas on common descent.
2. Why are **vestigial structures** considered critical evidence of evolution?

CRITICAL THINKING

3. **Hypothesize** Describe how some of the Galápagos finch species, which traditionally were seed eaters, evolved over generations to prefer insects over seeds.
4. **Apply** How can a bat's wing be considered both a **homologous structure** and an **analogous structure**?

***Connecting* CONCEPTS**

5. **Human Biology** Wisdom teeth are a third set of molars that usually appear in humans between the ages of 17 and 25, and often need removing because they crowd out other teeth. Explain why wisdom teeth are vestigial structures.

10.4 ASSESSMENT

1. Fossils found in deeper and therefore older rock layers were more primitive. Geography also affects the evolution of species. For example, islands with different habitats support species that evolved with adaptations for that environment. Similar features found in the earliest stage of embryonic development provide evidence of a common ancestor. Studying the anatomy of different organisms reveals homologous structures in some species. Vestigial structures provide evidence of evolutionary relationships.
2. They are homologous to full-size features and evidence of common ancestry among organisms that share them.
3. *Sample Answer:* On some islands, insects might have been more abundant than seeds, or there might have been less competition for insects than for seeds. The feeding behavior must have been heritable to become common in the population over time.
4. A bat wing is homologous to the forelimbs of other vertebrates. It is analogous to the wing of an insect because the wings are structurally different even though they perform the same function.
5. Wisdom teeth are vestigial structures because they serve no useful purpose. The human diet and jaw have changed over many generations. The wisdom teeth are no longer necessary.

MATERIALS
- piece of fabric
- bag of paper pieces

PROCESS SKILLS
- **Modeling**
- **Observing**
- **Predicting**

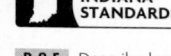

INDIANA STANDARDS

B.8.5 Describe how due to genetic variations, environmental forces, and reproductive pressures, organisms with beneficial traits are more likely to survive, reproduce, and pass on their genetic information.

NOS.6 Use analogies and models (mathematical and physical) to simplify and represent systems that are difficult to understand or directly experience due to their size, time scale, or complexity, and recognize the limitations of analogies and models.

Predator-Prey Pursuit

In this lab you will act like an owl in search of field mice. Your group will "consume" all the field mice that you see until only 25 percent of the population remains. These remaining field mice will then reproduce. These organisms pass an important trait for survival to their offspring—the ability to blend in with their surroundings. You will continue the process for several generations of mice, with some being consumed and others surviving to pass on their traits.

PROBLEM How does a population change as a result of natural selection?

PROCEDURE

1. Spread out the fabric habitat given to you on the tabletop.
2. Count out 20 pieces of paper of each of the five different colors for a total of 100 pieces. This will be your initial population of field mice.
3. One person should spread the pieces out randomly over the entire fabric habitat, making sure that none of the pieces cover the others. The remaining members of the group should not watch this process.
4. The other members of the group are now owls. They should pick up the pieces as they see them, one by one, until a total of 25 percent of the field mice remain in the habitat. Be sure to count carefully.
5. Carefully shake off the habitat to remove the surviving mice (a total of 25 pieces).
6. Group the survivors by color and record the numbers in your data table.
7. Next, assume that each survivor has three offspring. Place three additional pieces of the same color with each survivor.
8. Mix up the new set of pieces and have a different person spread them over the habitat. Note that there should again be 100 total pieces.
9. Repeat the entire process two more times, making a total of three generations of field mice being preyed upon.

OBSERVATIONS

TABLE 1. INFLUENCE OF SELECTIVE PREDATION ON FIELD MICE POPULATIONS

	Color 1	Color 2	Color 3	Color 4	Color 5
Number at start	20	20	20	20	20
Number after first predation					
Number after first reproduction					

ANALYZE AND CONCLUDE

1. **Compare** How do the original population and the survivor populations compare?
2. **Predict** How do you think the data would have changed if the experiment were continued until a total of five generations of field mice were preyed upon?
3. **Apply** Name one animal in real life that uses camouflage to avoid predators. What habitat is it most likely to survive in? What possible traits would give it a further advantage over members of its own species?

INVESTIGATION

Time 45 minutes	TEACHER TESTED
Teacher Preparation	
Student Difficulty	
Lab Binder Evolution, pp. 1–2	

Purpose Observe the effect of natural selection on a population.

Overview Students will use a model to examine predation as a selective agent and its effect on a prey population. They will
- observe the effect of predation on multiple "generations" of a prey population
- compare the effects of a beneficial adaptation (camouflage) on survivorship

LAB PREPARATION

- Each group of students will need approximately 30 pieces of each color to ensure they will have enough "prey" pieces for multiple generations.
- You may wish to use a paper punch and colored paper instead of tearing up strips of paper.
- It may take up to an hour to make enough paper pieces for the whole class.
- Have students use a bar graph to display data.

Teacher Note "This activity clearly demonstrated how camouflage affects natural selection. It made natural selection very concrete for the students."

POST-LAB DISCUSSION

Students will quickly see the selective advantage of camouflage. Point out some interesting examples of adaptive coloring in nature, such as white polar bears, sand-colored desert foxes, and striped tigers. Remind students that coloring that is adaptive in one habitat may not be adaptive in another (or if conditions change).

Answers

Sample Data

Go to page R102 for a sample graph.

Analyze and Conclude

1. Students should mention an increase in the camouflaged population.
2. Students should find that one color will be in much higher proportion than others.
3. Students should mention traits that are reasonable in terms of their benefit.

▼ Plan and Prepare

Objectives

- Summarize different types of evidence that support evolution.
- Recognize the importance of evolution in unifying all branches of biological study.

Section Resources

Unit Resource Book Study Guide pp. 17–18 Power Notes p. 19 Reinforcement p. 20 Pre-AP Activity pp. 25–26
Interactive Reader Chapter 10 **Spanish Study Guide** pp. 107–108
Biology Toolkit pp. C19, C23, C28, C38
Technology Power Presentation 10.5 Media Gallery DVD Online Quiz 10.5

Activate Prior Knowledge Tell students that in this section, the work of Darwin and Mendel come together. **Ask,** What was Darwin's mechanism for explaining the diversity of life? natural selection Mendel's mechanism? mixing of genes transmitted from parents to offspring

▼ Teach

Take It Further

Many missing links aren't missing anymore. In recent years, scientists have found transitional fossils that represent the links between birds and dinosaurs; four-legged terrestrial vertebrates (tetrapods) and fish; our species, *Homo sapiens,* and our apelike ancestors. Based on the fossil evidence of the dinosaur-bird link *(Archaeopteryx lithographica),* some scientists think that birds should be classified as dinosaurs.

Answers

A Infer They are intermediates between a modern species and its ancient ancestor, in this case, a modern whale and a terrestrial mammal.

10.5 Evolutionary Biology Today

KEY CONCEPT New technology is furthering our understanding of evolution.

MAIN IDEAS

- Fossils provide a record of evolution.
- Molecular and genetic evidence support fossil and anatomical evidence.
- Evolution unites all fields of biology.

VOCABULARY

paleontology, p. 316

INDIANA STANDARDS

B.8.7 Describe the modern scientific theory of the origins and history of life on earth, and evaluate the evidence that supports it.

Connect Darwin had spent many years collecting evidence of evolution from different fields of science before publishing his results. Since that time, technology has greatly advanced. Scientists can now examine evidence only dreamed about in the 1800s. In particular, the relatively new fields of genetics and molecular biology have added strong support to Darwin's theory of natural selection. They have shown how hereditary variation occurs.

MAIN IDEA

Fossils provide a record of evolution.

Paleontology (PAY-lee-ahn-TAHL-uh-jee), the study of fossils or extinct organisms, continues to provide new information and support current hypotheses about how evolution occurs. The fossil record is not complete, because most living things do not form into fossils after they die, and fossils have not been looked for in many areas of the world. However, no fossil evidence that contradicts evolution has ever been found.

VOCABULARY

Paleontology is the study of prehistoric life forms. *Paleo-* means "ancient," and *-ology* means "the study of."

In Darwin's time, paleontology was still a new science. Darwin worried about the lack of transitional fossils between groups of organisms. Since Darwin's time, however, many transitional forms have been discovered between species. Many of the large gaps in the fossil record have been filled in. The fossil record today includes many thousands of species that show the change in forms over time that Darwin outlined in his theory. These "missing links" demonstrate the evolution of traits within groups as well as the common ancestors between groups.

Although scientists classify organisms into groups, the mix of traits in transitional species often makes it difficult to tell where one group ends and another begins. One example of transitional species in the evolution of whales is shown in **FIGURE 10.14.** *Basilosaurus isis* had a whalelike body but also still had the limbs of land animals.

FIGURE 10.14 This skeleton of *Basilosaurus isis* was found in a desert in Egypt in 2005. It lived 40 million years ago and has characteristics of both land and marine animals.

A Infer Why are fossils such as *Basilosaurus isis* considered transitional fossils?

Differentiated Instruction

ENGLISH LEARNERS

Have pairs of students work together to provide support for the statement "Much evidence exists today to support the theory of evolution." Students can choose a graphic organizer they have used before. For example, have them place the statement in the center of a circle. Then have students extend four lines from the circle, and at the end of each line, write a statement that addresses molecular, genetic, fossil, and anatomical evidence.

Biology Toolkit, Mind Map, p. C28

BELOW-LEVEL

To ensure that students understand the difference between the theory of evolution and Darwin's theory of natural selection, have them write a paragraph or two on the subject.

Biology Toolkit, Quick-Write, p. C19

MAIN IDEA

Molecular and genetic evidence support fossil and anatomical evidence.

As with homologous traits, very different species have similar molecular and genetic mechanisms. Because all living things have DNA, they share the same genetic code and make most of the same proteins from the same 20 amino acids. DNA or protein sequence comparisons can be used to show probable evolutionary relationships between species.

DNA sequence analysis As you learned in Chapter 8, the sequences of nucleotides in a gene change over time due to mutations. DNA sequence analysis depends on the fact that the more related two organisms are, the more similar their DNA will be. Because there are thousands of genes in even simple organisms, DNA contains a huge amount of information on evolutionary history.

Pseudogenes Sequences of DNA nucleotides known as pseudogenes also provide evidence of evolution. Pseudogenes are like vestigial structures. They no longer function but are still carried along with functional DNA. They can also change as they are passed on through generations, so they provide another way to figure out evolutionary relationships. Functioning genes may be similar in organisms with similar lifestyles, such as a wolf and a coyote, due to natural selection. Similarities between pseudogenes, however, must reflect a common ancestor.

VOCABULARY

A pseudogene is a DNA sequence that resembles a gene but seems to have no function. *Pseudo-* means "false" or "deceptive."

Homeobox genes As you will learn in Chapter 23, homeobox genes control the development of specific structures. These sequences of genes are found in many organisms, from fruit flies to humans. They also indicate a very distant common ancestor. Evidence of homeobox gene clusters are found in organisms that lived as far back as 600 million years ago.

FIGURE 10.15 The eye spots of this marine worm have light-sensitive cells with a molecular fingerprint similar to that of a vertebrate eye.

Protein comparisons Similarities among cell types across organisms can be revealed by comparing their proteins, a technique called molecular fingerprinting. A unique set of proteins are found in specific types of cells, such as liver or muscle cells. Cells from different species that have the same proteins most likely come from a common ancestor. For example, the proteins of light-sensitive cells in the brain of an ancient marine worm, as shown in **FIGURE 10.15**, were found to closely resemble those of cells found in the vertebrate eye. This resemblance shows a shared ancestry between worms and vertebrates. It also shows that the cells of the vertebrate eye originally came from cells in the brain.

A Explain How have protein comparisons helped determine ancestral relationships between organisms?

Take It Further

Much of the molecular evidence used to support evolution and evolutionary relationships among organisms comes from comparisons of **mitochondrial DNA.** Unlike nuclear DNA, mitochondrial DNA ordinarily does not undergo recombination. Therefore, any differences between two sequences of mitochrondrial DNA are the result of mutations that occurred after the two species diverged from their common lineage.

Vocabulary

Academic Vocabulary The prefix **pseudo-** has been affixed to a number of nouns to suggest a fake or counterfeit.

pseudointellectual, someone who pretends to be more intelligent than he or she really is

pseudonym, a fictional name, or alias; the writer Stephen King wrote several books under the *pseudonym* Richard Bachman

pseudoscience, theories or methods that have no real scientific basis

Science Trivia

The photosensitive eyespots such as those found in marine and freshwater worms are called ocelli. Although the eyespots give these organisms a cross-eyed appearance, the difference between "whites" and "pupils" is merely a difference in pigment colors.

PRE-AP

On the board, use colored chalk or markers to represent chromosomes and colored sticky notes for genes to create this diagram comparing homeobox genes. Have students discuss what can be inferred from the similarities and differences between the gene clusters in the three species. The two insects are more closely related. The mouse's genes are laid out in a similar fashion, but on different chromosomes. Similarities suggest common ancestry; differences suggest evolution. (The diagram is included in Teacher Resources at **ClassZone.com.**)

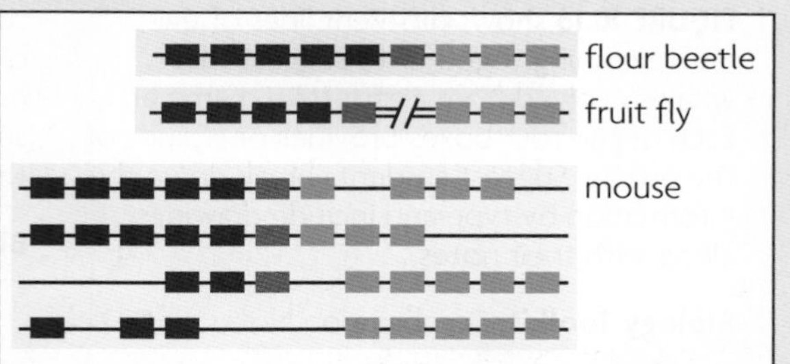

Answers

A Explain Cells from different species that have similar types of proteins are likely to be from related organisms.

▼ Teach *continued*

TEACH FROM VISUALS

FIGURE 10.16 Tell students that the term *ungulates,* which refers to hoofed mammals, is not a particularly useful term anymore. It makes sense for ungulates such as the horse, elephant, hippopotamus, and antelope. However, recent fossil and molecular evidence has brought sea cows and aardvarks into the group, and possibly whales and dolphins. All of these animals appear to share a common ancestor that dates back about 90 million years. The object of this diagram is to show the various lines of evidence that suggest whales are part of the ungulate family.

Ask, Looking at the fossil evidence, which features show clear homology among the three fossil species? Answers may include features such as jaws, teeth, and vertebrae, but certainly forelimbs. Ask students to relate the diagram of the vestigial pelvic and leg bones to the three fossils shown.

Take It Further

Whales are among the most distinctive groups of organisms on Earth. There are nearly 80 species of whales living today. They include the blue whale, which is the largest animal that ever lived, and the humpback whale, which courts mates by "singing." The California gray whale undertakes a remarkable journey each year, swimming from Baja California to the southern edge of the Arctic Ocean in spring and then returning to the Baja coast in the fall. This journey is 12,000 miles roundtrip, making it one of the longest known migrations of any animal.

Answers

Ⓐ **Critical Viewing** Tooth whales are more closely related to *Dorudon* because both species have teeth.

FIGURE 10.16 Evidence of Whale Evolution

The evidence that whales descended from hoofed mammals is supported by scientific research in several different fields of biology.

Modern-day whale

Vestigial Evidence

Many modern whale species have vestigial pelvic and leg bones. They also have vestigial nerves for the sense of smell, and small muscles devoted to external ears that no longer exist.

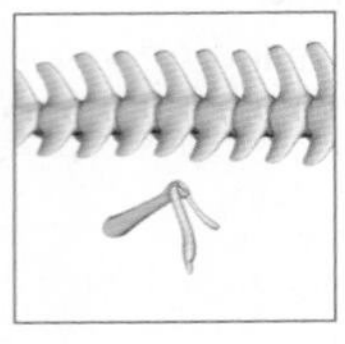

Embryological Evidence

Whale embryos have features such as hind leg buds and nostrils that resemble those of land animals. Nostrils are at the end of the whale's snout early in development but travel to the top of the head to form one or more blowholes before birth.

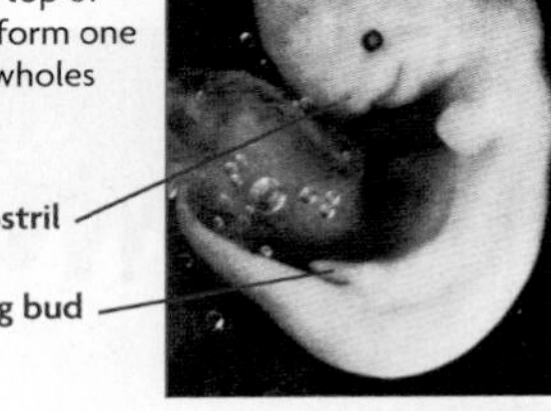

Molecular Evidence

The DNA sequences of milk protein genes in whales and ungulates are very similar, as demonstrated by the DNA fragments below.

Hippopotamus	TCC TGGCA GTCCA GTGGT
Humpback whale	CCC TGGCA GTGCA GTGCT

Fossil Evidence

There are many transitional fossils that have characteristics of both land mammals and whales. These are a few examples.

Dorudon 40 million years ago

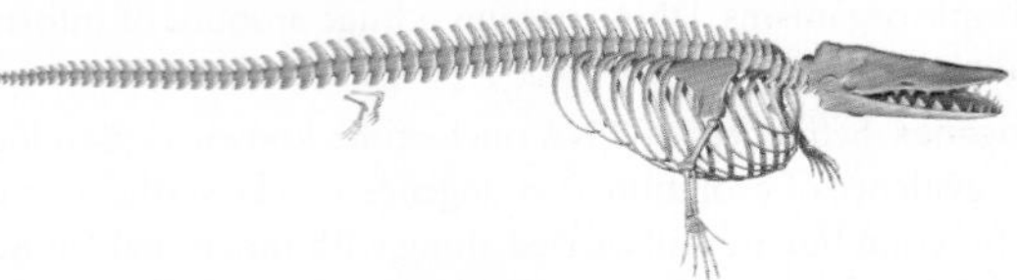

Tiny hind legs were useless on land, and a shorter neck and longer tail makes *Dorudon* similar to modern-day whales. Its ankle joints closely resemble those of modern ungulates.

Ambulocetus natans 50 million years ago

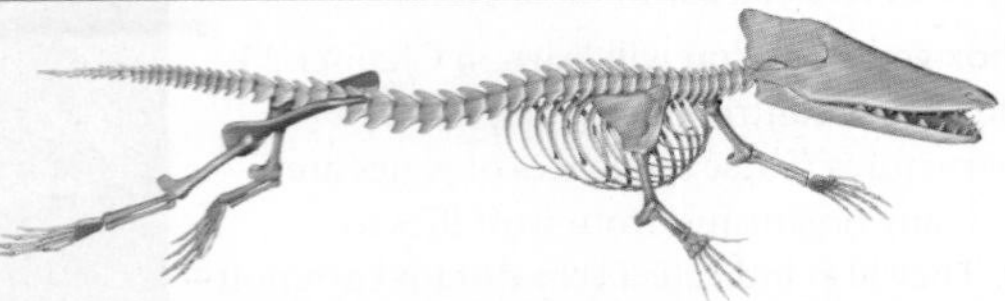

With a name that means "the walking whale that swims," *Ambulocetus natans* was an amphibious fish eater the size of a sea lion.

Pakicetus 52 million years ago

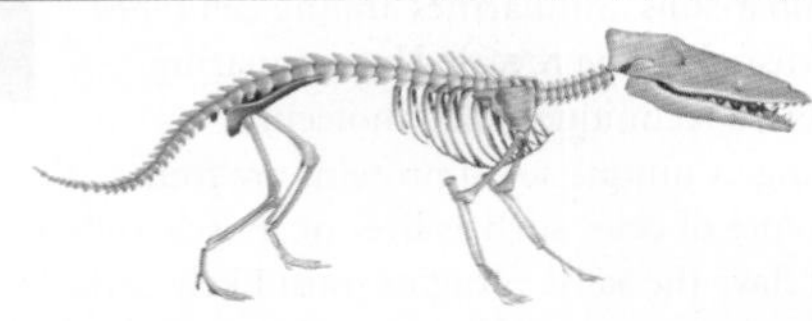

Pakicetus had a whale-shaped skull and teeth adapted for hunting fish. However, with ear bones that are in between those of land and aquatic mammals, it could not hear well underwater or make deep dives.

Ⓐ CRITICAL VIEWING **Whales are divided into two groups: tooth whales, such as the orca pictured above, and baleen whales, such as the humpback whale pictured on the next page. Which would you predict is most closely related to *Dorudon*? Explain.**

Differentiated Instruction

INCLUSION

For students who have difficulty processing complex visual information, describe how **FIGURE 10.16** shows different lines of evidence coming together to suggest that whales evolved from a terrestrial mammal. Each of the four boxes provides one piece of the puzzle. Suggest students break down the information by type and include drawings along with their notes.

Biology Toolkit, Combination Notes, p. C23

PRE-AP

Using the three fossil skeletons shown in **FIGURE 10.16,** have students prepare a sequence diagram. Tell them to start with the oldest organism and describe a series of events that could lead to the evolution of a sea mammal, the whale, from a land mammal, the *Pakicetus.*

Biology Toolkit, Sequence Diagram, p. C38

MAIN IDEA

Evolution unites all fields of biology.

FIGURE 10.17 Baleen whales, such as this humpback whale, have evolved a highly specialized adaptation for catching microscopic food. Molecular techniques have allowed scientists to discover the whale's relationship with hoofed animals.

Despite the advances talked about in this section, scientists are still actively studying evolution through natural selection. The theory of natural selection combined with genetics is sometimes called the modern synthesis of evolutionary theory. The 21st century is an exciting time to study evolutionary biology. New tools are providing more data than ever before. When you consider the number of proteins in a single organism, the amount of data that can be gathered through molecular evidence alone is overwhelming. New discoveries are limited only by the time and resources of scientists.

Scientists from many fields of science are shedding new light on the mechanisms and patterns of evolution. In some cases, modern tools add to what has been discovered through fossil evidence. For example, you have read that fossil evidence suggests that early ancestors of whales were hoofed land mammals. As shown in **FIGURE 10.16**, comparisons of milk protein genes confirm this relationship and even provide evidence that the hippopotamus is the closest living land animal related to whales.

The field of evolutionary biology is growing fast. The basic principles of evolution are used in fields such as medicine, geology, geography, chemistry, and ecology. For instance, the idea of common descent helps biologists understand where new diseases come from, as well as how to best manage endangered species. As much as we know about life on Earth, there is so much more waiting to be discovered. As the great geneticist Theodosius Dobzhansky (1900–1975) once noted, "Nothing in biology makes sense except in the light of evolution."

Infer How can the idea of a common ancestor help us understand new diseases?

History of Science

At the age of 15, **Theodosius Dobzhansky** read Darwin's *On the Origin of Species.* He went on to study biology at the University of Kiev. In 1927, he immigrated to the United States, where he worked on fruit fly genetics with Thomas Hunt Morgan. By that point, Darwin's theory of natural selection had lost momentum because many scientists found it difficult to reconcile the new understanding of genes with Darwin's ideas on species origins.

In his 1937 book *Genetics and the Origin of Species,* Dobzhansky defined species in terms of gene compatibility: organisms whose genomes are too different cannot successfully produce offspring. He also proposed that most mutations were neutral in their immediate effect, neither harmful nor helpful to an individual, but the variation they introduced could prove adaptive at some future point. His ideas helped lead to development of the **modern synthesis,** which proposed how mutations and natural selection could produce large-scale evolutionary changes.

Answers

A Infer Because their genes are similar, closely related species can be susceptible to the same diseases. Understanding how the disease-causing organism affects one species may help in preventing its spread to another or help in the treatment of the disease.

10.5 ASSESSMENT

ONLINE QUIZ ClassZone.com

B.8.7

REVIEWING MAIN IDEAS

1. How has our knowledge of the fossil record changed since Darwin proposed his theory of natural selection?
2. How has genetics, combined with **paleontology,** added to our understanding of evolution?
3. What are some of the fields of science to which evolutionary biology contributes?

CRITICAL THINKING

4. **Apply** Describe how similar protein comparisons of cells in two species can suggest a close evolutionary relationship.
5. **Synthesize** You have discovered the fossil remains of three organisms. One is mammalian, one is reptilian, and the third has both mammalian and reptilian features. What techniques could you apply to determine the relationship between these organisms?

Connecting CONCEPTS

6. **Genetics** Researchers have found that a gene controlling reproduction is linked to the gene for the number of digits an organism has. How does this help explain why many vertebrates have five digits per limb, despite the fact that there is no fitness benefit in having five rather than six or four?

10.5 ASSESSMENT

1. Many more fossils have been found, and many gaps in the fossil record, such as the gap between humans and our apelike ancestors, are being filled.
2. Genetics has provided the understanding of how traits can be inherited and adds supporting data about events that have been inferred from the fossil record.
3. *Sample Answers:* medicine, geology, geography, chemistry, and ecology
4. Proteins are encoded by an organism's DNA, which transmits heritable traits. If cells from different species have similar or identical proteins, this suggests an evolutionary relationship.
5. comparative anatomy, DNA sequence analysis, and protein comparisons
6. The gene that controls reproduction is important and likely to be conserved. Because this gene is linked to (close to) the gene affecting the digit number on limbs, this trait is likely to be conserved as well.

Assess and Reteach

Assess Use the Online Quiz or Section Quiz (*Assessment Book,* p. 195).

Reteach Have students work in groups to present an oral summary of the major lines of evidence (molecular, genetic, fossil, comparative anatomy, comparative embryology) supporting evolution.

OPTIONS FOR INQUIRY

INVESTIGATION

Time 45 minutes	TEACHER TESTED
Teacher Preparation	
Student Difficulty	
Lab Binder Evolution, pp. 3–6	

Purpose Make inferences based on observations of patterns.

Overview Students will use a model to observe patterns of data. They will

- work as a team to gather data
- use their observations to make a prediction about an unknown

LAB PREPARATION

- Use heavy construction paper, scissors, markers, and tape.
- Make one large cube according to the pattern for Cube 1 found in the *Lab Binder,* p. 6.
- Make several smaller cubes according to the pattern for Cube 2 found in the *Lab Binder,* p. 6.

Inclusion For students who are visually impaired, provide cubes that have sides with different textures.

LAB MANAGEMENT

- Be sure to keep the bottom of all cubes concealed.
- You can add more variables to the smaller cubes to make the bottom square more difficult to predict.

Teacher Note "Students were engaged in the scientific process throughout the activity. It clearly demonstrates the difference between observation and inference."

POST-LAB DISCUSSION

Reinforce the importance of forming predictions based on recognized patterns.

Use these inquiry-based labs and online activities to deepen your understanding of evolution.

B.8.5 Describe how due to genetic variations, environmental forces, and reproductive pressures, organisms with beneficial traits are more likely to survive, reproduce, and pass on their genetic information.

NOS.1 Develop explanations based on reproducible data and observations gathered during laboratory investigations.

INVESTIGATION

Using Patterns to Make Predictions

Scientists who study evolution and other processes in biology do not always have a complete set of information. They often form hypotheses and make predictions based on a limited number of observations and measurable data. In this lab, you will make your own prediction about an unknown using a set of observations.

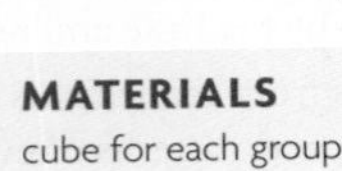

MATERIALS

cube for each group

SKILLS Predicting, Inferring, Analyzing, Drawing Conclusions

PROBLEM How do predictions change with new observations?

PROCEDURE

1. Observe the large cube your teacher has set out in the center of the room. Note the arrangement of the numbers and the colors of the sides.
2. Write your observations about the cube in your notebook.
3. Record what you predict will be found on the bottom section of the cube.
4. Split into groups of three or four students and get a different cube from your teacher. Do not look at the bottom side of the cube.
5. As a group, look for patterns on the cube. Observe the names and the numbers on the cube. If you need help determining the patterns, obtain a hint card from your teacher. Record any patterns you observe in your notebook.
6. Use the patterns that you have observed to predict the following information on the bottom section of the cube: the gender of the name, the number on the upper right corner, and the number on the bottom left corner. Use all three of these predictions as clues to predict the name on the bottom of the cube.
7. Write your group's prediction on a piece of paper and hand it to your teacher.

ANALYZE AND CONCLUDE

1. **Analyze** What patterns did you observe on each cube?
2. **Predict** Describe what you think is on the bottom of the first cube. Describe what you think is on the bottom of the second cube.
3. **Infer** How did you determine the name on the bottom of the second cube?
4. **Synthesize** After completing this exercise, what do you now know about the way scientists make their hypotheses?

EXTEND YOUR INVESTIGATION

In your group, create a cube with sides that follow patterns. Trade cubes with another group and repeat steps 5 through 7.

Answers

Analyze and Conclude

1. Answers will vary but students should come up with observations that match the hint cards.
2. Answers will vary but the first cube was a shaded "2" and the second box had "Samantha" with an "8" in the upper right-hand corner and a "1" in the lower left-hand corner.
3. Answers should reflect recognition of a pattern; the top of the box had a male name beginning with "S."
4. Answers should reflect that hypotheses are based on all available information. Students should recognize that many observations go into making a prediction, and often it is not possible to directly observe what you are studying.

320 Unit 4: Evolution

INVESTIGATION

Adaptations in Beaks

Differences in tools can affect the feeding efficiency, and therefore the survival, of a species. Similarly, beak variations in birds can influence their survival.

SKILL Inferring

MATERIALS

- aluminum pie plate
- petri dishes
- sunflower seeds
- forceps
- clothespins
- tongs
- chopsticks
- stopwatch

PROBLEM How do adaptations affect natural selection?

PROCEDURE

1. Gather a pan of seeds, four petri dishes, and four different tools, or "beaks."
2. Choose one member of the group to be the recorder and timer. The other members will be the "birds."
3. Create a data table with space to record three trials of each tool and an average of all of the trials.
4. Run three timed trials of 30 seconds each for each tool. Pick up as many seeds as you can during the 30 seconds and place them in a petri dish. At the end of each trial, count the number of seeds "eaten."
5. After the third trial, calculate the average for the "beak," and record the average in your data table.

ANALYZE AND CONCLUDE

1. **Conclude** Overall, which "beak" or "beaks" were most successful?
2. **Infer** Describe the beak of a bird that could have evolved to successfully eat these seeds. Which beak would not be suited to these particular seeds? Draw a rough sketch of each beak type.
3. **Apply** Use the terms *beak, seeds, natural selection, adaptation,* and *success* to describe what happened in the lab.

Online BIOLOGY
CLASSZONE.COM

ANIMATED BIOLOGY
Natural Selection
Watch a population evolve—or not. Discover how populations can evolve through natural selection, and how each principle is important to the entire mechanism.

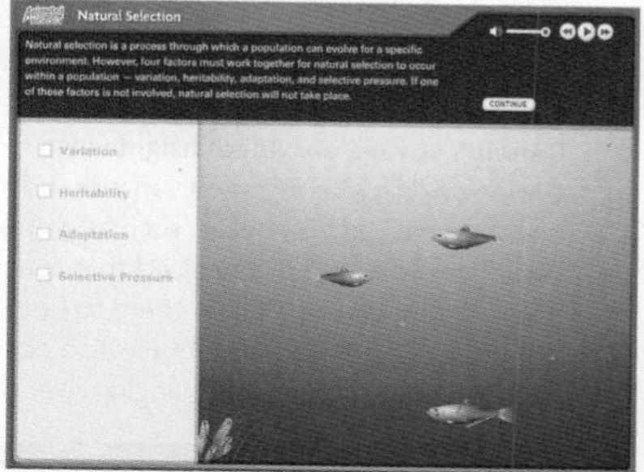

WEBQUEST
Are there living descendants of *Tyrannosaurus rex,* one of the most ferocious dinosaurs? Complete this WebQuest to find out. Explore the fossil evidence of a lineage extending from one group of dinosaurs, and determine which animals can call the *T. rex* their ancestor.

DATA ANALYSIS ONLINE
Bill depth in Darwin's finches is selected for mainly by the size and hardness of available seeds, but other factors can also affect bill depth. Graph and compare how bill depth in a species differs on one island with more competition and another island with less.

Online Biology ▼

ANIMATED BIOLOGY Students will learn about the factors needed for a population to evolve through natural selection. If a factor is not set to run, the population will not evolve with the selected trait. Use with **Section 10.3.**

WEBQUEST The WebQuest takes one full class period. Students complete the activity online and will need access to a printer to print out their answers. Sample answers, teacher notes, and alternative assessment ideas are available on **ClassZone.com.** Use with **Section 10.4.**

DATA ANALYSIS Students should use a bar graph to show that after a severe drought on Daphne Major, average beak depth of the surviving finches' offspring increased. Use with **Section 10.3.**

INVESTIGATION

TEACHER TESTED

Time	45 minutes
Teacher Preparation	(1 flask)
Student Difficulty	(1 flask)
Lab Binder	pp. 7–8

Purpose Have students infer how beak structure might affect food choices.

Safety Check with students for allergies to nuts. Make sure that garden seeds have not been treated with fungicides.

POST-LAB DISCUSSION

Have students compare their findings with the observations made by Peter and Rosemary Grant on p. 308 of **Section 10.3.**

Answers

Sample Data

Number of Seeds Captured

Trial #	Beak Tool 1	Beak Tool 2	Beak Tool 3	Beak Tool 4
1	25	11	37	4
2	19	16	53	9
3	27	12	54	6
Average	23.6	13	48	6.3

Analyze and Conclude

1. In general, larger "beaks," such as clothespins or tongs, are more successful with large seeds, and smaller "beaks," such as tweezers, are more successful with small seeds.
2. Answers will vary.
3. Answers will vary.

CHAPTER REVIEW

Interactive Review

Encourage students to go to **ClassZone.com** for a detailed review of each section, including visuals and vocabulary practice.

Unit Resource Book, Vocabulary Practice, pp. 27–30

ITEM CORRELATIONS	
Standard	**Items**
B.8.5	14, 15
B.8.7	16, 18
NOS.8	11
NOS.9	12, 21

CHAPTER 10 Interactive Review @ CLASSZONE.COM

KEY CONCEPTS | Vocabulary Games | Concept Maps | Animated Biology | Online Quiz

10.1 Early Ideas About Evolution

There were theories of biological and geologic change before Darwin. Early biologists suggested that different species might have shared ancestors, and geologists observed that new species appeared in the fossil record. Charles Lyell proposed the theory of uniformitarianism to explain how present observations explain past events.

10.2 Darwin's Observations

Darwin's voyage provided insights into evolution. Darwin observed variation between island species on his voyage, such as with the Galápagos tortoises. He noticed that species have adaptations that allow them to better survive in their environments. He also observed fossil evidence of species changing over time.

10.3 Theory of Natural Selection

Darwin proposed natural selection as a mechanism for evolution. Natural selection is a mechanism by which individuals that have inherited beneficial adaptations produce more offspring on average than do other individuals. Natural selection is based upon four principles: overproduction, variation, adaptation, and descent with modification.

10.4 Evidence of Evolution

Evidence of common ancestry among species comes from many sources. Fossil evidence is a record of change in a species over time. The study of biogeography showed that species could adapt to different environments. Two species that exhibit similar traits during development likely have a common ancestor. Vestigial and homologous structures also point to a shared ancestry.

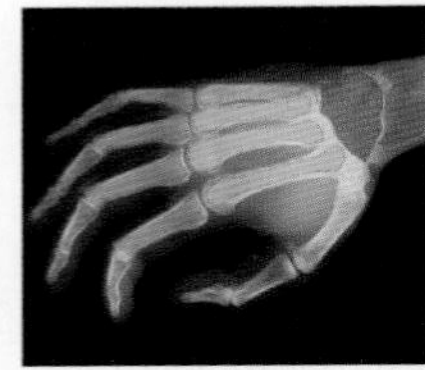

10.5 Evolutionary Biology Today

New technology is furthering our understanding of evolution. Modern techniques, such as DNA sequence analysis and molecular fingerprinting, continue to provide new information about how evolution occurs. Evolution is a unifying theme of all the fields of biology today.

Synthesize Your Notes

Main Idea Web Use a main idea web to summarize the four principles of natural selection.

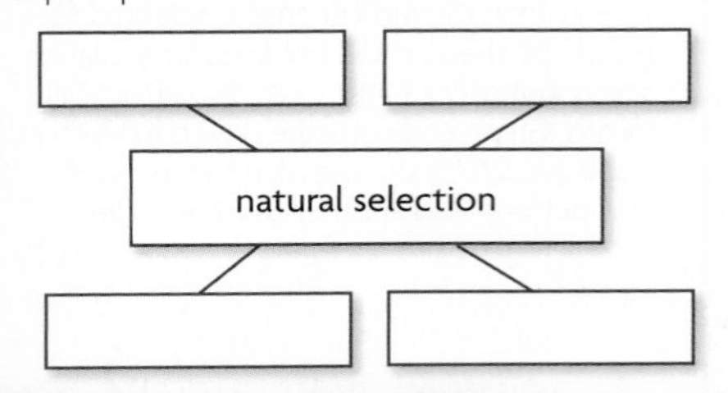

Concept Map Use a concept map like the one below to summarize what you know about evolutionary evidence.

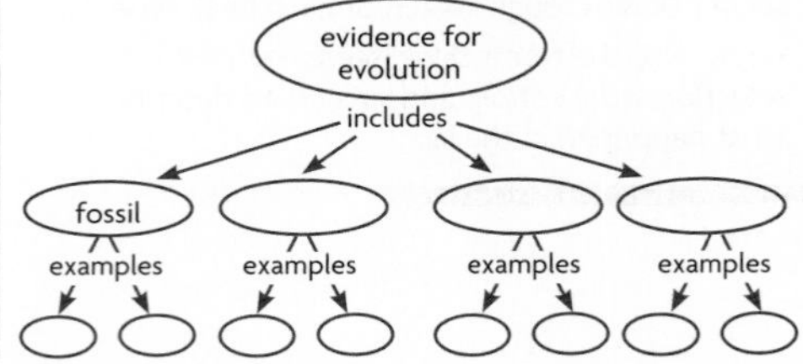

322 Unit 4: Evolution

Reviewing Vocabulary

1. **Catastrophism** is the theory that geologic change happened because of sudden large-scale events, while **gradualism** states that geologic change occurred slowly over a long span of time.
2. Within every **population,** there is natural **variation.**
3. **Evolution** occurs through natural selection as changes in the environment make different **adaptations** more or less beneficial for the survival of the species.
4. **Analogous structures** have similar functions but different structures. **Vestigial structures** have little or no function but are homologous to functional structures possessed by an ancestor.
5. **Fossils** are remains of past organisms that are studied by scientists in the field of **paleontology.**
6. The meaning of the prefix *homo-*, "same," refers to how homologous structures exhibit a similar structure and origin.
7. The meaning of the word *vestigium,* "track" or "footprint," refers to how a vestigial structure is like a footprint from the past, showing how an organism evolved.

Reviewing Main Ideas

8. Possible answers include ideas such as species could change over time, species shared common ancestors, more complex forms of life arose from less complex forms, or the environment affected organisms and could cause them to change over time.

Chapter Assessment

Chapter Vocabulary

10.1 evolution, p. 298
species, p. 298
fossil, p. 300
catastrophism, p. 301
gradualism, p. 301
uniformitarianism, p. 301

10.2 variation, p. 302
adaptation, p. 302

10.3 artificial selection, p. 304
heritability, p. 304
natural selection, p. 305
population, p. 306
fitness, p. 307

10.4 biogeography, p. 311
homologous structure, p. 312
analogous structure, p. 313
vestigial structure, p. 314

10.5 paleontology, p. 316

Reviewing Vocabulary

Vocabulary Connections

The vocabulary terms in this chapter are related to each other in various ways. For each group of words below, write a sentence or two to clearly explain how the terms are connected. For example, for the terms *variation* and *natural selection*, you could write "Natural selection depends on heritable variations."

1. catastrophism, gradualism
2. population, variation
3. adaptation, evolution
4. vestigial structure, analogous structure
5. fossil, paleontology

Greek and Latin Word Origins

6. The term *homologous* comes from the Greek word *homos*, which means "the same." Explain how this meaning relates to *homologous structures.*

7. The term *vestigial* come from the Latin word *vestigium*, which means "track or footprint." Explain how this meaning relates to *vestigial structures.*

Reviewing MAIN IDEAS

8. Describe one idea about evolution that was proposed before Darwin published his theory of natural selection.

9. Briefly explain how the geologist Charles Lyell influenced Darwin's ideas about how evolution works.

10. What insights did Darwin gain from observing island organisms such as the Galápagos tortoises and finches?

11. On his voyage, Darwin observed fossils of extinct organisms that resembled living organisms. He also found shells of marine organisms high up in the mountains. How did these observations provide evidence that Earth is very old? **NOS.8**

12. Thomas Malthus was an economist who proposed that resources such as food, water, and shelter are natural limits to human population growth. Explain how Darwin extended this idea in his theory of natural selection. **NOS.9**

13. Why is heritability important for both natural and artificial selection?

14. Natural selection is based on four main principles: variation, overproduction, adaptation, and descent with modification. Briefly explain how each of these principles is necessary for natural selection to occur. **B.8.5**

15. Explain what is meant by the sentence "Natural selection can act only on existing traits." **B.8.5**

16. Evidence of evolution comes from diverse sources, such as fossils, geography, embryology, and anatomy. Briefly describe one example of evidence for evolution from each of these sources. **B.8.7**

17. Give an example of a vestigial structure and explain how vestigial structures are significant to evolution.

18. Paleontology is the study of fossils or extinct organisms. Explain how this field is important to evolutionary biology. **B.8.7**

19. How are genes and proteins similar to homologous structures when determining evolutionary relationships among species?

20. Explain what the following quote by Theodosius Dobzhansky means: "Nothing in biology makes sense except in the light of evolution."

9. Lyell proposed the theory of uniformitarianism, which states that the geologic processes that shape Earth are uniform through time. For the changes that have been observed to occur, Earth must be very old. Darwin thought that species may also change through time and that this, too, could only be possible if Earth is much older than was commonly believed at the time.

10. Similar organisms on different islands have slight differences called variations.

11. The fact that fossils look like living species suggested that modern animals might have some relationship to fossil forms. For such changes to occur, Earth must be very old. Fossil shells of marine organisms high in the mountans also indicated change occurs over long periods of time.

CHAPTER REVIEW

12. Resources are limited in nature, and organisms have more offspring than can survive. Variation in a population makes it more likely that some individuals will survive and produce offspring with beneficial adaptations.

13. Only if traits are heritable can they be selected by either natural or artificial selection and passed on to offspring.

14. **Variation** in a population ensures that some traits will be beneficial in a given environment. **Overproduction** increases competition for resources and decreases chances that all individuals will survive to reproduce. **Adaptations** give an individual a survival advantage over competitors. **Descent with modification** occurs as environments "select" certain adaptations through differential reproductive success.

15. Natural selection cannot work directly on DNA. It selects for characteristics or traits, part of the phenotype, which in turn are coded within the genome of an organism.

16. *Sample Answers:* **Fossils** in older layers of rock tend to have more primitive forms than those in the newer layers, but there are often homologous structures, suggesting a shared ancestor. When comparing populations on neighboring islands or between other distinct **geographic** areas, we often see that variations have arisen that are well suited to each place, as with the Galápagos finches. **Embryology** shows that crabs and barnacles are different as adults yet nearly identical as larvae. **Anatomy** reveals homologous and vestigial structures.

17. *Sample Answers:* Snake pelvic bones and hind limbs, ostrich wings, and the human appendix are examples. They show evidence of common ancestry with other species possessing those structures.

18. Paleontology provides a record of past life forms and how they have changed over time, which illuminates relationships between species.

19. If very different species share a similar set of genes or proteins, they probably share a common ancestor.

20. Students should communicate that all fields of biology are based on evolutionary principles.

Critical Thinking

21. Both Darwin and Lamarck thought that traits that helped an organism survive were passed on to offspring, but neither of them knew how.
22. homologous because they came from a common ancestor
23. *Sample Answer:* Carrion eaters with fewer head feathers may have been less susceptible to disease because fewer feathers meant fewer ways for germs to collect. They survived longer or in greater numbers, allowing them to reproduce more than heavily feathered birds. If the number of head feathers was a heritable trait, then over generations, the carrion eaters with the highest fitness may have been those with no feathers on their head.
24. Many genes are on a single chromosome and are linked. It is possible that while humans were selecting one trait, such as a shiny coat, they were also unwittingly selecting an undesirable trait, such as weak hips.

Interpreting Visuals

25. The flower was emphasized to produce the cauliflower, and the leaves were emphasized to produce the cabbage.
26. Students should mention that plants with the desirable traits would have to be selected to reproduce for many generations to finally obtain broccoli with small flowers and thick stems.
27. A protein comparison of broccoli, cabbage, and cauliflower would confirm that they all share a common ancestor.

Critical Thinking

21. Compare Jean-Baptiste Lamarck hypothesized that changes in an environment led to an organism's greater or lesser use of a body part. Although his hypothesis was wrong, what ideas related to evolution did Lamarck and Charles Darwin share? **NOS.9**

22. Apply Both birds and crocodiles build nests, care for their young, and "sing" to defend territory and attract mates. They inherited these behaviors from a common ancestor. Are these homologous or analogous behaviors? Explain.

23. Analyze The turkey vulture and the California condor both feed upon dead animals, known as carrion. Neither species of bird has feathers on its head. Explain how natural selection may have played a role in the featherless heads of these carrion eaters.

24. Synthesize The Labrador retriever, a breed of dog, has been artificially selected for certain traits. However, these dogs are also prone to having weak hips. Use concepts from the chapter and your knowledge of genetics to explain how this situation may have arisen.

Interpreting Visuals

Use the following diagram, which shows the evolution of the wild mustard plant, to answer the next three questions.

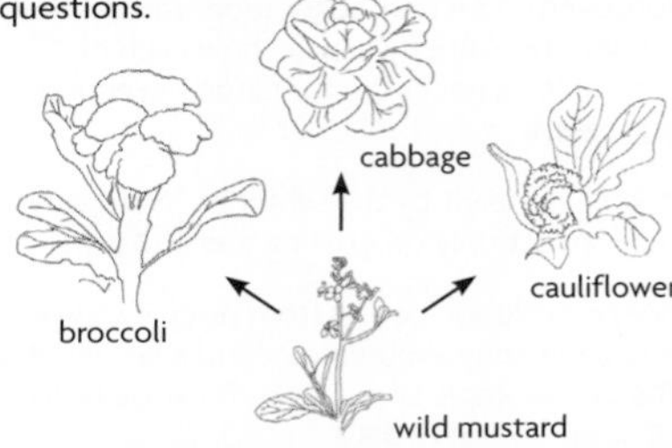

25. Infer Traits of the wild mustard plant have been emphasized by artificial selection to produce different vegetables. In some varieties, the flower heads were emphasized; in other vegetables, it is the leaves or the stems that are to be eaten. Which traits were emphasized to produce cauliflower? cabbage?

26. Apply Describe a procedure humans may have used to produce broccoli, which has small flowers and thick stems.

27. Predict What would a protein comparison of broccoli, cabbage, and cauliflower confirm about their relationships to each other?

Analyzing Data

One hundred million seabirds use the island of Gaugh, in the South Atlantic Ocean, as a critical nesting ground. Non-native carnivorous mice eat the helpless seabird chicks at a rate of about 1 million per year. Prior to the arrival of the mice, no natural predators existed on the island, so the birds did not evolve any defense mechanisms. Scientists estimate the current population of the mice at 700,000. The graph below displays a projection of seabird casualties and changes in the size of the mouse population.

SEABIRD CASUALTIES AND MOUSE POPULATION

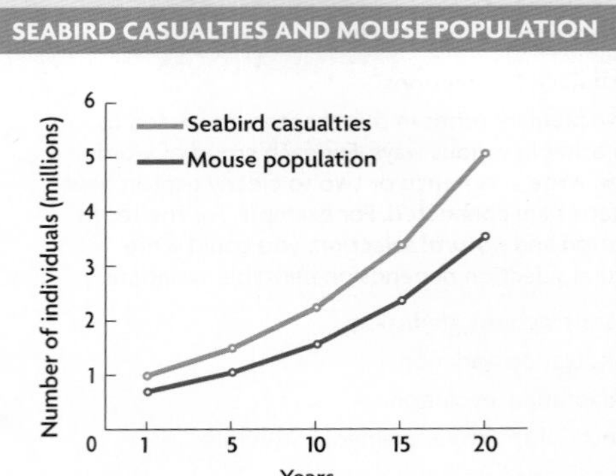

28. Interpret What does the graph show about seabird casualties and the mouse population over a 20-year period?

29. Predict Imagine some seabirds began defending their nests from the mice, and that this behavior is heritable. What changes might such a graph show over the next 20 years? Explain.

Connecting CONCEPTS

30. Write a Scenario Imagine a way in which seabirds could adapt to the mouse population and avoid predation upon their chicks. Then consider how, after many generations, the mouse population could counter this defense and again limit the seabird population. What are possible adaptations that could lead to this co-evolution of mice and seabirds?

31. Synthesize Look again at the picture of the star-nosed mole. Its claws are well adapted for breaking through soil. How could natural selection have played a role in this trait becoming common among star-nosed moles?

Analyzing Data

28. As the mouse population increased, the seabird casualties increased.
29. Accept all reasonable answers. *Sample Answer:* As seabirds began defending their nests and this became a common behavior in the population, the seabird casualty line would level off and then drop. The mouse population would also drop, possibly at a very similar rate and time.

INDIANA ISTEP+ Test Prep

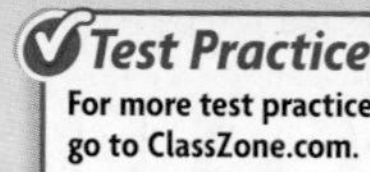

B.8.1; B.8.5; B.8.6

Test Practice
For more test practice, go to ClassZone.com.

1 The similarity in forelimb structure of humans, bats, and moles is evidence that they
- **A** share a common ancestor.
- **B** are members of the same genus.
- **C** use their forelimbs in similar ways.
- **D** evolved from each other.

2

The different neck lengths of the tortoises shown above is an example of
- **A** artificial selection.
- **B** adaptations as compromises.
- **C** vestigial structures.
- **D** variation between species.

3 After many generations, an insect species evolved resistance to a particular pesticide. This occurred because spraying pesticides
- **A** killed most of the insects in the population.
- **B** caused mutations in the insect species' gene pool.
- **C** caused another insect species to go extinct.
- **D** selected for insects that were able to survive and reproduce.

4 An herbicide killed 99% of a weed population. Which of the following is the best biological explanation for why some weeds were able to survive?
- **A** Some individuals were able to evolve before the spraying.
- **B** Genetic variation in the population allowed some weeds to survive.
- **C** The spray caused some individuals to mutate, and they were able to survive and reproduce.
- **D** Each individual occupied a different ecological niche and so some were unaffected.

THINK THROUGH THE QUESTION

This question is testing the same concept as number 3. Consider what conditions must be present for natural selection to occur.

5 In a population, natural selection acts on
- **A** heritable differences.
- **B** genetic mutations.
- **C** homologous structures.
- **D** analogous structures.

6 Define the terms "natural selection" and "evolution" and explain how they are different.

Standards-Based Assessment

1. A	4. B
2. D	5. A
3. D	6. See Below

Question 3 Answer D is correct. Answer A is incorrect because it explains only what happened to most of the insect population without explaining how the insects ultimately became resistant to the pesticide. Answers B and C are incorrect because while these side effects could possibly occur, they fail to explain how the insect population became resistant to the pesticide.

Question 5 Answer A is correct. Answers B, C, and D are incorrect because natural selection is a mechanism by which individuals that have inherited beneficial adaptations produce more offspring on average than do other individuals, thus it acts directly on phenotypic variation.

Question 6 Natural selection is the mechanism by which organisms with beneficial adaptations survive to reproduce, while those without such adaptations do not. Evolution is a change in a species, which is caused by natural selection over a long period of time.

Connecting Concepts

30. *Sample Answer:* The seabirds might use aggressive behavior, actively defending their nests. The mice start eating the eggs when the nests are not being watched rather than waiting for chicks to hatch. Possible seabird adaptations might be behavioral, such as loud squawking, wing-flapping, pecking. Mouse adaptations might include larger jaws or sharper teeth to pierce eggshells.

31. *Sample Answer:* Moles that had longer, stronger claws may have been able to find food faster and thus had better nutrition and achieved reproductive age more frequently than moles with shorter claws. Or, better nutrition meant they had larger numbers of offspring. If longer, stronger claws were heritable traits and continued to be beneficial to the moles, then over generations, they would become common throughout the star-nosed mole population.

ITEM CORRELATIONS

Standard	Items
B.8.1	1
B.8.5	3, 4, 5, 6
B.8.6	2

CHAPTER 11

Indiana Resource Preview

Print Resources

The Evolution of Populations

INDIANA STANDARDS		Sections	PAGES and PACING	UNIT RESOURCE BOOK
B.8.6	11.1	**Genetic Variation Within Populations** **KEY CONCEPT** A population shares a common gene pool.	pp. 328–329 30 minutes	URB pages 31–34
B.8.5	11.2	**Natural Selection in Populations** **KEY CONCEPT** Populations, not individuals, evolve.	pp. 330–333 30 minutes	URB pages 35–38
B.8.5, NOS.3		CHAPTER INVESTIGATION: Natural Selection in African Swallowtails	p. 334 45 minutes	**Lab Binder** Evolution pages 17–20
	11.3	**Other Mechanisms of Evolution** **KEY CONCEPT** Natural selection is not the only mechanism through which populations evolve.	pp. 335–338 45 minutes	URB pages 39–42
NOS.1		DATA ANALYSIS: Identifying Patterns	p. 339, 30 min.	URB page 55
	11.4	**Hardy-Weinberg Equilibrium** **KEY CONCEPT** Hardy-Weinberg equilibrium provides a framework for understanding how populations evolve.	pp. 340–343 45 minutes	URB pages 43–46
	11.5	**Speciation Through Isolation** **KEY CONCEPT** New species can arise when populations are isolated.	pp. 344–346 30 minutes	URB pages 47–50
	11.6	**Patterns in Evolution** **KEY CONCEPT** Evolution occurs in patterns.	pp. 347–351 30 minutes	URB pages 51–54
B.8.5, NOS.6		OPTIONS FOR INQUIRY	pp. 352–353 45, 20 min.	**Lab Binder** Evolution pages 21–24
		Chapter Review	pp. 354–357	**Assessment Book** Chapter Tests A, B pp. 217–224

INDIANA STANDARDS

B.8.5 Describe how due to genetic variations, environmental forces, and reproductive pressures, organisms with beneficial traits are more likely to survive, reproduce, and pass on their genetic information.

B.8.6 Explain how genetic variation within a population (a species) can be attributed to mutations as well as a random assortment of existing genes.

NOS.1 Develop explanations based on reproducible data and observations gathered during laboratory investigations.

NOS.3 Clearly communicate their ideas and results of investigations verbally and in written form using tables, graphs, diagrams, and photographs.

NOS.6 Use analogies and models (mathematical and physical) to simplify and represent systems that are difficult to understand or directly experience due to their size, time scale, or complexity, and recognize the limitations of analogies and models.

Labs

PUPIL EDITION LABS

Natural Selection in African Swallowtails, p. 334 Students model disruptive selection. **Lab Binder** pp. 17–20	**Time:** 45 minutes **Materials:** 15 small pieces of colored paper: 5 yellow, 5 orange, 5 red, extra paper of each color
Genetic Drift, Section 3, p. 337 Students model how isolation of a small population can affect allele frequency. **Lab Binder** p. 25	**Time:** 15 minutes **Materials:** deck of cards

OPTIONS FOR INQUIRY

Investigating an Anole Lizard Population, p. 352 Students observe whether a model population is evolving. **Lab Binder** pp. 21–22	**Time:** 45 minutes **Materials:** 10 large paper clips (mix of smooth and ribbed), 10 small paper clips, "extras" cup containing 20 additional large paper clips (10 smooth, 10 ribbed), graph paper
Exploring Adaptations, p. 353 Students analyze the natural process of adaptation. **Lab Binder** pp. 23–24	**Time:** 20 minutes **Materials:** wooden block, one wood screw, ruler

LAB BINDER Unit 4 Evolution

Additional Investigation: Population Genetics, pp. 27–30

Biotechnology Lab: Microevolution and Antibiotic-Resistant Bacteria, pp. 47–50

Real-World Lab: Exploring Dog Genetics and Evolution, pp. 51–54

Challenge Lab: Modeling Alleles, pp. 55–59; Investigating Plant Adaptations, pp. 60–63

Vernier Probeware Lab: Population Dynamics, pp. 64–69

LAB GENERATOR

A searchable CD of all labs in the program in editable format, including forensic, probeware, and biotechnology labs.

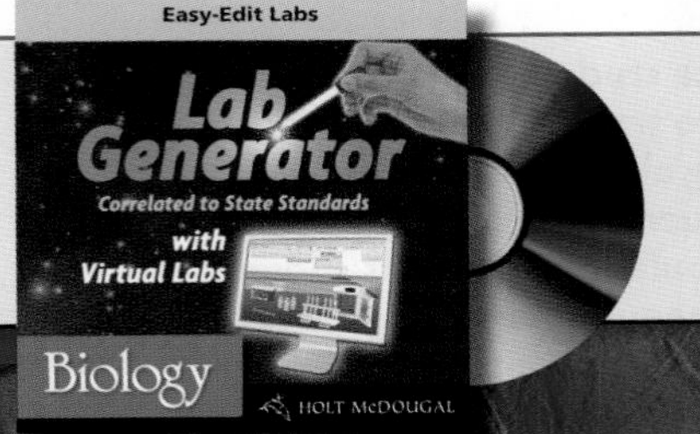

Presentation Tools

POWER PRESENTATIONS

Presentation Chapter 11
PowerPresentations for each section incorporate images and clips from the Media Gallery. Includes Note Navigator for each section.

MEDIA GALLERY

Contains the following images and video clips, as well as animations, simulations, and forms of visuals from the book.

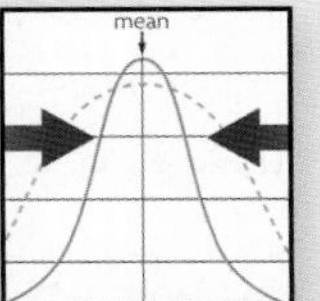

Stabilizing selection

Evolutionary arms race

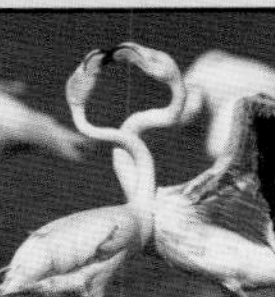
Flamingo courtship

Founder effect

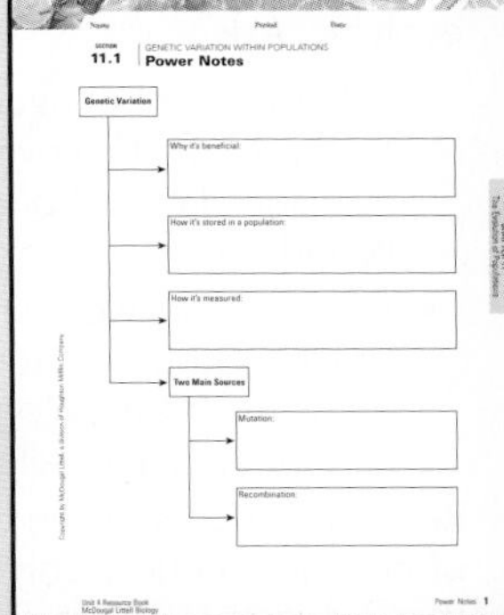

Power Notes

VIDEO

Check out a set of short video clips exploring the pressure on and evolution of populations.

ANIMATED BIOLOGY

Mechanisms of Evolution

Evolutionary Arms Race

Founder Effect

TRANSPARENCIES

Alleles T43
Directional Selection T44
Stabilizing Selection T45
Disruptive Selection T46
Factors That Can Lead to Evolution T47
Extinction Rates Through Time T48

Online BIOLOGY CLASSZONE.COM

BioZine
Animated Biology
Interactive Review
SciLinks
Resource Centers

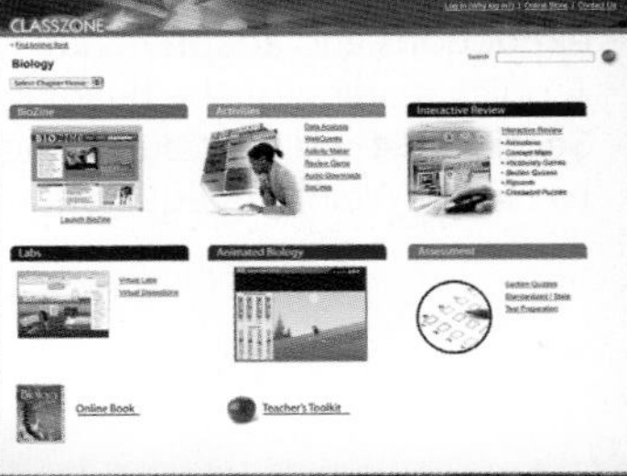

CHAPTER 11

▼ Focus and Motivate

How does a population of penguins evolve?

Have students discuss ways in which the penguin population could be evolving. **Ask**

- What traits of penguins are adaptive to the Antarctic environment? insulating layer of blubber, feathers, brood pouch
- What factors would result in changes to the genetic variation of the penguins in the colony? mutation, recombination of alleles

Remind students of the basic principle of natural selection: only those penguins that successfully reproduce and raise live, healthy chicks will pass on their genes and the phenotypes that they code for. Individuals do not evolve; populations do.

BIOZINE ClassZone.com

Students can access BioZine at **ClassZone.com** to look for topics suitable for research reports, writing assignments, or classroom debates.

In a Hurry?

The critical material of the chapter is found in **Sections 11.1, 11.2, 11.3, 11.5,** and **11.6,** which cover genetic variation in populations, patterns of natural selection, other mechanisms of evolution, speciation, and patterns such as mass extinctions and adaptive radiation. A quick reading of the headings in **Section 11.4** will introduce students to Hardy-Weinberg equilibrium.

CHAPTER 11

The Evolution of Populations

KEY CONCEPTS

11.1 Genetic Variation Within Populations
A population shares a common gene pool.

11.2 Natural Selection in Populations
Populations, not individuals, evolve.

11.3 Other Mechanisms of Evolution
Natural selection is not the only mechanism through which populations evolve.

11.4 Hardy-Weinberg Equilibrium
Hardy-Weinberg equilibrium provides a framework for understanding how populations evolve.

11.5 Speciation Through Isolation
New species can arise when populations are isolated.

11.6 Patterns in Evolution
Evolution occurs in patterns.

Online BIOLOGY CLASSZONE.COM

Animated BIOLOGY
View animated chapter concepts.
- Mechanisms of Evolution
- Evolutionary Arms Race
- Founder Effect

BIOZINE
Keep current with biology news.
- News feeds
- Polls
- Bio Bytes

RESOURCE CENTER
Get more information on
- Selective Pressures
- Mechanisms of Evolution
- Hardy-Weinberg Equilibrium
- Coevolution

Student Activity

Purpose Introduce students to phenotypic variation using two traits: hitchhiker's thumb and tongue-rolling ability. Students will calculate the frequency of each trait within the classroom population. Students should understand that frequency of a phenotype depends on the frequency of the genotype that codes for the trait.

Prepare On the board, create a table similar to the example shown below.

	Hitchhiker's Thumb	Tongue Rolling
Yes	8	16
No	18	10
Total pop.	26	26

How does a population of penguins evolve?

Connecting CONCEPTS

Every year, king penguins return to breed in the same colony in which they were born. These colonies help penguins to guard, protect, and defend their young. By ensuring the success of their young, penguins pass on their genes to future generations. Variation in these genes is the basis for the evolution of populations.

Homeostasis King penguins breed in harsh, cold conditions on sub-Antarctic islands. They have special adaptations that allow them to maintain a stable body temperature. One of the most difficult challenges for a penguin during this time is keeping the newly laid egg warm by balancing it on his feet. The egg is kept insulated by a thick roll of skin and feathers called a brood pouch.

Introduce Tell students that the abilities to roll one's tongue and flex a thumb tip backward into hitchhiker's thumb are traits that are coded for by genes. Have students work in pairs to determine who has these traits. Compile the data on the board. Ask students to calculate the frequency of each phenotype and express it as a percentage.

Discuss Explain that tongue rolling and hitchhiker's thumb provide examples of phenotypic variation within a population.

Discuss how this phenotypic variation is the result of different combinations of alleles on multiple genes.

Ask, What would happen to the genetic variation of the population if, for example, all the tongue-rolling students left the class or if ten hitchhiker-thumbed students were added to the class? Frequencies would change. Perhaps some traits would disappear completely.

Remind students that genetic variation is the basis for the evolution of populations.

Activate Prior Knowledge

Have students look at the picture of the penguins. **Ask,** Do you see any variation in this population of penguins? very hard to see **Ask,** How would you describe variation in a human population? tends to be much more obvious

Point out that one reason for phenotypic variation in humans is that our ancestors lived in very different environments over tens of thousands of years. Over many generations, certain traits were selected for in response to conditions in those environments.

Ask, How might this population of penguins change if Antarctica suddenly got much warmer? Over time you might see less blubber, fewer feathers.

Preview Vocabulary

Academic Vocabulary The concept of *variation* is important in this unit, particularly as it relates to differences in populations—both genotypic and phenotypic. Ask students to identify other words that share the Latin root *varius,* meaning "of different kinds."

vary	*variable*
variability	*variation*
variety	*various*
variance	*variant*

Have students write down these words in their science notebook, define them, and then use the words in sentences.

English Learners Suggest that if Mendel were looking at the penguins pictured here, he would be thinking about traits and genes. Remind students of the vocabulary in Chapter 6: *traits, genes, alleles, phenotype, genotype.*

Then suggest that if Darwin were looking at these penguins, he would be thinking about traits and natural selection. Remind students of the vocabulary in Chapter 10: *species, variation, natural selection.*

Have students make an outline of headings in this chapter to see how the work of Mendel and Darwin come together.

SECTION 11.1

▼ Plan and Prepare

Objectives

- Describe the significance of genetic variation within a population.
- Identify sources of genetic variation.

Section Resources

Unit Resource Book
Study Guide pp. 31–32
Power Notes p. 33
Reinforcement p. 34
Pre-AP Activity pp. 57–58

Interactive Reader Chapter 11
Spanish Study Guide pp. 109–110

Biology Toolkit pp. C17, C19

Technology
Power Presentation 11.1
Media Gallery DVD
Online Quiz 11.1

Activate Prior Knowledge Have students think about putting together a basketball team. **Ask,** What are the chances that you can put together a good team if just ten players try out? okay, but not great What about 30 players? much better Discuss with students that a larger group represents a larger pool of talent and skills. Tell them that the same applies to gene pools.

▼ Teach

Vocabulary

Word Origins Students will be familiar with the word **pool** in the context of swimming or billiards. Tell them that when applied to evolution and genetics, the word refers to the available supply, or pool, of alleles found in a population. This *pool* comes from the Old French *poule,* or "chicken," which goes back to the Latin *pullus,* "the young of an animal."

Answers

A Analyze Allele frequencies measure how common certain alleles are in a gene pool.

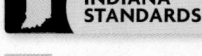

11.1 Genetic Variation Within Populations

KEY CONCEPT A population shares a common gene pool.

MAIN IDEAS
- Genetic variation in a population increases the chance that some individuals will survive.
- Genetic variation comes from several sources.

VOCABULARY
gene pool, p. 328
allele frequency, p. 328

Review
phenotype, gene, allele, meiosis, gamete

B.8.6 Explain how genetic variation within a population (a species) can be attributed to mutations as well as a random assortment of existing genes.

Connect You may think that if you've seen one penguin, you've seen them all. However, penguins can differ in body size, feather patterns, and many other traits. Just like humans, penguins are genetically different from one another. What is the nature of genetic variation in populations? And how is this variation measured by biologists?

MAIN IDEA

Genetic variation in a population increases the chance that some individuals will survive.

Body size and feather patterns in penguins are each examples of phenotypes. A phenotype is a trait produced by one or more genes. In a population, there may be a wide range of phenotypes. For example, some penguins may be short and rounded. Others could be tall and slim.

Natural selection acts on different phenotypes in a population. However, in order to have different phenotypes, a population must have genetic variation. A population with a lot of genetic variation likely has a wide range of phenotypes. The greater the variation in phenotypes, the more likely it is that some individuals can survive in a changing environment. For example, if an unusually cold winter occurs, short, rounded penguins might be able to stay warm more easily. But if there is a shortage of food, tall, slim penguins might be better divers, allowing them to catch more fish.

Genetic variation is stored in a population's **gene pool**—the combined alleles of all of the individuals in a population. Different combinations of alleles in a gene pool can be formed when organisms mate and have offspring. Each allele exists at a certain rate, or frequency. An **allele frequency** is a measure of how common a certain allele is in the population. As shown in **FIGURE 11.1**, you can calculate allele frequencies. First count the number of times an allele occurs in a gene pool. Then divide by the total number of alleles for that gene in the gene pool.

TAKING NOTES

Use mind maps to show relationships among related terms and concepts.

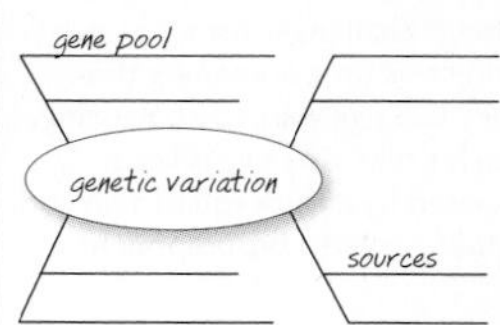

A Analyze What is the relationship between allele frequencies and a gene pool?

Differentiated Instruction

ENGLISH LEARNERS

This section has five review vocabulary words in addition to the new words. Help students recall the meanings of words by modeling the strategy Connect to Content Through Visuals: Picture Imaging. Choose one of the terms, such as *phenotype.* Share with students what you visualize when you see that word. Ask them to tell you what they "see" related to it. After studying the new vocabulary in context on this page, do the same with those words.

Biology Toolkit, Connect to Content Through Visuals, p. C17

PRE-AP

Have students take the concept of a gene pool and relate it to Mendel's work with garden peas. Ask students to write a paragraph or two about how Mendel manipulated the gene pool in his experiments with purebred peas.

Biology Toolkit, Quick-Write, p. C19

FIGURE 11.1 Allele Frequency

An allele frequency is the ratio of one allele to the total number of the alleles for that gene in the gene pool.

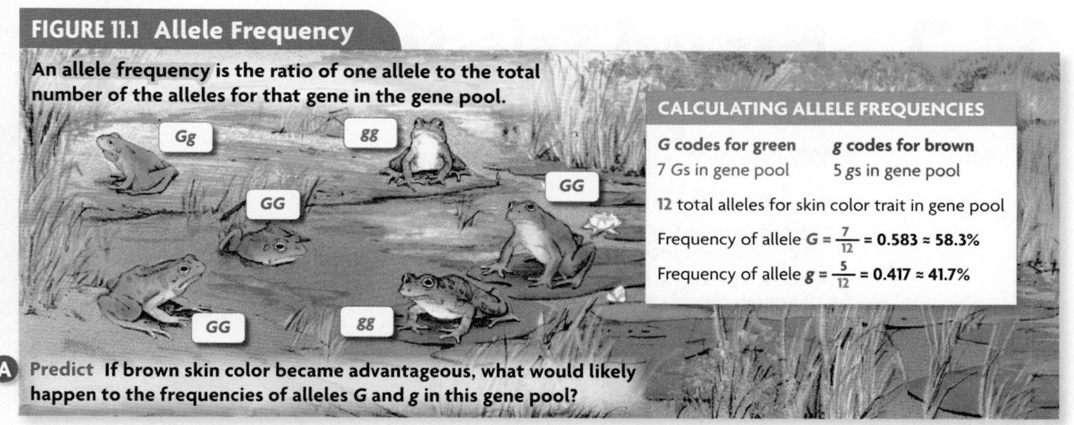

Gg
gg
GG
GG
GG
gg
CALCULATING ALLELE FREQUENCIES
G codes for green
g codes for brown
7 Gs in gene pool
5 gs in gene pool
12 total alleles for skin color trait in gene pool

Frequency of allele $G = \frac{7}{12} = 0.583 \approx 58.3\%$

Frequency of allele $g = \frac{5}{12} = 0.417 \approx 41.7\%$

A Predict **If brown skin color became advantageous, what would likely happen to the frequencies of alleles *G* and *g* in this gene pool?**

MAIN IDEA

Genetic variation comes from several sources.

Genetic variation comes from two main sources: mutation and recombination.

- **Mutation** A mutation is a random change in the DNA of a gene. This change can form a new allele. Mutations in reproductive cells can be passed on to offspring. This increases the genetic variation in the gene pool. Because there are many genes in each individual and many individuals in a population, new mutations form frequently in gene pools.
- **Recombination** New allele combinations form in offspring through a process called recombination. Most recombination occurs during meiosis—the type of cell division needed for sexual reproduction. When gametes are made, each parent's alleles are arranged in new ways. This shuffling of alleles results in many different genetic combinations.

Some biologists are studying hybridization as another source of genetic variation. Hybridization is the crossing of two different species that share common genes. Research suggests that this process occurs within many groups of animals, including birds and mammals, when similar species live in the same area and individuals cannot easily find mates of their own species.

B Infer **Why aren't mutations in nonreproductive cells sources of genetic variation?**

Connecting CONCEPTS

Genetics Recall from **Chapter 8** that mutations on noncoding regions of DNA do not affect phenotypes. Only mutations on coding regions of DNA can affect an organism's phenotype.

11.1 ASSESSMENT

ONLINE QUIZ ClassZone.com

B.8.6

REVIEWING MAIN IDEAS

1. Why does genetic variation increase the chance that some individuals in a population will survive?
2. Describe two main sources of genetic variation.

CRITICAL THINKING

3. **Analyze** In what way is a **gene pool** representative of a population?
4. **Apply** If a certain trait's **allele frequency** is 100 percent, describe the genetic variation for that trait in the population.

Connecting CONCEPTS

5. **Genetics** How does crossing over during meiosis provide a source of genetic variation? Draw a diagram to show this process.

11.1 ASSESSMENT

1. Genetically diverse populations display high phenotypic variation. If changing environmental conditions favor a particular phenotype—for example, resistance to a certain disease—there is a good chance that a genetically diverse population will have some individuals who have that advantageous phenotype.
2. Mutation is a random change in DNA that can result in a new allele. Recombination rearranges allele combinations on a chromosome, which can result in a new phenotype.
3. The gene pool contains all the alleles found within a population.
4. If an allele frequency for a trait is 100 percent, there is no genetic variation for that trait within the population (assuming the trait is a single-gene trait).
5. Diagrams should accurately illustrate prophase I of meiosis with homologous chromosomes crossing over, resulting in the exchange of alleles between the chromosomes and new combinations of alleles on the offspring's chromosomes.

Vocabulary

Academic Vocabulary In the word **inheritable,** the suffix *in-* does not mean "cannot" or "is not," as in incomplete or incorrect. Therefore, it is not the antonym, or opposite, of **heritable.** Rather it is a synonym that is used primarily in the context of inheriting money or property from a relative. In biology, the word *heritable* is more commonly used for the inheritance of traits. This might help students remember the distinction:

obtain the *inheritable* upon death
obtain the *heritable* upon birth

Ask, What are the antonyms? noninheritable, nonheritable

TEACH FROM VISUALS

FIGURE 11.1 The diagram shows a hypothetical population of frogs. **Ask,** What does *advantageous* mean in this example? It refers to fitness, meaning the trait improves the chances of an individual passing its genes on to offspring. Remind students that this advantage applies to this specific environment. An advantage in one environment could be a disadvantage in another environment.

Answers

A Predict The *G* allele would decrease in frequency, and the *g* allele would increase in frequency.

B Infer A source of genetic variation for a population must be heritable. Mutations in nonreproductive cells are not heritable.

Assess and Reteach

Assess Use the Online Quiz or Section Quiz (*Assessment Book*, p. 211).

Reteach Use the graphic organizer shown on page 328 to reteach the material. Work with students to incorporate review vocabulary words into this mind map: phenotype, gene, allele, meiosis, gametes.

▼ Plan and Prepare

Objectives

- Describe how natural selection acts on the distribution of traits in a population.
- Explain three ways natural selection can change the distribution of a trait in a population.

Section Resources

Unit Resource Book Study Guide pp. 35–36 Power Notes p. 37 Reinforcement p. 38
Interactive Reader Chapter 11 **Spanish Study Guide** pp. 111–112
Biology Toolkit pp. C10, C35
Technology Power Presentation 11.2 Media Gallery DVD Online Quiz 11.2

Activate Prior Knowledge Tell students that natural selection helps to determine not only which traits are found in a population, but also the range of a particular trait. Remind students of the Grants' study of Darwin's finches discussed in Chapter 10. **Ask,** When a drought caused more large-beak ground finches to survive than small-beaked ground finches, both of the same species, what was natural selection acting upon? alleles affecting beak size

▼ Teach

Vocabulary

Academic Vocabulary In everyday use, **normal** means common or average. When applied to a set of data, as in a *normal distribution* or *normal curve,* it is understood that most of the values tend to be near the average, while relatively few values are at or near the extremes.

Answers

A Synthesize body weight, average income, batting averages in baseball

11.2 Natural Selection in Populations

KEY CONCEPT Populations, not individuals, evolve.

MAIN IDEAS

- Natural selection acts on distributions of traits.
- Natural selection can change the distribution of a trait in one of three ways.

VOCABULARY

normal distribution, p. 330
microevolution, p. 331
directional selection, p. 331
stabilizing selection, p. 332
disruptive selection, p. 333

Review
natural selection

INDIANA STANDARDS

B.8.5 Describe how due to genetic variations, environmental forces, and reproductive pressures, organisms with beneficial traits are more likely to survive, reproduce, and pass on their genetic information.

Connect How do you describe a person's appearance? Perhaps you use height, hair color, and eye color. These traits are often used in descriptions because these traits vary widely among humans. In this section you will learn about how natural selection can act upon such variation.

MAIN IDEA

Natural selection acts on distributions of traits.

Any time you stand in a large crowd of people, you are likely to observe a wide range of heights. Imagine organizing this crowd across a football field according to each individual's height, with very short people at one end, people of average height in the middle, and very tall people at the other end. You would soon notice a pattern in the distribution for the human height trait. Relatively few people would be at each extreme height, very short or very tall. A majority of people would be in the middle due to their medium height.

This type of distribution, in which the frequency is highest near the mean value and decreases toward each extreme end of the range, is called a **normal distribution.** When these frequency values are graphed, the result is a bell-shaped curve like the one you see in **FIGURE 11.2.**

***Connecting* CONCEPTS**

Genetics As you learned in **Chapter 7,** single-gene traits are expressed in either one distinct form or another. However, the range of phenotypes common for most traits is the result of polygenic traits, which are controlled by multiple genes.

FIGURE 11.2 NORMAL DISTRIBUTION

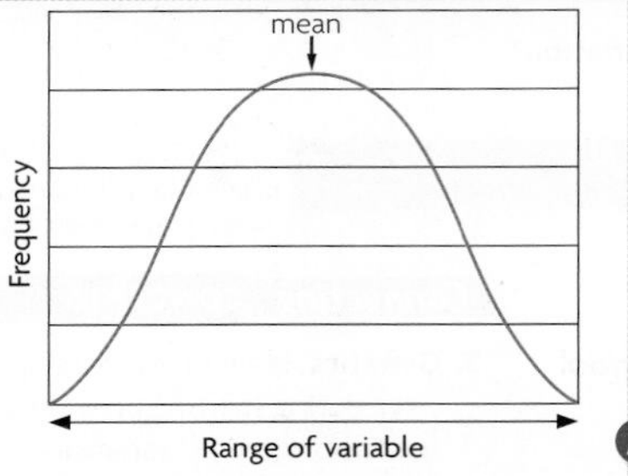

For some traits, all phenotypes provide an equal chance of survival. The distribution for these traits generally shows a normal distribution. Phenotypes near the middle of the range tend to be most common, while the extremes are less common. However, environmental conditions can change and a certain phenotype may become an advantage. Nature favors individuals with this phenotype. These individuals are able to survive and reproduce at higher rates than individuals with less favorable phenotypes. Therefore, alleles associated with favorable phenotypes increase in frequency.

A Synthesize What other types of data might follow a normal distribution?

Differentiated Instruction

ENGLISH LEARNERS

Plan for a round-table activity. Tell students upon finishing this section, to close their books and divide into groups. Each group will be given a sheet of paper labeled with one of the three types of natural selection: *Directional, Stabilizing,* or *Disruptive.* Each student in the group will write something he or she knows about the topic, then pass the sheet to the next person. Everyone has to write something different. Allow five minutes, then compile the information for the class.

Biology Toolkit, Round Table, p. C10

HANDS-ON ACTIVITY

To demonstrate a normal distribution, pass out sticky notes, using different colors for male and female. Ask each student to write his or her height on the note, then collect the data. Make the analogy that these are two populations and you want to find the distributions of a specific trait. Plot the two data sets on the same graph. Have students compare both the distribution and the range of sizes in the two populations. Point out that the mean is a useful statistic, but it is possible that it will not actually appear in the population.

MAIN IDEA

Natural selection can change the distribution of a trait in one of three ways.

Microevolution is the observable change in the allele frequencies of a population over time. Microevolution occurs on a small scale—within a single population. One process that can lead to microevolution is natural selection. Natural selection can change the distribution of a trait along one of three paths: directional, stabilizing, or disruptive selection. Such changes can have major effects on how a population looks and behaves.

Directional Selection

A type of selection that favors phenotypes at one extreme of a trait's range is called **directional selection.** Directional selection causes a shift in a population's phenotypic distribution. An extreme phenotype that was once rare in a population becomes more common. As shown in **FIGURE 11.3,** during directional selection, the mean value of a trait shifts in the direction of the more advantageous phenotype.

The rise of drug-resistant bacteria provides a classic example of this type of selection. Before antibiotics were developed in the 1940s, a trait for varying levels of drug resistance existed among bacteria. At the time, there was no advantage to having drug resistance. But once antibiotics came into use, the resistant bacteria had a great advantage.

The early success of antibiotics in controlling infectious diseases led to overuse of these drugs. This overuse favored even more resistant phenotypes. New drugs were then developed to fight the resistant bacteria. This resulted in the evolution of "superbugs" that are highly resistant to many drugs. Today, over 200 types of bacteria show some degree of antibiotic resistance.

***Connecting* CONCEPTS**

Bacteria Although many bacteria are helpful to other organisms, some do cause disease. You will learn more about how bacteria can evolve and become resistant to antibiotics in **Chapter 18.**

FIGURE 11.3 Directional Selection

Directional selection occurs when one extreme phenotype is favored by natural selection.

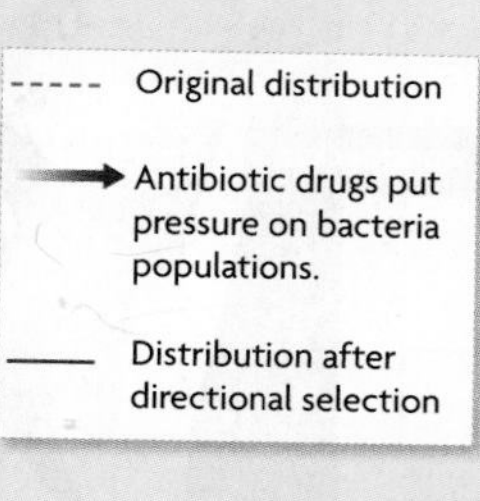

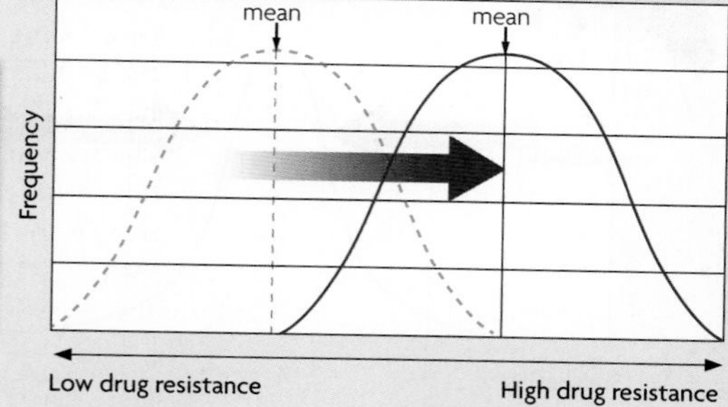

Today, scientists continue to research new drugs developed to treat infection-causing bacteria such as *Enterococcus faecalis,* which is resistant to many antibiotics.

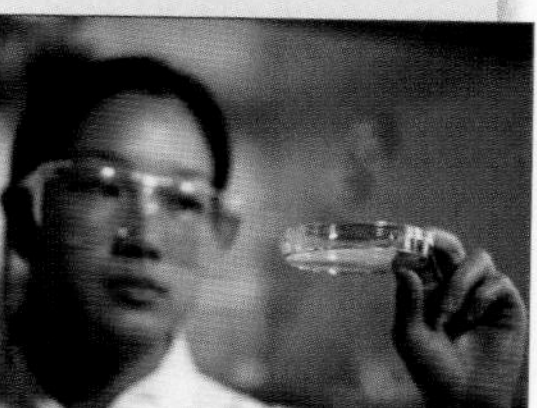

PRE-AP

Provide the following hypothetical data sets on Coho salmon reproduction and have students plot both on the same graph, using different colors for each data set.

# of eggs in 15 Coho salmon nests, 1985
813, 830, 830, 837, 839, 839, 839, 842, 843, 845, 847, 860, 881, 890, 893

# of eggs in 15 Coho salmon nests, 2005
853, 871, 876, 883, 883, 888, 889, 897, 899, 899, 905, 905, 905, 908, 912

Have students determine the mean, median (middle value), and mode (most common value) of each set.

1985: mean = 848.5; median = 842; mode = 839

2005: mean = 891.5; median = 897; mode = 905

Ask, Which phenotype does directional selection seem to be favoring? more eggs per nest

Vocabulary

Academic Vocabulary What follows are some terms commonly used in statistical analysis.

Frequency refers to the number of times a specific thing occurs or is found within a given interval or space.

Mean is the average. In a *normal distribution,* the *mean* is also the point at which the *frequency* is highest.

Range is the difference or interval between the smallest and largest values in a frequency distribution. For example, the *range* of heights is from the shortest to the tallest.

Median is the middle value in a distribution, with an equal number of values above and below. For example, in a range of integers from 0 to 10, the median is 5. There are five integers above and below. In a normal distribution, the median is equal to the mean.

Mode is the value occurring most frequently in a set of data. For example, if there are five flowers in a bunch, and three of them are red, one is white, and one is pink, the *mode* is red because it is the most common color. In a normal distribution, the mode is equal to the median and the mean.

Take It Further

One of the most threatening types of **antibiotic-resistant bacteria** is *Staphylococcus aureus,* or "Staph," a major cause of infections in hospitals. Mutations in these bacteria have resulted in antibiotic-resistant strains. The bacteria's resistance to penicillin began to show up in hospitals in the 1950s. By the 1980s, *Staphylococcus aureus* had become 100 percent resistant to penicillin. Since then, different strains have evolved to become resistant to methicillin and vancomycin, which are the drugs typically used as a last resort against infection.

▼ Teach continued

TEACH FROM VISUALS

FIGURE 11.5 To help students understand the difference between stabilizing and directional selection, have them compare **FIGURE 11.5** to **FIGURE 11.3. Ask**

- What type of selection would occur if only the woodpeckers were putting pressure on the gall fly population? directional selection
- What would the resulting graph look like? The graph would resemble Figure 11.3 but shifted to the left.
- How is the dashed line being used in the graph? It represents the distribution of gall fly phenotypes that produce various gall sizes in the absence of predators.

Integrating Earth Science

Many factors that put pressure on populations are the result of changes in the physical environment. For example, changes in sea level due to melting or freezing of polar ice, changes in land surface caused by earthquakes or volcanic eruptions, and glaciation or drought would force populations to adapt to the new conditions or migrate. Such changes might also lead to extinction for some populations.

Recent research and modeling in **climatology,** the study of the Earth's weather and climate, suggest that the huge extinction that marked the end of the Permian period may have been triggered by an increase in atmospheric carbon dioxide. Such an increase would have warmed the oceans, effectively shutting down the currents and upwelling that distribute oxygen and nutrients throughout the seas.

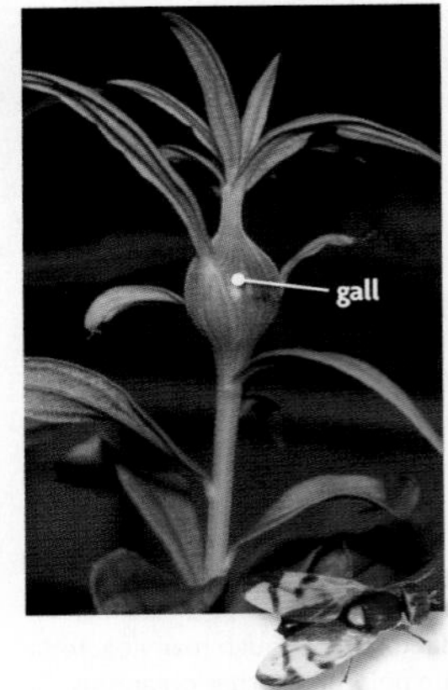

FIGURE 11.4 The gall fly and the goldenrod have a parasitic relationship. The fly benefits by receiving shelter and food during its larval stage, while the goldenrod is harmed, growing more slowly than a gall-free goldenrod.

Stabilizing Selection

The gall fly and its predators provide an excellent example of stabilizing selection. During **stabilizing selection,** the intermediate phenotype is favored and becomes more common in the population. That is, the distribution becomes stable at the intermediate phenotype rather than shifting toward one of the extremes. In the case of gall flies, something in nature selects against phenotypes at both extremes of the trait's range.

Gall flies lay their eggs in developing shoots of the tall goldenrod. The fly larvae produce a chemical that causes the plant tissue to swell around them. **FIGURE 11.4** shows the resulting mass of plant tissue, called a gall. The gall serves as a home where the larvae can develop. There is a range of phenotypes for body size in gall-fly larvae. Each body size causes a certain size gall to form, and each of the two main predators of gall flies specializes on a specific gall size.

- Downy woodpeckers attack larger galls and feed on the larvae inside.
- The parasitic wasp lays its own eggs inside small galls. After the wasp larvae emerge from the eggs, they eat the gall-fly larvae.

In this situation, selective pressure from predators works against fly phenotypes that produce galls at both extremes, large and small. As a result, flies that produce middle-sized galls become more common. As you can see in **FIGURE 11.5**, over time, stabilizing selection results in a higher frequency of flies that produce middle-sized galls.

Stabilizing selection increases the number of individuals with intermediate phenotypes. Notice, however, that selection against both extremes decreases the genetic diversity of the gall fly population. Flies that produce small and large galls become less common. In some populations, these extreme phenotypes may be lost altogether.

FIGURE 11.5 Stabilizing Selection

Stabilizing selection occurs when intermediate phenotypes are favored by natural selection.

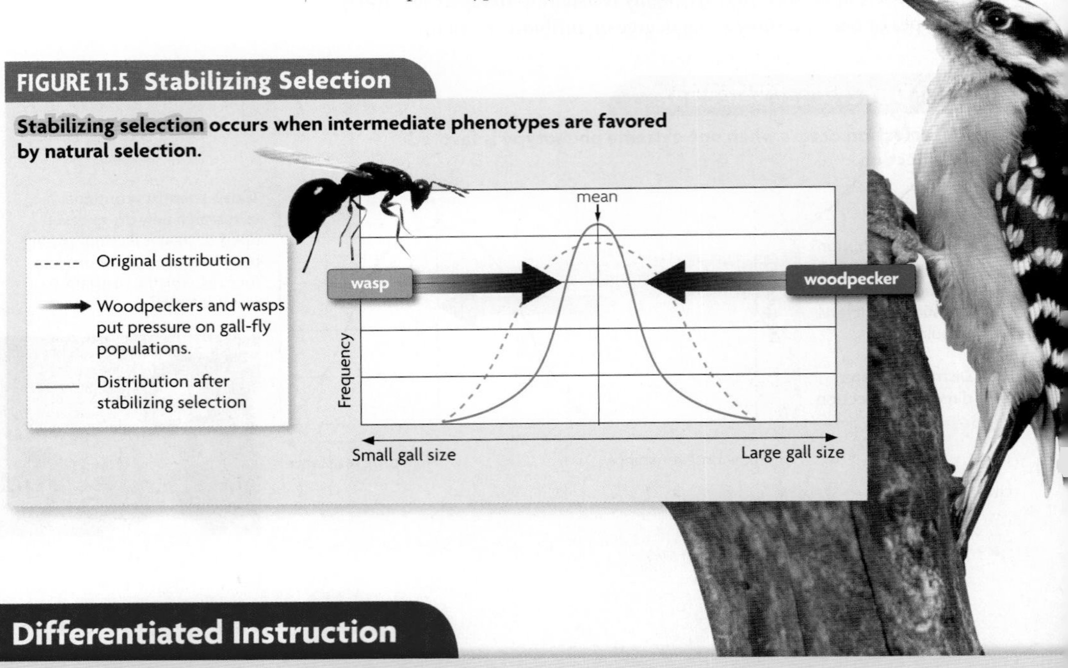

Differentiated Instruction

INCLUSION

For students who are literal thinkers, the graphs shown in **FIGURES 11.3, 11.5,** and **11.6** can be recreated by using a distribution of colored beads to represent different phenotypes. Using a horizontal line on a sheet of paper to represent the *x*-axis, align each set of phenotypic beads on a vertical, the uppermost bead representing a point on a graph. The resulting pattern of bead lines will suggest the shape of a distribution curve. Change the number of beads in response to "selection pressures" to model disruptive, directional, and stabilizing selection.

BELOW LEVEL

Make sure students see the connection between the gall fly and goldenrod pictured in **FIGURE 11.4** and the wasp and woodpecker pictured in **FIGURE 11.5.** Have students reinterpret the interaction of the four populations in a cause and effect diagram. Have them start with a goldenrod population with only gall flies present (the dashed curve of **FIGURE 11.5**), then add the wasp and woodpecker.

Biology Toolkit, Cause and Effect Diagram, p. C35

Disruptive Selection

Disruptive selection occurs when both extreme phenotypes are favored, while individuals with intermediate phenotypes are selected against by something in nature. As you can see in **FIGURE 11.6**, the middle of the distribution is disrupted. One example of this type of selection involves feather color in male lazuli buntings, a bird species native to North America.

Young male lazuli buntings vary widely in the brightness of their feathers, ranging from dull brown to bright blue. Dominant adult males are those with the brightest blue feathers on their heads and backs. These birds have their pick of the best territories. They also are most successful at attracting females. However, for young buntings, the brightest blue and dullest brown males are more likely to win mates than males with bluish brown feathers are.

Research suggests that dominant adult males are aggressive toward young buntings that they see as a threat, including bright blue and bluish brown males. The dullest brown birds can therefore win a mate because the adult males leave them alone. Meanwhile, the bright blue birds attract mates simply because of their color.

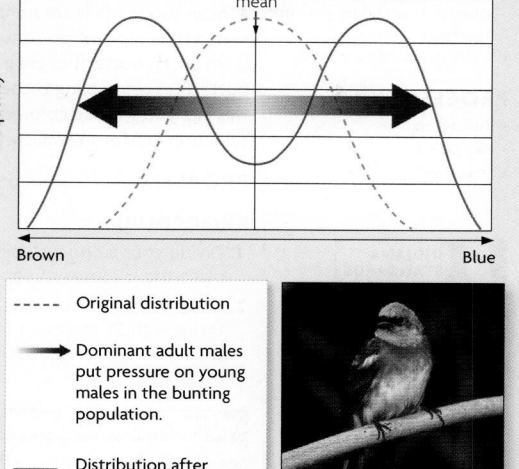

FIGURE 11.6 Disruptive Selection

Disruptive selection occurs when both extreme phenotypes are favored by selection.

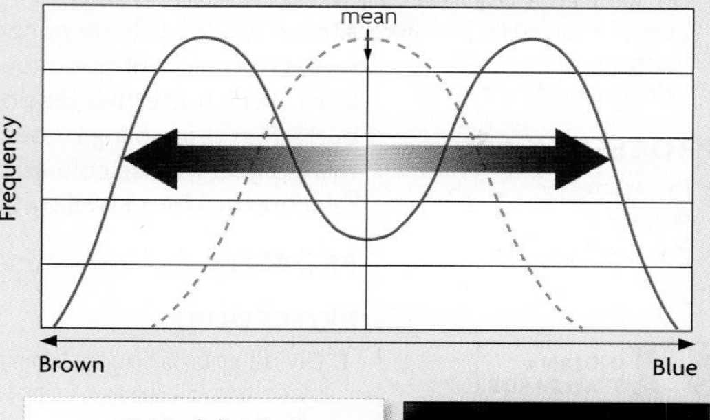

----- Original distribution

→ Dominant adult males put pressure on young males in the bunting population.

—— Distribution after disruptive selection

Adult male lazuli bunting

Both extreme phenotypes are favored in this situation, while intermediate forms are selected against. The bluish brown males are not as well adapted to compete for mates because they are too blue to be left alone by adult males, but not blue enough to win a mate based on color alone. By favoring both extreme phenotypes, disruptive selection can lead to the formation of new species.

A Apply If bluish brown coloring became advantageous for young males, what type of selection would likely occur in a lazuli bunting population?

11.2 ASSESSMENT

ONLINE QUIZ ClassZone.com

B.8.5

REVIEWING MAIN IDEAS

1. In terms of phenotypes, describe what is meant by the phrase "distribution of traits."
2. What are the three ways in which natural selection can change a distribution of traits?

CRITICAL THINKING

3. **Predict** How might the extinction of downy woodpeckers affect the phenotypic distribution of gall flies?
4. **Predict** How might overfishing of large pink salmon select for smaller body size in subsequent generations?

***Connecting* CONCEPTS**

5. **Genetics** For polygenic traits, a smooth curve results when the range of phenotypes is plotted against frequency. If you were to plot the frequencies of two phenotypes of a single-gene trait, you would end up with a double bar graph. Explain why.

ONLINE BIOLOGY Go to the chapter Resource Center at **ClassZone.com** for additional resources and information on selective pressures.

Answers

A Apply stabilizing selection toward bluish brown coloring in males

Assess and Reteach ▼

Assess Use the Online Quiz or Section Quiz (*Assessment Book,* p. 212).

Reteach Have students draw graphs to illustrate directional, stabilizing, and disruptive selection. They should be able to explain how populations change as a result of the three types of natural selection.

11.2 ASSESSMENT

1. The phrase "distribution of traits" refers to the frequencies of the different phenotypes of a particular trait within a population.
2. Directional selection: natural selection favors phenotypes at one extreme; stabilizing selection: natural selection favors intermediate phenotypes; and disruptive selection: natural selection favors phenotypes at both extremes.
3. Selection could become directional in favor of medium-sized to large-sized galls.
4. Smaller fish may be able to survive longer and reproduce more often than larger fish that are being fished. Alleles for small body size could then become more common in the population, and over generations, smaller adult salmon could become more and more common in the population. This is natural selection.
5. Only two phenotypes are being plotted, not a continuous range of phenotypes.

INVESTIGATION

Time 45 minutes	TEACHER TESTED
Teacher Preparation	
Student Difficulty	
Lab Binder Evolution, pp. 17–20	

Purpose Model disruptive selection.

Overview Students model disruptive selection within a population of African swallowtails. They will

- model predation by randomly selecting among swallowtails and the poisonous butterflies they mimic
- observe changes in the numbers of different-colored swallowtails in the population over time

LAB PREPARATION

- Write *X* on three yellow and three red pieces of paper (poisonous butterflies).
- Write *ST* on the remaining two yellow and two red pieces, as well as on all five orange pieces (swallowtails).

LAB MANAGEMENT

- If students cannot draw six pieces of paper from the table without selecting a color that previously made them "sick," have them draw as many as they can.
- Sometimes students will not be able to draw any pieces of paper.
- Students should record in the table only the number of swallowtails *(ST)*, not poisonous butterflies *(X)*.

POST-LAB DISCUSSION

Students should observe that swallowtails that are adapted to mimic the colors of poisonous butterflies have a greater chance of survival. Because of this advantage, we often see mimicry that very closely matches both the pattern and the coloration of poisonous species.

MATERIALS

- 15 small pieces of colored paper: 5 yellow, 5 orange, 5 red (These have been premarked by your teacher.)
- extra paper of each color

PROCESS SKILLS

- **Modeling**
- **Graphing**
- **Interpreting Data**

B.8.5 Describe how due to genetic variations, environmental forces, and reproductive pressures, organisms with beneficial traits are more likely to survive, reproduce, and pass on their genetic information.

NOS.3 Clearly communicate their ideas and results of investigations verbally and in written form using tables, graphs, diagrams, and photographs.

Natural Selection in African Swallowtails

African swallowtails are nonpoisonous butterflies that mimic the colors of poisonous butterflies. Predators learn which butterflies are poisonous and avoid eating butterflies resembling those that made them sick. In this lab, you will use colored paper to model natural selection in African swallowtails.

PROBLEM How can natural selection change the distribution of a trait?

PROCEDURE

1. Divide your group into birds and butterflies. Birds, close your eyes. Butterflies, place the 15 pieces of paper randomly on the table with the markings face up.
2. The pieces of paper with an *X* written on them represent poisonous butterflies; those with *ST* represent swallowtails, which are not poisonous. Butterflies, record the number of swallowtails of each color in your notebook, using a table similar to Table 1.

TABLE 1. NUMBER OF SWALLOWTAILS (MIMICS) OF EACH COLOR

	Yellow	Orange	Red
Original population			
Trial 1			
Trial 2			
Trial 3			

3. Butterflies, flip the pieces of paper over and tell the birds to open their eyes.
4. Birds, draw up to 6 pieces of paper (total) from the table to represent predation. If you "ate" any poisonous butterflies, do not draw another piece of paper that color for the rest of the activity. (Note: You may not always be able to draw 6.)
5. Birds, close your eyes. Butterflies, repopulate by duplicating every piece of paper that remains. Write *X* and *ST* on the appropriate new pieces of paper.
6. Butterflies, record the number of swallowtails on the table.
7. Repeat steps 3–6 two more times to complete three trials.

ANALYZE AND CONCLUDE

1. **Graph Data** Draw a line graph with three lines, one for each color. Put the trial number on the *x*-axis (including the original population) and the number of swallowtails on the *y*-axis. What trends can you identify in the data?
2. **Graph Data** Draw two bar graphs: one for the original population and one for the last trial. Set up your graphs with color on the *x*-axis (yellow, orange, and red) and number of swallowtails on the *y*-axis. How do these graphs differ?
3. **Analyze** What type of distribution best describes the original population?
4. **Apply** What type of selection (directional, stabilizing, or disruptive) is demonstrated in this activity? What caused this type of selection to occur?
5. **Predict** Suppose the poisonous butterflies were all orange. What type of selection would have likely occurred in the swallowtail population?

Answers

Sample Data

For sample of student data and graphs, go to page R103.

Analyze and Conclude

1. Over three trials, orange swallowtails become less common; yellow swallowtails and red swallowtails greatly increase.
2. first bar graph: normal distribution; second bar graph: high frequencies at each end, low frequency in the middle
3. normal distribution
4. disruptive selection; Butterflies representing the extreme phenotypes (yellow and red) are selected for because their colors mimic those of poisonous butterflies. Orange butterflies become the favored prey.
5. stabilizing selection

11.3 Other Mechanisms of Evolution

KEY CONCEPT Natural selection is not the only mechanism through which populations evolve.

MAIN IDEAS
- Gene flow is the movement of alleles between populations.
- Genetic drift is a change in allele frequencies due to chance.
- Sexual selection occurs when certain traits increase mating success.

VOCABULARY
gene flow, p. 335
genetic drift, p. 336
bottleneck effect, p. 336
founder effect, p. 336
sexual selection, p. 338

Review
homozygous, heterozygous

Connect Have you ever wondered why many male birds, such as cardinals, are brightly colored while females of the same species are dull brown? Such bright coloring may not make sense in terms of natural selection, since the male birds are more likely to be seen by predators. However, natural selection is not the whole story. There are other factors that can lead to the evolution of populations.

MAIN IDEA

Gene flow is the movement of alleles between populations.

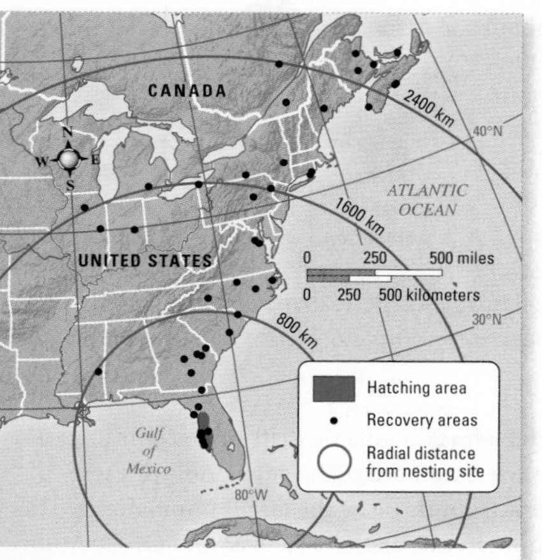

FIGURE 11.7 This map shows the locations where young banded eagles were found during the first summer after hatching.

Bird-banding studies have shown that certain birds leave their nesting areas once they are able to fly. As shown in **FIGURE 11.7**, bald eagles banded as nestlings have been tracked during the same summer more than 2500 kilometers away. These eagles have possibly joined a new population.

When an organism joins a new population and reproduces, its alleles become part of that population's gene pool. At the same time, these alleles are removed from the gene pool of its former population. The movement of alleles from one population to another is called **gene flow.** For many animals, gene flow occurs when individuals move between populations. Gene flow can occur in fungi and plant populations when spores or seeds are spread to new areas.

Gene flow increases the genetic variation of the receiving population. Gene flow between neighboring populations keeps their gene pools similar. However, the less gene flow that occurs between two populations, the more genetically different the two populations can become. A lack of gene flow also increases the chance that the two populations will evolve into different species.

A **Predict** **How does gene flow affect neighboring populations?**

Differentiated Instruction

ENGLISH LEARNERS

Have students use the technique of reciprocal teaching for this section. Assign students to small groups, with different members of each group taking responsibility to guide the discussion of different topics. Each topic leader first predicts what a selection is about by previewing the text, then uses questions to draw out information about the topic and identify any problems in understanding the material. Different members of the group alternate as topic leaders. Bring everyone back together to summarize.

Biology Toolkit, Reciprocal Teaching, p. C14

BELOW LEVEL

Have students set up a chart to compare and contrast different mechanisms of evolution. They should include natural selection, as well as gene flow, genetic drift, and sexual selection. Have them think about what causes the selection of certain genes and how that affects the gene pool of a population.

Biology Toolkit, Compare/Contrast Chart, p. C34

SECTION 11.3

Plan and Prepare

Objectives

- Explain how gene flow, genetic drift, and sexual selection can lead to the evolution of populations.

Section Resources

Unit Resource Book
Study Guide pp. 39–40
Power Notes p. 41
Reinforcement p. 42
Pre-AP Activity pp. 59–60

Interactive Reader Chapter 11
Spanish Study Guide pp. 113–114

Biology Toolkit pp. C14, C34, C40

Technology
Power Presentation 11.3
Media Gallery DVD
Online Quiz 11.3

Activate Prior Knowledge Have students think about how the human population in the United States has changed since 1776, when most settlers were of European origin. **Ask,** What effect has immigration had on the genetic variation of the U.S. population? Immigration from many different continents has increased the population's genetic variation by introducing new alleles to the gene pool.

Teach

TEACH FROM VISUALS

FIGURE 11.7 Direct students' attention to the map. **Ask,** With recovery areas in Maine, Michigan, Indiana, and Mississippi, which of these populations would you expect to have the most gene flow with the bald-eagle populations in Florida? Mississippi's populations

Answers

A **Predict** Gene flow between neighboring populations keeps their gene pools similar.

▼ Teach *continued*

ONLINE BIOLOGY Go to the chapter Resource Center at **ClassZone.com** for additional resources and information on mechanisms of evolution.

Vocabulary

Academic Vocabulary The word **founder** comes from the verb *found,* which means "to establish or set up." Remind students that those individuals who drafted the Constitution of the United States are referred to as the Founding Fathers.

Differentiate between the meaning of *found* and the past tense of *find* by using these examples:

My grandmother *founded* an organization that funds medical research.

I lost my watch last week but later *found* it under my bed.

Encourage students to think of the *founder effect* as the building of a new foundation for a population, in this case, from relatively few genetic resources.

Address Misconceptions

Common Misconception Genetic drift causes the bottleneck effect and founder effect.

Correcting the Misconception Genetic drift commonly occurs after processes such as a bottleneck or founder effects have resulted in a small population.

Take It Further

The **African cheetah** (*Acinonyx jubatus*) is endangered, in part, because of the population's extremely low **genetic variation.** A drastic reduction in the cheetah population about 10,000 years ago resulted in a bottleneck effect. The cause of this reduction is thought to be human beings widening their range and hunting the cheetahs. Because of low genetic variation, the cheetah population is not well equipped to resist disease or adapt to environmental changes.

MAIN IDEA

Genetic drift is a change in allele frequencies due to chance.

Imagine a patch of 100 flowers growing in a field. Fifty are white and fifty are purple. If you randomly pick flowers from this patch to create a bouquet, you would expect about half white and half purple flowers. The more flowers you randomly pick, the more likely you are to get these proportions. However, the fewer flowers you pick, the more likely you are to have a bouquet that is not representative of the patch. It might even be all one color.

VOCABULARY

Fixed means "not subject to change." If an allele increases to a frequency of 1.0 (100%), it is said to be fixed in the population.

A similar situation can occur in small populations. Small populations, like small sample sizes, are more likely to be affected by chance. Due to chance alone, some alleles will likely decrease in frequency and become eliminated. Other alleles will likely increase in frequency and become fixed. These changes in allele frequencies that are due to chance are called **genetic drift.** Genetic drift causes a loss of genetic diversity in a population.

Two processes commonly cause populations to become small enough for genetic drift to occur. Each of these processes results in a population with different allele frequencies than the original population.

Bottleneck Effect

The **bottleneck effect** is genetic drift that occurs after an event greatly reduces the size of a population. One example of the bottleneck effect is the overhunting of northern elephant seals during the 1800s. By the 1890s, the population was reduced to about 20 individuals. These 20 seals did not represent the genetic diversity of the original population. Since hunting has ended, the population has grown to over 100,000 individuals. However, it has very little genetic variation. Through genetic drift, certain alleles have become fixed while others have been lost completely from the gene pool.

VISUAL VOCAB

The **bottleneck effect** describes the effect of a destructive event that leaves only a few survivors in a population.

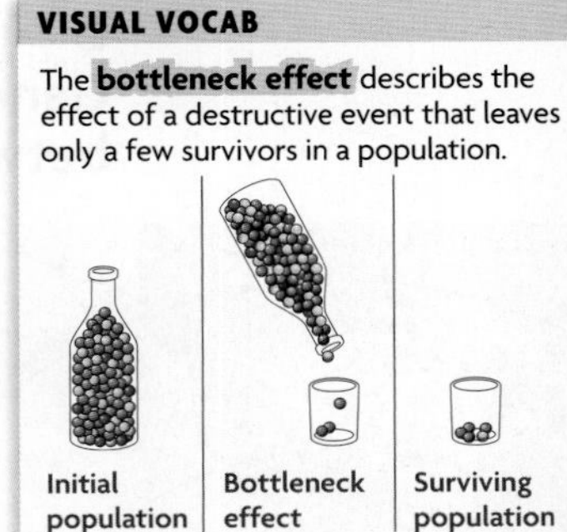

Founder Effect

As shown in **FIGURE 11.8**, the **founder effect** is genetic drift that occurs after a small number of individuals colonize a new area. The gene pools of these populations are often very different from those of the larger populations. The founder effect can be studied in human populations such as Old Order Amish communities. These communities were founded in North America by small numbers of migrants from Europe. For example, the Amish of Lancaster County, Pennsylvania, have a high rate of Ellis–van Creveld syndrome. Although this form of dwarfism is rare in other human populations, it has become common in this Amish population through genetic drift. Geneticists have traced this syndrome back to one of the community's founding couples.

Differentiated Instruction

HANDS-ON ACTIVITY

Have students model genetic drift in a small population by doing coin tosses. Working in pairs, have students state the results of their coin tosses for three flips of a coin. Some groups may see skewed ratios. Then continue on and record the results after ten flips of the coin. The results will probably shows that the more coin flips that are performed, the closer the ratio will be to 1:1. Use the early skewed ratios as an analogy to genetic drift occurring in a small population.

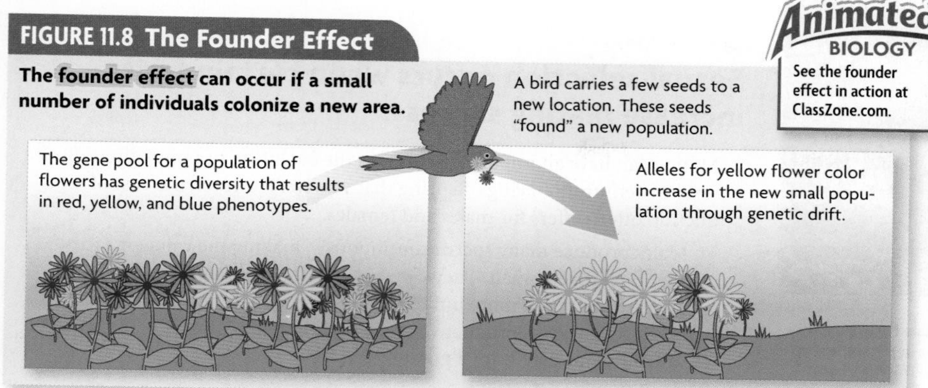

A bird carries a few seeds to a new location. These seeds "found" a new population.
The gene pool for a population of flowers has genetic diversity that results in red, yellow, and blue phenotypes.
Alleles for yellow flower color increase in the new small population through genetic drift.
Animated BIOLOGY
See the founder effect in action at ClassZone.com.

FIGURE 11.8 The Founder Effect

The founder effect can occur if a small number of individuals colonize a new area.

Effects of Genetic Drift

Genetic drift can cause several problems for populations. One problem is that the population loses genetic variation. With little genetic variation, a population is less likely to have some individuals that will be able to adapt to a changing environment. Another problem is that alleles that are lethal in homozygous individuals may be carried by heterozygous individuals, and become more common in the gene pool due to chance alone.

A Apply **Why is genetic drift more likely to occur in smaller populations?**

QUICK LAB **MODELING** NOS.6

Genetic Drift

Use a deck of cards to represent a population of island birds. The four suits represent different alleles for tail shape. The allele frequencies in the original population are 25% spade, 25% heart, 25% club, and 25% diamond tail shapes.

PROBLEM How does genetic drift occur?

MATERIALS
- deck of cards

PROCEDURE

1. Shuffle the cards and hold the deck face down. Turn over 40 cards to represent the alleles of 20 offspring produced by random matings in the initial population.
2. Separate the 40 cards by suit. Find the allele frequencies for the offspring by calculating the percentage of each suit.
3. Suppose a storm blows a few birds to another island. They are isolated on this island and start a new population. Reshuffle the deck and draw 10 cards to represent the alleles of five offspring produced in the smaller population.
4. Repeat step 2 to calculate the resulting allele frequencies.

ANALYZE AND CONCLUDE

1. **Analyze** Compare the original allele frequencies to those calculated in steps 2 and 4. How did they change?
2. **Analyze** Did step 1 or 3 demonstrate genetic drift?
3. **Evaluate** Does this activity demonstrate evolution? Why or why not? Does it demonstrate natural selection? Explain.

PRE-AP

Have students use the examples of over-hunting of elephant seals and the occurrence of Ellis-van Creveld syndrome in the Amish population to produce a concept map that shows how the bottleneck and founder effects yield a small population in which genetic drift can occur.

Biology Toolkit, Concept Map, p. C40

Answers

A **Apply** Small populations are more likely to be affected by chance events, whereas in large populations, these effects tend to be "averaged out."

QUICK LAB

Time 15 minutes — TEACHER TESTED

Lab Binder Evolution, p. 25

Purpose Model how isolation of a small population can affect allele frequency.

LAB MANAGEMENT

Realize that students may not see the purpose of what they are doing right away. **Ask,** In step 3, what effect are you modeling? founder effect

Inclusion Pair students who have visual impairments with partners. Have the partners call out the suit of the cards as they are drawn so that the students with visual impairments can complete the lab.

Sample Data

Trial 1

Diamond	Heart	Club	Spade
10	13	9	8
25%	32.5%	22.5%	20%

Trial 2

Diamond	Heart	Club	Spade
3	3	2	2
30%	30%	20%	20%

Analyze and Conclude

1. Answers will vary.
2. After either step 1 or 3, if the allele frequencies differ from the original distribution of 25 percent each, then genetic drift has occurred. It is more likely in step 3 because the population is smaller.
3. The activity demonstrates evolution because it shows how the allele frequencies in a population can change. The activity does not demonstrate natural selection, because changes in allele frequencies were due to chance alone.

▼ Teach *continued*

Vocabulary

Academic Vocabulary Point out the word **investment** used in the context of reproduction. Typically, an investment is a commitment of money in hope of a future return. In biology, the sperm and eggs of sexually reproducing organisms also represent an investment. In many species, males produce millions of sperm, while females produce a far smaller number of eggs. The male's *investment* in mating is far less than the female's. The difference helps to explain why competitive courtship behaviors are more common in males than in females, even when females are more numerous: sperm still vastly outnumber eggs.

Answers

A Apply An exaggerated trait would be advantageous if females associated the trait with "quality" and preferentially mated with such males. This trait and the female's response trait would be passed on to offspring.

FIGURE 11.9 Male frigate birds inflate an air sac in their chest to attract females. This trait has evolved through sexual selection.

VOCABULARY

Intra is Latin for "within." Intrasexual selection occurs within one sex.

Inter is Latin for "between." Intersexual selection occurs between both sexes.

MAIN IDEA

Sexual selection occurs when certain traits increase mating success.

Mating can have an important effect on the evolution of populations. Both sexes benefit from having offspring that survive. However, the cost of reproduction often differs for males and females.

- Males produce many sperm continuously, making the value of each sperm relatively small. They can make many investments at little cost.
- Females are much more limited in the number of offspring they can produce in each reproductive cycle. Each investment they make is more valuable, and they want a good return.

In many species, this difference in reproductive cost makes females choosy about mates. **Sexual selection** occurs when certain traits increase mating success. There are two types of sexual selection:

- Intrasexual selection involves competition among males, such as the head-butting of bighorn sheep. Whoever wins the competition wins the female.
- Intersexual selection occurs when males display certain traits that attract the female, such as peacocks fanning out their tails.

Traits that increase mating success are not always adaptive for the survival of the individual. As shown in **FIGURE 11.9**, bright red air sacs likely make male frigate birds very easy to spot by predators. How could such an exaggerated trait evolve?

Research has shown that some showy traits may be linked with genes for good health and fertility. Other traits are present in males that can offer better care for offspring or defense from predators. Therefore, females may use showy traits as signs of quality and health in males. These traits, such as the red air sacs of male frigate birds, can become very exaggerated over time through sexual selection.

A Apply Male Irish elks, which are now extinct, had 12-foot-wide antlers. Describe how sexual selection could have caused such an exaggerated trait to evolve.

11.3 ASSESSMENT

ONLINE QUIZ ClassZone.com

REVIEWING MAIN IDEAS

1. How does **gene flow** affect neighboring populations?
2. Name two processes through which **genetic drift** can occur.
3. How does **sexual selection** occur?

CRITICAL THINKING

4. **Analyze** Would a population of 10 individuals or 100 individuals be more vulnerable to genetic drift? Why?
5. **Infer** What impact can the **bottleneck effect** have on populations that have rebounded after near extinction?

***Connecting* CONCEPTS**

6. **Genetics** Ellis–van Creveld syndrome is a recessive trait. Explain why it has become common in the Amish of Lancaster County while remaining very rare in other human populations.

▼ Assess and Reteach

Assess Use the Online Quiz or Section Quiz (*Assessment Book*, p. 213).

Reteach Start with a population of imaginary animals and have students use the vocabulary in this section to describe different scenarios that cause the population to evolve.

11.3 ASSESSMENT

1. Gene flow decreases genetic diversity between neighboring populations.
2. bottleneck effect and founder effect
3. Certain male traits are favored by females when choosing a mate. Over time, the alleles associated with the preferred phenotype increase in the population.
4. A smaller population is more vulnerable to genetic drift because it has a smaller gene pool and is therefore more likely to be affected by chance events.
5. Bottleneck events can greatly reduce the size of a population, sometimes to only a few individuals. Such very small populations have little genetic variation, so even if the population rebounds, it will likely still have low genetic diversity.
6. Among the Amish founders, one couple carried the recessive allele for Ellis-van Creveld syndrome. Because marriages occurred primarily within the small Amish community, the frequency of the recessive allele increased within the gene pool over many generations. This increased the likelihood of a child getting two recessive alleles. Ellis-van Creveld syndrome is relatively rare in other populations because of the high frequency of dominant alleles in the larger gene pools.

NOS.1

DATA ANALYSIS ClassZone.com

Patterns in Sexual Selection

Identifying patterns in data from graphs and charts is essential for making future predictions and hypotheses.

EXAMPLE

The data in the graph below were collected during an experiment involving widowbirds in Kenya. The biologist was trying to determine the relationship between tail feather length and reproductive success in males of this species. The average number of nesting sites was used to measure reproductive success and was recorded for four groups of birds. Tail feathers were artificially shortened in one group, two groups were used as control groups, and tail feathers were artificially lengthened in the fourth group.

- Look at the bar representing the group with shortened tail feathers. Notice that this group averaged less than 0.5 nests.
- Next, notice that the bars for the two control groups show that these groups both averaged less than one nest.
- Now, look at the bar representing lengthened tail feathers. Notice that birds in this group averaged almost two nests.
- Finally, look for trends and patterns. The data show a trend that males with longer tail feathers have greater reproductive success: on average, they had more nesting sites.

GRAPH 1. TAIL FEATHER LENGTH AND REPRODUCTIVE SUCCESS

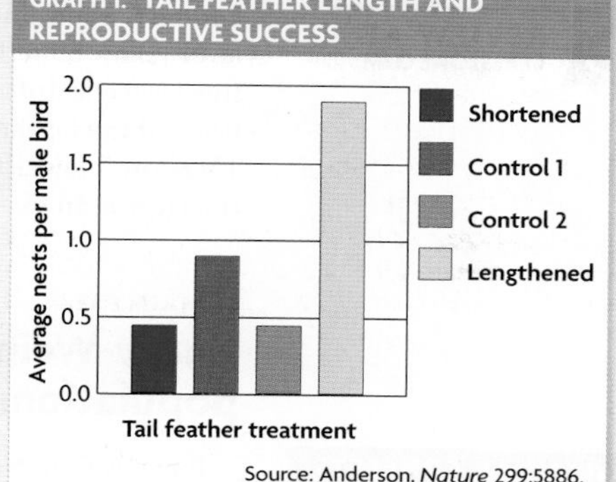

Source: Anderson, *Nature* 299:5886.

IDENTIFY PATTERNS

The graph at the right shows sexual selection patterns in guppies. Three experiments were run to determine if female guppies prefer males with specific tail sizes. In each experiment, female guppies were given the choice of two males to mate with, each having a different tail size: large versus small, large versus medium, and medium versus small.

1. **Analyze** What tail sizes were compared in each experiment?
2. **Analyze** What is the relationship between tail size in male guppies and female preference for mates?
3. **Infer** Why might the difference in preference be larger in Experiment 1 than in Experiment 2?

GRAPH 2. SEXUAL SELECTION IN GUPPIES

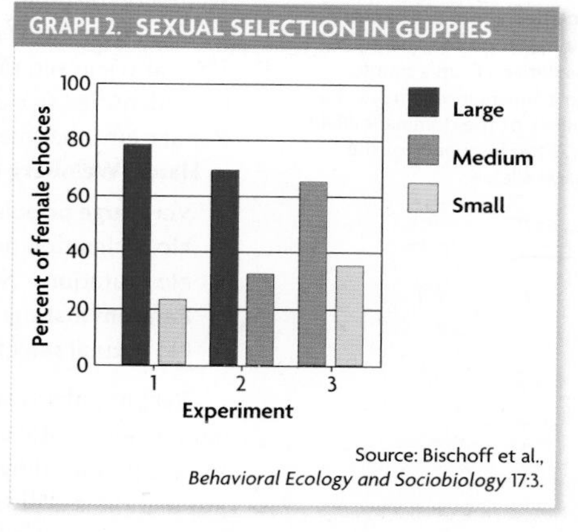

Source: Bischoff et al., *Behavioral Ecology and Sociobiology* 17:3.

Answers

1. Experiment 1: large and small; Experiment 2: large and medium; Experiment 3: medium and small
2. Female guppies prefer to mate with males that have larger tails.
3. The difference in the two tail sizes was greater in Experiment 1 (large vs. small) than in Experiment 2 (large vs. medium), meaning the female could more easily differentiate between her two choices in the first experiment.

DATA ANALYSIS

Introduce

Point out that in the widowbird experiment, the researchers made sure that the birds in the test groups had noticeably different tail lengths. **Ask,** Why didn't researchers simply choose birds with somewhat longer or shorter tails? By using birds that looked identical and then changing the tail length of some of them, researchers were able to control conditions to ensure that selection was in response to tail length.

Discuss

Make sure students focus on the trends in the data as displayed by the graphs. **Ask,** According to the data, what gives a male widowbird greater reproductive success? longer tail feathers What about the male guppy? larger tail

Take It Further

There is a communication element to sexual selection. The female response and the male display had to have coevolved for these traits to mean anything or be selected for. An Irish elk's huge antlers or a widowbird's long tail only mean something to potential mates if the females inherited the trait that makes them differentiate and value the male trait.

Sexual selection can arise because of a correlation between a display characteristic and a reproductive advantage. For example, a large-antlered elk might produce stronger, healthier offspring.

Unit Resource Book, Data Analysis, p. 55

SECTION 11.4

▼ Plan and Prepare

Objectives

- Identify the conditions that define Hardy-Weinberg equilibrium.
- Explain the predictive value of the Hardy-Weinberg equation.

Section Resources

Unit Resource Book Study Guide pp. 43–44 Power Notes p. 45 Reinforcement p. 46
Interactive Reader Chapter 11 **Spanish Study Guide** pp. 115–116
Biology Toolkit pp. C13, C18
Technology Power Presentation 11.4 Media Gallery DVD Online Quiz 11.4

Activate Prior Knowledge Discuss the idea of equilibrium. **Ask,** What does it mean to be in a state of equilibrium? Students may suggest it means a steady state, unchanging. Discuss equilibrium as being similar to an equation where values can be added or subtracted, but the result maintains equivalence.

11.4 Hardy-Weinberg Equilibrium

KEY CONCEPT Hardy-Weinberg equilibrium provides a framework for understanding how populations evolve.

MAIN IDEAS

- Hardy-Weinberg equilibrium describes populations that are not evolving.
- The Hardy-Weinberg equation is used to predict genotype frequencies in a population.
- There are five factors that can lead to evolution.

VOCABULARY

Hardy-Weinberg equilibrium, p. 340

Review

equilibrium, dominant, recessive, homozygous, heterozygous

REVIEW AT CLASSZONE.COM

Connect Many things affect how populations evolve. Natural selection may favor yellow butterflies over orange ones. But if a population of butterflies is small, genetic drift may also play a role. Studying populations in nature can be tricky. It can be hard to figure out what is causing a population to change. Therefore, biologists use models to learn more about how populations change over time.

MAIN IDEA

Hardy-Weinberg equilibrium describes populations that are not evolving.

Biologists often compare their data to a model to study how a population is changing. One important model is based on the research of a British mathematician named Godfrey Hardy and a German physician named Wilhelm Weinberg. In 1908, Hardy and Weinberg showed that genotype frequencies in a population stay the same over time as long as certain conditions are met. They also showed that these frequencies can be predicted. Hardy and Weinberg identified five conditions needed for a population to stay in equilibrium. Populations that meet these conditions are not evolving. They are said to be in **Hardy-Weinberg equilibrium.**

- **Very large population** No genetic drift can occur.
- **No emigration or immigration** No gene flow can occur.
- **No mutations** No new alleles can be added to the gene pool.
- **Random mating** No sexual selection can occur.
- **No natural selection** All traits must equally aid in survival.

Real populations rarely meet all five conditions. However, Hardy-Weinberg equilibrium is still a very important concept. Biologists can compare real data to data predicted by the model. Then they can learn more about how the population is evolving. The model also gives a framework for testing the factors that can lead to evolution.

Ⓐ Summarize **How are models used by population biologists?**

***Connecting* CONCEPTS**

Genetics The Hardy-Weinberg model and its equation are based on Mendelian genetics, which you learned about in **Chapter 6.** As you will soon see, the equation is derived from a simple Punnett square in which p is the frequency of the dominant allele and q is the frequency of the recessive allele.

	p	q
p	p^2	pq
q	pq	q^2

▼ Teach

Vocabulary

Academic Vocabulary Students will associate **immigration** and **emigration** with people who change citizenship and move to or from a country. In the study of populations and evolution, *immigration* refers to the flow of genes into a population, and *emigration* refers to the flow of genes out of a population. A good way to distinguish between the two: immigration begins with *i*, like *in;* emigration begins with *e*, like *exit*.

Answers

Ⓐ Summarize Population biologists compare real population data to a model to study how the population may be changing.

Differentiated Instruction

ENGLISH LEARNERS

Given the technical nature of the Hardy-Weinberg equilibrium, you might want to check students' comprehension as you discuss the material with the class. You can use signals such as thumbs up or thumbs down for comprehension, or a hand behind the ear to have students signal that they need to hear you repeat an explanation. Remember to periodically ask for feedback and scan the group for signals.

Biology Toolkit, Signals, p. C18

MAIN IDEA

The Hardy-Weinberg equation is used to predict genotype frequencies in a population.

For traits in simple dominant-recessive systems, biologists can predict genotype frequencies using the Hardy-Weinberg equation. Values predicted by the equation are those that would be present if the population is in equilibrium. If p equals the frequency of the dominant allele and q equals the frequency of the recessive allele, the equation can be written as follows:

$$p^2 + 2pq + q^2 = 1$$

Population biologists compare predicted genotype frequencies with actual frequencies. If they are the same, the population is in Hardy-Weinberg equilibrium for that trait. If the genetic data do not match the equation, the population is not in equilibrium; it is evolving.

FIGURE 11.10 Using the Hardy-Weinberg Equation

Use the Hardy-Weinberg equation to calculate predicted genotype frequencies for this population.

In a population of 1000 fish, 640 have forked tail fins and 360 have smooth tail fins. Tail fin shape is determined by two alleles: *T* is dominant for forked and *t* is recessive for smooth.

1 Find q^2, the frequency of smooth-finned fish (recessive homozygotes).

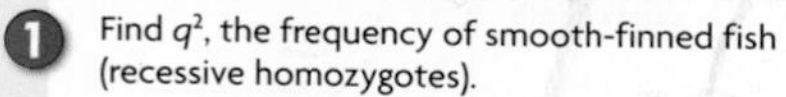

$$q^2 = \frac{\text{360 smooth-finned fish}}{\text{1000 fish in population}} = 0.36$$

2 To find the predicted value of q, take the square root of q^2.

$$q = \sqrt{0.36} = 0.6$$

3 Use the equation $p + q = 1$ to find the predicted value of p. Rearrange the equation to solve for p.

$$p = 1 - q$$
$$p = 1 - 0.6 = 0.4$$

These are the predicted allele frequencies: $p = 0.4$ and $q = 0.6$.

4 Calculate the predicted genotype frequencies from the predicted allele frequencies.

$p^2 = 0.4^2 = 0.16$ → 16% of fish have forked fins (*TT*)

$2pq = 2 \times (0.4) \times (0.6) = 0.48$ → 48% of fish have forked fins (*Tt*)

$q^2 = 0.6^2 = 0.36$ → 36% of fish have smooth fins (*tt*)

VARIABLES

p = frequency of allele *T* (dominant allele)

q = frequency of allele *t* (recessive allele)

p^2 = frequency of fish with *TT* (homozygous dominant genotype)

$2pq$ = frequency of fish with *Tt* (heterozygous genotype)

q^2 = frequency of fish with *tt* (homozygous recessive genotype)

A Analyze Through genetic analysis, scientists have found the genotype frequencies of the same fish population to be *TT* = 0.50, *Tt* = 0.14, *tt* = 0.36. What can you infer by comparing these data with the values predicted by the Hardy-Weinberg equation?

ONLINE BIOLOGY Students can study genetic drift in a population of fruit flies, using the Hardy-Weinberg equation. See Data Analysis Online in Options for Inquiry, page 353.

Integrating Medical Science

The **Hardy-Weinberg equation** may seem like something whose purpose is to prove the obvious: that evolution is occurring in most populations. However, the principles have practical value in population genetics and medicine. For example, researchers can apply the Hardy-Weinberg equation to a population to determine the prevalence of a recessive disease gene, such as **cystic fibrosis,** within a population. If scientists determine that 1 out of every 1700 Caucasian newborns is born with the disease, then they know that approximately 1 out of 21 Caucasians in the population is a carrier. It is important to stress that results of applying the Hardy-Weinberg equation to an evolving population (one that has genetic drift, sexual selection, and so on) are at best approximations.

TEACH FROM VISUALS

FIGURE 11.10 Before students follow the steps in solving the Hardy-Weinberg equation, have them review the variables listed in the chart. **Ask,** Why can't the frequency of fork-tailed fish be used to calculate p? Some fork-tailed fish have the heterozygous genotype. They carry both the dominant, forked-tail allele and the recessive, smooth-tail allele.

BELOW LEVEL

Draw a Punnett square on the board to show how the two alleles for tail fin shape in fish (*T* and *t*) result in two phenotypes (forked tail and smooth tail) but three genotypes (*TT*, *Tt*, and *tt*). Have students look at the Punnett square and discuss which genotype should be labeled with the following terms: heterozygous dominant, homozygous dominant, homozygous recessive. If students have difficulty distinguishing between these terms, point out the prefixes *homo-* and *hetero-*, and discuss what they mean.

PRE-AP

Provide students with a chance to work in pairs to predict genotype frequencies of a simple dominant-recessive system using the Hardy-Weinberg equation. Tell students that an earlier study of a population showed frequencies of 0.66, 0.31, and 0.03. Have students determine if the current population, with $p = 0.8$, has evolved. They should first get $q = 0.2$ by subtracting p from 1. The Hardy-Weinberg equation will show the population has evolved: 0.64, 0.32, 0.04.

Biology Toolkit, Think-Pair-Share, p. C13

Answers

A Analyze Because its genotype frequencies do not match those predicted by the Hardy-Weinberg equation, the fish population must be evolving.

▼ Teach *continued*

TEACH FROM VISUALS

FIGURE 11.11 Point out that the circle graphs show the relative frequencies of the different body-color alleles in the population, while each colored ball represents one allele. **Ask**

- What are the frequencies of the four different alleles in the initial population? 0.25 or 25% each
- Which of the factors led to a decrease in body-color variation in the population? genetic drift
- Which of the factors led to an increase in body-color variation in the population? mutation
- Which of the factors led to a change in the frequencies of different body colors in the population? all five factors

Take It Further

The fiber nylon was first synthesized in 1937. A type of bacterium has since evolved that feeds exclusively on nylon byproducts. The bacterium evolved as a result of a **frame-shift mutation** in a single gene, which produced a new protein that reacts with nylon products. The invention of nylon provided a niche for the new species of bacterium, but it was the mutation that enabled this species to diverge from another in the first place, similar to the example of bacteria that evolve to be resistant to antibiotics. Heavy use of antibiotics may pave the way for new strains or species of bacteria to arise, but without mutation, speciation and evolution cannot occur.

Answers

A Critical Viewing Accept any well-explained answer. For example, while sexual selection may increase blue alleles, natural selection may increase white alleles. This type of scenario can be seen in nature in many bird species. Brightly-colored males attract female mates, while female birds of the same species blend in with their surroundings, thereby avoiding predation and preserving their reproductive potential.

Animated BIOLOGY Explore the ways that populations can evolve at ClassZone.com.

FIGURE 11.11 Factors That Can Lead to Evolution

There are five factors that can lead to evolution at the population level.

INITIAL POPULATION

Here are the alleles associated with body color in a hypothetical population.

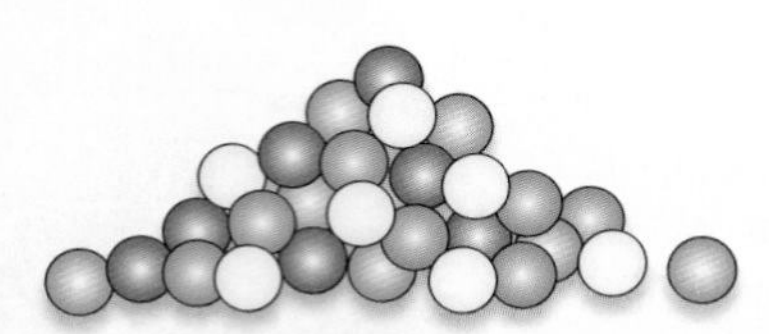

GENETIC DRIFT

After a bottleneck event, only orange and blue alleles remained in the small population. Through genetic drift, orange alleles increase in frequency.

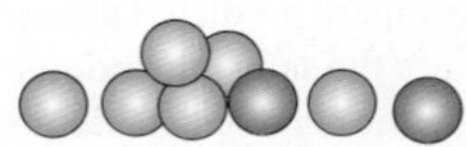

GENE FLOW

Green alleles increase in frequency because of immigration; orange alleles decrease in frequency because of emigration.

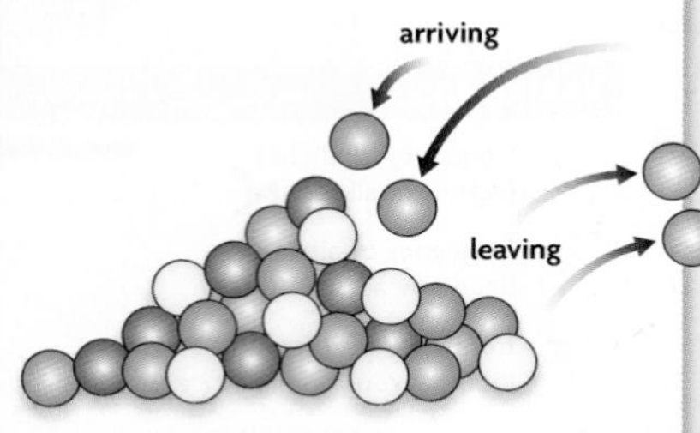

MUTATION

A new allele, associated with red body color, is formed through mutation. This could affect sexual selection if red body color improves mating success. It could affect natural selection if red body color increases the chance for survival.

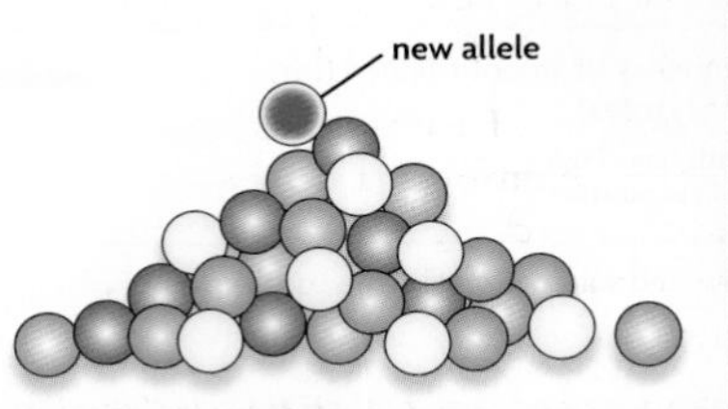

SEXUAL SELECTION

Blue alleles are associated with blue body color, which improves mating success. Blue alleles therefore increase in frequency.

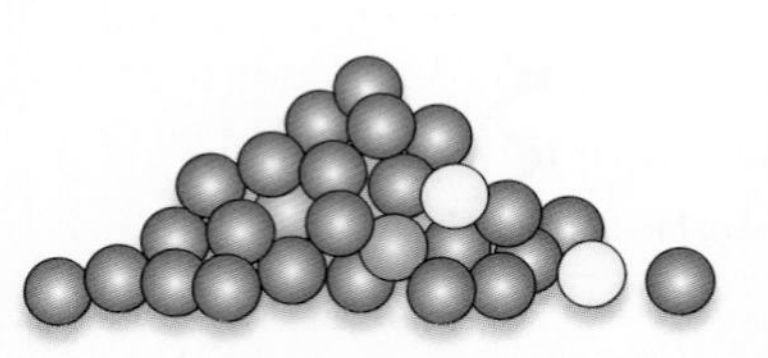

NATURAL SELECTION

White alleles are associated with white body color, which allows individuals to blend in with their environment and avoid predation. White alleles therefore increase in frequency.

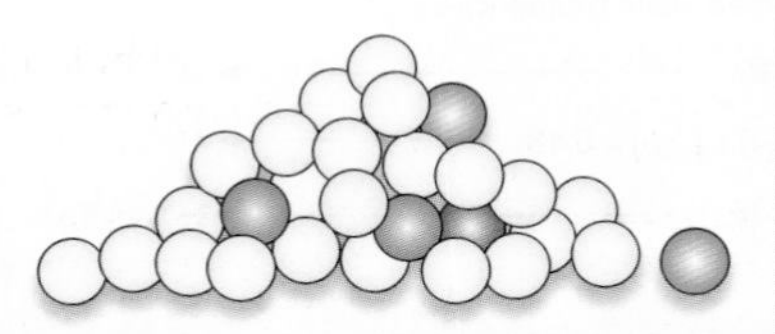

A CRITICAL VIEWING **Describe a scenario in which more than one factor could influence this population at the same time.**

Differentiated Instruction

HANDS-ON ACTIVITY

Have students work in groups with two sets of differently colored beads (about 50 of each color per group) to compare random changes in frequency to those brought about by natural (nonrandom) selection. Mix the beads together in a bowl, then have students randomly select ten beads to represent the initial population. One color will represent the value *p*, the other the value *q*. Have students create a data table for five rounds of selection, in which they record values for *p* and *q*.

With the initial population of ten established, have some groups remove three beads from this initial population at random (eyes covered). The other groups should, when possible, remove beads of just one color to model natural selection. The students should randomly select three replacements from the bowl and record the *p* and *q* values for the second round. Conduct at least five rounds before having students compare their results. You can have students compute the frequencies of each round and compare them to the Hardy-Weinberg equilibrium.

MAIN IDEA

There are five factors that can lead to evolution.

The conditions needed for Hardy-Weinberg equilibrium are not common in nature. Some parts of a population's environment may stay the same over time. However, other things will likely change. Perhaps a flood carries part of a population to a new place. This population may then go through genetic drift. A mutation may create a new allele that allows some individuals to run faster and get away from predators. The frequency of this allele may then increase in the gene pool as it is passed on to future generations.

In nature, populations evolve, or change in response to their environments. Populations that are not in Hardy-Weinberg equilibrium are evolving. In their studies, Hardy and Weinberg concluded that evolution should be expected in all populations almost all of the time. Their model shows that there are five factors that can lead to evolution. These factors are illustrated in **FIGURE 11.11.**

- **Genetic drift** Allele frequencies can change due to chance alone.
- **Gene flow** The movement of alleles from one population to another changes the allele frequencies in each population.
- **Mutation** New alleles can form through mutation. Mutations create the genetic variation needed for evolution.
- **Sexual selection** Certain traits may improve mating success. Alleles for these traits increase in frequency.
- **Natural selection** Certain traits may be an advantage for survival. Alleles for these traits increase in frequency.

Evolution is continuous. Environments are always changing, though often very slowly relative to a human's lifetime. Evolution is a response to these changes. As environments change, populations either adapt or go extinct. When a population becomes extinct, a different species can take its place, and the cycle continues.

Infer Why do real populations rarely reach Hardy-Weinberg equilibrium?

ONLINE BIOLOGY Go to the chapter Resource Center at **ClassZone.com** for additional resources and information on the Hardy-Weinberg equilibrium.

Answers

A Infer Real populations rarely reach the Hardy-Weinberg equilibrium because environments are constantly changing, which changes what traits are adaptive. Sexual selection in some species means mating is not random. Mutations and gene flow can occur, and not all populations are large enough to reach equilibrium.

Assess and Reteach ▼

Assess Use the Online Quiz or Section Quiz (*Assessment Book*, p. 214).

Reteach Use **FIGURE 11.11** to review the different factors that can lead to evolution in a population.

11.4 ASSESSMENT

ONLINE QUIZ ClassZone.com

REVIEWING MAIN IDEAS

1. What conditions are necessary for populations to remain in **Hardy-Weinberg equilibrium**?
2. What can be predicted using the Hardy-Weinberg equation?
3. What are the five factors that can lead to evolution?

CRITICAL THINKING

4. **Analyze** Why is phenotypic variation necessary for natural selection and sexual selection?
5. **Apply** Based on what you read in Section 11.3, is it likely that a population of peacocks would be in Hardy-Weinberg equilibrium? Why or why not?

Connecting CONCEPTS

6. **Genetics** How are the concepts of dominant, recessive, heterozygous, and homozygous related to the Hardy-Weinberg equation?

11.4 ASSESSMENT

1. very large population; no emigration or immigration; no mutations; random mating; no natural selection
2. genotype frequencies for a trait in a simple dominant-recessive system that is in equilibrium
3. genetic drift, gene flow, mutation, sexual selection, and natural selection
4. Individuals with advantageous phenotypes are better able to survive and/or reproduce. The alleles associated with these phenotypes may then become more common in the population.
5. no, because females are selecting males as mates based on the size of their tails, meaning sexual selection is occurring
6. In a simple dominant-recessive system, there are two homozygous genotypes (dominant-dominant; recessive-recessive) and one heterozygous genotype (dominant-recessive). One can calculate the frequency of these genotypes using the Hardy-Weinberg equation.

SECTION 11.5

▼ Plan and Prepare

Objectives

- Explain how isolation of populations can lead to speciation.
- Describe how populations can become isolated.

Section Resources

Unit Resource Book Study Guide pp. 47–48 Power Notes p. 49 Reinforcement p. 50
Interactive Reader Chapter 11 **Spanish Study Guide** pp. 117–118
Biology Toolkit pp. C15, C19, C30, C38
Technology Power Presentation 11.5 Media Gallery DVD Online Quiz 11.5

Activate Prior Knowledge Have students think about the potential for speciation in dog breeds. **Ask**

- How do we know that a three-foot-tall Irish wolfhound and a six-inch-high Chihuahua are the same species? capable of mating and producing fertile offspring
- At what point would the two breeds become separate species? unable to mate or produce fertile offspring Tell students that at that point, speciation has occurred.

▼ Teach

Science Trivia

- The common fruit fly, *Drosophila melanogaster,* is one of 900 fruit fly species.
- It has an estimated 13,600 genes on four chromosomes and over 3000 known mutations.
- It takes 11 days for a fertilized egg to develop into an adult fly capable of reproducing.

11.5 Speciation Through Isolation

KEY CONCEPT New species can arise when populations are isolated.

MAIN IDEAS

- The isolation of populations can lead to speciation.
- Populations can become isolated in several ways.

VOCABULARY

reproductive isolation, p. 344
speciation, p. 344
behavioral isolation, p. 345
geographic isolation, p. 346
temporal isolation, p. 346

Connect You have learned that gene flow helps to keep neighboring populations similar. The more gene flow that exists between populations, the more similar the populations will be. However, the less gene flow there is between two populations, the more likely the two populations are to become different. What happens if no gene flow occurs between two populations? This is one way that new species can arise.

MAIN IDEA

The isolation of populations can lead to speciation.

If gene flow between two populations stops for any reason, the populations are said to be isolated. As these populations adapt to their environments, their gene pools may change. Random processes like mutation and genetic drift can also change gene pools. All of these changes add up over many generations. With time, isolated populations become more and more genetically different. Members of the two populations may also begin to look and behave differently from one another.

Reproductive isolation occurs when members of different populations can no longer mate successfully with one another. Sometimes members of the two populations are not physically able to mate with each other. In other cases, they cannot produce offspring that survive and reproduce. Reproductive isolation between populations is the final step of becoming separate species. The rise of two or more species from one existing species is called **speciation.**

FIGURE 11.12 illustrates a recent experiment that shows how one mutation can result in reproductive isolation. Scientists studied the *ds2* gene of fruit flies. This gene affects how well fruit flies can deal with cold temperatures. Fruit flies living in tropical areas, where competition for food is high, have a tropical allele. Fruit flies living in cooler regions, where competition for food is less, have a temperate allele. The *ds2* gene also affects chemical scents called pheromones. Fruit flies use these scents to attracts mates of their own species.

***Connecting* CONCEPTS**

Genetics Fruit flies (*Drosophila melanogaster*) are very common in genetic research, as you may recall from **Unit 3.** Their popularity is based on several factors: they are easy to breed, they are common, and they have well understood genetic structures.

Differentiated Instruction

ENGLISH LEARNERS

Have students form into home groups of three and number off. Make all 1's responsible for the concept of behavioral isolation, 2's for geographic isolation, and 3's for temporal isolation. Ask each student to start a cluster diagram with the key concept of the section. Have students form into "expert" groups to complete their part of the cluster diagram and then return to the home group to construct a complete version.

Biology Toolkit, Jigsaw Reading, p. C15; Cluster Diagram, p. C30

FIGURE 11.12 Reproductive Isolation

Reproductive isolation occurs when members of isolated populations are no longer able to mate with each other successfully.

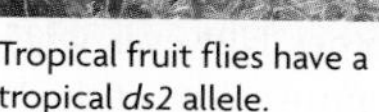

Tropical fruit flies have a tropical *ds2* allele.

Temperate fruit flies have a temperate *ds2* allele.

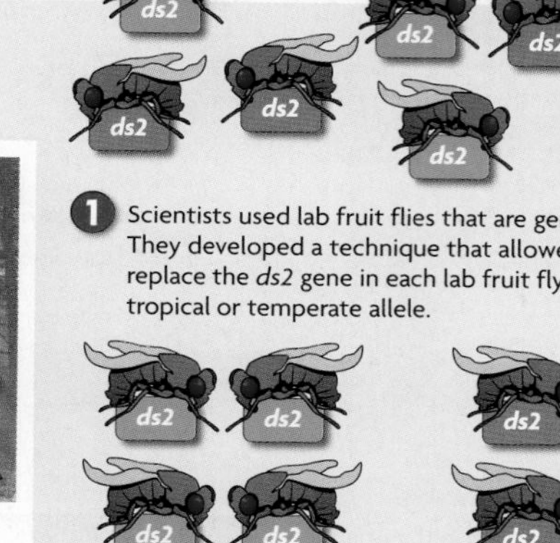

1. Scientists used lab fruit flies that are genetically similar. They developed a technique that allowed them to replace the *ds2* gene in each lab fruit fly with either the tropical or temperate allele.

2. Laboratory males that received the tropical allele were attracted to females that received the tropical allele. Males that received the temperate allele were attracted to females that received the temperate allele.

A **Synthesize** **Explain why fruit flies with a specific *ds2* allele prefer to mate with fruit flies with the same allele.**

This experiment shows how speciation may have occurred in natural fruit fly populations. Fruit flies migrating north from Africa to areas where there is less competition for food faced colder temperatures. A mutation in the *ds2* gene may have produced the temperate allele. This allele allows fruit flies to survive in cooler climates. Because the *ds2* gene also affects pheromones, mating behaviors changed. Fruit flies with the temperate allele and fruit flies with the tropical allele mated together less and less often. Eventually, these populations became reproductively isolated.

B **Summarize** **Why is reproductive isolation considered to be the final stage in speciation?**

MAIN IDEA

Populations can become isolated in several ways.

Several kinds of barriers can prevent mating between populations, leading to reproductive isolation. These include behavioral, geographic, and temporal barriers.

Behavioral Barriers

Chemical scents, courtship dances of birds, and courtship songs of frogs are sexual signals used to attract mates. Changes in these signals can prevent mating between populations. **Behavioral isolation** is isolation caused by differences in courtship or mating behaviors. Over 2000 species of fireflies are isolated in this way. Male and female fireflies produce patterns of flashes that attract mates of their own species. For example, *Photuris frontalis* emits one flash every second, *P. hebes* emits one flash every 2 seconds, and *P. fairchildi* produces a double flash every 5.5 seconds.

BELOW LEVEL

Have students use sequence diagrams to summarize how behavioral, geographic, and temporal isolation can lead to reproductive isolation and speciation.

Biology Toolkit, Sequence Diagram, p. C38

PRE-AP

Tell students that when the Isthmus of Panama formed about three million years ago, it separated the Pacific Ocean and Caribbean Sea between the two. The Panama Canal has reestablished a connection. Have students write a few paragraphs addressing the question of whether the long-isolated marine species could possibly interbreed if they were to migrate from one body of water to the other.

Biology Toolkit, Quick-Write, p. C19

TEACH FROM VISUALS

FIGURE 11.12 Have students read the captions. **Ask**

- Why didn't the scientists bring together flies from the original locations? wanted to be sure the flies would mate
- What type of isolation produced populations of tropical and temperate flies? geographic
- What type of isolation kept lab flies from mating? behavioral

Take It Further

When the two different *ds2* alleles became selected for in the different climates, mating behaviors were also affected. This is because the *ds2* gene codes for both temperature tolerance and mating behaviors. The two populations of fruit flies were first geographically isolated. Then, because of how the allele mutation affected mating behaviors, they became reproductively isolated.

Vocabulary

Word Origins A **pheromone** is a chemical secreted by an organism that affects others of the same species, often for the purpose of attracting a mate. The Greek root is *pherein,* meaning "to carry." Students may better remember what *pheromone* means if they think of the word **ferry,** which also means "to carry" and is derived from the Middle English word *ferein*—probably derived from the same Greek root.

Answers

A **Synthesize** Fruit flies with the temperate *ds2* allele produce a specific pheromone that only attracts mates that have the same *ds2* allele. The same is true for the tropical *ds2* allele.

B **Summarize** When populations can no longer mate successfully with one another, they are considered to be separate species. Until this occurs, other forms of isolation can be overcome as long as the two populations can still interbreed and have healthy, fertile offspring.

▼ Teach *continued*

TEACH FROM VISUALS

FIGURE 11.13 Have students find the Isthmus of Panama on the map. Tell them the isthmus formed about three million years ago from the shifting of Earth's tectonic plates. **Ask**

- How did the formation of the isthmus affect marine species? became geographically isolated
- How did the formation of the isthmus affect the land species of North and South America? Populations were no longer geographically isolated.
- What might it mean for marine species that there is now a canal connecting the Caribbean Sea and the Pacific Ocean? Some species may be able to migrate.

Answers

A Compare and Contrast Behavioral isolation involves differences in courtship or mating behaviors; temporal isolation involves differences in the *timing* of courtship or mating behaviors.

▼ Assess and Reteach

Assess Use the Online Quiz or Section Quiz (*Assessment Book,* p. 215).

Reteach Give students hypothetical examples of populations becoming isolated. Have them identify the type of isolation each example illustrates.

FIGURE 11.13 GEOGRAPHIC BARRIER

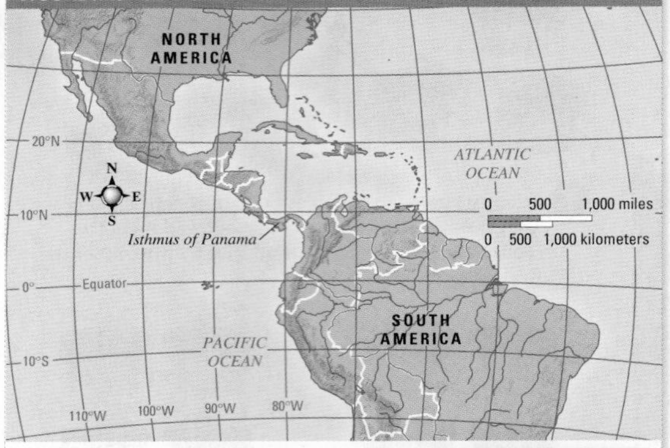

NORTH AMERICA
ATLANTIC OCEAN
Isthmus of Panama
PACIFIC OCEAN
SOUTH AMERICA
Equator
20°N
10°N
0°
10°S
110°W 100°W 90°W 80°W
0 500 1,000 miles
0 500 1,000 kilometers

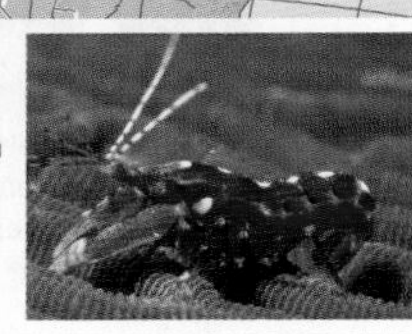

Although snapping shrimp in the Atlantic and Pacific oceans look similar, they are distinct species that have evolved through geographic isolation.

Geographic Barriers

The most commonly studied type of isolation is geographic isolation. **Geographic isolation** involves physical barriers that divide a population into two or more groups. These barriers can include rivers, mountains, and dried lakebeds. As shown in **FIGURE 11.13**, the formation of the Isthmus of Panama created a barrier for many marine species. Marine organisms could no longer easily cross between the Atlantic and Pacific oceans. Over time, the isolated populations became genetically different. Several species of snapping shrimp have evolved through geographic isolation. These species appear almost identical to one another. However, when males and females from opposite sides of the isthmus are placed together, they snap at each other instead of courting. Because they will no longer mate, these shrimp are classified as different species.

VOCABULARY

Temporal comes from the Latin word *tempus*, meaning "time."

Temporal Barriers

Barriers can also involve timing. **Temporal isolation** exists when timing prevents reproduction between populations. Some members of a population may show signs of courtship at different times if there is a lot of competition for mates. Reproductive periods may change to a different time of the year or a different part of the day. These differences in timing can lead to speciation. For example, two tree species that grow on the Monterey peninsula in California are very closely related. However, they have different pollination periods. The Monterey pine sheds its pollen in February, while the Bishop pine sheds its pollen in April. These pine species have likely evolved through temporal isolation.

To learn more about speciation, visit scilinks.org.
Keycode: MLB011

A Compare and Contrast What are the differences and similarities between behavioral isolation and temporal isolation?

11.5 ASSESSMENT

ONLINE QUIZ ClassZone.com

REVIEWING MAIN IDEAS

1. How can **reproductive isolation** lead to **speciation**?
2. What are three types of barriers that can lead to reproductive isolation?

CRITICAL THINKING

3. **Apply** Why are the flash patterns of fireflies considered to be **behavioral isolation**?
4. **Synthesize** How did **geographic isolation** affect the diversity Darwin observed in Galápagos finches?

Connecting CONCEPTS

5. **Scientific Process** What could have been used as a control group in the fruit fly experiment described on page 345?

11.5 ASSESSMENT

1. If populations cannot mate successfully with one another, genetic differences may accumulate in the populations. Over time, the populations may become so different that they become different species.
2. behavioral barriers, geographic barriers, and temporal barriers
3. The flash-pattern mating behaviors of fireflies are not related to the timing of mating, so this is considered behavioral isolation rather than temporal isolation.
4. The geographic isolation of the finches on different islands meant that each island's environment selected for traits that were beneficial on that particular island. Over time, genetic differences accumulated in the isolated populations, leading to many distinct finch species.
5. Flies bred in the laboratory with their original *ds2* genes could have been used as a control group, because they would not have received any kind of treatment. The effects of *ds2* insertions on the two treatment groups could have been compared against this group.

11.6 Patterns in Evolution

KEY CONCEPT Evolution occurs in patterns.

MAIN IDEAS

- Evolution through natural selection is not random.
- Species can shape each other over time.
- Species can become extinct.
- Speciation often occurs in patterns.

VOCABULARY

convergent evolution, p. 348
divergent evolution, p. 348
coevolution, p. 349
extinction, p. 350
punctuated equilibrium, p. 351
adaptive radiation, p. 351

Connect Even before the process of speciation is complete, individuals of an emerging new species are under pressure to survive. Adaptive traits are preserved in a population through natural selection. However, sudden changes in the environment can end the existence of a species. The rise and fall of species over time reveal clear evolutionary patterns.

MAIN IDEA

Evolution through natural selection is not random.

In science, the terms *chance* and *random* relate to how easily an outcome can be predicted. Because mutations and genetic drift cannot be predicted, they are called random events. These random events are sources of genetic diversity. However, natural selection, which acts on this diversity, is not random. Individuals with traits that are better adapted for their environment have a better chance of surviving and reproducing than do individuals without these traits.

You have learned about directional, stabilizing, and disruptive selection. In each of these modes of selection, the effects of natural selection add up over many generations. In other words, natural selection pushes a population's traits in an advantageous direction. As you can see in **FIGURE 11.14**, alleles associated with these traits add up in the population's gene pool.

Remember, however, that having direction is not the same as having purpose or intent. The environment controls the direction taken by natural selection. When the environment changes, different traits may become advantageous. The response of species to environmental challenges and opportunities is not random.

FIGURE 11.14 PATTERNS IN NATURAL SELECTION

In this hypothetical population, green body color is favored by natural selection. With each generation, alleles associated with green body color increase in frequency. Over time, more and more individuals in the population will have the advantageous phenotype.

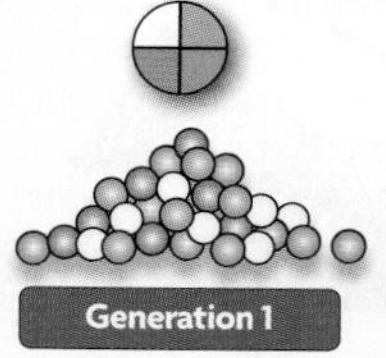

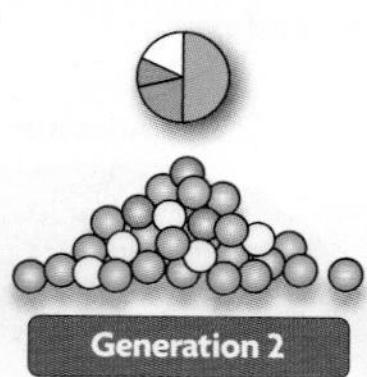

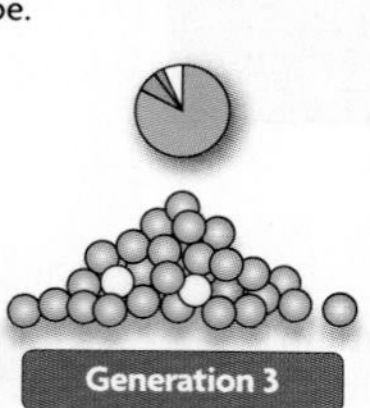

Differentiated Instruction

ENGLISH LEARNERS

Have students preview the section using the PLAN strategy: Predict, Locate, Add, and Note. Begin by having them read the Connect paragraph at the beginning of the section. Students should make a prediction about each main idea and how it relates to the vocabulary and the black headings in that part of the text (locate). Then they are ready to read the section, adding details and noting how the material describes patterns in both types and rates of evolution.

Biology Toolkit, PLAN, p. C7

BELOW LEVEL

Have a brainstorming session in which students develop a cluster diagram for the central idea that evolution occurs in patterns. Focus on patterns of evolution, including adaptive radiation. Have students include what is happening at the genetic level.

Biology Toolkit, Brainstorming, p. C11; Cluster Diagram, p. C30

SECTION 11.6

Plan and Prepare

Objectives

- Describe different types and rates of evolution.
- Compare different types and rates of extinction.

Section Resources

Unit Resource Book
Study Guide pp. 51–52
Power Notes p. 53
Reinforcement p. 54

Interactive Reader Chapter 11
Spanish Study Guide pp. 119–120

Biology Toolkit pp. C7, C11, C19, C30, C31, C38

Technology
Power Presentation 11.6
Media Gallery DVD
Online Quiz 11.6

Activate Prior Knowledge Make a list of organisms and their adaptations. **Ask,** What are some different adaptations in plants and animals that seem to relate directly to features of their environment? *Sample Answers:* heavy fur and layers of fat for warmth, camouflage for protection, food-pollen exchange between birds or insects and particular flowers Encourage students to distinguish between examples of divergent and convergent evolution based on whether the plants or animals are likely to share genes. Also discuss coevolution.

Teach

TEACH FROM VISUALS

FIGURE 11.14 Use the diagram to distinguish between the random and selective aspects of evolution. **Ask**

- What aspect of the initial population is random? different alleles, produced by mutation
- What aspect of the initial population is not random? natural selection, in this case for the green allele

▼ Teach *continued*

ONLINE BIOLOGY Have students complete a WebQuest on divergent evolution occurring within two insect populations. See Options for Inquiry on page 352.

Vocabulary

Greek and Latin Word Origins The terms **convergent** and **divergent** share the Latin root *vergere,* which means "to bend."

The prefixes in the words provide a sense of the direction, with *convergent* meaning "to bend or come together" and *divergent* meaning "to bend away or separate."

It is important for students to remember that in coming together in **convergent evolution,** populations had to start far apart. Have students associate *con-* with "come together." Populations come to have similar characteristics despite the lack of a close common ancestor: similar characteristics, dissimilar genes.

The opposite is true in **divergent evolution.** Have students associate *divergent* with *divide.* These populations start close together, but move apart: dissimilar characteristics, similar genes.

Answers

A Infer The shells of turtles and snails are examples of convergent evolution. Turtles and snails do not share a recent common ancestor. (Turtles are vertebrate reptiles, and snails are invertebrate mollusks.) The shells evolved as a means of protection from predators.

B Analyze In convergent evolution, a similar trait in unrelated species is selected for because of a common benefit the trait provides in a given environment. In divergent evolution, closely related species that are in different environments increasingly adapt to those differences with traits that are advantageous for survival in their different environments.

Convergent Evolution

Different species often must adapt to similar environments. Evolution toward similar characteristics in unrelated species is called **convergent evolution.** Analogous structures, such as wings on birds and insects, are common examples of convergent evolution. Another example is the tail fin of fish and marine mammals, as shown in **FIGURE 11.15.** Sharks, which are fish, and dolphins, which are mammals, are separated by about 300 million years of evolution. Separately, they have both evolved similar tail fins to propel themselves through the water. However, the tail fins of sharks and other fish are vertical, while those of dolphins are horizontal.

Divergent Evolution

When closely related species evolve in different directions, they become increasingly different through **divergent evolution.** The evolution of the red fox and the kit fox is an example of this trend. Though closely related, the two species have different appearances that have resulted from adapting to different environments. The red fox lives in temperate regions, usually in forests. Its dark reddish coat helps it to hide from predators. The sandy-colored coat of the kit fox allows it to blend in with its desert surroundings. Kit foxes also have large ears relative to their body size. This adaptation helps them to keep cool in the desert heat.

A Infer Are the shells of turtles and snails examples of convergent or divergent evolution? Explain.

FIGURE 11.15 Convergent and Divergent Evolution

Natural selection is not random. It can have direction, and its effects are cumulative through generations.

CONVERGENT EVOLUTION

Dolphins, which are mammals, and sharks, which are fish, have evolved similar tail fins, as each has adapted to similar environmental conditions.

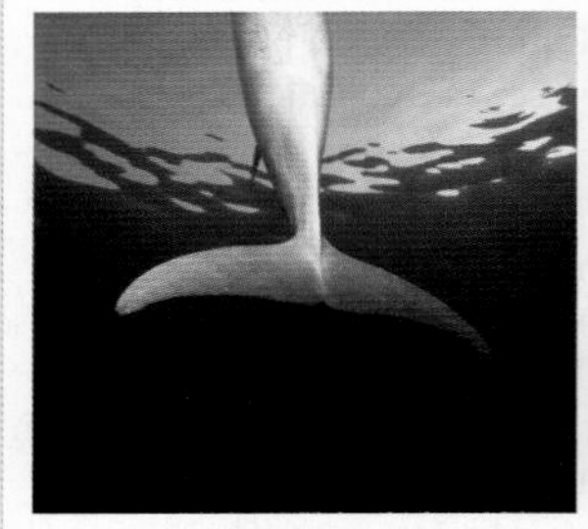

Dolphin

Shark

DIVERGENT EVOLUTION

The kit fox and red fox evolved from a common ancestor while adapting to different environments.

Kit fox

Red fox

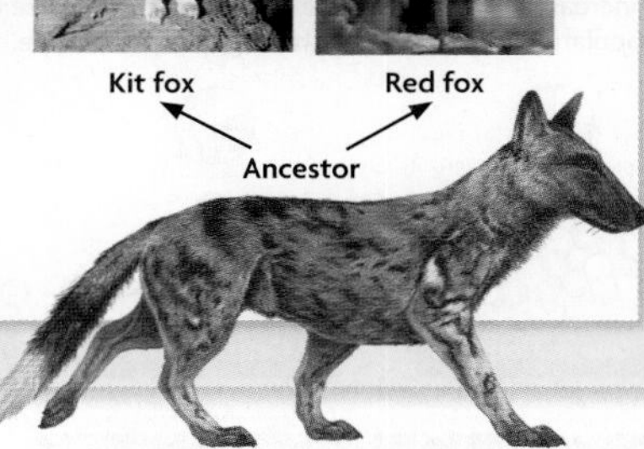

Ancestor

B Analyze How do convergent and divergent evolution illustrate the directional nature of natural selection?

Differentiated Instruction

TEACH WITH TECHNOLOGY

Create a PowerPoint presentation of images that convey different patterns in evolution. Build on the examples used in **FIGURE 11.15.**

Tail Fins Compare the various tail fins that have evolved through convergence and divergence in marine species. Thresher sharks have long, scythelike tails that are quite unlike those of their relatives, such as the mako or great white shark. In fact, the tails of the mako and great white sharks are more similar to those of tunas and billfishes—which are more distantly related than the thresher sharks.

Fur Color, Ear Size Compare the different coloration in fur and relative ear size in different species of fox, such as the kit fox, red fox, arctic fox, and fennec. Discuss how traits in these closely related species have diverged in response to different environments. The light brown fur of the fennec enables it to blend in with the sands of its desert environment, while its large ears provide a large surface area to release body heat. The arctic fox has a white winter coat that allows it to blend in with the snow, and small ears to limit heat loss.

MAIN IDEA

Species can shape each other over time.

Species interact with each other in many different ways. For example, they may compete for the same food source or be involved in a predator-prey relationship. Most of these interactions do not involve evolutionary changes. However, sometimes the evolutionary paths of two species become connected.

Beneficial Relationships Through Coevolution

The bull-thorn acacia is a plant species with branches covered in hollow thorns. Although the thorns protect the plant from being eaten by large animals, small herbivores such as caterpillars can fit between them. To the rescue comes *Pseudomyrmex ferrugineus,* a species of stinging ants. As shown in **FIGURE 11.16**, these ants live inside the thorns and feed on the plant's nectar. The ants protect the plant by stinging animals that try to eat the leaves.

Although this relationship may seem to be a simple cooperation between two species, it is much more than that. The acacia and the ants share an evolutionary history. The hollow thorns and nectar-producing leaves of the acacia and the stinging of the ants have evolved due to the relationship between the two species. Close relatives of these species that are not involved in this type of relationship do not have these traits. Such specialized relationships form through coevolution. **Coevolution** is the process in which two or more species evolve in response to changes in each other.

FIGURE 11.16 The relationship between this ant and the acacia plant has developed through coevolution. The ant lives inside the hollow thorn and protects the acacia by stinging any potential predators.

Evolutionary Arms Races

Coevolution can also occur in competitive relationships. These interactions can lead to evolutionary arms races, in which each species responds to pressure from the other through better adaptations over many generations.

For example, many plants produce defense chemicals to discourage herbivores from eating them. Natural selection then favors herbivores that can overcome the effects of the chemicals. After many generations, most herbivores have some level of resistance and are again able to safely eat the plant. Natural selection then favors plants that have evolved even more potent chemicals. In another case, the thick shells and spines of murex snails are an adaptive response to predation by crabs. In turn, crabs have evolved powerful claws strong enough to crack the snails' shells.

A Predict **What do you think will happen in future generations of crabs and snails?**

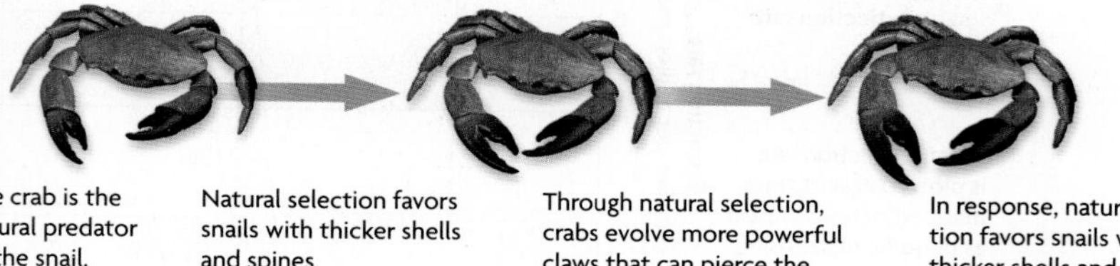

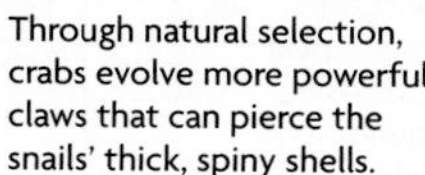

The crab is the natural predator of the snail.

Natural selection favors snails with thicker shells and spines.

Through natural selection, crabs evolve more powerful claws that can pierce the snails' thick, spiny shells.

In response, natural selection favors snails with even thicker shells and spines.

ONLINE BIOLOGY You can find additional resources and more information on coevolution in the chapter Resource Center at **ClassZone.com.**

Integrating Chemistry

Many plant species have evolved to produce chemicals whose sole purpose seems to be to make plants unpalatable to grazing herbivores. Some of these substances have, in fact, made the plants attractive to humans. These include **nicotine** from tobacco plants and **caffeine** from coffee plants.

Plants that belong to the mustard family produce **chemical deterrents** that keep most plant-eaters from feeding on their leaves. Among these substances are the oils used to make the condiments mustard and horseradish. In an evolutionary sense, these plants represent a ready source of food for any animal that could digest the oils. Certain species of bugs, beetles, and moths did evolve to take advantage of this unused food source.

ONLINE BIOLOGY The interactive animation provided in Options For Inquiry on page 353 looks at how populations of *Mycobacteruim tuberculosis* have changed in response to antibiotics. In this case, the arms race is between the bacteria that cause tuberculosis and the scientists who develop new drugs.

Answers

A Predict The history of competitive evolution between snails and crabs suggests that the shells of snails could continue to become thicker and spinier in response to the evolution of stronger claws in crabs. It is also possible that different mechanisms for protection and feeding could coevolve.

BELOW LEVEL

Have students trace the coevolution that occurs between the crab and snail populations by having them prepare a series of drawings similar to the photographs at the bottom of page 349. Students should alternate the crab and snail drawings, following the sequence of events described in the captions. Have students draw the crab claws noticeably bigger as they move through the sequence.

Biology Toolkit, Sequence Diagram, p. C38

PRE-AP

Have students recast the evolutionary arms race between the crab and snail species shown at the bottom of page 349 in terms of genes. Ask them to write one or two paragraphs describing the real winners and losers in this race: the alleles selected for in each species.

Biology Toolkit, Quick-Write, p. C19

▼ Teach *continued*

Science Trivia

The five largest mass-extinction events occurred at the ends of the Ordovician, Devonian, Permian, Triassic, and Cretaceous periods. One unit of measurement in extinctions is how many genera go extinct. (*Genera* is the plural form of *genus*, the taxonomic group just above species.)

- Terminal Ordovician event: ~ 443 million years ago, 57 percent of marine genera became extinct.
- Terminal Devonian event: ~ 359 million years ago, 57 percent of marine genera became extinct.
- Terminal Permian event: ~ 251 million years ago, 84 percent of marine genera and 70 percent of land species became extinct.
- Terminal Triassic event: ~ 199 million years ago, 52 percent of marine genera became extinct.
- Terminal Cretaceous event: ~ 65 million years ago, 47 percent of marine genera and 18 percent of land vertebrate families became extinct.

TEACH FROM VISUALS

FIGURE 11.18 Have students identify the mass extinction events on the graph and compare the scale of extinction. **Ask**

- What was the extinction rate 400 million years ago? about ten families per million years
- What does the blue dotted line represent? number of families that were going extinct per million years

Answers

A Compare and Contrast Background extinctions occur continuously, sometimes in a particular ecosystem or location, and they occur at low rate relative to those of mass extinctions. Mass extinctions, while rare, occur relatively suddenly and affect many species, often on a global level.

FIGURE 11.17 Native to Portugal and Spain, the Iberian lynx is the world's most endangered feline. The World Wildlife Federation estimates that there may be fewer than 200 individuals remaining in the wild.

MAIN IDEA

Species can become extinct.

Just as birth and death are natural events in the life of an individual, the rise and fall of species are natural processes of evolution. The elimination of a species from Earth is called **extinction.** Extinction often occurs when a species as a whole is unable to adapt to a change in its environment. Biologists divide extinction events into two categories—background extinctions and mass extinctions. Although they differ in degree, the effect of both is the same: the permanent loss of species from Earth.

Background Extinctions

Extinctions that occur continuously but at a very low rate are called background extinctions. They are part of the cycle of life on Earth. Background extinctions occur at roughly the same rate as speciation. Unlike catastrophic mass extinctions, background extinction events usually affect only one or a few species in a relatively small area, such as a rain forest or a mountain range. They can be caused by local changes in the environment, such as the introduction of a new predator species or a decrease in food supply. From a human perspective, such extinctions seem to occur randomly but at a fairly constant rate.

Mass Extinctions

Mass extinctions are much more rare than background extinctions. However, as illustrated in **FIGURE 11.18**, they are much more intense. These events often operate at the global level. Therefore, they destroy many species—even entire orders or families. Mass extinctions are thought to occur suddenly in geologic time, usually because of a catastrophic event such as an ice age or asteroid impact. The fossil record confirms that there have been at least five mass extinctions in the last 600 million years.

A Compare and Contrast **What are the differences and similarities between background extinctions and mass extinctions?**

FIGURE 11.18 EXTINCTION RATES THROUGH TIME

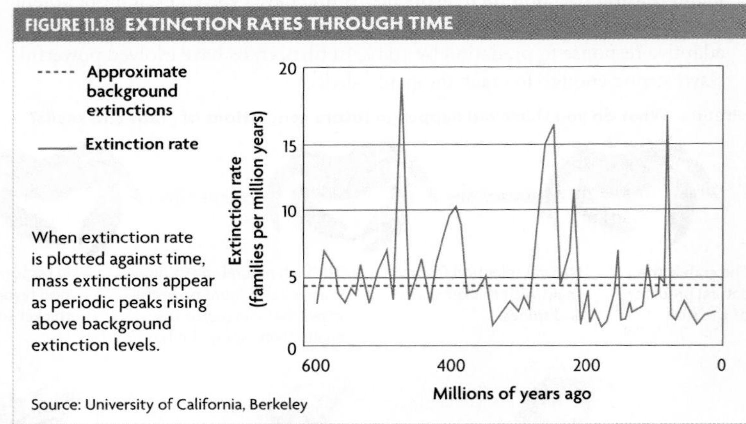

Differentiated Instruction

HANDS-ON ACTIVITY

Put together an extinction timeline with the class, using **Figure 11.18** as a starting point. Ask students to identify the time of extinction of a particular animal or plant that interests them. Encourage students to find not only examples from the distant past but also recent examples. These might include the passenger pigeon, dodo bird, mastodon, woolly mammoth, and Irish elk.

Biology Toolkit, Timeline, p. C31

MAIN IDEA

Speciation often occurs in patterns.

Paleontologists have long noticed a repeating pattern in the history of life, reflected in the fossil record. Bursts of evolutionary activity are followed by long periods of stability. This pattern is described by the theory of **punctuated equilibrium,** which states that episodes of speciation occur suddenly in geologic time and are followed by long periods of little evolutionary change. Niles Eldredge and Stephen Jay Gould originally proposed this theory in 1972. It was written as a revision of Darwin's idea that new species arise through gradual transformations of ancestral species.

The diversification of one ancestral species into many descendent species is called **adaptive radiation.** These descendent species are usually adapted to a wide range of environments. One example of adaptive radiation is the radiation of mammals following the mass extinction at the end of the Cretaceous period 65 million years ago.

VISUAL VOCAB

Adaptive radiation is the rapid evolution of many diverse species from ancestral species.

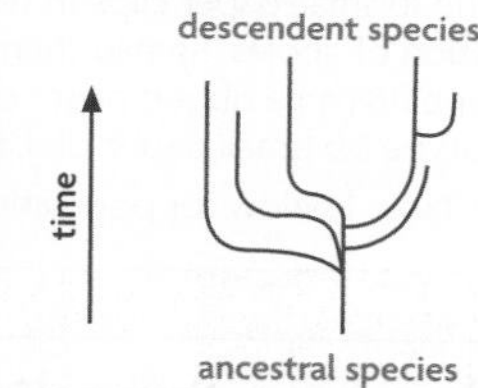

Although mammals had evolved for about 150 million years before the end of the Cretaceous period, they barely resembled the mammals we know today. The earliest mammals were tiny, usually insect eaters, and mostly nocturnal. These characteristics allowed them to coexist with the dinosaurs. The extinction of the dinosaurs left environments full of opportunities for other types of animals. In the first 10 million years following the dinosaurs' extinction, more than 4000 mammal species had evolved, including whales, bats, rodents, and primates.

Connecting CONCEPTS

Ecology Early mammals were able to coexist with dinosaurs because mammals and dinosaurs had different niches, or roles in the ecosystem. You will learn more about the concept of niches in **Chapter 14.**

A Synthesize The adaptive radiation of mammals followed the extinction of the dinosaurs. How do these events support the theory of punctuated equilibrium?

Vocabulary

Academic Vocabulary Students may first think of the word **radiation** as it relates to nuclear power, x-ray machines, or science fiction. In terms of evolution, *radiation* refers to organisms *radiating* out into new habitats and niches. As a result, new and distinct species evolve from a shared ancestor **(VISUAL VOCAB).** The roots of these words are Latin: *radius,* or "ray" and *radiät-,* or "to emit beams." Students may better remember the meaning of **adaptive radiation** if they think of how a radio emits signals that radiate outward.

Answers

A Synthesize When dinosaurs were dominant, most mammals were small, nocturnal insect-eaters. After the extinction of the dinosaurs, which left many niches empty, there was a period of sudden and rapid evolution of mammals, during which thousands of new and diverse species evolved and filled some of those niches.

11.6 ASSESSMENT

ONLINE QUIZ ClassZone.com

REVIEWING MAIN IDEAS

1. Explain what it means to say that natural selection is not random.
2. How does **coevolution** shape two species over time?
3. What are some of the causes of background and mass **extinctions**?
4. What pattern is described by the theory of **punctuated equilibrium**?

CRITICAL THINKING

5. **Synthesize** Defensive chemicals are usually found in unripe fruit but not in ripe fruit. In terms of coevolution, why might this be?
6. **Infer** If analogous structures are often examples of **convergent evolution,** what types of structures would likely be examples of **divergent evolution**?

Connecting CONCEPTS

7. **Human Biology** Through mutation, HIV can accumulate resistance to drugs developed for treatment. Describe the relationship between HIV and the humans who develop these drugs in terms of an evolutionary arms race.

Assess and Reteach

Assess Use the Online Quiz or Section Quiz (*Assessment Book,* p. 216).

Reteach Have students present an oral summary of the section content. Students should use the section heads to organize the content.

11.6 ASSESSMENT

1. Natural selection pushes a population's traits in an advantageous direction. There is nothing random about certain environmental conditions determining that some traits are beneficial, and therefore those traits become more common over time.
2. If two species share an evolutionary history, changes in one species can lead to changes in the other species, causing a continuous dynamic pattern.
3. background extinction: local changes in the environment, such as new predator species or a decrease in food supply; mass extinction: catastrophic events, such as an ice age
4. long periods of relatively little evolutionary change interspersed with sudden, rapid periods of speciation
5. Some fruit-eating animals act as seed dispersers for various plants. If the seeds are not ready for germination, it does the plant no good to have them dispersed by an animal. If the fruit is only edible when the seeds are ready to be dispersed, this greatly improves the chances of that plant having its genes passed on to offspring.
6. homologous structures
7. As humans develop new and improved drugs, some strains of HIV that are resistant to these drugs will have an advantage and will therefore become more common. Humans then must develop even more drugs, which leads to HIV evolving greater resistance, and so on.

OPTIONS FOR INQUIRY

INVESTIGATION

Time 45 minutes	TEACHER TESTED
Teacher Preparation	
Student Difficulty	
Lab Binder Evolution, pp. 21–22	

Purpose Observe whether a model population is evolving.

Overview Students model the predation of anole lizards over four generations. They will

- use different kinds of paper clips to represent different genotypes
- calculate and graph allele frequencies to determine whether each generation is in Hardy-Weinberg equilibrium

LAB PREPARATION

Use large paper clips to represent the large body size phenotype and rough and smooth textures to distinguish the two genotypes: *BB* and *Bb*, respectively.

LAB MANAGEMENT

A good ratio of paper clips to use is ten small: five large ribbed: five large smooth.

Teacher Note "I provide the frequency of several human genetic diseases and have students use the Hardy-Weinberg equation to predict allele frequencies."

Inclusion Use objects that are more visibly different and easily handled to represent different genotypes. For example, two vividly colored large markers and one skinnier one.

POST-LAB DISCUSSION

Discuss why the two alleles for body size would change in frequency in the anole population over time. **Ask,** Why would the frequency of the allele for small body size decrease over time? The small anoles fit more easily into the mouths of the curly-tailed lizards than do the large anoles, so the genotype that yields this trait will not be passed on as frequently as either of the large-body genotypes.

Use these inquiry-based labs and online activities to deepen your understanding of evolution.

B.8.5 Describe how due to genetic variations, environmental forces, and reproductive pressures, organisms with beneficial traits are more likely to survive, reproduce, and pass on their genetic information.

NOS.6 Use analogies and models (mathematical and physical) to simplify and represent systems that are difficult to understand or directly experience due to their size, time scale, or complexity, and recognize the limitations of analogies and models.

INVESTIGATION

Investigating an Anole Lizard Population

Curly-tailed lizards will eat any brown anole lizards that fit into their mouths. In this activity, you will model the effect of curly-tailed lizards on an anole population.

SKILL Modeling

PROBLEM Is this population evolving?

MATERIALS

- 10 large paper clips (mix of smooth and ribbed), 10 small paper clips
- "extras" cup containing 20 additional large paper clips (10 smooth, 10 ribbed)
- graph paper

PROCEDURE

1. Obtain 10 large and 10 small paper clips to represent the initial population of anoles. Spread them out in front of your group. Large anoles may have genotype *BB* (large ribbed paper clip) or *Bb* (large smooth paper clip). Small anoles have genotype *bb* (small paper clip). Keep extra paper clips in the "extras" cup.
2. Copy and fill out Table 1 below for population stage 1.

TABLE 1. EFFECT OF CURLY-TAILED LIZARDS ON A POPULATION OF BROWN ANOLE LIZARDS

Population Stage	Number of Anoles				Genotype Frequencies			Allele Frequencies	
	Total	*BB*	*Bb*	*bb*	*BB*	*Bb*	*bb*	*B*	*b*
1 (Generation 1)									
2 (Generations 1 + 2)									
3 (Generations 1 + 2 + 3)									
4 (Generations 1 + 2 + 3 + 4)									

3. Three small anoles are eaten by curly tails. Put 3 small paper clips in the "extras" cup.
4. Mix up the paper clips that remain in your population and randomly pull 3 aside. These represent the genotypes that get passed on to the next generation.
5. Take 3 paper clips from the cup—one to match each paper clip that you pulled aside in step 4. The new paper clips represent the new generation. Join the 3 pairs with the rest of the population, bringing the population total back up to 20.
6. Fill in the information for this population stage in the next row of Table 1.
7. Repeat steps 3–6 until you have produced generation 4.
8. Draw two line graphs, one each for each allele frequency—*B* and *b*. Put population stage (1 through 4) on the *x*-axis and allele frequency (from 0 to 1) on the *y*-axis.

ANALYZE AND CONCLUDE

1. **Analyze** What happens to the frequency of each allele over the four generations?
2. **Analyze** Is this population evolving, or is it in Hardy-Weinberg equilibrium? Explain.
3. **Predict** Which of the five conditions required for equilibrium are met and which are not?

Answers

Analyze and Conclude

1. The frequency of allele *B* (large body) increases, while the frequency of allele *b* (small body) decreases.
2. The change in allele frequencies over time shows that the population is evolving.
3. Genetic drift could be occurring because the population size is small, but it is not evident here. Conditions met: no gene flow, no mutation, and mating is random. Conditions not met: natural selection is occurring. The predation of anole lizards by curly-tail lizards is a selective pressure that favors the large-body phenotype in anoles.

INVESTIGATION

Exploring Adaptations

A toolbox has a wide variety of tools, each designed to perform a specific task. But what if the ideal tools are not available? In this activity, you will relate this problem to the natural process of adaptation.

SKILL Drawing Analogies

MATERIALS
- wooden block
- one wood screw
- ruler

PROBLEM What purposes do adaptations serve?

PROCEDURE
1. Obtain a wooden block and a wood screw from your teacher.
2. Find a way to insert the screw into the block of wood as far as possible. Use any device, method, or object to do this other than a tool designed for this purpose. Be sure not to do anything that could cause damage or injury.
3. After trying for five minutes, measure the length of the screw that remains outside of the wood block. Subtract this length from the total length of the screw to determine how far you were able to insert the screw into the wood.

ANALYZE AND CONCLUDE
1. **Summarize** List the objects you used and the strategies you tried to accomplish this task.
2. **Analyze** Which of your methods worked best?
3. **Evaluate** Compare your results and strategies with those of another group. Evaluate the effectiveness of each strategy.
4. **Contrast** How do adaptations differ from traits that you can acquire through a lifetime, such as bigger muscles from strength training?
5. **Apply** A woodpecker has adaptations for chipping wood and getting insects from cracks in tree bark. How might its beak, tongue, neck, and feet be different from those of other birds?

Online BIOLOGY
CLASSZONE.COM

ANIMATED BIOLOGY
Evolutionary Arms Race
Can you keep tuberculosis in check? See how the bacteria that cause tuberculosis have evolved resistance to a number of antibiotics.

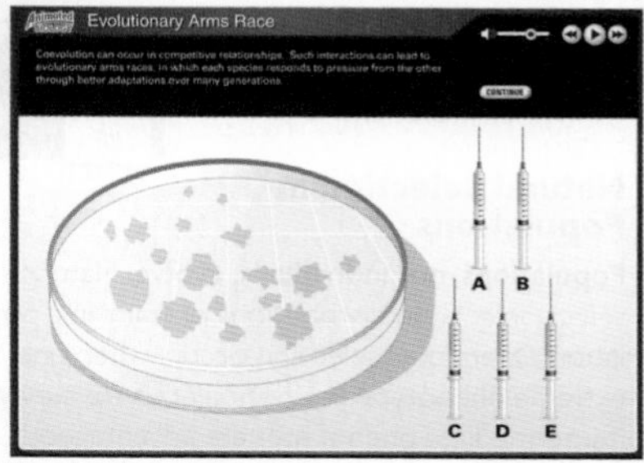

WEBQUEST
Speciation is an ongoing process, still active today. Complete this WebQuest to explore a butterfly population and a walking stick population that are each diverging into new species.

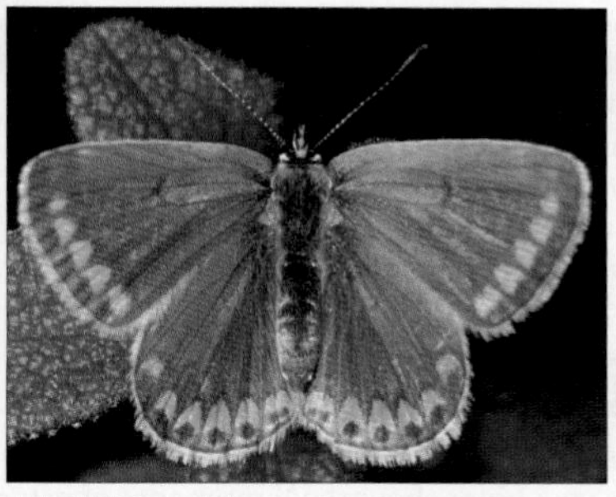

DATA ANALYSIS ONLINE
T. Dobzhansky and N.P. Spassky studied genetic drift in sample fruit fly populations. Graph the allele frequencies of the initial populations and the frequencies recorded at each stage of the experiment. Then determine if the populations are evolving.

Online Biology ▼

ANIMATED BIOLOGY Use this interactive animation to reinforce the concepts of **Section 11.6.**

WEBQUEST The WebQuest takes one full class period. Students complete the activity online and will need access to a printer to print out their answers. Sample answers, teacher notes, and alternative assessment ideas are available on **ClassZone.com.** Use with **Section 11.5.**

DATA ANALYSIS ONLINE
Students should use a bar graph. The two alleles move out of Hardy-Weinberg equilibrium (see **Section 11.4**). The fruit flies are evolving by means of genetic drift.

INVESTIGATION

Time 20 minutes	TEACHER TESTED
Teacher Preparation	
Student Difficulty	
Lab Binder Evolution, pp. 23–24	

LAB MANAGEMENT
- Check with the shop teacher to obtain pieces of scrap wood.
- Use soft woods, such as pine.
- Use a hammer and nail to create starter holes in the wood.

Answers

Sample Data

Depths ranged from 1/16 of an inch to about 1/2 inch.

Analyze and Conclude

1. Answers will vary, depending on resources available to students.
2. Answers will vary, depending on student results.
3. Answers will vary, depending on student results.
4. Adaptations evolve over time and are passed on to future generations only through genes. They cannot be acquired during an organism's lifetime.
5. beak: hard, straight, and long with chisel tip for drilling holes; tongue: long and slender, tipped with a "spear" to impale insects within the bark; neck: strong for pecking; feet: sharp claws that allow them to climb and provide leverage as they peck into the tree

CHAPTER REVIEW

Interactive Review

Encourage students to go to **ClassZone.com** for a detailed review of each section, including visuals and vocabulary practice.

Unit Resource Book, Vocabulary Practice, pp. 61–64

CHAPTER 11 Interactive Review @ CLASSZONE.COM

KEY CONCEPTS | Vocabulary Games | Concept Maps | Animated Biology | Online Quiz

11.1 Genetic Variation Within Populations

A population shares a common gene pool. Genetic variation in a gene pool can be measured through allele frequencies. Genetic variation increases the chance that some members of a population will be able to adapt to their environment.

11.2 Natural Selection in Populations

Populations, not individuals, evolve. Natural selection acts on distributions of traits in a population. Directional selection occurs when one extreme phenotype is advantageous for survival. If intermediate phenotypes are advantageous, they become more common through stabilizing selection. In the process of disruptive selection, extreme phenotypes are selected for.

11.3 Other Mechanisms of Evolution

Natural selection is not the only mechanism through which populations evolve. Gene flow is the movement of alleles between populations. Changes in allele frequencies due to chance alone can occur through genetic drift. If certain traits increase mating success, those traits can become more common through sexual selection.

11.4 Hardy-Weinberg Equilibrium

Hardy-Weinberg equilibrium provides a framework for understanding how populations evolve. A population in Hardy-Weinberg equilibrium is not evolving. The conditions required for this equilibrium are rarely met in nature. However, Hardy-Weinberg equilibrium provides a framework for understanding the factors that can lead to evolution. It is therefore very useful to population biologists.

11.5 Speciation Through Isolation

New species can arise when populations are isolated. Reproductive isolation occurs when members of two populations are no longer able to mate successfully. It is the final stage in speciation—the rise of two or more species from one existing species. Isolation can be due to behavioral, geographic, or temporal barriers.

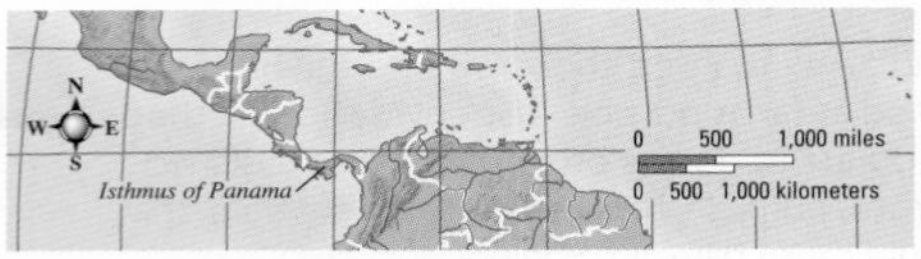

11.6 Patterns in Evolution

Evolution occurs in patterns. Evolution through natural selection can have direction, and its effects add up over many generations. The evolutionary paths of two or more species can become connected through the process of coevolution. Extinction and speciation events also appear in patterns in the fossil record.

Synthesize Your Notes

Two-Column Chart Make a two-column chart to synthesize your notes about the three modes of natural selection.

Type of Selection	Graph
Directional Selection Cause: Result:	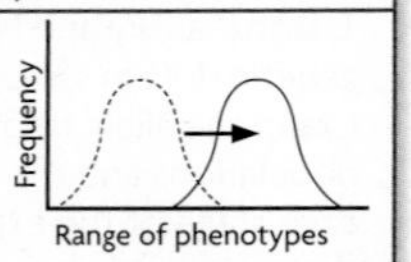

Concept Map Use concept maps to summarize factors that can lead to evolution.

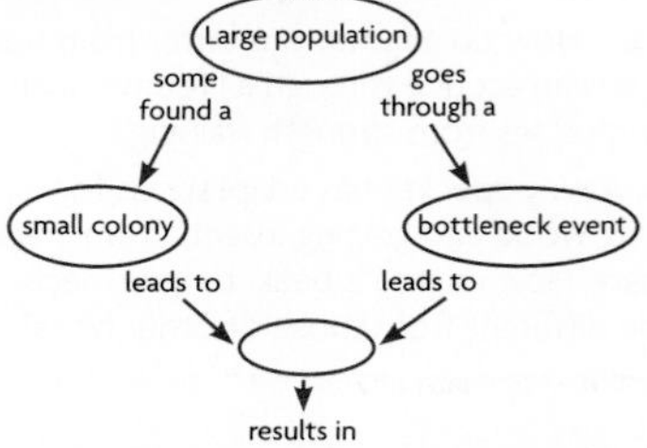

354 Unit 4: Evolution

ITEM CORRELATIONS	
Standard	**Items**
B.4.3	36
B.8.5	14, 17, 29
B.8.6	12

Reviewing Vocabulary

1. Picture could show a population of triangles and a population of squares with arrows pointing in both directions between them. Possible caption: Gene flow is the movement of alleles between populations.
2. Picture could show one population of circles separated from a mixed population of squares and X's by a mountain range. Possible caption: Mountains can geographically isolate the populations.
3. Picture could show a triangle with diverging arrows above it, one leading to a triangle with rounded corners and the other to a triangle with wavy edges. Possible caption: The two closely related species are evolving with different characteristics.
4. It is likely that students will draw a line graph that shows spikes in the rate of speciation over time. Possible caption: Long periods of little evolutionary change are separated by bursts of rapid speciation.
5. all the alleles in a population
6. unable to mate with one another
7. formation of new species
8. evolving toward similar characteristics
9. species evolving in response to each other
10. Many species evolve from one species.

Chapter Assessment

Chapter Vocabulary

11.1 gene pool, p. 328
allele frequency, p. 328

11.2 normal distribution, p. 330
microevolution, p. 331
directional selection, p. 331
stabilizing selection, p. 332
disruptive selection, p. 333

11.3 gene flow, p. 335
genetic drift, p. 336
bottleneck effect, p. 336
founder effect, p. 336
sexual selection, p. 338

11.4 Hardy-Weinberg equilibrium, p. 340

11.5 reproductive isolation, p. 344
speciation, p. 344
behavioral isolation, p. 345
geographic isolation, p. 346
temporal isolation, p. 346

11.6 convergent evolution, p. 348
divergent evolution, p. 348
coevolution, p. 349
extinction, p. 350
punctuated equilibrium, p. 351
adaptive radiation, p. 351

Reviewing Vocabulary

Visualizing Vocabulary

For each term below, use simple shapes, lines, or arrows to illustrate their meaning. Below each picture, write a short caption. Here's an example for *founder effect.*

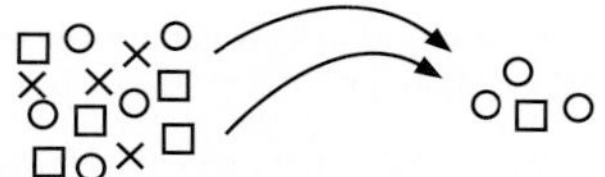

A small group of individuals starts a population that is subject to genetic drift.

1. gene flow
2. geographic isolation
3. divergent evolution
4. punctuated equilibrium

Keep It Short

For each vocabulary word below, write a short, precise phrase that describes its meaning. For example, a short phrase to describe *extinction* could be "gone forever."

5. gene pool
6. reproductive isolation
7. speciation
8. convergent evolution
9. coevolution
10. adaptive radiation

Reviewing MAIN IDEAS

11. Would a population with a lot of genetic variation or little genetic variation be more likely to have individuals that can adapt to a changing environment? Explain your answer.
12. Describe two major sources of genetic variation. **B.8.6**
13. A certain trait in a population is not under any selective pressure. Draw a curve showing the likely phenotypic distribution for this trait.
14. Over many generations, certain insect species have become more and more resistant to insecticides. What type of natural selection is this an example of, and how does it differ from the other types? **B.8.5**
15. Describe how gene flow can increase genetic variation within two neighboring populations.
16. How are the effects of genetic drift similar to the effects of having a small sample size in a scientific experiment?
17. Give an example of how sexual selection can cause extreme phenotypes in a population. **B.8.5**
18. What are the conditions necessary for a population to stay in Hardy-Weinberg equilibrium?
19. How can a lack of gene flow between populations lead to speciation?
20. Describe three types of barriers that can cause populations to become reproductively isolated from each other.
21. Explain why mutation and genetic drift are random events, while natural selection is not.
22. Speciation is the rise of two or more species from one existing species. What process keeps the number of total species on Earth from growing exponentially through speciation?
23. What is the relationship between speciation and the theory of punctuated equilibrium?

CHAPTER REVIEW

Reviewing Main Ideas

11. A population with a lot of genetic variation would likely have more phenotypic variation; therefore, such a population would more likely have individuals that can adapt to a changing environment.
12. Mutation can result in new alleles on chromosomes. Recombination rearranges alleles and produces new allele combinations on chromosomes.
13. The curve should show a normal distribution (bell-shaped curve).
14. Directional selection; it differs from stabilizing and disruptive selection in that one extreme phenotype is favored by natural selection.
15. New alleles can enter a population when an individual from a neighboring population mates with an individual from the original population.
16. A small sample size in an experiment can skew the results, because out-of-the-ordinary data will not be averaged out. This is the same effect that genetic drift can have on small populations. By chance, certain alleles may increase or decrease in frequency because of the small population size.
17. *Sample Answer:* Female widowbirds prefer to mate with male widowbirds that have longer tail feathers. Thus, alleles associated with longer tail feathers in males get passed on to future generations. Over time, males have longer and longer tail feathers.
18. very large population, no emigration or immigration, no mutations, random mating, and no natural selection
19. Without gene flow, the populations may begin to become more and more genetically different. They may become so genetically different that individuals from one population are no longer able to mate successfully with individuals from the other population. At this point, the two populations are different species.
20. Behavioral barriers are differences in courtship or mating behaviors, such as courtship dances and songs, between populations. Geographic barriers are physical barriers, such as mountains and rivers, that divide a population. Temporal barriers are differences in the timing of two populations' reproduction.
21. Mutation and genetic drift are random because they cannot be predicted and they are due to chance alone. Natural selection is not random because there is a cause-and-effect relationship: changes or new conditions in the environment result in the selection of traits that are adaptive to those changes.
22. extinction
23. The theory of punctuated equilibrium states that speciation occurs suddenly in geologic time and is followed by long periods of little evolutionary change or speciation.

Critical Thinking

24. Descendants of the common ancestor of honeycreepers became geographically isolated when they colonized different islands. Each population adapted to its island's environment, remaining reproductively isolated. In time, these populations evolved into distinct species.
25. Gene flow can introduce new alleles to a small population, and because the population is small to begin with, this flow can result in substantial changes in allele frequency.
26. Disruptive selection. In disruptive selection, the intermediate phenotype is selected against, whereas in stabilizing selection, the intermediate phenotype is selected for.
27. Genetic drift cannot be predicted. Certain alleles in small populations may increase or decrease due to chance alone, since there are so few individuals reproducing.
28. The allele frequencies in a gene pool always add up to 100 percent because a gene pool is the combined alleles of all the individuals in a population. It is the sum of all its parts.
29. Natural selection favors individuals that are best adapted to survive and reproduce in a given environment. Sexual selection favors individuals that are best adapted to win mates. Both types of selection are involved in reproductive success; however, traits that increase chances of winning a mate may sometimes be less advantageous for survival of that individual.

Interpreting Visuals

30. Disruptive selection; intermediate beak size has the lowest frequency, meaning it is selected against, while extreme phenotypes are selected for.
31. small beaks and large beaks
32. *Sample Answer:* Two main types of food are available: tiny insects and large, dry seeds. Small-beaked birds can pluck tiny insects from nooks and crannies; large-beaked birds have the ability to crack open the large seeds; medium-beaked birds are not good at either task.

Critical Thinking

24. Apply About 40 species of Hawaiian honeycreeper birds have likely descended from a common ancestor. These species occupy many different niches on the islands and they exhibit a variety of beak types, songs, and nesting behaviors. Describe how reproductive isolation and adaptive radiation likely played a role in the many species of honeycreepers in Hawaii today.

25. Apply How could gene flow affect a population that was founded by a small number of individuals?

26. Analyze What type of selection produces a distribution of phenotypes opposite to that produced by stabilizing selection? Explain your answer.

27. Analyze Explain how the process of genetic drift is completely due to chance.

28. Analyze Why must allele frequencies in a gene pool always add up to 100 percent?

29. Compare and Contrast What are the differences and similarities between natural selection and sexual selection? **B.8.5**

Interpreting Visuals

Below is a frequency distribution for beak size in a hypothetical population of birds. Use this graph to answer the next three questions.

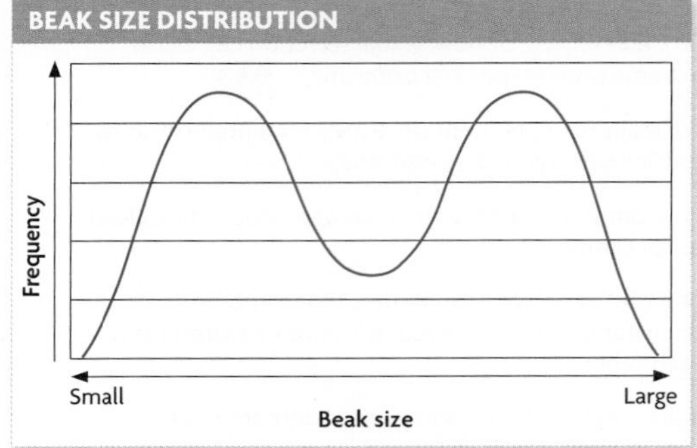

30. Analyze What type of selection is demonstrated by the data in this graph? Explain your answer.

31. Analyze Which phenotypes are the most common in this population?

32. Synthesize Describe a scenario that could realistically lead to this pattern of selection in a bird population.

Analyzing Data

Below is a graph showing the relationship between female chimpanzee rank and the survival of offspring. Use the graph to answer the next three questions.

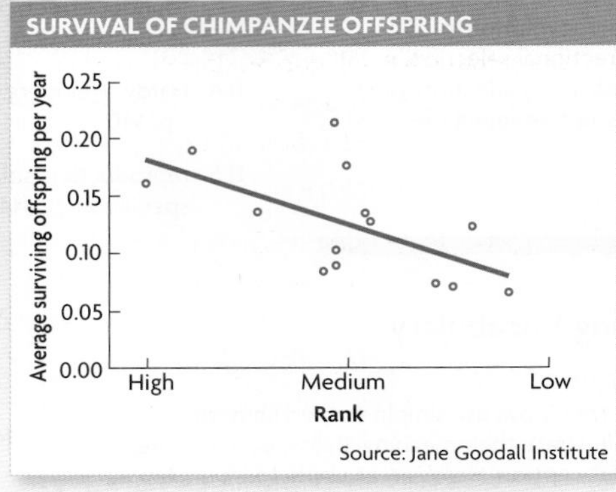

33. Analyze What is the relationship between female rank and the survival of her offspring?

34. Analyze Is there a level of rank that prevents a female chimp from reproducing? Explain.

35. Infer What can you infer by studying the scale of the *y*-axis on this graph?

Connecting CONCEPTS

36. Write a Proposal The explosive growth of nonnative species is a major global issue. A few individuals from one area act as founders of new populations on other continents or in other oceans. This is causing many native populations to decline. Human activities such as global commerce and travel are directly causing these destructive founding populations. Write a proposal to an international committee on the environment regarding this issue. Include in your proposal the significance of the changes to native populations, using terms and concepts from the chapter. **B.4.3**

37. Infer Hemoglobin, an oxygen-carrying protein found in the red blood cells of vertebrates, helps to circulate oxygen from the lungs to all parts of the body. In penguins, the blood has a very high concentration of hemoglobin. Penguin muscles have a high concentration of myoglobin, which also stores oxygen. What might be a reason for these adaptations?

Analyzing Data

33. In general, higher female rank means improved survival rate of offspring.
34. No, the lowest value on the graph is greater than zero (approximately 7 percent), so it would appear that every female is able to reproduce.
35. The survival rate of chimpanzee offspring is low. Even among the highest-ranked females, less than 20 percent of their offspring survive each year.

B.8.5, B.8.6

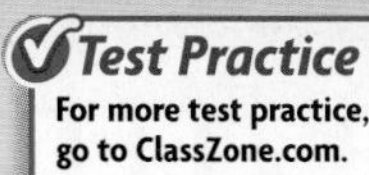

Test Practice
For more test practice, go to ClassZone.com.

1 An isolated population of bats goes through 100 generations with no immigration. However, genetic variation within the population increases. What ***best*** explains the cause of this increase?

A Reproductive isolation results in variation.
B Natural selection acts on the genotypes.
C Sexual selection has been disrupted.
D Random mutations can occur each generation.

2 How does genetic drift affect a population?

A It decreases genetic variability.
B It increases the number of individuals.
C It increases reproductive ability.
D It decrease the mutation rate.

3

Habitat Conditions		
	Old Habitat	New Habitat
Temp (°C)	14–22	15–21
Light level	low	low
Soil pH	5.3	5.4
Rainfall (cm/week)	4.2	2.2

Seeds from a plant species are introduced into a new habitat. The chart shows the environmental conditions in the old and new habitats. Based on this information, what is ***most*** likely to happen to the new population over the course of many generations?

A Individuals will require more sunlight.
B Individuals will require higher temperatures.
C Individuals that can survive with 2.2 cm/week of rainfall will become more common.
D Individuals that can survive with 2.2 cm/week of rainfall will become less common.

4 Due to severe flooding, 95 percent of a ground-nesting ant population dies. This event is different from natural selection in that any resulting change in allele frequencies is

A harmful to the population.
B beneficial to the population.
C random.
D directional.

5

The map shows the location of four populations of a bee species. Over time, population A is ***most*** likely to evolve into a new species due to

A geographic isolation.
B temporal isolation.
C convergent evolution.
D adaptive radiation.

6 The Irish potato famine in the 1840s was caused by a fungus that infected the potato crop. What is the ***most*** likely reason the potato population was vulnerable to infection?

Standards-Based Assessment

1. D	4. C
2. A	5. A
3. C	6. See Below

Question 3 Answer C is correct. Answer A is incorrect because the light level is the same in both habitats. Answer B is incorrect because the temperature range is approximately the same in both habitats. Answer D is incorrect because the new habitat has less rainfall than the old habitat, so only those plants that can survive with less water will survive to reproduce, making those that can survive with 2.2 cm/week more common.

Question 5 Answer A is correct. Answer B is incorrect because temporal isolation is a time-related barrier to mating between populations, not a geographic or physical barrier. Answer C is incorrect because convergent evolution is the evolution of similar characteristics in unrelated species, so it describes evolution but is not a contributing factor. Answer D is incorrect because adaptive radiation is the process by which one species evolves and gives rise to many descendant species that occupy different ecological niches.

Question 6 Genetic variability increases the likelihood that some members of a population can survive changing environmental conditions, including exposure to infection. Therefore, it is likely that this potato population lacked genetic variability.

Connecting Concepts

36. Students' answers should incorporate chapter concepts such as natural selection, gene flow, genetic drift, and extinction. Students could also incorporate concepts from ecology, including the fact that foreign founding populations will likely affect multiple species, such as those in a common food web and those that coevolved with the native species that are now in jeopardy.

37. These adaptations allow penguins to search for food under water for long periods of time, without needing to come up to the surface for oxygen.

ITEM CORRELATIONS	
Standard	**Items**
B.8.5	3, 6
B.8.6	1, 2, 4, 5

CHAPTER 12

Indiana Resource Preview

Print Resources

The History of Life

INDIANA STANDARDS		Sections	PAGES and PACING	UNIT RESOURCE BOOK
B.8.7	12.1	**The Fossil Record** **KEY CONCEPT** Fossils are a record of life that existed in the past.	pp. 360–363 30 minutes	URB pages 65–68
NOS.1, NOS.3		CHAPTER INVESTIGATION: Radioactive Decay	p. 364 30 minutes	**Lab Binder** Evolution pages 31–33
B.8.7	12.2	**The Geologic Time Scale** **KEY CONCEPT** The geologic time scale divides Earth's history based on major past events.	pp. 365–367 30 minutes	URB pages 69–72
B.8.7	12.3	**Origin of Life** **KEY CONCEPT** The origin of life on Earth remains a puzzle.	pp. 368–371 30 minutes	URB pages 73–76
B.8.7	12.4	**Early Single-Celled Organisms** **KEY CONCEPT** Single-celled organisms existed 3.8 billion years ago.	pp. 372–374 30 minutes	URB pages 77–80
NOS.3		DATA ANALYSIS: Calculating Axes Intervals Generation Times of Bacteria	p. 375 45 minutes	URB page 89
B.8.7	12.5	**Radiation of Multicellular Life** **KEY CONCEPT** Multicellular life evolved in distinct phases.	pp. 376–378 30 minutes	URB pages 81–84
B.8.7	12.6	**Primate Evolution** **KEY CONCEPT** Humans appeared late in Earth's history.	pp. 379–383 30 minutes	URB pages 85–88
NOS.1, NOS.3		OPTIONS FOR INQUIRY	pp. 384–385 45 min each	**Lab Binder** Evolution pages 34–39
		Chapter Review	pp. 386–389	**Assessment Book** Chapter Tests A, B pp. 237–244

INDIANA STANDARDS

B.8.7 Describe the modern scientific theory of the origins and history of life on earth, and evaluate the evidence that supports it.
NOS.1 Develop explanations based on reproducible data and observations gathered during laboratory investigations.
NOS.3 Clearly communicate their ideas and results of investigations verbally and in written form using tables, graphs, diagrams, and photographs.

Labs

PUPIL EDITION LABS

Radioactive Decay, p. 364 Students model the process of radioactive decay. **Lab Binder** pp. 31–33	**Time:** 45 minutes **Materials:** 10 pennies, graph paper, 3 pencils of different color
Geologic Clock, Section 6, p. 381 Students model relative interval lengths of the geologic time scale. **Lab Binder** p. 40	**Time:** 20 minutes **Materials:** paper, pencil

OPTIONS FOR INQUIRY

Stride Inferences, p. 384 Students infer characteristics of an organism based on trace fossil measurements. **Lab Binder** pp. 34–36	**Time:** 45 minutes **Materials:** meter stick, calculator (optional), graph paper
Understanding Geologic Time, p. 385 Students learn how past events contribute to the changing populations of life on Earth. **Lab Binder** pp. 37–39	**Time:** 45 minutes **Materials:** Geologic Time Scale datasheet

LAB BINDER Unit 4 Evolution

Additional Investigation: Comparing Indexes Among Primates, pp. 41–46

Virtual Lab Worksheet: Comparing Hominid Skulls, p. 70

LAB GENERATOR

A searchable CD of all labs in the program in editable format, including forensic, probeware, and biotechnology labs.

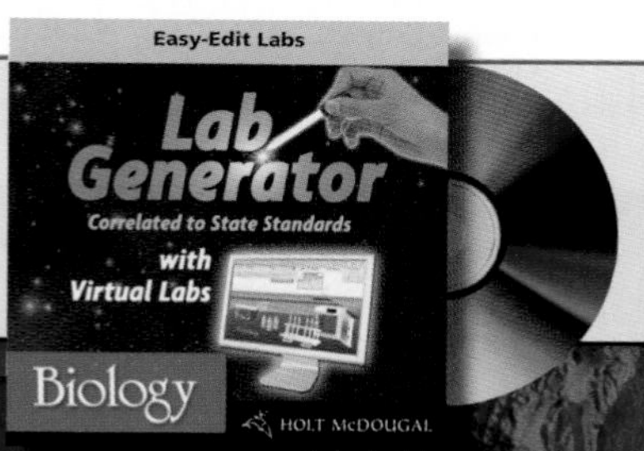

Presentation Tools

POWER PRESENTATIONS

Presentation Chapter 12
PowerPresentations for each section incorporate images and clips from the Media Gallery. Includes Note Navigator for each section.

MEDIA GALLERY

Contains the following images and video clips, as well as animations, simulations, and forms of visuals from the book.

Fossil formation

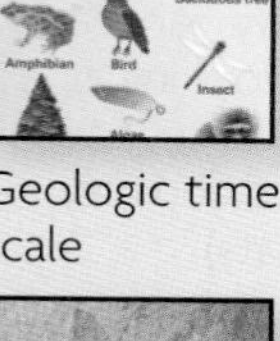
Geologic time scale

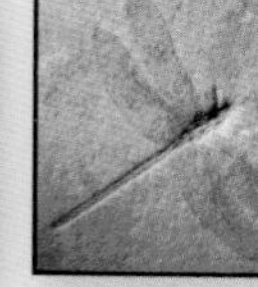
Chimpanzee

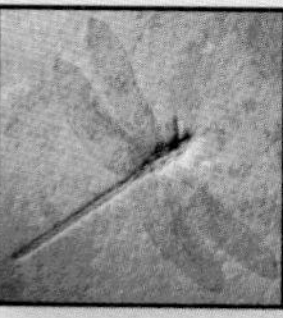
Dragonfly fossil

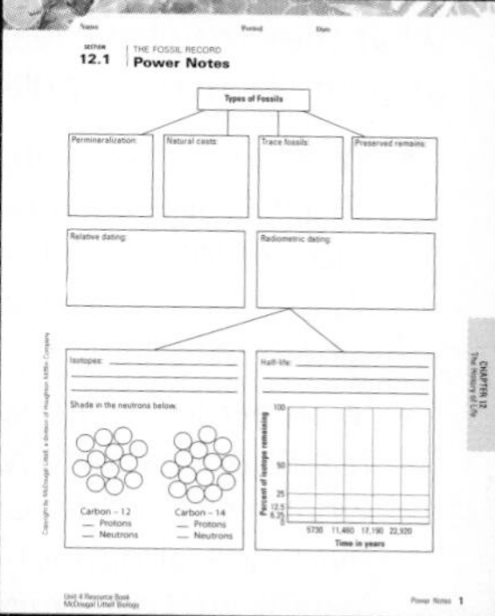
12.1 Power Notes

Types of Fossils

Power Notes

VIDEO

View a set of short video clips covering life over geologic time.

ANIMATED BIOLOGY

Endosymbiosis
Geologic Time Scale

TRANSPARENCIES

The Process of Permineralization T49
Radiometric Dating T50
Geologic Time Scale T51
Miller-Urey Experiment T52
Endosymbiosis T53
Evolutionary Relationships of Primates T54
Examples of Hominid Skulls T55

Online BIOLOGY CLASSZONE.COM

BioZine
Animated Biology
Interactive Review
SciLinks
Resource Centers

CHAPTER

12

▼ Focus and Motivate

What can fossils teach us about the past?

Have students think about fossils they may have seen in museums or about what they may have learned about ancient life from popular media. **Ask**

- What are some things we can learn about fossils by simply looking at them? what they looked like (size, shape), how they moved and ate, where they lived (habitats)
- In an evolutionary sense, relating fossils to the history of life on Earth, what else do they offer us? direct evidence of extinct organisms, insight into evolutionary relationships of both extinct and living organisms, evidence of climate change and continental drift

BIOZINE ClassZone.com

Students can access BioZine at **ClassZone.com** to take a poll about current issues in biology.

In a Hurry?

The critical material of the chapter is found in **Sections 12.3, 12.4,** and **12.5.** A survey of the heads in **Section 12.1** will provide information on fossil formation and dating techniques. The geologic time scale is presented visually on page 366 in **Section 12.2,** and **Section 12.6** presents primate and human evolution.

CHAPTER

12 The History of Life

KEY CONCEPTS

12.1 The Fossil Record
Fossils are a record of life that existed in the past.

12.2 The Geologic Time Scale
The geologic time scale divides Earth's history based on major past events.

12.3 Origin of Life
The origin of life on Earth remains a puzzle.

12.4 Early Single-Celled Organisms
Single-celled organisms existed 3.8 billion years ago.

12.5 Radiation of Multicellular Life
Multicellular life evolved in distinct phases.

12.6 Primate Evolution
Humans appeared late in Earth's history.

Online BIOLOGY CLASSZONE.COM

Animated BIOLOGY
View animated chapter concepts.
- Endosymbiosis
- Comparing Hominoid Skulls
- Geologic Time Scale

BIOZINE
Keep current with biology news.
- Featured stories
- News feeds
- Polls

RESOURCE CENTER
Get more information on
- Earth's Ancient Past
- Geologic Dating Methods
- History of Life

Student Activity

Purpose **Students will gain an appreciation for the information that can be obtained from trace fossils.**

Materials

- plaster of Paris
- petri dishes, jar lids, or other flat-bottomed containers
- petroleum jelly
- objects with distinct textures or shapes, such as shells, leaves, feathers, fern fronds, toy animals with feet or hands that will leave prints

What can fossils teach us about the past?

This man, known only as Tollund Man, died about 2200 years ago in what is now Denmark. Details such as his skin and hair were preserved by the acid of the bog in which he was found. A bog is a type of wetland that accumulates peat, the deposits of dead plant material. Older remains from bogs can add information to the fossil record, which tends to consist of mostly hard shells, teeth, and bones.

Connecting CONCEPTS

Arthropods This fossil of an extinct lobsterlike arthropod was discovered at a site where some of the world's oldest fossils are found—the Burgess Shale, in British Columbia, Canada. Arthropods are a large group of invertebrates that have segmented body parts and jointed legs. Fossils found at the Burgess Shale site offer a glimpse of what life was like during the Cambrian period, more than 500 million years ago. These fossils are special due to their great age and their remarkable state of preservation. In this chapter, you will read more about how fossils are preserved and about the time period during which this ancient arthropod lived.

Introduce Have students work in pairs or small groups. The petroleum jelly will make it easier to remove the specimens from the plaster. Each group should take one specimen and proceed as follows:

1. Pour some plaster of Paris into a petri dish.
2. Cover each specimen with a very thin layer of petroleum jelly.
3. When the plaster begins to set, press a specimen into the surface of the plaster.
4. When the plaster hardens, carefully remove the specimen.

Have students examine their fossil imprint and make notes and sketches of its characteristics. You can have the groups exchange fossils to see if other students make different inferences or observations.

Discuss When many students hear the word *fossil,* they think immediately of a fossilized bone or other mineralized body part. **Ask,** What types of information can be gathered from examining trace fossils? shape, general form, size, surface patterns (leaves and feathers), gait (footprints)

Activate Prior Knowledge

Point out the photograph of the Tollund Man and explain that he represents a rare type of preserved remains because his soft tissues are still present. **Ask,** What can we learn about Tollund Man that we can't from most fossils? features of his skin and muscles, hair, clothing **Ask,** What are some famous examples of preserved or fossilized remains? King Tut and other mummies, dinosaur bones and footprints, shark teeth, Lucy and other hominid bones, Pompeii

Preview Vocabulary

Academic Vocabulary The word *interval* is used frequently in this chapter. Remind students of the meaning of the prefix *inter-* as "between, among, or within." Furthermore, on the axes of a graph, intervals are uniform in length or value; in evolution, intervals are defined by characteristics and events that distinguish them from the ones they follow and precede, not by their length. In evolution, intervals are about how Earth and life have changed.

English Learners Encourage students to use the *Multilanguage Glossary* and the textbook Glossary to better understand the material in this chapter. They can use a strategy such as word squares and organize unfamiliar terms into subject groups such as "Earth history" and "primates." Within each group, they can organize terms by classification (primates) or levels of geologic time (epoch, period, era).

Integrating Earth Science

Some of the Burgess Shale fossils are *trace fossils,* meaning they appear as dark carbon and clay imprints on shale. The area that includes the Burgess Shale was a huge reef in a warm, shallow sea. Frequent mud slumps carried the organisms down into deeper water. Over time, the mud was compacted into shale. This muddy burial preserved the fossils, allowing for both hard and soft body parts to leave their impressions.

SECTION 12.1

▼ Plan and Prepare

Objectives

- Describe the ways that fossils can form.
- Identify the use of relative dating and absolute dating techniques.

Section Resources

Unit Resource Book Study Guide pp. 65–66 Power Notes p. 67 Reinforcement p. 68
Interactive Reader Chapter 12 **Spanish Study Guide** pp. 121–122
Biology Toolkit pp. C19, C22, C34
Technology Power Presentation 12.1 Media Gallery DVD Online Quiz 12.1

Activate Prior Knowledge Poll students to see how many have been to a natural history museum. **Ask,** What are some of the ancient life forms you remember? woolly mammoths, dinosaurs, armored fish, insects in amber Introduce to them the idea that not all species that have lived on Earth are represented in the fossil record and that we may never know of all the other kinds of life that have occupied the planet.

▼ Teach

Science Trivia

The dung or scat of an animal can reveal a great deal about its diet and habits. Even a piece of fossilized scat, or **coprolite,** can be very helpful to scientists. The largest dinosaur *coprolite* was uncovered in 1995 in Saskatchewan, Canada. It came from a *Tyrannosaurus rex.* The dung measured about 44 × 16 × 13 centimeters, weighed 7 kilograms (15 lb), had an estimated volume of 2.4 liters (0.6 gal.), and contained bone fragments of herbivorous dinosaurs.

12.1 The Fossil Record

KEY CONCEPT Fossils are a record of life that existed in the past.

MAIN IDEAS

- Fossils can form in several ways.
- Radiometric dating provides an accurate estimate of a fossil's age.

VOCABULARY

relative dating, p. 362
radiometric dating, p. 362
isotope, p. 362
half-life, p. 362

B.8.7 Describe the modern scientific theory of the origins and history of life on earth, and evaluate the evidence that supports it.

Connect Tollund Man and the arthropod found in the Burgess Shale site are both traces of Earth's history of life, although they lived about 500 million years apart. They were also preserved as fossils in different ways. In this section, you will learn about types of fossils, how fossils form, and how they can help us understand the history of life on Earth.

MAIN IDEA

Fossils can form in several ways.

Fossils are far more diverse than the giant dinosaur skeletons we see in museums. The following are some of the processes that make fossils. **FIGURE 12.1** shows examples of fossils produced in different ways.

- **Permineralization** occurs when minerals carried by water are deposited around a hard structure. They may also replace the hard structure itself.
- **Natural casts** form when flowing water removes all of the original bone or tissue, leaving just an impression in sediment. Minerals fill in the mold, recreating the original shape of the organism.
- **Trace fossils** record the activity of an organism. They include nests, burrows, imprints of leaves, and footprints.
- **Amber-preserved fossils** are organisms that become trapped in tree resin that hardens into amber after the tree gets buried underground.
- **Preserved remains** form when an entire organism becomes encased in material such as ice or volcanic ash or immersed in bogs.

FIGURE 12.1 The fossil record includes fossils that formed in many different ways.

Permineralized skeleton of a *Velociraptor* dinosaur

Natural cast of a crinoid, a marine animal

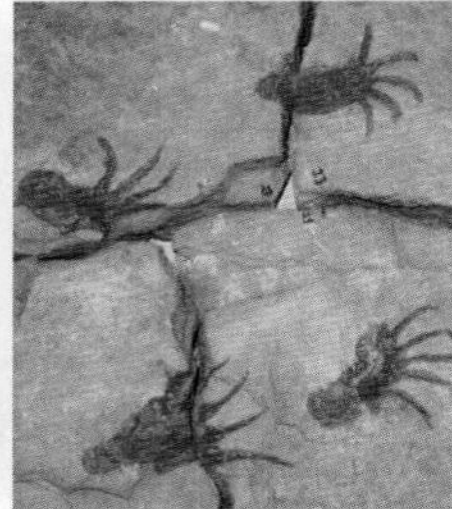
Trace fossils of footprints from a *Dimetrodon* dinosaur

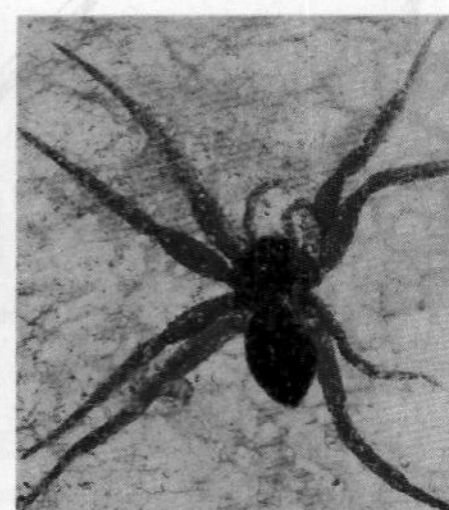
Amber-preserved spider

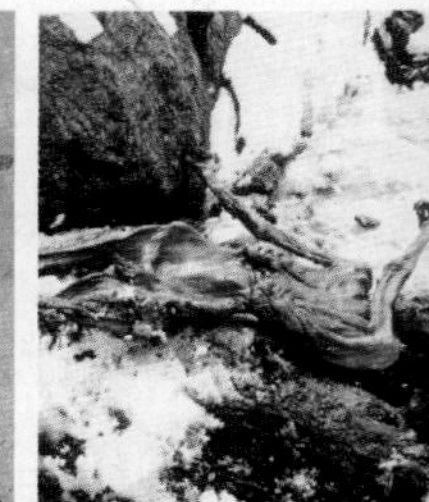
Ice-preserved 5000-year-old remains of a man found in the Italian Alps

Differentiated Instruction

ENGLISH LEARNERS

Have students create a compare-contrast chart to differentiate between the five fossil types shown on page 360. In one column, have them record the types in which the actual form or structures of an organism are preserved, while the other column gets the fossil types that do not preserve the structures themselves. Students can look for specific words, such as *impression* or *encased,* to help them identify which category the fossil types belong to.

Biology Toolkit, Compare/Contrast Chart, p. C34

FIGURE 12.2 The Process of Permineralization

The process of permineralization requires rapid burial in an area with water and continuous sedimentation.

An organism dies in a location, such as a riverbed, where sediments can rapidly cover its body.

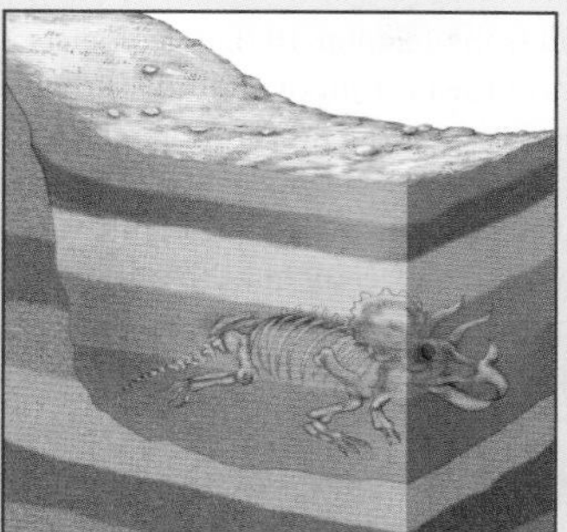

Over time, pressure from additional sediment compresses the body, and minerals slowly replace all hard structures, such as bone.

Earthquakes or erosion may expose the fossil millions of years after formation, or it may be uncovered by paleontologists, hikers, or road-building crews.

Infer What conditions could occur that would prevent an organism from being preserved through permineralization?

Most fossils form in sedimentary rock, which is made by many layers of sediment or small rock particles. The best environments for any type of fossilization include wetlands, bogs, and areas where sediment is continuously deposited, such as river mouths, lakebeds, and floodplains.

The most common fossils result from permineralization. Several circumstances are critical for this process, as shown in **FIGURE 12.2.** The organism must be buried or encased in some type of material—such as sand, sediment, mud, or tar—very soon after death, while the organism's features are still intact. After burial, groundwater trickles into tiny pores and spaces in plants, bones, and shells. During this process, the excess minerals in the water are deposited on the remaining cells and tissues. Many layers of mineral deposits are left behind, creating a fossilized record by replacing organic tissues with hard minerals. The resulting fossil has the same shape as the original structure and may contain some original tissue.

With such specific conditions needed for fossilization, it is easy to see why only a tiny percentage of living things that ever existed became fossils. Most remains decompose or are destroyed before they can be preserved. Even successful fossilization is no guarantee that an organism's remains will be added to the fossil record. Natural events such as earthquakes and the recycling of rock into magma can destroy fossils that took thousands of years to form.

Summarize Why are so few complete fossils discovered?

TAKING NOTES

Make a cause-and-effect chain of the conditions required for fossilization. Fill in important details.

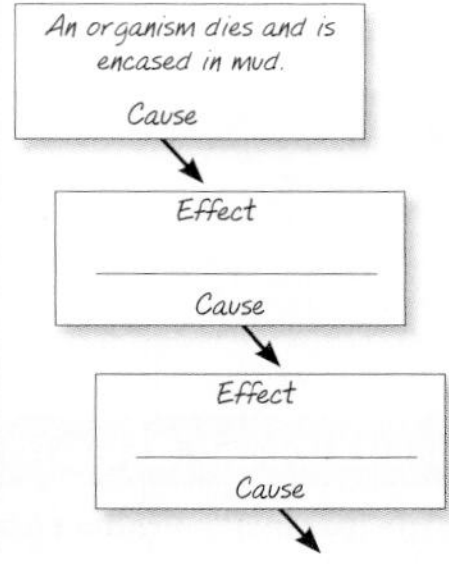
An organism dies and is encased in mud.
Cause
Effect
Cause
Effect
Cause

TEACH WITH TECHNOLOGY

When re-creations or models of extinct organisms are featured in movies or museum displays, their creators often take liberties when it comes to representing certain features, such as hair color, feathers, and, of course, behavior. Show a PowerPoint presentation of actual fossil remains alongside their re-creations, such as a *T. rex* skeleton next to a screen shot from a recent film. Discuss which features may be based on the fossil evidence and which are wholly assumed or invented by the model's creators.

TEACH FROM VISUALS

FIGURE 12.2 Use the figure to review conditions necessary for fossilization.
Ask

- Why are fossils commonly found near ancient or modern lakebeds and floodplains? These environments experience continuous sediment deposition, a necessary condition for fossilization.
- What role does groundwater play in the middle figure? Groundwater brings in dissolved minerals, which replace hard tissues such as bone and enamel.

Take It Further

Some of the world's best-preserved fossils come from the **Gobi** in central Asia. For many years, scientists thought that these animals had been buried by sandstorms that frequently occur in the region. Later studies revealed that the exquisite condition of many Gobi fossils was caused by the animals being buried alive when sand dunes collapsed suddenly during severe rainstorms. This rapid burial not only preserved the animals, but also preserved them while they were engaged in activities, such as fighting. One such amazing Gobi specimen consists of two dinosaurs—a *Velociraptor* and its prey, a *Protoceratops*—locked in combat. The *Velociraptor*'s foot claw is embedded in the neck of the *Protoceratops,* which, in turn, appears to have bitten and broken the *Velociraptor*'s right forelimb.

Answers

A Infer It may decompose before it is buried, be buried where there is no water, or get destroyed by geological processes.

B Summarize Because of the specific conditions and events that are required for fossilization to occur, only a tiny fraction of organisms can be preserved. Also, rock recycling destroys many fossils.

▼ Teach *continued*

ONLINE BIOLOGY Go to the chapter Resource Center at **ClassZone.com** for additional information on geologic dating methods. Students can do a WebQuest on dating methods; see Options for Inquiry on page 385.

Vocabulary

Greek and Latin Wo term **isotope** relates isotopes of an eleme the same place on th

isos = same or equa
topos = place

Integrating Molecular B

Scientists use **molecu** support evidence fro and to establish the c ary events. A molecul technique based on t mutations in DNA oc rate over time. After two species diverge from their ancestral lineage, each species continues to accumulate mutations in its DNA. The greater the number of differences in the DNA sequences of two species, the longer it has been since they shared a common ancestor.

Address Misconceptions

Common Misconception Students often think that fossils are rare and can be found only in certain areas.

Correcting the Misconception Fossils can be found almost anywhere that sedimentary rock has formed, and sedimentary rock is found all over the world. In places where conditions for fossilization were favorable, enormous numbers of fossils have been found.

MAIN IDEA

Radiometric dating provides an accurate estimate of a fossil's age.

Connecting CONCEPTS

Chemistry of Life Recall from Chapter 2 that all atoms of a given element have the same number of protons. Isotopes are named for the total number of protons and neutrons in their nuclei.

neutrons protons

Recall from Chapter 10 that geologists in the 1700s had realized that rock layers at the bottom of an undisturbed sequence of rocks were deposited before those at the top, and therefore are older. The same logic holds true for the fossils found in rock layers. **Relative dating** estimates the time during which an organism lived by comparing the placement of fossils of that organism with the placement of fossils in other layers of rock. Relative dating allows scientists to infer the order in which groups of species existed, although it does not provide the actual ages of fossils.

To estimate a fossil's actual, or absolute, age, scientists use **radiometric dating**—a technique that uses the natural decay rate of unstable isotopes found in materials in order to calculate the age of that material. **Isotopes** are atoms of an element that have the same number of protons but a different number of neutrons. Most elements have several isotopes. For example, the element carbon (C) has three naturally occurring isotopes. All carbon isotopes have six protons. Isotopes are named, however, by their number of protons plus their number of neutrons. Thus, carbon-12 (^{12}C) has six neutrons, carbon-13 (^{13}C) has seven neutrons, and carbon-14 (^{14}C) has eight neutrons. More than 98 percent of the carbon in a living organism is ^{12}C.

Some isotopes have unstable nuclei. As a result, their nuclei undergo radioactive decay—they break down—over time. This releases radiation in the form of particles and energy. As an isotope decays, it can transform into a different element. The decay rate of many radioactive isotopes has been measured and is expressed as the isotope's half-life, as shown in **FIGURE 12.3.** A **half-life** is the amount of time it takes for half of the isotope in a sample to decay into a different element, or its product isotope. An element's half-life is not affected by environmental conditions such as temperature or pressure. Both ^{12}C and ^{13}C are stable, but ^{14}C decays into nitrogen-14 (^{14}N), with a half-life of roughly 5700 years.

Radiocarbon Dating

The isotope ^{14}C is commonly used for radiometric dating of recent remains, such as those of Tollund Man shown at the beginning of this chapter. Organisms absorb carbon through eating and breathing, so ^{14}C is constantly being resupplied. When an organism dies, its intake of carbon stops, but the decay of ^{14}C continues. The fossil's age can be estimated by comparing the ratio of a stable isotope, such as ^{12}C, to ^{14}C. The longer the organism has been dead, the larger the difference between the amounts of ^{12}C and ^{14}C there will be. ^{14}C has a half-life of roughly 5700 years. This means that after 5700 years, half of the ^{14}C in a fossil will have decayed into ^{14}N, its decay product. The other half remains as ^{14}C. After 11,400 years, or two half-lives, 75 percent of the ^{14}C will have decayed.

FIGURE 12.3 DECAY OF ISOTOPES

Isotope (parent)	Product (daughter)	Half-life (years)
rubidium-87	strontium-87	48.8 billion
uranium-238	lead-206	4.5 billion
chlorine-36	argon-36	300,000
carbon-14	nitrogen-14	5730

Differentiated Instruction

PRE-AP

Give students the following scenario: On a research expedition, scientists uncover two different fossils in two different places. The first appears to be a humanlike skull in a stratum associated with a time period of approximately 4 million years ago; the second is a mummified human found in a crypt. Have students write proposals for how to determine the age of each set of remains and why their methods are the appropriate ones to use.

Biology Toolkit, Quick-Write, p. C19

INCLUSION

Have students create a matrix to compare different types of dating and what they are used for. They should compare both relative and absolute dating, and, within radiometric techniques, they should compare how isotopes with different half-lives can be used to date things that are as "young" as a few thousand years and as "old" as billions of years.

Biology Toolkit, Content Frame, p. C22

FIGURE 12.4 Radiometric Dating Using Carbon-14

Radiometric dating uses the natural decay rate of unstable isotopes to calculate the age of a fossil.

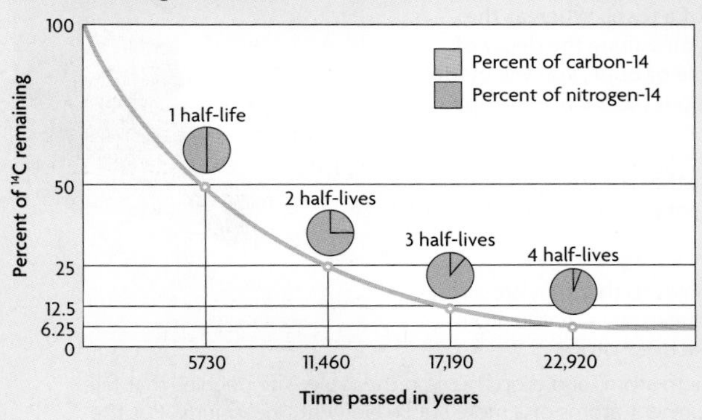

One-quarter of the original ^{14}C remains. Radioactive decay of ^{14}C is shown in **FIGURE 12.4.** Carbon-14 dating can be used to date objects only up to about 45,000 years old. If the objects are older than that, the fraction of ^{14}C will be too small to accurately measure. Older objects can be dated using isotopes with longer half-lives.

Determining Earth's Age

Scientists have used radiometric dating to determine the age of Earth. Because Earth constantly undergoes erosion and rock recycling, rocks on Earth do not remain in their original state. Unlike Earth, meteorites—which are mostly pieces of rock and iron that have fallen to Earth's surface from space—do not get recycled or undergo erosion. Meteorites are thought to have formed at about the same time as Earth. Therefore, meteorites provide an unspoiled sample for radiometric dating. Uranium-to-lead isotope ratios in many meteorite samples consistently estimate Earth's age at about 4.5 billion years.

Summarize **Why are meteorites helpful for determining the age of Earth?**

12.1 ASSESSMENT

B.8.7

REVIEWING MAIN IDEAS

1. What types of evidence of ancient life can be preserved as fossils?
2. Why is a uranium **isotope** often used rather than ^{14}C in **radiometric dating** to determine the age of Earth?

CRITICAL THINKING

3. **Apply** Considering that millions of species have lived on Earth, why are there relatively few fossils?
4. **Contrast** Explain the difference between **relative dating** and absolute dating.

Connecting CONCEPTS

5. **Earth Science** When mountains form, the order of rock layers can be disturbed. How could radiometric dating be used to sort out the relative ages of such rock layers?

TEACH FROM VISUALS

FIGURE 12.4 Have students examine the axes and other features of the graph. **Ask**

- Why do the intervals between the horizontal lines that intersect the points on the graph get smaller as time passes? The intervals really represent that percentage of decay relative to the initial sample, so even though it is being cut in half with each half-life, the number of carbon-14 atoms decaying into nitrogen-14 is getting smaller and smaller.
- What do the green portions of each circle graph on the curve represent? amount or portion of the sample that has decayed from carbon-14 ... 14
- ... the rate of formation ... on the same graph, ...-hand y-axis for ... would the curve look ... mirror image of the ... curve

...d Reteach ▼

...nline Quiz or Section ... *Book,* p. 231).

...dents add to or ...e-and-effect chains ...ating sequences that ...f fossil shown in ... page 360.

Answers

A Summarize They are thought to have formed at the same time as Earth. Because they have fallen to Earth from space relatively recently, they have not been spoiled by erosion or rock recycling.

12.1 ASSESSMENT

1. An organism itself, its shape, or some sense of its activities can be preserved.
2. It has a very long half-life, and Earth is very old.
3. Specific environmental conditions are required for a fossil to form, and many organisms have only soft body parts that do not preserve well. Rock cycling, erosion, and other geological processes also destroy fossils before they are found.
4. Both relative dating and absolute dating are used to find how old a site or fossil is. Relative dating does not give specific dates, but dates a sample in context with other samples. Absolute dating gives a specific age of a sample within a margin of error.
5. Disturbed rock strata may not be ordered sequentially. Radiometric dating of different layers can sort out the absolute ages of the rocks and determine the correct sequence of the strata.

INVESTIGATION

Time 45 minutes TEACHER TESTED
Teacher Preparation
Student Difficulty
Lab Binder Evolution, pp. 31–33

Purpose Model the process of radioactive decay.

Overview Students will use a model system to measure the decay of a fictitious radioactive isotope. They will

- toss each of ten pennies to determine its status as "tailsium," an unstable isotope, or "headsium," a stable isotope
- repeat this procedure only for the tailsium pennies until they are all gone or ten trials have been conducted
- graph their results as the rate of tailsium decay and compare these results with those of the average rate determined by the class

Teacher Note "Working with manipulatives materials makes the abstraction of radioactive decay more concrete. I feel students now have a better understanding of the process."

LAB PREPARATION

Make sure students have labeled their data sheets before beginning the coin tosses.

LAB MANAGEMENT

Teacher Note "I suggest doing the graphing in class so that the teacher can provide assistance to those students experiencing difficulty."

POST-LAB DISCUSSION

Discuss the benefit of using average values derived from many trials as opposed to using values from a single trial.

MATERIALS

- 10 pennies
- graph paper
- 3 pencils of different colors

PROCESS SKILLS

- **Analyzing**
- **Interpreting Data**
- **Modeling**

NOS.1 Develop explanations based on reproducible data and observations gathered during laboratory investigations.

NOS.3 Clearly communicate their ideas and results of investigations verbally and in written form using tables, graphs, diagrams, and photographs.

Radioactive Decay

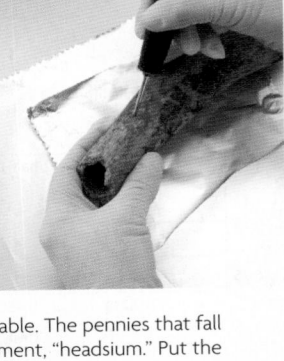

In this lab, you will model how scientists determine the age of a fossil. Whereas the scientist pictured is measuring the decay of carbon from a sample of bone, you will model the decay of a fictitious radioactive isotope called "tailsium."

PROBLEM How is the half-life of an unstable isotope used to determine the age of a material?

PROCEDURE

1. Arrange your pennies so that they are all tails-side-up. These pennies represent 10 atoms of "tailsium," a radioactive isotope.
2. Pick up all 10 tailsium atoms and drop them on the table. The pennies that fall heads-side-up represent atoms of a more stable element, "headsium." Put the headsium atoms off to the side. Count the number of tailsium atoms. Record that value in a table under toss 1.
3. Pick up only the tailsium atoms and drop them again. Put the newly formed headsium atoms off to the side with the other headsium atoms. Count the number of tailsium atoms and record this value in your table.
4. Repeat step 3 until there is no more tailsium, or until you have run 10 tosses.
5. Share your results with your class. Using the class data, determine the average number of tailsium atoms that remained after each toss.

ANALYZE AND CONCLUDE

1. **Graph Data** Graph your group results along with the average for the class on the same sheet of graph paper. The number of tosses should be on the *x*-axis, and the number of tailsium atoms remaining should be on the *y*-axis.
2. **Calculate** Using the class average, calculate an average half-life for tailsium. This is the number of tosses it took for half of the pennies to "decay" to headsium.
3. **Analyze** Below is the ideal rate of decay for tailsium. Graph these data on the same axes as your other graphs, using a different colored pencil to differentiate between the data sets. Which data set was closer to the ideal rate of decay, your group's data or the class average? Explain.

TABLE 1. IDEAL RATE OF TAILSIUM DECAY

Time	Start	1	2	3	4	5	6	7	8	9	10
# tailsium atoms	10	5	2.5	1.25	0.625	0.313	0.156	0.078	0.039	0.019	0

4. **Apply** Assume that there are 20 years between tosses. According to your data from the penny lab, how old would a material be that had 3 tailsium atoms and 7 headsium atoms? How old would it be according to the class data?

Answers

Sample Data

For a sample of students' data and graphs from this investigation, go to page R103.

Analyze and Conclude

1. The *x*-axis ("Number of Tosses") and *y*-axis ("Number of Talisium Atoms Remaining") should be numbered from 0 to 10. The graph should be a concave curve declining sharply in the first few tosses, then leveling off to 0.
2. Answers will vary, but should be around 1.
3. The class average should be closer to the ideal rate of tailsium decay. Individual answers may vary widely from this ideal rate. A larger sample size is more likely representative of true values.
4. Answers will vary, but should be near 35 years according to the class data if the material decays at the ideal rate of 1.

364 Unit 4: Evolution

12.2 The Geologic Time Scale

KEY CONCEPT The geologic time scale divides Earth's history based on major past events.

MAIN IDEAS
- Index fossils are another tool to determine the age of rock layers.
- The geologic time scale organizes Earth's history.

VOCABULARY
index fossil, p. 365
geologic time scale, p. 367
era, p. 367
period, p. 367
epoch, p. 367

Review
mass extinction, adaptive radiation

B.8.7 Describe the modern scientific theory of the origins and history of life on earth, and evaluate the evidence that supports it.

Connect As you just read, radiometric dating has shown that Earth is very old. It formed about 4.5 billion years ago. Scientists have divided this vast amount of time into manageable units based on major geologic changes.

MAIN IDEA
Index fossils are another tool to determine the age of rock layers.

You have learned that both relative dating and radiometric dating can help scientists determine the age of rock layers. Scientists who are trying to determine the age of a rock layer almost always use two or more methods to confirm results. Index fossils provide an additional tool to determine the age of fossils or the strata in which they are found. **Index fossils** are fossils of organisms that existed only during specific spans of time over large geographic areas.

Using index fossils for age estimates of rock layers is not a new idea. In the late 1700s, English geologist William Smith discovered that certain rock layers contained fossils unlike those in other layers. Using these key fossils as markers, Smith could identify a particular layer of rock wherever it was exposed.

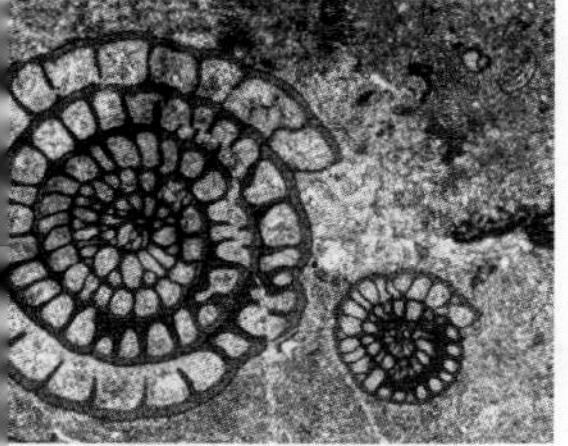

FIGURE 12.5 Fusulinids, tiny fossils usually less than 2 millimeters wide, make good index fossils. They are very abundant in marine sediment, widely distributed, and existed during a specific period of time.

The shorter the life span of a species, the more precisely the different strata can be correlated. The best index fossils are common, easy to identify, found widely around the world, and only existed for a relatively brief time. The extinct marine invertebrates known as fusulinids (FYOO-zuh-LY-nihdz), shown in **FIGURE 12.5**, are one example of an index fossil. They were at one time very common but disappeared after a mass extinction event about 251 million years ago. The presence of fusulinids indicates that a rock layer must be between 251 million and 359 million years old. Fossil fusulinids are useful for dating fossils of other organisms in strata because the presence of both organisms in one layer shows that they lived during the same time period.

A Apply **Could a rock layer with fusulinid fossils be 100 million years old? Explain.**

Differentiated Instruction

PRE-AP
Provide small groups of students with a stack of four colored index cards, ordered as shown. (Enlarged images are included in the Teacher Resources at **ClassZone.com.**) Students are to infer the time period for each stratum and for species 1 and 2. Tell students that if a species existed within the time period represented by a stratum, a well-defined rock layer, its fossil will appear there. Stratum 4 dates to 280–210 mya, stratum 3 dates to 210–150 mya, stratum 2 dates to 150-110 mya; species 1 existed 150–35 mya, species 2 existed 210–150 mya.

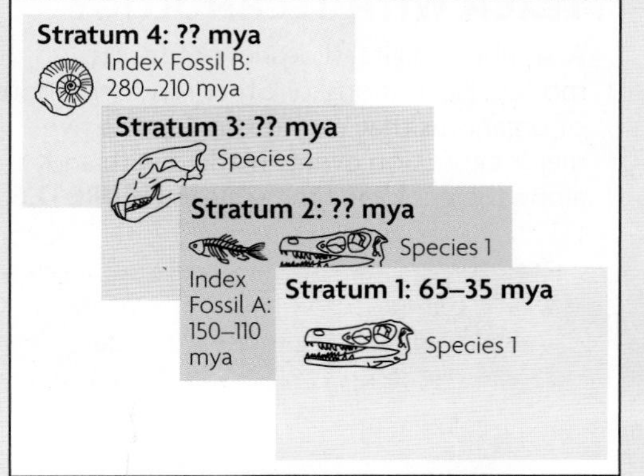

Plan and Prepare

Objectives
- Recognize the role of index fossils in determining the age of rocks.
- Identify the major intervals of the geologic time scale.

Section Resources

Unit Resource Book Study Guide pp. 69–70 Power Notes p. 71 Reinforcement p. 72 Pre-AP Activity pp. 91–92
Interactive Reader Chapter 12 **Spanish Study Guide** pp. 123–124
Biology Toolkit p. C22
Technology Power Presentation 12.2 Media Gallery DVD Online Quiz 12.2

Activate Prior Knowledge Scientists have identified five mass extinctions that have occurred since Earth formed. Many scientists have suggested that today we are in the midst of another mass extinction event because the extinction rate is so high. **Ask,** What are some reasons that species become extinct? habitat loss, climate change, increased predation, competition for resources, pollution, overfishing

Teach

Vocabulary
Academic Vocabulary The term **index** is used for fossils that serve as points of reference for different time periods. *Index* is a Latin word that means "indicator." The first finger, or pointer finger, is also called the index finger. Students can think of an index fossil as one that points, like a finger, to the time period that another fossil came from.

Answers
A **Apply** No, fusulinids lived between 360 and 248 million years ago, so the rock layers in which they are found must have formed in that time.

▼ Teach *continued*

ONLINE BIOLOGY In the chapter Resource Center at **ClassZone.com** students can get more information on the history of life.

TEACH FROM VISUALS

FIGURE 12.6 Have students review the geologic time scale. **Ask**

- What was significant about the Cambrian period? All existing animal phyla evolved during the Cambrian period.
- Did humans and dinosaurs coexist? Explain. No, dinosaurs became extinct at the end of the Cretaceous period, whereas the first primates did not evolve until well into the Tertiary period.
- In what period and era are we living today? Quaternary period, Cenozoic era

Science Trivia

The concept of one billion of anything is often difficult to grasp. Ask students to consider the following:

- If one billion children stood on each others' shoulders, they would reach past the Moon.
- If you laid one billion $1 bills end to end, they would encircle Earth nearly four times.
- If you stacked the bills on top of each other, the pile would be more than 47 miles high.
- If you wanted to count one billion $1 bills, it would take about 5787 days (almost 16 years) of counting without taking a break.

FIGURE 12.6 Geologic Time Scale

X = Major extinction

Millions of years ago (mya): 100, 250, 550, 1000, 2000

CENOZOIC ERA

QUATERNARY PERIOD (NEOGENE)
1.8 mya–present This period continues today and includes all modern forms of life.

TERTIARY PERIOD (PALEOGENE)
65–1.8 mya Mammals, flowering plants, grasslands, insects, fish, and birds diversified. Primates evolved.

Primate

MESOZOIC ERA

X

CRETACEOUS PERIOD
145–65 mya Dinosaur populations peaked and then went extinct. Birds survived to radiate in the Tertiary period. Flowering plants arose.

JURASSIC PERIOD
200–145 mya Dinosaurs diversified, as did early trees that are common today. Oceans were full of fish and squid. First birds

Mononykus

X

TRIASSIC PERIOD
251–200 mya Following the largest mass extinction to date, dinosaurs evolved, as did plants such as ferns and cycads. Mammals and flying reptiles (pterosaurs) arose.

PALEOZOIC ERA

X

PERMIAN PERIOD
299–251 mya Modern pine trees first appeared, and Pangaea supercontinent was formed as major landmasses joined together.

Pine tree

CARBONIFEROUS PERIOD
359–299 mya Coal-forming sediments were laid down in vast swamps. Fish continued to diversify. Life forms included amphibians, winged insects, early conifers, and small reptiles.

X

DEVONIAN PERIOD
416–359 mya Fish diversified. First sharks, amphibians, and insects appeared. First trees and forests arose.

SILURIAN PERIOD
444–416 mya Earliest land plants arose. Melting of glaciers allowed seas to form. Jawless and freshwater fishes evolved.

Jawless fish

X

ORDOVICIAN PERIOD
488–444 mya Diverse marine invertebrates evolved, as did the earliest vertebrates. Massive glaciers formed, causing sea levels to drop and a mass extinction of marine life to occur.

CAMBRIAN PERIOD
542–488 mya All existing animal phyla developed over a relatively short period of time known as the Cambrian Explosion.

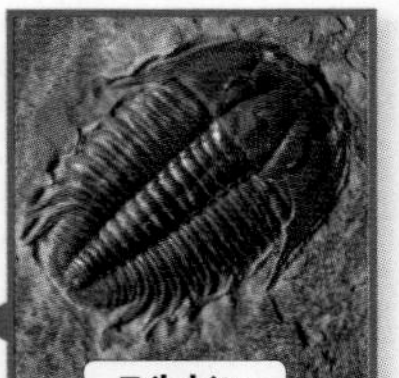

Trilobite

PRECAMBRIAN TIME

This time span makes up the vast majority of Earth's history. It includes the oldest known rocks and fossils, the origin of eukaryotes, and the oldest animal fossils. (colored SEM; magnification 50×)

Cyanobacteria

Differentiated Instruction

TEACH WITH TECHNOLOGY

Assemble a digital slideshow of fossils, models, illustrations, or other representations of organisms that went extinct in the five major extinction events marked with an X along the geologic time scale in **FIGURE 12.6.**

ENGLISH LEARNERS

Have students organize the geologic time scale in **FIGURE 12.6** into a content frame with these column heads: Years, Era, Period, Life Forms, Other Characteristics. Students may prefer to start with the oldest first. Make sure they realize that, in that case, they will need to read the diagram from bottom to top.

Biology Toolkit, Content Frame, p. C22

MAIN IDEA

The geologic time scale organizes Earth's history.

The **geologic time scale,** shown in **FIGURE 12.6**, is a representation of the history of Earth. It organizes Earth's history by major changes or events that have occurred, using evidence from the fossil and geologic records. Scientists worked out the entire geologic time scale during the 1800s and early 1900s. Although they are still being changed a little bit here and there, the main divisions of geologic time have stayed the same for over a hundred years.

The time scale is divided into a series of units based on the order in which different groups of rocks and fossils were formed. The geologic time scale consists of three basic units of time.

- **Eras** last tens to hundreds of millions of years and consist of two or more periods.
- **Periods** are the most commonly used units of time on the geologic time scale, lasting tens of millions of years. Each period is associated with a particular type of rock system.
- **Epochs** (EHP-uhks) are the smallest units of geologic time and last several million years.

The names of the eras came from early ideas about life forms preserved as fossils. *Paleozoic* means "ancient life," *Mesozoic* means "middle life," and *Cenozoic* means "recent life." Within the eras, the boundaries between many of the geologic periods are defined by mass extinction events. These events help to define when one period ends and another begins. The largest adaptive radiations tend to follow large mass extinctions. Recall that adaptive radiation happens when a group of organisms diversifies into several species. Those species adapt to different ecological niches because mass extinctions make many niches available. Over generations, the adaptive traits favored within these newly opened niches may become common for that population of organisms, and speciation may occur.

Connecting **CONCEPTS**

Adaptive Radiation Recall from **Chapter 11** that *adaptive radiation* refers to the change of a single species into several forms that are each adapted to a specific environmental niche.

Summarize **Why do adaptive radiations often occur after mass extinctions?**

12.2 ASSESSMENT

ONLINE QUIZ ClassZone.com

B.8.7

REVIEWING MAIN IDEAS

1. How are **index fossils** used to date rock layers?
2. What is the usefulness of categorizing Earth's history into the **geologic time scale**?

CRITICAL THINKING

3. **Infer** The most common index fossils are shells of invertebrates. Give two reasons why this is so.
4. **Analyze** Scientists have inferred that there have been at least five mass extinctions in Earth's history. How would fossil evidence support this inference?

Connecting **CONCEPTS**

5. **Scientific Process** French physicist Henri Becquerel discovered radioactivity in 1896, after geologists had developed the geologic time scale. How did Becquerel's discovery help later geologists as they refined the time scale?

Vocabulary

Academic Vocabulary Make the analogy between **period** in the geologic sense and a school period. Geologists identify periods not by uniform intervals of time but by their characteristics, such as what kinds of organisms were prevalent or dominant. Students have school periods that are defined not so much by their length or sequence but by their subject, such as math or science.

Assess and Reteach ▼

Assess Use the Online Quiz or Section Quiz (*Assessment Book*, p. 232).

Reteach Choose 11 students to represent the 11 periods. Students should describe the period without naming it. The rest of the class identifies the periods and directs the students to stand in a line in the proper chronological sequence.

Answers

A Summarize Mass extinctions create the opportunity for organisms to disperse across a wider range of habitats or environments. Over generations, populations evolve adaptations to the conditions of these environments.

12.2 ASSESSMENT

1. Index fossils are remains of organisms that are known to have lived during a specific span of time. They can be used to age other fossils by comparing their positions in strata.
2. The geologic time scale helps us organize Earth's history into periods that are characterized by conditions at Earth's surface and the forms of life found there.
3. Invertebrates have been abundant throughout much of Earth's history, and some had shells that are more easily fossilized than soft parts. Many shelled invertebrates lived in the ocean, where the conditions for preservation are better.
4. Abrupt changes in the fossil record support this inference, where species found in older (deeper) rock layers are not found in younger (upper) rock layers. Less species diversity in a younger layer may also suggest a mass extinction. After catastrophic events, there may also be boundary layers of changed sedimentation.
5. Prior to Becquerel's discovery, geologists relied exclusively on the relative dating of rock layers. Discovering radioactivity led to the development of radiometric dating, which offers absolute ages, rather than just the relative ages of rock layers.

SECTION 12.3

▼ Plan and Prepare

Objectives

- Describe the conditions on Earth billions of years ago.
- Summarize the main hypotheses of how life began on Earth.

Section Resources

Unit Resource Book Study Guide pp. 73–74 Power Notes p. 75 Reinforcement p. 76
Interactive Reader Chapter 12 **Spanish Study Guide** pp. 125–126
Biology Toolkit pp. C17, C38
Technology Power Presentation 12.3 Media Gallery DVD Online Quiz 12.3

Activate Prior Knowledge Gauge students' familiarity with theories of Earth's origins. **Ask,** What scientific theories or ideas have you heard of that deal with the formation of Earth and the solar system? "big bang," collapsing and expanding universe (matter squeezed into a grapefruit-sized mass) Discuss the role of the Hubble Space Telescope—direct observation of astronomical phenomena—in shaping or revising cosmological theories.

▼ Teach

Vocabulary

Greek and Latin Word Origins

Nebula is a Latin word meaning "cloud." Like many Latin words ending in *a*, the plural of *nebula* is *nebulae*. **Ask,** What other words ending in *a* are made plural by adding *e*? amoeba(e), antenna(e), nova(e), seta(e)

12.3 Origin of Life

KEY CONCEPT The origin of life on Earth remains a puzzle.

MAIN IDEAS

- Earth was very different billions of years ago.
- Several sets of hypotheses propose how life began on Earth.

VOCABULARY

nebula, p. 368
ribozyme, p. 370

B.8.7 Describe the modern scientific theory of the origins and history of life on earth, and evaluate the evidence that supports it.

Connect By studying the geologic time scale, it is clear that the farther back in Earth's history we go, the tougher it is to piece together what life at that time was like. Hypotheses of how Earth formed and life began have been proposed and researched. But as with any branch of science, questions still remain.

MAIN IDEA

Earth was very different billions of years ago.

For centuries, many of history's greatest minds have wondered about the origin of Earth and its living things. Despite differences over the details of Earth's origins, most scientists agree on two key points: (1) Earth is billions of years old, and (2) the conditions of the early planet and its atmosphere were very different from those of today.

Today, the most widely accepted hypothesis of Earth's origins suggests that the solar system was formed by a condensing **nebula,** a cloud of gas and dust in space, as shown in **FIGURE 12.7.** This hypothesis is supported by computer models and observations made with the Hubble Space Telescope. It suggests that about 4.6 billion years ago, the Sun formed from a nebula. Over time, most of the material in the nebula pulled together due to gravity. Materials that remained in the nebula's disk circled the newly formed Sun. Over millions of years, repeated collisions of this space debris built up into the planets of our solar system.

Earth was most likely violent and very hot for its first 700 million years, a time now called the Hadean eon. Many asteroids, meteorites, and comets struck the planet, releasing enormous amounts of heat. Meanwhile, the radioactive decay of elements trapped deep within Earth released heat as well. This intense heat kept the materials making up Earth in a molten state. Over time, these materials separated into Earth's layers. Hydrogen, carbon monoxide, and nitrogen gas were released from the interior. They combined to form an atmosphere containing compounds such as ammonia, water vapor, methane, and carbon dioxide. Most scientists agree that free oxygen was not abundant until about 2 billion years ago, after the first forms of life had begun to evolve.

FIGURE 12.7 One hypothesis proposes that the Sun and planets formed from a rotating disk of gas and dust about 4.6 billion years ago.

Toward the end of the Hadean eon, between 4 and 3.8 billion years ago, impacts became less frequent. That allowed Earth to cool down. Solar radiation and lightning produced energy for reactions on Earth and in the early atmosphere. The continents began to form. Water vapor condensed and fell as rain that collected in pools and larger bodies of water.

Differentiated Instruction

ENGLISH LEARNERS

Help students connect to content through visuals. They can use different-colored squares of paper to represent each sentence of the paragraphs on page 368, where the formation of the solar system is described. Have a student read a sentence and ask others to describe what they "see." Summarize each sentence description on a card, and post them all on the board until the paragraph is complete. Then ask for a picture summary of each square/sentence.

Biology Toolkit, Connect to Content through Visuals, p. C17

BELOW LEVEL

Have students do sequence diagrams for the nebular hypothesis of Earth's formation and the Miller-Urey experiment. Suggest that students connect the two ideas.

Biology Toolkit, Sequence Diagram, p. C38

Once liquid water was present, organic compounds could be formed from inorganic materials. All living matter is organic, as are the building blocks of life such as sugars and amino acids. However, you'll see below that the leap that resulted in life on Earth required conditions other than just the presence of water.

VOCABULARY

Organic compounds are carbon based and contain carbon–carbon bonds.

A Summarize Describe the nebular hypothesis of Earth's origin.

MAIN IDEA

Several sets of hypotheses propose how life began on Earth.

Since the 1950s, scientists have proposed several hypotheses to explain how life began on Earth. These hypotheses have looked at early organic molecules, how cell structures might have evolved, and early genetic material.

Organic Molecule Hypotheses

There are two general hypotheses about how life-supporting molecules appeared on early Earth.

Miller-Urey experiment In 1953 Stanley Miller and Harold Urey designed an experiment to test a hypothesis first proposed in the 1920s. Earlier scientists had proposed that an input of energy from lightning led to the formation of organic molecules from inorganic molecules present in the atmosphere of early Earth. Miller and Urey built a system to model conditions they thought existed on early Earth, as shown in **FIGURE 12.8.** They demonstrated that organic compounds could be made by passing an electrical current, to simulate lightning, through a mixture of gases. These gases—methane (CH_4), ammonia (NH_3), hydrogen (H_2), and water vapor (H_2O)—were thought to be present in the early atmosphere. The Miller-Urey experiment produced a variety of organic compounds, such as amino acids. Later, scientists suggested different compounds were present in the early atmosphere. However, similar experiments using more recent estimates of conditions on early Earth have also produced organic molecules, including amino acids and nucleotides.

FIGURE 12.8 Miller-Urey Experiment

A laboratory model is used to represent the conditions of early Earth. This experiment demonstrated that organic molecules can be made from inorganic molecules.

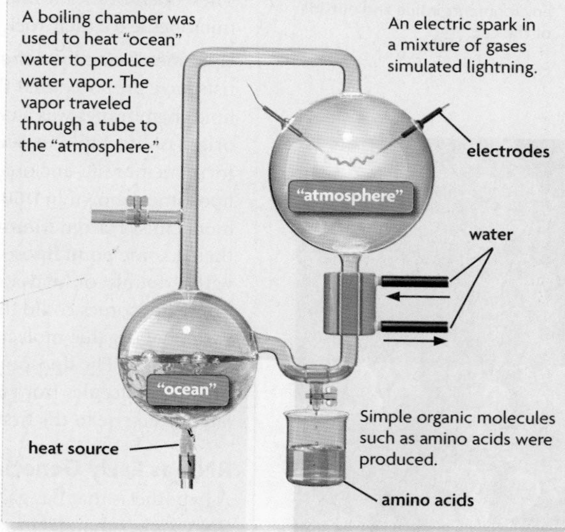
A boiling chamber was used to heat "ocean" water to produce water vapor. The vapor traveled through a tube to the "atmosphere."
An electric spark in a mixture of gases simulated lightning.
electrodes
"atmosphere"
water
"ocean"
heat source
Simple organic molecules such as amino acids were produced.
amino acids

Meteorite hypothesis Analysis of a meteorite that fell near Murchison, Australia, in 1969 revealed that organic molecules can be found in space. More than 90 amino acids have been identified from this meteorite. Nineteen of these amino acids are found on Earth, and many others have been made in experiments similar to the Miller-Urey study. This evidence suggests that amino acids could have been present when Earth formed, or that these organic molecules may have arrived on Earth through meteorite or asteroid impacts.

ONLINE BIOLOGY Go to the chapter Resource Center at **ClassZone.com** for additional resources and information on Earth's ancient past.

Integrating Chemistry

Chemists divide all chemical compounds into two major groups—**organic** and **inorganic.** Organic compounds contain both carbon and hydrogen atoms; inorganic compounds lack hydrocarbons. **Ask,** What inorganic compounds might be found in a living organism? water, carbon dioxide, sodium chloride, other salts

History of Science

The **Miller-Urey experiment** was one of the most famous scientific experiments of the 20th century. It was the first experiment to demonstrate that Earth's organic compounds, which are the building blocks of life, could have been synthesized from inorganic compounds already present on Earth. The results of the experiment stimulated many further inquiries in the scientific community. Later studies incorporated Miller's techniques to show how components of nucleic acids, such as adenine, could have been synthesized from atmospheric gases. The Miller-Urey experiment also laid the foundation for a new branch of science—**exobiology**—that is concerned with life outside Earth. A meteorite that landed in Australia in 1969 contained many organic compounds, some of which were similar to those produced in the Miller-Urey experiment, that are not found in living systems on Earth.

PRE-AP

Using the description of the Miller-Urey experiment in **FIGURE 12.8,** have students translate the information into an illustration of the early Earth. They should include active volcanoes, which were a likely source of carbon and nitrogen compounds as well as water vapor.

Answers

A Summarize Earth and the other planets in our solar system were formed through space debris collisions in a cloud of gas and dust, called a nebula, which circled the Sun.

▼ Teach *continued*

Science Trivia

- The water surrounding hydrothermal vents can reach temperatures as high as 380°C (716°F).
- Common inhabitants of hydrothermal vents include tube worms *(Riftia pachyptila)* that grow as long as 2–3 meters (7–10 ft), giant mussels *(Bathymodiolus thermophilus)* 20 centimeters (8 in.) in length, and giant clams *(Calyptogena magnifica)* 25 centimeters (10 in.) in length.

Integrating Medical Science

The structure and biochemistry of the liposome make it an excellent vehicle for delivering drugs directly to cancerous tumors. In the laboratory, scientists produce **artificial liposomes** that contain a particular drug (for example, a chemotherapy agent) enclosed in a phospholipid sac. Sequestering the drug inside the lipid memb
drug from being degra
patient's body. In stud
patients, researchers h
liposome-containing c
at the target site (such
of infection) in higher
nontarget sites. This a
delivery of the drug to
target and a lowered c
drugs at nontarget site
could cause undesirab

Connecting CONCEPTS

Cells Recall from **Chapter 3** that most cell membranes are composed of two layers of lipids, or fats. The cell membrane maintains a boundary between the environments inside and outside of the cell.

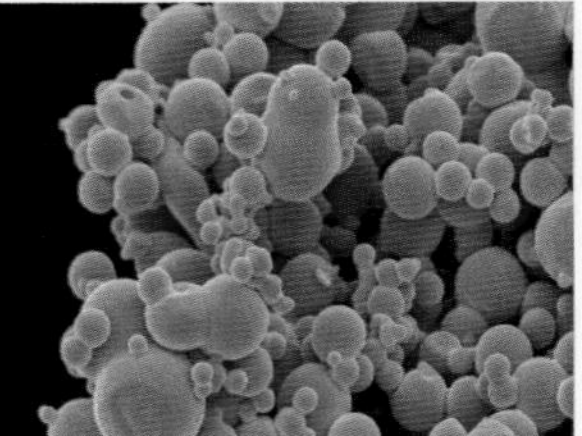

Early Cell Structure Hypotheses

There are several hypotheses of how the first cells may have formed. One concerns how organic molecules could have been brought together, and another addresses how cell membranes may have formed.

Iron-sulfide bubbles hypothesis In the 1990s, biologists William Martin and Michael Russell noted that hot iron sulfide rising from below the ocean floor combines with the cooler ocean water to form chimneylike structures made of many compartments. Russell modeled this process in the laboratory by injecting warm sodium sulfide into a cool iron-rich solution. Iron sulfide bubbles quickly formed, making a similar chimney structure within minutes. Russell proposed that around 4 billion years ago, biological molecules combined in the compartments of these chimneys. The compartment walls concentrated the basic organic molecules in a small space. Thus, the walls of the compartments, Russell proposed, acted as the first cell membranes. Once the right ingredients came together, the first organic cell membranes could form. These membranes would have let early microbes leave their rocky compartments.

FIGURE 12.9 Hydrothermal vents produce sulfur that mixes with ocean water to make compartments of rock. These structures may have created conditions necessary for early life to form.

Lipid membrane hypothesis Several scientists have proposed that the evolution of lipid membranes was a crucial step for the origin of life. Lipid molecules spontaneously form membrane-enclosed spheres, called liposomes, shown in **FIGURE 12.10.** In 1992 biochemist Harold Morowitz tested the idea that at some point liposomes were formed with a double, or bilayer, lipid membrane. These liposomes could then form around a variety of organic molecules, such as amino acids, fatty acids, sugars, and nucleotides. The liposomes would act as membranes that separated these organic molecules from the environment. These cell-like structures may have later given rise to the first true cells.

RNA as Early Genetic Material

A hypothesis that has gained much support in recent years proposes that RNA, rather than DNA, was the genetic material that stored information in living things on early Earth. In the 1980s, Thomas Cech from the University of Colorado and Sidney Altman from Yale University independently discovered that RNA can catalyze reactions. **Ribozymes** are RNA molecules that can catalyze specific chemical reactions. As **FIGURE 12.11** shows, ribozymes can catalyze their own replication and synthesis. RNA can copy itself, chop itself into pieces, and from these pieces make even more RNA. Unlike RNA, DNA needs enzymes to replicate itself.

ction

NOLOGY

Divide students into five groups and assign each group one of the hypotheses discussed in this section. Have each group present a digital slideshow or multimedia presentation on its assigned hypothesis, using visuals and other materials gathered from online resources.

ENGLISH LEARNERS

This section contains a number of familiar terms used in a new context. Have students use the *Multilanguage Glossary* to review the following terms: *replication, lipid, catalyst, prokaryotic cell, eukaryotic cell.*

FIGURE 12.11 RNA AND DNA

RNA, in the form of a ribozyme, is able to replicate itself without the help of additional enzymes.

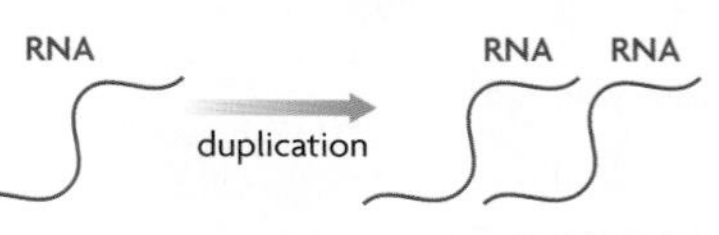

DNA requires many enzymes to replicate. Helicase enzymes separate the DNA strand and polymerase enzymes add nucleotides to the DNA strands.

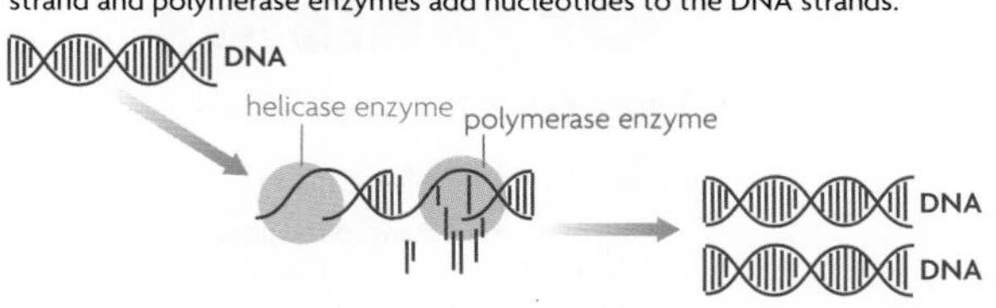

Along with the discovery of ribozymes, several other types of evidence support the RNA hypothesis. Short chains of RNA will form from inorganic materials in a test tube. If zinc is added as a catalyst, longer chains will grow. Also, RNA will fold into different shapes depending upon its sequence of nucleotides. Thus, it can perform more functions than DNA. But RNA does not catalyze chemical reactions as well as proteins do, nor does it store genetic information as well as DNA does. Over time, RNA may have become less important for these functions.

Perhaps the earliest replicating RNA molecule gained simple membranes over many generations through natural selection. Membranes might protect chemical reactions and make them work more efficiently. RNA molecules that made copies of themselves in a double-stranded form, similar to DNA, might eventually have been selected because fewer mutations would occur. Since DNA is more stable than RNA, it may have replaced RNA as the genetic material. Currently, there are several hypotheses about how RNA could have led to life as we know it today. Laboratory experiments in which RNA molecules survive and self-replicate support the idea of early cells being based on RNA. This model of the origins of life on Earth is sometimes called the RNA world.

Synthesize **Could cell structures or RNA have been present before organic molecules existed on Earth? Explain.**

12.3 ASSESSMENT

ONLINE QUIZ ClassZone.com

B.8.7

REVIEWING MAIN IDEAS

1. Describe the environmental conditions that are thought to have existed during the Hadean eon.
2. Describe two different hypotheses of the origin of early cell structure.

CRITICAL THINKING

3. **Evaluate** The theory of impact frustration proposes that life may have started several times during the Hadean eon, but was interrupted by space debris hitting Earth. What makes this theory difficult to test?
4. **Contrast** How are the two organic molecule hypotheses different?

Connecting CONCEPTS

5. **Protein Synthesis** RNA is hypothesized to be the earliest form of genetic material because it can store information, catalyze its own replication, and catalyze other reactions. Which two of these functions can DNA not do? Which two can proteins not do?

TEACH FROM VISUALS

FIGURE 12.11 Have students review the two parts of the figure. **Ask**

- What are ribozymes? RNA molecules that function as enzymes
- What is the primary difference between the replication of ribozymes and DNA as demonstrated in this figure? Ribozymes can replicate without the help of additional enzymes, whereas DNA requires several enzymes for replication.

Discuss the use of the word part *-zyme* as indicative of a chemical that promotes chemical activity.

Assess and Reteach ▼

Assess Use the Online Quiz or Section Quiz (*Assessment Book,* p. 233).

Reteach Work with students to map out a scenario that starts with the formation of Earth and leads to the creation of the first self-replicating "cell."

Answers

A **Synthesize** No, cell structures and RNA both require organic molecules in their synthesis.

12.3 ASSESSMENT

1. The environment was very hot, and Earth was bombarded by asteroids, meteorites, and comets; there was no liquid water; ammonia, water vapor, methane, and carbon dioxide existed in the atmosphere.
2. *Sample Answer:* The iron-sulfide bubbles hypothesis proposes that cells first formed in rocky compartments as organic materials were concentrated in a small space. The walls acted as the first cell membranes until organic cell membranes formed. The lipid membrane hypothesis proposes that a bilayer lipid membrane formed that could then wrap around a variety of organic molecules, isolating them as cell structures.
3. It was a very long time ago, and there is no fossil record. Even if a living thing had existed, it would have been unicellular and unlikely to fossilize.
4. The Miller-Urey hypothesis proposes that organic molecules were formed from inorganic molecules present in the atmosphere of early Earth. The meteorite hypothesis proposes that the first organic molecules fell to Earth on meteorites or asteroids, or were present when Earth formed.
5. DNA cannot catalyze its own replication or catalyze other reactions. Proteins cannot store information or catalyze their own replication.

SECTION 12.4

▼ Plan and Prepare

Objectives

- Recognize the role microbes played in shaping life on Earth.
- Summarize the theory of endosymbiosis.
- Relate increased biodiversity to sexual reproduction.

Section Resources

Unit Resource Book
Study Guide pp. 77–78
Power Notes p. 79
Reinforcement p. 80
Interactive Reader Chapter 12
Spanish Study Guide pp. 127–128
Biology Toolkit pp. C5, C13, C23, C36, D4
Technology
Power Presentation 12.4
Media Gallery DVD
Online Quiz 12.4

Activate Prior Knowledge When scientists look for signs of life, they often look for evidence of water. **Ask,** If you put photosynthetic organisms together with water, what do you get? oxygen as a product Discuss how oxygen first entered Earth's atmosphere.

▼ Teach

Vocabulary

cyanobacteria The prefix *cyano-* comes from *cyan,* a greenish blue color. These bacteria used to be called **blue-green algae.** Tell students that they may see *blue-green algae* in some books and references.

Answers

A Apply Stromatolite fossils can be as old as 3.5 billion years, which means that we know of at least one life form (cyanobacteria) that was alive at that time. Also, cyanobacteria, being photosynthetic, may have helped pave the way for aerobic life forms.

12.4 Early Single-Celled Organisms

KEY CONCEPT Single-celled organisms existed 3.8 billion years ago.

MAIN IDEAS

- Microbes have changed the physical and chemical composition of Earth.
- Eukaryotic cells may have evolved through endosymbiosis.
- The evolution of sexual reproduction led to increased diversity.

VOCABULARY

cyanobacteria, p. 372
endosymbiosis, p. 373

Review
prokaryote, anaerobic, eukaryote, aerobic, asexual reproduction, sexual reproduction

B.8.7 Describe the modern scientific theory of the origins and history of life on earth, and evaluate the evidence that supports it.

Connect By 3.8 billion years ago, the seas of the early Earth were full of organic molecules. As you have read, the leap from free-floating molecules to the first true cells has yet to be discovered. But once the first cells arose, they forever changed Earth's environment.

MAIN IDEA

Microbes have changed the physical and chemical composition of Earth.

Single-celled organisms changed Earth's surface by depositing minerals. They changed the atmosphere by giving off oxygen as a by-product of photosynthesis. However, before photosynthesis evolved, the first prokaryotes would have been anaerobic, living without oxygen. Many of these early prokaryotes probably got their energy from organic molecules.

Scientists have found evidence that photosynthetic life evolved more than 3.5 billion years ago, since that is the age of the oldest known fossils. These fossils are of a group of marine **cyanobacteria** (SY-uh-noh-bak-TEER-ee-uh), which are bacteria that can carry out photosynthesis. Like all early life forms, each cyanobacterium was a single prokaryotic cell. Recall from Chapter 3 that prokaryotic cells have no membrane-bound organelles.

Some cyanobacteria live in colonies and form stromatolites (stroh-MAT-l-yts). Stromatolites are domed, rocky structures made of layers of cyanobacteria and sediment. There are many stromatolite fossils, but some are living communities, as shown in **FIGURE 12.12.** Fossils of stromatolites as old as 3.5 billion years have been found. Communities of photosynthesizing cyanobacteria in stromatolites released oxygen as a by-product. Higher oxygen levels in the atmosphere and the ocean allowed the evolution of aerobic prokaryotes, which need oxygen to live.

FIGURE 12.12 Stromatolites, like these found in Australia, are made by cyanobacteria. Cyanobacteria are considered to have been among the first organisms on early Earth.

A Apply How are stromatolites evidence of Earth's early life?

Differentiated Instruction

ENGLISH LEARNERS

Students can get more out of this section if you incorporate a comprehensive vocabulary review. To the two new vocabulary words at the beginning of the chapter, add *stromatolite.* To the list of review vocabulary, add *photosynthesis (photosynthetic), organelle, chloroplast, mitochondria,* and *ribosome.* Have students work in pairs to create word squares, assigning one or two terms to each pair. When students finish, collect or review their squares.

Biology Toolkit, Word Squares, p. D4

INCLUSION

If there are students who have difficulty accessing the material, pair them with other students for a think-pair-share with a KWL focus. They will share what they know about the early Earth, what they want to know, and what they learn from the section.

Biology Toolkit, KWL, p. C5; Think-Pair-Share, p. C13

MAIN IDEA

Eukaryotic cells may have evolved through endosymbiosis.

The fossil record shows that eukaryotic organisms had evolved by 1.5 billion years ago. Unlike a prokaryote, a eukaryote has a nucleus and other membrane-bound organelles. While the first eukaryotes were made of only one cell, later eukaryotic organisms became multicellular, or made of many cells. All cells in multicellular organisms today are eukaryotic.

One hypothesis of eukaryote evolution, proposed more than a hundred years ago, did not get much attention until the 1970s. Biologist Lynn Margulis of the University of Massachusetts found evidence to support the theory of endosymbiosis. **Endosymbiosis** (EHN-doh-SIHM-bee-OH-sihs) is a relationship in which one organism lives within the body of another, and both benefit from the relationship.

VOCABULARY

Endosymbiosis can be broken down into *endo-*, meaning "within," *sym-*, meaning "together," and *biosis*, meaning "way of life."

The theory of endosymbiosis suggests that early mitochondria and chloroplasts were once simple prokaryotic cells that were taken up by larger prokaryotes around 1.5 billion years ago. Instead of being digested, some of the smaller prokaryotes may have survived inside the larger ones as illustrated in **FIGURE 12.13.** This relationship would have had its advantages. If it took in a prokaryote that acted as a mitochondrion, the larger cell got energy in the form of ATP. If it took in a prokaryote that acted as a chloroplast, the larger cell could use photosynthesis to make sugars. In exchange, the mitochondria and the chloroplasts found a stable environment and nutrients.

Margulis based her theory on several factors. Unlike other organelles, mitochondria and chloroplasts have their own DNA and ribosomes. They can copy themselves within the cell in which they are found. Mitochondria and chloroplasts are also about the same size as prokaryotes, their DNA forms a circle, and their gene structures are similar to that of prokaryotes.

Analyze **What evidence supports the theory of endosymbiosis?**

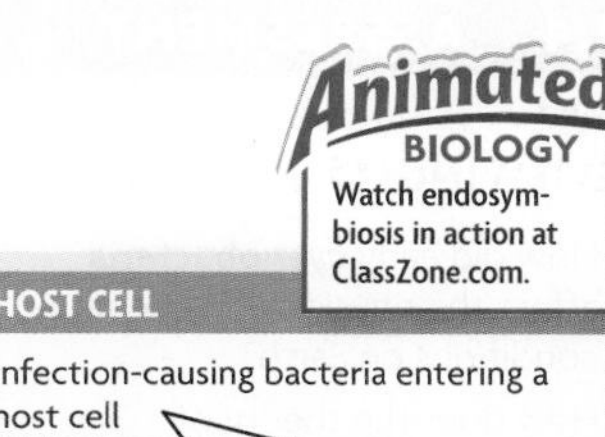

Animated
BIOLOGY
Watch endosymbiosis in action at ClassZone.com.

FIGURE 12.13 Endosymbiosis

The theory of endosymbiosis proposes that the mitochondria found in eukaryotic cells descended from ancestors of infection-causing bacteria. Likewise, chloroplasts are considered descendants of cyanobacteria.

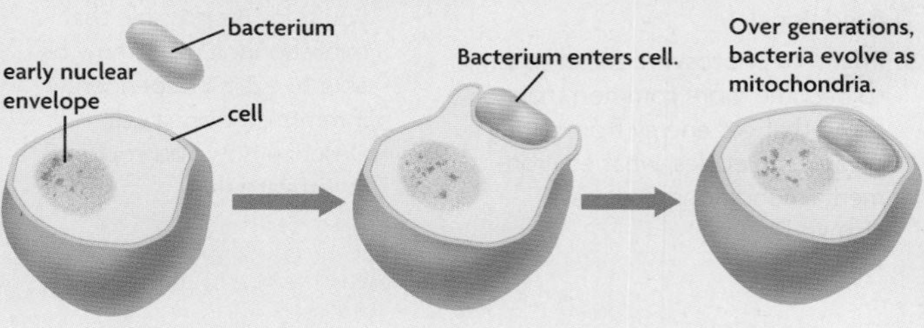

HOST CELL

Infection-causing bacteria entering a host cell

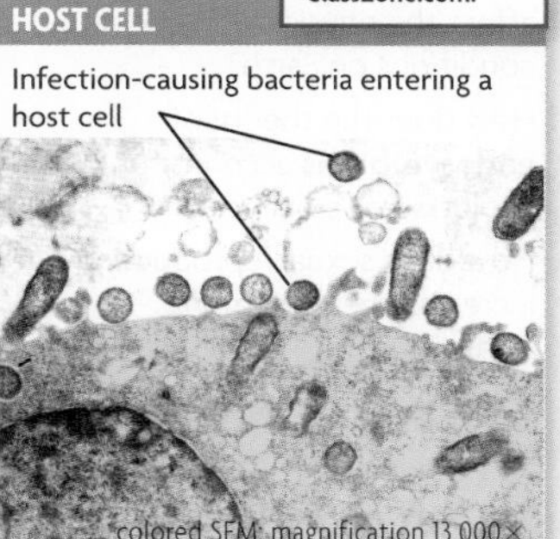

TEACH FROM VISUALS

FIGURE 12.13 Use the figure to review the theory of endosymbiosis. **Ask**

- What selective advantage did the host prokaryotes gain from taking in and maintaining the mitochondria-like prokaryotes? ability to process energy more efficiently And for taking in chloroplast-like prokaryotes? ability to make their own sugars via photosynthesis
- What advantages did the mitochondria-like and chloroplast-like prokaryotes get? stable environment, nutrients

Vocabulary

Greek and Latin Word Origins The roots of **endosymbiosis** can be found in many other words used in biology.

- *Endocytosis* is the process *(-osis)* of taking something into a cell *(cyto-).*
- *Endotherm* describes an organism that maintains a constant internal temperature *(-therm).*
- *Endoskeleton* is an internal skeleton.
- *Symbiosis* is a process *(-osis)* or relationship in which two organisms function together, in some cases for their mutual benefit.

Answers

A Analyze Mitochondria and chloroplasts copy themselves within the cell instead of relying on the cell's replication apparatus, indicating these organelles were once distinct organisms, probably ancestors of early prokaryotes. They are about the same size as prokaryotes, their DNA forms a circle like prokaryotes, and their gene structures also resemble those of prokaryotes.

PRE-AP

Have students spend five minutes creating cause and effect chains describing how life evolved, beginning with cyanobacteria, then aerobic prokaryotes, and finally eukaryotes. Have students incorporate key terms—*cyanobacterium, photosynthesis,* and *chloroplast*—in a way that defines each through context.

Biology Toolkit, Cause and Effect Chain, p. C36

BELOW LEVEL

Have students use a combination of descriptive sentences and diagrams to help them understand the theory of endosymbiosis. Encourage them to highlight the selective advantages to both host and infecting cells.

Biology Toolkit, Combination Notes, p. C23

▼ Teach *continued*

Address Misconceptions

Common Misconception Because sexual reproduction and genetic diversity are stressed as adaptive advantages, students may think that organisms that reproduce asexually are less successful.

Correcting the Misconception Although the genetic variation produced through sexual reproduction can be a selective advantage, some asexual species have survived for millions of years. One notable example is the bdelloid rotifers, a group of microscopic aquatic animals found around the world. All bdelloids are females that reproduce asexually and have been doing so for more than 40 million years. Not only has this group endured, but it has more than 360 species. One advantage of asexual reproduction, which is often prolific and frequent, is that the rate of mutations is greater, which is another way of achieving genetic variation in a population. Other groups, such as the echinoderms and sponges, have species that reproduce asexually and sexually.

▼ Assess and Reteach

Assess Use the Online Quiz or Section Quiz (*Assessment Book,* p. 234).

Reteach Divide students into three groups. Have each group prepare an oral summary based on a section head.

Answers

A Infer Mutations can provide a trait that is useful in the environment in which the organism exists.

MAIN IDEA

The evolution of sexual reproduction led to increased diversity.

The first prokaryotes and eukaryotes could only reproduce asexually. Some time later, eukaryotic cells began to reproduce sexually. Of the groups of organisms that reproduce asexually today, only a few—such as bacteria and certain groups of mites—appear to have ancient asexual origins.

Recall from Chapter 5 that in asexual reproduction, a single parent produces offspring that are genetically identical to itself. Asexual reproduction lets organisms have many offspring quickly. Sexual reproduction, on the other hand, needs two parents. Both parents give genes to their offspring. This means that individuals must use time and energy to find a mate, and each parent passes on only half of its genes to offspring.

The evolution of sexual reproduction is still an active area of research. The disadvantages of sexual reproduction—needing a partner and passing on only half of a set of genes—seem clear. One advantage to sexual reproduction, however, is genetic variation. Sexual reproduction allows new combinations of genes to come together. This process may mask harmful mutations, and in some cases it may also bring beneficial mutations together.

Sexual reproduction may also have resulted in an increase in the rate of evolution by natural selection. Sexual reproduction creates more genetic variation, which lets a population adapt quickly to new conditions. Over a long time, early eukaryotes may have gained variations that made living closely together, and eventually cooperating, beneficial. Thus, sexual reproduction may have been the first step in the evolution of multicellular life.

Connecting CONCEPTS

Genetics Recall from **Chapter 6** that recombination is an important source of genetic variation. Sexual reproduction results in many different phenotypes through the process of producing gametes and during crossing-over in meiosis.

 Infer **How can mutations be beneficial to organisms?**

12.4 ASSESSMENT

ONLINE QUIZ ClassZone.com

B.8.7

REVIEWING MAIN IDEAS

1. How did early **cyanobacteria** affect the physical and chemical conditions on Earth?
2. How does the theory of **endosymbiosis** account for the evolution of eukaryotes?
3. How does sexual reproduction increase diversity among living things?

CRITICAL THINKING

4. **Apply** How does sexual reproduction increase the chances that some individuals will survive changed environmental conditions?
5. **Infer** For photosynthetic organisms to become more common than those that get energy from eating organic molecules, what environmental conditions must have changed?

Connecting CONCEPTS

6. **Scientific Process** According to the theory of endosymbiosis, mitochondria were once independent organisms. Do you think it's possible that mitochondria might now be able to exist independently if removed from a cell? Describe how you could investigate this.

12.4 ASSESSMENT

1. Cyanobacteria created mineral structures and also supported aerobic life through the production of oxygen.
2. The theory of endosymbiosis proposes that larger prokaryotes engulfed smaller prokaryotes, resulting in a symbiotic relationship that was an adaptive advantage for all.
3. Through gamete production and crossing-over, sexual reproduction provides genetic variation.
4. In a sexually reproductive population, there is more mixing and combining of traits than in an asexual population. Rather than depending on mutation alone to create a trait that can be advantageous, recombination of alleles can yield new traits relatively quickly, possibly allowing a population to adapt to new environmental conditions more rapidly.
5. In order for photosynthetic organisms to evolve and thrive, there must have been increased levels of sunlight and plenty of carbon dioxide in the atmosphere and oceans.
6. Mitochondria could survive on their own perhaps if they were in a nutrient-rich environment. One test would be to try to raise excised mitochondria in a cell culture, with normal eukaryotic cells as a control.

NOS.3

DATA ANALYSIS ClassZone.com

Generation Times of Bacteria

Determining the correct scales of axes on graphs is important so that all data points can be plotted. The scale can also influence the reader's perception of the results. If the intervals are too far apart, the slope of the graph will seem steep—indicating a fast rate or a large change in the data. If the intervals are too small, the graph will be flatter, with change that seems small or nonexistent.

EXAMPLE

Some species that reproduce asexually have the benefit of short generation times. They may be able to adapt more quickly to changing environmental conditions. Bacteria populations, for instance, can quickly become resistant to antibiotics. Individual bacteria that survive antibiotic treatment will pass the gene for resistance to their offspring when they reproduce.

***E. coli* bacteria dividing** (colored SEM; magnification 32,000×)

The population of bacteria doubles with each generation. The following are the steps used to determine axis intervals of the line graph of the growth of *Escherichia coli* over 5 generations:

- Calculate the difference between the smallest and largest values of the variable and divide the difference by the number of data points. For the *E. coli* data, 85 – 17 = 68. Divided by 5, this equals 13.6.
- Round the result to the nearest convenient number, such as 2, 5, or 10. For *E. coli*, the interval was rounded down to 12.
- Use the rounded number as the interval.
- Begin the scale on the axis at zero (or at one interval lower than the lowest value if the values to be graphed are much larger than the interval).
- End the scale above the highest value. For *E. coli*, the scale ranges from 0 to 96.

GRAPH 1. GENERATION TIME IN *E. COLI*

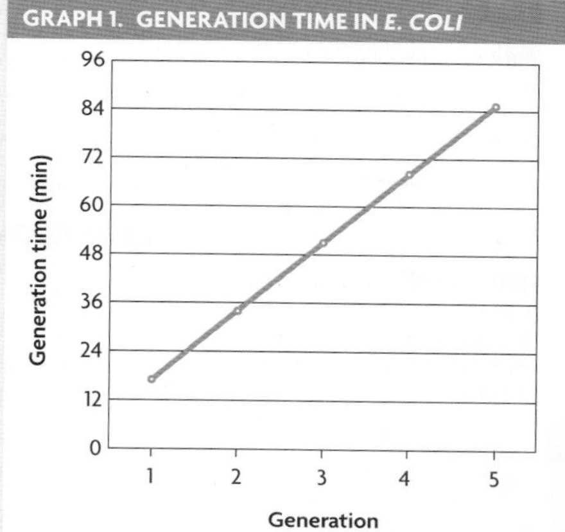

CALCULATE AXES INTERVALS

1. **Graph Data** Calculate the intervals for the *y*-axis and *x*-axis for a graph that compares the generation times of all three of the bacteria species listed below. Draw the axes, plot the data, and label each of the three plotted lines. Be sure to title your graph and label your axes.

TABLE 1. GENERATION TIMES FOR COMMON BACTERIA

Bacteria	Generation 1 Time (min)	Generation 2 Time (min)	Generation 3 Time (min)	Generation 4 Time (min)	Generation 5 Time (min)
	10 bacteria	20 bacteria	40 bacteria	80 bacteria	160 bacteria
E. coli	17	34	51	68	85
B. megaterium	25	50	75	100	125
S. lactis	48	96	144	192	240

2. **Analyze** Using your graph for *E. coli* as an example, explain how changing the axes of a graph can influence how data are interpreted.

Answers

1. Graphs will vary depending on how students calculate the intervals, but all should show three different linear curves of varying slopes and a *y*-axis that goes to approximately 250. See samples to the right.
2. The rate of change can be emphasized or minimized by changing the scales, thereby influencing the reader's interpretation of the results. For *E. coli*, the slope of the line is reduced if the intervals are set to suit the *S. lactis* data, making it appear as though *E. coli* population growth is relatively slow.

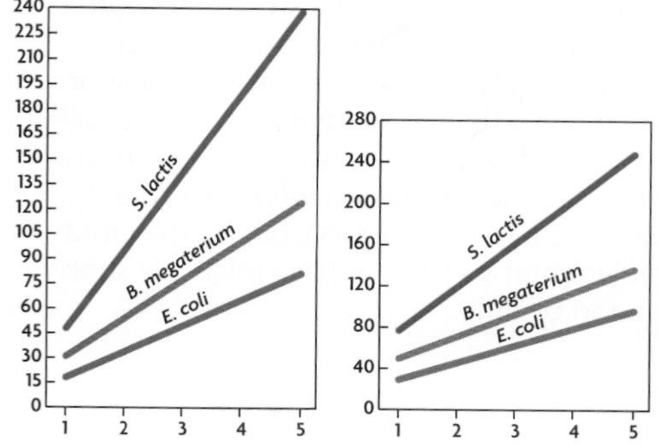

DATA ANALYSIS

Introduce

Graphs are powerful tools for communicating data, but if created incorrectly, they steer one's interpretations in a particular direction. **Ask**

- What would the slope of the *E. coli* graph look like if the *y*-axis scale had a range of 0 to 540 minutes? It would appear much flatter.
- What does the slope of the line on the graph represent? the rate at which the bacteria population doubles

Discuss

After the students have completed their graphs, have them consider what changes would need to be made if data from other species were added. **Ask**

- What is the value of placing all three curves on the same graph? The generation time of the different bacteria can be directly compared.
- What would three existing curves look like if data of a fourth bacterium—with generation times 150, 300, 600, 1200, and 2400 minutes—were added? The other curves would become very flat and hard to differentiate from each other.
- In such a graph, what would be easy to see and what would be difficult? It would be easy to see that the fourth bacterium's generation times are much longer than the other three. It would be hard to compare the original three bacteria to each other.
- Imagine you also have the data of generation times of three species of mammal. What kind of graph would you create to compare the generation times of the mammals with those of the bacteria? Graph all six species' data on the same graph.
- What would be difficult to see in such a graph? Explain. The data of the three bacteria would look like a single horizontal line on the bottom of the graph, because the intervals needed for the mammal generation times (years) would be enormous compared to what would be appropriate for bacteria.

Unit Resource Book, Data Analysis, p. 89

SECTION 12.5

▼ Plan and Prepare

Objectives

- Summarize the key events in the Paleozoic, Mesozoic, and Cenozoic eras.
- Identify how changes in environmental conditions affected the evolution and radiation of animal groups.

Section Resources

Unit Resource Book
Study Guide pp. 81–82
Power Notes p. 83
Reinforcement p. 84
Pre-AP Activity pp. 93–94

Interactive Reader Chapter 12
Spanish Study Guide pp. 129–130

Biology Toolkit p. C15

Technology
Power Presentation 12.5
Media Gallery DVD
Online Quiz 12.5

Activate Prior Knowledge Students will likely have some prior knowledge of dinosaurs and the Mesozoic era. **Ask,** To what kinds of habitats were dinosaurs and reptiles of the Mesozoic era adapted? tropical and temperate terrain, desert, oceans **Ask,** Assuming those habitats are similar to today's, why aren't there dinosaurs on Earth anymore? They were wiped out, possibly by a meteorite, climate change, or disease.

▼ Teach

Take It Further

An important development during the Paleozoic era was the **amniotic egg.** The amniotic egg is surrounded by a hard shell that prevents the interior structures from drying out. Inside the eggs fluid-filled membranes help the developing embryos survive. Both traits allowed for these eggs to be laid in nonaquatic habitats—a crucial step in the transition of animals from aquatic habitats to terrestrial ones.

12.5 Radiation of Multicellular Life

KEY CONCEPT Multicellular life evolved in distinct phases.

MAIN IDEAS
- Life moved onto land during the Paleozoic era.
- Reptiles radiated during the Mesozoic era.
- Mammals radiated during the Cenozoic era.

VOCABULARY
Paleozoic, p. 376
Cambrian explosion, p. 376
Mesozoic, p. 377
Cenozoic, p. 378

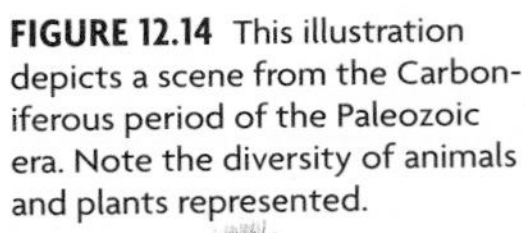

B.8.7 Describe the modern scientific theory of the origins and history of life on earth, and evaluate the evidence that supports it.

Connect Due to early photosynthetic organisms, oxygen levels in Earth's atmosphere began to increase dramatically about 2 billion years ago. As multicellular organisms evolved, the new environment produced new ecological opportunities for organisms.

MAIN IDEA

Life moved onto land during the Paleozoic era.

The trend toward multicellular organisms was one of the most important transitions in the history of life. One hypothesis suggests that it was an advantage for early one-celled organisms to increase in size by becoming multicellular. Cells that cooperated could compete more effectively for energy, by processes such as cooperative feeding. At some point, increased dependence on neighboring cells would have led the cells to function as a colony.

Multicellular organisms first appeared during the **Paleozoic** (PAY-lee-uh-ZOH-ihk) era, which began 542 million years ago. Members of every major animal group evolved within only a few million years. The era ended 251 million years ago with a mass extinction. More than 90 percent of marine animal species and 70 percent of land animal species of that time became extinct. In between these remarkable events, multicellular animals radiated, the first vertebrates evolved, and early plants moved onto land.

FIGURE 12.14 This illustration depicts a scene from the Carboniferous period of the Paleozoic era. Note the diversity of animals and plants represented.

The earliest part of the Paleozoic era is often called the **Cambrian explosion.** During the Cambrian explosion, a huge diversity of animal species evolved. At the start of the Paleozoic era, all life was found in the ocean. Among the earliest vertebrates was a group of jawless fishes. Marine invertebrates, such as the trilobites, were especially abundant. This highly diverse group of arthropods had thousands of species, though almost half of these species died in the mass extinction event at the end of the Cambrian period. Many other animals from this time period are also extinct. The best-known of these are found at the Burgess Shale site in British Columbia, where many fossils were well preserved.

Differentiated Instruction

ENGLISH LEARNERS

Point out to students that while the word *explosion* is commonly associated with bombs, *explosion* can mean the flowing or bursting forth in many directions of virtually anything, from physical things to emotions. The Cambrian explosion refers not to a violent physical explosion, but to the rapid radiation of species within a relatively short period of time.

The middle of the Paleozoic era was a time of great diversity as life moved onto land. The number and variety of plant groups greatly increased. Four-legged vertebrates, such as amphibians, became common. Most of the coal used in the United States formed during the Carboniferous period of this era, illustrated in **FIGURE 12.14.** The decomposed remains of millions of organisms were buried in sediment and changed over time into coal and the petroleum that fuels our cars today.

A **Summarize** **Why is part of the Cambrian period also called the Cambrian explosion?**

MAIN IDEA

Reptiles radiated during the Mesozoic era.

The **Mesozoic** (MEHZ-uh-ZOH-ihk) era began 251 million years ago and ended 65 million years ago. Called the Age of Reptiles because the dinosaurs roamed Earth during this era, the Mesozoic also featured birds and flowering plants. The oldest direct ancestor of mammals first appeared during this era. By the era's end, mammals—particularly marsupials, whose young develop in a pouch—had evolved numerous key traits that improved their chances of survival during the mass extinction at the end of the era.

The Mesozoic era is divided into three periods: the Triassic, the Jurassic, and the Cretaceous. Life took off slowly in the early Triassic, as organisms that survived earlier extinction events explored new environments. On land, the earliest crocodiles and dinosaurs arose. The fossil record shows that the first mammals also evolved during this time. An extinction event near the end of the Triassic destroyed many animal families. This mass extinction allowed the radiation of the dinosaurs in the Jurassic period, illustrated in **FIGURE 12.15.**

Although life had moved onto land, it was abundant under water as well. Ichthyosaurs (IK-thee-uh-SAWRZ), a specialized group of predatory marine reptiles, dominated the oceans. Sharks and bony fishes continued to evolve more complex forms.

The peak in dinosaur diversity, the Cretaceous period, also saw the rise of the first marsupial mammals. The period ended in the most famous of the mass extinctions, when a massive meteorite struck Earth. This impact sent enormous amounts of dust and debris into the atmosphere. Scientists think this airborne debris kept much of the Sun's light from reaching Earth, which in turn caused a change in climate and reduced photosynthesis. Without plants to eat, dinosaurs became extinct.

B **Analyze** **How had life on Earth changed from the beginning of the Paleozoic era to the end of the Mesozoic?**

FIGURE 12.15 This illustration depicts a scene from the Jurassic period of the Mesozoic era. Fossils of pterosaurs (above) have been found in groups, suggesting that they may have lived in colonies.

Vocabulary

Greek and Latin Word Origins The eras of the geologic time scale are named for when they occurred relative to the present time. The suffix *-zoic* comes from the Greek root *zōikos,* meaning "of animals." The prefixes refer to each era's relative age:

paleo = ancient
meso = middle
ceno = new

Science Trivia

When it was first discovered by paleontologists, the slender dinosaur *Oviraptor* was immediately labeled a thief. During a desert expedition to the Gobi in 1924, paleontologists uncovered a small fossilized theropod dinosaur on top of a clutch of broken dinosaur eggs. To paleontologists, the case seemed clear. The dinosaur, a biped with the powerful hind limbs and strong, clawed fingers of a predator, obviously had been preying on the eggs of another dinosaur—most likely a *Protoceratops,* because several fossils of that species lay nearby. So the newly discovered dinosaur was named *Oviraptor,* from the Latin words for *egg* and *thief.*

Then in the mid-1990s, scientists once again found a nest of dinosaur eggs underneath an *Oviraptor* skeleton. This skeleton, however, had the posture of a chicken or other animal that incubates its own eggs. Later the scientists found that one egg contained a tiny *Oviraptor* embryo. Far from being an egg predator, the *Oviraptor* was being a good mother.

BELOW LEVEL

Have students form groups of three and then number off and form expert groups, one for each era discussed in this section. After each expert group discusses and writes down the major characteristics and developments of each era, have the original groups form again and share what they have learned.

Biology Toolkit, Jigsaw Reading, p. C15

Answers

A **Summarize** There was a tremendous diversification of life forms and radiation of species during this time.

B **Analyze** There were relatively few types of organisms at the beginning of the Paleozoic era, and most were quite small. By the end of the Mesozoic era, many organisms had roamed Earth and the seas.

▼ Teach *continued*

Integrating Ecology

Why did mammals become so successful and undergo such a dramatic radiation in the early Cenozoic era? The sudden availability of many **niches** may have been a factor. A *niche* is the role that an organism plays in its environment. As the dominant land animals during the Mesozoic, dinosaurs occupied many varied niches. As the dinosaurs decreased in number, the niches they had occupied opened up. Mammals that had key adaptations (traits that allowed them to evolve to fill the niches) were better able to compete for and occupy these niches. Thus, the demise of the dinosaurs and many other animals at the close of the Cretaceous opened up new opportunities for mammals of the Cenozoic. Students will learn more about niches in Chapter 14.

Answers

A Infer Placental mammals and monotremes, egg-laying mammals, diversified during this era.

▼ Assess and Reteach

Assess Use the Online Quiz or Section Quiz (*Assessment Book*, p. 235).

Reteach Have students work in groups to summarize the major events of each era discussed in this section.

MAIN IDEA

Mammals radiated during the Cenozoic era.

The **Cenozoic** era (SEE-nuh-ZOH-ihk) began 65 million years ago and continues today. It is divided into two periods, the Tertiary (65–1.8 million years ago), illustrated in **FIGURE 12.16**, and the Quaternary (1.8 million years ago until today). During the Tertiary, placental mammals and monotremes—a small group of mammals that lay eggs—evolved and diversified. Their adaptive radiation rivaled that of the marsupials in the Mesozoic. The most dramatic radiation of the mammals, however, occurred with the placentals. Today, this group numbers roughly 4000 species. During the Tertiary period, birds, ray-finned fishes, and flowering plants also underwent dramatic radiations.

The earliest ancestors of modern humans evolved near the end of the Tertiary. However, *Homo sapiens*, anatomically modern humans, did not appear until about 100,000 years ago, very recently in Earth's history. The evolution of primates is covered in the next section.

Connecting CONCEPTS

Mammals Placental mammals include all monotremes, which lay eggs, and marsupials, which rear their underdeveloped young in a pouch. You will learn more about mammals in **Chapter 26**.

HORSE ANCESTOR (55 MYA)

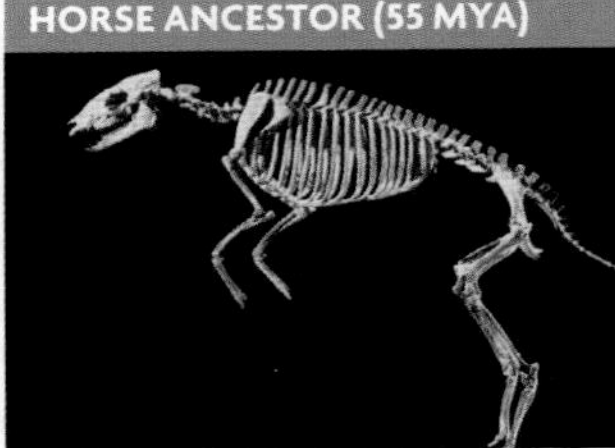

FIGURE 12.16 This illustration depicts a scene from the Tertiary period of the Cenozoic era. This ancestor of modern-day horses (above) was the size of a small dog.

NSTA SCILINKS scilinks.org

For more about the rise of mammals, go to scilinks.org. Keycode: MLB012

A Infer Why is the Cenozoic era sometimes referred to as the Age of Mammals?

12.5 ASSESSMENT

ONLINE QUIZ ClassZone.com

B.8.7

REVIEWING MAIN IDEAS

1. What important events occurred during the **Paleozoic** era?
2. What were some of the key appearances and radiations in the **Mesozoic** era?
3. What two groups of mammals evolved during the **Cenozoic** era?

CRITICAL THINKING

4. **Contrast** Examine the illustrations of the Paleozoic, Mesozoic, and Cenozoic eras in this section. What differences can you see in plant and animal diversity across these eras?
5. **Infer** How does a great diversity of organisms increase the chances that some will survive a major change in the environment?

Connecting CONCEPTS

6. **Ecology** How do you think the evolution of flowering plants affected the evolution and radiation of birds?

12.5 ASSESSMENT

1. Multicellular organisms arose, life moved from sea to land, and there were both the rapid diversification of the Cambrian explosion and a mass extinction event.
2. *Sample Answer:* dinosaurs, marsupial mammals, flowering plants, birds, predatory marine reptiles, bony fishes
3. placentals and monotremes
4. *Sample Answer:* Plants, aquatic reptiles, and insects dominate the scene of the Paleozoic era. The scene from the Mesozoic era depicts many dinosaurs and smaller reptiles that were on land and that could fly. The Cenozoic era scene shows a large predatory bird with smaller mammals in trees and roaming on the ground.
5. If there is a wide diversity among organisms, it is more likely that at least some will have characteristics that will be beneficial, or at least good enough, when environmental conditions change.
6. The evolution of flowering plants gave birds a greater diversity of habitats and foods.

12.6 Primate Evolution

KEY CONCEPT Humans appeared late in Earth's history.

MAIN IDEAS

- Humans share a common ancestor with other primates.
- There are many fossils of extinct hominids.
- Modern humans arose about 200,000 years ago.

VOCABULARY

primate, p. 379
prosimian, p. 379
anthropoid, p. 380
hominid, p. 380
bipedal, p. 381

INDIANA STANDARDS

B.8.7 Describe the modern scientific theory of the origins and history of life on earth, and evaluate the evidence that supports it.

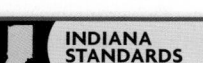

Connect In terms of the geologic time scale, the evolution of humans has occurred only very recently. Many fossils of our early ancestors consist of partial skeletons from which details must be inferred through careful study. Though far from complete, this fossil record offers a fascinating glimpse of our past.

MAIN IDEA

Humans share a common ancestor with other primates.

The common ancestor of all primates probably arose before the mass extinction that closed the Cretaceous period 65 million years ago. **Primates** make up a category of mammals with flexible hands and feet, forward-looking eyes—which allows for excellent three-dimensional vision—and enlarged brains relative to body size. Primates also have arms that can rotate in a circle around their shoulder joint, and many primates have thumbs that can move against their fingers. Primates include lemurs, monkeys, apes, and humans. In addition to sharing similar physical traits, primates share strong molecular similarities.

Primate Evolution

Similar to other groups of related organisms, the relationship among the primate groups forms a many-branched tree. At the tree's base is the common ancestor of all primates. Just above this base, the tree splits into two main subgroups: the prosimians and the anthropoids. **Prosimians** (proh-SIHM-ee-uhnz) are the oldest living primate group, and most are small and active at night. This group of nocturnal animals includes the lemurs, the lorises, and the tarsiers, like the ones shown in **FIGURE 12.17.** Tarsiers have been called living fossils, as their physical traits have changed little since their appearance in the fossil record more than 40 million years ago.

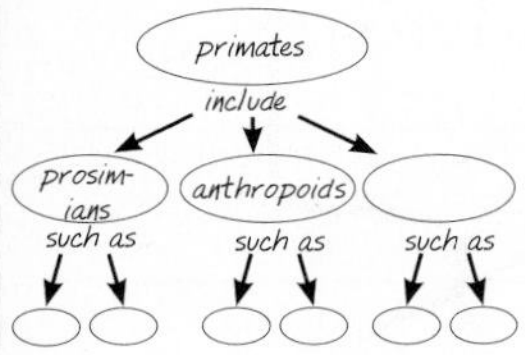

FIGURE 12.17 Prosimians, such as these tarsiers, are the oldest living primate group. They are active at night and have large eyes and ears.

TAKING NOTES

Make a concept map of primate classification. Add more shapes as needed.

primates
include
prosimians
anthropoids
such as
such as
such as

Differentiated Instruction

ENGLISH LEARNERS

In groups of approximately four, have students number off. Ask several questions about each of the section's three parts. Have students discuss for a few minutes to find and agree on an answer. Decide whether they can or cannot consult the text. Choose one number. Group members with that number say the answer or write it on the board. Provide feedback on their answers.

Biology Toolkit, Numbered Heads Together, p. C16

TEACH WITH TECHNOLOGY

Encourage students to use the Internet to learn more about primate phylogeny. Invite them to expand one branch of the cladogram in **FIGURE 12.18** (for example, Old World monkeys). Students should use a computer graphics program to construct their cladograms, or they can create multimedia presentations about their primate branch to be shared with the class.

Plan and Prepare

Objectives

- Examine the evolutionary relationships between humans and other primates.
- Recognize the names and relative ages of extinct hominids.
- Summarize the events and forces that shaped human evolution.

Section Resources

Humans & Primates

Ask: What living primate species is the closest relative to our species? the chimpanzee Its DNA differs from ours by less than 4 percent. One major difference between the two species is that in humans a gene called *FOXP2* codes for speech ability, while in chimps this gene does not.

Teach

Vocabulary

Greek and Latin Word Origins Students may become confused by the similarity between **hominoid** and **hominid.** Explain that the suffixes *-oid* and *-id* are from the Greek words meaning "resembles" and "belonging to." *Hominoid* is a more general group of primates that includes gibbons, orangutans, humans, chimpanzees, and gorillas. In contrast, *hominid* refers specifically to species in the human lineage.

▼ Teach *continued*

Take It Further

Anthropoid primates are divided into two main groups: the **platyrrhines** and the **catarrhines.**

- The New World, or Neotropical, monkeys are *platyrrhines* (plat-ih-RINES). They are so named because they have flattened (*platy-*) noses (*rhin-*) with nostrils that point to the side.
- The *catarrhines* (cat-ih-REENS) include the Old World monkeys, apes, and humans. Catarrhines have straight noses with nostrils that point downward (*cata-*).

TEACH FROM VISUALS

FIGURE 12.18 is structured like a family tree. At each point of separation, two distinct groups of organisms evolved from a common ancestor. **Ask,** Is a gorilla more closely related to a gibbon or an orangutan, and how can you tell? orangutan, because point of divergence for orangutans and hominids is about 8 million years after divergence of hominid/orangutan and gibbon group

Science Trivia

- Howler monkeys (of the genus *Alouatta*) are the largest monkeys and loudest animals in the Americas. They can grow up to 1.2 meters (4 ft) tall and may weigh up to 9 kilograms (20 lb). Their howl can be heard as far away as 4.8 kilometers (3 mi).
- The world's tiniest monkeys are the pygmy marmosets. Native to South American rain forests, these animals measure about 13 centimeters (5 in.) long (not including their tails) and weigh 113–199 grams (4–7 oz).

Answers

Ⓐ **Analyze** approximately 46 million years ago

VOCABULARY

The term *anthropoids* comes from the word root *anthropo*, which means "human."

Anthropoids (AN-thruh-POYDZ), the humanlike primates, are further subdivided into the New World monkeys, Old World monkeys, and hominoids, as shown in **FIGURE 12.18.** New World monkeys, which are native to the Americas, all live in trees. Many species have prehensile, or grasping, tails, an adaptation that allows them to hang by their tails from tree branches while feeding. Some Old World monkeys also spend time in trees, but most travel and forage on the ground as well. They have larger brains than do New World monkeys and a greater ability to manipulate objects.

The hominoids can be further divided into the lesser apes (gibbons), the great apes (orangutans, chimpanzees, and gorillas), and the hominids. **Hominids** walk upright, have long lower limbs, thumbs that oppose—or work against—the other four fingers, and relatively large brains. This group includes all of the species in the human lineage, both modern and extinct.

FIGURE 12.18 Evolutionary Relationships of Primates

Primates are divided into two groups: anthropoids and prosimians. Anthropoids are divided into hominoids and monkeys. The last division separates the lesser and the great apes from hominids, which include all species in the human lineage.

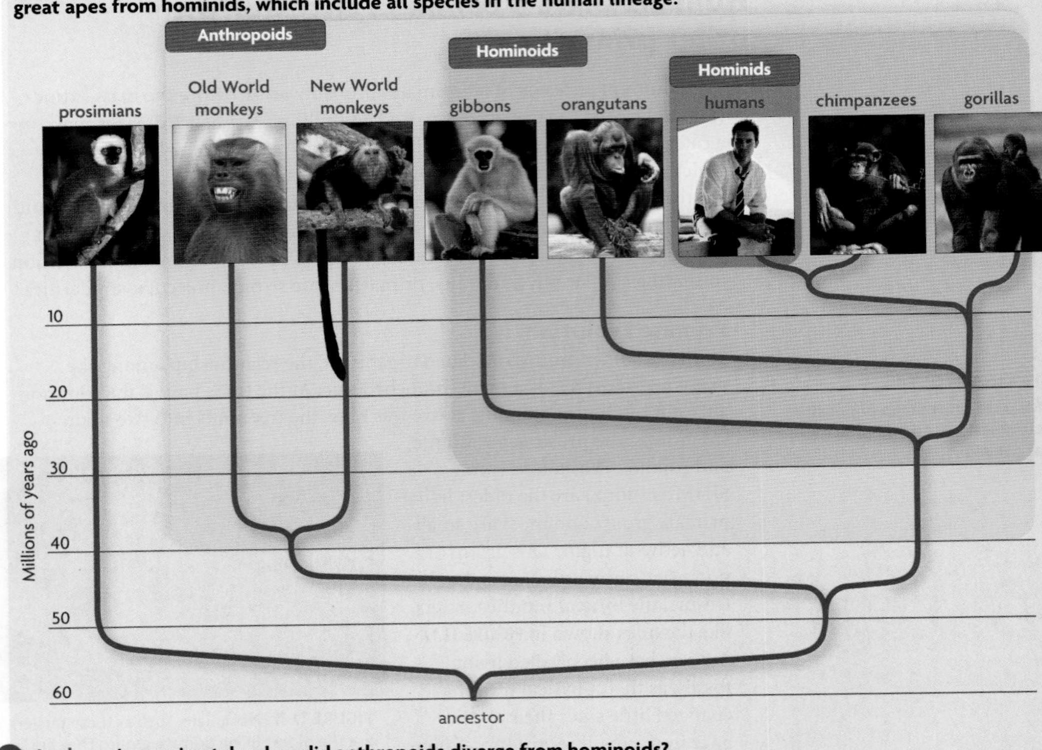

Ⓐ **Analyze Approximately when did anthropoids diverge from hominoids?**

Differentiated Instruction

BELOW LEVEL

Have students add distinguishing characteristics or more groups to their concept maps on page 379. From "anthropoids," they can draw diverging arrows to "hominid" and "hominoid" circles. As they proceed through the remaining sections, they can add more groups and species, including the extinct hominids discussed on page 382.

Walking Upright

Many hypotheses have been proposed to explain the evolutionary success of the hominids. Enlarged brain size and the ability to make and use tools were for many years among the most accepted ideas. However, fossil discoveries have revealed that another trait came before tool use and the large brains—walking upright on two legs. Upright posture and two-legged walking required changes in skeletal anatomy. These changes can be found in intermediate fossils between hominoids that walked only on all fours and early hominids that walked on two legs. Animals that can walk on two legs are called **bipedal** (BY-PEHD-l). This trait has important adaptive advantages. It allows higher reach into tree branches while foraging, and perhaps most importantly, it frees the hands for foraging, carrying infants and food, and using tools.

VISUAL VOCAB

Bipedal is an adjective that describes two-legged or upright walking. *Bi-* means "two," and *ped* means "foot."

A Connect **What is another common animal that is bipedal?**

QUICK LAB **MODELING** NOS.6

Geologic Clock

One way to understand the relative length of time in Earth's history is to compare its age to a clock face. Precambrian time goes from 12 noon to about 10:30 P.M. The time span from early human ancestors—more than 5 million years ago—to *Homo sapiens* covers less than a second on our 12-hour clock!

12
4800 MYA
9 ?
? 3
?
6

PROBLEM How do different geologic time periods compare?

PROCEDURE

1. Draw a large circle and mark the 12, 3, 6, and 9 positions of a clock face. Use the scale 1 hour = 400 million years ago, and label the four positions with the appropriate number of years, starting with 12 o'clock = 4800 million years ago. (Example: the three o'clock position = 3600 million years ago.)
2. Using the geological time scale, label Precambrian time and the three eras on your clock, along with the approximate time frames in which they occurred.
3. Label the following events on your clock in the appropriate positions, also filling in the approximate time frames they occurred: formation of Earth, oldest rocks, first stromatolites, first aerobic prokaryotes, first eukaryotes, first fishes, first flowering plants, first dinosaurs, first birds, and earliest hominids.

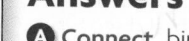

MATERIALS

- paper
- pencil

ANALYZE AND CONCLUDE

1. **Synthesize** How are eras and periods related? Where would the periods fit in this diagram?
2. **Calculate** Using your scale of 1 hour = 400 million years, how many millions of years in Earth's history would 1 minute represent?

PRE-AP

Have students write for five minutes describing the points of divergence in primate evolution and what they suggest about the genomes of the species that represent these groups today. For example, what can we infer about the similarities between the human genome and the genomes of the orangutan and Old World monkeys?

Biology Toolkit, Quick-Write, p. C19

History of Science

During a 1976 expedition to Laetoli in Tanzania, paleoanthropologist **Andrew Hill** accidentally discovered a trail of footprints that radically altered the time line of human evolution. The footprints were made by bipedal hominids about 3.6 million years ago. The trail, which measured approximately 24 meters (80 ft) long, was preserved in a deposit of volcanic ash. Further study suggested that the footprints were made by several *Australopithecus afarensis.* The discovery of the Laetoli footprints startled the scientific community. Before then, the oldest known evidence of hominid bipedalism was only tens of thousands of years old.

Answers

A Connect birds

QUICK LAB

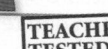

Time 20 minutes — TEACHER TESTED

Lab Binder Evolution, p. 40

Purpose Model relative interval lengths of the geologic time scale.

LAB MANAGEMENT

- If students are confusing time of day with time period, have them make marks without time labels.
- Have students first create a table of the ages and then label the circle.

Teacher Note "If a pie chart is referenced in the first step to assist students in picturing the final product, students will understand the step better."

Answers

Sample Data

For a sample clock, go to page R104.

Analyze and Conclude

1. Periods are the units within an era, as hours are the units within a day. On the diagram, periods would fit between the hours of the clock.
2. 6.7 million years (400 million years/hour divided by 60 minutes/hour)

▼ Teach *continued*

The Inside Story

In one of the all-time greatest hoaxes in science, a British amateur archaeologist, **Charles Dawson,** announced in 1912 that he had discovered a species of hominid that had lived a million years ago. His findings were two skulls that displayed the primitive jaws of an ape and the brow of a human. The remains were given the common name **Piltdown Man,** named for the region in which the bones were allegedly found, while Dawson used his own name in formulating the scientific name, *Eoanthropus dawsoni.*

Here, surely, was the missing link in the ancestry of both humans and apes. Some scientists, however, were skeptical. Details of the actual discovery of the skull and of subsequent Piltdown Man finds were murky, and there were obvious differences between the jaw and brow bones, suggesting they were from different individuals.

During a meeting of paleontologists in London in 1953, the teeth and other parts of the Piltdown Man were examined by several different scientists, who confirmed that the skulls were a deliberate fraud. They consisted of bones from a 500-year-old human and a modern orangutan.

Address Misconceptions

Common Misconception Humans are descended from modern apes.

Correcting the Misconception Humans did not descend from modern apes. Humans and the African apes (gorillas and chimpanzees) descended from a common ape ancestor that lived approximately 6–8 million years ago. The ancestor's descendants diverged into two lineages: one gradually evolved into gorillas; the other diverged into two lines, again about 5 million years ago, one giving rise to the ancestors of modern chimpanzees and the other leading to the early hominids.

Answers

A Hypothesize fossil specimens found in the same strata dated to the same time period

MAIN IDEA

There are many fossils of extinct hominids.

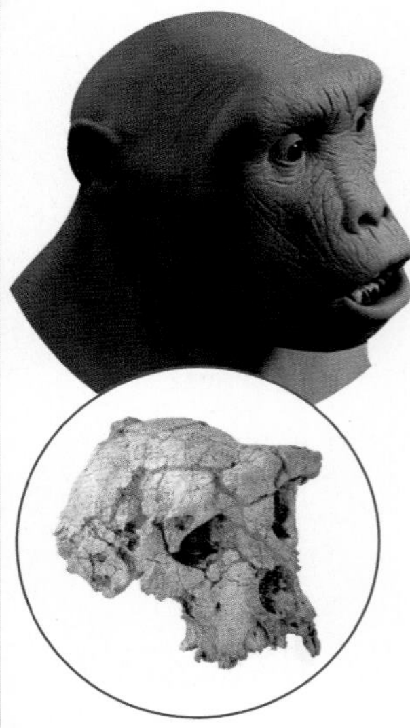

FIGURE 12.19 Computer technology allowed scientists to piece together 7-million-year-old skull fragments found in Africa. The three-dimensional reconstruction suggests that this may be the oldest known hominid ancestor of *Homo sapiens;* it has been named *Sahelanthropus tchadensis.*

Hominids are classified into several groups. Two important groups are the genus *Homo* and the older genus *Australopithecus* (aw-STRAY-loh-PIHTH-ih-kuhs). *Australopithecus* was a long-lived and successful genus. *Australopithecus afarensis* (AF-uh-REHN-sihs), who lived 3 to 4 million years ago in Africa, is one of the better known species of early hominids. Although its brain was much smaller than that of a modern human—about the size of a modern-day chimpanzee's brain—*A. afarensis* had very humanlike limbs.

The earliest member of the genus *Homo* was *Homo habilis.* Nicknamed "handy man" because of the crude stone tools associated with its skeletons, *H. habilis* lived 2.4–1.5 million years ago in what are now Kenya and Tanzania. This species may have lived alongside the australopithecine species for about 1 million years. *H. habilis* is the earliest known hominid to make stone tools. The brain of *H. habilis* was much larger than that of any of the australopithecines, and it more closely resembled the modern human brain in shape.

Another hominid species was *H. neanderthalensis,* commonly called Neanderthals for the Neander Valley in Germany, where their fossils were first found. This group lived from 200,000 to 30,000 years ago in Europe and the Middle East. Some evidence suggests that *H. neanderthalensis* coexisted with modern *Homo sapiens.* Did the two species live side by side? Or did they engage in a fierce competition for resources, causing the extinction of the Neanderthals by the better-adapted *H. sapiens?* This puzzle has not yet been solved.

Observations from the fossil record demonstrate a trend toward increased brain size in the human lineage. Although brain size can only be loosely related to intelligence, the combination of modern-day humans' physical and cultural adaptations has no doubt contributed to our success as a species.

A Hypothesize What type of evidence could indicate that *H. sapiens* and *H. neanderthalensis* coexisted?

MAIN IDEA

Modern humans arose about 100,000 years ago.

Fossil evidence reveals that the first appearance of modern *Homo sapiens,* or modern humans, dates to roughly 100,000 years ago in what is now Ethiopia. Many of their features are different than those of humans today. After becoming a distinct species, *H. sapiens* clearly did not stop evolving.

The Role of Culture

Human evolution is influenced by culture. Tools are among key markers of culture in human evolution, although they are used by some other animals as well. A comparison of tools from their first appearance some 2.5 million years ago, through their association with later *Homo* fossil sites, shows a steady trend of increasing sophistication and usefulness.

Differentiated Instruction

BELOW LEVEL

Have students make flash cards to help them keep track of the various species discussed in this section. They may wish to use some special method, such as color-coding, to identify the evolutionary relationships of groups. For example, they could draw a blue border around hominid cards, red around nonhuman anthropoid cards, and green for prosimians.

FIGURE 12.20 Examples of Hominid Skulls

Hominid evolution shows a progression in brain size.

4–3 MILLION YEARS AGO	2.4–1.5 MILLION YEARS AGO	200,000–30,000 YEARS AGO	200,000 YEARS AGO–PRESENT
Australopithecus afarensis	*Homo habilis*	*Homo neanderthalensis*	*Homo sapiens*
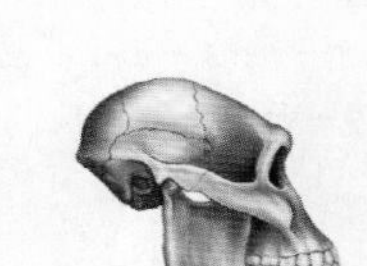	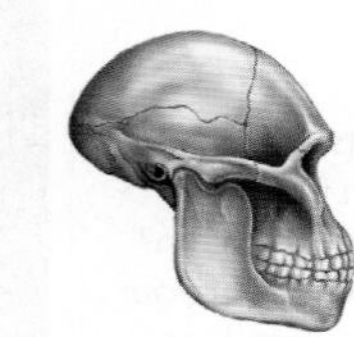	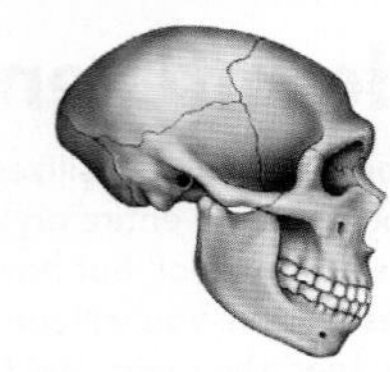	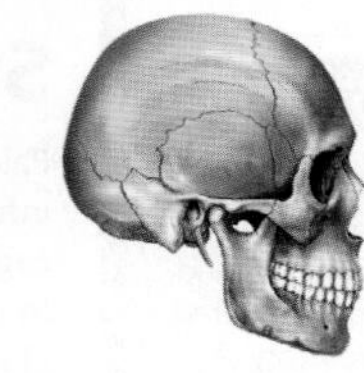
Australopithecus afarensis had a brain volume of 430 cm^3.	*Homo habilis* had a brain volume of about 700 cm^3.	*Homo neanderthalensis'* brain volume may have reached 1500 cm^3.	Modern *Homo sapiens* have a brain volume average of about 1300 cm^3.

A **Contrast** **What characteristics besides brain size differ among the species shown?**

Homo-
Sapiens
200,000
ya

The Evolution of the Human Brain

Human evolution would not have advanced as it did without an enlarging skull and brain size, as shown in **FIGURE 12.20.** One recent study has demonstrated that genes controlling the size and complexity of the human brain evolved faster than analogous genes in nonhuman primates. Researchers compared the DNA sequences for more than 200 genes affecting brain development in humans, Old World monkeys, rats, and mice. They found that these genes evolved at a much faster rate in the two primates than in the two rodents and that brain-related genes in humans evolved faster than did those in the monkeys. The results of the study support the hypothesis that the rapid evolution of large brain size posed an especially strong selective advantage among the hominids.

Connecting CONCEPTS

Classification A genus is a closely related group of species. You will learn more about categories for classification in Chapter 17.

B **Synthesize** **When might having an increasingly larger brain size no longer be a selective advantage?**

individuals of the same species, which the scientists named ***Homo floresiensis*** and jokingly referred to as "hobbits." Also associated with these bones were those of an extinct, tiny elephant called *Stegodon,* which the Flores human may have hunted.

What really caught scientists off guard was the age of the hominid: 18,000 years. Scientists speculate that the Flores human could have evolved from *Homo erectus,* which is known to have reached Java 1.6 million years ago, and that its small size is the result of inbreeding among a relatively small gene pool—a not uncommon evolutionary trend on isolated islands. Other scientists think that the Flores fossil may simply be a *Homo sapiens* that had microcephaly, a condition that causes the brain to be very small.

12.6 ASSESSMENT

ONLINE QUIZ ClassZone.com

B.8.7

REVIEWING MAIN IDEAS

1. What characteristics shared by humans and other **primates** suggest they have a common ancestor?
2. According to the fossil record, what other *Homo* species was present when modern humans arose?
3. From the **hominid** fossils described, what common trends can be found?

CRITICAL THINKING

4. **Apply** Explain why, according to the fossil record, it is not correct to say that humans evolved from chimpanzees.
5. **Infer** Scientists can often identify whether a fossil skull was from a **bipedal** primate. What characteristics of a skull might help them make this determination?

Connecting CONCEPTS

6. **Anatomy** Consider the skull illustrations above. Besides size, how did skull structure change as hominids evolved? What features are considered more apelike than humanlike?

12.6 ASSESSMENT

1. *Sample Answer:* flexible hands and feet, forward-looking eyes, enlarged brains relative to body size
2. *H. neanderthalensis*
3. Trends include larger skull size and greater sophistication of tools found near the fossils.
4. According to the fossil record, both chimps and humans diverged from a common ancestor at approximately the same time.
5. Accept all reasonable answers. *Sample Answer:* the location of the opening at the base of the skull, which shows how cervical vertebrae may have attached and therefore how the spine may have been positioned
6. *Sample Answer:* jaw size, teeth size, brow position. A low brow, protruding mouth, and sloping forehead are three features considered more apelike than humanlike.

Assess and Reteach

Assess Use the Online Quiz or Section Quiz (*Assessment Book,* p. 236).

Reteach Use **FIGURE 12.18** to review the material in this section. Have students identify distinguishing characteristics of each group.

Answers

A **Contrast** *Sample Answer:* the jaw size and position relative to eyes and nose, teeth size, brow position

B **Synthesize** *Sample Answer:* if the cranium becomes so large that it is too hard to carry around, or the larger brain does not confer reproductive success

OPTIONS FOR INQUIRY

INVESTIGATION

Time 45 minutes	TEACHER TESTED
Teacher Preparation	
Student Difficulty	
Lab Binder Evolution, pp. 34–36	

Purpose Infer characteristics of an organism based on trace fossil measurements.

Overview Students will measure classmates' characteristics to form inferences about the relationship between foot length, leg length, and stride. They will

- measure foot length and leg length on partners
- use these measurements to calculate stride length while walking and running
- display their findings in a bar graph

LAB PREPARATION

- Clear some space in the classroom or arrange to go outside or use a gym.

LAB MANAGEMENT

- The calculations may prove challenging for some students. Be sure to allow additional time for them to complete their work.

Inclusion Students who are physically challenged can use the Internet or library resources to gather data on stride length and speed of other species. They can then present this information to the class.

Teacher Note "An online data search revealed that there is a direct relationship between stride length and speed."

POST-LAB DISCUSSION

Discuss how scientists use inferences in paleontology. **Ask,** In addition to calculating speeds of locomotion, what other information could a paleontologist infer from trackways? *Sample Answers:* if the animal traveled alone or with a group, whether it could run fast enough to be an efficient predator, if it carried its young

Use these inquiry-based labs and online activities to deepen your understanding of the history of life on Earth.

INDIANA STANDARDS

NOS.1 Develop explanations based on reproducible data and observations gathered during laboratory investigations.

NOS.3 Clearly communicate their ideas and results of investigations verbally and in written from using tables, graphs, diagrams, and photographs.

DESIGN YOUR OWN INVESTIGATION

Stride Inferences

Paleontologists can use fossilized footprints to gain information about an entire organism, even if that organism is now extinct. But how much can they learn? In this investigation, you will measure the length of your classmates' feet, their legs, and their strides—walking and running—to see if there are any relationships between these variables.

SKILLS Measuring, Calculating, Interpreting Data

PROBLEM What relationship exists between foot length, leg length, and stride length?

MATERIALS

- meter stick
- calculator (optional)
- graph paper

PROCEDURE

1. Determine a procedure to measure foot length, leg length, and height of each person in your group.
2. Design a procedure for measuring both walking stride length and running stride length. Remember that repeated trials increase the validity of results.
3. Create a data table to organize the following information: foot length, leg length, height, stride length walking, and stride length running. Each person in your group will have these values measured and recorded.
4. Have your teacher approve your design. Then collect and record your data.
5. Each person in the group should make a bar graph of their own data for each of the following pairs of variables: foot length and leg length, foot length and height, leg length and height, stride length walking and leg length, and stride length walking and running. In addition, graph the average values.

ANALYZE AND CONCLUDE

1. **Analyze** Which of the above pairs of variables has a positive correlation? (As one increases, so does the other.) Which has a negative correlation? (As one increases, the other decreases.) Which pairs of variables have no clear relationship?
2. **Experimental Design** What steps in your design helped to avoid bias in your data collection?
3. **Experimental Design** What possible sources of error may have existed in your design? How could you change your experimental design to make the results more valid?
4. **Apply** Paleontologists have studied dinosaur footprints left as fossils in rock. What sort of information can they measure directly by looking at the footprints of these ancient animals? What information can they infer even if there are no fossilized skeletons?

Answers

Sample Data

For sample data and a sample graph from this investigation, go to page R104.

Analyze and Conclude

1. Students should find positive correlations among foot length, leg length, and height; and also between walking stride length and leg length. They should find a negative correlation between running and walking stride lengths. Student data may also demonstrate no clear correlation. Data should support student answers.
2. Multiple strides can be averaged, thereby enlarging sample size and reducing bias.
3. insufficient sample size, inconsistent methodology in taking measurements
4. They can directly measure foot size and stride length, then infer how the animal moved; infer its speed, size, skeletal anatomy; and, possibly, infer its herding behavior.

INVESTIGATION

Understanding Geologic Time

The history of Earth has spanned the past 4.6 billion years. During that time, the oceans and the atmosphere have formed, life has begun, and species have evolved and become extinct. The geologic time scale can be broken into eras, periods, and epochs, which your teacher has modeled for you around your classroom. In this exercise you will learn about major events in the history of Earth and explore how these events have led to the world we know today.

SKILL Modeling

MATERIALS
- Geologic Time Scale datasheet

PROBLEM How do past events contribute to the changing populations of life on Earth?

PROCEDURE

1. Your teacher will assign you an event to record on the geologic time scale that is displayed around the room.
2. Use your textbook to determine the appropriate place for the event you were assigned.
3. Once everyone has recorded their event on the geologic time scale, walk around the room, taking note of the major events in each era and period on the datasheet you were provided.

ANALYZE AND CONCLUDE

1. **Analyze** In what eon, era, period, and epoch are we living today?
2. **Calculate** What fraction of the total distance does the Quaternary period cover on the geologic time scale? (**Hint:** The time scale is 46 feet [14 m] long and each foot [30.5 cm] equals 100 million years.)

EXTEND YOUR INVESTIGATION

Choose one period of the geologic time scale and investigate it more. Learn about the era in which it occurred, providing specific examples of organisms, important events, and a physical description of Earth at that time. Write a summary of the period with an illustration. Post your summary near the appropriate flag.

Online BIOLOGY
CLASSZONE.COM

VIRTUAL LAB
Comparing Hominoid Skulls
How are modern humans similar to chimps and australopithecines. How are they different? In this interactive lab, you will examine hominoid skulls to determine the sequence in which select traits evolved.

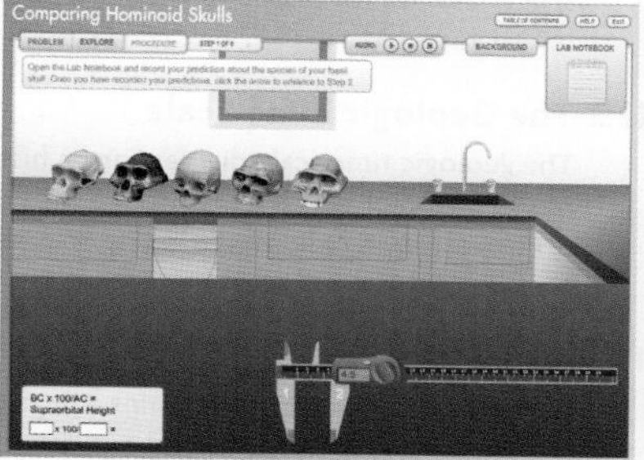

ANIMATED BIOLOGY
Geologic Time Scale
Which came first—flowering plants or coniferous trees? Use your knowledge of the history of life to place organisms in the correct order along a geologic time scale.

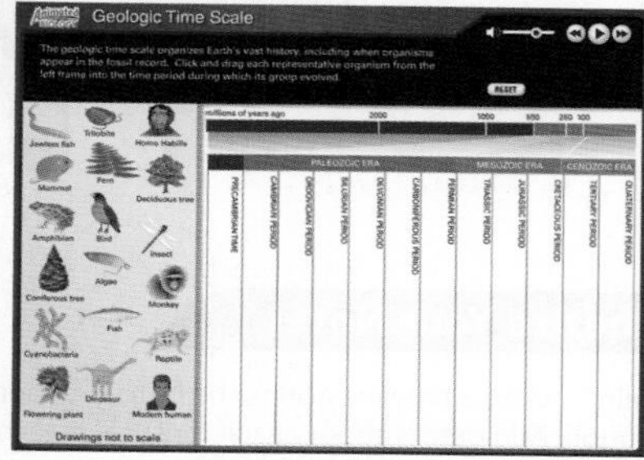

WEBQUEST
How do scientists decide which type of geologic dating to use for a sample? In this WebQuest, you will decide which method would be best to date two different types of fossil samples.

Answers

Analyze and Conclude

1. Cenozoic era, Quaternary period, Holocene epoch
2. About 1/2564, the Quaternary period began 1.8 million years ago = 0.018 hundred million years ago. 0.018/46 = 0.00039, or about 0.04%, which equals 1/2564.

Teacher Note "The majority of students simply divided with a calculator to achieve the Quaternary percent of the time scale. Most did not put it in a fraction."

Extend Your Investigation

Sample Answer: The Quaternary period of the Cenozoic era has featured the rise of the hominids, including *Homo sapiens,* from apelike ancestors. The Isthmus of Panama closes, linking the American continents. Extinction rates go up as humans affect habitats and populations through their widespread activities.

Online Biology ▼

VIRTUAL LAB Students will compare the features of four skulls and identify an unknown skull. Use with **Section 12.6.**

ANIMATED BIOLOGY Use this interactive animation to reinforce the concepts of **Section 12.2.**

WEBQUEST The WebQuest takes one full class period. Students complete the activity online and will need access to a printer to print their answers. Sample answers, teacher notes, and alternative assessment ideas are available on **ClassZone.com.** Use with **Section 12.1.**

INVESTIGATION TEACHER TESTED

Time 45 minutes	
Teacher Preparation	⚗⚗
Student Difficulty	⚗
Lab Binder Evolution, pp. 37–39	

LAB PREPARATION

Distribute copies of the geologic time scale, *Lab Binder,* pages 38–39.

LAB MANAGEMENT

Teacher Note "I liked this activity, and I would have advanced students hypothesize and investigate causes of the changes observed in the geologic time scale."

CHAPTER REVIEW

Interactive Review

Encourage students to go to **ClassZone.com** for a detailed review of each section, including visuals and vocabulary practice.

Unit Resource Book, Vocabulary Practice, pp. 95–98

ITEM CORRELATIONS

Standard	Items
B.8.5	20
B.8.7	14, 15, 17, 19, 24, 27

CHAPTER **12** Interactive Review @ CLASSZONE.COM

KEY CONCEPTS | Vocabulary Games | Concept Maps | Animated Biology | Online Quiz

12.1 The Fossil Record

Fossils are a record of life that existed in the past. Fossils can form in several different ways. The age of a fossil or rock can be determined by radiometric dating, which uses radioactive isotopes to determine the age of a fossil or the rock in which it is found. Through radiometric dating, scientists have estimated that Earth is about 4.5 billion years old.

12.2 The Geologic Time Scale

The geologic time scale divides Earth's history based on major past events. Index fossils can be used along with radiometric dating to determine the age of a fossil or rock.

12.3 Origin of Life

The origin of life on Earth remains a puzzle. There are several hypotheses about how early organic molecules appeared on Earth and about how early cells may have formed. The discovery of ribozymes, RNA molecules that can catalyze reactions without the help of proteins, led to the hypothesis that RNA arose before DNA as the first genetic material on Earth.

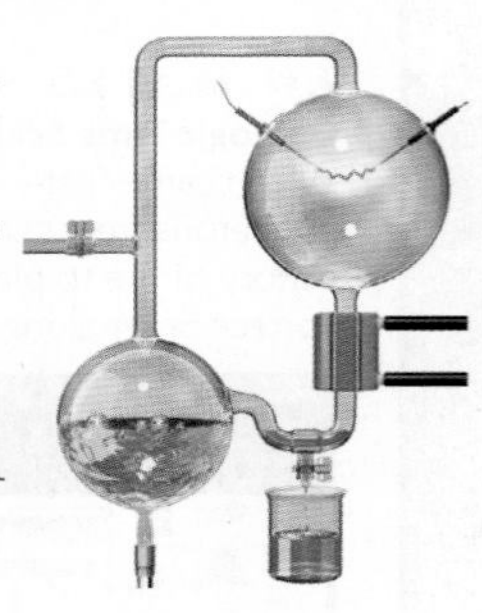

12.4 Early Single-Celled Organisms

Single-celled organisms existed 3.8 billion years ago. The first organisms on Earth were most likely anaerobic prokaryotes. The theory of endosymbiosis proposes that the first eukaryotic cells arose from a large prokaryote engulfing a smaller prokaryote.

12.5 Radiation of Multicellular Life

Multicellular life evolved in distinct phases. During the Paleozoic era, members of every major animal group evolved within only a few million years. During the Mesozoic era, dinosaurs, flowering plants, and birds inhabited the earth. Mammals also arose during this time. During the Cenozoic era, mammals diversified, as did birds, fishes, and flowering plants. Modern humans did not appear until 100,000 years ago.

12.6 Primate Evolution

Humans appeared late in Earth's history. Humans share a common ancestor with other primates. Primates include all mammals with flexible hands and feet, forward-looking eyes, and enlarged brains relative to their body size. The hominids include all species in the human lineage, both modern and extinct. Hominids walk upright, have long lower limbs, opposable thumbs, and relatively large brains. There are many fossils of extinct hominids.

Synthesize Your Notes

Timeline Make a timeline noting the history of hominid evolution. Add details about characteristics of each hominid that is on your diagram.

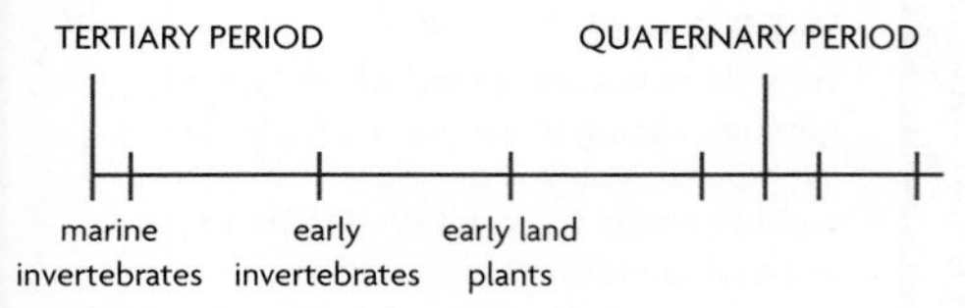

Concept Map Use a concept map to summarize hypotheses about the origin of life on Earth.

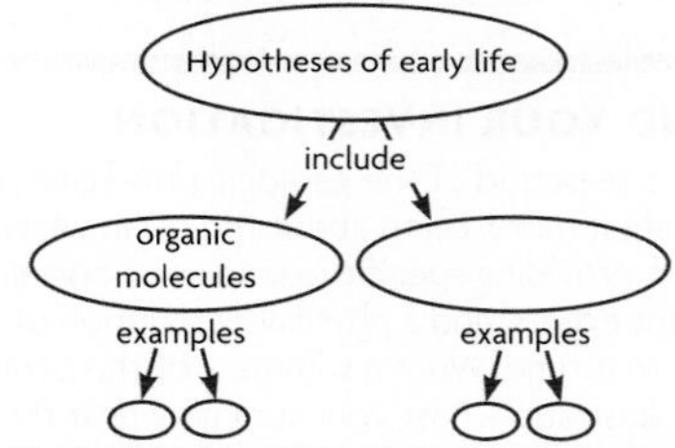

Reviewing Vocabulary

1. *Sample Answer:* Both relative dating and radiometric dating are methods of determining the age of artifacts or rock layer samples. Relative dating does this by comparing a sample's position in strata to that of other objects whose ages are known, while radiometric dating determines the absolute ages of a sample based upon the decay of radioactive elements.
2. *Sample Answer:* Both an isotope and half-life are used in radiometric dating, but only radioactive isotopes can be used in radiometric dating. The half-life of an isotope is the time it takes for half of the isotope to decay to another element.
3. *Sample Answer:* Both eras and periods are units of time used to organize the geologic time scale. Eras consist of two or more periods. Periods are the most common time unit used in the geologic time scale.
4. *Sample Answer:* Cyanobacteria are prokaryotes. Endosymbiosis is a theory that suggests that prokaryotes may have absorbed other prokaryotes, such as precursors of mitochondria and chloroplasts, and evolved into eukaryotes.
5. *Sample Answer:* The Paleozoic was an era, the Cambrian a period within the Paleozoic. Both are units of the geologic time scale. In the Cambrian, life was limited to the ocean environment. By the middle of the Paleozoic, life had also moved onto land.
6. *Sample Answer:* Hominids are a subgroup of primates that can walk upright on two feet. Primates are an order of mammals with flexible hands and feet, forward-looking eyes, and large brains relative to body size. Primates also have arms that can rotate in a circle around their shoulder joint, and many primates have opposable thumbs.
7. reference point to date other fossils
8. shortest unit of time in the geologic time scale
9. RNA that acts like an enzyme
10. walks on two feet
11. Astronomers observed what appeared to be a "cloud" of gas and dust.
12. Isotopes are forms of the same element differing only by the number of neutrons.

Chapter Assessment

Chapter Vocabulary

12.1 relative dating, p. 362
radiometric dating, p. 362
isotope, p. 362
half-life, p. 362

12.2 index fossil, p. 365
geologic time scale, p. 367
era, p. 367
period, p. 367
epoch, p. 367

12.3 nebula, p. 368
ribozyme, p. 370

12.4 cyanobacteria, p. 372
endosymbiosis, p. 373

12.5 Paleozoic, p. 376
Cambrian explosion, p. 376
Mesozoic, p. 377
Cenozoic, p. 378

12.6 primate, p. 379
prosimian, p. 379
anthropoid, p. 380
hominid, p. 380
bipedal, p. 381

Reviewing Vocabulary

Compare and Contrast

Describe one similarity and one difference between the two terms in each of the following pairs.

1. relative dating, radiometric dating
2. isotope, half-life
3. era, period
4. cyanobacteria, endosymbiosis
5. Paleozoic, Cambrian explosion
6. primate, hominid

Keep It Short

Write a short, precise phrase that describes the meaning of each vocabulary term below. For example, a short phrase to describe *geologic time scale* could be "organizes life's history."

7. index fossil
8. epoch
9. ribozyme
10. bipedal

Greek and Latin Word Origins

11. *Nebula* is a Latin word that means "cloud." Explain why you think astronomers chose this word as a name for what they were observing in outer space.

12. The prefix *iso-* means "the same." How does this meaning relate to the definition of *isotope*?

Reviewing MAIN IDEAS

13. Fossils can form in several ways, one of which is by permineralization. Describe the process of permineralization and give an example of the type of fossil that may result.

14. Give an example of how the concept of half-life is used in radiometric dating. **B.8.7**

15. How are index fossils used in relative dating? **B.8.7**

16. The geologic time scale organizes the history of Earth into eras, periods, and epochs. How are these units of time related to one another?

17. The Miller-Urey experiment and the meteorite hypothesis both suggest how the molecules that can support life might have appeared on early Earth. What is the main difference between these two hypotheses? Explain. **B.8.7**

18. What are two ways that cyanobacteria have changed the physical or chemical composition of Earth?

19. What evidence exists to support the endosymbiotic origins of eukaryotic cells? **B.8.7**

20. One evolutionary advantage of sexual reproduction is that it creates more genetic variation in a population than asexual reproduction. Why might this be an advantage? **B.8.5**

21. The earliest part of the Paleozoic era is called the Cambrian period. What was the Cambrian explosion?

22. In which era did mammals, dinosaurs, and birds appear on Earth? What happened to these groups in the following era?

23. Humans, apes, monkeys, and lemurs are all examples of primates. What characteristics do all primates share?

CHAPTER REVIEW

Reviewing Main Ideas

13. Permineralization can occur if an organism is buried quickly after death. Additional layers of sediment add pressure, and water flows through over time to distribute minerals that replace those present in the hard parts of the organism, such as bone. This maintains the shape of the organism. The resulting fossil is rocklike, or petrified.

14. *Sample Answer:* By measuring the ratio of an unstable isotope such as carbon-14 with a stable one such as carbon-12, one can determine how much the carbon-14 has decayed and then apply the known half-life value to calculate how long this decay has been occurring, in other words, how old the substance is.

15. Because the approximate age of an index fossil is already known, other fossils found within the same or nearby stratum can be dated on a relative time scale.

16. Eras (between ten million and hundreds of millions of years) are subdivided into periods (up to tens of millions of years), which are further subdivided into epochs (several million years).

17. The Miller-Urey experiment proposes that life began from the formation of organic compounds from available inorganic compounds. The meteorite hypothesis proposes that a meteor containing organic molecules, namely amino acids, hit Earth.

18. Cyanobacteria, being photosynthetic, have produced oxygen for Earth's atmosphere and oceans, and have also deposited minerals.

19. The endosymbiotic theory is based on mitochondria and chloroplasts of eukaryotes. Both structures have characteristics (such as their own DNA and the ability to self-replicate) of independent prokaryotes.

20. Genetic variation is advantageous because it increases the chances that some individuals will have genes that are beneficial for survival in a certain environment. Without genetic variation, the entire population is vulnerable to environmental change.

21. The Cambrian explosion was a time when a huge number of marine species evolved. Many forms of life appeared in the fossil record during this time.

22. Mammals, dinosaurs, and birds all appeared on Earth during the Mesozoic era. During the Mesozoic era, dinosaurs were dominant. At the end, dinosaurs became extinct. In the Cenozoic era, many mammals evolved, using the resources that became available once the dinosaurs were gone. Birds diversified during the Cenozoic era.

23. Primates make up a category of mammals with flexible hands and feet, forward-looking eyes, large brains relative to body size, arms that can rotate in a circle at the shoulder joints, and opposable thumbs.

Critical Thinking

24. 1.408 billion years old (704,000,000 + 704,000,000)
25. There wasn't enough oxygen to support aerobes until after autotrophs had produced enough through photosynthesis.
26. Accept all reasonable answers. *Sample Answer:* Although most life as we know it on Earth is supported by oxygen, other compounds could support other types of life, as we can see in hydrothermal vents of the deep ocean.
27. The fact that their brief simulation yielded more than half of the amino acids used by modern-day cells, it is reasonable to infer that reactions occurring on early Earth for billions of years could have worked in a similar way to produce the amino acids.

Interpreting Visuals

28. Accept all reasonable answers. *Sample Answer:* Within the past 7 million years, hominids have evolved from having small brains and large teeth to having larger brains and smaller teeth.
29. Only one representative of this species has been found, and in that case it was skull fragments (no jaw) which were pieced together by computer animation. It may have been impossible to tell how the spine was arranged beneath the base of the skull. One incomplete specimen is not enough to describe a species.
30. *Homo habilis* had many of the traits attributed to the members of the *Australopithecus* genus, such as a small brain, large teeth, and occasional bipedalism.

Critical Thinking

24. Calculate A sample is dated using uranium-235 (half-life 704,000,000 years), and it has 1/4 of the original amount of uranium. How old is the sample? **B.8.7**

25. Apply Why is it likely that autotrophs appeared on Earth before any aerobes, organisms that depended on oxygen?

26. Predict Astronomers determine the composition of the atmosphere around another planet by examining the light that travels from that planet to Earth. Would finding a lot of oxygen in the atmosphere of another planet strongly suggest that it supported life? Explain.

27. Evaluate Thirteen of the 20 amino acids used to make proteins in modern-day cells were made by Miller-Urey's simulation of early Earth's conditions. How does this result support Miller and Urey's hypothesis? **B.8.7**

Interpreting Visuals

The chart below shows when some human ancestors lived and traits that they had. Use the chart to answer the next three questions.

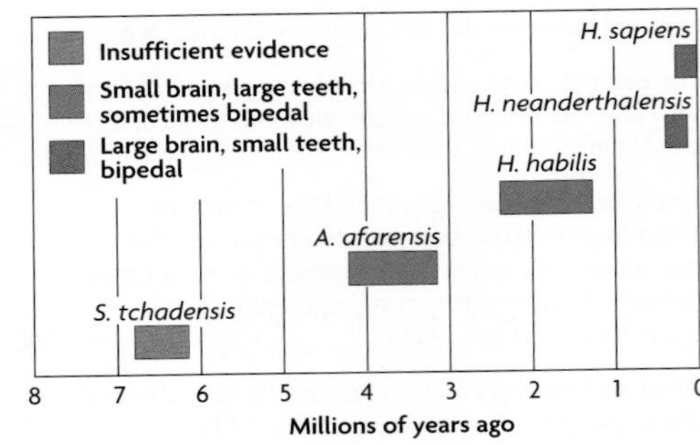

28. Summarize In one or two sentences, summarize the information in the chart.

29. Infer *Sahelanthropus tchadensis* was pictured on page 382 as a three-dimensional computer reconstruction. Although skull fragments have been found of this species, the chart above shows that there is not enough evidence to describe the traits of *S. tchadensis*. Explain why this might be so. Consider the scientific process in your explanation.

30. Analyze Some scientists suggest that *Homo habilis* should be classified as *Australopithecus habilis*. Based upon the information in the chart, explain why this might be the case.

Analyzing Data

Both graphs show the rate of decay of chlorine-36, which changes into argon-36. Use the graphs to answer the next two questions.

GRAPH 1 OF CHLORINE-36 DECAY

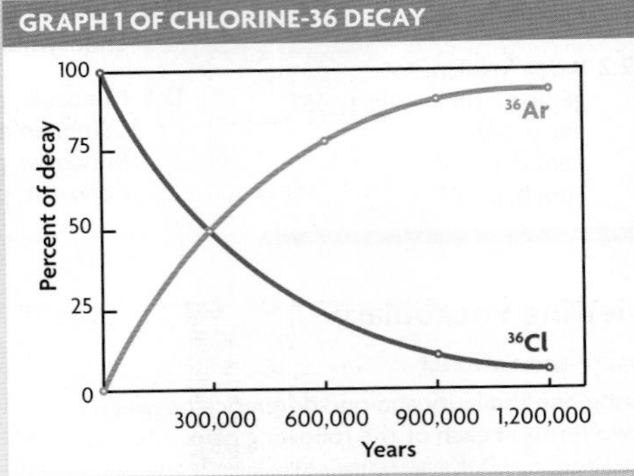

GRAPH 2 OF CHLORINE-36 DECAY

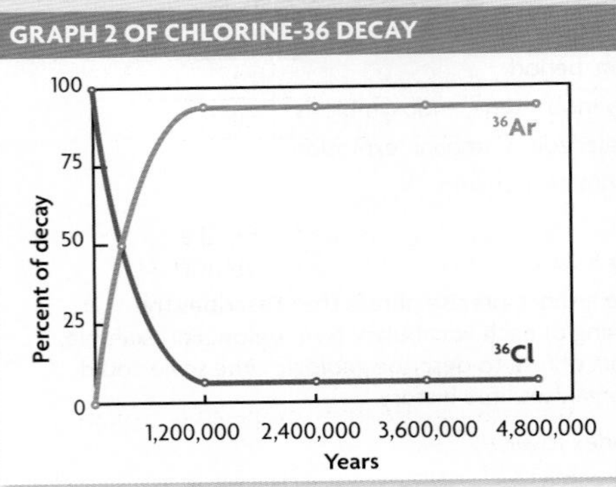

31. Analyze Which graph better shows the concept that the percentage change of ^{36}Cl and ^{36}Ar slows down dramatically over time? Explain.

32. Analyze From which graph can you more accurately determine the half-life in years of ^{36}Cl? Explain.

Connecting CONCEPTS

33. Write a Detailed Description Choose one of the periods in geological time and describe it in detail. Be sure to include vivid details about the organisms of the period.

34. Connect The time that the Tollund Man on page 359 lived was determined by radiocarbon dating. Why can't ^{14}C be used to date the Burgess Shale fossil shown on the same page?

Analyzing Data

31. The second graph shows that the rates of decay of these isotopes slow down to an almost imperceptible rate after 1.2 million years because the *x*-axis scale goes beyond that time. The first graph's time scale is too short to show this dramatic change.
32. The first graph is easier to use for determining half-life. Because the *x*-axis features a narrower span of time, the point at which the isotopes are at 50 percent is much more precisely represented.

INDIANA ISTEP+ Test Prep

B.8.7; NOS.1; NOS.2; NOS.6

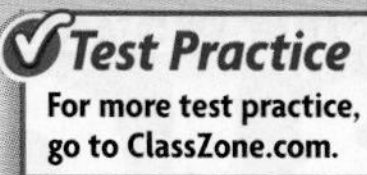

Test Practice
For more test practice, go to ClassZone.com.

1 Scientists hypothesize that complex organic molecules could have assembled in the environment of early Earth because

- **A** these molecules are found assembling under the conditions present today.
- **B** there are no other alternative hypotheses.
- **C** this process has been successfully modeled in the laboratory.
- **D** these molecules were present at extremely high concentrations.

2

Percent of Native Bird Fossils in Hawaii			
Excavated Section	^{14}C Dating (years before present)	% Bones from Non-native Species	% Bones from Native Species
I	390	100.0	0.0
II	770	98.8	1.2
III	4340	9.2	90.8
IV	7750	0.0	100.0

The table above shows the fossil evidence of birds in a section of cave wall in Hawaii. What can be determined from the data presented?

- **A** A catastrophic event occurred between 770 and 4340 years ago.
- **B** Native species out-competed non-native species.
- **C** Most native species died out over 800 years ago.
- **D** The disappearance of non-native species is a function of time.

3 Like modern plants, early photosynthetic organisms used light as the energy source for synthesizing sugar. Based on this fact, what substance had to be available to these organisms in the environment of early Earth?

- **A** nitrogen
- **B** ATP
- **C** oxygen
- **D** carbon dioxide

4

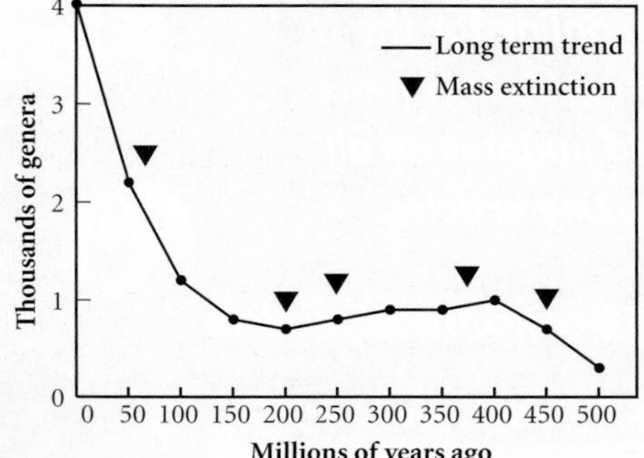

The graph above shows the estimated number of genera over time, with major extinction events indicated by arrows. Given that genera are made up of closely related species, what can be understood from these data?

- **A** The number of species always increases.
- **B** Mass extinctions wipe out all species.
- **C** Some species survive during mass extinctions.
- **D** A mass extinction is not likely to happen again.

5 As the oxygen content of Earth's atmosphere increased, what would have *best* allowed populations of anaerobic prokaryotes to adapt?

- **A** genetic mutation
- **B** sexual selection
- **C** competition
- **D** sexual reproduction

6 In the evolution of eukaryotes, why would cells that contained mitochondria-like organelles have an advantage?

THINK THROUGH THE QUESTION

This question is really just asking how mitochondria help a cell.

CHAPTER REVIEW

Standards-Based Assessment

1. C	4. C
2. C	5. A
3. D	6. See Below

TEST DOCTOR

Question 2 Answer C is correct. Answer A is incorrect because it cannot be determined from the data, and other explanations might better explain the shift in the data. Answer B is incorrect because the bones of the native species—and thus the native species itself—are no longer found in that area. Answer D is incorrect because the non-native species appears not to have disappeared but to have flourished given that only their bones are found as of 390 years ago, and there are no data suggesting that the non-native species will disappear in the future as a function of time.

Question 3 Answer D is correct. Answers A, B, and C are incorrect because the process of photosynthesis uses energy from light to convert carbon dioxide and water to sugars and oxygen.

Question 5 Answer A is correct. Answers B and D are incorrect because prokaryotes reproduce asexually. Answer C is incorrect because as the oxygen content increased, anaerobic prokaryotes would likely become less successful against their competitors.

Question 6 Cells with mitochondria-like organelles could better utilize available energy.

Connecting Concepts

33. Descriptions should include organisms that existed in the period, as well as overall trends such as extinctions and radiation.

34. Carbon-14 dating can only be used to age relatively recent fossils or remains because its half-life is only 5730 years. The amount of carbon-14 in a 500-million-year-old Burgess Shale fossil will be so minuscule that it will be imperceptible compared to the amount of carbon-12. An isotope with a much longer half-life must be used.

ITEM CORRELATIONS

Standard	Items
B.8.7	3, 5, 6
NOS.1	2
NOS.2	4
NOS.6	1

UNIT

4

Introduce

Tell students that people may be tempted to think of evolution as a theory about what happened in the past, and that it has no effect on them today. However, this is incorrect. Evolution involves the genetic changes in populations that occur over many generations. Evolution is constantly occurring in most populations of all species.

Evolutionary change occurs most rapidly in organisms that reproduce quickly and in large numbers. For example, a mutation forms in a population of bacteria, and this mutation allows individuals to survive exposure to a certain drug. Through natural selection, that entire population of bacteria may become resistant to the drug. This change can occur within a time scale easily observable by humans, because bacteria produce several generations per day.

Insect populations can evolve resistance to insecticides in a similar way. The use of insecticides on food crops creates a strong selective pressure on insect populations. The more resistant insects survive, and they pass on the resistant trait to their offspring. As a result, insecticides are becoming less and less effective in protecting crops. Resistant insects that are vectors for serious diseases can make the control of these diseases more difficult.

Viruses can also evolve quickly. The exchange of genetic material between different viral types results in constantly changing viruses. A virus that causes disease in a bird could mutate and infect a human. It could mutate again, evolving the ability to spread from one person to another.

Discuss with students how evolutionary changes affect the living world. **Ask**

- How might people be affected by evolving populations of bacteria, insects, and viruses?
- How might human populations evolve in response to a changing world?

UNIT 4: EVOLUTION

BIOZINE at CLASSZONE.COM

INTERNET MAGAZINE

Go online for the latest biology news and updates on all BioZine articles.

Expanding the Textbook

News Feeds

- Science Daily
- CNN
- BBC

Careers

Bio Bytes

Opinion Poll

Strange Biology

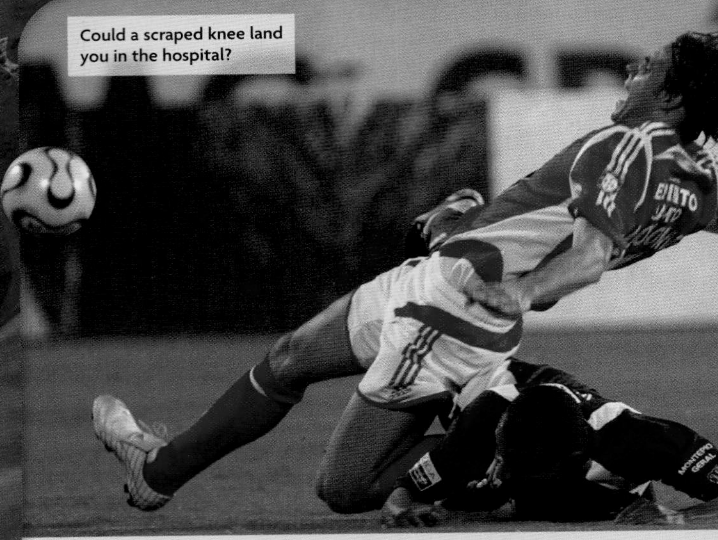

Could a scraped knee land you in the hospital?

Drug-Resistant Bacteria—A Global Health Issue

A bicyclist falls, scrapes his knees, and within a few days is unable to walk. Soccer players with turf burns suddenly find themselves in the hospital with skin infections that require intravenous antibiotics. Why are these young, healthy athletes developing such serious infections?

Current News

Arrange for students to have Internet access so that they can look for stories involving modern-day evolution featured in the Current News section of BioZine at **ClassZone.com.** Have students consider these questions:

- What organisms are mentioned as being recently evolved?
- What evolutionary pressures are causing these changes?
- What is the nature of the adaptation involved?
- How long did it take for the evolutionary change to be noticed by scientists?
- What impact might these changes have on humans or the environment?

Staph Infections

These athletes were infected by *Staphylococcus aureus*, or "staph." Staph is a common bacteria that most people carry on the surface of their skin and in their nose. To cause an infection, staph bacteria must get inside your body. The scrapes athletes commonly get provide an ideal entrance.

Serious problems caused by staph infections used to be rare. Doctors would prescribe antibiotics, such as penicillin, which killed the staph bacteria. Ordinary staph infections can still be treated this way. But the athletes in our examples did not have ordinary infections. These athletes' scrapes were infected by methicillin-resistant *Staphylococcus aureus* (MRSA) bacteria. This strain of bacteria is only one of many that has evolved resistance to antibiotics.

MRSA on the Rise

Percent of infections that are resistant: 0, 10, 20, 30, 40, 50, 60, 70, 80, 90, 100

1987, 1991, 1995, 1999, 2003

Source: NNIS System and Centers for Disease Control and Prevention

Drug-Resistant Bacteria

Bacteria that can survive antibiotic treatment are called drug-resistant bacteria. Some bacteria have resistance for one particular antibiotic, some have resistance for several, and a few cannot be treated with any known antibiotic.

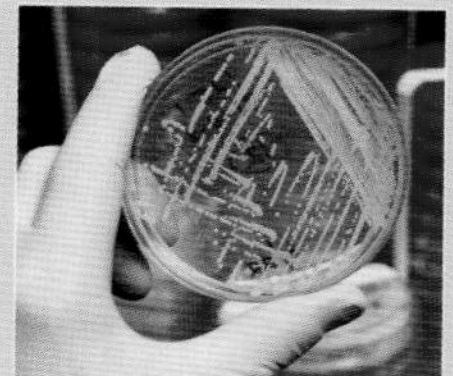

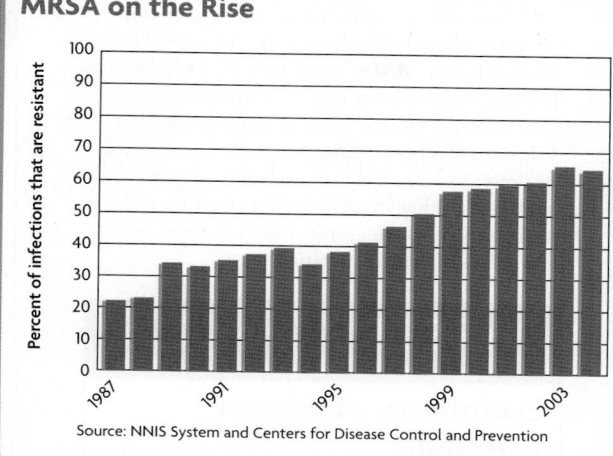

This petri dish contains *Staphylococcus aureus* bacteria.

MRSA can resist an entire class of antibiotics. Patients who have an MRSA infection must often be treated with what doctors call "the drug of last resort," vancomycin. Vancomycin is a drug that must be given intravenously. Not surprisingly, doctors began to see cases of vancomycin-resistant *Staphylococcus aureus* (VRSA) in 1997.

Staph isn't the only type of bacteria that is making a comeback with drug-resistant strains. For example, antibiotics developed to treat tuberculosis increased the survival rate of this disease to 98 percent. But now, drug-resistant strains of tuberculosis are killing 2.5 million people per year. Drug-resistant strains of cholera and bubonic plague also have been reported.

How Does Drug Resistance Evolve?

When you take antibiotics for a bacterial infection, billions of bacteria may be killed right away. However, there are likely to be a few that survive. Antibiotics kill the less resistant bacteria, leaving behind the more resistant bacteria to survive and reproduce. When resistant bacteria reproduce, the genes that make them resistant are passed on to their offspring; and bacteria reproduce rapidly. In six hours, one cell can produce as many as 500,000 offspring.

In addition to their ability to reproduce quickly, populations of bacteria evolve rapidly through another process as well. Bacteria use plasmids—small loops of DNA—to transfer genetic material between individual cells. This transfer of plasmids between cells is called conjugation. Some plasmids pass on resistance for one particular antibiotic. Others can transfer resistance for several antibiotics at once.

What characteristics do resistant bacteria pass on to their offspring? Some have cell walls that antibiotics cannot easily pass through. Others have pumps that remove antibiotics once they enter the cell. Some can even produce enzymes that attack the antibiotic drugs themselves.

Vocabulary of Drug-Resistant Bacteria

Students may not be familiar with all of the terms used to discuss drug-resistant bacteria.

bacteria—tiny, single-celled prokaryotic organisms. Many bacteria are helpful, but some cause serious infectious diseases.

selective pressure—the influence of some factor on natural selection that favors one group of organisms over another. Antibiotics cause a selective pressure by killing susceptible bacteria, allowing antibiotic-resistant bacteria to survive and reproduce.

conjugation—a type of bacterial recombination in which the organisms exchange genetic material through cell-to-cell contact. Bacteria can pass antibiotic resistance to other bacteria through conjugation.

antibiotic—a substance that destroys or inhibits bacterial growth that is used to treat diseases caused by bacteria.

penicillin—an antibiotic drug that is derived from penicillium molds or produced synthetically and used to treat various infections and diseases. It affects bacterial enzymes, inhibiting cell wall synthesis and causing the cell wall of the bacteria to break down.

methicillin—a synthetic antibiotic related to penicillin that is used to treat infections caused by staphylococci.

antibiotic resistance—a trait in microorganisms, especially bacteria, that enables them to survive in the presence of antibiotics.

plasmid—circular DNA that replicates within a cell independently of chromosomal DNA and is found in many bacterial strains. Plasmids are used in genetic engineering, gene cloning, gene therapy, and recombinant protein and DNA production research.

bacteriophage—a virus that infects a bacterium by attaching to it and inserting its genetic material into the bacterial cell. The bacteriophage may then destroy, or lyse, the bacterial cell.

Expanding the Textbook

Have students go to BioZine at **ClassZone.com** to read more about infections caused by drug-resistant bacteria and how they have become a global health issue. Students should take notes on the information and come to class prepared to discuss how drug resistance is a global problem. Have students identify diseases that are becoming more difficult to treat because of drug resistance and where outbreaks have occurred.

You could extend the discussion to include the role that people play in the development of drug resistance. **Ask**

- How has the use of antibiotics in farm animals contributed to drug resistance?
- How common are antibiotics in everyday products?
- What is the appropriate use of antibiotics?

Students can research how the use of antibiotics in humans, pets, and farm animals is changing.

Take It Further

According to the Centers for Disease Control and Prevention (CDC), over the last decade, almost every type of bacteria has become stronger and less responsive to antibiotic treatment. Diseases such as gonorrhea, head lice, malaria, streptococcus pneumoniae, and thyphoid fever are connected to antibiotic resistance and threaten public health. As a result, antibiotic resistance is among the CDC's top concerns.

Antibiotic-resistant bacteria can be spread throughout a population in various ways. Some bacteria are dispersed to new locations by wind or water. Modern transportation enables bacteria to travel great distances quickly. People, especially those in an enclosed space such as an airplane, can spread the bacteria when they cough or sneeze or when they touch a person or object without washing their hands.

Using proper sanitary practices, such as thorough hand washing with soap and water, can reduce the spread of bacteria. In hospitals, isolation is used to help keep antibiotic-resistant bacteria from spreading from one person to another. People visiting isolation rooms wear gowns and sometimes gloves and masks. Rooms may also provide antibacterial cleanser for visitors' hands.

Point out that to help reduce the speed with which antibiotic resistance develops, the overall use of antibiotics needs to be decreased. Antibiotics should only be used for bacterial infections when they are necessary and not for viral infections. All of an antibiotic prescription should be taken as directed and never shared.

Fighting Back

Some scientists are trying to develop ways to treat patients without killing the bacteria that are making them sick. Instead, they target the toxins produced by bacteria. If the bacteria are not harmed by the treatment, no selective pressure is produced. Scientists hope that by using this approach, bacteria will be slower to evolve defense mechanisms against the antibiotics. Other scientists hope to fight back by using bacteria's ancient rival, bacteriophages, which are viruses that infect bacteria.

CAREERS

Evolutionary Biologist in Action

DR. RICHARD LENSKI

TITLE Professor, Microbial Ecology, Michigan State University

EDUCATION Ph. D., Zoology, University of North Carolina, Chapel Hill

If you want to observe evolution in action, you must find populations that reproduce quickly. Dr. Richard Lenski, a professor at Michigan State University, has done just that. Dr. Lenski studies populations of *E. coli* bacteria, which he grows in flasks filled with a sugary broth. These bacteria produce about seven generations each day. Dr. Lenski has now observed more than 30,000 generations of *E. coli*.

The rapid rate of *E. coli* reproduction allows Dr. Lenski to watch evolution take place. Dr. Lenski can subject each generation of bacteria to the same environmental stresses, such as food shortages or antibiotics. He can then compare individuals from more recent generations with their ancestors, which he keeps in his laboratory freezer. By comparing generations in this way, Dr. Lenski can study how the population has evolved.

When Dr. Lenski began his research in 1988, watching evolution in action was still new. Now, many evolutionary biologists are following in his footsteps.

Read More >> at CLASSZONE.COM

TECHNOLOGY

New Drug Delivery System

Researchers at the University of South Florida decided to take on one of the most difficult bacterial infections of all, methicillin-resistant staph. They have developed a new class of antibiotics along with a new way to deliver it to the bacteria.

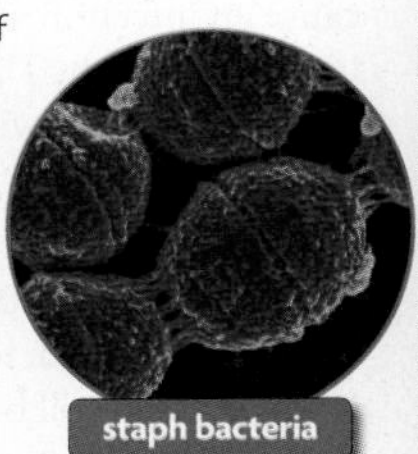
staph bacteria

- Antibiotics are bonded to nano-sized plastic balls. (One nanometer is one millionth of a millimeter.)
- The "nanoballs" are dissolved in water, and the solution is released into the patient's bloodstream. When the nanoballs reach the bacteria, the bacteria eat them.
- Nanoballs release antibiotics inside bacterial cells.

Because the bacteria are "eating" the nanoballs, cell wall adaptations that once kept antibiotics out are no longer an obstacle.

Read More >> at CLASSZONE.COM

Unanswered Questions

Some important research questions involving drug-resistant bacteria include the following:

- Can plasmids or bacteriophages be used in vaccines to fight bacteria?
- Are bacteria being exposed to antibiotics in sewage systems and evolving resistant strains there?
- How do antibacterial soaps and household cleaners contribute to the evolution of drug-resistant bacteria?
- Can drug-resistant bacteria be transferred from domestic animals to humans through food?

Read More >> at CLASSZONE.COM

Did You Know?

Have students access BioZine at **ClassZone.com** to read "Did you know?" Have students write a brief paragraph that addresses the following: Using information and examples from Unit 4, explain how the information in "Did you know?" can be viewed from an evolutionary perspective.

UNIT 5

Ecology

CHAPTER 13
Principles of Ecology 394

CHAPTER 14
Interactions in Ecosystems 426

CHAPTER 15
The Biosphere 454

CHAPTER 16
Human Impact on Ecosystems 482

BIOZINE

INTERNET MAGAZINE
Global Warming—Changing the Planet 512

TECHNOLOGY Deep Sea Sediment Coring

CAREER Oceanographer

Unit Project

Purpose **Consider an endangered species in the context of its benefit to biodiversity and describe conservation or recovery plans for an endangered species.**

Overview Students investigate an endangered species in their state and learn what measures are being taken to help the species survive. Students will

- search Internet, textbook, and/or library resources about an endangered species in their state
- analyze an existing recovery plan for the endangered species
- formulate a plan for improvement or support of the existing recovery plan, including how it would best be implemented
- prepare a report in an illustrated magazine-style article about their findings

Preparation Make a copy of the project description and rubric for each student (*Unit Resource Book*, pp. 125–126). Tell students that their article will be scored for organization and completeness.

Project Management Allow three weeks for the completion of the project. Have students check in weekly for progress monitoring.

Unit Resource Book Unit 5 Project, pp. 125–127

CHAPTER 13

Indiana Resource Preview

Print Resources

Principles of Ecology

INDIANA STANDARDS		Sections	PAGES and PACING	UNIT RESOURCE BOOK
	13.1	**Ecologists Study Relationships** **KEY CONCEPT** Ecology is the study of the relationships among organisms and their environment.	pp. 396–400 30 minutes	URB pages 1–4
		DATA ANALYSIS: Populations and Samples Quadrats and Population Size	p. 401 30 minutes	URB page 25
B.4.1	13.2	**Biotic and Abiotic Factors** **KEY CONCEPT** Every ecosystem includes both living and nonliving factors.	pp. 402–404 30 minutes	URB pages 5–8
B.4.1, NOS.3		CHAPTER INVESTIGATION: Design Your Own Abiotic Factors and Plant Growth	p. 405 20 minutes	**Lab Binder** Ecology pages 1–4
B.4.1	13.3	**Energy in Ecosystems** **KEY CONCEPT** Life in an ecosystem requires a source of energy.	pp. 406–407 30 minutes	URB pages 9–12
B.3.5	13.4	**Food Chains and Food Webs** **KEY CONCEPT** Food chains and food webs model the flow of energy in an ecosystem.	pp. 408–411 30 minutes	URB pages 13–16
B.3.4	13.5	**Cycling of Matter** **KEY CONCEPT** Matter cycles in and out of an ecosys-tem.	pp. 412–416 45 minutes	URB pages 17–20
B.3.5	13.6	**Pyramid Models** **KEY CONCEPT** Pyramids model the distribution of energy and matter in an ecosystem.	pp. 417–419 30 minutes	URB pages 21–24
NOS.6		OPTIONS FOR INQUIRY	pp. 420–421 45 min, 15 min	**Lab Binder** Ecology pages 5–8
		Chapter Review	pp. 422–425	**Assessment Book** Chapter Tests A, B pp. 259–266

INDIANA STANDARDS

B.3.4 Describe how matter cycles through an ecosystem by way of food chains and food webs and how organisms convert that matter into a vairety of organic molecules to be used in part in their own cellular structures.

B.3.5 Describe how energy from the sun flows through an ecosystem by way of food chains and food webs and only a small portion of that energy is used by individual organisms while the majority of energy is lost as heat.

B.4.1 Explain that the amount of life an environment can support is limited by the available energy, water, oxygen, and minerals, and by the ability of ecosystems to recycle the remains of dead organisms.

NOS.3 Clearly communicate their ideas and results of investigations verbally and in written form using tables, graphs, diagrams, and photographs.

NOS.6 Use analogies and models (mathematical and physical) to simplify and represent systems that are difficult to understand or directly experience due to their size, time scale, or complexity, and recognize the limitations of analogies and models.

Labs

PUPIL EDITION LABS

Quadrat Sampling, Section 1, p. 399 Students estimate population sizes by quadrat sampling. **Lab Binder** pp. 9–10	**Time:** 15 minutes **Materials:** quadrat, meter stick, calculator, objects to count
Abiotic Factors and Plant Growth, p. 405 Students test the effect of abiotic factors on plant growth. **Lab Binder** pp. 1–4	**Time:** 20 minutes **Materials:** 4 radish seedlings, 4 cups, ruler, cheesecloth, sand, gravel, potting soil, household-plant liquid fertilizer, plastic wrap in a variety of colors, graduated cylinder

OPTIONS FOR INQUIRY

Random Sampling, p. 420 Students estimate population size by random sampling. **Lab Binder** pp. 5–7	**Time:** 45 minutes **Materials:** ruler, scissors, paper, 2 containers, Calculation datasheet, calculator
Build a Terrarium, p. 421 Students model a self-sustaining ecosystem. **Lab Binder** p. 8	**Time:** 15 minutes **Materials:** glass jar with lid, gravel, potting soil, large sealable plastic bags, water, measuring cup, ruler, small plants, light source

LAB BINDER Unit 5 Ecology

Additional Investigation: Nitrogen Fixation, pp. 11–13

Virtual Lab Worksheet: Estimating Population Size, p. 86

LAB GENERATOR

A searchable CD of all labs in the program in editable format, including forensic, probeware, and biotechnology labs.

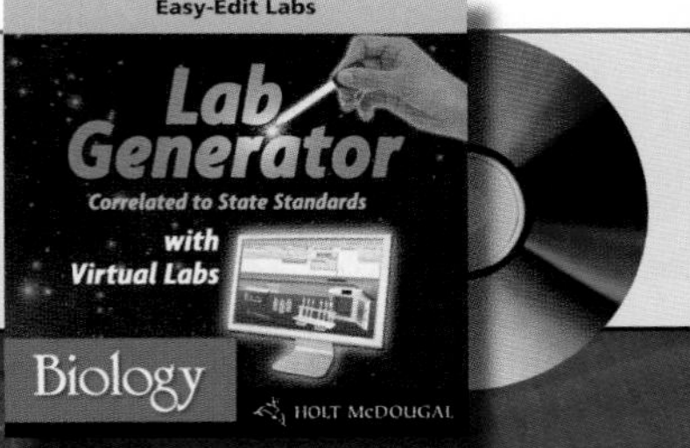

Presentation Tools

POWER PRESENTATIONS

Presentation Chapter 13
Power Presentations for each section incorporate images and clips from the Media Gallery: Includes Note Navigator for each section.

MEDIA GALLERY

Contains the following images and video clips, as well as animations, simulations and forms of visuals from the book.

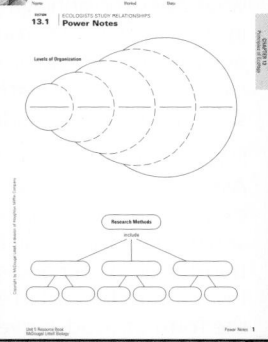

Levels of organization

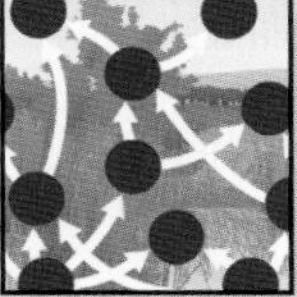
Food web

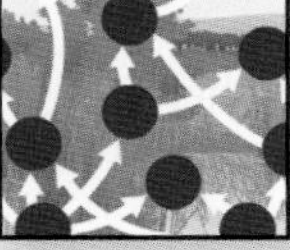

Power Notes

Coral reef

Beaver dam

VIDEO

Find a set of short video clips on ecology and ecosystems.

ANIMATED BIOLOGY

Distribution of Producers

Build a Food Web

TRANSPARENCIES

Levels of Organization T56
Food Web T57
The Hydrologic Cycle T58
The Oxygen Cycle T59
The Carbon Cycle T60
The Nitrogen Cycle T61
The Phosphorous Cycle T62
Energy Pyramid T63
Biomass Pyramid and Pyramid of Numbers T64

Online BIOLOGY CLASSZONE.COM

- BioZine
- Animated Biology
- Interactive Review
- SciLinks
- Resource Centers

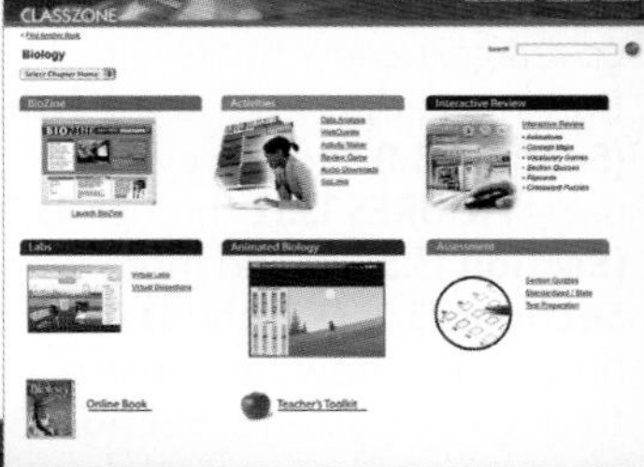

CHAPTER 13

▼ Focus and Motivate

How does this bird interact with its ecosystem?

Students may state the obvious answer, the bird gets food. **Ask,** In what other ways does the anhinga (an-HING-guh) interact with its environment? The environment provides water, shelter, oxygen, and other materials needed to support life and reproduction.

Have students look at the picture again. **Ask,** At a basic level, what type of exchange is happening between the anhinga and the fish in its beak? a transfer of matter and stored energy from fish to bird Matter and energy, in the form of food, move through an ecosystem from producers to consumers. **Ask,** Is the fish a consumer or producer? Why? a consumer because it, like the anhinga, gets energy from food Producers, such as plants and algae, are organisms that bring energy into an ecosystem. **Ask,** What is the original source of energy in this ecosystem? the sun

BIOZINE ClassZone.com

Students can access BioZine at **ClassZone.com** to receive updates to featured topics in the book.

In a Hurry?

Many students will be familiar with the material in this chapter. For quick coverage, review the levels of organization in an ecosystem, using **FIGURE 13.2 (Section 13.1)** and the cycles of matter, using **FIGURES 13.12** through **13.16 (Section 13.5).** Spend more time on **Sections 13.2, 13.3,** and **13.4** to reinforce how energy flows and matter cycles through ecosystems. **Section 13.6** provides a more in-depth look at trophic levels and biomass in ecosystems, using pyramid models.

CHAPTER 13 Principles of Ecology

KEY CONCEPTS

13.1 Ecologists Study Relationships
Ecology is the study of the relationships among organisms and their environment.

13.2 Biotic and Abiotic Factors
Every ecosystem includes both living and nonliving factors.

13.3 Energy in Ecosystems
Life in an ecosystem requires a source of energy.

13.4 Food Chains and Food Webs
Food chains and food webs model the flow of energy in an ecosystem.

13.5 Cycling of Matter
Matter cycles in and out of an ecosystem.

13.6 Pyramid Models
Pyramids model the distribution of energy and matter in an ecosystem.

Online BIOLOGY CLASSZONE.COM

Animated BIOLOGY
View animated chapter concepts.
- Distribution of Producers
- Estimating Population Size
- Build a Food Web

BIOZINE
Keep current with biology news.
- Featured stories
- News feeds
- Careers

RESOURCE CENTER
Get more information on
- Chemosynthesis
- Food Webs
- Cycles in Ecosystems
- Energy in Ecosystems

Student Activity

Purpose **Have teams of students model the flow of energy through food chains. Each team makes a food chain using pictures of organisms provided.**

Materials (per team)

Each team will need pictures of various producers and consumers. Examples:

- **Marine food chain** phytoplankton (for example, diatoms), zooplankton (for example, crustacean larvae), seaweed (green or brown algae), fish, sea turtle, heron, dolphin, shark
- **Woodland food chain** grass, fern, tree, insect, insect larva (for example, caterpillar), snail, spider, mouse, rabbit, weasel, sparrow, owl, fox

How does this bird interact with its ecosystem?

Connecting CONCEPTS

Anhingas live in freshwater marshes and swamps of the southeastern United States. While they are primarily consumers of fish, an anhinga's diet may also include aquatic insects and invertebrates. The anhinga and the fish are just two of the many organisms that interact in this complex wetland ecosystem.

Vertebrates Unlike other water birds, anhingas do not have oil glands to waterproof their feathers. Without the buoyancy of waterproof feathers, anhingas are effective underwater divers and swimmers. Because they cannot fly when their feathers are waterlogged, anhingas are often seen perched above water, drying their wings in the sun.

Introduce Describe how to make a food chain with the pictures, emphasizing that a food chain is a one-to-one linking of a producer and a series of consumers. Tell students that there are several different food chains possible with the organisms you provided, but that all food chains start with a producer.

Discuss Have teams critique one another's food chain. Make sure food chains are realistic. If time allows, arrange the food chains into a food web, showing how one food chain overlaps another.

Ask, How does energy flow in a food chain? Energy is first captured by a producer, then flows from each organism that is eaten to the organism that eats it.

Ask, Is all the energy captured by the producers kept within a food chain? No, each step of the way, energy is lost as heat or as other waste material.

Activate Prior Knowledge

In Chapter 1, students were introduced to the idea of systems as a unifying theme in biology. Ecologists study ecosystems. **Ask**

- What is a system? smaller parts working together, organized into a larger whole
- What systems are you a part of? Students will probably think in terms of social constructs, such as a school system.

Focus on the idea that, as animals, humans are part of an ecosystem. We interact with the environment to get energy and materials.

Preview Vocabulary

Greek and Latin Word Origins Two word roots are important to the vocabulary in this chapter.

The Latin root *vorare* means "to swallow or devour." The emphasis is on the act of eating and what is eaten:

herbivore *omnivore*
carnivore *detrivore*

The word *trophic* comes from the Greek root *trephein,* "to nourish." Point out that the emphasis is different. For example, the words

autotroph *heterotroph*

are broader in scope. The term *trophic level* refers to the source of nutrition for a whole group of organisms.

Academic Vocabulary Point out to students the important distinction between the words *flow* and *cycle.* Energy flows into and out of an ecosystem, whereas matter cycles within, remaining part of the system.

English Learners Students will see vocabulary words from everyday language that are used as scientific terminology:

producer *consumer*
community
generalist *specialist*

Give students a few minutes to check the words in the *Multilanguage Glossary.* Discuss how the meaning in this context differs from everyday use.

▼ Plan and Prepare

Objectives

- Summarize the levels of organization that ecologists study.
- Describe research methods ecologists use to study the environment.

Section Resources

Unit Resource Book Study Guide pp. 1–2 Power Notes p. 3 Reinforcement p. 4 Pre-AP Activity pp. 27–28
Interactive Reader Chapter 13 **Spanish Study Guide** pp. 133–134
Biology Toolkit pp. C4, C7, C20, D4
Technology Power Presentation 13.1 Media Gallery DVD Online Quiz 13.1

Activate Prior Knowledge Ask, What does the word *relationship* mean to you? family, friends, team, job In each instance, the word suggests a connection, an *interaction,* typically with other human beings. An ecologist studies the close connection all organisms have with their natural environment. This is not just how the environment affects the organism, but also how the organism affects the environment as well as other organisms in that environment.

▼ Teach

Vocabulary

Word Origins The root of **environment** is from the French *environner,* meaning "to encircle." **Environmental science** considers not just the natural world but also the effects of human activity, including social institutions, cultural attitudes, agricultural practices, and industrial conditions. **Ecology** focuses specifically on the interdependent relationship between living things and their environment.

13.1 Ecologists Study Relationships

KEY CONCEPT Ecology is the study of the relationships among organisms and their environment.

MAIN IDEAS

- Ecologists study environments at different levels of organization.
- Ecological research methods include observation, experimentation, and modeling.

VOCABULARY

ecology, p. 396
community, p. 397
ecosystem, p. 397
biome, p. 397

Review
organism, population

Connect Water birds such as anhingas, along with a variety of other plants and animals, rely on the presence of wetlands for their survival. How might the loss of wetland areas affect these aquatic species? Learning about organisms and how they interact with one another, with other species, and with their environment is what the study of ecology is all about.

MAIN IDEA

Ecologists study environments at different levels of organization.

Over their life cycle, Pacific salmon are the main food source for more than 140 species of wildlife, including grizzly bears, as shown in **FIGURE 13.1.** If they are not eaten, their bodies return vital nutrients back into the river system, some of which are used by plants to grow. In addition to their role in the health of river systems, salmon are also important to the Pacific Northwest's economy. Today, many species of wild Pacific salmon are threatened with extinction due to competition from hatchery fish, blocked river paths, and loss of spawning grounds. As salmon populations decline, how are other species affected? What effect would the loss of salmon have on a local and a global scale? These are the types of questions ecologists are trying to answer.

FIGURE 13.1 Salmon are a primary food source for many species, including grizzly bears. If salmon disappeared, species dependent on them would also suffer.

What Is Ecology?

Ecology is the study of the interactions among living things, and between living things and their surroundings. The word *ecology* comes from the Greek word *oikos,* which means "house." This word origin makes sense if you think of Earth as home and all organisms as members of Earth's household. Ernst Haeckel, a German biologist, coined the term *ecology* in 1866 to encourage biologists to consider the ways organisms interact. Until that time, most scientists studied a plant or an animal as though it existed in isolation—as if it did not affect its surroundings, and its surroundings did not affect it.

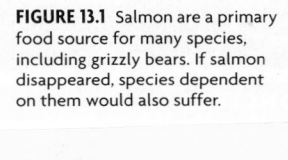

- What is ecology?
- What types of relationships and interactions does an ecologist study?
- What are some ways an ecologist can get information about an ecosystem?

Have them study the section, close their books, and write answers to the questions.

Biology Toolkit, Questions to Guide Reading, p. C4

BELOW LEVEL

Students can preview each section, using this strategy:

- Predict what the section is about using the headings.
- Locate key terms.
- Add details and definitions as they read.
- Note how the text supports the section's main ideas, summarizing the main ideas in their own words.

Biology Toolkit, PLAN, p. C7

Levels of Organization

Ecologists study nature on different levels, from a local to a global scale. These levels, shown in **FIGURE 13.2**, reveal the complex relationships found in nature.

- **Organism** An organism is an individual living thing, such as an alligator.
- **Population** A population is a group of the same species that lives in one area, such as all the alligators that live in a swamp.
- **Community** A **community** is a group of different species that live together in one area, such as groups of alligators, turtles, birds, fish, and plants that live together in the Florida Everglades.
- **Ecosystem** An **ecosystem** includes all of the organisms as well as the climate, soil, water, rocks, and other nonliving things in a given area. Ecosystems can vary in size. An entire ecosystem may live within a decaying log, which in turn may be part of a larger wetland ecosystem.
- **Biome** A **biome** (BY-OHM) is a major regional or global community of organisms. Biomes are usually characterized by the climate conditions and plant communities that thrive there.

Ecologists study relationships within each level of organization and also between levels. For example, researchers may study the relationships within a population of alligators, as well as the relationships between alligators and turtles in a community.

A Apply What level of organization describes a flock of pigeons in a park?

Community? levels of organization

FIGURE 13.2 Levels of Organization

The Florida Everglades is an example of the subtropical savanna biome. Many organisms live in this aquatic ecosystem.

e

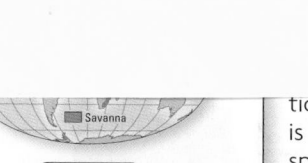

ant roles that go
g diverse biologi-
ands act as
purify water by
ring toxins.
odwaters. In
p stabilize
uce storm
it loss of wetlands
ast exacerbated
ne Katrina in 2005.

LS

llustration to walk
levels of organiza-
tion that ecologists study. The organism is one individual and represents a single species. The population also represents a single species but includes more than one individual. **Ask**

- What populations besides alligators could you find in this ecosystem? grasses, mangroves, osprey, herons, egrets, turtles, fish
- What do these different populations taken together represent? a community
- What does the ecosystem include in addition to the living things you see here? physical conditions; nonliving components, such as water, soil, sunlight

Answers

A Apply population

BELOW LEVEL

Remind students that mnemonic devices, or memory aids, can help with recall. For example, to remember the levels of organization, ask students to come up with a sentence that uses the first letter of each level. Example: <u>O</u>ver<u>p</u>opulation <u>c</u>rowds <u>e</u>very<u>b</u>ody. To help students interpret the relationship between levels, discuss the significance of the nested circles in **FIGURE 13.2.**

ENGLISH LEARNERS

Have students extend the note-taking diagram shown in their textbook to include a word square for each of the levels of organization. The first square includes the term accompanied by the word's translation in the student's native language. All of these terms appear in the *Multilanguage Glossary*. In the remaining squares, students draw a picture, rewrite the definition in their own words, and then write the English definition (also found in the *Multilanguage Glossary*).

Biology Toolkit, Word Squares, p. D4

Chapter 13: Principles of Ecology **397**

▼ Teach *continued*

History of Science

During the 1700s and 1800s, many scientists, including **Charles Darwin** and **Alfred Russell Wallace,** traveled to different parts of the world to catalog new species. The work of Darwin and Wallace made clear the connection between the physical characteristics of a place and the types of species found there—**biogeography.** The British botanist **Arthur Tansley** coined the word **ecosystem** in 1935 to describe the interactive system that exists *between* the living and nonliving components of an environment. From 1903 to 1907, Tansley had coordinated field studies that surveyed and mapped the types of vegetation found across the British Isles. As an educator, he strongly advocated fieldwork as being necessary to the education of any good ecologist.

Take It Further

Prairie dogs are not only an important food source for the black-footed ferret but also a critical part of the **prairie ecosystem.** Prairie ecosystems that have healthy prairie-dog populations support a greater number of animals overall and have greater species diversity than prairies without them. **Ask,** In what ways, other than as a food source, might prairie dogs support other species? Their burrows provide shelter for other animals. In digging burrows, prairie dogs increase the nitrogen content in the soil and open up more area for oxygen and water absorption, all of which aid plant growth.

Answers

A Apply A scientist might directly survey mountain goats by using binoculars or might indirectly survey them by looking for signs of feces (commonly called *scat*). A scientist could also use radio telemetry to track the goats.

MAIN IDEA

Ecological research methods include observation, experimentation, and modeling.

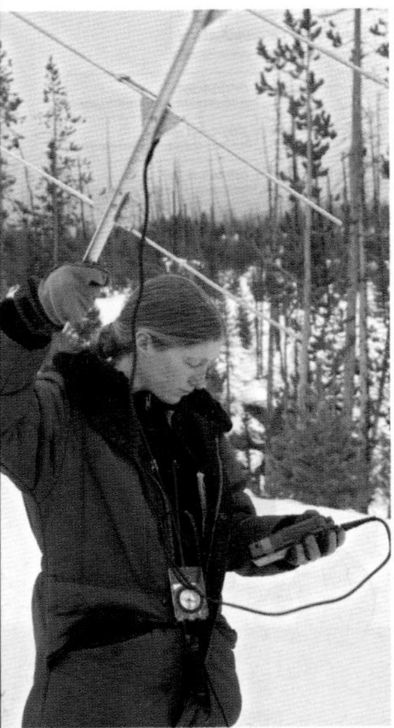

FIGURE 13.3 Much of the data gathered by ecologists results from long hours of observation in the field. This ecologist is using radio telemetry to track gray wolves.

Scientists rely on a variety of methods and tools to conduct research. Tools can range from a simple tape measure used to find an organism's size to a sophisticated computer system used to create a model of an entire ecosystem.

Observation

Observation is the act of carefully watching something over time. Such observations may occur over short or long periods of time. Long-term studies are a key part of a scientist's toolkit because most environmental changes happen over a long period of time. For example, studies of prairie-dog populations are helping scientists to determine which locations are most appropriate for the reintroduction of the black-footed ferret. The black-footed ferret is an endangered species that relies on the prairie dog as its main food source.

One way that scientists monitor and observe populations is by conducting surveys. Visual surveys may be direct or indirect.

- Direct surveys are used for species that are easy to follow. In these surveys, scientists watch animals either with the naked eye or with tools such as binoculars or scopes.
- Indirect surveys are used for species that are difficult to track. In these surveys, scientists search for other signs of its presence, such as feces or a recent kill.

Radio telemetry is another method used by scientists to monitor populations. Scientists fit an animal with a radio collar that emits a signal and then use the signal to track the animal's movement, as shown in **FIGURE 13.3.** This practice is especially useful when studying a species that has a broad range, such as the gray wolf.

In addition to observing the activities of a species, scientists may want to determine its population size. Rather than count every individual organism in a large study area, scientists often sample the population instead. Mark-recapture is a method used by scientists to estimate the population size of mobile organisms. For example, to monitor prairie-dog populations, scientists capture and mark prairie dogs with ear tags and then release them back into the wild. When scientists later repeat the survey, the captured prairie dogs will include both marked and unmarked animals. Scientists calculate the ratio of marked to unmarked animals and use this value to estimate the total population size.

To monitor plant populations, scientists use a method called quadrat sampling. In this method, quadrats, or rectangular frames, are randomly placed on the study site. To determine plant population numbers, scientists identify and count the number of plants within each randomly selected plot. The total number of counted plants is then plugged into a mathematical formula to determine the plant population of the entire study site.

 Apply **How might a scientist use observation to study a population of mountain goats? Explain your answer.**

Differentiated Instruction

PRE-AP

Have students use a graphic organizer to compare the advantages and disadvantages of direct animal surveys with those of indirect surveys. To get students started, have them consider these questions:

- How invasive is the technique to the animal?
- How easy is it to identify individuals?
- Is there the possibility of counting individuals more than once?
- How might weather conditions affect observations?

Biology Toolkit, T-Chart, p. C20

TEACH WITH TECHNOLOGY

Using a mapping database such as Google Earth or NASA's Visible Earth, print out images of natural areas in your area. Ask students to identify ecosystems from these images. For more information on mapping resources, visit **ClassZone.com.** Have students suggest strategies for mapping the vegetation in an area.

QUICK LAB SAMPLING

Quadrat Sampling

Ecologists often use quadrats—square or rectangular grids—to collect data about population numbers in an ecosystem. In this lab, you will use a quadrat to collect data on three "species."

PROBLEM What is the population size of each species?

PROCEDURE

1. Obtain a quadrat frame. Measure, calculate, and record the area of the quadrat.
2. Stand at the edge of the area you will sample and randomly throw your quadrat.
3. Move your quadrat so that it does not overlap with any other quadrat. Each different object represents a different species. Count how many individuals of each species are in your quadrat and record your data in a data table. Repeat this procedure three times.
4. Combine your data with that of your classmates. Find the average number of each species for all of the samples. Obtain the area of the sampling plot from your teacher. Calculate how many quadrats would fit in the area of the sampling plot. Multiply this by the average number of each species found in one quadrat to estimate the population of each species.

MATERIALS

- quadrat
- meter stick
- calculator
- objects to count

ANALYZE AND CONCLUDE

1. **Analyze** Compare your population estimate for each species to the actual number that your teacher provides. Is the estimate accurate? Why or why not?
2. **Evaluate** How can you ensure that your estimate of population size will be as accurate as possible?

Experimentation

Scientists may perform experiments in the lab or in the field. There are benefits and drawbacks to each type of experiment. While a lab experiment gives the researcher more control, the artificial setting does not reflect the complex interactions that occur in nature. A field experiment, on the other hand, gives a more accurate picture of how organisms interact in a natural setting. However, in a field study, it is more difficult to determine cause and effect due to the large number of factors at work in nature.

A lab experiment is conducted in a controlled, indoor environment. This isolation helps scientists to focus each experiment on a very specific part of an ecosystem, such as a single organism. For example, to find out how climate change affects the growth rates of plants, scientists can grow plants in a lab and adjust temperature settings. Working in a lab allows scientists to control variables in a way that would not be possible in the field.

A field experiment is performed where the organisms live. Like lab experiments, field experiments also have controls and manipulated variables. For example, to determine how browsing by deer affects plant and small-animal communities, scientists might fence off large study plots to keep out the deer. By monitoring the fenced and unfenced plots over a period of time, scientists can determine whether deer significantly change the areas in which they browse for food.

Connecting CONCEPTS

Scientific Method As you learned in **Chapter 1**, all fields of science, including ecology, use the scientific method to investigate and answer scientific questions. Applied ecology uses the principles of ecology along with the scientific method to solve environmental problems.

A **Contrast** **What is the difference between a lab experiment and a field experiment?**

BELOW LEVEL

To illustrate the importance of a random sample, draw a square on a sheet of acetate and scatter paper dots across the square. Use a second sheet of acetate to cover the dots. Place on an overhead projector. With a small cardboard quadrat, show how different placements of the quadrat can affect the estimate. Discuss what would happen to the estimate if the quadrat were placed only where there were lots of dots to count. **Ask,** What is it called if a person's own preferences influence a choice? bias

PRE-AP

Calculations of population density will be covered in Chapter 14. **Ask,** Knowing the size of a population for a given area, how could you predict the size of a population for a similar but much larger area? Calculate average number of individuals per unit of area and apply to the larger area.

QUICK LAB

Time 15 minutes 

Lab Binder Ecology, pp. 9–10

Purpose Estimate population sizes by quadrat sampling.

LAB MANAGEMENT

- Conduct the lab indoors using common objects, such as paper clips, pencils, and erasers, placed randomly in a location whose area you have measured ahead of time.
- Count and record the objects before distributing them.
- Have students count any object within or touched by the quadrat.
- It is possible a very small population might not be sampled, depending on the placement of the quadrats.

Safety Avoid quadrats made from wire hangers.

Teacher Note "I used to make quadrats out of hangers and had a couple of accidents with overzealous students. Surprisingly, a Hula-Hoop® is almost a perfect square meter."

Answers

Analyze and Conclude

1. Accept all reasonable answers. If the estimate is inaccurate, it could be because of inaccurate counting, miscalculation of averages, nonrandom sampling, or nonrandom distribution of species in a population.
2. *Sample Answer:* Increase the number of samples taken, be sure quadrat size is appropriate for the size of the area sampled, obtain random samples, count accurately, and calculate averages accurately.

Answers

A **Contrast** A lab experiment is conducted in the controlled setting of a laboratory; a field experiment is conducted in a less-controlled natural setting.

▼ Teach *continued*

TEACH FROM VISUALS

FIGURE 13.4 Discuss the challenges involved in developing and deploying transmitters on wild animals. **Ask,** What concerns must scientists address in developing transmitters to be placed on animals in their natural environments? safety in placing the unit; remote control of the unit; battery life; adequate storage space for data; size of unit (small, lightweight); durability; ability to access data without disturbing the animal; data retention if animal moves out of study area

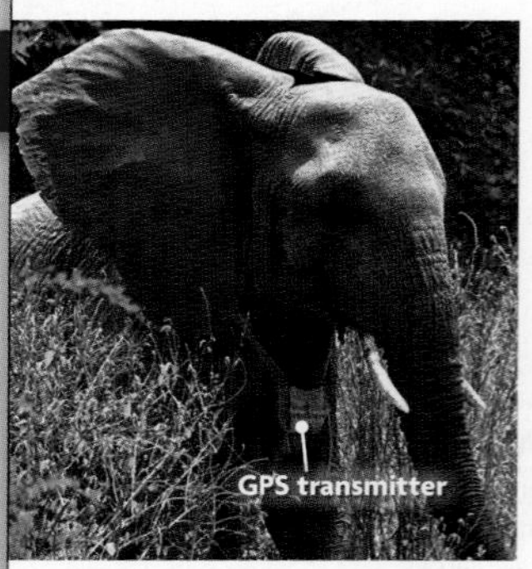

FIGURE 13.4 Ecologists use data transmitted by GPS receivers worn by elephants to develop computer models of the animals' movements.

Modeling

Sometimes the questions scientists wish to ask cannot be easily answered through observation or experimentation. Instead, scientists use computer and mathematical models to describe and model nature. Scientists can manipulate different model variables to learn about organisms or whole ecosystems in ways that would not be possible in a natural setting.

Although they are used to test hypothetical situations, models are created with the use of real data. For example, in Kenya, scientists are using satellite technology to track the movement of elephants, as shown in **FIGURE 13.4.** These data, in turn, can be used to create a model to study how changes to the ecosystem might affect elephant movement patterns. Before putting the model to use, scientists can test it by inserting actual data values. Such testing allows scientists to make sure that the values predicted by the model are similar to actual observations in the field.

In the United States, scientists developed a computer software program to create a virtual model of the Greater Yellowstone ecosystem. A variety of data were used to create this model, including

- the movements of elk, bison, bear, and wolf populations
- the location of different vegetation, such as meadows and forests
- the amount of snow
- the activities of geysers and other geothermal landforms

The combination of these data together with computer-generated maps creates a virtual ecosystem that scientists can use to model how one variable affects another. This type of modeling program sometimes plays a role in the development of wildlife conservation plans. Computer programs modeled population dynamics with and without the presence of the gray wolf. These programs were used to study how the reintroduction of gray wolves into Yellowstone might affect other species within the park and the surrounding area. By understanding how different organisms and factors within an ecosystem interact, wildlife managers are able to make well-informed decisions.

To learn more about ecology, go to scilinks.org.
Keycode: MLB013

Ⓐ **Contrast** **How does modeling differ from experimentation?**

Answers

Ⓐ **Contrast** Modeling is computer-based or math-based and relies on large amounts of data to make predictions. Experimentation involves the direct study of organisms, either in the lab or in the field.

▼ Assess and Reteach

Assess Use the Online Quiz or Section Quiz *(Assessment Book,* p. 253).

Reteach Project on the board the image of **FIGURE 13.2** from the Media Gallery. Have students take turns writing the types of research methods that would be appropriate at each level of the ecosystem. Have students explain their choices.

13.1 ASSESSMENT

ONLINE QUIZ
ClassZone.com

REVIEWING MAIN IDEAS

1. What are the five different levels of organization studied by ecologists?
2. Describe the three general methods used by ecologists to study organisms.

CRITICAL THINKING

3. **Apply** What ecological research methods would you use to study bird migration? Explain your choices.
4. **Apply** How might an ecologist use modeling to study fire in a forest **ecosystem**? What might be some key variables used to create the model?

***Connecting* CONCEPTS**

5. **Evolution** Ernst Haeckel was greatly influenced by the writings of Charles Darwin. How do the principles of **ecology** relate to understanding how adaptations occur?

13.1 ASSESSMENT

1. organism, population, community, ecosystem, biome
2. Observation is the act of watching something over time, such as a population of birds; experimentation can occur in the lab or in the field and involves testing a hypothesis; modeling is a computer-based or math-based method used to predict how changes in one variable may affect another.
3. observation—band birds and capture them at each end of their migratory route to record their movement; experimentation—devise an experiment to test what triggers migration; modeling—develop a computer model that includes different variables that might predict the time and path of migration
4. *Sample Answer:* Ecologists could use models to determine movement of fire, locations where prescribed burns should take place, and areas with the potential for fire outbreaks. Key variables might include forest density, types of trees, plant and animal populations, wind patterns, and weather conditions.
5. Species are adapted to their environments. This concept is directly related to the study of ecology, in which the interactions between organisms and the environment are studied. By understanding the interactions within an ecosystem, scientists can develop an understanding of how populations evolve in response to their environments.

Quadrats and Population Size

One part of studying a population is to record its size. Often, it is possible to count all of the individuals in a population of organisms, such as large mammals or trees. With smaller organisms or more numerous populations, the population must be estimated based on representative samples. A **sample** is a portion of the population that is defined and counted.

Quadrat sampling is most often used to survey plant populations. This method can be used to identify species, calculate species' frequency, and monitor changes in plant communities over time.

EXAMPLE

One method used to estimate populations is to count the number of individuals within a known sample area. To sample plants, quadrats are randomly placed over a large area and the number of individuals of the same species within the quadrat is counted. The number of quadrats sampled depends on the size of the entire area under study. In the example shown here, a scientist used quadrats to estimate the population of shrubs in a field. A simple equation can be used to find the population estimate: $T = NA$

$$T = NA$$

T = Total population estimate

$$N = \frac{\text{Total number of individuals counted}}{\text{Number of quadrats}}$$

$$A = \frac{\text{Total area}}{\text{Area of quadrat}}$$

In the example, each darkly shaded area represents a quadrat. Six shrubs were counted in five quadrats. The area of each quadrat is 1 m^2. The total area of the sampling plot is 200 m^2.

$$T = NA$$
$$T = \frac{6}{5} \cdot \frac{200\ m^2}{1\ m^2}$$
$$T = 1.20 \cdot 200 = 240$$

T = 240 individuals = estimated population of shrubs in the field

ESTIMATE A POPULATION FROM A SAMPLE

For each example, calculate the estimated population. Use the formula and show all of your work.

1. **Calculate** A scientist uses a quadrat of 2 m^2 to estimate the population of daisies in a field. She counts 173 individuals in 15 quadrats. The total area of the field is 250 m^2.
2. **Calculate** A scientist uses a 0.25 m^2 quadrat to sample a population of dandelions in a garden that is 500 m^2. The number of dandelions counted in 10 quadrats is 63.

Answers

1. 1442 individuals ($173/15 = 11.53 = N$; $250/2 = 125 = A$; $11.53 \cdot 125 = 1441.67$)
2. 12,600 individuals ($63/10 = 6.3 = N$; $500/0.25 = 2000 = A$; $6.3 \cdot 2000 = 12{,}600$)

DATA ANALYSIS

Introduce

Scientists use very carefully calculated sampling techniques and statistical analysis to estimate population sizes with a high degree of confidence. **Ask**

- Why is sampling important to the study of ecology? No scientist can count every member of a wild population or all members of all the interacting populations within a community.
- What does the sample represent? population as a whole
- What does a different count for each sample suggest? Individuals in the sampling areas are not spaced uniformly.
- What does the expression *level of confidence* mean when discussing data? It describes the degree to which a scientist trusts the data to be accurate, typically expressed as a percentage. The higher the percentage, the greater is the confidence.

Discuss

Have students look at the population shown in the diagram. **Ask**

- If the quadrats were placed in very sparse areas or very dense areas, how would that affect the estimate of the population's size? low estimates for sparse areas, high estimates for dense areas
- What might a biased choice look like in this example? *Sample Answer:* choosing quadrats that have at least one shrub in them.

Unit Resource Book, Data Analysis, p. 25

SECTION 13.2

▼ Plan and Prepare

Objectives

- Identify biotic and abiotic factors in an ecosystem.
- Describe how a change in one factor in an ecosystem can affect others.

Section Resources

Unit Resource Book
Study Guide pp. 5–6
Power Notes p. 7
Reinforcement p. 8

Interactive Reader Chapter 13
Spanish Study Gui

Biology Toolkit p.

Technology
Power Presentatio
Media Gallery DVD
Online Quiz 13.2

Activate Prior Know students imagine the woodland, then a des picked up a handful c place, what differenc Woodland soil is rich matter and holds wat has little organic matt water. Discuss the eff plant type.

▼ Teach

Take It Further

Mangrove forests, which are typically home to biting insects, crocodiles, and snakes, are often cut back to make room for hotels and housing along the coast. However, the very tropical fish and coral reefs that attract tourists may be threatened if some portion of the forest is not preserved.

Answers

A Contrast Biotic factors are living components; abiotic factors are nonliving.

13.2 Biotic and Abiotic Factors

KEY CONCEPT Every ecosystem includes both living and nonliving factors.

MAIN IDEAS
- An ecosystem includes both biotic and abiotic factors.
- Changing one factor in an ecosystem can affect many other factors.

VOCABULARY
biotic, p. 402
abiotic, p. 402
biodiversity, p. 403
keystone species, p. 403

INDIANA STANDARDS

B.4.1 Explain that the amount of life an environment can support is limited by the available energy, water, oxygen, and minerals, and by the ability of ecosystems to recycle the remains of dead organisms.

Connect A vegetable garden is a small ecosystem, and its success depends on many factors. You can probably list several without too much thought. You might think of sunlight, fertilizer, or insects to pollinate the plants' flowers. Gardeners usually don't think of themselves as scientists, but they must take into account how these factors affect their plants in order for the plants to flourish.

MAIN IDEA

An ecosystem includes both biotic and abiotic factors.

All ecosystems are made up of living and nonliving components. These parts are referred to as biotic and abiotic factors.

- **Biotic** (by-AHT-ihk) factors are living things, such as plants, animals, fungi, and bacteria. Each organism plays a particular role in the ecosystem. For example, earthworms play a key role in enriching the soil.
- **Abiotic** (AY-by-AHT-ihk) factors are nonliving things such as moisture, temperature, wind, sunlight, and soil. The balance of these factors determines which living things can survive in a particular environment.

In the Caribbean Sea, scientists found that coral reefs located near saltwater marshes have more fish than do reefs farther out at sea. As shown in **FIGURE 13.5,** the key biotic factor is the mangrove trees that live in the marshes. The trees provide food and shelter for newly hatched fish, protecting them from predators. After the fish mature, they swim to the reefs. Abiotic factors that affect the growth of mangrove trees include low levels of oxygen in the mud where they grow and changing levels of salinity, or saltiness, due to daily tidal changes.

An ecosystem may look similar from one year to the next, with similar numbers of animals and plants. However, an ecosystem is always undergoing some changes. For example, a long period of increased precipitation might allow one plant species to grow better than others. As the plant continues to grow, it may crowd out other plant species, changing the community's composition. Though the total number of plants in the community may remain the same, the species have changed. As these cyclic changes occur, an ecosystem falls into a balance, which is known as approximate equilibrium.

A Contrast What is the difference between biotic and abiotic factors?

Differentiated Instruction

BELOW LEVEL

Make use of a terrarium or an aquarium to help students identify biotic and abiotic factors. Encourage them to go beyond the obvious plants and animals, water, and soil. Ask about unseen factors, such as microorganisms, oxygen, pH, and temperature. A similar activity can be done with matter cycles in **Section 13.5.**

MAIN IDEA

Changing one factor in an ecosystem can affect many other factors.

An ecosystem is a complex web of connected biotic and abiotic factors. You may not always think of yourself as part of the ecosystem, but humans, like other species, rely on the environment for survival. All species are affected by changes to the biotic and abiotic factors in an ecosystem.

Biodiversity

The relationships within an ecosystem are very complicated. If you attached a separate string between a forest tree and each of the living and nonliving things in the ecosystem that influenced it, and did the same for each of those living and nonliving things, the forest would quickly become a huge web of strings. The web would also reveal the biodiversity in the forest. **Biodiversity** (BY-oh-dih-VUR-sih-tee) is the assortment, or variety, of living things in an ecosystem. An area with a high level of biodiversity, such as a rain forest, has a large assortment of different species living near one another. The amount of biodiversity found in an area depends on many factors, including moisture and temperature.

Some areas of the world have an unusually large amount of biodiversity in comparison to other locations. For example, tropical rain forests, which are moist and warm environments, cover less than 7 percent of Earth's ground surface. However, they account for over 50 percent of the planet's plant and animal species. This large amount of biodiversity emphasizes the importance of conserving such areas. Tropical rain forests are one of several areas referred to as hot spots. These hot spots, located across the globe, are areas that are rich in biodiversity, but are threatened by human activities.

Connecting CONCEPTS

Biodiversity The discovery of potential medicines and new species are two reasons why it is important to maintain biodiversity. In **Chapter 16**, you will learn how human activities impact biodiversity and how the loss of biodiversity affects us all.

Keystone Species

The complex relationships in ecosystems mean that a change in a single biotic or abiotic factor—a few broken strings in the web—can have a variety of effects. The change may barely be noticed, or it may have a deep impact. In some cases, the loss of a single species may cause a ripple effect felt across an entire ecosystem. Such an organism is called a keystone species. A **keystone species** is a species that has an unusually large effect on its ecosystem.

One example of a keystone species is the beaver. By felling trees to construct dams, beavers change free-flowing stream habitats into ponds, wetlands, and meadows. This modification leads to a cascade of changes within their ecosystem.

VISUAL VOCAB

Like a keystone that holds up an arch, a **keystone species** holds together a dynamic ecosystem.

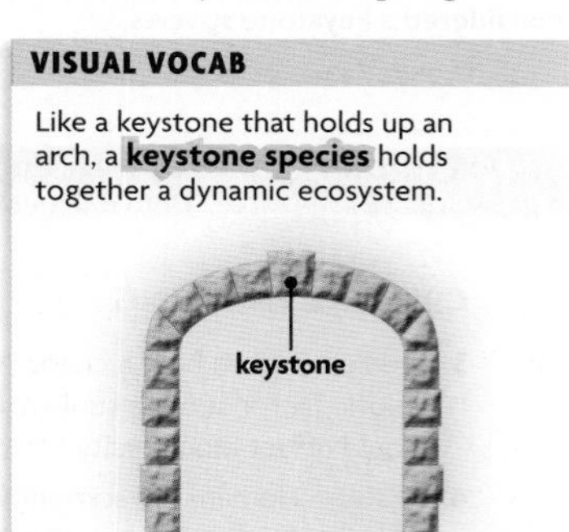

Keystone species

ONLINE BIOLOGY Have students learn more about keystone species by taking a look at the story of California's sea otter in the WebQuest in Options for Inquiry on page 421.

Vocabulary

Academic Vocabulary The word **diversity,** in a general sense, encompasses the idea of differences. In biology, *diversity* becomes **biodiversity,** the measure of the number of species in a given area or system or even the world. **Genetic diversity** refers to the range of different alleles within a species. Just as populations with greater genetic diversity are more stable, so too are ecosystems with greater biodiversity more stable.

Take It Further

Neither precious minerals nor exotic spices drew explorers into the vast expanses of the North American ... ne late 17th and early ... s a rodent—a rather ... with webbed feet, ... h, and a flat rudder- ... American beaver ... elt and the water- ... l be compressed into ... coats and hats.

... ast its skin, found ... heads of royalty, ... , and statesmen alike. ... of President Abraham ... om beaver pelt. The ... ned coats of arms, a ... d, coinage, and ... s Wars were fought, ... of the beaver trade. ... s the beaver pelt that the animal was on the brink of extinction by the mid 19th century. The emergence of the silk top hat, which unlike the beaver top hat, could be collapsed for easy handling, helped to save the animal. Such are the vagaries of fashion.

PRE-AP

Have students map out a possible sequence of events to predict what would happen if a population of fast-growing trees took root in a meadow. As they plot the transformation of the ecosystem, students should indicate whether each successive step results from a change in a biotic factor, an abiotic factor, or both.

Biology Toolkit, Sequence Diagram, p. C38

BELOW LEVEL

Build on the metaphor of the arch. Tell students that with the keystone in place, more rows of stone can be placed above. The choice of the word *keystone* signals the importance of a keystone species to an ecosystem. To underscore the point, give students playing cards to construct a house of cards. **Ask,** What happens if the keystone species is removed?

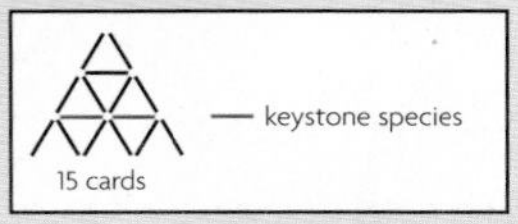

▼ Teach *continued*

TEACH FROM VISUALS

FIGURE 13.6 Beavers are considered a keystone species partly because of their dam-building behavior. **Ask**

- How does dam building affect fish populations? The dam creates a pond from free-flowing water, which allows a greater number and variety of fish to live and reproduce in the water.
- What effect does the increase in fish populations have on the pond? Fish attract species to the pond that feed on them.
- What is the overall effect of damming? increase in biodiversity

Answers

A Connect Salmon are the main food source for more than 140 species. They return vital nutrients to the river system when they die and decompose. Many species would suffer without their presence.

▼ Assess and Reteach

Assess Use the Online Quiz or Section Quiz (*Assessment Book,* p. 254).

Reteach Have pairs of students take turns quizzing each other on the main ideas and terms in this section. Let one student write a question and the other student answer it. Have partners switch roles and repeat the activity until they have covered all the main ideas and terms.

FIGURE 13.6 Keystone Species

Beavers are a keystone species. By constructing dams, beavers create an ecosystem used by a wide variety of species.

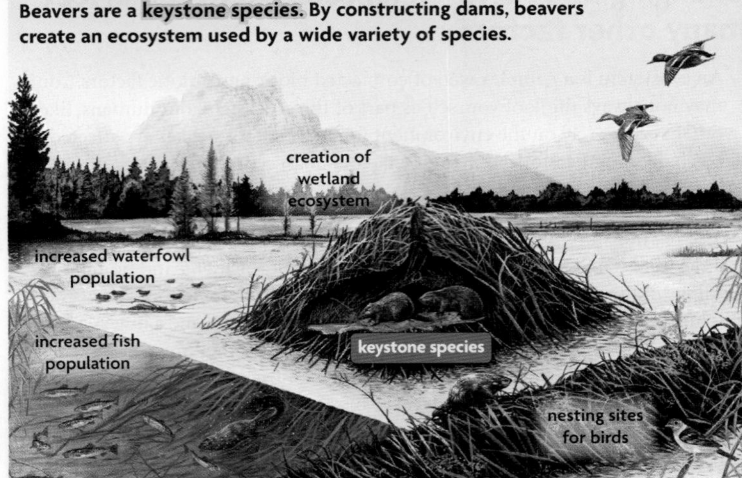

As **FIGURE 13.6** shows, beavers cause changes that create an ecosystem used by a variety of different species, leading to an overall increase in biodiversity.

- A greater number and wider variety of fish are able to live in the still waters of the pond.
- The fish attract fish-eating birds, such as herons and kingfishers.
- Insects inhabit the pond and the dead trees along the shore, attracting insect-eating birds, such as great-crested flycatchers, that nest in the tree cavities.
- Waterfowl nest among the shrubs and grasses along the pond's edge.
- Animals that prey on birds or their eggs are also attracted to the pond.

Keystone species form and maintain a complex web of life. Whatever happens to that species affects all the other species connected to it.

A Connect Explain why the Pacific salmon, introduced in Section 13.1, could be considered a keystone species.

13.2 ASSESSMENT

ONLINE QUIZ ClassZone.com

B.4.1

REVIEWING ▶ MAIN IDEAS

1. Select an ecosystem that is familiar to you and describe the **biotic** and **abiotic** factors that exist there.
2. How would the removal of a **keystone species** affect an ecosystem's **biodiversity**?

CRITICAL THINKING

3. **Predict** Explain how a change in an abiotic factor such as sunlight would affect biodiversity.
4. **Analyze** Humans are sometimes described as being a keystone species. Does this label fit? Why or why not?

***Connecting* CONCEPTS**

5. **Evolution** What role might an abiotic factor such as temperature play in the evolution of a species?

13.2 ASSESSMENT

1. Answers should show that students understand that biotic factors are living things and abiotic factors are nonliving.
2. The removal of a keystone species would decrease the ecosystem's biodiversity.
3. Changes in amount of sunlight might affect local temperatures, leading to a change in the numbers and types of species in the ecosystem. New species may move into the area, taking the place of those that cannot survive.
4. Keystone species are those that help to establish and maintain a complex web of life. Humans do not fit this label because human activities often decrease, rather than increase, biodiversity.
5. A long-term temperature change could result in selective pressure that selects for individuals better adapted to the temperature, causing populations to evolve. It could alter the types of food available, again creating selective pressure toward individuals that can take advantage of different food sources.

Abiotic Factors and Plant Growth

MATERIALS

- 4 radish seedlings
- 4 cups
- ruler
- cheesecloth
- sand
- gravel
- potting soil
- household-plant liquid fertilizer
- plastic wrap in a variety of colors
- graduated cylinder

PROCESS SKILLS

- **Designing Experiments**
- **Collecting Data**

B.4.1 Explain that the amount of life an environment can support is limited by the available energy, water, oxygen, and minerals, and by the ability of ecosystems to recycle the residue of dead materials.

NOS.3 Clearly communicate their ideas and results of investigations verbally and in written form using tables, graphs, diagrams, and photographs.

Many factors affect plant growth. Is it possible to test some in a laboratory setting? In this investigation you will choose an abiotic factor and attempt to test how (or if) it affects the growth of radish seedlings.

PROBLEM How do abiotic factors affect plant growth?

PROCEDURE

1. Choose an abiotic factor to test on the growth of radish seedlings. Possible factors include amount of sunlight, amount of water, soil type, light color available to plants, or amount of fertilizer.
2. Determine a way to vary the factor you have chosen. Be sure to include at least three different settings of your variable and to keep all other factors constant. Write out a procedure for your investigation.
3. Obtain 4 plants. Label one "Control" and the remaining three "A," "B," and "C."
4. Measure the height of your control and variable plants over a period of seven days. Use the same method to repeat measurements each day. Be sure to keep plants watered.
5. Record all data you generate in a well-organized data table.

ANALYZE AND CONCLUDE

1. **Operational Definitions** On the basis of your procedure, how are you defining plant growth?
2. **Identify Variables** What are your independent and dependent variables? What are your constants? What is your control?
3. **Graph Data** Make a bar graph to present the data you obtained on plant growth.
4. **Conclude** By studying your data, what can you conclude about how (or if) your variable affects the growth of radish seedlings?
5. **Conclude** Is your experiment a failure if your variable did not apparently affect the growth? Explain.
6. **Experimental Design** What possible sources of error may have occurred in your experiment? Why might they have occurred?

EXTEND YOUR INVESTIGATION

How would you design an experiment to determine whether a specific biotic factor influences plant growth?

INVESTIGATION

Time 20 minutes	TEACHER TESTED
Teacher Preparation	
Student Difficulty	
Lab Binder Ecology, pp. 1–4	

Purpose Test the effect of abiotic factors on plant growth.

Overview Students will vary one abiotic factor to test its effect on the growth of a seedling. They will

- write an experimental procedure that describes how they will test their independent variable
- measure the height of seedlings over a period of seven days

LAB PREPARATION

- Germinate the seeds two weeks before. Use a baking sheet and place the seeds on several layers of damp, not soaking, paper towels. Lay another dampened towel on top. Allow four radish plants per team.
- Keep the towels moist.
- Seeds will germinate in about one week. Plant each seed in a small plastic cup.

LAB MANAGEMENT

- Use sand, gravel, and potting soil to test soil type.
- Use cheesecloth to filter light and plastic wrap to test different wavelengths of light. Use a stick to keep materials off the plant.
- Remind students to record data and water the plants each day.

Safety Remind students to wash their hands after handling plants or materials.

POST-LAB DISCUSSION

Discuss results. **Ask,** How might the vulnerability of a seedling affect results? Students' handling of plants may have damaged plants to the point where any testing of abiotic factors was meaningless.

Answers

Expected Results

more growth in red and blue light than green; more growth in soil than sand or gravel

Analyze and Conclude

1. *Sample Answer:* height in centimeters
2. independent, abiotic factor varied; dependent, plant growth; constants, factors not varied; control plant, factors held constant
4. No difference in height suggests abiotic factor tested may not affect plant growth.
5. No; knowing what does not affect plant growth is useful information.
6. *Sample Answers:* inaccuracies in measuring, not providing consistent watering each day

Extend Your Investigation

Plant density could be tested or the characteristics of different plant types could be compared. Seedlings could be placed in a terrarium that includes animals and plants.

▼ Plan and Prepare

Objectives

- Describe the roles of producers and consumers in ecosystems.
- Compare photosynthesis to chemosynthesis.

Section Resources

Unit Resource Book
- Study Guide pp. 9–10
- Power Notes p. 11
- Reinforcement p. 12

Interactive Reader Chapter 13
Spanish Study Guide pp. 137–138

Biology Toolkit p.

Technology
- Power Presentatio
- Media Gallery DVI
- Online Quiz 13.3

Consumer,
Producer
autotrophs
heterotrophs
-Photosynthesis

Activate Prior Know
board the equation fo

$6H_2O + 6CO_2$ light er

Ask, Why does life a
depend upon this fo
thesis captures the s
transforms it to cher
can be used by othe
the products.

▼ Teach

TEACH FROM VISUALS

FIGURE 13.7 Remind students that chlorophyll is a pigment found in the cells of most producers. **Ask,** What does chlorophyll have to do with energy? Excitation of chlorophyll molecules by sunlight sets up a series of chemical reactions that end with glucose, which stores energy.

Answers

A Predict Many producers would die. Fewer plant-eating consumers would survive and reproduce, affecting food available to other consumers.

13.3 Energy in Ecosystems

KEY CONCEPT Life in an ecosystem requires a source of energy.

MAIN IDEAS
- Producers provide energy for other organisms in an ecosystem.
- Almost all producers obtain energy from sunlight.

VOCABULARY
- **producer,** p. 406
- **autotroph,** p. 406
- **consumer,** p. 406
- **heterotroph,** p. 406
- **chemosynthesis,** p. 407

Review
photosynthesis

INDIANA STANDARDS

B.4.1 Explain that the amount of life an environment can support is limited by the available energy, water, oxygen, and minerals, and by the ability of ecosystems to recycle the remains of dead organisms.

Connect In the previous section, you learned that every ecosystem includes biotic and abiotic factors. Another important part of an ecosystem is the flow of energy. This energy is needed to fuel life processes, such as breathing and growing. Where does this energy come from, and what role does it play within an ecosystem?

MAIN IDEA

Producers provide energy for other organisms in an ecosystem.

All organisms must have a source of energy in order to survive. However, not all organisms obtain their energy by eating other organisms.

- **Producers** are organisms that get their energy from nonliving resources, meaning they make their own food. Their distribution is shown in **FIGURE 13.7.** Producers are also called **autotrophs** (AW-tuh-TRAHFS). In the word *autotroph,* the suffix *-troph* comes from a Greek word meaning "nourishment." The prefix *auto-* means "self."
- **Consumers** are organisms that get their energy by eating other living or once-living resources, such as plants and animals. Consumers are also called **heterotrophs** (HEHT-uhr-uh-TRAHFS). In the word *heterotroph,* the prefix *hetero-* means "different."

All ecosystems depend on producers, because they provide the basis for the ecosystem's energy. Even animals that eat only meat rely on producers. One such species is the gray wolf. Gray wolves are consumers that eat elk and moose. Elk and moose are consumers that eat plants, such as grasses and shrubs. Plants are producers that make their own food. If the grasses and shrubs disappeared, the elk and moose would either have to find some other producer to eat or they would starve. The wolves would also be affected because they eat elk and moose. Although the wolves do not eat plants, their lives are tied to the grasses and shrubs that feed their prey. Likewise, all consumers are connected in some way to producers.

Most producers need sunlight to make food. These producers depend directly on the sun as their source of energy. For this reason, all the consumers connected to these producers depend indirectly on the sun for their energy.

FIGURE 13.7 This satellite image uses chlorophyll abundance to show the distribution of producers in the Western Hemisphere. Dark green areas are heavily forested, while yellow areas have limited vegetation.

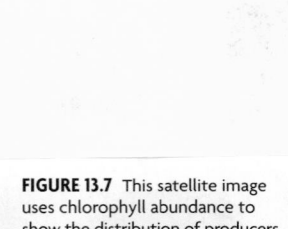

A Predict How would a long-term drought affect producers and consumers?

Differentiated Instruction

BELOW LEVEL

To test student understanding, write a series of declarative statements about the main points of the section. Focus on the word pairs *producer-consumer* and *autotroph-heterotroph.* Connect the word pairs to the process words *photosynthesis* and *chemosynthesis.* Have students react to the statements as being true or false before reading the section, and then again after reading.

Biology Toolkit, Anticipation Guide, p. C3

PRE-AP

Write on the board the equation for chemosynthesis just below that of photosynthesis:

$$6CO_2 + 6H_2O + 3H_2S \longrightarrow C_6H_{12}O_6 + 3H_2SO_4$$

Have students compare and contrast the two equations, considering both reactants and products. You may want to label hydrogen sulfide and sulfuric acid. Chemosynthesis occurs in extreme environments.

MAIN IDEA

Almost all producers obtain energy from sunlight.

Most producers on Earth use sunlight as their energy source. Photosynthesis is the two-stage process that green plants, cyanobacteria, and some protists use to produce energy. Chemical reactions form carbohydrates from carbon dioxide and water. Oxygen is released as a waste product.

Photosynthesis in plants begins when energy from the sun hits chloroplasts and is absorbed by chlorophyll. In the first stage of photosynthesis, energy from sunlight is converted to chemical energy. In the second stage, this chemical energy is used to change carbon dioxide into carbohydrates, such as glucose. Plants use these carbohydrates as an energy source to fuel cellular respiration.

Not all producers depend on sunlight for their energy. Scientists were stunned in 1977 when they first visited deep-sea vents on the bottom of the ocean. There they found thriving ecosystems in places where super-heated water shoots up from the ocean floor. Studies showed that tiny prokaryotes were making their own food from minerals in the water. They had no need for sunlight. **Chemosynthesis** (KEE-moh-SIHN-thih-sihs) is the process by which an organism forms carbohydrates using chemicals, rather than light, as an energy source. A series of reactions changes the chemicals into a usable energy form. Different reactions occur depending on which chemicals are present.

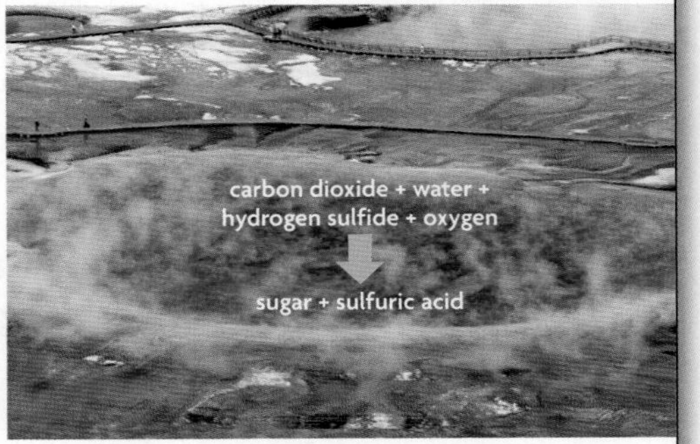

FIGURE 13.8 Chemosynthetic bacteria thrive in many of Yellowstone National Park's hydrothermal pools.

In addition to deep-sea vents, chemosynthetic organisms are also found in sulfur-rich salt marsh flats and in hydrothermal pools, such as those in Yellowstone National Park, shown in **FIGURE 13.8.** In this case, chemical energy is used to change carbon dioxide (CO_2), water (H_2O), hydrogen sulfide (H_2S), and oxygen (O_2) into an energy-rich sugar molecule. Sulfuric acid (H_2SO_4) is released as a waste product.

Contrast **How do photosynthesis and chemosynthesis differ?**

13.3 ASSESSMENT

ONLINE QUIZ ClassZone.com

B.4.1

REVIEWING MAIN IDEAS

1. How does the stability of an ecosystem depend on its **producers**?
2. What are the two processes used by producers to obtain energy?

CRITICAL THINKING

3. **Hypothesize** Few producers live deep below a lake's surface. Suggest an explanation for this pattern.
4. **Infer** Could producers survive without **consumers**? Explain why or why not.

***Connecting* CONCEPTS**

5. **History of Life** How might chemosynthetic organisms help scientists to understand how life developed on Earth?

13.3 ASSESSMENT

1. Producers bring energy into an ecosystem.
2. photosynthesis and chemosynthesis
3. Sunlight cannot penetrate the water to a great depth, so photosynthesizing organisms are more common near the surface.
4. Producers do not require consumers to fill material needs as a food source. So in that sense, producers do not need consumers to survive.
5. Chemosynthetic organisms live in environments that may be similar to those that existed on Earth billions of years ago, when life was beginning to develop. Studying these organisms enables scientists to infer how different life forms may have evolved as Earth changed.

ONLINE BIOLOGY Go to the chapter Resource Center at **ClassZone.com** for additional resources and information on energy in ecosystems.

Vocabulary

Academic Vocabulary Review the definition of the word **synthesis** in the context of **photosynthesis** and **chemosynthesis.**

synthesis, combining of separate elements or substances to form a complex whole

Students may have a general sense of the word as meaning "to make or produce" and so might be tempted, for example, to interpret *photosynthesis* as producing light. The root of synthesis actually means

"to put together with"

A carbohydrate, a complex whole, is put together *(synthesized)* using light *(photo-)* or chemicals *(chemo-)* as the initial source of energy.

Answers

A Contrast Both photosynthesis and chemosynthesis are processes by which producers capture energy. In photosynthesis, sunlight is the energy source. In chemosynthesis, chemicals are the energy source.

Assess and Reteach

Assess Use the Online Quiz or Section Quiz (*Assessment Book,* p. 255).

Reteach Work with the class to put the following terms into a concept map: *producer, consumer, autotroph, heterotroph, photosynthesis,* and *chemosynthesis.* Have students supply details and tell you which terms to connect as you write them on the board. Then have students write a paragraph using the terms in context.

SECTION 13.4

▼ Plan and Prepare

Objectives

- Describe the structure of a food chain.
- Explain how food chains and trophic levels are related.
- Analyze feeding relationships in a food web.

Section Resources

Unit Resource Book Study Guide pp. 13–14 Power Notes p. 15 Reinforcement p. 16 Pre-AP Activity pp. 00–00
Interactive Reader Chapter 13 **Spanish Study Guide** pp. 139–140
Biology Toolkit pp. C38, D6, D9
Technology Power Presentation 13.4 Media Gallery DVD Online Quiz 13.4

Activate Prior Knowledge Have students describe a typical meal. **Ask**

- What do you get from these foods? matter, energy
- How does energy and matter come to be in these foods? Help students trace back to a producer.
- What other way could you obtain energy for your body? There is none.

▼ Teach

TEACH FROM VISUALS

FIGURE 13.9 Point out the yellow arrows used to depict energy flow. They are used here and in other diagrams. **Ask**

- What is the original source of energy? sunlight
- How do the cottontail and hawk differ as consumers? Cottontail feeds on producer; hawk feeds on another consumer.

13.4 Food Chains and Food Webs

KEY CONCEPT Food chains and food webs model the flow of energy in an ecosystem.

MAIN IDEAS

- A food chain is a model that shows a sequence of feeding relationships.
- A food web shows a complex network of feeding relationships.

VOCABULARY

food chain, p. 408
herbivore, p. 409
carnivore, p. 409
omnivore, p. 409
detritivore, p. 409
decomposer, p. 409
specialist, p. 409
generalist, p. 409
trophic level, p. 409
food web, p. 411

INDIANA STANDARDS

B.3.5 Describe how energy from the sun flows through an ecosystem by way of food chains and food webs and only a small portion of that energy is used by individual organisms while the majority of energy is lost as heat.

Connect As we have seen, energy flows through an ecosystem in one direction—from producers to consumers. However, since an ecosystem can have hundreds or even thousands of different species, determining the relationship between species can be quite tricky. Food chains and food webs are used to model these relationships.

MAIN IDEA

A food chain is a model that shows a sequence of feeding relationships.

The simplest way to look at energy flow in an ecosystem is through a food chain. A **food chain** is a sequence that links species by their feeding relationships. Rather than describe every potential relationship, this model chain only follows the connection between one producer and a single chain of consumers within an ecosystem. For example, in a desert ecosystem, a desert cottontail eats grass. The food chain is, therefore, grass–desert cottontail. If another consumer such as a Harris's hawk eats a desert cottontail, the food chain gets longer: grass–desert cottontail–Harris's hawk, as shown in **FIGURE 13.9.**

FIGURE 13.9 Food Chain

Energy flows through a food chain.

GRAMA GRASS

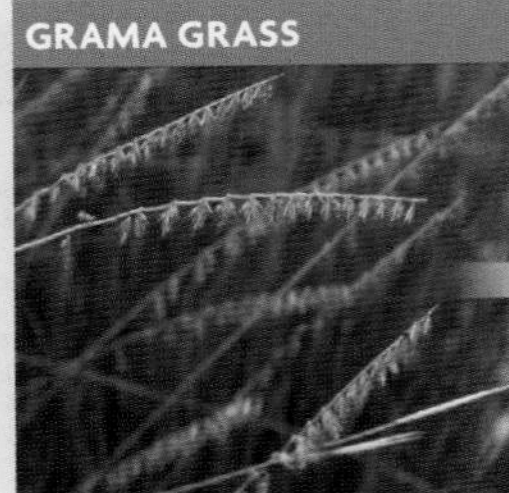

Grama grass, a producer, obtains its energy through photosynthesis.

DESERT COTTONTAIL

The desert cottontail, a consumer, obtains its energy by eating the seeds of plants, such as grama grass.

HARRIS'S HAWK

The Harris's hawk, a consumer, obtains its energy by eating other animals, such as desert cottontails.

Differentiated Instruction

ENGLISH LEARNERS

Use analogies to help students remember the meanings of new vocabulary words. Ask them to make a three-column chart with the heads *Key Concept, Definition,* and *Analogy.* Have them complete the first two columns on their own by writing the ten new vocabulary words in the first and finding definitions in context to complete the second. Help them create analogies for the third column, such as "an herbivore is to a carnivore as a plant is to meat."

Biology Toolkit, Analogies, p. D9

PRE-AP

Have students list and then group keywords in this section:

consumer-producer-decomposer

herbivore-carnivore-omnivore-detrivore

Have students differentiate between the groups by describing the type of information each set of terms provides.

Biology Toolkit, List-Group-Label, p. D6

Types of Consumers

As you read in Section 13.3, consumers are organisms that eat other organisms. All consumers, however, are not alike.

- **Herbivores,** such as desert cottontails, are organisms that eat only plants.
- **Carnivores** are organisms that eat only animals. Harris's hawks are carnivores that eat desert cottontails.
- **Omnivores** are organisms that eat both plants and animals. Kangaroo rats are omnivores that eat both seeds and insects.
- **Detritivores** (dih-TRY-tuh-VOHRZ) are organisms that eat detritus, or dead organic matter. A millipede is a detritivore that feeds on particles of detritus on the ground.
- **Decomposers** are detritivores that break down organic matter into simpler compounds. Fungi, for example, are decomposers. Decomposers are important to the stability of an ecosystem because they return vital nutrients back into the environment.

VOCABULARY

Most words for consumers come from Latin words.

- *Vorāre* means "to swallow or devour."
- *Herba* means "vegetation."
- *Carnus* means "flesh."
- *Omnis* means "all."
- *Dētrere* means "to wear away."

Food chains are especially helpful in describing feeding relationships among extremely selective eaters, known as specialists. A **specialist** is a consumer that primarily eats one specific organism or feeds on a very small number of organisms.

FIGURE 13.10 Florida snail kites are specialists that rely on apple snails as their primary food source.

Specialists are very sensitive to changes in the availability of prey. For example, the Florida snail kite, shown in **FIGURE 13.10**, is a specialist that depends on the apple snail as its main source of food. In the early 1900s, apple snails became less common in Florida as a result of land development. Florida snail kite populations declined suddenly, and in 1967, the bird was listed as an endangered species. Currently, the snails and the birds continue to survive in lower numbers in protected areas, such as the Everglades.

Most species do not rely on a single source of food. These species are called generalists. **Generalists** are consumers that have a varying diet. For example, the diet of a gray wolf may include a number of animals, including elk, moose, white-tailed deer, beavers, and even mice.

Trophic Levels

Trophic levels are the levels of nourishment in a food chain. For example, the producer–herbivore–carnivore chain has three trophic levels. Carnivores are at the highest trophic level. Herbivores are at the second trophic level. Producers are at the first, or bottom, trophic level. Energy flows up the food chain from the lowest trophic level to the highest.

- Primary consumers are herbivores because they are the first consumer above the producer trophic level.
- Secondary consumers are carnivores that eat herbivores.
- Tertiary consumers are carnivores that eat secondary consumers.

Omnivores, such as humans that eat both plants and animals, may be listed at different trophic levels in different food chains. When a person eats a salad, the trophic levels in the food chain are producer–omnivore. When a person eats a steak, the trophic levels are producer–herbivore–omnivore.

A Connect **What is the connection between food chains and trophic levels?**

HANDS-ON ACTIVITY

Unlike snail kites, owls are generalists. They often feed on small animals, which they swallow whole. Because an owl cannot digest bones, fur, or feathers, these remains are pressed into a tight mass and regurgitated some hours after eating. The result is an owl pellet.

With enough owl pellets, identification keys, and needle tools or tweezers for every two students, have students form pairs. Each pair will need gloves and a paper towel or tray. Have students pull apart the pellet and identify the remains. Remind students to wash their hands after the materials are discarded and the tools cleaned.

At the end of the activity, **ask**

- Why doesn't a consumer digest all the food it consumes? Not all food matter can be digested, for example bones and seeds.
- What happens to the waste material left behind by consumers? It can become a source of nutrition for detrivores and decomposers.

Take It Further

What was a beneficial adaptation for the **Florida snail kite** has now become a serious liability. The kite beak evolved a hook that enabled it to feed on a once-plentiful food supply: **apple snails.** The beak is so deeply hooked that the population's survival is now linked to this single food source.

The Florida snail kite is endangered in part because of a reduced habitat, but also because of changes to water levels throughout the Florida Everglades. Water height affects the behavior and availability of apple snails. Water that is too shallow restricts the snails' breeding and movement. Water that is too high covers that vegetation where the kite can prey upon the snails.

Address Misconceptions

Common Misconception A number of misconceptions about food chains and food webs are based on an association of higher trophic levels with higher numbers. **Ask,** Are the following statements true or false?

- Organisms higher in a food chain eat everything that is lower. F
- Populations higher in a food chain increase in number because they deplete those lower in the chain. F
- The top of the food chain has the most energy because it accumulates up the chain. F

Correcting the Misconception Remind students of the specialization that occurs as populations adapt to the conditions of their environment and of the patterns of evolution described in Chapter 11. **Section 13.6** will address the loss of energy as matter moves from producer to consumers, but students may already be familiar with the concept of entropy.

Answers

A Connect Food chains illustrate the flow of energy from one trophic level to the next.

▼ Teach *continued*

ONLINE BIOLOGY Students can build their own food web. See the interactive animation described on page 421 of Options for Inquiry.

TEACH FROM VISUALS

FIGURE 13.11 Point out that all food webs require an initial source of energy, usually from sunlight. Have students use the color key of the diagram to identify different trophic levels. **Ask**

- What do the yellow arrows represent? the flow of energy
- Which organisms bring energy into this ecosystem? the producers phytoplankton and algae
- Starting with a producer, identify three food chains in this food web. *Sample Answer:* algae-parrotfish-reef shark; phytoplankton-sea sponge; phytoplankton-shrimp-triggerfish-reef shark
- Which organism is a tertiary consumer? reef shark

Answers

A Critical Viewing The removal of phytoplankton or algae would have the most impact because they are producers, and many consumers rely on them as a food source, either directly or indirectly.

FIGURE 13.11 Food Web

A **food web** shows the network of feeding relationships between trophic levels within an ecosystem. The food web in a coral reef can be quite complex because many organisms feed on a variety of other species.

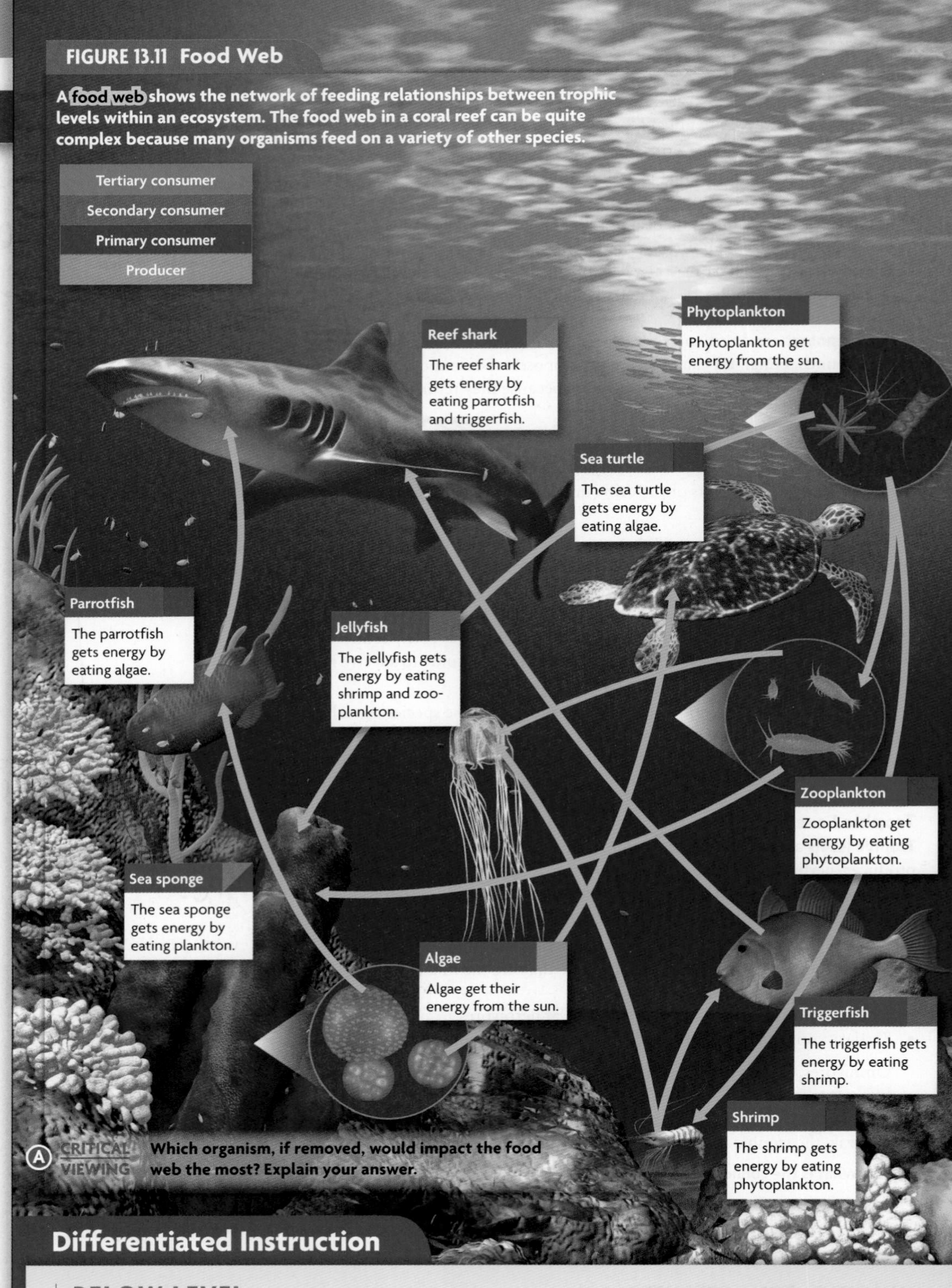

Tertiary consumer
Secondary consumer
Primary consumer
Producer
Phytoplankton
Phytoplankton get energy from the sun.
Reef shark
The reef shark gets energy by eating parrotfish and triggerfish.
Sea turtle
The sea turtle gets energy by eating algae.
Parrotfish
The parrotfish gets energy by eating algae.
Jellyfish
The jellyfish gets energy by eating shrimp and zooplankton.
Zooplankton
Zooplankton get energy by eating phytoplankton.
Sea sponge
The sea sponge gets energy by eating plankton.
Algae
Algae get their energy from the sun.
Triggerfish
The triggerfish gets energy by eating shrimp.
Shrimp
The shrimp gets energy by eating phytoplankton.

A CRITICAL VIEWING Which organism, if removed, would impact the food web the most? Explain your answer.

Differentiated Instruction

BELOW LEVEL

Have students who will have difficulty following the arrows use their fingers to trace the arrows. Tell them that an arrow pointing toward an organism indicates what that organism eats. Have them identify individual food chains by drawing sequence diagrams. Show them that when more than one arrow leads from an organism, they have a choice of which arrow to follow.

Biology Toolkit, Sequence Diagram, p. C38

MAIN IDEA
A food web shows a complex network of feeding relationships.

Generalists may be involved in many food chains, depending on which links are in the chain. Each of the organisms in those links, in turn, may be part of many other food chains. As a result, scientists use food webs to describe these interconnections. A **food web** is a model that shows the complex network of feeding relationships and the flow of energy within and sometimes beyond an ecosystem. At each link in a food web, some energy is stored within an organism, and some energy is dissipated into the environment.

Coral reefs are often referred to as rain forests of the sea, due to the abundance and diversity of species found there. The complex connections in a coral reef ecosystem, illustrated in **FIGURE 13.11**, are created by the feeding relationships within the food web.

The stability of any food web depends on the presence of producers, as they form the base of the food web. In the case of a marine ecosystem such as a coral reef, algae and phytoplankton are two of the producers that play this important role.

An organism may have multiple feeding relationships within a food web. For example, reef sharks are generalists that eat several different food items. When a reef shark eats a parrotfish, it is a secondary consumer, because a parrotfish is a primary consumer that eats algae. However, a reef shark is a tertiary consumer when it eats a triggerfish. This difference in trophic levels occurs because a triggerfish is a secondary consumer that feeds on shrimp. The shrimp, in turn, is a primary consumer that eats phytoplankton. Food webs like this one emphasize both the complicated nature of feeding relationships and the flow of energy within an ecosystem.

Connecting CONCEPTS

Marine Ecosystems Coral reefs are ecosystems that are rich in diversity. In **Chapter 15** you will learn about the complex relationships found in these underwater ecosystems.

Analyze **How might the introduction of a new predator affect the flow of energy through a food web?**

ONLINE BIOLOGY Go to the chapter Resource Center at **ClassZone.com** for additional resources and information on food webs.

Answers

A Analyze A new predator might cause other populations in the food web to decrease in size, thus decreasing the amount of energy available.

Assess and Reteach

Assess Use the Online Quiz or Section Quiz (*Assessment Book,* p. 256).

Reteach Have students prepare a list of the vocabulary in this section. Have them use each term as they describe what they see in **FIGURE 13.11.**

13.4 ASSESSMENT

ONLINE QUIZ ClassZone.com

B.3.5

REVIEWING MAIN IDEAS

1. Why are **food chains** especially useful for describing the relationships of **specialists**?
2. What happens to energy as it flows through a **food web**?

CRITICAL THINKING

3. **Compare and Contrast** Only a small percentage of all consumers are specialists. What danger does a specialist face that a **generalist** does not?
4. **Predict** How might the stability of an ecosystem be affected if all of the **decomposers** were suddenly removed?

Connecting CONCEPTS

5. **Pollution** How might an oil spill in the ocean affect an aquatic food web? What might happen to the food web on land located near the spill? Explain your answers.

13.4 ASSESSMENT

1. Specialists have specific diets that include only one type of organism, which produces a simple food chain.
2. Some energy is stored in the organism, but much energy is dissipated into the environment.
3. If a specialist's food source becomes scarce or disappears, the population may die out. A generalist facing the loss of one of its food sources can shift to a different food source.
4. The stability of the ecosystem would be negatively affected because without decomposers, vital nutrients would not be returned to the environment.
5. The entire food web would be affected by an oil spill. Oily water may kill off phytoplankton. The loss of smaller fish would affect the larger fish, which would, in turn, affect tertiary consumers. Plants and animals that live along the coast would also be affected as the oil seeped onto the shore. The overall effect would be a decline in the availability of food sources both within and outside the ocean.

▼ Plan and Prepare

Objectives

- Summarize Earth's hydrologic and biogeochemical cycles.
- Relate cycling of matter to ecosystems.

Section Resources

Unit Resource Book
Study Guide pp. 17–18
Power Notes p. 19
Reinforcement p. 20

Interactive Reader Chapter 13
Spanish Study Guide pp. 141–142

Biology Toolkit pp. C8, C13, C19, C23

Technology
Power Presentation 13.5
Media Gallery DVD
Online Quiz 13.5

Activate Prior Knowledge Remind students that a human being that begins life as a single cell ends up with anywhere from 10–100 trillion cells as an adult. **Ask,** Where does all that material come from? It cycles from Earth into the living parts of an ecosystem. Humans absorb most through food. **Ask,** What would you include on a shopping list for elements that are critical to a human? The list should include oxygen, carbon, hydrogen, and nitrogen.

▼ Teach

Science Trivia

- The total volume of water on Earth is about 326 million trillion gallons.
- If Earth's water could fit into a gallon container, only about 3 tablespoons would be available to us. The rest would be either frozen or salty.

Answers

A Analyze So little of Earth's water is fresh water. Increasing population puts a strain on available supply.

13.5 Cycling of Matter

KEY CONCEPT Matter cycles in and out of an ecosystem.

MAIN IDEAS
- Water cycles through the environment.
- Elements essential for life also cycle through ecosystems.

VOCABULARY
hydrologic cycle, p. 412
biogeochemical cycle, p. 413
nitrogen fixation, p. 415

B.3.4 Describe how matter cycles through an ecosystem by way of food chains and food webs and how organisms convert that matter into a vairety of organic molecules to be used in part in their own cellular structures.

Connect Since life in most ecosystems requires a constant inflow of energy from the sun, Earth is an open system in terms of energy. However, in terms of matter, such as oxygen and carbon, Earth is a closed system. Today's Earth has roughly the same amount of carbon as it had billions of years ago, meaning that the same carbon atoms that make up your body may once have been part of a tree, or gases spewed by a volcano, or even part of a dinosaur.

MAIN IDEA

Water cycles through the environment.

Matter changes form, but it does not disappear. It can be used over and over again in a continuous cycle. If you crush a rock, for example, it does not vanish. Instead, it turns into sand and other bits of minerals. Although matter may change form over time, the total amount of matter remains the same.

As you learned earlier, a major part of life on Earth is water, which has a cycle of its own. The **hydrologic cycle** (HY-druh-LAHJ-ihk), also known as the water cycle, is the circular pathway of water on Earth from the atmosphere, to the surface, below ground, and back. Part of that pathway involves humans and other organisms, which all have bodies made mostly of water.

As shown in **FIGURE 13.12**, precipitation, such as rain or snow, falls to Earth. Some of this precipitation seeps into the ground, some drops into ponds, streams, lakes, or other waterways, and some forms puddles or other temporary pools. Depending on the type of soil and rocks surrounding it and also on its location, groundwater may empty directly into oceans. Sometimes water flows first into lakes, swamps, or wetlands, but these—along with rivers, streams, and other freshwater sources—also feed into oceans.

In addition, some droplets of water quickly reenter the atmosphere through evaporation. Since oceans cover over 70 percent of Earth's surface, about 85 percent of Earth's evaporation occurs between the oceans and the atmosphere. On land, water vapor is released by plants during transpiration, which is evaporation that occurs between plant leaves and the atmosphere. The cycle is completed as water vapor in the atmosphere condenses and forms clouds, returning water to the surface once again in the form of precipitation.

A Analyze If the total amount of water on Earth does not change, why are there concerns about global freshwater shortages?

***Connecting* CONCEPTS**

Properties of Water The presence of water is necessary for life on Earth. All organisms depend on the simple structure of the water molecule. As you learned in **Chapter 2,** water has several unique properties. Water's high specific heat helps keep cells at the right temperature to carry out life processes.

Differentiated Instruction

ENGLISH LEARNERS

Have students form five small groups and ask questions about one of five cycles described in this section. They can use the strategy Survey/Question/Read/Recite/Review to monitor learning as they read. They gather information by surveying headings, vocabulary, visuals, and end-of-section questions. They develop questions and read to fill in information. Then students stop to recall the questions, answer them, and then review if needed.

Biology Toolkit, SQ3R, p. C8

BELOW LEVEL

To organize the notes for this section, have students draw each cycle as a simple diagram (like the one shown on page 414) and then annotate it with notes, including:

- the role of the substance in supporting life
- how the substance cycles into and out of the living parts of an ecosystem
- where the cycles overlap

Biology Toolkit, Combination Notes, p. C23

FIGURE 13.12 Hydrologic Cycle

The hydrologic cycle is the circular pathway of water on Earth.

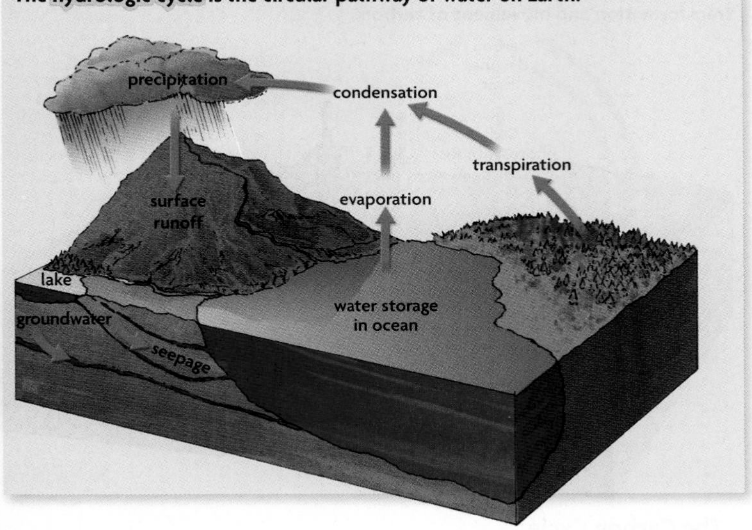

Know water cycle -

- Know biogeochemical cycle - & how it relates to photosynthesis

MAIN IDEA
Elements essential for life also cycle through ecosystems.

Many elements are essential to the structure and function of organisms. Elements are basic chemical substances, such as the oxygen and hydrogen found in the chemical compound of water. Additional elements important to life include carbon, nitrogen, phosphorus, and sulfur. As you learned in Chapter 2, oxygen, carbon, nitrogen, and hydrogen make up 96 percent of the mass of the human body. This is just one reason why the cycling of these elements is so important. All of these elements cycle through ecosystems, just as water does.

A **biogeochemical cycle** (BY-oh-JEE-oh-KEHM-ih-kuhl) is the movement of a particular chemical through the biological and geological, or living and nonliving, parts of an ecosystem. Just as water changes from solid form (ice or snow) to liquid form (rain) or gaseous form (water vapor), other substances may also change state as they move through their cycles.

The Oxygen Cycle

Plants, animals, and most other organisms need oxygen for cellular respiration. As shown in **FIGURE 13.13**, plants release oxygen as a waste product during photosynthesis. In turn, humans and other organisms take in this oxygen and release it as carbon dioxide through respiration. Oxygen is also indirectly transferred through an ecosystem by the cycling of other nutrients, including carbon, nitrogen, and phosphorus.

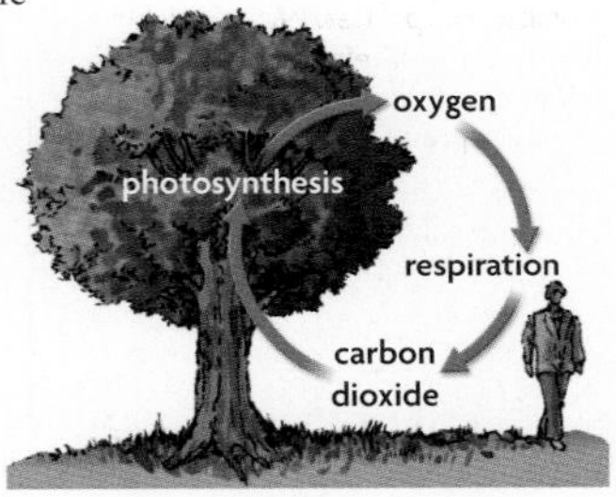

FIGURE 13.13 In the oxygen cycle, oxygen flows into the atmosphere as a byproduct of photosynthesis. Organisms take in this oxygen and release it as carbon dioxide through respiration.

Apply **Explain how deforestation might affect the oxygen cycle.**

INCLUSION

Have a student who is visually impaired work with a small group of students, each of whom will walk through one of the cycles described in the section as if relating a journey. Each student should give a brief description of how one atom or molecule makes its way through a cycle. All the participants should ask questions to clarify.

BELOW LEVEL

Working in pairs, have students address the question of why the cycles shown in this section are referred to as *biogeochemical.* Each pair should think through and answer the question, and then share it with the class.

Biology Toolkit, Think-Pair-Share, p. C13

TEACH FROM VISUALS

...e water cycle,
...lternating
...nd vapor. **Ask**
...e water cycle is
...state? precipita-
...d water, ocean
...ge
...ater are used for
...by plants for their
..., ground water,
...n
...turn water vapor
...? transpiration,

...sforms water
...ter? condensation
...ter is not shown in
...still an important
reservoir of water? solid: ice, snow

Vocabulary

Academic Vocabulary Students will be familiar with the word **cycle,** which in a literal sense means to move in a circle. However, the word often refers to a sequence of events, for example, a life cycle. Matter in a cycle doesn't literally move in circles, but it does repeatedly move from Earth's physical environment, into living matter, and then back in the environment again.

TEACH FROM VISUALS

FIGURE 13.13 Remind students that both plants and animals respire. Cellular respiration is the process by which eukaryotic cells release energy. Plants, like animals, need oxygen to break down carbohydrates for energy. **Ask,** What organelles use oxygen to release energy? mitochondria

Answers

A Apply The loss of trees would result in less oxygen being released into the atmosphere.

▼ Teach *continued*

Integrating Earth Science

As the theory of **uniformitarianism** states, the same processes that shape Earth's past are at work in the world today. **Ask,** Does that mean that new supplies of fossil fuels are being generated today? The tectonic processes by which these fuels were generated still occur. Carbon-rich organic matter still falls to Earth. The difficulty is that to generate more fuel, that organic matter must fall undisturbed into a layer of sediment, get covered by still more layers of sediment or sand, and be compressed into rock under great pressure over millions of years to produce a deposit of coal, oil, or natural gas.

Science Trivia

- The total amount of carbon on Earth is estimated to be 450 quadrillion kilograms.
- There is 50 times as much carbon dissolved in the ocean as exists in the atmosphere, but the majority of carbon is stored in Earth's crust.

FIGURE 13.14 Carbon Cycle

Photosynthesis and respiration account for much of the transformation and movement of carbon.

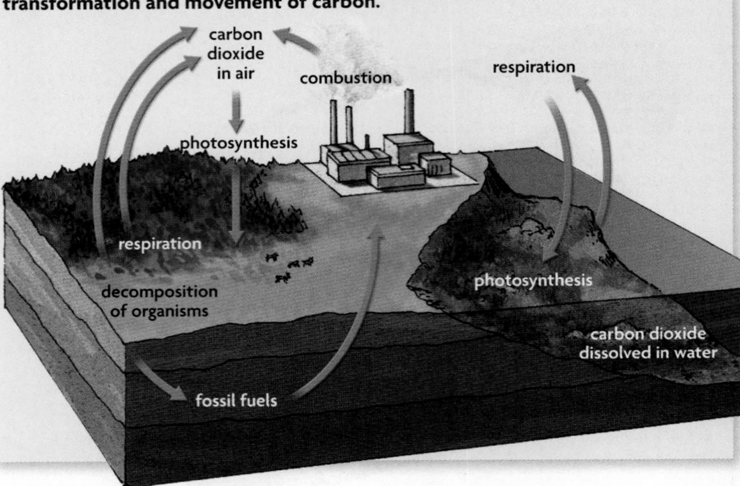

TAKING NOTES

For each cycle, draw and label a simple diagram in your notes.

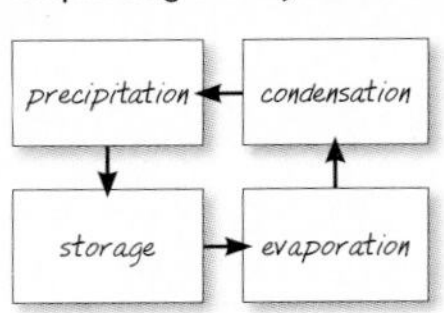

The Carbon Cycle

Carbon is the building block of life—it is key to the structure of all organisms on our planet. It is an essential component of carbohydrates, proteins, fats, and all the other organic molecules that make up your body. Carbon continually flows from the environment to living organisms and back again in the carbon cycle, shown in **FIGURE 13.14.**

Carbon exists in the abiotic world in several forms. Carbon can be found in solid, liquid, and gaseous states. Sources of carbon include

- carbon dioxide (CO_2) gas in the atmosphere
- bicarbonate (HCO_3^-) dissolved in water
- fossil fuels, which are underground deposits of oil, natural gas, and coal
- carbonate rocks, such as limestone
- dead organic matter, such as humus, in the soil

The simplest transfer of carbon occurs between plants and animals. Plants use energy from the sun to convert carbon dioxide from the air into organic material that becomes a part of the plant's structure. The carbon then moves through the biotic world as one organism eats another.

Carbon is returned to the atmosphere as carbon dioxide by respiration or through the decomposition of dead organisms. The burning of fossil fuels and wood, as well as emissions from factories and automobiles, adds to carbon dioxide in the atmosphere. Another source of atmospheric carbon is methane, which is emitted from wetlands, landfills, and livestock.

Not all carbon molecules move freely through the cycle. Areas that store carbon over a long period of time are called carbon sinks. One example is forest land, where large amounts of carbon are stored in the cellulose of wood.

Differentiated Instruction

TEACH WITH TECHNOLOGY

If you have pressure sensors available and the appropriate probeware or CBL technology, you can demonstrate the participation of organisms in biogeochemical cycles. Introducing hydrogen peroxide to a suspension of yeast and glucose in skim milk or antacid will cause hydrogen peroxide to break down into water and oxygen gas. Students can measure the pressure of the oxygen gas released.

PRE-AP

Point out to students that matter that makes up organisms—such as oxygen, carbon, nitrogen, and phosphorus—can cycle through the atmosphere or through sediments at Earth's surface. Have students write a brief analysis of which nutrients cycle through the atmosphere and which cycle through sediments. Have them consider which cycle is more likely to return materials more quickly into an ecosystem.

Biology Toolkit, Quick-Write, p. C19

The Nitrogen Cycle

About 78 percent of Earth's atmosphere is made of nitrogen gas. However, most organisms can use nitrogen only in the form of ions such as ammonium (NH_4^+) or nitrate (NO_3^-). As shown in **FIGURE 13.15,** much of the nitrogen cycle takes place underground.

Certain types of bacteria convert gaseous nitrogen into ammonia (NH_3) through a process called **nitrogen fixation.** A few types of cyanobacteria fix nitrogen in aquatic ecosystems. On land, some nitrogen-fixing bacteria live in small outgrowths, called nodules, on the roots of plants such as beans and peas. Other nitrogen-fixing bacteria live freely in the soil. The ammonia released by these bacteria is transformed into ammonium by the addition of hydrogen ions found in acidic soil. Some ammonium is taken up by plants, but most is used by nitrifying bacteria as an energy source. Through the process called nitrification, these bacteria change ammonium into nitrate.

Nitrates released by soil bacteria are taken up by plants, which convert them into organic compounds such as amino acids and proteins. Nitrogen continues along the cycle as animals eat plant or animal matter. When decomposers break down animal excretions or dead animal and plant matter, nitrogen is returned to the soil as ammonium, in a process called ammonification.

Denitrifying bacteria use nitrate as an oxygen source, releasing nitrogen gas into the atmosphere as a waste product. Some nitrogen also enters the soil as a result of atmospheric fixation by lightning. Lightning's energy breaks apart nitrogen molecules in the atmosphere. Nitrogen recombines with oxygen in the air, forming nitrogen oxide. The combination of nitrogen oxide with rainwater forms nitrates, which are absorbed by the soil.

FIGURE 13.15 Nitrogen Cycle

Much of the nitrogen cycle occurs underground, where bacteria transform ammonium into nitrates, which are used by plants to make amino acids.

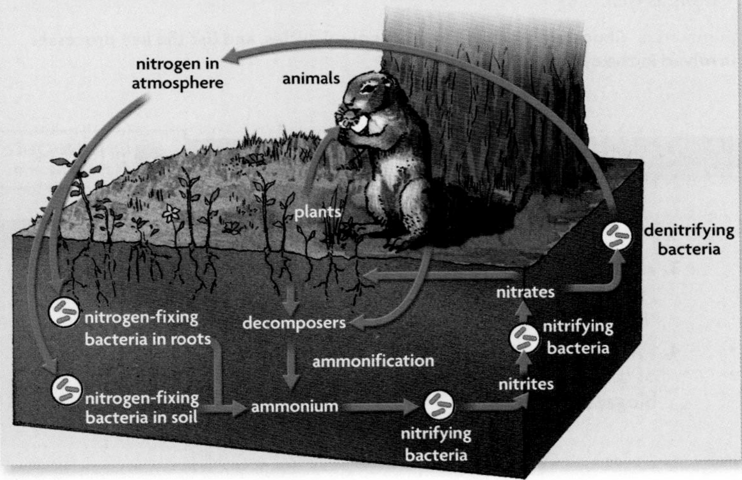

ONLINE BIOLOGY Go to the chapter Resource Center at **ClassZone.com** for additional resources and information on cycles in ecosystems.

Integrating Chemistry

Nitrogen makes up nearly 80% of Earth's atmosphere. As a component of DNA and the amino acids that make up proteins, nitrogen is an element essential to all life. However, nitrogen gas, N_2, is very unreactive because of the strong bonds between the nitrogen atoms. To make nitrogen chemically reactive and available to enter into biochemical reactions, the nitrogen must go through **nitrogen fixation,** which in essence means to convert atmospheric nitrogen into useable nitrogen.

Vocabulary

Word Origins Students will probably be most familiar with the sense of fixing as a process of repair. The root of **fix** actually means "to fasten," which is how it is used in this context. Nitrogen gas must be "fastened" into a compound that can then be taken up by plants, bacteria, and ultimately all other living things. Students might be familiar with another derivative of *fix* that has a similar meaning: *affix.*

TEACH FROM VISUALS

FIGURE 13.15 Suggest students think of the nitrogen cycle diagram as divided into two spheres: atmosphere and lithosphere as represented by the soil. Have students look carefully at the figure. **Ask**

- What is the source of nitrogen for the animal? plant matter
- What is the source of nitrogen for plants? decomposers, bacteria
- What is the source of nitrogen for decomposers? once-living matter
- Which organisms act as a bridge between the nitrogen in the atmosphere and the organisms of the biosphere? bacteria

ENGLISH LEARNERS

It might be helpful to students if you model your own analysis of the nitrogen cycle by reading aloud from the text. Show students how to use the text and **FIGURE 13.15** together to clarify the details of what is happening. Once you have demonstrated how to decode the text for meaning, model for students how to summarize the main points.

▼ Teach continued

TEACH FROM VISUALS

FIGURE 13.16 Have students note the two smaller cycles that make up the phosphorus cycle. **Ask,** What are the sources of phosphates in the soil? weathering of rocks and decomposition

Answers

A Summarize *Sample Answer:* Phosphate is released by the weathering of rocks; plants and fungi take up the phosphate; it is then transferred by the food chain from producers to consumers; phosphate reenters soil or water through decomposition.

▼ Assess and Reteach

Assess Use the Online Quiz or Section Quiz (*Assessment Book*, p. 257).

Reteach Have student groups summarize the different cycles. Suggest that they use the figures in the section and trace the movement of water or an element through the ecosystem. Assign each student a different cycle to summarize for the group, or have students divide up the work among themselves.

The Phosphorus Cycle

Unlike the other cycles, the phosphorus cycle does not include an atmospheric portion. Instead, most of the cycle takes place at and below ground level, as shown in **FIGURE 13.16.**

FIGURE 13.16 Phosphorus Cycle

The phosphorus cycle occurs on a local, rather than global, scale. Its cycle is limited to water, soil, and ocean sediment.

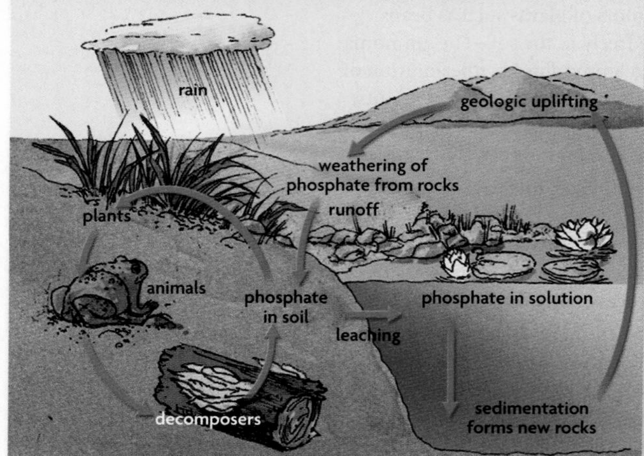

The phosphorus cycle begins when phosphate is released by the weathering of rocks. Plants and some fungi found near plant roots are able to take up phosphate. Phosphorus moves from producers to consumers through the food web. When the producers and consumers die, decomposers break down the organisms. This process releases phosphorus back into the soil or water for use by producers. Some phosphorus may leach into groundwater from the soil. This groundwater may flow into a lake or other body of water, where the phosphorus becomes locked in sediments at the bottom. Over many thousands of years, these sediments eventually become rock again, and the cycle starts again as phosphate is released by the weathering of these newly formed rocks.

Mining and agricultural runoff also add to the overall amount of phosphorus in the environment. The excessive flow of phosphorus into an aquatic ecosystem from sewage and agricultural runoff can cause significant problems. Phosphorus is a limiting factor for the growth of plants. Large amounts of phosphorus within an aquatic environment can lead to algal blooms. These blooms crowd out other plant species and negatively impact wildlife populations as well.

A Summarize Choose one of the biogeochemical cycles, and list the key processes involved in the cycling of the element.

13.5 ASSESSMENT

ONLINE QUIZ ClassZone.com

B.3.5

REVIEWING ▶ MAIN IDEAS

1. How does the **hydrologic cycle** move water through the environment?
2. What are four elements that cycle through ecosystems, and why are they important?

CRITICAL THINKING

3. **Apply** Why might farmers plant legumes such as peas to improve the nitrogen levels in their soil?
4. **Synthesize** Explain the importance of decomposers to the overall **biogeochemical cycle.**

***Connecting* CONCEPTS**

5. **Evolution** How might Earth's biogeochemical cycles help scientists to understand the early history of life on Earth?

13.5 ASSESSMENT

1. Precipitation falls to Earth, and transpiration and evaporation transfer water back into the atmosphere as water vapor.
2. Oxygen, carbon, nitrogen, and phosphorus; they are all necessary for life on Earth.
3. Legumes have root nodules, which contain nitrogen-fixing bacteria. Increased nitrogen levels increase the fertility of the soil.
4. Decomposers break down organisms and release various elements, including nitrogen and phosphorus, which other organisms can then use.
5. Studies of the biogeochemical cycles and how they interact may help scientists reconstruct the sequence of events that led to changes at Earth's surface that would enable different types of organisms to evolve.

13.6 Pyramid Models

KEY CONCEPT Pyramids model the distribution of energy and matter in an ecosystem.

MAIN IDEAS

- An energy pyramid shows the distribution of energy among trophic levels.
- Other pyramid models illustrate an ecosystem's biomass and distribution of organisms.

VOCABULARY

biomass, p. 417
energy pyramid, p. 418

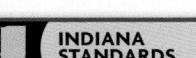

INDIANA STANDARDS

B.3.5 Describe how energy from the sun flows through an ecosystem by way of food chains and food webs and only a small portion of that energy is used by individual organisms while the majority of energy is lost as heat.

Connect You have seen that ecosystems have a structure, with large numbers of producers supporting several levels of consumers. Ecologists often model this structure as a pyramid, in terms of both matter and energy. The pyramids can represent the general flow of energy through an ecosystem, from producers to consumers. They can also represent the mass or numbers of organisms at each trophic level.

MAIN IDEA

An energy pyramid shows the distribution of energy among trophic levels.

Ecosystems get their energy from sunlight. Sunlight provides the energy for photosynthesis, and that energy flows up the food chain. However, along the way, some of the energy is dissipated, or lost. Producers use energy from sunlight to make food. Herbivores eat the plants, but burn some energy in the process. This energy is given off as heat, and the heat escapes into space. Carnivores then eat the herbivores, but again lose energy as heat. In other words, each level in the food chain contains much less energy than the level below it. Fortunately, the Sun pumps new energy into the system and allows life to continue.

Loss of Available Energy

Each meal that you consume is packed with energy in the form of proteins, fats, and carbohydrates. Your body uses this energy for many purposes such as movement and growth. The majority of the food you consume is used to keep your body at its normal temperature. Your body is very inefficient at converting what you consume into useful energy, so there will always be some material that is not used. Unused material is simply excreted as waste.

Energy in an ecosystem works in much the same way, only on a larger scale. **Biomass** is a measure of the total dry mass of organisms in a given area. When a consumer incorporates the biomass of a producer into its own biomass, a great deal of energy is lost in the process as heat and waste. The conversion of biomass from a producer into biomass of the consumer is inefficient.

Consider the simple producer-to-consumer food chain of grass–prairie dog. Photosynthesis traps energy as carbohydrates, which can be thought of as a high-quality form of energy. A hungry prairie dog then eats the grass.

***Connecting* CONCEPTS**

Cellular Respiration As you learned in **Chapter 4**, the processes of cellular respiration use ATP to maintain your body's functions. While the chemical reactions of metabolism are relatively efficient, there will always be some loss of available energy.

Differentiated Instruction

ENGLISH LEARNERS

Students will see a series of pyramid models in this section that appear almost identical. Have students copy the diagrams into their notebooks and then look carefully at the captions and labels. Have students summarize for you the differences between these models.

Biology Toolkit, Context Clues, p. D10

Plan and Prepare

Objectives

- Trace the flow of energy through an ecosystem, using an energy pyramid.
- Relate energy pyramids to food chains and trophic levels.
- Compare and contrast a biomass pyramid and a pyramid of numbers.

Section Resources

Unit Resource Book Study Guide pp. 21–22 Power Notes p. 23 Reinforcement p. 24 Pre-AP Activity pp. 29–30
Interactive Reader Chapter 13 **Spanish Study Guide** pp. 143–144
Biology Toolkit pp. C22, D10
Technology Power Presentation 13.6 Media Gallery DVD Online Quiz 13.6

Activate Prior Knowledge Tell students that the unit of measure of energy in an ecosystem is one they can readily find by looking on just about any package of the food they buy. **Ask**

- How is food energy measured? in Calories
- What do Calories measure? the amount of energy needed to produce a certain amount of heat

Teach

Vocabulary

Academic Vocabulary The word **efficiency** is often associated with business, describing the least wasteful use of time, materials, and energy. In ecology, *efficiency* is a measure of how much of the energy stored in producers as biomass is available to support the consumers of an ecosystem.

▼ Teach *continued*

ONLINE BIOLOGY Go to the chapter Resource Center at **ClassZone.com** for additional resources and information on energy in ecosystems.

TEACH FROM VISUALS

FIGURE 13.17 Make sure students understand that the shape of an energy pyramid represents the amount of energy available at each trophic level. The pyramid shape works because each succeeding trophic level typically supports fewer individuals.

Ask, Why are there fewer owls than prairie dogs in a prairie ecosystem? less energy available to support the owl population because energy is lost at each trophic level

Vocabulary

kilocalorie A kilocalorie (kcal) is equal to 1000 calories, also referred to as a gram or small calorie, written with a lowercase c. The Calories (capital C) listed on food labels are each equivalent to 1 kilocalorie, or 1000 small calories.

Answers

A Connect Pyramids should show grass in the bottom level, cottontails in the middle level, and hawks in the top level. Arrows should point from the bottom level to the middle level and from the middle level to the top level. Each level should also include outward-pointing arrows to show energy loss.

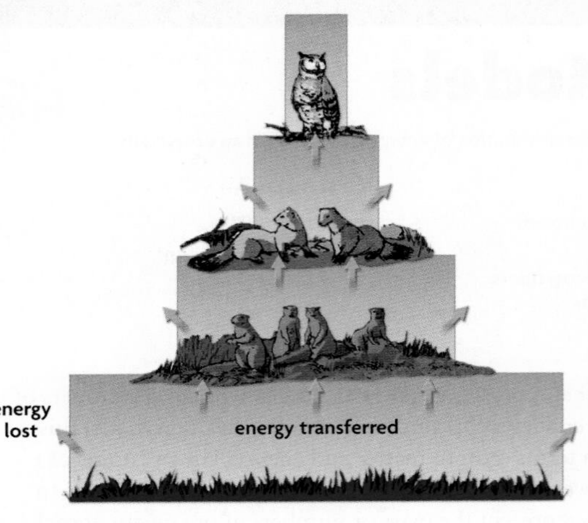

FIGURE 13.17 An energy pyramid illustrates the energy flow between trophic levels in an ecosystem. Between each tier, up to 90 percent of the energy is lost as heat into the atmosphere.

Some of the energy is used by the animal to grow. The remaining energy may be used to fuel cellular respiration or remains undigested. The dissipation, or loss, of energy between trophic levels may be as much as 90 percent, meaning that only 10 percent of the available energy is left to transfer from one trophic level to another.

Energy Pyramids

Because energy is lost at each stage of a food chain, the longer the chain is, the more energy is lost overall. The total energy used by producers far exceeds the energy used by the consumers they support. This concept can be illustrated with an energy pyramid. An **energy pyramid** is a diagram that compares energy used by producers, primary consumers, and other trophic levels. The pyramid, therefore, illustrates how available energy is distributed among trophic levels in an ecosystem. The unit of measurement used to describe the amount of energy at each trophic level in an energy pyramid is the kilocalorie (kcal).

A typical energy pyramid has a very large section at the base for the producers, and sections that become progressively smaller above. For example, in a prairie ecosystem, as illustrated in **FIGURE 13.17**, energy flows from grass at the producer level, to prairie dogs at the primary consumer level, to black-footed ferrets at the secondary consumer level, to a great horned owl at the tertiary consumer level.

A Connect **Draw an energy pyramid for the desert food chain introduced in Section 13.4. Use arrows to illustrate the flow of energy.**

MAIN IDEA

Other pyramid models illustrate an ecosystem's biomass and distribution of organisms.

FIGURE 13.18 The biomass pyramid depicts the total dry mass of organisms found at each trophic level.

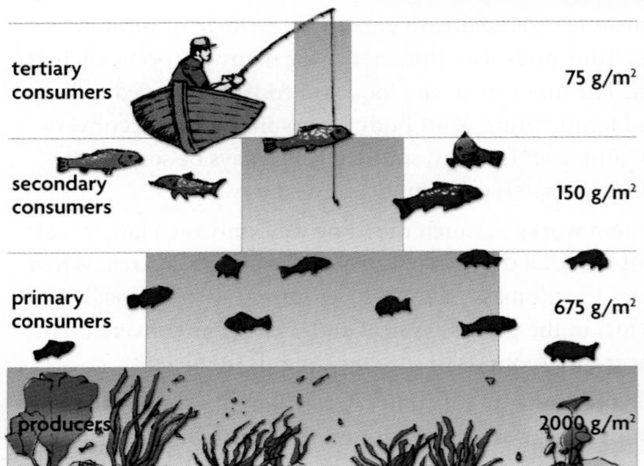

A biomass pyramid is a diagram that compares the biomass of different trophic levels within an ecosystem. Unlike an energy pyramid, which represents energy use, a biomass pyramid provides a picture of the mass of producers needed to support primary consumers, the mass of primary consumers required to support secondary consumers, and so on.

In a pond ecosystem, such as the one illustrated in **FIGURE 13.18**, a biomass pyramid shows that the total dry mass (given in grams per square meter, or g/m^2) of algae within the pond is far greater than the dry mass of fish. This example illustrates yet again the important role producers play in maintaining a stable ecosystem.

Differentiated Instruction

BELOW LEVEL

Have students use a chart to compare all the pyramids shown in this section. Tell them to identify at least two features common to all the pyramids. Tell them not to use shape as one of the features. Have them note the key difference that makes each pyramid distinctive.

Biology Toolkit, Content Frame, p. C22

PRE-AP

For students to see how quickly energy flows from an ecosystem, have them calculate the loss of energy in a sample ecosystem, using percents. Students should start with a pyramid that has 15,000 energy units. Remind them that 90 percent of available energy is lost from one trophic level to the next. Have them continue to make the calculation until they reach a value less than one. Have them do a calculation for a system twice the size of the first to see if there is an appreciable difference.

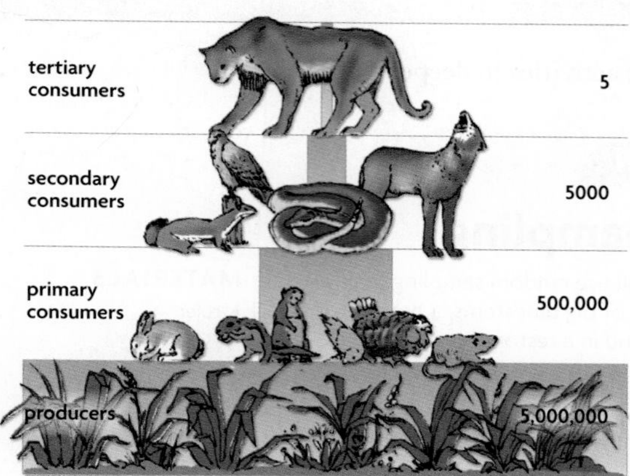

FIGURE 13.19 In a pyramid of numbers, each tier represents the actual number of individual organisms present in each trophic level.

A pyramid of numbers shows the numbers of individual organisms at each trophic level in an ecosystem. For example, a pyramid of numbers depicting a mountainous habitat, as shown in **FIGURE 13.19**, might include organisms such as grasses, snowshoe hares, gophers, coyotes, snakes, and mountain lions. This type of pyramid is particularly effective in showing the vast number of producers required to support even a few top level consumers.

In certain situations, both biomass pyramids and pyramids of numbers may occur in an inverted, or upside down, formation. Consider, for example, a pyramid of numbers based on a single tree. This single tree would be greatly outnumbered by the primary and secondary consumers, such as insects and birds, that live within it. In this case, the upper tiers of the pyramid of numbers would be much larger than the bottom tier representing the single tree.

A **Apply** **If a scientist wanted to compare the exact number of organisms at each trophic level within a desert ecosystem, which pyramid model would he or she use?**

13.6 ASSESSMENT

ONLINE QUIZ ClassZone.com

B.3.5

REVIEWING MAIN IDEAS

1. How does an **energy pyramid** help to describe energy flow in a food web?
2. What is the difference between a **biomass** pyramid and a pyramid of numbers?

CRITICAL THINKING

3. **Apply** How would you draw a pyramid of numbers for a dog with fleas? What shape would the pyramid take?
4. **Calculate** If each level in a food chain typically loses 90 percent of the energy it takes in, and the producer level uses 1000 kcal of energy, how much of that energy is left after the third trophic level?

Connecting CONCEPTS

5. **Nutrition** Why is an herbivorous diet more energy efficient than a carnivorous diet? Explain your answer.

Vocabulary

Academic Vocabulary The word **distribution** is used to describe the pyramid models shown in this section. The word is also used in business, as in the distribution of goods, and in law, as in the distribution of property. The concept that is common to these two uses is the idea of an *allotment,* a share or portion of a larger whole that is divided among different groups or individuals. The distribution shown in ecological pyramids is somewhat different. The word refers to the *arrangement* of organisms through which energy flows.

Answers

A **Apply** pyramid of numbers

Assess and Reteach ▼

Assess Use the Online Quiz or Section Quiz (*Assessment Book,* p. 258).

Reteach Draw on the board a pyramid with three levels. Pointing to each trophic level, ask students what each level represents and what units are used for each pyramid type: energy, biomass, and numbers.

13.6 ASSESSMENT

1. An energy pyramid shows the relative contribution to energy flow made by each trophic level in an ecosystem.
2. A biomass pyramid compares the mass of organisms that make up each trophic level in an ecosystem; a pyramid of numbers compares the number of individual organisms that make up each trophic level.
3. The bottom level of the pyramid would be the dog, and the fleas would be the top level. This would be an inverted pyramid because there are many fleas to just one dog.
4. The first trophic level uses 1000 kcal; the second trophic level uses 100 kcal; the third trophic level uses 10 kcal, leaving 1 kcal.
5. A herbivorous diet is more energy efficient because it is the closest trophic level to the producers, meaning there is more available energy to use.

OPTIONS FOR INQUIRY

INVESTIGATION

Time	45 minutes
Teacher Preparation	(1 flask)
Student Difficulty	(1 flask)
Lab Binder	Ecology, pp. 5–7

TEACHER TESTED

Purpose Estimate population size by random sampling.

Overview Students will use a grid to model random sampling and estimate population size. They will

- calculate average number of "plants" in 12 squares of a 49-square grid to estimate population size
- calculate percent error of estimate

LAB PREPARATION

- Make copies of the calculation data sheet from the *Lab Binder*, p. 7.

LAB MANAGEMENT

- You can use white kidney beans instead of pieces of paper for randomizing. Use a marker to write letters and numbers on the beans.
- Have groups of three or four students pool their data in step 6 before calculating percent error.

Teacher Note "I have students do the calculations as a group to help students who have math problems."

Inclusion For students who have difficulty seeing the dots, copy the grid twice at 200 percent. Use a pushpin to pierce the dots. By running a hand over the other side of the paper, a student with visual impairment will get a sense of the variation within the grid.

POST-LAB DISCUSSION

Discuss why this method is suited to sessile organisms, such as plants. **Ask,** Can you think of an underwater application of this sampling method? It could be used on a coral reef or with other sessile marine organisms.

Use these inquiry-based labs and online activities to deepen your understanding of ecological principles.

NOS.6 Use analogies and models (mathematical and physical) to simplify and represent systems that are difficult to understand or directly experience due to their size, time scale, or complexity, and recognize the limitations of analogies and models.

INVESTIGATION

Random Sampling

In this activity, you will use random sampling to calculate the number of big bluestems, a typical tall-grass species, found in a restored prairie.

MATERIALS
- ruler
- scissors
- paper
- 2 containers
- Calculation datasheet
- calculator

SKILL Sampling

PROBLEM How many big bluestems are in the field?

PROCEDURE

1. Cut 14 equal-sized paper squares.
2. Letter seven of the squares A through G. Number seven of the squares 1 through 7. Place the lettered squares and numbered squares in separate containers.
3. In your notebook, draw a data table like the one below. Include 12 rows in your table.
4. The pictured grid is your study plot. It is part of a larger grassland. The study plot measures 7 meters on each side, and each grid segment measures 1 meter by 1 meter. A single big bluestem plant is represented by each dot.
5. Determine which segment you will count by taking one square from each container without looking. Locate the letter-number combination on the grid and count the number of big bluestem plants. Record this number in your data table. Place each square back in its container.
6. Repeat step 5 until you have collected data for 12 different grid segments. Do not count the same segment twice.

CALCULATE Complete the calculation datasheet to estimate the population size.

TABLE 1. RANDOM SAMPLE DATA

Grid Letter	Grid Number	No. of Big Bluestems in Grid Segment

ANALYZE AND CONCLUDE

1. **Experimental Design** Why were paper squares used to determine which grid segment to count? Why didn't you just choose ten grid segments on your own?
2. **Evaluate** How could you change the procedure to reduce your percent error?
3. **Analyze** What are the advantages of using random sampling to estimate population size? What are the disadvantages?

Answers

Sample Data

For a sample of student data from this lab, go to page R105. There are 110 dots in the grid.

Analyze and Conclude

1. Using the paper squares reduces the chance of introducing bias. Choosing squares randomly means that each grid segment has an equal chance of being selected.
2. Increasing sample size would help reduce percent error.
3. Advantages include ease of use, time-saving, and ability to calculate population size without counting every individual. Disadvantages include inaccurate estimate because of nonrandom dispersal of individuals, inaccurate (skewed) results if sample size is too small, and inexact population count.

INVESTIGATION

Build a Terrarium

In this activity, you will construct a miniature self-sustaining ecosystem and monitor its stability.

SKILL Modeling

PROBLEM How does an ecosystem change or maintain its equilibrium over time?

MATERIALS

- glass jar with lid
- gravel
- potting soil
- large sealable plastic bags
- water
- measuring cup
- ruler
- small plants
- light source

PROCEDURE

1. Cover the bottom of the jar with a layer of gravel about 2 centimeters deep.
2. Place 2 cups of potting soil and 1/2 cup of water in the plastic bag. Seal the bag and mix well until the soil is moist.
3. Add the moistened soil into the jar over the gravel layer.
4. Select and plant the small plants in the soil. Cover the jar with the lid and tighten it shut.
5. Observe and record changes in your terrarium over time.

ANALYZE AND CONCLUDE

1. **Operational Definitions** What criteria did you use to select the size and number of plants for your terrarium?
2. **Identify Variables** What are the key variables involved in maintaining your ecosystem?
3. **Observe** How did your terrarium ecosystem change over time?
4. **Conclude** Was your terrarium a success? Explain.

Online BIOLOGY CLASSZONE.COM

VIRTUAL LAB

Estimating Population Size

How does a scientist count a mobile population? In this interactive lab, capture, mark, then recapture individual animals to estimate the size of a sample population.

ANIMATED BIOLOGY

Build a Food Web

Build a food web. Use your knowledge of producers and consumers to place a set of organisms in a food web.

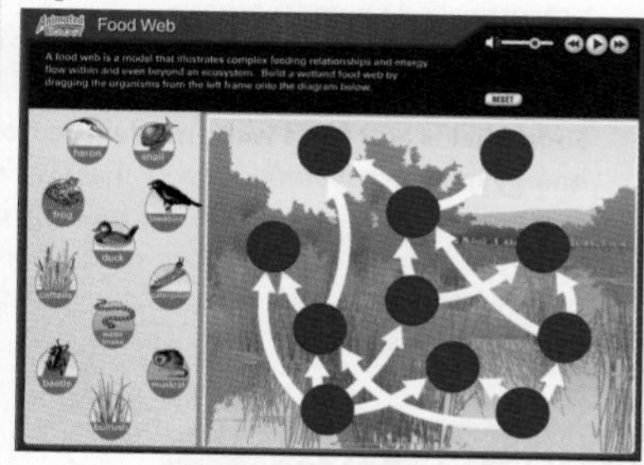

WEBQUEST

A sea otter is playful, fun to watch, and very critical to its ecosystem. In this WebQuest, you will explore its role as a keystone species within the aquatic environment of the California coast. Learn what happened after sea otters were almost wiped out. Finally, think of ways you can protect sea otter populations and the ecosystems in which they live.

Answers

Analyze and Conclude

1. size of jar compared to plant size; amount of soil and water used
2. amount of light, water, oxygen, carbon dioxide, number of plants, soil nutrients, and structure
3. Students may mention plant growth or formation of condensation.
4. Success will be indicated by the health of the plants.

Online Biology ▼

VIRTUAL LAB Use this lab to reinforce the concepts in **Section 13.1.**

ANIMATED BIOLOGY Use this interactive animation to reinforce the concepts in **Section 13.4.**

WEBQUEST The WebQuest will take one full class period. Students complete the activity online and then will need access to a printer to print their answers. Sample answers, teacher notes, and alternative assessment ideas are available on **ClassZone.com.** Use with **Section 13.4.**

INVESTIGATION TEACHER TESTED

Time	15 minutes
Teacher Preparation	
Student Difficulty	
Lab Binder	Ecology, p. 8

Purpose Model a self-sustaining ecosystem.

Overview Students will make a terrarium ecosystem and observe changes in the ecosystem over time.

LAB PREPARATION

- Use fast plants or plants grown from radish or mustard seeds.

Safety Avoid potting soil that includes chemicals for insect control.

LAB MANAGEMENT

- Establish an operational definition for *equilibrium.*
- Check potting soil for nutrients.
- Set aside a time each day for making observations.

POST-LAB DISCUSSION

Potting soil contains nitrogen and phosphorus, but not microbes. Discuss soil pH, soil structure, and how gravel acts as a reservoir for water.

Interactive Review

Encourage students to go to **ClassZone.com** for a detailed review of each section, including visuals and vocabulary practice.

Unit Resource Book, Vocabulary Practice, pp. 31–34

ITEM CORRELATIONS	
Standard	**Items**
B.3.4	18, 19, 21, 28, 29, 39
B.3.5	16, 17, 20, 30, 31
B.4.1	38
B.4.2	26, 27
B.4.4	13, 14, 25

CHAPTER 13 Interactive Review @ CLASSZONE.COM

KEY CONCEPTS | Vocabulary Games | Concept Maps | Animated Biology | Online Quiz

13.1 Ecologists Study Relationships

Ecology is the study of the relationships among organisms and their environment. Ecologists study environments at different levels of organization. Ecologists use methods such as observation, experimentation, and modeling to study ecological principles.

13.2 Biotic and Abiotic Factors

Every ecosystem includes both living and nonliving factors. Changing one factor in an ecosystem can affect many other factors. The removal of a keystone species may lead to changes in an ecosystem's biodiversity.

13.3 Energy in Ecosystems

Life in an ecosystem requires a source of energy. Producers provide energy for other organisms in an ecosystem. Most producers obtain their energy from sunlight through photosynthesis. Other producers obtain their energy through a process called chemosynthesis.

13.4 Food Chains and Food Webs

Food chains and food webs model the flow of energy in an ecosystem. A food chain is a simple model that shows a sequence of feeding relationships. A food web provides a more complex picture of the network of feeding relationships among organisms in an ecosystem.

13.5 Cycling of Matter

Matter cycles in and out of an ecosystem. The hydrologic cycle is the circular pathway of water through the environment. Elements essential for life on Earth, such as oxygen, carbon, nitrogen, and phosphorus, also cycle through ecosystems.

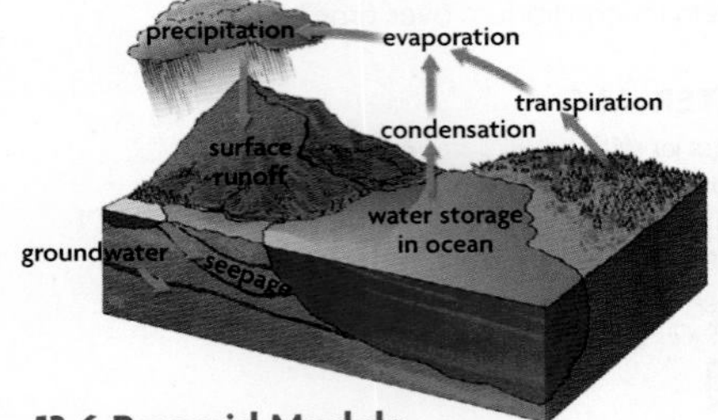

13.6 Pyramid Models

Pyramids model the distribution of energy and matter in an ecosystem. An energy pyramid shows the distribution of energy in a food chain. Energy flows upward from producers to consumers. Between each tier of the energy pyramid, energy is lost as heat. Sometimes only 10 percent of the original energy is transferred to the next trophic level. A biomass pyramid shows the total mass of organisms at each trophic level, while a pyramid of numbers shows the actual number of organisms present in each trophic level.

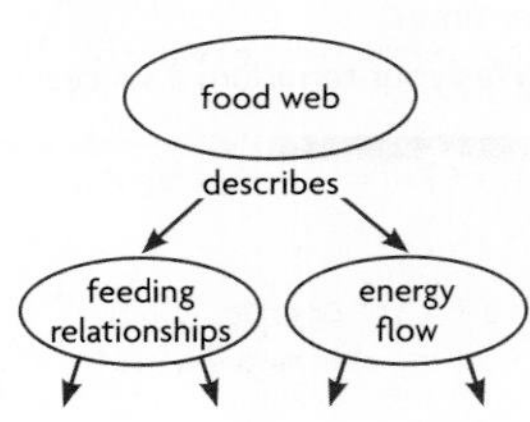

Synthesize Your Notes

Energy Pyramid Add labels and organisms that belong in each trophic level to this energy pyramid.

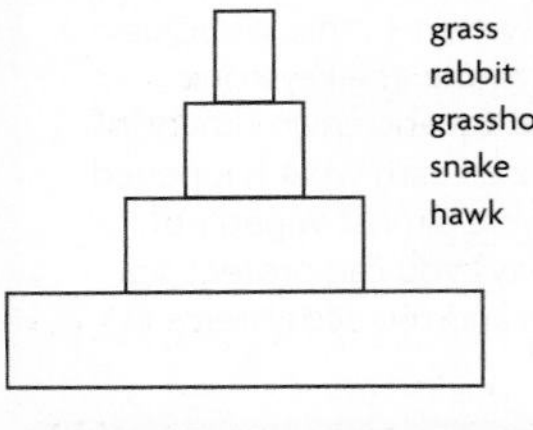

Concept Map Use a concept map to summarize what you know about food webs.

food web → describes → feeding relationships; energy flow

Reviewing Vocabulary

1. Biotic factor—both are parts of an ecosystem. Biotic factors are living things; abiotic factors are nonliving things.
2. Consumer—both get energy from food. Consumers obtain food from producers; producers make their own food.
3. Autotroph—both get energy from food. Heterotrophs obtain food from producers; autotrophs make their own food.
4. Herbivore—both are types of consumers. Carnivores eat only animals; herbivores eat only plants.
5. Generalist—both are types of consumers. Specialists eat only one or a few types of food; generalists eat many types of food.
6. The root *vore* means "to eat." It is used in the names of consumers, which eat other organisms.
7. All but one of the terms refers to the living components of ecosystems, describing different aspects. The exception is "abiotic," which refers to the nonliving components.
8. An ecosystem is a home to both living and nonliving things in an area.
9. Both processes are involved in making carbohydrates by chemically combining other substances.

Chapter Assessment

Chapter Vocabulary

13.1 ecology, p. 396
community, p. 397
ecosystem, p. 397
biome, p. 397

13.2 biotic, p. 402
abiotic, p. 402
biodiversity, p. 403
keystone species, p. 403

13.3 producer, p. 406
autotroph, p. 406
consumer, p. 406
heterotroph, p. 406
chemosynthesis, p. 407

13.4 food chain, p. 408
herbivore, p. 409
carnivore, p. 409
omnivore, p. 409
detritivore, p. 409
decomposer, p. 409
specialist, p. 409
generalist, p. 409
trophic level, p. 409
food web, p. 411

13.5 hydrologic cycle, p. 412
biogeochemical cycle, p. 413
nitrogen fixation, p. 415

13.6 biomass, p. 417
energy pyramid, p. 418

Reviewing Vocabulary

Find an Opposite

Pair each of the words listed below with a different vocabulary term that has an opposing definition. Then, write one sentence describing a difference.

1. abiotic factor
2. producer
3. heterotroph
4. carnivore
5. specialist

Greek and Latin Word Origins

Use the definitions of the word parts to answer the following questions.

Part	Meaning
bio-	life
eco-	home
syn-	together, joined
vore	eat

6. Explain why the root *vore* is used in the appropriate vocabulary terms.

7. Six vocabulary terms include the prefix *bio-*. Describe how they are all related.

8. Use the meaning of *eco-* to write your own definition of *ecosystem.*

9. *Photo-* means "light," and *chemo-* means "chemical." Explain why *photosynthesis* and *chemosynthesis* both include the prefix *syn-*.

Reviewing MAIN IDEAS

10. How can an individual organism simultaneously be part of a population, community, ecosystem, and biome?

11. What are the major differences between observation, experimentation, and modeling?

12. List some biotic and abiotic factors you would expect to find in a city park.

13. What is a keystone species and how might the removal of it affect the stability of and biodiversity within its ecosystem? **B.4.4**

14. What would happen to a forest ecosystem if a fire killed most of its producers? **B.4.4**

15. Describe one similarity and one difference between photosynthesis and chemosynthesis.

16. An acorn is eaten by a squirrel, which is eaten by an owl. What model best describes this simple relationship, and how does it show energy flow? **B.3.5**

17. How is a food web related to energy flow within an ecosystem? **B.3.5**

18. Describe the main processes involved in the hydrologic cycle. **B.3.4**

19. Give an example of one biogeochemical cycle and explain how it is important to living things. **B.3.4**

20. How does an energy pyramid show the flow of energy in an ecosystem? **B.3.5**

21. A biomass pyramid and a pyramid of numbers are two ways of modeling the flow of matter in an ecosystem. What is the main difference between the two? **B.3.4**

Reviewing Main Ideas

10. An individual organism is involved in many interactions within its environment. It interacts with others of the same species in a population, with different species in a community, and with abiotic factors in an ecosystem, which is part of a biome.

11. Observation involves watching and recording what is occurring naturally, experimentation is a controlled procedure designed to answer a question, and modeling is used to determine what might happen in the future.

12. Biotic factors might include birds, squirrels, insects, trees, and grasses. Abiotic factors might include sunlight, air, moisture, and soil.

13. A keystone species has an unusually large effect on shaping an ecosystem. Its removal may change an ecosystem by decreasing its stability and amount of biodiversity.

14. Primary consumers might die out or move to a new location because their food source is gone. Secondary consumers might die out or move to a new location because of the lack of primary consumers to eat.

15. Similarity: both form carbohydrates. Difference: photosynthesis uses sunlight as an energy source; chemosynthesis uses chemicals.

16. A food chain would best describe this relationship. Energy flows from the acorn to the squirrel to the owl.

17. A food web is made up of many interconnected food chains. At each trophic level in a food chain, some energy is stored in new structures within organisms, but most energy is dissipated into the environment.

18. Precipitation moves water from the atmosphere to Earth's surface, evaporation and transpiration return water to the atmosphere as water vapor, and condensation leads to cloud formation and precipitation.

19. Answers should describe how an element or compound cycles between the environment and living matter. *Sample Answer:* Carbon, an element found in all living matter, is brought into an ecosystem through producers by photosynthesis. Producers are the source of carbon compounds for consumers. Some carbon returns to the atmosphere through respiration. The rest returns to the environment as organisms die and their remains are broken down by decomposers.

20. An energy pyramid compares energy used by producers, primary consumers, and other trophic levels. The pyramid shows that while some energy is transferred between levels, at each level, most energy is dissipated into the environment.

21. A biomass pyramid compares the mass of organisms at each trophic level, whereas a pyramid of numbers compares the total number of organisms at each trophic level.

Critical Thinking

22. The community level; seals and polar bears are different species.
23. Beavers use trees to block moving water, which in turn changes the habitat and allows for more types of organisms to populate the ecosystem.
24. Chemosynthetic organisms use chemicals instead of sunlight as an energy source to make food.
25. Producers might die out because of water loss, which might reduce the number of herbivores who have less food available. Carnivores would also be affected by loss of prey. The producer populations might be most affected because they cannot move from the drought area.
26. Omnivores and generalists would be the most likely to adapt to changes in their environments because they eat a wide variety of foods. Specialists and carnivores would have the most difficult time adapting to changes in the environment because their diets are more restricted.
27. Carbon is the central element in organic molecules that make up all organisms. Carbon compounds incorporate different elements such as oxygen, nitrogen, phosphorous—all of which are needed for carbohydrates, nucleic acids, lipids, and proteins. The source of these materials for humans are biogeochemical cycles that make carbon compounds available as food.
28. Decomposers release nitrogen into the soil as ammonia as they break down dead organic matter.
29. Consumers at the top of a pyramid are often larger carnivores. If their number increases, this may reduce the number of prey animals at the middle levels of the pyramid. Producers might increase in number as a result of fewer herbivores.

Critical Thinking

22. Apply At what level of organization would a scientist study the interaction between seals and polar bears in the Arctic? Explain your answer.

23. Apply Explain which biotic factors used by the beaver are related to its role as a keystone species.

24. Evaluate Scientists used to say that all living things depend on the sun. Explain why this statement is no longer valid.

25. Analyze How might a drought affect a grassland food web? Which trophic level would the drought affect the most? Explain your answer. **B.4.4**

26. Synthesize Humans have changed many ecosystems on Earth. Compare different types of consumers, and predict which types would be more likely to adapt to these changes and which would not. Explain your answers. **B.4.2**

27. Synthesize Use the information you learned about carbon-based molecules to explain a human's need to participate in the biogeochemical cycles. **B.4.2**

28. Connect What role do decomposers play in the nitrogen cycle? **B.3.4**

29. Predict In a pyramid of numbers, the highest organism has the smallest number of individuals in a community. What might happen if this organism increased its numbers significantly? Explain the effect this increase would have on the other members of the community. **B.3.4**

Interpreting Visuals

Use the energy pyramid below to answer the following questions.

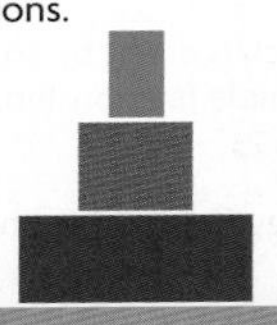

10,000 kcal energy

30. Apply Use the energy pyramid to describe the flow of energy within an ecosystem. Identify which tier represents producers, primary consumers, and so on. **B.3.5**

31. Calculate If 90 percent of the energy is lost as heat between trophic levels, approximately how much energy is available to the secondary consumers in this energy pyramid? Show your calculations. **B.3.5**

Analyzing Data

Use the equation T = N × A to estimate the population size in questions 32–33. Show all of your work.

32. Calculate A scientist wants to estimate the population of mushrooms on a forest floor with an area of 300 m^2. Each quadrat is 2 m^2. She counts 13 mushrooms in 20 quadrats. What is the population of mushrooms in the forest?

33. Calculate A scientist uses quadrats to sample the population of strawberry cactus plants in a section of the Chihuahuan desert that is 150 m^2. He counts 5 cacti in 10 quadrats. Each quadrat is 2 m^2. What is the population of strawberry cacti in the desert?

34. Analyze What are the advantages and disadvantages of using random sampling to obtain an estimate of the population size?

35. Evaluate A scientist uses quadrats to determine the population size of lupines in a field 500 m^2 in size. She uses ten 1 m^2 quadrats. Is this an adequate sample size? Explain your answer.

36. Apply Scientists often use tables of random numbers to determine where to place quadrats on their study site. Why might they do this? Why can't they choose where to place the quadrats?

37. Apply A scientist wants to determine the population size of whiptail lizards within a 15-acre area. What sampling method should she use? How can she ensure that she obtains an accurate estimate of the lizard population? Explain your answer.

Connecting CONCEPTS

38. Write About Your Own Ecosystem Imagine you built a large greenhouse in your home to create your own ecosystem. What types of organisms would you include? How would you ensure that the biogeochemical cycles were in place? Describe in detail an ecosystem you would like to have in your home. Be sure to include the biotic and abiotic factors in your explanation of how the ecosystem would sustain itself. **B.4.1**

39. Make a Food Web Read the description of anhingas on page 395 and draw a partial food web of a freshwater marsh ecosystem. Include producers and consumers in your web. **B.3.4**

Interpreting Visuals

30. As you move up the energy pyramid from one trophic level to the next, less energy is available for organisms to use. Typically 90 percent of the energy is lost between trophic levels, meaning only 10 percent is transferred from one trophic level to the next. The bottom level is producers, then primary consumers, secondary consumers, and tertiary consumers.
31. 100 kcal (10,000 − 9000 = 1000; 1000 − 900 = 100)

Analyzing Data

32. 98 mushrooms
33. 38 cacti
34. Random sampling lets scientists estimate population size without having to count every single organism within the population. However, there is a chance that the sample is not representative of the group as a whole, so the estimate may be too high or too low.
35. This would not be an adequate sample size, because for such a large area, more quadrats should be used.
36. Scientists use random number tables to avoid introducing bias into the sampling process. Avoiding bias is also why they cannot choose the plot sites themselves.

INDIANA ISTEP+ Test Prep

B.3.4; B.3.5; B.4.2; B.4.4

Test Practice For more test practice, go to ClassZone.com.

1 In the carbon cycle, through what process does carbon move from an abiotic resource into organic matter?

A immigration
B combustion
C respiration
D photosynthesis

2

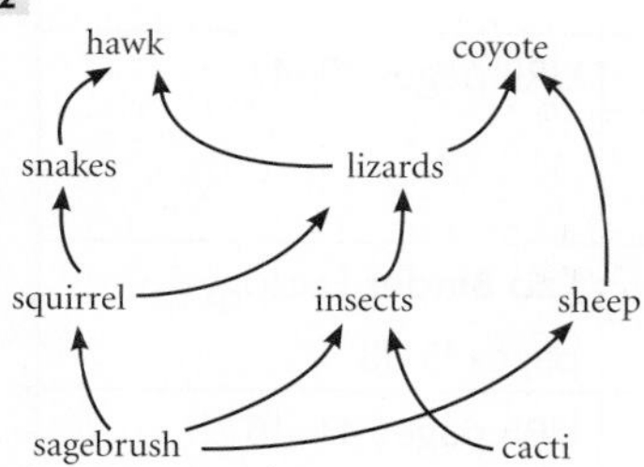

This food web shows the relationships between organisms in an ecosystem. Which type of organism ***not*** shown in this food web is important to the stability of the ecosystem?

A producer
B consumer
C herbivore
D decomposer

3 Several different plant species grew in an empty lot. The city council decided to turn the lot into a park, so they had the ground torn up and planted with grass to create a playing field. The ecological factor that was most likely affected by the change was the lot's

A biomass.
B temperature.
C biodiversity.
D hydrologic cycle.

4

4
3
2
1

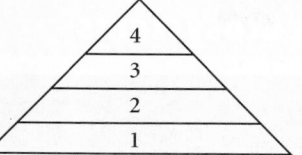

In which direction does energy flow through this energy pyramid?

A 4, 3, 2, 1
B 1, 2, 3, 4
C 2, 1, 3, 4
D 3, 4, 2, 1

THINK THROUGH THE QUESTION

Remember that an energy pyramid shows the amount of energy in each trophic level, with producers at the bottom of the pyramid, and consumers at the top.

5 Which of the following groups is most important for bringing energy into an ecosystem?

A consumers
B producers
C decomposers
D generalists

6 Energy pyramids trace the passage of energy from the organisms of one trophic level to the organisms of the next. Why type of organisms occupies the base of the energy pyramid?

Standards-Based Assessment

1. D	4. B
2. D	5. B
3. C	6. See Below

Question 2 Answer D is correct. Answer A is incorrect because producers (sagebrush, cacti) are shown in the diagram. Answer B is incorrect because consumers (squirrel, insects, sheep, snakes, lizards, hawk, coyote) are shown in the diagram. Answer C is incorrect because herbivores, a type of consumer, are shown in the diagram (squirrel, insects, sheep).
Question 4 Answer B is correct. Answers A, C, and D are incorrect because energy flows upward in the energy pyramid model, from producers through several tiers of consumers; only answer B represents energy flowing in order from bottom to top.
Question 5 Answer B is correct. Answers A, C, and D are incorrect because they do not obtain energy from abiotic sources such as sunlight or inorganic chemicals, therefore they rely upon producers to obtain energy for themselves.
Question 6 Producers, or green plants, occupy the base of the energy pyramid. They are the only organisms on Earth that obtain energy directly from the sun, which means that they are the largest source of energy for other organisms on Earth.

37. The scientist could use the mark-recapture method to determine the population size. She should set out a number of traps that evenly cover the entire study site area to be sure that all the lizards within the area have an equal chance of being caught.

Connecting Concepts

38. Students should include plants, bacteria, soil, and water at a minimum to maintain an ecosystem. Any animals would need to have continuing food sources and adequate space.
39. *Sample Answers:* Producers include algae and aquatic plants. Primary consumers include insects, secondary consumers include fish, and tertiary consumers include . Other animals in the ecosystem might include alligators (tertiary consumers) and other aquatic birds, such as herons or cormorants (both tertiary consumers).

ITEM CORRELATIONS

Standard	Items
B.3.4	1
B.3.5	4, 5, 6
B.4.2	3
B.4.4	2

CHAPTER 14

Indiana Resource Preview

Print Resources

Interactions in Ecosystems

INDIANA STANDARDS		Sections	PAGES and PACING	UNIT RESOURCE BOOK
B.4.4	14.1	**Habitat and Niche** **KEY CONCEPT** Every organism has a habitat and a niche.	pp. 428–430 30 minutes	URB pages 35–38
B.4.4	14.2	**Community Interactions** **KEY CONCEPT** Organisms interact as individuals and as populations.	pp. 431–434 30 minutes	URB pages 39–42
NOS.3		CHAPTER INVESTIGATION: Modeling Predation	p. 435 30 minutes	**Lab Binder** Ecology pages 15–18
	14.3	**Population Density and Distribution** **KEY CONCEPT** Each population has a density, a dispersion, and a reproductive strategy.	pp. 436–439 30 minutes	URB pages 43–46
B.4.1	14.4	**Population Growth Patterns** **KEY CONCEPT** Populations grow in predictable patterns.	pp. 440–444 45 minutes	URB pages 47–50
NOS.1		DATA ANALYSIS: Reading Combination Graphs	p. 442 30 minutes	URB page 55
B.4.2	14.5	**Ecological Succession** **KEY CONCEPT** Ecological succession is a process of change in the species that make up a community.	pp. 445–447 30 minutes	URB pages 51–54
NOS.1, NOS.3		OPTIONS FOR INQUIRY	pp. 448–449 45 minutes, 45 minutes	**Lab Binder** Ecology pages 19–21
		Chapter Review	pp. 450–453	**Assessment Book** Chapter Tests A, B pp. 279–286

INDIANA STANDARDS

B.4.1 Explain that the amount of life an environment can support is limited by the available energy, water, oxygen, and minerals, and by the ability of ecosystems to recycle the remains of dead organisms.
B.4.2 Describe how human activities and natural phenomena can change the flow of matter and energy in an ecosystem and how those changes impact other species.
B.4.4 Describe how climate, the pattern of matter and energy flow, the birth and death of new organisms, and the interaction between those organisms contribute to the long term stability of an ecosystem.

NOS.1 Develop explanations based on reproducible data and observations gathered during laboratory investigations.
NOS.3 Clearly communicate their ideas and results of investigations verbally and in written form using tables, graphs, diagrams, and photographs.

Labs

PUPIL EDITION LABS

Modeling Predation, p. 435 Students model predation under different environmental conditions. **Lab Binder** pp. 15–18	**Time:** 45 minutes **Materials:** 21 × 27 cm^3 grid paper, 400 uncooked rice grains, toothpick
Survivorship Curves, Section 3, p. 438 Students model a survivorship curve, using obituary data. **Lab Binder** pp. 23–24	**Time:** 15 minutes **Materials:** obituary section of a newspaper, graph paper

OPTIONS FOR INQUIRY

Limiting Nutrients for Algae, p. 448 Students determine if nitrogen and phosphorus are limiting nutrients for algae. **Lab Binder** pp. 19–20	**Time:** 45 minutes **Materials:** 3 baby food jars with lids, glass marking pencil, 200 mL pond water, 3 eyedroppers, 50 mL algae culture, 5 drops 10% trisodium phosphate solution, 5 drops 10% ammonium sulfate or urea solution, 50-mL graduated cylinder
Making a Local Field Guide, p. 449 Students observe specimens near their home or school to create their own local field guide. **Lab Binder** p. 21	**Time:** 45 minutes **Materials:** several field guides, hand lens, blank notebook, pencil, colored pencils, camera (optional)

LAB BINDER Unit 5 Ecology

Additional Investigation: Predator-Prey Interactions, pp. 25–30

Real-World Lab: Monitoring Bird Populations, pp. 54–57

Challenge Lab: Using GPS in Ecological Surveys, pp. 62–66; Modeling the Effects of Habitat Fragmentation, pp. 67–72

Vernier Probeware Lab: Interdependence of Plants and Animals, pp. 73–80

LAB GENERATOR

A searchable CD of all labs in the program in editable format, including forensic, probeware, and biotechnology labs.

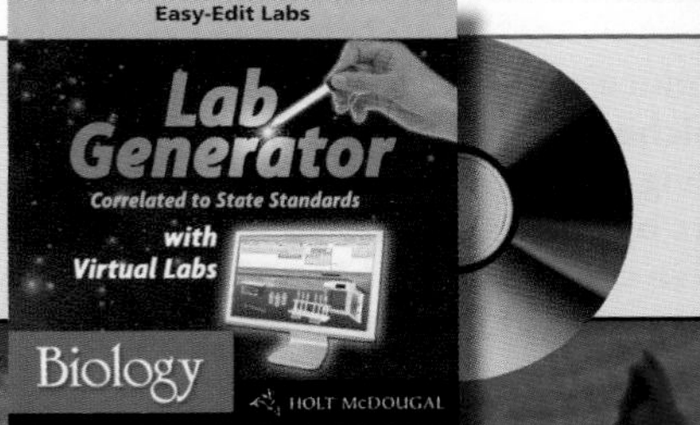

Presentation Tools

POWER PRESENTATIONS

Presentation Chapter 14
Power Presentations for each section incorporate images and clips from the Media Gallery: Includes Note Navigator for each section.

MEDIA GALLERY

Contains the following images and video clips, as well as animations, simulations and forms of visuals from the book.

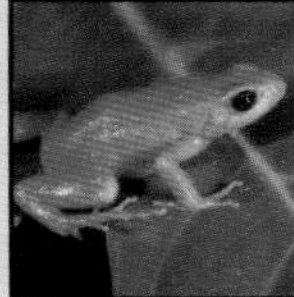
Ecological equivalents

Limits to population growth

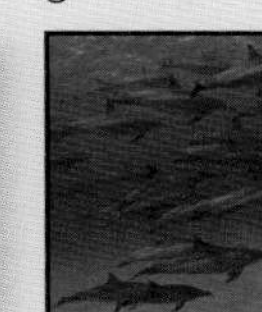
School of dolphins

Dry river bed

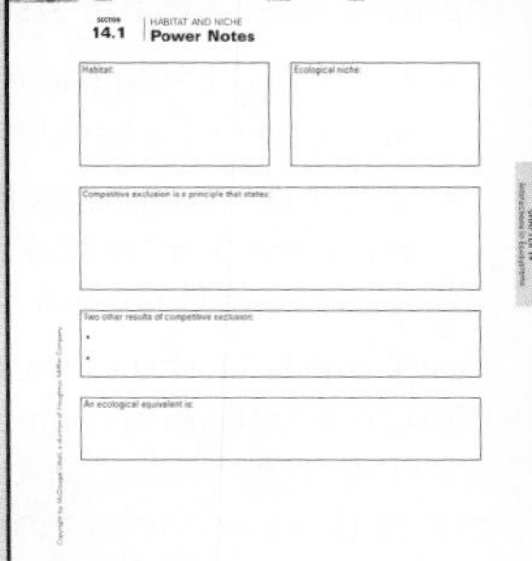

Power Notes

VIDEO

View a set of short video clips exploring predator and prey relationships.

ANIMATED BIOLOGY

Survive Within a Niche
What Limits Population Growth?

TRANSPARENCIES

Population Graphs T65
Primary Succession T66
Secondary Succession T67
Warbler Feeding Zones T68

Online BIOLOGY CLASSZONE.COM

BioZine
Animated Biology
Interactive Review
SciLinks
Resource Centers

CHAPTER

14

▼ Focus and Motivate

Why are these zebras fighting?

Have students speculate on reasons why the zebras are fighting. two males fighting over a mate **Ask**

- Is *fighting* really the right word? Can you think of a better one? competing
- What do organisms in an ecosystem compete for? resources such as food, water, shelter, and a mate

Point out that the competition in the picture is between males of the same species. In general, most competition for mates does not result in significant harm to either animal. The fights are rituals. **Ask,** In terms of evolution, why might nonviolent competitive behavior within a group tend to be the rule, not the exception, in the natural world? When a dominant male dies, other males are needed for reproduction. Also, other males in a group contribute in other ways, for example, providing protection.

BIOZINE ClassZone.com

Students can access BioZine at **ClassZone.com** to check the daily science news feeds.

In a Hurry?

The critical material of the chapter is found in **Sections 14.2, 14.3,** and **14.4,** which cover species interactions, population parameters, and patterns of population growth. A quick read of vocabulary in **Section 14.1** will enable students to review concepts of habitat, ecological niche, competitive exclusion, and ecological equivalent. Students may also be familiar with the concept of ecological succession covered in **Section 14.5.** Use **FIGURES 14.16** and **14.17** to review primary and secondary succession.

CHAPTER

14 Interactions in Ecosystems

KEY CONCEPTS

14.1 Habitat and Niche
Every organism has a habitat and a niche.

14.2 Community Interactions
Organisms interact as individuals and as populations.

14.3 Population Density and Distribution
Each population has a density, a dispersion, and a reproductive strategy.

14.4 Population Growth Patterns
Populations grow in predictable patterns.

14.5 Ecological Succession
Ecological succession is a process of change in the species that make up a community.

Online BIOLOGY CLASSZONE.COM

Animated BIOLOGY
View animated chapter concepts.
- Survive Within a Niche
- What Limits Population Growth?

BIOZINE
Keep current with biology news.
- News feeds
- Strange Biology
- Bio Bytes

RESOURCE CENTER
Get more information on
- Symbiotic Relationships
- Succession

Teacher Demo

Eye Opener **Introduce students to the idea of an ecological niche by using the classic study of the feeding habits of North American warblers by ecologist Robert MacArthur. The five species of warblers are about the same size and eat insects commonly found in fir and pine trees. MacArthur discovered that each bird fed in different parts of the tree, dividing up the resources of their shared habitat.**

Demonstrate Reproduce on individual acetates the diagrams shown on the next page, and also prepare a simple outline of the tree and its feeding zones. Place the tree outline on an overhead projector, then layer on the acetate for each warbler. (Diagrams available in Media Gallery and Transparencies.)

Point out how little overlap there is. Make sure students don't jump to the conclusion that a niche is simply a feeding location. Each bird feeds on different insects, at different times of day, and has different feeding behaviors.

Why are these zebras fighting?

Connecting CONCEPTS

For the zebra, life on the African savannah is about survival. Whether escaping the ambush of a pride of lions, walking vast distances to drink fresh water, or competing for the right to mate with females, only the best adapted zebras will survive and pass on their genes. The interactions among organisms, and between organisms and their environment, make ecosystems function.

Adaptation The zebra's stripes are not just for show. They are an adaptation that protect zebras against predators. As the herd moves, the stripes of all the zebras blend together, creating a kind of camouflage that makes it difficult for a predator to pick out just one.

Warbler Feeding Zones Enlarge as needed.

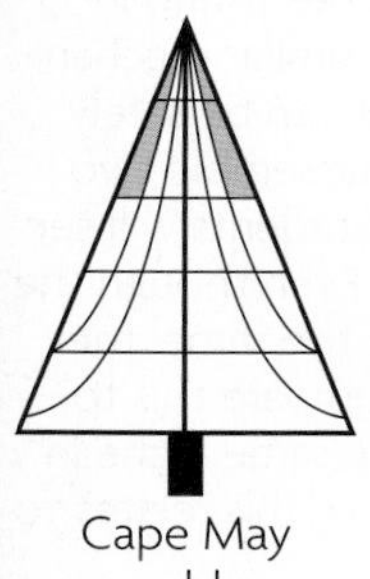

Cape May warbler

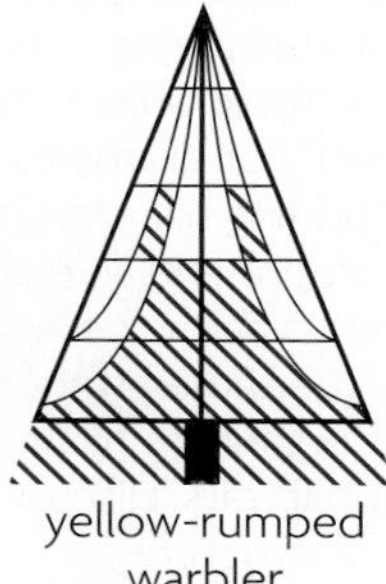

yellow-rumped warbler

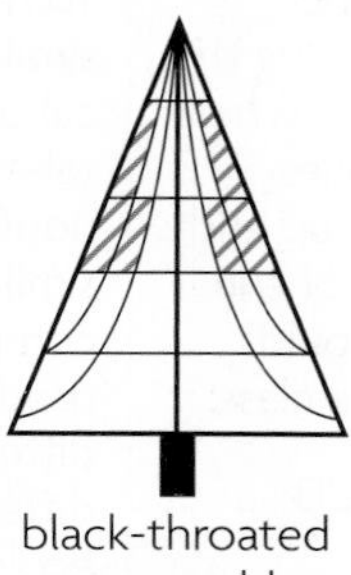

black-throated green warbler

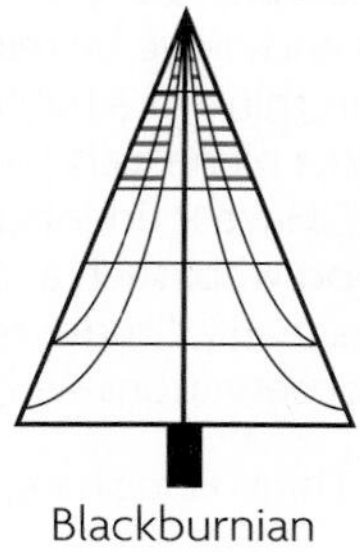

Blackburnian warbler

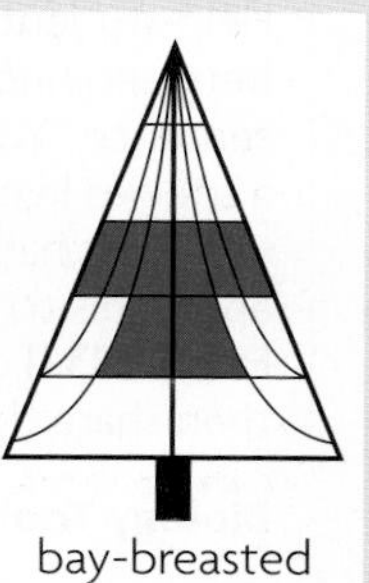

bay-breasted warbler

Activate Prior Knowledge

Direct students' attention to the word *interaction* in the chapter title and references to *population* in the Key Concepts list. **Ask,** What are some interactions common to human population? How do you interact with others? Students might mention family interactions that involve cooperation in maintaining shelter, preparing food, caring for family members or competition for parents' attention or household resources. In school, students cooperate in learning activities but also compete for school resources and in sports.

Remind students that living things must obtain matter and energy to survive. In an ecosystem, different populations live in the same environment and share or compete for resources. How individuals and populations interact in getting resources helps to explain how populations are distributed within an ecosystem.

Preview Vocabulary

Academic Vocabulary In this chapter students will consider the *logistics* of biological populations. The word typically applies to military operations and the procurement, distribution, maintenance, and replacement of material and personnel. Have students to consider the "logistics" of an ecosystem. **Ask,** What are terms you expect to see in a discussion of population trends? distribution, density, limits, growth, decline, emigration, immigration, carrying capacity

English Learners Prepare an anticipation guide to test students' understanding of the way that terms describing behavior are applied in ecology. Students are probably familiar with the words *competition* and *parasitic,* but may not see how they relate to resources.

Integrating Earth Science

Because of the climate in Africa and the zebras' need for food and water, large herds of plains zebras migrate more than 480 kilometers (300 mi) every year. When one area becomes dry, they move to another that has rain and fresh grass.

▼ Plan and Prepare

Objectives

- Differentiate between habitat and niche.
- Differentiate between competitive exclusion and ecological equivalents.

Section Resources

Unit Resource Book Study Guide pp. 35–36 Power Notes p. 37 Reinforcement p. 38
Interactive Reader Chapter 14 **Spanish Study Guide** pp. 145–146
Biology Toolkit pp. C11, C13, C30
Technology Power Presentation 14.1 Media Gallery DVD Online Quiz 14.1

Activate Prior Knowledge Students will probably be familiar with the word **niche** as a marketing term. **Ask,** How would you define the word *niche*? highly specialized taste, function People are also said to fill a niche in the functions they perform. **Ask,** What are some niches found in a school community? teacher, coach, counselor, student, janitor Discuss that while all schools have these niches, different people in different schools fill the niches.

▼ Teach

Vocabulary

Academic Vocabulary Sometimes a word that has a general meaning in everyday language takes on a specialized meaning in science. For example, **niche** comes from the Latin "to nest." An **ecological niche** describes the role an organism plays in an ecosystem as well as its living conditions. Another example is the word **habitat,** from the Latin root "to dwell." In ecology, *habitat* refers to the place where the niche conditions are found.

14.1 Habitat and Niche

KEY CONCEPT Every organism has a habitat and a niche.

MAIN IDEAS

- A habitat differs from a niche.
- Resource availability gives structure to a community.

VOCABULARY

habitat, p. 428
ecological niche, p. 428
competitive exclusion, p. 429
ecological equivalent, p. 430

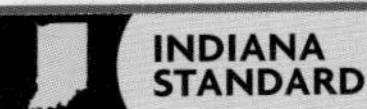

INDIANA STANDARDS

B.4.4 Describe how climate, the pattern of matter and energy flow, the birth and death of new organisms, and the interaction between those organisms contribute to the long term stability of an ecosystem.

Connect The ways in which a zebra interacts with its environment and other organisms are only a small part of the ecology of the African plains. To understand what individuals, populations, and communities need to survive, ecologists study the interactions among species and between species and their environment. Why does a zebra fit so well into the African savannah?

MAIN IDEA

A habitat differs from a niche.

On the vast plains of Africa, tall grasses grow among trees and shrubs, and small pools of water surrounded by thirsty animals dot the landscape. This challenging environment is the home of the African lion, shown in **FIGURE 14.1.** Here, lions stalk through tall grass to hunt zebras and antelope, find places to rest in the shade of trees, and never stray far from valuable pools of water. These are just a few of the environmental features that make up the lion's habitat. A **habitat** can be described as all of the biotic and abiotic factors in the area where an organism lives. These factors include all aspects of the environment, including the grass, the trees, and the watering holes.

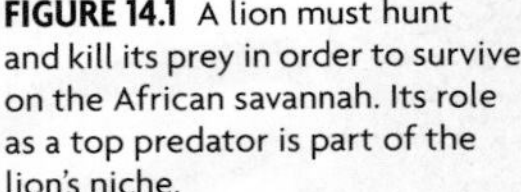

FIGURE 14.1 A lion must hunt and kill its prey in order to survive on the African savannah. Its role as a top predator is part of the lion's niche.

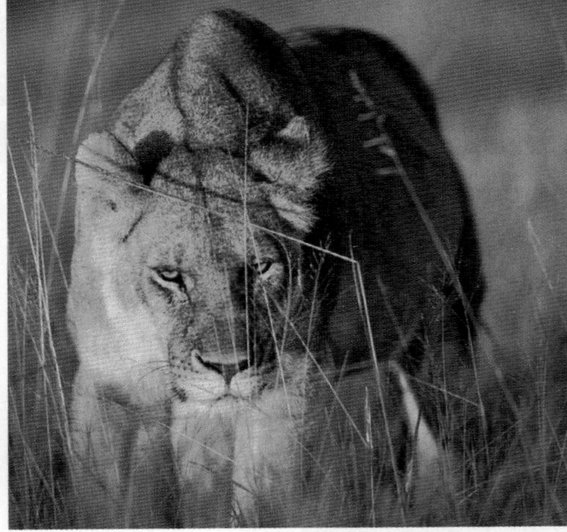

Each species interacts with its environment in a different way. Within an ecosystem, each species has an ecological niche. An **ecological niche** (nihch) is composed of all of the physical, chemical, and biological factors that a species needs to survive, stay healthy, and reproduce.

You can think of a habitat as *where* a species lives and a niche as *how* it lives within its habitat. A niche includes

- **Food** The type of food a species eats, how a species competes with others for food, and where it fits in the food web are all part of its niche.
- **Abiotic conditions** A niche includes the range of conditions, such as air temperature and amount of water, that a species can tolerate.
- **Behavior** The time of day a species is active as well as where and when it reproduces are factors in the niche of a species.

Differentiated Instruction

BELOW LEVEL

Help students understand the difference between *habitat* and *niche* by reinforcing the sentence "You can think of a habitat as *where* a species lives and a niche as *how* it lives within its habitat." Have students pair up and apply this to a food web, such as the one in **FIGURE 13.11** on page 410. Students should then share their observations with the class.

Biology Toolkit, Think-Pair-Share, p. C13

HANDS-ON ACTIVITY

To model the concept of niches found in similar habitats, bring in two similar mechanical or electronic objects that can be safely taken apart. For example, disassemble two nonfunctioning hair dryers. Students will see similar components in each. Even though the components are not exactly the same, they produce the same effect. Compare this to different organisms filling the same niche in different habitats. Discuss how this relates to ecological structure.

Looking closely at all of these factors, we can see that while an antelope may use the tall grasses of the African plains as a food resource, a lion may use the same grasses as camouflage for hunting. A lion uses the antelope as a food resource and hunts primarily during low-light times like dawn or dusk. In order to avoid the intense heat of the savannah, lions often spend afternoons in the shade. These examples are only a few parts of the lion's ecological niche, but they help to give a picture of how a lion fits into the African savannah.

A Connect What are some of the abiotic and biotic factors of your habitat?

TAKING NOTES

Define *ecological niche* by organizing your notes into a chart.

Ecological Niche
- Food
- Abiotic conditions
- Behavior

MAIN IDEA

Resource availability gives structure to a community.

As you learned in Chapter 10, the ability of an individual to survive and reproduce is the driving force behind natural selection. A species needs resources such as food, water, and shelter to be successful in its habitat. The organism that is best suited to obtain these resources is most likely to survive and reproduce. But what if two species are competing over limited resources?

Competitive Exclusion

We have already seen that many species can share similar habitats and that they may use some of the same resources, as shown in **FIGURE 14.2.** But when two species use the same resources in the same ways, one species will always be better adapted to the environment. The principle of **competitive exclusion** states that when two species are competing for the same resources, one species will be better suited to the niche, and the other species will be pushed into another niche or become extinct.

The North American gray squirrel was introduced to Great Britain in the late 1800s. The native European red squirrel was forced to compete with the newcomer for the same food resources, habitat, and space. In this case the gray squirrel was better adapted to the niche and pushed out its smaller competitor. Currently, the red squirrel population is declining due to competition with its larger, more aggressive cousin. But competitive exclusion can also result in other outcomes.

- **Niche partitioning** The two squirrel species could have naturally divided different resources based on competitive advantages. If one type of squirrel ate nuts from the tops of trees while others ate nuts from the ground, the niche would have been divided.
- **Evolutionary response** The two species of squirrel could have experienced divergent evolution. Selection for larger teeth might have allowed one type of squirrel to become better at cracking large nuts, while selection for smaller teeth might have allowed the other to eat small seeds.

FIGURE 14.2 Even though bees and butterflies both use these flowers for food, they occupy different niches. Many species with similar niches can coexist.

PRE-AP

Remind students that selective pressures can result in divergent evolution occurring between related populations in a shared habitat or can result in convergent evolution occurring with unrelated populations in separate but similar habitats. Work with students to develop a concept map that links these ideas from Section 11.6 to the discussion of structure in an ecological community, as described in this section.

Biology Toolkit, Brainstorming, p. C11

ENGLISH LEARNERS

Use the example of competition between the American gray squirrel and European red squirrel described on page 429 to help students understand the concepts of ecological niches and competitive exclusion. Use a cluster diagram to explore possible outcomes of this competition.

Biology Toolkit, Cluster Diagram, p. C30

Answers

A Connect Abiotic factors might include air, temperature, buildings, roads, and water. Biotic factors might include pets, plants, and people.

History of Science

The principles of **competitive exclusion** and **niche partitioning** apply to organisms of all sizes and types in an ecosystem. Yet, they were discovered by a scientist observing tiny protists, single-cell organisms, interacting in a laboratory. In 1934, **G.F. Gause,** a Russian ecologist, observed two cultures of closely related species of protists in the genus *Paramecium*. The paramecia fed on bacteria in culture flasks. Both species grew well when they were in separate flasks, but when placed in the same flask, *Paramecium aurelia* grew well and *Paramecium caudatum* died. Gause inferred that one species was better adapted to take advantage of limited resources and prevented the other from doing the same. Ecologists call this the competitive exclusion principle.

Gause also grew two other species of protists in the same flask and observed these species separating from each other. One species lived exclusively in the medium while the other species lived on the flask's walls. He had observed niche partitioning.

Vocabulary

niche partitioning Have students notice the roots *part* and *partition* in the word *partitioning*. A part is a "portion, piece, or segment of a whole." *Partition* is "the act or process of dividing something into parts." **Ask,** How would niche partitioning be described using the word roots? Two organisms use or divide up different parts of the same niche.

▼ Teach *continued*

TEACH FROM VISUALS

FIGURE 14.3 Use a globe or map to locate the frog habitats. **Ask**

- Where is each frog found? mantella frog on Madagascar, off southeastern coast of Africa, poison dart frog in northern part of South America
- How are the frogs similar? similar insect prey, defense mechanisms, bright coloration, and poisonous toxin
- In what ways are these frogs ecological equivalents? similar niches in geographically separate areas

Answers

A Synthesize *Sample Answer:* Two species in similar niches were exposed to similar adaptive pressures, resulting in similar adaptations. This is known as convergent evolution.

B Apply This is not an example of competitive exclusion because the frogs are not in the same community, competing for the same limited resources.

FIGURE 14.3 Ecological Equivalents

Ecological equivalents are two species that occupy similar niches in geographically separate areas.

Animated BIOLOGY — Explore survival in a niche at ClassZone.com.

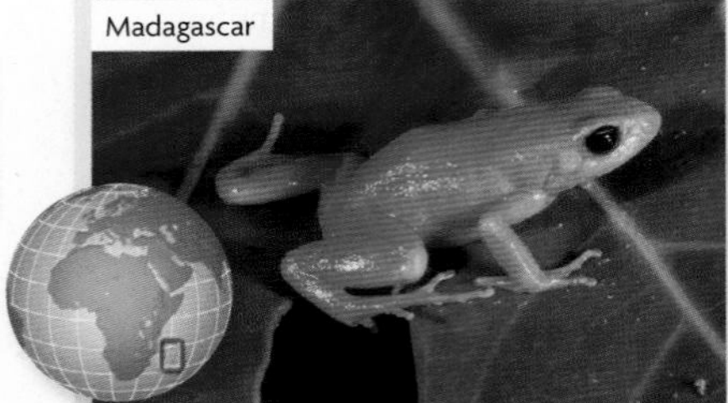

The mantella frog (left) and the poison dart frog (right) have evolved similar defense mechanisms. The bright coloration of each is a warning to predators. Each frog secretes a highly poisonous toxin through its skin that makes it an unpleasant meal for a predator.

A Synthesize Explain how natural selection resulted in the evolution of two similar frog species in two similar niches.

Connecting CONCEPTS

Amphibians Amphibians were the first vertebrates to move out of the water and onto land. In **Chapter 25,** you will learn more about amphibians.

Ecological Equivalents

The competitive exclusion principle involves species competing for resources in the same community. In different communities, ecological equivalents occur in very similar niches. In mathematics, numbers that are equal are called equivalents. Similarly, **ecological equivalents** are species that occupy similar niches but live in different geographical regions. Pictured in **FIGURE 14.3,** the mantella frog of Madagascar and the poison dart frog of South America have much the same niche in similar habitats. They both have brightly colored skin that secretes a highly poisonous toxin to ward off predators. Both prey on similar insects and live in a similar habitat, but because they live in different regions of the world, they never compete for the same resources.

B Apply Are these frogs experiencing competitive exclusion? Explain.

14.1 ASSESSMENT

ONLINE QUIZ ClassZone.com

B.4.4

REVIEWING MAIN IDEAS

1. What are the three parts of an organism's **ecological niche**?
2. What does the principle of **competitive exclusion** say will happen when two species compete for the same resource?

CRITICAL THINKING

3. **Predict** If a group of mantella frogs were transported to the ecosystem of the poison dart frogs, what might happen to the two species' populations?
4. **Analyze** A bison and an elk live in the same **habitat** and feed on the same grasses. Does this mean that the competitive exclusion principle does not apply? Explain.

Connecting CONCEPTS

5. **Exotic Species** Considering the competitive exclusion principle, why may it be harmful to transport a species, such as a rabbit, to another habitat where it currently does not exist?

▼ Assess and Reteach

Assess Use the Online Quiz or Section Quiz (*Assessment Book,* p. 273).

Reteach Have students summarize the section's content by comparing and contrasting the examples in **FIGURES 14.2** and **14.3,** using vocabulary listed on page 428.

14.1 ASSESSMENT

1. Three parts of a niche include food type, abiotic conditions, and behavior.
2. One species will be better suited to the niche and the other species will either be pushed into another niche or become extinct.
3. As ecological equivalents, they share a similar niche. The population better suited to the niche might deprive the other of resources, causing the other to die off. Or one population might respond to limited resources by altering its niche.
4. *Sample Answer:* The competitive exclusion principle only applies if the two species occupy the same niche and habitat. These two species use the same food resource but occupy different niches.
5. *Sample Answer:* If a new species is introduced to an area, it may occupy a similar niche as a native species and be better adapted for the niche or have no natural predators. This could drive the native species to extinction.

14.2 Community Interactions

KEY CONCEPT Organisms interact as individuals and as populations.

MAIN IDEAS

- Competition and predation are two important ways in which organisms interact.
- Symbiosis is a close relationship between species.

VOCABULARY

competition, p. 431
predation, p. 431
symbiosis, p. 432
mutualism, p. 432
commensalism, p. 432
parasitism, p. 432

Review
community

INDIANA STANDARDS

B.4.4 Describe how climate, the pattern of matter and energy flow, the birth and death of new organisms, and the interaction between those organisms contribute to the long term stability of an ecosystem.

Connect Each day, two hot dog vendors sell virtually identical products to anyone who is hungry. They may be on different sides of the street, but they are still trying to sell hot dogs to the same hungry consumers. A vendor selling hot pretzels may also be trying to sell to the same customers, but with a slightly varied product. Just like these vendors, organisms constantly compete with one another.

MAIN IDEA

Competition and predation are two important ways in which organisms interact.

Two birds may fight over territories. A fish may prey on insects floating on the water. These are just two examples of the many interactions between species in an ecosystem.

Competition

Competition occurs when two organisms fight for the same limited resources. There are two different types of competition: interspecific competition and intraspecific competition.

Even though they may have different niches, two species may still use similar resources. Interspecific competition occurs when two different species compete for a limited resource, such as space. In a lawn, for example, grass, dandelions, and many other plants all compete for nutrients and water.

Competition also occurs among members of the same species. This is known as intraspecific competition. Individuals of a particular species struggle against one another for limited resources. You can observe intraspecific competition during the spring breeding season of birds. A typical male will share a particular territory with males of different bird species but will not tolerate another male of its own species in the same area.

FIGURE 14.4 Snakes are predators that swallow their prey whole. The hollow fangs of this timber rattlesnake inject venom to paralyze and kill its prey.

Predation

Another way species interact with one another is through predation. **Predation** is the process by which one organism captures and feeds upon another organism. Many organisms, such as the snake in **FIGURE 14.4**, have become highly adapted to hunting and killing their prey.

Plan and Prepare

Objectives

- Compare and contrast interspecific and intraspecific competition.
- Describe three types of symbiosis.

Section Resources

Unit Resource Book
Study Guide pp. 39–40
Power Notes p. 41
Reinforcement p. 42
Pre-AP Activity pp. 57–58

Interactive Reader Chapter 14
Spanish Study Guide pp. 147–148

Biology Toolkit pp. C19, D5, D7, D9

Technology
Power Presentation 14.2
Media Gallery DVD
Online Quiz 14.2

Activate Prior Knowledge Mention that competition and cooperation occur in ecosystems just as they do in human interactions. **Ask,** What are some ways that you compete or cooperate with others? *Sample Answers:* compete in grades, cooperate in learning; compete in sports, cooperate on teams

Ask, How does cooperation and competition among organisms differ from human cooperation and competition? Cooperation and competition in nature relate to survival. Organisms are not making a conscious choice.

Teach

Vocabulary

Latin Word Origins Point out that prefixes can help students remember the difference between *interspecific* and *intraspecific competition.*

inter- = between *intra-* = within

Ask, How does an international competition differ from an intramural competition? (Hint: *Mural* derives from a Latin root meaning "wall.") International occurs between nations; intramural occurs within the same school.

Differentiated Instruction

INCLUSION

Students who are literal thinkers may assume that all competition (fighting) for resources results in an actual battle between organisms. Use the analogy of a habitat as a market with limited supplies. A shopper's business is with the market, not with other shoppers. The shopper who buys all of a particular product deprives others who shop for the same thing even though there is no direct interaction. Have students work on analogies for other terms in the section.

Biology Toolkit, Analogies, p. D9

▼ Teach *continued*

ONLINE BIOLOGY Go to the chapter Resource Center at **ClassZone.com** for additional resources on symbiotic relationships.

Answers

A Evaluate Predators that are better adapted to catching and consuming prey and prey that are better adapted to avoiding and escaping from predators are more likely to survive and reproduce

Take It Furt

The Brazil nuts we bu
from a complex **sym**
among four species i
forests of South Am
the Brazil nut tree is
species of orchid be
flower's nectar (relati
pollinated, the Brazil
duces a large, hard se
contains up to 24 see

The seed pod falls to
the agouti, a small m
like teeth, breaks into
other animal does th
on some of the nuts,
rest to bury for later (relationship #2). Some seeds may germinate before the agoutis can retrieve them, and thus new trees grow.

Another part of the story is that of male orchid bees. To attract a mate, the bees gather a fragrant chemical from orchids also growing in the forest. The bees pollinate the orchids in the process (relationship #3).

Ask, How would you describe the complex interactions between Brazil nut trees, orchid bees, orchids, and agoutis? mutualism

These complex interactions make it difficult to cultivate Brazil nut trees away from the forest.

know symbiotic relationships

The timber rattlesnake, for example, is a predator that preys on small animals such as mice, voles, rabbits, and squirrels. Lying silent, hidden among leaf litter on the forest floor, the rattlesnake has found a niche as an ambush predator. A swift bite from the snake's fangs injects its venom. The venom attacks the nervous system and eventually paralyzes the prey. The snake swallows the paralyzed animal whole.

Herbivores can also be considered predators. The deer that eats grass in fields and leaves from trees is preying on the plants.

A Evaluate How does natural selection shape predator–prey relationships?

VOCABULARY

The word *symbiosis* comes

MAIN IDEA

Symbiosis is a close relationship between species.

A honeybee buzzes away from a flower with its reward of nectar. Small pollen grains have become attached to the bee's back. When the bee arrives at the next flower, the pollen fertilizes the egg of the next plant. In this way, a relationship, or symbiosis, between the bee and the flower has evolved. **Symbiosis** is a close ecological relationship between two or more organisms of different species that live in direct contact with one another. There are three major types of symbiosis: mutualism, commensalism, and parasitism.

Mutualism

Mutualism is an interspecies interaction in which both organisms benefit from one another. The relationship between the lesser long-nosed bat and the saguaro cactus is another example of mutualism. During the spring, bats help pollinate the cacti through the indirect transfer of pollen as they fly from one cactus to another to feed on flower nectar. When the fruit ripens in the summer, bats become fruit eaters, as shown in **FIGURE 14.5.** The cactus benefits when bats spread its indigestible seeds across the desert.

Commensalism

Another type of symbiotic relationship is commensalism. **Commensalism** is a relationship between two organisms in which one receives an ecological benefit from another, while the other neither benefits nor is harmed. Right now you may be a part of a commensal relationship. Buried deep in the hair follicles of your eyelashes are microscopic mites that feed on the secretions and dead skin cells of your body. These harmless organisms are called demodicids, and they have found their highly specialized niche in your hair follicles.

Parasitism

Parasitism is a symbiotic relationship involving a species that directly harms its host. **Parasitism** is a relationship similar to predation in that one organism benefits while the other is harmed. But unlike a predator, which quickly kills and eats its prey, a parasite benefits by keeping its host alive for days or years. For example, the braconid wasp lays its eggs inside a caterpillar. When the larvae hatch, they eat the caterpillar from the inside out, consuming the nutrients they need to grow into adults.

Differentiated Instruction

BELOW LEVEL

To help students remember the different terms introduced in the section, have them draw a 2-by-2 matrix, with a circle at the center. Students place the term in the circle and then fill in the surrounding cells with the following information:

- definition
- characteristics
- examples
- nonexamples

Biology Toolkit, Frayer Model, p. D5

ENGLISH LEARNERS

Work with students to analyze the interactions of organisms described in this section by listing the characteristics of those given as examples. Features to have students consider are whether the relationships are interspecific or intraspecific, whether they are symbiotic and if so, of what type, and what resources are involved in the interaction.

Biology Toolkit, Semantic Feature Analysis, p. D7

FIGURE 14.5 Symbiotic Relationships

The interactions between species in an ecosystem can take many different forms. A symbiotic relationship involves interactions between organisms of different species that live in direct contact.

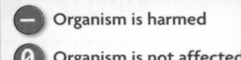

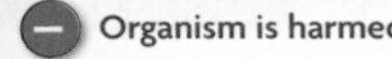

− Organism is harmed

∅ Organism is not affected

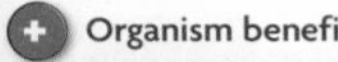

+ Organism benefits

Parasitism

− **Hornworm caterpillar** The host hornworm will eventually die as its organs are consumed by wasp larvae.

+ **Braconid wasp** Braconid larvae feed on their host and release themselves shortly before reaching the pupae stage of development.

Commensalism

∅ **Human** Our eyelashes are home to tiny mites that feast on oil secretions and dead skin. Without harming us, up to 20 mites may be living in one eyelash follicle.

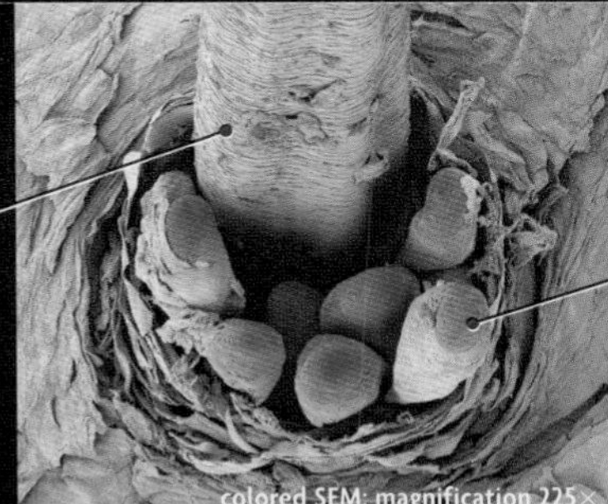

colored SEM; magnification 225×

+ **Demodicids** Eyelash mites find all they need to survive in the tiny follicles of eyelashes. Magnified here 225 times, these creatures measure 0.4 mm in length and can be seen only with a microscope.

Mutualism

+ **Lesser long-nosed bat** The bat depends on night-blooming cacti as its primary source of food. Cacti are a rich source of fruit and nectar, staples of the bat's diet.

+ **Saguaro cactus** As the bat feeds on the cactus' fruit, it also ingests the seeds. These indigestible seeds are dispersed to new locations as the bat flies across the desert.

CRITICAL VIEWING **How might the symbiotic relationship change if eyelash mites destroyed hair follicles?**

Chapter 14: Interactions in Ecosystems 433

TEACH FROM VISUALS

FIGURE 14.5 Point out the symbols in the key and have students use them as a memory aid. **Ask**

- What symbols are used for parasitism, and what do they mean? − and +; one organism is harmed, the other benefits
- What symbols are used for commensalism, and what do they mean? ∅ and +; one organism is not affected, the other benefits
- Why are two of the same symbols needed for mutualism? Both organisms benefit.

Science Trivia

- Mites are arachnids, as are spiders.
- Most people have follicle mites. A human head has about 100,000 follicles.
- The mite's elongated body enables it to fit into a hair follicle.

Take It Further

The human body is home to billions of microorganisms, not just mites. Most are different species of bacteria that colonize the body upon birth. They inhabit the skin, as well as the respiratory, digestive, and urinary tracts. Referred to as the **normal flora** of the human body, they perform important physiological, nutritional, and protective functions. It is possible that there are more bacterial cells at work in the human body than there are body cells. Though some flora cause illness, scientists think that most such relationships are mutually beneficial to both the host and its unseen guests.

PRE-AP

Have students write for five minutes on the question: In what ways are symbiotic relationships distinct from other interactions such as predator-prey interactions? Have them consider the role coevolution plays in symbiotic relationships, and whether coevolution is a factor in nonsymbiotic relationships.

Biology Toolkit, Quick-Write, p. C19

Answers

A Critical Viewing The relationship would be classified as parasitic.

▼ Teach *continued*

Integrating Medical Science

Leeches, once used by doctors to remove the "bad" blood that caused illness, are back. A species of freshwater leech, raised in laboratories, is being used as a medical device for some **skin grafts** and **reattachment surgeries.** Two or three leeches attach to the injured site of the body and remove blood that the body is unable to circulate. After about 40 minutes, the leeches drop off and new leeches are applied. The used leeches are treated as infectious waste material and destroyed. **Ask,** How does this change the natural type of symbiosis between these two organisms? The person benefits instead of being harmed by the parasite. Although the leech initially benefits, it is eventually harmed as a result of the relationship. The parasitism is reversed.

Answers

A Hypothesize Hosts remove ectoparasites if they detect them.

B Connect mutualism

▼ Assess and Reteach

Assess Use the Online Quiz or Section Quiz (*Assessment Book*, p. 274).

Reteach Make sure students complete their note-taking graphic organizer on page 432. Have them work together to add examples of their own for each type of symbiosis.

FIGURE 14.6 Human Parasites: Inside and Out

Humans can get parasites in many ways. Leeches attach to the exposed skin of humans. By penetrating human skin, hookworms find their home in the digestive tract.

Many leeches feed on the blood of a host organism. Freshwater leeches such as this one can grow to lengths of 12 cm or more.

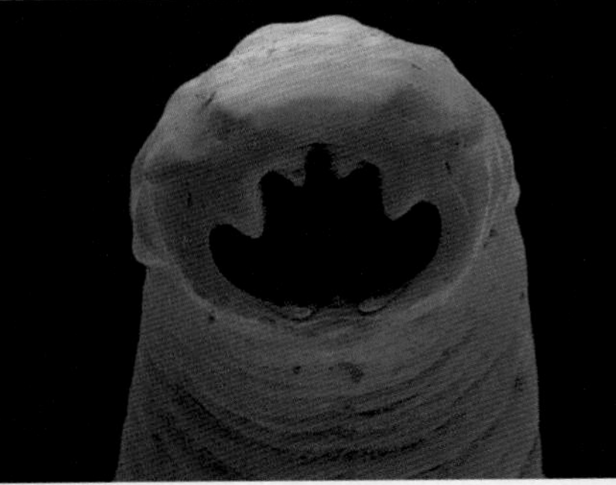

Hookworms are endoparasites with sharp teeth that attach to the intestinal wall of a host organism and absorb nutrients for food. (colored SEM; magnification 200×)

A Hypothesize Why is it important for ectoparasites to stay undetected by their hosts?

Connecting **CONCEPTS**

Invertebrates Leeches and hookworms are classified as invertebrates. In **Chapter 23,** you will learn more about invertebrate diversity.

The needs of a parasite are met by a host—the victim of the parasite. There are two different ways that parasites can use their host. An ectoparasite makes its home on the exterior of an organism, attaching itself to the outside of the host and usually feeding on its fluids. Common ectoparasites include fleas, ticks, and leeches, such as the one seen in **FIGURE 14.6.** Many types of ectoparasites are also known to carry a wide variety of diseases that can affect their host. Parasites can also be found inside of living organisms. Endoparasites live in the tissues and organs of a host where, safely hidden, they feed on the nutrients ingested by their host. Large endoparasites, such as tapeworms and hookworms, and smaller protozoan endoparasites can kill their host if not treated.

B Connect What type of symbiosis is the relationship between a dog and its owner?

14.2 ASSESSMENT

ONLINE QUIZ ClassZone.com

B.4.4

REVIEWING ▶ MAIN IDEAS

1. During the fall spawning of salmon, grizzly bears fight over space on the banks of a river. What type of **competition** is this?
2. Describe and give examples of the three types of **symbiosis.**

CRITICAL THINKING

3. **Compare and Contrast** How are **predation** and **parasitism** similar? How do they differ?
4. **Synthesize** After a lion has made a kill, birds will sometimes arrive to pick at the leftover carcass. Which are the predators: the birds, the lion, or both? Why?

Connecting **CONCEPTS**

5. **Animal Behavior** You have probably heard the saying "There is safety in numbers." Why might traveling in a large group be beneficial to prey species?

14.2 ASSESSMENT

1. The bears are fighting among themselves, so it is considered intraspecific competition.
2. Mutualism, commensalism, and parasitism; examples may vary.
3. Predation and parasitism are both relationships in which one organism benefits while the other is harmed. In predation, the predator needs to kill its prey in order to benefit. In parasitism, the parasite benefits by keeping the host alive.
4. The term *predator* is restricted to an organism that finds and eats another living organism. The lion is the predator; the birds are scavengers.
5. *Sample Answer:* A predator may become overwhelmed when facing a large number of prey. Although a predator may have the speed to chase down and kill a single prey animal, it may switch from chasing one individual to another when faced with a large group of prey and tire before it is successful.

MATERIALS
- 21 × 27 cm² grid paper
- 400 uncooked rice grains
- toothpick

PROCESS SKILLS
- **Modeling**
- **Analyzing Data**

NOS.3 Clearly communicate their ideas and results of investigations verbally and in written form using tables, graphs, diagrams, and photographs.

Modeling Predation

In this lab, you will model predation and the effects of changes in the environment on organisms. Blue herons are large birds that live in aquatic habitats and feed on fish, frogs, salamanders, lizards, small snakes, and dragonflies. You will model a lake filled with fish.

PROBLEM How do changes in environmental factors affect the predation habits of the blue heron?

PROCEDURE

1. Spread 200 rice grains over the grid. The grid represents the lake from which the heron feeds, and the rice grains represent fish.
2. A blue heron will catch an average of two fish per hour during daylight. To model the heron hunting for fish, close your eyes and lower the end of the toothpick slowly down onto the grid.
3. Remove the grains that are in the square touching the toothpick. Count the grains.
4. Rearrange the remaining grains on the grid, and repeat steps 2 and 3 five more times to model one day's worth of feeding for the heron. Count the total number of grains removed, and record this number in a data table like the one shown below.
5. Repeat steps 2–4 five more times to represent six total days of feeding by the heron.
6. Return all of the removed rice grains to the grid. Runoff containing large amounts of nitrates causes an algal bloom in the lake. When the algae die and decomposition occurs, the oxygen level in the lake becomes very low, causing fish to die. Remove 150 grains from the grid. Repeat steps 2–5. Make a second data table and record your data.
7. Return all of the removed grains to the grid. The fish in the lake spawn during the spring. To model this, add another 200 grains to the grid. Repeat steps 2–5. Make a third data table and record your data.

TABLE 1. NUMBER OF FISH CAUGHT PER DAY

Day	1	2	3	4	5	6
No. of Fish Caught						

ANALYZE AND CONCLUDE

1. **Graph Data** Construct a graph to represent your data.
2. **Analyze** How was the amount of food caught by a heron related to changes in biotic and abiotic factors?
3. **Infer** How might abundant amounts of food allow herons to reproduce more often?
4. **Predict** How would the populations of amphibians and small reptiles be affected if the fish population in the lake remained low for an extended period of time?

INVESTIGATION

Time 45 minutes	TEACHER TESTED
Teacher Preparation	
Student Difficulty	
Lab Binder Ecology, pp. 15–18	

Purpose Model predation under different environmental conditions.

Overview Students will use rice grains and grid paper to model predation of fish by blue herons. Students will then

- model predation after an algal bloom caused by runoff of nitrates
- model predation after fish spawn

LAB PREPARATION

- Students will need additional grid paper for graphing their results.

LAB MANAGEMENT

- Have students read the procedure and make three data tables before they start step 1.
- Provide each group with a small paper cup to hold the fish caught for the day in step 4.
- Mention that availability of resources can affect a population's reproductive rate. Abundant resources can lead to higher rates of reproduction. Limited resources can have the opposite effect.

Teacher Note "Initially I thought counting out the grains of rice would take students forever. It did not and that amount of rice worked."

POST-LAB DISCUSSION

Discuss the limitations of modeling natural events by using simple simulations. The numbers are not important, but the patterns of change are. **Ask,** What is a model? a conceptual, theoretical, or mathematical representation of a natural phenomenon or a system that can be used for further study or prediction

Answers

Sample Data

For a sample of student data and line graph from this lab, go to page R105.

Analyze and Conclude

1. Students should make a line graph with different colored lines to represent the different conditions that they modeled. "Days" should be on the *x*-axis, and "Number of fish caught" should be on the *y*-axis.
2. *Sample Answer:* The amount of food caught decreased when nitrate runoff caused an algae bloom, which then caused fish to die by lowering the level of oxygen. Fish spawning increased the number of fish caught.
3. Students may infer that herons eat more when fish are abundant and can reproduce more when they have more energy and nutrients.
4. They would increase in size if the herons start targeting amphibians and reptiles.

SECTION 14.3

▼ Plan and Prepare

Objectives

- Consider density and geographic dispersal as characteristics of populations.
- Describe three basic types of survivorship curves in relation to reproductive strategies.

Section Resources

Unit Resource Book Study Guide pp. 43–44 Power Notes p. 45 Reinforcement p. 46
Interactive Reader Chapter 14 **Spanish Study Guide** pp. 149–150
Biology Toolkit pp. C15, C19
Technology Power Presentation 14.3 Media Gallery DVD Online Quiz 14.3

Activate Prior Knowledge Describe density as the number of objects in an area. Suggest students think of this as a measure of how crowded the area is. **Ask,** Which parking lot has a higher density of cars—a 40-car lot with 40 cars parked in it or a 1000-car lot with 40 cars parked in it? 40-car lot

▼ Teach

Integrating Mathematics

Density is expressed as a **ratio,** a mathematical expression that describes a direct relationship between two quantities. With **population density,** the relationship is between the number of individuals and the size of the area they occupy.

Answers

A Connect Resources may be depleted or the community may have changed due to, for example, the arrival of a new predator.

14.3 Population Density and Distribution

KEY CONCEPT Each population has a density, a dispersion, and a reproductive strategy.

MAIN IDEAS

- Population density is the number of individuals that live in a defined area.
- Geographic dispersion of a population shows how individuals in a population are spaced.
- Survivorship curves help to describe the reproductive strategy of a species.

VOCABULARY

population density, p. 436
population dispersion, p. 437
survivorship curve, p. 438

Connect If you have ever traveled from a rural area into a city, you may have noticed a change in population density. Cities have more dense populations, while rural areas have more widely dispersed populations. Scientists measure species populations in a similar way. What can we learn from population data?

MAIN IDEA

Population density is the number of individuals that live in a defined area.

The wandering albatross may fly over open ocean waters for days or weeks at a time without ever encountering another bird. In contrast to this solitary lifestyle, elephant seals may gather in groups of a thousand or more on California beaches. By collecting data about a population in a particular area, scientists can calculate the density of a population. **Population density** is a measurement of the number of individuals living in a defined space.

Calculating an accurate population density can tell scientists a great deal about a species. When scientists notice changes in population densities over time, they work to determine whether the changes are the result of environmental factors or are simply due to normal variation in the life history of a species. In this way a wildlife biologist can work to make changes that will help to keep the population healthy. One way to calculate population density is to create a ratio of the number of individuals that live in a particular area to the size of the area. This formula is simplified as follows:

$$\frac{\text{\# of individuals}}{\text{area (units}^2\text{)}} = \text{population density}$$

For example, if scientists sampling a population of deer counted 200 individuals in an area of 10 square kilometers, the density of this deer population would be 20 deer per square kilometer.

A Connect What might a decrease in the density of a deer population over a specific time period tell scientists about the habitat in the area?

***Connecting* CONCEPTS**

Gene Flow Recall that in **Chapter 11** you learned about gene flow and geographic isolation. Population dispersion patterns influence the rate of gene flow among and between species.

Differentiated Instruction

ENGLISH LEARNERS

Have students form into home groups of three, numbering off one to three. By the number, have them re-form into "expert" groups to study the key concepts of dispersion patterns, population density, and survivorship curves. Have them return to the home groups to share what they have learned.

Biology Toolkit, Jigsaw Reading, p. C15

BELOW LEVEL

Discuss population density in terms of a school. Different areas of a school will have different population densities. The same area may have different densities at different times. **Ask**

- What areas of your school have the most students at lunch? cafeteria before the bell rings? hallway after the bell rings? classroom, gym
- What factors affect the population density of a school? time of day, day of the week, time of the year

FIGURE 14.7 Dispersion Patterns

Dispersion patterns help us understand species interactions by showing how populations group together.

CLUMPED DISPERSION

Many species of fish swim together in large groups called schools. By moving as a large mass, individuals have an advantage in avoiding predators.

UNIFORM DISPERSION

Nesting sites of the gannet show uniform distances for protection of eggs from other males. Territorial organisms generally display uniform dispersion.

RANDOM DISPERSION

The three-toed tree sloth, a solitary animal, spends most of its life in the canopy of tropical forests. The sloth has almost no competitors and has few natural predators.

MAIN IDEA

Geographic dispersion of a population shows how individuals in a population are spaced.

Other information can be gained from population density measurements. Patterns of geographical dispersion give us ideas of how individuals of the same species interact and how different species interact with one another. **Population dispersion** is the way in which individuals of a population are spread in an area or a volume. **FIGURE 14.7** shows the three types of population dispersion.

- **Clumped dispersion** Individuals may live close together in groups in order to facilitate mating, gain protection, or access food resources.
- **Uniform dispersion** Territoriality and intraspecies competition for limited resources lead to individuals living at specific distances from one another.
- **Random dispersion** Individuals are spread randomly within an area or a volume.

VISUAL VOCAB

Population dispersion is the way in which individuals of a population are spread in an area or a volume.

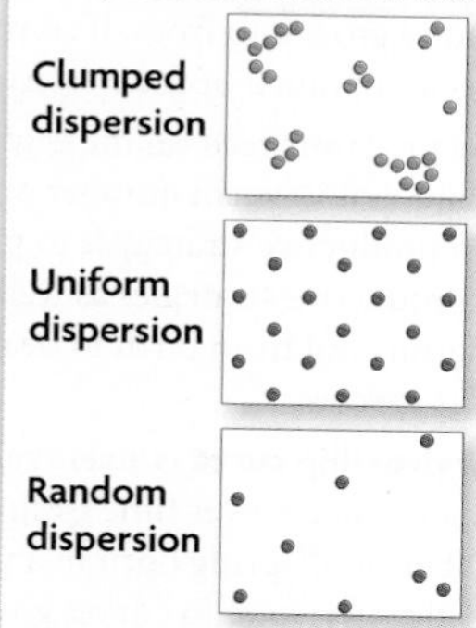

Infer **What type of intraspecies interaction might cause uniform dispersion?**

INCLUSION

For students who are visually impaired, look for ways to incorporate concrete representations into the lesson. For example, in the Quick Lab, a pile of 35 pennies can be subdivided to represent age groups. For the survivorship curves on page 439, overlay string or yarn on the curves to emphasize the characteristic shapes of each.

TEACH FROM VISUALS

FIGURE 14.7 Have students observe the animals in each photograph and then match each pattern to the corresponding pattern in the **VISUAL VOCAB. Ask**

- In what type of dispersion pattern can the distance between individual organisms be predicted accurately? uniform dispersion
- What type of dispersion would a herd of wild horses have? clumped dispersion

Take It Further

Plants also exhibit the same dispersion patterns as those of animals. A clumped dispersion pattern is most common. Different **plant populations** tend to grow in clumps where the soil type and amounts of water, nutrients, and sunlight are what they are best adapted to. Some species of plants have populations with a uniform dispersion pattern. This pattern results when plants growing closely together would compete for the same resources. In other cases, some plants add a toxic substance to the soil that keeps plants of the same species equally distant from each other. A random dispersion pattern is less common in plants, but can occur with plants that are adapted to a variety of conditions and have windblown seeds.

Vocabulary

Academic Vocabulary Have students consider the difference between the term **density** and the terms **distribution** and **dispersion.** The words all relate to the same physical quality but describe different aspects of it. *Density* provides the number of objects or organisms to be found in a given unit of measure. *Distribution* and *dispersion* describe the manner in which those objects or organisms are placed relative to one another.

Answers

A Infer competition for limited resources

▼ Teach *continued*

QUICK LAB

Time 15 minutes	TEACHER TESTED
Lab Binder Ecology, p. 23	

Purpose Model a survivorship curve, using obituary data.

LAB MANAGEMENT

- Students record the number of deaths by age group, using 35 obituary notices from a newspaper and use the data to suggest the proportion of survivors within each age group. Note that the data collected is number of deaths, not number of survivors.
- To get a large sampling, check online for death notices published in a large metropolitan newspaper.
- Tell students that the lines in the "Death" column of the table represent hatch marks, not numerals.

Answers

Sample Data

For a sample of student data and a chart of precalculated percentages, go to page R105.

Analyze and Conclude

1. The graph should show few or no deaths through middle age, with a downward trend as age increases. Note the graph might rise at the end because the model assumes an equivalent population size for each group, including people in their 90s.
2. *Sample Answer:* The data showed few deaths before age 50. Most people live until old age.

Vocabulary

Word Origins The origin of the word **strategy** is a military one. It refers to the "office of general," the commander who prepares and executes a plan. Ecologists consider patterns of survivorship as characteristics of species and refer to them as **reproductive strategies.** In this case, the strategy does not result from planning but rather from response to evolutionary pressures.

QUICK LAB **INTERPRETING DATA** NOS.3

Survivorship Curves

In this lab, you will make a type 1 survivorship curve using data from the obituary section of a newspaper.

MATERIALS
- obituary section of a newspaper
- graph paper

PROBLEM What is the trend in data for type 1 survivorship curves?

PROCEDURE

1. Obtain the obituary section of the newspaper.
2. Create a data table like the one at right that extends to include five-year age groups up to 91–95 years.
3. For 35 obituaries, place a tally next to the age group in which the individual died.
4. Subtract the number of individuals that died from the number of remaining survivors, and record the answer in the third column of your data table. Calculate the percent surviving in each age group by dividing the number of survivors by 35 and multiplying by 100. Repeat this step for all age groups.

TABLE 1. SURVIVORSHIP DATA

Age (years)	Deaths	Survivors	% Surviving
0–5	I	35 – 1 = 34	97
6–10	I	34 – 1 = 33	94
11–15	0	33 – 0 = 33	94
16–20	IIII	33 – 4 = 29	83
21–25	I	29 – 1 = 28	80

ANALYZE AND CONCLUDE

1. **Graph Data** Draw a survivorship curve by plotting the age group on the *x*-axis, and the percent survivors on the *y*-axis.
2. **Analyze** Explain the trend in the data.

MAIN IDEA

Survivorship curves help to describe the reproductive strategy of a species.

The California red-legged frog of the western United States is an amphibian that reproduces by laying 2000 to 5000 eggs in late winter and early spring. In one to two weeks, these eggs hatch, and over the next four to seven months, the tadpoles grow into frogs. If so many eggs are laid, why is this frog a threatened species in much of the western United States?

Many predators feed on the eggs of the red-legged frog, so of the thousands of eggs laid, only a small number of offspring will survive to adulthood. This type of reproductive strategy is to produce a lot of offspring. Species use many other reproductive strategies as well. Survivorship curves illustrate how offspring survival from birth to death fits in with the survival strategies of a particular species.

A **survivorship curve** is a generalized diagram showing the number of surviving members over time from a measured set of births. By measuring the number of offspring born in a year and following those offspring through until death, survivorship curves give information about the life history of a species. For example, we will begin with 100 coyotes born in year zero. After one year, 10 of those baby coyotes died from disease or predation. Of the original 100, 90 are left. During year two, 4 more coyotes die, leaving 86 of

Differentiated Instruction

PRE-AP

Ask students to write a paragraph or two on what a reproductive strategy characterized by a high number of births might suggest about conditions in a habitat. It could suggest unlimited resources, as with an insect population, or a slim chance of survival for offspring, as with fish or frog eggs.

Biology Toolkit, Quick-Write, p. C19

the original 100. In year three, 3 more die, leaving 83 of the original 100. The number of individuals surviving from year to year decreases, but a substantial portion of the group will live a full life and reproduce. In **FIGURE 14.8,** you can see the three basic patterns of animal survivorship curves.

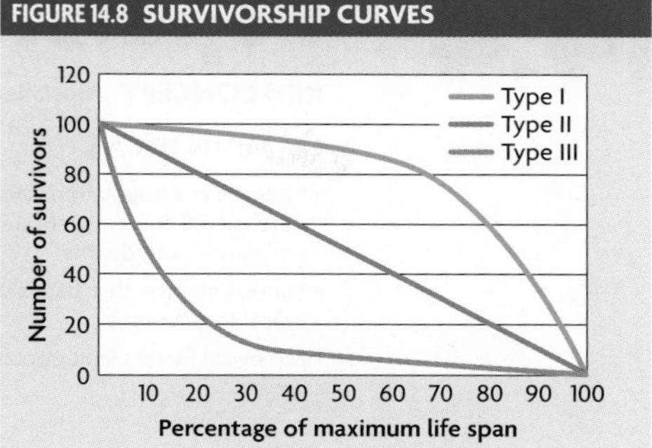

FIGURE 14.8 SURVIVORSHIP CURVES

Type I The graph shows a type I survivorship curve in orange. Type I survivorship represents a life history that is common among large mammals, including humans. The curve shows a low level of infant mortality and a population that generally will survive until old age. A behavior that most organisms showing type I survivorship share is parental care for the young. Most infant organisms are unable to care for themselves. By protecting their young, parents are better able to ensure that their offspring stay alive until they can survive on their own.

Type II Organisms such as birds, small mammals, and some reptiles show a survivorship rate that is roughly equal at all ages of an organism's life. At all times, these species have equal chances of living and dying, whether from disease or as a result of predation. A type II survivorship curve is shown in green on the graph.

Type III Organisms with type III survivorship (shown in blue) have a very high birth rate and also a very high infant mortality rate. Species with type III survivorship are generally invertebrates, fish, amphibians, and plants. Many of their offspring will die from predation, but inevitably a few will survive to adulthood and be able to pass their genes on to the next generation. Though the California red-legged frogs are threatened largely because of habitat loss and pollution, the frogs are also targets of high levels of predation at an early age, making recovery for this species especially difficult.

A Synthesize Is there any connection between survivorship curves and reproductive strategies? Explain.

NSTA scilinks.org SCiLINKS
For more information about populations and communities, go to scilinks.org.
Keycode: MLB014

TEACH FROM VISUALS

FIGURE 14.8 Help students interpret the graph. **Ask**

- In any of the curves, what do the 100 individuals have in common? They are from the same population and were born in the same year.
- How many of the individuals in the type I curve live 10 percent of their maximum life span? about 97 How many in the type II curve? about 90 How many in the type III curve? about 50
- How many of the individuals in the type I curve live 70 percent of their maximum life span? about 80 How many in the type II curve? about 30 How many in the type III curve? about 5

Answers

A Synthesize Type I organisms tend to produce fewer offspring. Type III individuals produce a large number of offspring but provide little or no parental care.

14.3 ASSESSMENT

ONLINE QUIZ ClassZone.com

REVIEWING MAIN IDEAS

1. A shoreline mussel species has a **population density** of one organism per square meter. Will all mussels be found one meter apart? Explain.
2. Draw and label a diagram showing the three **population dispersion** patterns.
3. How do **survivorship curves** show three types of reproductive strategies?

CRITICAL THINKING

4. **Analyze** What might be the advantages of having a clumped dispersal pattern?
5. **Infer** An organism has ten offspring. Two of these offspring die each year over a five-year period. Is the organism more likely to be a bird or an insect? Explain.

Connecting CONCEPTS

6. **Abiotic Factors** On the African savannah, what types of abiotic factors may lead to high population density and clumped dispersion patterns?

Assess and Reteach ▼

Assess Use the Online Quiz or Section Quiz (*Assessment Book,* p. 275).

Reteach Choose a particular organism, such as a bird, and discuss its individual characteristics. Then extend the discussion to a population of birds and the types of characteristics an ecologist uses to describe that population.

14.3 ASSESSMENT

1. No, population density simply describes the number of individuals per unit area, not the dispersion pattern.
2. Student diagrams should include three dispersion patterns: clumped, uniform, and random. Diagrams should be similar to those in Visual Vocab on page 437.
3. *Sample Answer:* If the curve shows a low level of infant mortality, the parents probably care for their young. If the curve shows a very high infant mortality rate, the organisms probably have a high birth rate and provide little or no parental care.
4. *Sample Answer:* Individuals do not have to move very much to find mates, organisms have better protection from predators, and there is more access to food resources from other population members.
5. The organism is a bird because the mortality pattern described is closest to type II. Insects tend to be type III, with many offspring and high mortality in early life stages.
6. Answers may include limited water supplies, high temperature, and little or no precipitation.

▼ Plan and Prepare

Objectives

- Describe four factors that affect population size.
- Compare exponential and logistic population growth.
- Identify factors that limit population growth.

Section Resources

Unit Resource Book
Study Guide pp. 47–48
Power Notes p. 49
Reinforcement p. 50
Pre-AP Activity pp. 59–60

Interactive Reader Chapter 14
Spanish Study Guide pp. 151–152

Biology Toolkit p

Technology
Power Presentat
Media Gallery D
Online Quiz 14.4

Activate Prior Kn
population size of y
Ask, What are som
affect the size of a
immigration, emigr
availability of reso

Know
immigration
Emigration
Births/deaths
Exponential growth
& logistic growth

▼ Teach

Take It Further

Charles Darwin realized that species have the capacity to increase in number beyond what is needed to replace existing members of a population. Yet populations tend to remain constant in size, given limits on available resources. **Ask,** How does Darwin's observation connect to natural selection? Competition for limited resources causes a struggle for survival between individuals. Individuals with advantages over others are more likely to survive and have offspring.

Answers

Ⓐ Apply Deaths and emigration are outpacing births and immigration.

14.4 Population Growth Patterns

KEY CONCEPT Populations grow in predictable patterns.

MAIN IDEAS

- Changes in a population's size are determined by immigration, births, emigration, and deaths.
- Population growth is based on available resources.
- Ecological factors limit population growth.

VOCABULARY

immigration, p. 440
emigration, p. 440
exponential growth, p. 441
logistic growth, p. 441
carrying capacity, p. 442
population crash, p. 442
limiting factor, p. 443
density-dependent limiting factor, p. 443
density-independent limiting factor, p. 444

INDIANA STANDARDS

B.4.1 Explain that the amount of life an environment can support is limited by the available energy, water, oxygen, and minerals, and by the ability of ecosystems to recycle the remains of dead organisms.

Connect That banana you left in your backpack did not go unnoticed. After one week, you open your bag and dozens of tiny insects swarm out. The smell of rotting fruit follows close behind. Only a week ago, the population of fruit flies in your backpack was zero. Just before you opened it, the population had grown to several dozen. How did this population grow so quickly?

MAIN IDEA

Changes in a population's size are determined by immigration, births, emigration, and deaths.

The size of a population is usually changing. If resources such as food and water are abundant, or plentiful, a population may grow. On the other hand, if resources are in short supply, the population may decrease in size. Hopefully, the normal fruit fly population in your backpack is zero. But if an abundance of resources, such as an overripe banana, becomes available, the population will increase dramatically. However, when the resources are removed, the fruit fly population in your backpack will once again return to zero. Four factors affect the size of a population.

- **Immigration** When one or two fruit flies found the banana, they immigrated into your backpack. **Immigration** is the movement of individuals into a population from another population.
- **Births** Additional fruit flies were born in your backpack. Births increase the number of individuals in a population.
- **Emigration** After you opened your backpack, some fruit flies flew out and left to find other rotting fruit. **Emigration** is the movement of individuals out of a population and into another population.
- **Deaths** You might have squashed a couple of unlucky fruit flies as you were opening your backpack. The size of a population decreases when individuals die.

Ⓐ Apply When a population is declining, what two factors are likely outpacing what other two factors?

Differentiated Instruction

BELOW LEVEL

Have students use a two-column format to take notes on new terms. In the first column, they should include their notes and definitions. In the second column, they should draw a diagram that illustrates the concept.

Biology Toolkit, Combination Notes, p. C23

ENGLISH LEARNERS

When students have read the section, reinforce vocabulary by asking them to write for three minutes on each of these pairs of contrasting concepts: immigration/emigration; exponential growth/logistic growth; density-dependent limiting factor/density-independent limiting factor.

Biology Toolkit, Quick-Write, p. C19

MAIN IDEA

Population growth is based on available resources.

Population growth is a function of the environment. The rate of growth for a population is directly determined by the amount of resources available. A population may grow very rapidly, or it may take a bit of time to grow. There are two distinct types of population growth.

Exponential Growth

When resources are abundant, a population has the opportunity to grow rapidly. This type of growth, called **exponential growth,** occurs when a population size increases dramatically over a period of time. In **FIGURE 14.9,** you can see that exponential growth appears as a J-shaped curve.

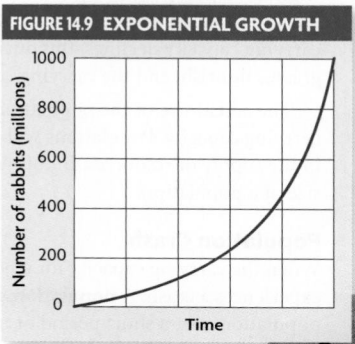

FIGURE 14.9 EXPONENTIAL GROWTH

Number of rabbits (millions): 0, 200, 400, 600, 800, 1000

Time

Exponential growth may occur when a species moves to a previously uninhabited area. For example, in 1859 an Australian landowner returning home from England brought 24 European rabbits to the country for the purpose of sport hunting. The rabbits were introduced into an environment that had abundant space and food and no predators fast enough to catch them. The initial population of 24 rabbits grew exponentially and spread across the country. After many attempts to control the population, today there are between 200 million and 300 million rabbits in Australia.

FIGURE 14.10 In Australia during the early 1900s, the introduced European rabbit population exhibited exponential growth.

Logistic Growth

Most populations face limited resources and thus show a logistic growth rate. During **logistic growth,** a population begins with a period of slow growth followed by a brief period of exponential growth before leveling off at a stable size. A graph of logistic growth takes the form of an S-shaped curve and can be seen in **FIGURE 14.11,** which models a population's change in size over time. During initial growth, resources are abundant, and the population is able to grow. Over time, resources begin to deplete, and growth starts to slow. As resources become limited, the population levels off at a size the environment can support.

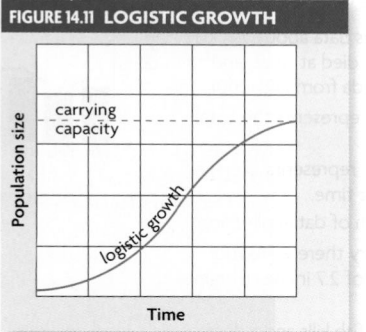

FIGURE 14.11 LOGISTIC GROWTH

Population size

carrying capacity

logistic growth

Time

ONLINE BIOLOGY Have students do the Data Analysis in Options for Inquiry on page 449 to plot the logistic growth curve of a bison population.

TEACH FROM VISUALS

FIGURES 14.9 AND 14.11 Point out that both the J-shaped and S-shaped curves are models that approximate patterns of growth seen in actual populations. **Ask,** Do you see any similarities between the two models? Both show a pattern of exponential growth at the beginning.

Explain that the exponential growth model represents a situation that cannot be sustained in the real world. No population can grow unchecked because the resources available are finite; they have a limit. The logistic growth model can be described as what happens to a growing population when the effects of those limits are felt. **Ask**

- Looking at the dotted line in the logistic growth model, what do you infer the *carrying capacity* to be? the maximum number of organisms in a population that the resources can support
- Which of the two models relates population growth to population density? Logistic growth; population growth decreases as population density increases.

Take It Further

Biotic potential is the rate that a population increases under ideal circumstances, including unlimited resources. It is the maximum rate at which a species can reproduce and results in exponential growth. The giant puffball mushroom has a very impressive biotic potential. It is capable of producing 7 trillion offspring in a single generation. If all offspring survived and reproduced, then together all descendants would weigh more than Earth in just two generations.

The same environmental factors, such as food, water, shelter, and low predation that affect biotic potential, also combine to determine the carrying capacity of an environment. There are limits.

HANDS-ON ACTIVITY

To model exponential growth, use the story of the king who receives the gift of a beautiful chessboard. He offers to reward the giver and is surprised by what seems to be so insignificant a request: 1 grain of rice on the first square, 2 on the second, 4 on the third, and so on, doubling the amount for each of the 64 squares. The king soon realizes he doesn't have enough rice in the kingdom to honor the request. To establish the pattern, use sticky notes to mark the amount on the first two rows of a chessboard.

Chapter 14: Interactions in Ecosystems **441**

▼ Teach *continued*

DATA ANALYSIS

Discuss

A fish kill event is reported when dead or dying fish are observed in a body of water. It can involve a small number of fish or thousands of fish. The combination graph shows data from 1991 to 2001. The bars represent the total number of fish kill events for each month. The line graph represents the average rainfall for each month. **Ask,** What is the advantage of graphing 10 years of data? more reliable comparison and to see long-term trends

Address Misconceptions

Common Misconception M
events are caused by human

Correcting the Misconcept
Florida, most fish kill events h
causes. The most common ca
dissolved oxygen levels in wat
number of cloudy days, temp
number of organisms living in
affect oxygen levels in water.
fertilizers and herbicides can
low dissolved oxygen levels.

Answers

1. July, November, and Dec
2. *Sample Answer:* The nun kill events rises slowly fro through May, are the most numerous from June through August, decrease in September and October, and then begin to rise again in November. The most fish kill events occur during the summer months. The amount of rainfall is low from January through April, increases in May and June, decreases in July, rises in August, levels off in September, and decreases from October through December.
3. *Sample Answer:* Increased rainfall may lead to more fish kills, at least until another factor or set of factors come into play and the correlation between rainfall and fish kill events becomes less evident.

Unit Resource Book, Data Analysis, p. 55

Carrying Capacity

The environment determines how many individuals of the species can be supported based on natural cycles and species diversity. An environment, therefore, has a carrying capacity for each species living in it. The **carrying capacity** of an environment is the maximum number of individuals of a particular species that the environment can normally and consistently support.

In nature, a carrying capacity can change when the environment changes. Consider a population of grasshoppers that feed on meadow grasses. If a fire burns part of the meadow, the insects' food resources diminish, and the carrying capacity declines. But during years with plentiful rain, the meadow grasses flourish, and the carrying capacity rises.

The actual size of the population usually is higher or lower than the carrying capacity. Populations will rise and fall as a result of natural changes in the supply of resources. In this way, the environment naturally controls the size of a population.

Population Crash

When the carrying capacity for a population suddenly drops, the population experiences a crash. A **population crash** is a dramatic decline in the size of a population over a short period of time. There are many reasons why a population might experience a crash.

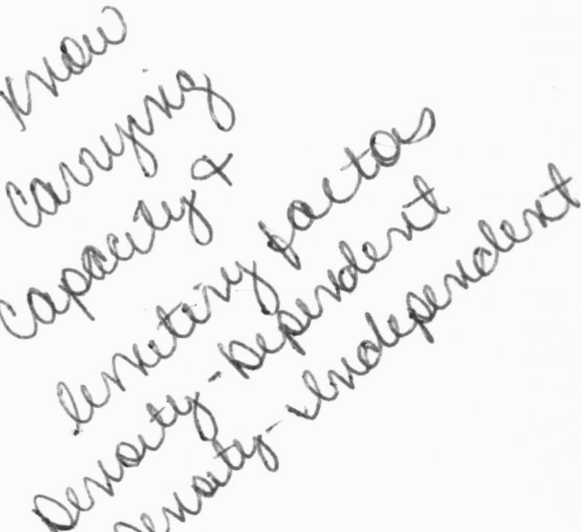

DATA ANALYSIS NOS.1

ta on the
n as a
wn as a
he same
ists can

t fish kill
ce, and
91–2001.
the total

s average

ollection.
ere four
es of rain.

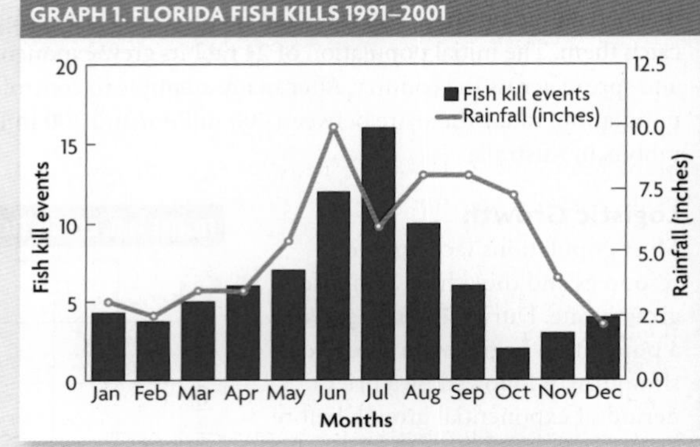

Source: The University of Florida Extension Information Circular 107. Used by permission.

d a decrease in rainfall occurs in what months?

2. **Analyze** Describe the trend in the fish kill events throughout the year. Describe the trend in rainfall data throughout the year.
3. **Hypothesize** What relationship might exist between fish kill events and rainfall?

Differentiated Instruction

BELOW LEVEL

Go over the structure of the Fish Kill graph in Data Analysis. Point out that the two *y*-axes enable two sets of data to be graphed on the same *x*-axis. Point out that a similar setup is used in **FIGURE 14.13.**

PRE-AP

Prepare a list of 6–10 statements about limiting factors—some true, some false. Give students the list before discussing the topic in class. Have students react to the statements, indicating whether the statements are true or false based on their understanding of population dynamics. Then have them correct any mistakes following class.

Biology Toolkit, Anticipation Guide, p. C3

For example, in 1944, 29 reindeer were introduced to St. Matthew Island off the coast of Alaska. At the time of the introduction, the entire island was covered with a rich mat of lichens. Plenty of good food allowed the reindeer herd to grow at an exponential rate. By the summer of 1963, the island population had grown to 6000 reindeer. However, over the winter, large amounts of snow fell on food resources that had already become greatly depleted by the large herd. By the spring of 1964, only 50 reindeer remained. The population crash on St. Matthew Island came as the result of two factors that limited resources: the harsh winter and the scarcity of food.

Predict What would have eventually happened to the reindeer herd if the winter had not made foraging so difficult? Explain.

MAIN IDEA

Ecological factors limit population growth.

Many factors can affect the carrying capacity of an environment for a population of organisms. The factor that has the greatest effect in keeping down the size of a population is called the **limiting factor.** There are two categories of limiting factors—density dependent and density independent.

Density-Dependent Limiting Factors

Density-dependent limiting factors are limiting factors that are affected by the number of individuals in a given area. Density-dependent limiting factors include many different types of species interactions.

Competition Members of populations compete with one another for resources such as food and shelter. As a population becomes denser, the resources are used up, limiting how large the population can grow.

Predation The population of a predator can be limited by the available prey, and the population of prey can be limited by being caught for food. On Isle Royale in Michigan, changes in wolf and moose populations, shown in **FIGURE 14.13**, provide an example. As the moose population grows, so does the wolf population. But at a certain point, the wolves eat so many moose that there are not enough left to feed all the wolves. The result is a decrease in the wolf population. Over time, the two populations rise and fall in a pattern, shown in **FIGURE 14.13**.

Parasitism and disease Parasites and diseases can spread more quickly through dense populations. The more crowded an area becomes, the easier it is for parasites or diseases to spread. The parasites or diseases can then cause the size of the population to decrease.

Analyze How does the wolf population on Isle Royale affect the carrying capacity of the moose population?

FIGURE 14.12 Taking down prey as large as a moose requires that the members of a pack work together. As many as ten wolves may take hours or even days to wear down this moose.

FIGURE 14.13 DENSITY-DEPENDENT LIMITING FACTORS

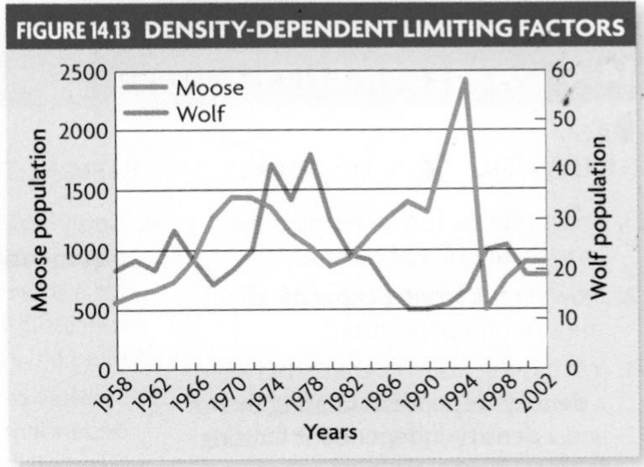

Source: Isle Royale Research Data

TEACH WITH TECHNOLOGY

Use the Internet to gather data on prey/predator populations, for example, the Hudson Bay Company data on hare/lynx populations or Isle Royal data on moose/wolf populations. Place the data into a spreadsheet program and use an interactive white board to demonstrate different ways to format the data. Go to the Teacher Resources at **ClassZone.com.**

ONLINE BIOLOGY Have students use the simulation in Options for Inquiry on page 449 to apply a limiting factor to an oak forest with chipmunks and foxes.

TEACH FROM VISUALS

FIGURE 14.13 Point out the inverse relationship between the size of each population shown in the two graphs.

Ask

- What happens to the moose population as the wolf population increases? It decreases.
- What happens to the moose population as the wolf population decreases? It increases.
- Is there something in the data to suggest that the wolf population crashed? a dramatic drop in the wolf population starting about 1978
- In what way does the data suggest that something other than availability of prey caused the wolf population to crash? The wolf population continued to fall even though the moose population rebounded dramatically and plenty of prey was available. What might have caused the crash? The initial decrease in prey may have caused the birth rate of the wolf population to decrease.
- Is there something in the data to suggest that the moose population crashed? a dramatic drop in the moose population starting about 1994
- What might have caused the moose population to crash? With few predators to control their numbers, the moose exceeded the carrying capacity of their environment.

Answers

A Predict Because of the limited quantity of food, the population would have stopped growing and then leveled off and eventually decreased as food became scarce.

B Analyze Wolves keep the population of moose at a level that the environment can support.

▼ Teach *continued*

ONLINE BIOLOGY Have students explore density-independent factors in the WebQuest in Options for Inquiry on page 449.

Answers

A Apply It is density-independent unless the algae population becomes large enough to block sunlight.

▼ Assess and Reteach

Assess Use the Online Quiz or Section Quiz (*Assessment Book,* p. 276).

Reteach Collect from the Media Gallery all the graphs presented in this section. Use the graphs to review the patterns of population growth. Have students refer to the vocabulary listed on page 440.

FIGURE 14.14 The storm surge accompanying a hurricane can cause dangerous flooding.

Density-Independent Limiting Factors

Density-independent limiting factors are the aspects of the environment that limit a population's growth regardless of the density of the population.

Unusual weather Weather can affect the size of a population regardless of its density. For example, along the western coast of the United States, a lack of southerly winds can prevent nutrient-poor warm water from being replaced, as it normally is, with nutrient-rich cold water. The lack of nutrients in the water along the coast can prevent phytoplankton, which form the base of the marine ecosystem, from growing in their usual large numbers. In turn, zooplankton, tiny organisms that feed on phytoplankton, have smaller populations. The effects are felt all the way up the food chain, with smaller populations of fish and birds.

Natural disasters Volcanoes, tsunamis, tornados, and hurricanes, shown in **FIGURE 14.14**, can wipe out populations regardless of density. For example, the large wave of a tsunami can damage fragile coral reefs, knock down entire mangrove forests, and destroy sea turtle nesting beaches.

Human activities Destruction of a wetland habitat along the Platte River in Nebraska has threatened an important feeding ground for the sandhill crane. Urbanization in this area is depleting the resources these migratory birds need during their trek to nesting grounds in northern Canada and in Alaska. By clearing forests, filling wetlands, and polluting the air, land, and water, humans threaten habitats and the organisms that live in them. As we will discuss in Chapter 16, human influence as a limiting factor has had a profound effect on populations. For example, the introduction of nonnative species has caused population crashes in many parts of the world where biodiversity is an important part of the ecosystem's functioning.

A Apply A population of algae in a pond is limited in size by the amount of sunlight that strikes the pond's surface. Is sunlight a density-dependent or density-independent limiting factor for the algae population?

14.4 ASSESSMENT

ONLINE QUIZ ClassZone.com

B.4.1

REVIEWING MAIN IDEAS

1. What four factors determine the growth rate of a population?
2. How does **carrying capacity** affect the size of a population?
3. What is the main difference between a **density-dependent limiting factor** and a **density-independent limiting factor**? Give examples of each.

CRITICAL THINKING

4. **Apply** What might cause **exponential growth** to occur only for a short period when a new species is introduced to a resource-filled environment?
5. **Synthesize** How might density-dependent limiting factors be affected by a flood or some other natural disaster?

***Connecting* CONCEPTS**

6. **Symbiosis** Give an example of how a symbiotic relationship could cause a population crash.

14.4 ASSESSMENT

1. immigration, births, deaths, emigration
2. Carrying capacity limits the size of a population.
3. A density-dependent limiting factor is affected by the number of individuals in a given area, but a density-independent limiting factor is not affected by population size. Examples of density-dependent limiting factors include predation, competition, and disease. Examples of density-independent limiting factors include weather, natural disasters, and human activities.
4. Eventually, the growing population will consume all available resources, and the species may experience a population crash.
5. Answers might include effects such as a flood or other natural disaster destroying resources, predators, or prey in an area, which are density-dependent factors.
6. If a parasite or disease spreads in a dense population, it could cause a population to decline dramatically over a short period of time.

14.5 Ecological Succession

KEY CONCEPT Ecological succession is a process of change in the species that make up a community.

MAIN IDEA

- Succession occurs following a disturbance in an ecosystem.

VOCABULARY

succession, p. 445
primary succession, p. 446
pioneer species, p. 446
secondary succession, p. 447

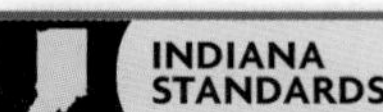

B.4.2 Describe how human activities and natural phenomena can change the flow of matter and energy in an ecosystem and how those changes impact other species.

Connect It begins with a dirty sock. Then a discarded homework assignment. But this is only the start. If you have ever spent a Saturday afternoon cleaning your bedroom, you may have wondered how a perfectly clean room could manage to become such a cluttered mess. A clean room becoming cluttered is a gradual process much like the process that rebuilds damaged ecosystems.

MAIN IDEA

Succession occurs following a disturbance in an ecosystem.

After an ecosystem experiences a devastating catastrophe and begins to regrow, the space re-forms itself through a process known as succession. **Succession** is the sequence of biotic changes that regenerate a damaged community or create a community in a previously uninhabited area.

The Hawaiian Islands began to form more than 70 million years ago. Over time, volcanic eruptions like the one shown in **FIGURE 14.15** created these islands in the middle of the Pacific Ocean. Eventually, the bare volcanic rock began to break down into soil, which provided a place for plants to grow. As time passed, the process of succession created unique tropical ecosystems. Succession from bare rock to such highly diverse vegetation takes a great deal of time.

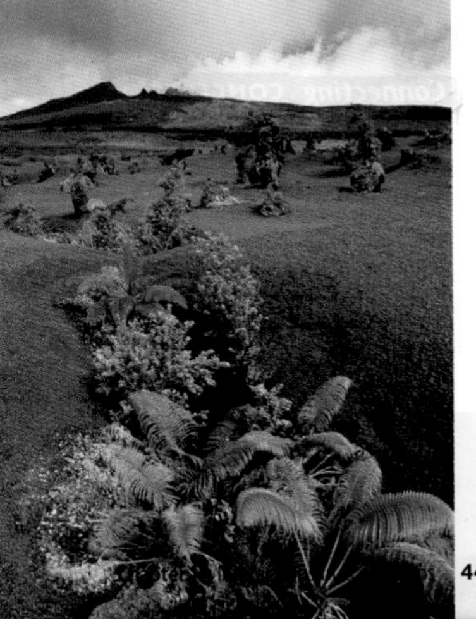

FIGURE 14.15 The path of a lava flow, like this one on the island of Hawaii (left), leaves behind nothing but solid rock. Over time, primary succession will turn this harsh landscape into a fertile ecosystem (right).

Differentiated Instruction

BELOW LEVEL

Make sure the sequence of events shown by the two photographs in **FIGURE 14.15** is clear. The lava flow in the first photograph hardens to form a surface layer of rock. The plants in the second photograph take root much later, after pioneer species, such as moss or lichen, have begun to break down the rock into soil.

Plan and Prepare

Objectives

- Describe the process of primary succession.
- Explain the difference between primary and secondary succession.

Section Resources

Unit Resource Book
Study Guide pp. 51–52
Power Notes p. 53
Reinforcement p. 54

Interactive Reader Chapter 14
Spanish Study Guide pp. 153–154

Biology Toolkit p. C38

Technology
Power Presentation 14.5
Media Gallery DVD
Online Quiz 14.5

Activate Prior Knowledge Most students will have observed some form of secondary succession. Remind students that an ecosystem can be a large forest or a small, empty lot and that a disturbance is a change to the existing ecological community. **Ask,** What happens to a garden or field when plants are removed in the fall and not replanted in spring? Seeds or roots from the original plants may regrow, or weeds, grasses, wildflowers, or saplings might take root. **Ask,** What term is used to describe the arrival of new plants? immigration

Teach

Vocabulary

succession The shared root of the words *succeed* and *succession* refers to a sequence of events, not to success or victory. A team can have a succession of wins, or a prince can succeed his father to the throne. **Ask,** How are these uses similar to its use in ecology? Succession in an ecosystem follows a sequence of events that enable new species to colonize a habitat.

▼ Teach *continued*

TEACH FROM VISUALS

FIGURE 14.16 Point out how the cross section of soil changes during the process of primary succession. The land goes from having large rocks to soil with smaller and smaller rocks. Changes in the soil correspond to changes in surface vegetation as plant roots break down the rock and add organic matter. **Ask**

- What are the first organisms to break down rock? lichens and mosses
- What types of trees are the first to appear in primary succession? alders, cottonwoods, shrubs

Integrating Earth Scien

The process of brea
smaller and smaller
weathering. Plants
help break down ro
weathering is cause
Over a long period
weathered rock ev

Answers

A Apply Mosses
up the rock and ad
they aid in soil for

Succession

Primary & Secondary Succession

FIGURE 14.16 Primary Succession

Melting glaciers, volcanic eruptions, landslides, and strip mines can all begin the process of primary succession.

0–15 years Moss, lichens, grasses

15–80 years Shrubs, cottonwoods, alder thicket

80–115 years Transition to forest, alder, spruce

115–200 years Hemlock-spruce forest

Glacier Bay National Park in Alaska has given scientists an opportunity to witness primary succession as the glacier recedes.

A Apply What function might the mosses and lichens serve in primary succession?

Primary Succession

One of the best ways to understand succession is to watch it progress. **Primary succession** is the establishment and development of an ecosystem in an area that was previously uninhabited. The first organisms that live in a previously uninhabited area are called **pioneer species.** Typical examples of pioneer species are lichens and some mosses, which can break down solid rock into smaller pieces. The process of primary succession, which is illustrated in **FIGURE 14.16**, follows this basic pattern:

- Bare rock is exposed by a retreating glacier or is created when lava cools. Wind, rain, and ice begin to break down the surface of the rock, forming cracks and breaking the rock into smaller pieces.
- Lichen and moss spores are blown in by wind. As they grow, they break up the rock further. When they die, their remains mix with the rock pieces to form a thin layer of soil.
- Over time, seeds are blown into the area or are dropped by birds. Small flowers and hardy shrubs grow from these seeds. These new plants provide a habitat for small animals, break up the rock with their roots, and add material to the soil when they die.
- As the soil continues to grow thicker, small trees take root, and different animals move into the area. These trees provide shade.
- Different tree species take root in the shade and eventually replace the original trees, which need direct sunlight to thrive.

Differentiated Instruction

PRE-AP

Have students prepare sequence diagrams of primary and secondary succession. Tell them to pay attention not only to descriptions in the text but to the details of the diagrams. For example, have students look carefully at how the community of trees changes over the course of secondary succession.

Biology Toolkit, Sequence Diagram, p. C38

HANDS-ON ACTIVITY

Collect some historical pictures of your area and share these with students. Have them look for changes in the natural landscape that point to ecological succession.

FIGURE 14.17 Secondary Succession

Following a flood or a fire, a community is given a chance for new life. Plants remaining after the disturbance reestablish the ecosystem.

Analyze **Why does secondary succession take less time than primary succession?**

Secondary Succession

Succession does not always begin from bare rock. More often, a disturbance, such as a fire or hurricane, halts the progress of succession or destroys an established community. **Secondary succession,** which is illustrated in **FIGURE 14.17,** is the reestablishment of a damaged ecosystem in an area where the soil was left intact. Plants and other organisms that remain start the process of regrowth. There is no end to secondary succession. Small disturbances, such as a tree falling, start the process again and again. The dynamic processes of succession are always changing the face of an ecosystem.

Connect **Where might succession occur in the ocean?**

14.5 ASSESSMENT

ONLINE QUIZ ClassZone.com

B.4.2

REVIEWING MAIN IDEAS

1. How is **primary succession** different from **secondary succession**?
2. Why are **pioneer species** so important for primary succession?

CRITICAL THINKING

3. **Infer** Does the process of primary succession take longer in tropical or arctic areas? Explain.
4. **Predict** During **succession,** what might become the limiting factor for sun-loving mosses as taller plants begin to grow?

***Connecting* CONCEPTS**

5. **Niche** At what point during primary succession does an ecosystem provide the fewest habitats for organisms? Explain your reasoning.

TEACH FROM VISUALS

FIGURE 14.17 Point out to students the passage of time noted in the labels and compare it to the passage of time shown in **FIGURE 14.16. Ask**

- Which process takes longer? primary succession
- Why are shrubs and grasses able to take root so quickly with secondary succession? The ecosystem already has soil, so these plants can grow in the first stage of the process. They may have been growing there before the fire.
- What part of the ecosystem undergoes very little change with secondary succession? the quality of the soil

Answers

A Analyze Secondary succession starts with soil instead of bare rock.

B Connect in a coral reef

Assess and Reteach ▼

Assess Use the Online Quiz or Section Quiz (*Assessment Book,* p. 277).

Reteach Have students summarize the section's content by explaining the meaning of each vocabulary term listed on page 445.

14.5 ASSESSMENT

1. Primary succession begins with bare rock, worn down and colonized by pioneer species. Secondary succession begins with established soil in which many different plants can grow.
2. Pioneer species, such as mosses and lichens, can break down rock into smaller pieces. When they die, their remains mix with tiny pieces of rock to form a thin layer of soil. They change the ecosystem in ways that enable the support of more diverse species.
3. *Sample Answer:* Primary succession takes longer in arctic areas because rock is covered with snow part of the year, the growing season is shorter, and cold temperatures slow growth and decomposition. Soil takes much longer to form.
4. the amount of sunlight that reaches them
5. *Sample Answer:* There are no habitable areas in the earliest stages of succession because there is no soil to support producers. Land becomes habitable once rock has weathered enough to support mosses and lichens. Over time, the mosses and lichens will provide the resources needed to support other organisms.

OPTIONS FOR INQUIRY

INVESTIGATION

Time 45 minutes	TEACHER TESTED
Teacher Preparation	
Student Difficulty	
Lab Binder Ecology, pp. 19–20	

Purpose Determine if nitrogen and phosphorus are limiting nutrients for algae.

Overview Students will grow algae in pond water, pond water with added nitrogen, and pond water with added phosphorus and note differences.

LAB PREPARATION

- Algae culture can be purchased from a scientific supply house.
- Test tubes with stoppers can be substituted for baby food jars.
- Trisodium phosphate is a cleaning agent found at hardware stores. Sulfates or urea are available in granular form at garden stores. Prepare a 10% solution of each.

Safety Use caution when preparing solutions. Material Safety Data Sheets (MSDS) note trisodium phosphate is destructive of mucous membranes; an irritant for upper respiratory tract, eyes, and skin; and corrosive. Ammonium sulfate causes irritation to skin, eyes, and respiratory tract and may be harmful if swallowed. Remind students to wash their hands.

LAB MANAGEMENT

- If test tubes are used, add 19 mL of pond water in step 1, 20 drops of algae culture in step 2, 2 drops of trisodium phosphate in step 3, and 2 drops of ammonium sulfate in step 4.
- Demonstrate how to smell the jars without inhaling the air above the jars.

POST-LAB DISCUSSION

Discuss the operational definition students used for a limiting effect.

Use these inquiry-based labs and online activities to deepen your understanding of ecosystems.

INDIANA STANDARDS

NOS.1 Develop explanations based on reproducible data and observations gathered during laboratory investigations.

NOS.3 Clearly communicate their ideas and results of investigations verbally and in written from using tables, graphs, diagrams, and photographs.

INVESTIGATION

Limiting Nutrients for Algae

All organisms require sufficient nutrients to grow. In many ecosystems, two important limiting nutrients, nitrogen and phosphorus, may limit plant growth.

SKILL Interpreting Data

PROBLEM Are nitrogen and phosphorus limiting nutrients for algae growth?

MATERIALS

- 3 baby food jars with lids
- glass marking pencil
- 200 mL pond water
- 3 eyedroppers
- 50 mL algae culture
- 5 drops 10% trisodium phosphate solution
- 5 drops 10% ammonium sulfate or urea solution
- 50-mL graduated cylinder

PROCEDURE

1. Mark the three jars *control*, *A*, and *B*, and add pond water until each is two-thirds full.
2. Add 40 to 50 mL of algae culture to each jar.
3. Add 4 or 5 drops of the trisodium phosphate solution to jar A. This is a source of phosphorous. Swirl to mix.
4. Add 4 or 5 drops of the ammonium sulfate or urea solution to jar B. This is a source of nitrogen. Swirl to mix.
5. Cap the jars and place them in a sunny window.
6. Design a data table to record your observations.
7. Predict how algae levels will change in each jar after seven days.
8. Observe every day for seven days. Record your observations.

ANALYZE AND CONCLUDE

1. **Observe** After seven days, how did the appearances of the three jars differ? How did their smells differ?
2. **Evaluate** Use your data to determine whether your results support your prediction.
3. **Conclude** Explain how you know whether phosphorus or nitrogen was a limiting nutrient.
4. **Experimental Design** In what way did your experiment fall short in revealing limiting nutrients for algae?
5. **Application** Based on what you learned in this experiment, which nutrients would you add to a vegetable garden?

EXTEND YOUR INVESTIGATION

Excess nutrients in waterways can cause an environmental problem called eutrophication. Sources of excess nutrients include sewage treatment runoff, agriculture runoff, industrial waste, storm water runoff, and atmospheric fallout. Do research on eutrophication and the effects of excess amounts of nitrogen and phosphorus on algae growth.

Answers

Analyze and Conclude

1. Jar B (ammonium sulfate) had the strongest smell and the most algae; jar A (trisodium phosphate) had the weakest smell, least algae; control jar was in between.
2. Answers should compare students' predictions in step 7 with their results.
3. Phosphorus was a limiting factor because jar A had the least algae. Nitrogen was not a limiting factor because that jar had the most algae growth.
4. Experiment does not reveal the role that quantity or concentration may play. Perhaps less of the phosphate would have encouraged growth.
5. *Sample Answer:* I would add nitrogen and a little phosphorus. Too much phosphorus might have a limiting effect.

Extend Your Investigation

Students will find that eutrophication of waterways can deprive other organisms of oxygen and sunlight.

INVESTIGATION

Making a Local Field Guide

Field guides contain descriptions and pictures of plant, insect, and animal species. In this activity, you will observe specimens near your home or school to create your own local field guide.

SKILL Observing

PROBLEM What plant and animal species can you identify in your region?

MATERIALS
- several field guides appropriate to the plants and animals in your area
- hand lens
- blank notebook
- pencil
- colored pencils
- camera (optional)

PROCEDURE
1. Find an area near your home or school with as many different species as possible, such as an open field or a pond. Choose a category of species from your teacher's list, and find as many different species in that category as you can.
2. Draw pictures in your notebook or take photographs of each species.
3. Use field guides to identify each species. Write down both the common and scientific names, and note any interesting species information.
4. Make a field-guide page for each species you identified in your local ecosystem. Include the drawing or photograph of each species, along with its common and scientific names, when and where you collected it, and interesting information about it.
5. Compile your field guide in a binder or folder. Give your guide a title and a table of contents.

ANALYZE AND CONCLUDE
1. **Analyze** How diverse is the ecosystem you studied? Compare the species richness you observed with what your classmates discovered.
2. **Conclude** Summarize what you learned about the ecosystem you surveyed. How did creating your own field guide affect your understanding of the ecosystem?

Online BIOLOGY
CLASSZONE.COM

ANIMATED BIOLOGY
What Limits Population Growth?
Apply a limiting factor within a sample environment and see how the populations of organisms react.

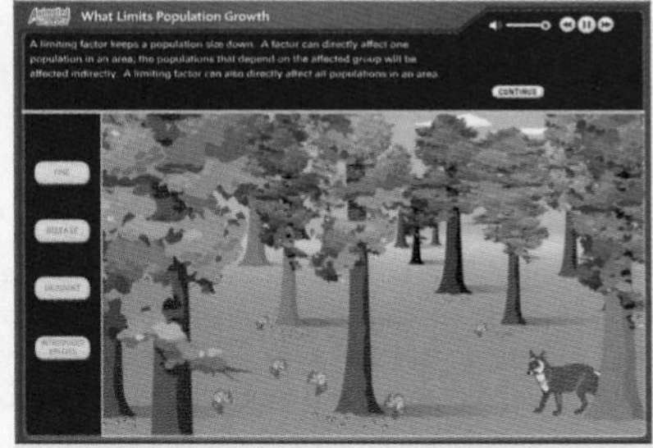

WEBQUEST
In this WebQuest, you will examine how Hurricane Hugo affected endangered Puerto Rican parrots. Explore how healthy parrot populations weathered hurricanes in the past, then determine if the current population recovered from the hurricane.

DATA ANALYSIS ONLINE
By 1900, most bison in Yellowstone Park had been wiped out. Between 1902 and 1968, scientists gathered data on the reemerging bison population. Make a graph of the data to analyze how the population grew and when the population reached its carrying capacity.

Answers

Analyze and Conclude

1. *Sample Answer:* It is very diverse because there are many different types of species living in it. We have 15 species in our field guide. Other groups have 4, 11, 20, and 22.
2. *Sample Answer:* I learned that in the schoolyard there were many different species of plants and animals. In only 30 minutes, a diverse number of species were found. Some of them were in cool, shady areas, while others were in the sun. Making the field guide helps me understand and remember the diversity of species in the ecosystem.

Online Biology ▼

ANIMATED BIOLOGY Limiting factors in this simulation include fire, disease, drought, and invasive species. Use with **Section 14.4.**

WEBQUEST The WebQuest takes one full class period. Students complete the activity online and will need access to a printer to print out their answers. Sample answers, teacher notes, and alternative assessment ideas are available on **ClassZone.com.** Use with **Section 14.4.**

DATA ANALYSIS ONLINE
The bison population follows a logistic growth pattern and then declines. Use with **Section 14.4.**

INVESTIGATION

Time 45 minutes	TEACHER TESTED
Teacher Preparation	
Student Difficulty	
Lab Binder Ecology, p. 21	

LAB MANAGEMENT

To narrow the scope, assign groups of students different types of organisms, for example, grasses, trees, insects, and other animals.

Safety Be sure to identify for students any poisonous plants or animals in your area. Also, be aware of students with allergies and assign them a role that allows them to avoid allergens.

Teacher Note "This activity is very appropriate and authentic for all classroom settings! I had fun doing it as well!"

Interactive Review

Encourage students to go to **ClassZone.com** for a detailed review of each section, including visuals and vocabulary practice.

Unit Resource Book, Vocabulary Practice, pp. 61–64

CHAPTER 14

Interactive Review @ CLASSZONE.COM

KEY CONCEPTS | Vocabulary Games | Concept Maps | Animated Biology | Online Quiz

14.1 Habitat and Niche

Every organism has a habitat and a niche. Each organism in an ecosystem has an ecological niche, which includes the type of food it consumes, its behavior, and its habitat—the place where it lives. Competitive exclusion prevents two species from sharing the same niche. In different geographical regions, ecological equivalents may have similar ecological niches.

14.2 Community Interactions

Organisms interact as individuals and as populations. Interactions between species include competition and predation. Interactions shape ecosystem dynamics. Parasitism, commensalism, and mutualism are symbiotic relationships involving two species living in direct contact with one another.

14.3 Population Density and Distribution

Each population has a density, a dispersion, and a reproductive strategy. The distribution of a population can be measured by population density. Species can have clumped, uniform, or random dispersion patterns. Survivorship curves describe the reproductive strategies of different species.

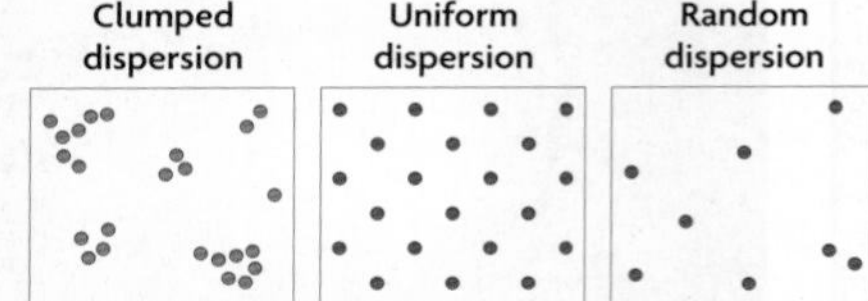

14.4 Population Growth Patterns

Populations grow in predictable patterns. Population growth accommodates changes in population size due to births and deaths as well as immigration and emigration. Populations experiencing exponential growth increase dramatically over time. When resources become a limiting factor, a population will grow logistically until it reaches the environmental carrying capacity, or the maximum population size the environment can support. Density-dependent limiting factors affect dense populations, but density-independent limiting factors affect populations regardless of density.

14.5 Ecological Succession

Ecological succession is a process of change in the species that make up a community. *Succession* refers to the progression of plants and animals that repopulate a region after an ecological disturbance. Primary succession begins in a previously uninhabited area, such as bare rock exposed by the receding of a glacier or created by a volcanic eruption. Secondary succession occurs in a previously inhabited area that is damaged by an ecological disturbance, such as a fire or a flood.

Synthesize Your Notes

Concept Map Use a concept map to display the differences between exponential and logistic growth.

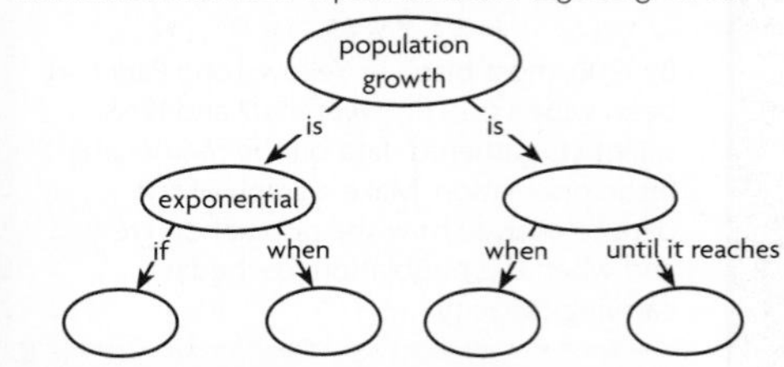

Main Idea Chart Use the main idea chart to explain and give examples of density-independent and density-dependent limiting factors.

Density Independent	Density Dependent

Reviewing Vocabulary

1. mutualism
2. parasitism
3. commensalism
4. clumped
5. random
6. uniform
7. exponential
8. population crash
9. carrying capacity
10. *Sample Answer:* A niche is a unique set of characteristics that describe how a species lives in its environment. Therefore, it can be considered special because a niche is unique to a species.
11. *Sample Answer:* The place a person inhabits includes all the living and nonliving things surrounding him or her. Likewise, a habitat of an organism includes all of the biotic and abiotic factors in its surroundings.

Chapter Assessment

CHAPTER REVIEW

16. The population density increases.
17. A type I survivorship curve shows a low level of infant mortality and a population that generally will survive until old age. This curve is associated with organisms that take care of their young until the young can care for themselves. A type II survivorship curve shows a survivorship rate that is roughly equal at all ages of an organism's life. A type III survivorship curve shows a very high birth rate and a very high infant mortality rate. There is generally little or no parental care in organisms showing a type III curve.
18. Answers should include deaths and emigration.
19. *Sample Answer:* A population experiencing exponential growth is likely to exceed the carrying capacity of the ecosystem and consequently run out of resources such as food.
20. The carrying capacity for a species could decline because an unusually long and harsh winter could reduce the food resources for the species.
21. Answers should describe and give examples of two of the following density-dependent limiting factors: competition, predation, and parasitism and disease.
22. Succession is an ongoing, dynamic, and long-term process. Even small disturbances, such as a tree falling, restart the process.

Chapter Vocabulary

14.1 habitat, p. 428
ecological niche, p. 428
competitive exclusion, p. 429
ecological equivalent, p. 430

14.2 competition, p. 431
predation, p. 431
symbiosis, p. 432
mutualism, p. 432
commensalism, p. 432
parasitism, p. 432

14.3 population density, p. 436
population dispersion, p. 437
survivorship curve, p. 438

14.4 immigration, p. 440
emigration, p. 440
exponential growth, p. 441
logistic growth, p. 441
carrying capacity, p. 442
population crash, p. 442
limiting factor, p. 443
density-dependent limiting factor, p. 443
density-independent limiting factor, p. 444

14.5 succession, p. 445
primary succession, p. 446
pioneer species, p. 446
secondary succession, p. 447

Reviewing Vocabulary

Category Clues

For each clue in the category group, list the appropriate vocabulary words from the chapter.

Category: Types of Symbiosis

1. two-way benefit
2. host is harmed
3. no effect on host

Category: Types of Dispersion

4. a herd
5. no pattern
6. territories

Category: Population Growth

7. quick growth
8. sudden decrease in size
9. number environment can sustain

Word Origins

10. *Niche* is an English word with a French origin. In general, it means "a special place." How does this meaning relate to the ecological definition of the word?

11. *Habitat* comes from a Latin word meaning "it inhabits." Connect this meaning with the definition in Section 14.1.

Reviewing MAIN IDEAS

12. A deer is a large herbivore that usually lives in a forest. What is the deer's habitat, and what is its niche?

13. How does competitive exclusion differ from ecological equivalents?

14. A brown bear is an omnivore. Explain how a brown bear and a squirrel can be in interspecific competition and have a predatory–prey relationship. **B.4.4**

15. The remora fish has an adaptation that allows it to attach to a shark, and it feeds on scraps of food left over from the shark's meal. What type of symbiotic relationship is this? Explain.

16. If you were to add two goldfish into a fish tank that already contains three goldfish, explain what happens to the population density of the fish tank.

17. Explain how the three types of survivorship curves align with different reproductive strategies.

18. If a large number of individuals immigrated into a population of bison, what two things could happen to return the population to its original size?

19. Why does a population that experiences exponential growth have a high chance of having a population crash?

20. How might the carrying capacity of an environment for a particular species change in response to an unusually long and harsh winter? Why? **B.4.1**

21. Describe and give examples of two limiting factors that affect a dense population.

22. Why is succession considered an ongoing process? **B.4.2**

Reviewing Main Ideas

12. The deer's habitat is the forest. Its niche is an herbivore that lives in the forest.
13. Competitive exclusion occurs between two species competing for the same resources in the same environment. These two species would be considered ecological equivalents if they lived in different geographical regions.
14. A brown bear and a squirrel are in interspecific competition when they both eat the same resources, such as acorns. They have a predator-prey relationship when the bear eats the squirrel.
15. It is commensalism because the remora fish benefits by getting food, and the shark apparently is not harmed and does not benefit.

ITEM CORRELATIONS

Standard	Items
B.4.1	20, 24
B.4.2	22, 28, 29
B.4.4	14

CHAPTER REVIEW

Critical Thinking

23. mutualism
24. The prairie dogs could experience a population crash, or growth could slow down and level off to a level the environment can support.
25. This is a density-dependent factor because it is the high numbers of beetles that make the population more susceptible to competition.
26. The crash was caused by a density-dependent limiting factor because disease can spread more easily in a dense population.
27. Students should draw and label a type III survivorship curve in which the squid have a very high birth rate and a very high infant mortality rate. The *y*-axis should represent number of survivors, and the *x*-axis should represent the percentage of maximum life span.

Analyzing a Diagram

28. The left side of the diagram depicts pioneer species because it shows mosses and lichens growing on bare rock. These species are pioneer species because they are the first species to grow in a previously uninhabited area.
29. *Sample Answer:* Any disturbance, such as a fire, hurricane, or volcano, that destroys or damages the ecosystem could make it revert to an earlier stage of succession. Human activity could also cause the ecosystem to regress.

Critical Thinking

23. Apply A bee gathers nectar from a flower by using a strawlike appendage called a proboscis. While on the flower, grains of pollen attach to the bee's back. When the bee travels to another flower, the pollen fertilizes the new plant. What type of symbiosis is this?

24. Predict A population of prairie dogs is experiencing high immigration and birthrates, but resources are beginning to deplete. What could eventually happen to this population? Give two possibilities. **B.4.1**

25. Synthesize A species of beetle is in a period of exponential growth, but a competing species has started sharing the same space. Is the competing species an example of a density-dependent or a density-independent limiting factor? Explain.

26. Evaluate Imagine that scientists introduced a disease into the rabbit population of Australia, and the rabbit population crashed. Was the crash caused by a density-dependent or density-independent limiting factor? Justify your answer.

27. Apply Each year, thousands of California market squid swim up from the ocean depths and lay millions of eggs along California shorelines. The squid then die, leaving their offspring to fend for themselves. Draw and label a graph that illustrates a likely survivorship curve of the California market squid.

Analyzing a Diagram

Use the diagram below to answer the next two questions.

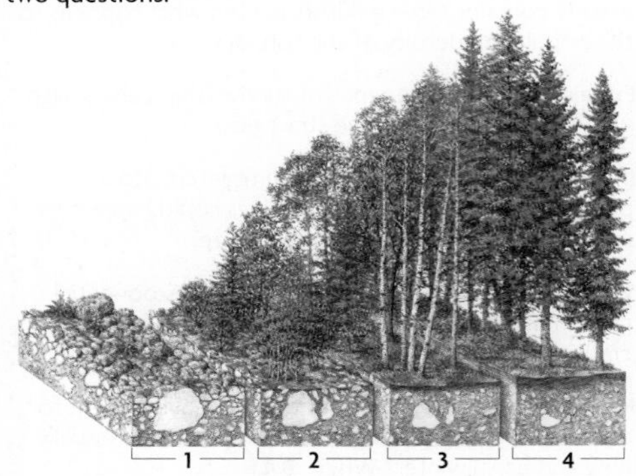

28. Apply What part of the diagram depicts pioneer species? Explain your answer. **B.4.2**

29. Infer What could happen in the ecosystem shown that could make it revert to an earlier stage of succession? **B.4.2**

Analyzing Data

Use the graph to answer the next three questions.

The combination graph below shows changes in the sizes of bee and mite populations in one area of the Midwest. The mites live as parasites on the bees.

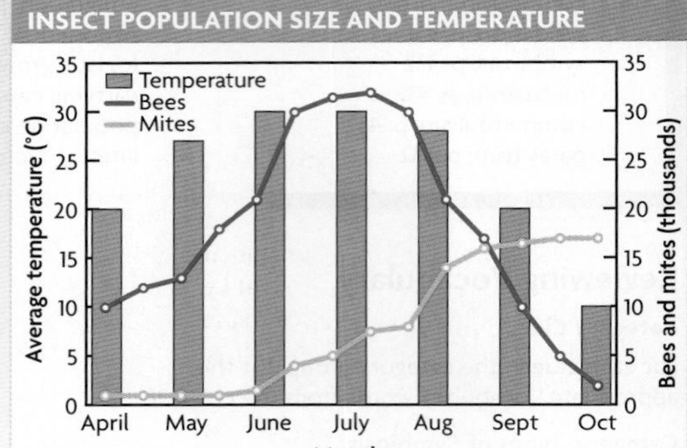

30. Interpret A decrease in the number of bees occurs during which months?

31. Analyze Describe the trends in the bee and mite populations from April through October.

32. Hypothesize What might explain the relationship between the bee and mite population numbers?

Connecting CONCEPTS

33. Write Ad Copy Imagine that you are an advertising agent trying to encourage a new species to move into an environment. Design an advertisement using the concepts from the chapter. Keep in mind that a population will not want to move to a new area without abundant resources. Choose a target species and make sure that your advertisement answers the following questions: What resources and environmental factors would make this species want to move? What abiotic and biotic factors does it need? Include several vocabulary terms from the chapter.

34. Apply The two zebras on page 427 are competing for the right to mate with females. Are they engaging in intraspecific or interspecific competition? Explain your answer.

Analyzing Data

30. A decrease in the number of bees occurs during August, September, and October.
31. The bee population slowly and steadily increases from early spring through midsummer. After this point, the bee population steadily declines through the fall. The mite population starts very low in the spring and then starts increasing significantly as the bee population begins to fall in mid-summer. It continues its increase inversely to the bee decline.
32. *Sample Answer:* As the bee population grows, so can the mite population. Then, as temperatures fall and bees begin to die, the mites continue to reproduce because there are still enough bees for them to live on, though their rate of population growth is slowed.

452 Unit 5: Ecology

INDIANA ISTEP+ Test Prep

Test Practice For more test practice, go to ClassZone.com.

1 Archaeologists find that the disappearance of a large mammal occurred shortly after the arrival of hominids in a certain region. What most likely occurred between these two species?

A dispersion
B predation
C commensalism
D parasitism

2 Officials attempt to control the spread of an exotic wildflower species by introducing its natural predator, a beetle. Unexpectedly, the beetle population grows exponentially and begins to eat local crops. What best accounts for this unexpected population explosion?

A Adaptive radiation allowed the beetle population to evolve faster.
B The beetle population has few predators in the new habitat.
C The wildflower and the local crops are genetically similar kinds of plants.
D The beetle has different nutritional requirements in the new habitat.

3

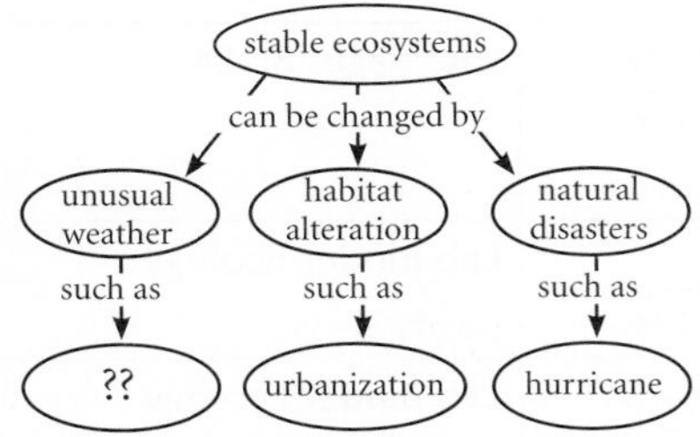

Which of these best completes this concept map?

A acid rain
B pollution
C an earthquake
D extended drought

THINK THROUGH THE QUESTION

Keep in mind that unusual weather is a natural part of ecosystem function.

4 In many parts of the United States, native plants that once grew on the forest floor have been replaced by garlic mustard, an invasive species that thrives in cool forest understories. This situation is an example of

A parasitism between species.
B primary succession between species.
C predation between species.
D competition between species.

5

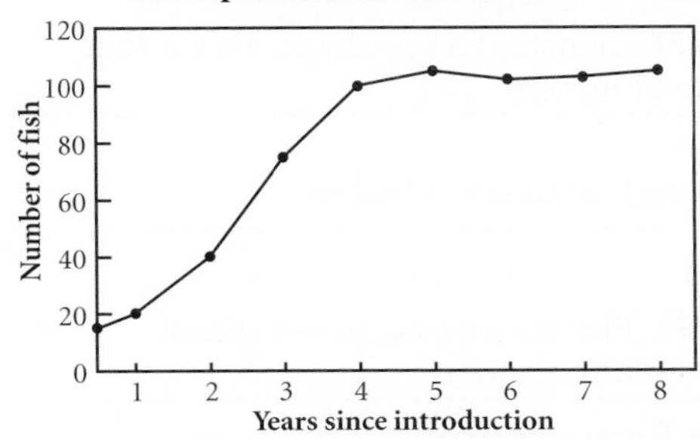

A fish species is introduced to a park pond. Which statement best describes the population growth of these fish shown in the graph?

A The population stopped growing because the fish stopped reproducing.
B The population stopped growing because this species of fish lives less than one year.
C The population grew until disease caused the population to level off.
D The population grew until it reached the pond's carrying capacity.

6 Explain why human impact on ecosystems poses a threat to Earth's biodiversity.

CHAPTER REVIEW

Standards-Based Assessment

1. B	4. D
2. B	5. D
3. D	6. See Below

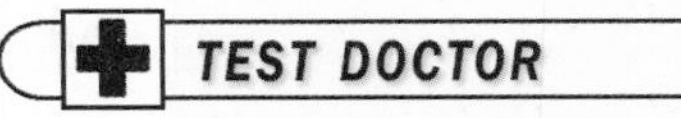

TEST DOCTOR

Question 2 Answer B is correct. Answer A is incorrect because there is no evidence that the beetles have changed, yet adaptive radiation is the process by which one species evolves and gives rise to many descendant species that occupy different ecological niches. Answer C is incorrect because it cannot be determined from the information given in the question, and the beetles can likely eat a wide range of plants. Answer D is incorrect because there is no evidence that the beetles have changed, thus they would continue to have the same nutritional requirements.

Question 3 Answer D is correct. Answer A is incorrect because acid rain is rain with a low pH caused by pollutants in the atmosphere, so it is not a naturally occurring example of unusual weather. Answers B and C are incorrect because pollution and an earthquake are not examples of unusual weather.

Question 4 Answer D is correct. Answer A is incorrect because a parasite is an organism that benefits by harming another organism. Answer B is incorrect because primary succession is the establishment and development of an ecosystem in an area that was previously uninhabited. Answer C is incorrect because predation is the hunting and killing of one organism by another.

Question 6 Human influences include many types of habitat destruction, pollution, and introduction of foreign species. All of these influences alter an ecosystem's biodiversity.

Connecting Concepts

33. The ad copy should be directed at a target species and include resources and environmental factors that would make the species want to move, abiotic and biotic factors it needs, and several vocabulary terms from the chapter.

34. The two zebras are engaging in intraspecific competition because the competition is between members of the same species.

ITEM CORRELATIONS

Standard	Items
B.4.1	5
B.4.2	6
B.4.3	1, 2, 4
B.4.4	3

CHAPTER 15

Indiana Resource Preview

Print Resources

The Biosphere

INDIANA STANDARDS		Sections	PAGES and PACING	UNIT RESOURCE BOOK
B.4.1	15.1	**Life in the Earth System** **KEY CONCEPT** The biosphere is one of Earth's four interconnected systems.	pp. 456–457 30 minutes	URB pages 65–68
B.4.4	15.2	**Climate** **KEY CONCEPT** Climate is a key abiotic factor that affects the biosphere.	pp. 458–461 30 minutes	URB pages 69–72
NOS.3		DATA ANALYSIS: Constructing Combination Graphs	p. 461 45 minutes	URB page 85
	15.3	**Biomes** **KEY CONCEPT** Biomes are land-based, global communities of organisms.	pp. 462–467 30 minutes	URB pages 73–76
	15.4	**Marine Ecosystems** **KEY CONCEPT** Marine ecosystems are global.	pp. 468–470 30 minutes	URB pages 77–80
	15.5	**Estuaries and Freshwater Ecosystems** **KEY CONCEPT** Freshwater ecosystems include estuaries as well as flowing and standing water.	pp. 471–474 45 minutes	URB pages 81–84
NOS.3, NOS.4		CHAPTER INVESTIGATION: Design Your Own Winter Water Chemistry	p. 475 45 minutes	**Lab Binder** Ecology pages 31–33
NOS.5, NOS.6		OPTIONS FOR INQUIRY	pp. 476–477 45 minutes, 45 minutes	**Lab Binder** Ecology pages 35–37
		Chapter Review	pp. 478–481	**Assessment Book** Chapter Tests A, B pp. 299–306

INDIANA STANDARDS

B.4.1 Explain that the amount of life an environment can support is limited by the available energy, water, oxygen, and minerals, and by the ability of ecosystems to recycle the remains of dead organisms.

B.4.4 Describe how climate, the pattern of matter and energy flow, the birth and death of new organisms, and the interaction between those organisms contribute to the long term stability of an ecosystem.

NOS.3 Clearly communicate their ideas and results of investigations verbally and in written form using tables, graphs, diagrams, and photographs.

NOS.4 Regularly evaluate the work of their peers and in turn have their work evaluated by their peers.

NOS.5 Apply standard techniques in laboratory investigations to measure physical quantities in appropriate units and convert known quantities to other units as necessary.

NOS.6 Use analogies and models (mathematical and physical) to simplify and represent systems that are difficult to understand or directly experience due to their size, time scale, or complexity, and recognize the limitations of analogies and models.

Labs

PUPIL EDITION LABS	
Microclimates, Section 2, p. 460 Students identify microclimates in and around school grounds. **Lab Binder** p. 38	**Time:** 15 minutes **Materials:** thermometer, stopwatch
Winter Water Chemistry, p. 475 Students investigate seasonal changes in a lake ecosystem. **Lab Binder** pp. 31–33	**Time:** 45 minutes **Materials:** 2 plastic bowls, sample water and sediment, 500 mL beaker, *Elodea* leaves, wax paper, plastic food wrap, large rubber band, warm water bath, cold water bath, 2 thermometers, dissolved oxygen kits, pH strips

OPTIONS FOR INQUIRY	
Modeling Biomes, p. 476 Students model and compare abiotic factors for plant growth in different biomes. **Lab Binder** pp. 35–36	**Time:** 45 minutes to set up biomes **Materials:** cardboard container, scissors, stapler, plastic or aluminum tray, sandy soil, potting soil, 30 wheatgrass seeds, 10 lima bean seeds, 5 sunflower seeds, permanent marker, masking tape, water, light source, refrigerator access, metric ruler
Heating and Cooling Rates of Water and Soil, p. 477 Students compare heating and cooling rates of soil and water. **Lab Binder** p. 37	**Time:** 45 minutes **Materials:** marker, 2 clear plastic cups, ruler, soil, water at room temperature, 2 thermometers, lamp

LAB BINDER Unit 5 Ecology

Additional Investigation: Modeling the Water Cycle, pp. 39–42

LAB GENERATOR

A searchable CD of all labs in the program in editable format, including forensic, probeware, and biotechnology labs.

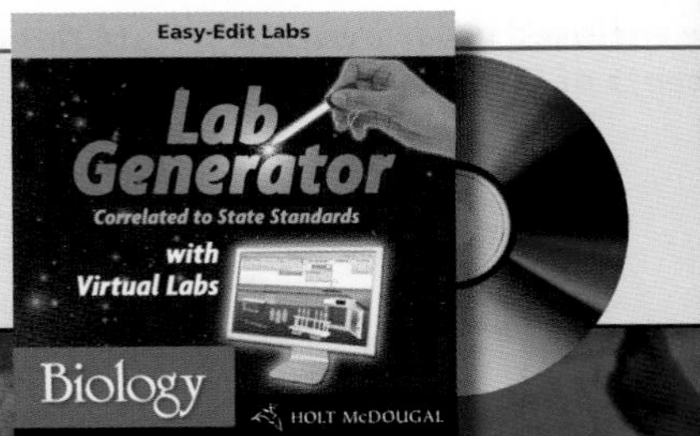

Presentation Tools

POWER PRESENTATIONS

Presentation Chapter 15
Power Presentations for each section incorporate images and clips from the Media Gallery: Includes Note Navigator for each section.

MEDIA GALLERY

Contains the following images and video clips, as well as animations, simulations and forms of visuals from the book.

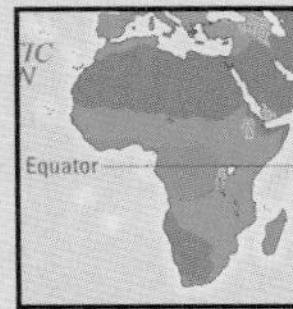

Biomes

Marine habitats

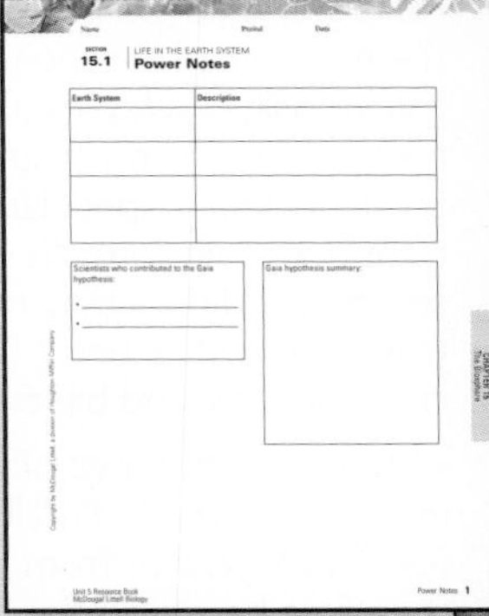

Power Notes

Temperate deciduous forest

Temperate rainforest

VIDEO

Examine a set of short video clips on different types of ecosystems.

ANIMATED BIOLOGY

Lake Turnover

Where Do They Live?

TRANSPARENCIES

Climate Zones T69

Biomes T70

Ocean Zones T71

Online BIOLOGY CLASSZONE.COM

BioZine

Animated Biology

Interactive Review

SciLinks

Resource Centers

CHAPTER 15

▼ Focus and Motivate

What species would you expect to find in a rain forest?

Have students read the caption below the photograph of the temperate rain forest. **Ask,** How does a temperate rain forest differ from a tropical rain forest? Students might speculate that the temperate rain forest is cooler and has seasons, and they may think of the tropical forest as being full of monkeys, colorful birds, and big cats.

Although both types of rain forests receive abundant rainfall, temperate rain forests are farther from the equator and therefore have a cooler climate. **Ask,** In terms of organisms adapted to these two types of rain forests, what are some differences you might expect in the mammal species of each? Temperate mammals might have more fur or seasonal hibernation or migration behaviors to avoid cold temperatures. Tropical mammals could be short-haired.

BIOZINE ClassZone.com

Students can access BioZine at **ClassZone.com** to receive updates to topics featured in the book.

In a Hurry?

The critical material in this chapter is found in **Sections 15.3, 15.4,** and **15.5,** which cover Earth's biomes. **Section 15.1** explains Earth's interconnected systems, and **Section 15.2** details the importance of climate in the characterization of a biome.

CHAPTER 15

The Biosphere

KEY CONCEPTS

15.1 Life in the Earth System
The biosphere is one of Earth's four interconnected systems.

15.2 Climate
Climate is a key abiotic factor that affects the biosphere.

15.3 Biomes
Biomes are land-based, global communities of organisms.

15.4 Marine Ecosystems
Marine ecosystems are global.

15.5 Estuaries and Freshwater Ecosystems
Freshwater ecosystems include estuaries as well as flowing and standing water.

Online BIOLOGY CLASSZONE.COM

Animated BIOLOGY
View animated chapter concepts.
- Lake Turnover
- Where Do They Live?

BIOZINE
Keep current with biology news.
- Strange Biology
- News feeds
- Careers

RESOURCE CENTER
Get more information on
- Biosphere
- Biomes
- Aquatic Ecosystems

Student Activity

Purpose **Observe enclosed ecosystems to visualize the concepts of biosphere and biome.**

Materials (per class)
- a self-contained terrarium (terrestrial ecosystem) or photos of such a terrarium
- a self-contained aquarium (aquatic ecosystem) or photos of such an aquarium

What species would you expect to find in a rain forest?

Connecting CONCEPTS

Not all rain forests are teeming with monkeys and macaws. The temperate rain forest of the Pacific Northwest is inhabited by an entirely different community of plants and animals than is found in tropical rain forests. Location, climatic conditions, and other abiotic factors determine what species you will find in a particular area.

Plant Evolution Ferns, which are abundant in the temperate rain forest, first appeared during the early Carboniferous period (360 to 320 million years ago). These plants diversified before the evolution of flowering plants. Instead of reproducing through pollen, ferns reproduce through spores. The early evolution of ferns makes them among the oldest plants still in existence today.

Introduce Display the two environments so students can examine them. Tell students that each represents an ecosystem that has boundaries, just as Earth does. **Ask**

- What is Earth's boundary? The upper reaches of the atmosphere. The atmosphere marks the boundary of the biosphere—where all living things on Earth live.
- What abiotic factors may be affecting these systems from the inside? oxygen, carbon dioxide levels, humidity from the outside? the Sun
- What areas within the ecosystem might some of the living things prefer? any spaces in which to hide, areas of different height or temperature or light exposure

Discuss Have students observe different areas within each ecosystem. Discuss how these different areas might support different organisms, relating back to what they learned about evolution, habitats, and niches. For example, there may be organisms in the soil that are adapted to its conditions, or organisms adapted to different zones within the water column.

Activate Prior Knowledge

Encourage students to think about Earth's regions and climates. **Ask,** What types of environments might you go through if you get in a car and travel from coast to coast in the United States? forest, prairie, desert, wetland, swamp Discuss the conditions that exist in these different environments, such as the humidity, temperature, air quality, and winds. **Ask,** What are some ways in which we organize or categorize Earth's regions? continents, oceans, seas, hemispheres, time zones, countries Tell students that some of these environments and major features of Earth are known as biomes, and that all of them are in the biosphere.

Preview Vocabulary

Academic Vocabulary Words that are often used in business or commerce have different meanings in biology. In everyday language, *global community* may refer to the interconnectedness of international cultures due to advances in trade and communication. However, in science, a global community is a biological community—the interacting populations in a particular place—that appears in many places throughout the world. Other words that are used commonly to describe cultural situations or conditions, such as *sphere, climate,* and *productivity,* have different meanings in biology. The common thread, though, is that in both everyday language and biological language, these terms suggest relatedness and interconnections between systems.

English Learners Tell students that in the context of biology, *sphere* rarely refers to an actual shape. *Hydrosphere, biosphere, atmosphere,* and *geosphere* are terms that organize the contents of the spherical Earth—liquid, solid, gas, and what is alive in all three. However, these spheres have no particular shape, and their boundaries are often unclear. Have students think of a seashore, where the atmosphere, hydrosphere, and geosphere are mixing and colliding, and among all three are living things such as bacteria, fish, crabs, birds, humans, and much more. Point out that all four spheres are present, but their shapes are constantly shifting.

SECTION 15.1

▼ Plan and Prepare

Objectives

- Describe the interactions of the biosphere, atmosphere, hydrosphere, and geosphere.
- Describe the interactions of biotic and abiotic factors in the biosphere.

Section Resources

Unit Resource Book Study Guide pp. 65–66 Power Notes p. 67 Reinforcement p. 68
Interactive Reader Chapter 15 **Spanish Study Guide** pp. 155–156
Biology Toolkit pp. C19, D2
Technology Power Presentation 15.1 Media Gallery DVD Online Quiz 15.1

Activate Prior K
deal with many b
everyday lives. A
how many boun
what are they? S
doorways, yards,
Discuss the diffic
boundaries of th

Biosphere
biota
hydrosphere
atmosphere
geosphere

▼ Teach

Vocabular

Greek and Latin
Flora, which is Lat
the plant life of a
"animals," refers to
given area. Once bacteria were discovered, the scientific community was not sure whether to group them in with the flora or the fauna. The word **biota,** which comes from the Greek *bios,* meaning "life," functions as a catchall word for the flora, fauna, and bacteria of our world.

Answers

A Connect The air is part of the biosphere. It contains living things such as bacteria, but air itself is not alive.

15.1 Life in the Earth System

KEY CONCEPT The biosphere is one of Earth's four interconnected systems.

MAIN IDEAS

- The biosphere is the portion of Earth that is inhabited by life.
- Biotic and abiotic factors interact in the biosphere.

VOCABULARY

biosphere, p. 456
biota, p. 456
hydrosphere, p. 456
atmosphere, p. 456
geosphere, p. 456

Review
biotic, abiotic

INDIANA STANDARDS

B.4.1 Explain that the amount of life an environment can support is limited by the available energy, water, oxygen, and minerals, and by the ability of ecosystems to recycle the remains of dead organisms.

Connect You've probably seen many photos of tropical rain forests, complete with monkeys and brightly colored frogs. But did you know that there are also temperate rain forests? They get just as much rain but have cooler temperatures and different types of plants and animals. These are just two of the biomes found within the biosphere.

MAIN IDEA

The biosphere is the portion of Earth that is inhabited by life.

The **biosphere** is the part of Earth where life exists. All of Earth's ecosystems, taken together, form the biosphere. If you could remove all the nonliving parts of the biosphere—all the water, air, rocks, and so on—you would be left with the biota. The **biota** is the collection of living things that live in the biosphere.

VISUAL VOCAB

The **biosphere** includes living organisms and the land, air, and water on Earth where living things reside.

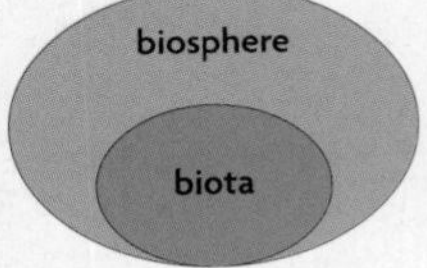

The collection of living things in the biosphere may also be called the **biota.**

The biosphere is one of Earth's four major interconnected systems. The other three Earth systems are

- the **hydrosphere,** all of Earth's water, ice, and water vapor
- the **atmosphere,** the air blanketing Earth's solid and liquid surface
- the **geosphere,** the features of Earth's surface—such as the continents, rocks, and the sea floor—and everything below Earth's surface

You need to look at how all four Earth systems interact to really understand how an ecosystem works. For example, a plant growing in a swamp depends on the soil in which it grows just as much as on the water in the swamp. It uses carbon dioxide from the atmosphere to make sugars, and it gives off excess oxygen, slightly changing the air around it. One plant growing in one swamp has a small effect on the Earth system as a whole. But all living things together throughout the planet's history have had a vast effect.

A Connect Is the air in your classroom part of the biosphere or the biota? Explain.

Differentiated Instruction

ENGLISH LEARNERS

Have students study the parts of the words *biosphere, atmosphere, hydrosphere,* and *geosphere.* For each prefix, have students write a list of any other words they know in which it appears. To reinforce the meaning of the prefixes and the whole terms, have students use the *Multilanguage Glossary* and practice writing sentences that use these terms in a way that clarifies their meanings through context.

Biology Toolkit, New Word Analysis, p. D2

PRE-AP

Draw this figure on the board:

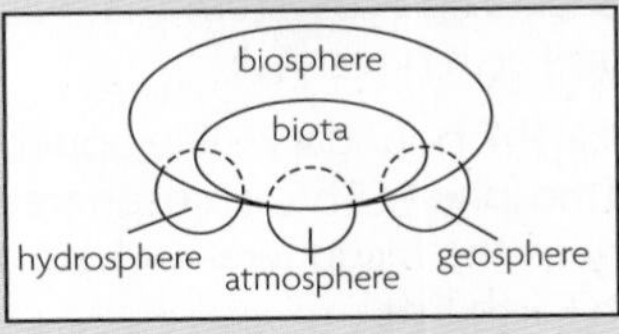

Have students look at this figure and write a paragraph on the interactions and overlaps between the five circles.

Biology Toolkit, Quick-Write, p. C19

MAIN IDEA

Biotic and abiotic factors interact in the biosphere.

Just as one ecosystem is connected to another, all four Earth systems are also connected. A change in one sphere can affect the others. If plants are removed from a riverbank, for example, rain may flow more easily from the land to the water. This increased flow would likely carry more sediment and therefore make the river water murkier, as shown in **FIGURE 15.1.** The murky water might block sunlight, affecting the growth of aquatic plants. This change might in turn prevent these plants from taking up carbon dioxide and releasing oxygen.

FIGURE 15.1 Deforestation, or the removal of forests, along the Mahajamba Bay in Madagascar has led to erosion along the waterway, clogging the water with silt and soil.

James Lovelock, an atmospheric scientist from the United Kingdom, proposed the Gaia hypothesis to explain how biotic and abiotic factors interact in the biosphere. This hypothesis considers Earth itself a kind of living organism. Its atmosphere, geosphere, and hydrosphere are cooperating systems that yield a biosphere full of life. He called this living planet Gaia after the Greek goddess of Earth. In the early 1970s, Lynn Margulis, a microbiologist from the United States, added to the hypothesis, specifically noting the ties between the biosphere and other Earth systems. For example, when carbon dioxide levels increase in the atmosphere, plants grow more quickly. As their growth continues, they remove more and more carbon dioxide from the atmosphere. The atmospheric carbon dioxide level drops, and plant growth slows. This give-and-take, known as a feedback loop, helps maintain a fairly constant level of carbon dioxide in the atmosphere.

Sometimes, people mistakenly believe that the Gaia hypothesis suggests that Earth is a thinking being that regulates the geosphere, the atmosphere, and the hydrosphere. This is obviously not the case. Rather, the Gaia hypothesis recognizes the extensive connections and feedback loops between the living and nonliving parts of the planet. Many scientists are now devoting their careers to organizing new fields of study, such as geobiology and geomicrobiology, to examine these intriguing relationships.

Summarize **Explain the Gaia hypothesis in your own words.**

15.1 ASSESSMENT

ONLINE QUIZ ClassZone.com

B.4.1

REVIEWING MAIN IDEAS

1. What is the relationship between the **biota** and the **biosphere**?
2. How does the Gaia hypothesis explain the interaction between biotic and abiotic factors in the biosphere?

CRITICAL THINKING

3. **Apply** A frog jumps into a pond and it's skin absorbs water. What spheres has the water moved through?
4. **Predict** How might a rise in global temperatures affect the biosphere?

***Connecting* CONCEPTS**

5. **Predator-Prey** Explain how feedback loops, such as those described in the Gaia hypothesis, might apply to predator-prey relationships.

15.1 ASSESSMENT

1. The biosphere contains the biota—all the living things on Earth—as well as portions of the hydrosphere, atmosphere, and geosphere.
2. According to the Gaia hypothesis, Earth itself is analogous to a living organism. The interactions between the atmosphere, geosphere, biosphere, and hydrosphere are like the interactions of an organism's vital organs.
3. hydrosphere and biosphere
4. A rise in global temperatures might affect the distribution of living things in the biosphere. Some species might increase in number; others could decrease or become extinct.
5. When a prey population increases in size, the predator population has more food to eat. As a result, the predator population increases in size. When the predators become so plentiful that the prey population decreases, the predators have less food to eat. As a result, the predator population decreases in size.

ONLINE BIOLOGY Go to the chapter Resource Center at **ClassZone.com** for additional resources and information on the biosphere.

Integrating Chemistry

Carbon dioxide constitutes only about 0.035 percent of the atmosphere. Carbon dioxide, along with methane, nitrous oxide, and water vapor, is a **greenhouse gas.** These gases tend to hold heat inside Earth's atmosphere, keeping Earth's average temperature at about 16°C (60°F). Without these gases, Earth's average temperature would be about −18°C (0°F). Too much greenhouse gas, however, can lead to an increase in average temperature. Most scientists think that the increase of carbon dioxide in the atmosphere is leading to an overall warming of Earth.

Answers

A Summarize Answers will vary but should include that the Gaia hypothesis proposes that Earth is a kind of living organism in which the hydrosphere, geosphere, biosphere, and atmosphere are interacting systems that maintain one another's balance.

Assess and Reteach ▼

Assess Use the Online Quiz or Section Quiz (*Assessment Book,* p. 293).

Reteach Have students draw a graphic, such as a series of nested circles, that summarizes the hierarchy of the organization of life within the biosphere as follows: organisms, populations, communities, ecosystems, biomes, biosphere.

Chapter 15: The Biosphere 457

SECTION 15.2

▼ Plan and Prepare

Objectives

- Differentiate between weather, climate, and microclimates.
- Identify factors that determine Earth's climate zones.

Section Resources

Unit Resource Book Study Guide pp. 69–70 Power Notes p. 71 Reinforcement p. 72 Pre-AP Activity pp. 87–88
Interactive Reader Chapter 15 **Spanish Study Guide** pp. 157–158
Biology Toolkit pp. C19, C22
Technology Power Presentation 15.2 Media Gallery DVD Online Quiz 15.2

Activate Prior Knowledge Have students describe different types of climates they are familiar with. **Ask**

- Why are there different climates on Earth? The main factor is the angle at which sunlight hits Earth's surface.
- If you were on the equator and wanted to take a trip on which you would experience each climate type, would you travel in a north/south direction or east/west? north/south, because climate change is most pronounced as you move into different latitudes

▼ Teach

Vocabulary

Greek and Latin Word Origins Remind students of the Greek prefixes *micro-* and *macro-*, and relate them to climate.

micro- = exceptionally small
macro- = large

Answers

A Analyze *Sample Answer:* forest canopy, (more sunlight) or the forest floor (less sunlight)

15.2 Climate

KEY CONCEPT Climate is a key abiotic factor that affects the biosphere.

MAIN IDEAS

- Climate is the prevailing weather of a region.
- Earth has three main climate zones.

VOCABULARY

climate, p. 458
microclimate, p. 458

Review
biosphere

B.4.4 Describe how climate, the pattern of matter and energy flow, the birth and death of new organisms, and the interaction between those organisms contribute to the long term stability of an ecosystem.

Connect Although you might sometimes check the local weather report to see if you'll need an umbrella, you are already familiar with the general climate where you live. If you live in the Midwest, you know that winter means cold temperatures, while if you live in the Southwest, winter temperatures are much milder. The long-term weather patterns of an area help determine which plants and animals you will find living there.

MAIN IDEA

Climate is the prevailing weather of a region.

The weather of an area may change from day to day, and even from hour to hour. In contrast, the **climate** is the long-term pattern of weather conditions in a region. Climate includes factors such as average temperature and precipitation and relative humidity. It also includes the seasonal variations an area experiences, such as rainy or dry seasons, cold winters, or hot summers.

The key factors that shape an area's climate include temperature, sunlight, water, and wind. Among these abiotic factors, temperature and moisture play a large role in the shaping of ecosystems. Descriptions of a specific region's climate take these abiotic factors into consideration. For example, a specific region such as a desert may be described as hot and dry, while a rain forest may be described as warm and moist.

FIGURE 15.2 The cavity in this log provides a humid microclimate that supports the growth of mushrooms.

Even within a specific region, climate conditions may vary dramatically. A **microclimate** is the climate of a small specific place within a larger area. A microclimate may be as small as a hole in a decaying log where mushrooms grow, as pictured in **FIGURE 15.2**, or as large as a city neighborhood. San Francisco, for example, is characterized by frequent fog and cool temperatures. However, not far beyond the city limits, and even within other sections of the city itself, the weather may be quite different.

Microclimates can be very important to living things. The same grassy meadow, for example, may be home to both frogs and grasshoppers. The frogs may tend toward areas that are moist, often at the base of the grasses, while the grasshoppers may prefer drier sites and cling to the tops of the grass blades. Each of these locations is a microclimate.

A Analyze **Where in a forest might you find different microclimates?**

Differentiated Instruction

ENGLISH LEARNERS

Have students work in small groups to create a content frame that lists the three different climates, the range of latitudes associated with each, the characteristics of each climate, and some examples of real places within each climate.

Biology Toolkit, Content Frame, p. C22

TEACH WITH TECHNOLOGY

Prepare a digital slide show depicting habitats in which there could be microclimates very different from the general climate. Ask students to identify the likely areas of microclimates and explain why conditions there might differ from those of the general area. Mix natural examples with human ones such as a tall apartment building (air conditioners in some windows) or a standard refrigerator/freezer appliance.

MAIN IDEA

Earth has three main climate zones.

Scientists use average temperature and precipitation levels to categorize a region's climate. Using this system, Earth can be divided into three main climate zones, as shown in **FIGURE 15.3.** These three zones are the polar, tropical, and temperate climates. The polar climate is found at the far northern and southern regions of Earth. The tropical zone surrounds the equator. The temperate zone is the wide area in between the polar and tropical zones.

Influence of Sunlight

What determines an area's climate? The answer begins with the Sun. The Sun's rays are most intense, and therefore hottest, on the portion of the planet that sunlight strikes most directly. Earth's surface is heated unevenly due to its curved shape. The area of Earth that receives the most direct radiation from the Sun all year is the region at and around the equator, where the tropical climate zone is found. Near the north and south poles, or polar climate zones, the Sun's rays strike Earth's surface at a lower angle, diffusing their heat over a larger area.

Earth's tilt on its axis also plays a role in seasonal change. As Earth orbits the Sun, different regions of the planet receive higher or lower amounts of sunlight. When the North Pole is at its maximum tilt away from the Sun, it is winter in the Northern Hemisphere and summer in the Southern Hemisphere. When the North Pole reaches its maximum tilt toward the Sun, the opposite is true.

Connecting CONCEPTS

Seasons At the March and September equinoxes, both hemispheres receive equal amounts of sunlight. At the June solstice, the Northern Hemisphere enters summer and the Southern Hemisphere enters winter. The opposite is true at the December solstice.

FIGURE 15.3 Climate Zones

The uneven heating of Earth by the Sun results in three different climate zones.

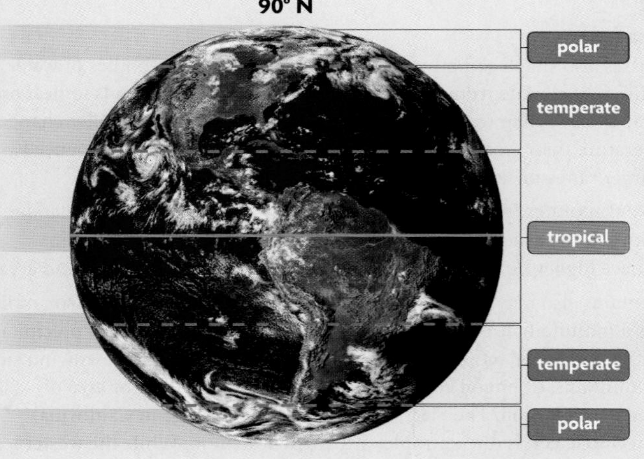

POLAR CLIMATE

The polar climate zone is located in far northern and far southern reaches of the planet, where the temperature is typically cold and often below freezing.

TROPICAL CLIMATE

The tropical climate zone, which surrounds the equator, runs from the tropic of Cancer to the tropic of Capricorn and is characterized by warm, moist conditions.

TEMPERATE CLIMATE

The temperate climate zone is located in the broad area lying between the polar and tropical climate zones. This zone experiences summer and winter seasons of about equal length.

A Apply **What is the relationship between sunlight and climate zone?**

BELOW LEVEL

Have students write for five minutes about the climate in which they live, including descriptions of any seasonal variations in temperature and precipitation. Have students address the effect of their region's position on Earth's surface in terms of the angle of sunlight and the hours of daylight.

Biology Toolkit, Quick-Write, p. C19

Connecting CONCEPTS

Seasons Remind students that an **equinox** is the day of a year when the Sun's rays hit corresponding latitudes in both hemispheres equally, meaning the day is precisely as long in Philadelphia (40°N) as it is in the north island of New Zealand (40°S), though one is in spring and the other is in fall.

A **solstice** occurs when the Sun's rays are at their most direct in one hemisphere while at their most indirect in the other. The summer solstice is the longest day of the year, with the most hours of daylight; the winter solstice has the longest night. At the poles, things are especially extreme during a solstice: 24 hours of the Sun at the same height in the sky, or 24 hours of extreme cold and darkness.

TEACH FROM VISUALS

FIGURE 15.3 Tell students that the yellow bars running horizontally into the left side of Earth represent rays of sunlight. **Ask**

- At which latitude or area is the sunlight striking Earth most directly? 0° (equator, tropical zone)
- Where is sunlight striking at the steepest angle? highest latitudes (polar)
- Where is sunlight striking at a slight angle? temperate latitudes (halfway between the equator and either pole)

Vocabulary

Academic Vocabulary Lines of **longitude** indicate east/west positions on Earth, whereas lines of **latitude** indicate north/south positions. Tell students that to help remember the orientation of the lines they can think of the shape their mouth takes when saying the vowel sounds of the first syllable of each word.

Answers

A Apply Intense sunlight indicates tropical climates, less intense sunlight indicates temperate climates, and weak sunlight indicates polar climates.

▼ Teach *continued*

QUICK LAB

Time 15 minutes	TEACHER TESTED ✓
Lab Binder Ecology, p. 38	

Purpose Identify microclimates in and around school grounds.

LAB MANAGEMENT

- Group students for this activity and assign one student in each group to be in charge of handling the thermometer.
- Assist students in choosing their locations.
- Have students prepare their data tables prior to the investigation.

Safety Avoid mercury thermometers.

Answers

Analyze and Conclude

Sunlit locations with low wind will register higher temperatures than nearby shaded locations or windy areas.

Integrating Earth Science

Global warming may be causing a slowdown of one of the Atlantic Ocean's most powerful currents. The **Gulf Stream** works like a conveyor belt. Cold, dense seawater in the Arctic sinks and flows to the south as water in the tropics warms, rises to the surface, and flows northward to take the place of the sinking cold water. This warm surface current gives off heat as it travels north, keeping western Europe's winters relatively mild. As the ice sheets of the Arctic melt into the sea and atmospheric temperatures are not chilling the waters of the Arctic as quickly, the conveyor is slowing down, meaning colder winters for Europe.

QUICK LAB OBSERVING NOS.5

Microclimates

Determine the temperature of inside and outside areas of your school to identify different microclimates.

PROBLEM Where are different microclimates in and around your school grounds?

PROCEDURE

1. Identify one place inside and one place outside your school where microclimates may exist.
2. Place a thermometer at each location. Wait at least five minutes before recording the temperature.

MATERIALS

- thermometer
- stopwatch

ANALYZE AND CONCLUDE

Compare the temperatures you collected with those recorded by your classmates at different locations.

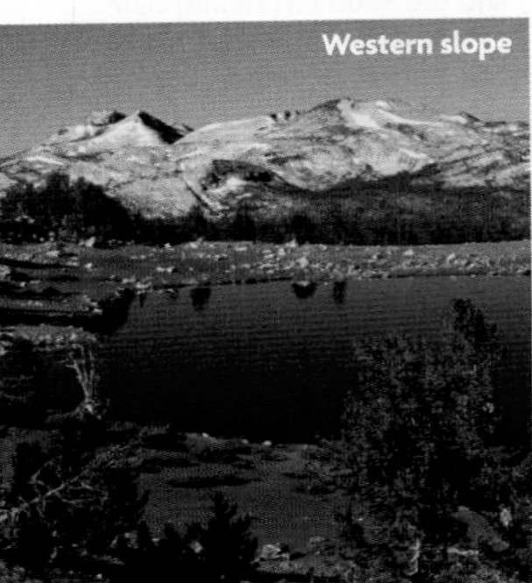

FIGURE 15.4 The western slope of the Sierra Nevada, which faces the prevailing winds, receives precipitation throughout the year. Due to the rain shadow, the eastern slope of the Sierras is much drier.

Air and Water Movement

When the Sun heats Earth, it warms not only the land and the rocks but also the water and the air. This heating causes movements in both water and air. Warm air and warm water are less dense than cooler air and water, and therefore they rise. Since the tropics near the equator are especially warm, the warm air here rises and the cooler air from areas to the north or south moves in to take its place. As the warm air rises, it cools. Since cold air holds less moisture than warm air does, a large amount of precipitation drops as rain. This large amount of precipitation, along with warm temperatures, defines the tropical rain forest regions found near the equator. The movement of air also leads to movement in water, forming currents. The rotation of Earth, water temperatures, and salinity levels also interact to form currents.

Landmasses

Landmasses also shape climates. For example, areas closer to bodies of water have a different climate from areas farther away because land tends to heat and cool more quickly than water. Thus, coastal areas tend to have smaller changes in temperature than areas farther inland. Farther inland, areas experience a much larger range of seasonal high and low temperatures.

Water evaporates from open bodies such as lakes or oceans faster than it does from soil or through plant transpiration. As a result, coastal sites in general have higher humidity and receive more precipitation than inland areas.

Mountains also may have a large effect on an area's climate. As warm, moist air nears a mountain, it rises and cools. This cooling of air results in precipitation on the side of the mountain range facing the wind. On the downwind side of the mountains, drier and cooler air produces a rain shadow, or area of decreased precipitation. The Sierra Nevada mountain range in California, shown in **FIGURE 15.4**, is one example of this phenomenon. While the western slope receives a large amount of precipitation, the Great Basin to the east of the mountains is dry.

Differentiated Instruction

HANDS-ON ACTIVITY

Have students bring in weather maps from newspapers or online sources and analyze the movement or development of weather fronts in relation to mountains, bodies of water, and other features of Earth's surface. Are there signs of rain shadow effect? What are the sources of the water that is coming down as rain or snow?

DATA ANALYSIS

NOS.3

CONSTRUCTING COMBINATION GRAPHS

Climatograms are combination graphs that represent weather data for a specific location or biome over a period of time. Refer to the Data Analysis Feature on page 442 to recall what a combination graph looks like.

1. **Graph Data** Plot the average precipitation as a bar graph, and plot the average temperature as a line graph.
2. **Analyze** How would you describe the temperature change throughout the year in this location?
3. **Identify** During which month is the precipitation level lowest for this location?
4. **Analyze** Is there a relationship between temperature and precipitation in Albuquerque, New Mexico? If so, explain how they are related.
5. **Explain** What is the benefit of using a combination graph to illustrate an area's climate?

TABLE 1. AVERAGE CLIMATE IN ALBUQUERQUE, NM

Month	Precipitation (mm)	Temperature (°C)
January	12.4	2.1
February	11.2	5.2
March	15.5	8.9
April	12.7	13.1
May	15.2	18.2
June	16.5	23.8
July	32.3	25.8
August	43.9	24.5
September	27.2	20.6
October	25.4	14.1
November	15.7	6.9
December	12.4	2.3

Source: National Oceanic and Atmospheric Administration

Adaptations to Climate

Many organisms have adaptations that allow them to survive in a specific climate. The water-holding frog shown in **FIGURE 15.5** is a dramatic example. It lives in the dry grasslands and deserts of inland Australia, where the rainy season comes only once a year. Dry periods can last 10 months or more. The frog survives the dry season by burrowing underground, where water evaporates more slowly. Moisture loss is further reduced by a cocoonlike structure formed from the frog's shed skin. When rains soak the ground, the frogs crawl out of their burrows to mate, and the females lay eggs in water puddles that form in depressions along the ground. Within a matter of weeks, the eggs hatch into tadpoles, and the tadpoles change into frogs. This frog must move through its life cycle very quickly because the water evaporates quickly once the rains end. If the tadpoles are not ready to leave the ponds, they will die.

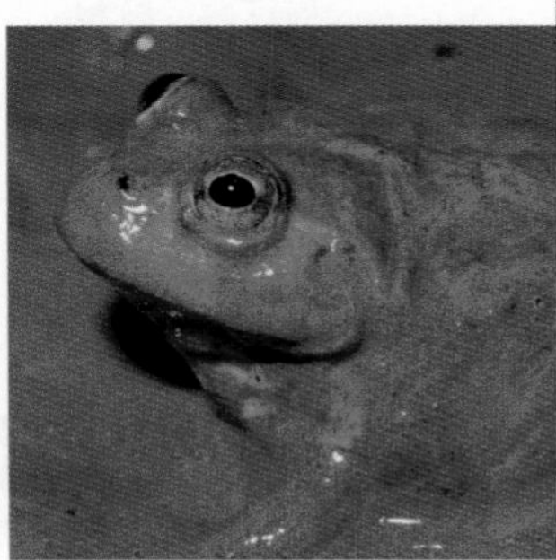

FIGURE 15.5 Water-holding frogs crawl out of their burrows to mate during the rainy season.

Connect **Describe the climate where you live.**

15.2 ASSESSMENT

ONLINE QUIZ ClassZone.com

B.4.4

REVIEWING MAIN IDEAS

1. What is the difference between **climate** and weather?
2. What are the three different climate zones, and where are they located?

CRITICAL THINKING

3. **Connect** Where might there be **microclimates** in your area?
4. **Infer** Would areas along the shores of the Great Lakes have warmer summers and colder winters than other inland areas? Explain.

Connecting CONCEPTS

5. **Niches** Would you expect an area with several microclimates to have more or fewer ecological niches? Explain your answer.

15.2 ASSESSMENT

1. Weather is the day-to-day temperature, precipitation, and wind conditions in a region. Climate is the long-term pattern of weather.
2. The polar climate is found at the North and South poles. The tropical climate is located near the equator. The temperate climate is found between the tropical and polar climates.
3. Answers will vary and may include forests, gardens, alleys, and open lots.
4. No, because of the buffering effects of the water, shoreline areas have moderate seasonal temperature changes compared to inland areas.
5. An area with several microclimates would have more ecological niches, allowing for a wider variety of organisms to find suitable habitats.

DATA ANALYSIS

Discuss

Climatograms are usually constructed with precipitation on one *y*-axis and temperature on the other. **Ask**

- What is the benefit of using a climatogram instead of simply studying the data? Trends in the data are much easier to see when organized into a graph.
- On many climatograms, temperature on the *y*-axis begins at −30° C. What is the benefit of having the temperature scale run so low if temperatures do not get that low? It sets the temperature curve well above that of precipitation, so the curves are more easily seen and compared.

Answers

1. Temperatures are lowest in winter, rise in spring, peak in summer, and decrease in autumn.
2. February
3. Precipitation increases slightly as temperatures rise in spring. The highest amounts of precipitation occur with the summer peak in temperature. Precipitation decreases as temperatures decrease throughout autumn and winter.
4. It illustrates relationships between temperature and precipitation, two main factors in characterizing a climate.

Unit Resource Book, Data Analysis, p. 85

Answers

A Connect Descriptions should include temperature, precipitation, wind conditions, and other climatic factors.

Assess and Reteach ▼

Assess Use the Online Quiz or Section Quiz (*Assessment Book*, p. 294).

Reteach Have students use a globe to describe Earth's three climate zones, identify their locations, and indicate how the angle of sunlight is involved.

SECTION 15.3

Plan and Prepare

Objectives

- Describe biotic and abiotic features of Earth's six major biomes.
- Explain why polar ice caps and mountains are not considered biomes.

Section Resources

Unit Resource Book	
Study Guide	pp. 73–74
Power Notes	p. 75
Reinforcement	p. 76
Pre-AP Activity	pp. 89–90
Interactive Reader	Chapter 15
Spanish Study Guide	pp. 159–160
Biology Toolkit	pp. C12, C19, C22
Technology	
Power Presentation	15.3
Media Gallery DVD	
Online Quiz	15.3

Activate Prior Knowledge Because the United States has several biomes, students should be familiar with them without necessarily knowing them as biomes. **Ask,** Thinking in terms of both climate and terrain, what kinds of general environments can we see in the United States? hardwood forests, desert, prairie (grassland), mountain, beach, tundra (Alaska)

Teach

TEACH FROM VISUALS

FIGURE 15.6 Remind students that a biome is a classification based on abiotic factors, not a location. **Ask,** Which continents have all six biomes? Asia, North America Remind students that biomes often do not have well-defined borders as shown on the map. There are often transition zones—including non-biome areas—in between biomes.

Answers

A Identify all six biomes

15.3 Biomes

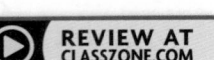

KEY CONCEPT Biomes are land-based, global communities of organisms.

MAIN IDEAS

- Earth has six major biomes.
- Polar ice caps and mountains are not considered biomes.

VOCABULARY

canopy, p. 464
grassland, p. 464
desert, p. 464
deciduous, p. 465
coniferous, p. 465
taiga, p. 465
tundra, p. 466
chaparral, p. 466

Review
biome

Connect You wouldn't find a cactus in a tropical rain forest or a penguin in a desert. Individual plant and animal species have adaptations that let them thrive only in certain biomes. In this section, you will learn about the major biomes of the world and the characteristics of each.

MAIN IDEA

Earth has six major biomes.

The global distribution of biomes is shown in **FIGURE 15.6.** Characteristics of each biome are given in **FIGURE 15.7.** As you will see, these broad biome types can be divided into even more specific zones. For example, the grassland biome can be further separated into zones of temperate and tropical grassland.

A variety of different ecosystems are found within a biome. However, because a biome is characterized by a certain set of abiotic factors, ecosystems located across the globe in the same biome—the tropical rain forest of Brazil or Madagascar, for example—tend to have similar plant and animal species.

***Connecting* CONCEPTS**

Levels of Organization Recall from **Chapter 13** that a biome is a major community of organisms, usually characterized by the climate conditions and plant communities that live there.

FIGURE 15.6 World Biomes

A biome is defined by its climate and by the plant communities that live there.

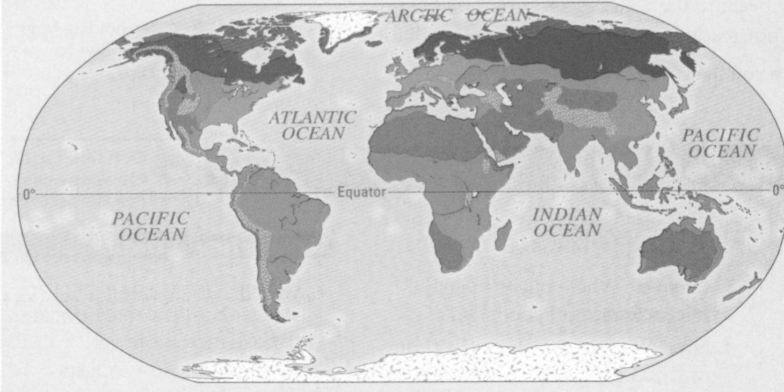

A Identify Which biomes are found in North America?

Differentiated Instruction

PRE-AP

Though they are so small that they are scarcely represented in maps such as **FIGURE 15.6,** the Pacific Islands are home to millions of people, dozens of languages, and a diversity of organisms both above and below the water. Have students write a paragraph speculating on what kinds of biomes may exist in the Pacific Islands, the majority of which are between 20°N and 20°S. Students should think about how the ocean, latitude, and elevations of the islands are involved in affecting climates.

Biology Toolkit, Quick-Write, p. C19

TEACH WITH TECHNOLOGY

Show the class a digital slide show of labeled photographs of the six biomes. After you have run through a number of photographs of each biome type, test students' ability to recognize biomes by showing them unfamiliar photographs that have telltale characteristics or species. You could also show them climatograms and give them a few minutes to infer in what biome or biomes the data could have been recorded. Go to **ClassZone.com** for visual resources.

FIGURE 15.7 Biomes

TROPICAL	
Tropical rain forest	• Warm temperatures and abundant rainfall occur all year. • Vegetation includes lush thick forests. • Animals that live within the thick cover of the upper-most branches of rain forest trees use loud vocalizations to defend their territory and attract mates.
GRASSLAND	
Tropical grassland	• Temperatures are warm throughout the year, with definite dry and rainy seasons. • Vegetation includes tall grasses with scattered trees and shrubs. • Hoofed animals, such as gazelles and other herbivores, dominate this biome.
Temperate grassland	• This biome is dry and warm during the summer; most precipitation falls as snow during the winter. • Vegetation includes short or tall grasses, depending on the amount of precipitation. • Many animals live below ground to survive the dry and windy conditions in this biome.
DESERT	
Desert	• This biome has a very dry climate. • Plants, such as cacti, store water or have deep root systems. • Many animals are nocturnal; they limit their activities during the day.
TEMPERATE	
Temperate deciduous forest	• Temperatures are hot in the summer and cold in the winter; precipitation is spaced evenly over the year. • Broadleaf forest dominates this biome, and deciduous trees lose their leaves in the winter.
Temperate rain forest	• This biome has one long wet season and a relatively dry summer. • Evergreen conifers, which retain their leaves (needles) year-round, dominate this biome. • While some species remain active in the winter, others migrate to warmer climates or hibernate.
TAIGA	
Taiga	• This biome has long, cold winters and short, warm, humid summers. • Coniferous trees dominate this biome. • Mammals have heavy fur coats to withstand the cold winters.
TUNDRA	
Tundra	• Subzero temperatures are the norm during the long winter, and there is little precipitation. • The ground is permanently frozen; only mosses and other low-lying plants survive. • Animal diversity is low.

BELOW LEVEL

Have students create a content frame that lists the six biomes and their characteristics such as temperature, precipitation, plants, and animals. If content frames are made for climates, as suggested in **Section 15.2,** students can study both to reinforce the differences between a climate and a biome.

Biology Toolkit, Content Frame, p. C22

Address Misconceptions

Common Misconception All deserts are hot and dry.

Correcting the Misconception It is the amount of rainfall an area receives that defines a desert, not the temperature range. **FIGURE 15.6** illustrates the wide range of latitudes in which deserts exist.

Take It Further

Biodiversity tends to decrease the farther an ecosystem is located from the equator. As one moves from the tropics to the poles, the tendency is to find larger and larger populations of fewer and fewer species. This is one reason much of the current loss of species is occurring most swiftly in the tropics. Populations there are smaller and more vulnerable to habitat loss, overfishing, and other factors.

Vocabulary

Greek and Latin Word Origins

- **Temperate** comes from the Latin *temperatus,* "to temper." To temper something, whether it is a material (glass, metal) or an emotion (anger), means to moderate or adjust it into a milder or more moderate state. Students can think of temperate climates and biomes as the mild middle ground between polar and tropical biomes and climates.
- **Pole,** from the Greek *polos,* refers to either extremity of an axis through a sphere, in this case, Earth.
- **Tropical** comes from Greek and Latin roots meaning "turning." If students think of Earth turning on its axis, it is at the equator that a given point on Earth is "turning" the fastest. Relative to Earth's axis, a person in Ecuador is traveling about 1000 miles an hour, while someone at one of the poles is barely moving.

▼ Teach continued

ONLINE BIOLOGY For an exercise in analyzing the distribution of amphibians in the world's biomes, see Data Analysis Online in Options for Inquiry, page 477.

Integrating Pharmacology

Because a tropical rain forest is the most biologically diverse biome, it offers medical scientists abundant opportunities to find compounds that can function as anesthetics and treatments for diseases. For example, **poison-dart frogs** of Central and South American rain forests have been studied closely for their medical and pharmaceutical potential.

Scientists observed native forest hunters dipping their blowgun darts in the **alkaloids** secreted by three species of these colorful amphibians. Epibatidine, which is an alkaloid in the skin secretion of the South America poison-dart frog, *Epipedobates tricolor,* is a painkiller 200 times more powerful than morphine. The alkaloids of another species, *Dendrobates auratus,* have been shown to stimulate heart activity. Unfortunately, much of the rain forest is now threatened by slash-and-burn agriculture and the timber industry.

Vocabulary

Greek and Latin Word Origins Plants that have evolved strategies that enable them to survive the hot, dry climate of a desert are called **xerophytes.** The prefix *xero-* comes from the Greek word *xeros,* meaning "dry." The suffix *-phyte* is from the Greek phyton, meaning "plant." *Xerophyte* ("dry plant") adaptations include reduced leaf surface area, stems that collect and hold water, and very short reproductive cycles so that they can bloom and make seeds during brief periods of rain.

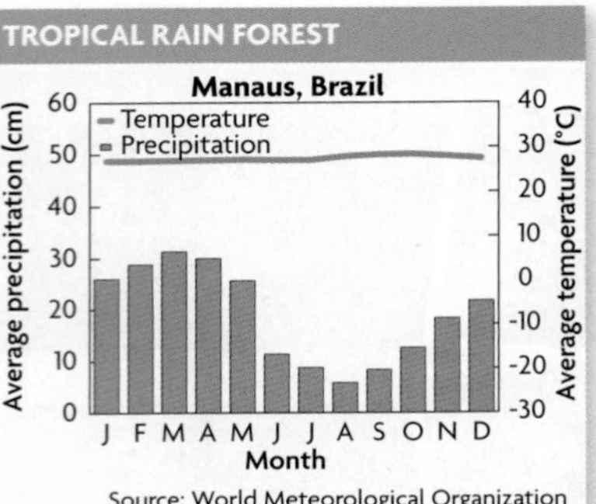

Tropical Rain Forest Biome

A tropical rain forest has warm temperatures and abundant precipitation throughout most, if not all, of the year. This climate typically produces lush, thick forests that can completely shade the forest floor. The limiting factor for plants that live on the forest floor is sunlight. In fact, as little as 1 percent of the sunlight that strikes the uppermost branches of the trees, called the **canopy,** may make it through to the ground. The soil is very thin and low in nutrients. Most organisms that live in this biome inhabit branches of the upper canopy. Some plants, called epiphytes, grow above the ground on the branches of trees. A few of these, such as some figs, sprout and develop on branches and then send down long lengths of roots that grow into the ground below.

Grassland Biomes

Grassland biomes occur in a variety of climates. A **grassland** is an area where the primary plant life is grass. Tropical grasslands are found in the tropical climate zones of South America, Africa, and Australia. Temperate grasslands are found in the temperate climate zones of South Africa, eastern Europe, and central North America.

Tropical grasslands, also called savannas, are covered with grass plants that may stand 1–2 meters (3–7 ft) in height. Some grasslands have scattered trees or shrubs, but the trees are never as thick and lush as in the tropical rain forests. The limiting factor in the savanna is rainfall. For five months or more each year, precipitation averages at most 10 centimeters (4 in.) a month; often there is much less. During the rainy season, however, water can replenish lakes, rivers, streams, and wetlands and form temporary ponds. This biome is home to plants and animals that have adapted to the extreme shifts in moisture.

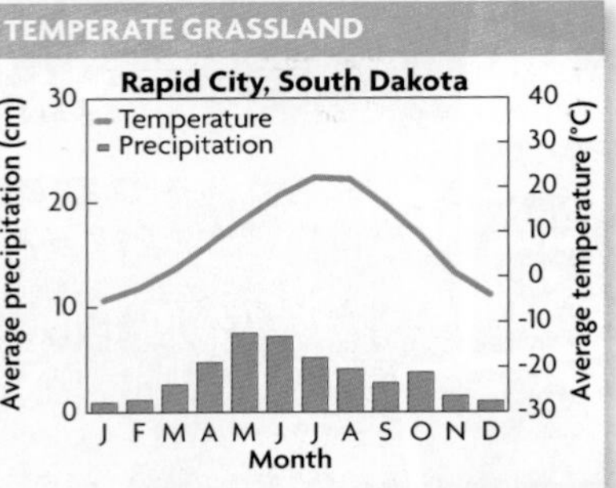

Temperate grasslands receive 50–90 centimeters (20–35 in.) of annual precipitation, most occurring as rain in the late spring and early summer. Summers may be warm or quite hot, depending on the latitude of the grassland. Under such arid conditions, fast-spreading fires are common. Some plants in temperate grasslands have adapted to fire by producing fire-resistant seeds that require the fire's heat to start germination.

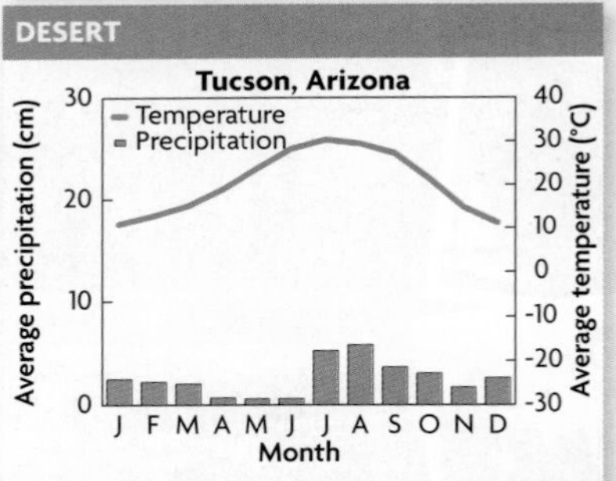

Desert Biome

Desert biomes receive less than 25 centimeters (10 in.) of precipitation annually, and are always characterized by a very dry, or arid, climate. There are four different types of deserts: hot, semiarid, coastal, and cold.

In hot deserts, such as the Sonoran Desert in Arizona, the daily summer temperature may easily top 38°C (100°F). At night, however, the temperature can drop by 10 degrees Celsius or more. During the winter, the temperature may be as low as 0°C (32°F). The precipitation falls as rain in hot deserts.

Differentiated Instruction

ENGLISH LEARNERS

After students have read and reviewed this section, organize students into six groups. Around the classroom, place six stations, each featuring a large sheet of paper displaying the name of one of the major biomes along with several questions about its characteristics. Have the groups rotate through the six stations and answer the questions by working together. Afterwards, regroup as a class to review and discuss.

Biology Toolkit, Carousel Review, p. C12

Semiarid deserts, like hot deserts, have long and dry summers and low amounts of rain in the winter. In comparison with hot deserts, however, temperatures are cooler and rarely exceed 38°C. Coastal deserts are characterized by cool winters followed by relatively long, warm summers. Temperatures range from a maximum of 35°C (95°F) in the summer to –4°C (25°F) in the winter. In cold deserts, such as the Great Basin of the western United States, precipitation falls evenly throughout the year and often occurs as snow in the winter. Summer temperatures range between 10°C (50°F) at night to 24°C (75°F) during the day, and winter temperatures can drop below freezing.

Plants use a variety of strategies to survive a desert's heat and lack of moisture. The reduced surface area of a cactus's spines helps it to retain more water by avoiding moisture loss from transpiration. Many desert plants have the ability to conserve or store water over a long period of time. Some desert plants, such as mesquite, have extremely long root systems that absorb water by reaching down to the water table. Desert plants also have heat- and drought-resistant seeds.

Contrast How do rainfall amounts differ in deserts and in tropical rain forests?

Temperate Forest Biomes

A key feature of temperate biomes is their distinguishable seasons. The growing season occurs during the warmer temperatures from mid-spring to mid-fall and depends upon the availability of water.

The **temperate deciduous forest** typically receives about 75–150 centimeters (30–59 in.) of precipitation spread over the entire year as rain or snow. This biome is characterized by hot summers and cold winters. **Deciduous** trees have adapted to winter temperatures by dropping their leaves and going dormant during the cold season. Trees, such as oaks, beeches, and maples, along with shrubs, lichens, and mosses, make up the main vegetation.

The **temperate rain forest** does not receive precipitation evenly spaced across the year. Instead, it has one long wet season and a relatively dry summer, during which fog and low-lying clouds provide the needed moisture. Precipitation in the temperate rain forest averages over 250 centimeters (98 in.) per year. Evergreen conifers, such as spruces, Douglas firs, and redwoods, dominate this biome. **Coniferous** trees retain their needles all year. Mosses, lichens, and ferns are plant species found on the forest floor.

TEMPERATE FOREST

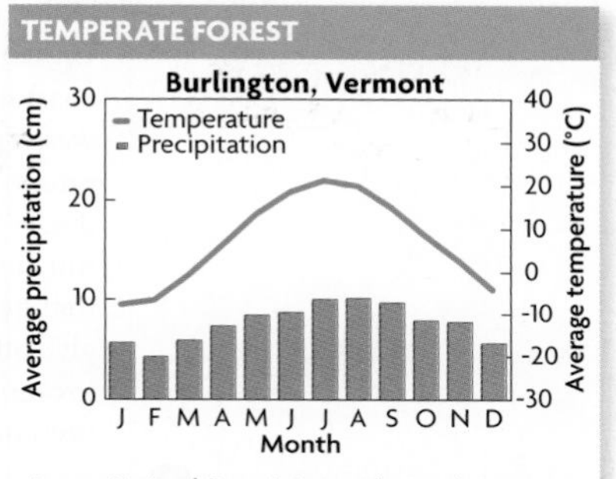

Source: National Oceanic Atmospheric Administration

Taiga Biome

The **taiga** (TY-guh), also known as the boreal forest, is located in cooler climates. Winters are long and cold, often lasting six months or more. The average winter temperature is below freezing. Summers are short, typically with only two to three months of frost-free days. However, they may be quite humid and warm, sometimes reaching 21°C (70°F). Precipitation in the taiga is 30–85 centimeters (12–33 in.) per year, which is similar to that in the arid temperate grasslands. Coniferous forest is dominant in the taiga.

TAIGA

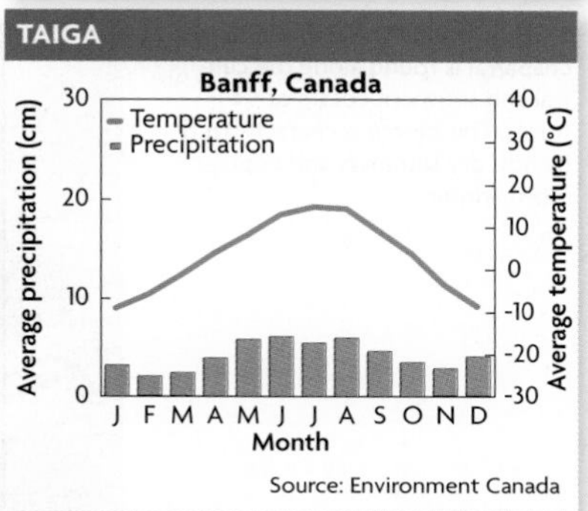

Source: Environment Canada

Answers

A Contrast Deserts receive less than 25 centimeters (10 in.) of rain a year, while tropical rain forests are characterized by abundant levels of rainfall throughout the year, as shown in the climatogram on page 464.

Take It Further

Giant sequoias, also known as Sierra redwoods, are the largest trees in the world. Sequoias depend on fire as an abiotic factor to clear away competing saplings from the forest floor and to dry out their cones so that seeds will fall and germinate. For years the U.S. Forest Service used fire suppression to protect the trees. With a better understanding of the ecosystem, the Forest Service recently began a program of **prescribed burning.** Prescribed burns help maintain and promote the growth of redwood forests, as well as other plant communities, such as prairies, that depend on fire for long-term stability.

Science Trivia

- Giant sequoias can approach 90 meters (300 feet) in height and 11 meters (37 feet) in trunk diameter.
- Probably the largest single organism on Earth is a giant sequoia named General Sherman.
- The General Sherman sequoia is estimated to weigh more than 1000 tons, equivalent to about 10 blue whales—the largest animals on Earth.
- Some giant sequoias are ancient, having lived as long as 3200 years.

INCLUSION

The differences between the leaves and seed pods of deciduous and coniferous trees can be appreciated visually, but also through touch. Give students who are visually impaired a chance to handle various pinecones, pine branches, deciduous leaves, and deciduous seed pods so they can better understand how these groups are adapted to life in the temperate forests or taiga. Be sure to ask students about plant allergies and have them wash their hands after handling the plants.

▼ Teach *continued*

Vocabulary

Tundra comes from the Finnish word *tunturia,* meaning "barren land" or "treeless plain." While trees cannot grow in the *tundra* because permafrost prevents root growth, there are shrubs, sedges, mosses, lichens, and grasses, some of which provide food for migrating herds of caribou.

Take It Further

Plants of the chaparral are adapted to fire in several different ways. Plants known as **obligate resprouters** cope with fire by resprouting from root systems in the ground. **Obligate seeders** depend on their offspring (seedlings) to maintain the population. Seeds of these plants often will germinate only if some fire-related cue, such as smoke or heat, is abundant in the soil. The Tecate cypress, a conifer, has cones that open only when there is a fire.

This is not to say that these plants are dependent on fire. These adaptations simply mean that when fires do occur, the plants can survive or at least pass on their genes to their offspring.

Answers

A Connect Answers will vary according to students' geographic location.

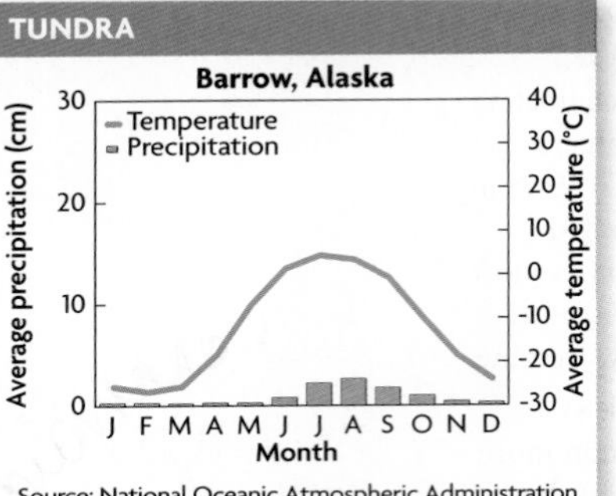

Tundra Biome

Often described as bleak, the **tundra** is located beyond the taiga in far northern latitudes. Winter lasts as long as 10 months a year. The average winter temperature is below freezing. The ground below the surface is always frozen. This frozen ground is known as permafrost. Summers last just 6 to 10 weeks. Precipitation is meager, averaging less than 13 centimeters (5 in.) annually.

In addition to limited precipitation, permafrost captures and holds moisture, making very little available to plants. Therefore, the tundra is quite barren. Only mosses, other tiny, low-lying plants, and a few scattered shrubs are able to survive. Trees and most flowering plants do not grow here.

Minor Biomes

In addition to the six major biomes, there are also some other biomes that occur globally, but on a smaller scale. One example is chaparral, shown in **FIGURE 15.8**. **Chaparral** (SHAP-uh-RAL), also called Mediterranean shrubland, is characterized by its hot, dry summers and cool, moist winters. Over the year, temperatures in the chaparral range from 10°C (50°F) to 40°C (104°F). Annual precipitation ranges from 38–102 centimeters (15–40 in.), and occurs mostly during the winter as rain. The dominant plants in the chaparral are small-leaved evergreen shrubs. This biome is found in small areas across the globe, including the central and southern coast of California in the western United States, the coast of Chile in South America, the Mediterranean Sea coast in Europe, the southern and western coasts of Australia, and the southwestern tip of South Africa. Because of the fairly hot climate, the plants in this biome exhibit some of the same adaptations to heat as those found in the desert biome. Many plants have shallow root systems that let them take in as much water as possible when it rains. The leaves of shrubs have thick cuticles that help in water retention. Many plant species, such as sage and rosemary, give off a strong smell. These aromatic oils are also highly flammable, and promote fire. As in temperate grasslands, chaparral plants have adapted to the presence of fire, and some plants need fire in order for their seeds to germinate.

A Connect **What biome includes the area where you live?**

FIGURE 15.8 In the United States, chaparral is found along the central and southern coasts of California. This biome is characterized by hot, dry summers and cool, moist winters.

Differentiated Instruction

PRE-AP

It may be difficult for students to understand how fire could be anything but a disaster for any system. Have them think of reasons why some chaparral plants have evolved to withstand or depend on fire. What would be the selective advantage of reproducing after a fire has devastated the standing plants in a community? Why would plants secrete oils that are flammable?

Biology Toolkit, Quick-Write, p. C19

MAIN IDEA

Polar ice caps and mountains are not considered biomes.

FIGURE 15.9 A polar bear's thick layer of fat, or blubber, keeps it well insulated from the cold as it rests on an ice floe or swims in Arctic waters to catch food.

Polar ice caps are ice-covered areas that have no soil and do not have a specific plant community. In mountains, the climate and the animal and plant communities change depending on elevation. Because of these characteristics, polar caps and mountains are not categorized as biomes.

Polar ice caps occur around the poles at the top and bottom of Earth. In the Northern Hemisphere, the polar ice cap includes parts of Greenland and permanently frozen portions of the Arctic Ocean and surrounding islands. In the Southern Hemisphere, the polar ice cap includes the glacier-covered continent of Antarctica. At the ice caps, ice and snow cover the surface all year. Very few plants or fungi are able to survive the harsh conditions found in the polar regions. Some species found in Antarctica include mosses and lichens. Most animals in this region depend on the sea for their food. Animals such as polar bears, shown in **FIGURE 15.9**, have layers of fat that keep them warm in the cold polar conditions. Different animals are found in the northern and southern polar regions. For example, polar bears are found only in the north, while penguins are found only in the south.

Mountains are often rich with life. Different communities of species have adapted to the variety of ecosystems found at different mountain elevations. As you move up a mountain, the different communities that you see are similar to the biomes found in different latitudes across the globe. For example, you may begin a hike in a grassland at the base of the mountain, continue upward through a coniferous forest, and finally reach a desolate tundralike zone at the mountain's top. While the life zones found on mountains are similar across biomes, their species of plants and animals differ as a result of the different abiotic factors that shape each biome.

Summarize **Explain why neither polar ice caps nor mountains are considered**

15.3 ASSESSMENT

ONLINE QUIZ ClassZone.com

REVIEWING MAIN IDEAS

1. List and describe the six major biome types.
2. What are some characteristics of mountains and polar ice caps?

CRITICAL THINKING

3. **Predict** How might stopping fires change a temperate **grassland**?
4. **Infer** Polar bears have white fur but black skin underneath. Consider the climate in which the bears live. What might be the adaptive advantage of the bears' black skin?

Connecting CONCEPTS

5. **Animal Behavior** Male birds that migrate the earliest to their summer nesting sites can usually secure the best territories. What limiting factor keeps birds from arriving too early in the **taiga**?

Take It Further

The current warming trend in the Arctic has spelled trouble for the **polar bear.** These carnivores hunt seals for food, but they do so from the stability of the ice shelf or an ice floe. Because the ice pack is breaking up and retreating northward earlier and farther than it used to, bears now have to swim great distances—sometimes between 50 and 100 miles—to get to hunting grounds. Some bears that attempt these exhausting swims end up drowning; others end up starving.

Answers

A Summarize Polar ice caps have no characteristic plant life. Mountains may exhibit the characteristics of several biomes in sequence from top to bottom, because an increase in elevation is analogous to an increase in latitude.

Assess and Reteach

Assess Use the Online Quiz or Section Quiz (*Assessment Book*, p. 295).

Reteach Print out copies of **FIGURE 15.6** from the Media Gallery and distribute to students. Have students create an expanded map key that includes the characteristics of each biome type.

15.3 ASSESSMENT

1. tropical rain forest: warm temperatures and abundant precipitation; grassland: temperatures warm throughout the year with distinct dry and rainy seasons; desert: very dry, temperatures can be very high in daytime and cold at night; temperate forest: distinguishable seasons; taiga: long, cold winters and short, humid summers; tundra: long, cold winters and little precipitation
2. Different communities that are analogous to biomes are found at different elevations of mountains. Polar ice caps are ice-covered, have no soil, and lack plant communities.
3. Stopping fires would change the grassland landscape, as some plants that grow there need fire as part of their growth cycle. Without fire, seeds would be unable to germinate, and other plants that are suppressed by fire could thrive and dominate. In time, the grassland could become a forest.
4. The black skin on a polar bear absorbs heat from the Sun.
5. temperature, because it dictates how much water is available for drinking and also the growth of food that birds rely on

SECTION 15.4

▼ Plan and Prepare

Objectives

- Identify the four major ocean zones and organisms unique to each zone.
- Describe the unique habitats of coastal waters.

Section Resources

Unit Resource Book Study Guide pp. 77–78 Power Notes p. 79 Reinforcement p. 80
Interactive Reader Chapter 15 **Spanish Study Guide** pp. 161–162
Biology Toolkit pp. C19, C23
Technology Power Presentation 15.4 Media Gallery DVD Online Quiz 15.4

Activate Prior K
marine ecosyste
be familiar with:
salt marshes, kel
thermal vents, al
ocean. **Ask,** Wha
define, affect, ar
systems? sunligh
turbidity, depth,

Know
Ocean zones -
Neritic zone - biomass
Chemosynthetic
organisms live in
Abyssal zone
No light
Bathyal zone
high pressure

▼ Teach

Take It Fu

Intertidal zones c
bays, estuaries, m
shorelines, and ev
jetty. Intertidal zones offer various niches in which different species and adaptations have evolved. **Ask,** In intertidal zones where there is periodic battering by waves, what kinds of adaptations might be seen in animals that live there? features that allow the animals to attach to rocks and withstand the force of the waves

ONLINE BIOLOGY Go to the chapter Resource Center at **ClassZone.com** for additional resources and information on aquatic ecosystems.

15.4 Marine Ecosystems

KEY CONCEPT Marine ecosystems are global.

MAIN IDEAS

- The ocean can be divided into zones.
- Coastal waters contain unique habitats.

VOCABULARY

intertidal zone, p. 468
neritic zone, p. 468
bathyal zone, p. 469
abyssal zone, p. 469
plankton, p. 469
zooplankton, p. 469
phytoplankton, p. 469
coral reef, p. 470
kelp forest, p. 470

Connect If you've ever been to the ocean, you are already familiar with some ocean zones. If you walked on the beach at the edge of the surf, you were in the intertidal zone. If you went into the water, you were swimming in the neritic zone. In this section, you will learn about these and other zones that divide the ocean. You will also read about the unique habitats found along the ocean's coasts.

MAIN IDEA

The ocean can be divided into zones.

The oceans are a global expanse of water containing a large variety of living things that dwell from coastline shallows to the great depths of the deep-sea vents.

Ocean Zones

Scientists use several systems to divide the ocean into different zones. The simplest division of the ocean separates the water of the open sea, or pelagic zone, from the ocean floor, which is called the benthic zone.

The presence of light is also used to differentiate between areas of the ocean. The photic zone is the portion of the ocean that receives plentiful sunlight. In contrast, the aphotic zone refers to the depths of the ocean where sunlight does not reach.

In a third system, as shown in **FIGURE 15.11,** the ocean is separated into zones using distance from the shoreline and water depth as dividing factors.

The **intertidal zone** is the strip of land between the high and low tide lines. If you have ever walked on the beach, you have been in the intertidal zone. Organisms in this zone, such as those that inhabit tidal pools, must tolerate a variety of conditions that result from changing water levels. Organisms must contend with changes in temperature, amount of moisture, and salinity. The sea anemone, for example, opens up when underwater during high tide. It avoids drying out during low tide by closing up.

The **neritic zone** (nuh-RIHT-ihk) extends from the intertidal zone out to the edge of the continental shelf. The depth of the neritic zone may range from a few centimeters at low tide to more than 200 meters deep.

FIGURE 15.10 Organisms that live in tidal pools, such as this one off the Washington coast

Differentiated Instruction

HANDS-ON ACTIVITY

Display an assortment of once-living marine organisms, such as dried sea stars, shells of bivalves and snails, crab and lobster carapaces, dried plants, and pieces of coral. Have students speculate on the kinds of habitats or zones these organisms may have lived in. Even if students know the answer already, they should explain why the characteristics and adaptations of the organism are well suited to a specific habitat or zone.

ENGLISH LEARNERS

Students may wonder why the word *zone* is used to define parts of a marine ecosystem. Point out that the word suggests subdivisions of a whole.

FIGURE 15.11 Ocean Zones

The ocean is divided into four major zones.

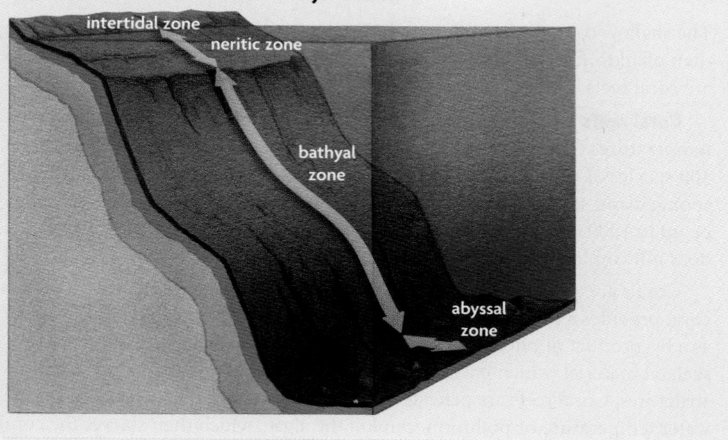

The **bathyal zone** (BATH-ee-uhl) extends from the edge of the neritic zone to the base of the continental shelf. The bathyal zone lies between the depths of 200 and 2000 meters. This zone is characterized by water that is turbid, or murky, due to the accumulation of silt. Fish that have adapted to living in areas of high pressure live in the bathyal zone. Burrowing animals thrive in this zone.

The **abyssal zone** (uh-BIHS-uhl) lies below 2000 meters and is in complete darkness. While deep-sea vents support a large number of organisms, the total number of species found in this zone is much smaller than the number found in the neritic zone. Since there is no light, photosynthetic organisms do not exist. Chemosynthetic organisms are the base of the food webs at the deep-sea vents. Many organisms that live in the abyssal zone make their own light, much as a firefly produces its glow. This light is often used to attract mates and prey.

VOCABULARY

In the word *bathyal,* the prefix *bathy-* comes from a Greek word meaning "deep." In the word *abyssal,* the word part *abyss* comes from a Greek word meaning "bottomless."

Life in the Neritic Zone

Although the neritic zone represents less than one-tenth of the total ocean area, it contains 40 times more biomass than the rest of the ocean. Much of the biomass consists of organisms called plankton. **Plankton** are tiny free-floating organisms that live in the water. These organisms include both animals and protists. **Zooplankton** is another term for animal plankton. **Phytoplankton** are photosynthetic plankton, which include microscopic protists such as algae.

Marine phytoplankton, especially blue-green algae and other types of algae, are critical to life on the planet. These organisms carry out the bulk of photosynthesis on Earth, and therefore provide most of the oxygen. According to many estimates, 70 percent or more of the oxygen in every breath you take can be traced back to marine phytoplankton. In addition to their role in oxygen production, phytoplankton also form the base of the oceanic food web.

***Connecting* CONCEPTS**

Invertebrates Some invertebrates, such as sea stars and lobsters, are plankton during their larval stage. You will learn more about the life stages of invertebrates in **Chapter 23.**

 Hypothesize **What other adaptations might organisms have in the abyssal zone?**

ONLINE BIOLOGY Have students view an interactive animation on ocean zones. See Options for Inquiry on page 477.

TEACH FROM VISUALS

FIGURE 15.11 Have students locate each of the major ocean zones. **Ask,** What are some abiotic factors that affect organisms in each zone? intertidal zone: wave action, exposure to air, temperature fluctuations; neritic zone: sunlight, surface currents; bathyal zone: little or no sunlight, high pressure; abyssal zone: no light, cold temperatures, high pressure, thermal vents

Vocabulary

Greek and Latin Word Origins The prefix *zoo-* in **zooplankton** (ZOH-oh-playng tuhn) comes from the Greek *zöion,* meaning "animals." **Zoology,** meaning "the study of animals," has the same prefix.

Science Trivia

- Zooplankton is one food source of whales, the world's largest animals.
- A typical humpback whale may eat up to 1800 kilograms (4000 lb) of plankton per day.

Answers

A Hypothesize ability to withstand high pressure, light organs, large eyes for light detection

BELOW LEVEL

Have students make a drawing similar to **FIGURE 15.11** and label each zone with its characteristics and depth profile.

Biology Toolkit, Combination Notes, p. C23

PRE-AP

Have students imagine that they are equipped with special diving suits or submersibles that allow them to dive down through the different ocean zones. Give them five minutes to describe in writing what they see and feel as they descend through the zones.

Biology Toolkit, Quick-Write, p. C19

▼ Teach *continued*

The Inside Story

Jacques-Yves Cousteau was famous for his explorations of the underwater world and his influence on generations of marine enthusiasts. Perhaps his greatest contribution to science was the invention of **scuba** (self-contained underwater breathing apparatus). This invention allowed divers to go deeper under water and explore for longer periods without being tethered to the ship by a breathing tube.

Science Trivia

- The Great Barrier Reef (GBR) is the largest tropical coral reef system on Earth.
- It is roughly the length of Japan, stretching 2300 kilometers (1429 mi) along the northeastern coast of Australia.
- The GBR is not a single reef, but a chain of over 3000 reefs and 900 small islands.

Answers

A Compare Both are highly productive and support enormous biological diversity.

▼ Assess and Reteach

Assess Use the Online Quiz or Section Quiz (*Assessment Book,* p. 296).

Reteach Have students study **FIGURE 15.11** for a few minutes. Then ask them to close their books and make a diagram of the ocean zones that shows their relative locations from the shore and their approximate depths.

MAIN IDEA

Coastal waters contain unique habitats.

FIGURE 15.12 Ecologists are working to rebuild coral reef ecosystems by building artificial reefs, such as this network of cables, onto which corals can adhere.

The shallow coastal waters that make up the neritic zone contain much more than plankton. Two highly diverse habitats found within these coastal waters are coral reefs and kelp forests.

Coral reefs are found within the tropical climate zone. In this area, water temperatures remain warm all year. A single coral reef may be home to 50 to 400 species of corals, along with hundreds of other species, including fishes, sponges, and sea urchins. Studies indicate that the biomass in coral reefs may be up to 1000 times greater than the biomass in a similar area of ocean that does not contain a reef.

Corals are animals that have a mutualistic relationship with algae. The coral provides a home for the algae, and algae provide nutrients for the coral as a by-product of photosynthesis. Coral reefs are made mostly of coral skeletal material, which packs together over thousands of years into solid structures. Coral reefs are delicate. A change in conditions, such as increased water temperature or pollution, can kill the algae, which then starves the coral. With global ocean temperatures on the rise, coral reefs are in decline around the world.

Ecologists are trying to reintroduce these diverse communities in some areas by making artificial reefs, shown in **FIGURE 15.12**, where organisms can find shelter. In addition, some shipwrecks and sunken oil rigs have become artificial reefs that can support fishes and other species associated with coral reefs.

To learn more about coral reefs, visit scilinks.org.
Keycode: MLB015

In contrast to coral reefs, **kelp forests** exist in cold, nutrient-rich waters, such as those found in California's Monterey Bay. These forests are composed of large communities of kelp, a seaweed. Kelp grows from the ocean floor up to the water's surface, sometimes extending up to a height of over 30 meters (about 100 ft). Kelp forests are areas of high productivity that provide habitat and food sources to many marine species ranging from tiny invertebrates to large mammals, such as sea lions.

 **Compare** **What are the similarities between coral reefs and kelp forests?**

15.4 ASSESSMENT

ONLINE QUIZ ClassZone.com

REVIEWING MAIN IDEAS

1. What criteria do scientists use to divide the ocean into different zones?
2. What conditions account for the development of highly diverse habitats in coastal waters?

CRITICAL THINKING

3. **Connect** A red tide occurs when a bloom of **plankton** causes a reddish discoloration of coastal ocean waters. What might cause such an increase in plankton populations?
4. **Predict** What might organisms that inhabit the **abyssal zone** eat?

***Connecting* CONCEPTS**

5. **Food Webs** How might the disappearance of coastal habitats affect an oceanic food web?

15.4 ASSESSMENT

1. open sea and ocean floor; presence of light; distance from shoreline and water depth
2. sunlight, upwelling of nutrients, temperature variations, currents, wind, waves, tides
3. Answers may include increased amounts of nutrients in the water and temperature that is conducive to this kind of alga.
4. Organisms in the abyssal zone might eat other organisms that inhabit the zone or organic matter that sinks from the bathyl zone. This organic matter may be bits of dead plants or animals or the feces of living animals.
5. Because many fish species spend an early stage of their lives in coastal habitats and many marine organisms feed on these and other coastal organisms, the disappearance of these habitats would be devastating to oceanic food webs.

15.5 Estuaries and Freshwater Ecosystems

KEY CONCEPT Freshwater ecosystems include estuaries as well as flowing and standing water.

MAIN IDEAS
- Estuaries are dynamic environments where rivers flow into the ocean.
- Freshwater ecosystems include moving and standing water.
- Ponds and lakes share common features.

VOCABULARY
estuary, p. 471
watershed, p. 473
littoral zone, p. 474
limnetic zone, p. 474
benthic zone, p. 474

Review
ecosystem

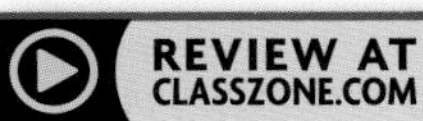

Connect You rely on aquatic ecosystems more than you might realize. Many of the fish and shellfish that you might eat depend, at least for a part of their lives, on estuaries. But more importantly for you, freshwater ecosystems provide the water that you need to survive.

MAIN IDEA
Estuaries are dynamic environments where rivers flow into the ocean.

An **estuary** is a partially enclosed body of water formed where a river flows into an ocean. The San Francisco and Chesapeake bays are estuaries. So are the Louisiana bayous, Florida Bay in the Everglades, and many other harbors, sounds, and inlets around the world.

The distinctive feature of an estuary is the mixture of fresh water from a river with salt water from the ocean. The river carries high levels of nutrients from inland areas. The tidal movements of water in the ocean also bring in large volumes of organic matter and a variety of marine species from the ocean. Large numbers of species thrive in this rich mixture of fresh water and salt water.

Estuaries are highly productive ecosystems, on a level comparable to tropical rain forests and coral reefs. Photosynthetic organisms thrive in estuaries throughout the year, providing the basis for the aquatic food web. Estuaries also have thriving detritivore communities that decompose the enormous amounts of dead plant and animal matter that build up in the estuary's waters. These decomposers return vital nutrients back to the ecosystem. Estuaries also provide the necessary habitat for a number of endangered and threatened species. For example, the brown pelican, the Morro Bay kangaroo rat, and a plant called the Morro manzanita are all threatened or endangered species that depend on the Morro Bay estuary in California, shown in **FIGURE 15.13.**

FIGURE 15.13 An estuary occurs where a river flows into the ocean. Estuaries are high in biodiversity and provide habitat for a number of different species.

Differentiated Instruction

ENGLISH LEARNERS
Have students draw an estuarine system and label its features and characteristics, such as the flow of fresh water and salt water, the presence of larval and juvenile fish, and the role of reefs, sandbars, and barrier islands.

Biology Toolkit, Combination Notes, p. C23

SECTION 15.5

Plan and Prepare ▼

Objectives
- Summarize the characteristics of estuaries and the organisms that inhabit them.
- Describe moving and standing freshwater ecosystems and the adaptations of the organisms that inhabit them.
- Identify common features of ponds and lakes.

Section Resources

Unit Resource Book
Study Guide pp. 81–82
Power Notes p. 83
Reinforcement p. 84

Interactive Reader Chapter 15
Spanish Study Guide pp. 161–162

Biology Toolkit pp. C23, C34

Technology
Power Presentation 15.4
Media Gallery DVD
Online Quiz 15.4

Activate Prior Knowledge Have students describe an experience they have had on or near an estuary or a freshwater ecosystem, such as a lake or river. Tell them to include any organisms they remember seeing. **Ask,** What kinds of abiotic factors influence organisms in an estuary or a freshwater ecosystem? climate, salinity, water movements, sunlight, sedimentation

Teach ▼

Vocabulary
Academic Vocabulary Tell students the word **dynamic** relates to objects or energy in motion, often continuously. This word is often applied to systems, such as an estuary, where various factors and forces are interacting in a dynamic way. The often-used idea of a "balance of nature" is more accurately termed "dynamic equilibria," as this refers to the cyclical nature of many natural systems and to the fact that few ever arrive at some kind of final phase.

▼ Teach *continued*

Take It Further

The **San Francisco Bay** is the largest estuary on the west coast of the United States. The San Joaquin and Sacramento rivers flow into the bay, and salt water from the Pacific comes in on the high tide. In the last century, the bay's estuarine system has been changed by the introduction of as many as 250 exotic or non-native species. The striped bass, *Morone saxatilis,* arrived by way of boxcars from the east coast in 1879 so that San Franciscans would have another fish to dine on. Since then, it has become a rival of the indigenous salmon, competing for food and eating young salmon. The Asian clam, *Corbula amurensis,* arrived to the bay in the ballast water released from large trans-Pacific ships. It is a small bivalve, but it is now the dominant invertebrate in the bay.

Answers

A Analyze The area is rich in nutrients carried by the river(s) from inland areas. Tidal movements bring in nutrients from the ocean. Reefs and barrier islands provide protection to species within an estuary, particularly those who spend their larval or juvenile stages there.

FIGURE 15.14 The Tejo Estuary in Portugal is an important stop-over point for migratory birds such as these greater flamingos.

***Connecting* CONCEPTS**

Keystone Species Recall from **Chapter 13** that a keystone species is a species that has a large effect on its ecosystem. Migratory birds in the Delaware Bay depend on horseshoe crab eggs as a main food source. This dependence illustrates the importance of the horseshoe crab in its estuarine ecosystem.

Estuary Characteristics

The large number of phytoplankton and zooplankton in an estuary support a variety of species. Populations of fish and crustaceans depend on plankton as their primary food source. In turn, birds and other secondary consumers eat fish and crustaceans. Humans also rely on estuaries as a food source. In fact, 75 percent of the fish we eat depend on estuary ecosystems, making estuaries an important resource for the commercial fishing industry.

Estuaries provide a protected refuge for many species. Reefs and barrier islands along an estuary's boundary with the ocean protect estuary species from storms and the ocean's strong currents and waves. In an estuary's calm waters, many aquatic species lay eggs, and their young mature there before venturing into the ocean. The use of estuaries as spawning grounds explains why these areas are often called nurseries of the sea. Estuaries are also a key part of the migration paths of many bird species, as shown in **FIGURE 15.14.** Birds rely on estuaries as a refuge from the cold weather that occurs in the northern parts of their range during certain parts of the year.

Changing conditions in estuaries present challenges for species that live there. For example, in order to withstand changing salinities, some organisms have glands that remove the excess salt that builds up in their bodies. This adaptation helps organisms cope with an estuary's changing salinity level. Salt levels may lower with the tide and during periods of drought or heavy rainfall.

Threats to Estuary Ecosystems

Estuaries are made up of a variety of ecosystems, including salt marshes, mud flats, open water, mangrove forests, and tidal pools. When estuaries are lost to land development and other human activities, these ecosystems and the organisms that live within them are also lost.

The removal of estuaries also makes coastal areas more vulnerable to flood damage from catastrophic storms such as hurricanes. Estuaries act as a buffer between the ocean and coastal land. In some coastal areas of the United States, over 80 percent of the original estuary habitat has been lost to land development.

A Analyze **What characteristics make an estuary such a productive ecosystem?**

Differentiated Instruction

HANDS-ON

Have students work in pairs or small groups to create a guided tour of a freshwater or marine ecosystem in the area. The tour should include all parts and depths of the ecosystem and point out biotic and abiotic factors through the use of digital images. Have the groups use a digital slide show, poster, or other medium to serve as the virtual ecosystem for their tour.

BELOW LEVEL

Have students make a compare/contrast chart for the zones of marine and freshwater ecosystems. They can set up a table in which the systems are in the rows and their zones' characteristics are compared within columns. For example, littoral zone should be matched up with intertidal, and limnetic with neritic.

Biology Toolkit, Compare/Contrast, p. C34

MAIN IDEA

Freshwater ecosystems include moving and standing water.

Rivers and streams are the flowing bodies of fresh water that serve as paths through many different ecosystems. Rivers and streams, along with lakes and ponds, originate from watersheds. A **watershed** is a region of land that drains into a river, a river system, or another body of water.

Freshwater Ecosystems

If you have ever paddled down a river in a canoe, you have probably witnessed the change in shoreline ecosystems, perhaps with a forest along one stretch and sand dunes along another. Along its course, a river may vary in many ways. For example, the speed of its flow is greater in narrow areas than in wide ones. The river bottom may be alternately sandy, gravel-covered, or rock-strewn. The water level may differ across seasons. In some areas, spring brings about the melting of snow and causes river water levels to rise. Humans also affect water levels by damming rivers or by draining water for irrigation or drinking water.

Unlike rivers and streams, wetlands have very little water flowing through them. A wetland is an area of land that is saturated by ground or surface water for at least part of the year. Bogs, marshes, and swamps are different types of wetlands that are identified by their plant communities. Common wetland plants include cattails, duckweed, and sedges.

Like estuaries, wetlands are among the most productive ecosystems on Earth. They provide a home for a large number of species, some of which are only found in wetlands. Wetlands also help maintain a clean water supply. A wetland filters dirty water and renews underground stores of water.

FIGURE 15.15 As the Colorado River travels southward from Colorado to Mexico, it flows through different ecosystems, including forests and deserts.

Adaptations of Freshwater Organisms

The particular variety of freshwater organisms found in a body of water depends on a number of factors. These factors include water temperature, oxygen levels, pH, and the water flow rate. Each type of freshwater ecosystem is home to species with adaptations suited to its conditions. In fast-moving rivers, for example, trout are adapted to swim against the current. They have streamlined bodies that can slice through the water easily. Some aquatic insects, such as the stonefly, have hooks on their bodies. The stonefly uses the hooks to attach itself to a solid surface in fast-running water to avoid being swept away. Similarly, tadpoles that live in fast-running water often have sucker mouths that they use to attach to a surface while feeding. These tadpoles also have streamlined bodies with long tails and low fins that help them to move in the fast water. Tadpoles that live in pools or in slower moving water often lack sucker mouths and have more rounded bodies and higher fins.

Predict **What effect would the construction of a dam have on a river ecosystem?**

Integrating Earth Science

Pollution resulting from urban buildup along the margins of estuaries and the rivers that feed them presents a series of challenges to the health of estuary systems and the species that live there. Discharge of sewage, runoff from paved roads, and fertilizers that leach into the system from upriver are all sources of pollution. **Soil erosion** is another problem, as it contributes to turbidity of the water, loss of tree cover, and warmer temperatures of the estuary.

Science Trivia

The Great Salt Lake in Utah is the largest lake west of the Mississippi River. It is three to five times saltier than the ocean. Runoff flows into the lake from the surrounding area, carrying dissolved salts from rocks. Because the lake has no outlet, water can escape only by evaporation, leaving the salts behind to accumulate over time. The Great Salt Lake has no fish but is teeming with brine shrimp.

Answers

A Predict Water would no longer flow at the same speed, water temperature might change, and erosion would occur at a slower rate. Species that depend on fast-flowing water might be threatened.

PRE-AP

Have students consult a map to determine the biomes, ecosystems, ocean zones, and other systems that the waters of the Colorado River flow through as they descend from the western United States to the Gulf of California. Students can draw their own map or diagram that illustrates this flow through these systems, and can use arrows to show how water from the ocean then is recycled back to the river through evaporation and precipitation.

▼ Teach *continued*

ONLINE BIOLOGY Have students explore different ecosystems in the WebQuest in Options for Inquiry, page 477.

Vocabulary

Greek and Latin Word Origins The prefix *thermo-*, as in **thermocline,** comes from the Greek word *thermē*, meaning "heat." The suffix *-cline* comes from the Greek word *klīnein*, meaning "to lean." As in *decline* and *recline*, *-cline* means "a gradual change." Thus, *thermocline* means "a gradual change in heat."

Answers

A Analyze Lake turnover brings nutrients from the bottom of the lake to the top, where they are used by organisms.

▼ Assess and Reteach

Assess Use the Online Quiz or Section Quiz (*Assessment Book*, p. 297).

Reteach Ask students to call out answers and provide details by creating a cluster diagram to contrast estuaries, rivers, streams, wetlands, lakes, and ponds. You might include the terms *fresh water, salt water, moving water, standing water, productive ecosystem,* and *zones.*

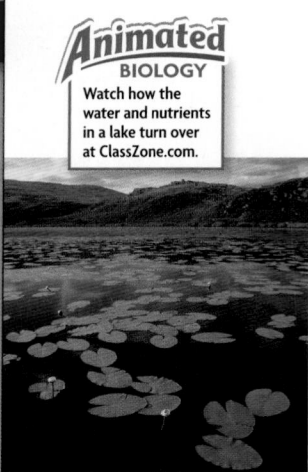

Animated BIOLOGY Watch how the water and nutrients in a lake turn over at ClassZone.com.

FIGURE 15.16 In the spring and fall, the water in a lake turns over, bringing nutrients from the bottom of the lake to the top.

MAIN IDEA

Ponds and lakes share common features.

Although they are much smaller in size than oceans, freshwater ponds and lakes are also divided into zones. Scientists use the terms *littoral, limnetic,* and *benthic* to identify and separate these zones.

- The freshwater **littoral zone** is similar to the oceanic intertidal zone, and it is located between the high and low water marks along the shoreline. The waters of the littoral zone are well-lit, warm, and shallow. A diverse set of organisms, including water lilies, dragonflies, and snails, live in this zone.
- The **limnetic zone** (also called the pelagic zone) refers to the open water located farther out from shore. This zone is characterized by an abundance of plankton communities, which support populations of fish.
- The **benthic zone** is the lake or pond bottom, where less sunlight reaches. Decomposers, such as bacteria, live in the mud and sand of the benthic zone.

During the summer and the winter, the water temperature within a lake is stratified, which means that different layers of the lake have different temperatures. In the summer, water is warmer near the surface and colder at the bottom of the lake. These warm and cold regions are separated by a thin zone called the thermocline.

All of the water within a lake "turns over" periodically. This happens because water is most dense at 4°C (39°F). When water reaches this temperature, it will sink beneath water that is either warmer or cooler. In autumn, colder air temperatures cool the surface layer of water to 4°C, causing it to sink and mix with the water underneath. During the winter, the surface layer of water cools to less than 4°C. In the spring, when the surface water warms to 4°C, it sinks and mixes with the layers of water below. In both autumn and spring, the underlying water flows upward and switches places with the surface water. This upwelling brings nutrients such as bits of decaying plants and animals from the benthic zone to the surface, where they are eaten by surface-dwelling organisms.

A Analyze What is the significance of lake turnover to the lake ecosystem?

15.5 ASSESSMENT

ONLINE QUIZ ClassZone.com

REVIEWING MAIN IDEAS

1. What are the characteristics of an **estuary** ecosystem?
2. What abiotic factors might affect a river ecosystem?
3. How is a lake different from the ocean? How is it the same?

CRITICAL THINKING

4. **Compare and Contrast** How are coastal wetlands different from and similar to estuaries?
5. **Predict** If an oil spill wipes out most of the producers in an estuary, how might the food web in the surrounding area be affected?

***Connecting* CONCEPTS**

6. **Adaptation** Many fish species and other aquatic animals have colorations that closely resemble the rocks or silt found on the bottom of their aquatic habitat. What types of ecological advantages might such an adaptation give an aquatic species?

15.5 ASSESSMENT

1. An estuary is a partially enclosed body of fresh water and salt water mixing together. Estuaries have a large amount of biodiversity and are important breeding grounds for a variety of species.
2. seasonal changes in water level, geology of the water bed, siltation, erosion
3. A lake is smaller than an ocean and has seasonal water turnover that is similar to downwelling and upwelling in oceans. Like an ocean, a lake can be divided into zones based on depth.
4. An estuary is a shallow area with a mix of fresh water and salt water. A coastal wetland also is a shallow area, but it is fresh water.
5. Primary consumers would have no food and would die off, leaving secondary consumers without food. Offshore fisheries could collapse, along with ocean food webs.
6. Such colorations provide aquatic animals protection from predators, as the colors help camouflage the animals.

Winter Water Chemistry

MATERIALS

- 2 plastic bowls
- sample water and sediment
- 500 mL beaker
- Elodea leaves
- wax paper
- plastic food wrap
- large rubber band
- warm water bath
- cold water bath
- 2 thermometers
- dissolved oxygen kits
- pH strips

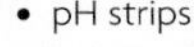

PROCESS SKILLS

- **Designing Experiments**
- **Collecting Data**
- **Analyzing Data**

NOS.3 Clearly communicate their ideas and results of investigations verbally and in written form using tables, graphs, diagrams, and photographs.

NOS.4 Regularly evaluate the work of their peers and in turn have their work evaluated by their peers.

Seasonal changes in temperature cause changes in lake ecosystems and the organisms that live there. Chemical cycles can vary from winter to summer, and the presence of ice on the surface of a lake also can alter oxygen levels. In this lab, you will design an experiment that models the conditions of lake water in the summer and in the winter. You will collect data from both models to determine how a layer of surface ice can affect lake water chemistry.

PROBLEM How does a layer of winter ice affect the chemistry of lake water?

DESIGN YOUR EXPERIMENT

1. Using the materials listed, design an experiment to determine differences between lake water chemistry in winter conditions and in summer conditions. Keep in mind that dissolved oxygen and pH are two variables that are influenced by lake surface ice.
2. Write a procedure to explain how you will set up your experiment, and which variable you will test. Identify a control group and experimental group, the data you will collect, and how often you will collect it.
3. Have your experimental design approved by your teacher.
4. Design a table to organize your results.
5. Conduct your experiment.

ANALYZE AND CONCLUDE

1. **Graph Data** Determine the best way to present how the variable in the experimental group changed over time. Determine whether you should draw a line graph or a bar graph, and then construct that type of graph.
2. **Analyze Data** How did the variable in each experimental group change over time? Why did these changes occur? What differences occurred between the two set-ups? What accounts for these differences?
3. **Experimental Design** What discrepancies exist between your simulation of summer and winter water conditions and real conditions? How might these discrepancies affect your results?
4. **Communicate** Discuss your results with other groups. Are the trends in their results similar to yours? If not, compare your experimental designs. Can any differences in experimental design or procedure account for differences in results? As a class, discuss what factors in this experiment are most important to obtaining accurate results.
5. **Apply** Review your data. How would the changes in the chemistry of the water affect aquatic organisms?

EXTEND YOUR INVESTIGATION

Design an experiment in which you would track the changes in these variables in a real lake over a year. Include information on how you would measure the effects of the changes on the organisms living in the lake. What other variables, besides dissolved oxygen and pH, would you want to track as part of this experiment?

INVESTIGATION

TEACHER TESTED

Time	45 minutes
Teacher Preparation	2 flasks
Student Difficulty	3 flasks
Lab Binder	Ecology, pp. 31–33

Purpose Investigate seasonal changes in a lake ecosystem.

Overview Students model summer and winter lake conditions to determine how surface ice affects the water chemistry of a lake. They will

- write an experimental procedure, identifying the control group and the experimental group
- collect data each day for six days

LAB MANAGEMENT

- Allow 15 minutes per day for six days to collect data.
- Keep "Summer" bowls uncovered in warm water, about 24°C (75.2°F).
- Keep "Winter" bowls in cold water, about 2°C (35.6°F). Cover these bowls with plastic wrap to simulate the effect of an ice layer.

Safety Students should use hand protection (gloves) when handling lake/pond water and sediment, and wash their hands after class.

POST-LAB DISCUSSION

Relate lab results to photosynthesis and cellular respiration. **Ask,** What effect does the "ice" have on producers? prevents gas exchange, plants unable to undergo photosynthesis, so water lacks dissolved oxygen required by aquatic animals

Answers

Analyze and Conclude

1. Students should graph changes in DO and pH over time: time on the *x*-axis; DO and pH on two *y*-axes.
2. "Summer" model: There is little change, because gas exchange and photosynthesis occur. "Winter" model: DO and pH decrease over time because gas exchange and sunlight are blocked. pH decreases as CO_2 increases; DO decreases due to respiration and lack of photosynthesis.
3. Amounts of sunlight differ in summer and winter. Real lake could be more stratified in the summer because of thermoclines; have more gas exchange because of wind and wave action; have water coming in via rain, streams, rivers, and runoff.
4. Controlling all variables except the experimental one is important.
5. Low DO levels or highly acidic water may mean that organisms cannot survive.

Extend Your Investigation

Other variables could include lake turbidity, precipitation, introduction of nutrients from runoff or pollution, temperature, thickness of ice, and presence of surface algae (blocking sunlight).

OPTIONS FOR INQUIRY

INVESTIGATION

Time 45 minutes TEACHER TESTED

Teacher Preparation

Student Difficulty

Lab Binder Ecology, pp. 35–36

Purpose Model and compare abiotic factors for plant growth in different biomes.

Overview Students will design two biomes. They will

- choose soil types and seeds
- determine the temperature, water, and light levels of each biome
- measure plant growth in each biome

LAB PREPARATION

- Have students bring in enough cartons for two biomes per group.
- Have students poke holes in the bottom of the cartons for drainage and put the same amount of soil in each biome.
- Students will need 10 minutes a day for 2–3 weeks to collect data.

Teacher Note "Students should review the characteristics of each biome they are modeling to determine how much light and water the models should receive."

Safety Check for plant allergies. Remind students to wash their hands and caution them not to eat the seeds.

POST-LAB DISCUSSION

Discuss possible reasons for seeds that failed to germinate or grow after germination.

Use these inquiry-based labs and online activities to deepen your understanding about the biosphere.

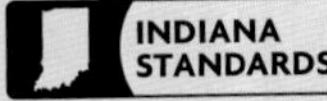

NOS.5 Apply standard techniques in laboratory investigations to measure physical quantities in appropriate units and convert known quantities to other units as necessary.

NOS.6 Use analogies and models (mathematical and physical) to simplify and represent systems that are difficult to understand or directly experience due to their size, time scale, or complexity, and recognize the limitations of analogies and models.

INVESTIGATION

Modeling Biomes

You have already learned about the characteristics of Earth's different biomes, including temperature ranges and how much water and light they receive. In this lab, you will model several biomes.

SKILL Modeling

PROBLEM What types of plants grow in certain biomes?

PROCEDURE

1. Choose two of the following biomes to model: desert, grassland, or tropical rain forest.
2. Choose which soil you will use in each biome and which seeds you will plant in each. Decide how much light and water each biome will receive each day. Determine how you will measure which type of plant grows in each biome.
3. Determine what type of data you need to collect and how often you need to collect it; construct a data table to record the data you collect.

MATERIALS

- cardboard container
- scissors
- stapler
- plastic or aluminum tray
- sandy soil
- potting soil
- 30 wheatgrass seeds
- 10 lima bean seeds
- 5 sunflower seeds
- permanent marker
- masking tape
- water
- light source
- refrigerator
- metric ruler

ANALYZE AND CONCLUDE

1. **Analyze** How did seed growth differ between the biomes? Which seeds were the most and least successful? Under which conditions did these situations occur?
2. **Experimental Design** What other variables could you control to make your model biomes as realistic as possible?
3. **Synthesize** How would you model an aquatic biome such as a wetland or a lake?

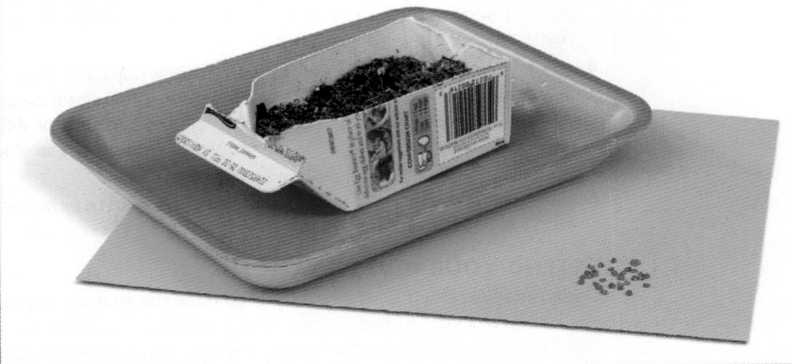

Answers

Analyze and Conclude

1. Answers will vary depending on the biomes and seeds students chose.
2. Answers may include animal species and wind conditions.
3. Answers will vary but may include using a plastic or glass container with water of controlled salinity, sediment, aquatic inhabitants, temperature, and light. Wave or river effects could be modeled using an aerator, a fan, or another device.

INVESTIGATION

Heating and Cooling Rates of Water and Soil

Water and soil have many different qualities. One quality is the rate at which each substance heats up and cools down. In this lab, you will compare the heating and cooling rates of water and soil.

SKILL Comparing

MATERIALS
- marker
- 2 clear plastic cups
- ruler
- soil
- water at room temperature
- 2 thermometers
- lamp

PROBLEM What are the heating and cooling rates of water and soil?

PROCEDURE
1. Mark a line 3 centimeters from the bottom of each cup. Fill one cup to the line with water and the other with soil.
2. Design a table in which to record your data.
3. Place a thermometer into the contents of each cup. Allow the thermometer to sit in each cup for 3 minutes, then take an initial temperature reading. Record your data in your data table.
4. Put the cups side by side under a lamp. Do not allow the lamp bulb to touch the water. Keep all electrical cords away from the water. After 15 minutes, record the temperature in each cup.
5. Turn off the lamp and move the cups away from the lamp to simulate shade. After 15 minutes, record the temperature in each cup.

ANALYZE AND CONCLUDE
1. **Analyze Data** Which substance had the faster rate of heating? Which had the faster rate of cooling?
2. **Apply** How do the heating and cooling rates of water and soil affect aquatic and land ecosystems?
3. **Connect** How do the differences in heating and cooling rates affect climates of coastal cities?

Online BIOLOGY
CLASSZONE.COM

ANIMATED BIOLOGY
Where Do They Live?
Species have adapted to life in specific ocean zones. Use their adaptations as well as other clues to place organisms in the appropriate ocean environments.

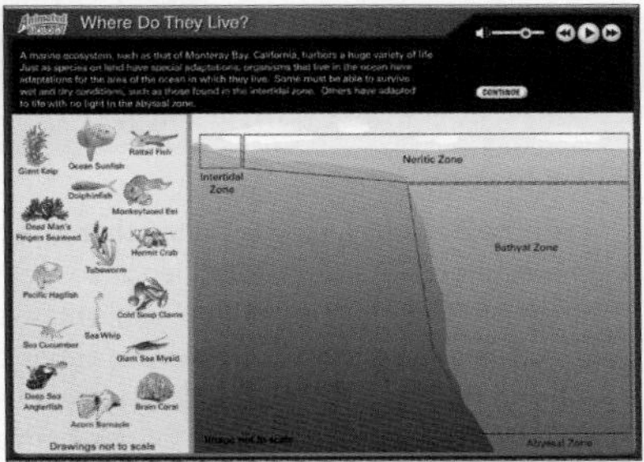

WEBQUEST
In this chapter you read overviews of the major ecosystems on Earth. Use this WebQuest to focus on one ecosystem and dig further. Explore the organisms, geology, soils, climate, and other characteristics specific to that environment. Then compare that ecosystem with your observations of the one in which you live.

DATA ANALYSIS ONLINE
Amphibians are found all over the world, but they are not evenly distributed. Some areas have many more types of amphibians than others. Graph the number of known amphibian species by region and analyze the distribution.

Online Biology ▼

ANIMATED BIOLOGY Use this interactive animation to reinforce concepts covered in **Section 15.4.**

WEBQUEST The WebQuest takes one full class period. Students complete the activity online and will need access to a printer to print their answers. Sample answers, teacher notes, and alternative assessment ideas are available at **ClassZone.com.** Use with **Section 15.5.**

DATA ANALYSIS ONLINE
Students should use a bar graph to determine the distribution of amphibians. Amphibian biodiversity is greatest in regions near the equator and generally decreases as latitude increases. Use with **Section 15.3.**

INVESTIGATION TEACHER TESTED

Time	45 minutes
Teacher Preparation	⚗
Student Difficulty	⚗
Lab Binder	Ecology, p. 37

Purpose Compare heating and cooling rates of soil and water.

Safety Students should exercise caution with the hot bulb and keep the lamp cord away from water. Students should wash their hands before leaving the lab each day.

Answers

Analyze and Conclude

1. The soil had the faster rate of both heating and cooling.
2. Aquatic ecosystems do not experience the daily temperature extremes that terrestrial ecosystems do, so aquatic species have not evolved the kind of behavioral or metabolic adaptations that many terrestrial species have. What this means, though, is that if an extreme change occurs, the organisms in an aquatic ecosystem may be less able to cope than those in a terrestrial system. The bleaching events seen in coral reef ecosystems is an example.
3. Coastal cities have smaller temperature ranges than inland areas have because the large body of water nearby tends to moderate the climate of the city. In summer, the water can offer evaporative cooling, and in winter, heat remaining from the warmer months can radiate out and warm the city somewhat.

CHAPTER REVIEW

Interactive Review

Encourage students to go to **ClassZone.com** for a detailed review of each section, including visuals and vocabulary practice.

Unit Resource Book, Vocabulary Practice, pp. 91–94

CHAPTER 15

Interactive Review @ CLASSZONE.COM

KEY CONCEPTS | Vocabulary Games | Concept Maps | Animated Biology | Online Quiz

15.1 Life in the Earth System

The biosphere is one of Earth's four interconnected systems. The biosphere includes living organisms, called the biota, and the land, air, and water on Earth where the biota live. Biotic and abiotic factors interact in the biosphere, and a change in one Earth system can affect the others.

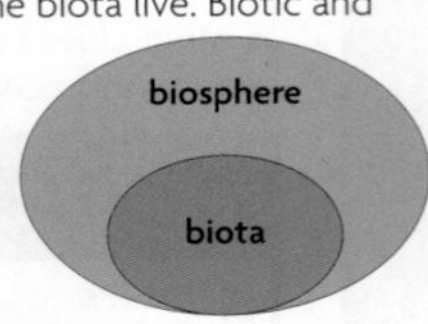

15.2 Climate

Climate is a key abiotic factor that affects the biosphere. Factors that influence an area's climate include temperature, sunlight, water, and wind. The three main climate zones on Earth are polar, tropical, and temperate. The polar zone is located at the far northern and far southern reaches of the planet. The tropical zone surrounds the equator. The temperate zone is located in the broad area between the polar and tropical zones.

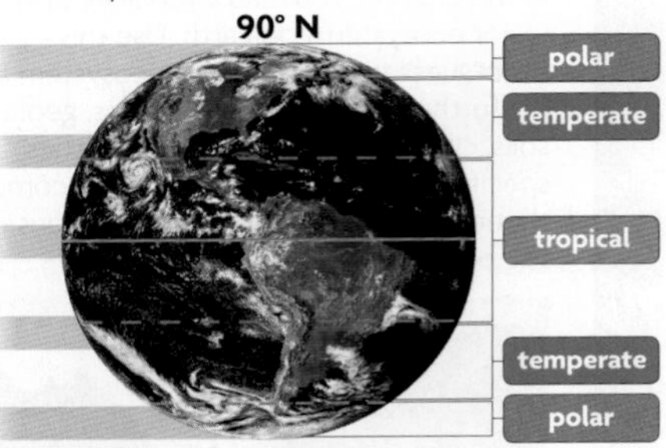

15.3 Biomes

Biomes are land-based, global communities of organisms. Earth has six major biomes. These biomes include tropical rain forest, grassland, desert, temperate forest, taiga, and tundra. Polar ice caps and mountains are not considered biomes.

15.4 Marine Ecosystems

Marine ecosystems are global. Scientists use different criteria to separate the ocean into different zones. One system separates the ocean into zones using distance from the shoreline and water depth as dividing factors. The neritic zone contains 40 times more biomass than the open ocean. Coral reefs are found in the warm, shallow waters of the tropical climate zone. Kelp forests thrive in cold, nutrient-rich waters.

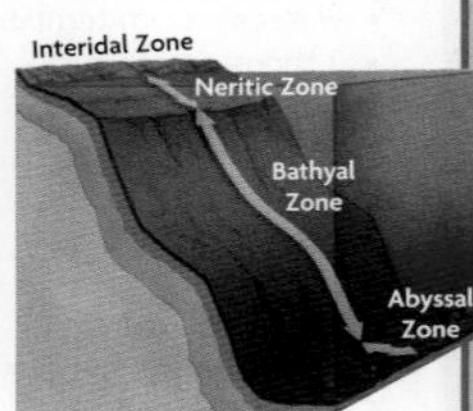

15.5 Estuaries and Freshwater Ecosystems

Freshwater ecosystems include estuaries as well as flowing and standing water. An estuary is a partially enclosed body of water that exists where a river flows into an ocean. A variety of organisms are adapted to the constant change in salinity found in an estuarine ecosystem. Freshwater ecosystems include rivers and streams, wetlands, and lakes and ponds.

Synthesize Your Notes

Concept Map Use a concept map to summarize what you know about climate zones.

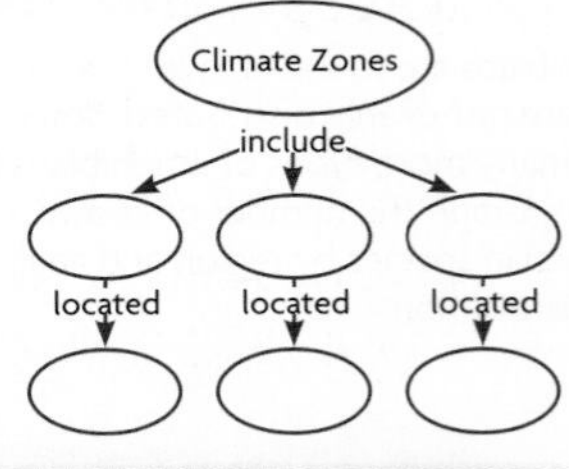

Supporting Main Ideas Use a diagram like the one below to summarize what you know about biomes.

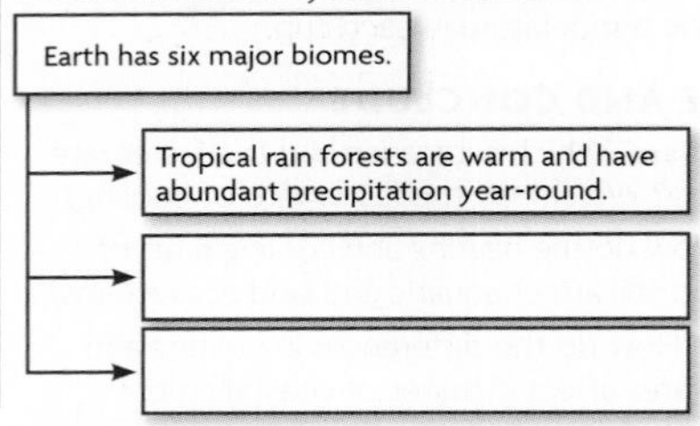

Reviewing Vocabulary

1. Both include living things, but the biosphere also includes nonliving things.
2. Both are tiny free-floating organisms that live in water. Zooplankton is animal plankton. Phytoplankton is photosynthetic plankton.
3. Both are Earth systems. The atmosphere is the air blanketing Earth's solid and liquid surface. The hydrosphere is all of Earth's water.
4. Both refer to the long-term pattern of weather conditions in a specific area. Microclimate is the climate of a small specific place within a larger area and climate.
5. Both are biomes. The taiga is located in cool climates, and coniferous forests are dominant. The tundra is located beyond the taiga in far northern latitudes, and few plants grow there.
6. Both are ocean zones. The intertidal zone is in the range between high and low tides. The neritic zone extends from the intertidal zone to the edge of the continental shelf.
7. Both are diverse habitats found in shallow coastal waters of the ocean. Kelp forests are found in cold waters. Coral reefs are found in warm tropical waters.
8. Plankton are organisms that drift in water, as though wandering. Their primary mode of movement is being carried by currents.
9. Climate is the long-term weather pattern of a specific region on Earth's solid and liquid surface.
10. An estuary is a body of water that forms where ocean and river water meet. This ecosystem is affected by both tidal movement and river flow.
11. The littoral zone is the area of a lake or pond nearest the shore.
12. Every year, in autumn, the leaves of deciduous trees fall off.

Chapter Assessment

Chapter Vocabulary

15.1 biosphere, p. 456
biota, p. 456
hydrosphere, p. 456
atmosphere, p. 456
geosphere, p. 456

15.2 climate, p. 458
microclimate, p. 458

15.3 canopy, p. 464
grassland, p. 464
desert, p. 464
deciduous, p. 465
coniferous, p. 465
taiga, p. 465
tundra, p. 466
chaparral, p. 466

15.4 intertidal zone, p. 468
neritic zone p. 468
bathyal zone, p. 469
abyssal zone, p. 469
plankton, p. 469
zooplankton, p. 469
phytoplankton, p. 469
coral reef, p. 470
kelp forest, p. 470

15.5 estuary, p. 471
watershed, p. 473
littoral zone, p. 474
limnetic zone, p. 474
benthic zone, p. 474

Reviewing Vocabulary

Compare and Contrast

Describe one similarity and one difference between the two terms in each of the following pairs.

1. biosphere, biota
2. zooplankton, phytoplankton
3. hydrosphere, atmosphere
4. climate, microclimate
5. taiga, tundra
6. neritic, intertidal
7. kelp forest, coral reef

Greek and Latin Word Origins

8. The term *plankton* comes from the Greek word *planktos,* which means "wandering." Explain how this meaning relates to plankton.

9. The term *climate* comes from the Greek word *klima,* which means "surface of the earth." Explain how this meaning relates to the definition of *climate.*

10. The term *estuary* comes from the Latin word *æstus,* which means "tide" or "surges." Using this meaning, explain how it relates to what an estuary is.

11. The term *littoral* comes from the Latin word *litoralis,* meaning "shore." Explain how this meaning relates to the definition of *littoral zone.*

12. The term *deciduous* comes from the Latin word *decidere,* which means "to fall off." How is this meaning related to the definition of *deciduous?*

Reviewing MAIN IDEAS

13. Explain the difference between the terms *biota, biosphere,* and *biome.*

14. After a forest fire wipes out plants growing on a hill, rainwater washes soil down into a stream, and the stream fills with silt. In this example, what are the interactions between biotic and abiotic factors? **B.4.2**

15. If the temperature in an area drops five degrees between one day and the next, has the climate of the area changed? Explain.

16. What is the connection between sunlight, the curved shape of Earth, and Earth's three main climate zones?

17. Earth has six major biomes—tropical rain forest, grassland, desert, temperate forest, taiga, and tundra. Why are two different deserts, each on a separate continent, considered to be the same biome?

18. Why are polar caps and mountains not considered biomes?

19. Briefly compare the four ocean zones—intertidal, neritic, bathyal, and abyssal—based on their distance from the shoreline and their water depth.

20. Where, in terms of water depth, would you expect to find a coral reef? a kelp forest?

21. Estuaries occur where rivers flow into the ocean. What conditions in estuaries make them suitable as nurseries for organisms that live out in the open ocean as adults?

22. The ecosystem of a river upstream in the mountains and downstream in a valley can be very different. Describe the adaptations of an upstream organism and an organism that lives downstream in the same river.

CHAPTER REVIEW

Reviewing Main Ideas

13. The biosphere is the part of Earth where life exists. The biota is the collection of living things in the biosphere. A biome includes living things, meaning it overlaps with both the biosphere and the biota.

14. The forest fire (abiotic factor) interacts with the plants (biotic factor) when it kills the plants. Rainwater, soil, the hill, and the stream (all abiotic factors) interact when rainwater washes soil down the hill and into the stream. When silt (abiotic factor) accumulates in the stream, it may harm the organisms (biotic factor) living in the stream.

15. The climate has not changed; the weather has. Climate characteristics are long-term.

16. Because of Earth's curved shape, there is variability in how sunlight strikes and heats Earth's surface. It is most indirect and seasonally variable in the polar zone (temperature is low, daylight varies greatly), most direct and less seasonably variable in the tropical zone (high temperatures, little or no variability in daylight), and generally moderate in the temperate zone (temperature and daylight vary but within a smaller range).

17. They have the same climate and plant communities.

18. polar ice caps: no soil, no characteristic plant community; mountains: a range of climates and plant communities

19. intertidal zone: between the high and low tide extremes; neritic zone: from the intertidal zone to 200 m deep; bathyal zone: edge of the neritic zone to the base of the continental shelf (2000 m); abyssal zone: below 2000 m

20. Both are found in the neritic zone, where they receive sunlight.

21. Estuaries are rich in nutrients, and many feature outer reefs, sandbars, and barrier islands, which offer small organisms shelter.

22. Organisms living in the swift, cool waters of a mountain stream will be streamlined and may have ways (such as suckers) to grasp rocks or burrow into gravelly substrate. Organisms downstream, where the water may move more slowly and be more turbid, might be wider, slower, and capable of burrowing or hiding in the softer substrata.

ITEM CORRELATIONS

Standard	Items
B.4.2	14, 35
B.4.4	26, 27

Critical Thinking

23. hydrosphere, biosphere, atmosphere
24. The polar climate zone and the temperate climate zone would not have extreme seasonal changes of temperature or daylight.
25. A change in climate could cause a biome to change into another type of biome. For example, if a grassland receives very little rainfall over the course of many years, it could become a desert.
26. Algae provide the nutrients needed for coral to survive. Algae are at the base of a coral reef food web.
27. *Sample Answer:* Estuaries support a large variety of species, especially fishes in their early life stages. They are a major stopover location for migratory birds, and they are among the most productive ecosystems on Earth.

Interpreting Visuals

28. The organisms get water from precipitation and the ocean spray during high tide.
29. Species in the spray zone must be able to retain moisture and protect themselves from terrestrial consumers. Species in the low-tide zone must be able to withstand tidal movements, surf, and fluctuations of temperature.
30. Some fish commute to the intertidal zone (especially on the high tide), but most need to go out with the tide in order to have enough water to respire and enough room to maneuver. They may divide their time between the neritic and intertidal zones.

Critical Thinking

23. Apply A deer drinks water from a stream, and then later it breathes out some of the water as vapor into the air. Through which three Earth spheres has this water moved?

24. Infer How would Earth's three main climate zones be different if Earth's axis were not tilted in relation to the Sun? (**Hint:** The tropical climate zone would likely be the most similar to how it is now.)

25. Infer Do you think it is possible for a biome to change from one type into another? Explain a situation in which this might happen.

26. Connect Why does the health of an entire coral reef ecosystem depend on algae? **B.4.4**

27. Analyze Describe two reasons why it is critical to protect estuary ecosystems. **B.4.4**

Interpreting Visuals

Use the diagram of a rocky intertidal zone to answer the next three questions.

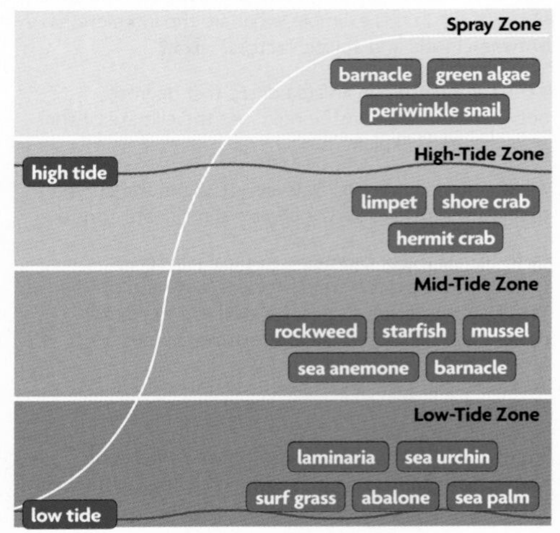

28. Predict How do you think the organisms above the high-tide mark are able to obtain the water they need to survive?

29. Compare What adaptations are necessary for a species to survive in the spray zone compared with a species in the low-tide zone?

30. Hypothesize Why do you think there aren't any fish shown in the diagram? Why wouldn't fish be a major part of the rocky intertidal zone?

Analyzing Data

Below is a climatogram for the city of Portland, Oregon. Use the graph to answer the next four questions.

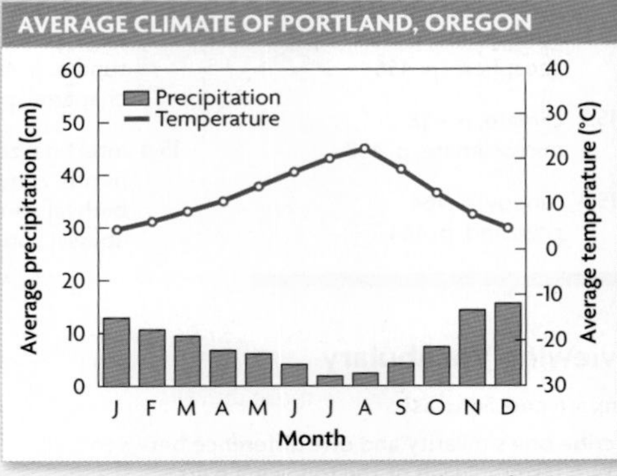

Source: National Oceanic Atmospheric Administration

31. Analyze Which month receives the highest amount of rain? the highest temperature?

32. Summarize Describe in one or two sentences the climate of Portland throughout the year.

33. Analyze A family is planning to vacation in Portland. Many of their planned activities occur outdoors. If they wish to avoid rain, in which month should they travel?

34. Connect Based on the data in the graph, which biome is Portland a part of? Explain your choice.

Connecting CONCEPTS

35. Write a Policy The majority of the wetlands in the United States have been drained and used for development. A company has submitted a proposal to purchase an area of 100 acres of wetland that it plans to develop. If you were an official in the area, how would you respond to this proposal? What would you say to a local environmental group that opposes the proposal? What might be a possible compromise? Use information from the chapter to convince your fellow elected officials to take your position. **B.4.2**

36. Synthesize Reread the information about the temperate rain forest at the beginning of the chapter. Using your knowledge of climate, biomes, and evolution, explain why different species are found in temperate and tropical rain forests.

Analyzing Data

31. December, August
32. Portland is rainy and cool from fall through spring, but dry and warm in summer.
33. July
34. temperate rain forest: long wet season, dry summer

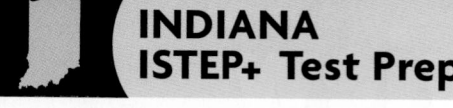

INDIANA ISTEP+ Test Prep

B.3.1; B.4.1; B.4.2; B.4.4; B.8.5; NOS.1

Test Practice For more test practice, go to ClassZone.com.

1

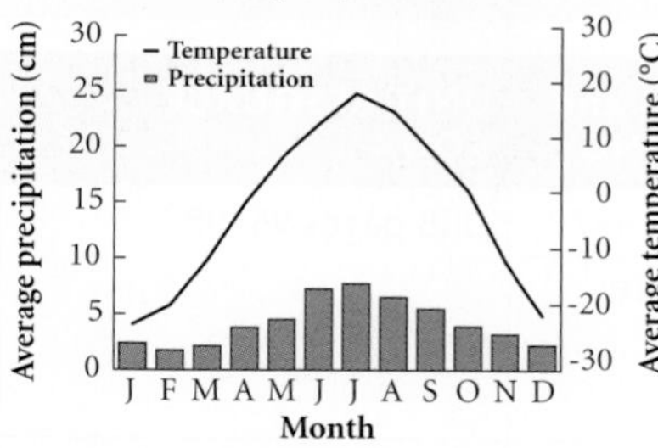

This graph shows the average monthly temperature and precipitation for a location in Canada. What can you conclude from these data?

A An increase in temperature causes an increase in precipitation.
B An increase in precipitation causes an increase in temperature.
C Temperature and precipitation both peak in the month of July.
D It never rains more than 5 cm per month.

2 Over thousands of years, the plant life in a region gradually changes from plants with lush green foliage to hardy, deep-rooted plants adapted to dry conditions. This shift is most likely the result of a change in

A predators.
B climate.
C sunlight.
D weather.

3 Tropical rain forests have the greatest number of species of any biome. However, the alteration of rain forest habitats into farmland threatens to decrease this

A biomass.
B biosphere.
C bioindicator.
D biodiversity.

4 High concentrations of sediment in the water can block out sunlight needed by aquatic plants for photosynthesis. This condition will most likely result in

A increased concentrations of nitrogen.
B decreased concentrations of nitrogen.
C increased concentrations of oxygen.
D decreased concentrations of oxygen.

THINK THROUGH THE QUESTION

Think about what is produced and what is consumed during photosynthesis. If rates of photosynthesis decrease, the products of photosynthesis will decrease in the ecosystem.

5

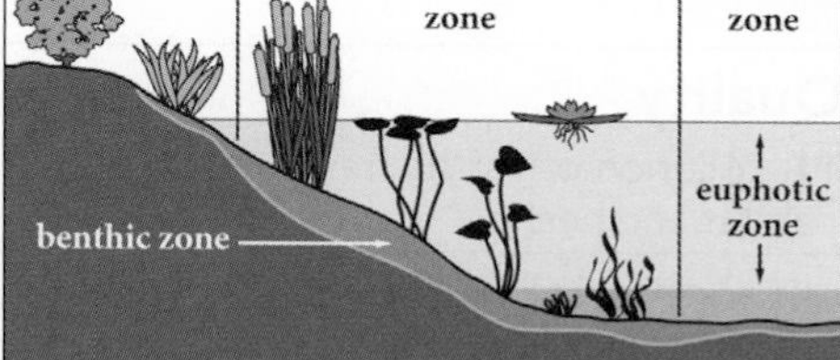

This diagram shows the zones that exist in freshwater lakes. In the benthic zone, dead organic material is converted into nutrients that can be used by other organisms. What type of organisms carry out this conversion?

A decomposers
B consumers
C carnivores
D producers

6 Organisms develop adaptations that allow them to better survive in their environments. Compare the adaptations of plants that live in the rainforest with plants that live in the tundra.

Standards-Based Assessment

1. C	4. D
2. B	5. A
3. D	6. See Below

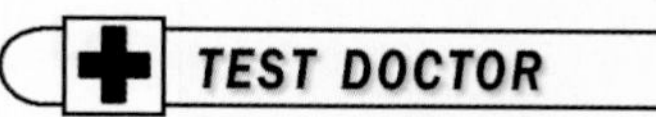

Question 3 Answer D is correct because biodiversity is the variety of life within an area. Answer A is incorrect because biomass is the total dry mass of all organisms in a given area. Answer B is incorrect because the biosphere is all organisms and the part of Earth where they exist. Answer C is incorrect because a bioindicator is a species that provides a sign, or indication, of the quality of the ecosystem's environmental conditions.
Question 5 Answer A is correct. Answer B is incorrect because consumers obtain energy by eating other organisms. Answer C is incorrect because carnivores obtain energy by eating other animals. Answer D is incorrect because producers obtain energy from light or inorganic chemicals.
Question 6 Plants in the rainforest and in the tundra obtain energy from the sun. However, they are different in many ways. Plants in the tundra are short and have shallow root systems due to the permafrost in the biome. Plants in the rainforest are taller and usually have broad leaves. They must be tall to compete for sunlight in the densely packed forest, and they use their broad leaves to obtain as much access to sun as possible.

Connecting Concepts

35. Answers will vary. A negative response to the proposal should include a discussion of the importance of wetlands in maintaining biodiversity and a clean water supply. A positive response to the proposal should include a discussion of the economic benefits of the proposed development to the local community. A possible compromise might be not developing the entire 100 acres or setting aside other wetland areas for protection.

36. While both types of rain forests are characterized by abundant rainfall, there are climatic differences between these two biomes that have necessitated the evolution of adaptations suited to the specifics of the two climates. For example, the cooler temperate zone may require that an organism be able to build or find shelter, or migrate elsewhere.

ITEM CORRELATIONS

Standard	Items
B.3.1	4
B.4.1	5
B.4.2	3
B.4.4	2
B.8.5	6
NOS.1	1

CHAPTER 16

Indiana Resource Preview

Print Resources

Human Impact on Ecosystems

INDIANA STANDARDS		Sections	PAGES and PACING	UNIT RESOURCE BOOK
B.4.2	16.1	**Human Population Growth and Natural Resources** **KEY CONCEPT** As the human population grows, the demand for Earth's resources increases.	pp. 484–487 30 minutes	URB pages 95–98
B.4.2	16.2	**Air Quality** **KEY CONCEPT** Fossil fuel emissions affect the biosphere.	pp. 488–492 45 minutes	URB pages 99–102
B.4.4, NOS.5		CHAPTER INVESTIGATION: DESIGN YOUR OWN Acid Rain	p. 493 45 minutes	**Lab Binder** Ecology pages 43–46
B.4.2	16.3	**Water Quality** **KEY CONCEPT** Pollution of Earth's freshwater supply threatens habitat and health.	pp. 494–496 30 minutes	URB pages 103–106
NOS.1		DATA ANALYSIS: Discrete and Continuous Data Types of Quantitative Data	p. 497 30 minutes	URB page 115
B.4.2	16.4	**Threats to Biodiversity** **KEY CONCEPT** The impact of a growing human population threatens biodiversity.	pp. 498–501 30 minutes	URB pages 107–110
B.4.2	16.5	**Conservation** **KEY CONCEPT** Conservation methods can help protect and restore ecosystems.	pp. 502–505 30 minutes	URB pages 111–114
NOS.1, NOS.3		OPTIONS FOR INQUIRY	pp. 506–507 20 minutes, 30 minutes	**Lab Binder** Ecology pages 47–49
		Chapter Review	pp. 508–511	**Assessment Book** Chapter Tests A, B pp. 319–326

INDIANA STANDARDS

B.4.2 Describe how human activities and natural phenomena can change the flow and of matter and energy in an ecosystem and how those changes impact other species.
NOS.1 Develop explanations based on reproducible data and observations gathered during laboratory investigations.
NOS.3 Clearly communicate their ideas and results of investigations verbally and in written form using tables, graphs, diagrams, and photographs.
NOS.5 Apply standard techniques in laboratory investigations to measure physical quantities in appropriate units and convert known quantities to other units as necessary.

Labs

PUPIL EDITION LABS

Acid Rain, p. 493 Students investigate how acid rain affects plant growth. **Lab Binder** pp. 43–46	**Time:** 45 minutes **Materials:** 4 potted radish seedlings; sharpened pencil; marker; water, pH6; water, pH 5; water, pH 4; water, pH 3; 250-mL beaker; metric ruler
Modeling Biomagnification, Section 3, p. 496 Students model the way fat-soluble toxic chemicals are biomagnified up a food chain. **Lab Binder** p. 50	**Time:** 20 minutes **Materials:** 4 small paper cups, 2 medium paper cups, 1 large paper cup, marker, sharpened pencil, 10 cm masking tape, 400 mL salt, 16 beads, 500-mL beaker

OPTIONS FOR INQUIRY

Water Quality Testing, p. 506 Students test water samples to determine if they meet EPA standards. **Lab Binder** pp. 47–48	**Time:** 20 minutes **Materials:** 2 plastic cups, marker, 2 100-mL graduated cylinders, 100 mL water sample A, 100 mL water sample B, 2 chlorine test strips, 2 copper test strips, 2 iron test strips, 2 nitrate test strips, 2 nitrite test strips
Contamination of Groundwater, p. 507 Students model the contamination of an area by a leaking underground storage tank (UST). **Lab Binder** p. 49	**Time:** 30 minutes **Materials:** shoebox, balloon, 1 m string, 10 cm masking tape, toothpick, craft stick, graph paper, ruler

LAB BINDER Unit 5 Ecology

Additional Investigation: Caffeine and Seed Germination, pp. 51–53

Biotechnology Lab Design Your Own: Investigating How Pollution Affects Plant Life, pp. 58–61

Vernier Probeware Lab: Biodiversity and Ecosystems, pp. 81–85

LAB GENERATOR

A searchable CD of all labs in the program in editable format, including forensic, probeware, and biotechnology labs.

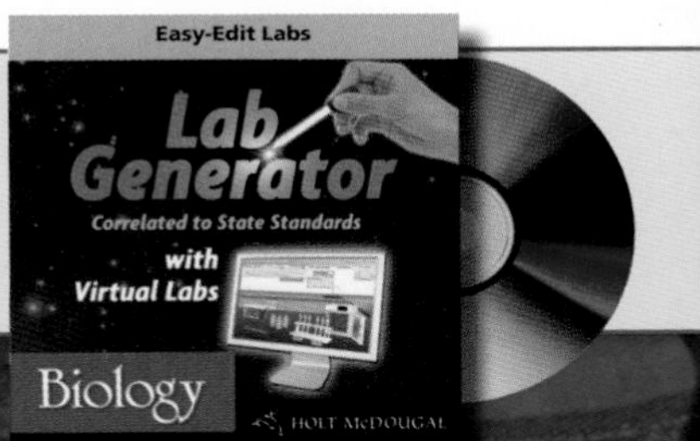

Presentation Tools

POWER PRESENTATIONS

Presentation Chapter 16
Power Presentations for each section incorporate images and clips from the Media Gallery: Includes Note Navigator for each section.

MEDIA GALLERY

Contains the following images and video clips, as well as animations, simulations and forms of visuals from the book.

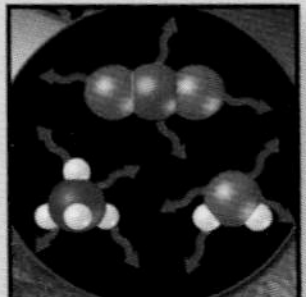
Greenhouse effect

Human effects on a food web

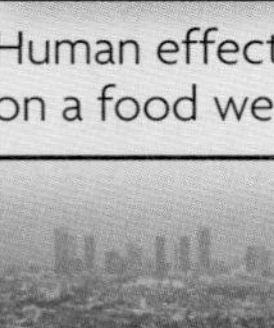
Wildlife corridor

Smog

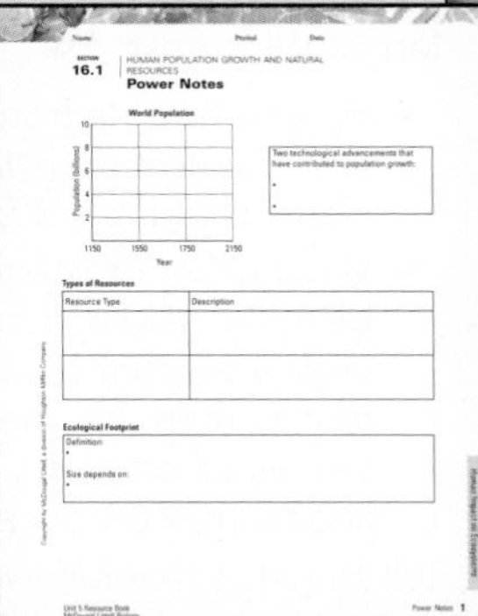

Power Notes

VIDEO

Check out a set of short video clips examining the human effects on bog lands and fish reproduction.

ANIMATED BIOLOGY

Human Population Growth

Global Warming

Human Effects on a Food Web

TRANSPARENCIES

Global Warming T72

Biomagnification T73

Online BIOLOGY CLASSZONE.COM

BioZine
Animated Biology
Interactive Review
SciLinks
Resource Centers

CHAPTER 16

▼ Focus and Motivate

What happened to this forest?

Discuss the fact that there is very little green anywhere to be seen in what is left of this forest. **Ask**

- What is missing from the forest floor? almost no evidence of other plants growing in succession
- What other organisms are likely to be indirectly impacted by acid rain? Organisms that feed on the plants or rely on them for shelter or nesting will die or emigrate, as will secondary and tertiary producers.

Tell students that rain water naturally has a slight acidity, typically a pH of 5.6. Acid rain has a lower pH, usually starting at 4.6. To put this in perspective, tell students that their bodies can tolerate liquids with pH values lower than that. Cola, for example, has a pH of 3, as does vinegar.

BIOZINE ClassZone.com

Students can access BioZine at **ClassZone.com** to receive updates to featured topics in the book.

In a Hurry?

The critical material of the chapter is found in **Sections 16.2, 16.3,** and **16.5,** which discuss the impact of human activity on air and water quality. Use **FIGURE 16.1** in **Section 16.1** to review the problem of Earth's growing human population. A quick read of the Main Ideas of **Section 16.4** can be used to summarize the importance of biodiversity and human activities that threaten it.

CHAPTER 16 Human Impact on Ecosystems

KEY CONCEPTS

16.1 Human Population Growth and Natural Resources
As the human population grows, the demand for Earth's resources increases.

16.2 Air Quality
Fossil fuel emissions affect the biosphere.

16.3 Water Quality
Pollution of Earth's freshwater supply threatens habitat and health.

16.4 Threats to Biodiversity
The impact of a growing human population threatens biodiversity.

16.5 Conservation
Conservation methods can help protect and restore ecosystems.

Online BIOLOGY CLASSZONE.COM

Animated BIOLOGY
View animated chapter concepts.
- Human Population Growth
- Global Warming
- Human Effects on a Food Web

BIOZINE
Keep current with biology news.
- Featured stories
- News feeds
- Polls

RESOURCE CENTER
Get more information on
- Global Warming
- Introduced Species
- Sustainable Development

Teacher Demo

Eye Opener Demonstrate the change in acidity represented by a difference of one pH unit.

Materials
- 100-mL graduated cylinder
- 100-mL beaker
- water sample adjusted to pH 6 (use vinegar or baking soda)
- pH strips
- distilled water

What happened to this forest?

Connecting CONCEPTS

This once lush hillside has been destroyed by acid rain. Emissions from a nearby steel plant release chemical compounds that change the natural pH of rain, forming acid rain. Not only does acid rain damage leaves and branches, but because it lowers soil pH, it can damage plant root systems and kill useful microorganisms that release nutrients from dead organic material.

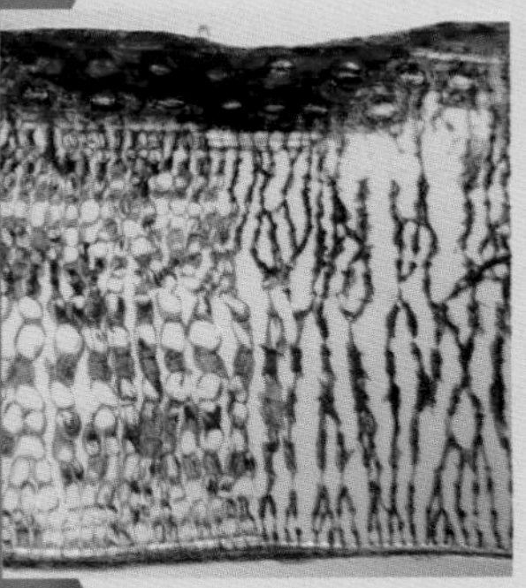

Plant Cells The acidity of rain affects plants at the cellular level. As you can see in this cross-section of a leaf, the plant cells on the left are healthy, but the cells on the right have been greatly damaged by water with a lowered pH. Acid rain destroys cell walls and can damage or even kill plants. (LM; magnification 30×)

Demonstrate Ask a volunteer to measure the pH of a water sample that you have adjusted to pH 6, which is close to the pH of normal rainwater (~pH 5.6). Tell students that pure water has a neutral pH of 7. Then pour 10 mL of the water into a beaker and add 90 mL of distilled water to it. Have the volunteer measure the pH of the second water sample. This ten-fold dilution should result in a one-unit change in pH, to pH 7.

Discuss Students often have difficulty conceptualizing the actual difference in acidity between two solutions that differ by only one pH unit. Lead students to recognize from the demonstration that a difference of one pH unit is equivalent to a ten-fold difference in acid concentration. **Ask,** If unpolluted rain has a pH of 5.6, and acid rain has a pH of 4.6, how many times more acidic is acid rain than normal rain? 10 times **Ask,** If distilled water has a neutral pH of 7, how much more acidic is acid rain? about 240 times

Activate Prior Knowledge

Discuss how manufacturing, agriculture, mining, and transportation have improved people's lives. **Ask,** How have these improvements created problems for Earth's ecosystems? Students should mention air and water pollution, buildup of solid waste, depletion of resources, and habitat loss. **Ask,** What steps can people take to help address these problems? *Sample Answer:* reducing activities that produce pollution, reducing waste by recycling, conserving resources, protecting habitats

Preview Vocabulary

Word Origins The words *conserve* and *preserve* share the same Indo-European root, which is related to the Greek *seros,* "protector," and the Latin *sera,* "a locking bolt."

conserve, to protect from loss or harm

preserve, to keep in unaltered condition

Discuss with students the difference between the two words. For example, compare the terms *nature preserve* and *habitat conservation.*

Academic Vocabulary Students are introduced to the word *particulate* in this chapter. The difference between a *particle* and *particulate* is one of relative size, a *particle* being "a small piece or portion of something," whereas *particulate* refers to "minute particles." A particulate, sometimes referred to as particulate matter, is typically a minute particle of solid or liquid that can be suspended in a gas, either as smoke or an aerosol.

English Learners This chapter features a number of nouns that have specific meanings in the contexts of biology and conservation, but their verb forms are often applied in many other contexts. As students read and learn these terms (*sustainable, renewable, fragmentation, biomagnification, pollution*), discuss the meanings of the verbs *sustain, renew, fragment, magnify,* and *pollute,* and have students use them in sentences relating both to the material in the text and to everyday contexts.

SECTION 16.1

▼ Plan and Prepare

Objectives

- Summarize the current state and effects of human population growth.
- Explain the importance of effective resource management.

Section Resources

Unit Resource Book Study Guide pp. 95–96 Power Notes p. 97 Reinforcement p. 98
Interactive Reader Chapter 16 **Spanish Study Guide** pp. 165–166
Biology Toolkit pp. C19, C26, C27
Technology Power Presentation 16.1 Media Gallery DVD Online Quiz 16.1

Activate Prior Knowledge Tell students that in 1963 Buckminster Fuller published his *Operating Manual for Spaceship Earth.* **Ask,** Have you ever heard the expression "Spaceship Earth"? What does it suggest to you? Earth is a closed system, like a spaceship, moving through space. Tell students that Earth has also been likened to an island. **Ask,** What do both of these images convey about Earth resources? a limit, a carrying capacity Remind students that many of Earth's resources are finite. How long they last depends largely on how many people inhabit Earth and the amount of resources used.

16.1 Human Population Growth and Natural Resources

KEY CONCEPT As the human population grows, the demand for Earth's resources increases.

MAIN IDEA
- Earth's human population continues to grow.
- The growing human population exerts pressure on Earth's natural resources.
- Effective management of Earth's resources will help meet the needs of the future.

VOCABULARY
nonrenewable resource, p. 485
renewable resource, p. 485
ecological footprint, p. 487

Review
carrying capacity, population, limiting factor

INDIANA STANDARDS

B.4.2 Describe how human activities and natural phenomena can change the flow and of matter and energy in an ecosystem and how those changes impact other species.

Connect Humans depend upon Earth's nutrient and energy cycles. We harness Earth's energy to power our televisions, radios, streetlights, automobiles, airplanes—and everything else in our homes and cities. Your cotton T-shirt and this paper page came from plants that depend on Earth's nutrient cycles. The water you drink comes from water sources replenished by the hydrologic cycle. We do not just use Earth's cycles, we are a part of Earth's cycles. Everything we eat, drink, and use comes from Earth. But the overuse of resources and the production of waste can cause disruptions in the energy and nutrient cycles of Earth.

MAIN IDEA

Earth's human population continues to grow.

How many people can Earth support? In other words, what is the carrying capacity for humans on Earth? Recall that carrying capacity refers to the maximum population size that an environment can consistently support.

Animated BIOLOGY Watch human population growth over time at ClassZone.com.

FIGURE 16.1 WORLD POPULATION

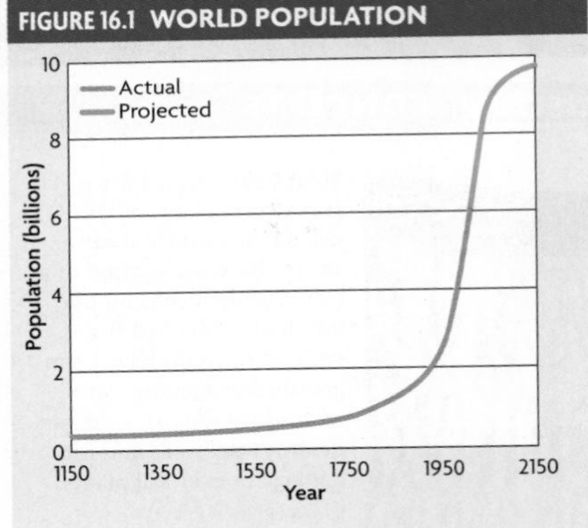

Source: United Nations, World Population Prospects, Population Reference Bureau

Earth's Carrying Capacity

Our predictions of Earth's human carrying capacity have changed over time. In the late 1700s, a young economist named Thomas Malthus wrote a controversial essay in which he claimed that the human population was growing faster than Earth's resources could support. Today, scientists use his observations and predictions when they are describing the concept of an ecosystem's carrying capacity. In Malthus's lifetime, the world population was around 1 billion. The graph in **FIGURE 16.1** shows how population size has changed over time. Today's human population of more than 6 billion has exceeded many earlier predictions. In the future, will Earth support 10 billion people, 20 billion, or even 50 billion people? Although we do not know of a fixed limit to the number of people that Earth can support, some limit must exist—Earth cannot support an infinite number of people.

▼ Teach

TEACH FROM VISUALS

FIGURE 16.1 Have students study the graph. **Ask,** What kind of growth does the human population show? exponential **Ask,** In approximately what year does the graph predict that human population growth will begin to slow? 2050

Differentiated Instruction

ENGLISH LEARNERS

Have students write each of the main ideas in this section in a central box, each on a separate sheet of paper. From each central box, have them draw several lines that connect to other boxes. Within each of these boxes, have students write details that support the main idea. For example, "ecological footprint" would be in a box branching off from "resource management."

Biology Toolkit, Main Idea Web, p. C27

BELOW LEVEL

Suggest that students take notes using the Cornell method. Tell students to take abbreviated notes in outline form in the second column of a T-chart, with key points in the column on the left. Students can then create a large box beneath both columns that puts the terms and notes into a summary paragraph.

Biology Toolkit, Cornell Notes, p. C26

Technology and Human Population

Recall that the carrying capacity of an environment can change as the environment changes. As humans have modified their environment through agriculture, transportation, medical advances, and sanitation, the carrying capacity of Earth has greatly increased.

Technologies developed by humans have allowed Earth to support many more people than Malthus could ever have imagined. Gas-powered farm equipment, for example, made possible the production of huge quantities of food—much more than could be produced by human and animal power. Medical advances have also contributed to population growth. For example, infant mortality rates in the United States have dropped steadily over the last 70 years. In 1940, more than 40 infants died for every 1000 births. In 2002, only 7 infants died in 1000 births. Antibiotics and antiseptic cleaners have lowered infant mortality and the spread of diseases.

For a moment, think about how much we depend on technology. How have human lives changed with the help of plumbing to bring fresh water into homes and to take human waste out of homes? What if there were no transportation to move food and materials around the globe? What if there were no medicines? How many people could Earth support without electricity or gas, or if all construction had to be done by hand? Technological advances have allowed for continued human population growth.

A Connect **What technologies do you depend on each day?**

Renewable & nonrenewable Resources -

MAIN IDEA

The growing human population exerts pressure on Earth's natural resources.

Two resources, oil and coal, currently support the majority of our country's energy use. Oil and coal are the result of natural processes. Over millions of years, natural processes transformed dead organisms into the concentrated carbon substances we use today as oil and coal. Oil and coal are **nonrenewable resources** because they are used faster than they form. In 2006, the human population was using oil at a rate of about 77 million barrels per day, and world oil use continues to rise. The growing use of this limited resource will lead to energy crises in the decades ahead unless technologies are developed to use other forms of energy.

Not all resources are nonrenewable. Resources that cannot be used up or can replenish themselves over time are called **renewable resources.** For example, wind energy—captured by wind turbines such as those shown in **FIGURE 16.2**—and solar energy are renewable resources because they cannot be used up by humans. Other resources, such as those that come from plants and animals, can be used up, but because they could last indefinitely through regrowth and reproduction, they are renewable. As long as these resources are replenished faster than they are used, they are considered renewable. But if renewable resources are not used carefully, they can become nonrenewable.

FIGURE 16.2 Giant wind turbines such as these capture renewable energy from Earth's natural processes.

her

:her limited
part because of the
n population, but it
modern technolo-
accessible and
here they were
t used to be the
cars, air condition-
re now common-
ies.

urrently generates
ctricity that the
despite having a
ur times bigger. As
ws, however, and
re able to tap into
onsumption of
electricity is expected to triple over the next 20 years, equivalent to a 4.3 percent increase per year.

Integrating Physics

Tell students that wind turbines convert the **kinetic energy** of the wind into **mechanical energy.** A generator converts this mechanical energy into electricity. A wind farm contains dozens or hundreds of wind turbines. The Nysted wind farm, located in the Baltic Sea off the coast of Denmark, has 72 turbines that provide about 20 percent of Denmark's electricity.

Answers

A Connect *Sample Answer:* automobiles, microwave ovens, computers, digital music players, wireless phones

PRE-AP

Tell students that the metaphor of "Spaceship Earth" popularized in the mid-20th century may have come from a once popular book *Progress and Poverty,* self-published in 1879 by Henry George. He wrote:

It is a well-provisioned ship, this on which we sail through space. If the bread and beef above decks seem to grow scarce, we but open a hatch and there is a new supply, of which before we never dreamed.

Have students write for five minutes on how our view of Earth resources has changed since the 18th century.

Biology Toolkit, Quick-Write, p. C19

▼ Teach *continued*

Science Trivia

Americans produce a lot of solid waste. In 2003, according to the Environmental Protection Agency, Americans produced 236 million tons of household garbage. The composition was as follows:

- 35.2% paper
- 23.8% food scraps and yard trimmings
- 11.3% plastics
- 8.0% metals
- 7.4% rubber, leather, and textiles
- 5.8% wood
- 5.3% glass
- 3.4% other

Of this, about 30 percent was recycled or composted, 14 percent was burned, and 56 percent was buried in landfills.

Per capita generation of garbage rose from 2.7 pounds per day in 1960 to 4.5 pounds in 1990. From 1990 to 2003, however, this number stayed the same, suggesting that some people are finding ways to reduce the amount of garbage they produce.

Answers

A Analyze If water becomes contaminated with toxic chemicals, or if it continues to be extracted from aquifers faster than it is replaced, it will become a nonrenewable resource.

***Connecting* CONCEPTS**

Hydrologic Cycle In **Chapter 13**, you learned how the hydrologic cycle moves water through Earth's atmosphere and back to Earth's surface. This cycling of water from resources such as lakes, rivers, and aquifers sustains the needs of the surrounding ecosystem.

Drinking water is a renewable resource, but pollution and overuse threaten its supply. Pesticides, industrial waste, and other contaminants have been found in water sources that supply tens of millions of people across the United States with fresh water. Groundwater is also being extracted from aquifers faster than it is replaced.

As Earth's human population continues to grow, the management of renewable and nonrenewable resources will play an important role. Today, the United States uses more resources and produces more waste than any other country on Earth. Each year, the United States generates about 230 million tons of garbage. That is about 4.2 pounds per day, per person, or almost 1 ton per year. What would happen if each of Earth's 6 billion humans generated 1 ton of garbage each year?

A Analyze Explain how a renewable resource such as water could become a nonrenewable resource.

MAIN IDEA

Effective management of Earth's resources will help meet the needs of the future.

Management of Earth's resources affects both current and future generations. The responsible use of Earth's resources can help to maintain these resources for future generations.

The story of Easter Island is a cautionary tale of destruction caused by careless use of resources. When humans first landed on Easter Island between A.D. 400 and 700, it was thickly forested on rich soil, with many bird species. The human colony grew quickly over the next 1000 years, building the stone monuments for which the island is now famous. The island inhabitants cut down the forests for lumber and for building boats. The trees were cut down faster than they could grow back. Eventually, Easter Island was left with no trees, as shown in **FIGURE 16.3.** Without trees, there was no wood for shelter or boats, the rich soil washed away, and habitat for the island's animal populations was lost. Without boats, there was no offshore fishing. With no food and island resources nearly gone, the Easter Island human population crashed and the Easter Islanders disappeared.

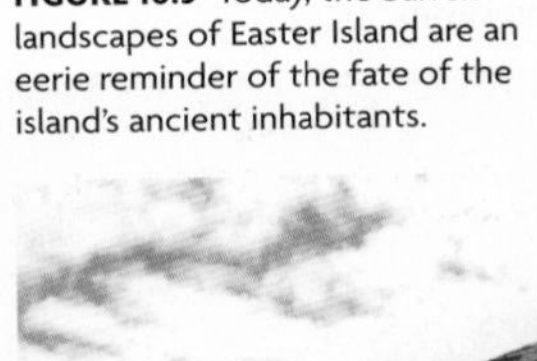

FIGURE 16.3 Today, the barren landscapes of Easter Island are an eerie reminder of the fate of the island's ancient inhabitants.

The Easter Islanders' use of trees was unsustainable. In other words, the islanders used trees to meet their short-term needs. But this resource could not be maintained into the future, and its use had negative long-term effects. In contrast, sustainable use of resources means using resources in such a way that they will be available for future generations.

Differentiated Instruction

HANDS-ON ACTIVITY

Tell students that between 10 and 50 percent of the cost of most products bought in supermarkets goes into packaging and that such packaging is one of the major sources of solid waste in landfills. Ask students to look at the packaged products in their homes and in stores. Have each of them bring in an example of an over-packaged product.

Students can then compare the actual volume, weight, or surface area of the product with the volume, weight, or surface area of the packaging.

Ecological Footprint

Humans need natural resources to survive, but the way resources are used threatens the welfare of the human population. Earth's carrying capacity depends on how much land is needed to support each person on Earth. The amount of land necessary to produce and maintain enough food and water, shelter, energy, and waste is called an **ecological footprint.** The size of an ecological footprint depends on a number of factors. These include the amount and efficiency of resource use, and the amount and toxicity of waste produced.

As shown in **FIGURE 16.4**, individuals and populations vary in their use of resources and production of waste, and therefore in the size of their ecological footprints. The average U.S. citizen's ecological footprint covers an area larger than 24 football fields (9.7 hectares) and is one of the largest in the world. But the ecological footprint of individuals in developing nations is growing, and nations such as China and India have populations that are more than three times the size of the U.S. population. Individuals in the United States may have a large footprint, but other nations have a lot more "feet."

As the world population continues to grow, we face many challenging decisions. Waste production and management is an issue that will become more important as we move into the future. Should we have rules to regulate resource use and waste production? If so, how much resource use and waste production should individuals and populations be allowed? How much land needs to be maintained for agriculture, how much for living space, and how much for other uses? How much fresh water should be used for crop irrigation and how much reserved for humans to drink? Our welfare, and the welfare of future generations, depends on sustainable management of Earth's resources.

AVERAGE ECOLOGICAL FOOTPRINTS BY REGION

Population (millions): 0, 1000, 2000, 3000, 4000
Ecological footprint (hectares per person): 0–10
■ Population (millions) ■ Ecological footprint
North America, Europe, Middle East, Central and South America, Asia Pacific, Africa

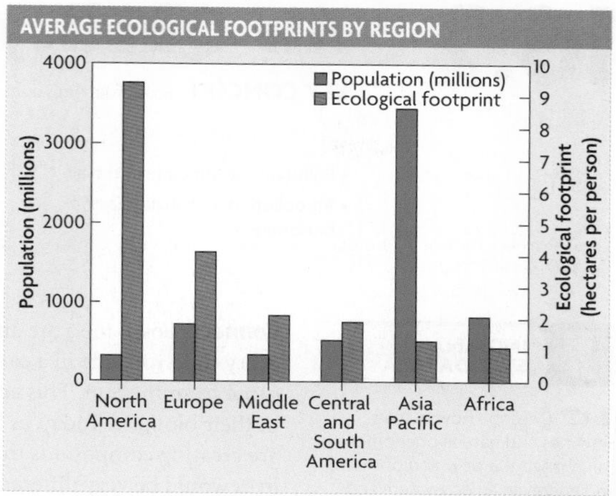

Source: Global Footprint Network

FIGURE 16.4 Different regions of the world have varying levels of impact on their environment. This graph shows the average ecological footprint of individuals around the world.

NSTA SCILINKS scilinks.org
To learn more about Earth's human population, go to scilinks.org.
Keycode: MLB016

A Analyze **Why is our ecological footprint related to an area of land?**

Ecological footprint

- and use of resources, how do North America and Asia/Pacific compare? They are about the same.
- In terms of Earth's resources, what is missing from the ecological footprint? oceans

Answers

A Analyze The production of all the material goods we use each day, including our homes, food, and clothing, at some point required use of or access to land. Also our waste products are return to the land.

16.1 ASSESSMENT

ONLINE QUIZ ClassZone.com

B.4.2

REVIEWING MAIN IDEAS

1. Give three examples of how technology has influenced human population growth.
2. What is the difference between **renewable** and **nonrenewable resources**?
3. Describe how a population can use resources in a sustainable way.

CRITICAL THINKING

4. **Connect** What factors can limit the growth of the human population?
5. **Synthesize** How could the Easter Islanders have prevented their population crash?

Connecting CONCEPTS

6. **Carrying Capacity** The progressive increase in Earth's human carrying capacity came from advances in technology. What density-independent and density-dependent limiting factors may prevent the human population from continued growth?

Assess and Reteach ▼

Assess Use the Online Quiz or Section Quiz (*Assessment Book*, p. 313).

Reteach On the board, make a T-chart in which students list renewable resources and nonrenewable resources in separate columns. Ask students to give their reasons for categorizing the resources as they did.

16.1 ASSESSMENT

1. Advances in medicine have reduced infant mortality and prolonged lifespans. Industrial technologies have made transportation and agriculture much easier, allowing for increased food production and distribution. Plumbing and sewage treatment have improved sanitation, reducing incidence of water-borne illness.
2. Renewable resources can be replenished by Earth's natural processes, whereas nonrenewable resources are difficult to replenish in a time span meaningful to humans.
3. Humans can use recyclable goods, use renewable energy sources such as wind and solar power, support only sustainable fisheries and agriculture, and minimize their use of products that contain toxins.
4. *Sample Answer:* disease, drought, overexploitation of limited resources, crop pests, war
5. They could have limited their use of the island's forests.
6. density-dependent factors: disease, lack of food, limited water supplies; density-independent factors: exhaustion of nonrenewable resources, medical and cultural practices

SECTION 16.2

Plan and Prepare

Objectives

- Describe the sources, types, and effects of air pollution.
- Explain how air pollution contributes to acid rain.

Section Resources

Unit Resource Book Study Guide pp. 99–100 Power Notes p. 101 Reinforcement p. 102
Interactive Reader Chapter 16 **Spanish Study Guide** pp. 167–168
Biology Toolkit pp. C35, C37, C40
Technology Power Presentation 16.2 Media Gallery DVD Online Quiz 16.2

Activate Prior Knowledge Initiate a class discussion of pollution problems that students have heard about. Encourage students to identify the pollutant and its effect on people and other organisms. **Ask,** In general, why is pollution a problem for Earth? It harms ecosystems. Discuss what steps are being taken to solve the problems students have discussed.

Teach

Vocabulary

Academic Vocabulary New technologies, processes, and discoveries sometimes require new words. **Smog** is one of these. It comes from the combination of **smoke** and **fog.**

smoke, a suspension of fine solid or liquid particles in a gaseous medium

fog, condensed water vapor in cloudlike masses lying close to the ground

smog, fog that has become mixed and polluted with smoke

16.2 Air Quality

KEY CONCEPT Fossil fuel emissions affect the biosphere.

MAIN IDEA

- Pollutants accumulate in the air.
- Air pollution is changing Earth's biosphere.

VOCABULARY

pollution, p. 488
smog, p. 488
particulate, p. 488
acid rain, p. 489
greenhouse effect, p. 490
global warming, p. 492

B.4.2 Describe how human activities and natural phenomena can change the flow and of matter and energy in an ecosystem and how those changes impact other species.

Connect Fossil fuels are an important part of modern society. Consider that every time you ride in a car, you are being transported by energy that originally came from the Sun. This energy was absorbed by ancient organisms and stored in their biomass. Today, as humans burn these fuels in the form of gas and oil, we are creating compounds that pollute Earth's biosphere. Without this energy our lives would be very different, but how does air pollution from fossil fuels affect the biosphere?

MAIN IDEA

Pollutants accumulate in the air.

Although it is sometimes easy to forget, humans are an important part of the biosphere. Our actions have direct and indirect effects on Earth's natural cycles. Each year humans add synthetic chemicals and materials to the Earth. Many of them cannot be integrated into normal ecosystem functions. The addition of these materials to the environment is called pollution. **Pollution** describes any undesirable factor, or pollutant, that is added to the air, water, or soil. Pollution can take the form of microscopic air particles, or waste products from factories and sewers, or household chemicals that are poured down the kitchen sink. The harmful effects of pollutants can be immediate or delayed, but these effects may add up over time and can disrupt the function of ecosystems.

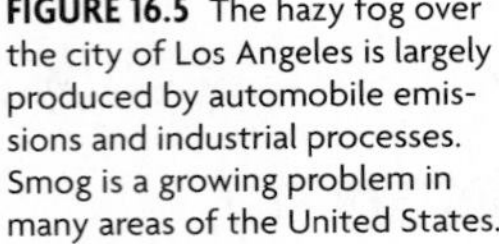

FIGURE 16.5 The hazy fog over the city of Los Angeles is largely produced by automobile emissions and industrial processes. Smog is a growing problem in many areas of the United States.

Smog and Ozone

The most common air pollution comes from the waste products produced by burning fossil fuels such as gas and oil. Chemical compounds released through this process can combine to form a haze of matter called smog, shown in **FIGURE 16.5. Smog** is a type of air pollution caused by the interaction of sunlight with pollutants produced by fossil fuel emissions. There are several components of smog, including particulate matter and ground-level ozone. **Particulates** are microscopic bits of dust, metal, and unburned fuel, 1–10 microns in size, that are produced by many different industrial processes. Once in the air, some particulates may stay in the atmosphere for weeks before they settle to the ground. Fine particulates can be inhaled and can cause many different types of health problems.

Differentiated Instruction

ENGLISH LEARNERS

Write on the board the six vocabulary terms listed at the top of the page. Before reading the section, have students discuss the relationships between the words. Then have them read the section. Next, have them write sentences that include two or more of the terms. Students should be able to include all the terms and the proper context in two sentences. Then have students format their sentences into a concept map.

Biology Toolkit, Concept Map, p. C40

TEACH WITH TECHNOLOGY

Assemble images of air pollution, such as smog, into a digital slide show. Show images taken by satellites as well as from the ground. See **ClassZone.com** for links to sources of online images, such as NASA's Earth Observatory. See also the Power Presentation for this section.

The second component of smog is ground-level ozone. In the presence of sunlight, two types of chemicals react to produce ground-level ozone (O_3). Nitrogen oxides are produced during fossil fuel combustion, and these chemicals give smog a yellowish color. Ozone is formed when nitrogen dioxide (NO_2) reacts with oxygen (O_2) present in the atmosphere. In this reaction, one oxygen from an NO_2 molecule is transferred to an O_2 molecule, forming ozone (O_3). The ozone produced by reactions of nitrogen oxide and oxygen tends to stay close to the ground, where it can be harmful to human health and ecosystem functions. Although ozone is harmful to organisms, it also plays an important, protective role in the Earth's upper atmosphere. High concentrations of ozone in the stratosphere, also known as the ozonosphere or ozone layer, act as a shield protecting Earth's biosphere against harmful ultraviolet rays found in sunlight.

Acid Rain

The chemicals produced by the burning of fossil fuels become part of the ecosystem and can change the products of natural cycles. For example, nitrogen oxides and sulfur oxides from fossil fuel emissions can lead to the formation of acid rain. **Acid rain** is a type of precipitation produced when pollutants in the water cycle cause rain pH to drop below normal levels.

VISUAL VOCAB

Acid rain is a type of precipitation produced when pollutants in the water cycle cause rain pH to drop below normal levels.

Acid rain pH 4.6 — H+ ions — Normal rain pH 5.6

Connecting CONCEPTS

pH Recall from **Chapter 2** that the pH is a measure of the concentration of H+ ions in a solution. Concentrations of H+ ions in acid rain are very high, giving the rain a lower pH level.

During the water cycle, rain falls through Earth's atmosphere and interacts with carbon dioxide molecules. As it falls, water molecules react with carbon dioxide molecules to form a weak carbonic acid, which then breaks apart, leaving lone hydrogen ions. This is normal. All rain that falls is slightly acidic, with a pH around 5.6. When pollutants such as nitrogen oxides and sulfur oxides become a part of the water cycle, acid rain is the result. Reactions between these chemicals and the oxygen and water normally present in the atmosphere create sulfuric and nitric acids that can cause pH levels to fall below 5.6.

Acid rain falls in many areas of the United States and has a major effect on ecosystems. By decreasing pH levels in lakes and streams, acid rain threatens water supplies and species habitat. Acid rain can cause a decline in growth rates, as shown in **FIGURE 16.6.** It can also cause leaves and bark to break down more quickly and make trees more vulnerable to disease and weather.

FIGURE 16.6 The wide growth rings of this tree indicate a healthy environment. The smaller growth rings illustrate how acid rain directly impacts plant growth.

A Synthesize As the human population continues to increase and use more fossil fuels, why might acid rain become a bigger problem?

BELOW LEVEL

Have students create cause and effect diagrams for acid rain, smog, and global warming. Diagrams should include chemical reactions and the elements and energy sources that are involved.

Biology Toolkit, Cause and Effect Diagram, p. C35

The Inside Story

The word *smog* first appeared in print in 1905, in a London newspaper's account of a meeting of the Public Health Congress at which **Dr. Harold Antoine des Voeux** presented his paper "Fog and Smoke." In his paper, Dr. des Voeux reported "something produced in great cities which was not found in the country, and that was **smoky fog,** or what was known as *smog.*" Dr. des Voeux's coinage of *smog* occurred a half-century after smog first appeared in the atmosphere as a byproduct of England's Industrial Revolution.

Take It Further

Acid rain refers to all types of precipitation (rain, snow, sleet, and hail) that is acidic in nature. Acid rain does not just affect forests. It kills aquatic life, crops, and other vegetation; damages buildings and monuments; corrodes copper and lead pipes; damages automobiles; reduces soil fertility; and can cause toxic metals to leach into groundwater. In lakes, as acidity increases, aquatic plants die off and waterfowl lose their food source.

TEACH FROM VISUALS

FIGURE 16.6 Explain that the photo shows a cross section of a tree trunk. The rings consist of vascular tissue that carries water up the tree from the roots. When the drier, colder season occurs, growth of this tissue is very limited and the vessels are very narrow, creating the darker concentric lines shown in the figure. Each ring represents one year of growth, or one year in the life of the tree. The rings to the left are the innermost rings, and the rings on the right are nearer the outside of the tree trunk, or the younger part of the tree. **Ask,** For approximately how many years has acid rain inhibited the growth of the tree? 20

Answers

A Synthesize There is a positive correlation between fossil fuel emissions and acid rain. More fossil fuel combustion means more acid rain.

Chapter 16: Human Impact on Ecosystems 489

▼ Teach *continued*

TEACH FROM VISUALS

FIGURE 16.7 Review the graph with students. Tell them to note the pattern of a high in both temperature and carbon dioxide followed by a decline to a low point and then a relatively sudden rise back up. Describe this as a climate cycle. **Ask**

- According to the graph, about how long does it take for Earth to complete one climate cycle? 100,000 years
- From the graph, what can you infer about Earth's temperature and Earth's carbon dioxide level? There is a direct positive correlation between the two; as one goes up or down, so does the other.

History of Science

Researchers working at Vostok Station at Lake Vostok in Antarctica produced one of the **world's longest ice cores** in 1998. A joint Russian, French, and U.S. team drilled and analyzed the core, which is 3623 meters (11,886 ft) long. The tip of the ice core is estimated to be as old as 420,000 years. The data in **FIGURE 16.7** came from the analysis of the chemical composition of this ice core and air bubbles trapped in the ice.

Integrating Physics

The **type of surface** that sunlight first encounters is an important factor in the greenhouse effect. Forests, ocean surfaces, grasslands, ice caps, cities, and deserts all reflect sunlight to different degrees. For example, a white glacier strongly reflects sunlight, resulting in very little heating of the surface. Dark desert soil and concrete strongly absorb sunlight, resulting in high surface temperatures, as anyone who has walked across a parking lot on a hot day knows.

MAIN IDEA

Air pollution is changing Earth's biosphere.

Earth's atmosphere naturally includes molecules of carbon dioxide that play an important part in keeping the biosphere at a temperature that can support life. The levels of atmospheric carbon dioxide rise and fall over time as a normal part of the climate cycles of Earth. Collections of data from arctic ice cores allow scientists to look deep into Earth's atmospheric history. They have discovered that cycles of rising and falling carbon dioxide levels follow known patterns of periodic warming and cooling. The relationship between changes in global average temperatures and carbon dioxide levels is shown in **FIGURE 16.7.** We know that high levels of carbon dioxide are typical of Earth's warmer periods, while low levels are associated with cool climates, eventually leading to periods of extreme cold called ice ages.

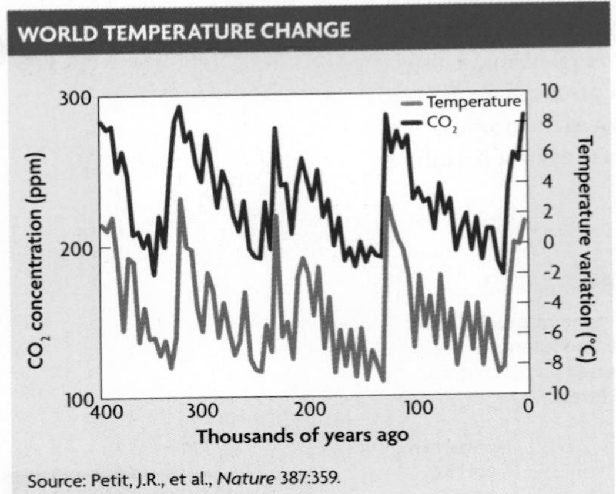

FIGURE 16.7 Scientists have found that changes in Earth's temperature correspond with fluctuations in global carbon dioxide levels.

The Greenhouse Effect

Earth gets nearly all of its energy from the wavelengths of both visible and invisible light emitted by the Sun. When the Sun's waves reach Earth, some are absorbed by Earth's atmosphere, but many of these rays pass through the atmosphere and reach Earth's surface. Some of this energy is absorbed by Earth's surface, but it is later reradiated as invisible infrared radiation—heat. After being reradiated from Earth's surface, this energy could travel away from Earth, be lost into space, and leave an extremely cold Earth that could never sustain life. But Earth is not cold and does have life. So what keeps Earth's temperature from dropping to extreme freezing conditions?

To answer this question, think about the greenhouses that scientists and gardeners use to grow plants. Greenhouses use glass that allows sunlight to pass radiation through and provide energy for plant growth. The glass also prevents infrared radiation from escaping. This infrared radiation keeps the inside of the greenhouse warm. This same phenomenon occurs in a car, causing the inside to heat up when the windows are closed.

In the same way that greenhouse glass creates an environment for plants to grow, the chemical composition of Earth's atmosphere plays an important role in maintaining an environment that is suitable for life. Earth's atmosphere contains gases called greenhouse gases that act as insulators and slow the loss of heat through the atmosphere. Water vapor, carbon dioxide, and methane are three of the most common greenhouse gases found in the atmosphere. Greenhouse gases absorb wavelengths of infrared radiation. This process is called the greenhouse effect and is illustrated in **FIGURE 16.8.** The **greenhouse effect** occurs when carbon dioxide, water, and methane molecules absorb energy reradiated by Earth's surface and slow the release of this energy from Earth's atmosphere.

Differentiated Instruction

HANDS-ON ACTIVITY

To demonstrate the greenhouse effect, have students work in pairs to make greenhouse models. Provide each pair with a clear-plastic 2-liter bottle with its cap on and its bottom cut out, two thermometers, cellophane tape, and graph paper. Tell students to punch a small hole near the top of the bottle and insert the thermometer into the hole, bulb end first. Have them use tape to secure the thermometer in place so that it can be easily read. Have students record the temperature on both thermometers before placing the bottle in a sunny area. Tell students to place the second thermometer near the bottle, but not to allow its bulb to be hit by direct sunlight. Have students record both thermometers' temperature readings every five minutes for half an hour. Then have students graph their data and write conclusions. Students should find that in the sunlight, the temperatures in the greenhouse bottle were higher than those of the other thermometer.

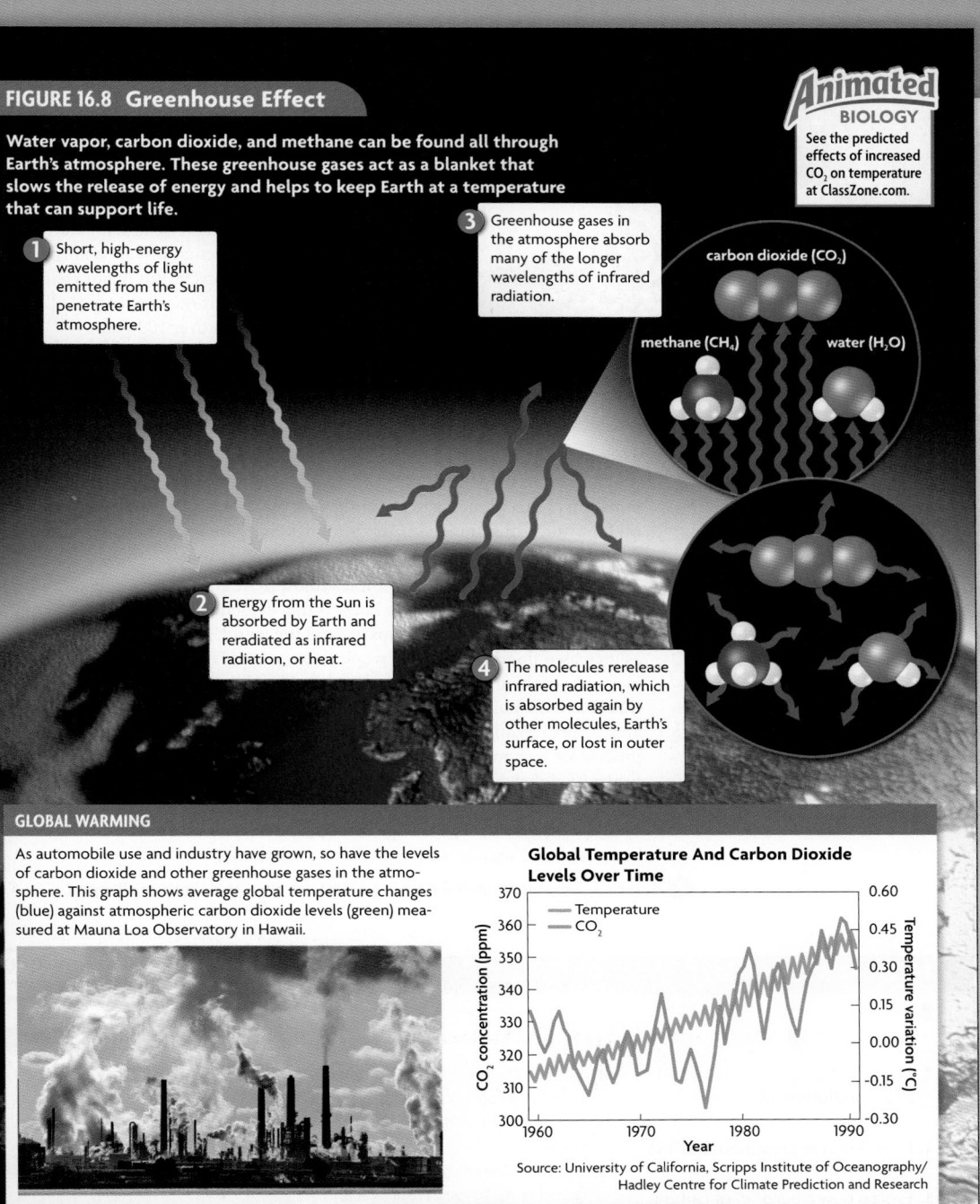

FIGURE 16.8 Greenhouse Effect

Water vapor, carbon dioxide, and methane can be found all through Earth's atmosphere. These greenhouse gases act as a blanket that slows the release of energy and helps to keep Earth at a temperature that can support life.

Animated BIOLOGY See the predicted effects of increased CO_2 on temperature at ClassZone.com.

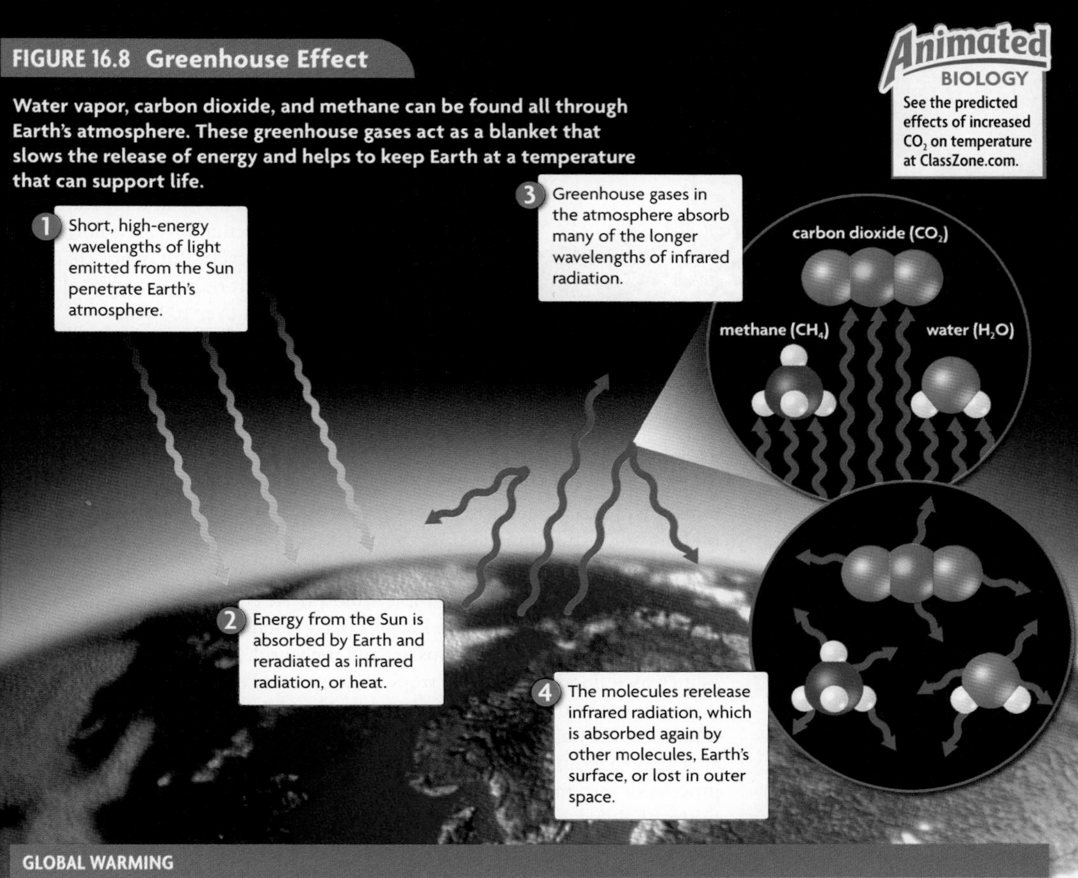

1 Short, high-energy wavelengths of light emitted from the Sun penetrate Earth's atmosphere.
2 Energy from the Sun is absorbed by Earth and reradiated as infrared radiation, or heat.
3 Greenhouse gases in the atmosphere absorb many of the longer wavelengths of infrared radiation.
4 The molecules rerelease infrared radiation, which is absorbed again by other molecules, Earth's surface, or lost in outer space.
carbon dioxide (CO_2)
methane (CH_4)
water (H_2O)

GLOBAL WARMING

As automobile use and industry have grown, so have the levels of carbon dioxide and other greenhouse gases in the atmosphere. This graph shows average global temperature changes (blue) against atmospheric carbon dioxide levels (green) measured at Mauna Loa Observatory in Hawaii.

Global Temperature And Carbon Dioxide Levels Over Time

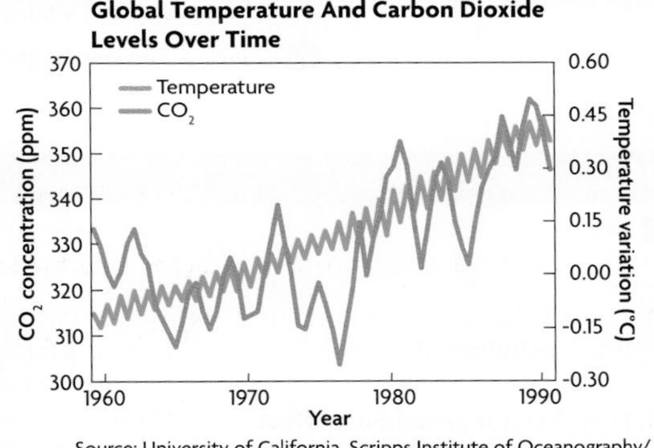

Source: University of California, Scripps Institute of Oceanography/ Hadley Centre for Climate Prediction and Research

A CRITICAL VIEWING **How would an increase in atmospheric greenhouse gases contribute to an increase in average global temperatures?**

491

PRE-AP

Suggest students use the graphic organizer known as a fishbone to sort out all the pressures and effects that have an impact on air quality. The head of the "fish" would be Air Quality, with the "bones" coming from the central backbone being Smog/Ozone, Acid Rain, and Greenhouse Effect. Students may also want a separate "bone" for Global Warming. Attached to each of these contributing factors would be the attributes or effects of each.

Biology Toolkit, Fishbone Diagram, p. C37

ONLINE BIOLOGY Go to the chapter resources at **ClassZone.com** for more on global warming.

TEACH FROM VISUALS

FIGURE 16.8 Discuss each step of the figure with students. **Ask,** What would happen to the infrared radiation produced in step 2 if there were no greenhouse gases? Much of it would be released from the atmosphere. Point out the regular sawtooth appearance in the CO_2 curve. Explain that in many locations, such as the Mauna Loa Observatory in Hawaii, CO_2 levels fluctuate with the seasons. During the winter, trees do not take up CO_2 at as high a rate as they do in the summer, so there is more atmospheric CO_2. **Ask,** What is the general trend in both temperature and CO_2 concentration? increasing

Address Misconceptions

Common Misconception The greenhouse effect and global warming are the same thing.

Correcting the Misconception The greenhouse effect is essential for keeping the atmosphere warm enough for living things to survive. This is the natural greenhouse effect. Human activities, especially the burning of fossil fuels, can enhance the natural greenhouse effect by increasing the level of greenhouse gases, causing a general warming trend that is called global warming.

Answers

A Critical Viewing The gases would trap more heat in the atmosphere.

▼ Teach *continued*

ONLINE BIOLOGY Go to the chapter Resource Center at **ClassZone.com** for additional resources and information on global warming.

TEACH FROM VISUALS

FIGURE 16.9 Have students trace the red line, indicating where the North Pole ice boundary used to be. Explain that Arctic ice is thinning, melting, and rupturing. The largest single block of ice in the Arctic, the Ward Hunt Ice Shelf, started cracking in 2000. By 2002, it had split all the way through and is now breaking into pieces. **Ask,** What effect will the melting of Arctic ice have on global warming? There will be less white surface to reflect solar radiation, so there will be more infrared radiation. Increased absorption of solar radiation will lead to more infrared radiation in the atmosphere. Tell students that wildlife also is being affected. Polar bears have to swim as far as 97 kilometers (60 mi) between ice floes to find food, and some are drowning in the process.

Answers

A Connect Seasonal temperature changes could be less pronounced.

▼ Assess and Reteach

Assess Use the Online Quiz or Section Quiz (*Assessment Book*, p. 314).

Reteach Create cause and effect diagrams for global warming, acid rain, and smog. Leave blanks in the diagrams and ask students to complete them.

FIGURE 16.9 Over the past 20 years, increasing global temperatures have decreased summer ice pack around the North Pole by about 20 percent.

Global Warming

Over the past 100 years, the average global temperature has risen 0.6°C (1.2°F), with the most dramatic change occurring over the past 40 years. What is causing this rise in temperature? Global temperature fluctuations are a normal part of Earth's climate cycle. But major changes in temperature generally occur over tens of thousands of years, not over 100 years.

The trend of increasing global temperatures is known as **global warming.** From a variety of evidence, scientists can infer that the changes in temperature are the result of increased levels of greenhouse gases such as carbon dioxide, water, and methane. There is no doubt that the growth of industry and use of automobiles has increased the emission of greenhouse gases over the past 100 years. Scientists may disagree on how much this human impact is influencing global warming, but most agree that we must take steps to slow the warming process.

Scientists do not know how these atmospheric changes will affect the global biosphere. What they do know is that evidence shows global warming is already threatening ecosystems around the world. Ecological disasters, such as increased flooding, stronger tropical storms, and the loss of biodiversity, are just a few of the threats that may be caused by global warming. As shown in **FIGURE 16.9**, the polar ice pack is melting at a rapid pace, which may eventually affect global weather patterns. These changes may be part of a slow warming process, or they may be the beginning of a rapid global climate change. The future of global warming is uncertain, but scientists predict that average temperatures on Earth could increase anywhere from 1.4 to 5.8°C (2.2 to 10°F) by the year 2100, a change that could have dramatic effects on Earth's biosphere, and change the planet that we call home.

A Connect How might global warming affect seasonal temperature changes?

16.2 ASSESSMENT

ONLINE QUIZ ClassZone.com

B.4.2

REVIEWING MAIN IDEAS

1. Name and describe two ways in which **pollution** affects ecosystems.
2. How does the **greenhouse effect** keep Earth warm?
3. Explain how a build-up of carbon dioxide in the atmosphere could increase Earth's global temperature.

CRITICAL THINKING

4. **Predict** Describe how **acid rain** falling in a forest could disrupt the trophic structure of the ecosystem.
5. **Connect** Greenhouse gases are found close to Earth's surface and high above in the atmosphere. Name two important functions of greenhouse gases at Earth's surface.

***Connecting* CONCEPTS**

6. **Food Webs** Ocean producers such as phytoplankton are an important part of food webs, but they need a specific temperature to survive. How might increased water temperatures affect these ocean food webs?

16.2 ASSESSMENT

1. Pollution can result in smog and acid rain. Smog is caused by the interaction of sunlight with pollutants produced by fossil fuel emissions. Acid rain results from the mixture of these emissions with water vapor.
2. Infrared energy radiating from Earth's surface is absorbed by greenhouse molecules such as water, carbon dioxide, and methane. This energy, also called heat, is then released and absorbed by other molecules of Earth's surface or the atmosphere.
3. With more greenhouse molecules in the atmosphere, less heat would be allowed to escape, causing Earth to become warmer.
4. The destruction of leaves in the forest canopy would let more sunlight reach the forest floor. Here plants adapted for less sunlight might be excluded by plants that thrive on more light. Herbivorous animals that feed on any of these plants could starve, as could the carnivores they sustain.
5. At Earth's surface, water vapor condenses to form precipitation that is part of the hydrologic cycle. Carbon dioxide is essential for photosynthesis.
6. If increased water temperatures kill the phytoplankton, the lowest trophic level of ocean ecosystems will be gone, and the food webs will probably collapse.

MATERIALS

- 4 potted radish seedlings
- sharpened pencil
- marker
- water, pH 6
- water, pH 5
- water, pH 4
- water, pH 3
- 250-mL beaker
- metric ruler

PROCESS SKILLS

- **Designing Experiments**
- **Hypothesizing**
- **Collecting Data**
- **Analyzing Data**

INDIANA STANDARDS

B.4.2 Describe how human activities and natural phenomena can change the flow and of matter and energy in an ecosystem and how those changes impact other species.

NOS.5 Apply standard techniques in laboratory investigations to measure physical quantities in appropriate units and convert known quantities to other units as necessary.

Acid Rain

In this lab, you will determine the effects of acid rain on plant growth. You will use water with different levels of acidity to water plants and monitor how it affects plant growth over a two-week period.

PROBLEM How does acid rain affect plant growth?

DESIGN YOUR EXPERIMENT

1. Write a procedure to explain how you will set up and conduct an experiment to test how acid rain affects plant growth. Identify the independent and dependent variables and constants you will maintain. For example:
   - What amount of water will you use to water the plants?
   - How often will you water the plants?
   - How will you measure the effects of acid rain on plant growth, both quantitatively and qualitatively?
   - How often will you collect data?
2. Form a hypothesis about the effects of acidic water on plant growth.
3. Design a data table to organize your results.
4. Have your teacher approve your experimental design.
5. Obtain your materials. Set up and conduct your experiment.

ANALYZE AND CONCLUDE

1. **Analyze** What were the independent and dependent variables in your experiment? What variables were held constant?
2. **Graph Data** Determine the best way to graph the data you collected. Determine whether a line graph or bar graph is appropriate, and construct that type of graph.
3. **Analyze Data** Write a summary statement that describes the results of your experiment. Include the qualitative data as well as the quantitative data. Is your hypothesis supported by the data you collected? Why or why not?
4. **Experimental Design** Identify possible sources of unavoidable experimental error in your design. List possible reasons for inconsistent results you may have observed.
5. **Apply** How does acid rain appear to affect plant growth?

EXTEND YOUR INVESTIGATION

Measure the pH of rain in your area. Based on the results of your experiment, what could you conclude about how the pH of rain might affect the growth of plants?

Answers

Analyze and Conclude

1. independent variable: pH of water; dependent variable: growth rate and plants' appearance; constants: species of plant, type of soil, amount of soil, cup size, amount of water, and amount of light
2. Students can make a line graph with time (days) on the *x*-axis and plant growth (cm) on the *y*-axis.
3. Students should report that the greater the acidity of the water, the less the plant grew. Plants exposed to acidity may have had brown or yellow leaves, or the leaves may have been drooping or wilting.
4. watering at different times of the day, failure to water on weekends, not using the same amount of water
5. Acid rain inhibits or slows plant growth.

Extend Your Investigation

Students can make a conclusion based on the pH of the rainwater they collect. If it is acidic, they should conclude that plant growth will be negatively affected.

INVESTIGATION

Time 45 minutes	TEACHER TESTED
Teacher Preparation	
Student Difficulty	
Lab Binder Ecology, pp. 43–46	

Purpose Investigate how acid rain affects plant growth.

Overview Students will treat radish seedlings with water of different pH levels. They will

- write an experimental procedure that describes how they will test their independent variable
- observe and measure the growth of the radish seedlings over a two-week period

LAB PREPARATION

- Prepare water samples with pH adjusted to pH 6, pH 5, pH 4, and pH 3.
- Provide pre-germinated radish seedlings. Each seedling should be approximately the same height and should have just put on its first true leaves when students begin the investigation.

LAB MANAGEMENT

- Remind students that they should water the plants at regular intervals with an amount of water that is adequate for thoroughly drenching the soil.

Safety Remind students not to taste any materials used in a lab. Also remind them to wash their hands each day after handling materials.

POST-LAB DISCUSSION

Have students discuss their data and the conclusions they can draw about the effects of acid rain on plant growth. **Ask,** Did your data support your hypothesis? Answers will vary, but students should see that the decreased pH consistent with acid rain has detrimental effects on plant growth and health.

SECTION 16.3

▼ Plan and Prepare

Objectives

- Describe how water pollution affects ecosystems.
- Explain how biomagnification causes accumulation of toxins in food chains.

Section Resources

Unit Resource Book
Study Guide pp. 103–104
Power Notes p. 105
Reinforcement p. 106
Pre-AP Activity pp. 117–118

Interactive Reader Chapter 16
Spanish Study Guide pp. 169–170

Biology Toolkit p. C39

Technology
Power Presentation 16.3
Media Gallery DVD
Online Quiz 16.3

Activate Prior Knowledge Many people assume that water pollution is the deliberate dumping of hazardous chemicals or wastes into bodies of water, but actually it is any pollut that ends up in water. **Ask,** What about water that allows so much pollution to be dispersed across thousands of miles of ocean? It i powerful solvent, and it flows.

▼ Teach

Vocabulary

Greek and Latin Word Origins word **eutrophication** comes fron Greek *eutrophos,* which means "nourished."

16.3 Water Quality

KEY CONCEPT Pollution of Earth's freshwater supply threatens habitat and health.

MAIN IDEA
- Water pollution affects ecosystems.
- Biomagnification causes accumulation of toxins in the food chain.

VOCABULARY
indicator species, p. 494
biomagnification, p. 495

Review
pollution

B.4.2 Describe how human activities and natural phenomena can change the flow and of matter and energy in an ecosystem and how those changes impact other species.

Connect When you swallow a pill, your body only uses a part of the medicine in the pill and gets rid of the rest as waste, which is flushed away. Scientists have detected traces of many prescription drugs in freshwater supplies. Several fish species that live in fresh waters have been exposed to the female hormone, estrogen. Some of the male fish have begun showing female characteristics. These "gender-bending" fish are only one effect of water pollution. What other pollutants can be found in our water?

MAIN IDEA

Water pollution affects ecosystems.

Pollution can have a major impact on water ecosystems. Chemical contaminants, raw sewage, trash, and other waste products are only a few pollutants that make their way into rivers, lakes, and aquifers all over the world.

Runoff from farms and cities may contain toxic chemicals and debris that can disrupt the chemical balance of freshwater lakes and streams and put entire freshwater ecosystems at risk. For example, detergents and fertilizers used in fields can affect a lake ecosystem by stimulating plant and algae overgrowth. A buildup of algae, such as the one shown in **FIGURE 16.10,** can drastically lower the levels of dissolved oxygen, leading to the dying off of fish populations. A lack of oxygen can also keep detritivores from breaking down waste materials. Over time, lakes and ponds slowly begin to fill in through a process called eutrophication.

FIGURE 16.10 A buildup of algae in lakes such as this one is the direct result of pollution. Eventually, the process of eutrophication will lead to the disappearance of the lake.

One way in which scientists can determine the health of an ecosystem is through the study of natural indicator species. An **indicator species,** also known as a bioindicator, is a species that provides a sign, or indication, of the quality of the ecosystem's environmental conditions. The gender-bending fish discussed above is an example of an aquatic indicator species. Frogs are sometimes considered an indicator species for water quality. Because the skin of tadpoles and adults is water-permeable, they come into direct contact with pollutants that can cause deformities such as extra arms and legs, as well as body tumors. Terrestrial ecosystems have indicator species as well, but the environmental impacts on these species are shown in different ways. Aquatic indicator species show the direct effects of pollution.

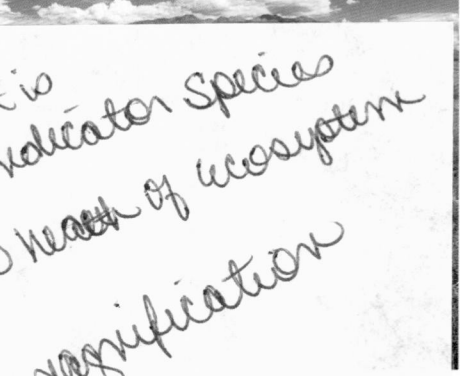

Y

pond, ... er-collection protocol, for students to test for pH by using a pH meter. Samples from several sites would provide a good opportunity for comparison. Prepare the buffer solutions and calibrate the pH meters before class. If you have samples from several sites, group students according to the number of site samples you have. Provide each group with five 50-mL portions of a sample. Demonstrate the proper use of the pH meter. Have groups measure and record the pH of each 50-mL portion and determine the average pH.

If the entire class is testing water from a single site, determine a class average for the water's pH. If groups are testing water from different sites, have them compare the pHs. Ask each group to write a summary of their procedure, present their data, and form conclusions about the quality of the body of water from which their water sample was taken.

The Forster's tern, a bird species native to coastal regions of the United States, has provided scientists with clues about pollution in the San Francisco Bay. This indicator species occupies a niche at the top of this ecosystem's food web. An important part of the tern's diet is fish it catches in the San Francisco Bay. By studying the tissues of dead tern chicks, scientists are finding large amounts of chemical contaminants such as mercury and PCBs, or polychlorinated biphenyls. These chemicals can harm developing eggs and can cause problems in the nervous system of adult birds. The high levels of these pollutants found in birds could lead to a decrease in the tern population and disrupt the balance of this aquatic ecosystem.

A Apply If the population of an indicator species is increasing, what might you infer about the conditions of the ecosystem?

MAIN IDEA

Biomagnification causes accumulation of toxins in the food chain.

The high death rates in young Forster's terns are due to high levels of toxic compounds found in the parents. How did these chemicals get into the adult birds?

Some pollutants are water-soluble, which means that they dissolve in water and will exit an organism through its wastes. Other pollutants are fat-soluble and stay in the body fat of an organism. Fat-soluble pollutants can also move from one organism to another in a process known as biomagnification. In **biomagnification,** a pollutant moves up the food chain as predators eat prey, accumulating in higher concentrations in the bodies of predators. Scientists measure pollutants in parts per million (ppm). The illustration in **FIGURE 16.11** shows how biomagnification moves small traces of a pollutant to higher concentrations further up the food chain.

FIGURE 16.11 Biomagnification

The movement of fat-soluble pollutants through a food chain results in higher concentrations in the top consumer.

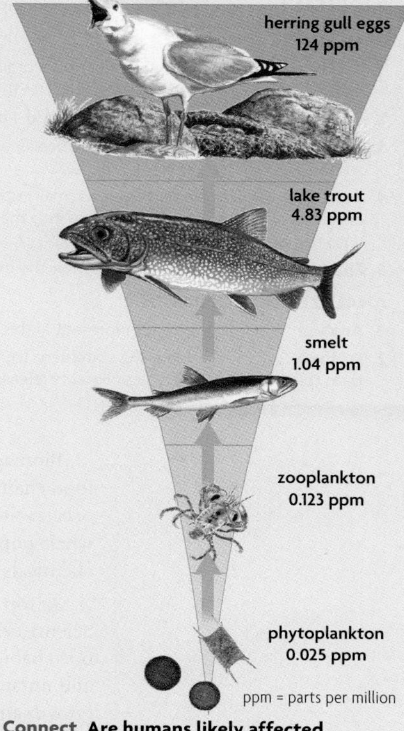

B Connect Are humans likely affected by biomagnification? If so, what foods might be dangerous?

After a pesticide is sprayed onto fields, large amounts of the chemical are washed into ponds and lakes, where phytoplankton pick up the chemical from their environment. The phytoplankton contain very small concentrations of the chemical, but when zooplankton feed on phytoplankton, they are also eating the chemical. Because the zooplankton eat many phytoplankton, higher levels of the chemical build up in the zooplankton. Secondary consumers such as small fish eat zooplankton and collect larger concentrations in their own body fat. Larger fish eat the chemical-laden fish, and the amount of the chemical in their fat builds up as they eat more and more. The increase in contamination is dramatic and causes the consumer at the top of the food chain, often a large predator such as an eagle or hawk, to receive the most concentrated dose of the pollutant.

***Connecting* CONCEPTS**

Energy Pyramid In Chapter 13, you learned how energy is lost as it moves up through trophic levels. In comparison, the process of biomagnification increases toxic material as it moves up the trophic structure.

BELOW LEVEL

Help students make a diagram of the hydrologic cycle. Diagrams should include evaporation, precipitation, runoff, transpiration, and root uptake. Have students note in their diagrams the points in the water cycle where pollution can occur and what kind of pollution is likely. They can also trace this pollution from the water up through a food chain, such as the one shown in **FIGURE 16.11.**

Biology Toolkit, Cycle Diagram, p. C39

ONLINE BIOLOGY Students can apply a human-induced change to a food web and observe its effects. Go to Animated Biology in Options for Inquiry on page 507.

Take It Further

In the 1950s, eating fish contaminated with methylmercury resulted in death, illness, or birth defects for thousands of people living around Minamata Bay in Japan. The cause of the contamination was mercury-containing wastes that had been dumped into the bay by a manufacturing company. **Minamata disease** is now the name given to the disorder caused by methylmercury poisoning.

Besides being dumped into waterways, mercury can be discharged into the air by such sources as coal-burning power plants, incinerators, and mining. It eventually contaminates waterways, where it is converted by bacteria into methylmercury, which becomes concentrated in the bodies of fish through biomagnification.

Address Misconceptions

Common Misconception Industry is the biggest water polluter in the United States.

Correcting the Misconception The runoff of silt, pesticides, and fertilizers from agricultural land is the largest single source of water pollution.

Answers

A Apply It is likely that the ecosystem is healthy and resources are abundant.

B Connect Yes, fish that are high in marine food chains could be dangerous.

▼ Teach *continued*

QUICK LAB

Time 20 minutes	TEACHER TESTED
Lab Binder Ecology, p. 50	

Purpose Model the way fat-soluble toxic chemicals are biomagnified up a food chain.

LAB MANAGEMENT

- Fine, dry sand can substitute for salt.
- Dried pinto or kidney beans can substitute for beads.
- Make the holes in the cups large enough for the salt to pass through but small enough to prevent the beads from passing through.

Safety Caution students to handle sharp objects carefully. Remind them to wash their hands before leaving the lab.

Answers

Analyze and Conclude

1. The beads represent fat-soluble water pollutants.
2. Large carnivores end up accumulating the pollutants that are within their prey.

Answers

A Compare Because they occupy a higher trophic level, tertiary consumers accumulate more toxins than primary consumers do.

▼ Assess and Reteach

Assess Use the Online Quiz or Section Quiz (*Assessment Book,* p. 315).

Reteach Make a chain of events diagram that traces a pollutant released from the smokestack of an industrial complex to the eggs of a sea bird thousands of miles away.

QUICK LAB MODELING NOS.6

Modeling Biomagnification

In this lab, you will model biomagnification. Small cups represent smelt, a fish that feeds on zooplankton. Medium-sized cups represent trout, which feed on smelt. The large cup represents an eagle, which feeds on trout.

PROBLEM How are contaminants magnified up the food chain?

PROCEDURE

1. Label the cups, smelt, trout, and eagle according to size. Punch holes in the bottom of each cup with the pencil. Cover the holes with masking tape.
2. Fill each of the cups halfway with salt. Add 4 beads to each small cup.
3. Hold each of the small cups over the beaker and remove the tape. Allow the salt to flow through the holes into the beaker.
4. Pour the remaining contents of two small cups into one medium cup. Pour the contents of the other two small cups into the second medium cup. Repeat step 3 with the medium-sized cups.
5. Pour the remaining contents of both of the medium cups into the large cup.

MATERIALS

- 4 small paper cups
- 2 medium paper cups
- 1 large paper cup
- marker
- sharpened pencil
- 10 cm masking tape
- 400 mL salt
- 16 beads
- 500-mL beaker

ANALYZE AND CONCLUDE

1. **Analyze** What do the beads represent in this model of biomagnification?
2. **Evaluate** Why is the following statement true: "Carnivores at the top of the food chain tend to be most affected by pollutants released into the environment"?

Biomagnification has the most serious effect on species near the top of the food chain. For example, the beluga whale is a top predator that lives in cold ocean waters and feeds on a wide variety of fish species. Studies of a beluga whale population in eastern Canada have shown such extreme levels of toxic chemicals that some whale carcasses have been treated as hazardous waste.

As top level consumers, humans can also be affected by biomagnification. Scientists have recently found small amounts of PCBs in the blood of newborn babies. Exposure to fat-soluble toxins such as PCBs during pregnancy and nursing can be dangerous to the developing fetus, and may also affect growth and development in young children.

A Compare **Why would tertiary consumers have higher concentrations of toxins than primary consumers?**

16.3 ASSESSMENT

ONLINE QUIZ ClassZone.com

B.4.2

REVIEWING ▶ MAIN IDEAS

1. What does an **indicator species** tell us about the health of an ecosystem?
2. How do PCBs affect bird populations through **biomagnification**?

CRITICAL THINKING

3. **Compare** How are the concepts of carrying capacity and indicator species related?
4. **Synthesize** Would a buffalo or a mountain lion be more affected by biomagnification? Why?

***Connecting* CONCEPTS**

5. **Energy Pyramid** How does the biomagnification "pyramid" compare with the energy pyramid?

16.3 ASSESSMENT

1. It reveals what types of pollutants are in the ecosystem. A decrease in an indicator species population is probably the result of high levels of pollutants in the environment.
2. PCBs travel up through the trophic structure of an ecosystem and accumulate in large amounts in the eggs of large birds. PCBs can negatively impact growth and development within the egg, causing genetic mutations, deformities, and death. The population of birds may crash as a result.
3. If the population of an indicator species is far below an ecosystem's carrying capacity for that species, it may indicate the presence of toxins or another pollutant that is causing a decline in the species' population.
4. A mountain lion would be more affected because it is higher on the food chain and would ingest more contaminants from its food supply.
5. They are opposite. Energy decreases as you move up the food chain, but pollutants increase.

DATA ANALYSIS ClassZone.com

NOS.1

ypes of Quantitative Data

ollecting data is a fundamental part of the scientific process. efore you design and carry out an experiment, it is important to nderstand the two different types of quantitative data: discrete nd continuous.

iscrete data Data that cannot be broken down into maller units and have meaning, such as the number of ogs in a pond, are called discrete data. Bar graphs are sually used for discrete data.

ontinuous data Data that have fractional values—that e not whole numbers—are called continuous data. The ngth and mass of a frog are continuous data. Continuous ata are usually shown on a line graph. The values of oints that were not actually measured in an experiment an be inferred from the graph.

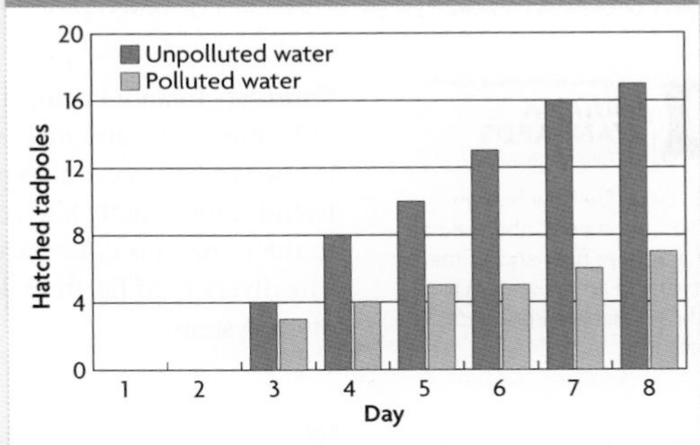

XAMPLE

rogs are commonly used as a biological indicator for ater quality. A classroom of students wishes to test ow water quality affects growth rates in frogs. Frogs atch from eggs into tadpoles and then slowly mature nto adult frogs.

tudents compared hatching rates in frog eggs over an ight-day period. Eggs were raised in one of two water amples, a sample from a known polluted pond, and a ample from an unpolluted pond. These data are discrete ecause a certain number of eggs hatched. There were no alf or quarter tadpoles.

fter hatching, students measured tadpole growth in both olluted and unpolluted water over the next five days. hese data are continuous because they can be broken own further and data points between measurements can e inferred.

GRAPH 1. HATCHED TADPOLES (DISCRETE DATA)

Unpolluted water
Polluted water
Hatched tadpoles
Day

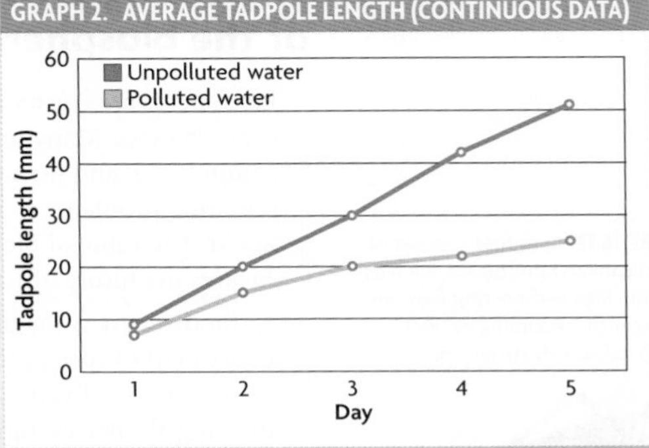

GRAPH 2. AVERAGE TADPOLE LENGTH (CONTINUOUS DATA)

IDENTIFY DISCRETE AND CONTINUOUS DATA

For each example, identify whether the data are discrete or continuous.

1. **Apply** A student collects data each spring and summer for five years about populations of endangered frogs in a wetland by counting the number of individual frogs in quadrats.
2. **Classify** The EPA compiles data about the mass of recycled aluminum (millions of tons) for every year since 1990.
3. **Analyze** Since 1860, the National Oceanic and Atmospheric Administration has collected data about the change in Earth's surface temperature and the concentration of carbon dioxide in the atmosphere.

Answers

1. discrete
2. continuous
3. continuous

DATA ANALYSIS

Introduce

There are generally two types of quantitative data—discrete and continuous. The type of data you have will determine the kind of graph you prepare to display your data.

Discuss

Tell students that sometimes it is difficult to determine whether data are discrete or continuous. One way to think about the difference between the two types of data is that discrete data involve counting, and continuous data involve measurement. For example, if you are surveying the number of children each family on a certain street has, you are counting and therefore collecting discrete data. If you are surveying the number of children on a certain street over the course of 30 years, you are collecting continuous data.

Another way to tell discrete data from continuous data is to ask yourself "When I plot the data on a graph, does it make sense to connect the dots on the graph?" **Ask**

- Which type of data should you plot and then connect the dots? continuous data
- What kind of graph will you produce? line graph
- Which type of data should you plot without connecting the dots? discrete data
- What kind of graph will you produce? bar graph

Point out to students that they can also differentiate discrete data from continuous data by asking themselves "Are these data whole numbers (discrete), or are there possible fractional quantities (continuous)?"

Unit Resource Book, Data Analysis, p. 115

▼ Plan and Prepare

Objectives

- Assess the consequences of loss of biodiversity.
- Explain how loss of habitat and introduced species affect ecosystems and biodiversity.

Section Resources

Unit Resource Book
Study Guide pp. 107–108
Power Notes p. 109
Reinforcement p. 110
Pre-AP Activity pp. 119–120

Interactive Reader Chapter 16
Spanish Study Guide pp. 171–172

Biology Toolkit pp. C19, D3

Technology
Power Presentation 16.4
Media Gallery DVD
Online Quiz 16.4

Activate Prior Knowledge Discuss with students the meaning of biodiversity. **Ask,** How would you describe the species diversity locally? Answers will depend on how urban the area is, the climate, and how observant students are.

▼ Teach

Science Trivia

Many of the most biologically diverse ecosystems, including coral reefs, are found in the tropics. A recent survey of the reefs of the Raja Ampats, a cluster of islands in Indonesia, found

- 450 species of hard coral
- more than 600 mollusk species
- over 1000 species of fish.

One fish expert counted 283 different fish species during a single one-hour dive.

16.4 Threats to Biodiversity

KEY CONCEPT The impact of a growing human population threatens biodiversity.

MAIN IDEA
- Preserving biodiversity is important to the future of the biosphere.
- Loss of habitat eliminates species.
- Introduced species can disrupt stable relationships in an ecosystem.

VOCABULARY
habitat fragmentation, p. 499
introduced species, p. 500

Review
biodiversity

B.4.2 Describe how human activities and natural phenomena can change the flow and of matter and energy in an ecosystem and how those changes impact other species.

Connect Imagine yourself taking a walk down your favorite street. But instead of bright colors and interesting sights, you see only one type of everything. There is one type of tree, one type of flower, and one type of car. At school all of your friends look exactly like you, lunch is the same every day, and everyone listens to the same music. We rarely think of the diversity we experience each day. The diversity of Earth makes our planet unique and maintains the stability of ecosystems.

MAIN IDEA

Preserving biodiversity is important to the future of the biosphere.

Ecosystems are constantly changing, and populations are always adjusting to these changes. Many times, human actions alter ecosystems in ways that harm a population and threaten biodiversity. The loss of habitat and the growing pollution problem are affecting animal and plant populations around the world. The value of biodiversity is not just measured in dollars. Biodiversity ensures the future of Earth.

Biodiversity is the diverse world of living things—the wide array and assortment of species that are found in any ecosystem. A decrease in an ecosystem's biodiversity will have a ripple effect through the entire ecosystem, affecting all species. Biodiversity is the foundation of much of our world.

Many medical and technological advancements come from nature. Nearly half of prescribed medicines are derived from plants. On the technological front, scientists in many fields continue to get inspiration from nature. For example, an adhesive from a mussel is being used as the pattern for a new coating for medical implants.

The loss of biodiversity has long-term effects. When a species goes extinct, it is gone forever. In many cases, all that remains of extinct species is a few dead specimens in a museum that can give little information other than where they were discovered. A loss of biodiversity can reduce an ecosystem's stability and make it more difficult for the ecosystem to handle future change.

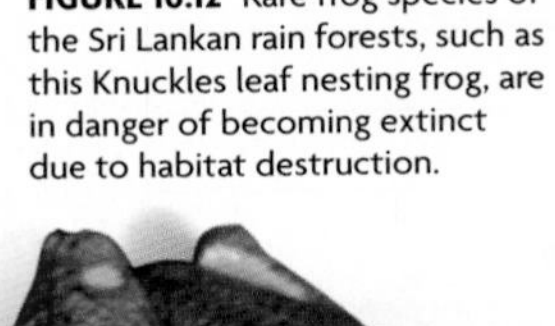
FIGURE 16.12 Rare frog species of the Sri Lankan rain forests, such as this Knuckles leaf nesting frog, are in danger of becoming extinct due to habitat destruction.

Differentiated Instruction

ENGLISH LEARNERS

Have students create a four-column chart to help them learn vocabulary in this section. The columns should include: (1) the word; (2) a personal definition; (3) a definition from a dictionary or the *Multilanguage Glossary;* and (4) a visual interpretation of the word. For example, from page 498 students might select *mussel, adhesive, array,* and *biodiversity.* Students' word lists should be of their own choosing, based on their own level of familiarity with the terms.

Biology Toolkit, Student Vocabulary, p. D3

PRE-AP

Obtain a list of the endangered species per state from Internet sources listed on **ClassZone.com.** Have students look for correlations between each state's human population density, total area, climate type, and diversity of habitats, and its number of endangered species. Have students infer why a small, remote state, such as Hawaii, has more than 300 endangered species, while larger states, such as Montana, have barely more than a dozen. Tell students to note how many species listed are aquatic or marine, and what might be threatening these species.

For example, as the nation of Sri Lanka has modernized, the natural resources of the island have become increasingly depleted. Ninety-five percent of the island's rain forests have been lost, and with them more than 19 different frog species have gone extinct. In addition, numerous other species, such as the rare frog species shown in **FIGURE 16.12**, are endangered. The loss of even a single species can harm the overall stability of an island ecosystem.

Biodiversity is highest in the rain forest biomes of the world, and it is these areas that are most threatened. Currently, about 1 percent of this biome is lost each year to logging or to clearing for agricultural use. Preserving the rain forests of the world will do a great deal to protect and preserve the biodiversity of our planet.

Connecting CONCEPTS

Carbon Cycle Rain forests around the world play an integral role in Earth's carbon cycle, storing large amounts of carbon in their structures.

A Connect **Why is biodiversity highest in tropical rain forests?**

MAIN IDEA

Loss of habitat eliminates species.

One way to protect species is to monitor and manage their numbers, and to ensure they have adequate habitat for survival. Governments and organizations around the world are developing programs to protect species that are threatened by overhunting, overcollecting, and habitat loss.

As the human population moves into what was formerly wilderness, people are moving into the territory of many different species of wildlife. In many parts of the world, the loss of habitat can put species in danger of becoming extinct. Historically, for example, wetland habitats were viewed as breeding grounds for disease and as "wasted land." Between the 1780s and the 1980s, more than 53 percent of wetland habitat in the United States was eliminated. This destruction displaced large numbers of wildlife and disrupted migration patterns for many species of water birds.

Efforts to ensure adequate habitat must take into account the life history of the organism, including mating habits and migration patterns. Ecologists have become particularly worried about habitat fragmentation. **Habitat fragmentation** occurs when a barrier forms that prevents an organism from accessing its entire home range. Often, habitat fragmentation is caused by the building of roadways or the harvesting of forests. Bears, deer, raccoons, and opossums are just a few of the animals that find their home ranges fragmented as urban sprawl increases. To try to fix this growing problem, some states are building underpasses and overpasses so that wildlife can avoid busy roadways. Corridors such as the one shown in **FIGURE 16.13** help to maintain continuous tracts of habitat for those species that move between different areas.

FIGURE 16.13 By providing a safe way to cross barriers such as roads and highways, land bridges such as this one in Canada allow animals to move safely from one part of their habitat to the next.

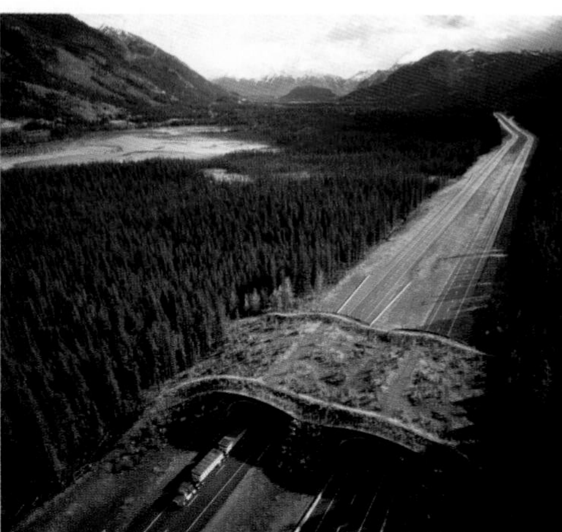

B Connect **Why is wetland habitat important for migrating birds?**

BELOW LEVEL

Tell students that salmon are anadromous. They are born upriver in fresh water, live most of their lives in the oceans, and then return to their birthplace to reproduce. Have students write about how the construction of a dam on a large river could result in the habitat fragmentation of salmon species' home ranges. Have them also write a proposal for how the dam could be constructed or modified to eliminate or lessen this problem.

Biology Toolkit, Quick-Write, p. C19

TEACH FROM VISUALS

FIGURE 16.13 Tell students that animals often use "islands" of habitat—one for watering, one for hunting, one for nesting, and so on. When obstructions, such as the highway in the photo, get between these areas, the animal's habitat is fragmented. **Ask**

- How is the problem of habitat fragmentation dealt with in this photo? The bridge allows animals to cross the highway safely.
- In order to ensure that animals cross the highway only at these bridges, what must be constructed on either side? fences running the entire length of the roadway, with openings only at the corridors

Take It Further

In 1968, a massive oil field was discovered on the north coast of Alaska near **Prudhoe Bay,** but the ice-packed waters were inaccessible to oil tankers. Plans were made to begin construction of a pipeline more than 1200 kilometers (800 mi) long that would carry oil to the ice-free port at Valdez, Alaska. Conservation groups argued that the pipeline would fragment the caribou habitats of the Arctic, so 50 percent of the pipeline was built high enough above the ground to permit passage of caribou herds underneath. As of 2006, more than 550,000 gallons of crude oil have been spilled from the pipeline onto the land.

Answers

A Connect Tropical rain forests are found in areas where both temperature and precipitation are high, which are key to the survival of many species.

B Connect Wetlands provide all the essentials that birds need for a long journey: a variety of fish and plants for food, and abundant water to drink.

▼ Teach *continued*

ONLINE BIOLOGY Students can learn about an invasive species in their local area and find out what can be done to control its damage. Go to the WebQuest in Options for Inquiry on page 507. Go to the chapter Resource Center at **ClassZone.com** for additional resources and information on introduced species.

Vocabulary

Academic Vocabulary Any species that is brought by humans into a new ecosystem is **introduced,** but only those that prove highly successful in their new homes are referred to as **invasive.** If someone releases a carp from Asia into a pond ecosystem in Wisconsin, the carp is an introduced species. But if the carp dies or does not reproduce, it will not be considered invasive.

Take It Further

Tiny Macquarie Island lies about 1500 kilometers (932 mi) southeast of Tasmania in the Southern Ocean about halfway between Australia and Antarctica. Millions of sea birds go there to breed each year. The island was also home to **feral cats,** the wild descendants of cats brought there as pets by seal hunters in 1820. Feral cat numbers reached about 500 at one time, and they were killing up to 60,000 sea birds a year. The Tasmanian government began a trapping program to eradicate cats from the island. Between 1974 and 2000, a total of 2450 cats were caught on the island. No feral cats have been seen since 2000. Today, mice and rats are being targeted through baiting programs to prevent population explosions of these animals.

FIGURE 16.14 Mice plagues in Australia and China can cost farmers millions of dollars in lost crops.

MAIN IDEA

Introduced species can disrupt stable relationships in an ecosystem.

Introduced species have a direct impact on the biodiversity and natural flow of energy in an ecosystem. An **introduced species** is any organism that was brought to an ecosystem as the result of human actions. Introduced species can pose a great threat to the stability of an ecosystem if they prey on or crowd out native species. In some instances, introduced species can cause economic damage. Just as native species interact with one another and their habitat, nonnative or introduced species are active and sometimes disruptive in their new ecosystems. Invasive species are successful in environments under many different circumstances. If an environment has a niche that the invasive species can exploit, or if the invasive species is a better competitor in a particular niche, native species may be pushed out. Invasive species are also successful if there is a lack of predators to keep the population stable.

Effect on Native Species

The Florida Everglades is a dynamic ecosystem where unique plants and animals have evolved for tens of thousands of years. The climate is similar to that of a tropical jungle, and the Everglades can support a great diversity of organisms. One species that has been introduced to this region originally came from the tropical jungles of Southeastern Asia. The Burmese python, shown in **FIGURE 16.15,** came to the United States as a pet species. Growing more than 6 meters (20 ft) in length, this massive snake can be difficult to care for. Irresponsible owners have released many of the snakes back into the wild. A large number of Burmese pythons have been captured and removed from Everglades National Park, and officials say that there is a good chance that a breeding population is present. As a constrictor species, the Burmese python feeds on small animals such as rats, birds, raccoons, and even dogs. Threats to endangered bird species in the park worry officials. As the python population begins to grow, endangered species protected in the Everglades could be affected.

FIGURE 16.15 Introduced species such as the Burmese python are growing in numbers in places like the Florida Everglades.

Differentiated Instruction

TEACH WITH TECHNOLOGY

The National Park Service has a list of alien plant species that are invading natural areas of the United States. Visit their Weeds Gone Wild website via **ClassZone.com** to look at different species on the list, where they can be found, and what they look like. Check for invasive plant species in your area.

Introduced animals are not the only problem. Plant species such as kudzu, another native of southeastern Asia, are invasive in the United States and are choking out native species of plants across the southeastern United States. The kudzu plant, shown in **FIGURE 16.16,** was introduced in 1876 as an ornamental tropical houseplant enjoyed for its fragrant flowers and large leaves. It was planted as field cover to prevent soil loss from erosion, but it rapidly began to spread out of the fields. Currently, kudzu is a classified as a problematic weed species in much of the eastern United States. Kudzu is a hardy plant, at home in virtually any soil, and it can grow up to 18 meters (60 ft) in a single growing season. This growth rate makes it difficult to control. Very few plant species can survive in an environment once kudzu is introduced. By blanketing trees and shrubs with its large leaves, kudzu deprives other plants of the sunlight they need to survive. The plant is resistant to most types of herbicides and can live for many years.

FIGURE 16.16 After a few months of being left in a single place, this car has become covered with kudzu. Fast-growing kudzu can destroy natural habitats in just a few years.

Economic Damage

Invasive species can have a major impact on humans as well as ecosystems. The common house mouse is an introduced species to the Australian continent. During the late 1700s, mice came from Europe as stowaways on British cargo ships. Today, mice are considered a major pest species in Australia and have caused widespread economic damage. Every four or five years, mice populations increase exponentially. Seasons of heavy rainfall lead to bumper crops of corn and grain, causing a dramatic rise in mouse populations and leading to huge numbers of mice moving from one food source to another. It was estimated that during the 1993–1994 season, the mouse population in Australia cost farmers about $65 million in lost revenue. Mice continue to be a problem throughout the region.

A Predict **How might a species of carnivorous fish introduced into a lake have a negative impact on the lake ecosystem?**

16.4 ASSESSMENT

ONLINE QUIZ ClassZone.com

B.4.2

REVIEWING MAIN IDEAS

1. Give two reasons why biodiversity is important to humans.
2. How does **habitat fragmentation** affect migrating bird populations?
3. What types of damage can **introduced species** cause?

CRITICAL THINKING

4. **Analyze** How could continued habitat fragmentation reduce biodiversity?
5. **Connect** How might the introduction of a mouse predator help with the mouse problem in Australia? What problems might it cause?

***Connecting* CONCEPTS**

6. **Population Growth** Using your knowledge of populations, describe what will eventually happen to mouse populations in Australia as they run out of food.

16.4 ASSESSMENT

1. Numerous medicines and technological advances have come from wild plant and animal species. We depend on ecosystems for food. A loss of diversity could mean a loss of food, medicine, and economic activity.
2. Birds need large areas of land or water on which to rest and feed during long migrations. If these habitats are not available, the birds may not be able to complete a migration.
3. Introduced species can disrupt ecosystems, threaten human health, and physically dominate or overtake waterways and humanmade structures.
4. If species are cut off from habitats they need for survival or reproduction, they could become extinct, thereby reducing biodiversity.
5. The mouse predator might keep the mouse populations in check, but it could also prey on other species and affect their populations.
6. It is likely that the mouse populations will eventually experience a population crash when they exceed their ecosystem's carrying capacity.

ONLINE BIOLOGY Have students graph and analyze data to determine how the introduction of trout to lakes affects the lakes' frog population. Go to Data Analysis Online in Options for Inquiry on page 507.

Take It Further

One of the more disastrous introductions of a non-native species to a new habitat occurred around 1950 in Guam, a Micronesian island in the western Pacific Ocean. The **brown tree snake,** *Boiga irregularis,* a venomous species native to Australia, Papua New Guinea, and other islands of Melanesia, established a population on Guam after individuals had stowed away on cargo ships and airplanes. Because Guam's forests offered plenty of prey species and no natural predators, the brown tree snake population exploded to a density of 13,000 per square mile.

Over the course of 50 years, this species has killed off much of Guam's native forest vertebrate species, caused thousands of power outages by biting electric cables, killed domestic pets, and delivered venomous bites to humans. Despite various controls aimed at ridding Guam of this species and preventing it from making its way to other Pacific islands, the brown tree snake has been found in Hawaii and Saipan.

Answers

A Predict The fish might increase pressure on prey species beyond what their populations can withstand. The introduced fish could also compete with other predators and drive them out of the lake ecosystem.

Assess and Reteach ▼

Assess Use the Online Quiz or Section Quiz (*Assessment Book,* p. 316).

Reteach On the board, create a concept map. Begin with the word *Biodiversity,* and then form two branches with the connecting phrases *is important because* and *is threatened by.* Encourage students to include as many examples as they can.

SECTION 16.5

▼ Plan and Prepare

Objectives

- Define sustainable development and describe some of its methods.
- Explain how protecting an umbrella species can protect an entire ecosystem.

Section Resources

Unit Resource Book
Study Guide pp. 111–112
Power Notes p. 113
Reinforcement p. 114
Pre-AP Activity pp. 00–00

Interactive Reader Chapter 16
Spanish Study Guide pp. 173–174

Biology Toolkit p. C19

Technology
Power Presentation 16.5
Media Gallery DVD
Online Quiz 16.5

Activate Prior Knowledge Discuss with students the conservation practices or movements with which they are familiar. **Ask,** What are some species you know of that are endangered? *Sample Answer:* giant pandas, whales, rhinos, elephants, gorillas **Ask,** What might be an added benefit of passing a law that protects a single species that lives in a specific forest ecosystem? The whole forest, including other species that live in it, could also be protected.

16.5 Conservation

KEY CONCEPT Conservation methods can help protect and restore ecosystems.

MAIN IDEA
- Sustainable development manages resources for present and future generations.
- Conservation practices focus on a few species but benefit entire ecosystems.
- Protecting Earth's resources helps protect our future.

VOCABULARY
sustainable development, p. 502
umbrella species, p. 503
Review
ecosystem, habitat, keystone species

B.4.2 Describe how human activities and natural phenomena can change the flow and of matter and energy in an ecosystem and how those changes impact other species.

Connect When Rachel Carson's book *Silent Spring* was published in 1962, the wheels were set in motion for the creation of the modern environmental movement. The book, which described how the pesticide DDT was affecting wildlife, brought about a public uproar and helped lead to a ban on the use of DDT in the United States. Since then, a variety of measures have been put into place, both to restore Earth's biosphere and to protect it from further degradation.

MAIN IDEA

Sustainable development manages resources for present and future generations.

To ensure that Earth can continue to support, or sustain, a growing human population, it is important to secure the future of the Earth's ecosystems. This way of thinking is known as sustainable development. **Sustainable development** is a practice in which natural resources are used and managed in a way that meets current needs without hurting future generations.

Sustainable development covers a wide range of resource management methods. Concerns about the condition of the environment have led to changes in methods of harvesting natural resources. In the timber industry, for example, old growth forests are being lost at a fast rate due to a method called clear cutting. By cutting down large sections of wooded areas and removing entire forest ecosystems, lumber companies serve a growing need for building supplies. Today, with the raised awareness of forest ecosystem

FIGURE 16.17 Forests of bamboo in China grow quickly and can provide an abundant supply of wood to support the growing demand for building materials.

▼ Teach

Take It Further

DDT, which **Rachel Carson** wrote about in *Silent Spring,* is another chemical that accumulates up food chains through biomagnification. It has been banned in many countries, but it is still used to kill mosquitoes in countries where malaria is still a severe public health problem. DDT's potential for eradicating malaria was so celebrated that in 1948, the Swiss chemist **Paul Müller,** who had discovered DDT's insecticidal properties, was awarded a Nobel Prize for his work.

Differentiated Instruction

PRE-AP

Write the following quotation on the board:

> *The raging monster upon the land is population growth. In its presence, sustainability is but a fragile theoretical construct.*
>
> —E. O. Wilson (1992)

Have students write a five-minute essay about what they think the quotation means. When they are finished, they can form small groups for discussion. (Wilson means that talk of conservation and sustainability for the future has limited value unless we control population growth first.)

Biology Toolkit, Quick-Write, p. C19

safety, several companies are choosing to cut selected trees rather than clear-cutting forests. This practice encourages rapid regrowth of trees, and makes sure there is only minimal impact to the forest ecosystem. When choosing where and when to harvest trees, foresters must consider how the soil, water, and wildlife of the area will be affected and change their harvest strategy accordingly.

Global fisheries are also in need of sustainable development practices. Overfishing has depleted fish populations worldwide. Fish stocks are not as hardy as they once were. One reason for this is that the fish that are caught represent the healthy, reproducing age groups of the fish population. By removing the reproducing individuals from the population, the fishing industry is actually hurting itself. Without fish to reproduce now, there will be no fish for the future. In addition, unsustainable fishing techniques damage marine and coastal environments. A number of techniques can be adopted by fisheries to make the industry sustainable:

- **Rotation** Rotating catches between different species gives the "off" species time to recover their numbers following a harvest.
- **Fishing gear review** The gear used to catch fish can damage the sea floor and often unintentionally catches other species. Reviewing and possibly banning certain fishing gear could help avoid damaging the sea floor and prevent ecologically important organisms from being killed.
- **Harvest reduction** Slowing the harvests of deep-water species that grow very slowly allows them more time to recover their populations.
- **Fishing bans** Creating and enforcing fishing bans in certain areas helps to replenish populations within that area, which may lead to greater fish numbers in nearby locations.

A **Connect What important services do forests provide? How might their destruction have an effect on humans?**

Connecting CONCEPTS

Natural Selection Recall from **Chapter 11** that in natural selection the environment favors certain traits over others. In a fish's environment, nets used by humans catch fish that are large and slow. Fish that may be smaller and faster have a distinct advantage, thus leading to a genetic shift in the population.

MAIN IDEA

Conservation practices focus on a few species but benefit entire ecosystems.

Laws written to protect individual species also help to protect their habitats. The Endangered Species Act in the United States, for example, is designed to protect individual species that are near extinction by establishing protection for the organism and its environment. When a single species within an ecosystem is placed on a list of endangered species, many other species within the ecosystem also benefit. The listed species is often called an **umbrella species** because its protection means a wide range of other species will also be protected. Such is the case with the West Indian manatee. These aquatic mammals, shown in **FIGURE 16.18,** live in the waters of the Gulf of Mexico and Atlantic Ocean along the coast of the southeastern United States. Their range extends as far west as Texas and as far north as Virginia.

FIGURE 16.18 The West Indian manatee is an umbrella species whose protection helps to re-establish marine habitats.

ONLINE BIOLOGY Go to the chapter Resource Center at **ClassZone.com** for additional resources and information on sustainable development.

Address Misconceptions

Common Misconception Planting trees after clear-cutting a forest restores the ecosystem.

Correcting the Misconception When a forest or part of one is clear-cut, every tree is removed. All the living things that depend on those trees die out or are pushed into new territory for which they may not be adapted. Simply replanting trees does not re-create a fully interacting ecosystem that took decades, hundreds of years, or thousands of years to develop. Replanting trees is only the first step in a process that nature must complete.

Take It Further

The growing human population, coupled with highly effective fishing techniques and technologies, has meant that numerous fish populations are being harvested beyond what is known as their **maximum sustainable yield,** the maximum amount of fish that can be caught without destroying the population's ability to replenish itself. Whether or not populations are overfished is due in part to the demand for them in world markets, but it is also a matter of the species' reproductive biology. Some fish species take years to reach maturity, and produce a relatively small number of offspring after a long pregnancy. These species are especially vulnerable to overfishing because the few individuals who avoid being caught will only produce a few young at a time. Species that reproduce at an early age and yield large numbers of offspring can recover much more quickly from overfishing.

BELOW LEVEL

To illustrate the concept of an umbrella species, provide students with the following scenario: Commercial longline fishing for swordfish sometimes results in the death or injury of endangered sea turtles. Other species caught by the longline fleets include yellowfin, bigeye, albacore, and skipjack tunas; blue and mako sharks; pelagic stingrays, and mahi mahi. Because the turtles are endangered, these fisheries have been shut down several times. Have students draw umbrella figures that illustrate how the protection of the sea turtles ends up protecting populations of other species as well. Point out that if regulations were aimed at protecting the swordfish instead of the turtles, it is likely that the same species would still be protected.

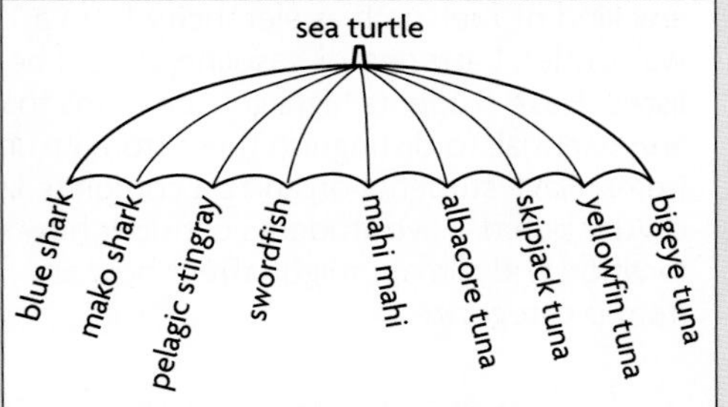

Answers

A **Connect** Forests help to convert CO_2 to oxygen, purify water, and prevent the erosion of soil. Their destruction could lead to degradation and erosion of land, the increased pollution of water, and an increase in atmospheric CO_2.

▼ Teach *continued*

Science Trivia

The bald eagle, *Haliaeetus leucocephalus,* has been the emblem of the United States since 1782.

- Their wingspans can reach up to 2.5 m (8 ft), and they can live for at least 28 years in the wild.
- The pesticide DDT was largely responsible for the bald eagle population crash that only recently has abated. DDT weakened the shells of bald eagle eggs to the point where they would collapse under the weight of the mother eagle.
- Bald eagles mate for life and will reuse nests over and over again, adding new building materials, such as mosses, twigs, and branches, each year. Nests can eventually weigh as much as 2 tons and be 2 m wide.

Take It Further

In June 1969, the Cuyahoga River in Cleveland, Ohio, caught fire. Debris and pollutants in the river were ignited by a worker's blowtorch. Though the actual blaze was relatively short-lived, the fire gained the attention of the nation, creating a national concern for our waterways, which eventually led to both the **Great Lakes Water Quality Act** and the **Clean Water Act** in the 1970s.

Answers

A Apply They might consider what other species and habitats might be affected by the recovery plan, and how the plan could affect economies and cultures.

The manatee was placed on the endangered species list in 1967. Its listing resulted from a variety of factors including loss of habitat, overhunting, and deaths due to collisions with powerboats. Today, the situation for manatees is difficult, and fewer than 3000 manatees remain in the United States. To promote their survival, local, state, and federal agencies are working to develop policies to protect their habitat. When developing recovery plans for an endangered species, scientists must consider many factors. For example, since manatees rely on seagrass as their main food source, areas rich in this resource must also be protected. By protecting waterways from pollution, restoring damaged areas, and limiting boating, the marine ecosystem that is the natural habitat for manatees is also protected. As a result, entire ecosystems can benefit from efforts to save a single species from extinction.

A Apply What factors might scientists consider when developing a recovery plan for the endangered grizzly bear of western North America?

MAIN IDEA

Protecting Earth's resources helps protect our future.

All living things, including humans, share Earth and its resources, and the value of the services our planet provides is priceless. The cycling of nutrients and the regulation of water provide essential resources that are almost impossible for humans to manufacture. If we were to put a human economic value on it, the total value of the services Earth's natural ecosystems provide has been estimated to be over $30 trillion a year.

Global warming, pollution, and the loss of biodiversity are only a few of the direct threats our planet is facing. To prevent further loss of the valuable resources of Earth, public actions are helping to preserve and protect the future of our planet.

FIGURE 16.19 Yosemite Falls in California is the tallest waterfall in the United States, and is just one of the wonders that the founders of the National Park System hoped to preserve.

Protecting Natural Resources

The Environmental Protection Agency was created as part of the National Environmental Policy Act in 1970. Its creation paved the way for the development of policies and regulations to protect the environment across the United States. Laws such as the Clean Air Act, Clean Water Act, and Endangered Species Act have had a major impact on the environment. The Clean Air Act, signed into law in 1970, has helped to increase air quality across the nation. It regulates emissions from industrial factories and automobiles. In 1970, only 36 percent of the lakes and waterways in the United States were considered safe for swimming. Since the Clean Water Act was signed in 1972, regulations against pollution and an increased public awareness have helped to double the number of waterways that are safe today. Since 1973, when the Endangered Species Act was signed, breeding pairs of the bald eagle, once in danger of extinction, grew from 791 pairs to almost 6500 pairs in 2000.

Setting aside areas as public land is another way that governments can protect ecosystems. The Yosemite Grant of 1864 was the United States' first step to protect nature from development. This grant established what would

Differentiated Instruction

HANDS-ON ACTIVITY

Ask students to make a list of all the energy-using devices they have in their homes. Remind students that any device that needs any kind of fuel, such as electricity from a wall outlet, batteries, or gasoline, should be listed. Have students highlight the items that are essential, to distinguish them from luxury items. Have students organize a complete list on the board. Have students consider how location and climate might affect how an item is categorized.

PRE-AP

Have students bring in articles on conservation and other ecological issues from newspapers, magazines, and online sources. Set aside class time to discuss articles and students' views.

eventually become Yosemite National Park, part of which is shown in **FIGURE 16.19.** The success of this grant eventually led to the formation of the National Park Service. The management of multiple-use areas and wilderness areas balances recreation for visitors with protection of the natural ecosystem. Today, grassroots environmental organizations are working with local governments and private citizens to purchase and restore areas of land across the country to increase the amount of suitable habitat for wildlife.

A Sustainable Earth

As we have seen, humans represent an integral part of Earth's ecosystems and are subject to the same limitations as other species living on the planet. However, unlike other organisms, we have a much larger impact on our environment because of our population size and the fact that we are found over the entire globe. At the same time, we have the ability and technology to change the extent of our impact on Earth's biosphere and ultimately control our destiny.

- We have the ability to control how fast our population grows, through controlling birth rates.
- We can develop technology to produce more food and produce less waste.
- Most importantly, we have the ability to change our practices and take action to protect and maintain ecosystems. In some cases, we can reduce or even eliminate the pressures we place on the planet's biogeochemical processes.

FIGURE 16.20 Each year on Arbor Day, people around the world plant trees and play an important role in rebuilding ecosystems for future generations.

No places on Earth are untouched by humans. While we may not have directly visited each square inch of the planet, human-caused pollutants, invasive species, or ecosystem alterations have reached the world over. Yet our economies, and our very lives, depend on a healthy, thriving, sustainable Earth.

A Connect **How could you reduce the amount of waste produced by your school?**

Take It Further

Since the 1960s, many companies that once packaged their products in paper, which is biodegradable, have switched to **plastic packaging.** Plastic does not leak like paper does and is lightweight and economical to ship. Most plastics are not biodegradable and therefore their disposal contributes to the solid waste problem. However, plastics are recyclable. Plastic packaging, such as plastic milk jugs and polystyrene food containers, is marked with a number that indicates the type of plastic, allowing for easy sorting of recyclables.

Some plastics are biodegradable. For example, polylactide (PLA) is a biodegradable plastic made from starch fermented by microorganisms.

Answers

A Connect *Sample Answer:* Use less packaging material, participate in or start a recycling program, campaign for more natural foods in the lunchroom, and urge students and teachers to limit paper use.

16.5 ASSESSMENT

ONLINE QUIZ ClassZone.com

B.4.2

REVIEWING MAIN IDEAS

1. Give two examples of **sustainable development.**
2. Describe how the protection of an **umbrella species** can be beneficial to an ecosystem.
3. How do governmental actions help to preserve natural habitats and protect resources?

CRITICAL THINKING

4. **Connect** What can humans do to minimize the impact of urban sprawl on wildlife?
5. **Evaluate** Could the West Indian manatee be considered a keystone species? Justify your answer.

Connecting CONCEPTS

6. **Nutrient Cycling** Natural ecosystems provide important cleansing and recycling functions to humans. What specific products do Earth's natural cycles provide for humans?

Assess and Reteach

Assess Use the Online Quiz or Section Quiz (*Assessment Book,* p. 317).

Reteach Have students list five ways in which they can personally become involved in conservation and then write these suggestions on the board. For each idea, ask students to discuss how sustainable development and umbrella species could be targeted in order to ensure and maximize conservation.

16.5 ASSESSMENT

1. *Sample Answer:* selective cutting of trees from a forest, fishing gear modification to target certain species and exclude others
2. Actions taken to protect a certain species may result in protection for other species, or even whole habitats or ecosystems.
3. The development of legislation can create consequences for harming the environment. The establishment of parks sets aside wilderness so that it will not be used by industry.
4. reduce or eliminate pollution in urban areas, construct corridors so animals can migrate through urban areas, limit the growth or sprawl of the urban area
5. *Sample Answer:* yes, if it plays an integral role in maintaining the marine ecosystem it lives in, such as controlling the growth of eelgrass
6. oxygen, carbon, nitrogen, water, all of which are needed by us for respiration or for the production of foods

OPTIONS FOR INQUIRY

INVESTIGATION

Time 20 minutes	TEACHER TESTED
Teacher Preparation	
Student Difficulty	
Lab Binder Ecology, pp. 47–48	

Purpose Test water samples to determine if they meet EPA standards.

Overview Students will use test strips to determine if two water samples meet EPA standards for safe levels of chlorine, copper, iron, nitrate, and nitrite.

LAB MANAGEMENT

- Review the proper use of the test strips before beginning the lab.
- Obtain two different water samples, for example, one from home and one from school.

Safety Remind students not to taste any of the solutions or put anything in their mouths while in the lab. Also remind students to wash their hands before leaving the lab.

Teacher Note "The students enjoyed testing the water samples. I think it helped them to better understand the concept of contamination."

Inclusion Group students so that students with physical disabilities will not have to handle test strips and water samples alone.

POST-LAB DISCUSSION

Discuss the results of the tests and have students form conclusions about which of the water samples would be safe to drink. **Ask**

- Why does the EPA set standards for drinking water? to help guarantee that water is safe for drinking
- If a sample is free of the contaminants you tested for, can you be certain the water is safe to drink, assuming you don't know the source of the water? No, the water could be contaminated with other harmful chemicals or pathogens, such as certain bacteria.

Use these inquiry-based labs and online activities to deepen your understanding of human impact on ecosystems.

INDIANA STANDARDS

NOS.1 Develop explanations based on reproducible data and observations gathered during laboratory investigations.
NOS.3 Clearly communicate their ideas and results of investigations verbally and in written form using tables, graphs, diagrams, and photographs.

INVESTIGATION

Water Quality Testing

The United States Environmental Protection Agency (EPA) regulates the drinking water that comes from public water systems. In this lab, you will test two water samples to determine if they meet EPA standards.

SKILLS Measuring, Comparing

PROBLEM Which sample meets EPA standards?

MATERIALS

- 2 plastic cups
- marker
- 2 100-mL graduated cylinders
- 100 mL water sample A
- 100 mL water sample B
- 2 chlorine test strips
- 2 copper test strips
- 2 iron test strips
- 2 nitrate test strips
- 2 nitrite test strips

PROCEDURE

1. Label one cup water sample A and the second cup water sample B. Fill each cup half full with the corresponding water sample.
2. Read the instructions for each type of testing strip and then collect data on both water samples. Record your data in a chart like the one below.

TABLE 1. TEST RESULTS AND EPA STANDARDS FOR DRINKING WATER

Possible Contaminant	EPA Maximum Level (mg/L)	Sample A	Sample B
Chlorine	4		
Copper	1.3		
Iron*	0.3		
Nitrate	100		
Nitrite	1		

*EPA Recommended Standard

ANALYZE AND CONCLUDE

1. **Analyze** Compare the results of your tests with the EPA standards listed in Table 1. Does either of the water samples not meet the recommended standards? What conclusions can you reach about the water samples based on your results? (**Note:** Check to make sure you are comparing the same units between your tests and the EPA standards.)
2. **Apply** Suppose you collect and analyze a water sample that receives runoff from a large area of farmland. Predict how the quality of the water may be affected. Assume that you test for the same contaminants listed in the table above.

EXTEND YOUR INVESTIGATION

Research how exposure to high levels of the toxins listed above can affect human health.

Answers

Sample Data

For a sample of student data from this lab, go to page R106.

Analyze and Conclude

1. Answers will vary, but water samples should meet EPA standards.
2. The nitrogen-based fertilizers might result in a high concentration of nitrites or nitrates in the sample.

Extend Your Investigation

Chlorine can cause irritation to the eyes, nose, and stomach. Short-term exposure to copper can lead to gastrointestinal discomfort. Long-term exposure to copper can cause liver and kidney damage. Exposure to nitrates and nitrites to infants under six months can lead to blue-baby syndrome (methemoglobinemia), in which the oxygen-carrying capacity of the blood is reduced. Increased level of iron in water is not considered a health hazard.

INVESTIGATION

Contamination of Groundwater

Leakage of toxic chemicals from underground storage tanks (USTs) is the leading threat to the security of the U.S. drinking water supply. This contamination can have devastating effects on nearby ecosystems. In this activity, you will work to map an area and locate a UST contaminated area.

SKILL Modeling

PROBLEM How much land can be contaminated by a leaking UST?

MATERIALS

- shoebox containing hidden water balloon
- 1 m string
- 10 cm masking tape
- toothpick
- craft stick
- graph paper
- ruler

PROCEDURE

1. Obtain a container with a water balloon (UST) buried in surrounding kitty litter.
2. Using string and masking tape, section the container into quadrats about 2.5 cm × 2.5 cm. Copy the quadrats onto graph paper and label with a grid system.
3. Systematically, gently insert the craftstick in each grid to locate all quadrats the UST sits inside.
4. Sketch on your map the location of the UST.
5. Insert a toothpick to break the UST to determine the number of quadrats contaminated.

ANALYZE AND CONCLUDE

1. **Conclude** what effect might a leaking UST have on an ecosystem?
2. **Predict** what other problems might result when a UST must be removed from the ground?

Online BIOLOGY CLASSZONE.COM

ANIMATED BIOLOGY

Human Effects on a Food Web

Humans can have a profound effect on the organisms in an ecosystem. Apply a human-induced change to a food web and see how the change ripples through the system.

WEBQUEST

Invasive species are a leading cause of extinctions of native species around the world. In this WebQuest, you will explore an invasive species in your area. Determine if the species has a harmful effect within your local environment and what can be done to control its damage.

DATA ANALYSIS ONLINE

Humans introduced trout into wilderness lakes of the Sierra Nevada in California for sport fishing. Since the fish were introduced, the number of mountain yellow-legged frogs has declined significantly. Graph frog density in lakes with no trout and in lakes from which trout were removed over time to see if the fish do affect frog population size.

Answers

Analyze and Conclude

1. A leaking UST could negatively impact an ecosystem by harming or killing organisms and disrupting chemical processes.
2. The use of heavy equipment to remove the tank could result in damage to the habitat around it.

Online Biology ▼

ANIMATED BIOLOGY Use this simulation to see what happens when humans induce a change in an ecosystem. Use with **Section 16.3.**

WEBQUEST The WebQuest takes one full class period. Students complete the activity online and will need access to a printer to print their answers. Sample answers, teacher notes, and alternative assessment ideas are available on **ClassZone.com.** Use with **Section 16.4.**

DATA ANALYSIS ONLINE
Students should find that frog density increases when trout are removed from a lake. Use with **Section 16.4.**

INVESTIGATION TEACHER TESTED

Time	30 minutes
Teacher Preparation	(1 flask)
Student Difficulty	(1 flask)
Lab Binder	Ecology, p. 49

INVESTIGATION

Purpose Model contamination by a leaking underground storage tank.

Overview Students will use a grid system to locate and map a simulated leak.

LAB PREPARATION

- The balloon should be completely covered so there is no hint as to where the balloon is.
- Review with students how to set up an area in quadrats.

Safety Remind students to wash their hands.

Interactive Review

Encourage students to go to **ClassZone.com** for a detailed review of each section, including visuals and vocabulary practice.

Unit Resource Book, Vocabulary Practice, pp. 121–124

CHAPTER 16 **Interactive Review** @ CLASSZONE.COM

KEY CONCEPTS | Vocabulary Games | Concept Maps | Animated Biology | Online Quiz

16.1 Human Population Growth and Natural Resources

As the human population grows, the demand for Earth's resources increases. The human population has grown tremendously due to advancements in technology. But a large population puts pressure on nonrenewable resources such as fossil fuels as well as on renewable resources such as water. Balancing the needs of our population with the resources of our environments will help to reduce our ecological footprint to sustainable levels.

16.2 Air Quality

Fossil fuel emissions affect the biosphere. Pollution is the addition of undesirable factors to the air, water, and soil. Fossil fuel emissions from industrial processes are causing an increase in smog and acid rain, which both threaten Earth's ecosystems. Carbon dioxide, methane, and other greenhouse gases slow the release of energy from Earth's atmosphere. But increased fossil fuel emissions appear to be contributing to rapid climate change in a process called global warming.

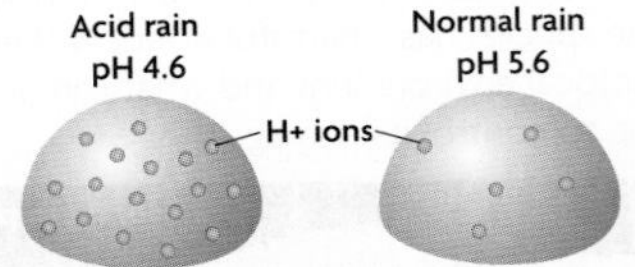

16.3 Water Quality

Pollution of Earth's freshwater supply threatens habitat and health. Indicator species help us understand the effects of pollution on an ecosystem. The process of biomagnification is a threat to both humans and ecosystems, as toxins accumulate at the top of food chains.

16.4 Threats to Biodiversity

The impact of a growing human population threatens biodiversity. The biodiversity of a region helps keep ecosystems stable. Habitat fragmentation and destruction are threatening biodiversity. Nonnative species can have a negative effect on ecosystems by pushing out native species and using up resources.

16.5 Conservation

Conservation methods can help protect and restore ecosystems. To protect Earth's natural resources for future generations, we need to plan for sustainable development. In addition, the protection of umbrella species and the positive support of government and industry can help to ensure Earth is protected for future generations.

Synthesize Your Notes

Concept Map Use a concept map like the one below to display the effects of pollution.

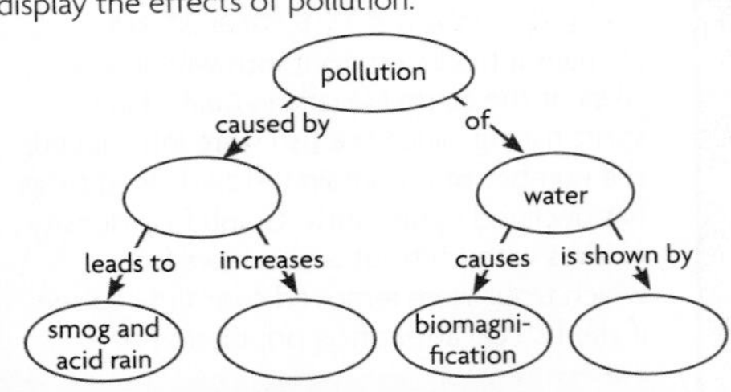

Process Diagram Use the process diagram like the one below to explain the greenhouse effect.

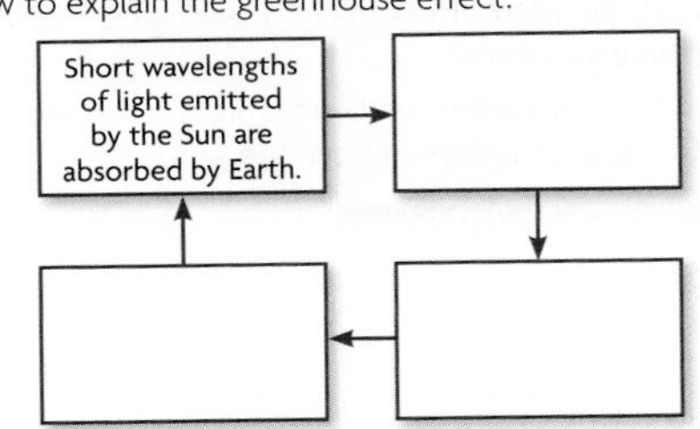

Reviewing Vocabulary

1. Both are things that humans use for energy and materials. Nonrenewable resources are used faster than they can be replenished, whereas renewable resources cannot be used up or are replenished as they are used.
2. Both are products of air pollution that comes from the combustion of fossil fuels. Smog involves particulates and ground-level ozone; acid rain involves sulfuric and nitric acids that cause the pH of rain to become more acidic.
3. The greenhouse effect is a natural phenomenon, whereas global warming is the consequence of human activities enhancing the greenhouse effect. Both terms describe processes that inhibit the release of heat energy from the atmosphere.
4. Both are used in conservation science. An indicator species is one that provides information about the health of an ecosystem, whereas an umbrella species is one whose conservation benefits other species or the ecosystem it lives in.
5. Sustainable development is development that holds or maintains the use of resources at or below the level that allows them to replenish or survive.
6. Biomagnification occurs when the concentration of a toxin in animals becomes greater, or is magnified, up through a food chain.
7. Anything within the shadow of an umbrella is protected from rain. An umbrella species is one whose protection affords protection to other organisms of its habitat or ecosystem.
8. Drawings will vary, but may compare the amount of resources required to support the life and lifestyle of humans from different countries.
9. Drawings will vary, but should relate fossil fuel emissions with increasing atmospheric temperatures.
10. Drawings will vary, but should show a species in an ecosystem or a habitat in which it has not lived before, and should show the effects of its introduction.

Chapter Assessment

Chapter Vocabulary

16.1 nonrenewable resource, p. 485
renewable resource, p. 485
ecological footprint, p. 487

16.2 pollution, p. 488
smog, p. 488
particulate, p. 488
acid rain, p. 489
greenhouse effect, p. 490
global warming, p. 492

16.3 indicator species, p. 494
biomagnification, p. 495

16.4 habitat fragmentation, p. 499
introduced species, p. 500

16.5 sustainable development, p. 502
umbrella species, p. 503

Reviewing Vocabulary

Compare and Contrast

Describe one similarity and one difference between the two terms in each of the following pairs.

1. renewable resource, nonrenewable resource
2. smog, acid rain
3. greenhouse effect, global warming
4. indicator species, umbrella species

Word Origins

5. The word *sustain* comes from the Latin words *sub-*, which means "below," and *tenere*, which means "to hold." Explain how these meanings relate to the term *sustainable development*.

6. The term *biomagnification* is comprised of the prefix *bio-*, which means "life," and the word *magnify*, which comes from a Latin word meaning "great" or "large." Explain how the meanings of the word parts make up the meaning of the term.

7. The word *umbrella* comes from the Latin word *umbra*, which means "shadow." How does the everyday meaning of the word *umbrella* relate to the ecological meaning of the term *umbrella species*?

Draw Cartoons

For each vocabulary term below, draw a cartoon that will best summarize the definition.

8. ecological footprint
9. global warming
10. introduced species

Reviewing MAIN IDEAS

11. Earth's human carrying capacity has exceeded many earlier predictions. How has technology affected human population growth? **B.4.2**

12. The United States uses more resources and produces more waste than any other country. How is this resource use reflected in the ecological footprint of the United States? **B.4.2**

13. What are the major causes of smog and acid rain? What are the effects of each type of pollution? **B.4.2**

14. Since the 1970s, human activity has released approximately 150 billion tons of carbon dioxide into the atmosphere. How could the increase in atmospheric carbon dioxide impact the greenhouse effect? **B.4.2**

15. Which organism is most likely to have accumulated toxins through biomagnification: plankton, a small plankton-eating fish, or a large fish that eats smaller fish? Explain. **B.4.2**

16. How could the extinction of a single species, such as a predatory bird, affect an entire ecosystem? **B.4.4**

17. In what ways can an introduced species impact an ecosystem it has colonized? **B.4.3**

18. The North American grizzly bear is considered an umbrella species. Explain how the protection of the grizzly bear may affect the larger ecosystem to which the bear belongs. **B.4.4**

CHAPTER REVIEW

Reviewing Main Ideas

11. Technology has improved human health and survival; made agriculture more intensive and productive; increased the speed of construction of living spaces, production of tools, equipment, and clothing; and has provided heating, air conditioning, plumbing, sanitation, water purification, transportation, and many other things that have allowed the human population to grow at an exponential rate.

12. The United States' ecological footprint is the largest in the world.

13. Smog forms from particulates and ozone produced by fossil fuel emissions. Acid rain forms from nitrogen oxides and sulfuric oxides in fossil fuel emissions. Smog is a hazy air pollution that can cause human health problems. Acid rain increases the acidity of water systems and can damage plants, soil, and other things.

14. The high carbon dioxide emissions could enhance the greenhouse effect, because each carbon dioxide molecule can absorb infrared radiation.

15. The large fish, because the toxins accumulate as they are passed up through the food chain. The plankton may have a small amount of the toxin in its system, and then the plankton-eating fish eats a lot of plankton, so the toxins in the plankton accumulate in the small fish. Then the larger fish eats a lot of the smaller fish, and the toxins from all of the smaller fish accumulate in the larger fish.

16. Each organism is part of a complex web of life, and the extinction of any part or strand of that web will affect the others. If a predatory bird, for example, becomes extinct, the population of its prey species, such as mice and other rodents, could increase greatly. These larger populations would, in turn, reduce the populations of the organisms they feed on. Also, the populations of species that competed with the extinct bird could now increase due to reduced competition for resources.

17. Introduced species can disrupt a stable ecosystem, for example, by preying on, crowding out, or competing with native species.

18. Protection of the grizzly bear would involve protecting the grizzly bear's habitat. Therefore, all the other organisms that lived in that habitat would be protected. If populations of grizzly bears rebound, populations of their prey could be reduced.

ITEM CORRELATIONS

Standard	Items
B.3.4	24, 25
B.4.2	11-15, 19-21, 29, 30
B.4.3	17, 23, 26
B.4.4	16, 18

Critical Thinking

19. Cattle, chicken, and other meat sources are higher up on the food chain than vegetables (which are autotrophs), so the land required to raise these animals includes the land required to raise all of the things that go into their feed as well as the land required to dispose of their waste.
20. *Sample Answer:* ride the bus, walk, ride a bike, carpool
21. Everything that is used to produce the carton of milk contributes to a person's ecological footprint. Land was used to produce the tree that yielded pulp to be made into the carton and also to feed the cow that made the milk.
22. Larger predators can be used as indicator species because their presence, and a healthy population of them, suggests that the ecosystem is functioning and the lower levels of the food chain are present. If a large carnivore population is dwindling, this may mean that there are few prey items and there may be a loss of producers. In addition, if an individual carnivore has high levels of toxins in its body, this may be an indication of a pollutant that has infiltrated the environment and is being magnified as it moves up through the food chain.
23. The predator insect may feed on or otherwise affect species other than the pest.

Critical Thinking

19. Analyze Assuming all other factors are the same, the more meat in a person's diet, the larger that person's ecological footprint. Why might this be the case? **B.4.2**

20. Connect Nationwide, automobiles are the major source of carbon monoxide, carbon dioxide, nitrogen oxides, particulate matter, and cancer-causing toxins. What can you do to decrease your fossil fuel use? **B.4.2**

21. Evaluate An ecological footprint is a measure of the impact of the resources we use on the environment. Explain how buying a carton of milk relates to your ecological footprint. **B.4.2**

22. Infer Frogs are commonly used as an indicator species in aquatic habitats. Could a large predator such as a bear or an eagle be used as an indicator species? Explain.

23. Synthesize Explain how a predator insect species, introduced to help control insect pests, could become a threat to an ecosystem. **B.4.3**

Interpreting Visuals

Use the simple food web outlined below to answer the next three questions.

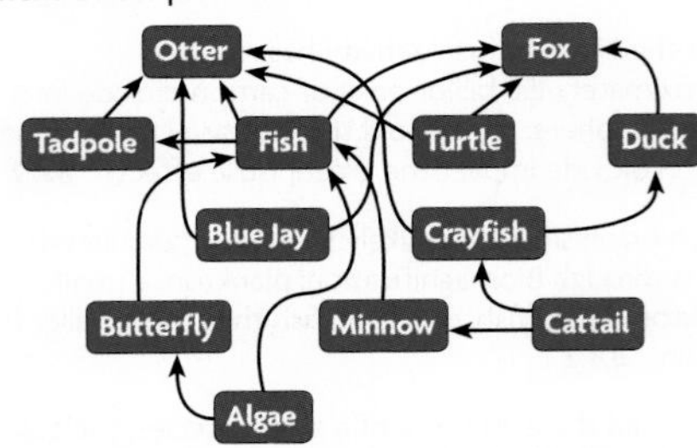

24. Apply Which of these organisms is likely to be most affected by biomagnification of toxins? Explain your answer. **B.3.4**

25. Predict This food web includes both aquatic and terrestrial organisms. Imagine that a new road separates the aquatic environment from the nearby terrestrial environment. Do you think the turtle or the duck would be more affected by this habitat fragmentation? Explain. **B.3.4**

26. Predict Imagine that an introduced species results in the local extermination of crayfish. How might this change affect the larger ecosystem? **B.4.3**

Analyzing Data

This circle graph shows the components of the ecological footprint for a resident of a North American city. Use the graph to answer the next two questions.

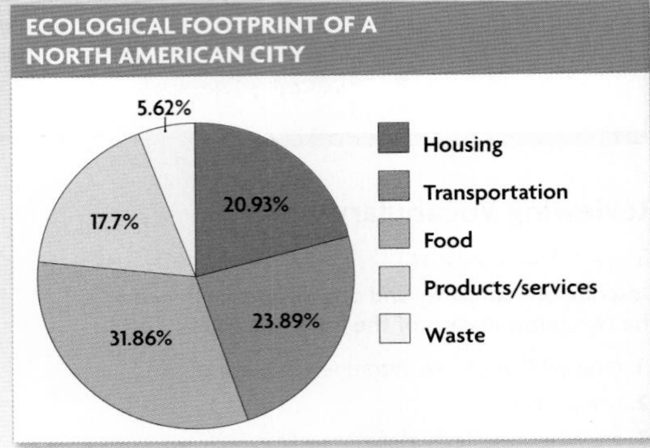

27. Apply Does the circle graph show discrete or continuous data? Explain.

28. Analyze In order of biggest to smallest impact, list the components of human activity that make up the average ecological footprint, according to this graph.

Connecting CONCEPTS

29. Write a Scenario Imagine that successful efforts in sustainable development have made global resource use and waste production fully sustainable by the year 2099. Write a few paragraphs that describe what a sustainable world might look like in 2099. Include information about resource use, waste production, pollution, biodiversity, and conservation. **B.4.2**

30. Connect Look again at the damaged forest ecosystem on page 483. The emissions produced in this region have led to the rapid decline in the biodiversity of this area. How might this decline affect the resources of local animal populations? **B.4.2**

Interpreting Visuals

24. The fox or otter, because both are at the top of the food chain and will absorb the toxins in their prey.
25. The turtle would be more affected. The duck can fly, so it could more easily cross over the barrier that the road represents; the turtle runs the risk of being hit by cars or spotted by foxes if it walks across the road.
26. *Sample Answer:* Otters and ducks may become less common because they have less food to eat. This may result in fewer foxes. Reduced consumption of cattails will allow minnows to flourish, which could lead to more fish and tadpoles. Fish could exert pressure on algae and butterfly populations, which are related.

Analyzing Data

27. discrete, because the data are specific to the footprint of someone in a city at a given time
28. food, transportation, housing, products/services, waste

510 Unit 5: Ecology

INDIANA ISTEP+ Test Prep

B.3.4; B.4.2; B.4.3; NOS.6

Test Practice For more test practice, go to ClassZone.com.

1

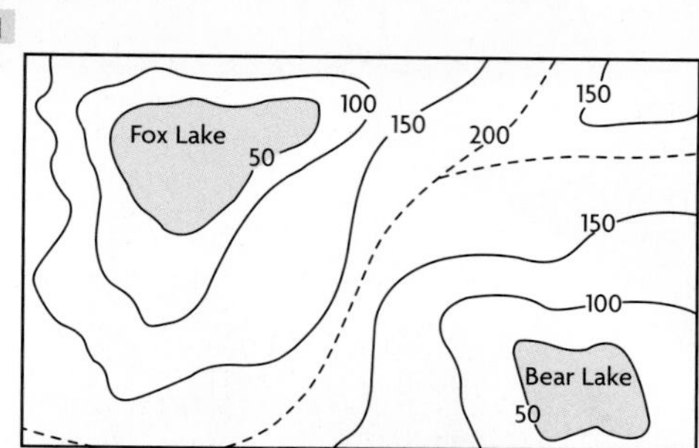

This topographic map shows the Fox Lake and Bear Lake watersheds, or regions that drain into these lakes. The watershed boundary, shown with a dashed line, determines which lake water will flow into. According to the map, this boundary follows

A the highest elevation points between the lakes.
B the lowest elevation points between the lakes.
C a river that likely flows between the lakes.
D exactly halfway between the two lakes.

2 Fertilizers used to improve lawns and gardens may interfere with the equilibrium of an ecosystem because they

A cause mutations in all plants
B cannot be absorbed by roots
C can be carried to local water supplies
D cause atmospheric pollution

3 The nonnative zebra mussel was first found in a lake near Detroit in 1988. By 1989, it had colonized all Great Lakes waterways. Which scenario is most likely true regarding the introduction of this species?

A Native fish naturally eat zebra mussels.
B The higher biodiversity leads to healthier lakes.
C They compete with native mussels for food and other resources.
D Native mussel populations are growing rapidly.

4

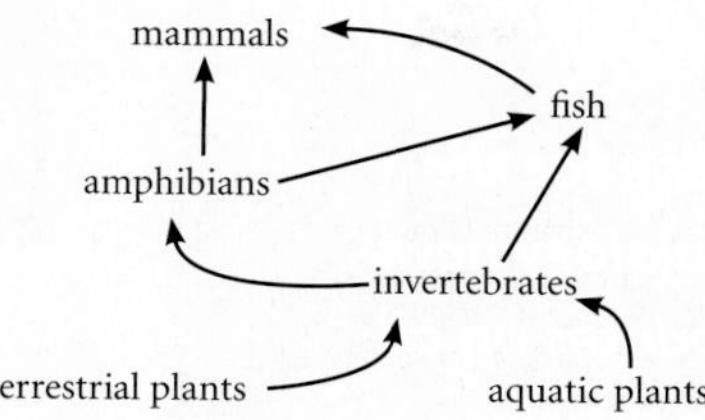

Through the process of biomagnification, certain pollutants build up at each link of a food web. In a polluted river, at what link in the food web above would pollutant concentrations be the highest?

A aquatic plants
B fish
C invertebrates
D mammals

5 Biodiversity is measured and compared for four adjacent spreads of forest that vary in how they have been managed. Which of the following will likely have the highest biodiversity?

A forest surrounded by a fence to keep out predators
B forest managed to control wildfires and insect pests
C forest left unmanaged, not treated for fires or pests
D forest left unmanaged but divided by roads that cross it.

6 CO_2 is important in our atmosphere because it is required for photosynthesis and it traps some heat, keeping the Earth warm. Why is human produced CO_2 a problem?

CHAPTER REVIEW

Standards-Based Assessment

1. A	4. D
2. C	5. C
3. C	6. See Below

TEST DOCTOR

Question 3 Answer C is correct. Answer A is incorrect because if it were true, the nonnative mussel would not likely be found in such abundance. Answer B is incorrect because it appears that the nonnative mussel is taking over many niches and is likely outcompeting other species, thereby decreasing biodiversity. Answer D is incorrect because the nonnative mussel population is growing so rapidly that it is likely outcompeting the native mussel population.

Question 4 Answer D is correct. Answers A, B, and C are incorrect because biomagnification is the concentration of toxic substances in tissues of organisms higher on the food chain than ones lower in the food chain, and aquatic plants, fish, and invertebrates are all lower than mammals in this food chain.

Question 6 Carbon dioxide is a natural part of Earth's atmosphere. The levels of carbon dioxide rise and fall over time as a natural part of Earth's climate cycles. Times of high carbon dioxide levels are also times of warmer global climate. Global temperature changes are a normal part of Earth's climate cycle. However, changes in temperature usually happen over tens of thousands of years. Temperature change caused by human produced CO2 has caused temperatures to rise in only 100 years, endangering ecosystems around the world.

Connecting Concepts

29. Answers will vary, but should include a description of nonrenewable resources being the primary sources of energy and materials, little or no pollution occurring, preservation of biodiversity, recycling, and production of very little non-biodegradable solid waste.

30. Acid rain would lead to a decline in the resources of the area and in turn will decrease animal populations.

ITEM CORRELATIONS

Standard	Items
B.3.4	4
B.4.2	2, 5, 6
B.4.3	3
NOS.6	1

UNIT 5

Introduce

Each day science information is reported in newspapers, magazines, television and radio news, and on the Internet. The scientific research that generates this information often consists of complex data, lengthy reports, and scientific jargon. The information that is of interest to the general public is typically simplified. Sometimes key information is not accurately represented. In addition, people with a certain point of view regarding a controversial issue may take the data out of context and draw conclusions that are not supported.

In 2002, a paper on the climate of Antarctica was published in the January 31 issue of the journal *Nature*. The paper included data collected on temperatures in different areas of Antarctica over a period of time. The researchers, lead by Peter Doran, concluded that the evidence showed an overwhelming warming trend. However select areas did show a lowering of temperatures. These particular data were used as evidence that Earth's temperatures are actually cooling. This is not what Doran's team reported.

When reading about or listening to news reports about science, students should consider whether or not the scientific data involved have been simplified and possibly misinterpreted. Tell students that Peter Doran says his paper is often cited but not often read. **Ask,** What does it mean that something is taken out of context? don't have complete picture

UNIT 5: ECOLOGY

BIOZINE at CLASSZONE.COM

INTERNET MAGAZINE

Go online for the latest biology news and updates on all BioZine articles.

Expanding the Textbook

News Feeds

- Science Daily
- CNN
- BBC

Careers

Bio Bytes

Opinion Poll

Strange Biology

As global temperatures rise and arctic ice melts, polar bears are losing important hunting grounds.

Global Warming—Changing the Planet

Polar bears are beginning to drown. In the summer, the area of arctic sea ice on which these carnivores hunt seals has declined 10 to 15 percent as worldwide temperatures rise. As this ice is lost, polar bears must swim as far as 100 kilometers (about 60 mi) to find their prey. Some of these polar bears do not make it. If global warming is changing the shape of one of Earth's coldest regions, how will it affect the rest of our planet?

Current News

Using the Current News section of BioZine at **ClassZone.com,** have students find articles reporting on ecological or environmental issues. Have students consider these questions:

- How do the articles distinguish between short- and long-term effects?
- What data are included in the articles?
- Do you think the information was simplified or altered in such a way that making an informed decision about the issue is difficult?

Opinion Poll

Have students participate in the BioZine online poll and check the results. **Ask**

- Why do you think questions involving the relative health of ecosystems are so contentious?
- How would you describe human impact on the environment?

Ecosystems at Risk

In the 21st century, the average global temperature is expected to rise about 0.22°C (0.4°F) per decade. This may seem like a small change, but this change is magnified in the seasonal temperature changes of a region. In some parts of the world, such as the Arctic, the temperature is changing much faster. Average annual temperatures in Alaska have risen 3.3°C (5.9°F) since 1949. Sea ice area has been shrinking over the past 100 years, and the ice has become 40 percent thinner in the past several decades, leaving coastal land vulnerable to erosion.

Good and Bad News?

In the rest of the world, the impact of global warming on Earth's species may not be as bad. Many animal species, such as birds and butterflies, can move to cooler areas as the climate warms. But the microorganisms that cause infectious diseases, such as malaria and yellow fever, are also spreading toward the poles. Plant species are moving as well, but many are not able to move as quickly as the climate is expected to change.

Researchers are also finding that changing temperatures can affect animals in surprising ways. The sex of some reptiles, for example, is partially determined by the temperature of the developing egg. A consistent warming trend could cause some reptiles to become extinct by creating entire generations that are all the same sex. Migratory birds and marine mammals also face challenges. For example, birds that wait until their normal migration time to fly north in the spring may arrive too late, missing the best weeks for laying eggs and catching the insects they need to raise their young. In addition, marine mammals face challenges in their own food webs. Several researchers are predicting that the productivity of phytoplankton, the algae on which ocean food webs are based, may decline in some areas. A change of this sort could cause a domino effect in marine food webs. If phytoplankton levels decline, fish will have less food and will be less numerous. If fish are less numerous, marine mammals and birds will have less to eat too.

TECHNOLOGY

Deep Sea Sediment Coring

Analyzing ocean floor sediments can provide scientists with data about how plants and animals were affected during past climate changes. The process of collecting deep sea sediments is expensive and time-consuming, but the results of this research give scientists a look at what life in the oceans was like millions of years ago.

To study these ancient organisms, scientists need sediment samples that are hundreds of meters long. To obtain these, they must use drills similar to the drills used by the oil and gas industry. Taking these samples requires many hours and can be dangerous if the seas are rough or full of ice. Once scientists have obtained the cores, they first split the core in half lengthwise. One half is sampled for fossils of ancient organisms. This is the "working half." The other half, the "archive half," is saved and stored away so that future scientists who may develop other questions can have access to this difficult-to-obtain material.

By carefully dissecting the working half of the sample, scientists discover microscopic fossils of marine animals. Scientists know that these ancient animals were very sensitive to slight changes in temperature and chemistry. These microfossils can tell scientists how Earth's climate has changed over millions of years.

Read More >> at CLASSZONE.COM

These "working half" cores will be carefully dissected and analyzed to better understand Earth's changing climate.

Expanding the Textbook

Have students go to BioZine at **ClassZone.com** to read more about plants and animals affected by global warming. Have students take notes on different organisms. Students should come to class prepared to discuss the organisms and how they are affected by global warming. Have students identify the conditions that are most often cited as sources of concern.

You could extend the discussion to include students' understanding of the factors that are causing global warming. What is the appropriate role of government in controlling global warming? What is the role of individuals? What groups, organizations, or parties might have a vested interest in the global warming debate? Students can research possible effects of global warming on ecosystems and organisms in their state.

Vocabulary of Global Warming

Students may need clarification of some of the terms used in the discussion of global warming.

global warming—an increase in the average global temperature. This temperature is calculated from data of temperatures from all over Earth. A particular area may have warmer temperatures one year and cooler temperatures the next year, but the average temperature for Earth is increasing.

greenhouse effect—the trapping of heat by Earth's atmosphere. This is a natural process without which Earth's average temperature would be around −18 °C. The greenhouse effect increases as the amount of carbon dioxide in the atmosphere increases.

greenhouse gases—gases in the atmosphere that absorb infrared radiation and produce the greenhouse effect. Water vapor, carbon dioxide, and methane are three of the greenhouse gases.

climate—the average weather over a period of time. Weather is the specific conditions of the atmosphere at a particular time and place.

sea ice—ice that forms when ocean water freezes. During the coldest season, sea ice covers about 14 to 16 million square kilometers of the Arctic Ocean and 17 to 20 million square kilometers of the ocean around Antarctica. Glaciers, ice sheets, and ice caps are made up of freshwater ice and are located on land.

permafrost—a layer of permanently frozen soil or ice at or near the surface of the ground. Permafrost may be under a thin layer of soil or a body of water.

Take It Further

Another effect of global warming on ecosystems involves the melting permafrost. Permafrost, as its name suggests, is soil or ice that remains frozen all year. It is located under the surface of the ground or bodies of water. More than half of Alaska's surface rests on a layer of permafrost. Most of the state's permafrost is shallow, but in northern Alaska, the permafrost is very deep. Areas farther south in the state may have little or no permafrost.

When permafrost under a body of water melts, water in the lake or pond can drain out. This has a devastating effect on aquatic ecosystems. Scientists have noticed that in many areas of Alaska, lakes and ponds are getting smaller while others have dried up and disappeared.

In areas where permafrost melts and over-saturates the ground, trees begin to die. As the trees die, the boreal forest changes into a wetland. If permafrost melts in well-drained areas, the water will move away from the area, causing the groundwater content to decrease. With less groundwater, the boreal forest changes into a grassland.

As ecosystems change, the plant and animal communities found there also change. This can affect an ecosystem's food web by disrupting feeding relationships among the different trophic levels and the flow of energy.

Computer modeling programs such as this one work to predict the effects of global warming by simulating different temperature increases.

The news may not be all bad. Global warming is caused by increased levels of carbon dioxide in the atmosphere. Many plants, including crops such as cotton, soybeans, wheat, and rice, can benefit from the increase in CO_2. They can absorb the CO_2 and yield more at harvest time as a result. On the other hand, in warmer weather crops may also be more at risk from insect pests and from severe storms or droughts.

Unanswered Questions

Scientists have little doubt that Earth's climate is changing. Unfortunately, it is impossible to predict exactly how any particular ecosystem will be affected by global warming. However, biologists and climatologists are collecting data about processes including solar radiation, precipitation, evaporation, the transfer of heat energy by winds and by ocean currents, and the ways in which plants affect climate. Then, by using computer models that interpret this information, they can begin to answer questions about how global warming will affect Earth.

- Does global warming cause the number of tropical storms and hurricanes to increase?
- Could global warming alter certain ocean currents, changing Earth's temperatures further?
- How quickly might the polar ice caps melt?
- How have global climate changes affected Earth's ecosystems in the past?

Read More >> at CLASSZONE.COM

CAREERS

Oceanographer in Action

RUTH CURRY

TITLE Oceanographer, Woods Hole Oceanographic Institution

EDUCATION B.S., Geology, Brown University

For Ruth Curry, spending time on the ocean waves has nothing to do with surfing or vacationing. She spends her time studying the ocean currents that affect our lives each day. Ruth Curry is an oceanographer at the Woods Hole Oceanographic Institute, an organization of scientists who research and study how the ocean affects the global environment.

Curry's research focuses on the North Atlantic circulation and the currents that carry warm waters from tropical regions northward. As these warm waters reach higher latitudes, they release heat that warms the air above them and warms the climate of western Europe. As warm water cools, its density increases and it sinks to the bottom of the ocean. There it begins a southward journey back to the tropics. This conveyor belt of water plays an important role in maintaining Earth's climate. Normally, the salinity, or saltiness, of ocean water stays about the same. But changes in global temperatures are melting large sheets of ice in Greenland, which is introducing large amounts of fresh water into the ocean. This fresh water is diluting the ocean water, making it less salty. A decrease in salinity makes ocean waters less dense and prevents them from sinking to the bottom of the ocean. Eventually, the melting of ice sheets in Greenland could cause the North Atlantic currents to slow and eventually stop, leading to dramatic changes in the Northern Hemisphere's climate.

Read More >> at CLASSZONE.COM

BIOZINE ClassZone.com

Have students use the resources available in the Unit 5 BioZine at **ClassZone.com** to report about recent research on ecosystems and global warming. In addition to the resources available in BioZine, have students work with a librarian to locate the original, primary-source materials. Have students compare data in the reports. **Ask**

- How do different accounts of a research report present the findings?
- What different opinions, if any, were expressed by the researchers themselves?
- What information from the primary source could be taken out of context and used to support an alternate viewpoint?

UNIT 6

Classification and Diversity

CHAPTER 17
The Tree of Life 516

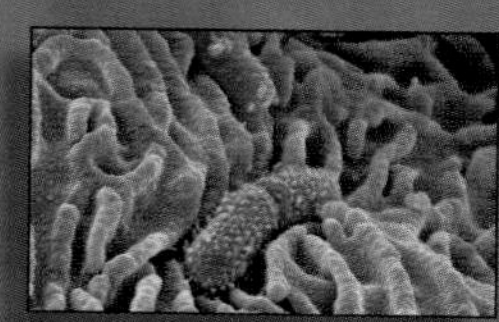

CHAPTER 18
Viruses and Prokaryotes 542

CHAPTER 19
Protists and Fungi 572

INTERNET MAGAZINE
Pandemics—Is the Next One on the Way? 606

TECHNOLOGY Dissecting a Virus

CAREER Epidemiologist

Unit Project

Purpose **Investigate disease-causing organisms of the Amazon, vaccines required for travel to the area, and measures needed to prevent illness.**

Overview Students write an information packet about health precautions to take for a trip to the Amazon. Students will

- search Internet, textbook, and/or library resources about the Amazon and health concerns for travelers
- provide detailed information about the diseases, the organisms that cause the diseases, and the vaccines and behaviors that tend to prevent illness
- prepare an information packet designed to inform parents, teachers, and students about health precautions involved in traveling to the Amazon

Preparation Make a copy of the project description and rubric for each student (*Unit Resource Book*, pp. 95–96). Tell students that their packets will be scored on organization and completeness.

Project Management Allow three weeks for the completion of the project. Have students check in weekly to monitor progress.

Unit Resource Book Unit 6 Project, pp. 95–97

CHAPTER 17

Indiana Resource Preview

Print Resources

The Tree of Life

INDIANA STANDARDS		Sections	PAGES and PACING	UNIT RESOURCE BOOK
	17.1	**The Linnaean System of Classification** **KEY CONCEPT** Organisms can be classified based on physical similarities.	pp. 518–521 30 minutes	URB pages 1–4
		CHAPTER INVESTIGATION: Creating a Dichotomous Key for Limpet Shells	pp. 522–523 90 minutes	**Lab Binder** Classification and Diversity pages 1–3
B.8.2	17.2	**Classification Based on Evolutionary Relationships** **KEY CONCEPT** Modern classification is based on evolutionary relationships.	pp. 524–528 45 minutes	URB pages 5–8
B.8.3		DATA ANALYSIS: Transforming Data Amino Acid Differences Among Species	p. 529 30 minutes	URB page 17
B.8.3	17.3	**Molecular Clocks** **KEY CONCEPT** Molecular clocks provide clues to evolutionary history.	pp. 530–532 30 minutes	URB pages 9–12
B.8.2	17.4	**Domains and Kingdoms** **KEY CONCEPT** The current tree of life has three domains.	pp. 533–535 30 minutes	URB pages 13–16
B.8.2		OPTIONS FOR INQUIRY	pp. 536–537 45 minutes, 45 minutes	**Lab Binder** Classification and Diversity pages 5–9
		Chapter Review	pp. 538–541	**Assessment Book** Chapter Tests A, B pp. 339–346

INDIANA STANDARDS

B.8.2 Explain how organisms are classified and named based on their evolutionary relationships into taxonomic categories.
B.8.3 Use anatomical and molecular evidence to establish evolutionary relationships between organisms.

Labs

PUPIL EDITION LABS

Creating a Dichotomous Key for Limpet Shells, pp. 522–523 Students construct and use a dichotomous key to identify limpet shells. **Lab Binder** pp. 1–3	**Time:** 90 minutes **Material:** set of or photographs of limpet shells
Construct a Cladogram, Section 2, p. 525 Students learn how cladograms are constructed using shared characteristics. **Lab Binder** p. 10	**Time:** 15 minutes **Materials:** paper, pencil

OPTIONS FOR INQUIRY

Modeling DNA Hybridization, p. 536 Students model DNA hybridization and determine relatedness of species. **Lab Binder**, pp. 5–7	**Time:** 45 minutes **Materials:** DNA Hybridization Sequences, 5 different colored pencils
Defining Species, p. 537 Students determine different ways to define species. **Lab Binder** p. 9	**Time:** 45 minutes **Material:** computer with Internet access

LAB BINDER Unit 6 Classification and Diversity

Additional Investigation: Constructing a Phylogenetic Tree, pp. 11–13

Biotechnology Lab: Bioinformatics, pp. 43–45

LAB GENERATOR

A searchable CD of all labs in the program in editable format, including forensic, probeware, and biotechnology labs.

Presentation Tools

POWER PRESENTATIONS

Presentation Chapter 17
Power Presentations for each section incorporate images and clips from the Media Gallery: Includes Note Navigator for each section.

MEDIA GALLERY

Contains the following images and video clips, as well as animations, simulations and forms of visuals from the book.

Linnaean classification

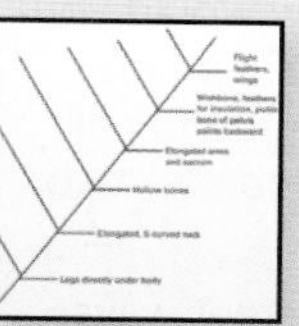
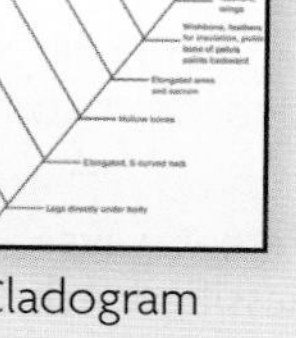

Cladogram

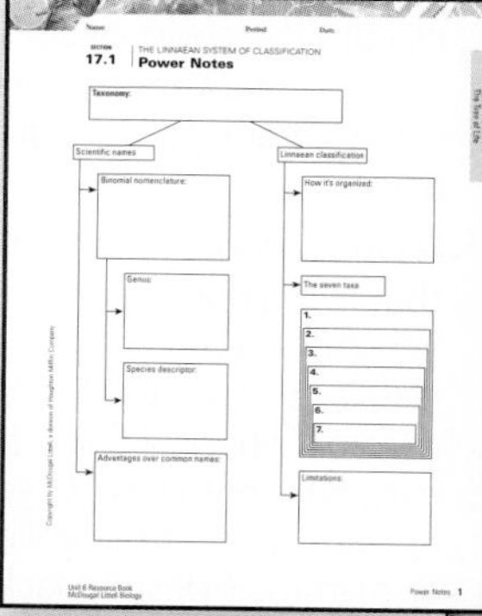

Power Notes

Red handfish

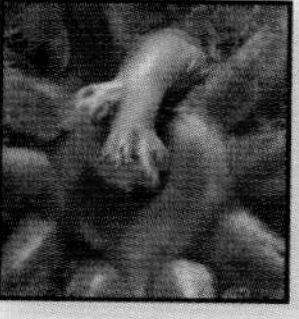

Sea cucumber

VIDEO

View a short video clip exploring classification.

ANIMATED BIOLOGY

Molecular Clock

Build a Cladogram

TRANSPARENCIES

The Linnaean Classification System T74

Tetrapod Cladogram T75

The Tree of Life T76

Online BIOLOGY CLASSZONE.COM

BioZine

Animated Biology

Interactive Review

SciLinks

Resource Centers

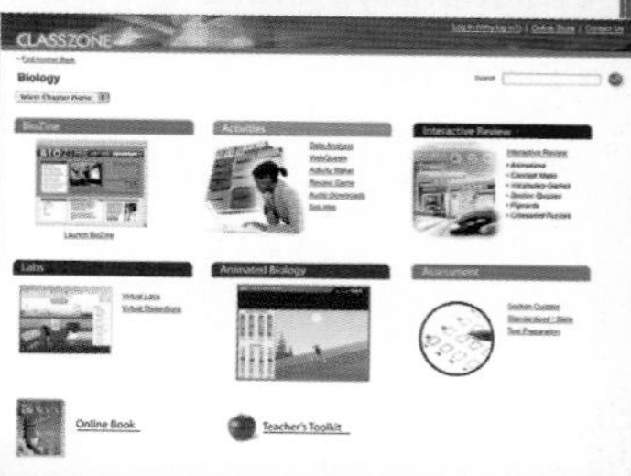

CHAPTER

17

▼ Focus and Motivate

How would you classify this organism?

Help students think about how classifications are made. **Ask,** How would you classify the sport of soccer? *Sample Answer:* team sport, uses a round ball, non-contact, game is divided into two halves

Have students discuss different ways that living things can be classified. **Ask,** What characteristics could you use to classify the pangolin in the photograph? external physical traits, behavior, what it eats, where it lives, its genetic make-up Explain that pangolins are classified as mammals despite lacking hair because they nourish their young with milk.

BIOZINE ClassZone.com

Students can access BioZine at **ClassZone.com** to check the daily science news feeds.

In a Hurry?

The critical material of the chapter is found in **Sections 17.1, 17.2,** and **17.4,** which cover the Linnaean system of classification; classification based on evolutionary relationships; and the current classification system using domains and kingdoms. **Section 17.3** contains more advanced material on how molecular clocks can reveal evolutionary history.

CHAPTER 17 The Tree of Life

KEY CONCEPTS

17.1 The Linnaean System of Classification
Organisms can be classified based on physical similarities.

17.2 Classification Based on Evolutionary Relationships
Modern classification is based on evolutionary relationships.

17.3 Molecular Clocks
Molecular clocks provide clues to evolutionary history.

17.4 Domains and Kingdoms
The current tree of life has three domains.

Online BIOLOGY CLASSZONE.COM

Animated BIOLOGY
View animated chapter concepts.
- Molecular Clock
- Build a Cladogram

BIOZINE
Keep current with biology news.
- Featured stories
- News feeds
- Strange Biology

RESOURCE CENTER
Get more information on
- Modern Classification
- Molecular Clocks

Student Activity

Purpose **Have teams of students practice making the kinds of observations and decisions that are required to develop and use a classification system.**

Materials (per team)

Provide to each group five books of varying subjects and physical characteristics. Include one or two books from the school library, which will have already been marked by a classification method such as the Dewey decimal classification.

How would you classify this organism?

Connecting CONCEPTS

Pangolins, native to Africa and Asia, are not closely related to any other living mammals. Their backs and tails are covered with large scales similar in arrangement to dinosaur bone plates. Pangolins do not have teeth. Instead, they have an organ similar to a bird's gizzard. Due to these unique traits, pangolins are classified into their own group within class Mammalia.

Evolution The pangolin's long snout and tongue, sharp claws for digging, and the absence of teeth are all adaptations to an ant-eating lifestyle. Anteaters and aardvarks have similar traits. However, these animals are not closely related. Instead, pangolins, anteaters, and aardvarks display convergent evolution. Their similar characteristics arose independently as natural selection acted upon species with similar diets.

Introduce Have students form small teams. Tell them to examine the books provided and develop their own book classification system that places the books into categories based on similarities.

Discuss Have students describe their classification systems. **Ask**

- What criteria did you select in setting up your system? similarities of physical attributes; subject area or genre; language
- Would these systems work if additional books were added? Answers will depend on how well the systems anticipate new additions.
- Do you think any of these books have already been classified by another system? Students may recognize the Dewey decimal classification or the Library of Congress cataloging system if books are marked in these ways.

Explain that there have been many different systems for classifying living things, and that most modern classification schemes are based on evolutionary relationships.

Activate Prior Knowledge

Introduce the "tree of life" as a metaphor of the relationships and evolution of all the life on Earth. **Ask**

- If we imagine a tree of life that represents the evolution of life over billions of years, what might the leaves represent? species, or different groups of closely related organisms (families)
- What might the branches, both the small and the large, represent? Large branches could represent ancestral species from which the smaller branches diverged and evolved over time.
- What might the trunk represent? the earliest life forms from which all living organisms have evolved

Preview Vocabulary

Word Origins The words *kingdom* and *domain* share the same word part *dom.* This old English root means "state" or "power." Both *kingdom* and *domain* relate to a territory that someone either controls or owns, a king, for example. In biology, the words relate to a sense of belonging by shared characteristics. Tell students they can think of a biological domain as a "superkingdom," one that encompasses smaller biological kingdoms.

Academic Vocabulary In this chapter, students will encounter the word *system* in a new way. A classification system is an organized method of grouping organisms based on similarities. *Systematics* is the science of classification.

English Learners Have students apply a vocabulary strategy to help them learn new words or new meanings of familiar words, such as the way in which *system* is used in this chapter. They can write the sentence in which a word appears in the text, try to understand the meaning based on its context, and then use resources such as the *Multilanguage Glossary* to find out the exact meaning.

SECTION 17.1

▼ Plan and Prepare

Objectives

- Examine the scientific naming system developed by Linnaeus.
- Identify the limitations of the Linnaean system.

Section Resources

Unit Resource Book
Study Guide pp. 1–2
Power Notes p. 3
Reinforcement p. 4
Pre-AP Activity pp. 19–20

Interactive Reader Chapter 17
Spanish Study Guide pp. 175–176

Biology Toolkit p. C3

Technology
Power Presentation 17.1
Media Gallery DVD
Online Quiz 17.1

Activate Prior Knowledge Explain to students that while common names are how we identify species in everyday life, science requires a single scientific name for each species. **Ask,** What would be the problem with using common names? There can be many names for the same organism in one language, and the names are entirely different in another language. The large number of common names makes it difficult for scientists to communicate or share data.

▼ Teach

Vocabulary

Academic Vocabulary The terms **diverse** and **diversity** come from a Latin word meaning "in different directions." These terms appear in the context of classification because to understand and quantify the **biodiversity** of Earth, biologists need to know how two or more species are related. By analyzing evolutionary relationships, biologists can sometimes pinpoint when two species diverged from a common ancestor.

17.1 The Linnaean System of Classification

KEY CONCEPT Organisms can be classified based on physical similarities.

MAIN IDEAS
- Linnaeus developed the scientific naming system still used today.
- Linnaeus' classification system has seven levels.
- The Linnaean classification system has limitations.

VOCABULARY
taxonomy, p. 518
taxon, p. 518
binomial nomenclature, p. 519
genus, p. 519

Review
species

Connect The pangolin shown on the previous page may not look like any other animal that you are familiar with. However, scientists classify pangolins as mammals—the same group of animals that includes dogs, cats, mice, and humans. All female mammals have the ability to produce milk. Unlike pangolins, most mammals have hair. Scientists use key characteristics such as these to classify all living things.

MAIN IDEA

Linnaeus developed the scientific naming system still used today.

TAKING NOTES
Use a main idea web to take notes about the Linnaean system of classification.

taxonomy | binomial nomenclature | Linnaeus' naming system

Before Swedish botanist Carolus Linnaeus introduced his scientific naming system, naturalists named newly discovered organisms however they wanted. In fact, they often named organisms after themselves. Because they had no agreed-upon way to name living things, it was difficult for naturalists to talk about their findings with one another. This all changed in the 1750s, when Linnaeus devised a system that standardized the way organisms are classified and named.

Taxonomy

Taxonomy is the science of naming and classifying organisms. Taxonomy gives scientists a standard way to refer to species and organize the diversity of living things. Linnaean taxonomy classifies organisms based on their physical and structural similarities. Organisms are placed into different levels in a hierarchy—a multilevel scale in which each level is "nested" in the next-higher level. In other words, each level is included in a larger, more general level, which in turn is included in an even larger, more general level.

VOCABULARY
Taxonomy comes from the Greek *taxis,* which means "arrangement," and *nomie,* which means "method."

A group of organisms in a classification system is called a **taxon** (plural, *taxa*). The basic taxon in the Linnaean system is the species. In this system, species are most commonly defined as a group of organisms that can breed and produce offspring that can reproduce. Linnaeus' system gives each species a scientific name. With few changes, this method of naming is still used today.

Differentiated Instruction

BELOW LEVEL

Create an anticipation guide to evaluate students' comprehension before and after they read the section. Pose true/false statements such as the following:
Within a phylum, a class has more species than an order. T
If two species both have the word fish in their name, they must be in the same family. F
The best name for scientists to use for a species is its most popular common name. F

Biology Toolkit, Anticipation Guide, p. C3

PRE-AP

To help students understand how organisms are classified in a hierarchical system, give them the analogy of the United States postal system and how it gives each home a unique address. Have students come up with a seven-step hierarchical order of geographical detail that would lead someone who is outside the continent to their front door. Remind students that the goal is to arrive at a unique place by following a universally understood convention. A good sequence would be North America, United States, state, county, city/town, street, number.

Scientific Names

Binomial nomenclature (by-NOH-mee-uhl NOH-muhn-KLAY-chuhr) is a system that gives each species a two-part scientific name using Latin words. The first part of the name is the genus. A **genus** (plural, *genera*) includes one or more physically similar species that are thought to be closely related. For example, the genus *Quercus* includes more than 500 species of oak trees. Genus names are always capitalized. They are written in italics or underlined.

VISUAL VOCAB

Binomial nomenclature is a standard naming system that gives each species a two-part name using Latin words.

two — bi; name — nomial; naming — nomen; system — clature

(1) *Genus* (2) *species*

The second part of the name is the species descriptor. It can refer to a trait of the species, the scientist who first described it, or its native location. Like the genus, the species descriptor is written in italics or underlined. However, it is always lowercase. The species descriptor is never written alone because, as **FIGURE 17.1** shows, the same word may be used in different genera. *Quercus alba* is the scientific name for white oak trees (*alba* means "white"), but *Tyto alba* is the scientific name for barn owls.

You may wonder why biologists use scientific names. It may seem easier to use terms such as *white oak* instead of remembering two-part Latin names. However, scientific names are helpful in a number of ways. First, genera such as *Quercus* contain hundreds of species. Many of these species have very similar common names. Scientific names allow scientists to talk about particular species without confusion. Also, remember that biology is studied all over the world. One species may have many different common names. In fact, a species may have several different common names within a single country. *Armidillidium vulgare* is the scientific name for pill bugs. However, this species is also called roly-poly, sow bug, and potato bug. Scientific names allow scientists around the world to communicate clearly about living things.

FIGURE 17.1 The white oak (*Quercus alba*) and the barn owl (*Tyto alba*) belong to different genera. The species parts of their scientific names are both *alba*, meaning "white."

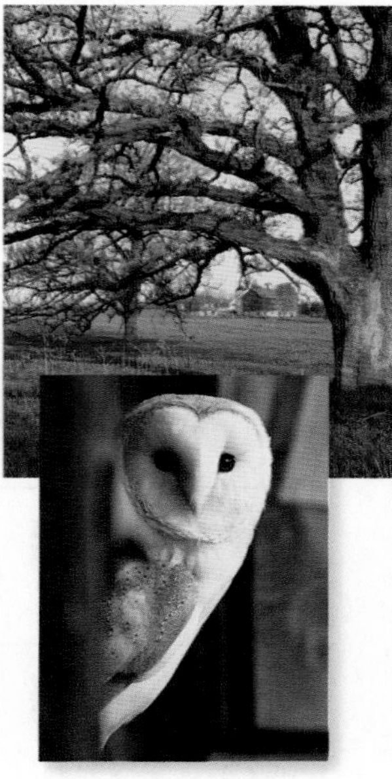

A **Contrast** **Describe the difference between a genus and a species.**

FIGURE 17.2 SCIENTIFIC AND COMMON NAMES

COMMON NAMES	SCIENTIFIC NAME	
	Genus	**species**
Roly-poly, pill bug, sow bug, potato bug	*Armadillidium*	*vulgare*
Dandelion, Irish daisy, lion's tooth	*Taraxacum*	*officinale*
House sparrow, English sparrow	*Passer*	*domesticus*
Mountain lion, cougar, puma	*Puma*	*concolor*
Red maple, scarlet maple, swamp maple	*Acer*	*rubrum*

ONLINE BIOLOGY Go to the chapter Resource Center at **ClassZone.com** for additional resources and information about classification.

The Inside Story

He was so serious about his classification work that **Carl Linnaeus** changed his first name to **Carolus,** a Latin transliteration. Linnaeus was compulsive about organizing life on Earth and matters in his own life. Even his private letters were classified into groups and subgroups. At first, he did not think much of his idea to give a species descriptor in addition to the genus, so he referred to them as "trivial names." In time, though, he realized how helpful descriptors were in differentiating between species.

Though his system is still the basis for classification, he classified some animals in ways that now seem odd. For example, he placed the rhinoceros among rodents. To his credit, he bravely suggested the relationship between humankind and apes—an idea that is still unsettling to many people.

Answers

A Contrast Both are groups of the biological classification system. A *species,* however, is a subset of a genus consisting of a single type of organism. A *genus* is a group of one or more closely related and physically similar species.

TEACH WITH TECHNOLOGY

Plan an Internet activity, either in your classroom or in a computer lab. Provide students with a list of six scientific names of marine fish species who among them have several species descriptors or genus names in common. Have students organize the species into a classification scheme. Students can look up each species online at FishBase or other sites to learn common names as well as the family, class, and order of each species. English learners can use their home language's version of FishBase and share with the class the common names of the species in their language.

Students can also print out illustrations or photos of these species to illustrate their tree or classification scheme. Here is a sample list of species, representing three families, two orders, and two classes:

Makaira nigricans
Acanthurus nigricans
Naso unicornis
Naso brevirostris
Negaprion brevirostris
Negaprion acutidens
Tetrapturus audax
Makaira indica

▼ Teach *continued*

TEACH FROM VISUALS

FIGURE 17.3 Have students follow the diversity of organisms through the different levels. **Ask**

- What animals are dropped as we move from kingdom to phylum? invertebrates
- What well-known Australian animal is excluded from the Carnivora order, which includes all true bears? koala bear
- How can this be? Sharing a common name or having a similar name means very little in terms of actual relatedness. An animal called a bear may not be a true bear.
- From what you can infer from the figure, what are characteristics of animals in the order Carnivora? terrestrial, toothed, four-legged, meat-eating mammals

Vocabulary

Word Origins Students may wonder what relationship the word **tax** has to **taxonomy.** Despite the similarity, the words come from different roots. *Tax* relates to an expression in Old French that means "to touch," which developed into the idea of "touching" someone for a payment or tax. The word **taxi** has the same root, which derives from the **taximeter** that calculates the cost of a ride.

The words *taxonomy* and **taxidermy** share the same root *taxis,* meaning "arrangement." The first is a methodical arrangement of organisms; the second is the preparation and arrangement of, literally, skin—as in the stuffing of animal skin to create a lifelike form.

Answers

A Analyze cats

MAIN IDEA

Linnaeus' classification system has seven levels.

***Connecting* CONCEPTS**

Domains The tree of life has been updated since Linnaeus' time. Scientists now classify organisms into an even broader category, called the domain, above the kingdom level. You will learn more about domains and kingdoms in **Section 17.4.**

The Linnaean system of classification has seven levels, or taxa. From the most general to the most specific, these levels are kingdom, phylum (the term *division* is often used instead of *phylum* for plants and fungi), class, order, family, genus, and species. Each level in Linnaeus' system is nested, or included, in the level above it. A kingdom contains one or more phyla, a phylum contains one or more classes, and so forth. The classification of the gray wolf, *Canis lupis,* is shown in **FIGURE 17.3.** Moving down, the levels represent taxa that become more and more specific, until you reach the species level at the bottom.

FIGURE 17.3 The Linnaean Classification System

Linnaean taxonomy classifies living things into a hierarchy of groups called taxa. The classification of the gray wolf is illustrated here.

A Analyze Based on the taxonomy shown here, are bats or cats more closely related to gray wolves?

Differentiated Instruction

ENGLISH LEARNERS

Mnemonics are helpful in learning the order of the nested levels of Linnaean classification. Write on the board the seven levels in order, from kingdom to species, with the first letter of each underlined. Have students think of a phrase that matches up the first letters of the Linnaean levels with the first letters of words they will remember. Example: King Philip called out for good spaghetti.

TEACH WITH TECHNOLOGY

Have students work in groups or as a class to put together a digital slide show of the classification of a species of their choice. They should prepare a visual hierarchy similar to **FIGURE 17.3** with notes on the characteristics of each level. Encourage students to select species from several different orders so that students will learn about different branches of the tree of life as they view one another's presentations.

The top level represents all of the species in kingdom Animalia. As you move down, the levels show examples of species from phylum Chordata, class Mammalia, order Carnivora, family Canidae, genus *Canis,* and the species *Canis lupis*. Each level is included in all of the more general levels above it.

Notice that gray wolves are in the same genus, *Canis,* as dogs and coyotes. Because the Linnaean system is a nested hierarchy, wolves, dogs, and coyotes also belong to the same family, order, class, phylum, and kingdom. Foxes do not belong to the *Canis* genus, but they do belong to Canidae—the same family as wolves, dogs, and coyotes. Therefore, foxes also belong to the same order, class, phylum, and kingdom as wolves, dogs, and coyotes.

Apply If two species belong to the same order, what other levels in the Linnaean system must they have in common?

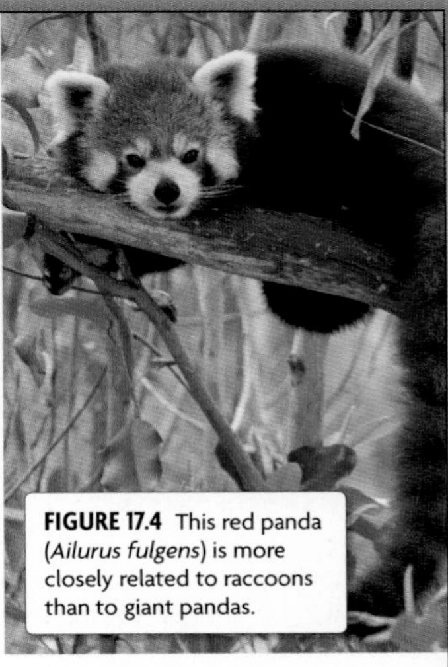

FIGURE 17.4 This red panda (*Ailurus fulgens*) is more closely related to raccoons than to giant pandas.

MAIN IDEA

The Linnaean classification system has limitations.

Linnaeus created his classification system before technology allowed us to study organisms at the molecular level. His system focuses on physical similarities alone. Remember that physical similarities between two species are not always a result of the species' being closely related. Unrelated species can evolve similar traits through convergent evolution. Linnaeus' system does not account for similarities that evolved this way. So today, scientists use genetic research to help classify living things. Genetic similarities between two species are more likely than physical similarities to be due to a common ancestor.

For example, the giant panda and the raccoon have similar ears and snouts. Because of these similarities, they have been placed in the same family in the Linnaean system. However, molecular biologists have found that the giant panda is more closely related to members of the bear family than it is to raccoons. Furthermore, the red panda, shown in **FIGURE 17.4**, is more closely related to the raccoon than to the giant panda.

Infer Why is the common name *red panda* misleading in terms of classification based on relatedness?

Connecting CONCEPTS

Classification Refer to the **Appendix** for a complete list of the kingdoms and their phyla.

NSTA scilinks.org SCILINKS

To learn more about taxonomy, go to scilinks.org.
Keycode: MLB017

17.1 ASSESSMENT

ONLINE QUIZ ClassZone.com

REVIEWING MAIN IDEAS

1. What is **binomial nomenclature**?
2. Name each **taxon** in the Linnaean system of classification, from most general to most specific.
3. What are some limitations of the Linnaean classification system?

CRITICAL THINKING

4. **Compare** How is a scientific name similar to an address that includes city and state?
5. **Apply** Which two species are more closely related: *Ursus maritimus, Ursus americanus,* or *Bufo americanus?* Explain your answer.

Connecting CONCEPTS

6. **History of Science** During his voyages, Darwin collected thousands of organisms, which he classified using the Linnaean classification system. How did this system help him share his findings with other naturalists?

Take It Further

Our species, ***Homo sapiens,*** is in the same kingdom, phylum, and class as the dogs, cats, and bears of **FIGURE 17.3,** but we are in the order Primates and the family Hominidae. Our closest living relatives are the chimpanzees, whose DNA is 98 percent identical to our own. Other extinct hominids have been placed in the same genus as ours. ***Homo habilis*** is believed to have lived as recently as 1.5 million years ago in what is now Java. ***Homo floresiensis,*** a hominid whose bones were recently found on the island of Flores in Indonesia, lived as recently as 18,000 years ago. It is conceivable that this hominid encountered our species as we spread out from Asia toward Australia.

Answers

A Apply class, phylum, kingdom

B Infer because red pandas are actually more closely related to raccoons than to giant pandas, which are in turn more closely related to other bears

Assess and Reteach

Assess Use the Online Quiz or Section Quiz (*Assessment Book,* p. 335).

Reteach Have students use a graphic organizer such as a cluster diagram to review the Linnaean system of classification.

17.1 ASSESSMENT

1. It is a system that gives every species a unique two-part name that identifies it. The first part is the genus, and the second part is the species descriptor.
2. kingdom, phylum, class, order, family, genus, species
3. It only accounts for physical and structural similarities between organisms, which can be the result of convergent evolution and therefore not indicative of relatedness.
4. A state has many cities as a genus has many species. Like species descriptors, city names cannot be used alone because the same city names can occur in different states, as with Portland (Maine and Oregon).
5. *Ursus maritimus* (polar bear) and *Ursus americanus* (black bear) are most closely related; they belong to the same genus.
6. Others could understand the relationships between organisms, such as Darwin's finches, and there was uniformity in terms of language. Had he used common names alone, they would have required translation into many languages.

INVESTIGATION

Time 90 minutes	TEACHER TESTED
Teacher Preparation	
Student Difficulty	
Lab Binder Diversity, pp. 1–3	

Purpose Construct and use a dichotomous key to identify limpet shells.

Overview Students will identify characteristics of limpet shells that can be used to categorize the shells. Students will then

- construct a dichotomous key using the characteristics of limpet shells
- use the dichotomous keys of other students to identify the limpet shells

LAB PREPARATION

Become familiar with important limpet shell characteristics that students could include in their dichotomous keys, including:

- presence or absence of a hole in the top of the shell
- size, shape, and color of the shell (inside and outside)
- pattern of coloration
- margin variation (smooth or crenulated)
- presence or absence of ribs or ridges on the outside of the shell

LAB MANAGEMENT

- If students are having difficulty deciding what characteristics of limpet shells to use for their dichotomous keys, you may want to describe the characteristics of one limpet shell together as a class.
- Students can find additional information on the nine limpet species on the Internet or in field guides to shells. Field guides to coral reefs, seashores, or to a particular geographic area, such as the Caribbean, may also be useful.

MATERIAL
set of or photographs of limpet shells

PROCESS SKILLS
- Observing
- Identifying
- Classifying

Creating a Dichotomous Key for Limpet Shells

Limpets are marine invertebrates found along rocky shorelines around the world. The flattened shape of a limpet's shell allows it to withstand the impact of waves, and its muscular foot allows it to cling tightly to rocks. Although biologists today classify limpets by using traits of the entire organism, for this activity you will construct a dichotomous key based on shell characteristics.

Dichotomous keys are used to identify objects or organisms that have already been described by another scientist. As its name implies (*di-* means "two"), a dichotomous key is made up of paired statements. Each pair of statements divides the objects to be classified into two categories. This means that each object must fit into one category or the other, but not both. At the right is a simple example of a dichotomous key that identifies five common beans. As you proceed from step to step, the classification is narrowed down until all five beans are identified.

SAMPLE DICHOTOMOUS KEY FOR BEANS

1.a. If the bean is round .... it is a garbanzo bean.
1.b. If the bean is oblong .... go to step 2.

2.a. If the bean is white ..... it is a white northern bean.
2.b. If the bean is dark-colored .... go to step 3.

3.a. If the bean is a solid color .... go to step 4.
3.b. If the bean is speckled .... it is a pinto bean.

4.a. If the bean is black .... it is a black bean.
4.b. If the bean is reddish-brown .... it is a kidney bean.

PROBLEM What characteristics can you use to make a dichotomous key for limpet shells?

PROCEDURE

1. Identify some characteristics of each limpet shell. Characteristics may include margin (edge) variation, shape, color, and features on the shell.
2. Construct a dichotomous key, using the above sample for beans as a guide. Start with a general characteristic that separates your limpets into two groups. (**Example:** Keyhole limpets have a hole at the highest point of their shell; true limpets do not.)
3. Continue making paired statements that become more detailed.
   - Each pair of statements must contain only two choices, and these choices must refer to the same characteristic. (**Example:** Do not compare size and color in the same pair of statements.) Every limpet that has not yet been identified must fit one of the two choices.
   - Do not use vague terms such as *big* and *little*. Be as specific as possible.
   - Each statement must either identify a limpet or lead to another step in the key.
4. Trade dichotomous keys with another student or group in your class. Check to make sure you can identify each limpet using your classmates' key.

Answers

Sample Data

Sample of students' description of *Fissurella barbadensis:*

- hole in center
- very dullish color
- rings of brown going around hole
- combination of yellow and brown spots
- rough edges

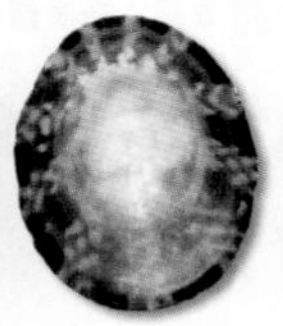

Cellana testudinaria
Common turtle limpet

Collisella striata
Striate limpet

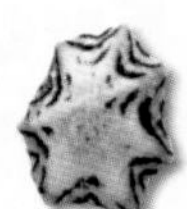

Patelloida saccharina
Sugar limpet

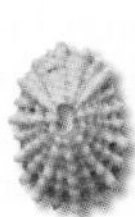

Fissurella nodosa
Knobbed keyhole limpet

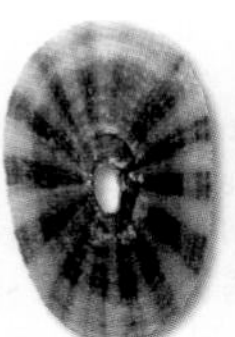

Fissurella maxima
Giant keyhole limpet

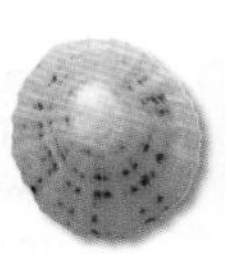

Cellana radiata
Rayed limpet

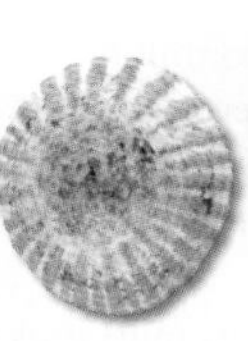

Nacella deaurata
Patagonian copper limpet

Fissurella barbadensis
Barbados keyhole limpet

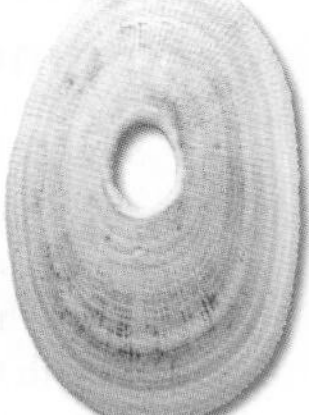
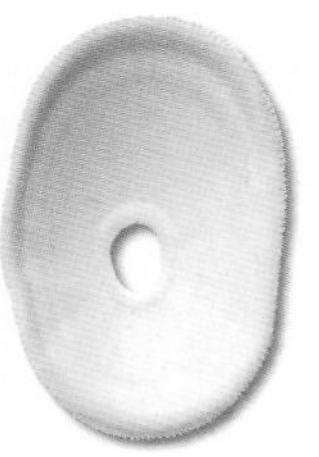

Megathura crenulata
Great keyhole limpet

ANALYZE AND CONCLUDE

1. **Summarize** How did you organize the limpet shells?
2. **Analyze** What different categories did other groups use to organize the shells?
3. **Identify Problems** What problems arose as you constructed your key?
4. **Infer** If you were given the actual shells, what additional characteristics could you have used to make your key?
5. **Apply** Two outcomes are said to be mutually exclusive if they cannot both occur at the same time. For example, heads and tails are mutually exclusive outcomes of flipping a coin. Why is it important that the paired statements in a dichotomous key describe mutually exclusive characteristics?

INVESTIGATION

Inclusion Tell students that one of the world's foremost experts on mollusks, **Dr. Geerat J. Vermeij** of the University of California, Davis, is visually impaired. He identifies and classifies mollusk shells exclusively by touch. If, however, the shells are too worn or small, non-expert students who are visually impaired may have difficulty identifying them. These students can be given larger types of shells or other objects that can be categorized by touch.

POST-LAB DISCUSSION

Have students discuss the various ways in which they categorized the limpet shells. **Ask**

- What characteristic seemed like the best option for the first paired statements in your key? presence or absence of keyhole
- If you wanted to select out a limpet right away, in the first paired statements, what characteristic could you focus on? star-shaped shell, because only one species has this distinct feature

Determine whose key had the least number of paired statements or steps, and have that student explain his or her strategy.

This activity can be related to the use of marine mollusk shells as index fossils. Because the shapes and textures of shells are often very well preserved, as in the Burgess Shale, it is relatively easy to identify the species and use them to determine the relative age of other fossils in the same or nearby strata.

Analyze and Conclude

1. Keys should have nine or more pairs of statements. Most will have nine. If they start with keyhole/no keyhole, they will have nine, at least.
2. Answers could include presence or absence of keyhole; shape, coloration, size of shell; and fissures in the shell.
3. Answers may include problems determining the order of the paired statements that best divides the shells into mutually exclusive groups.
4. Texture, mass; microscope could be used to see surface details of the shells.
5. because otherwise an organism could qualify for inclusion in more than one group or species, or may fit neither group

SECTION 17.2

▼ Plan and Prepare

Objectives

- Describe classification by cladistics.
- Summarize how molecular evidence reveals species' relatedness.

Section Resources

Unit Resource Book
Study Guide pp. 5–6
Power Notes p. 7
Reinforcement p. 8
Pre-AP Activity pp. 21–22

Interactive Reader Chapter 17
Spanish Study Guide pp. 177–178

Biology Toolkit pp. C14, C19, D4

Technology
Power Presentation 17.2
Media Gallery DVD
Online Quiz 17.2

Activate Prior Knowledge Discuss the tree of life as a symbol of evolutionary relationships. Have students compare a genealogy or family tree to the phylogeny or evolution of a group of species. **Ask,** If you think of yourself as a species, who represents the genus, family, and order? Genus would be yourself + parents; family would be yourself + parents + grandparents; order would be yourself + parents + grandparents + great-grandparents.

To take the analogy further, ask a student to volunteer the surnames through several generations of his or her family, which can be strung together to create names for the "taxa."

17.2 Classification Based on Evolutionary Relationships

KEY CONCEPT Modern classification is based on evolutionary relationships.

MAIN IDEAS

- Cladistics is classification based on common ancestry.
- Molecular evidence reveals species' relatedness.

VOCABULARY

phylogeny, p. 524
cladistics, p. 525
cladogram, p. 525
derived character, p. 525

Review
taxon

B.8.2 Explain how organisms are classified and named based on their evolutionary relationships into taxonomic categories.

Connect If you've ever observed bats in a zoo or in the night sky, you've likely noticed that they have several features in common with birds, such as wings. However, bats are actually more closely related to rodents and primates than they are to birds. Today, scientists agree that species should be classified based on evolutionary relationships rather than just physical similarities.

MAIN IDEA

Cladistics is classification based on common ancestry.

Similar traits between species are often the result of sharing a common ancestor, such as the ancestor shared by dogs and wolves. However, scientists now know that similar traits, such as the wings of bats and birds, can also evolve in species that are adapting to similar environmental conditions. As you read in Chapter 11, this process is called convergent evolution.

To classify species according to how they are related, scientists must look at more than just physical traits. Modern classification is based on figuring out evolutionary relationships using evidence from living species, the fossil record, and molecular data. The evolutionary history for a group of species is called a **phylogeny** (fy-LAHJ-uh-nee).

Phylogenies can be shown as branching tree diagrams. In a way, these diagrams are like family trees. The branches of a family tree show how family members are related to each other. The branches of an evolutionary tree show how different groups of species are related to each other.

FIGURE 17.5 The glyptodon (*Glyptotherium arizonae*), illustrated here, was the size of a small car and lived more than 10,000 years ago. It is the common ancestor to about 20 modern armadillo species, including the nine-banded armadillo (*Dasypus novemcinctus*).

▼ Teach

Vocabulary

Greek and Latin Word Origins The word **phylogeny** comes from the following Greek words:

phylon = class or race
geneia = origin

The first root is also the origin of the words **phylogenic, phylum,** and **phylogenetic.**

Differentiated Instruction

ENGLISH LEARNERS

Have students work in small groups to preview the section, ask questions about the main ideas or unfamiliar terms, identify things that are difficult to comprehend, and then summarize the material. Students should give special attention in this section to cladograms, how they are constructed, and what each part represents in relation to evolutionary history or phylogeny.

Biology Toolkit, Reciprocal Teaching, p. C14

Cladistics

The most common method used to make evolutionary trees is called cladistics. **Cladistics** (kluh-DIHS-tihks) is classification based on common ancestry. The goal of cladistics is to place species in the order in which they descended from a common ancestor. A **cladogram** is an evolutionary tree that proposes how species may be related to each other through common ancestors.

At the root of the words *cladistics* and *cladogram* is the word *clade*. A clade is a group of species that shares a common ancestor. For example, the glyptodon in **FIGURE 17.5** is the common ancestor of about 20 modern species of armadillos. Together, the glyptodon and all of its descendants form a clade.

Through the course of evolution, certain traits change in some species of a clade but stay the same in other species. Therefore, each species in a clade has some traits that have not changed from its ancestors, such as the similar shells of glyptodons and modern armadillos. However, each species also has traits that have changed over evolutionary time.

The traits that can be used to figure out evolutionary relationships among a group of species are those that are shared by some species but are not present in others. These traits are called **derived characters.** As you will soon see, cladograms are made by figuring out which derived characters are shared by which species. The more closely related species are, the more derived characters they will share. A group of species that shares no derived characters with the other groups being studied is called an outgroup.

VOCABULARY

The word *derived* comes from the Latin *de-*, meaning "from," and *rivus*, meaning "stream." Therefore, *derived* refers to something that has "flowed" from a source. The term *derived characters* refers to characters that have evolved in a species since sharing a common ancestor.

QUICK LAB **CLASSIFYING** B.8.2

Construct a Cladogram

You can think of a cladogram as an evolutionary family tree in which things that are more closely related share more characteristics. As an analogy, processes that have evolved due to new technologies can be organized using cladistics. In this lab, you will fill in a cladogram for methods of transportation.

PROBLEM How can methods of transportation be organized using a cladogram?

PROCEDURE

1. Copy the cladogram axes on the right into your notebook.
2. Think about the characteristics of the following methods of transportation: bicycle, car, motorcycle, airplane, and on foot.
3. Complete your cladogram by filling in each method of transportation listed in step 2 on the appropriate line at the top.

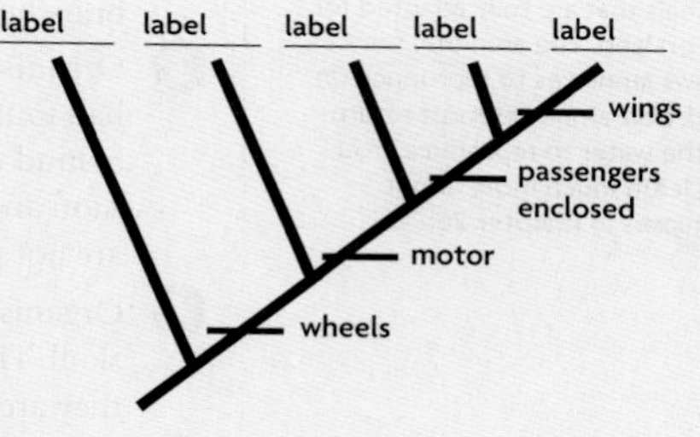

ANALYZE AND CONCLUDE

1. **Identify** What "derived characters" are used in this cladogram?
2. **Analyze** Which mode of transportation may be considered an "outgroup"—a group that has none of the characteristics labeled on the cladogram?
3. **Connect** A species that has evolved a new trait is not better than a species without that trait. Each species is just adapted to a certain way of life. When might riding a bike have an advantage over flying in an airplane?

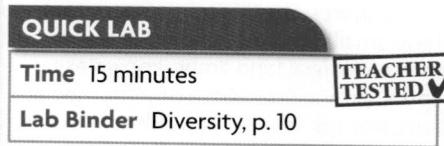

ONLINE BIOLOGY Go to the chapter Resource Center at **ClassZone.com** for additional resources and information on modern classification and cladistics.

Vocabulary

Greek and Latin Word Origins The words **clade** and **cladistics** come from the Greek *klados,* meaning "branch."

Academic Vocabulary Point out to students that the words **trait** and **character** are similar, but not synonymous. Both are heritable features, but characters relate specifically to different "states," such as "hair present" versus "hair absent," that are used for classification purposes. The word **characteristic,** meaning "a distinguishing feature," is more akin to the word *trait* in a general sense, though when referring to a phenotype, *trait* is the appropriate term.

QUICK LAB

Time 15 minutes	TEACHER TESTED
Lab Binder Diversity, p. 10	

Purpose Learn how cladograms are constructed using shared characteristics.

Teacher Note "I've only taught cladograms in a 'traditional' sense. This lab was more meaningful, and students related to it."

Answers

Sample Data

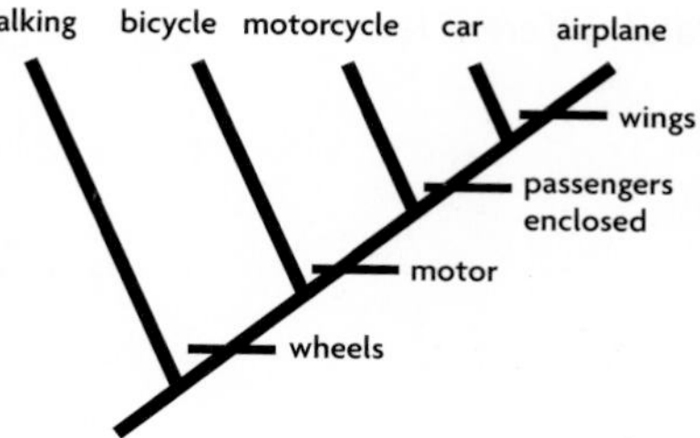

Analyze and Conclude

1. wheels, motor, passengers enclosed, wings
2. walking
3. It is not practical to board an airplane just to fly a few miles, so biking is better.

BELOW LEVEL

To distinguish among the terms *clade, cladistics, cladogram,* and *derived characters,* have students create word squares in which they draw a cladogram, label its parts, and then define each term. They should write one or two sentences that capture the meanings of these terms. It may be helpful to use different colors of ink or pencil to distinguish one clade from another, or for the hash marks that represent derived characters.

Biology Toolkit, Word Squares, p. D4

▼ Teach *continued*

Vocabulary

Academic Vocabulary The word **node** comes from a root meaning "knot." It has several applications that relate to a point of connection. In mathematics, a *node* exists where a continuous curve crosses itself. In computer science, a node is a terminal in a computer network, such as a wireless router in a series of routers. In botany, a node describes the point on a stem where a leaf is or was attached. Students can think of the node in a cladogram as the point where the rest of the branch carries on evolving while the group that is diverging and will not have the next derived character—is now off on its own.

Take It Further

One of the main characteristics of snakes is the absence of limbs. However, some snakes, such as boa constrictors, have small remnants of hind-limb bones. These vestigial hind limbs, known as **spurs,** provide evidence of a four-legged ancestor for snakes. The oldest known fossil snakes have been dated to the early Cretaceous period.

Answers

A Contrast A taxon is a group of organisms classified together in a system such as that of Linnaeus. A clade is any group of organisms that share a common ancestor, so it can contain many taxa of different levels.

Interpreting a Cladogram

The main features of a cladogram are shown in **FIGURE 17.6.** Tetrapods are vertebrates that have four limbs—amphibians, reptiles, birds, and mammals. Some tetrapods, such as snakes and marine mammals, no longer have the four limbs that their known ancestors had. However, they are still members of the tetrapoda clade because they share a common ancestor.

Derived characters In a cladogram, groups of species are placed in order by the derived characters that have added up in their lineage over time. This order is hypothesized to be the order in which they descended from their common ancestor. Derived characters are shown as hash marks between the branches of the cladogram. All species above a hash mark share the derived character it represents.

Nodes Each place where a branch splits is called a node. There are five nodes on the tetrapod cladogram. The first node is where the amphibian branch splits off from the rest of the cladogram. Nodes represent the most recent common ancestor shared by a clade. Therefore, the first node of the tetrapod cladogram represents a common ancestor for the whole tetrapod clade.

Identifying clades You can identify clades by using the "snip rule." Whenever you "snip" a branch under a node, a clade falls off. In this cladogram, if you were to "snip" below the node where turtles and tortoises branch off, you would be left with the reptilia clade. This clade includes turtles and tortoises, lizards and snakes, crocodiles and alligators, and birds. As you can see, each clade is nested within the clade that forms just before it. There are five clades in the tetrapod cladogram. Crocodiles, alligators, and birds belong to all five clades.

1. All of the organisms in this cladogram belong to the tetrapoda clade (brown). They all share the derived character of four limbs.
2. An embryo protected by a fluid filled sac is a derived character for all organisms in the amniota clade (blue). Because amphibians do not produce an amniotic sac, the amphibian branch splits off from rest of the branches before the mark that represents this trait.
3. Organisms in the reptilia clade (yellow) have a common ancestor that had four legs, produced protected eggs, and had a skull with openings behind the eyes. The third node in the cladogram represents this common ancestor. Because mammal skulls do not have these openings, they are not part of the reptilia clade.
4. Organisms in the diapsida clade (green) have openings in the side of the skull. The skulls of turtles and tortoises do not have these openings, so they are not part of the diapsida clade.
5. Lizards and snakes branch off of the cladogram next. Their skulls do not have certain openings in the jaw that are found in crocodiles, alligators, and birds. This is the derived character shared by all organisms in the archosauria clade (pink). Feathers and toothless beaks separate crocodiles and alligators from birds within the archosauria clade.

Connecting CONCEPTS

Animals The amniotic sac is a key characteristic of amniotes, animals that are fully adapted for life on land. The amniotic sac allows amniotes to reproduce on land; non-amniotes must return to the water to reproduce. You will learn much more about amniotes in **Chapter 26.**

A Contrast What is the difference between a clade and a taxon?

Differentiated Instruction

PRE-AP

Have students take ten minutes to review **FIGURE 17.6** and write a brief essay that answers the following question: What would it mean if a new species of mammal were discovered that had skull openings behind the eyes? Students' answers should suggest that a revision to the derived character scheme of the clade might be necessary, but that the new mammal's trait may be the result of convergent evolution rather than a trait shared with archosaurs, diapsids, and reptiles.

Biology Toolkit, Quick-Write, p. C19

BELOW LEVEL

Help students understand the structure and meaning of the cladogram by modeling for them how you read page 526 for meaning and relate your reading to **FIGURE 17.6.** Relate the branched nature of the cladogram to divergence. For example, the turtles and tortoises diverge from the other reptiles because they do not have openings in the sides of their skulls. Point out that if the cladogram went further, it would branch off into the orders, families, genera, and species within each of the clades.

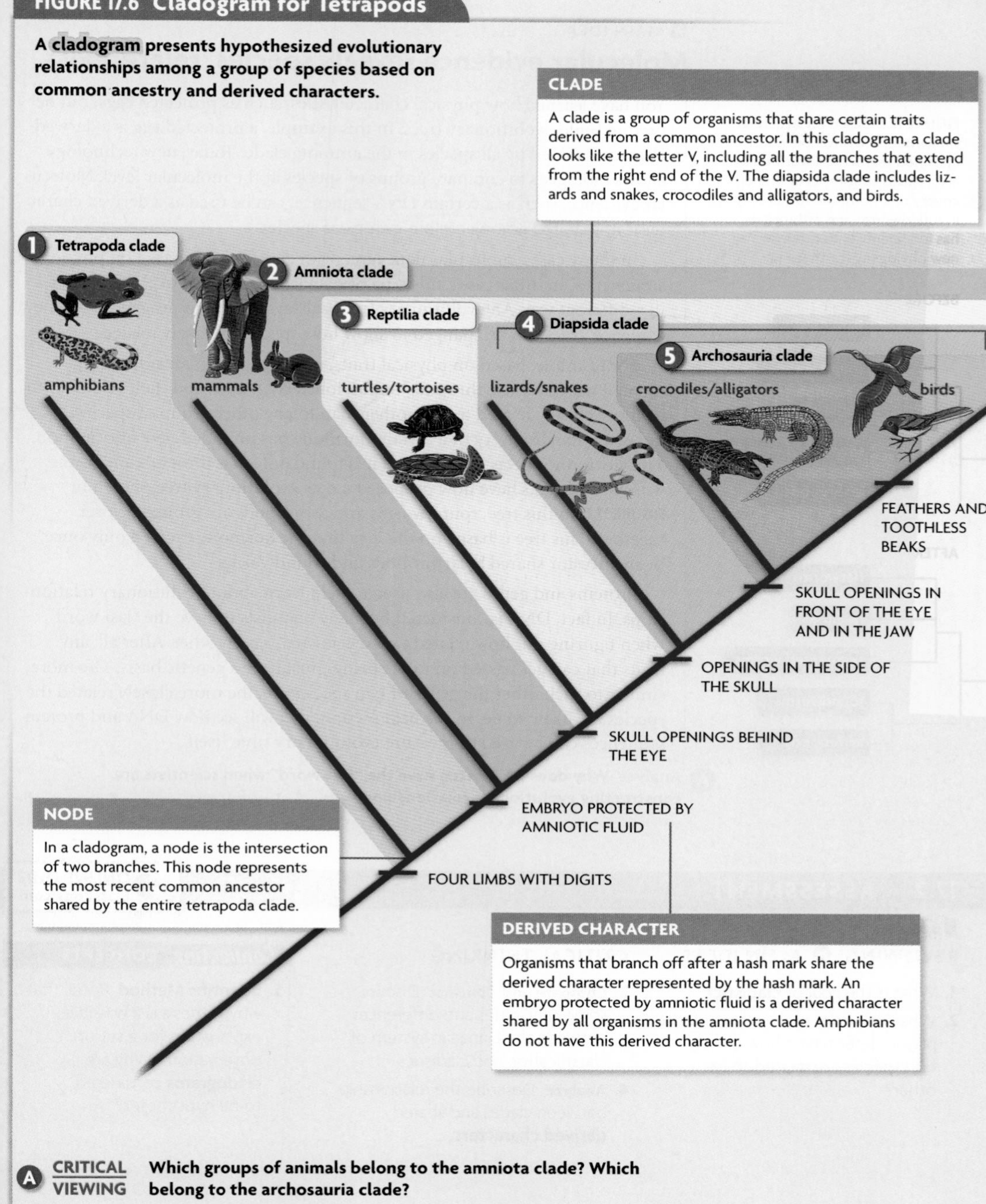
CLADE
A clade is a group of organisms that share certain traits derived from a common ancestor. In this cladogram, a clade looks like the letter V, including all the branches that extend from the right end of the V. The diapsida clade includes lizards and snakes, crocodiles and alligators, and birds.
1 Tetrapoda clade
2 Amniota clade
3 Reptilia clade
4 Diapsida clade
5 Archosauria clade
amphibians
mammals
turtles/tortoises
lizards/snakes
crocodiles/alligators
birds
FEATHERS AND TOOTHLESS BEAKS
SKULL OPENINGS IN FRONT OF THE EYE AND IN THE JAW
OPENINGS IN THE SIDE OF THE SKULL
SKULL OPENINGS BEHIND THE EYE
EMBRYO PROTECTED BY AMNIOTIC FLUID
FOUR LIMBS WITH DIGITS
NODE
In a cladogram, a node is the intersection of two branches. This node represents the most recent common ancestor shared by the entire tetrapoda clade.
DERIVED CHARACTER
Organisms that branch off after a hash mark share the derived character represented by the hash mark. An embryo protected by amniotic fluid is a derived character shared by all organisms in the amniota clade. Amphibians do not have this derived character.

FIGURE 17.6 Cladogram for Tetrapods

A cladogram presents hypothesized evolutionary relationships among a group of species based on common ancestry and derived characters.

Ⓐ **CRITICAL VIEWING** **Which groups of animals belong to the amniota clade? Which belong to the archosauria clade?**

ONLINE BIOLOGY Have students view the interactive animation to build a cladogram of reptiles. See Options for Inquiry, page 537.

TEACH FROM VISUALS

FIGURE 17.6 Point out to students that the clades shown are nested within larger ones like the seven taxonomic levels of the Linnaean classification system. **Ask,** What types of taxonomic levels are not shown in this figure? None of the Linnaean taxa are shown in this figure. The animal kingdom has phyla that are not characterized by four limbs with digits, and we know that even the smaller groups shown, such as the crocodiles/alligators, have more than two species once we account for all the living and extinct species. **Ask**

- How could we include other taxa? can add clades that are more general or more specific, such as the orders, families, and genera within the bird class
- What would be some derived characters we might see if we added more general clades to this cladogram? *Sample Answer:* vertebrae, bilateral symmetry, eukaryotic cells

Answers

Ⓐ **Critical Viewing** Amniota includes everything but the amphibians; archosauria includes the crocodiles/alligators and birds.

INCLUSION

Have a visually impaired student work with a classmate who will construct and describe the cladogram shown in **FIGURE 17.6.** Supply pipe cleaners and cloth or paper of varying textures, which can be used to signify derived characters. Clades should be bent away from the larger ones so that the student can feel that they are distinct but also nested within other clades.

▼ Teach *continued*

TEACH FROM VISUALS

FIGURE 17.7 This figure shows what can happen to a phylogenic tree or clade

Modern classification is common ancestry

being discussed or compared, they can be referred to as *taxa*. For example, "The bee and spider *taxa* in the phylum Arthropoda are two of the most feared groups of animals, but the spider *taxon* has only about a dozen species whose venom can hurt humans."

Answers

A Analyze Shared or identical sequences of DNA is hard proof of common ancestry, whereas shared traits or similar characteristics can be the result of convergent evolution.

FIGURE 17.7 Based on structural similarities, scientists previously classified segmented worms and arthropods as sister taxa. The discovery of a hormone found only …undworms and arthropods …ed scientists to propose a … phylogeny for these taxa.

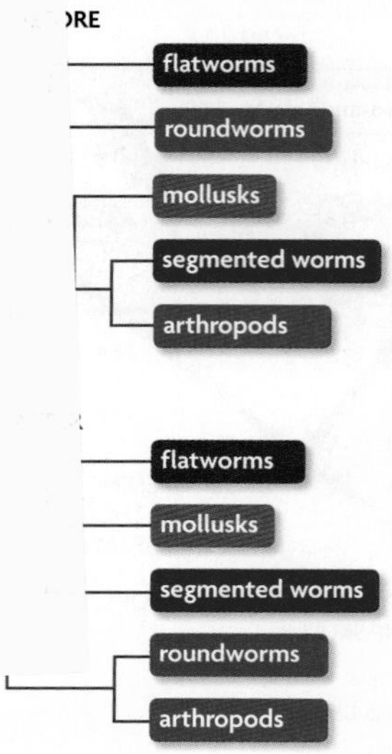

MAIN IDEA

Molecular evidence reveals species' relatedness.

You have learned how physical characteristics, such as protected eggs, can be used to build evolutionary trees. In this example, a protected egg is a derived character shared by all species in the amniota clade. Today, new technology allows biologists to compare groups of species at the molecular level. Molecular evidence, such as a certain DNA sequence, can be used as a derived character if it is shared among certain groups of species.

In many cases, molecular data agree with classification based on physical similarities. In other cases, this type of data leads scientists to classify species in a different way. An evolutionary tree is always a work in progress. With new evidence, trees can be changed to show how species are likely related.

For example, based on physical traits, most biologists considered segmented worms and arthropods (crabs, lobsters, insects, and their relatives) to be more closely related to each other than to any other group of species. However, the discovery of a certain hormone has provided new information. This hormone affects molting, and it is found only in arthropods and roundworms. Biologists have now proposed a new evolutionary tree, shown in **FIGURE 17.7.** In this tree, roundworms and arthropods are grouped closer together. This tree is based on the idea that the hormone evolved only once, in an ancestor shared by arthropods and roundworms.

Proteins and genes are also used to help learn about evolutionary relationships. In fact, DNA is considered by many scientists to have the "last word" when figuring out how related two species are to each other. After all, any traits that can get passed on to offspring must have a genetic basis. The more similar to each other the genes of two species are, the more closely related the species are likely to be. In the next section, you will see how DNA and protein sequences can be used to measure evolutionary time itself.

A Analyze Why does DNA often have the "last word" when scientists are constructing evolutionary relationships?

17.2 ASSESSMENT

ONLINE QUIZ ClassZone.com

B.8.2

REVIEWING MAIN IDEAS

1. What is the goal of **cladistics**?
2. What role does molecular evidence play in determining how closely two species are related to each other?

CRITICAL THINKING

3. **Compare and Contrast** Discuss some similarities and differences between the Linnaean system of classification and cladistics.
4. **Analyze** Describe the relationship between clades and shared **derived characters.**

***Connecting* CONCEPTS**

5. **Scientific Method** Recall that a hypothesis is a possible explanation for a set of observations. Why are **cladograms** considered to be hypotheses?

▼ Assess and Reteach

Assess Use the Online Quiz or Section Quiz (*Assessment Book,* p. 336).

Reteach Discuss how cladistics could be used to classify Darwin's finches or another group of organisms. Create a hypothetical cladogram by having students come up with the derived characters, branches, and clades.

17.2 ASSESSMENT

1. to arrange groups and species in the order in which they diverged from a common ancestor
2. Analysis of DNA and protein sequences can reveal differences among species. The more biomolecular similarities, the more closely related are the species.
3. Both systems attempt to classify organisms on the basis of similarities—the Linnaean by physical/structural similarities and cladistics by analyzing evolutionary relationships and species relatedness.
4. A derived character is one that emerges over time in a group of organisms and is the distinguishing trait between a diverging group, or clade, and the clades that have evolved previously. Every member of a clade can be traced back to a common ancestor that possessed and passed on that derived character.
5. Hypotheses are educated explanations that form a basis for future investigation or research. Cladistics is ongoing, and cladograms represent explanations based on the most current research.

B.8.3

Amino Acid Differences Among Species

DATA ANALYSIS ClassZone.com

Researchers rarely publish raw data by itself. Instead, data are usually analyzed in some way. This is because certain types of observations and patterns can be made clearer when data are presented in different ways. For example, data that show change or difference may be best represented as percentage difference.

EXAMPLE

Cytochrome C is a protein that functions in cellular respiration. A sequence of 104 amino acids make up the cytochrome C protein. Scientists have compared this sequence of amino acids in humans with the sequence in a variety of other species. The number of amino acid differences between cytochrome C in humans and in other species has been used to help determine species' relatedness.

Lampreys such as this one are jawless fish with a round sucking mouth.

Look at the data table at the right. Notice that the cytochrome C of chimpanzees most closely resembles that of humans, while the cytochrome C of lampreys, a type of jawless fish, has more differences. To more clearly represent how different they are, these data can be transformed into percentage differences. To calculate the percentage difference of cytochrome C between humans and lampreys, follow this procedure.

1. First, transform the number of amino acid differences into a fraction of the total number of amino acids that make up the cytochrome C protein (104).

   $\frac{\textbf{20 differences}}{\textbf{104 total amino acids}}$

2. Next, perform the division.

   20 ÷ 104 = 0.1923

3. Transform this number into a percentage by multiplying by 100.

   0.1923 × 100 = 19.23% difference

TABLE 1. AMINO ACID DIFFERENCES COMPARED WITH HUMAN CYTOCHROME C

Organism	Number of Differences
Chimpanzee	0
Rhesus monkey	1
Whale	10
Turtle	15
Bullfrog	18
Lamprey	20
Tuna	21

Source: M. Dayhoff, *Atlas of Protein Sequence and Structure.*

TRANSFORM DATA

1. **Calculate** Use the procedure outlined above to find percentage differences in cytochrome C between humans and the following animals: tunas, bullfrogs, turtles, whales, rhesus monkeys, and chimpanzees.
2. **Apply** What do the transformed data suggest about how related each type of animal is to humans?
3. **Infer** What percentage of the human cytochrome C protein is the same as that of whales?
   Hint: 100 percent − percentage difference = percentage similarity.

Answers

1. tuna: 20.19% difference; bullfrog: 17.31%; turtle: 14.42%; whale: 9.62%; rhesus monkey: 0.96%; chimpanzee: 0%
2. Of the animals in this data set, tuna and lamprey, which are fish, are least related to humans. Chimpanzees and rhesus monkeys, which are primate mammals, are the most related to humans.
3. 90.38%

DATA ANALYSIS

Introduce

Review with students the structure and function of amino acids. **Ask**

- What is the basic function of amino acids? They are the building blocks of proteins.
- What determines the nature and function of a protein? its sequence of amino acids
- In what ways can raw data from an investigation be analyzed and displayed? Data can be analyzed statistically or mathematically and then displayed in data tables and in different types of graphs and diagrams.

Discuss

Have students look at the types of organisms being compared in the activity. **Ask**

- Given what we know about human origins and taxonomy, should we expect humans, rhesus monkeys, and chimpanzees to have the most similar amino acid sequences? Yes, they are all members of the order Primates, so they are more closely related to each other than to any of the other organisms.
- If there are no differences between the amino acid sequences in the cytochrome C protein of humans and chimps, why aren't we the same species? Cytochrome C is just one protein that is being compared. There are many others in which we would find differences between our species and the chimpanzee.

Unit Resource Book, Data Analysis, p. 17

SECTION 17.3

▼ Plan and Prepare

Objectives

- Explain how molecular clocks work.
- Describe two types of molecular clocks: mitochondrial DNA and ribosomal RNA.

Section Resources

Unit Resource Book
Study Guide pp. 9–10
Power Notes p. 11
Reinforcement p. 12

Interactive Reader Chapter 17
Spanish Study Gu

Biology Toolkit p

Technology
Power Presentati
Media Gallery DV
Online Quiz 17.3

Activate Prior Kno students to think of estimate age. **Ask**

- How would you someone you d hair color, physi
- How can a botar age of a tree? c rings
- How are rocks ar radiometric dating, index fossils

Explain that just as the ages of fossils and trees can be determined through direct or relative means, scientists can use pieces of living organisms to reveal how long their species has existed.

17.3 Molecular Clocks

KEY CONCEPT Molecular clocks provide clues to evolutionary history.

MAIN IDEAS

- Molecular clocks use mutations to estimate evolutionary time.
- Mitochondrial DNA and ribosomal RNA provide two types of molecular clocks.

VOCABULARY

molecular clock, p. 530
mitochondrial DNA, p. 532
ribosomal RNA, p. 532

B.8.3 Use anatomical and molecular evidence to establish evolutionary relationships between organisms.

Connect Have you ever played the game telephone? One person whispers a message to another person, who repeats it to yet another person, and so on. By the time it reaches the final person, the message has changed. In a similar way, DNA changes slightly each time it is passed from generation to generation.

MAIN IDEA

Molecular clocks use mutations to estimate evolutionary time.

In the early 1960s, biochemists Linus Pauling and Emile Zuckerkandl proposed a new way to measure evolutionary time. They compared the amino acid sequences of hemoglobin from a wide range of species. Their findings show that the more distantly related two species are, the more amino acid differences there are in their hemoglobin. Using this data, they were able to calculate a mutation rate for part of the hemoglobin protein.

Molecular Evolution

Molecular clocks are models that use mutation rates to measure evolutionary time. Recall that mutations are nucleotide substitutions in DNA, some of which cause amino acid substitutions in proteins. Pauling and Zuckerkandl found that mutations tend to add up at a constant rate for a group of related species. As shown in **FIGURE 17.8,** the rate of mutations is the "ticking" that powers a molecular clock. The more time that has passed since two species have diverged from a common ancestor, the more mutations will have built up in each lineage, and the more different the two species will be at the molecular level.

TION

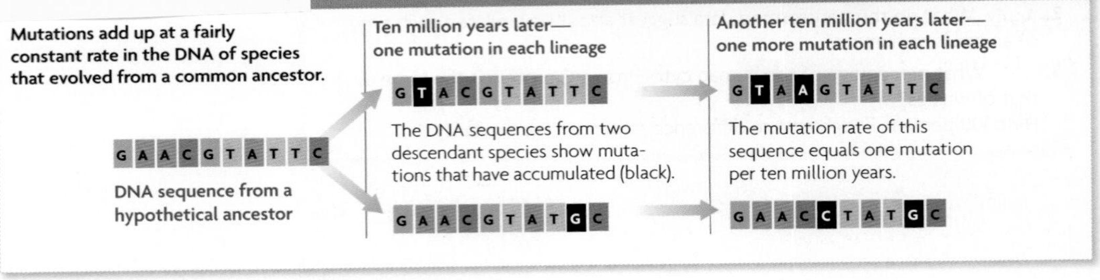

Mutations add up at a fairly constant rate in the DNA of species that evolved from a common ancestor.

G A A C G T A T T C

DNA sequence from a hypothetical ancestor

Ten million years later— one mutation in each lineage

G T A C G T A T T C

The DNA sequences from two descendant species show mutations that have accumulated (black).

G A A C G T A T G C

Another ten million years later— one more mutation in each lineage

G T A A G T A T T C

The mutation rate of this sequence equals one mutation per ten million years.

G A A C C T A T G C

▼ Teach

TEACH FROM VISUALS

FIGURE 17.8 **Ask,** What DNA base pairs change in the top lineage after 10 million years? A to T after another 10 million years? C to A

Differentiated Instruction

PRE-AP

Draw the following graphic on the board and have students compare it to **FIGURE 17.8.** Tell them to determine how long ago the two lineages diverged if the rate of mutation is 1 per 5 million years. For the sequences shown here, the answer is 20 million years ago.

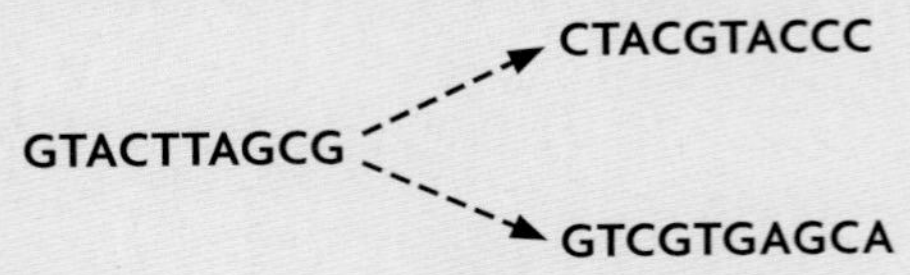

Linking Molecular Data with Real Time

To estimate mutation rates, scientists must find links between molecular data and real time. Often this link comes from the timing of a geologic event that is known to have separated the species they are studying. If scientists know when the species began to diverge from a common ancestor, they can find the mutation rate for the molecule they are studying. For example, scientists know that marsupials of Australia and those of South America diverged about 200 million years ago, when these two continents split.

A link can also come from fossil evidence. Pauling and Zuckerkandl compared their molecular data with the first appearance of each type of organism in the fossil record. Using these dates, they confirmed that the number of amino acid differences increases with the evolutionary time between each group of species. The number of amino acid differences between human hemoglobin and the hemoglobin of several other types of organisms is shown in **FIGURE 17.9.** Human hemoglobin is most different from species that diverged earliest in evolutionary time.

A Infer Why is the hemoglobin of humans more different from that of sharks than that of birds?

Animated BIOLOGY Learn how a molecular clock works at ClassZone.com.

FIGURE 17.9 LINKING MOLECULAR AND FOSSIL DATA

Animal species that evolved longer ago compared with humans have more amino acid differences in the beta chain of their hemoglobin.

ANIMAL	AMINO ACID DIFFERENCES COMPARED WITH HUMANS	APPEARANCE IN FOSSIL RECORD (millions of years ago)
Mouse	16	70
Horse	18	70
Bird	35	270
Frog	62	350
Shark	79	450

B Analyze Which two animals in this table are least related to humans?

Frogs and humans have 62 differences in the beta chain of hemoglobin.

MAIN IDEA

Mitochondrial DNA and ribosomal RNA provide two types of molecular clocks.

Different molecules have different mutation rates. For example, some sequences of DNA accumulate mutations relatively quickly in a lineage, while others have very low mutation rates. Depending on how closely two species are related, scientists choose a molecule with an appropriate mutation rate to use as a molecular clock.

ONLINE BIOLOGY Go to the chapter Resource Center at **ClassZone.com** for additional resources and information on molecular clocks.

Take It Further

Sharks are **cartilaginous fish,** meaning their skeletal system is made of cartilage rather than bone. Because cartilage is not easily fossilized, the **fossil record** of sharks consists almost entirely of preserved teeth. A single tooth of an extinct ancestor of the great white shark can be over 6 inches (15 cm) long and weigh as much as a pound, a size that suggests that *Carcharodon megalodon,* a shark that lived between 5 and 1.6 million years ago, was over 50 feet (15 m) long. Some scientists believe that this species was so large that it could have hunted large whales.

Science Trivia

The Human Genome Project successfully listed and mapped all 3 billion base pairs in human DNA.

- Of all of those, only about 1–2 percent actually carry genetic information.
- The beta hemoglobin gene is found on the 11th chromosome, from base pairs 5,203,271 to 5,204,876.

Answers

A Infer Humans and birds diverged more recently than sharks.

B Analyze frog and shark

ENGLISH LEARNERS

Develop a list of questions to give students before they begin the sections. For example, *How can the changes that occur as species evolve be a measure of time?* *What do the changes consist of?* *Where do scientists look for these changes?* Remind students of these questions as you discuss the section.

Biology Toolkit, Questions to Guide Reading, p. C4

▼ Teach *continued*

The Inside Story

The Y chromosome can be used to trace descent from paternal lineages (father to son). Researchers **Moore, Laoise,** and **Bradley** of Trinity College in Dublin, Ireland, have analyzed the Y chromosomes in almost 800 males throughout Ireland. In northwestern Ireland, 1 out of 5 men share a chromosomal marker, a sort of signature that can be traced to the 5th-century Irish king Niall. Niall, who reportedly had 12 sons, founded a dynasty that dominated Ireland for centuries. Eight percent of the males in modern Ireland—and as many as 2 to 3 million men worldwide—are thought to be descendants of Niall.

Answers

A Summarize It accumulates mutations at a relatively low rate, allowing patterns of change to remain or become clear over long periods of time.

▼ Assess and Reteach

Assess Use the Online Quiz or Section Quiz (*Assessment Book*, p. 337).

Reteach Tell students to imagine a fossil find that includes some tissue remains. Have them describe how scientists could use the fossil as a source of molecular clocks.

FIGURE 17.10 INHERITANCE OF MITOCHONDRIAL DNA

grandparents
parents
child
● mitochondrial DNA
|| nuclear DNA
Mitochondrial DNA is passed down only from the mother of each generation, so it is not subject to recombination.
Nuclear DNA is inherited from both parents, making it more difficult to trace back through generations.

Mitochondrial DNA

Mitochondrial DNA (mtDNA) is DNA found only in mitochondria, the energy factories of cells. The mutation rate of mtDNA is about ten times faster than that of nuclear DNA, which makes mtDNA a good molecular clock for closely related species. Furthermore, as shown in **FIGURE 17.10**, mtDNA is always inherited from the mother because the mitochondria in a sperm cell are lost after fertilization. This type of inheritance is different from that of nuclear DNA, which is a combination of DNA from both parents. Scientists use the fact that mtDNA is passed down unshuffled to trace mutations back through many generations in a single species. In fact, mutations in mtDNA have been used to study the migration routes of humans over the past 200,000 years.

VOCABULARY

In this context, the word *conservative* means "resistant to change." Because ribosomes play such a crucial role in cell function, even small changes can be very disruptive and damaging to the cell. Therefore, most mutations in rRNA do not accumulate within the genome.

Ribosomal RNA

Ribosomes, the organelles that manufacture proteins in cells, contain **ribosomal RNA** (rRNA). Ribosomal RNA is useful for studying distantly related species, such as species that are in different kingdoms or phyla. When studying the relationships among species over longer time scales, it is best to use a molecule that has a lower mutation rate. Ribosomal RNA has conservative regions that accumulate mutations at a low rate relative to most DNA. Over long periods of geologic time, mutations that do build up in the rRNA of different lineages are relatively clear and can be compared. American microbiologist Carl Woese first used rRNA to establish that archaea diverged from the common ancestor they share with bacteria almost 4 billion years ago. As you will learn in the next section, these findings supported a restructuring of the tree of life at its highest level.

Summarize **Why is rRNA useful for studying more distantly related species?**

17.3 ASSESSMENT

ONLINE QUIZ ClassZone.com

B.8.3

REVIEWING MAIN IDEAS

1. How are **molecular clocks** used to measure evolutionary time?
2. What are the benefits of **mitochondrial DNA** and **ribosomal RNA** as molecular clocks?

CRITICAL THINKING

3. **Explain** How do rates of mutation "power" molecular clocks?
4. **Apply** What molecular clock might be useful to examine the evolutionary relationship between several phyla in the kingdom Plantae? Explain your answer.

***Connecting* CONCEPTS**

5. **History of Life** The theory of endosymbiosis explains how eukaryotic cells may have evolved from prokaryotic cells. According to this theory, explain why mitochondria have their own DNA, separate from nuclear DNA.

17.3 ASSESSMENT

1. The clocks presume that mutations occur at a constant rate for any clade or group of related taxa. Because these changes occur at a relatively constant and predictable rate, the changes can be used to measure how long ago different lineages diverged.
2. Mitochondrial DNA accumulates mutations relatively quickly, so it is most useful for analyzing relatedness within closely related species or change within a species. Ribosomal RNA has many conservative regions that accumulate mutations relatively slowly, so it is useful for studying taxa that are more distantly related.
3. Mutations tend to occur at relatively constant rates in certain proteins and DNA sequences among related taxa. Once a scale has been applied to the rate of mutation, it can function as a clock.
4. rRNA, because it accumulates mutations relatively slowly
5. Because mitochondria and chloroplasts were once free-living prokaryotes, they have their own DNA.

532 Unit 6: Classification and Diversity

17.4 Domains and Kingdoms

KEY CONCEPT The current tree of life has three domains.

MAIN IDEAS
- Classification is always a work in progress.
- The three domains in the tree of life are Bacteria, Archaea, and Eukarya.

VOCABULARY
Bacteria, p. 534
Archaea, p. 534
Eukarya, p. 534

Review
prokaryote, eukaryote

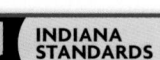

B.8.2 Explain how organisms are classified and named based on their evolutionary relationships into taxonomic categories.

Connect Have you ever swum in a pond? Every drop of pond water is teeming with single-celled organisms. At one time, scientists classified these organisms as either plants or animals. However, classification schemes change. Single-celled eukaryotes such as these pond dwellers now have a kingdom of their own.

MAIN IDEA
Classification is always a work in progress.

The tree of life is a model that shows the most current understanding of how living things are related. Some new discoveries confirm parts of the tree that were once based on similarities in form alone. But as **FIGURE 17.11** shows, new findings can also lead scientists to change how they classify certain organisms.

- The two-kingdom system was accepted by biologists until 1866, when German biologist Ernst Haeckel proposed moving all single-celled organisms to the kingdom Protista.
- In 1938, American biologist Herbert Copeland argued that the prokaryotes deserved their own kingdom, called Monera. Prokaryotes are single-celled organisms that do not have membrane-bound nuclei or organelles.
- In 1959, American ecologist Robert Whittaker proposed that because of how they feed, fungi should be placed into their own kingdom apart from plants. The kingdom Fungi includes molds and mushrooms.
- In 1977, rRNA research by Carl Woese revealed two genetically different groups of prokaryotes. His findings led scientists to split the kingdom Monera into two kingdoms, called Bacteria and Archaea.

***Connecting* CONCEPTS**

Fungi Fungi are heterotrophs that feed by absorbing dead organic materials from the environment. This is one characteristic that distinguishes fungi from plants, which are autotrophs, or organisms that make their own food. You will learn more about fungi in **Chapter 19.**

FIGURE 17.11 HISTORY OF THE KINGDOM SYSTEM

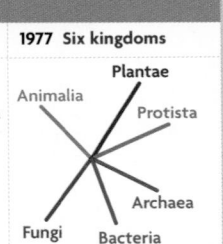

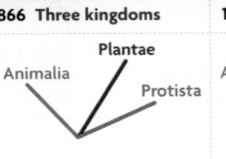

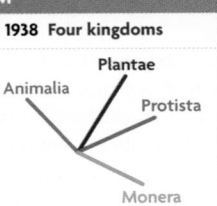

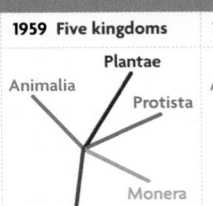

1753 Two kingdoms	1866 Three kingdoms	1938 Four kingdoms	1959 Five kingdoms	1977 Six kingdoms
Animalia, Plantae	Animalia, Plantae, Protista	Animalia, Plantae, Protista, Monera	Animalia, Plantae, Protista, Monera, Fungi	Animalia, Plantae, Protista, Archaea, Bacteria, Fungi

Differentiated Instruction

ENGLISH LEARNERS

Have students compare and contrast the diagram of the six kingdoms shown in **FIGURE 17.11** on page 533 with the diagram of the three domains shown in **FIGURE 17.13** on page 535. Have students describe the reason for the change.

Biology Toolkit, Quick-Write, p. C19

TEACH WITH TECHNOLOGY

Organize students into nine groups. Six will prepare digital slide show presentations of organisms in a particular kingdom; three will do the same for the characteristics of life forms in the major domains. Have the two groups representing the Archaea and Bacteria kingdoms present in tandem with the groups representing those domains. The other four kingdom groups should follow the Eukarya domain group.

Plan and Prepare ▼

Objectives

- Describe classification as a work in progress.
- Identify the three domains in the tree of life as Bacteria, Archaea, and Eukarya.

Section Resources

Unit Resource Book Study Guide pp. 13–14 Power Notes p. 15 Reinforcement p. 16
Interactive Reader Chapter 17 **Spanish Study Guide** pp. 181–182
Biology Toolkit pp. C19, C22
Technology Power Presentation 17.4 Media Gallery DVD Online Quiz 17.4

Activate Prior Knowledge Lead a discussion about how various things in a culture are often reclassified based on new attitudes, ideas, or evidence. **Ask,** How do you classify a type of music? kinds of instruments used, beat or rhythm, region or time period it comes from The same discussion can be had about film, food, and much more. Make the point that the way science classifies Earth's biodiversity is similar to how we classify things in our culture: always changing.

Teach ▼

***Connecting* CONCEPTS**

Fungi Fungi differ from plants in other fundamental ways. Unlike plants, fungi lack structural specialization, and their cell walls contain chitin instead of cellulose.

▼ Teach *continued*

Vocabulary

Greek and Latin Word Origins Tell students that **Archaea** is derived from the Greek *arkhaio,* meaning "ancient" or "primitive." The prefixes *archeo-* and *archaeo-* indicate an ancient origin. Other words in which students may recognize these roots are **archaeology** and **archaic.**

Address Misconceptions

Common Misconception Viruses and bacteria are the same thing.

Correcting the Misconception Viruses are not classified in any of the six kingdoms. Viruses cannot metabolize or reproduce independently, so many scientists do not even consider them to be living things. Because viruses have many properties that are unique and different from known life forms, they require their own classification system. Viruses and prokaryotes will be discussed in Chapter 18.

Science Trivia

- The total number of species on Earth is estimated to be between 10 and 100 million, with less than 2 million having been described, named, and classified by scientists.
- It's estimated that 99 percent of all plant and animal species that have ever lived are already extinct.
- Of the known animal species, 99 percent are smaller than bumblebees.

Answers

A Analyze The genetic difference between these groups of prokaryotes is greater than the genetic difference between the four eukaryotic kingdoms.

Woese's discovery did more than split the kingdom Monera. The two groups of prokaryotes that he studied have very different cell wall chemistry. In terms of genes, these two groups are more different from each other than animals are from plants, fungi, and protists. Based on these differences, Woese proposed that all life be divided into three domains. These domains are above the kingdom level.

A Analyze Why did Woese propose classifying bacteria and archaea into separate domains, rather than just separate kingdoms?

MAIN IDEA

The three domains in the tree of life are Bacteria, Archaea, and Eukarya.

Most biologists now accept Woese's domain system. This system more clearly shows the great diversity of prokaryotes in the tree of life by dividing them into two domains. These domains are called Bacteria and Archaea. All eukaryotes are placed into a third domain, called Eukarya.

TAKING NOTES

Use a three-column chart to take notes about the three domains and six kingdoms in the modern classification of life.

Domain Name	Characteristics	Kingdoms Included

Bacteria

The domain **Bacteria** includes single-celled prokaryotes in the kingdom Bacteria. The domain Bacteria is one of the largest groups of organisms on Earth. In fact, there are more bacteria in your mouth than there are people that have ever lived! Bacteria can be classified by many traits, such as their shape, their need for oxygen, and whether they cause disease.

Archaea

Like bacteria, organisms in the domain **Archaea** (ahr-KEE-uh) are single-celled prokaryotes. However, the cell walls of archaea and bacteria are chemically different. Archaea, like those in **FIGURE 17.12**, are known for their ability to live in extreme environments, such as deep sea vents, hot geysers, Antarctic waters, and salt lakes. All archaea are classified in the kingdom Archaea.

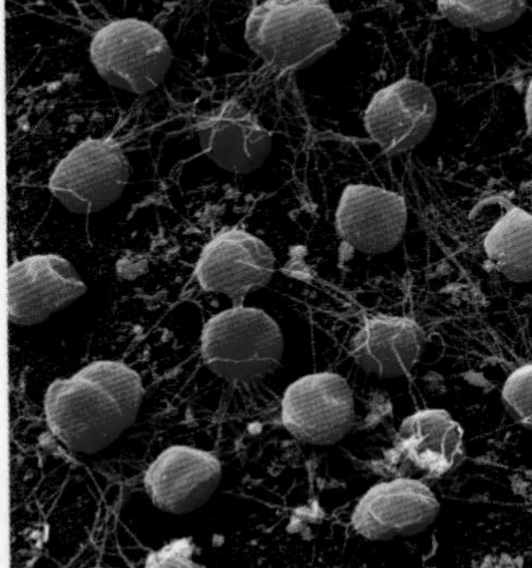

FIGURE 17.12 This archaean species, *Pyrococcus furiosus*, can be found in undersea hot vents and in the sand surrounding sulfurous volcanoes. These organisms live without oxygen and can grow in temperatures higher than the boiling point of water. (colored SEM; magnification 6500×)

Eukarya

The domain **Eukarya** (yoo-KAR-ee-uh) is made up of all organisms with eukaryotic cells. Eukaryotic cells have a distinct nucleus and membrane-bound organelles. Eukarya may be single-celled, such as most protists. They can also be colonial, such as some algae, or multicellular, like you. The domain Eukarya includes the kingdoms Protista, Plantae, Fungi, and Animalia.

Differentiated Instruction

BELOW LEVEL

Have students identify the characteristics and properties of the three domains. Help them identify examples of several organisms that fit into each domain. They can use the note-taking graphic organizer shown in their textbooks to compare the relationship between domains and kingdoms.

Biology Toolkit, Content Frame, p. C22

PRE-AP

Have students think about what kingdoms might be more able to withstand the effects of climate change. Give them a scenario, such as an ice age or a major global warming, and have them discuss or write explanations for why the organisms of one kingdom might be more likely to withstand extreme climate change more than another. Students should mention the Archaea prokaryotes' ability to live in hot geysers, hydrothermal vents, frigid ocean water, and other extreme environments.

Biology Toolkit, Quick-Write, p. C19

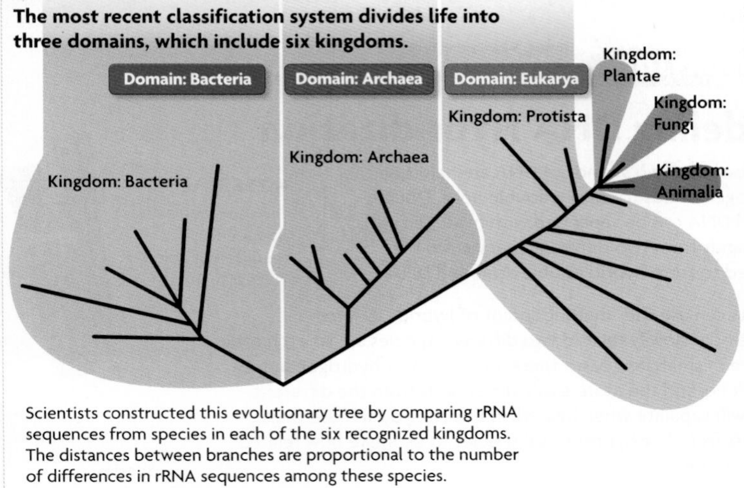

Scientists constructed this evolutionary tree by comparing rRNA sequences from species in each of the six recognized kingdoms. The distances between branches are proportional to the number of differences in rRNA sequences among these species.

Source: C. Woese, *PNAS* 97:15.

Connecting CONCEPTS

Kingdoms and Phyla See the **Appendix** for a detailed description of each kingdom and its phyla.

Classifying Bacteria and Archaea

Some scientists think that bacteria and archaea have no true species. This is because many of these organisms transfer genes among themselves outside of typical reproduction. This sharing of genes blurs the lines between "species" as we define them in the Linnaean system. One study found that almost a quarter of the genes in the bacterium *Thermotoga maritima* are similar to archaean genes. Our understanding of how to classify prokaryotes is just beginning. You will learn more about these organisms in Chapter 18.

Analyze **Why are protists, plants, fungi, and animals classified into the same domain but into different kingdoms?**

17.4 ASSESSMENT

ONLINE QUIZ ClassZone.com

B.8.2

REVIEWING MAIN IDEAS

1. Why is the classification of life considered a work in progress?
2. What kingdoms are included in each of the three domains in the modern tree of life?

CRITICAL THINKING

3. **Apply** If you come across an unusual single-celled organism, what parts of the cell would you study in order to classify it into one of the three domains?
4. **Analyze** Explain, using the traditional definition of species, why it is difficult to classify some **bacteria** and **archaea** at the species level.

Connecting CONCEPTS

5. **History of Life** The Archaea lineage may include the first life on Earth, which began under much different environmental conditions from those present today. What characteristics of archaea help to support this statement?

ONLINE BIOLOGY Students can go through the process of classifying a sea cucumber in the WebQuest in Options for Inquiry, on page 537.

Integrating Human Biology

The human mouth is full of bacteria. Some are helpful; some are harmful. Bacteria in the ***mutans streptococci*** group are especially harmful when they are well fed. Whenever we eat simple carbohydrates, such as the sugars common in many processed foods and drinks, these bacteria are getting a meal, too. The acid produced by these bacteria when they metabolize sugar eats away at the enamel of our teeth, causing cavities and tooth loss.

Answers

A **Analyze** They all have eukaryotic cells, but are classified in different kingdoms based on differences in other characteristics.

Assess and Reteach

Assess Use the Online Quiz or Section Quiz (*Assessment Book,* p. 338).

Reteach Have students present an oral summary of the content in the section based on the section heads.

17.4 ASSESSMENT

1. Scientists are always finding new information about organisms that forces a re-examination of classification schemes.
2. Bacteria—Bacteria; Archaea—Archaea; Eukarya—Protista, Fungi, Plantae, and Animalia
3. nucleus (or lack thereof) and cell wall
4. A species can be defined as an interbreeding group of organisms that produce fertile offspring. But bacteria and archaea do not breed to produce offspring; they reproduce by binary fission. In reproduction, as it is generally defined, parents also pass genetic material to their offspring. However, many bacteria and archaea can take up genetic material from their environment—a transfer of genes outside of typical reproduction that does not occur in eukaryotes.
5. Archaea exist in extreme environments that are similar to those of early Earth.

OPTIONS FOR INQUIRY

INVESTIGATION

Time 45 minutes	TEACHER TESTED
Teacher Preparation	
Student Difficulty	
Lab Binder Diversity, pp. 5–7	

Purpose Model DNA hybridization and determine relatedness of species.

Overview Students will model DNA hybridization and analyze the results to infer the relatedness of five hypothetical species. They will

- pair single strands of DNA from the same species and with each of the other species
- count the number of hydrogen bonds that would form in each pair and record the numbers in a grid
- compare the results for hybrid strands and normal strands

LAB PREPARATION

- Copy the sequences from the data sheet in the *Lab Binder* (p. 7) and distribute a set to each lab group. Students can cut them apart for easier side-by-side comparison and formation of hybrid molecules.

Teacher Note "Students will understand how DNA evidence can determine evolutionary relationships."

Use these inquiry-based labs and online activities to deepen your understanding of classification.

B.8.2 Explain how organisms are classified and named based on their evolutionary relationships into taxonomic categories.

INVESTIGATION

Modeling DNA Hybridization

Remember that two strands of DNA are held together by hydrogen bonds to form a double helix. Double-stranded DNA can be separated with heat. Separated DNA strands from two different species can then be combined to form hybrid double-stranded DNA.

MATERIALS
- DNA Hybridization Sequences
- 5 different colored pencils

Scientists can use the "melting" point of hybrid DNA to estimate how closely related two different species are to each other. The more mismatched bases there are, the fewer hydrogen bonds there will be, and the more easily the strands from the different species will separate when heated. In this lab, you will use DNA fragments from five hypothetical species to estimate how related the species are.

SKILL Modeling

PROBLEM How is DNA hybridization used to study species relatedness?

PROCEDURE

1. Copy the grid shown here into your notebook.
2. Recall the base-pairing rules for DNA:
   - A pairs with T, forming two hydrogen bonds.
   - C pairs with G, forming three hydrogen bonds.

   If adjoining bases do not form one of these pairs, no hydrogen bonds form.
3. Using the DNA sequence fragments, put the strands from the original species (same color) together. Count the number of hydrogen bonds that would form for each species' DNA fragment. Record this number in your grid. Notice that these counts will go in the gray diagonal boxes of the grid.
4. Form hybrid DNA fragments for each possible combination of species by matching the strands up with the arrows pointing in opposite directions. Count and record the number of hydrogen bonds holding each hybrid together. Notice that each of these counts will be recorded in one of the white boxes of the grid.

Species

Species	1	2	3	4	5
1					
2					
3					
4					
5					

ANALYZE AND CONCLUDE

1. **Analyze** Which DNA hybrid had the most hydrogen bonds? Which had the fewest?
2. **Analyze** Which species is the least related to the other four species?
3. **Synthesize** How has DNA technology changed the way scientists classify some organisms?

Answers

Sample Data

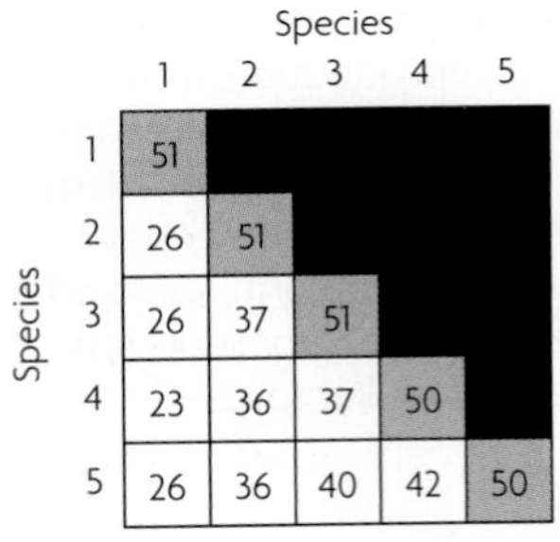

Species

Species	1	2	3	4	5
1	51				
2	26	51			
3	26	37	51		
4	23	36	37	50	
5	26	36	40	42	50

Analyze and Conclude

1. Hybrids of species 4 and 5 had the most hydrogen bonds. Hybrids of species 1 and 4 had the fewest.
2. species 1
3. Originally, classification was based only on similarity of physical characteristics (morphology). Nowadays, DNA fragments can be compared to analyze true evolutionary relatedness, based on genetic makeup. The classifications of many organisms have changed as a result.

INVESTIGATION

Defining Species

The biological species concept is often used to define species. According to this definition, a species is a group of individuals that can mate and produce offspring that are able to reproduce. However, this definition has limitations. For example, a liger is the offspring of a male lion and a female tiger. Some female ligers have been able to reproduce. This ability blurs the line between lions and tigers as species, as defined by the biological species concept.

SKILL Evaluating

PROBLEM What are some different ways to define species?

PROCEDURE

1. Research the definition of one of the species concepts listed below.
   - morphological species concept
   - paleontological species concept
   - ecological species concept
   - phylogenetic species concept
2. Write two paragraphs evaluating the species concept you have chosen. Be sure to include answers to the following questions:
   - How are species defined by this concept?
   - What are the advantages and limitations of the concept?
   - In what types of scientific research might this concept be the most useful?
   - Would this concept be more appropriate than the biological species concept in classifying bacteria and archaea?

The liger shown here, named Patrick, lives in the Shambala Preserve in California. He has a mane like a lion and stripes like a tiger.

Online BIOLOGY
CLASSZONE.COM

ANIMATED BIOLOGY
Build a Cladogram
How are crocodiles related to birds? Use derived characters to build a cladogram of taxa within the archosauria clade.

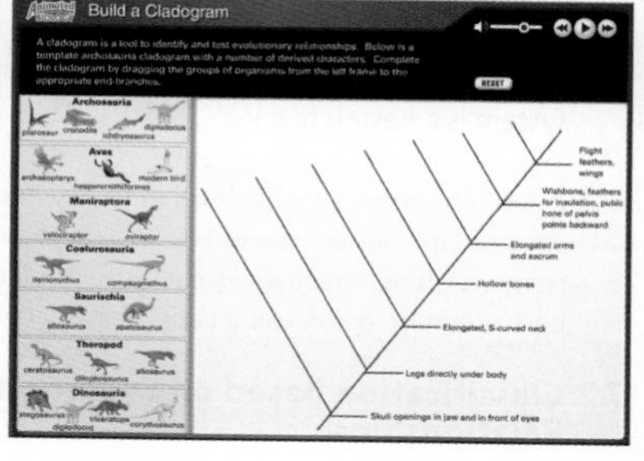

WEBQUEST
How do you classify a sea cucumber, an animal that looks like a water balloon? Complete this WebQuest to find out. Discover the evolutionary history of these animals and examine the traits that define them. Explore how sea cucumbers fit in the tree of life.

BIOZINE
Stories about the diversity of life— such as "New Species Found in New York's Central Park" and "Parasitic Fungus Drives Ant to Self-Destruction"—are often in the headlines. Read the latest news about the diversity of life in the BioZine.

Online Biology ▼

ANIMATED BIOLOGY Students learn derived characters of certain reptiles and use them to build a clado-gram. Use this interactive animation to reinforce the concepts of **Section 17.2.**

WEBQUEST The WebQuest takes one full class period. Students complete the activity online and will need access to a printer to print their answers. Sample answers, teacher notes, and alternative assessment ideas are available on **ClassZone.com.** Use with **Section 17.4.**

INVESTIGATION

Time 45 minutes	TEACHER TESTED ✓
Teacher Preparation	
Student Difficulty	
Lab Binder Diversity, p. 9	

Purpose Determine different ways to define species.

Overview Students will conduct research in the library or on the Internet to answer the questions.

Answers

1. • morphological: individuals that have a similar body shape and size and other physiological and structural characteristics in common. One advantage of this concept is that it can be applied to organisms that reproduce sexually or asexually. A disadvantage is that scientists cannot always agree on what characteristics distinguish different species from each other.
   • paleontological: concept used to classify extinct organisms. Evidence can only be obtained from the fossil record.
   • ecological: species defined by niche. Advantage is that it includes both asexual and sexual organisms, but the blurred distinction between two niches can be a disadvantage.
   • phylogenetic: species defined on the basis of genetic history. The physical and molecular characteristics of organisms are compared. Disadvantage is that genetic analysis is necessary, which is not always easy.
2. Answers will vary.

CHAPTER REVIEW

Interactive Review

Encourage students to go to **ClassZone.com** for a detailed review of each section, including visuals and vocabulary practice.

Unit Resource Book, Vocabulary Practice, pp. 23–26

CHAPTER 17

Interactive Review @ CLASSZONE.COM

KEY CONCEPTS | Vocabulary Games | Concept Maps | Animated Biology | Online Quiz

17.1 The Linnaean System of Classification

Organisms can be classified based on physical similarities. The Linnaean system of classification groups organisms based on shared physical or structural characteristics. This system is a nested hierarchy with seven taxa, or levels. The most specific level in this system is a species. Species are named according to binomial nomenclature, which gives each species a two-part scientific name using Latin words.

GENUS: *Canis*
SPECIES: *Canis lupis*

Common name: gray wolf

17.2 Classification Based on Evolutionary Relationships

Modern classification is based on evolutionary relationships. Cladistics is a common method used to group species based on the order in which they diverged from a common ancestor. These evolutionary relationships can be presented in a branching diagram called a cladogram. Cladograms are constructed by identifying which derived characters are shared by which species in the group being analyzed.

Glyptodon

Armadillo

17.3 Molecular Clocks

Molecular clocks provide clues to evolutionary history. Mutations tend to accumulate at a constant rate for a group of related species. The longer that two species are separated after diverging from a common ancestor, the more different the two species will be at the molecular level. Biologists use molecular clocks by linking molecular data to real time. They can then measure the rate of evolution for these species. Ribosomal RNA and mitochondrial DNA provide two types of molecular clocks, used to measure evolution at different time scales.

17.4 Domains and Kingdoms

The current tree of life has three domains. The domains are based on fundamental differences at the cellular level. Within these domains are a total of six kingdoms. The Bacteria and Archaea domains include all organisms in the Bacteria and Archaea kingdoms, respectively. Bacteria and archaea are unicellular prokaryotes, but the genetic and cellular differences between these groups are greater than the differences between any other two kingdoms. The domain Eukarya includes all organisms with eukaryotic cells—kingdoms Protista, Fungi, Plantae, and Animalia.

Tree of life

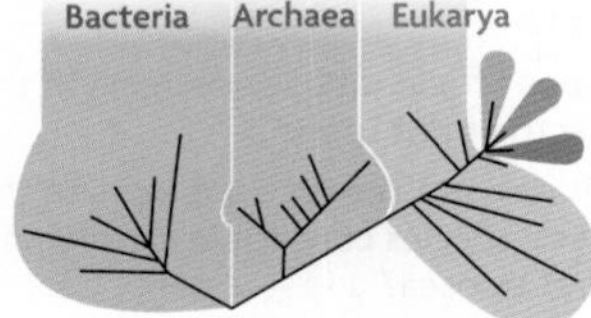

Synthesize Your Notes

Main Idea Web Use a main idea web to take notes about cladograms.

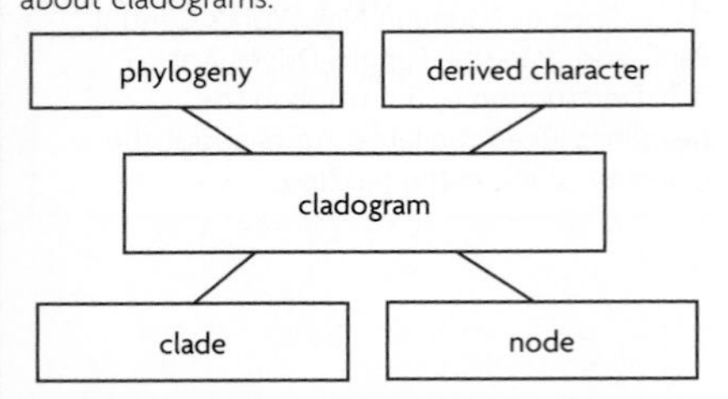

Concept Map Summarize what you know about taxonomy using a concept map.

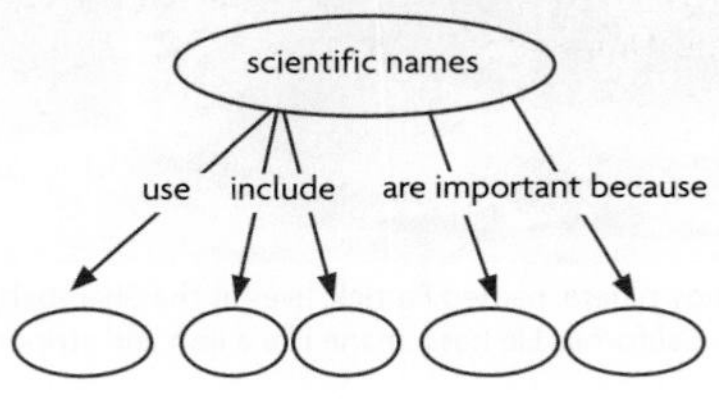

538 **Unit 6:** Classification and Diversity

Reviewing Vocabulary

1. Binomial nomenclature is a system used to give each species a two-part scientific name, which includes a genus name and a species descriptor.
2. Life forms are currently divided into three domains: Bacteria, Archaea, and Eukarya.
3. Two molecules that are used as molecular clocks are mtDNA and rRNA.
4. *Sample Question:* What method of constructing evolutionary trees makes use of the phylogeny of a species? *Answer:* cladistics
5. *Sample Question:* In a cladogram, what distinguishes one clade from the next? *Answer:* derived characters
6. A cladogram is a type of chart with many branches.
7. The Archaean lineage is thought to possibly include the first, or most ancient and most primitive, life on Earth.

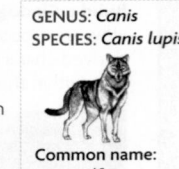

Chapter Assessment

Chapter Vocabulary

17.1 taxonomy, p. 518
taxon, p. 518
binomial nomenclature, p. 519
genus, p. 519

17.2 phylogeny, p. 524
cladistics, p. 525
cladogram, p. 525
derived character, p. 525

17.3 molecular clock, p. 530
mitochondrial DNA, p. 532
ribosomal RNA, p. 532

17.4 Bacteria, p. 534
Archaea, p. 534
Eukarya, p. 534

Reviewing Vocabulary

Vocabulary Connections

For each group of words below, write a sentence or two to clearly explain how the terms are connected. For example, for the terms *taxonomy* and *taxon,* you could write "In Linnaean taxonomy, each level of classification is called a taxon."

1. binomial nomenclature, genus, species
2. Bacteria, Archaea, Eukarya
3. molecular clock, mitochondrial DNA, ribosomal RNA

Write Your Own Questions

Think about the relationship between each pair of terms below. Then write a question about the first term that uses the second term as the answer. For the pair *taxonomy, taxon,* the question could be "In Linnaean taxonomy, what is each level of classification called?" Answer: taxon

4. phylogeny, cladistics
5. cladogram, derived characters

Greek and Latin Word Origins

6. *Klados* is Greek for "branch," and *-gram* is a suffix meaning "something written or drawn." Explain how this meaning relates to *cladogram.*
7. The prefix *archaeo-* comes from the Greek word *arkhaio,* which means "ancient" or "primitive." Explain how this meaning relates to *Archaea.*

Reviewing MAIN IDEAS

8. The scientific name for humans is *Homo sapiens.* What genus do humans belong to?
9. Why is it important for biologists to include scientific names when reporting their research to other biologists around the world?
10. Name the seven levels of organization in Linnaean taxonomy, from the most general to the most specific.
11. Current technology allows scientists to examine organisms at the molecular level. How has this technology exposed limitations in Linnaean taxonomy? **B.8.3**
12. What basic idea does cladistics use to classify groups of organisms? **B.8.3**
13. Two species with similar adaptations are found to have key differences at the molecular level. Scientists conclude that these species are not as closely related as previously thought. Why should the molecular evidence outweigh physical similarities that the species share? **B.8.4**
14. A particular DNA sequence accumulated three mutations over 10,000 years. After how much time would you expect this sequence to have accumulated six more mutations? Explain. **B.8.3**
15. Mutations accumulate more slowly in ribosomal RNA than in mitochondrial DNA. Which of these molecules would provide a better molecular clock for studying the evolution of species from different kingdoms? **B.8.3**
16. The original Linnaean system of classification had two kingdoms. Biologists now use six kingdoms. What does this change suggest about the nature of classification? **B.8.4**
17. What distinguishes the three domains in the tree of life from one another? **B.8.4**

CHAPTER REVIEW

12. common ancestry, or descent from a common ancestor
13. Physical similarities may be due to convergent evolution, while similarities at the molecular level are more likely due to relatedness based on sharing a common ancestor.
14. 20,000 years. Mutations occur at a fairly constant rate, so if three mutations took place in 10,000 years, you could expect to double the number of mutations in double the amount of time.
15. rRNA. Molecules with low mutation rates accumulate fewer mutations over long periods of time. Species in different kingdoms have been diverging genetically for very long periods of time. Molecules that accumulate mutations at relatively high rates would have accumulated so many mutations that they would be almost impossible to compare between species in two different kingdoms.
16. Classification is a work in progress; it is always changing as scientists make more and more discoveries about species' relatedness.
17. The structure of cells distinguishes the three domains. Bacteria and Archaea both have prokaryotic cells, but their cell walls are chemically different. Eukarya have eukaryotic cells.

Reviewing Main Ideas

8. *Homo*
9. Scientific names are recognized by scientists around the world, no matter what languages they speak. This allows for clear communication. Also, there is only one scientific name given to each species, whereas one species may have many common names in just one language, and hundreds across multiple languages.
10. kingdom, phylum, class, order, family, genus, species
11. By studying species at the molecular level, scientists can compare the DNA of different species. Similarities in DNA are likely due to relatedness, while physical and structural similarities between species may be the result of convergent evolution and therefore not indicative of actual relatedness. Molecular evidence has led scientists to reclassify into different groups some species that were originally thought to be closely related based on physical similarities alone.

ITEM CORRELATIONS

Standard	Items
B.8.3	11, 12, 14, 15, 19, 20, 21, 23-25
B.8.4	13, 16, 17, 22

Critical Thinking

18. Organisms in the same family are more closely related than organisms in the same class. Class is a more general taxon than family in Linnaean taxonomy.
19. There are likely not enough rRNA mutations in the human lineage for comparison between different sub-groups because rRNA mutations occur very slowly.
20. birds. Crocodiles and alligators share a more recent common ancestor with birds, and both groups share the derived character of skull openings in the jaw.
21. In the Linnaean system, organisms are grouped by physical appearance and structural similarities. To classify organisms by evolutionary relation-ships, scientists also analyze molecu-lar/genetic evidence, which often supports the Linnaean system but sometimes does not.
22. The three domains account for the huge genetic difference among bacteria, archaea, and eukaryotes. Eukaryotes (protists, fungi, plants, and animals) are more genetically similar to each other than bacteria are to archaea. The domain model makes this distinction more clear than the six-kingdom system alone.

Critical Thinking

18. Apply Are species in the same family more or less closely related than species in the same class? Explain your answer.

19. Synthesize Scientists have used mtDNA as a molecular clock to trace human evolution and early migration routes. Explain why mtDNA would be more useful in this research than rRNA. **B.8.3**

20. Apply Refer to the cladogram on page 527. Are crocodiles and alligators more closely related to snakes or to birds? Explain your answer using the terms *common ancestor* and *derived characters*. **B.8.3**

21. Compare and Contrast What types of evidence are used for classifying organisms in the Linnaean classification system? What types of evidence are used for classifying organisms based on evolutionary relationships? **B.8.3**

22. Evaluate What is the significance of grouping the six kingdoms into three domains? How does the domain model more clearly represent the diversity of prokaryotes than a system with the six kingdoms as its broadest divisions? **B.8.4**

Interpreting Visuals

Use the cladogram, which classifies species A, B, C, and D, to answer the next three questions.

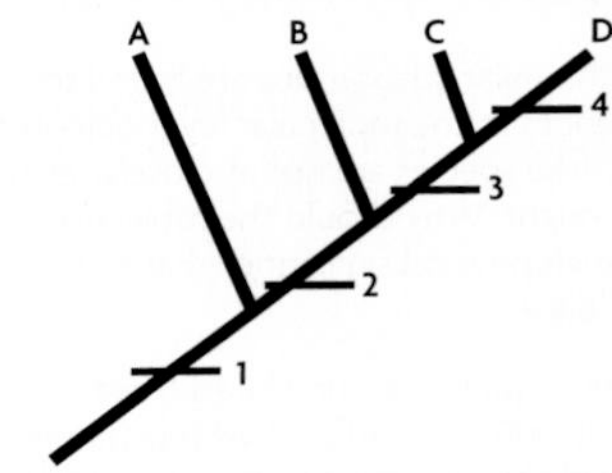

23. Apply What represents the derived characters that were used to construct this cladogram? **B.8.3**

24. Analyze Where are the nodes in this cladogram, and what do they represent? **B.8.3**

25. Analyze How many clades are represented in this cladogram? **B.8.3**

Analyzing Data

The family Ursidae contains all bear species. The data below show the number of species in each of the five genera of this family. Use this data to answer the next three questions.

GENERA OF THE FAMILY URSIDAE

Genus Names	Number of Species
Ailuropoda	1
Helarctos	1
Melursus	1
Tremarctos	1
Ursus	4

Source: University of Michigan Museum of Zoology

26. Analyze How many species belong to family Ursidae?

27. Transform Data Transform the number of species in each genus to a percent of the total number of bear species in family Ursidae.

28. Analyze What do the transformed data show that raw data do not show?

Connecting CONCEPTS

29. Write a Letter Imagine that you are a modern-day molecular biologist. Write a letter to Linnaeus explaining how advances in technology have affected the way that scientists classify living organisms. Describe the parts of his classification system that are still used in the same way today. Also describe the aspects of his system that have changed over the years.

30. Compare and Contrast The pangolin on page 517 shares many physical traits, such as a long snout, with anteaters and aardvarks. However, these traits are known to have evolved separately in each of these groups of species. Write a paragraph that compares how Linnaeus and a modern taxonomist would likely classify pangolins. Include in your paragraph the kinds of additional infor-mation that a modern taxonomist might look for in order to classify the pangolin.

Interpreting Visuals

23. hash marks 1, 2, 3, and 4
24. Nodes are where the side branches intersect with the main branch. They represent the common ancestor of the species in each clade.
25. 3; one with A, B, C, and D; one with B, C, and D; and one with C and D

Analyzing Data

26. 8
27. *Ailuropoda, Helarctos, Melursus, Tremarc-tos:* 12.5 percent each; *Ursus:* 50 percent
28. Half of family Ursidae is in the genus *Ursus.*

INDIANA ISTEP+ Test Prep

B.8.2; B.8.6; NOS.9

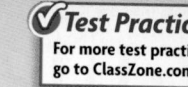

Test Practice For more test practice, go to ClassZone.com.

1 In the past 150 years, the classification of life has changed through the addition and restructuring of kingdoms and domains. This system is always changing because

A scientific study keeps producing more data.
B evolution keeps producing unique organisms.
C extinctions change evolutionary relationships.
D humans increase the rate of speciation.

2 Birds and snakes share a common ancestor from over 250 million years ago, but now they show many physical differences. These differences are ***most*** directly the result of

A coevolution between species.
B molecular clocks ticking at different rates.
C the long-term accumulation of mutations.
D differences in the alleles of the ancestor.

3

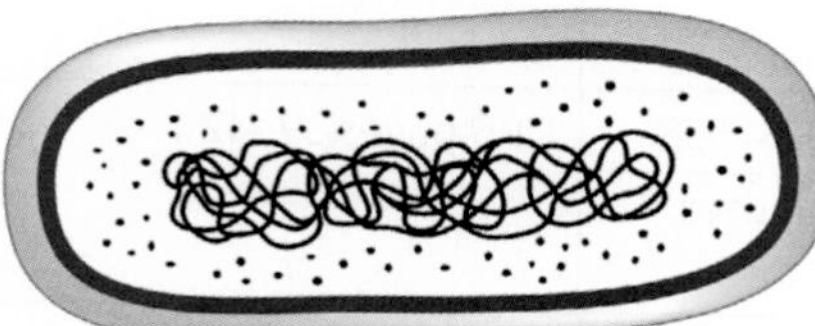

Scientists isolate this organism from marsh water. Based on this illustration, the organism would ***most*** likely be classified as a

A protist.
B bacterium.
C plant.
D fungus.

4 Mammals are multicellular organisms with about 3 billion base pairs in their genome. Yeasts are single-celled organisms with about 13 million base pairs in their genome. Both of these groups are classified as eukaryotes because they

A have over one million base pairs.
B can reproduce sexually.
C utilize aerobic respiration.
D have a similar basic cellular structure.

THINK THROUGH THE QUESTION

Do not get confused by extra information provided in this question. Focus on the definition of eukaryotes. The number of base pairs is not relevant to this question.

5 Scientists notice very few differences in the DNA sequences of individual cheetahs. This indicates that modern cheetahs likely descended from only a few individuals because

A smaller populations have less genetic variation.
B genetically different individuals are less fit.
C the mutation rate depends on population size.
D mutations do not affect small populations.

6 How might new technology lead to changes in the way scientists have classified organisms?

Standards-Based Assessment

1. A	4. D
2. C	5. A
3. B	6. See Below

Question 3 Answer B is correct. Answers A, C, and D are incorrect because protists, plants, and fungi are all eukaryotes.
Question 4 Answer D is correct. Answers A, B, and C are incorrect because eukaryotes are classified according to basic cellular structure (presence of a nucleus and other membrane-bound organelles), not according to genome size, mode of reproduction, or type of cellular respiration.
Question 5 Answer A is correct. Answer B is incorrect because this statement is not a logical answer to the question, and whether or not it is true depends on the types of genetic differences and the environmental conditions. Answer C is incorrect because mutation rate depends on a variety of factors unrelated to population size. Answer D is incorrect because mutations affect populations of all sizes.
Question 6 The ability to look at the DNA of organisms has allowed scientists to determine that some organisms previously thought to be relatives are less closely related than originally thought. On the other hand, DNA evidence has also allowed scientists to make connections between organisms that were previously thought to be unrelated.

Connecting Concepts

29. Letters should include current molecular technologies and explanations of what they are, how they work, and why they are important. Linnaeus' scientific naming system and classification categories are still used today, but the way organisms are assigned to groups has changed.

30. *Sample Answer:* Linnaeus would likely classify the three types of organisms very closely together since they share so many physical similarities. A modern taxonomist would realize that these similar traits may have resulted from convergent evolution. The modern taxonomist would then analyze molecular/genetic data to further investigate how closely related the three types of organisms are to each other.

ITEM CORRELATIONS

Standard	Items
B.8.2	3, 4
B.8.6	2, 5
NOS.9	1
NOS.10	6

CHAPTER 18

Indiana Resource Preview

Print Resources

Viruses and Prokaryotes

INDIANA STANDARDS		Sections	PAGES and PACING	UNIT RESOURCE BOOK
	18.1	**Studying Viruses and Prokaryotes** **KEY CONCEPT** Infections can be caused in several ways.	pp. 544–545 30 minutes	URB pages 27–30
NOS.1		DATA ANALYSIS: Choosing Data Representation Trends in Infectious Disease	p. 546 45 minutes	URB page 51
	18.2	**Viral Structure and Reproduction** **KEY CONCEPT** Viruses exist in a variety of shapes and sizes.	pp. 547–551 30 minutes	URB pages 31–34
	18.3	**Viral Diseases** **KEY CONCEPT** Some viral diseases can be prevented with vaccines.	pp. 552–554 30 minutes	URB pages 35–38
B.8.3	18.4	**Bacteria and Archaea** **KEY CONCEPT** Bacteria and archaea are both single-celled prokaryotes.	pp. 555–558 30 minutes	URB pages 39–42
B.4.4	18.5	**Beneficial Roles of Prokaryotes** **KEY CONCEPT** Prokaryotes perform important functions for organisms and ecosystems.	pp. 559–561 30 minutes	URB pages 43–46
NOS.1, NOS.3		CHAPTER INVESTIGATION: Leaf Print Bacteria	p. 562 45 minutes	**Lab Binder** Diversity pages 15–17
	18.6	**Bacterial Diseases and Antibiotics** **KEY CONCEPT** Understanding bacteria is necessary to prevent and treat disease.	pp. 563–565 30 minutes	URB pages 47–50
NOS.1, NOS.6		OPTIONS FOR INQUIRY	pp. 566–567 45, 90 min.	**Lab Binder** Diversity pages 18–21
		Chapter Review	pp. 568–571	**Assessment Book** Chapter Tests A, B pp. 359–366

INDIANA STANDARDS

B.4.4 Describe how climate, the pattern of matter and energy flow, the birth and death of new organisms, and the interaction between those organisms contribute to the long term stability of an ecosystem.
B.8.3 Use anatomical and molecular evidence to establish evolutionary relationships between organisms.
NOS.1 Develop explanations based on reproducible data and observations gathered during laboratory investigations.
NOS.3 Clearly communicate their ideas and results of investigations verbally and in written form using tables, graphs, diagrams, and photographs.
NOS.6 Use analogies and models (mathematical and physical) to simplify and represent systems that are difficult to understand or directly experience due to their size, time scale, or complexity, and recognize the limitations of analogies and models.

Labs

PUPIL EDITION LABS

Examining Bacteria in Yogurt, Section 5, p. 560 Students observe bacteria on a microscope slide of yogurt. **Lab Binder** p. 22	**Time:** 15 minutes **Materials:** toothpick, dab of yogurt, microscope slide, drop of water, cover slip, microscope
Leaf Print Bacteria, p. 562 Students compare the growth of bacteria on different media. **Lab Binder** pp. 15–17	**Time:** 45 minutes **Materials:** petri dish containing a selective medium, petri dish containing a nonselective medium, permanent marker, 2 leaves from the same plant, pencil with eraser, transparent tape

OPTIONS FOR INQUIRY

Using Bacteria to Break Down Oil, p. 566 Students test the effectiveness of bacterial enzymes at degrading oil. **Lab Binder** pp. 18–20	**Time:** 45 minutes **Materials:** 4 10-mL test tubes with caps, 6 cm masking tape, marker, test tube rack, 5 plastic droppers, 3 10-mL graduated cylinders, 2 mL cooking oil, 2 mL 0.02% tetrazolium indicator solution, 2 mL each of three types of enzymatic drain cleaner
Modeling Viruses, p. 567 Students make a model of a virus to understand how the virus attacks a cell. **Lab Binder** p. 21	**Time:** 90 minutes **Materials:** research materials (books, scientific journals, Internet), markers, pipe cleaners, clay, toothpicks, construction paper, white paper

LAB BINDER Unit 6 Classification and Diversity

Additional Investigation: Viruses and Cancer, pp. 23–25

Biotechnology Lab: Bacteria's Role in Wastewater Treatment, pp. 39–42

Virtual Lab Worksheet: Testing Antibacterial Agents, p. 54

LAB GENERATOR

A searchable CD of all labs in the program in editable format, including forensic, probeware, and biotechnology labs.

Presentation Tools

POWER PRESENTATIONS

Presentation Chapter 18
Power Presentations for each section incorporate images and clips from the Media Gallery: Includes Note Navigator for each section.

MEDIA GALLERY

Contains the following images and video clips, as well as animations, simulations and forms of visuals from the book.

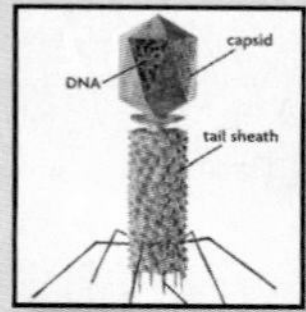

Bacteriophage

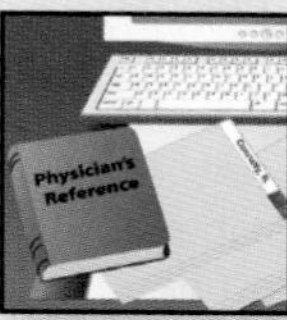

Antibiotics and illness

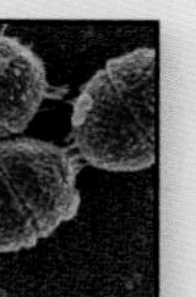
Streptococcus bacteria

Ebola virus testing

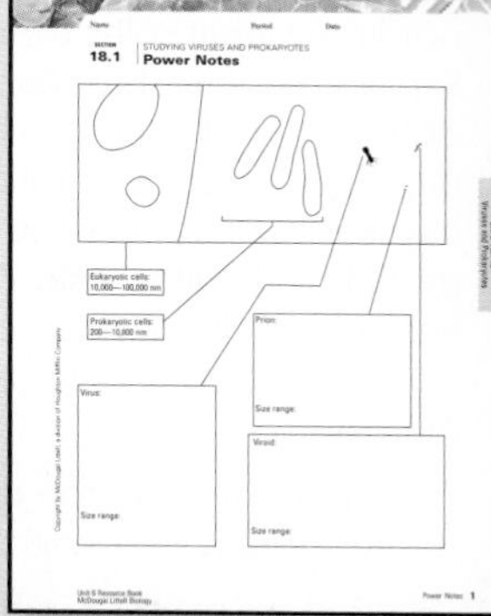

Power Notes

VIDEO

Check out a set of short video clips examining bacteria and antibiotic resistance.

ANIMATED BIOLOGY

Viral Infections

What Would You Prescribe?

TRANSPARENCIES

Viral Structures T77

Lytic and Lysogenic Infections T78

Prokaryote Structures T79

Online BIOLOGY CLASSZONE.COM

BioZine

Animated Biology

Interactive Review

SciLinks

Resource Centers

CHAPTER

18

▼ Focus and Motivate

How are bacteria helpful to humans?

Students may be aware that bacteria live in the human intestine, but they may not know what roles the bacteria play. Explain that intestinal bacteria break down nutrients we could not otherwise digest and keep harmful microbes at bay. For the bacteria, the intestine provides a habitat. **Ask,** What type of ecological relationship does this situation describe? symbiosis, specifically mutualism

Have students read the description of the bacterium shown in the picture. **Ask**

- How are bacteria in the esophagus part of an ecosystem? They are living things that interact with their environment.
- How might the bacteria protect humans from throat and stomach cancers? Accept all reasonable answers. Tell students that scientists think the bacteria in the esophagus produce a toxin that kills cancer cells.

BIOZINE ClassZone.com

Students can access BioZine at **ClassZone.com** to learn about avian flu, antibiotic resistance, and viruses.

In a Hurry?

The critical material of the chapter is found in **Sections 18.2, 18.3, 18.4,** and **18.6,** which cover viral and prokaryote structure and reproduction, viral and bacterial diseases, and antibiotic use. **Section 18.1** presents an overview of infectious agents, including prokaryotes, viruses, viroids, and prions. **Section 18.5** shows the benefits and utility of bacterial species in ecosystems as well as in industry.

CHAPTER 18

Viruses and Prokaryotes

KEY CONCEPTS

18.1 Studying Viruses and Prokaryotes
Infections can be caused in several ways.

18.2 Viral Structure and Reproduction
Viruses exist in a variety of shapes and sizes.

18.3 Viral Diseases
Some viral diseases can be prevented with vaccines.

18.4 Bacteria and Archaea
Bacteria and archaea are both single-celled prokaryotes.

18.5 Beneficial Roles of Prokaryotes
Prokaryotes perform important functions for organisms and ecosystems.

18.6 Bacterial Diseases and Antibiotics
Understanding bacteria is necessary to prevent and treat disease.

Online BIOLOGY CLASSZONE.COM

Animated BIOLOGY
View animated chapter concepts.
- Viral Infections
- Testing Antibacterial Products
- What Would You Prescribe?

BIOZINE
Keep current with biology news.
- News feeds
- Careers
- Polls

RESOURCE CENTER
Get more information on
- Research Applications
- Vaccines
- Bacteria
- Archaea

Student Activity

Purpose **Have students assess the effectiveness of hand washing for removing microbes.**

Materials (per team)
- GloGerm lotion
- black-light lamp
- liquid soap
- paper towels

If GloGerm and black lights are too expensive, use a mixture of ground cinnamon and baby oil as "germs."

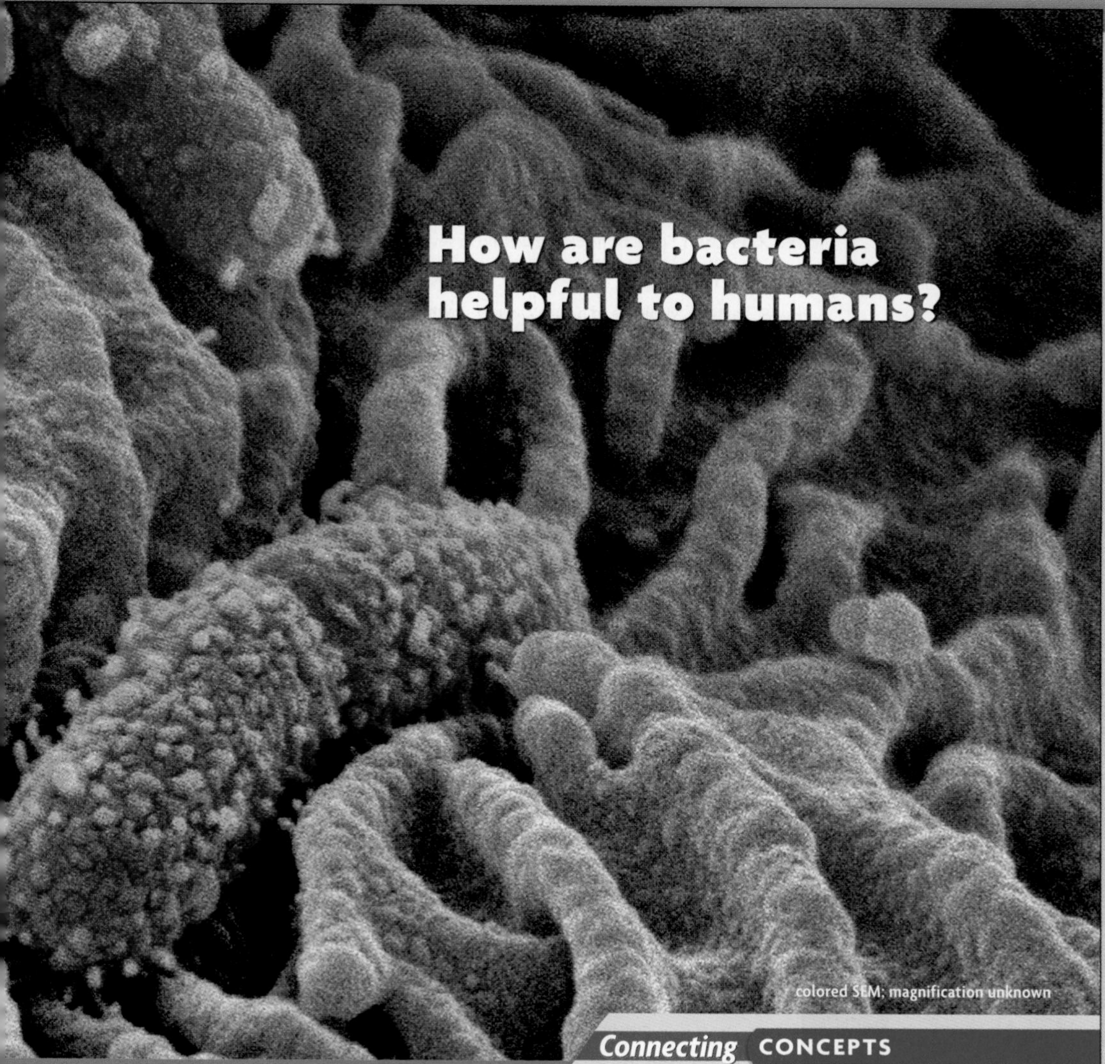

How are bacteria helpful to humans?

colored SEM; magnification unknown

These bacteria live in the lining of an esophagus, the tube that leads from your mouth to your stomach. Only a few years ago, it was thought that nothing could survive in an esophagus, but the entire digestive tract is home for many types of bacteria. Being a home to bacteria isn't bad, though. Some doctors hypothesize that these bacteria may protect us from some throat and stomach cancers.

Connecting CONCEPTS

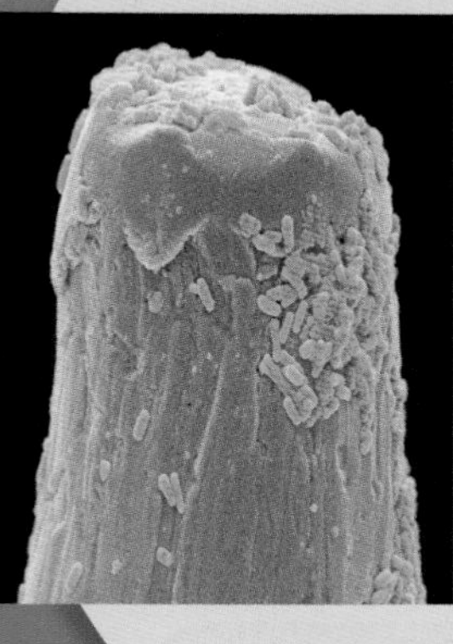

Biotechnology Hundreds of bacteria can fit on the tip of a pin, as shown at left. About the same number of bacteria will fit on a silicon chip. Scientists have made a device that can collect signals from bacteria joined to silicon chips. These bacteria have been specially altered to glow when near pollutants. The chips then measure the amount of light emitted—the more light, the more pollution present. (colored SEM; magnification 1100×)

Introduce Have students rub a small amount of GloGerm lotion onto their hands, making sure to rub it into the fingernails and between the fingers. Explain that GloGerm is meant to simulate microbes—invisible to the eye but present everywhere. Have students look at their hands under the black light. Their hands should glow. Ask students to wash their hands thoroughly for 15–20 seconds with soap and warm water, trying to remove as many of the "microbes" as possible. After rinsing and drying their hands, have students examine their hands under the black light again.

Discuss GloGerm is useful for those who work in industries that demand a high level of hygiene, such as medicine and food service. **Ask**

- What areas of the hand need particular attention when washing? around the nails and between the fingers
- When is it important to wash hands to minimize the spread of disease-causing microbes? before and after handling food, after using the toilet, after handling animals or their waste, after contact with someone with an infectious illness, before performing medical procedures

Activate Prior Knowledge

Students will be familiar with computer viruses designed to disrupt or destroy. Tell them that the concept of a self-replicating agent that proliferates over the Internet has now been adapted to marketing techniques. **Ask,** Have you ever signed up for a free email account? How can such a service pay for itself? Students may recognize that the provider is supported by advertising. What students may not realize is that their emails may also pass along marketing materials to the recipient. This is called *viral marketing.* In the case of email providers, "susceptible" users sign up and then "infect" others in their social circle with promotional information from the provider. Real biological viruses are passed on in a similar way, often without the transmitter or recipient knowing they have the virus.

Preview Vocabulary

Academic Vocabulary In everyday language, we use the word *contagious* to describe the spread of laughter, fear, and other behaviors or states of mind. In biology, *contagious* describes a disease that is passed from one organism to another by direct or indirect physical contact. The term *infectious* is similar.

Both words come from the Latin:

contingere = to touch

inficere = to stain

English Learners Throughout the chapter, the analogy of a virus or bacterium acting like an uninvited or unseen guest should be pointed out. Students should look for terms in the text that relate to this analogy, such as *host, door, intruder,* and *guest.* The idea of entry is important. Students need to think about how pathogens move into hosts and how they behave once they are inside.

SECTION 18.1

▼ Plan and Prepare

Objective

- Compare and contrast different types of infectious agents.

Section Resources

Unit Resource Book Study Guide pp. 27–28 Power Notes p. 29 Reinforcement p. 30
Interactive Reader Chapter 18 **Spanish Study Guide** pp. 183–184
Biology Toolkit pp. C33, D7
Technology Power Presentation 18.1 Media Gallery DVD Online Quiz 18.1

Activate Prior Knowledge Many people wonder why some illnesses are easily treatable or curable, while others are not. **Ask,** Why is it that when you go to a doctor, explain your symptoms, and undergo testing, sometimes you are given an antibiotic and sometimes you are not? Antibiotics do not work on viruses. Viruses, such as those that cause the common cold, cannot be treated with antibiotics because they do not have the cellular structures that bacteria have that can be destroyed or inhibited.

▼ Teach

Vocabulary

Academic Vocabulary Tell students that the suffix *-oid* is attached to objects or beings that are similar or related to another. For example, *humanoid* describes something that has characteristics associated with humans, though is not human. Often that which is described is *diminutive,* less substantial or smaller than the original, as is the case with **viroids** and **viruses.**

18.1 Studying Viruses and Prokaryotes

KEY CONCEPT Infections can be caused in several ways.

MAIN IDEA

- Viruses, bacteria, viroids, and prions can all cause infection.

VOCABULARY

virus, p. 544
pathogen, p. 544
viroid, p. 544
prion, p. 545

Review
prokaryote, archaea

REVIEW AT CLASSZONE.COM

Connect Bacteria are everywhere, including in and on your own body—such as the bacteria that live in our digestive tracts. The relationship between you and the microorganisms in your body is usually mutually beneficial. Under certain conditions, however, normally harmless microorganisms can cause disease, and some types of microorganisms are particularly nasty—they always make you sick.

MAIN IDEA

Viruses, bacteria, viroids, and prions can all cause infection.

You are probably familiar with the terms *virus* and *bacteria,* but you may not know exactly what they are. A **virus** is an infectious particle made only of a strand of DNA or RNA surrounded by a protein coat. Bacteria, on the other hand, are one-celled microorganisms that can also cause infection. Any living organism or particle that can cause an infectious disease is called an infectious agent, or **pathogen.**

In Chapter 1, you learned that all living things share certain key characteristics: the abilities to reproduce, to use nutrients and energy, to grow and develop, and to respond to their environments. They also contain genetic material that carries the code of life. Prokaryotes—such as the bacterium shown in **FIGURE 18.1**—are clearly living things, since they have each of the traits of life. But are viruses living things? Like living cells, viruses respond to their environment. Viruses have genes and can reproduce. Unlike cells, however, viruses cannot reproduce on their own. Instead, they need living cells to help them reproduce and make proteins. Viruses are also much smaller than most cells, as you can see in **FIGURE 18.2.** While viruses have key traits similar to living cells, they also have many differences. In fact, viruses are not even given a place in the Linnaean system of biological classification.

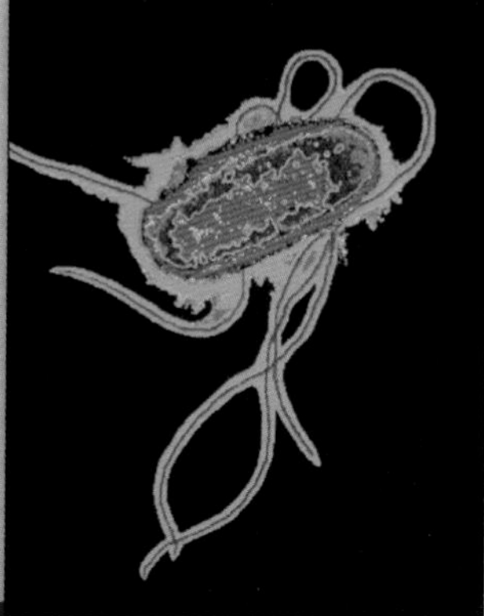

FIGURE 18.1 Prokaryotes, such as this *Escherichia coli* bacterium, are single cells that have all of the characteristics of living things. (colored TEM; magnification 6000×)

A viroid has even less in common with living things than do viruses. **Viroids** are infectious particles that cause disease in plants. Viroids are made of single-stranded RNA without a protein coat. They are passed through seeds or pollen. Viroids have had a major economic impact on agriculture because they can stunt the growth of plants.

Differentiated Instruction

ENGLISH LEARNERS

Students can use a Venn diagram to compare viruses with living things such as bacteria. In the overlapping areas, they can list the commonalities, such as "have genes," and in the other areas, they can list the differences that exclude viruses from the three domains.

Biology Toolkit, Venn Diagram, p. C33

PRE-AP

Have students create a table to organize the material of the chapter. Tell them that they will study different infectious agents, how they are structured, how they reproduce, and how they interact with other organisms, including humans, in ways that are beneficial, harmful, or benign.

Biology Toolkit, Semantic Feature Analysis, p. D7

FIGURE 18.2 Relative Sizes of Cells and Infectious Particles

Although eukaryotic and prokaryotic cells can be microscopic, they are large in comparison to **viruses, viroids,** and **prions.**

A Infer **Why are viroids and prions sometimes called subviral particles?**

At the boundary between living and nonliving, perhaps the strangest entity of all is the prion. A **prion** (PREE-ahn) is an infectious particle made only of proteins that can cause other proteins to fold incorrectly. When proteins misfold, the protein will not work properly. Prions are unusual in that they are infectious yet have no genetic material. They play a part in certain diseases of the brain such as mad cow disease, known to scientists as bovine spongiform encephalopathy, or BSE. Humans may become infected with BSE when they eat meat from animals that are infected. Food safety laws in the United States, however, try to reduce the risk of infection. Creutzfeld-Jakob (KROYTS-fehlt YAH-kawp) disease (CJD), another brain disease that affects humans, is also associated with prions. Prion diseases can incubate for a long time with no effect on their host. However, once symptoms appear, they worsen quickly and are always fatal, because the body has no immune response against a protein.

TAKING NOTES

Use a two-column chart to take notes on viruses, viroids, and prions.

Main Idea	Detail
Virus	
Viroid	
Prion	

Synthesize **Why are viruses, viroids, and prions not included in the Linnaean system**

18.1 ASSESSMENT

ONLINE QUIZ ClassZone.com

REVIEWING MAIN IDEAS

1. What are the main differences between living cells and **viruses**?
2. Viruses, **viroids, prions,** and some bacteria can all be considered **pathogens.** What do all pathogens have in common?

CRITICAL THINKING

3. **Infer** Prions were not widely known to be infectious agents until the 1980s. Give two reasons why this might be so.
4. **Apply** An RNA-based disease spreads through pollen. Is it likely due to a virus, viroid, or prion? Explain.

Connecting CONCEPTS

5. **Medicine** To multiply, viruses must take over the functions of the cells they infect. Why does this make it difficult to make effective antiviral drugs?

TEACH FROM VISUALS

FIGURE 18.2 Have students compare the sizes of eukaryotic cells, prokaryotic cells, viruses, viroids, and prions. **Ask,** How many times larger are the largest eukaryotic cells than the largest prions? 10,000 times larger

Integrating Epidemiology

Kuru is a **prion disease** found only among the **Fore** people of the New Guinea highlands. *Kuru* means "shiver," denoting the tremors and wobbly gait caused by the disease. Other symptoms include slurred speech and sudden maniacal laughter. The disease reached epidemic levels during the 1950s and 1960s, before scientists realized that the means of transmission was a practice known as mortuary cannibalism.

According to Fore culture, family members of a dead relative absorb that person back into the living family by cooking and eating the tissue of the deceased, including the brain. Because the incubation time of Kuru was sometimes many years, the Fore people never made the connection between their ritual and the disease. The New Guinean government's discouragement of the practice has produced a steady decline of the disease.

Answers

A Infer They are smaller than viruses.

B Synthesize They are not considered to be organisms.

18.1 ASSESSMENT

1. Cells can use energy and nutrients and reproduce independently of other cells, whereas viruses rely on cells to help them reproduce and make proteins.
2. They cause infectious diseases.
3. They are very small, and prion diseases often incubate for many years before taking effect.
4. Viroids, because they are made of RNA, are passed through seeds or pollen, and infect plants.
5. Most drugs that would interfere with viral replication would also kill the host cell.

Assess and Reteach ▼

Assess Use the Online Quiz or Section Quiz (*Assessment Book,* p. 353).

Reteach Create a table on the board to compare prions, viruses, bacteria, and viroids. Have students call out the characteristics of each. Headings could include size, living or nonliving, type of genetic material (if any), and type of organisms affected.

DATA ANALYSIS

Introduce

Explain that TB is a major public health threat globally. One-third of the world's population is infected with TB, and 3 million people die from the disease each year. Worldwide, TB infection rates are increasing, and multidrug resistance is becoming more prevalent. **Ask**

- Why is it important to collect data on the spread of disease in a population? helps monitor trends, can determine what treatments are effective
- Is it better to collect discrete data, continuous data, or both? Both discrete data and continuous data are valuable for analyzing the effects of disease. Discrete data can give specifics on how many people are suffering from a disease, where they are living, and how many have died, among other things. Continuous data help to reveal trends, such as a rise or fall in the incidence or mortality of a disease.

Discuss

Have students consider the implications of the TB data. **Ask**

- What hypotheses might account for the decrease in TB prevalence in the United States since 1955? Answers will vary but could include increased availability of drugs, compliance in completing full drug regimens, and improved public health science.
- Do the high numbers of TB cases in California, New York, Florida, and Texas suggest that residents of these states are more likely to get TB than residents of other states? No, the numbers of cases in these states may be high only because they are the most populous states.
- What would be a better way to compare the incidence of TB in different states? convert the number of cases to a rate, such as cases per 100,000 people

Unit Resource Book, Data Analysis, p. 51

DATA ANALYSIS CHOOSING DATA REPRESENTATION

NOS.1

Trends in Infectious Disease

Collecting data on the spread of infectious disease in a population is an important part of monitoring trends and determining a course of treatment. Different methods of displaying data, such as bar graphs or line graphs, often convey different information. Recall from page 497 in Chapter 16 the difference between discrete and continuous data.

DATA ANALYSIS ClassZone.com

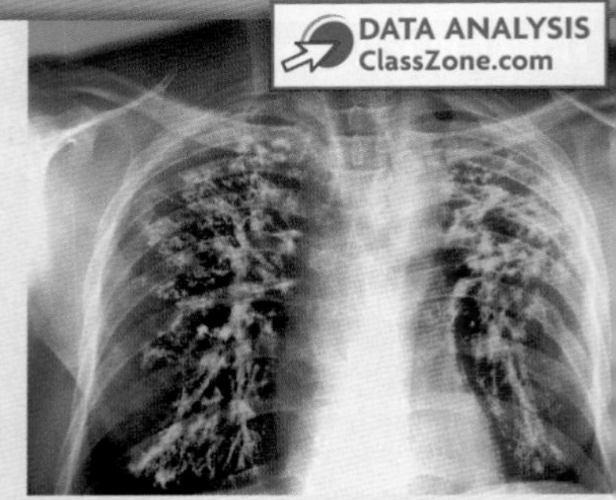
Lungs infected by tuberculosis

TABLE 1. STATES WITH MOST TB CASES IN 2005

State	Number of Cases
California	2900
Texas	1535
New York	1294
Florida	1094
Illinois	596
Georgia	510
New Jersey	485
Virginia	355
North Carolina	329
Pennsylvania	325

TABLE 2. RATE OF TB FOR U.S. RESIDENTS

Year	TB Cases per 100,000 Persons
1955	46.6
1960	30.7
1965	25.2
1970	18.1
1975	15.7
1980	12.2
1985	9.3
1990	10.3
1995	8.7
2000	5.8
2005	4.8

Source: Centers for Disease Control and Prevention

CHOOSE DATA REPRESENTATION

The tables above show two sets of data describing tuberculosis (TB) infection in the United States.

1. **Connect** For each of the tables above, identify whether the data are continuous or discrete.
2. **Graph Data** Determine which type of graph would best represent each set of data and construct the graph for each set.
3. **Analyze** What trend did your graph show in rates of tuberculosis cases in the United States between the years 1955 and 2005?
4. **Analyze** Which table gives a more complete picture of TB infection in the United States? Explain.
5. **Predict** What trend do you expect the rate of TB cases to show in 2010?

Answers

Sample Data

See sample graphs of student data, p. R106.

Analyze and Conclude

1. Table 1: discrete; Table 2: continuous
2. Discrete data should be constructed as a bar graph. Continuous data should be constructed as a line graph.
3. The rate of TB cases declined between 1955 and 2005.
4. Table 2, because it shows how the rate of infection has declined in the United States over time, whereas Table 1 does not reveal trends and has data from only ten states in one year.
5. From the data given, one would predict a further decline in the rate of TB cases in the United States in 2010.

18.2 Viral Structure and Reproduction

KEY CONCEPT Viruses exist in a variety of shapes and sizes.

MAIN IDEAS

- Viruses differ in shape and in ways of entering host cells.
- Viruses cause two types of infections.

VOCABULARY

capsid, p. 547
bacteriophage, p. 549
lytic infection, p. 551
lysogenic infection, p. 551
prophage, p. 551

Review
endocytosis, lipid

Connect Just like the computer viruses that you hear about in the news, viruses that affect living things pass from one host to the next. While computer viruses pass through networks from one computer to another, human viruses pass from person to person. Also like computer viruses, viruses of living things can be simple or complex in structure, and have several different ways to get into their hosts.

MAIN IDEA

Viruses differ in shape and in ways of entering host cells.

The idea that infectious agents cause certain diseases was a fairly new concept in 1892 when Russian scientist Dmitri Ivanovsky made a surprising observation. He was studying tobacco mosaic disease, named for the scar pattern left on affected leaves of tobacco or tomato plants. Mosaic disease, shown in **FIGURE 18.3,** was thought to be caused by a bacterium. But so far no one had been able to prove it. Ivanovsky passed extracts of diseased tobacco leaves through filter pores small enough to strain out bacteria and found that the extracts could still pass on the disease. Was this a new bacterium? Or was it some unknown type of organism?

In 1898, Dutch microbiologist Martinus Beijerinck built upon Ivanovsky's work. He showed that the disease agent passed through agar gel. He proposed that tiny particles within the extracts caused infection, and he called the particles *viruses,* from the Latin for "poison." The observations of Ivanovsky and Beijerinck laid the groundwork for more discoveries. Scientists began finding that many diseases of unknown causes could be explained by viruses.

FIGURE 18.3 These pictures compare a healthy leaf and a leaf infected by tobacco mosaic virus (TMV). TMV was the first virus identified by scientists.

The Structure of Viruses

Viruses have an amazingly simple basic structure. A single viral particle, called a *virion,* is made up of genetic material surrounded by a protein shell called a **capsid.** Capsids can have different shapes. In some viruses, the capsid itself is surrounded by a lipid envelope. A lipid envelope is the protective outer coat of a virus, from which spiky structures of proteins and sugars may stick out.

Differentiated Instruction

BELOW LEVEL

Suggest that students use a combination of diagrams and notes to summarize the content of this section. Students need to answer two basic questions:

- What are the structural parts of a virus?
- How do those different parts enable a virus to infect its host?

Biology Toolkit, Combination Notes, p. C23

SECTION 18.2

Plan and Prepare

Objectives

- Identify the structures and shapes of viruses.
- Describe different types of viral infection.

Section Resources

Unit Resource Book Study Guide pp. 31–32 Power Notes p. 33 Reinforcement p. 34
Interactive Reader Chapter 18 **Spanish Study Guide** pp. 185–186
Biology Toolkit pp. C15, C23, C33, C38
Technology Power Presentation 18.2 Media Gallery DVD Online Quiz 18.2

Activate Prior Knowledge Have students think about a piece of computer code that makes up a computer virus. **Ask,** At what point does the virus become dangerous? when it enters into the computer's operating system and the virus's code becomes a set of instructions Discuss that any virus has to have a way inside. **Ask,** How do viruses enter into a human population? contact with infected organisms; mosquito bites, water, food, bodily fluids

Teach

History of Science

The first person to see a virus was **Wendell Stanley.** In the 1930s at the Rockefeller Institute, Stanley purified the juices of 4000 kilograms (8800 lb) of tobacco leaves to produce about one tablespoon of pure, crystallized **tobacco mosaic virus,** which scientists then examined using x-ray crystallography.

▼ Teach *continued*

Take It Further

In addition to bearing the surface proteins that function as connecting points to host cells, the capsid offers a virus' vulnerable genetic material some basic protection from

- physical damage that can result from mechanical forces
- chemical damage, such as UV radiation from sunlight
- damage from enzymes secreted by organisms as a defense against viruses

TEACH FROM VISUALS

FIGURE 18.4 Have students look at the diagrams of the three viruses. **Ask,** What are three parts common to all viruses, and what are they used for? nucleic acid for replication, capsid for protection, surface protein for host recognition

Integrating Immunology

The structure of viral surface proteins not only helps viruses infect host cells, in some cases, it enables a virus to elude capture by the host's immune system. In humans and other animals, the immune system targets invading viruses by recognizing their surface proteins. In viruses such as **HIV** and **hepatitis C,** the genes coding for surface proteins have a high mutation rate, producing rapid changes to surface proteins that make it difficult for the immune system to detect the virus.

Answers

Ⓐ Compare and Contrast All the viruses have nucleic acids and surface proteins, and all three types have different shapes. Two have outer capsids, and one has capsids on its genetic material. Two have lipid envelopes, and one does not.

Some viruses attach to host cells by these spikes. The spikes are such an obvious trait of some viruses that they can be used for identification.

Viruses can only reproduce after they have infected host cells. Viruses are simply packaged sets of genes that move from one host cell to another. Unlike bacteria and other living parasites, a virus has no structures to maintain—no membranes or organelles needing ATP, oxygen, or glucose. All it carries into the cell is what it needs to reproduce—its genes.

The structure and shape of viruses play an important role in how they work. Each type of virus can infect only certain hosts. A virus identifies its host by fitting its surface proteins to receptor molecules on the surface of the host cell, like a key fitting a lock. Some viruses are able to infect several species, while other viruses can infect only a single species. Common viral shapes are shown in **FIGURE 18.4.**

FIGURE 18.4 Viral Shapes

The different proteins that make up a viral capsid give viruses a variety of shapes.

ENVELOPED

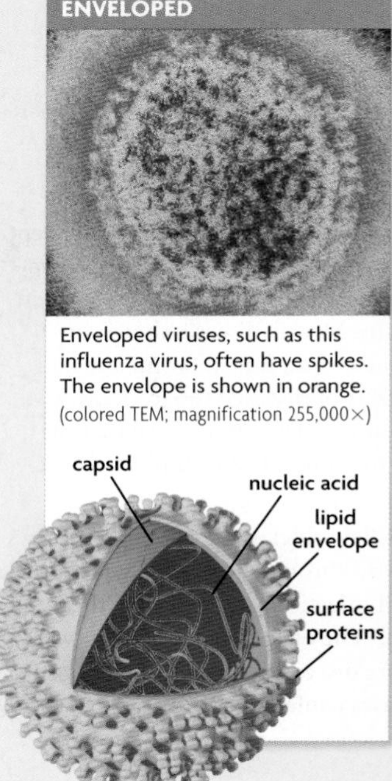

Enveloped viruses, such as this influenza virus, often have spikes. The envelope is shown in orange. (colored TEM; magnification 255,000×)

HELICAL

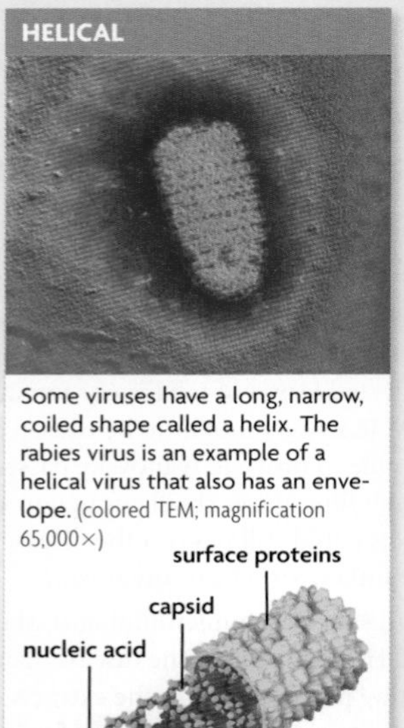

Some viruses have a long, narrow, coiled shape called a helix. The rabies virus is an example of a helical virus that also has an envelope. (colored TEM; magnification 65,000×)

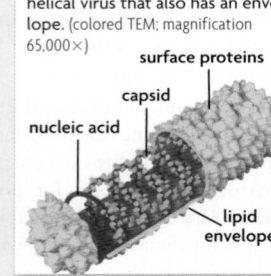

POLYHEDRAL

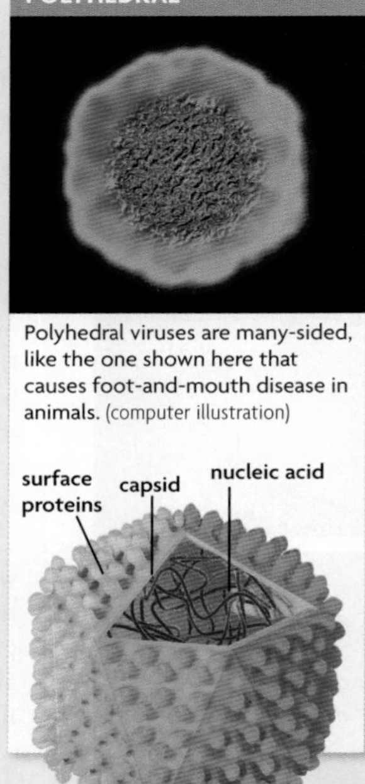

Polyhedral viruses are many-sided, like the one shown here that causes foot-and-mouth disease in animals. (computer illustration)

Ⓐ Compare and Contrast What are the similarities and differences between the three types of viruses shown above?

Differentiated Instruction

TEACH WITH TECHNOLOGY

Show students an animation of viral infection to help them see the role each part of the virus plays in enabling the viral DNA to take over the machinery of a cell. If possible, use the pause feature to enable students to diagram the process in their science notebooks. Go to the chapter Resource Center at **ClassZone.com.**

In some viruses, capsids form a 20-sided polyhedral. Rod-shaped and strandlike viruses often have capsids shaped in coils, like a spring or helix.

In contrast to prokaryotes and eukaryotes, in which DNA is always the main genetic material, a virus can have either DNA or RNA but never both. The genetic material of viruses can be single-stranded or double-stranded, and linear, circular, or segmented.

Viruses that Infect Bacteria

One group of viruses is the bacteriophages, often called simply "phages." **Bacteriophages** (bak-TEER-ee-uh-FAYJ-ihz) are viruses that infect bacteria. One example is the T-bacteriophage that infects *Escherichia coli,* the bacteria commonly found in the intestines of mammals. The T-bacteriophage shown in **FIGURE 18.5** has a 20-sided capsid connected to a long protein tail with spiky footlike fibers. The capsid contains the genetic material. The tail and its spikes help attach the virus to the host cell. After attachment, the bacteriophage's tail releases an enzyme that breaks down part of the bacterial cell wall. The tail sheath contracts, and the tail core punches through the cell wall, injecting the phage's DNA. The phage works like a syringe, injecting its genes into the host cell's cytoplasm, where its DNA is found.

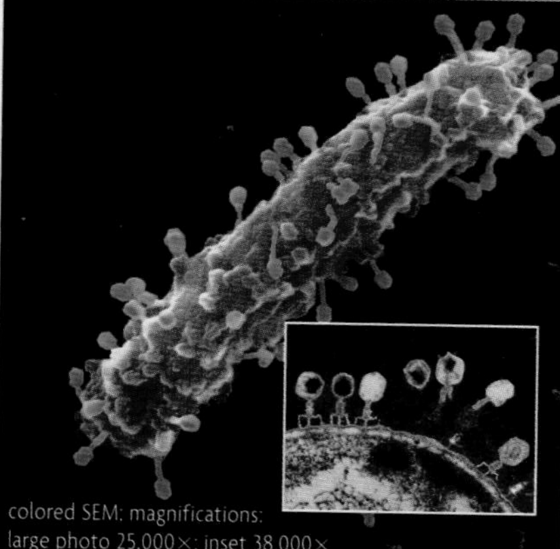

FIGURE 18.5 The SEM above shows bacteriophages attacking an *E. coli* bacterium. While injecting their genetic material into the bacterium, the protein coats remain outside the cell (inset). The unique structure of a bacteriophage is shown below.

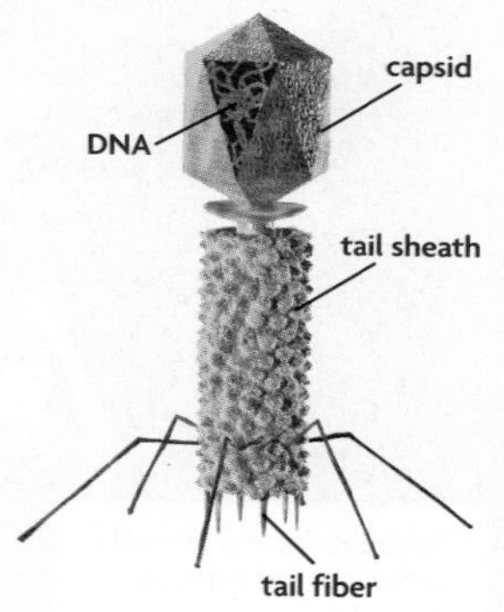

Viruses that Infect Eukaryotes

Viruses that infect eukaryotes differ from bacteriophages in their methods of entering the host cell. For example, these viruses may enter the cells by endocytosis. Recall from Chapter 3 that endocytosis is an active method of bringing molecules into a cell by forming vesicles, or membrane-bound sacs, around the molecules. If the viruses are enveloped, they can also enter a host cell by fusing with the plasma membrane of the host cell and releasing the capsid into the cell's cytoplasm. HIV is a virus that enters cells in this way. Once inside the cell, eukaryotic viruses target the nucleus of the cell.

A Summarize Describe how the structures of a bacteriophage are well-suited for their functions.

MAIN IDEA

Viruses cause two types of infections.

The ways in which viruses enter and leave a cell may vary, but two basic pathways of infection are similar for all viruses. These pathways are shown for the most studied viruses, the bacteriophages, in **FIGURE 18.6**.

Once inside the host cell, phages follow one of two general paths in causing disease. In one path, the phage behaves like a bad houseguest. It takes over the household, eats all of the food in the refrigerator, and then blows up the house when it leaves. The other path of infection is somewhat more subtle. Instead of destroying the house, the phage becomes a permanent houseguest. Neither path is good for the host.

PRE-AP

Have students draw diagrams to sequence viral infections of a bacterial cell and a eukaryotic cell. Students can review the process of endocytosis in Chapter 3 on page 90.

Biology Toolkit, Sequence Diagram, p. C38

Vocabulary

bacteriophage Point out that word roots can sometimes be confusing. For example, a bacteriophage is a virus, not a bacterium. The root *phage* comes from the Greek *phagein,* "to eat." *Bacteriophage* means "bacteria eater." However, a virus is smaller than a bacterium, with no mouth in sight. Suggest students think of this term functioning in the same way as *dragon-slayer.*

TEACH FROM VISUALS

FIGURE 18.5 Have students use the labeled diagram of the bacteriophage to identify phage capsids, tail sheaths, and tail fibers in the SEM image. **Ask,** How would you describe the movement of a bacteriophage's DNA during an infection? from the bacteriophage's capsid, through its tail, and into the cytoplasm of the bacterium

Vocabulary

Academic Vocabulary Point out to students that three of the structural elements associated with viruses involve a form of casing.

envelope, wrapping, typically the paper wrapping for a letter

sheath, close-fitting covering, as in the case for a sword or blade

capsid, a protective shell, a term specifically used in biology

Answers

A Summarize The capsid houses the nucleic acids, the tail fibers help with attachment, and the tail sheath helps with injecting the genetic material of the virus.

▼ Teach *continued*

TEACH FROM VISUALS

FIGURE 18.6 Have students compare the two pathways. **Ask,** What is the difference in the way viral DNA interacts with host DNA in a lytic infection compared to a lysogenic infection? Lytic: viral DNA uses host DNA to construct new viruses but then separates from it; lysogenic: viral DNA and host DNA merge. **Ask,** If you were a researcher, which type of infection would be more obvious in a culture of bacteria? lytic: producing large number of viruses in a short period of time, and killing bacterial cells Lysogenic infections first use the host cells to produce virus-host cell DNA that is passed on to daughter cells through mitosis. Until or unless the prophage is activated, the virus is dormant.

Vocabulary

lysogenic, lytic Students can use features of the words *lysogenic* and *lytic* to remember which is which. The *-gen* root in *lysogenic* can remind them of new generations of cells that carry the viral DNA. The word *lytic* is shorter, just like the lives of the cells that are infected.

Answers

Ⓐ Critical Viewing The virus is not making parts; it is just replicating its DNA.

FIGURE 18.6 General Pathways of Viral Infection

A **lytic infection** results in the lysis, or breaking apart, of the host cell and release of new viral particles. A **lysogenic infection** does not destroy the host cell.

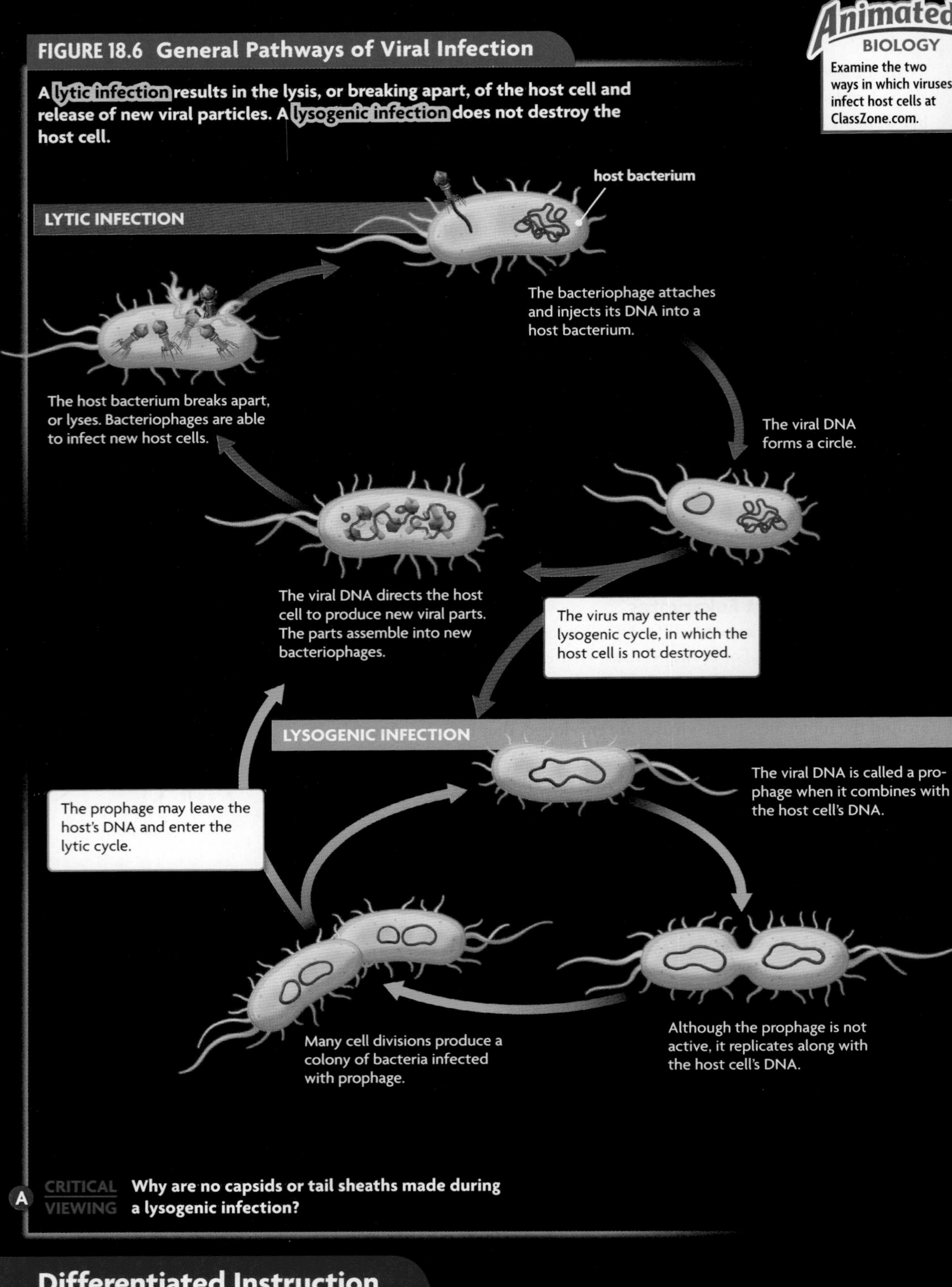
Animated BIOLOGY
Examine the two ways in which viruses infect host cells at ClassZone.com.
LYTIC INFECTION
host bacterium
The bacteriophage attaches and injects its DNA into a host bacterium.
The viral DNA forms a circle.
The virus may enter the lysogenic cycle, in which the host cell is not destroyed.
The viral DNA directs the host cell to produce new viral parts. The parts assemble into new bacteriophages.
The host bacterium breaks apart, or lyses. Bacteriophages are able to infect new host cells.
LYSOGENIC INFECTION
The viral DNA is called a prophage when it combines with the host cell's DNA.
Although the prophage is not active, it replicates along with the host cell's DNA.
Many cell divisions produce a colony of bacteria infected with prophage.
The prophage may leave the host's DNA and enter the lytic cycle.

Ⓐ CRITICAL VIEWING **Why are no capsids or tail sheaths made during a lysogenic infection?**

Differentiated Instruction

BELOW LEVEL

Have students make a Venn diagram to compare and contrast lytic infection and lysogenic infection. Suggest that students consider the advantages and disadvantages of each type of infection for the virus as well as the host cell. Have them include expectations of how each type of infection will affect the host organism. Ask students which infection is likely to lie dormant for a time and which is likely to create symptoms more immediately.

Biology Toolkit, Venn Diagram, p. C33

ENGLISH LEARNERS

Have students form home groups and then number off 1 and 2 for a modified jigsaw reading on lysogenic and lytic infection. The 1s go to the lytic expert group, and the 2s to the lysogenic group. Within the groups, half the students should study **FIGURE 18.6** on page 550, and half should study the text on page 551. After the expert groups convene to discuss what they know, have students return to home groups to share what they have learned.

Biology Toolkit, Jigsaw Reading, p. C15

Lytic Infection

A **lytic infection** (LIHT-ihk) is an infection pathway in which the host cell bursts, releasing the new viral offspring into the host's system, where each then infects another cell.

- When the viral DNA enters the host cell, it takes over control of the host's own DNA, turning on the genes necessary to copy the viral genes.
- Under direction of the viral genes, the host's DNA undergoes transcription and translation, and produces capsids and enzymes. The enzymes then help in the copying of the virus's DNA.
- Using energy from the host cell, the capsids and viral DNA assemble into new virions. Viral enzymes dissolve the host cell membrane, releasing the new virus particles into the host's bloodstream or tissues—and destroying the host cell in the process.

Lysogenic Infection

In a **lysogenic infection** (LY-suh-JEHN-ihk), a phage combines its DNA into the host cell's DNA.

- After entering the host cell, the viral DNA combines with the host's DNA, forming a new set of genes called a prophage. A **prophage** is the phage DNA inserted into the host cell's DNA. In organisms other than bacteria, this stage is called a provirus.
- The prophage is copied and passed to daughter cells, with the host's own DNA, when the host cell undergoes mitosis. Although this process doesn't destroy the cell, it can change some of the cell's traits.
- After the cell has been copied, the prophage faces two possible paths. A trigger, such as stress, can activate the prophage, which then uses the cell to produce new viruses. Or the prophage can remain as a permanent gene.

A Connect **Using the analogy of viral infections resembling houseguests, explain which describes a lytic and which describes a lysogenic infection.**

VOCABULARY

The term *lytic* comes from the Greek word *lutikos*, meaning "able to loosen." The word *lysis* is often used in biology to describe a cell breaking apart.

NSTA SCILINKS scilinks.org

For more information on viruses, visit scilinks.org.
Keycode: MLB018

The Inside Story

The **Ebola virus** is one of the world's deadliest pathogens. The first known outbreak occurred in 1976 in Zaire (now Republic of Congo). The virus produces a hemorrhagic fever by attacking and weakening the cells of veins and arteries. This produces severe blood loss, resulting in 50–90 percent mortality of infected people in as little as two weeks.

Of the several strains identified, all but one were restricted to Africa. In 1989, a strain was detected in a colony of macaque monkeys in a research lab in Reston, Virginia. The outbreak caused panic among government personnel, but this strain was lethal only to the monkeys. Although the outbreak was swiftly contained, the research facility was later torn down.

Answers

A Connect The house guest that takes over the household, eats all the food, and then blows up the house is similar to a lytic infection. The permanent house guest is similar to a lysogenic infection.

18.2 ASSESSMENT

ONLINE QUIZ ClassZone.com

REVIEWING MAIN IDEAS

1. Name and describe the main parts of a typical virus.
2. What are the differences between a **lytic infection** and a **lysogenic infection**? Include the effects of each type of infection on the cells of the host organism in your answer.

CRITICAL THINKING

3. **Apply** Researchers studying infection can often grow bacteria more easily than they can grow viruses. What conditions must scientists provide for viruses to multiply?
4. **Classify** A wart is caused by a virus that may lie dormant for years before any symptoms appear. Does this resemble a lytic or lysogenic infection? Explain.

Connecting CONCEPTS

5. **Evolution** If the virus is a foreign invader, how is it possible for the proteins of its **capsid** to match the receptors on the host cell's surface? Consider natural selection in your answer.

Assess and Reteach

Assess Use the Online Quiz or Section Quiz (*Assessment Book,* p. 354).

Reteach Have students draw their own labeled diagrams that illustrate the processes of lytic infection and lysogenic infection.

18.2 ASSESSMENT

1. capsid: protein shell; genetic material: single-stranded or double-stranded DNA or RNA; some viruses have a lipid envelope covering the capsid.
2. lytic infection: virus replicates many times, producing many offspring; lysogenic infection: virus integrates into the host cell's DNA, with the viral genes passed to the host cell's daughter cells during mitosis. Lytic infection destroys the host cell after viral replication and release of offspring, whereas lysogenic infection generally causes no initial harm to the cell, though it can alter some of the cell's traits.
3. In order to replicate, viruses need living cells they can infect.
4. lysogenic infection; it is characterized by a virus that lies dormant.
5. Over time, viruses that happened to have the right protein "keys" would survive and pass on these traits to their offspring. Viruses without the right proteins would not be able to successfully infect the host and would probably become extinct.

SECTION 18.3

▼ Plan and Prepare

Objectives

- Identify the names and symptoms of several viral diseases.
- Describe how vaccines are made.

Section Resources

Unit Resource Book	
Study Guide	pp. 35–36
Power Notes	p. 37
Reinforcement	p. 38
Pre-AP Activity	pp. 53–54
Interactive Reader	Chapter 18
Spanish Study Guide	pp. 187–188
Biology Toolkit	pp. C19, C38
Technology	
Power Presentation	18.3
Media Gallery DVD	
Online Quiz	18.3

Activate Prior Knowledge Have students think about the difference between getting a vaccination shot and taking an antibiotic. Mention that vaccines are used to prevent viral diseases. **Ask,** What vaccinations are commonly given to young children? measles, mumps, hepatitis, tetanus, polio Discuss how vaccination uses the body's own defenses to fight infection, unlike an antibiotic, which is an outside agent.

18.3 Viral Diseases

KEY CONCEPT Some viral diseases can be prevented with vaccines.

MAIN IDEAS

- Viruses cause many infectious diseases.
- Vaccines are made from weakened pathogens.

VOCABULARY

epidemic, p. 553
vaccine, p. 553
retrovirus, p. 553

Connect Why do we worry about catching a cold or the flu every winter? Cold weather itself does not cause us to get sick, but spending time close to other people can. For most people, winter means spending more time indoors. Cold and flu viruses then easily transfer to hands from doorknobs and other objects. That's why frequently washing your hands can help keep you healthy.

MAIN IDEA

Viruses cause many infectious diseases.

As you have read, viruses follow two pathways of infection once they encounter their target cells. But to enter the host's body in the first place, the virus must first pass a major obstacle.

First Defenses

In vertebrates, the first obstacle a virus must pass is the skin, but in other organisms it might be an outer skeleton or a tough cell wall. Viruses can penetrate the skin only through an opening such as a cut or scrape. Or they can take another route—the mucous membranes and body openings. It's no accident that some of the most common points of entry for infection are the mouth, nose, genital area, eyes, and ears.

Once inside the body, the virus finds its way to its target organ or tissue. However, the targeted cells don't just open the door to this unwanted guest. Body cells have receptors that guard against foreign intruders. These receptors act almost like locks. When the virus arrives at the host cell, it uses its own surface proteins as keys to trick the cell into allowing it to enter.

***Connecting* CONCEPTS**

Cells Recall from **Chapter 3** that receptors are proteins that detect chemical signals and perform an action in response. In the case of a host-specific infection, these normally helpful receptors provide little protection to the cell.

Examples of Viral Infections

Viruses can cause symptoms that range from merely bothersome to life-threatening. Below are a few of the many human illnesses caused by viruses.

The common cold The most familiar viral disease is the common cold. More than 200 viruses are known to cause this seasonal nuisance. One such cold virus is shown in **FIGURE 18.7.** With so many viruses, it's not easy to find a cure. In fact, cold viruses can mutate as they move from one person to another. Although they're unpleasant to have, colds usually last only about one week.

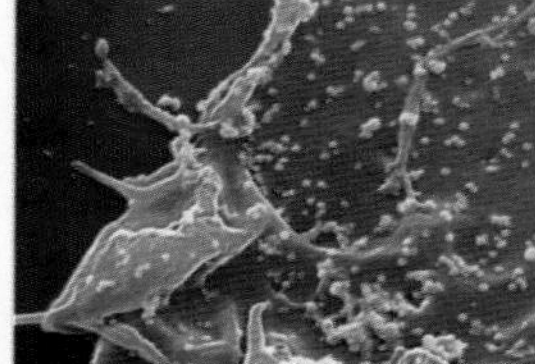

FIGURE 18.7 Cold virus particles (yellow) on the surface of a cell culture (blue). (colored SEM; magnification 10,000×)

▼ Teach

Integrating Epidemiology

Smallpox, caused by a virus, is the only infectious disease that has been globally eradicated. Highly contagious and often deadly, it originated about 10,000 B.C. in Egypt or India. Smallpox epidemics throughout history claimed commoners and royalty alike. Queen Mary II of England and Louis XV of France were among its victims. In the 1950s, the annual global incidence of smallpox was 50 million. A global vaccination program began in 1967, leading to the eradication of the disease by 1980.

Differentiated Instruction

BELOW LEVEL

Have students organize the material in this section, using the idea of a single infection—a flu virus. Ask students to create a sequence that describes the events involved: pathogen enters host, production of more pathogen, transmission to other hosts. Then have students repeat the sequence with the host having been immunized by a vaccine.

Biology Toolkit, Sequence Diagram, p. C38

Influenza Winter usually causes concern about the influenza, or "flu" virus—and with good reason. The flu spreads quickly and can result in frequent local epidemics. An **epidemic** is a rapid outbreak of an infection that affects many people. In the United States, up to 20 percent of the population is infected with the flu each year.

At this time, only three influenza subtypes infect humans; other subtypes may infect horses, pigs, whales, and seals. More than fifteen subtypes infect birds, and are all referred to as avian influenza, or bird flu. Sometimes a mutation enables a virus to jump from one species to another, making the spread of infection difficult to control. The high mutation rate of surface proteins on viral capsids makes it necessary for a new influenza vaccine to be made every year. A **vaccine** (vak-SEEN) is a substance that stimulates the body's own immune response against invasion by microbes.

SARS Severe acute respiratory syndrome (SARS) is another viral respiratory disease. It has symptoms similar to influenza, such as fever and coughing or difficulty in breathing. SARS is a relatively recent concern. It first appeared in Asia in late 2002. By the following summer, it had spread to other countries. SARS continues to be monitored globally by the World Health Organization.

HIV Human immunodeficiency virus, or HIV, is a retrovirus. *Retro-* means "backward," which describes how retroviruses work. Usually, DNA is used to make an RNA copy in a cell, but a **retrovirus** is a virus that contains RNA and uses an enzyme called reverse transcriptase to make a DNA copy. Double-stranded DNA then enters the nucleus and combines with the host's genes as a lysogenic infection. The viral DNA can remain dormant for years as a provirus, causing no symptoms to its human host.

When the virus becomes active, it directs the formation of new viral parts. The new viruses leave, either by budding or bursting through cell membranes, and infect new cells. This stage of the disease is a lytic infection that destroys white blood cells of the host's immune system, as shown in **FIGURE 18.9.** The loss of white blood cells ultimately causes AIDS, acquired immune deficiency syndrome. Once a person's immune system is affected, he or she may be unable to fight off even the common microorganisms that humans encounter every day. HIV's unusually high mutation rate has made it a challenge to treat. The combined use of several antiviral drugs—medications that treat viral infection—has proved somewhat effective in slowing the spread of the virus once a person is infected.

A Analyze How do retroviruses work differently from other viruses?

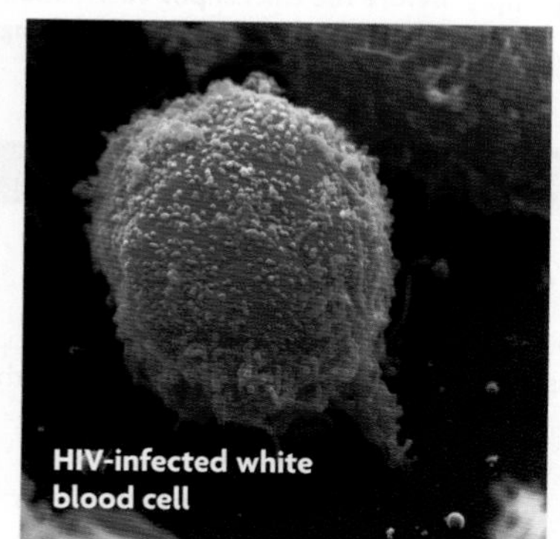

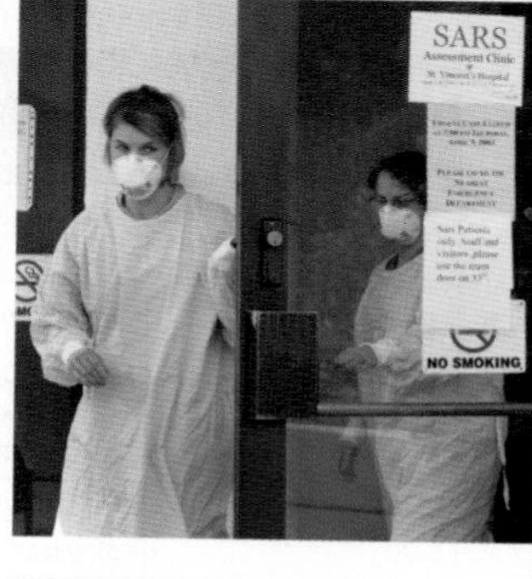

FIGURE 18.8 Nurses in Canada walk outside an emergency SARS clinic, which was opened to deal with an outbreak.

Connecting CONCEPTS

HIV Certain types of white blood cells of the human immune system are targeted by HIV to cause AIDS. You will learn more about HIV transmission and how this virus targets the immune system in **Chapter 31.**

FIGURE 18.9 This scanning electron micrograph (SEM) shows the HIV virus as purple dots on an infected white blood cell. Destruction of white blood cells weakens the immune system and causes AIDS. (colored SEM; magnification: 3500×)

ONLINE BIOLOGY Go to the chapter Resource Center at **ClassZone.com** for additional information and resources on pandemics and vaccines.

Vocabulary

Greek and Latin Word Origins
Epidemic comes from Greek roots meaning "prevalence" and "people." **Epidemiology** is the study of diseases in populations. **Pandemic** comes from a Greek word meaning "of all the people." A pandemic is an epidemic that has spread across a very wide range and is infecting a large percentage of the population, such as the Spanish flu of 1918–1919.

Take It Further

The flu pandemic of 1918 and 1919 got the name **Spanish flu** because it was first reported in Spanish newspapers. More than 20 million Americans became sick, and an estimataed 675,000 died, many within 24 hours of infection. Health departments restricted public gatherings and distributed gauze facemasks. Stores could not have sales, and funerals were limited to 15 minutes. More than 400 million people (one-fifth of the world's population) were affected, and 20 million died within one year.

Answers

A Analyze A retrovirus contains RNA and uses the enzyme reverse transcriptase to make a DNA copy.

PRE-AP

Tell students that in 2003, the SARS virus spread to several continents by way of infected air travelers. Have students write a five-minute essay describing what needs to occur on both a cellular level and a population level in order for a virus to move from one person in Asia to another person in North America. They should track the virus from lysogenic infection in the carrier to a lytic infection in the recipient.

Biology Toolkit, Quick-Write, p. C19

TEACH WITH TECHNOLOGY

Show students an animation depicting how a retrovirus works. If possible, use the pause function so students can sketch the process of retroviral infection in their notebooks. Go to the chapter Resource Center at **ClassZone.com.**

▼ Teach *continued*

The Inside Story

In 18th-century England, more than one-third of children died of **smallpox** before the age of three. People who managed to survive the infection were immune for life, so scientists were eager to find a way to administer a strain of the virus that would be strong enough to immunize the patient from further infection yet weak enough that it would not kill the patient.

Edward Jenner, a physician, had observed that people who had contracted cowpox, a disease affecting cow udders, were immune to smallpox. For two years, he experimented with cowpox, giving it to children and then testing their immunity to smallpox a few weeks later. In 1798, he published a pamphlet describing his techniques, and **vaccination,** which comes from the Latin *vacca,* meaning "cow," was coined.

FIGURE 18.10 Viral Diseases

VIRAL INFECTION	SYMPTOMS OF DISEASE	TRANSMISSION OF DISEASE	U.S. VACCINE RECOMMENDATION
Chickenpox	rash, itchy skin, fever, fatigue	contact with rash, droplet inhalation	for children between 12 and 18 months
Hepatitis A	yellow skin, fatigue, abdominal pain	contact with contaminated feces	for people traveling to infected locations and protection during outbreaks
Mumps	painful swelling in salivary glands, fever	droplet inhalation	for children between 12 and 15 months and again at 4 to 6 years
Rabies	anxiety, paralysis, fear of water	bite from infected animal	for veterinarians and biologists in contact with wildlife
West Nile	fever, headache, body ache	bite from infected mosquito	no available vaccine

MAIN IDEA

Vaccines are made from weakened pathogens.

Chances are good that you have had vaccinations. In the United States, children are vaccinated at an early age against diseases such as measles, mumps, rubella (MMR), and chickenpox. Every year, millions of people are vaccinated against influenza. How does a simple shot provide protection against disease?

A vaccine is made from the same pathogen—disease-causing agent—that it is supposed to protect against. Vaccines consist of weakened versions of the virus, or parts of the virus, that will cause the body to produce a response. The immune system is triggered by the surface proteins of a pathogen. In the host's body, the vaccine works by preparing the host's immune system for a future attack. Vaccines can prevent some bacterial and some viral infections, including the viral diseases shown in **FIGURE 18.10.** Whereas bacterial diseases can also be treated with medicine once they occur, viral diseases are not easily treated. Vaccination is often the only way of controlling the spread of viral disease.

Vaccines cause a mild immune response. If the body is invaded again, it will be able to start an immune defense before the virus can cause damage.

Connecting CONCEPTS

Human Biology Vaccines help build up the immune system to prepare for exposure to a pathogen by recognizing its surface proteins. You will learn more about the immune system in Chapter 31.

Apply **Before the chickenpox vaccination was available, children were often purposely exposed to the virus at a young age. What was the reason for doing this?**

Answers

A Apply Exposing children to chickenpox once should prevent the disease from occurring again, just as a vaccine prevents the real virus from causing the viral disease.

18.3 ASSESSMENT

ONLINE QUIZ ClassZone.com

REVIEWING MAIN IDEAS

1. Name and describe two infectious viruses and a body's first defense against infection.
2. Briefly describe how a **vaccine** can prevent some viral infections.

CRITICAL THINKING

3. **Infer** If a vaccine is in short supply, why is it often recommended that older adults and children get vaccinated first?
4. **Apply** Why might getting a flu vaccination sometimes cause you to get a mild case of the flu?

Connecting CONCEPTS

5. **Human Biology** People infected with HIV, the virus that causes the disease AIDS, can become unable to fight off infections by organisms that normally do not harm people. Why is this so?

▼ Assess and Reteach

Assess Use the Online Quiz or Section Quiz (*Assessment Book,* p. 355).

Reteach Have students make a crossword puzzle using terms and information from this section. Students can exchange puzzles and complete them, using the text for help.

18.3 ASSESSMENT

1. Answers may include the common cold, flu, SARS, HIV, chickenpox, or viruses not discussed in this section. The skin is the body's first defense against infection.
2. A vaccine is made from a weakened pathogen or parts of a virus. When given, it stimulates the host's own immune system, preparing it for future infection by the real virus.
3. The immune systems of older adults and children are often weaker than those of the rest of the population, so they are more likely to become infected than a healthy person who is not very young or very old.
4. because you may be getting a weakened strain of the live virus in order to build up your immune system
5. HIV affects the immune system of an infected person, making him or her susceptible to organisms that normally are harmless.

18.4 Bacteria and Archaea

KEY CONCEPT Bacteria and archaea are both single-celled prokaryotes.

MAIN IDEAS
- Prokaryotes are widespread on Earth.
- Bacteria and archaea are structurally similar but have different molecular characteristics.
- Bacteria have various strategies for survival.

VOCABULARY
obligate anaerobe, p. 555
obligate aerobe, p. 555
facultative aerobe, p. 555
plasmid, p. 556
flagellum, p. 556
conjugation, p. 558
endospore, p. 558

INDIANA STANDARDS

B.8.3 Use anatomical and molecular evidence to establish evolutionary relationships between organisms.

Connect Humans not only share the environment with prokaryotes—for many species, we *are* the environment. Up to 500 types of prokaryotes can live in the human mouth. In fact, you may have as many as 25 different types in your mouth right now. One milliliter of saliva can contain up to 40 million bacterial cells.

MAIN IDEA

Prokaryotes are widespread on Earth.

Prokaryotes, which include bacteria and archaea, are the most widespread and abundant organisms on Earth. Consider that humans are one species with about 6 billion individuals. In contrast, scientists estimate there are more than 1 billion (10^9) types of bacteria and more than 10^{30} individual prokaryotic cells on, above, and under Earth's surface. Bacteria and archaea are an important part of every community they inhabit. These tiny organisms live in just about every habitat on Earth, including the air we breathe. Prokaryotes have been found living inside rocks, in deserts, and in polar ice caps. One gram of soil may contain as many as 5 billion bacterial cells from up to 10,000 types of bacteria.

Prokaryotes can be grouped based on their need for oxygen. Prokaryotes that cannot live in the presence of oxygen are called obligate anaerobes. An **obligate anaerobe** (AHB-lih-giht AN-uh-ROHB) is actually poisoned by oxygen. As you have learned, archaea are prokaryotes that can live in extreme environments. The archaea that produce methane gas are obligate anaerobes. They live in marshes, at the bottom of lakes, and in the digestive tracts of herbivores such as deer, sheep, and cows, as shown in **FIGURE 18.11.** These microorganisms release nutrients from plants that animals are unable to digest on their own.

FIGURE 18.11 A "window" made into a cow's rumen, the first of its four stomachs, allows scientists to study digestion. Anaerobic bacteria live mutualistically within a cow's stomach. The bacteria have shelter and nutrients, and break down plant material for the cow to digest.

In contrast, some prokaryotes need the presence of oxygen in their environment. Organisms that need oxygen in their environment are called **obligate aerobes** (AHB-lih-giht AIR-OHBZ). This group includes several familiar pathogens, such as those that cause the diseases tuberculosis and leprosy. There are also prokaryotes that can survive whether oxygen is present in the environment or not. This type of prokaryote is called a **facultative aerobe** (FAK-uhl-TAY-tihv AIR-OHB).

A Evaluate **Bacteria are often associated with illness. Why is this a misconception?**

Differentiated Instruction

ENGLISH LEARNERS

Model asking key questions for before, during, and after reading. For example, before: *What do you already know about bacteria and archaea? What do you want to know?* during: *What types of shapes do we see in prokaryotes? What do you expect to learn next?* after: *What questions are still unanswered about prokaryotes?* Guide students to ask one another such questions and to listen actively to the answers.

Biology Toolkit, Questions to Guide Reading, p. C4

BELOW LEVEL

Students who are confused by the terms *obligate* and *facultative* can use contextual clues to understand what these words mean. Point out to students that they may already be familiar with the term *obligation* as something that must be done. Explain that *facultative* comes from *faculty,* meaning "an aptitude for something." Have students reread the material and then write a brief definition of each term.

Biology Toolkit, New Word Analysis, p. D2

Plan and Prepare

Objectives

- Describe different types of prokaryotes.
- Summarize the similarities and differences between bacteria and archaea.
- Describe the survival strategies of bacteria.

Section Resources

Unit Resource Book
Study Guide pp. 39–40
Power Notes p. 41
Reinforcement p. 42

Interactive Reader Chapter 18
Spanish Study Guide pp. 189–190

Biology Toolkit pp. C4, C20, D2

Technology
Power Presentation 18.4
Media Gallery DVD
Online Quiz 18.4

Activate Prior Knowledge In general, students' ideas of bacteria are probably negative. **Ask,** What kinds of products and innovations can we use that kill bacteria or keep them away from us? various soaps and detergents, antibiotics, sewer systems, indoor plumbing, refrigeration, bleach Tell students that while there are bacteria that threaten our health, there are many types that are harmless, and others that we rely on for good health and other benefits.

Teach

Science Trivia

- It is estimated that just 1 percent of bacteria and archaea have been discovered.
- Of the more than 3000 bacteria named by science, it is estimated that fewer than 10 percent are human pathogens.

Answers

A Evaluate Only a small number of bacteria are pathogenic.

▼ Teach *continued*

Connecting CONCEPTS

Classification The domain **Archaea** is subdivided into four main groups:

- **Methanogens** produce methane gas as a waste product of making energy.
- **Psychrophiles** live at unusually low temperatures.
- **Halophiles** live in salty environments.
- **Thermophiles** live at extremely high temperatures.

Thermophiles are equipped with enzymes that help keep the shape of their proteins. Normally, high heat undoes the bonds that hold a protein in its functional shape. The **extremozymes** in thermophiles are folded up much tighter than normal proteins, and there are chemical bonds that further strengthen their shape and structure. Some thermophiles also have a protein called **chaperonin** that actually refolds other proteins back into their original shape.

Vocabulary

Academic Vocabulary The word **flagella** is the plural form of **flagellum.** Other plural/singular word pairs worth reviewing are

- *data/datum*
- *media/medium*
- *phyla/phylum*
- *bacteria/bacterium*
- *millennia/millennium*

MAIN IDEA

Bacteria and archaea are structurally similar but have different molecular characteristics.

Connecting CONCEPTS

Classification Recall from Chapter 17 that archaea and bacteria are in separate kingdoms and in separate domains as well. Both their kingdoms and their domains have the same names, Archaea and Bacteria.

Members of domain Bacteria and domain Archaea comprise all of Earth's prokaryotes. Domain Bacteria is the more diverse and widespread of the two domains, while many archaea are found in Earth's extreme environments. Some archaea are even able to grow at temperatures greater than 100°C (212°F). Bacteria and archaea have many structural similarities but important genetic and biochemical differences.

Structural Comparisons

Even under the microscope, archaea look very similar to bacteria. For example, both archaea and bacteria are small, single-celled organisms that have cell walls and plasma membranes. Archaea come in many shapes, while the three most common forms of bacteria are shown in **FIGURE 18.12.** Bacteria are often named based upon their shapes. Rod-shaped bacteria are called *bacilli.* Spiral-shaped bacteria are called *spirilla* or *spirochetes,* and spherical bacteria are called *cocci.*

TAKING NOTES

Create a Venn diagram to compare bacteria and archaea using information from this section.

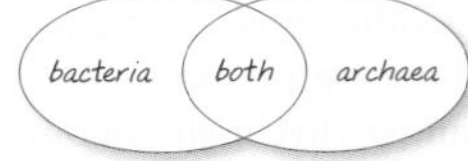

Prokaryotes do not have any membrane-bound organelles, such as a nucleus containing double-stranded DNA. Instead, their DNA is in the form of a circle and is surrounded by cytoplasm. Prokaryotes may also have plasmids. A **plasmid** is a small piece of genetic material that can replicate separately from the prokaryote's main chromosome.

Most prokaryotes can move on their own. Many bacteria and archaea move by gliding or using flagella. A **flagellum** (fluh-JEHL-uhm) is a long, whiplike structure outside of a cell that is used for movement. The flagella of prokaryotes are attached to the plasma membrane and cell wall. They may be at one end of an organism, or they may have different arrangements over the entire cell. Although similar in appearance, the flagella of bacteria and archaea are structurally different from each other. In addition, their flagella are both structurally different from the flagella of eukaryotes. You will learn more about the flagella of eukaryotes in Chapter 19.

Many prokaryotes also contain structures called pili that are thinner, shorter, and often more numerous than flagella. Pili help prokaryotes stick to surfaces and to other prokaryotes. A typical prokaryote is shown in **FIGURE 18.13.**

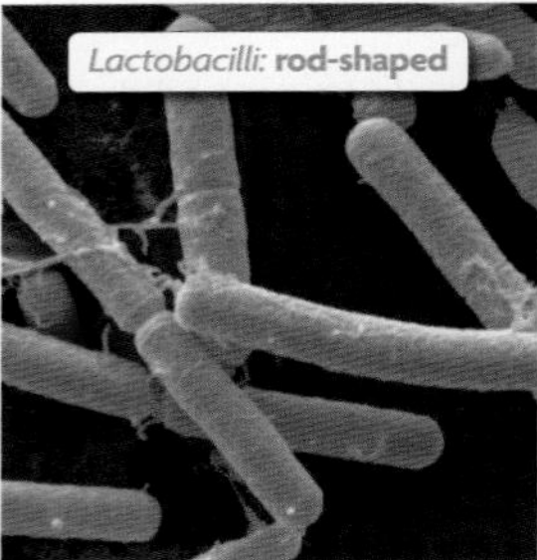

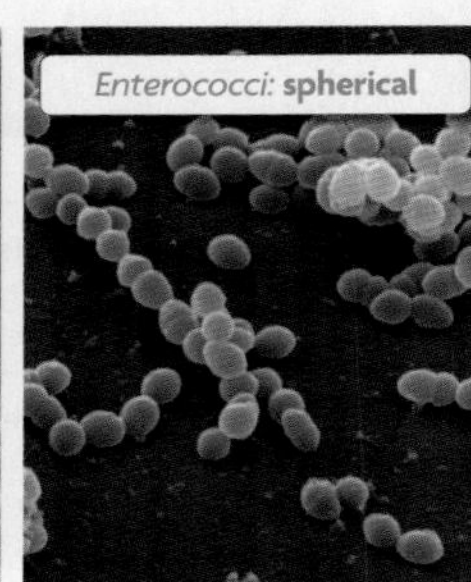

FIGURE 18.12 The most common shapes of bacteria are rods, spirals, and spheres. Many bacteria are named after these shapes. Some examples are shown at right. (colored SEMs; magnifications: *lactobacilli* magnification unknown; *spirochaeta* 5000×; *enterococci* 7000×)

Differentiated Instruction

PRE-AP

Have students make a T-chart to compare archaea and bacteria. To get them started, have them consider these questions:

- How widespread is each group?
- What environments does each group inhabit?
- What are some differences in each group's physical traits?

Biology Toolkit, T-chart, p. C20

FIGURE 18.13 Prokaryote Structure

This diagram shows the typical structure of a prokaryote. Archaea and bacteria look very similar, although they have important molecular differences.

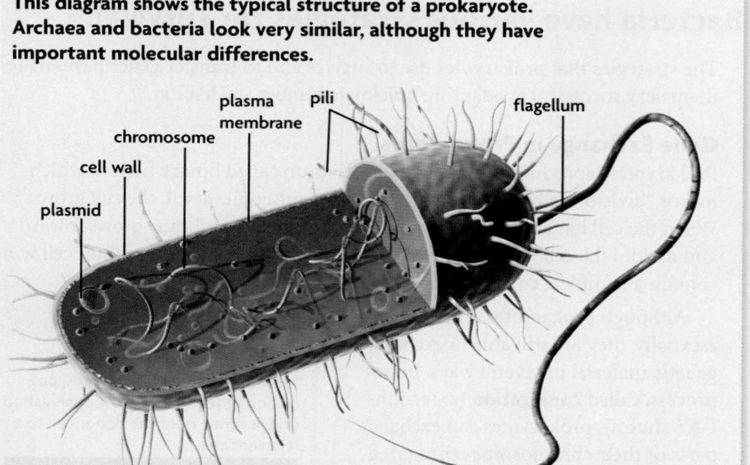

Molecular Comparisons

It was not until molecular analysis techniques were available that the many differences between bacteria and archaea became clear. Despite their similarities in function and appearance, bacteria and archaea are not closely related. Molecular evidence suggests that archaea have at least as much in common with eukaryotes as they do with bacteria. For example, archaea cell walls and membranes are chemically different from those of bacteria. The membranes of archaea contain lipids that are not found in any other type of organism on Earth, and bacteria have a polymer called peptidoglycan (PEHP-tih-doh-GLY-cuhn) in their cell walls, which archaea do not.

The amount of peptidoglycan in their cell walls is an important characteristic of bacteria. Bacteria are often classified into one of two groups based on this difference, as shown in **FIGURE 18.14**. A staining method called a Gram stain is used to tell the two groups apart. The Gram stain is important for diagnosing infectious bacterial diseases, and it sometimes helps determine the type of medicine a doctor chooses to fight infection. Because of their cell wall differences, archaea are often not affected by medicine used to treat bacterial infection.

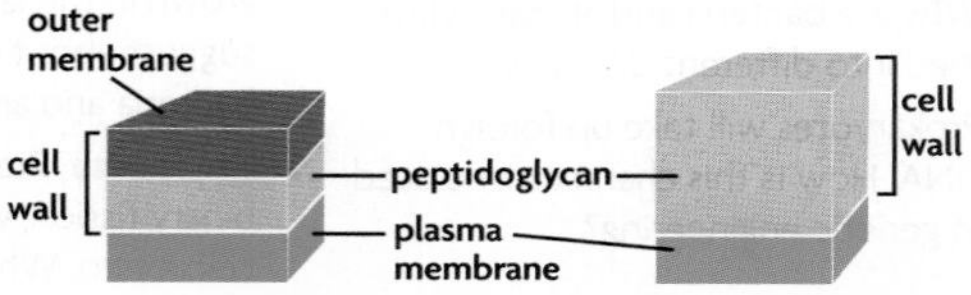

A Contrast Archaea were first named archaeabacteria, a term that you may still find in some books and articles. What are two differences between archaea and bacteria?

FIGURE 18.14 GRAM STAINING

A staining technique called a Gram stain is used to identify types of bacteria. This stain identifies the amount of a polymer, called peptidoglycan, that is present. The result is either gram positive or gram negative. (LMs; gram-negative 2,500×; gram-positive 550×)

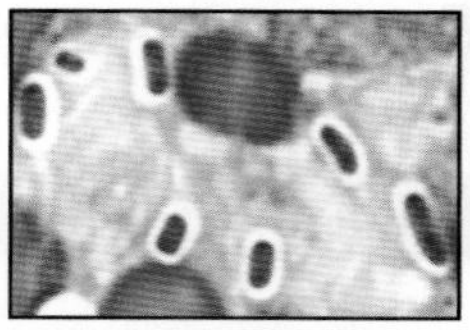

Gram-negative bacteria have a thin layer of peptidoglycan and stain red.

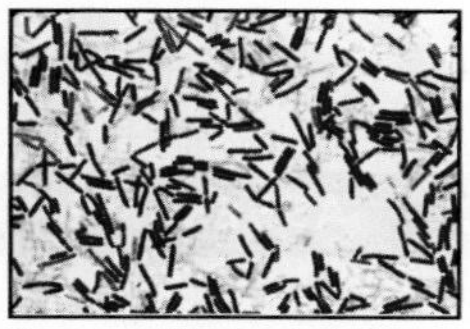

Gram-positive bacteria have a thicker peptidoglycan layer and stain purple.

ONLINE BIOLOGY Go to the chapter Resource Center at **ClassZone.com** for additional resources and information on bacteria and archaea.

Integrating Microbiology

In addition to the cell wall and plasma membrane shown in **FIGURE 18.13,** some bacterial species have a thick polysaccharide or polypeptide envelope surrounding the cell. In some species, the envelope is well defined; in others, it is looser, forming a slime layer that may trail behind the bacteria as they move. Envelopes are common among pathogenic species and are thought to play a role in resisting the host's immune defenses. Among the encapsulated pathogens are types of influenza, pneumonia, and meningitis.

Answers

A Contrast Answers will vary but could include differences in their flagella, cell wall, or plasma membrane composition.

TEACH WITH TECHNOLOGY

Prepare a digital slide show of the process of Gram staining. Use the Internet to find images that show each step in the process, as well as photographs of slides of Gram-stained bacteria. Try to find images of bacteria with distinctive shapes or other features. Remind students that Gram staining is one of the first tests done to identify bacteria.

▼ Teach *continued*

Take It Further

One notable group of **endospore-forming bacteria** is the genus *Bacillus,* notably *B. anthracis,* more commonly known as anthrax—the first bacterium shown to be the cause of disease. Endospores are an evolutionary adaptation that enables the cell to lie dormant when conditions are dry or otherwise unfavorable. Endospores are covered with a tough layer of keratin and are highly resistant to heat and chemicals.

Bacillus species can be difficult to identify under the microscope. Younger bacteria stain Gram-positive, but may become Gram-negative as they age. Endospores do not respond to typical lab stains and require a special staining or other identification procedure. The location of the spore in the rod-shaped bacillus—at the cell center (central), at either end (terminal), or between the middle and end (subterminal)—offers a clue to the organism's identity.

Answers

A Connect Some bacteria form endospores, which can withstand exposure to disinfectants.

▼ Assess and Reteach

Assess Use the Online Quiz or Section Quiz (*Assessment Book,* p. 356).

Reteach Have students define or describe each of the labeled structures in **FIGURE 18.13.**

MAIN IDEA

Bacteria have various strategies for survival.

The strategies that prokaryotes use to survive and to transfer genes have made them very successful at adapting quickly to almost any habitat.

Gene Exchange in Prokaryotes

Prokaryotes reproduce by a type of cell division called binary fission, which means "division in half." While the chromosome copies itself, the cell grows. When the cell has about doubled in size, its plasma membrane grows inward and divides the cell into two equal-sized daughter cells. Each daughter cell will contain a complete copy of the parent cell's genes.

Although prokaryotes reproduce asexually, they are still able to exchange genetic material in several ways. In one process, called **conjugation** (KAHN-juh-GAY-shuhn), prokaryotes can exchange parts of their chromosomes through a hollow bridge of pili formed to connect two or more cells.

VISUAL VOCAB

In **conjugation,** genetic material transfers between prokaryotes, producing genetic variation. A conjugation bridge forms from the donor cell to a recipient cell.

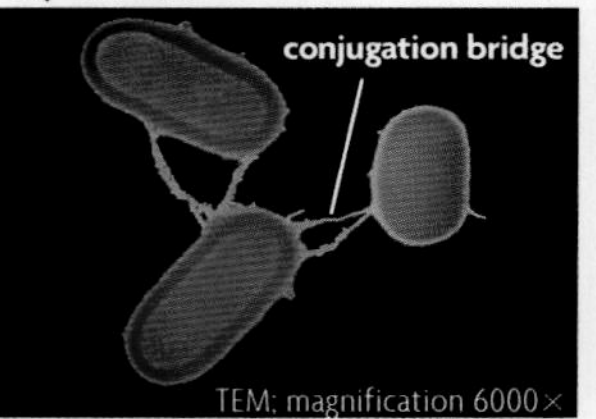

Surviving Harsh Conditions

During conditions unfavorable for survival, some bacteria can produce an **endospore,** a specialized cell with a thick, protective wall. To form an endospore, the bacterium copies its chromosome and produces a wall around the copy. This thick wall around the bacterial DNA helps it survive harsh conditions such as drying out, temperature change, and disinfectants. Endospores can last for centuries. Some have even been found in Egyptian mummies!

A Connect **Why are disinfectants alone not enough to kill all types of bacteria?**

18.4 ASSESSMENT

ONLINE QUIZ ClassZone.com

B.8.3

REVIEWING MAIN IDEAS

1. What are the three most common shapes of bacteria?
2. Why are bacteria and archaea classified into different domains?
3. Prokaryotes will take up foreign DNA. How is this characteristic used in genetic engineering?

CRITICAL THINKING

4. **Infer** Scientists estimate that only 1 percent of prokaryotes can be grown in the lab. What does this suggest about our knowledge of bacteria and archaea?
5. **Synthesize** Prokaryotes multiply by binary fission, which simply divides a cell in two. Why are mutations and **conjugation** important for natural selection in prokaryotes?

***Connecting* CONCEPTS**

6. **Health** Bacteria in your mouth convert foods containing sugar and starch into acids that can then cause cavities in your teeth. These bacteria will be present even if you brush your teeth, floss, or use mouthwash. So why are these hygiene habits so important?

18.4 ASSESSMENT

1. rod, spiral, sphere
2. Archaea are biochemically and genetically different from bacteria.
3. Pieces of genes can be inserted into the genetic material of prokaryotes so that they will make the protein products encoded in the genes or copies of the genes themselves.
4. We do not know much about prokaryotes. Our understanding of prokaryotes will likely change as scientists learn more about prokaryotes that have not been able to be cultured, or grown, in the lab.
5. Binary fission produces no variation, but mutations and conjugation do. Natural selection requires variation in a population.
6. Brushing teeth is important to keep the populations of these bacteria down and to remove the food that the bacteria convert into acids.

18.5 Beneficial Roles of Prokaryotes

KEY CONCEPT Prokaryotes perform important functions for organisms and ecosystems.

MAIN IDEAS

- Prokaryotes provide nutrients to humans and other animals.
- Prokaryotes play important roles in ecosystems.

VOCABULARY

bioremediation, p. 561

Review
nitrogen fixation

B.4.4 Describe how climate, the pattern of matter and energy flow, the birth and death of new organisms, and the interaction between those organisms contribute to the long term stability of an ecosystem.

Connect People usually think bacteria in or on food are harmful, and it is true that food poisoning caused by bacteria can be a serious problem. However, some bacteria are safe in food, and actually provide a taste or texture that many people enjoy. Swiss cheese, sour cream, and butter are just a few products that are made with the help of bacteria. Eating food produced by bacteria is not dangerous, as long as they are the right kind of bacteria!

MAIN IDEA

Prokaryotes provide nutrients to humans and other animals.

Prokaryotes, such as the bacteria shown in **FIGURE 18.15,** are a key part of animal digestive systems. A balanced community of prokaryotes in our bodies is important for our health. Prokaryotes have a beneficial relationship, or mutualistic symbiosis, with the host animal and break down food while getting a place to live. They also make vitamins and other compounds, and keep away harmful microbes by filling niches that might otherwise be filled by disease-causing bacteria. In turn, the host animal provides the bacteria with food and a home with a stable pH and temperature.

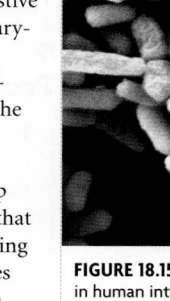

FIGURE 18.15 These bacteria, found in human intestines, are beneficial to our health. They produce B vitamins and keep out harmful microbes. (colored SEM; magnification: 6300×)

Humans can get nutrients from prokaryotes in other ways as well. Many foods that humans enjoy are fermented by bacteria. Bacteria help ferment, or chemically break down, many dairy products people eat every day, such as yogurt and cheeses. Pickles, soy sauce, sauerkraut, and vinegar also depend on fermentation by prokaryotes to produce their flavors.

Connecting CONCEPTS

Ecology Recall from **Chapter 14** that *symbiosis* is the close association of two or more species. A *niche* is a specific role an organism plays in its environment.

A Summarize **What are two ways in which prokaryotes that live within our bodies are helpful to us?**

Differentiated Instruction

BELOW LEVEL

After reading through the section, have students write for five minutes about the ways in which prokaryotes are beneficial to humans. They should mention nitrogen fixation, oxygen production, digestion-aiding bacteria, fermentation, and bioremediation.

Biology Toolkit, Quick-Write, p. C19

PRE-AP

Have students list and then group keywords in this section, such as *photosynthesis/cyanobacteria, biodegradable/bioremediation,* and *nitrogen fixation/symbiosis.* Have students differentiate between the groups by describing the subjects or phenomena that each involves.

Biology Toolkit, List-Group-Label, p. D6

Plan and Prepare

Objectives

- Describe ways prokaryotes provide nutrients to humans and other animals.
- Recognize the roles prokaryotes play in ecosystems.

Section Resources

Unit Resource Book
Study Guide pp. 43–44
Power Notes p. 45
Reinforcement p. 46
Interactive Reader Chapter 18
Spanish Study Guide pp. 191–192
Biology Toolkit pp. C19, D6
Technology
Power Presentation 18.5
Media Gallery DVD
Online Quiz 18.5

Activate Prior Knowledge See if students are aware of the role prokaryotes play in making some of our favorite foods. **Ask**

- What kinds of foods require bacteria for their production? dairy products such as cheese and yogurt, soy products such as tofu and soy sauce, alcoholic beverages, and pickled foods
- What role do bacteria play in agriculture? nitrogen fixation

Teach

Science Trivia

- The holes in Swiss cheese are produced by carbon dioxide gas released by bacteria.
- Vitamin K, which is crucial in helping blood clot, is synthesized by bacteria living in the large intestine.

Answers

A Summarize They provide nutrients, and they exclude pathogenic bacteria.

Chapter 18: Viruses and Prokaryotes **559**

▼ Teach *continued*

QUICK LAB

Time 15 minutes TEACHER TESTED

Lab Binder Diversity, p. 22

Purpose Observe bacteria on a microscope slide of yogurt.

LAB MANAGEMENT

Safety Tell students to be careful handling the sharp-edged cover slips and to carefully clean the lenses of the microscopes to avoid contamination.

Answers

Analyze and Conclude

1. Answers will vary, but students are likely to see bacilli and cocci-shaped bacteria. (This may include *Lactobacillus bulgaricus, Lactobacillus acidophilus,* and *Streptococcus thermophilus.*)
2. Many of the bacteria in yogurt produce lactase, which metabolizes the lactose in yogurt.

Take It Further

The flashlight fish (*Photoblepharon palpebratus*) gets its name from **bioluminescent bacteria,** with which it has a symbiotic relationship. The bacteria live in a sac under the fish's eyes and produce the enzyme luciferase, which glows. The glowing blue-green light helps the fish hunt for food and navigate its dark habitat. In return, the fish provides the bacteria with a safe habitat, oxygen, and nutrients. When threatened by a predator, the fish covers its light sac with a film, which effectively turns out the light, hiding the fish.

QUICK LAB **OBSERVING** NOS.3

Examining Bacteria in Yogurt

Some types of bacteria can ferment milk, producing lactic acid in the process. Yogurt is a product of fermentation. It is acidic and stays fresh longer than milk, and it is also digested more easily. In this exercise, you will prepare a microscope slide of yogurt.

PROBLEM What types of bacteria can you observe in yogurt?

PROCEDURE

1. Using a toothpick, place a dab of yogurt on a microscope slide. **Caution:** Do not eat in the laboratory.
2. Mix the yogurt in a drop of water and carefully add a coverslip.
3. Examine the slide with a compound microscope.
4. Record your observations by drawing a picture of what you see through the microscope.

MATERIALS

- toothpick
- dab of yogurt
- microscope slide
- drop of water
- coverslip
- microscope

ANALYZE AND CONCLUDE

1. **Identify** Recall the terms *bacillus, coccus,* and *spirilla* from the previous section. Which type or types of bacteria did you observe in your slides?
2. **Analyze** Many people do not produce lactase, which is an enzyme that breaks down the milk sugar lactose. As a result, lactose-intolerant people have trouble digesting dairy products. Why might they have fewer problems eating yogurt?

MAIN IDEA

Prokaryotes play important roles in ecosystems.

Even though you can't easily see them, prokaryotes play important roles in every ecosystem they occupy. Some, such as cyanobacteria, produce oxygen through photosynthesis. Others help recycle carbon, nitrogen, hydrogen, and sulfur through the ecosystem. The absence of prokaryotes in the environment can disrupt an ecosystem, since other organisms rely on them for survival.

Photosynthesizing prokaryotes include purple and green photosynthetic bacteria and cyanobacteria. Whereas purple and green bacteria use light to make carbohydrates, they do not produce oxygen. Cyanobacteria, however, are similar to plants in how they produce oxygen as a byproduct of photosynthesis. Cyanobacteria are named for their greenish blue (cyan) color. Recall from Chapter 12 that cyanobacteria played an important part on early Earth, supporting the life forms we are familiar with today. Fossil evidence suggests there was very little oxygen on Earth prior to the appearance of cyanobacteria.

Some colonies of photosynthesizing cyanobacteria, as well as other bacteria, are also able to fix nitrogen. Although much of the atmosphere is made up of nitrogen gas (N_2), this is not in a form that plants or animals can use to make amino acids or proteins.

Differentiated Instruction

TEACH WITH TECHNOLOGY

Students can perform a probeware lab that explores the use of bacteria in bioremediation.

Lab Binder, Diversity, pp. 39–42

HANDS-ON ACTIVITY

Students can see how fermentation is involved in the production of some foods and drinks by working in small groups to brew root beer, make apple cider, bake bread, or create other simple-to-make foods from basic ingredients or inexpensive kits. You can make such an activity more experimental by trying slightly different recipes or using a control group (such as no yeast).

Recall from Chapter 13 that nitrogen fixation is the process of converting atmospheric nitrogen into ammonia (NH_3) and other nitrogen compounds that plants can then use. Prokaryotes supply usable nitrogen to ecosystems ranging from grasslands and forests to the arctic tundra.

Some types of nitrogen-fixing bacteria are free-living, while others live along with other organisms. Legumes, a group of plants including peas, beans, alfalfa, and clover, have a mutualistic relationship with nitrogen-fixing bacteria. These bacteria live in the plant's nodules, small rounded lumps that form the roots, as shown in **FIGURE 18.16.** The bacteria provide usable nitrogen to the plant by capturing nitrogen gas from air trapped in the soil. They combine the nitrogen with hydrogen to produce ammonia. In return, the plant supplies food and shelter to the bacteria.

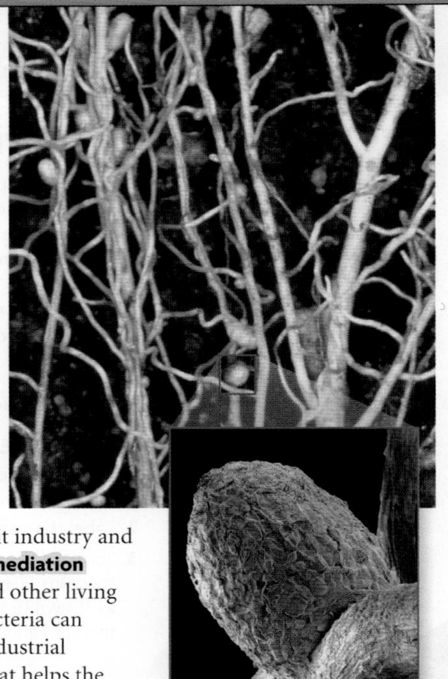

FIGURE 18.16 Root nodules of this white clover contain nitrogen-fixing bacteria. The symbiotic bacteria convert nitrogen from the atmosphere (N_2) into a form usable by the clover. In return, the plant produces carbohydrates through photosynthesis that the bacteria can consume. (inset colored SEM; magnification 90×)

Scientists have found many ways to use prokaryotes to benefit industry and the environment. One important use of prokaryotes is in **bioremediation** (BY-oh-rih-MEE-dee-AY-shuhn), a process that uses microbes and other living things to break down pollutants. For example, some types of bacteria can digest oil, which is helpful for cleaning up oil spills and other industrial accidents. Workers spray oil-polluted beaches with a fertilizer that helps the bacteria grow.

Bacteria can digest almost any product that humans can make, including poisons. Therefore, they play an important role in recycling and composting. When you hear the term *biodegradable,* it often refers to the ability of bacteria to break down a material. Some of the only materials made by humans that cannot be biodegraded are certain types of plastics.

A Apply When there is a toxic chemical spill, sometimes workers will spray bacteria over the contaminated area. Why might they do this?

Integrating Earth Science

In 1975 in Hanahan, South Carolina, about 300,000 liters (80,000 gal) of jet fuel leaked from a nearby military fuel-storage facility. The fuel soaked into the soil and slowly spread to the groundwater. Scientists with the United States Geological Survey had discovered that certain soil microorganisms consume fuel-derived toxic compounds, changing them into carbon dioxide, and that this process can be enhanced by adding nutrients to the soil. Using this knowledge, in 1992, scientists added nutrients to the fuel-contaminated soil around Hanahan. A year later, the contamination was reduced by more than 75 percent. The Hanahan Bioremediation Project was a success.

Answers

A Apply The bacteria can digest the chemicals, converting them into harmless or less harmful compounds.

18.5 ASSESSMENT

ONLINE QUIZ ClassZone.com

B.4.4

REVIEWING MAIN IDEAS

1. Describe two ways bacteria provide nutrients to humans.
2. What are two roles prokaryotes play in the cycling of elements in an ecosytem?

CRITICAL THINKING

3. **Connect** Think of an example in which the use of **bioremediation** either has improved the environment or has the potential to do so.
4. **Synthesize** How do prokaryotes lend stability to an ecosystem?

Connecting CONCEPTS

5. **Ecology** Prokaryotes in cow intestines produce more methane if the cow is fed a diet high in grains rather than grass. Some scientists propose that overfeeding grain to cows contributes to global warming. How did these scientists arrive at this hypothesis, and how could it be tested?

Assess and Reteach

Assess Use the Online Quiz or Section Quiz (*Assessment Book,* p. 357).

Reteach Tell students that the class has been given government funding to improve the reputation of prokaryotes, which has suffered from their association with disease. Have students design posters describing the benefits of having prokaryotes in our lives.

18.5 ASSESSMENT

1. Bacteria in our bodies make vitamins that we absorb, and some bacteria are needed to make foods that we eat, such as soy and dairy products.
2. *Sample Answer:* producing oxygen through photosynthesis, fixing nitrogen, decomposing other organisms
3. *Sample Answer:* cleaning up industrial accidents, sewage, and other waste
4. Prokaryotes lend stability to an ecosystem through their role as decomposers. Other organisms rely on prokaryotes for nitrogen and other compounds that are broken down through prokaryote metabolic activity. Some prokaryotes also help the stability of an ecosystem by releasing oxygen into the environment during photosynthesis.
5. Students can infer that the amount of methane produced by the intestines of a grain-fed cow can be compared to that produced by a grass-fed cow, perhaps by measuring concentrations of methane in closed environments after cows have fed and lived inside them for some time. The effect of methane concentration on the heat retention of the atmosphere can also presumably be tested in a small, enclosed space that is open to sunlight.

INVESTIGATION

Time 45 minutes	TEACHER TESTED ✓
Teacher Preparation	
Student Difficulty	
Lab Binder Diversity, pp. 15–17	

Purpose Compare the growth of bacteria on different media.

Overview Students will test the effect of medium type on the growth of PPFM and other bacteria. They will

- test nonselective and selective media by making leaf prints
- predict results based on their understanding of the bacteria
- record qualitative and quantitative results for 1–2 weeks

LAB PREPARATION

- Prepare 1 L of medium, enough for about 30 petri dishes.
- Selective media—M9 Salts: dissolve the salts according to directions, add agar to 1.5% and, after pressure cooling or autoclaving, add methanol to 0.5%.
- Nonselective media—Nutrient Agar or Tryptic Soy Agar: Rehydrate according to package instructions.
- Avoid using hard, shiny leaves.

LAB MANAGEMENT

- Allow 5–10 minutes per day for observations.
- Make sure students do not touch the media inside the dishes.
- Dishes should not be reopened.

Safety Remind students to wash their hands before and after handling leaves and petri dishes. Properly dispose of dishes after the investigation is complete.

POST-LAB DISCUSSION

Discuss results with the class. **Ask,** Why was it important to seal the petri dishes before storing them? to minimize the chance of contamination by airborne bacteria or molds

MATERIALS

- petri dish containing a selective medium
- petri dish containing a nonselective medium
- permanent marker
- 2 leaves from the same plant
- pencil with eraser
- transparent tape

PROCESS SKILLS

- **Observing**
- **Evaluating Outcomes**

Leaf Print Bacteria

PPFM are pink-pigmented bacteria that grow on plant surfaces. They help plants by stimulating seed germination and plant growth. A unique feature of PPFM bacteria is that they use methanol as their sole source of carbon. Therefore, a simple nutrient mixture that contains only methanol as a carbon source will "select" for PPFM bacteria. This type of mixture is called a selective medium. A mixture that contains many nutrients is called a nonselective medium. In this lab, you will make leaf prints on selective and nonselective media to study the growth of PPFM and other bacteria.

PROBLEM How do populations of bacteria grown on various media differ?

PROCEDURE

1. Obtain two petri dishes, one containing a selective medium (methanol carbon source only) and the other containing a nonselective, nutrient-rich medium.
2. Label the petri dishes with your name, the date, and "selective" or "nonselective."
3. To make the first leaf print, lay one of the leaves on the surface of the selective medium. Use the eraser end of a pencil to gently press the leaf into the medium, as shown below. After making the impression, carefully lift the leaf away from the medium and discard. Close the petri dish.

4. Repeat step 3 using your other leaf and the nonselective medium.
5. Seal the petri dishes with tape. Store them upside down at room temperature.

   Caution: Once the dishes are sealed, they should not be opened again. Follow your teacher's directions for disposal of the petri dishes at the end of the lab.
6. Write a prediction based on what you know about PPFM bacteria and the selective and nonselective media.
7. Observe the dishes over a period of one or two weeks. Record your observations daily. These should be both qualitative (shape, color, and size of colonies) and quantitative (number of colonies). To count colonies, it may help to create a grid on the underside of each petri dish.
8. At the end of the observation period, compare your results with those from the rest of the class.

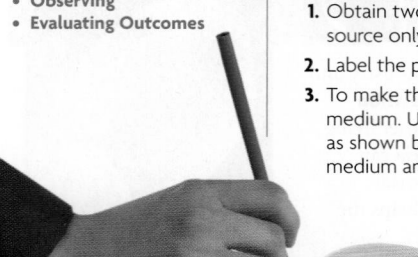

INDIANA STANDARDS

NOS.1 Develop explanations based on reproducible data and observations gathered during laboratory investigations.

NOS.3 Clearly communicate their ideas and results of investigations verbally and in written form using tables, graphs, diagrams, and photographs.

ANALYZE AND CONCLUDE

1. **Analyze** How many types of bacteria were present on the nonselective medium? the selective medium? What might account for differences between the two?
2. **Analyze** Is PPFM bacteria growth the same on both types of media? Which observations support this conclusion?
3. **Analyze** Do all bacteria grow at the same rate? Which observations support this conclusion?
4. **Infer** Why might bacteria grow faster on the nonselective medium?

EXTEND YOUR INVESTIGATION

Design an experimental procedure to test the hypothesis that different types of PPFM bacteria are found on different plants.

Answers

Analyze and Conclude

1. Answers will vary, but the nonselective medium should have more types of bacteria present than the selective medium, because the nonselective medium is richer in nutrients.
2. Answers will vary, but PPFM growth should be greater on the selective medium, as evidenced by the presence of pink colonies.
3. Answers will vary, but students should find that bacteria do not grow at the same rate. Some colonies will be larger than others.
4. The nonselective medium has many nutrients in it.

Extend Your Investigation

Leaves from a variety of plants could be tested in separate petri dishes. Ideally, students would plan an experimental design that included a control and at least three replicates per leaf.

Teacher Note "I never did an activity quite like this before. It was as much a learning experience for me as it was for my students. Nicely done."

18.6 Bacterial Diseases and Antibiotics

KEY CONCEPT Understanding bacteria is necessary to prevent and treat disease.

MAIN IDEAS
- Some bacteria cause disease.
- Antibiotics are used to fight bacterial disease.
- Bacteria can evolve resistance to antibiotics.

VOCABULARY
toxin, p. 563
antibiotic, p. 564

Review
homeostasis

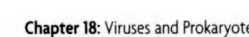

Connect In the early 1900s, most deaths in the United States were caused by infectious diseases, such as bacterial pneumonia and tuberculosis. Thanks to new medicines, infectious diseases were among the least common causes of death by the century's end. In recent years, however, many diseases are making a comeback due to a new problem—antibiotic resistance.

MAIN IDEA

Some bacteria cause disease.

Some bacteria cause disease in plants and animals by disrupting the host organism's homeostasis, or the stability of its internal environment. Bacteria can cause illness to a host in two basic ways: by invading tissues and attacking cells or by making poisons, or toxins, that can be carried by blood to sites throughout the body. A **toxin** is a poison released by an organism.

The disease tuberculosis (TB) is an example of bacteria invading the host's tissues, and using the tissues for nutrients. *Mycobacterium tuberculosis* bacteria multiply in the lungs, killing white blood cells that respond to the invasion. The host's reaction to an invasion by bacteria may itself cause serious problems. In the case of TB, the host responds to the infection by releasing enzymes that cause swelling. That swelling, in turn, damages the host's lungs.

TB is a good example of the changing ecological balance between host and pathogen in an infectious disease. A host is not usually aware of pathogens that its immune system defeats. It is when the host's immune system fails that the host becomes aware of the pathogen's presence. Most healthy people can defeat a potential TB infection, especially if there are not many bacteria present.

Bacteria, such as *Staphylococcus aureus* and *Clostridium botulinum,* shown in **FIGURE 18.17,** can also make their hosts sick through food poisoning. *S. aureus,* which normally lives in nasal passages, can be transferred to food when food handlers don't wash their hands after they blow their nose. This transfer can result in serious food poisoning, known as staph poisoning. Even high temperatures cannot destroy a toxin produced by *S. aureus.* The most common source of food poisoning by *S. aureus,* however, is from foods that were contaminated after they were cooked. If contaminated food is not refrigerated, bacteria can multiply and produce a large amount of toxin.

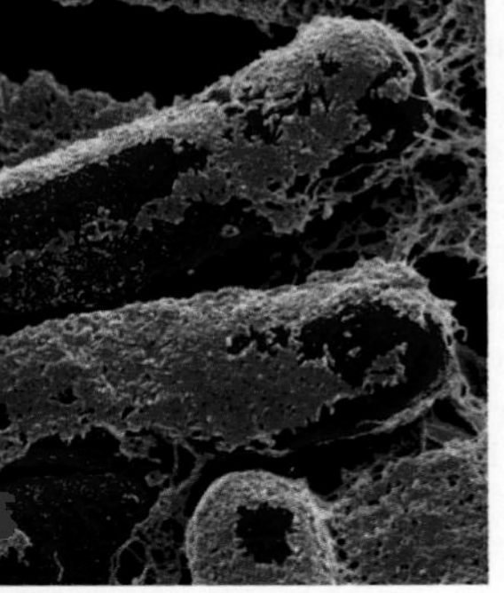

FIGURE 18.17 *Clostridium botulinum* causes a serious illness called botulism. Food contamination by this bacterium often comes from improper home canning. (magnification unknown)

Differentiated Instruction

ENGLISH LEARNERS

Tell students that at the end of the section, they will do a five-minute quick-write on what they have learned about bacterial diseases and antibiotics. After reading the section, separate the class into two groups, one that will write on diseases and the other on antibiotics. After students have written for five minutes on their topic, have them gather in their topic groups and pool their ideas into a single essay.

Biology Toolkit, Quick-Write, p. C19; Pair-Share, p. C13

BELOW LEVEL

To test students' understanding, write five to ten true/false statements about the main points of the section, such as:

Bacteria can develop a resistance to an antibiotic. (T)

Have students react to the statements as being true or false both before and after reading the section. If any questions are answered incorrectly after the reading, go over the relevant material one more time and retest students for comprehension.

Biology Toolkit, Anticipation Guide, p. C3

Plan and Prepare

Objectives

- Explain how bacteria cause disease.
- Describe how antibiotics work and the potential for antibiotic resistance.

Section Resources

Unit Resource Book
Study Guide pp. 47–48
Power Notes p. 49
Reinforcement p. 50
Pre-AP Activity pp. 55–56

Interactive Reader Chapter 18
Spanish Study Guide pp. 193–194

Biology Toolkit pp. C3, C13, C19, C38

Technology
Power Presentation 18.6
Media Gallery DVD
Online Quiz 18.6

Activate Prior Knowledge Have students consider the language of treating infectious disease. **Ask,** If we regard ourselves as being under attack by viruses and bacteria, how do we fight back? For some viruses, we have vaccines; for bacteria, we have antibiotics. Antibiotics offer a way to win battles against bacteria, but because the lifespans of bacteria are brief and ours are long, they have an advantage. **Ask,** Who can adapt faster to the tactics of the other—humans or bacteria? bacteria; because bacterial lifespans are so brief, mutations accumulate much faster, allowing them to quickly adapt to the challenges we create, like antibiotics.

Teach

Take It Further

Some bacteria that are normally harmless can become pathogenic when a change in circumstances provides new opportunities. These are called **opportunistic pathogens.** For example, *E. coli,* one of the normal intestinal floras, causes illness if it invades the urinary system or contaminates a wound. Hosts whose health is compromised, such as AIDS patients, are especially vulnerable to opportunistic pathogens.

▼ Teach *continued*

ONLINE BIOLOGY See Options for Inquiry on page 567 for a virtual lab on testing the effectiveness of antibacterial products. Or use Animated Biology to let students test their understanding of antibiotics.

History of Science

In medicine, **carriers** are people who have recovered from an infectious disease but can still infect other people, often by poor hygienic practices. One especially notorious carrier was a young cook named **Mary Mallon.** Over a 10-year period in the early 20th century, she infected with typhoid fever eight families she had worked for. Typhoid fever is a severe illness caused by the bacterium *Salmonella typhi.*

Officials investigating a typhoid outbreak in a wealthy family noted that they had become ill shortly after Mary had come to cook for them. She had since left their employ, but subsequent tracking revealed that typhoid outbreaks occurred in every family she worked for. When officials finally located Mallon, she resisted being tested and had to be forced into quarantine by several police officers.

She was released from quarantine three years later on condition that she never work again handling food. However, in 1915, she took a cooking job, infecting 25 people. Seized again by authorities, **Typhoid Mary,** as she came to be called, was again placed in quarantine, where she remained for the rest of her life.

Answers

A Apply *Staphylococcus aureus* is the most likely culprit, as the potato salad was not refrigerated.

B Infer Antibiotics act on characteristics that are unique to bacterial cells, such as their cell walls.

FIGURE 18.18 Common Bacterial Infections

INFECTION	BACTERIUM	SYMPTOMS	CAUSES
Acne	*Propionibacterium*	chronic cysts, blackheads	increased oil production in skin
Anthrax	*Bacillus anthracis*	fever, trouble breathing	inhaling endospores
Lyme disease	*Borrelia burgdorferi*	rash, aching, fever, swelling of joints	bite from infected tick
Tetanus	*Clostridium tetani*	severe muscle spasms, fever, lockjaw	wound contaminated with soil
Tooth decay	*Streptococcus mutans*	tooth cavities	large populations of bacteria in mouth

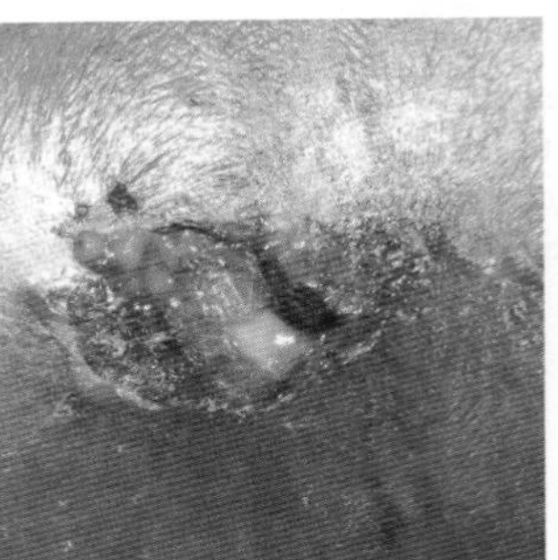

FIGURE 18.19 *Streptococcus* bacteria are commonly found on skin. They are fairly harmless unless they come in contact with tissues they do not normally colonize, such as muscle or fat. This can occur through open wounds.

Staph food poisoning can make you pretty sick, but botulism can kill you. *C. botulinum* produces a deadly toxin. Botulism is usually caused by the eating of improperly canned foods that were contaminated with endospores before being sealed. Bulging cans are a sign that *C. botulinum* may be present.

Normally harmless bacteria can be destructive when introduced to a part of the host that is not adapted to them. Disease can result if these bacteria get into tissues they do not usually colonize through a cut, scrape, or surgical incision. You can see one result of typically harmless *Streptococci*, which we have normally in our mouths and noses—and often on our skin—becoming pathogenic in **FIGURE 18.19.** These are also the bacteria that can cause what is commonly known as strep throat.

A Apply **Potato salad left out at a picnic is sometimes a source of food poisoning. Which bacterium mentioned above is the most likely culprit? Explain.**

Connecting CONCEPTS

Immune System Although antibiotics do not work on viruses, vaccines may work on both viruses and bacteria. This is because vaccines trigger the immune system. You will learn more about how the immune system works in **Chapter 31.**

MAIN IDEA

Antibiotics are used to fight bacterial disease.

If you've ever had a cold, your doctor may have told you that the only cure was to let the cold "run its course." If you had strep throat, however, the doctor would prescribe a powerful antibiotic. Why do you get antibiotics for strep throat but not for the common cold?

Colds and strep throat are treated differently because they are caused by different pathogens. Viruses cause colds, while the bacterium *Streptococcus* causes strep throat. Many types of **antibiotics**—or chemicals that kill or slow the growth of bacteria—work by stopping bacteria from making cell walls.

Antibiotics are produced naturally by some species of bacteria and fungi. They can be used as medicine for humans and other animals without damaging their cells, since animal cells do not have cell walls. Because viruses also lack cell walls, antibiotics do not work on viral infections.

Antibiotics can be effective when used properly, but they should not be the first line of defense against bacterial infection; prevention should. Overuse of antibiotics can completely wipe out the community of intestinal microbes, resulting in illness.

B Infer **Why don't antibiotics affect our bodies' own cells?**

Differentiated Instruction

PRE-AP

Have students map out a possible sequence of events predicting the spread of *pneumococcus,* a bacterium that causes pneumonia, in a crowded nursing home. Remind students that most residents in the nursing home are elderly and their immune systems are impaired. As they plot the movement of the bacteria, students should consider all the people that pass through a nursing home each day and the other people they interact with outside the home.

Biology Toolkit, Sequence Diagram, p. C38

MAIN IDEA

Bacteria can evolve resistance to antibiotics.

Although antibiotics should certainly be used when needed, the inappropriate and incomplete use of antibiotics has produced a serious public health issue—multidrug-resistant bacteria. Resistance occurs as a result of natural selection, as individuals who are more resistant are more likely to survive and reproduce. This has led to the evolution of multidrug-resistant strains of "superbugs" that are almost impossible to treat. As you can see in **FIGURE 18.20**, bacteria can acquire genes for resistance through plasmid exchange. This has happened with many bacteria with a wide range of commonly used antibiotics. This problem has arisen due to various factors.

Overuse The potential problem with antibiotics is that they may create a selective pressure that favors the very bacteria they are intended to destroy. Using antibiotics when bacteria are not causing an illness may make some bacteria resistant.

FIGURE 18.20 ANTIBIOTIC RESISTANCE

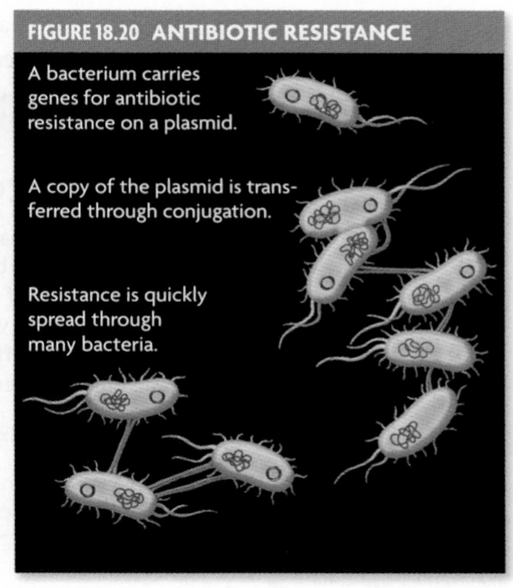

A bacterium carries genes for antibiotic resistance on a plasmid.
A copy of the plasmid is transferred through conjugation.
Resistance is quickly spread through many bacteria.

Underuse Failure to take the entire course of antibiotics prescribed for a bacterial infection is one of the main factors leading to drug resistance. If your doctor prescribed a ten-day course of an antibiotic, you must finish the entire prescription. Otherwise, you may not have destroyed all of the bacteria—only the weakest ones.

Misuse A large portion of the antibiotics distributed in the United States are fed to livestock. Antibiotics are often misused in agriculture to increase the animals' rate of growth. However, when antibiotics are added to the food of healthy animals, bacteria within the food—including pathogens—can become resistant to multiple antibiotics.

Connect How can you use "superbugs" as an example of natural selection?

18.6 ASSESSMENT

ONLINE QUIZ ClassZone.com

REVIEWING MAIN IDEAS

1. What are two ways in which bacteria can cause disease?
2. How can **antibiotics** stop bacterial infections?
3. What is antibiotic resistance, and how does it occur?

CRITICAL THINKING

4. **Apply** Why are antibiotics not effective against viruses?
5. **Synthesize** Evolution is often thought of as taking thousands, or even millions, of years to occur. What are two reasons that antibiotic resistance has been able to evolve in bacteria so quickly?

Connecting CONCEPTS

6. **Ecology** Pesticide resistance occurs in much the same way as antibiotic resistance. How could we apply what we have learned about antibiotic resistance to how pesticides are used in the environment?

18.6 ASSESSMENT

1. invade tissues and attack cells directly or make a toxin that is carried by the blood
2. by disrupting cell wall synthesis in bacteria
3. Genetic mutations occur that render bacteria resistant to antibiotics. The genes are on plasmids, which are exchanged frequently between bacteria. Over time, more bacteria in the population have the antibiotic-resistant genes because these bacteria have a selective advantage.
4. Antibiotics act on parts of cells that viruses do not have, such as cell walls.
5. Bacteria can transfer genes directly to each other through conjugation, and generation times in bacteria are very brief, so mutations can occur and build up fairly quickly.
6. If pesticides are used without being needed, resistance will build up so that when pesticides are needed, they will not work.

ONLINE BIOLOGY To explore the role of antibiotics in agriculture and its effect, see the WebQuest in Options for Inquiry on page 567.

Take It Further

The resistance of certain strains of bacteria to common antibiotics is forcing pharmaceutical scientists to find new antibiotics. **Platensimycin,** a compound isolated from a soil microbe found in South Africa, was recently found to be effective in destroying *S. aureus* and enterococci pathogens without doing harm to the host animal's cells. When the compound was tested in mice infected with *S. aureus,* the bacteria were decreased 10,000-fold within 24 hours. If platensimycin is deemed safe enough for use in humans, it could be the most potent antibiotic to reach patients in decades.

Answers

A Connect Mutations allow bacteria to become drug resistant, and the trait is passed on to the next generation. As the drugs change, certain bacteria that are resistant to the new drug will survive, produce offspring, and through conjugation, spread the resistant genes on to offspring.

Assess and Reteach

Assess Use the Online Quiz or Section Quiz (*Assessment Book,* p. 358).

Reteach As a class, make a concept map that relates to the issue of bacterial antibiotic resistance. You might begin with the following terms: *bacterial diseases, antibiotics, inappropriate uses,* and *antibiotic resistance.* Have students add terms to the map and show how to connect them.

OPTIONS FOR INQUIRY

INVESTIGATION

Time 45 minutes	TEACHER TESTED
Teacher Preparation	
Student Difficulty	
Lab Binder Diversity, pp. 18–20	

Purpose Test the effectiveness of bacterial enzymes at degrading oil.

Overview Students will test the effectiveness of different enzymatic drain cleaners on cooking oils. They will

- design a procedure to test the cleaners
- observe and record results for 5+ days
- compare their results with those of other groups using different cooking oils

LAB PREPARATION

- Test several types of cooking oil.
- Prepare a 0.02% tetrazolium solution. Mix 0.1 g of tetrazolium power with 50 mL of distilled water. Store in the refrigerator. On the day of the lab, mix 1 part of tetrazolium solution with 9 parts distilled water. Put solution in a flask and provide a 1-mL eyedropper or pipette.
- Do not use lye-based drain cleaners. Some appropriate cleaners are Drain Care Build-Up Remover, Roebic K-67 Bacterial Drain and Trap Cleaner, and Rid-X Septic System Treatment.

LAB MANAGEMENT

Make sure students use separate droppers for each drain cleaner, type of cooking oil, and the tetrazolium solution. Allow ten minutes each day for students to record observations.

POST-LAB DISCUSSION

Discuss students' results. **Ask**

- Why do bacteria make enzymes that break down oil? Oil is a source of energy.
- What is a possible application of this process? bioremediation

Use these inquiry-based labs and online activities to deepen your understanding of viruses and prokaryotes.

NOS.1 Develop explanations based on reproducible data and observations gathered during laboratory investigations.

NOS.6 Use analogies and models (mathematical and physical) to simplify and represent systems that are difficult to understand or directly experience due to their size, time scale, or complexity, and recognize the limitations of analogies and models.

DESIGN YOUR OWN INVESTIGATION

Using Bacteria to Break Down Oil

Some types of bacteria have enzymes that can break down oil and are used by scientists to help clean up an oil spill. Some types of drain cleaners contain bacteria that work in the same way to clear drain pipes. In this lab, you will test the effectiveness of different types of enzymatic drain cleaners at breaking down cooking oil.

MATERIALS

- 4 10-mL test tubes with caps
- 6 cm masking tape
- marker
- test tube rack
- 5 plastic droppers
- 3 10-mL graduated cylinders
- 2 mL cooking oil
- 2 mL 0.02% tetrazolium indicator solution
- 2 mL each of three types of enzymatic drain cleaner

SKILLS Designing Experiments, Concluding

PROBLEM Which enzymatic drain cleaner is most effective at breaking down oil?

PROCEDURE

1. Label four test tubes A, B, C, and D.
2. Determine a procedure for your experiment, using small amounts of the materials. Decide which materials and how much of each will be placed in each test tube. You will test the effectiveness of each type of drain cleaner at breaking down cooking oil. Each class group will use a different type of oil. The tetrazolium indicator solution turns pink when oil is broken down.
3. Identify the independent and dependent variables in your experiment. Identify the controls and constants in your experiment. Develop an operational definition of your dependent variable.
4. Get approval from your teacher to carry out your experiment. Wear gloves.
5. Use a separate dropper for the oil, the tetrazolium solution, and each type of drain cleaner. Once they are prepared, place the caps on the test tubes and gently swirl the test tubes to thoroughly mix solutions.
6. Observe your test tubes every day for at least five days. Record your data in a table like the one below. Day 0 represents the observations you make immediately after your test tubes have been prepared.

TABLE 1. DRAIN CLEANER EFFECTIVENESS

Day	Tube A	Tube B	Tube C	Tube D
0				
1				

ANALYZE AND CONCLUDE

1. **Analyze** Which drain cleaner was most effective at breaking down the oil?
2. **Compare** Compare your results to those of other groups in the class that used different types of cooking oil. Which type of oil was broken down most effectively?
3. **Conclude** Which drain cleaner would you buy? Explain.

Answers

Sample Data

See a sample table of student data on page R106.

Analyze and Conclude

1. Students' responses will vary depending on the combinations of oil and drain cleaner used. Whichever test tube took the least number of days to turn pink contained the most effective drain cleaner for breaking down that specific oil.
2. Answers will vary.
3. Students' responses will vary depending on the effectiveness of the drain cleaners used in the class.

INVESTIGATION

Modeling Viruses

The structure of a virus actually helps the virus to enter into a host cell and multiply. In this exercise, you will create a model to help understand how a virus attacks a healthy cell.

SKILL Modeling

PROBLEM How does the shape of a virus relate to how it functions?

MATERIALS
- research materials (books, scientific journals, Internet)
- markers
- pipe cleaners
- clay
- tooth picks
- construction paper
- white paper

PROCEDURE

1. In your group, select one of the following viral illnesses:
   - chickenpox
   - common cold
   - influenza
   - mumps
   - polio
   - measles
   - AIDS
   - West Nile
   - hemorrhagic fever
2. Research the structure of the virus that causes the illness. State the scientific name of the virus (or virus family) that causes the illness.
3. Using the provided craft materials, construct a model of the virus based on the micrographs that you find.

ANALYZE AND CONCLUDE

1. **Analyze** Look at all the models. What differences do you see? How are they similar?
2. **Apply** How does the specific shape of your virus enable it to attack healthy cells?
3. **Evaluate** What characteristics of the virus are not represented by your model?

Online BIOLOGY
CLASSZONE.COM

VIRTUAL LAB
Testing Antibacterial Products
Do antibacterial products really kill germs as they claim? In this interactive lab, you will culture bacteria, and then determine the effectiveness of different germ-killing agents.

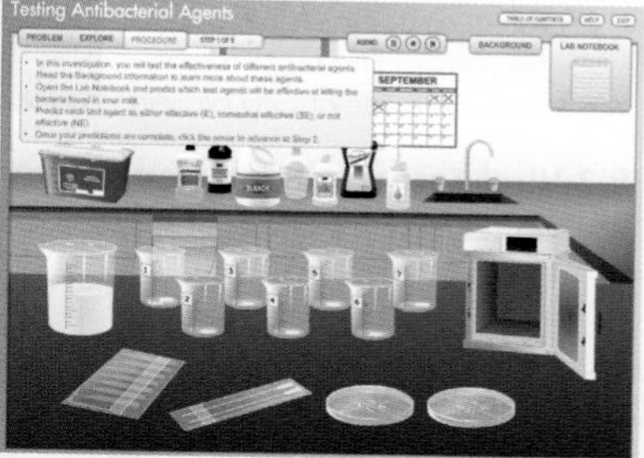

ANIMATED BIOLOGY
What Would You Prescribe?
Is an antibiotic always the best medicine? Review patients' symptoms and diagnoses, then determine if an antibiotic should be used to treat the patients.

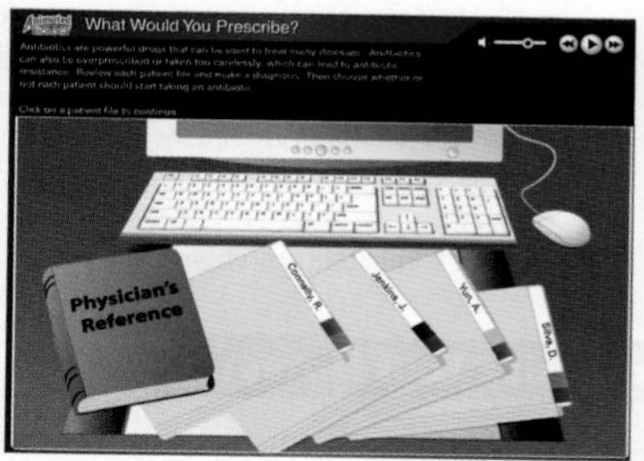

WEBQUEST
Modern agriculture uses antibiotics to keep livestock healthy. Is there a downside to giving livestock antibiotics? Complete this WebQuest to find out. Explore links between antibiotic resistance and antibiotic use in agriculture.

Online Biology ▼

VIRTUAL LAB Use this lab to reinforce the concepts in **Section 18.6.**

ANIMATED BIOLOGY Use this interactive animation to reinforce the concepts in **Section 18.6.**

WEBQUEST The WebQuest takes one full class period. Students complete the activity online and will need access to a printer to print their answers. Sample answers, teacher notes, and alternative assessment ideas are available on **ClassZone.com.** Use with **Section 18.6.**

INVESTIGATION

TEACHER TESTED

Time	90 minutes
Teacher Preparation	
Student Difficulty	
Lab Binder	Diversity, p. 21

Purpose Make a model of a virus to understand how the virus attacks a cell.

Overview Students will research the structure of a particular virus and then construct a model.

LAB PREPARATION

- Gather ahead of time research materials such as books and journals.
- If your classroom does not have a computer, plan ahead to reserve time in your school computer lab.

Teacher Note "The rhinovirus was nice because of its tube shape."

POST-LAB DISCUSSION

Discuss the model-building process with students. **Ask,** How did building a model help you understand the process of viral infection? Answers will vary but may include that seeing the structure of a virus helps to visualize how the virus uses its structure to infect a cell.

Answers

Sample Models
- rhinovirus: toothpicks wrapped in ribbon glued onto cardboard
- adenovirus: plastic foam balls studded with toothpicks
- poliovirus: cardboard triangles glued together

Analyze and Conclude
1. Answers will vary but may include type of genetic material, shape of capsid, and presence or absence of envelope and spiky surface proteins. Models are similar in that each has a capsid and genetic material.
2. Answers will vary but may include ability to attach to host cell receptors or fuse to cells.
3. Answers will vary but may include the chemical makeup of the virus. Also, the model may not have accurate scale measurements, possibly might not use 3-dimensional representation, or may be limited by the materials used in construction.

CHAPTER REVIEW

Interactive Review

Encourage students to go to **ClassZone.com** for a detailed review of each section, including visuals and vocabulary practice.

Unit Resource Book, Vocabulary Practice, pp. 57–60

CHAPTER 18 Interactive Review @ CLASSZONE.COM

KEY CONCEPTS | Vocabulary Games | Concept Maps | Animated Biology | Online Quiz

18.1 Studying Viruses and Prokaryotes

Infections can be caused in several ways. Viruses, viroids, and prions have characteristics of both living and nonliving things. Unlike bacteria, viruses cannot reproduce on their own. A virus has genetic material and a protein coat. Viroids have only RNA and no protein coat. Prions are made of only protein.

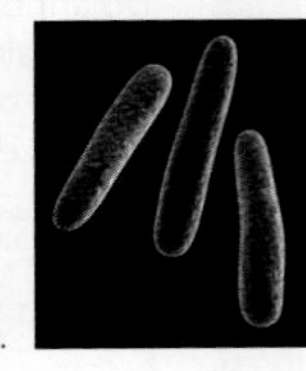

18.2 Viral Structure and Reproduction

Viruses exist in a variety of shapes and sizes. Viruses can be helical like a spring, many-sided, or enveloped. Bacteriophages, or viruses that attack bacteria, have a many-sided capsid with a long protein tail and spiky footlike fibers. There are two basic types of viral infections: lytic and lysogenic. A lytic infection results in the host cells bursting open, while the virions in a lysogenic infection do not immediately destroy the host.

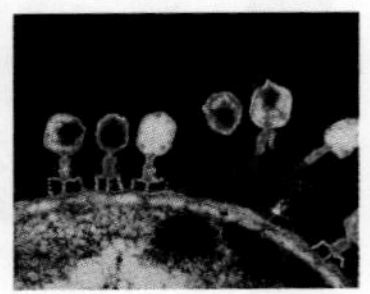

18.3 Viral Diseases

Some viral diseases can be prevented with vaccines. Viruses can enter a body through wounds or body openings such as mouths or noses. Many infectious viruses exist. Examples of illnesses caused by viruses include the common cold, influenza, SARS, and AIDS. Vaccines can prevent some, but not all, viral diseases.

18.4 Bacteria and Archaea

Bacteria and archaea are both single-celled prokaryotes. Prokaryotes are widespread on Earth. Archaea look very similar to bacteria, but many of their structures are made of different compounds. Some prokaryotes can survive harsh conditions by forming endospores. Prokaryotes can transfer genes to each other through conjugation.

18.5 Beneficial Roles of Prokaryotes

Prokaryotes perform important functions for organisms and ecosystems. Prokaryotes that live in an animal's digestive tract help the animal absorb nutrients from the food that it eats. Animals and plants also depend on prokaryotes to fix atmospheric nitrogen. Nitrogen is necessary to make amino acids and proteins. Bioremediation uses prokaryotes to help break down pollutants in the environment.

18.6 Bacterial Diseases and Antibiotics

Understanding bacteria is necessary to prevent and treat disease. Although the majority of bacteria are not pathogenic, some do cause disease. Bacteria can also cause conditions such as food poisoning, chronic acne, Lyme disease, and tooth decay. Antibiotics are used to fight bacterial infection. However, through natural selection, many bacteria have become resistant to commonly used antibiotics.

Synthesize Your Notes

Concept Map Use a concept map like the one below to summarize what you know about infectious agents. Include details about genetic material and types of hosts they infect.

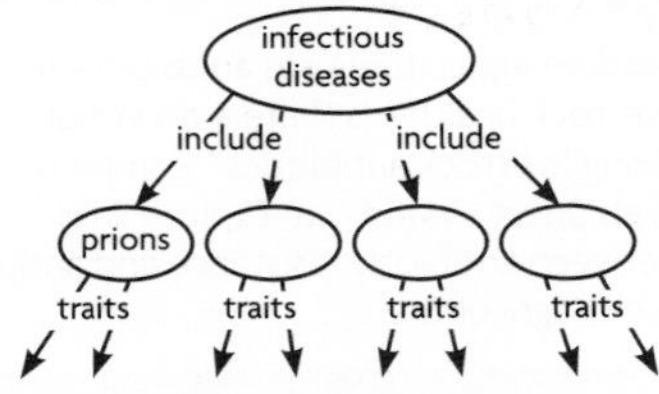

Cycle Diagram Use two cycle diagrams like the one below to summarize lytic and lysogenic infections.

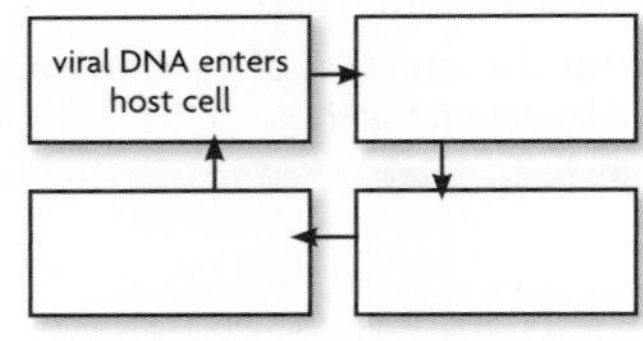

Reviewing Vocabulary

1. vaccine
2. viroid
3. prophage
4. bacteriophage
5. antibiotic
6. bioremediation
7. A flagellum is a whiplike structure of single-celled organisms.
8. Conjugation is the transfer of genetic material between prokaryotes. It occurs when two or more cells join together through a conjugation bridge of pili.
9. An epidemic is a large-scale spread of infection among a group of people or among a community.
10. An anaerobe lives without oxygen.

Chapter Assessment

Chapter Vocabulary

18.1 virus, p. 544
pathogen, p. 544
viroid, p. 544
prion, p. 545

18.2 capsid, p. 547
bacteriophage, p. 549
lytic infection, p. 551
lysogenic infection, p. 551
prophage, p. 551

18.3 epidemic, p. 553
vaccine, p. 553
retrovirus, p. 553

18.4 obligate anaerobe, p. 555
obligate aerobe, p. 555
facultative aerobe, p. 555
plasmid, p. 556
flagellum, p. 556
conjugation, p. 558
endospore, p. 558

18.5 bioremediation, p. 561

18.6 toxin, p. 563
antibiotic, p. 564

Reviewing Vocabulary

Category Clues

For each clue, list the appropriate vocabulary term from the chapter.

Category: Viral Infection

1. protects against infection
2. plant virus
3. host and viral DNA

Category: Bacteria

4. virus of bacteria
5. fights bacterial infection
6. pollution digestion

Greek and Latin Word Origins

7. The term *flagellum* comes from the Latin word *flagrum,* which means "whip." Explain how this meaning relates to flagellum.
8. The term *conjugation* comes from the Latin word *conjugare,* which means "to join together." Using this meaning, explain how it relates to what conjugation is.
9. The term *epidemic* comes from the Greek words *epi-*, which means "upon," and *demos,* which means "people." Explain how these meanings relate to an epidemic.
10. The term *aerobe* means "an organism that requires oxygen to live." The prefixes *a-* or *an-* mean "without, or not." How do these meanings relate to the term *anaerobe*?

Reviewing MAIN IDEAS

11. Viruses, viroids, and prions are not considered to be living things. Which of their traits resemble living organisms, and which traits do not?
12. The flu virus has an envelope with surface proteins that allow it to infect its host cells. What structures help viruses infect bacterial cells? Explain.
13. Explain the differences between the two ways viruses infect their host cells.
14. Children across the United States get "shots," or injections, during their physical exams. Explain what these shots are and why they are recommended for all children.
15. The success of prokaryotes is due to special characteristics they have, such as the ability to form endospores and perform conjugation. Explain how each of these abilities helps prokaryotes survive changing environments.
16. It surprises most people to learn that their lives depend on bacteria. Describe three roles bacteria play in human health and survival.
17. Due to their unique ability to break down an enormous array of substances, prokaryotes play critical roles in ecosystems. Summarize two of these roles.
18. Doctors recommend washing hands before eating to prevent the spread of disease. What is the connection between bacteria and disease?
19. Prokaryotes have the ability to carry genes other than their own. How is this trait important for genetic engineering?
20. Recently, doctors have been advised to limit the use of antibiotics whenever possible. Why is this recommendation important?

CHAPTER REVIEW

Reviewing Main Ideas

11. Viruses, viroids, and prions can multiply, and viruses and viroids have genes. None of them, however, can reproduce on their own. They all require living organisms in order to reproduce.
12. Spiky footlike fibers help attach to host cells; tails break down bacterial cell walls and then punch through, injecting the virus's genes.
13. Lytic infections cause the host cells to burst and release new virions; lysogenic infections can remain in the host cell undetected for long periods of time. In lysogenic infections, the genetic material of the virus becomes incorporated within the genetic material of the host cell.
14. Shots are usually vaccines, a preparation of weakened microbes that can prepare an individual's immune system for any future encounter with a specific virus.
15. Endospores offer protection from harsh, unfavorable conditions such as high heat or lack of water. Conjugation allows genes to quickly transfer between prokaryotes, allowing rapid adaptation to environmental conditions.
16. Bacteria break down food that we would otherwise be unable to absorb. They also make vitamins and other compounds and keep harmful microbes away by filling niches that might otherwise be filled by disease-causing bacteria.
17. Some prokaryotes can fix atmospheric nitrogen into compounds that plants and later, animals require. Others can break down pollutants and waste products into less harmful compounds.
18. Some bacteria cause diseases in humans when they are exposed to certain types of cells or tissues.
19. Genes from other organisms can be inserted into prokaryotes that will then deliver them into other cells.
20. Many bacteria are showing resistance to multiple antibiotics. Limiting the use of antibiotics to times when they are really needed will lessen the exposure of bacteria to antibiotics and slow the rate at which they gain resistance.

CHAPTER REVIEW

Critical Thinking

21. Bacteria that consume toxic materials can clean up pollution in the environment by metabolizing the toxins and producing a less toxic or nontoxic waste product. This is the basis of bioremediation.
22. In the lysogenic infection, the virus can go undetected for a long period of time, producing copies of its genes for as long as it remains integrated with the host's genes. In the lytic cycle, the virus works quickly, and the host can release a large number of new virions at once.
23. A virus that kills the host quickly may not get the chance to infect others because the host (or its cells) are no longer interacting with others.
24. Because endospores are so resistant to harsh conditions, they give some bacteria the chance to survive freezing, canning, cooking, chemical cleaning, and other treatments designed to preserve or sterilize.

Interpreting Visuals

25. lytic infection; we see new viral parts being made and new virions leaving the host cell.
26. The viral genes direct the host to make copies of the viral parts.
27. If the host cell were eukaryotic, the virus might enter the cell by endocytosis. If the virus is enveloped, it may enter by fusing to the plasma membrane of the host cell.

Critical Thinking

21. Apply Many bacteria cause food spoilage because they have dietary needs similar to humans. However, some bacteria consume chemicals such as heavy metals, sulfur, petroleum, and mercury. How are these bacteria being used to help humans?

22. Compare and Contrast In the lysogenic infection, viral genes can become a part of the host's cell. In the lytic infection, the host cell is destroyed. What might be the benefit of each type of infection to the virus?

23. Infer New viruses may quickly kill their host after infection, but after many generations viruses tend to weaken and cause fewer deaths. Why might it be a disadvantage for a virus to quickly kill its host?

24. Synthesize Endospore-forming bacteria include those that cause the diseases tetanus, botulism, and anthrax. Endospores themselves, however, do not cause illness and cannot reproduce. Why, then, are endospores such a concern to the food and healthcare industries?

Interpreting Visuals

Use the diagram below to answer the next three questions.

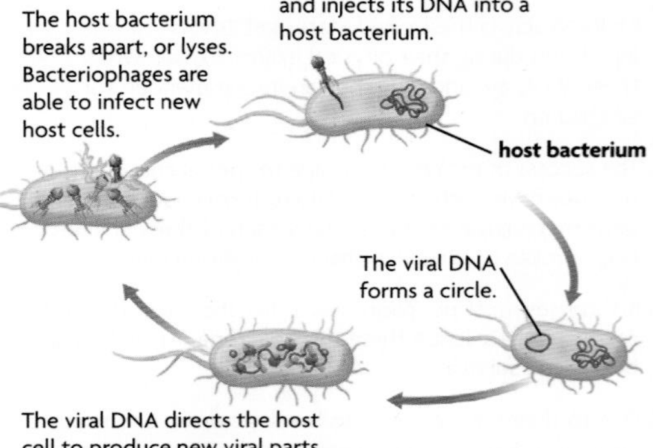
The bacteriophage attaches and injects its DNA into a host bacterium.
host bacterium
The viral DNA forms a circle.
The viral DNA directs the host cell to produce new viral parts. The parts assemble into new bacteriophages.
The host bacterium breaks apart, or lyses. Bacteriophages are able to infect new host cells.

25. Apply What type of viral infection is shown above? Explain your answer.

26. Apply Why is it necessary for the viral genes to enter the host cell?

27. Analyze How would the way that the virion enters the host cell change if the virus were a type that infected animals, and the host cell were eukaryotic rather than prokaryotic?

Analyzing Data

Use the hypothetical data below to answer the next questions.

TYPE OF BACTERIA AND LENGTH	
Type of bacteria	**Average length (nm)**
Streptococcus	500
Staphylococcus	900
Vibrio	2600
Aquaspirillum	2800

REPLICATION TIME OF STREPTOCOCCUS	
Time (min)	**Number of streptococcus cells**
0	1
28	2
56	4
84	8

28. Connect For each of the tables above, identify whether the data are continuous or discrete. Explain.

29. Calculate Assuming that nutrients are unlimited, how many *Streptococcus* cells will there be after 112 minutes? Explain.

Connecting CONCEPTS

30. Writing a Pamphlet Scientists agree that a form of the avian flu virus has the potential to cause a worldwide flu epidemic. This type of virus is known to mutate easily and adapt quickly to host changes. Imagine you are a representative from the Centers for Disease Control and are writing a pamphlet to educate citizens about the virus and how it actually causes infection. Using your knowledge of cells and viruses, make a detailed pamphlet that the general public could understand.

31. Synthesize The bacteria in the esophagus shown on page 543 are one of the many types of symbiotic prokaryotes living within our bodies. How might these types of mutualistic relationships have arisen? Consider natural selection in your answer.

Analyzing Data

28. The table of the type of bacteria displays discrete data; the other table displays continuous data. Discrete data are for specific subjects, such as the bacteria listed. Continuous data are sequential and can reveal change.
29. 16 cells; the population is doubling every 28 minutes. At 112 minutes, the population at 84 minutes (8 cells) will have doubled.

INDIANA ISTEP+ Test Prep

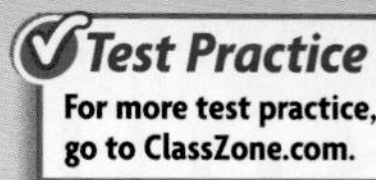
B.4.1; B.8.2; B.8.5; NOS.1

Test Practice
For more test practice, go to ClassZone.com.

1

Set-up for Antibiotic Testing			
Antibiotic	A	B	C
Infected mice tested	30	15	5
% Effectiveness	83%	25%	100%

Scientists are testing three antibiotics—A, B, and C—on 50 mice with bacterial infections. Their experimental design is shown above. They conclude that they need to do more testing on antibiotic C because

A it unexpectedly worked better than A and B.
B 100 percent of the mice were cured.
C the sample size was too small.
D it will likely have the worst side effects.

2 Impetigo is a highly contagious skin infection caused by staph or strep bacteria that are normally found on the skin, where they are harmless. This infection is ***most*** likely to occur when

A scraped skin provides the bacteria with access to tissues they do not normally contact.
B the bacteria have been genetically altered by scientists doing research.
C the infected person did not receive regularly scheduled vaccinations.
D the bacteria form endospores on the surface of the skin.

3 Some scientists think that measures of an ecosystem's health—such as usable nitrogen levels in the soil—may become more variable as the diversity of organisms on Earth declines. This is because usable soil nitrogen depends on a variety of

A animals that return nitrogen to the soil through respiration.
B animals that return nitrogen to the soil after they die.
C bacteria and other decomposers that fix nitrogen into a usable form.
D plants, which produce nitrogen as a byproduct of photosynthesis.

4 The main reason that viruses are not considered to be living things is that they do not

A die when exposed to antibiotics.
B reproduce on their own.
C contain a nucleus.
D undergo meiosis before replication.

THINK THROUGH THE QUESTION

All of these answer choices correctly describe viruses, so do not be tricked! Look at each answer choice and try to think of a living organism that fits the characteristic described, making that answer choice wrong.

5

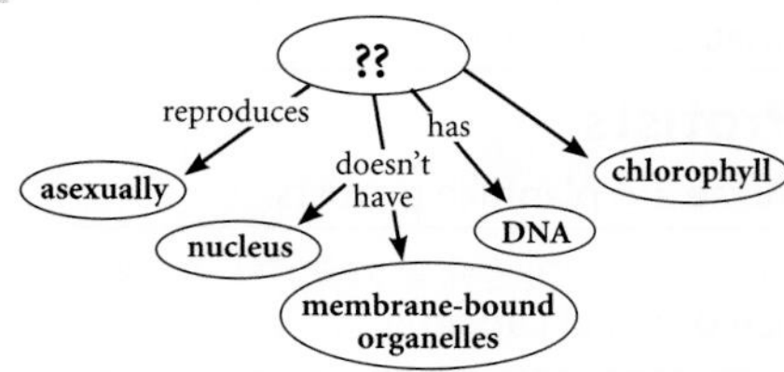

Which of the following is described by this concept map?

A animal cell
B plant cell
C bacterium
D virus

6 The purpose of a vaccination is to allow your body to develop antibodies to a specific virus, so that it will be able to fight that virus if you are ever exposed to it. Why do doctors recommend that individuals get flu shots every year?

Standards-Based Assessment

1. C	4. B
2. A	5. C
3. C	6. See Below

TEST DOCTOR

Question 2 Answer A is correct. Answer B is incorrect because the genetic alteration of bacteria is by no means the most likely cause of a staph or strep infection. Answer C is incorrect because people typically are not vaccinated against staph and strep. Answer D is incorrect because staph and strep do not form endospores.

Question 3 Answer C is correct. Answers A and B are incorrect because animals cannot convert nitrogen from its gaseous form into ions that can be used in organic compounds. Answer D is incorrect because plants produce oxygen as a byproduct of photosynthesis, not nitrogen.

Question 5 Answer C is correct. Answers A and B are incorrect because animal cells and plant cells do, for example, have a nucleus and membrane-bound organelles. Answer D is incorrect because viruses do not have chlorophyll and are incapable of reproducing on their own.

Question 6 Influenza virus mutates over time, producing new strains. Though your body might be protected against the virus it has already been exposed to, it will not be protected against new strains that it is exposed to in the future.

Connecting Concepts

30. Students' pamphlets should explain how viruses can cause infection, mutate, and be transmitted from one organism to another.

31. *Sample Answer:* These bacteria may have conferred a benefit to the animal host by protecting it from serious pathogens. The improved survivability of hosts carrying these bacteria would give a selective advantage for the bacteria because their environment would not be dying early or often.

ITEM CORRELATIONS

Standard	Items
B.4.1	3
B.8.2	4, 5
B.8.5	6
NOS.1	1

CHAPTER 19

Indiana Resource Preview

Print Resources

Interactions in Ecosystems

INDIANA STANDARDS		Sections	PAGES and PACING	UNIT RESOURCE BOOK
B.8.2	19.1	**Diversity of Protists** **KEY CONCEPT** Kingdom Protista is the most diverse of all the king DOMS.	pp. 574–576 30 minutes	URB pages 61–64
	19.2	**Animal-like Protists** **KEY CONCEPT** Animal-like protists are single-celled heterotrophs that can move.	pp. 577–580 30 minutes	URB pages 65–68
	19.3	**Plantlike Protists** **KEY CONCEPT** Algae are plantlike protists.	pp. 581–585 30 minutes	URB pages 69–72
		DATA ANALYSIS: Analyzing Experimental Design Algae Preference of Coral Larvae	p. 586 30 minutes	URB page 85
	19.4	**Funguslike Protists** **KEY CONCEPT** Funguslike protists decompose organic matter.	pp. 587–588 30 minutes	URB pages 73–76
	19.5	**Diversity of Fungi** **KEY CONCEPT** Fungi are heterotrophs that absorb their food.	pp. 589–594 30 minutes	URB pages 77–80
NOS.1		CHAPTER INVESTIGATION: Exploring Mushroom Anatomy	p. 595 45 minutes	**Lab Binder** Classification and Diversity pages 27–29
B.4.4	19.6	**Ecology of Fungi** **KEY CONCEPT** Fungi recycle nutrients in the environment.	pp. 596–599 30 minutes	URB pages 81–84
NOS.1, NOS.3		OPTIONS FOR INQUIRY	pp. 600–601 45 minutes, 20 minutes	**Lab Binder** Classification and Diversity pages 30–33
		Chapter Review	pp. 602–605	**Assessment Book** Chapter Tests A, B pp. 379–386

INDIANA STANDARDS

B.4.4 Describe how climate, the pattern of matter and energy flow, the birth and death of new organisms, and the interaction between those organisms, and the interaction between those organisms contribute to the long term stability of an ecosystem.
B.8.2 Explain how organisms are classified and named based on their evolutionary relationships into taxonomic categories.
NOS.1 Develop explanations based on reproducible data and observations gathered during laboratory investigations.
NOS.3 Clearly communicate their ideas and results of investigations verbally and in written form using tables, graphs, diagrams, and photographs.

Labs

PUPIL EDITION LABS

Investigating Motion in Protists, Section 2, p. 579 Students observe the movement of protozoa. **Lab Binder** p. 34	**Time:** 20 minutes **Materials:** 4 eyedroppers, 4 drops bottled spring water, 3 microscope slides, 2 cover slips, culture of *Paramecium,* 3 drops methylcellulose solution, culture of *Amoeba,* culture of *Euglena,* microscope
Exploring Mushroom Anatomy, p. 595 Students identify features of a mushroom. **Lab Binder** pp. 27–29	**Time:** 45 minutes **Materials:** mushroom; plastic knife; 1/2 sheet of white paper; plastic cup; hairspray; dissecting scope, or magnifying lens

OPTIONS FOR INQUIRY

Quantifying Mold Growth, p. 600 Students quantify the growth of mold on a slice of bread. **Lab Binder** pp. 30–32	**Time:** 45 minutes **Materials:** slice of white bread, 10 mL water, eyedropper, sealable plastic lunch bag, straw cut into pieces, scale, clear plastic grid, prepared slide (optional), microscope (optional)
Algae in Products, p. 601 Students identify common household products and foods that contain algae. **Lab Binder** p. 33	**Time:** 20 minutes **Materials:** common household products

LAB BINDER Unit 6 Classification and Diversity

Additional Investigation: Investigating Meiosis in *Sordaria fimicola,* pp. 35–38

Challenge Lab: Chemotaxis in *Physarum*, pp. 46–49; Exploring Bioluminescence, pp. 50–53

LAB GENERATOR

A searchable CD of all labs in the program in editable format, including forensic, probeware, and biotechnology labs.

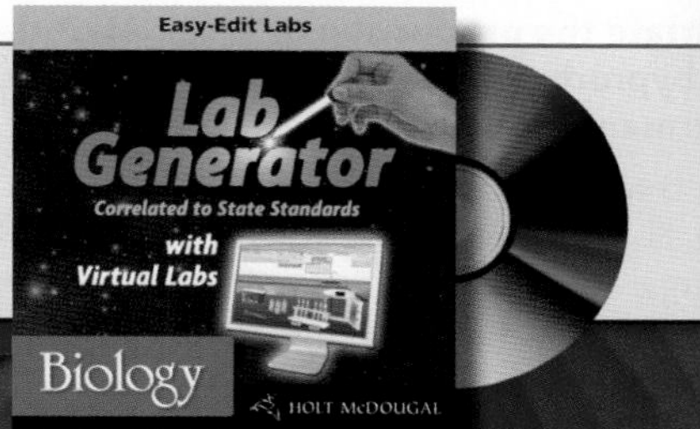

Presentation Tools

POWER PRESENTATIONS

Presentation Chapter 19
Power Presentations for each section incorporate images and clips from the Media Gallery: Includes Note Navigator for each section.

MEDIA GALLERY

Contains the following images and video clips, as well as animations, simulations and forms of visuals from the book.

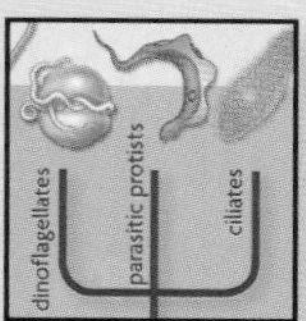

Protist phylogenetic tree

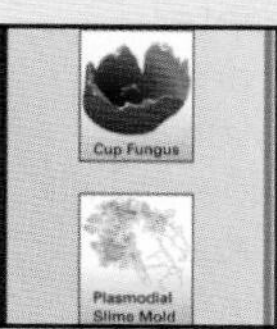

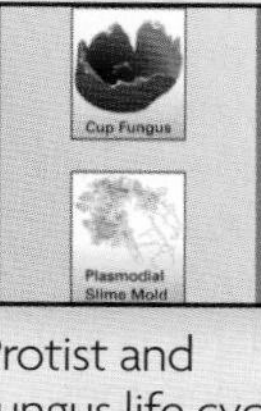

Protist and fungus life cycles

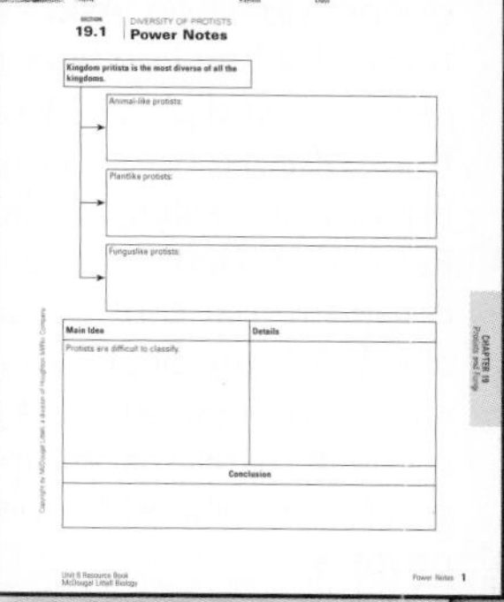

Power Notes

Fungi on a tree

Diatoms

VIDEO

Explore a set of short video clips on protozoa, algae, and fungi.

ANIMATED BIOLOGY

Protist Movement
Protist and Fungus Life Cycles
Algae Concentrations

TRANSPARENCIES

Phylogeny of Protists T80
Paramecium T81
Euglena T82
Life Cycle of Single-celled Green Algae T83
Life Cycle of Club Fungi T84
Life Cycle of Bread Molds T85

Online BIOLOGY CLASSZONE.COM

BioZine
Animated Biology
Interactive Review
SciLinks
Resource Centers

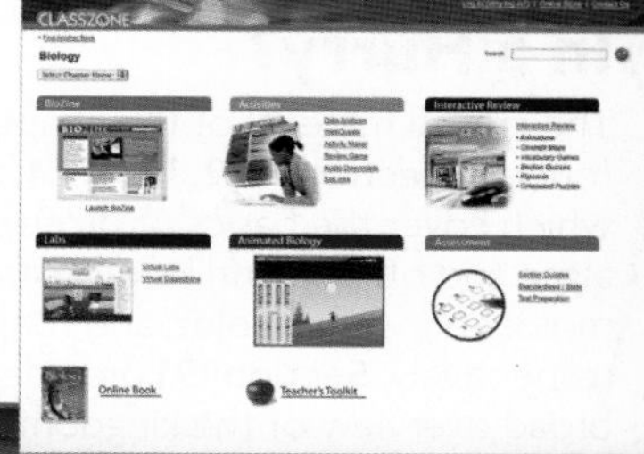

CHAPTER

19

▼ Focus and Motivate

When these two protists meet, who is the prey?

Have students look at the photograph on page 573 and read the chapter opener question. **Ask,** What do you think of when you hear the words *predator* and *prey*? Most students will think of large carnivorous animals hunting and killing smaller animals. Remind students that a predator is any organism that captures and consumes another living organism and that the captured organism is its prey. Predators come in many shapes and sizes, from great white sharks to microscopic protists.

Explain that we encounter protists and fungi daily. Fungi that students may contact include yeast in bread, mildew that grows in bathrooms, and the fungus that causes athlete's foot. Tell students that they eat certain protists (algae) or substances they produce in some of their favorite foods, such as ice cream and various candies. Many protists and fungi have applications for agriculture, industry, and health care. Research on protists and fungi is among the hottest areas in biological research today.

BIOZINE ClassZone.com

Students can access BioZine at **ClassZone.com** to check out articles featured in "Strange Biology."

In a Hurry?

The critical material of the chapter is found in **Sections 19.2, 19.3, 19.4,** and **19.5,** which cover the basics of protozoa, algae and other plantlike protists, slime molds and water molds, and fungi, respectively. **Section 19.1** provides a broad overview of the kingdom Protista, and **Section 19.6** discusses the ecology of fungi.

CHAPTER

19 Protists and Fungi

KEY CONCEPTS

19.1 Diversity of Protists
Kingdom Protista is the most diverse of all the kingdoms.

19.2 Animal-like Protists
Animal-like protists are single-celled heterotrophs that can move.

19.3 Plantlike Protists
Algae are plantlike protists.

19.4 Funguslike Protists
Funguslike protists decompose organic matter.

19.5 Diversity of Fungi
Fungi are heterotrophs that absorb their food.

19.6 Ecology of Fungi
Fungi recycle nutrients in the environment.

Online BIOLOGY CLASSZONE.COM

Animated BIOLOGY
View animated chapter concepts.
- Protist Movement
- Algae Concentrations
- Protist and Fungus Life Cycles

BIOZINE
Keep current with biology news.
- Featured stories
- Strange Biology
- Bio Bytes

RESOURCE CENTER
Get more information on
- Protozoa
- Algae
- Slime Molds

Teacher Demo

Purpose **Demonstrate the production of CO_2 by yeast as a byproduct of cellular respiration and fermentation.**

Introduce Explain that yeasts are unicellular fungi and that, like all cells, must break down glucose to get energy. Tell students that yeast is used in baking bread. The yeast cells feed on the sugars in flour and produce carbon dioxide gas, which makes the bread rise.

Materials
- packet of active dry yeast
- very warm water (105°F–115°F)
- 2 tablespoons sugar
- large rubber balloon
- small, plastic water bottle
- safety goggles

Safety Wear safety goggles during the demonstration.

When these two protists meet, who is the prey?

colored SEM; magnification 2000×

Although they are both protists, the round *Didinium* hunts live paramecia almost exclusively. Paramecia are much longer than this predator, but that doesn't stop *Didinium*. It captures, paralyzes, and reels in paramecia like fish on a line. It then eats its prey whole, expanding its own body just so that its meal will fit.

Connecting CONCEPTS

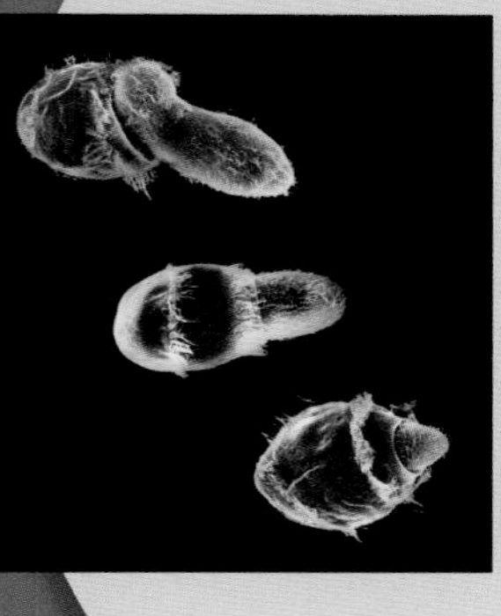

Ecology Most organisms follow one of two basic strategies for finding food, acting as specialists or generalists. *Didinium* is a specialist that eats only paramecia. In fact, when no paramecia are around, *Didinium* just turns into a cyst and waits until more come along. Paramecia are considered generalists, because they will eat anything smaller than themselves.

Demonstrate

1. Prepare the balloon by inflating and deflating it several times, then set it aside.
2. Add the yeast and sugar to 1 cup of warm water, and stir until they are dissolved.
3. Pour the mixture into the bottle. Bubbles should form as the yeast produces carbon dioxide. If no bubbles form, try another packet.
4. Attach the balloon to the mouth of the bottle, and set both aside.

After several minutes, the balloon will inflate and stand upright.

Discuss

Explain that when oxygen is available, cellular respiration yields carbon dioxide, water, and energy. Remind students that when oxygen is used up, cells can continue to break down glucose for energy through fermentation. Point out that in yeast, the products of fermentation are ethyl alcohol and carbon dioxide. **Ask,** What could have caused the bubbling in the bottle? production of carbon dioxide, first through cellular respiration and later by fermentation of sugar

Activate Prior Knowledge

Point out that, like bacteria, protists and fungi are living things that play a critical role in ecosystems. **Ask**

- What are some examples of fungi? mushrooms, bread mold, athlete's foot
- What is the name of the giant algae that grows in the coastal waters of California? kelp

Preview Vocabulary

Greek and Latin Roots Point out to students these important Greek prefixes that appear in different words in this chapter:

myc- = fungus
poly- = many
proto- = first
rhiz- = root
eu- = true

Academic Vocabulary In everyday life, a *strategy* is a plan of action that is consciously plotted and carried out in order to achieve a goal. In biology, a strategy is a series of activities that has evolved over time and increases evolutionary fitness. In this sense, a strategy can be anything from protective coloration to a mode of locomotion. Emphasize that a biological strategy is not consciously chosen by a species; instead, it is a trait that is adaptive given the species' environmental circumstances.

English Learners Students will learn many new terms to describe protists and fungi that won't easily match up to cognates in the students' native language. Suggest students associate images with the organisms and when possible make the image relate to the English term used to identify the organism. As an example, mention flagellates and ciliates and how the names relate to their form of locomotion.

SECTION 19.1

▼ Plan and Prepare

Objectives

- Identify the three main types of protists.
- Discuss the difficulty of classifying protists.

Section Resources

Unit Resource Book Study Guide pp. 61–62 Power Notes p. 63 Reinforcement p. 64 Pre-AP Activity pp. 87–88
Interactive Reader Chapter 19 **Spanish Study Guide** pp. 195–196
Biology Toolkit pp. C11, C30, C40, D7
Technology Power Presentation 19.1 Media Gallery DVD Online Quiz 19.1

Activate Prior Knowledge Suggest to students that in much the same way that record stores have had to completely rework their classifications of musical genres since 1977, so too have biologists been forced to rethink how life forms are classified given the discovery of archaeans in 1977. **Ask,** How would a music store your parents visited as teenagers be different from one you visit today? Students should mention new musical genres. Tell students that scientists are still trying to sort out how best to classify protists in light of all they are learning about this diverse and varied group of organisms.

19.1 Diversity of Protists

KEY CONCEPT Kingdom Protista is the most diverse of all the kingdoms.

MAIN IDEAS
- Protists can be animal-like, plantlike, or funguslike.
- Protists are difficult to classify.

VOCABULARY
protist, p. 574

INDIANA STANDARDS

B.8.2 Explain how organisms are classified and named based on their evolutionary relationships into taxonomic categories.

Connect If you looked at a drop of water from a pond, a roadside puddle, or a bird bath, you might find specimens of both *Didinium* and *Paramecium.* Despite their unique appearances, they are single-celled. That is what makes single-celled protists so amazing—they can carry out all life functions within just one cell. As you will see, one cell can be quite complex.

MAIN IDEA

Protists can be animal-like, plantlike, or funguslike.

Large yellow globs of slime seemed to come out of nowhere. They were spreading across lawns and pulsing up telephone poles. Afraid that this was an alien invasion, residents of the Dallas neighborhood called police and firefighters. The firefighters turned their hoses on the blobs, but water only made the invaders grow.

Scientists came to the rescue. What the people in the Dallas neighborhood were seeing on this sunny day in 1973 wasn't an alien life form, but a slime mold. Specifically, it was *Fuligo septica,* shown in **FIGURE 19.1,** a species commonly called dog-vomit slime mold because of its resemblance to—well, dog vomit.

FIGURE 19.1 *Fuligo septica,* commonly known as the dog-vomit slime mold, is just one member of the diverse kingdom Protista.

TAKING NOTES

Use a three-column chart to take notes about the groups of protists mentioned in this section.

Group	Description	Examples
animal-like		

Slime molds usually don't grow large enough to scare a neighborhood, but they are unusual. Slime molds are one of several groups of living things classified in kingdom Protista, a very diverse kingdom that includes hundreds of phyla. Members of this kingdom are often simply called protists. A **protist** is a eukaryote that is not an animal, a plant, or a fungus. Protists are generally grouped together because, although they share some features with animals, plants, and fungi, they also lack one or more traits that would place them in any of these three kingdoms. Protists may be single-celled or multicellular, microscopic or very large. They have different ways of moving around and of responding to the environment. Some protists reproduce asexually, whereas others reproduce both asexually and sexually.

▼ Teach

Vocabulary

Greek and Latin Word Origins The word **protist** comes from the Greek *prōtistos,* which means "the very first" and comes from the simpler Greek *prōtos,* or "first." Students will recognize this root in other words, such as *prototype, proton,* and *protocol.*

Differentiated Instruction

ENGLISH LEARNERS

After students read this short section, have them close their books, and call out main ideas and details about the great diversity of protists. Record them in a concept map. Start with a central circle that contains the main concept: protist diversity. Then draw three arrows radiating out from the central circle, each one ending with a square labeled with a type of protist. Add details under or branching off from each square, such as examples of these protist types.

Biology Toolkit, Concept Map, p. C40

BELOW LEVEL

Have students preview this section and all the rest to develop a note-taking strategy for the chapter. This section gives a broad overview of protist diversity, whereas later sections go into more detail. Suggest that students use a matrix to classify different protists by their distinguishing characteristics, including examples of each, and aspects that may make them beneficial or detrimental to humans.

Biology Toolkit, Semantic Feature Analysis, p. D7

Protists can be divided informally into three broad categories based on how they get their food. Categorizing protists in this way does not reflect evolutionary relationships, but it is a convenient way to study their diversity.

- **Animal-like protists** Animal-like protists, such as the *Euplotes* in **FIGURE 19.2**, are heterotrophs—organisms that consume other organisms. However, all animal-like protists are single-celled, while all animals—no matter how simple—are multicellular.
- **Plantlike protists** Plantlike protists, such as the algae *Pediastrum* in **FIGURE 19.2**, make their own food by photosynthesis just as plants do. Although these protists may have chloroplasts, they do not have roots, stems, or leaves. And while all plants are multicellular, plantlike protists may be either single-celled, colonial, or multicellular.
- **Funguslike protists** Funguslike protists, such as slime molds, decompose dead organisms. Because of this trait, these protists were once classified in kingdom Fungi. However, funguslike protists can move during part of their life cycle, whereas fungi cannot. You will learn about fungi later in this chapter.

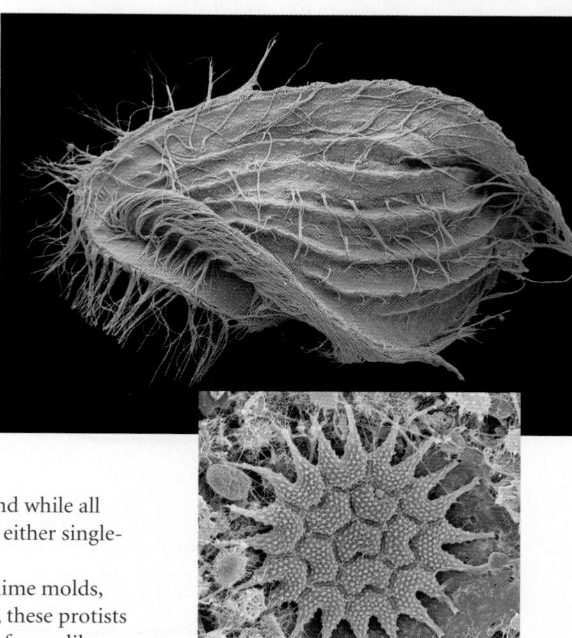

FIGURE 19.2 *Euplotes* (top) is an example of an animal-like protist. It can move around quickly to find its food. *Pediastrum* (bottom) are algae that live in colonies. Like plants, they use sunlight to make food. (colored SEMs; magnifications unknown)

Apply **What one characteristic do all protists share?**

MAIN IDEA

Protists are difficult to classify.

Recall from Chapter 17 that the three-domain system of classification divides prokaryotes into two domains, Archaea and Bacteria, and places all eukaryotes in one domain, Eukarya. There are four kingdoms within the domain Eukarya: Animalia, Fungi, Plantae, and Protista. The kingdom Protista includes many phyla. These phyla are very different from one another, and most are only distantly related. In fact, many protists are more closely related to members of other kingdoms than to other protists.

Kingdom Protista can be considered the junk-drawer of the kingdoms. It is a kingdom for all the eukaryotes that don't seem to fit in the animal, plant, or fungi definitions. Now that molecular biology techniques have revealed the genetic relationships between groups of organisms, many biologists think the protist kingdom will eventually be divided into several kingdoms within the domain Eukarya. If the genetic differences used to classify fungi, plants, and animals were used as a guide for classifying protists, we'd end up with more than 15 kingdoms of eukaryotes rather than the four we currently use. Until there is a widely accepted division of kingdom Protista into multiple kingdoms, the term *protist* remains useful when studying the group.

Connecting CONCEPTS

Classification Recall from **Chapter 17** that the six-kingdom model is made of two prokaryotic kingdoms and four eukaryotic kingdoms.

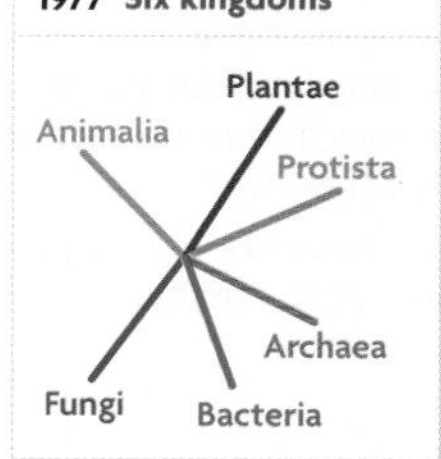

Science Trivia

- The largest slime mold on record was 91 centimeters (3 ft) wide and 914 centimeters (30 ft) long.
- Giant kelp, a type of alga, can grow 30 meters (100 ft) in one year and 35 centimeters (14 in.) in a single day.

Take It Further

Can **slime molds** think? Not really, but they can negotiate a maze. A team of Japanese scientists placed chunks of the slime mold *Physarum polycephalum* in a small gel maze that contained four pathways out. The mold extended its mass randomly, filling all available space in the maze. Next, the scientists placed pieces of food at two of the four exit points. The mold then changed position, extending its entirety between the two sources of nutrients, taking the shortest route possible. This suggests that the presence of food caused a chemical response in the slime mold that made it contract, extending it toward both food locations. Scientists surmise that such a cellular response is a type of primitive intelligence.

Answers

A Apply All protists are eukaryotes.

PRE-AP

Have students speculate why single-celled organisms might be more of a challenge to classify than multicellular organisms. Suggest they organize their thoughts into a cluster diagram. They should consider the "body" that is being classified as well as how modes of reproduction might affect diversity.

Biology Toolkit, Brainstorming, p. C11; Cluster Diagram, p. C30

▼ Teach *continued*

TEACH FROM VISUALS

FIGURE 19.3 Review the phylogenetic tree shown in the figure. **Ask**

- To which kingdoms are the slime molds most closely related? Fungi and Animalia
- Which of the following are more closely related—green algae and oak trees, or green algae and red algae? green algae and oak trees

Answers

A Summarize Techniques in molecular biology have revealed how different some groups of protists are compared to each other. They have as many differences as the fungi, plant, and animal kingdoms have compared to each other.

▼ Assess and Reteach

Assess Use the Online Quiz or Section Quiz (*Assessment Book*, p. 373).

Reteach Create a three-column chart on the board and have students describe the three types of protists and some examples of each.

FIGURE 19.3 Relationships of Protists to Other Eukaryotes

All protists currently belong to kingdom Protista, but some protists are more closely related to other kingdoms than to members of their own kingdom.

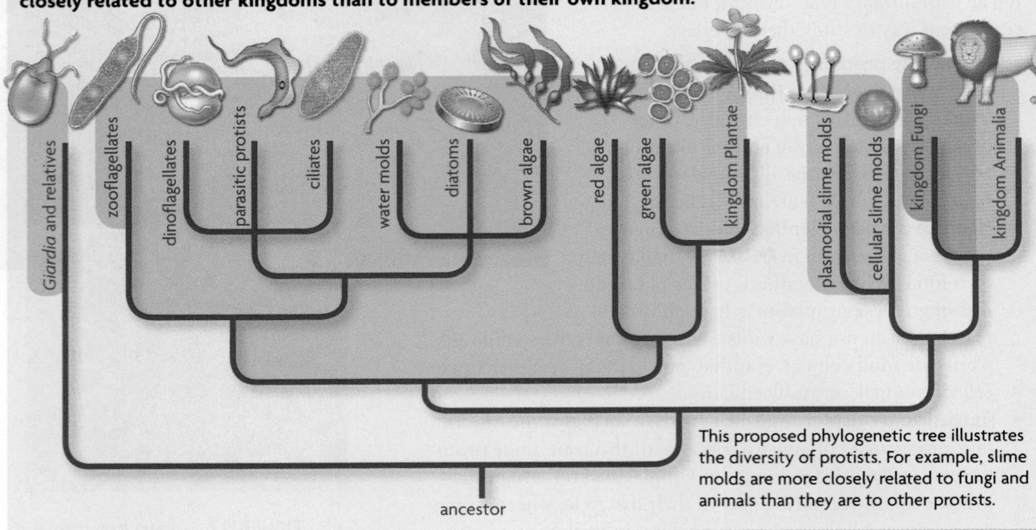

This proposed phylogenetic tree illustrates the diversity of protists. For example, slime molds are more closely related to fungi and animals than they are to other protists.

You can see the genetic relationship of protists to each other and to other kingdoms in **FIGURE 19.3.** For example, a comparison of RNA sequences between plants and green algae indicates that green algae are more closely related to plants than to other algae. Protist classification is a very active area of research, and in the future may provide insight into areas of study such as preventing or treating protist-caused diseases.

 **Summarize What is the argument for placing protists in more than one kingdom?**

19.1 ASSESSMENT

ONLINE QUIZ ClassZone.com

B.8.2

REVIEWING MAIN IDEAS

1. Name the three main groups within the kingdom Protista. What characteristics distinguish each group from the other two?
2. Give two reasons why **protists** are difficult to classify.

CRITICAL THINKING

3. **Infer** What observable traits might green algae and plants share that support the molecular evidence that these two groups are closely related?
4. **Contrast** At one time, scientists grouped all single-celled organisms together. What are the main differences between single-celled protists and bacteria or archaea?

***Connecting* CONCEPTS**

5. **Ecology** Organisms that get their food by ingesting it are called heterotrophs, while those that make their own food are called autotrophs. Categorize animal-like, plant-like, and funguslike protists using these two terms.

19.1 ASSESSMENT

1. protozoa—heterotrophic consumers; algae—autotrophic producers; slime molds—heterotrophic decomposers
2. Answers should include two of the following: Some protist phyla are very distantly related, and some are more closely related to members of other kingdoms than they are to other protists. The definition of protists is based on the absence of traits that characterize the other kingdoms.
3. *Sample Answer:* Both are green, have chloroplasts, are eukaryotic, and are (sometimes) multicellular.
4. Protists are eukaryotic, meaning they are made up of cells that have a nucleus and membrane-bound organelles; bacteria and archaea are prokaryotic, meaning their cells do not have a nucleus or organelles.
5. Animal-like protists and funguslike protists are heterotrophs; plantlike protists are autotrophs.

19.2 Animal-like Protists

KEY CONCEPT Animal-like protists are single-celled heterotrophs that can move.

MAIN IDEAS

- Animal-like protists move in various ways.
- Some animal-like protists cause disease.

VOCABULARY

protozoa, p. 577
pseudopod, p. 578
cilia, p. 578

Review
flagella, heterotroph, phagocytosis, conjugation

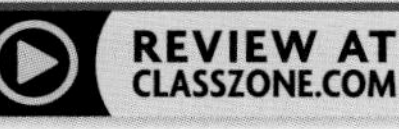

Connect Think of all the ways that different animals move. Some walk on two legs, while others walk on four. Some spend most of their time flying, while others can only swim. Just like animals, animal-like protists use different ways to get around.

MAIN IDEA

Animal-like protists move in various ways.

The animal-like protists represent the largest number of species in the kingdom Protista. In the early two-kingdom classification system, some protists were classified as animals because they had many animal-like traits. Like animals, they can move around, they consume other organisms, and their cells lack chloroplasts. The key difference between animal-like protists and animals is their body organization: all animal-like protists are unicellular, while animals are multicellular. The term **protozoa** is often used informally to describe the many phyla of animal-like protists. A few common protozoan groups are discussed below.

Protozoa with Flagella

The zooflagellates (zoh-uh-FLAJ-uh-lihts) are animal-like protists that have one or more flagella at some point in their life cycle. Recall from Chapter 18 that flagella are tail-like structures that help unicellular organisms swim. Although the flagella of zooflagellates (phylum Zoomastigophora) look like the flagella of prokaryotes, they are structurally very different. Prokaryotic flagella attach to the surface of the cell. In contrast, eukaryotic flagella, such as those of the zooflagellate shown in **FIGURE 19.4**, are extensions of the cytoplasm. They are made of bundles of small tubes called microtubules and are enclosed by the plasma membrane. Prokaryotic flagella are also much smaller than the flagella of protists. You can easily see protist flagella with the aid of a light microscope, but prokaryotic flagella are invisible at the same magnification.

More than 2000 species of zooflagellates exist. All free-living zooflagellates are heterotrophs. For example, some zooflagellates eat prokaryotes that feed on dissolved organic matter, playing an important role in recycling nutrients through aquatic ecosystems. Other zooflagellates are pathogens, or disease-causing parasites of humans and other animals. Some zooflagellates live inside other organisms in mutualism—a relationship in which both organisms benefit.

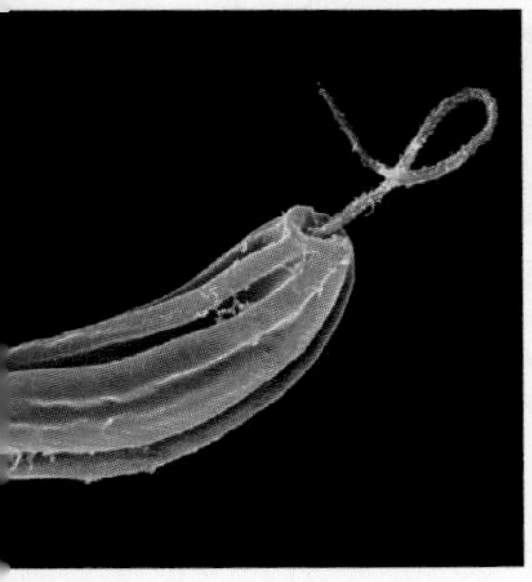

FIGURE 19.4 Zooflagellates have flagella that help them move through water. (colored SEM; magnification unknown)

Differentiated Instruction

ENGLISH LEARNERS

Have students record definitions of the words *zooflagellate, amoeba, foraminifera,* and *paramecium* in the left column of a two-column chart. In the right column, they should make a simple drawing of each, using the figures from the section as guides. Have students pair up to show each other their drawings. Tell students to use vocabulary and information from the section to describe and label the features of the four protozoa.

Biology Toolkit, Combination Notes, p. C23

SECTION 19.2

Plan and Prepare

Objectives

- Recognize the three types of locomotion used by protozoa.
- Identify three parasitic protozoa and the diseases they cause.

Section Resources

Unit Resource Book
Study Guide pp. 65–66
Power Notes p. 67
Reinforcement p. 68

Interactive Reader Chapter 19
Spanish Study Guide pp. 197–198

Biology Toolkit pp. C19, C23, C38

Technology
Power Presentation 19.2
Media Gallery DVD
Online Quiz 19.2

Activate Prior Knowledge Discuss the characteristics of animals. **Ask,** When you think of an animal, what are its basic characteristics? It moves, gets its nutrients from other organisms, does not have chloroplasts, and is multicellular. Tell students that animal-like protists, or protozoa, are like animals except that protozoa have only one cell.

Teach

Vocabulary

Greek and Latin Word Origins The word **protozoa** comes from the Greek *proto-*, meaning "first," and *zoion*, meaning "animal." The term *protozoa* was coined in the early 19th century when these organisms were still classified in the animal kingdom. The term was intended to distinguish the more primitive single-celled animals from the so-called true animals.

▼ Teach *continued*

Take It Further

Paramecium bursaria has an interesting strategy for survival. It is capable of farming *Chlorella,* a species of algae, within its own cytoplasm. The paramecium receives nutrients produced by the photosynthetic alga, and the alga receives a safe home. When other sources of nutrients are scarce, however, *P. bursaria* digests its algal symbionts as a source of nutrition.

History of Science

Dutch scientist **Antonie van Leeuwenhoek** (1632–1723) was the first person to observe protozoa under a microscope. Van Leeuwenhoek was untrained as a scientist, but he became fascinated with observing the miniscule and the invisible. He improved upon the first simple microscope that used a single small lens to produce a clear image of the specimen being observed. While examining a drop of pond water under his microscope, he observed little animal-like organisms swimming rapidly around. Van Leeuwenhoek called these organisms **animalcules,** a name that endured for almost 200 years, until it was discarded in the 1920s in favor of protozoa.

Integrating Epidemiology

Amoebic dysentery is a severe form of amoebiasis, an infection caused by a parasitic amoeba, *Entamoeba histolytica.* Usually transmitted through fecal contamination of drinking water, this amoeba causes gastrointestinal pain and diarrhea. At the 1933 World's Fair in Chicago, sewage contaminated the drinking water, causing amoebiasis in 1000 people, and killing 58.

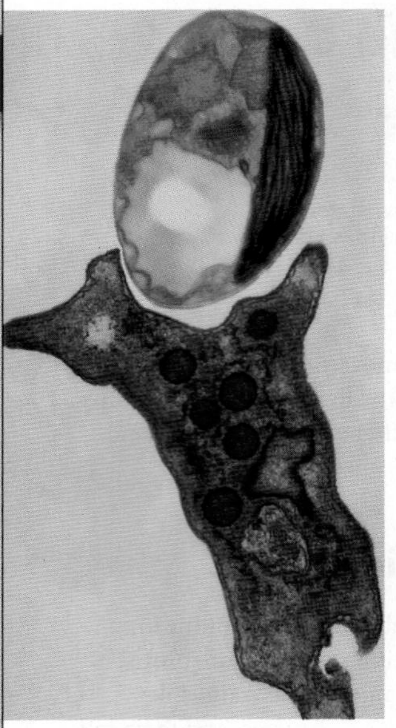

FIGURE 19.5 An amoeba extends a pseudopod to surround and ingest an algal cell. (LM; magnification 4,200×)

Sometimes zooflagellates play a crucial role in another organism's life. For example, termites cannot digest the wood they eat. Inside the gut of a termite is a complex community made of zooflagellates and bacteria that *can* digest wood. The termites get nutrition from the zooflagellate's activity, and the zooflagellates get free meals and a place to live.

Protozoa with Pseudopods

Two groups of protozoa that can easily change shape as they move are the amoebas and the foraminifera.

Amoebas The amoebas (uh-MEE-buhz) are very flexible. Amoebas (phylum Rhizopoda) form pseudopods to move. A **pseudopod** (SOO-duh-PAHD), which means "fake foot," is a temporary extension of cytoplasm and plasma membrane that helps protozoa move and feed. To form a pseudopod, the cell cytoplasm flows outward, forming a bulge. This bulge spreads, anchors itself to the surface it is on, and pulls the rest of the cell toward it. Pseudopod formation uses energy. When the amoeba is not moving or feeding, it does not form pseudopods.

An amoeba's method of getting food is shown in **FIGURE 19.5.** Ingestion takes place by the process of phagocytosis. Recall from Chapter 3 that phagocytosis is the engulfing of solid material by a cell. The amoeba surrounds the food with its pseudopod, and the outer membrane of the amoeba then forms a food vacuole, or sac. Digestive enzymes enter the food vacuole from the surrounding cytoplasm, and digestion takes place.

Amoebas live in fresh water, salt water, and soil. The majority of amoebas are free-living, but some species are parasites. Most amoebas are microscopic. However, *Pelomyxa palustris* is an amoeba that can grow as large as five millimeters in diameter—a huge size for a single-celled organism—and can be seen without a microscope.

Connecting CONCEPTS

Cell Organelles Recall from **Chapter 3** that a vacuole is a fluid-filled sac used for the temporary storage of materials needed by the cell.

Foraminifera Another group of protozoa with pseudopods are members of phylum Foraminifera (fuh-RAM-uh-NIHF-uhr-uh). Foraminifera, sometimes simply called forams, are named for their multichambered shell, shown in **FIGURE 19.6.** The Latin word *foramen* means "little hole." Their shells are made of organic matter, sand, or other materials, depending on the species. Forams make up a large group of marine protozoa that, like amoeba, use pseudopods to move.

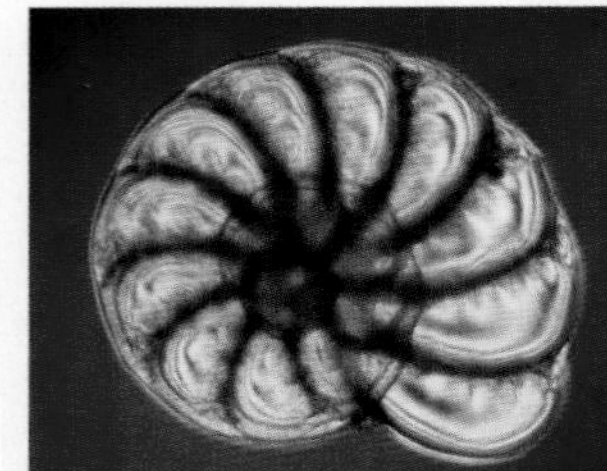

FIGURE 19.6 Pseudopods can extend from pores in a foraminifera's multichambered shell. This shell is smaller than the head of a matchstick.

Protozoa with Cilia

This group's name, Ciliates, comes from its most obvious feature—cilia. **Cilia** are short, hairlike structures that cover some or all of the cell surface and help the organism swim and capture food. Cilia are usually much shorter than flagella and found in much greater numbers. Some ciliates have many rows of cilia all over their surface, whereas other ciliates just have clusters of cilia.

Differentiated Instruction

TEACH WITH TECHNOLOGY

Go to the Media Gallery and the chapter resources at **ClassZone.com** to show students movies of protist movement.

About 8000 species of ciliates make up the phylum Ciliophora. Some ciliates are parasites that cause disease. However, most ciliates are free-living cells found in fresh water, such as the common pondwater protists in the genus *Paramecium*.

Structures of a paramecium are shown in **FIGURE 19.7.** Food is swept into the oral groove by the cilia, and is sent to the gullet. Eventually the food is digested in food vacuoles. Two organs that act like pumps, called contractile vacuoles, control the amount of water inside the cell. An unusual trait found in paramecia and other ciliates is the presence of two types of nuclei. Each cell has one large macronucleus, but there can be many small micronuclei. The macronucleus controls the cell's structures and activities. The micronuclei contain all of the cell's chromosomes. They function only during conjugation, a process of genetic exchange. Two paramecia unite at the oral grooves and exchange micronuclei. Some species of the genus *Paramecium* have up to 80 micronuclei. Because micronuclei can be exchanged during conjugation, having so many micronuclei allows for a huge amount of genetic variation.

A **Summarize** **What functions do the two kinds of nuclei within *Paramecium* perform?**

FIGURE 19.7 PARAMECIUM

A paramecium is a single-celled protist covered with thousands of cilia. Its organelles can be identified through its transparent cell membrane.

Animated BIOLOGY Watch how protists move at ClassZone.com.

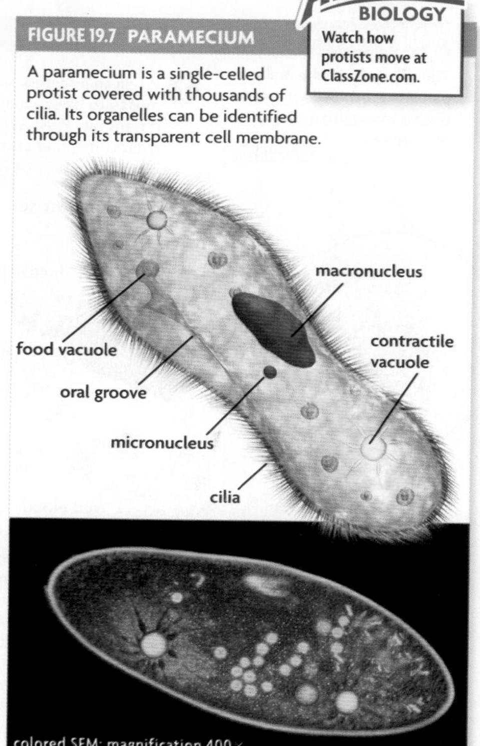

colored SEM; magnification 400×

QUICK LAB OBSERVING

NOS.3

Investigating Motion in Protists

In this investigation you will observe the movement of one or more of the following protists: *Paramecium, Amoeba,* or *Euglena.*

PROBLEM What does a protist's movement look like?

1. Make a wet mount slide of the protist. You may need to add a drop of methylcellulose solution to the wet mount so that you can slow down the organism enough to observe. **Caution:** Do not use a cover slip on the amoeba slide, as you will crush the organism.
2. Observe how the organism moves. Make a series of three drawings that depict the movement of the organism.
3. If time allows, repeat steps 1 and 2 with the other two protists.

ANALYZE AND CONCLUDE

1. **Analyze** Describe the movement of the protist(s) you observed.
2. **Analyze** What structures did the protist that you observed use to move?
3. **Infer** Based on the structures you observed, do you think the species of protist that you observed swims in the water or crawls in the bottom sediments? Explain.

MATERIALS

- 4 eyedroppers
- 4 drops bottled spring water
- 3 microscope slides
- 2 cover slips
- culture of *Paramecium*
- 3 drops methylcellulose solution
- culture of *Amoeba*
- culture of *Euglena*
- microscope

ONLINE BIOLOGY Go to the chapter Resource Center at **ClassZone.com** for additional resources and information on protozoa.

TEACH FROM VISUALS

FIGURE 19.7 Review the labeled structures in **FIGURE 19.7.** Point out that paramecia live in a hypotonic environment. **Ask**

- What is one of the biggest challenges of living in such an environment? Water tends to flow into the cell and must be removed to maintain homeostasis.
- Which structures help the paramecium pump out water? contractile vacuoles
- What would happen if the contractile vacuoles stopped working? Water would keep moving into the cell until it burst.

Answers

A **Summarize** The macronucleus controls cell structures and activities. Micronuclei contain all the cell's chromosomes and function only during conjugation, a process of genetic exchange.

QUICK LAB TEACHER TESTED

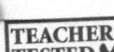

Time 20 minutes
Lab Binder Diversity, p. 34

Purpose Observe the movement of protozoa.

Answers

Analyze and Conclude

1. Paramecia glide, amoeba creep, and euglena swim.
2. Paramecia use cilia, amoebas use pseudopods, and euglena use flagella.
3. Euglena swim; amoebas crawl on the bottom; paramecia do both.

PRE-AP

Have students review the functions of the organelles and other structures shown in the paramecium diagram in **FIGURE 19.7.** Then ask them to write a paragraph entitled "A Day in the Life of a Paramecium," describing how the organism finds food, what happens to ingested food, how it mates, and how it maintains homeostasis. The paragraph should incorporate all the structures shown in the diagram.

Biology Toolkit, Quick-Write, p. C19

BELOW LEVEL

Have students create a sequence diagram for the life cycle of the malaria parasite shown in **FIGURE 19.8** on page 580. Students should begin with a mosquito biting an infected human host. Have students compare their sequence diagrams with a partner to ensure that their diagrams begin with the mosquito's ingestion of *Plasmodium* cells from the infected human, and end with red blood cells bursting and releasing *Plasmodium* cells.

Biology Toolkit, Sequence Diagram, p. C38

▼ Teach *continued*

ONLINE BIOLOGY For more on sleeping sickness, malaria, and giardiasis, see the WebQuest in Options for Inquiry on page 601.

History of Science

One of the great engineering feats of the 20th century was the construction of the **Panama Canal.** One of the great feats of public health was that the loss of life among construction workers to **malaria** and **yellow fever** during the canal's construction was not higher.

The United States began work on the canal in 1904. By late 1906, the death rate due to malaria among workers was 11.59 per 1000. Public health officials implemented a multifaceted program to make the environment less mosquito-friendly, largely by draining ponds and cutting brush. By December 1909, the death rate from malaria had dropped to 1.23 per 1000.

Answers

A Compare *Plasmodium* is transmitted by mosquito bites, whereas *Giardia* is ingested through contaminated water.

▼ Assess and Reteach

Assess Use the Online Quiz or Section Quiz (*Assessment Book,* p. 374).

Reteach Project images of **FIGURES 19.4, 19.5,** and **19.7** from the Media Gallery and have students describe the lifestyles of these protists.

FIGURE 19.8 LIFE CYCLE OF THE MALARIA PARASITE

The life cycle of the malaria parasite *Plasmodium* requires both a mosquito and a human host.

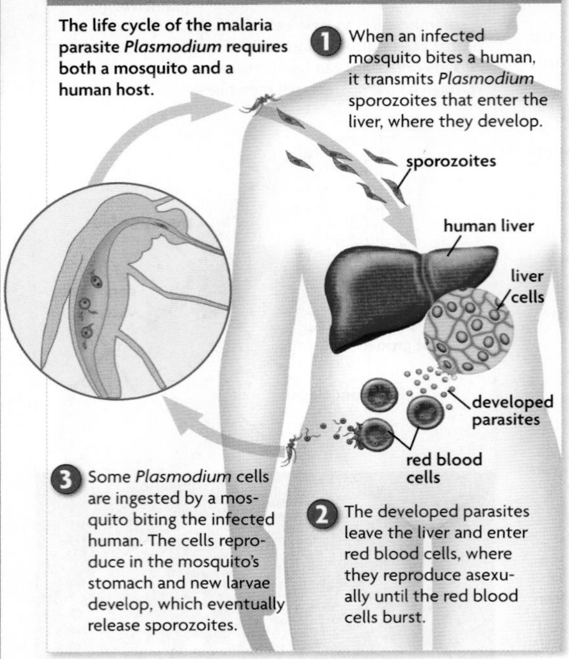

1 When an infected mosquito bites a human, it transmits *Plasmodium* sporozoites that enter the liver, where they develop.

sporozoites

human liver

liver cells

developed parasites

red blood cells

2 The developed parasites leave the liver and enter red blood cells, where they reproduce asexually until the red blood cells burst.

3 Some *Plasmodium* cells are ingested by a mosquito biting the infected human. The cells reproduce in the mosquito's stomach and new larvae develop, which eventually release sporozoites.

MAIN IDEA

Some animal-like protists cause disease.

Protists cause some of the world's most well-known infectious diseases. The phylum Apicomplexa (A-pih-kuhm-PLEHK-suh) includes about 4000 species, all of which are parasites of animals. Many members of this phylum are known as sporozoans because they form sporozoites—infectious cells that have tough outer coats. Malaria is an example of a disease caused by sporozoans. It is caused by infection with the protozoan *Plasmodium*, shown in **FIGURE 19.8.**

Malaria is passed to humans and other animals through the bite of the *Anopheles* mosquito. Symptoms of malaria include high fever and vomiting. In some cases, the parasite can severely affect kidney and liver function, leading to coma and even death. Although the disease was once on the decline, today more than 1 million people—mostly children in developing countries—die from malaria each year. Mosquitoes have developed resistance to the insecticides that once would kill them, and *Plasmodium* species have become resistant to antimalarial drugs.

Two other parasitic protists that cause disease are the zooflagellates *Trypanosoma* and *Giardia.* In Africa, several species of *Trypanosoma* cause the disease known as sleeping sickness in humans and other mammals. Trypanosomes are transmitted through the bite of the tsetse fly, and can cause coma and death. *Giardia* causes intestinal disease in humans. People can become infected with *Giardia* by drinking water contaminated with feces of infected animals. Campers and hikers must be careful of *Giardia*, as even streams or rivers that appear clean could be contaminated.

A Compare How do the parasites *Plasmodium* and *Giardia* each infect humans?

19.2 ASSESSMENT

ONLINE QUIZ ClassZone.com

REVIEWING MAIN IDEAS

1. Name and describe the three basic means of movement used by animal-like protists.
2. Describe how the parasite *Plasmodium* causes disease in humans.

CRITICAL THINKING

3. **Compare and Contrast** In what ways are **cilia** and flagella similar? How are they different?
4. **Infer** Why do amoebas form **pseudopods** only when they need them?

***Connecting* CONCEPTS**

5. **Analogous Structures** The flagella of eukaryotes and prokaryotes serve the same function, but they are structurally very different. What does this suggest about the evolution of flagella?

19.2 ASSESSMENT

1. flagella: tail-like extensions of cytoplasm that are used in a whiplike motion to propel the organism forward; pseudopods: the plasma membrane and cytoplasm extend to form a bulge that anchors to the surface and pulls the rest of the organism along; cilia: short hairlike structures on the surface of the organism that wave
2. The bite of a mosquito carrying *Plasmodium* transmits sporozoites into a human's bloodstream. The sporozoites enter the liver, where they develop and then move to red blood cells. They reproduce asexually until the red blood cells burst open, releasing *Plasmodium* cells that can then be ingested by mosquitoes that bite the infected host. Symptoms include severe fever, vomiting, and possibly liver and kidney problems.
3. Cilia and flagella are both used for movement in protists. Both are formed from the cell membrane and are permanent structures. However, cilia are shorter and more hairlike and can be in rows or clusters that cover parts of a cell or the entire cell. Flagella are longer, and there are usually only one or two per cell.
4. because pseudopod formation requires energy
5. The flagella of eukaryotes and prokaryotes arose separately and are an example of convergent evolution.

19.3 Plantlike Protists

KEY CONCEPT Algae are plantlike protists.

MAIN IDEAS

- Plantlike protists can be single-celled or multicellular.
- Many plantlike protists can reproduce both sexually and asexually.

VOCABULARY

algae, p. 581

Review

phytoplankton, gamete, plankton, haploid, mitosis, diploid, meiosis

Connect On your birthday, do you enjoy decorations on your cake, or do you prefer it topped with ice cream? Both cake decorations and ice cream are among the many products that commonly contain substances from seaweeds, types of plantlike protists.

MAIN IDEA

Plantlike protists can be single-celled or multicellular.

Just as animal-like protists were once classified as animals, it is not surprising that many plantlike protists used to be classified as plants. Although many plantlike protists look like plants, they are different in many ways. Unlike plants, plantlike protists do not have roots, stems, leaves, specialized tissues, or the same reproductive structures that plants have. All plants are multicellular, while plantlike protists may be single-celled or multicellular.

Many single-celled plantlike protists are free-living aquatic organisms that, together with photosynthetic bacteria, are known as phytoplankton. Recall from Chapter 15 that phytoplankton form the base of aquatic food chains and provide about half of the oxygen in Earth's atmosphere. Several species of single-celled plantlike protists, such as *Volvox,* shown in **FIGURE 19.9,** live in colonies. Multicellular plantlike protists include the seaweeds or kelps. Some species eat other organisms, but most plantlike protists have chloroplasts and can produce their own food through photosynthesis. Photosynthetic plantlike protists are called **algae.**

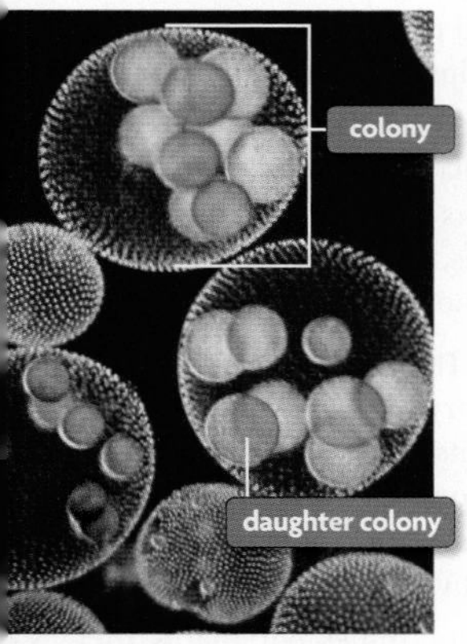

colony

daughter colony

FIGURE 19.9 *Volvox* are actually hundreds of individual algae cells that join together to form a colony in the shape of a hollow ball. Offspring form smaller daughter colonies inside the parent colony. (LM; magnification 50×)

From Single-Celled to Multicellular

In the distant past, single-celled organisms combined to become multicellular. It is likely that multicellular algae arose from colonies of algae such as *Volvox.* Members of the order Volvocales include three kinds of forms: single-celled, multicellular forms with every cell acting independently, and multicellular forms in which the cells are specialized. In the evolution from single-celled to multicellular algae, some individual cells in colonies were probably very efficient at certain tasks, such as digesting food or producing gametes. These cells and their offspring would have become more specialized over time, and eventually may have become dependent on each other. Over many generations, colonies could have led to multicellular forms.

Differentiated Instruction

ENGLISH LEARNERS

After students read the section, set up a round table by dividing them into four groups. Give each group a sheet of paper, and write this topic sentence on the board: *There are many types of single-celled and multicellular plantlike protists.* Give students three minutes to review the chapter, and then ask them to close their books. Have one student in each group write something he or she knows about the topic on the paper and pass it to the next student. That student should write something different about the topic, and so on. After a minute or two, circulate to see if students have listed the categories of euglenoids, dinoflagellates, diatoms, green algae, brown algae, and red algae. If not, write at least some of these categories on the board to start the brainstorming process. After students write for ten minutes, ask one student from each group to read the group list. Then have students compile a class list.

Biology Toolkit, Round Table, p. C10

Plan and Prepare

Objectives

- Identify six major groups of plantlike protists.
- Recognize the reproductive strategies used by plantlike protists.

Section Resources

Unit Resource Book Study Guide pp. 69–70 Power Notes p. 71 Reinforcement p. 72
Interactive Reader Chapter 19 **Spanish Study Guide** pp. 199–200
Biology Toolkit pp. C10, C36, C40
Technology Power Presentation 19.3 Media Gallery DVD Online Quiz 19.3

Activate Prior Knowledge Algae is commonly viewed as a slimy green scum that floats on ponds and covers rocks near the seashore. So it is not surprising that many people cringe at the thought of eating algae. **Ask,** Who has eaten sushi? Answers will vary. Explain that the dark green *nori* around maki rolls is a kind of seaweed, which is a type of algae. You may also want to mention that algae and algal products have many commercial applications such as in food processing and cosmetics manufacture.

Teach

Vocabulary

algae The plural forms of some Latin words can be confusing. Words ending in *a,* such as *alga,* are generally made plural by adding an *e,* forming *algae;* some words, such as *amoeba,* are commonly made plural by adding either an *s* or an *e.* Tell students that both *amoebas* and *amoebae* are correct plural forms.

▼ Teach *continued*

Science Trivia

- The eyespot on a euglenoid shades a light-sensitive receptor that helps orient the organism toward light.
- If kept in darkness, a euglenoid's green chloroplasts will disappear.

Integrating Ecology

The toxic dinoflagellate alga *Alexandrium fundyense* is responsible for the harmful algal blooms commonly called **red tides.** In 2005, a bloom of this alga in the marine waters of New England caused the closure of shellfish beds for much of the summer—the peak season for shellfishing and shellfish consumption. It was estimated that the bloom cost the New England shellfish industry $3 million per week. The danger of such a bloom is that filter-feeding mollusks such as soft-shell clams (steamers), quahogs, oysters, and blue mussels accumulate the toxin of the abundant algae and that this buildup of toxin can then be ingested by humans, causing an illness known as paralytic shellfish poisoning (PSP).

Scientists suspected that the high levels of precipitation in the previous winter and spring created ideal conditions for the alga by flushing more nutrients into the coastal waters. The fresh water running off from land may have also created a buoyant surface layer of water to carry the algal bloom—a natural summertime phenomenon in the colder waters of the Gulf of Maine—south towards Cape Cod and the rest of southern New England. About 15,000 square miles of ocean were closed to shellfishing as a result of the 2005 red tide.

FIGURE 19.10 EUGLENA

A euglena has both animal-like structures—such as an eyespot, contractile vacuoles, and flagella—and plantlike structures, such as chloroplasts.

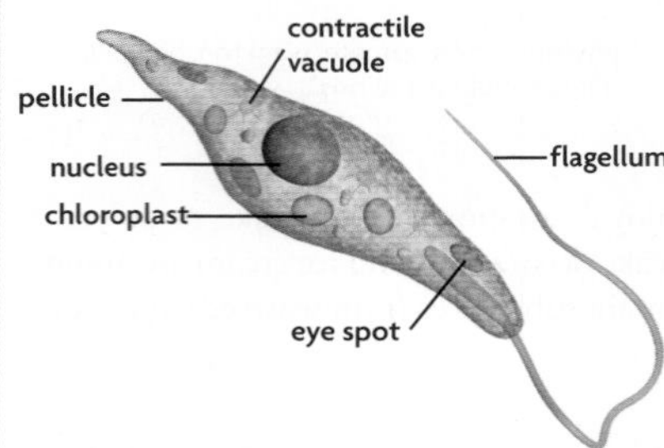

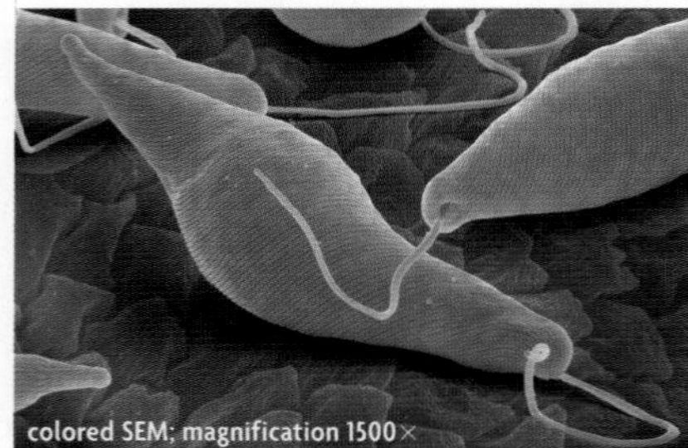

Diversity of Plantlike Protists

Plantlike protists are found in most habitats on Earth. Most are aquatic organisms that live in freshwater and marine ecosystems. Some species live in deserts, while others live in the tundra. Despite their great diversity, plantlike protists have certain features in common, such as the chlorophyll they use for photosynthesis. Also, most plantlike protists have flagella at some point in their life cycle. Although their classification will likely change, for now many biologists group the plantlike protists into several phyla based on their photosynthetic pigments and cell wall structure.

Euglenoids The euglenoids (phylum Euglenophyta) are a large group of single-celled organisms that swim with the aid of one or two flagella. Although most of these species are found in fresh water, some live in ocean environments. Members of this group are both animal-like and plantlike. Like animals, these protists can move around easily. Euglenoids have a pellicle, a flexible coatlike covering on their cell surface. The pellicle allows the cell to change shape. In some species, the pellicle helps the organism to creep across solid surfaces using a type of movement that resembles the inching movement of worms. Although some colorless species of euglenoids eat other organisms, most make their own food through photosynthesis.

Plantlike photosynthetic euglenoids are green, such as the euglena shown in **FIGURE 19.10.** Their bright green color comes from two different chlorophyll pigments, called chlorophyll *a* and *b*. Chlorophyll *a* is found in all photosynthesizing organisms. Chlorophyll *b* is found only in green algae and plants.

VOCABULARY

The name *dinoflagellates* comes from the Greek word *dinos,* meaning "whirling," and the Latin word *flagrum,* meaning "whip." This name describes how dinoflagellates move.

Dinoflagellates The dinoflagellates (phylum Dinoflagellata) are single-celled. About 90 percent of dinoflagellates are marine plankton. Recall from Chapter 15 that plankton are often microscopic organisms that live suspended in the water. Some dinoflagellates are freshwater species, and a few species have even been found in snow. About half of all marine dinoflagellates photosynthesize.

Dinoflagellates have two flagella, as shown in **FIGURE 19.11.** One flagellum extends from the rear of the cell and propels it forward. The other is a ribbonlike strand that circles the cell in a groove along its body. This flagellum allows the cell to turn over and change direction. The combination of the two flagella cause this protist to turn in a spiral as it moves forward. Some species also have a covering of stiff plates that form a protective armor.

Some dinoflagellates, such as *Noctiluca,* are bioluminescent; that is, they can produce light through internal chemical reactions. The name *Noctiluca* means "night-light." If you have ever visited the ocean at night, you may have seen these tiny, blue glowing organisms along the surface of the water. They give off light when they are disturbed. The light may act as an alarm to help them avoid being eaten.

Differentiated Instruction

INCLUSION

Students who have a hard time sorting out information may need to create a table or an outline that identifies each major plantlike protist group and then gives details about that group. Students can adapt the style of the chart depending on their needs; for example, students who are visually impaired may need to use heavy markers and large lettering, while students who have learning disabilities may want to color-code each group.

Certain other photosynthetic dinoflagellates help build coral reefs through their symbiotic partnership with corals. These dinoflagellates live in the inner tissues of the corals. In return for shelter from the corals, the dinoflagellates provide the corals with nutrients in tropical waters that are usually nutrient-poor.

Some species of dinoflagellates produce toxins. A large population of these dinoflagellates can create what is known as a red tide, due to the reddish color produced by a high density of these species. Red tides, shown in **FIGURE 19.11**, occur when changes in ocean currents bring up nutrients from far below the ocean surface. The higher nutrient levels produce a rapid increase, or bloom, in the dinoflagellate population. A toxic bloom in the waters can kill large numbers of fish. The toxins can also build up in the tissues of shellfish, which then can be dangerous to humans who eat the contaminated seafood.

Diatoms Most diatoms (phylum Bacillariophyta) are easy to recognize when viewed through a microscope. These tiny single-celled algae are covered with delicately patterned glasslike shells. The shells of diatoms serve almost as an external skeleton, helping the cell to hold a rigid shape. Diatom shells, such as those shown in **FIGURE 19.12**, are made of silica, the same brittle substance that is used to make glass. The silica shell is divided into two parts that overlap each other, like the lid of a box.

Like other autotrophs, all diatoms release oxygen into the environment. In fact, diatoms could be considered the world champions of photosynthesis. They play a critical role in the uptake of carbon dioxide on Earth and produce about half of the oxygen we breathe. Diatoms may be freshwater or marine. Many species are phytoplankton. Others live clinging to rocks, plants, soil, and even animals—diatoms have been found growing on crustaceans, turtles, and even whales. Because of their glassy, mineralized shells, diatoms have been well preserved in the fossil record. Some fossil rocks consist almost entirely of diatoms. These diatom skeletons have many industrial uses, such as an ingredient in scrubbing products, because of their rough texture.

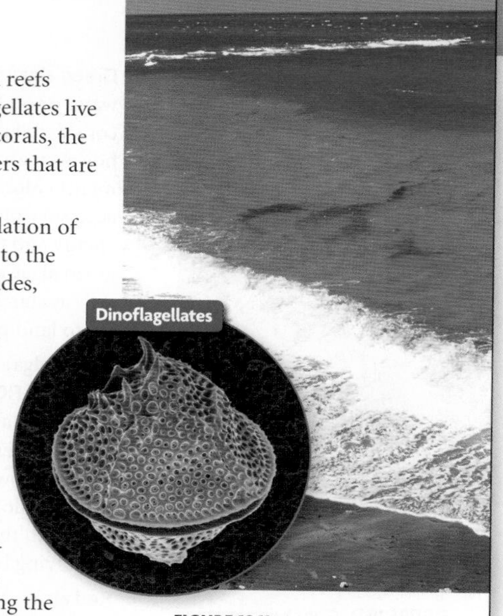

FIGURE 19.11 A high density of dinoflagellates causes reddish coloration of ocean waters, called a red tide. The toxins produced during a red tide can kill sea life and cause illness in humans. (colored SEM; magnification about 850×)

VOCABULARY

The name *diatom* comes from the Greek term *diatomos*, meaning "cut in half." This refers to the appearance of the diatom's overlapping shell.

FIGURE 19.12 DIATOMS

Diatoms are known for their delicate glasslike cell walls, or shells, that can have many shapes. They are common in both freshwater and marine environments.

Animated BIOLOGY Explore algae diatom concentrations over time at ClassZone.com.

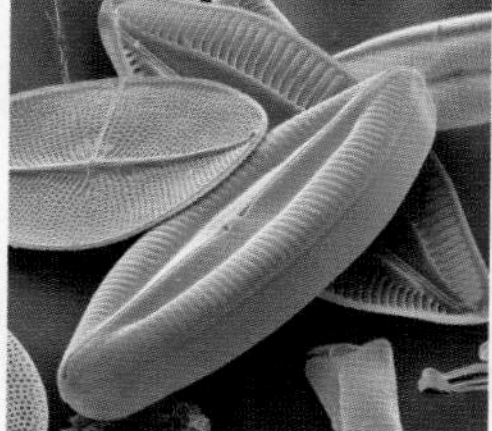

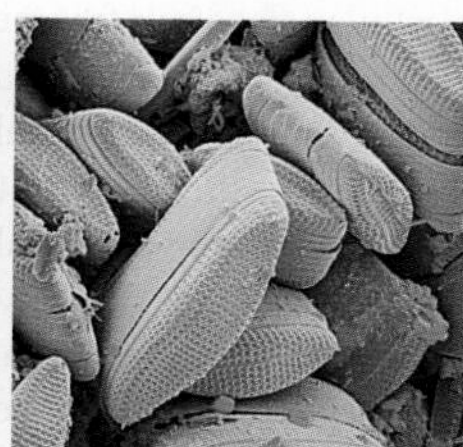

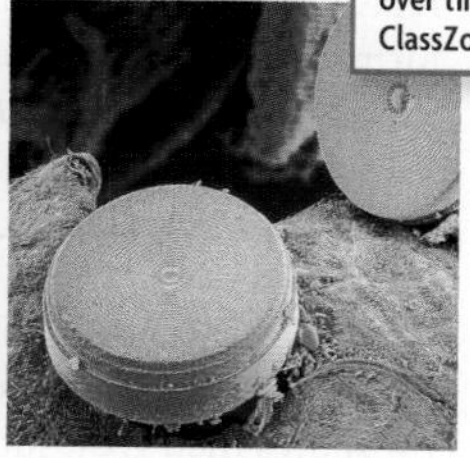

(all colored SEMs; magnification 750×; magnification 250×; magnification unknown)

Address Misconceptions

Common Misconception When the shallow coastal waters are red, it is because of a red tide.

Correcting the Misconception While some harmful algal blooms do create a reddish hue in seawater, there are others that are invisible to the human eye. A harmful red tide may not be red at all. A red color in the water may be due to a bloom or buildup of harmless red algae.

Take It Further

Phytoplankton (free-floating photosynthetic protists such as marine algae, diatoms, and dinoflagellates) play a critical role in global climate and the carbon cycle. They are responsible for roughly half of Earth's photosynthetic activity; as a result, they have a key part in regulating atmospheric CO_2 levels.

Atmospheric CO_2 not taken up by photosynthesis dissolves in oceans and lakes and is converted into carbonate, a form not usable by most plants and algae. Diatoms and other phytoplankton are able to convert carbonate back to CO_2 and use it for photosynthesis. The silica in diatom shells speeds this conversion and helps increase carbon fixation by photosynthesis. When they die, diatoms, along with the carbon they fixed, sink to the ocean floor. As the diatoms decay, the stored carbon is converted into fossil fuel.

PRE-AP

Tell students that the danger of harmful algal blooms to humans is that toxins produced by these particular algae will accumulate in shellfish and then accumulate in a person who eats clams, mussels, or oysters. Have students create a cause and effect chain to show how nutrient runoff from a farm upriver could result in humans getting sick from shellfish in a bay downriver.

Biology Toolkit, Cause and Effect Chain, p. C36

▼ Teach continued

ONLINE BIOLOGY The tropical seaweed *Caulerpa,* accidentally introduced into the Mediterranean Sea in the 1980s, has undergone dramatic and exponential growth. Students can analyze and chart the spread of this organism using the Data Analysis in Options for Inquiry on page 601.

Integrating Ecology

Brown kelp, sea urchins, and sea otters form a food chain in the coastal **kelp forests** of the northeastern Pacific Ocean. As primary producers, brown kelp provides food and shelter for a wide range of organisms. Sea urchins are primary consumers that graze on kelp, and sea otters are the dominant predators of sea urchins. By preying on sea urchins, sea otters keep sea-urchin populations in check, so the forests are not overgrazed.

In the 1990s, the sea-otter population in western Alaska began declining due to predation by killer whales. The whales normally feed on sea lions and seals; however, when these prey populations began declining, whales began hunting sea otters. Scientists attribute the decline in numbers of sea lions and seals to a decline in fish species that they feed on. Thus, the decline in the fish triggered a chain reaction that ultimately led to a population explosion of sea urchins, which are rapidly stripping the kelp forests. If the problem continues, the kelp-forest ecosystem off the coast of Alaska could collapse.

Answers

A Compare and Contrast Green, red, and brown algae are photosynthetic and aquatic. They are usually all multicellular. They all have chlorophyll *a*. Green algae also have chlorophyll *b*, and brown algae also have chlorophyll *c*. Red algae can grow deeper than green and brown algae due to the blue light-absorption properties of the red pigments.

FIGURE 19.13 Giant kelp are a type of brown algae that form underwater forests. The forests are home to a large variety of marine organisms.

Green algae The green algae (phylum Chlorophyta) may be found in the water or on land, although most species are aquatic. Recall that algae are not considered plants because they do not have roots, stems, or leaves. Like plants, however, green algae are multicellular and contain the photosynthetic pigments chlorophyll *a* and chlorophyll *b*. Both plants and green algae also have accessory pigments called carotenoids. Accessory pigments capture light energy and transfer it to chlorophyll during photosynthesis. Both plants and green algae also have cell walls made of cellulose and store food within their cells as starch. These similarities suggest that green algae were an early ancestor to land plants.

Brown algae The brown algae (phylum Phaeophyta) include the giant kelps, shown in **FIGURE 19.13,** that form thick underwater forests. Brown algae are multicellular and can grow to be extremely large. Some giant kelp can grow up to 100 meters high (about 330 ft). Most brown algae live in marine environments. Brown algae are photosynthetic but have a different form of chlorophyll—chlorophyll *c*—than do plants or green algae. Brown algae share this trait with the diatoms. This observation has led some biologists to propose classifying brown algae and diatoms together in their own kingdom.

Red algae Most red algae are found in the ocean, though a few live in freshwater habitats. Red algae (phylum Rhodophyta) use chlorophyll *a* for photosynthesis, but they get their color from the pigment phycoerythrin. Red algae can grow at deeper depths than other algae because the red pigments allow red algae to absorb the blue light that reaches deepest into the ocean. Some species secrete calcium carbonate, forming thick crusts that look like corals and provide habitats for tiny invertebrates. Red algae provide many products for the food industry. Carrageenan and agar, thickening agents used in products such as ice cream, come from red algae. In Japan, red algae is dried to make nori, a seaweed wrap used for sushi.

A Compare and Contrast **What are the similarities and differences between green, brown, and red algae?**

MAIN IDEA

Many plantlike protists can reproduce both sexually and asexually.

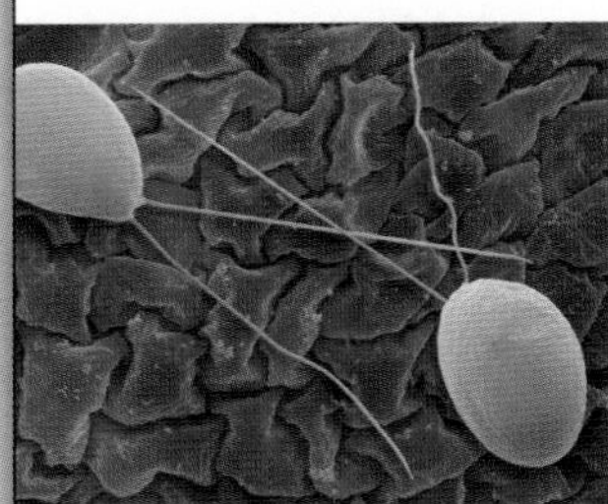

FIGURE 19.14 *Chlamydomonas* are single-celled green algae with two flagella. (colored SEM; magnification 1600×)

Most protists can undergo both sexual and asexual reproduction. All algae can reproduce asexually. Multicellular algae can fragment; each piece is capable of forming a new body. When a single-celled alga, such as the green alga *Chlamydomonas* shown in **FIGURE 19.14,** reproduces asexually, its life cycle is a bit more complex. The dominant phase of the life cycle for this species is haploid. Before reproducing asexually, the haploid parent alga absorbs its flagella and then divides by mitosis. This division may occur two or more times, producing up to eight cells. The daughter cells develop flagella and cell walls. These daughter cells, called zoospores, leave the parent cell, disperse, and grow. The zoospores then grow into mature haploid cells.

Differentiated Instruction

BELOW LEVEL

Draw a concept map to differentiate between asexual reproduction in multicellular and unicellular algae. Begin the map with the sentence "All algae can reproduce asexually." in a circle. The next two circles, branching off from the first, should be labeled "single-celled algae" and "multicellular algae." Help students complete the map.

Biology Toolkit, Concept Map, p. C40

FIGURE 19.15 Life Cycle of Single-Celled Green Algae

Some single-celled green algae, such as *Chlamydomonas*, undergo sexual as well as asexual reproduction.

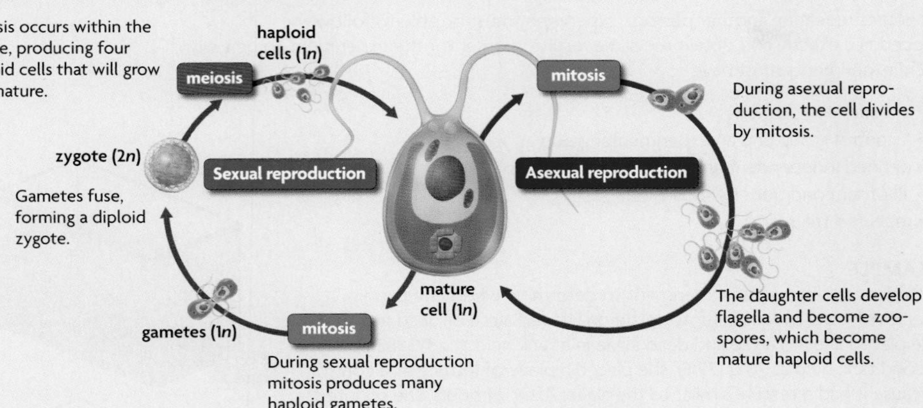

Sexual reproduction occurs in algae as well. Some species alternate generations so that the offspring from sexual reproduction reproduce asexually, and the next generation then reproduces sexually. In other species, asexual reproduction occurs for several generations until conditions change. For the single-celled *Chlamydomonas,* sexual reproduction is triggered by stress such as lack of moisture or food. As shown in **FIGURE 19.15,** it begins with cells dividing by mitosis to produce one of two types of gametes. Because the gametes look identical in most species of *Chlamydomonas,* they are usually identified as different mating types, labeled + and –. When the gametes come together, they join and form a diploid zygote. The zygote may develop into a zygospore by making a thick wall that can protect it during unfavorable conditions. When favorable conditions return, meiosis occurs, producing four haploid cells.

Apply Explain how sudden population increases, or "blooms," of algae may occur.

19.3 ASSESSMENT

ONLINE QUIZ ClassZone.com

REVIEWING  MAIN IDEAS

1. Give an example of each of the following: a single-celled, a colonial, and a multicellular plantlike protist.
2. Many plantlike protists, or **algae,** reproduce sexually when conditions are harsh. Why might this be beneficial for a species?

CRITICAL THINKING

3. **Classify** If a multicellular organism contains chlorophyll *c* but no silica, to which phylum does it likely belong?
4. **Analyze** Many biologists argue that the euglenoids should be classified as an animal-like protist rather than a plantlike protist. Explain.

Connecting CONCEPTS

5. **Ecology** Draw a simple food web for a marine ecosystem. Include dinoflagellates, fish and shellfish, diving birds, and humans in your diagram. What might happen if nutrient levels in the water increased?

ONLINE BIOLOGY Go to the chapter Resource Center at **ClassZone.com** for additional resources and information about algae.

TEACH FROM VISUALS

FIGURE 19.15 Compare sexual and asexual reproduction as illustrated in the figure. **Ask**

- What happens when *Chlamydomonas* undergoes mitosis during asexual reproduction? produces flagellated daughter cells that become zoospores, which become mature haploid cells
- What is the result of mitosis in sexual reproduction of *Chlamydomonas*? produces haploid gametes, which then fuse to become a diploid zygote that undergoes meiosis

Answers

A Apply Changes in conditions, such as a high level of nutrients, can trigger a change in the reproductive strategy of the algae species. For example, they may begin rapidly reproducing asexually, dramatically increasing the population in a short amount of time.

Assess and Reteach ▼

Assess Use the Online Quiz or Section Quiz (*Assessment Book*, p. 375).

Reteach Use the Power Presentation in the Unit Resource Book to review the material in this section.

19.3 ASSESSMENT

1. *Sample Answer:* single-celled plantlike protist: dinoflagellates, euglena, diatoms, Chlamydomonas; colonial protist: volvox; multicellular protist: green, brown, or red algae
2. Sexual reproduction will increase genetic variability within the population, improving the chances that some of the individuals will have traits that will be adaptive to harsh conditions.
3. phylum Phaeophyta, the brown algae
4. Some eugleniods lack chlorophyll and eat other organisms, while others use an animal-like creeping method of locomotion.
5. Food webs should have dinoflagellates as producers and the other organisms as consumers. If nutrient levels in the water increased, the population of dinoflagellates could drastically increase. This could harm humans if the dinoflagellates produce toxins that accumulate up the food chain.

DATA ANALYSIS

Introduce

Remind students that one of the major tenets of science is that an experiment must be repeatable by other scientists, which means that, if students follow the same protocol, they will get the same results as the original scientist. **Ask**

- What is meant by the term *experimental design*? the way that an experiment is to be carried out
- What are the characteristics of a good experiment design? All well-designed experiments have certain features in common: all are built on testable hypotheses; all contain clearly defined constants, variables, and controls; and all can be repeated.

Discuss

Work with students to write a list of the steps taken according to the flawed experimental design described. **Ask**

- What are potential problems in using different species of coral larvae for this experiment? One species may be inhibited from settling on the alga more than another species would.
- What could be the problem with releasing different numbers of larvae into each tank? A small number of larvae in any of the tanks could yield unreliable data due to small sample size. Depending on how the chemical actually inhibits the coral larvae from settling, a large number of larvae could improve the odds of at least some of them settling compared to a small number.

Unit Resource Book, Data Analysis, p. 85

DATA ANALYSIS ClassZone.com

Algae Preference of Coral Larvae

Scientists repeating another person's experiment must be able to follow the procedures exactly and obtain the same results in order for the experiment to be valid. Valid experiments must have

- a testable hypothesis
- a control group and an experimental group
- defined independent and dependent variables
- all other conditions held constant
- repeated trials

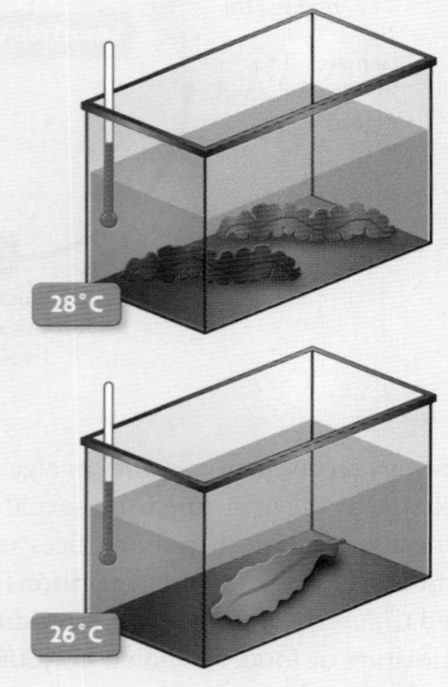

EXAMPLE

A student performed an experiment to determine whether a certain species of coral larvae prefer to settle on live red algae or dead red algae. She placed live red algae and dead algae in a tank held at 28°C (82°F). In a second tank held at 26°C (79°F), she placed a piece of lettuce as a control because it had a texture similar to the algae. After 24 hours, she counted the number of larvae that settled on each type of algae. The following flaws exist in this experiment:

- A controlled variable—temperature—was not held constant.
- The lettuce control was separated from the algae choices.
- There were no repeated trials.

A valid experimental design would have all of the choices in a single aquarium, which makes it easier to maintain constants, and allows accurate observation of which surface types the larvae prefer. At least three aquariums should be used with the same setup so that the results could be compared.

IDENTIFY EXPERIMENTAL DESIGN FLAWS

A student wanted to determine what concentration—low, medium, or high—of a chemical released from brown algae prevented coral larvae from settling and growing on the algae. Each concentration level of the chemical from one brown alga was added to the water of each tank. Tank size, water temperature, and algae species were held constant. A different number and species of larvae were dropped into each tank. After three days, the percent of settled larvae for each concentration of inhibiting chemical was found.

TABLE 1. RESULTS OF INHIBITING CHEMICAL ON LARVAL SETTLEMENT

Inhibiting Chemical Concentration	Low	Medium	High
Percent of Larvae Settled	85%	40%	1%

1. **Evaluate** What are the design flaws in this experiment? How would you change the experiment to make the results more valid?
2. **Analyze** The student concluded that at all levels the inhibiting chemical affected the rate of settlement of marine larvae. Is this an accurate conclusion based on the data collected? Explain.

Answers

1. There is no control group, and the numbers and species of larvae are not constant. A fourth tank with no chemical inhibitor added could be used as a control group. The same species and number of larvae should be used in each tank.
2. No, without a control group to compare, one cannot know if the chemical lowered settlement rates at all levels of concentration. If a control group was included with no chemical added and the settlement rates were also about 85 percent, it could mean that at low concentrations, the chemical does not affect settlement rates. Also, this experiment tests the effects of an inhibiting chemical on coral larvae—not all marine larvae.

586 Unit 6: Classification and Diversity

19.4 Funguslike Protists

KEY CONCEPT Funguslike protists decompose organic matter.

MAIN IDEAS
- Slime molds and water molds are funguslike protists.

VOCABULARY
slime mold, p. 587
water mold, p. 588

Review
decomposer

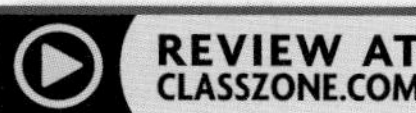

Connect Perhaps you have seen a funguslike protist and didn't recognize it, like the Dallas residents you read about at the start of this chapter. Most funguslike protists don't grow large enough to scare people. In fact, some you can barely see.

MAIN IDEA
Slime molds and water molds are funguslike protists.

As decomposers, funguslike protists play an important role in ecosystems by recycling nutrients such as carbon and nitrogen back into the soil. For a long time, funguslike protists were classified as fungi because they are all decomposers and have similar reproductive structures and cycles. However, funguslike protists can move during part of their life cycle, while fungi cannot.

***Connecting* CONCEPTS**
Biogeochemical Cycles Recall from **Chapter 13** that a biogeochemical cycle is the movement of a particular chemical, such as carbon or nitrogen, through the living and nonliving parts of an ecosystem.

Slime Molds
Slime molds are eukaryotic organisms that have both funguslike and animal-like traits. They can be divided into two phyla: plasmodial slime molds (phylum Myxomycota) and cellular slime molds (phylum Acrasiomycota).

Plasmodial slime molds For most of their life, plasmodial slime molds live as a single mass of cytoplasm that actually is a large single cell with many nuclei, called a plasmodium. They can grow as large as a meter or more in diameter. A plasmodium, shown in **FIGURE 19.16,** moves like a giant amoeba, creeping over the ground as it absorbs bacteria and nutrients from decaying matter. *Fuligo septica,* the dog-vomit slime mold, is typical of this group.

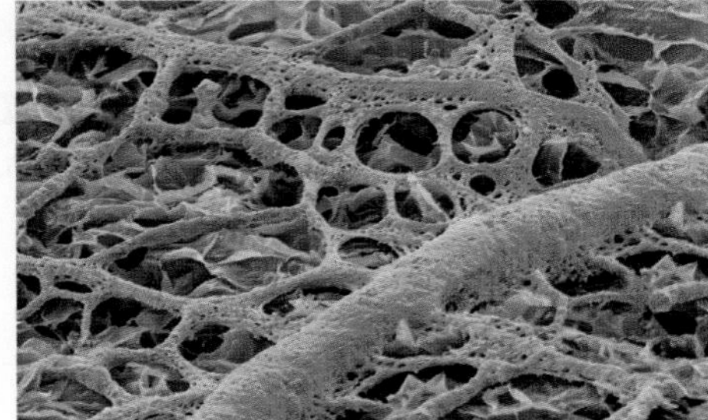
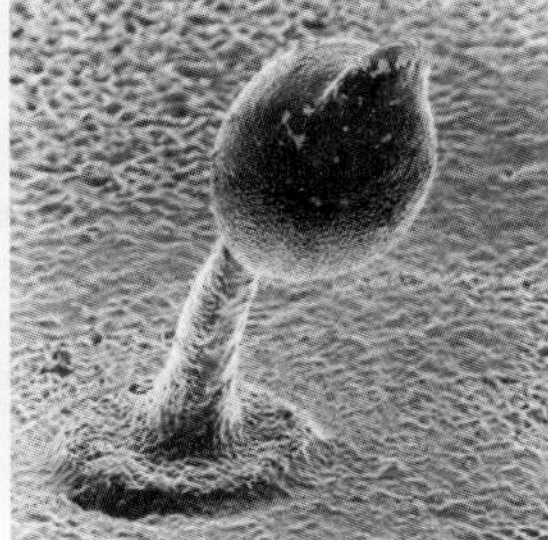

FIGURE 19.16 A plasmodial slime mold (left) in the plasmodium stage resembles a giant amoeba. A cellular slime mold (right) forms a stalk in the spore-producing stage. (colored SEMs; plasmodial slime mold magnification 80×; cellular slime mold magnification 100×)

Differentiated Instruction

ENGLISH LEARNERS
Tell students to work in pairs to create a content frame comparing the organisms featured in this section. Students might create a chart with these column heads: Type of Funguslike Protists, Size, Number of Cells, Parasitic Appearance, Movement, Diet. Students can use these row heads: Plasmodial Slime Mold, Cellular Slime Mold, Water Mold. When all pairs are finished, have them ask each other questions based on their content frames.

Biology Toolkit, Content Frame, p. C22

BELOW LEVEL
Have students use a Venn diagram to compare slime molds and water molds. Have students consider characteristics such as habitat, type of movement, and growth patterns. Also, have students consider what roles each type of mold plays in its community.

Biology Toolkit, Venn Diagram, p. C33

Plan and Prepare ▼

Objectives
- Identify the three phyla of funguslike protists, their role in ecosystems, and how they differ from true fungi.

Section Resources

Unit Resource Book Study Guide pp. 73–74 Power Notes p. 75 Reinforcement p. 76
Interactive Reader Chapter 19 **Spanish Study Guide** pp. 201–202
Biology Toolkit pp. C22, C33
Technology Power Presentation 19.4 Media Gallery DVD Online Quiz 19.4

Activate Prior Knowledge Have students imagine their room if they could not put away their clothes, even if they wanted to. Instead, they would get new clothes to wear each day. **Ask,** What would happen if the natural world had no means to "clean its room," that is remove dead or decaying organic matter? Decaying organic matter would pile up, soil would be deprived of essential nutrients, and phytoplankton would not have a source of nutrients in the oceans. Tell students that funguslike protists play the role of decomposers in the environment.

Teach ▼

Vocabulary
plasmodium The word *plasmodium* has two distinct definitions in biology:
- a multinucleated mass of "naked" cytoplasm typical of plasmodial slime molds
- a genus of protozoan parasites, four of which cause malaria

In the first context, the word begins with a lower-case letter (plasmodium). When used to denote the protozoan genus, the word is capitalized and italicized (*Plasmodium*).

▼ Teach *continued*

ONLINE BIOLOGY Go to the chapter Resource Center at **ClassZone.com** for additional resources and information on slime molds.

Integrating Social Science

In the early 1800s, potatoes were a staple food in Ireland. Many families relied entirely on potatoes for food. The famine that followed the devastation of the potato crop by potato blight stimulated mass emigration. By 1854, almost two million Irish people had left Ireland to move abroad. One of the largest waves of immigration was to the United States. More than half a million Irish immigrants arrived in the United States in the 1840s. The **Great Potato Famine** is still remembered in Ireland, as well as in cities around the world that have large populations descended from Irish immigrants.

Answers

A Infer Having two modes of reproduction gives organisms the ability to reproduce regardless of the conditions. They can switch modes of reproduction when conditions change.

FIGURE 19.17 The water mold *Phytophthora infestans* causes disease, including potato blight in many plants. This disease was the cause of a seven-year famine in Ireland in the 1800s. (colored SEM; magnification 100×)

Plasmodial slime molds are common on the underside of logs and on dead leaves. When food or moisture is in short supply, the plasmodial slime mold stops growing and develops nonmoving reproductive structures that produce spores. Such a structure is a resistant, resting form of the slime mold. When the spores are released, they are often able to move on their own. They may creep like an amoeba, or, if water is present, they can develop up to four flagella per cell. Eventually, the spores swarm together and form a new plasmodium.

Cellular slime molds The cellular slime molds are common in soil. Each spore released by a cellular slime mold becomes a single amoeba-like cell. However, when food is scarce, individual cells can release chemical signals that cause the cells to swarm together. They form a sluglike body that moves as though it were one organism. This form of a cellular slime mold is called a pseudoplasmodium, meaning "fake plasmodium," because each cell is independent—the membranes of each cell do not fuse. These slime molds are of interest to biologists who study how cells can communicate with each other.

Water Molds

Water molds are funguslike protists (phylum Oomycota) that are made up of branching strands of cells. They are common in freshwater habitats. Like slime molds, many water molds are decomposers. However, some water molds are parasites of plants or fish. For example, if you keep an aquarium, you may have seen a water mold that infects fish. The mold appears first as a cottony coating on the skin and gills but later causes deep wounds.

Perhaps the best known water mold is the downy mildew *Phytophthora infestans,* shown in **FIGURE 19.17,** which causes a disease called potato blight. An outbreak of this disease in Ireland from 1845 to 1849 destroyed almost all of the country's potato crops. As a result, more than 1 million people died of starvation in what became known as the Great Potato Famine.

A Infer Many protists have two modes of reproduction. How does having two modes of reproduction affect when and how they reproduce?

19.4 ASSESSMENT

ONLINE QUIZ ClassZone.com

REVIEWING MAIN IDEAS

1. In what ways are **slime molds** and **water molds** similar to fungi?
2. Describe how slime molds help other organisms within an ecosystem obtain nutrients.

CRITICAL THINKING

3. **Compare** Make a three-column chart comparing plasmodial slime molds, cellular slime molds, and water molds.
4. **Analyze** Why doesn't spraying water on slime molds work to destroy them?

***Connecting* CONCEPTS**

5. **Natural Selection** What might be the advantage of being able to switch from living as separate cells to become a coordinated unit acting like a single organism?

▼ Assess and Reteach

Assess Use the Online Quiz or Section Quiz (*Assessment Book*, p. 376).

Reteach Create a simple table comparing the three types of funguslike protists discussed in this chapter.

19.4 ASSESSMENT

1. These funguslike protists also are decomposers that recycle nutrients back into the soil.
2. They decompose organic matter, breaking it down so that the nutrients return to the soil.
3. Charts should include all that are eukaryotic decomposers.

   Plasmodial slime molds: live as a single large cell with many nuclei (a plasmodium) that moves like a giant amoeba; are common under logs or on dead leaves; can produce spores that can have flagella or that can move like an amoeba. The spores will swarm and form a new plasmodium.

   Cellular slime molds: common in soil; their spores become amoeba-like; they swarm together to move as one organism, but each cell is independent of the others.

   Water molds: have branching strands of cells; are common in freshwater habitats; they are sometimes parasites of plants or fish.
4. Spraying water actually encourages the slime mold to grow larger, because they thrive on water and wet conditions.
5. The different body forms can be an advantage when conditions change. When there is plenty of food, the individual cells can find food easily. When food becomes scarce, they may be more likely to survive by working together to find and share food.

19.5 Diversity of Fungi

KEY CONCEPT: Fungi are heterotrophs that absorb their food.

MAIN IDEAS

- Fungi are adapted to absorb their food from the environment.
- Fungi come in many shapes and sizes.
- Fungi reproduce sexually and asexually.

VOCABULARY

chitin, p. 589
hyphae, p. 589
mycelium, p. 590
fruiting body, p. 590
mycorrhizae, p. 591
sporangia, p. 592

Connect What is the largest living thing in the world? The blue whale? A giant redwood tree? Although they are big, both species are tiny compared with a fungus growing in Oregon—a single honey mushroom, *Armillaria ostoyae*. Most of it is underground, but this mushroom could cover more than 1500 football fields. It is thought to be at least 2400 years old. As amazing as it sounds, there are other fungi throughout the world nearly as large.

MAIN IDEA

Fungi are adapted to absorb their food from the environment.

Despite how little most people know about fungi, they are all around us—in soil, water, and even in the air. Many forms live in and on plants and animals. Scientists have named about 70,000 species but estimate there may be a total of 1.5 million fungi species in the world.

Comparing Fungi and Plants

Members of the kingdom Fungi fall into one of three groups—the single-celled yeasts, the molds, and the true fungi. For many years, biologists classified fungi as plants. But there are a few traits that separate these two kingdoms.

- Plants contain chlorophyll and photosynthesize. Fungi do not have chlorophyll and get food by absorbing it from their environment.
- Plants have true roots, leaves, and stems, but fungi do not.
- Plant cell walls are made of the polysaccharide cellulose. Fungal cell walls are made of **chitin** (KYT-uhn), a tough polysaccharide that is also found in the shells of insects and their close relatives.

FIGURE 19.18 A mushroom is actually just the reproductive, or fruiting, body of a fungus. Most of the fungus grows in the ground, as a mycelium.

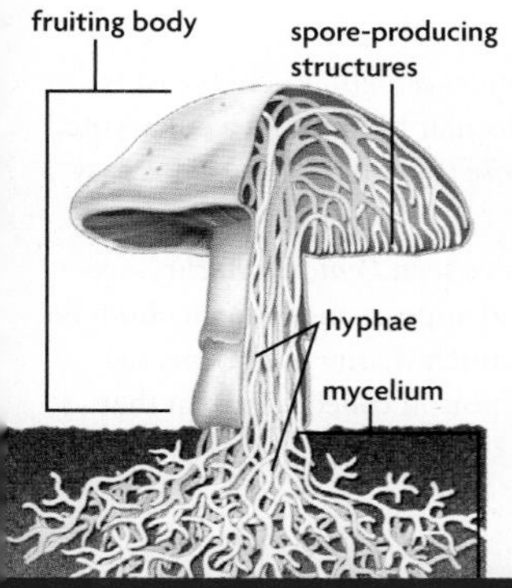

fruiting body
spore-producing structures
hyphae
mycelium

Anatomy of Fungi

With the exception of the yeasts, fungi are multicellular organisms. The bodies of multicellular fungi are made of long strands called **hyphae** (HY-fee). Hyphae (singular, *hypha*) are shown in **FIGURE 19.18.** Depending on the species, each hypha may consist of a chain of cells or may contain one large, long cell with many nuclei. In both cases, cytoplasm can flow freely throughout the hyphae, and each hypha is surrounded by a plasma membrane and a cell wall of chitin.

Plan and Prepare ▼

Objectives

- Describe how fungi obtain nutrients.
- Identify the four main types of fungi.
- Summarize the life cycles of club fungus and bread mold.

Section Resources

Unit Resource Book
Study Guide pp. 77–78
Power Notes p. 79
Reinforcement p. 80
Pre-AP Activity pp. 89–90

Interactive Reader Chapter 19
Spanish Study Guide pp. 203–204

Biology Toolkit pp. C15, C19, D6, D7

Technology
Power Presentation 19.5
Media Gallery DVD
Online Quiz 19.5

Activate Prior Knowledge Remind students that fungi, like algae, have many everyday uses. **Ask,** What are some ways that people use fungi? as food, for example, mushrooms; as leavening or fermenting agents, for example, yeast; also as antibiotics, as in penicillin

Teach ▼

Vocabulary

polysaccharide Remind students that the prefix *poly-* means "many" and is used in science and mathematics to indicate something made up of many units. A polysaccharide is "a molecule composed of many sugars." The prefix *poly-* is found in many words:

polypeptide, a protein composed of many amino acids

polymer, a compound composed of many repeating units

polygonal, in geometry, a figure composed of many sides

polyglot, someone who speaks many languages

Differentiated Instruction

ENGLISH LEARNERS

Have individual students skim the section for the positive, negative, and neutral effects of fungi on human life and then create a semantic feature analysis of their findings. Students can choose their variables or use the following column heads: Type of Fungus, Subtype, Effect(s), + (for positive), – (for negative), 0 (for neutral); first column: primitive, sac, mold, club; second column: morels, truffles, *Penicillium,* rusts, smuts, yeast; third column: delicious to eat, prevents disease, cures disease, ruins plants, makes bread rise. Give students ten minutes to skim the section and find and record the information. If they do not find information for all cells in a row, they can use a question mark. Have students share and discuss findings by making statements about their matrices and using input from other students to revise their work.

Biology Toolkit, Semantic Feature Analysis, p. D7

▼ Teach *continued*

Take It Further

Mushrooms make frequent appearances in folklore and myths. One of these is **fairy rings**—large rings of mushrooms typically found in meadows and open areas in forests. According to legend, the rings were made by fairies that gathered in the open area to dance in the moonlight. The fairies danced inside the ring and rested on the tiny stools. The actual cause of the ring pattern of these mushrooms is more down-to-earth. The rings result from the growth underground of certain fungi, such as *Marasmius oreades.* The mycelia of the fungus grow outward in a spokelike manner. The toadstools seen in a ring aboveground form at the ends of the spokes and are the fungus's fruiting bodies.

Vocabulary

Academic Vocabulary The words **primitive** and **advanced** are used differently in science than they are in everyday life. Both terms are used to describe the relative stage in the evolution of an organism or a trait. A primitive characteristic is one that developed in an ancestral species and has remained unchanged over time.

Primitive fungi are so-named because in both form and function, they more closely resemble early fungi rather than fungi that evolved more recently. Similarly, an advanced characteristic is one that developed relatively late in evolution. Because the terms *primitive* and *advanced* may imply a judgment of the sophistication of a trait or an organism, the terms *ancestral* and *derived* are frequently used in their place.

Answers

A Contrast Fungi absorb their food directly from the environment, using enzymes to digest it before it enters the fungi.

Hyphae often group together in long tangled masses to form a mycelium. A **mycelium** (my-SEE-lee-uhm) is an underground network of hyphae. Under certain conditions, such as a moist environment, a mycelium (plural, *mycelia*) can grow quickly to cover a large area. Mycelia may produce fruiting bodies. A **fruiting body** is a reproductive structure of a fungus that grows above ground. Mushrooms are one type of fruiting body.

Fungi absorb their food from their environment. The food can be from a wide variety of food sources—including tree bark, bread, cheese, and even flesh. As fungi grow, hyphae extend into the food source and release enzymes. These enzymes break down their food so that it can be absorbed across their cell walls. Fungi can take in large amounts of nutrients due to their mycelia, which in turn allows mycelia to grow very quickly.

A Contrast How is the way that fungi get their food different from that of any other group of organisms?

MAIN IDEA

Fungi come in many shapes and sizes.

The kingdom Fungi is diverse, and it is commonly divided into four main groups—primitive fungi (phylum Chytridiomycota), sac fungi (phylum Ascomycota), bread molds (phylum Zygomycota), and club fungi (phylum Basidiomycota).

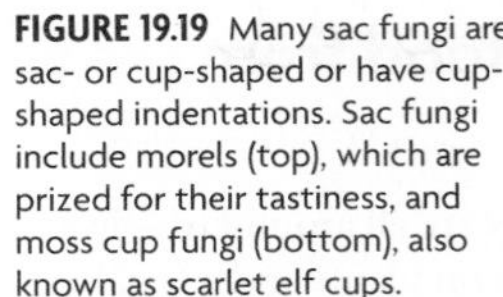

FIGURE 19.19 Many sac fungi are sac- or cup-shaped or have cup-shaped indentations. Sac fungi include morels (top), which are prized for their tastiness, and moss cup fungi (bottom), also known as scarlet elf cups.

Primitive Fungi

The primitive fungi, or chytrids, are the smallest and simplest group of fungi. They are mostly aquatic, and their spores have flagella, which help propel them through the water. They are the only fungi with flagellated spores. Some primitive fungi are decomposers, while others are parasites of protists, plants, or animals. One explanation for the global decrease of amphibians such as frogs may be due to a parasitic type of chytrid fungi.

Sac Fungi

Yeasts, certain molds such as *Penicillium,* and morels and truffles—which many people consider delicious to eat—are all sac fungi. The sac fungi are a diverse group, but they have one key trait in common. They all form a sac, called an ascus, that contains spores for reproduction. Some examples of sac fungi are shown in **FIGURE 19.19.**

The yeast that makes bread rise is *Saccharomyces cerevisiae*. This yeast is also an important model organism used in molecular biology. As a eukaryote, it has many of the same genes as humans. Because it is single-celled, it is easy to work with in a laboratory.

If you've ever let an orange grow moldy, you've seen *Penicillium chrysogenum*. This mold is usually a deep green color and appears fuzzy. *Penicillium* is also the source for the antibiotic penicillin. In contrast, one dangerous sac fungus is *Aspergillis flavus,* a mold that makes a poison called aflatoxin that can contaminate cereals, nuts, and milk.

Differentiated Instruction

BELOW LEVEL

Divide the class into four groups. Then have students number off into four expert groups, one for each of the four main groups of the kingdom Fungi. Have expert groups read and review the characteristics of their fungus. Then home groups reassemble so that experts can teach one another about their subject.

Biology Toolkit, Jigsaw Reading, p. C15

Bread Molds

The bread molds range from the molds you see on spoiled foods to fungi used to ferment certain foods such as soy sauce. Most members of this phylum get food by decomposing dead or decaying matter. At least one group of symbiotic fungi belongs to this group. **Mycorrhizae** (MY-kuh-RY-zuh) are mutualistic partnerships between fungi and the roots of certain plants. Mycorrhizae help these plants to fix nitrogen—that is, they take inorganic nitrogen from the soil and convert it to nitrates and ammonia, which the plants use.

Club Fungi

The club fungi get their name because their fruiting bodies are club-shaped. This phylum includes mushrooms, puffballs, and bracket, or shelf, fungi. It also includes the rusts and smuts, which are two types of fungi that cause diseases in plants. Puffballs, shown in **FIGURE 19.20**, form dry-looking structures that release their spores when someone or something strikes the mature fruiting body. Bracket fungi are a common sight in forests, where they grow outward from tree trunks, forming a little shelf.

FIGURE 19.20 Puffballs release a cloud of spores when the fruiting body matures and bursts.

Identify **What two organisms share a mutualistic partnership in the formation of mycorrhizae?**

MAIN IDEA

Fungi reproduce sexually and asexually.

Most fungi reproduce both sexually and asexually through a wide variety of strategies.

Reproduction in Single-Celled Fungi

Yeasts are single-celled fungi. They reproduce asexually, either through simple fission or through a process called budding, shown in **FIGURE 19.21.** Fission is identical to mitosis—the cell's DNA is copied and the nucleus and cytoplasm divide, making two identical daughter cells. During budding, the parent cell forms a small bud of cytoplasm that also contains a copy of the nucleus. When these buds reach a certain size, they detach and form a cell.

Some yeasts undergo sexual reproduction. A diploid yeast cell undergoes meiosis, producing four haploid nuclei. However, the parent cell's cytoplasm does not divide. Recall that a yeast is a type of sac fungi. Instead of the cytoplasm dividing, it produces the characteristic saclike structure of this phylum called an ascus. The haploid nuclei it contains are actually a type of spore. The ascus undergoes budding, releasing each of the haploid spores. Some spores may then reproduce more haploid spores through budding. Others may fuse with other haploid spores to form diploid yeast cells.

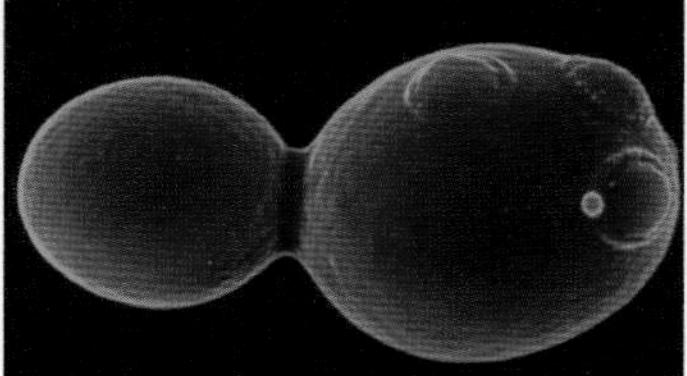

FIGURE 19.21 Yeast can reproduce by budding, the pinching of small cells off the parent cell. (colored SEM; magnification 6000×)

Integrating Agricultural Science

The **mycorrhiza** is one of the most important and common types of **symbiosis** in the natural and agricultural world. More than 90 percent of all known plant species form associations with mycorrhizal fungi. Many fruit and vegetable plants, such as corn, carrots, leeks, potatoes, legumes, tomatoes, strawberries, citrus, and apples, form mycorrhizae with soil fungi. Often, the soil in which crops are planted for the first time must be inoculated with the mycorrhizal fungi that the plants form associations with in their native environments.

Mycorrhizae greatly increase the plants' ability to absorb nutrients from the soil. Some of these fungi can be cultured and applied to soil or seedlings. Mycorrhizae greatly increase the plants' ability to absorb nutrients from the soil. The indiscriminate use of **fungicides** targeting fungi that are harmful to plants can end up killing the mycorrhizal fungi that are so beneficial.

Answers

A **Identify** a fungus and a plant

Vocabulary

Greek and Latin Word Origins The prefix *myc-* is derived from the Greek word *mykes,* meaning "fungus."

mycology, the branch of biology devoted to the study of fungi

mycologist, a scientist who studies fungi

mycorrhizae, mutualistic associations between plant roots (*rhiz-*) and fungi

PRE-AP

Tell students that puffballs release their spores when an external pressure is applied to their bellowslike fruiting body. Have students write about what natural events might trigger spore dispersal (animals, raindrops), spread spores (water, wind, animals), and how this reproductive strategy may have evolved (would confer a reproductive advantage by casting spores into a wide area).

Biology Toolkit, Quick-Write, p. C19

▼ Teach *continued*

ONLINE BIOLOGY Have students go to Animated Biology in Options for Inquiry on page 601 for an interactive animation on fungus life cycles.

Science Trivia

- In ancient Egypt, only the pharaoh and his family could eat mushrooms. Commoners were forbidden even to touch a mushroom.
- Shiitake mushrooms have been used medicinally by the Chinese for more than 6000 years.
- Current studies of shiitake mushrooms show that they contain a compound called lentinan that strengthens the immune system and may fight cancer.

Take It Further

As with bacteria and algae, fungi are key ingredients in many processed foods, not just as mushrooms.

- Soy sauce is fermented first with the mold *Aspergillus oryz,* and then with the yeast *Saccharomyces rouxii.*
- The blue streaks and pungent flavor of blue cheeses such as Roquefort and Gorgonzola result from inoculation with *Penicillium roquefortii.*
- Chocolate is made from cacao beans, which are fermented with the yeasts *Candida krusei* and *Geotrichum.*

FIGURE 19.22 REPRODUCTIVE STRUCTURES OF FUNGI

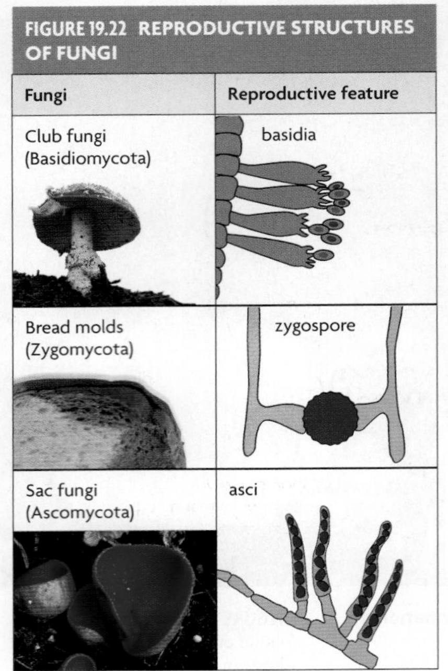

Fungi	Reproductive feature
Club fungi (Basidiomycota)	basidia
Bread molds (Zygomycota)	zygospore
Sac fungi (Ascomycota)	asci

Reproduction in Multicellular Fungi

The multicellular fungi have complex reproductive cycles. Examples of life cycles for two phyla of fungi are shown in **FIGURE 19.23.**

Club fungi Basidiomycota are named for their club-shaped structures called basidia, where spores are produced during sexual reproduction. Basidia are found on the undersides of mushrooms. They form within the leaflike gills that you can easily see. In club fungi, unlike the other phyla, spores are most often formed by sexual reproduction.

- Nuclei within the basidia fuse to form diploid zygotes.
- The zygotes undergo meiosis to form haploid spores.
- The spores drop from the gills and are carried away by wind or by contact with animals.
- If the spores land in a favorable environment, they grow and form haploid hyphae.
- Some cells of the haploid mycelium may fuse with the cells of another haploid mycelium, producing a diploid mycelium underground.
- An environmental cue, such as rain or change in temperature, can trigger the formation of aboveground fruiting bodies such as mushrooms.

Connecting CONCEPTS

Asexual Reproduction Recall from **Chapter 5** that asexual reproduction is the creation of offspring from a single parent that does not involve the joining of gametes. The offspring are genetically identical to each other and to the parent.

Bread molds Members of Zygomycota are also known as zygote fungi because of the structures they form during sexual reproduction. Bread molds reproduce sexually when the food supply is low but can also reproduce asexually when there is plenty of food. They reproduce asexually by producing spores in **sporangia,** spore-forming structures at the tips of their hyphae. The term *sporangium* is used to describe similar reproductive structures of a variety of organisms, including some fungi, mosses, algae, and ferns.

VISUAL VOCAB

Sporangia are structures that produce spores.

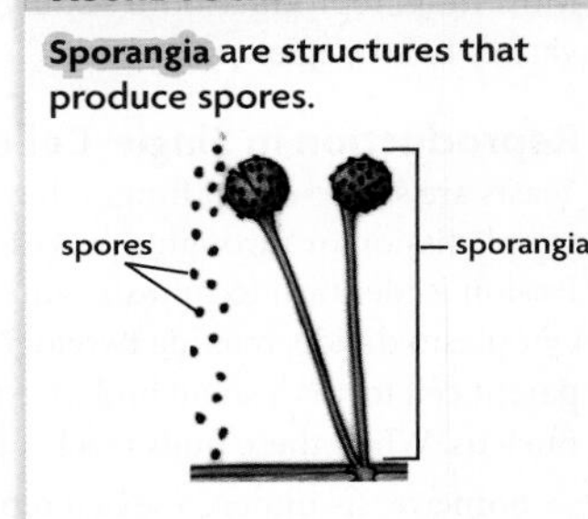

- As in the club fungi, sexual reproduction in zygote fungi involves hyphae that look alike but are different mating types.
- The two types of hyphae fuse their nuclei to produce a diploid zygospore that can tolerate long periods of extreme conditions.
- When the conditions become favorable, a sporangium grows and produces haploid spores.
- The spores are released and can grow into new hyphae.
- The new hyphae in turn may reproduce asexually, by forming haploid spores in sporangia. Or they may reproduce sexually, by fusing hyphae to produce more zygospores.

Differentiated Instruction

BELOW LEVEL

Have students list and then group keywords in this section, such as *sporangia-basidia-asci* and *hyphae-mycelium-fruiting body.* Have students differentiate between the groups by describing the type of information each set of terms provides.

Biology Toolkit, List-Group-Label, p. D6

FIGURE 19.23 Typical Life Cycles of Fungi

Reproduction in fungi can occur in several ways. Although most club fungi reproduce sexually, bread molds can reproduce both sexually and asexually.

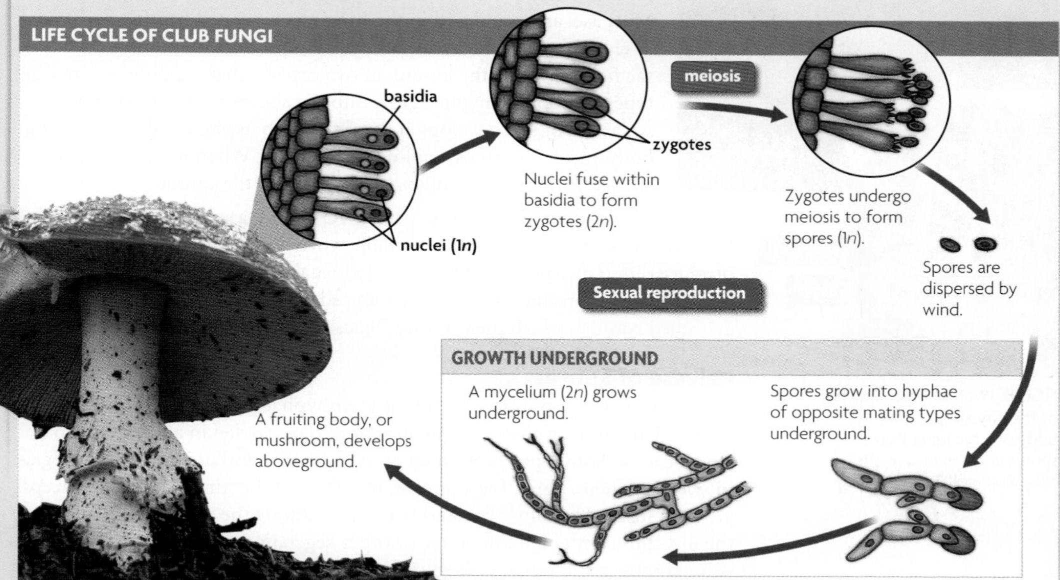

LIFE CYCLE OF CLUB FUNGI
basidia
nuclei (1n)
meiosis
zygotes
Nuclei fuse within basidia to form zygotes (2n).
Zygotes undergo meiosis to form spores (1n).
Spores are dispersed by wind.
Sexual reproduction
GROWTH UNDERGROUND
A mycelium (2n) grows underground.
Spores grow into hyphae of opposite mating types underground.
A fruiting body, or mushroom, develops aboveground.

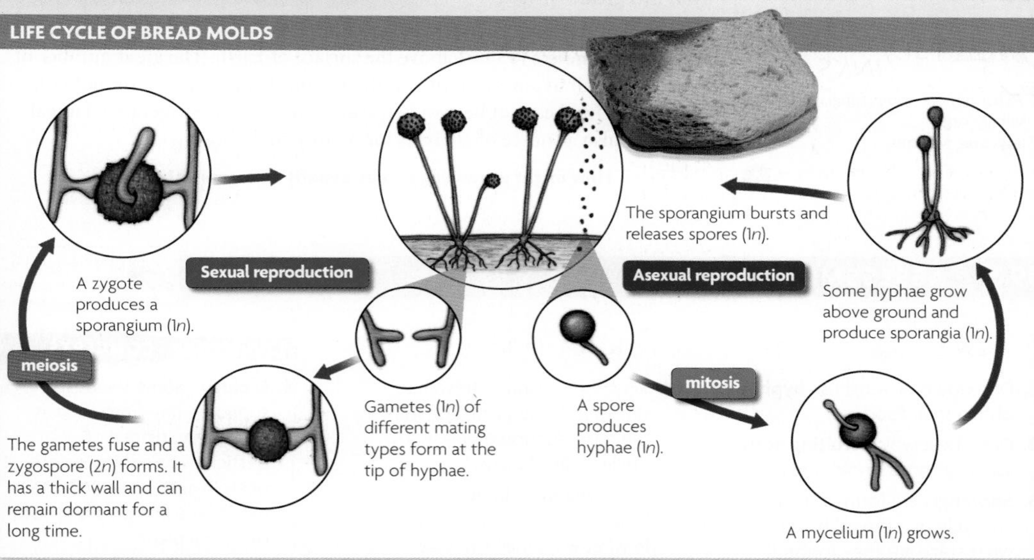

LIFE CYCLE OF BREAD MOLDS
A zygote produces a sporangium (1n).
Sexual reproduction
meiosis
The gametes fuse and a zygospore (2n) forms. It has a thick wall and can remain dormant for a long time.
Gametes (1n) of different mating types form at the tip of hyphae.
The sporangium bursts and releases spores (1n).
Asexual reproduction
A spore produces hyphae (1n).
mitosis
Some hyphae grow above ground and produce sporangia (1n).
A mycelium (1n) grows.

A CRITICAL VIEWING **How are the life cycles of club fungi and bread molds similar? How are they different?**

History of Science

Piptoporus betulinus is a bracket fungus that grows horizontally from the sides of trees. The hard, leathery upper surface of the fungus can be peeled off in strips and was used to make razor strops for sharpening straight-edge razors. The fungus has numerous medicinal properties as well. It contains antibiotic substances and substances that attack intestinal whipworms, *Trichurus trichiura*. Perhaps this is why pieces of the fungus were found threaded into a necklace worn by Ötzi, a man whose 5300-year-old frozen body was found in the Alps in 1991. An autopsy revealed that he was suffering from a whipworm infestation at the time of his death.

TEACH FROM VISUALS

FIGURE 19.23 Have students review the life cycles of bread molds and club fungi.
Ask

- Which type of fungus produces a zygospore? bread mold
- What are three characteristics of a zygospore? diploid, has a thick wall, can remain dormant for long periods
- What is a basidium, and in which type of fungus is it found? reproductive structure of a club fungus

Answers

A Critical Viewing Both club fungi and bread molds produce spores and hyphae with different mating types. They both form zygotes and undergo meiosis during sexual reproduction. A club fungus usually undergoes only sexual reproduction, whereas a bread mold may undergo both sexual and asexual reproduction. Bread mold zygotes produce sporangia, whereas club fungus zygotes produce spores directly.

INCLUSION

Students who are visually impaired or who have difficulty assimilating large amounts of complex information may have difficulty interpreting **FIGURE 19.23.** Have students draw each cycle in a way that is useful to them, such as a sequence diagram. Some students may wish to color-code different stages, while other students may need to draw an enlarged chart or use mnemonics.

▼ Teach *continued*

Address Misconceptions

Common Misconception Fungi need a warm, moist, dark environment in order to grow.

Correcting the Misconception Most fungi do grow best under such conditions; however, some fungi thrive at very high temperatures, while others exist in cold environments, including the Arctic tundra. *Aspergillus niger,* or black mold, grows on onions and garlic that grow in warm, dry areas such as the California deserts. Some fungi are very light-sensitive and require light stimulation to form spores.

Answers

A Hypothesize *Sample Answer:* Spores allow offspring to grow far from the parent organism, colonize a new area, and thereby minimize competition for space in the original location. Spores allow many more offspring to be produced.

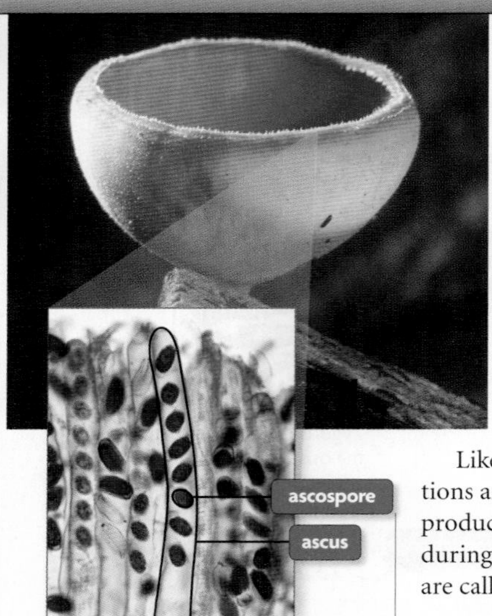

FIGURE 19.24 A cross-section of the cup-shaped fruiting body of a sac fungi shows spores encased in an ascus. (magnification 400×)

Sac fungi Members of Ascomycota are called the sac fungi due to the saclike case, or ascus (plural, *asci*), that forms during sexual reproduction. These reproductive structures are shown in **FIGURE 19.24.** Most asci are found within the fungi's cup-shaped fruiting body. As in club fungi and bread molds, sexual reproduction in multicellular sac fungi involves the joining of two mycelia that are different mating types. The joined hyphae grow into the aboveground fruiting body. An ascus, or sac, develops at the tip of each hypha within the fruiting body. Inside the ascus, haploid spores form. When mature, the cup-shaped fruiting body collapses, and releases the spores.

Like the bread molds, sac fungi usually reproduce asexually when conditions are favorable and reproduce sexually when conditions are harsh. They produce different types of spores during asexual reproduction than they do during sexual reproduction. Spores produced during asexual reproduction are called conidia, which means "dust," because they travel easily through air.

Release of Spores

Fungi release their spores at the tips of their hyphae, high above their food source. This strategy allows the small spores to be carried in air currents to a new location. Some species of fungi go even further and use unusual strategies in releasing their spores. For example, members of the fungal genus *Cordyceps* grow on insects. In some species, the fungi penetrate the insect's brain, causing the insect to climb high into a tree or other vegetation. Eventually, the insect stops climbing and remains fixed in place. The fungus then releases its spores from this greater height.

Spores of fungi are everywhere, and have even been found in the air more than 150 kilometers (93 mi) above the surface of Earth. The great number of spores in the air at any given time is the reason that the growth of mold on our leftover food cannot be avoided, even if the food is refrigerated. Fungal spores are also a source of allergies for many people worldwide.

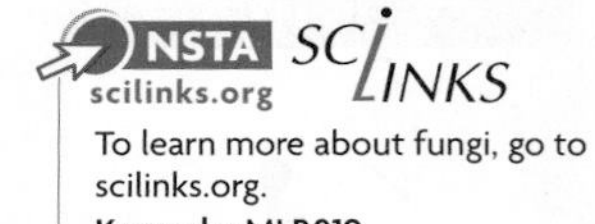

To learn more about fungi, go to scilinks.org.
Keycode: MLB019

A Hypothesize How might producing spores benefit an organism?

19.5 ASSESSMENT

ONLINE QUIZ ClassZone.com

REVIEWING MAIN IDEAS

1. Describe how fungi use **hyphae** to obtain their food.
2. Describe a typical **fruiting body** of sac fungi, bread mold, and club fungi.
3. **Sporangia** are formed during the life cycle of a typical bread mold. At what stage are they formed?

CRITICAL THINKING

4. **Summarize** Draw a flowchart showing the sequence of steps in the reproduction of yeast, a single-celled fungus.
5. **Infer** The **mycelium** of a fungus grows underground. In what ways might this be helpful for the fungus?

***Connecting* CONCEPTS**

6. **Ecology** Some scientists support using fungi such as *Cordyceps* instead of pesticides to control insect pests in agriculture. What might be some pros and cons of such a plan?

▼ Assess and Reteach

Assess Use the Online Quiz or Section Quiz (*Assessment Book,* p. 377).

Reteach Review the visuals in this section and have students visit Animated Biology at **ClassZone.com** to view the animation of the life cycle of a cup fungus.

19.5 ASSESSMENT

1. The hyphae extend into the food source and release enzymes that break the food down. Nutrients are then absorbed across the cell walls.
2. The typical fruiting body of sac fungi is cup-shaped. A fruiting body of a bread mold is on a stalk as a sporangium. The typical fruiting body of club fungi is a mushroom.
3. Sporangia are formed during sexual reproduction by the zygote or during asexual reproduction after a spore produces hyphae.
4. Accept all reasonable drawings. Steps should include yeast cell undergoing meiosis, producing four haploid nuclei; production of an ascus; the ascus undergoing budding; and releasing the haploid spores. Spores may then bud, producing more haploid spores or may fuse with other spores to form diploid yeast cells.
5. It might provide protection from the environment to be underground. Even if the aboveground fruiting body is harmed, the fungus is likely to survive.
6. Using fungi rather than pesticides could help reduce the amount of toxic chemicals released into the environment. However, *Cordyceps* may affect beneficial insects or other species, not just the pests.

MATERIALS

- mushroom
- plastic knife
- 1/2 sheet of white paper
- plastic cup
- hairspray
- dissecting scope, or magnifying lens

PROCESS SKILLS

- **Observing**
- **Predicting**
- **Inferring**

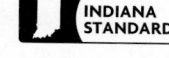

INDIANA STANDARDS

NOS.1 Develop explanations based on reproducible data and observations gathered during laboratory investigations.

Exploring Mushroom Anatomy

In this lab, you will first identify the main parts of a mushroom. Then you will make a spore print to reveal the color of its spores.

PROBLEM What are the structures of a mushroom?

PROCEDURE

1. Obtain a mushroom from your teacher and look at it carefully. Using the illustration and terms below as a guide, draw a diagram of your mushroom, and label the parts of its anatomy that are present. **Note:** Many mushrooms do not have all of these parts!
   - cap—top part of mushroom
   - scales—rough patches on cap surface
   - gills—radially arranged flat surfaces on the underside of the cap
   - ring—skirt of tissue circling stalk
   - stalk—main support of mushroom
   - cup—at the base of the mushroom

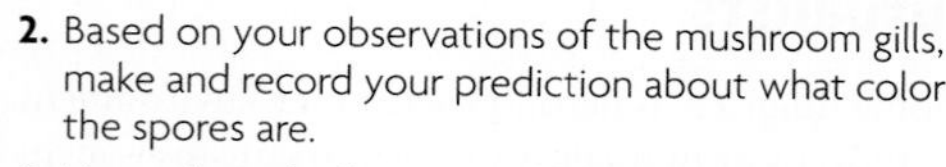

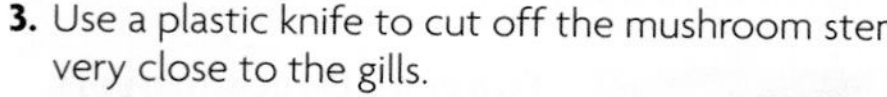

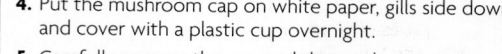

2. Based on your observations of the mushroom gills, make and record your prediction about what color the spores are.
3. Use a plastic knife to cut off the mushroom stem very close to the gills.
4. Put the mushroom cap on white paper, gills side down, and cover with a plastic cup overnight.
5. Carefully remove the cup and the mushroom cap. Thousands of spores should have fallen onto the paper, creating an outline of the gills.
6. Spray the print with hairspray to preserve it.
7. Examine the spore print, using a dissecting scope or magnifying lens if available. **Note:** If the spores are light-colored, hold the paper at an angle toward the light to see them better.

ANALYZE AND CONCLUDE

1. **Analyze** Was your prediction of spore color correct? Why might it be difficult to predict spore color?
2. **Infer** Why do you think the spores are located where they are in the mushroom?
3. **Experimental Design** Why was it necessary to cover the mushroom cap when you left it out overnight?
4. **Predict** Under what type of environmental conditions do you think these spores would be most likely to grow into new mycelia?
5. **Apply** The color of external mushroom parts can vary within one species since they may be affected by environmental conditions. Knowing this, why do you think spore prints are a valuable technique for mushroom identification?

Answers

Analyze and Conclude

1. The spore color is often not the same color as the basidia or the rest of the mushroom, as students may have predicted.
2. The cap of the mushroom protects the developing spores. Also, they are raised up by the stalk and have a better chance of being dispersed than if they were down low.
3. to shield the mushroom and spores from air currents or other forces that could move the spores
4. Fungi generally grow best in moist soil and shady areas.
5. Spore shape could be examined under a microscope to help identify the type of mushroom. Spore color could help distinguish the type of mushroom, provided that a reliable dichotomous key or field guide of mushroom spore colors is available.

INVESTIGATION

Time 45 minutes	TEACHER TESTED
Teacher Preparation (1 flask)	
Student Difficulty (1 flask)	
Lab Binder Diversity, pp. 27–29	

Purpose Identify features of a mushroom.

Overview Students will observe a mushroom. They will

- identify the main structures of the mushroom
- make a spore print to determine the color of its spores

LAB PREPARATION

- Use only mushrooms from a grocery store. Do not collect wild mushrooms.
- Wash your hands after touching fungi.

LAB MANAGEMENT

Have students use the freshest-looking mushrooms for spore prints and make spore prints with both black paper and white paper. Some spore colors will be more visible on either light paper or dark paper.

Safety Remind students to wash their hands after handling mushrooms.

POST-LAB DISCUSSION

Discuss the results of the activity with students. Point out that if no pattern of spores was observed, the mushroom might have been too old or too dry, or should have been left on the paper longer. Explain that mushrooms can take up to 24 hours to release their spores. Also, the gills of store-bought fungi can be disrupted during transport.

SECTION 19.6

▼ Plan and Prepare

Objectives

- Recognize three roles fungi play in ecosystems.
- Describe the ways that humans use fungi.

Section Resources

Unit Resource Book Study Guide pp. 81–82 Power Notes p. 83 Reinforcement p. 84
Interactive Reader Chapter 19 **Spanish Study Guide** pp. 205–206
Biology Toolkit pp. C19, C26, C27
Technology Power Presentation 19.6 Media Gallery DVD Online Quiz 19.6

Activate Prior Knowledge Remind students that the largest living organism on Earth is a honey mushroom thought to be at least 2400 years old, which covers more than 890 hectares (8,900,000 m^2) in eastern Oregon. **Ask,** How is it possible for a mushroom to live so long and grow so large? Traits of the fungus are adaptive to the conditions of its environment. Tell students that some scientists speculate that the dry climate of eastern Oregon is not conducive for most fungi to grow, meaning there isn't much competition for the honey mushroom. Remind them that the ability to occupy unique niches is an evolutionary advantage.

▼ Teach

Vocabulary

Academic Vocabulary The word **organic** in everyday life indicates a food or material that is made or grown naturally, without the use of pesticides, synthetic fertilizers, or hormones. In science, the word *organic* indicates matter that is derived from organisms or that contains hydrocarbons.

19.6 Ecology of Fungi

KEY CONCEPT Fungi recycle nutrients in the environment.

MAIN IDEAS
- Fungi may be decomposers, pathogens, or mutualists.
- Fungi are studied for many purposes.

VOCABULARY
lichen, p. 598

Review
mycorrhizae

INDIANA STANDARDS

B.4.4 Describe how climate, the pattern of matter and energy flow, the birth and death of new organisms, and the interaction between those organisms contribute to the long term stability of an ecosystem.

Connect Fungi just might be the most overlooked and unappreciated organisms on Earth. Fungi grow on shower curtains, spoil food, and cause illnesses to humans. But humans also eat some fungi and use them to make things that range from bread to antibiotics. Perhaps most importantly, these unusual organisms play a major role in every ecosystem on Earth.

MAIN IDEA

Fungi may be decomposers, pathogens, or mutualists.

Some fungi act as decomposers in the environment. Others act as either pathogens or mutualists to other organisms—including humans.

FIGURE 19.25 Fungi produce enzymes that help break down the complex molecules in wood to simpler molecules that fungi can absorb and use.

Fungi as Decomposers

Fungi and bacteria are the main decomposers in any ecosystem. Fungi, such as those shown in **FIGURE 19.25,** decompose dead and decaying organic matter such as leaves, twigs, logs, and animals. They return nutrients such as carbon, nitrogen, and minerals back into the soil. Because of the large surface area of their mycelia, fungi are well adapted for absorbing their food and can recycle nutrients quickly. This constant cycling of nutrients helps enrich soil with organic compounds. The nutrients can then be taken up by other organisms.

Plants and animals could not survive without the activity of decomposers. The ability of fungi to break down tough plant materials such as lignin and cellulose is especially important in woodland ecosystems. Fungi are the main decomposers of these hard parts of plants, which cannot be used by animals without being first broken down by decomposers.

The decomposing activity of fungi is not always helpful to humans, however. Fungi can damage fruit trees, and they can also cause damage inside wooden houses and boats. Molds and other fungi inside a house can weaken its walls, and their spores can cause respiratory illness. Homeowners should check for and remove molds that are established in their homes.

Differentiated Instruction

ENGLISH LEARNERS

Have students use a graphic organizer such as a main idea web to organize their notes for this section. Have students start by writing a main idea in a box. Lines should be angled off the box to outer boxes that contain details relating to the central concept. Another layer of boxes can be added to the second layer, and more layers added to set up a hierarchy.

Biology Toolkit, Main Idea Web, C27

Fungi as Pathogens

Like bacteria, some fungi can be pathogenic, or disease-causing. A few pathogenic fungi always cause disease. These fungi are called obligate pathogens—the term *obligate* means necessary or obliged. Other fungi are normally harmless, coexisting with other organisms in a delicate ecological balance. However, changes in environmental circumstances can upset this balance and lead to disease. Organisms that normally don't cause a problem until there is a change in the host's homeostasis are called opportunistic pathogens. A change in the host's body provides them an opportunity to grow unchecked and cause infection.

Connecting CONCEPTS

Prokaryotes In biology, the term *obligate* means requiring a particular environment to survive. Recall from **Chapter 18** that prokaryotes can be obligate anaerobes, meaning they cannot have oxygen in their environment. Some bacteria, protists, and fungi can also be obligate pathogens or obligate parasites.

Fungi and humans The overuse and incorrect use of antibiotics is one example of how humans allow pathogens an opportunity to cause infection. Antibiotics can destroy certain beneficial bacteria in the human digestive system, allowing other organisms such as fungi to thrive. Typically harmless fungi also cause disease when the immune system is not functioning at its best. For instance, all healthy humans have populations of the yeast *Candida* that occupy certain parts of the body, such as the skin and mouth. If a human's immune system is damaged, populations may grow and cause disease.

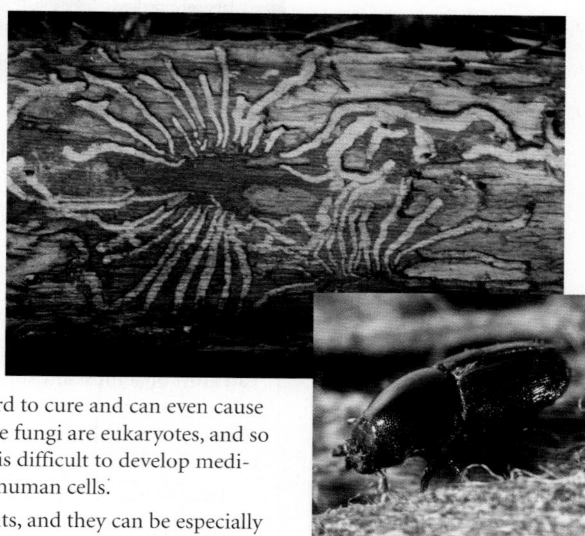

FIGURE 19.26 A fungus is responsible for Dutch elm disease. Adult elm bark beetles tunnel into the bark of elms to lay their eggs. If the trees are diseased, fungus spores stick to the adults as they visit new trees.

Some fungal pathogens, such as those that cause ringworm and athlete's foot, have fairly mild effects. But several fungi cause severe diseases, such as some lung illnesses, that are hard to cure and can even cause death. Fungal infections are hard to treat because fungi are eukaryotes, and so their cellular structure is very similar to ours. It is difficult to develop medicine that will harm fungal cells but not damage human cells.

Fungi and plants Fungal diseases also affect plants, and they can be especially devastating in agriculture and horticulture. Dutch elm disease is caused by a fungus that is transmitted by elm bark beetles, shown in **FIGURE 19.26.** In the United States, the first cases of Dutch elm disease were reported in Ohio in 1930. Today, the disease has destroyed more than half of the elms in the northern United States. Fungi also destroy a large portion of the world's fruit crops. A disease of peaches called peach scab is caused by a fungus and results in millions of dollars in losses to growers each year. Gray mold is a disease of produce such as strawberries. This fungus can grow even in refrigerated fruit and is a major cause of fruit spoilage during shipment and storage.

Fungal diseases in agriculture are often treated with chemical sprays called fungicides. Today, however, crops that are genetically engineered to resist fungi are becoming more common. Fungal diseases in animals, including those in humans, are usually treated with antifungal medications. These treatments usually come from fungi themselves, which produce them as a defense against other fungi. Like bacteria and protists, however, fungi can develop resistance to treatments if they are overused. These products should be used carefully.

BELOW LEVEL

Have students use Cornell notes to outline this section. They can record key terms and their definitions in a left column across from the appropriate point in the outline. Then students can add a summary in the bottom section. Encourage them to be concise but still try to include all key information.

Biology Toolkit, Cornell Notes, p. C26

TEACH FROM VISUALS

FIGURE 19.26 Review the figure with students. Explain that the squiggly lines in the tree bark are made by larval bark beetles as they emerge. **Ask,** What is significant about the fungus's spores sticking to adult elm bark beetles? It explains how the fungus is transmitted between elm trees.

The Inside Story

The convulsive fits that affected several young girls in Salem, Massachusetts, in 1692 were thought at the time to be caused by **witchcraft.** Modern research by a number of scientists suggests that the symptoms displayed by the girls resulted from poisoning with a fungus, *Claviceps purpurea,* that commonly contaminates stored grains. The fungus, commonly called **ergot,** grows on stored cereal grains, notably rye. It produces a substance that has marked effects on several body systems, including the nervous system. Common symptoms include convulsions, twitching, and sometimes a feeling that the limbs are on fire.

The bizarre symptoms, coupled with certain social prejudices of the period, led to accusations that some of the people of Salem, mostly women, had put the young girls under a spell. As a result, some of the accused were executed for participating in witchcraft. Studies begun in the 1970s pointed to ergot poisoning as a possible cause of the bizarre behavior of these young women. There is some evidence that ergot was growing on stored rye in Salem homes.

Other instances of similar bizarre behavior have led scientists to suspect ergotism as a factor. Among these was the Dancing Mania that occurred across Europe during the Middle Ages. During this epidemic, groups of people would run and dance through the streets, often foaming at the mouth and screaming in an unintelligible language, until they collapsed from exhaustion or, in some cases, died.

▼ Teach *continued*

Vocabulary

saprophyte Decomposers have wrongly been tagged with the name *saprophytes,* which translates as "putrid plants." The root *sapro-* comes from the Greek word *sapros,* meaning "putrid." The term *saprophyte* was coined when fungi were still considered members of the plant kingdom. Even though incorrect, *saprophyte* is still commonly used to describe all decomposers. The more appropriate but less commonly used scientific term is *saprotroph.*

Science Trivia

- Lichens are extremely sensitive to air pollution and are used in environmental science as air-quality indicators.
- Litmus paper is made from the lichens *Ochrolechia tartarea* and *Roccella tinctoria.*
- Reindeer moss, a crusty vegetation much favored by reindeer, is actually *Cladonia rangiferina,* a lichen that grows in alpine tundra.

FIGURE 19.27 Lichens

A **lichen** is a symbiotic relationship between an alga and a fungus. Algae cells feed the fungus through photosynthesis, and the fungal mycelium provides habitat for the algae.

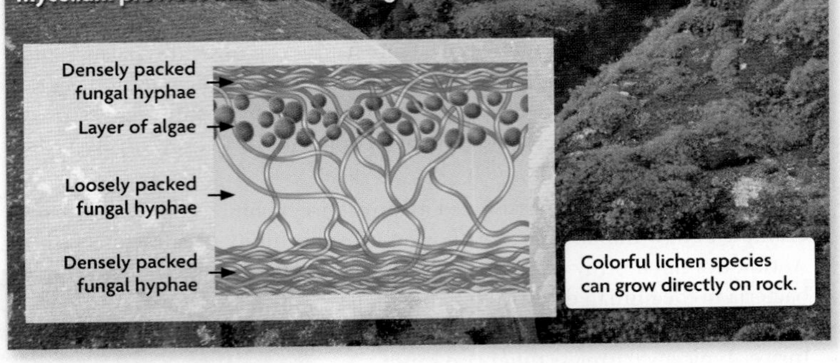

Fungi as Mutualists

Mutualism is a symbiotic relationship in which both organisms benefit. Fungi form mutualistic relationships with several types of organisms.

Lichens A **lichen** (LY-kuhn) is a mutualistic relationship between a fungus and algae or photosynthetic bacteria. Only certain fungi, algae, or cyanobacteria can combine to form a lichen body. The body itself consists mainly of fungal hyphae that surround and grow into the algal cells, as shown in **FIGURE 19.27.** The algal part of the lichen carries out photosynthesis, making sugars that feed both the alga and the fungus. Lichens (phylum Mycomycota) can grow on almost any solid surface, from tree trunks to soil to rocks. They are common in cool, dry environments. They can also withstand severe temperatures. This characteristic of lichens allows them to live in habitats such as tundra, where fungi could not survive alone.

Lichens play several different roles in the environment and in the lives of humans. For example, they are extremely important during primary succession, because they can live on bare rock. Many species of lichens are sensitive to air pollution and can be used as indicators of air quality. Lichens are also important in nutrient cycling, because they function as both a decomposer and a producer. Lichens produce hundreds of unique chemicals, including pigments used as dyes in traditional cultures and compounds that have antibiotic properties.

***Connecting* CONCEPTS**

Ecology Recall from **Chapter 14** that primary succession occurs after disruptive events such as fires and volcanic eruptions. The first organisms to recolonize an area, such as lichens, are called pioneer species.

Mycorrhizae Mutualistic associations between plant roots and soil fungi are called mycorrhizae. More than 80 percent of the world's plants have mycorrhizae on their roots. Mycorrhizae form when the hyphae of a fungus colonize the roots of a nearby plant. The huge surface area of the fungal mycelium is much larger than the root surface area of the plants, so the mycelium can absorb soil nutrients and water faster than the plant's roots could alone. In return, the fungus benefits because it gets sugars and other nutrients from the plant. Mycorrhizae can boost plant growth and reduce the need for fertilizers, which can cause soil and water pollution. Mycorrhizae also produce chemicals with antibiotic properties that help fight harmful bacteria.

Differentiated Instruction

PRE-AP

Point out that in spite of the three fungal trophic strategies (decomposer, mutualist, and pathogen), all fungi still fall into the primary category of decomposer. Ask students to analyze the three strategies and their utility to fungi and other organisms. Then have students write a five-minute essay that identifies each trophic strategy and gives an example of a fungus that employs the strategy.

Biology Toolkit, Quick-Write, p. C19

TEACH WITH TECHNOLOGY

Use the Internet to obtain photos, video clips, and information on *Atta cephalotes,* better known as the leaf-cutter ant. Assemble a digital slide show and discuss the importance of the fungus-ant mutualism to the health of the forest ecosystem. See **ClassZone.com** for links.

Fungal gardens and insects Some insects also live as partners in a mutualistic symbiosis with fungi. The leafcutter ants of Central and South America, shown in **FIGURE 19.28**, don't just use fungi—they actually grow them. These ants cut tiny pieces of leaf from plants with their jaws. They carry these leaf pieces back to an underground nest area, where they build a garden of leaf pieces. Next, the ants add pieces of the fungus. The fungus breaks down the leaf pieces and absorbs nutrients from them. The ants in turn feed on the fungal mycelium.

FIGURE 19.28 Leafcutter ants carry leaves back to their nests to provide food for fungi. The ants then eat the growing fungal mycelium.

A Summarize **Describe three ways that fungi are important to the environment.**

MAIN IDEA

Fungi are studied for many purposes.

Many species of fungi are edible, such as the mushrooms we eat on pizza and the yeast we use to bake bread. In addition, fungi make citric acid, which is used in soft drinks and some candy. Fungi are also useful in the health care industry. Since the discovery of antibiotics in the 1900s, scientists have been researching how pathogens interact with their natural environments. This knowledge is then applied to develop useful medicines. For example, in their natural habitats fungi and bacteria compete for similar resources, such as space and nutrients. This is true whether they live on a forest floor or in a human digestive tract. Over time, fungi have evolved natural defenses against bacteria.

Studies of yeast have produced equally valuable insights. These tiny single-celled organisms are among the most important model systems used in molecular biology. Most yeasts have many of the same genes and proteins found in plants and animals. Insights gained from studies of a yeast's genome can often be applied to multicellular organisms. Yeast are small, grow quickly, and are easy to culture, or raise, in the laboratory.

B Summarize **What are three ways that fungi benefit humans?**

Connecting CONCEPTS

Antibiotics Recall from **Chapter 18** that an antibiotic is a chemical that kills or slows the growth of bacteria.

Take It Further

Like leaf-cutter ants, termites also cultivate **fungal gardens,** growing the fungus *Termitomyces* in giant termitaria. More than 300 termite species are completely dependent on their fungal gardens for food. *Termitomyces* is grown on termite feces inside **termitaria.** A termitarium is a large, moundlike structure that houses the fungal garden and the termites. Termitaria can be quite large. Some can house as many as several million individual termites and their crop of fungus. These structures may rise as high as nine feet into the air.

Answers

A Summarize Fungi are important to the environment as decomposers, as pathogens, and as mutualists that help their autotrophic partners obtain important nutrients or provide food for them.

B Summarize Fungi decompose dead matter and return it to the soil as nutrients; they boost plant productivity; and they are used for food and medicine.

19.6 ASSESSMENT

ONLINE QUIZ ClassZone.com

B.4.4

REVIEWING MAIN IDEAS

1. How do fungi contribute to the balance of an ecosystem?
2. What are three reasons **lichens** are useful to humans?

CRITICAL THINKING

3. **Compare** Draw a Venn diagram comparing lichens and mycorrhizae. Include terms such as *roots, photosynthesis,* and *mutualism.*
4. **Analyze** Some antifungal medications can damage the patient's own tissues. Why doesn't this problem occur with antibiotics?

Connecting CONCEPTS

5. **Natural Selection** A peach farmer is faced every year with an outbreak of peach scab, a fungal disease of peaches. Every year he sprays his crop carefully with fungicides, but each time these seem less effective than the year before. Why might this be?

Assess and Reteach

Assess Use the Online Quiz or Section Quiz (*Assessment Book,* p. 378).

Reteach Use the Power Presentation for **Section 19.6** to review the material presented in this section. Have students use this review to fill in any gaps in their notes for the section.

19.6 ASSESSMENT

1. Fungi contribute to the balance of an ecosystem by decomposing organic matter and recycling nutrients.
2. Answers should include three of the following: lichens produce oxygen; they grow in unfavorable environments, which then allows other organisms to grow; they are indicators of air quality; they are important decomposers that return nutrients to the soil; they can be used to produce antibiotic compounds; their pigments are used as dyes.
3. features specific to lichens: algae, photosynthesis; features specific to mycorrhizae: roots, surface area; common features: mutualism, fungus
4. Antibiotics affect prokaryotes, whereas fungi and humans are eukaryotes.
5. Fungi that survived the initial spraying may have conferred resistance to later generations. Over time, the population of fungicide-resistant fungi could increase.

OPTIONS FOR INQUIRY

INVESTIGATION

Time 45 minutes	TEACHER TESTED
Teacher Preparation	
Student Difficulty	
Lab Binder Diversity, pp. 30–32	

Purpose Quantify the growth of mold on a slice of bread.

Overview Students will design an experiment to quantify the mold growing on a slice of bread. They will

- write an experimental procedure that describes how they will test their independent variable
- make quantitative measurements and qualitative observations of mold growth on bread

LAB PREPARATION

- Plan to allow ten minutes of class time each day to check mold growth and a full day for lab wrap-up.
- Discuss quantitative and qualitative data with the class. Have students give an example of each one. Examples: quantitative—size of mold patch; qualitative—color of mold

LAB MANAGEMENT

Point out that students can decide where to place water droplets. Students may place these in one corner, in the center, or spread evenly across the bread.

Safety Provide latex gloves for students to wear whenever handling bread or bags that contain bread. Remind them to properly dispose of the gloves and to wash their hands after each lab session.

POST-LAB DISCUSSION

Discuss the results of the investigation. **Ask,** What changes did you observe in the bread over the course of the experiment? the colors of the mold, the spread of the mold on the bread, increased mass of the bread-and-mold Students may wonder why the total mass of the bread, bag, air, and mold increases when the bag is sealed.

Use these inquiry-based labs and online activities to deepen your understanding of protists and fungi observed in everyday life.

INDIANA STANDARDS

NOS.1 Develop explanations based on reproducible data and observations gathered during laboratory investigations.

NOS.3 Clearly communicate their ideas and results of investigations verbally and in written form using tables, graphs, diagrams, and photographs.

DESIGN YOUR OWN INVESTIGATION

Quantifying Mold Growth

Mold grows in many places. For example, baked goods will eventually grow mold when left out on the counter. In this experiment, you will grow mold on the surface of a slice of bread. You will gather quantitative and qualitative data to study the growth and structure of this mold.

SKILLS Designing Experiments, Analyzing Data

PROBLEM How can you best quantify mold growth on a slice of bread?

MATERIALS

- slice of white bread
- 10 mL water
- eyedropper
- sealable plastic lunch bag
- straw cut into pieces
- scale
- clear plastic grid
- prepared slide (optional)
- microscope (optional)

PROCEDURE

1. Use a piece of bread, water, pieces of straw, and a sandwich bag to design an experiment to determine how much mold grows on a slice of bread.
2. Your experiment should take place over a week. Once you have placed the bread in the bag you will never open the bag again.
3. Choose the quantitative data that your group wishes to record. Examples include mass, or approximate percentage of the bread slice that is covered in mold (using a plastic grid). If you will be recording mass, record the initial mass of the bag with the bread.
4. Have your teacher approve your experimental design, and then set up your experiment.
5. Keeping the bag sealed, record your data every day for a week. Also record a daily qualitative description of the mold growth (color, size, texture, growth pattern, and so on). Wash your hands after you take data. Keep the bag sealed and dispose of it at the end of the week according to your teacher's directions.

ANALYZE AND CONCLUDE

1. **Analyze** Using the quantitative and qualitative data that you recorded, describe how the amount of mold growing on the bread changed each day.
2. **Analyze** Was there a pattern that the mold growth followed or was it random? Explain.
3. **Experimental Design** What are the potential disadvantages with the quantitative method that you decided to use? What are methods that would make your results more accurate?

EXTEND YOUR INVESTIGATION

If a prepared slide of bread mold is available, examine it under the microscope. Draw a sketch of what you see. Label the sketch, referring to the life cycle illustrations on page 593.

Answers

Sample Data

For a sample of student data, go to page R107.

Analyze and Conclude

1. Students should have seen an increase in the quantity of mold throughout their observation period.
2. Often the molds grow by spreading out over the bread.
3. Measuring bread mass can be misleading, because while the total mass increases, it is the mold's mass that is growing, not the bread's mass. Measuring percent coverage of mold could be difficult if the pattern of coverage is spotting or oddly shaped.

Extend Your Investigation

The sketches should resemble the images on the slides and should be labeled correctly.

600 Unit 6: Classification and Diversity

INVESTIGATION

Algae in Products

Do you enjoy eating algae? Even if you don't like seaweed-wrapped sushi, you might be surprised to find that you like other products made from algae. Algal products are found in many foods, including ice cream and chocolate milk. Algae contain important nutrients, such as iodine, potassium, magnesium, iron, and selenium. Look through your refrigerator and cabinets at home to see what other household products you can find that contain algae.

SKILL Researching

PROBLEM What products in your home contain algae?

RESEARCH

All of the ingredients listed below come from different types of algae.

- *Carrageenan* is found in the cell walls of some red algae. It is used as a thickener in foods, cosmetics, and medicines.
- *Agar* is another product made from red algae. It is often used as a replacement for gelatin. It is also used in science laboratories to grow bacteria.
- *Alginates,* also called *alginin* or *algin,* are compounds from brown algae that help form smooth, creamy liquids. They also make products more stable over a range of temperatures, making the products last longer.
- *Beta carotene* is a pigment from green algae, as well as other sources. It is used as a yellow-orange food coloring.

1. Find an item in your home that contains algae.
2. How do you think the algal compounds are used in the product that you found?
3. Perform research to describe how the red, brown, or green alga that your product contains grows naturally.
4. How is the algae found in your product farmed in order to produce enough for industry?

Online BIOLOGY
CLASSZONE.COM

ANIMATED BIOLOGY
Protist and Fungus Life Cycles
Build the life cycles of a slime mold, a cup fungus, and a brown algae. Compare and contrast the ways by which these diverse organisms reproduce.

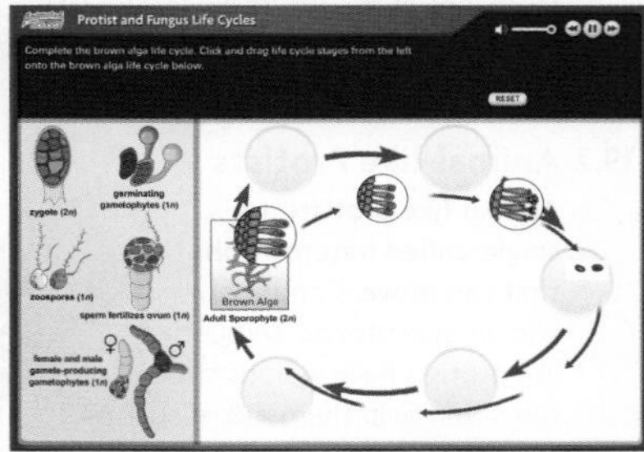

WEBQUEST
Some of the world's most dangerous diseases are caused by protists. In this WebQuest, you will learn more about three of these diseases: sleeping sickness, giardiasis, and malaria. Use your knowledge to diagnose and treat three patients.

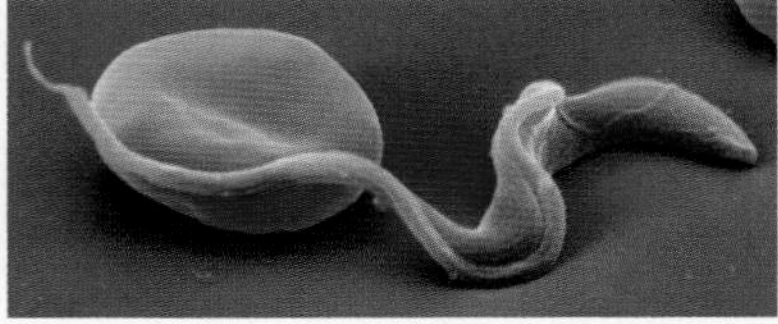

DATA ANALYSIS ONLINE
The Mediterranean strain of *Caulerpa taxifolia* is a tropical seaweed that was bred for use in aquariums. It was accidentally released in 1984 into the Mediterranean Sea. Graph the spread of *Cualerpa* from 1984 until 2000 and determine if *Caulerpa* has been successful in its new environment.

Answers

Analyze and Conclude

1. Students should correctly identify a product that contains a derivative of algae.
2. Carrageenan is a thickener, agar replaces gelatin, alginates make the temperature of products stable or make products creamy, and beta carotene gives products a yellow-orange color.
3. *Sample Answer:* Red algae grow at a deeper depth than do green or brown algae.
4. Answers may vary, but might include being grown in tanks or farmed directly in the ocean.

Online Biology ▼

ANIMATED BIOLOGY Use this interactive animation to reinforce the concepts in **Sections 19.3, 19.4,** and **19.5.**

WEBQUEST The WebQuest takes one full class period. Students complete the activity online and will need access to a printer to print their answers. Sample answers, teacher notes, and alternative assessment ideas are available on **ClassZone.com.** Use with **Section 19.2.**

DATA ANALYSIS ONLINE
Use this lab to reinforce the concepts of **Section 19.3.** Students should find that *Caulerpa* spread exponentially through a 10,000 hectare (100,000,000 m^2) range off the coast of the French Riviera. *Caulerpa* had a sigmoidal growth curve—a slow start with an exponential increase over a short period of time that slows or levels off when carrying capacity is reached.

INVESTIGATION

TEACHER TESTED

Time	20 minutes
Teacher Preparation	(1 flask)
Student Difficulty	(1 flask)
Lab Binder	Diversity, p. 33

Purpose Identify common household products and foods that contain algae.

Overview Students will research foods and household products to determine which, if any, contain algae or products made from algae.

POST-LAB DISCUSSION

Have students describe their findings. **Ask,** What products surprised you the most in terms of containing algae? Answers will vary.

CHAPTER REVIEW

Interactive Review

Encourage students to go to **ClassZone.com** for a detailed review of each section, including visuals and vocabulary practice.

Unit Resource Book, Vocabulary Practice, pp. 91–94

CHAPTER 19 Interactive Review @ CLASSZONE.COM

KEY CONCEPTS | Vocabulary Games | Concept Maps | Animated Biology | Online Quiz

19.1 Diversity of Protists

Kingdom Protista is the most diverse of all the kingdoms. It includes organisms that are animal-like, plantlike, and funguslike. Protists may be single-celled or multicellular, and may be microscopic or very large. Protist classification is likely to change in the future, as some protists are more closely related to members of other kingdoms than they are to other protists.

19.2 Animal-like Protists

Animal-like protists are single-celled heterotrophs that can move. Commonly known as protozoa, animal-like protists have various structures that help them move, such as flagella, pseudopods, or cilia. Some animal-like protists can cause diseases such as malaria and sleeping sickness.

19.3 Plantlike Protists

Algae are plantlike protists. Unlike animal-like protists, which are all single-celled, plantlike protists can be either single-celled or multicellular. Most plantlike protists can make their own food through photosynthesis. Plantlike protists are not classified as plants because they do not have roots, stems, leaves, or the specialized tissues and reproductive structures that plants have. However, like many plants, most plantlike protists can reproduce both sexually and asexually.

19.4 Funguslike Protists

Funguslike protists decompose organic matter. These protists have an important role in recycling nutrients through ecosystems. Unlike fungi, funguslike protists can move during part of their life cycle. Funguslike protists include slime molds and water molds.

19.5 Diversity of Fungi

Fungi are heterotrophs that absorb their food. Their bodies are made of long strands, called hyphae, which grow underground in a tangled mass called a mycelium. The parts of fungi that humans normally recognize, such as mushrooms, are actually only the reproductive structures of the fungi, called fruiting bodies.

19.6 Ecology of Fungi

Fungi recycle nutrients in the environment. Some fungi cause illness to humans, such as those that cause athlete's foot and ringworm. Other fungi, such as those that cause Dutch elm disease, cause illness to plants or other organisms. Some fungi share a mutualistic relationship with organisms such as algae to form lichens, or plant roots, which form mycorrhizae. Humans use fungi for foods, medicine, and as model organisms in scientific research.

Synthesize Your Notes

Supporting Main Ideas Use a supporting main ideas diagram to summarize how the three groups of protists get their food.

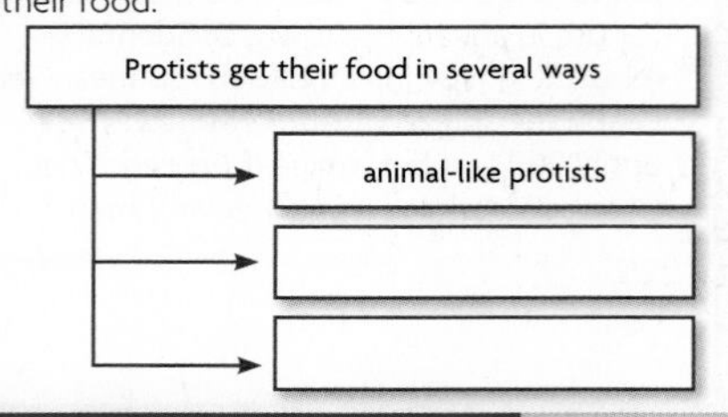

Concept Map Use a concept map like the one below to summarize what you know about the roles of fungi in the environment.

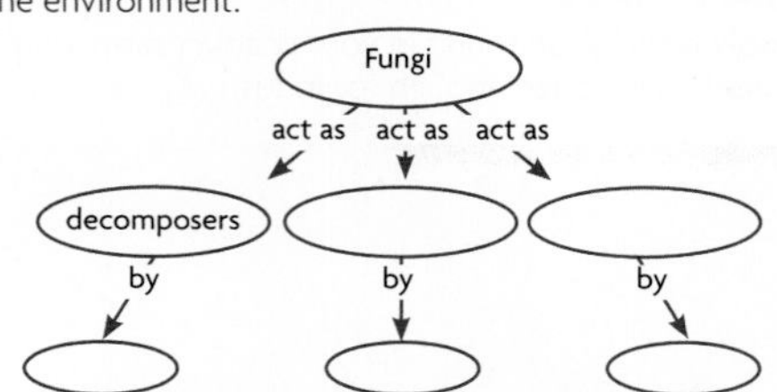

Reviewing Vocabulary

1. Both are structures that help animal-like protists move and capture food. A pseudopod is a temporary extension of the cell's cytoplasm and plasma membrane. Cilia are short, hairlike structures.
2. Both are funguslike protists and are decomposers. Slime molds can be single cells, each with many nuclei, or a single amoeba with one nucleus. Water molds are branching filaments of cells. Slime molds also have animal-like traits, and water molds do not.
3. Both are symbiotic partnerships and examples of mutualism. Mycorrhizae are symbiotic partnerships between plant roots and fungi. Lichens are composed of a fungus and an alga or a photosynthetic bacterium.
4. Both are protists. Protozoa have animal-like characteristics. Algae have plantlike characteristics.
5. Both are reproductive structures of fungi. *Fruiting body* refers to the reproductive structures of any fungus, whereas sporangia are fruiting bodies that form spores at the tips of hyphae.
6. Both help the fungus obtain nutrients. Hyphae are long individual filaments that excrete enzymes to digest and absorb food. Mycelia are a mass of hyphae.
7. Hyphae grow into a weblike mycelium.
8. Mycorrhizae are mutualistic relationships between a fungus mycelium and plant roots.
9. fruiting body
10. hyphae
11. mycelium

Chapter Assessment

Chapter Vocabulary

19.1 protist, p. 574

19.2 protozoa, p. 577
pseudopod, p. 578
cilia, p. 578

19.3 algae, p. 581

19.4 slime mold, p. 587
water mold, p. 588

19.5 chitin, p. 589
hyphae, p. 589
mycelium, p. 590
fruiting body, p. 590
mycorrhizae, p. 591
sporangia, p. 592

19.6 lichen, p. 598

Reviewing Vocabulary

Compare and Contrast

Describe one similarity and one difference between the two terms in each of the following pairs.

1. pseudopod, cilia
2. slime mold, water mold
3. mycorrhizae, lichen
4. protozoa, algae
5. fruiting body, sporangia
6. hyphae, mycelium

Greek and Latin Word Origins

7. The term *hyphae* comes from the Greek word *huphe,* which means "web." Explain how this meaning relates to hyphae.
8. The term *mycorrhizae* comes from the Greek words *mukes,* which means "fungus," and *rhiza,* which means "root." Explain how these meanings relate to mycorrhizae.

Labeling Diagrams

In your notebook, write the vocabulary term that matches each numbered item below.

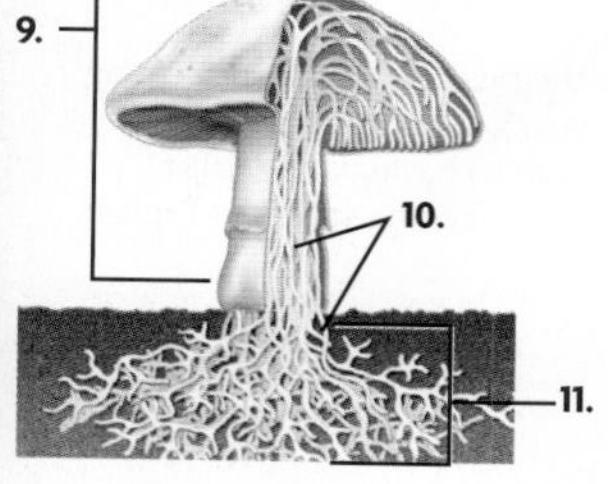

Reviewing MAIN IDEAS

12. Give one characteristic of each type of protist that explains why it is animal-like, plantlike, or funguslike. **B.8.3**
13. Explain why the phyla of the kingdom Protista might be regrouped into several kingdoms and what would likely be the basis for this reclassification. **B.8.3**
14. What are three types of structures that help some protists move?
15. When does an amoeba form a pseudopod?
16. Name two animal-like protists that cause disease and briefly describe the diseases that they cause.
17. Are protists classified on the basis of being single-celled or multicellular? Give an example to support your answer.
18. How do multicellular algae reproduce asexually?
19. Slime molds have animal-like traits. What might be one reason they are classified with water molds as funguslike protists?
20. Explain how hyphae help a fungus absorb food.
21. The phyla Ascomycota and Basidiomycota are both in the kingdom Fungi. What structures are the basis for placing organisms in one or the other of these phyla?
22. Describe sexual reproduction in yeast, or single-celled fungi.
23. How can the hyphae of bread molds be involved in both asexual and sexual reproduction?
24. Why are yeasts useful to scientific research?
25. How is the decomposing activity of fungi both beneficial and harmful?

CHAPTER REVIEW

Reviewing Main Ideas

12. Animal-like protists are heterotrophic. Most plantlike protists photosynthesize their own food. Funguslike protists are decomposers.
13. Many of the phyla are distantly related to one another and are more closely related to members of other kingdoms. DNA analysis would likely provide the basis for reclassifying protists into several kingdoms.
14. flagella, pseudopods, cilia
15. when it needs to move or capture food
16. *Sample Answer:* malaria from *Plasmodium;* sleeping sickness from *Trypanosoma;* intestinal diseases from *Giardia*
17. No, both unicellular and multicellular plantlike protists are classified according to their photosynthetic pigments, food storage strategies, and cell wall structure. Examples include the three phyla of green, brown, and red algae. Green algae can be multicellular or unicellular; red and brown algae are multicellular.
18. By fragmenting; each piece can then grow into another alga.
19. Slime molds are decomposers, as are water molds.
20. The hyphae extend into the food source and release enzymes that break down the food so it can be absorbed across the cell walls of the hyphae.
21. The reproductive structure that contains the spores in the Ascomycota, or sac fungi, is a sac (an ascus). The fruiting body of the Basidiomycota, or club fungi, is club-shaped (a basidium).
22. A diploid cell produces four haploid nuclei through meiosis. They are contained within a saclike structure called an ascus in the parent cell's cytoplasm. The haploid nuclei are called ascospores. These are released from the ascus through the budding process. Some of these ascospores might fuse with other haploid ascospores to form diploid cells.
23. The hyphae can form haploid spores in sporangia (asexual), or they can fuse to produce a diploid zygospore (sexual).
24. Most yeasts have many of the same genes and proteins that are found in higher eukaryotes. Therefore, studies of their genomes can be applied to multicellular organisms.
25. As decomposers, fungi help recycle nutrients such as carbon, nitrogen, and minerals back into the soil. But this same decomposing action can harm fruit trees and wooden houses and boats.

ITEM CORRELATIONS

Standard	Items
B.8.3	12, 13, 26, 28, 31, 32, 35

Critical Thinking

26. All animal-like protists, and some plantlike protists, are unicellular; all animals and plants are multicellular. Plantlike protists also do not have roots, stems, or leaves that characterize plants. Funguslike protists can move during part of their life cycle; fungi cannot.
27. Amoebas would be found on land and in water, and zooflagellates and ciliates would be found only in water environments. Flagella and cilia are structures that help protists swim. They are of no use on land or in any environment that does include moisture. Amoebas can live in water—as long as there is a surface on which they can anchor their pseudopods—and on land in moist environments.
28. Dinoflagellata
29. The pseudoplasmodium form of a cellular slime mold moves as though it is a single individual, like a plasmodium. However, in a pseudoplasmodium, the cells remain independent, and their membranes do not fuse.
30. The broad-spectrum fungicide will also kill off beneficial fungi needed to recycle nutrients back into the soil, as well as the fungal part of the mycorrhizae on plant roots. Without proper nutrients in the soil to draw up through their roots, the crops will not grow well.

Interpreting Visuals

31. Fungi and animals are more closely related than fungi and plants.
32. Green algae are more closely related to plants than they are to red algae. The diagram shows them branching off from the common ancestor with plants at a later time than they do from the common ancestor with red algae.

Critical Thinking

26. Analyze What characteristics of protists prevent them from being classified as animals, plants, or fungi? **B.8.3**

27. Analyze Amoebas have pseudopods, zooflagellates have flagella, and ciliates have cilia to help them move. Would you expect to find each of these types of protists on land or water? Explain your answer.

28. Classify A new plantlike protist has been discovered. It has the following characteristics: two flagella, found in a marine environment, body covering made of cellulose. What phylum would it likely be placed in? **B.8.3**

29. Infer The prefix *pseudo-* means "false" or "fake." Why is the term *pseudoplasmodium* used to describe one form of a cellular slime mold?

30. Predict A grape crop is infected with a fungus. There is a fungicide that targets only this kind of fungus and kills it. But a broad-spectrum fungicide that kills many different kinds of fungi is cheaper, and the farmer decides to use it instead. Explain why the farmer's crops may actually become less healthy.

Interpreting Visuals

Use the diagram below to answer the next two questions.

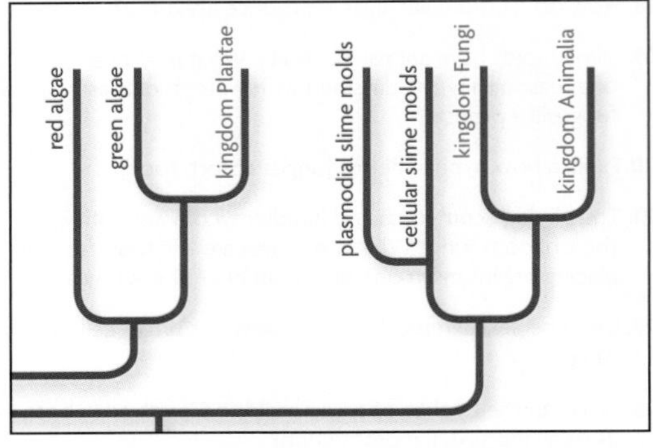

31. Analyze What does this diagram suggest about the relationship between fungi and animals, as compared with fungi and plants? **B.8.3**

32. Analyze Are green algae more closely related to red algae or plants? Explain your answer. **B.8.3**

Analyzing Data

Use the text and the data below to answer the next two questions. The following experiment was conducted by two students to determine if adding yeast to a decomposing fruit would speed up the rate of decomposition.

Two 3-cm^2 pieces of banana were cut. Each was placed in a different plastic bag and the bags were sealed. Each student took one of the banana pieces home.

- Student A placed her banana piece on a bookshelf.
- Student B put some dry yeast on his banana and resealed the bag. He also put his banana piece on a bookshelf.

Both students looked at the banana pieces every day for the next four days and recorded their observations.

PERCENT DECOMPOSITION

Organism	Day 1	Day 2	Day 3	Day 4
Student A's banana	1%	5%	7%	10%
Student B's banana	0%	4%	7%	10%

33. Experimental Design What is the main design flaw in this experiment?

34. Analyze Does the experimental design clearly indicate the question that the students were trying to answer? Explain.

Connecting CONCEPTS

35. Write an Argument Write an argument between two euglenoids in which one wants to be placed with animals and the other wants to be placed with plants. Include the decision of the referee who explains why they can be neither plants nor animals. **B.8.3**

36. Evaluate Look again at the picture of *Didinium* eating the *Paramecium* on page 573. What might be one advantage and disadvantage to having a specialist feeding strategy? a generalist feeding strategy? Explain your answer.

Analyzing Data

33. The banana without the yeast is supposed to be the control, but the two bananas are not held under the same conditions. Student B's banana piece was placed in a sealed bag; Student A's was not.
34. No, their design appears to be testing whether yeast or a closed container affects decomposition. Other conditions (temperature, light) may differ as well, meaning the purpose of the experiment is unclear.

604 Unit 6: Classification and Diversity

INDIANA ISTEP+ Test Prep

B.3.4, B.4.1, B.8.2, NOS.9

Test Practice For more test practice, go to ClassZone.com.

1 When scientists first saw protists with chlorophyll, they thought the protists were actually single-celled plants. With more recent molecular techniques, scientists have determined that these organisms are genetically different from plants. This is an example of

A how our scientific understanding of the world can change with new information.
B how scientists can sometimes form bad conclusions.
C the limitations of using a model to explain scientific discoveries.
D the importance of statistical analysis in science.

2

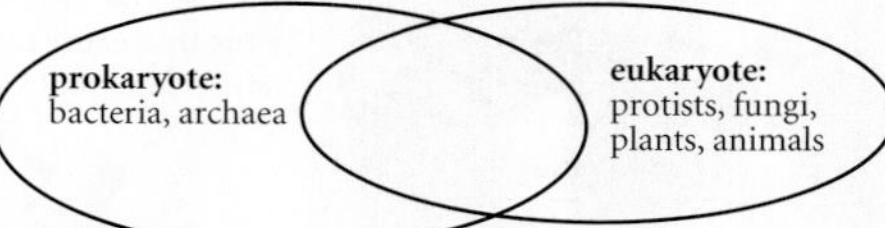

The grouping of kingdoms into prokaryotes and eukaryotes is shown in the Venn diagram above. One characteristic that could be placed in the area that overlaps both groups is

A nucleus.
B organelles.
C chloroplasts.
D cell membranes.

3 Diatoms carry out a large portion of the photosynthesis that occurs on Earth. In which biogeochemical cycle do diatoms probably have the ***greatest*** effect?

A phosphorus cycle
B nitrogen cycle
C carbon cycle
D water cycle

4 Most fungi are decomposers. How do their life processes affect other organisms in the community?

A Fungi keep other populations under control by preying on weak organisms.
B Fungi make stored nutrients available to other organisms.
C Fungi compete with plants for soil nutrients.
D Fungi compete with plants and animals for space.

THINK THROUGH THE QUESTION

If you are having a hard time answering this question in terms of fungi, try to consider it based on the role of decomposers in general.

5

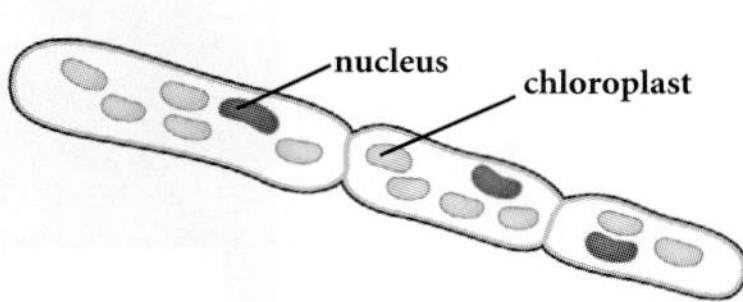

A researcher discovers a new type of organism. Only some structures, labeled above, can be clearly seen. Based on this information alone, the researcher is able to conclude that the organism

A is a protist that lives in colonies.
B is a multicellular protist.
C can capture energy from the sun.
D will not prey upon other organisms.

6 Protists are a diverse group of organisms generally grouped into three different categories. What are these categories and how are they defined?

Standards-Based Assessment

1. A	4. B
2. D	5. C
3. C	6. See Below

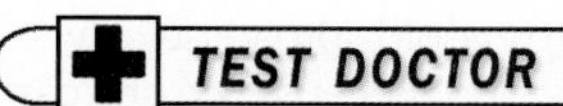

Question 1 Answer A is correct. Answer B is incorrect because the scientists' first conclusion was based on evidence, but new evidence enabled them to gain a new understanding of the data. Answer C is incorrect because the question does not involve scientific models. Answer D is incorrect because the question does not involve statistical analysis.

Question 2 Answer D is correct because all cells have a cell membrane. Answer A is incorrect because a nucleus is unique to eukaryotes. Answer B is incorrect because membrane-bound organelles are unique to eukaryotes. Answer C is incorrect because chloroplasts, a type of membrane-bound organelle, are unique to eukaryotes.

Question 3 Answer C is correct. Answers A, B, and D are incorrect because photosynthesis is a process in which plants take in carbon dioxide, store energy in the form of sugars, and release oxygen; therefore, the phosphorus, nitrogen, and water cycles will likely be less affected by diatoms than is the carbon cycle.

Question 6 Protists can be plant-like, animal-like, or fungus-like. They are categorized, primarily, by the method they use to obtain energy. Plant-like protests posses chloroplasts, and are able to synthesize their own food from the Sun's energy.Animal-like protests obtain their energy from other organisms. Fungus-like protists break down dead or dying organisms to obtain energy.

Connecting Concepts

35. The argument for being classified as an animal should point out that euglenoids do not have cell walls and can move easily. The argument for being classified as a plant should point out that many euglenoids are autotrophs and have chlorophyll. The referee should explain that both plants and animals are multicellular and that euglenoids are unicellular.

36. *Sample Answer:* A specialist may have less competition for food but must have a way to survive during times of food shortages. A generalist has many more food choices available but might face greater competition for some or all of those food sources from many other organisms.

ITEM CORRELATIONS

Standard	Items
B.3.4	3
B.4.1	4
B.8.2	2, 5, 6
NOS.9	1

UNIT
6

Introduce

Tell students that a disease caused by an emerging virus could spread quickly around the world. Because viruses can cross continental boundaries easily, a global network of specialized agencies and their partners work together to monitor and track these viruses and have plans in place in case the viruses spread.

The World Health Organization (WHO) is the United Nations' specialized agency for health. This agency is responsible for global monitoring and the coordination of information. Global surveillance networks report suspected disease outbreaks or the presence of viruses in humans and in animals. Once the disease is detected, cases are verified, data is analyzed, and information is made available around the world. In addition, WHO coordinates a rapid response to outbreaks of diseases.

The Centers for Disease Control and Prevention (CDC) is part of the United States Department of Health and Human Services. The CDC conducts research, monitors outbreaks, develops national plans for response to disease outbreaks, and provides information to the United States government. The CDC works closely with the World Health Organization and public and private associations, organizations, departments, universities, and health professionals to try to prevent the spread of disease.

Discuss with students the importance of global monitoring and a central source for the latest information. **Ask**

- If you needed the most recent data on cases of avian flu, where would you get it? WHO or CDC Internet websites
- Why is a global network for monitoring and tracking disease important? *Sample Answer:* Diseases can spread quickly around the world. Health professionals need to trade disease information to make sure preventative measures are taken and medical supplies get to where they are needed.

UNIT 6: CLASSIFICATION AND DIVERSITY

BIOZINE at CLASSZONE.COM

INTERNET MAGAZINE

Go online for the latest biology news and updates on all BioZine articles.

Expanding the Textbook

News Feeds
- Science Daily
- CNN
- BBC

Careers

Bio Bytes

Opinion Poll

Strange Biology

Could one of these travelers be carrying a virus that causes the next pandemic?

Pandemics— Is the Next One on the Way?

Imagine that a new virus emerges and people have no immunity. There is no vaccine. If this were to happen, there could be mandatory travel restrictions, quarantines, and social distancing—including staying out of all crowded places. In the United States alone, such an outbreak could kill up to 2 million people. But how can such a virus emerge, and how can we prepare for it?

Current News

Using a computer and the Internet, have students look at the stories being covered in the Current News section of BioZine at **ClassZone.com.** Have students consider these questions:

- What stories deal with microbial diseases?
- How often is the word **pandemic** used? **epidemic?** How are these terms defined?
- What local agencies track or report on disease in your area?

Careers

Have students go to BioZine to read about featured careers. Have students check the career listings in the local area. **Ask**

- What percentage of careers in your area relate to the health sciences?
- What risks do health professionals have to be aware of when working with disease-causing agents?

Pandemics

When a new virus emerges, the species that it infects has had little or no opportunity to evolve immunity. If the virus infects people, there is often little time to produce vaccines. For these reasons, a new virus may be able to spread easily from person to person.

A new virus can cause a pandemic, which is a disease outbreak that affects large areas of the world and has a high fatality rate. The 1918 flu pandemic was the most devastating pandemic recorded in world history. This virus infected nearly one-fifth of the world's population, killing about 50 million people worldwide. It spread mainly along global trade routes and with the movement of soldiers during World War I.

If a new and deadly disease emerges today, a carrier could travel around the world in 24 hours. More than a million people travel internationally by plane every year, easily reaching their destinations before symptoms of any diseases they may be harboring appear.

The "Perfect" Virus

Not every virus is well-suited to cause massive human casualties. For many viruses, humans represent a dead-end infection because they cannot be passed from human to human. For other viruses, victims die too quickly for the virus to reproduce. Quarantines can contain this type of virus relatively easily.

What characteristics would make an emerging virus likely to cause a pandemic? The virus would need to be adapted to humans as hosts and easily spread through casual contact. Victims would also have to survive infection long enough without symptoms to go about their daily business and infect other people. Finally, the most deadly virus would mutate rapidly, foiling the attempts of scientists to develop a vaccine or a drug that targets it.

TECHNOLOGY

Dissecting a Virus

Scientists have long debated how the genetic material of influenza A viruses, RNA, is likely arranged. In 2005 virologist Yoshihiro Kawaoka and his team of researchers at the University of Wisconsin unraveled the mystery using a technique called electron tomography.

Electron tomography is a way to construct a three-dimensional image from a series of electron microscope images taken at different angles. By making slices along flu virus particles that cut them into "top" and "bottom" halves, researchers found that all influenza A viruses have a total of eight RNA strands. As shown at the right, seven strands form a circle just inside the edge of the virus particle, surrounding an eighth strand in the center.

The researchers concluded that all influenza A viruses, including those responsible for regular seasonal outbreaks as well as the avian flu, must share a specific mechanism for packaging their genetic material. By knowing how these viruses package their genetic material, it may be possible to engineer viruses that can be used to mass produce vaccines.

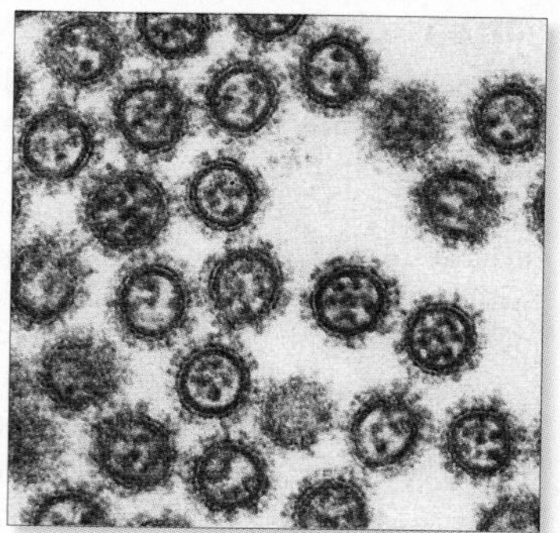

Read More >> at CLASSZONE.COM

Strange Biology

Have students access BioZine at **ClassZone.com** and read the information in the Strange Biology section. Have students relate that information to the key concepts in Unit 6. Then ask students why the information presented in the Strange Biology section could be viewed as being strange or unusual.

Vocabulary of Viruses

Students may need clarification of some of the terms relating to viruses.

emerging virus—a virus that suddenly appears or comes to the attention of medical scientists. An emerging virus is an existing species of virus that mutates, spreads more quickly, or spreads to a new host species. People have little or no immunity to emerging viruses and vaccines are not available.

epidemic—an outbreak of a contagious disease that spreads rapidly in a certain area or country and occurs in a larger-than-normal number of people. An epidemic differs from a pandemic in that the area of the outbreak is more confined.

pandemic—an outbreak of a contagious disease that occurs in a large number of people. A pandemic is an epidemic that occurs over a wide geographic area. The greatest risk of a pandemic today is from emerging viruses.

avian flu—a highly contagious viral disease affecting birds. All birds are susceptible, but outbreaks occur most often in chickens and turkeys. Migratory birds with no symptoms can act as carriers of the virus by transporting the virus from one country to another. Health officials are concerned that the virus could mutate into a highly infectious form and cause a pandemic in humans.

carrier—an organism that acts as host to a disease-causing bacterium or virus, transmitting the bacterium or virus to other organisms, but showing no symptoms of the disease.

mutation—any change in DNA. Specific mutations cannot be predicted. This makes it difficult or impossible to know if or when the avian flu virus could mutate and spread to people.

zoonoses—diseases that are transferable from animals to humans. The SARS virus and avian flu virus cause zoonoses.

strain—a group of organisms of the same species that have distinctive characteristics but are not different enough to be considered a separate breed.

species barrier—the limited transmission of a disease from one species to another.

UNIT
6

Take It Further

Scientists often refer to the viruses that cause influenza by their subtypes. For example, H5N1 is an emerging virus that has crossed the species barrier and moved from birds to some humans. The letters and numbers represent certain proteins on the surface of a virus and the way proteins combine. Scientists are concerned that the H5N1 virus could mutate and potentially cause a pandemic.

Scientists continue to track new influenza viruses that infect humans. Although other strains of influenza viruses continue to appear in small numbers of people, the H5N1 strain continues to be a concern to scientists. The virus first appeared in humans in 1997 in Hong Kong after being transmitted by poultry. Six of the eighteen people known to have the disease died. Since then the virus has only infected small numbers of people, but the area where people have been found with the disease has expanded to other Asian countries and Africa.

CAREERS

Epidemiologist in Action

DR. BEN MUNETA
TITLE Medical Epidemiologist, Indian Health Service
EDUCATION M.D., Stanford University

In 1993 a mystery disease began to kill people in the southwestern United States. One of the experts that the Centers for Disease Control (CDC) consulted was Dr. Ben Muneta. Dr. Muneta is an epidemiologist, a scientist who studies the causes, transmission, and control of diseases within a population. He works at the Indian Health Service National Epidemiology Program in Albuquerque, New Mexico.

Dr. Muneta consulted a traditional Navajo healer. From him, Dr. Muneta learned that the disease was associated with extra rainfall, which had caused the pinon trees to produce more nuts than usual. This in turn had led to a population explosion among mice that feed on these nuts.

Using this lead, CDC researchers determined that the disease was caused by hantavirus, a virus spread through the droppings of deer mice. With further research, Dr. Muneta confirmed that some Navajo healers had even predicted the 1993 outbreak.

Read More >> at CLASSZONE.COM

Diseases that Jump to New Species

Some diseases, called zoonoses, can jump between species. If a virus evolves the ability to jump from a nonhuman animal species to humans, our immune systems will have had little opportunity to evolve defenses. And if this virus exchanges genetic material with another human virus, a new virus that is capable of spreading from person to person may form.

Perhaps the most familiar zoonosis is the avian flu virus. Sometimes called the bird flu, this virus normally infects wild birds such as ducks and geese as well as domestic birds such as chickens. The spread of avian flu does not rely on any human form of transportation, since migrating birds can carry it to other continents.

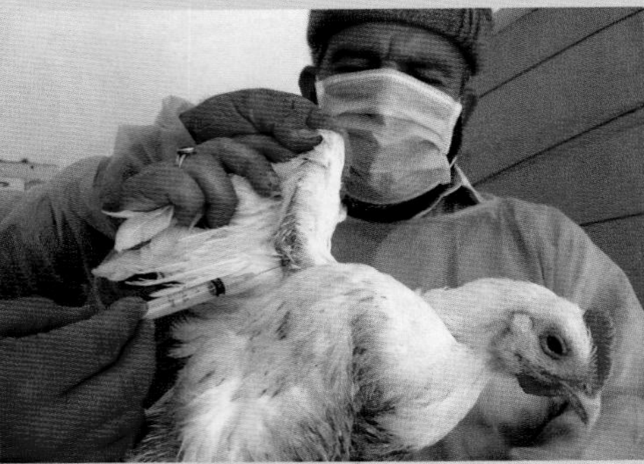

China, Thailand, Russia, Turkey, and Pakistan are among the countries that have confirmed cases of avian flu in poultry farms. Here, a Pakistani health worker vaccinates a healthy chicken.

Avian Flu H5N1

Is avian flu the perfect killer virus? Researchers are currently tracking a form of avian flu called H5N1. Like other flu viruses, H5N1 mutates rapidly. However, mutations are random and may or may not help the virus adapt to new host species.

Unfortunately, a faster, less random way for viruses to mutate exists. Some animals can be infected with viruses from two different species at the same time. For example, if a pig becomes infected by both avian and human flu viruses at the same time, the viruses can exchange genetic information. If this happens, the avian flu can jump the species barrier, becoming a flu virus that can be transmitted from one human to another.

Unanswered Questions

Despite the danger that a new virus represents, no one knows how the virus may mutate or whether it will cause a pandemic. Some of the most important questions include the following:

- How can vaccines be developed quickly enough to stop a disease that can spread in hours or days?
- Can a broad-spectrum antiviral drug be developed that could target more than one flu virus?
- What specific molecular factors allow a virus to jump from one species to another?

Read More >> at CLASSZONE.COM

BIOZINE ClassZone.com

Have students use the resources available in the Unit 6 BioZine at **ClassZone.com** to report about recent discoveries about viruses. In addition to sources available in BioZine, have students locate information from the World Health Organization and the Centers for Disease Control and Prevention. **Ask**

- What research is being done on vaccines for viral diseases?
- How can scientists study the evolution of viruses?
- How do sources of information about viral disease get disseminated?

UNIT 7

Plants

CHAPTER 20
Plant Diversity 610

CHAPTER 21
Plant Structure and Function 638

CHAPTER 22
Plant Growth, Reproduction, and Response 662

BIOZINE

INTERNET MAGAZINE
Genetically Modified Foods—Do Potential Problems Outweigh Benefits? 690

TECHNOLOGY Gene Gun

CAREER Research Engineer

Unit Project

Purpose **Explore natural plant diversity through the biological requirements of a xeriscape design.**

Overview Students prepare a presentation in the form of a landscape design for a five-acre municipal park. Students will

- research and incorporate xeriscaping principles in their landscape designs
- use native or adapted plantings from their regional ecosystem
- incorporate natural topographical elements, water conservation methods, natural pest control, and address runoff and erosion
- present and explain their designs

Preparation Make a copy of the project description and rubric for each student (*Unit Resource Book,* pp. 83–84). Tell students that their design will be scored for organization, neatness, and completeness.

Project Management Allow three weeks for the completion of the project. Have students check in weekly for progress monitoring.

Unit Resource Book Unit 7 Project, pp. 83–85

CHAPTER 20

Indiana Resource Preview

Print Resources

Plant Diversity

INDIANA STANDARDS		Sections	PAGES and PACING	UNIT RESOURCE BOOK
B.8.3	20.1	**Origins of Plant Life** **KEY CONCEPT** Plant life began in the water and became adapted to land.	pp. 612–616 30 minutes	URB pages 1–4
B.8.2	20.2	**Classification of Plants** **KEY CONCEPT** Plants can be classified into nine phyla.	pp. 617–622 30 minutes	URB pages 5–8
NOS.1		CHAPTER INVESTIGATION: Habitat Clues	p. 623 60 minutes	**Lab Binder** Plants pages 1–4
	20.3	**Diversity of Flowering Plants** **KEY CONCEPT** The largest phylum in the plant kingdom is the flowering plants.	pp. 624–627 30 minutes	URB pages 9–12
		DATA ANALYSIS: Mean, Median, and Mode Measures of Central Tendency	p. 628 30 minutes	URB page 17
	20.4	**Plants in Human Culture** **KEY CONCEPT** Humans rely on plants in many ways.	pp. 629–631 30 minutes	URB pages 13–16
NOS.3		OPTIONS FOR INQUIRY	pp. 632–633 45 minutes, 20 minutes	**Lab Binder** Plants pages 5–7
		Chapter Review	pp. 634–637	**Assessment Book** Chapter Tests A, B pp. 399–406

INDIANA STANDARDS

B.8.2 Explain how organisms are classified and named based on their evolutionary relationships into taxonomic categories.
B.8.3 Use anatomical and molecular evidence to establish evolutionary relationships between organisms.
NOS.1 Develop explanations based on reproducible data and observations gathered during laboratory investigations.
NOS.3 Clearly communicate their ideas and results of investigations verbally and in written form using tables, graphs, diagrams, and photographs.

Labs

PUPIL EDITION LABS

Classifying Plants as Vascular or Nonvascular, Section 2, p. 620 Students observe and compare prepared slides of vascular and nonvascular plant tissue under a microscope. **Lab Binder** p. 8	**Time:** 15 minutes **Materials:** prepared slides of plant tissue, microscope
Habitat Clues, p. 623 Students draw conclusions about the natural habitat of plants based on observations of their leaves. **Lab Binder** pp. 1–4	**Time:** 45 minutes **Materials:** 2 plant samples, hand lens, ruler, razor tool, forceps, 2 microscope slides, 2 cover slips, microscope

OPTIONS FOR INQUIRY

Comparing Monocots and Dicots, p. 632 Students classify plant samples as monocots or dicots. **Lab Binder** pp. 5–6	**Time:** 90 minutes **Materials:** 2–4 plant samples, razor tool, dissecting microscope
Investigating Medicinal Plants, p. 633 Students research medicinal qualities found in rainforest plants. **Lab Binder** p. 7	**Time:** 45 minutes **Material:** computer with Internet access

LAB BINDER Unit 7 Plants

Additional Investigation: Plants and Pollinators, pp. 9–14

Biotechnology Lab: Phytoremediation, pp. 45–48

LAB GENERATOR

A searchable CD of all labs in the program in editable format, including forensic, probeware, and biotechnology labs.

Presentation Tools

POWER PRESENTATIONS

Presentation Chapter 20

Power Presentations for each section incorporate images and clips from the Media Gallery: Includes Note Navigator for each section.

MEDIA GALLERY

Contains the following images and video clips, as well as animations, simulations and forms of visuals from the book.

Plant adaptations

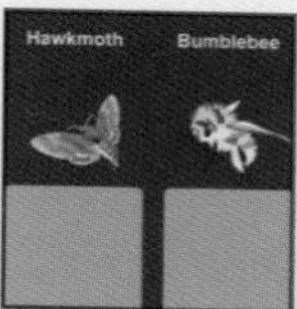

Plants and pollinators

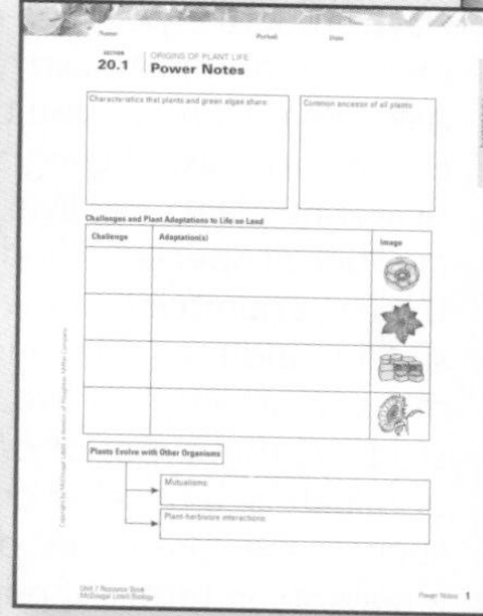

Power Notes

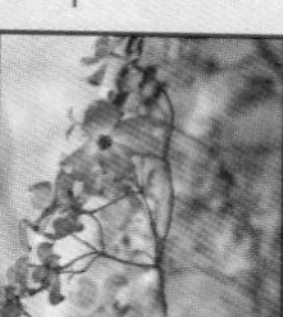
Flowering dogwood

Rabbit eating clover

VIDEO

Check out a set of short video clips exploring plant pollinators and plant resources.

ANIMATED BIOLOGY

Plant and Pollinator Matching Game

TRANSPARENCIES

Adaptations of Land Plants T86

Monocots and Dicots T87

Online BIOLOGY CLASSZONE.COM

- BioZine
- Animated Biology
- Interactive Review
- SciLinks
- Resource Centers

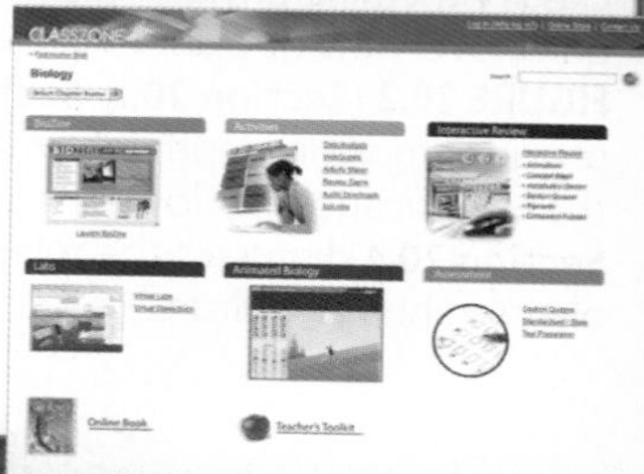

CHAPTER 20

▼ Focus and Motivate

How have flowering plants come to dominate Earth's landscapes?

Have students speculate on what it means to dominate Earth's landscapes. **Ask,** What form do you think this domination takes? geographic—where flowering plants can live; numeric—number of species or individuals Discuss the large number of flowering plant species and the wide range of environments in which they live. Remind students that types of organisms that dominate in a tangible or obvious way, such as large predators, do not represent a majority in terms of numbers of organisms. Bacteria are dominant despite being relatively invisible to the eye. So are plants, which are visible but not necessarily things we notice.

BIOZINE ClassZone.com

Students can access BioZine at **ClassZone.com** to look for topics suitable for research reports, writing assignments, or classroom debates.

In a Hurry?

The critical material of the chapter is found in **Sections 20.1** and **20.2,** which cover the evolution of plants from green algae, adaptations that allow plants to live on land, and characteristics used to classify the nine phyla of plants. For a quick overview of plant evolution, use **FIGURE 20.2 (Section 20.1). Section 20.3** provides more in-depth information on the classification of flowering plants. **Section 20.4** discusses the roles of plants in human culture.

CHAPTER 20 Plant Diversity

KEY CONCEPTS

20.1 Origins of Plant Life
Plant life began in the water and became adapted to land.

20.2 Classification of Plants
Plants can be classified into nine phyla.

20.3 Diversity of Flowering Plants
The largest phylum in the plant kingdom is the flowering plants.

20.4 Plants in Human Culture
Humans rely on plants in many ways.

Online BIOLOGY CLASSZONE.COM

Animated BIOLOGY
View animated chapter concepts.
- Plant and Pollinator Matching Game

BIOZINE
Keep current with biology news.
- Featured stories
- News feeds
- Careers

RESOURCE CENTER
Get more information on
- Plant Evolution
- Plant Classification
- Plant Resources

Student Activity

Purpose Have teams of students model plant classification. Each team classifies a variety of plants into groups based on characteristics observed in real specimens or photographs.

Materials (per team)

Each team will need pictures or actual specimens of a variety of plants from different phyla with as many identifying characteristics as possible. Examples:

- liverworts, hornworts, and mosses
- club mosses, whisk ferns, horsetails, and ferns
- seed plants including cone-bearing plants (cycads, ginkgo, conifers) and flowering plants

How have flowering plants come to dominate Earth's landscapes?

From the mosses that live in Antarctica to these flowering protea plants of South Africa, the plant kingdom is diverse. Proteas are native to one region of South Africa, called the Cape floristic region, which can go through long periods of drought. This small region is home to over 9,000 plant species, including at least 6,000 that are found nowhere else on Earth.

Connecting CONCEPTS

Habitat Protea plants are a necessary part of the habitat for Cape sugarbirds, such as the one shown at left. These birds depend on proteas for both food and shelter. They drink the nectar produced inside protea flowers. They build their nests in tangled protea branches and line them with the soft, short hairs that cover protea leaves. During the mating season, male Cape sugarbirds perch on top of the highest protea plants to defend their territories in an effort to attract a mate.

Introduce Tell students that the photographs represent a variety of plants that scientists classify into different phyla based on their characteristics. Point out that students do not have to base their groups on scientific phyla, but can classify their pictures on whatever characteristics they choose. However, make sure students know that they must explain the characteristics they used for grouping the plants.

Discuss Have teams explain how they classified their plants. **Ask**

- What characteristics did you use for your groups? Accept all reasonable observable characteristics.
- What made classifying plants using pictures difficult? life cycles and some structures that cannot be observed; limited characteristics shown in photographs

Point out that scientists consider many different characteristics when classifying plants, such as internal structures, molecular data, and evolutionary relationships.

Activate Prior Knowledge

Discuss with students the wide variety of plants used by different cultures. **Ask**

- What are some of the most important plants in the United States for farming? grains, corn, vegetables, fruits, sugar cane
- What value do other plants have? lumber for construction, oxygen for our atmosphere, ecological value, medicinal value

Discuss the potential value of having high plant diversity. You may want to discuss this in terms of quality of life.

Preview Vocabulary

Academic Vocabulary Use the context of plant classification to introduce students to these terms:

criterion = standard, rule, or test on which a judgment or decision can be based

criteria = plural of *criterion*

Like the words *datum* and *data,* students often use the plural form when they should use the singular. Encourage students to use the words in class when discussing the criteria used to classify plant groups: seed/seedless, vascular/nonvascular, flowering/cone-bearing.

English Learners Have students use the strategy list-group-label (*Biology Toolkit,* p. D6) for as many plant-related terms as they can think of. You can provide ideas by giving examples of categories, such as plant parts, types of plants, and different environments where plants are found. After ten minutes, divide students into teams to group their words by commonalities and label them. Have students share their results. You can sort these words and display them for the class.

Integrating Ecology

Have students recall that an ecological niche encompasses the physical, chemical, and biological factors that a species needs to survive and reproduce. The protea essentially is the Cape sugarbird's niche, because the bird depends on it for feeding, nesting, and mating.

SECTION 20.1

▼ Plan and Prepare

Objectives

- Identify evidence of land plants having evolved from green algae.
- Describe adaptations of land plants.
- Explain the coevolution of plants and other organisms.

Section Resources

Unit Resource Book
Study Guide pp. 1–2
Power Notes p. 3
Reinforcement p. 4
Pre-AP Activity pp. 19–20

Interactive Reader Chapter 20
Spanish Study Guide pp. 207–208

Biology Toolkit pp. C3, C17, C19, D4

Technology
Power Presentation 20.1
Media Gallery DVD
Online Quiz 20.1

Activate Prior Knowledge Have students think about taking a hike that puts them far away from the resources they use every day. **Ask,** What do you take with you on a long hike? food, water, clothing Discuss the idea that plant ancestors are considered pioneers that moved from the shores of early Earth's lakes and oceans inland. **Ask,** What did organisms need to adapt to in order to survive the move inland? lack of moisture, fluctuations of temperature, variations in climate

20.1 Origins of Plant Life

KEY CONCEPT Plant life began in the water and became adapted to land.

MAIN IDEAS
- Land plants evolved from green algae.
- Plants have adaptations that allow them to live on land.
- Plants evolve with other organisms in their environment.

VOCABULARY
plant, p. 612
cuticle, p. 614
stomata, p. 614
vascular system, p. 614
lignin, p. 614
pollen grain, p. 614
seed, p. 614

Review
algae, eukaryote, photosynthesis, chlorophyll, herbivore

B.8.3 Use anatomical and molecular evidence to establish evolutionary relationships between organisms.

Connect The flowering proteas shown on the previous page are not just plants with beautiful flowers. Various birds, rodents, and insects rely on protea nectar and pollen as food sources. Green protea beetles even live inside of protea flowers. Without plants, animal life as we know it would not exist on land.

MAIN IDEA

Land plants evolved from green algae.

All green algae share certain characteristics with plants. **Plants** are multicellular eukaryotes, most of which produce their own food through photosynthesis and have adapted to life on land. Like plants, green algae are photosynthetic eukaryotes. They have chlorophyll that captures energy from sunlight during photosynthesis. Chlorophyll is what makes these algae—and most of the plants that we are familiar with—green. Green algae and plants have the same types of chlorophyll. Another feature both green algae and plants share is that they use starch as a storage product. Most green algae also have cell walls that contain cellulose, a complex carbohydrate that is found in the cell walls of all plants.

Evidence from genetic analysis points to one ancient species of green algae that is the common ancestor of all plants. If it were alive today, this species would be classified as a member of the class Charophyceae, like the algae in **FIGURE 20.1.** Several other important plant characteristics likely originated in charophyceans.

- A multicellular body, which led to the specialization of cells and tissues
- A method of cell division that produces cells with small channels in their walls, which allows cells to communicate with each other chemically
- Reproduction that involves sperm traveling to and fertilizing an egg cell

FIGURE 20.1 Multicellular green algae of the genus *Chara* can be found in many lakes and ponds. They are charophyceans, which are thought to be the closest living relatives of the common ancestor of all plants.

Today, charophyceans are common in freshwater habitats. Scientists hypothesize that the ancestral charophycean species may have grown in areas of shallow water that dried out from time to time. Natural selection likely favored individuals that could withstand longer dry periods. Eventually, the first true plant species evolved, as shown in **FIGURE 20.2.** True plants have multicellular embryos that remain attached to the female parent as they develop.

▼ Teach

Take it Further

Existing species of the class Charophyceae are often called **stoneworts** because over time, calcium carbonate builds up on the plants, creating a hardened texture. Stoneworts are eaten by waterfowl and other aquatic animals, and provide shelter for fish.

Differentiated Instruction

ENGLISH LEARNERS

Suggest students use word squares as their vocabulary strategy for the section. You can review the strategy by completing one for *plant.* In the first quadrant, provide a translation of the word in several home languages, using the *Multilanguage Glossary.* Include a symbol or picture and then have students provide their own definition, in addition to one taken from the Glossary. Finally have them write a sentence that demonstrates meaning through context.

Biology Toolkit, Word Squares, p. D4

BELOW LEVEL

To test students' understanding, write five to ten true or false statements about the main points of the section. Focus on the characteristics that green algae and plants have in common, the challenges of living on land, and the adaptations that allow plants to meet these challenges. Have students react to the statements as being true or false before reading the section and then after.

Biology Toolkit, Anticipation Guide, p. C3

FIGURE 20.2 Evolution of Plants

Plants have evolved from green algae. An extinct charophycean species is the common ancestor of all plants.

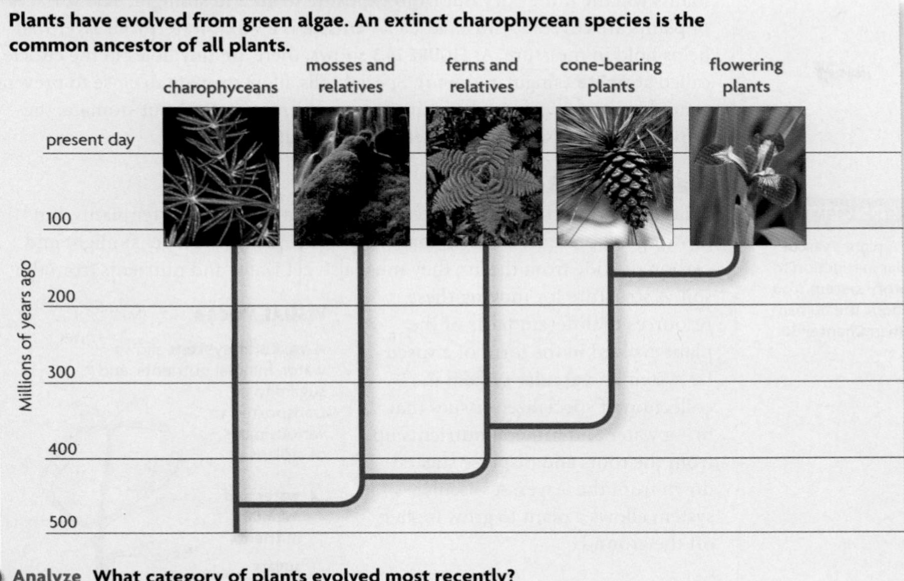

Analyze **What category of plants evolved most recently?**

The earliest plant fossils date to more than 450 million years ago. The first true plants probably grew on the edges of lakes and streams. Like modern-day mosses, they relied on droplets of water that brought sperm to eggs to produce the next generation of plants. They also had a fairly simple structure similar to that of moss, keeping low to the ground to retain moisture. Over time, the descendants of these plants were able to live in even drier areas.

Apply **What evidence suggests that green algae are close relatives of land plants?**

Connecting CONCEPTS

Algae Recall from **Chapter 19** that algae are plantlike protists. Photosynthetic pigments give various types of algae their distinct colors.

MAIN IDEA

Plants have adaptations that allow them to live on land.

Life on land presents different challenges than does life in the water. Unlike land plants, algae are constantly surrounded by water, which is needed for photosynthesis. The buoyancy of water supports the weight of most algae. For algae, water provides a medium through which sperm and spores can travel, allowing for reproduction and dispersal. Finally, water prevents sperm, eggs, and developing offspring from drying out.

The challenges of living on drier land have acted as selective pressures for plant life on Earth. In turn, many land plants have evolved adaptations that allow them to retain moisture, transport water and other resources between plant parts, grow upright, and reproduce without free-standing water.

TAKING NOTES

Use a main idea web to take notes about the challenges of life on land and plants' adaptations to these challenges.

ONLINE BIOLOGY Go to the chapter Resource Center at **ClassZone.com** for additional resources and information on plant evolution.

TEACH FROM VISUALS

FIGURE 20.2 Use the diagram to help students understand the evolution of plants. **Ask**

- What is the common ancestor of all plants? an extinct charophycean
- What is the first category of plants to evolve from the ancestral charophyceans? mosses and relatives
- When did the flowering plant lineage diverge from the cone-bearing plant lineage? about 150 mya

Answers

A Analyze flowering plants

B Apply Green algae have the same types of chlorophyll as plants have. Some green algae, such as charophyceans, are multicellular, and some have a method of cell division similar to that of plants that produces cells with small channels in their walls that allow for communication. Charophycean reproduction involves sperm swimming to and fertilizing an egg, which is also characteristic of plant reproduction.

INCLUSION

Help students who are literal thinkers interpret **FIGURE 20.2.** Suggest that they use their fingers to trace the lines, starting with the photograph of the charophyceans traced down to the point where it branches off. Relate that branch to the date on the left side of the diagram. Then have them trace the new line up to the photograph of mosses and their relatives. Tell students that all plants evolved from charophyceans. Each point where new branches diverge represents a common ancestor.

Biology Toolkit, Connect to Content through Visuals, p. C17

▼ Teach *continued*

Integrating Ecology

The **vascular systems** of trees and other plants function not only to keep these organisms alive, but also to help mitigate the sometimes violent effects of severe rainstorms and flooding. By drawing water out of the soil, trees lessen the volume of water that would otherwise flow into a river or other low-lying area.

Trees also help to keep landforms intact by preventing erosion—lessening the impact of rainfall on the ground and holding the soil in place by the vast network of roots weaving through the ground. If trees and other plants are removed from a hillside, mudslides are far more likely, as is siltation of rivers and other bodies of water.

Vocabulary

Greek and Latin Word Origins Tell students that the term **cuticle** comes from the Latin *cuticula,* which means "little skin." In plants, the cuticle is a waxy, waterproof layer that covers the stems and leaves. In vertebrates, it is the outermost layer of skin known as the epidermis. In arthropods, such as grasshoppers, it is a tough exoskeleton. Tell students that what the cuticles of different organisms have in common is that they are outer coverings that offer protection.

Answers

A Analyze Algae are surrounded by water, so they do not have to support their own weight or cope with dry periods. Water contains dissolved minerals and nutrients, which algal cells absorb directly. Algal cells do not need to transport resources in the same way as some land plants do. Finally, water provides a medium through which sperm and spores can travel.

***Connecting* CONCEPTS**

Human Biology A plant's vascular system is similar in function to a human's circulatory system. You will learn more about the human circulatory system in **Chapter 30**.

Retaining Moisture

Plants will die if they dry out from exposure to air and sunlight. The surfaces of plants are covered with a cuticle. A **cuticle** is a waxy, waterproof layer that helps hold in moisture. As **FIGURE 20.3** shows, there are tiny holes in the cuticle, called **stomata** (singular, *stoma*). Special cells allow stomata to close to prevent water loss, or to open to allow air to move in and out. Without stomata, the movement of air would be prevented by the cuticle.

Transporting Resources

Taller plants often have more access to sunlight than do shorter plants, but growing tall presents another challenge. While plants must get sunlight and carbon dioxide from the air, they must also get water and nutrients from the soil. A structure for moving these resources to different parts of the plant evolved in the form of a vascular system. A **vascular system** is a collection of specialized tissues that bring water and mineral nutrients up from the roots and disperse sugars down from the leaves. A vascular system allows a plant to grow higher off the ground.

VISUAL VOCAB

A **vascular system** allows water, mineral nutrients, and sugars to be transported to various parts of a plant.

water and mineral nutrients

sugars

Growing Upright

Plant height is also limited by the ability of a plant to support its own weight. Plants need structure to support their weight and provide space for vascular tissues. This support comes from a material called **lignin** (LIHG-nihn), which hardens the cell walls of some vascular tissues. Lignin is also responsible for the strength of wood and provides stiffness to the stems of other plants. As a result, plants can retain their upright structure as they grow toward the sun.

Reproducing on Land

In all plants, eggs are fertilized within the tissue of the parent plant. There, the fertilized egg develops into an embryo, the earliest stage of growth and development for a plant. Some plants reproduce with the help of rainwater or dew, while others do not need free-standing water to reproduce. Pollen and seeds are adaptations that allow seed plants to reproduce completely free of water. A **pollen grain** is a two-celled structure that contains a cell that will divide to form sperm. Pollen can be carried by wind or animals to female reproductive structures. A **seed** is a storage device for a plant embryo. A seed has a hard coat that protects the embryo from drying wind and sunlight. Once a seed encounters the right conditions, the embryo can develop into an adult plant.

 Analyze **Discuss why the four challenges on this page do not apply to most algae.**

Differentiated Instruction

PRE-AP

Have students write a brief essay describing the selective advantages that both pollen and seeds offer to plants that reproduce this way. They should consider the effect of these adaptations on genetic diversity as well as how they might relate to seasonal changes. Also, encourage them to think about how seeds and pollen may have been advantageous for early human agriculture. Ask students what farming would be like if we did not have seeds to work with.

Biology Toolkit, Quick-Write, p. C19

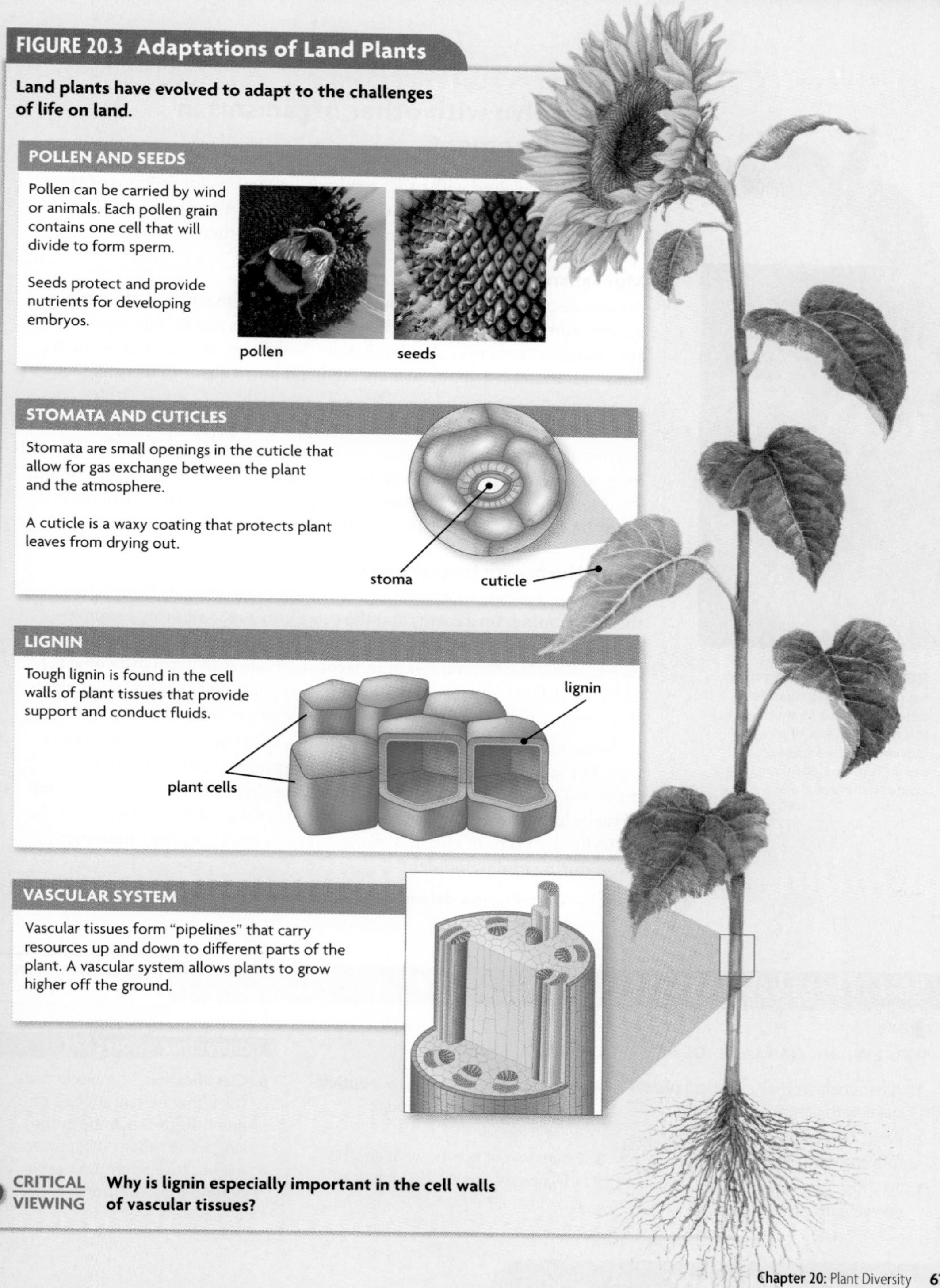

FIGURE 20.3 Adaptations of Land Plants
Land plants have evolved to adapt to the challenges of life on land.
POLLEN AND SEEDS
Pollen can be carried by wind or animals. Each pollen grain contains one cell that will divide to form sperm.
Seeds protect and provide nutrients for developing embryos.
pollen
seeds
STOMATA AND CUTICLES
Stomata are small openings in the cuticle that allow for gas exchange between the plant and the atmosphere.
A cuticle is a waxy coating that protects plant leaves from drying out.
stoma
cuticle
LIGNIN
Tough lignin is found in the cell walls of plant tissues that provide support and conduct fluids.
lignin
plant cells
VASCULAR SYSTEM
Vascular tissues form "pipelines" that carry resources up and down to different parts of the plant. A vascular system allows plants to grow higher off the ground.

A CRITICAL VIEWING **Why is lignin especially important in the cell walls of vascular tissues?**

TEACH FROM VISUALS

FIGURE 20.3 Have students study the photographs and diagrams as they read the information about plant adaptations. **Ask**

- What do pollen and seeds allow plants to do on land? reproduce in the absence of water
- What do stomata and cuticles allow plants to do? exchange gases while retaining moisture
- What does lignin help plants do? grow upright
- What does a vascular system allow plants to do? transport resources and grow tall

Mention that not all have the adaptations shown. For example, the presence or absence of a vascular system is one criterion used to classify plant groups.

Vocabulary

Greek and Latin Word Origins The word **vascular** comes from the Latin *vasculum,* which means "small vessel." Organisms that have vessels for transporting resources are said to have vascular systems. In plants, the fluid that flows through the vascular system is called **sap;** in most animals it is called **blood.**

Science Trivia

Lignin has been extracted and used by various industries since the 1880s, when it was used for tanning leather.

- Lignin functions as a binder in charcoal briquettes, ceramics, fiberglass insulation, dust suppressants, plywood, and animal feed pellets.
- As an emulsifier, lignin keeps products such as asphalt and pesticides from breaking down.

HANDS-ON ACTIVITY

To illustrate the importance of lignin in vascular tissues of plants, have students try drawing water from a cup, using both an oversized plastic straw and a piece of hard tubular plastic, such as a snorkel. Both should work well.

Try this again, only this time have another student try to squeeze each drinking tube closed. The weaker plastic straw will be compressed by the pressure, while the hard plastic tube will not.

Tell students that the hard plastic tube is analogous to the lignin-strengthened vascular system of a plant, which would be crimped closed if the plant could be bent or twisted. If vessels cannot withstand pressure, they will not be able to transport water and other resources. Discuss human-made systems or shapes that are analogous, such as underground tunnels, scuba equipment, submarines, water mains, and gas lines.

Answers

A Critical Viewing Lignin stiffens the cell walls in vascular tissues, allowing for the flow of water and sugars through the vessels.

▼ Teach *continued*

ONLINE BIOLOGY For more on the relationship between plants and their pollinators, have students view the interactive animation in Options for Inquiry. See page 633.

TEACH FROM VISUALS

FIGURE 20.4 Discuss the relationship between the hawk moth and the orchid.

Ask

- What adaptations do the moth and the orchid have that make them dependent on each other? long tongue; nectar deep inside the flower
- How does the plant benefit from its relationship with the moth? Pollination enables fertilization of eggs.
- What is the significance of the orchid blooming at night? Moths feed at night.

Answers

A Synthesize As a result of a mutation, the leaves of a certain plant may have contained a small amount of a chemical that tasted bad to herbivores. Because the plant was not eaten, it survived longer or reproduced more than other plants in the population, and over time, the trait became more common.

▼ Assess and Reteach

Assess Use the Online Quiz or Section Quiz (*Assessment Book*, p. 395).

Reteach Create a digital slide show of images from the Media Gallery that illustrate the parts of land plants and their functions, and also interactions between plants and other animals. Have students call out the name of the features or describe what is being shown.

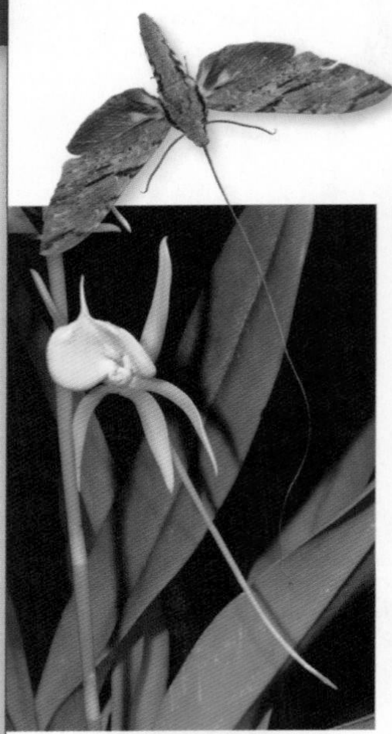

FIGURE 20.4 The hawk moth has a tongue that measures between 30 and 35 cm (12–14 in.). It is the pollinator of a night-blooming orchid whose nectar is produced 30 cm down inside the flower.

MAIN IDEA

Plants evolve with other organisms in their environment.

Plants have coevolved with other terrestrial organisms for millions of years. Some of these relationships are cooperative, while others have evolved between plant species and the animal species that eat them.

Mutualisms

A mutualism is an interaction between two species in which both species benefit. Some mutualisms exist between plant roots and certain types of fungi and bacteria. Roots provide a habitat for these fungi and bacteria, while the fungi and bacteria help the plant get mineral nutrients from the soil.

Many flowering plants depend on specific animal species for pollination or seed dispersal. In turn, these animals are fed by the plant's pollen, nectar, or fruit. For example, in Madagascar, Darwin noticed a variety of orchids with long, tubular flower parts. He predicted that a nocturnal moth with a tongue 10 to 12 inches long must be the pollinator. That very moth, shown in **FIGURE 20.4**, was discovered 40 years after Darwin's prediction.

Plant-Herbivore Interactions

Plants have a variety of adaptations that discourage animals from eating them. The spines on a cactus and the thorns on a rose stem are examples. Other plants produce defensive chemicals that act as pesticides against plant-eating predators. Natural selection favors herbivores that can overcome the effects of defensive plant adaptations. In turn, natural selection favors plants that produce even sharper spines or thorns or even more toxic chemicals.

Some insects use defensive chemicals produced by plants to their advantage. The larvae of monarch butterflies, for example, feed exclusively on milkweed species. Milkweed plants produce a chemical that makes monarch larvae, adults, and even eggs taste bad to potential predators. In this way, the butterfly has a type of chemical protection as a result of eating milkweed leaves during its development.

A Synthesize Describe how defensive chemicals in plant leaves may have evolved.

20.1 ASSESSMENT

ONLINE QUIZ ClassZone.com

B.8.3

REVIEWING MAIN IDEAS

1. What characteristics do land **plants** share with green algae?
2. What adaptations allow plants to thrive on dry land?
3. Describe two ways in which plants evolve with other organisms.

CRITICAL THINKING

4. **Synthesize** Describe how a **cuticle** could have evolved through natural selection.
5. **Evaluate** For plants, what are the advantages and disadvantages of growing tall?

***Connecting* CONCEPTS**

6. **Classification** Some scientists think that certain species of green algae should be in the kingdom Plantae. What reasons might these scientists use to defend their position?

20.1 ASSESSMENT

1. Both are eukaryotic, photosynthetic, contain the same types of chlorophyll, and use starch as a storage product.
2. cuticles and stomata, vascular systems, lignin, pollen grains, and seeds
3. Plants and other types of organisms can coevolve through mutualistic relationships and through predator-prey relationships.
4. As a result of a mutation, the leaves of a certain plant may have been covered by a waterproof layer. Through natural selection, this trait increased in frequency among the plant population.
5. Taller plants may have better access to sunlight, but they also have a longer distance to transport resources from the soil, such as water and minerals, up to the highest leaves.
6. Both green algae and plants are photosynthetic eukaryotes. Green algae have the same types of chlorophyll as plants do. Both also use starch as a storage product. Finally, plants and most green algae have cell walls that contain cellulose.

20.2 Classification of Plants

KEY CONCEPTS Plants can be classified into nine phyla.

MAIN IDEAS
- Mosses and their relatives are seedless nonvascular plants.
- Club mosses and ferns are seedless vascular plants.
- Seed plants include cone-bearing plants and flowering plants.

VOCABULARY
pollination, p. 620
gymnosperm, p. 621
angiosperm, p. 621
cone, p. 621
flower, p. 622
fruit, p. 622

Review
seed, vascular system, pollen

INDIANA STANDARDS

B.8.2 Explain how organisms are classified and named based on their evolutionary relationships into taxonomic categories.

Connect Scientists have described about 300,000 plant species, and many more probably remain to be found. All plants belong to the kingdom Plantae. While modern plants can be classified into nine phyla, DNA analysis continues to reveal new relationships that keep taxonomists updating the plant family tree.

MAIN IDEA

Mosses and their relatives are seedless nonvascular plants.

Connecting CONCEPTS

Classification Recall from **Chapter 17** that the term *division* is sometimes used instead of *phylum* for the classification of plants and fungi.

In a damp forest, mosses lend an emerald green color to the landscape. These plants do not produce seeds. They have no vascular systems. Instead, they grow close to the ground or on surfaces such as tree trunks, where they can absorb water and nutrients directly. They also rely on free-standing water to allow their sperm to swim to and fertilize eggs. Mosses belong to Bryophyta, one of the three phyla of nonvascular plants. The other phyla in this category are Hepatophyta, the liverworts, and Anthocerophyta, the hornworts.

Liverworts

Most liverworts live in damp environments and get moisture directly from the surface of the soil. They are often found growing on wet rocks, in greenhouse flowerpots, and in other areas with plenty of moisture. Liverworts can have one of two basic forms: thallose or leafy. The name *liverwort* refers to thallose liverworts, which look like the lobes of a liver flat on the ground. Eggs are produced on umbrella-like structures of the thallose liverwort, shown in **FIGURE 20.5.** Though thallose liverworts may be easier to recognize, leafy liverworts are much more common. Leafy liverworts have stemlike and leaflike structures. These leaflike structures are most often arranged in three rows.

FIGURE 20.5 Thallose liverworts, like the one shown here, can grow from 2 mm to 25 cm in length.

Differentiated Instruction

BELOW LEVEL

To organize notes for this section, have students identify important ideas and arrange them in a concept map. Have students start with the section's Key Concept as the central box. Have them extend it to include the three major groups at the second level—seedless vascular, seedless nonvascular, seed. Then extend to a third level to include the subgroups. Tell students to identify the characteristics of each grouping.

Biology Toolkit, Concept Map, p. C40

ENGLISH LEARNERS

Have students organize the information in this section into a chart that identifies each plant phylum by its distinguishing characteristics. Students should list all possible characteristics as column heads, and indicate with a plus or minus sign which ones a particular phylum has.

Biology Toolkit, Semantic Feature Analysis, p. D7

Plan and Prepare

Objectives

- Identify mosses and their relatives as seedless nonvascular plants.
- Identify club mosses and ferns as seedless vascular plants.
- Describe the characteristics of seed plants, including cone-bearing plants and flowering plants.

Section Resources

Unit Resource Book
Study Guide pp. 5–6
Power Notes p. 7
Reinforcement p. 8

Interactive Reader Chapter 20
Spanish Study Guide pp. 209–210

Biology Toolkit pp. C22, C32, C40, D7

Technology
Power Presentation 20.2
Media Gallery DVD
Online Quiz 20.2

Activate Prior Knowledge Have students think about the plants that live in the local area. **Ask,** What general categories of plants are found where you live? Answers will vary but may include pines or evergreens, deciduous, or "leafy," trees, flowers, vines, cacti, mosses, shrubs, and grasses. Discuss any plants that are distinctive to your area because of climate.

Teach

Vocabulary

Word Origins The word **wort** is often used in combination with others to form the names of plants, such as *liverworts, stoneworts* (Charophyceans), and *hornworts.* It comes from an Old English word *wyrte,* meaning "plant or root." The unrelated word **wart** is a variation on the original Old English word *wearte* and refers to a growth or lump.

▼ Teach *continued*

ONLINE BIOLOGY Go to the chapter Resource Center at **ClassZone.com** for additional resources and information on plant classification.

Vocabulary

Academic Vocabulary Point out the use of the words **colonize** and **pioneer** with reference to mosses. Their general meanings fit well with the idea of a pioneer species:

pioneer—one who ventures into unknown or unclaimed territory to settle

colonize—to migrate to and settle in a distant territory

Point out in this use that not only is the land occupied by mosses originally uninhabited, is it uninhabited because the conditions are harsh and inhospitable to other forms of life. Students may be accustomed to seeing mosses in their yards and will not necessarily make this association.

Science Trivia

- An estimated 400 billion tons of carbon are stored in peat.
- Deposits of fossilized peat—better know as coal—have been mined for centuries to produce fuel for electric plants, steam engines, and other industrial purposes.
- The Chinese used coal as long ago as 1000 B.C., to smelt copper.
- The purest form of coal is graphite, the substance that is the lead in pencils.

Answers

A Apply They have no vascular system to transport resources, so water and nutrients must be absorbed directly by the entire plant.

Hornworts

Hornworts are a widespread group of plants that are found in tropical forests and along streams around the world. Hornworts grow low to the ground, and the main plant body has a flat, lobed appearance similar to that of thallose liverworts. Little green horns rising above the flat plant body, as shown in **FIGURE 20.6**, produce spores.

FIGURE 20.6 The stalks of these hornworts are 2 to 5 cm long.

Mosses

Mosses are the most common nonvascular plants. Some look like clumps of grass, others look like tiny trees, and still others look like strands of green yarn. Mosses do not have true leaves. Instead, they have leaflike structures that are just one cell thick. While they lack vascular systems, some moss species do have cuticles, and most of them have stomata. Mosses can anchor themselves to surfaces such as soil, rocks, or tree trunks, as shown in **FIGURE 20.7**, with structures called rhizoids (RY-ZOYDZ).

Connecting CONCEPTS

Ecology Recall from **Chapter 14** that primary succession is the establishment of an ecosystem in an area that was previously uninhabited. Mosses are common pioneer species that help to break down solid rock into smaller pieces—one of the first steps in producing soil.

Mosses are often tolerant of harsh weather conditions and nutrient-poor soils. They can grow in many places where other plants are unable to grow. Some mosses can survive in deserts and tundras by entering a stage of dormancy until water is available. In fact, mosses are often among the first plants to colonize bare land and begin the soil-making process in the early stages of primary succession.

One moss that is commonly used by humans is sphagnum (SFAG-nuhm), which grows in acidic bogs. Sphagnum does not decay when it dies, so thick deposits of this dead moss, called peat, build up over time. Peat can be cut from the ground and burned as fuel. Dried peat can absorb water, and it has antibacterial properties. In fact, dried peat has been used in products such as diapers and bandages. Peat also has an important role in the carbon cycle, as a reservoir that holds carbon in an organic form.

A Apply Why can't nonvascular plants grow tall?

FIGURE 20.7 Like all nonvascular plants, mosses need to live in moist environments.

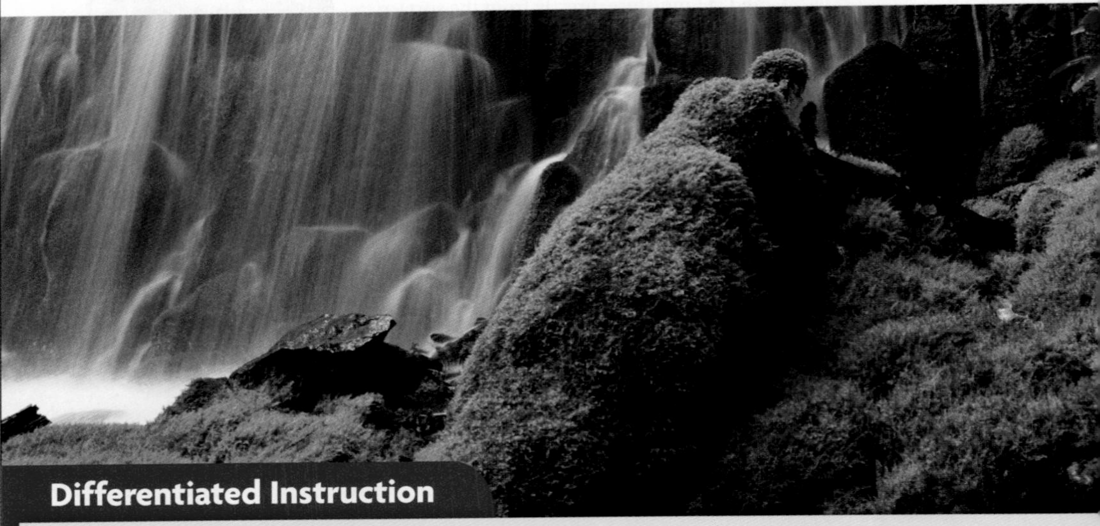

Differentiated Instruction

HANDS-ON ACTIVITY

Provide pairs of students with samples of peat and a graduated cylinder, beaker, or scale. Have students predict the absorptive ability of a piece of peat. Calculations could include what percent the peat's mass increases when it is saturated or what volume of water a specific volume or mass of peat can absorb. Have students share their answers with the class and discuss the usefulness of peat in gardening as a reservoir for water available to plants.

MAIN IDEA

Club mosses and ferns are seedless vascular plants.

About 300 million years ago, during the Carboniferous period, shallow swamps were home to enormous seedless vascular plants. Over time, the dead remains of these plants were pressed and heated underground, where they gradually turned into coal. This is why we call coal a fossil fuel.

Club mosses (phylum Lycophyta) and ferns (phylum Pterophyta) are modern seedless vascular plants. Like nonvascular plants, they depend on water for reproduction. However, a vascular system allows these plants to grow higher above the ground and still get materials they need from the soil.

FIGURE 20.8 Club mosses, such as this *Lycopodium* species, are able to grow up off of the ground because they have vascular systems.

Club Mosses

Club mosses, which are not true mosses, belong to the oldest living group of vascular plants. Some ancient species looked like modern trees, growing more than ten stories tall. These giant plants were wiped out when the Carboniferous climate cooled, but some of the smaller species survived. One common living genus of club moss is *Lycopodium*. Some *Lycopodium* species, such as the one shown in **FIGURE 20.8**, look like tiny pine trees and are sometimes called "ground pines."

Whisk Ferns, Horsetails, and Ferns

Ferns and their relatives, whisk ferns and horsetails, can be grouped together in one phylum. Whisk ferns grow mostly in the tropics and subtropics. Although they lack true roots and leaves, DNA analysis indicates that whisk ferns are closely related to ferns.

Horsetails grow in wetland areas and along rivers and streams. They have tan, scalelike leaves that grow in whorls around a tubular stem. Like club mosses, horsetails were much larger and more common in the Carboniferous period. Because horsetails' cell walls contain a rough compound called silica, colonial settlers used the plant, also called "scouring rush," to scrub pots.

Ferns are the most successful survivors of the Carboniferous period, with about 12,000 species alive today. Most ferns grow from underground stems called rhizomes (RY-zohmz). Their large leaves, shown in **FIGURE 20.9**, are called fronds. Newly forming fronds, called fiddleheads, uncurl as they grow. Some ferns are grown as houseplants. Others, called tree ferns, live in the tropics and can grow over three stories tall.

FIGURE 20.9 FERNS

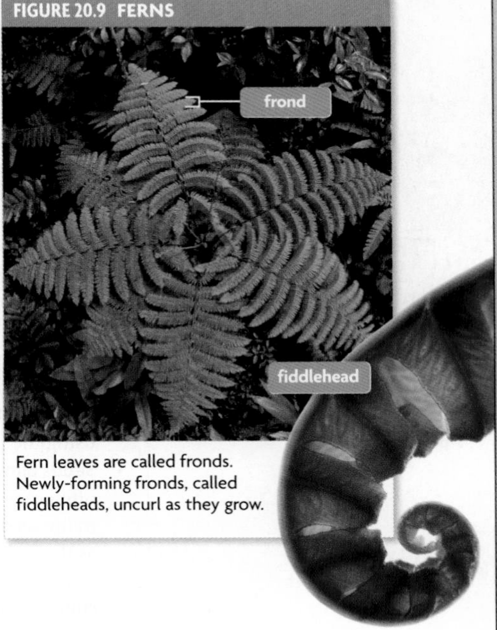

Fern leaves are called fronds. Newly-forming fronds, called fiddleheads, uncurl as they grow.

A Infer Why do most seedless vascular plants live in moist areas?

Science Trivia

One of the most dominant plant genera in the world is *Pteridium,* a fern genus that is commonly called bracken.

- Bracken is found on every continent except Antarctica, and in all regions except for arctic, alpine, and desert.
- The fiddleheads of bracken are edible and highly prized in Korea and Japan, where they are eaten fresh, cooked, and pickled.
- Bracken is highly resistant to fire. Its dead fronds can form a carpet of flammable material, which, if ignited, can burn up competing woody plants. Later, the bracken's rhizomes sprout new fronds, allowing the ferns to dominate the blackened landscape.
- The Maori, a Polynesian people that colonized New Zealand in the 13th century, ate the starchy rhizomes of bracken. By clearing and burning forest to hunt terrestrial birds and grow crops, the Maori may have provided bracken with new areas in which to grow.

Answers

A Infer They rely on water for reproduction.

BELOW LEVEL

Have students use a Y diagram to help them identify the differences and similarities between the two general categories of seedless plants, nonvascular and vascular. Students should list the characteristics of each in the "arms" of the Y, including some examples, and then identify those characteristics common to both in the "stem" of the Y.

Biology Toolkit, Y Diagram, p. C32

INCLUSION

Bring in examples of the three major groups of plants for students who are visually impaired. Have students work with a classmate who describes the distinguishing features of each group in a way that will enable the student to identify each plant.

▼ Teach *continued*

QUICK LAB

Time 15 minutes	TEACHER TESTED
Lab Binder Plants, p. 8	

Purpose Observe and compare prepared slides of vascular and nonvascular plant tissue under a microscope.

LAB MANAGEMENT

- When making comparisons, students should look for specialized cells that look like they could be "pipelines" that transport materials.

Safety Caution students to be careful in handling the slides. Remind students to wipe down the eyepieces with alcohol wipes after use.

Answers

Analyze and Conclude

1. Answers will vary depending on plants used. Both are likely green. Students should see that the tissue of vascular plants is more complex, containing "pipelines," while the tissue of nonvascular plants appears less specialized.
2. Students should have observed both types. The presence or absence of pipe-like structures should serve as evidence.
3. Nonvascular plants must absorb all water and nutrients at their surfaces (osmosis) and pass these resources from cell to cell (diffusion). This means that all cells must be relatively close to sources of water, which greatly limits their ability to grow tall.

QUICK LAB CLASSIFYING NOS.3

Classifying Plants as Vascular or Nonvascular

In this lab, you will examine tissues from several plants to determine whether they are vascular or nonvascular. This is the first step in classifying plants into one of the nine phyla.

PROBLEM Are the plants vascular or nonvascular?

PROCEDURE

1. Observe each slide under the microscope.
2. Make a sketch of each plant tissue you examine.

MATERIALS

- prepared slides of plant tissue
- microscope

ANALYZE AND CONCLUDE

1. **Analyze** In what ways are the plant tissues similar? In what ways are they different?
2. **Analyze** Based on your observations, are the plants vascular or nonvascular? What evidence did you use to determine their identity?
3. **Apply** How does the absence of vascular tissue affect the size (height) of nonvascular plants?

MAIN IDEA

Seed plants include cone-bearing plants and flowering plants.

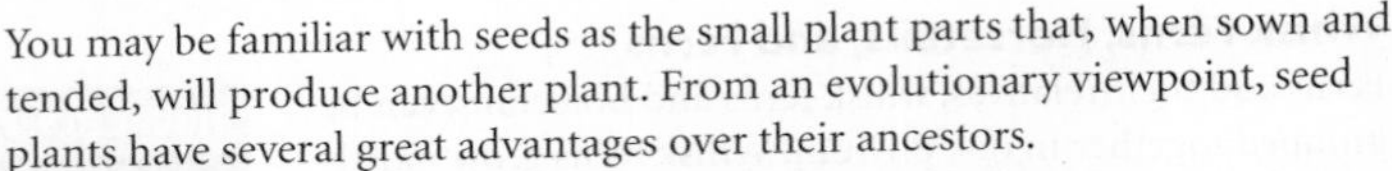

You may be familiar with seeds as the small plant parts that, when sown and tended, will produce another plant. From an evolutionary viewpoint, seed plants have several great advantages over their ancestors.

- **Seed plants can reproduce without free-standing water.** Seedless plants depend on water through which sperm swim to fertilize an egg. However, seed plants do not depend on water in this way. Seed plants, such as the pine tree in **FIGURE 20.10**, produce pollen. Pollen can be carried by the wind or on the body of an animal pollinator, such as a bee. **Pollination** occurs when pollen meets female reproductive parts of the same plant species. Each pollen grain has a cell that will then divide to form sperm. Fertilization occurs when a sperm meets an egg. The ability to reproduce without free-standing water allows many seed plants to live in drier climates.
- **Seeds nourish and protect plant embryos.** A seed consists of a protective coat that contains a plant embryo and a food supply. A seed can survive for many months, or even years, in a dormant state. During this time, the seed can withstand harsh conditions, such as drought or cold, that might kill an adult plant. When conditions are right, the embryo will begin growing, using the food supply provided by the seed.
- **Seeds allow plants to disperse to new places.** Wind, water, or animals often carry seeds far from the individual plant that produced them. In fact, many seed plants have adaptations that aid in the dispersal of seeds, such as the "wings" that carry maple seeds in the wind. Because seeds can remain dormant, the embryo will not begin to develop until it reaches a suitable environment.

FIGURE 20.10 Seed plants produce pollen. In pine trees such as the one shown here, clouds of pollen are released from male pine cones.

Differentiated Instruction

PRE-AP

Students can use a content frame to analyze and organize information about the nine plant phyla. Tell students to use the first column to list phyla, the second column to describe the main adaptations of the plants in that phylum, and any remaining columns to add more detail. Suggest that students list the phyla in the order in which they evolved, using **FIGURE 20.2** on page 613, and explain how each adaptation affected their ability to live in different environments.

Biology Toolkit, Content Frame, p. C22

Scientists hypothesize that seed plants evolved as the Earth's climate changed from warm and moist to hot and dry during the Devonian period, 410 to 360 million years ago. Fossil evidence suggests that seed plants evolved about 360 million years ago. Seed plants can be grouped according to whether their seeds are enclosed in fruit.

- A **gymnosperm** (JIHM-nuh-SPURM) is a seed plant whose seeds are not enclosed in fruit.
- An **angiosperm** (AN-jee-uh-SPURM) is a seed plant that has seeds enclosed in some type of fruit.

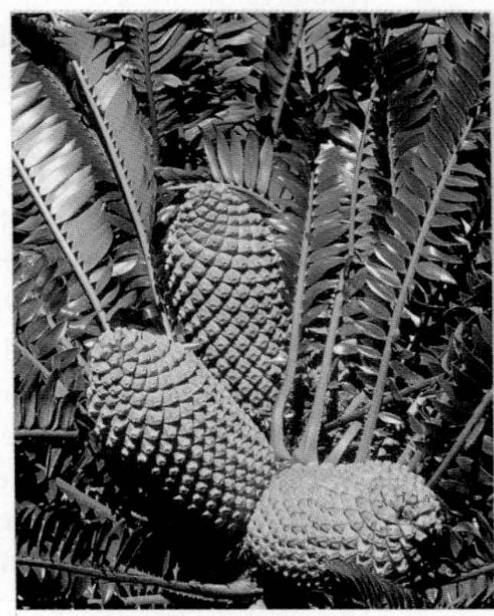

FIGURE 20.11 Cycads, such as the one shown here, produce seeds on large, protective, female cones.

Most gymnosperms are cone-bearing and evergreen, such as pine trees. A woody **cone** is the reproductive structure of most gymnosperms. It contains hard protective scales. Pollen is produced in male cones, while eggs are produced in female cones. Seeds also develop on the scales of female cones, which protect fertilized eggs. There are three living phyla of gymnosperms: cycads (phylum Cycadophyta), *Ginkgo biloba* (phylum Ginkgophyta), and conifers (phylum Coniferophyta).

VOCABULARY

Gymnosperm comes from the Greek words *gumnos*, which means "naked," and *sperma*, which means "seed." *Angiosperm* comes from the Greek words *angos*, which means "vessel," and *sperma*, which means "seed."

Cycads

Cycads look like palm trees with large cones, as shown in **FIGURE 20.11.** Huge forests of cycads grew during the Mesozoic era, 248 million to 65 million years ago. These plants provided food for dinosaurs. In fact, the Jurassic period of this era is commonly called the Age of the Cycads. Today, cycads grow in tropical areas in the Americas, Asia, Africa, and Australia. Many cycad species are endangered because of their slow growth and loss of habitat in these tropical areas.

Ginkgo

Like cycads, ginkgoes were abundant while the dinosaurs lived. Only one species lives today, *Ginkgo biloba*, shown in **FIGURE 20.12.** This species is native to China, and it has survived in part due to its cultivation by Buddhist monks since the year 1100. Because it so closely resembles its fossil ancestors, Darwin called this species a living fossil. In fact, the ginkgo may be the oldest living species of seed plants. Today, it is grown around the world in gardens and used in urban landscaping.

FIGURE 20.12 The name *Ginkgo biloba* refers to the two-lobed leaves of this plant. Ginkgo trees are used commonly in garden landscapes.

Science Trivia

- The female cones of gymnosperms vary in weight from less than 25 grams to more than 45 kilograms.
- Female cones vary from a few millimeters in diameter to more than a meter long.

Integrating Pharmacology

Ginkgo biloba is the oldest living tree species and one of the oldest known sources of medicine. Chinese herbal medicine has relied on the leaves and seeds of *Ginkgo biloba* for centuries, but modern medicine uses a concentrated extract made from dried leaves. Two compounds (**flavonoids** and **terpenoids**) are believed to be the most beneficial of the 40 known compounds isolated in the *Ginkgo biloba* extract. Terpenoids dilate blood vessels, allowing for improved circulation that can improve cognitive functions and memory. Flavonoids are beneficial because they destroy particles called **free radicals,** which can damage tissues and organs by attacking DNA and changing cell membranes.

HANDS-ON ACTIVITY

Have students examine a variety of seeds. For gymnosperms, students can collect pinecones and use tweezers to take apart the scales. For the seeds of angiosperms, include bare seeds and their ripened fruits, or allow students to dissect fruits to find the seeds within. Students can also go outside to gather seeds, depending on the season and the area. Students can draw detailed illustrations of the seeds and speculate on the function of any fruit that surrounds them, such as the "wings" of maple or the flesh of an apple.

▼ Teach *continued*

Address Misconceptions

Common Misconception Our culture tends to divide produce into fruits and vegetables, yet the distinction between the two is often artificial, based on taste or appearance more than on botanical classification. For example, students may think of tomatoes as vegetables and grapes as fruit, when in fact both are fruits.

Correcting the Misconception In botany, a fruit is simply the ripened ovary of any flowering plant. This means that peppers, tomatoes, squash, green beans, eggplant, watermelon, apples, bananas, cherries, blueberries, peaches, and cucumbers are all fruits, even though in cuisine we refer to some as vegetables. *Vegetable* really refers to the edible leaves, stalks, flower buds, or roots of a plant.

Answers

A Apply pollen grains

▼ Assess and Reteach

Assess Use the Online Quiz or Section Quiz (*Assessment Book,* p. 396).

Reteach Draw the evolutionary tree of plants on the board, using **FIGURE 20.2** from page 613. Ask students to identify plants that belong to each category and the adaptations that make them separate.

FIGURE 20.13 This Ponderosa pine is a typical evergreen conifer with needlelike leaves.

Conifers

By far the most diverse and common gymnosperms alive today are the conifers—familiar trees with needlelike leaves, such as those in FIGURE 20.13. Pines, redwood, spruce, cedar, fir, and juniper all belong to this phylum. Conifers supply most of the timber used for paper, cardboard, housing lumber, and plywood. They grow quickly, and large tree farms help produce enough wood to meet demand.

Many conifers are evergreen, or green all year-round. However, a few lose their needles in the winter. Conifers are well adapted to high altitudes, sloping hillsides, and poor soil. These characteristics allow conifers to thrive in mountainous regions.

Conifers tend to grow old and grow tall. Two conifers living in California hold world records. At more than 4700 years of age, one bristlecone pine in California's White Mountains is the oldest known living tree. And a giant sequoia tree in Sequoia National Park is the world's most massive living thing. It has a mass of 1.2 million kilograms, which is about the mass of 40 buses.

Flowering Plants

Angiosperms belong to a phylum of their own (phylum Anthophyta) and are commonly called flowering plants. A **flower** is the reproductive structure of flowering plants. Flowers protect a plant's gametes and fertilized eggs, as woody cones do for most gymnosperms. A **fruit** is the mature ovary of a flower. Fruit can take the form of a juicy peach, the wings attached to a maple seed, or the fluff surrounding dandelion seeds. As you will learn in the next section, flowers and fruits have played a large role in the dominance and diversity of flowering plants today.

A Apply What adaptation of seed plants allows sperm to reach and fertilize an egg in the absence of water?

20.2 ASSESSMENT

ONLINE QUIZ ClassZone.com

B.8.2

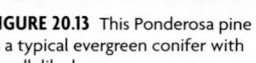

REVIEWING ▶ MAIN IDEAS

1. What are the habitat requirements for seedless nonvascular plants?
2. What are the evolutionary advantages of a vascular system?
3. What are the evolutionary advantages of seeds?

CRITICAL THINKING

4. **Infer** In what type of environment might you find nonvascular plants, seedless vascular plants, and seed plants growing together? Explain.
5. **Apply** Consider the characteristics of pollen grains. Why do people with pollen allergies find it difficult to avoid exposure to pollen?

***Connecting* CONCEPTS**

6. **History of Life** According to the fossil record, seed plants date back to 360 million years ago, when the Earth's climate was becoming hotter and drier. What role did this global climate change likely play in the evolution of seed plants?

20.2 ASSESSMENT

1. environment where water and nutrients can be absorbed directly into plant body; must have free-standing water for reproduction
2. allows plants to grow higher off the ground, which can mean better access to sunlight
3. Seeds allow an embryo to remain dormant until the environmental conditions are right for growth.
4. moist environments, because all seedless plants require free-standing water for reproduction
5. Pollen grains are tiny (only two cells), and they are blown around by the wind. When pollen counts are high outdoors, it is difficult to avoid exposure unless you stay inside.
6. As the climate became drier, there was less standing water in which seedless plants could reproduce. Plants that could reproduce without free-standing water had an adaptive advantage in this situation, and they became more and more common.

MATERIALS

- 2 plant samples
- hand lens
- ruler
- razor tool
- forceps
- 2 microscope slides
- 2 cover slips
- microscope

PROCESS SKILLS

- Observing
- Analyzing
- Classifying

NOS.1 Develop explanations based on reproducible data and observations gathered during laboratory investigations.

Habitat Clues

By examining different parts of a plant, you can often tell a lot about its habitat. In this lab, you will examine external features to help you determine the natural habitat of several different plants. You will also examine the epidermal tissue—the "skin" of the plant—which you will learn more about in Chapter 21. This tissue is in direct contact with the air. It has adaptive traits that allow the plant to survive and reproduce in a specific type of environment.

PROBLEM What kinds of adaptations allow plants to live in different habitats?

PROCEDURE

1. Record descriptions for each plant in a data table. Include leaf blade size, shape, thickness, and appearance (dull, shiny, and so on).
2. Using a hand lens, closely examine each plant sample. Look for differences as well as similarities between the plant samples. Record these observations in your data table.
3. Gently bend a leaf from each plant to determine how flexible the leaf is. If the leaf bends quite easily without snapping, then it is flexible. If the leaf is stiff, it may be difficult to bend, or it may snap while you are trying to bend it. Record this information in your table.
4. Carefully prepare a wet mount slide of epidermal tissue from each plant. For some plants, you may be able to tear the leaf at an angle, and then "peel" the leaf apart gently by hand. For others, it will be easier to cut the leaf at an angle with a razor tool. Be very cautious using razors, always cut away from yourself. Forceps may also be helpful for peeling off layers of tissue.
5. Examine the epidermal tissue under a microscope. Pay close attention to differences between the plant samples. Record your observations for each slide.

step 4

ANALYZE AND CONCLUDE

1. **Analyze** What visible characteristics do these plants share? What characteristics are unique for each plant?
2. **Analyze** How is the epidermal tissue from each plant different?
3. **Infer** Based on your observations, what conclusions can you make about the natural habitat of each plant?
4. **Infer** How are stiff leaves and flexible leaves adapted for different habitats?
5. **Apply** Describe a characteristic of a plant that lives in the same area that you do. How might this characteristic help the plant to survive in its habitat?

EXTEND YOUR INVESTIGATION

Research the adaptations of plants that live in one of the following types of environments: aquatic, acidic, or salty.

Answers

Analyze and Conclude

1. Both are likely green. Differences may include the shape, size, and texture of the leaves.
2. desert plant's epidermis: thicker, because it has a thick, waxy cuticle; woodland plant epidermis: much thinner
3. One plant is adapted to a dry environment, the other to a more moist environment.
4. Leaves that hold more water and have thicker cuticles are more stiff. These adaptations help to slow down water loss and keep the plants from drying out. Woodland plants have a much thinner epidermis, which makes them more flexible.
5. *Sample Answer:* Water lilies have flat, broad leaves that float on water. Their flexibility helps them withstand wave energy.

Extend Your Investigation

Results of students' research will vary. Aquatic plants should have long roots with means of anchoring firmly to substrate. Some plants that live in acidic environments, such as bogs, have to catch and digest insects for nutrients. Some salt-tolerant plants simply excrete salt.

INVESTIGATION

Time 45 minutes TEACHER TESTED
Teacher Preparation
Student Difficulty
Lab Binder Plants, pp. 1–4

Purpose Draw conclusions about the natural habitat of plants based on observations of their leaves.

Overview Students will record descriptions of visible characteristics of the leaves of different plants. They will

- prepare and observe slides of the plants' epidermal tissues
- draw conclusions about the adaptations of a plant's leaves and its habitat

LAB PREPARATION

- Obtain leaves from plants with thick and thin cuticles.
- If possible, use a microtone to get thin slices of epidermal tissue.

LAB MANAGEMENT

- If students' samples are too thick to mount on slides, have them examine their samples under a dissecting microscope.
- Discuss terms students can use to describe plant characteristics.

Safety Remind students to wear gloves if they have plant allergies. Remind students to clean the eyepieces of the microscopes with alcohol wipes after use.

Inclusion For students who lack fine motor skills, prepare the slides of epidermal tissue and focus the microscope. As an alternative, have students skip steps 4 and 5.

POST-LAB DISCUSSION

Discuss results. **Ask,** How might the preparation of the slides have affected your descriptions of the plants' epidermal tissues? Tissue might not have been thin enough to observe; tissue might have been damaged; observations could be inaccurate.

▼ Plan and Prepare

Objectives

- Describe adaptations of flowering plants.
- Describe the two groups of flowering plants.

Section Resources

Unit Resource Book Study Guide pp. 9–10 Power Notes p. 11 Reinforcement p. 12
Interactive Reader Chapter 20 **Spanish Study Guide** pp. 211–212
Biology Toolkit pp. C5, C19, C40
Technology Power Presentation 20.3 Media Gallery DVD Online Quiz 20.3

Activate Prior Knowledge Discuss the appeal flowers have that makes growing and selling flowering plants a multibillion dollar industry in the United States. **Ask**

- What might be the evolutionary advantage for a plant to have flowers that smell good or are bright and colorful? attracts animals that will aid in pollination or spread the seeds of the plant
- What is the evolutionary advantage of having sweet, edible fruits? Animals will eat the fruit in one location and excrete the seeds in another. The offspring can take advantage of more resources in more locations.

20.3 Diversity of Flowering Plants

KEY CONCEPT The largest phylum in the plant kingdom is the flowering plants.

MAIN IDEAS

- Flowering plants have unique adaptations that allow them to dominate in today's world.
- Botanists classify flowering plants into two groups based on seed type.
- Flowering plants are also categorized by stem type and lifespan.

VOCABULARY

cotyledon, p. 625
monocot, p. 626
dicot, p. 626
wood, p. 627

Review
fruit, flower, pollination, pollen, lignin

Connect Sunflower seeds in the shell aren't just a tasty snack. They are an example of one of the great adaptations of flowering plants. Like all flowering plants, sunflowers produce fruits. Technically, the fruit is the shell surrounding the sunflower seed. As you will soon learn, fruits can take many forms beyond the juicy apple or peach that first comes to mind.

MAIN IDEA

Flowering plants have unique adaptations that allow them to dominate in today's world.

***Connecting* CONCEPTS**

Evolution Recall from **Chapter 11** that mammals also went through a period of adaptive radiation after the mass extinction that killed the dinosaurs 65 million years ago.

Up until about 65 million years ago, there were far fewer flowering plants than there are today. After the mass extinction event that ended the Cretaceous period, the fossil record reveals that a major shift took place in species that dominated the Earth. Dinosaurs disappeared, as did many seedless plant species. These plant extinctions left open niches into which flowering plants, such as the dogwoods in **FIGURE 20.14**, could radiate and prosper. Their diversification happened quickly in geologic terms and was closely tied to the diversification of land animals such as insects and birds. The same adaptations that were important to the success of flowering plants long ago continue to be important today.

FIGURE 20.14 Many trees, including dogwoods, are flowering plants.

Flowers and Pollination

Flowers allow for more efficient pollination than occurs in most gymnosperms, which rely on wind for pollination. You have probably observed a bee or a butterfly hovering around the center of a flower. These insects and other animals feed on pollen, which is high in protein, or on nectar, a sugary solution produced in the flowers of some plant species. As an animal feeds from a flower, it gets pollen on itself. Then, when it moves to another flower for more food, some of the pollen brushes off onto the new flower. Thus, animal pollinators transfer pollen from flower to flower in a very targeted way. For this reason, flowering plants pollinated by animals don't need to produce nearly as much pollen as do plants that rely on the wind to randomly transfer their pollen.

▼ Teach

Vocabulary

Greek and Latin Word Origins The word **nectar** comes from the Greek *nektar,* meaning "drink of the gods." The glands that produce nectar are called **nectaries.**

Differentiated Instruction

ENGLISH LEARNERS

Work with students to create a KWL chart in their science notebooks. Discuss with them what they already know, including plant names, uses, parts, and habitats. Have students list what they know in the *K* column. Under *W,* ask students to list what they would like to learn. Guide them in thinking about seed and stem types, and lifespans of various plants. Tell them to fill out the *L* column as they read the section. Have them compare what they have in the *K* column with what they have learned.

Biology Toolkit, KWL Chart, p. C5

BELOW LEVEL

Suggest students use a concept map to organize material for this section, as described in **Section 20.2** on page 617. Make sure students realize that after the division of flowering plants into monocots and dicots, the other characteristics described (stem type and lifespan) apply to both monocots and dicots.

Biology Toolkit, Concept Map, p. C40

FIGURE 20.15 Adaptations of Flowering Plants

Flowers and fruits are unique adaptations of all flowering plants.

Many flowering plants are pollinated by animals.

Fruits protect the seeds of flowering plants and often play a role in seed dispersal.

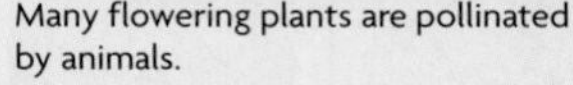

Synthesize **How is each photograph showing a coevolutionary relationship?**

Fruits and Seed Dispersal

The many types of fruits include some very unlike the kinds you see in a grocery store. In biological terms, a fruit is a flower's ripened ovary, which surrounds and protects the seed or seeds. For example, the shells of sunflower seeds and peanuts are fruits. Fruit play an important role in seed dispersal. As shown in **FIGURE 20.15**, the more familiar fleshy fruits are tasty food sources for animals, which digest the fruit tissue but not the seeds. Seeds pass through the animal, and are deposited along with a convenient supply of fecal fertilizer that is helpful during germination. Others take the form of burrs that cling to passing wildlife, or fibers that help spread seeds by wind. You will learn more about flowers, fruits, and seed dispersal in Chapter 22.

Infer **Why is pollination by animals more efficient than wind pollination?**

MAIN IDEA

Botanists classify flowering plants into two groups based on seed type.

There are at least 250,000 identified flowering plant species. Compared with other living plant phyla—the three gymnosperm phyla have a total of 720 species—the number of flowering plants is impressive.

Botanists classify flowering plants into two groups based on two basic kinds of seed: seeds with one or two cotyledons. A **cotyledon** (KAHT-uhl-EED-uhn) is an embryonic leaf inside a seed. For this reason, cotyledons are often called "seed leaves." As an embryo develops into a seedling, the seed leaf of some species remains inside the seed coat. In other species, cotyledons break out of the seed and turn green.

HANDS-ON ACTIVITY

Have students gather samples of plants from the area outside the school or around their homes. Put students in teams and give each team several different plants to analyze. They should search for characteristics that identify the plants as either monocots or dicots. After students have successfully identified the types of plants, give them samples in which there is only one feature to analyze. For example, supply only a flower head and have students infer what type of plant the sample came from.

TEACH FROM VISUALS

FIGURE 20.15 Have students focus on the coevolution shown in the photographs. Point out the long, slender beak; the tubular red flowers; and the size correlation between the blueberry and field mouse. **Ask**

- What would happen if a bird with a short, thick beak tried to collect nectar from the flower? would not be able to reach the nectar or would destroy the flower in the process
- How would the seed dispersal of the fruit be affected if the fruit were the same size as the field mouse? The mouse may eat the fruit from around the seed instead of carrying it away or eating it whole. The seed would not be dispersed very far from the plant.

Take it Further

Fruit and seeds can be dispersed by water, as well. The **coconut,** one of the most important foods in the tropical Pacific, is thought to have spread to remote islands by both humankind and ocean currents. On the shores of islands, many coconuts that fall to the ground from the coconut palm trees roll into the sea and get carried off by outgoing tides. The major ocean currents can then carry the coconuts, which feature a dense, fibrous husk around a hard shell, to distant shores. Many islands were probably planted with coconuts by humans, but dispersal by sea is another means of carrying some seeds.

Answers

A Synthesize Because the bird has a long, slender beak, it can get food from the tubular-shaped flower. At the same time, the flower is pollinated and can reproduce. The fruit provides food for the mouse, and the mouse disperses the seeds.

B Infer Wind pollination is less targeted; pollen grains land wherever the wind takes them. Animal pollinators, on the other hand, often move from flower to flower while they are feeding.

▼ Teach *continued*

The Inside Story

Carolus Linnaeus tried to classify plants by looking almost exclusively at plant reproductive organs. Any plant that lacked obvious reproductive organs was put in a class called Cryptogamia, which means "hidden marriage." This class included algae, mosses, fungi, ferns, and lichens. Meanwhile, conifers were placed in an order that included several flowering plants, as the difference between true flowers and cones was not yet understood.

Many scientists complained that Linnaeus's classification scheme for plants was artificial. **Johann Siegesbeck** criticized Linnaeus for having a scheme that was so sexually based, and called it "loathsome harlotry." Linnaeus got back at him by naming a particular weed *Siegesbeckia.*

TEACH FROM VISUALS

FIGURE 20.16 Point out the potential difficulty of determining a flowering plant's classification based solely on the number of flower parts. **Ask,** Can you think of two scenarios in which counting the number of flower parts would not tell you conclusively that a plant was a monocot or dicot? There could be 12 or 15 petals, or another number that is a multiple of both 3 and 4 or 3 and 5. Petals could be missing because the flower is damaged or dying.

Answers

A Predict No, because they are not photosynthetic. They are called "seed leaves" only because they are embryonic leaves inside of the seed.

FIGURE 20.16 Monocots and Dicots

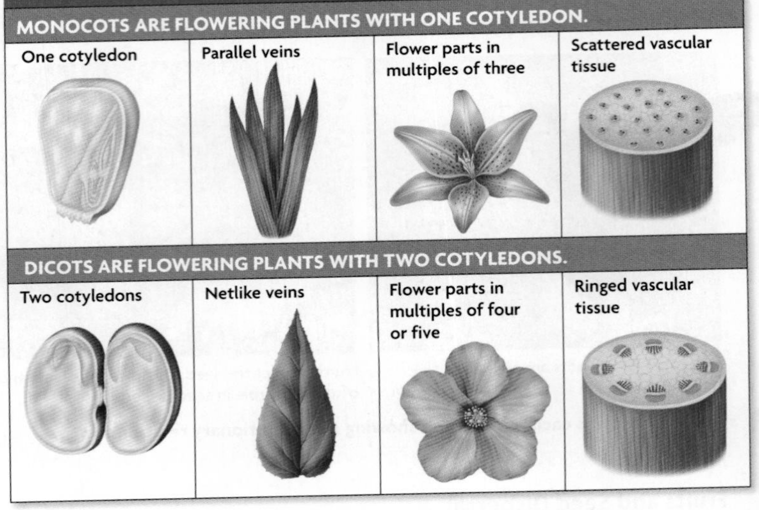

MONOCOTS ARE FLOWERING PLANTS WITH ONE COTYLEDON.			
One cotyledon	Parallel veins	Flower parts in multiples of three	Scattered vascular tissue
DICOTS ARE FLOWERING PLANTS WITH TWO COTYLEDONS.			
Two cotyledons	Netlike veins	Flower parts in multiples of four or five	Ringed vascular tissue

VOCABULARY

Mono- and *di-* are prefixes meaning "one" and "two." *Cot* is a shortened form of the word *cotyledon.* Therefore, monocots have one cotyledon and dicots have two.

Monocots

Flowering plants whose embryos have one seed leaf are called monocotyledons, or **monocots** (MAHN-uh-KAHTS). As **FIGURE 20.16** shows, monocot plants generally have parallel veins in long, narrow leaves, such as those of an iris or lily. Their flower parts usually occur in multiples of three, and bundles of vascular tissues are scattered throughout the stem. The cereal plants we depend on—corn, wheat, rice—are monocots, as are all other grasses, irises, and lilies.

Dicots

Dicotyledons, or **dicots** (DY-KAHTS), are flowering plants whose embryos have two seed leaves. In contrast to monocots, dicots have leaves with netlike veins. Flower parts in dicots usually occur in multiples of four or five, and bundles of vascular tissue are arranged in rings. Most deciduous trees, which lose their leaves in the fall, are dicots. Peanuts are also dicots. Each "half" of a peanut that has been removed from its shell is a cotyledon.

A Predict **Would you expect that cotyledons are green inside a seed? Explain.**

MAIN IDEA

Flowering plants are also categorized by stem type and lifespan.

Flowering plants can also be categorized by stem type and lifespan, as shown in **FIGURE 20.17**. These characteristics help describe mature flowering plants and are commonly used by botanists, gardeners, landscape designers, and horticulturists.

Differentiated Instruction

PRE-AP

Students have just read about different modes of dispersal for seeds. Have them consider how the involvement of humans in the process of seed dispersal and production has altered a process that was originally driven by selective pressures. Have them write for five minutes on this question.

Biology Toolkit, Quick-Write, p. C19

Iris Monocot, herbaceous, perennial

Wheat Monocot, herbaceous, annual

Foxglove Dicot, herbacious, biennial

Oak Dicot, woody, perennial

Big bluestem Monocot, herbaceous, perennial

FIGURE 20.17 Flowering plants are the largest and most diverse of the plant phyla. They are commonly categorized according to seed type, stem type, and lifespan.

Herbaceous or Woody Stems

Some flowering plants develop woody stems, while others do not. **Wood** is a fibrous material made up of dead cells that are part of the vascular system of some plants. High concentrations of lignin and cellulose make the cell walls of these cells thick and stiff. Woody plants therefore have stiff stems and branches. Wood also accounts for the thickness of many woody plant stems. Trees, shrubs, and most vines have woody stems. Plants that do not produce wood, such as cucumbers, cacti, and marigolds, are called herbaceous plants.

Three Types of Lifespans

It is also helpful for gardeners to classify plants in terms of their lifespans, since lifespan determines which plants they need to replace each year.

- **Annual** Flowering plants that mature from seeds, produce flowers, and die all in one year are called annuals. Corn and lettuce are common annuals, as are some garden flowers such as zinnias.
- **Biennial** Flowering plants that take two years to complete their life cycle are called biennials. During the first year, a biennial produces a short stem, leaves that grow close to the ground, and underground food reserves. During the second year, these reserves are used to produce a taller stem, leaves, flowers, and seeds. Carrots are common biennial garden plants.
- **Perennial** Any flowering plant that lives for more than two years is a perennial. Most woody plants, including trees, are perennials. The stems and leaves of some herbaceous perennials, such as some grasses and dandelions, die at the end of the fall and grow back in the spring.

To learn more about flowering plants, visit scilinks.org.
Keycode: MLB020

Contrast **How do the lifespans of annuals, biennials, and perennials differ?**

20.3 ASSESSMENT

ONLINE QUIZ ClassZone.com

REVIEWING MAIN IDEAS

1. What adaptations give flowering plants a reproductive advantage over gymnosperms?
2. What are the primary differences between **monocots** and **dicots**?
3. Name three ways in which flowering plants can be categorized.

CRITICAL THINKING

4. **Contrast** In what ways does pollination in gymnosperms differ from pollination in angiosperms?
5. **Apply** How would you take plant lifespan type into account when planning a garden?

Connecting CONCEPTS

6. **Mass Extinctions** The fossil record reveals a mass extinction at the end of the Cretaceous period. Discuss why mass extinctions are commonly followed by a period of adaptive radiation, in this case, of flowering plants.

Vocabulary

Academic Vocabulary The word **annual** in everyday language usually is used to describe something that occurs every year, such as a holiday or the first day of school. In botany, the terms *annual,* **biennial,** and **perennial** refer to the lifespans of plants—not to how often they grow or reappear. An annual is a plant that lives for just one year—not a plant that sprouts or grows back every year. That is a perennial. In a similar way, certain sports teams are sometimes called "perennial favorites" because they perform well year after year.

Answers

A **Contrast** Annuals mature from seeds, produce flowers, and die within one year. Biennials take two years to complete their life cycle, producing a short stem, leaves, and underground food reserves in the first year and a taller stem, more leaves, flowers, and seeds during the second year. Perennials live for more than two years.

Assess and Reteach ▼

Assess Use the Online Quiz or Section Quiz (*Assessment Book,* p. 397).

Reteach Work with students to explore the idea that special adaptations in flowering plants are associated with a plant's "lifestyle." Organize the information into a cluster diagram and ask students to identify any patterns that emerge involving these adaptations.

20.3 ASSESSMENT

1. Animal pollination is more efficient than wind pollination, flower ovaries protect gametes and seeds, and fruit protects seeds and helps to disperse them.
2. monocots: one cotyledon per seed; dicots: two cotyledons per seed
3. by number of cotyledons: monocot or dicot; by stem type: woody or herbaceous; or by lifespan: annual, biennial, or perennial
4. Gymnosperms rely on wind for pollination; angiosperms are pollinated by wind or animals.
5. Annuals will need to be replanted every year. Biennial plants will not flower the first year if planted from seed, and they will need to be replanted after their second year of growth. Perennial plants will grow back every spring.
6. A mass extinction leaves open niches and unused abiotic resources. Surviving organisms may be able to adapt to these niches, expanding their range and possibly radiating into new species over many generations.

DATA ANALYSIS

Introduce

Scientists collect large amounts of numerical data. One way scientists make sense of this data is by using measures of central tendency to find a single number that summarizes the data. Point out that scientists usually have so much data that they use computer programs to find the mean, median, and mode.

Ask

- Why is ordering the data points from least to greatest important when finding the median? so the point that falls in the middle can be located
- How can a data set have more than one mode? There can be several different values that occur with the same high frequency.

Inclusion Provide smaller sets of data for students who have difficulty with numbers.

Discuss

Discuss when mean, median, and mode are used when dealing with statistics. **Ask,** Which measure of central tendency is less useful if the data set contains outliers? mean

Discuss with students which measure of central tendency would be the most appropriate for determining how much money the typical worker makes in the United States. **Ask**

- Is the mean a good measure? Explain. No. The relatively few people who make millions or billions of dollars would inflate the mean far above what most people actually make.
- What measure is most appropriate, and why? median, because there would be an equal number of workers earning less and more than this value, and outliers would have no influence

Unit Resources Book, Data Analysis, p. 17

Measures of Central Tendency

One way to analyze data is to use measures of **central tendency,** which are measures that indicate the center of a data set. The three most common measures of central tendency are the mean, median, and mode. It is often helpful to look at all three of these measures because they may each point out different characteristics of a data set.

The **mean** is calculated by adding all of the data points together and dividing by the number of data points. The mean considers the full range of data, and is therefore affected by **outliers**—data points that vary greatly from all of the other points in the data set.

The **median** is the data point that falls in the middle when all of the data points are ordered from least to greatest. If there is an even number of data points, the median is the average of the two middle numbers. Since outliers do not affect the median, this may be a good measure to use with a data set that includes outliers.

The **mode** is the value that occurs most frequently. It is not affected by outliers. Some data sets have more than one mode. If there are several modes that dominate the data set, it is a good idea to study these data points more closely.

EXAMPLES

A class counted the number of seeds found in some common fruits. These data are shown in Table 1.

- **Oranges** The mean is an appropriate measure to use for this data set because there are no obvious outliers.
- **Watermelons** The mean is affected by an outlier, 582 seeds. The median is a good measure to represent this data set.
- **Apples** The two modes represent a trend in these results that the students may want to investigate further.

TABLE 1. NUMBER OF SEEDS IN VARIOUS FRUIT

Fruit	Number of Seeds per Fruit	Mean	Median	Mode
Oranges	14, 6, 10, 8, 4, 11, 6, 3, 5, 13	8	7	6
Watermelons	582, 133, 207, 87, 164, 290, 98, 155, 196, 278	219	180	none
Apples	6, 7, 6, 4, 4, 4, 3, 6, 4, 6	5	5	4 and 6
Strawberries	171, 208, 230, 171, 159, 182, 217, 238, 165, 179	?	?	?

CHOOSE AN APPROPRIATE MEASURE OF CENTRAL TENDENCY

Use the data for the number of seeds counted in each of 10 strawberries to answer the questions below.

1. **Calculate** Find the mean, median, and mode for this set of data.
2. **Evaluate** Which measure of central tendency best represents this data set? Why?

Answers

1. mean = 192, median = 180.5, mode = 171
2. The mean best represents this data set because there are no outliers.

20.4 Plants in Human Culture

KEY CONCEPTS Humans rely on plants in many ways.

MAIN IDEAS
- Agriculture provides stable food supplies for people in permanent settlements.
- Plant products are important economic resources.
- Plant compounds are essential to modern medicine.

VOCABULARY
botany, p. 629
ethnobotany, p. 629
pharmacology, p. 631
alkaloid, p. 631

Connect Books are made from plants. The pages are pulverized wood from trees, the ink contains plant oil, and the glue that binds them together is made from petroleum—the ancient leftovers of algae and plants. Humans rely on plants for nearly everything in daily life. Today, crop plants are so important to our economy that their changing prices are reported in the media alongside those of stocks and bonds.

MAIN IDEA

Agriculture provides stable food supplies for people in permanent settlements.

VOCABULARY
Ethnobotany comes from the Greek words *ethnos*, which means "people," and *botanē*, which means "plants."

Some of the plants that are considered important by humans have changed over time, but plants have always been used to fill the basic needs of our species: food, shelter, clothing, and medicine. While **botany** is the study of plants, **ethnobotany** explores how people in different cultures use plants.

For most of human history, people survived by hunting and gathering. This requires a very thorough understanding of local botany—plant locations, life cycles, and characteristics. Hunting and gathering also requires people to change locations if resources are diminished by weather, disease, or overuse. People then must become familiar with the resources of the new area.

FIGURE 20.18 Agriculture has become an important part of our global economy. Many river deltas, such as the Sacramento River delta in California, are used for farmland because of their nutrient-rich soils and water.

Differentiated Instruction

BELOW LEVEL

Have students organize the material in this section by constructing a timeline from the dates provided in the text.

Biology Toolkit, Timeline, p. C31

PRE-AP

Explain to students that cereals are grain-producing grasses. The first wild wheat had stalks that opened easily, scattering their seeds. Today, the stalks of cultivated wheat are tough and do not yield the seeds until harvested. Have students create a cause and effect chain to suggest how the first farmers may have affected the evolution of wheat species. Tell students to consider factors such as how easily the seeds could be dispersed.

Biology Toolkit, Cause and Effect Chain, p. C36

SECTION 20.4

Plan and Prepare

Objectives

- Describe the importance of plants and agriculture to humans.
- Discuss plant compounds that are essential to modern medicine.

Section Resources

Unit Resource Book
Study Guide pp. 13–14
Power Notes p. 15
Reinforcement p. 16
Pre-AP Activity pp. 21–22

Interactive Reader Chapter 20
Spanish Study Guide pp. 213–214

Biology Toolkit pp. C31, C36

Technology
Power Presentation 20.4
Media Gallery DVD
Online Quiz 20.4

Activate Prior Knowledge Ask, What plant products have you used so far today? *Sample Answer:* food, clothing, books, furniture Point out that most of the plants that people rely on are seed plants. One exception dates back to the Carboniferous period, when mosslike plants and ferns became peat and were eventually compressed and heated into coal.

Teach

Vocabulary

Academic Vocabulary In biology, the word **culture** is often used as a verb that means "to grow or cultivate." To specify what is being grown, *culture* is often combined with other words or prefixes. The root *agri-* of **agriculture** comes from a Latin root meaning "field." **Aquaculture** is the cultivation of aquatic organisms such as fish and shellfish.

▼ Teach continued

ONLINE BIOLOGY Go to the chapter Resource Center at **ClassZone.com** for additional resources and information on plant resources and genetically modified foods.

Take It Further

One treatment for malaria is **quinine,** an alkaloid from the bark of the cinchona tree. Peruvian Indians used this bark to treat fevers before the 1600s. During the 1600s, missionaries took the bark back to Europe. Eventually, demand for the bark increased, and the number of trees began decreasing rapidly. Today, quinine is produced synthetically for use in anti-malarial medicines and as a bitter flavoring in tonic water.

Tonic water was created specifically to be taken as a preventive medicine for malaria. To make it more palatable, because tonic water was much more bitter than it is now, Englishmen in the tropics began to mix in a little gin, making the first gin and tonic. Today's tonic water has so little quinine that one would need to drink an enormous quantity to ward off malaria, which still kills about one million people every year.

Integrating Genetics

Today's crops are changing quickly as a result of **genetic engineering.** Scientists no longer rely on artificial selection. They can transfer a gene from an unrelated species into the seeds of crops. The resulting plants may be more resistant to insects and disease or may be more nutritious. Many of our crops today are grown from genetically modified seeds. However, some scientists are concerned about unknown risks to human health or to the environment. See the Unit Feature on page 690 for more on genetically modified foods.

Answers

A Summarize how different cultures use plants

B Connect *Sample Answer:* cotton plants for t-shirts, trees for notebook paper and pencils

FIGURE 20.19 An ear of teosinte, the ancestor of modern corn, is shown along with a kernel of modern corn (top). Modern corn evolved through artificial selection. Humans likely selected individual plants that had the most numerous and accessible seeds.

Archaeological evidence suggests that people started intentionally planting for harvest about 10,000 years ago. Over the centuries, ancient farmers "tamed" wild species by a process of artificial selection, as shown in **FIGURE 20.19.** They chose plants with the best traits, saved their seeds, and planted them the next year. Most of the world's staple foods—corn, rice, and wheat—were developed from wild grasses in this way. These farmers became more closely tied to particular areas.

Because farming requires people to stay in one place, agriculture gave rise to more socially complex centers of human populations. A benefit of farming was a more reliable source of food that could support a growing population. Eventually, farmers grew enough excess food to sell it to neighbors as a cash crop. In this way, farming became part of a culture's economy.

A Summarize What does an ethnobotanist study?

MAIN IDEA

Plant products are important economic resources.

Plant products have been traded among various regions for thousands of years. Spices such as pepper, cinnamon, and cloves were so valuable that they were commonly used as a form of currency during the early Middle Ages. In fact, many of the seafaring explorations to Asia and the Americas during the 1400s and 1500s were prompted by the value of spices, like those shown in **FIGURE 20.20.** Among these explorers, Columbus, Magellan, and da Gama were all in search of a new route to the valuable commodities of the East.

Today, plants are important economic resources on a global scale. The values of rice, corn, wheat, soybeans, coffee, sugar, cotton, and forest products traded in world markets every year are each billions of dollars. Paper, textiles, and lumber are just a few of the plant-derived products that are the basis of industries contributing to our economy.

B Connect What plants were used to make the clothes that you are wearing and the contents of your backpack?

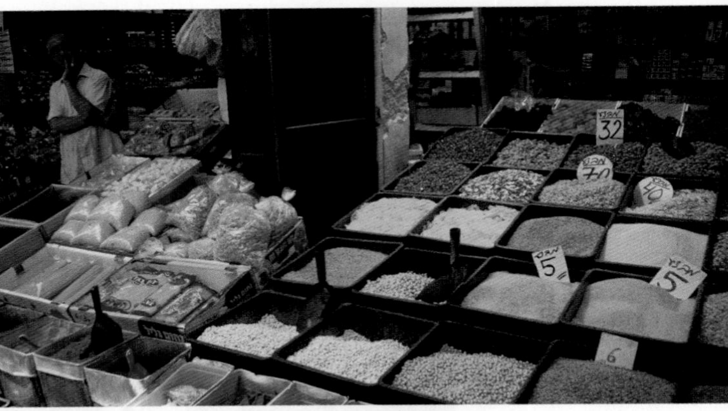

FIGURE 20.20 Spices have been an economically important resource for at least 4000 years.

Differentiated Instruction

HANDS-ON ACTIVITY

Have students work in pairs to look around the classroom and identify as many things as they can that are plant products. Give students five minutes and see which pair can come up with the longest list. When students misidentify something as a plant product when it is, in fact, synthetic, take the opportunity to discuss synthetics such as nylon and polyester. Encourage students to think of all possible plant products, including invisible things such as oxygen.

MAIN IDEA

Plant compounds are essential to modern medicine.

The study of drugs and their effects on the body is called **pharmacology.** Many of the drugs used today are derived from plants, and much of the knowledge of these plants comes from traditional cultures. We still use some plants medicinally in the same way they have been used for thousands of years. For instance, the aloe vera gel you can buy to soothe sunburn was used for the same purpose by the Egyptians 3500 years ago.

As shown in **FIGURE 20.21**, scientists continue to look for and find new uses for plants that have been used medicinally for centuries. For example, Native Americans have long used the Pacific yew to treat a variety of conditions. In the 1960s, scientists isolated a compound called taxol from the tree, which has been used as a cancer treatment since 1993. Salicin, which comes from willow trees, is another plant compound that you are likely familiar with. It is the active ingredient in aspirin, the most widely used medicine in the world.

While plant oils and resins are common in traditional medicines, other plant compounds, including gums, steroids, and alkaloids, have found their way into modern medicines. **Alkaloids** are potent plant chemicals that contain nitrogen. In small amounts, many alkaloids are medicinal. By interfering with cell division, some alkaloids—such as taxol—have anti-cancer properties. Two alkaloids produced by the Madagascar periwinkle are used to treat childhood leukemia and Hodgkin's disease. Other alkaloids have been identified to treat conditions ranging from a nasty cough to high blood pressure.

Today, much medical research focuses on the chemical properties of various plant compounds—especially compounds from plants that have been used medicinally in traditional cultures. Chemists also work to develop synthetic drugs based on the structure of these natural compounds, often changing the structures slightly to increase effectiveness and reduce side effects.

A Infer **Why might certain plant compounds have healing effects in small quantities but be dangerous in larger doses?**

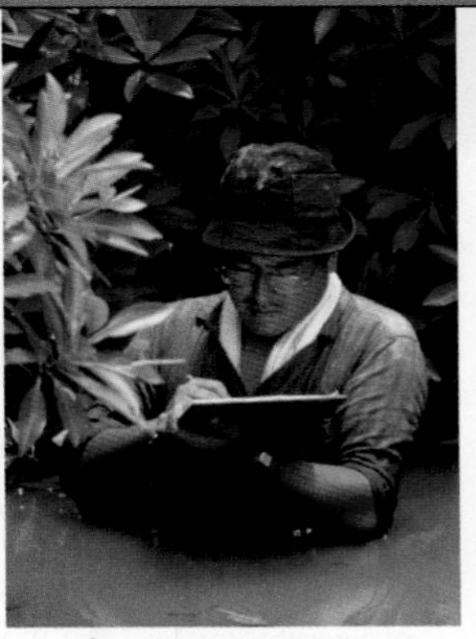

FIGURE 20.21 This scientist, standing waist-high in water, is studying a mangrove forest in Thailand. Mangrove forests grow in intertidal zones in the tropics. These diverse ecosystems may hold treatments for a variety of medical conditions.

Connecting CONCEPTS

Cells Some alkaloids help stop the spread of cancer by interfering with mitosis. Recall from **Chapter 5** that mitosis is the phase of the cell cycle when the duplicated chromosomes separate so that two new cells form.

20.4 ASSESSMENT

ONLINE QUIZ ClassZone.com

REVIEWING MAIN IDEAS

1. How has agriculture affected the day-to-day life of humans?
2. In what ways are plants an important part of our culture today?
3. Why is a knowledge of plants so important to **pharmacology**?

CRITICAL THINKING

4. **Analyze** How did the average person's knowledge of plants change in societies that adopted agriculture? Explain your answer.
5. **Connect** Aside from food and medicine, in what ways are plants used in your life?

Connecting CONCEPTS

6. **Human Impact on Ecosystems** Many plants harvested for medicinal purposes grow in rain forests of developing countries. How might this fact affect the ecosystems and economies of these countries?

20.4 ASSESSMENT

1. Today, most humans do not rely on hunting and gathering to obtain food. Agriculture makes large quantities of food available.
2. We use plants for food, drink, medicine, construction, and numerous other products by which our cultures are largely defined.
3. Many modern medicines are derived from plants or have chemical structures based on the structures of plant chemicals.
4. In an agricultural society, the growers are the ones who know about plants; people who buy food do not need to know. In hunter-gather societies, everyone had to know where and when to find plants, and which were edible.
5. *Sample Answers:* grass playing fields, cotton clothing, paper, wooden furniture, wooden pencils
6. When harvesting of a plant becomes very profitable, it can lead to overharvesting or planting of cash crops instead of food crops.

ONLINE BIOLOGY For information on threatened or endangered plant species, see the WebQuest in Options for Inquiry, page 633.

Take It Further

Only a very small percentage of plants has been studied for potential use as medicines. The areas of Earth with the greatest potential for research are the **tropics** because of the great diversity of plants that grow there. However, more than half of Earth's human population lives in the tropics. As human demands for space and resources increase, many plant species are becoming endangered or extinct. Discuss what the extinction of plant species might mean for pharmacology and the discovery of new medicines.

Vocabulary

Greek and Latin Word Origins The term **pharmacology** is from the Greek word *pharmakon,* which means "drug." Other common words related to pharmacology include *pharmacist* and *pharmacy.* The word *pharmaceutical* can be used as an adjective or noun; its root is the Greek word *pharmakeutikos,* which means "preparer of drugs."

Students may have also heard of or read the term **apothecary,** which refers to a shop that or person who dispenses drugs or other medicines. It has a Greek root meaning "storehouse."

Answers

A Infer Large amounts of any chemical can disrupt equilibrium in body systems.

Assess and Reteach

Assess Use the Online Quiz or Section Quiz (*Assessment Book,* p. 398).

Reteach Create a cycle diagram on the board that illustrates the relationships between humans, plants, atmosphere, hydrosphere, and other systems.

OPTIONS FOR INQUIRY

INVESTIGATION

Time 90 minutes	TEACHER TESTED
Teacher Preparation	
Student Difficulty	
Lab Binder Plants, pp. 5–6	

Purpose Classify plant samples as monocots or dicots.

Overview Students will observe and classify plant samples. They will

- observe the vein pattern of leaves, the number of petals on flowers, and the presence of wood or bark
- examine vascular bundles by using thin cross sections of stems

LAB PREPARATION

- Collect 2–4 plant samples per group: half monocot, half dicot

Teacher Note "For some grasses, it was tough to see flower parts and count the parts. Use gladiolus, iris, or tulips."

LAB MANAGEMENT

- For a simpler alternative, have students prepare and examine tissue samples of moss and a bean plant and classify each as vascular or nonvascular.
- Remind students to always cut away from their bodies when using razors.

Safety Caution students who have plant allergies to wear gloves or avoid contact. Remind students to clean the eyepieces of the microscopes with alcohol wipes and wash their hands after the investigation.

POST-LAB DISCUSSION

Discuss other characteristics that are used to classify plants. **Ask,** What characteristic would you look for if you were classifying plants as angiosperms or gymnosperms? fruit or no fruit What characteristic would you look for if you were classifying a moss and a fern? vascular tissue

Use these inquiry-based labs and online activities to deepen your understanding of plant diversity.

NOS.3 Clearly communicate their ideas and results of investigations verbally and in written form using tables, graphs, diagrams, and photographs.

INVESTIGATION

Comparing Monocots and Dicots

Several characteristics can be used to distinguish between monocots and dicots. In this activity, you will use these characteristics to classify plants as either monocots or dicots.

MATERIALS

- 2–4 plant samples
- razor tool
- dissecting microscope

SKILLS Observing, Classifying

PROBLEM Is the plant that you are observing a monocot or a dicot?

PROCEDURE

1. Select a plant to classify.
2. Draw a detailed illustration of the plant, including stem, leaves, and flower (if present). Save space to add labels and observations.
3. Examine the leaves of the plant. Draw a sketch of the vein pattern.
4. If the plant has a flower, record the number of petals on your drawing.
5. Using a razor tool, carefully cut off a very thin cross-section of the stem. Examine the cross-section of the stem under a dissecting microscope. Draw what you see next to the stem in your drawing. Record whether the vascular bundles are arranged in a simple ring or several rings, or if they are more scattered throughout the stem cross-section.
6. Record whether the plant has wood or bark.
7. Compare your observations with the characteristics listed in Table 1. Based on this information, classify the plant as a monocot or a dicot, and label it in your drawing.
8. Repeat steps 1–7 for each plant sample.

TABLE 1. CHARACTERISTICS OF MONOCOTS AND DICOTS

Monocots	Dicots
Veins in leaves are parallel.	Veins in leaves are netlike.
Flower parts are usually in multiples of 3.	Flower parts are usually in multiples of 4 or 5.
Vascular bundles in stem are scattered.	Vascular bundles in stem form a ring.
Wood and bark are not common.	Wood and bark are common.

ANALYZE AND CONCLUDE

1. **Analyze** Which characteristics do you think were the easiest to use in classifying the plants as monocots or dicots?
2. **Analyze** List the plants that you were able to classify, and include whether you identified them as monocots or dicots.
3. **Apply** Why do you think that botanists rely on the number of cotyledons to classify flowering plants, rather than using a characteristic such as number of flower parts?

Answers

Analyze and Conclude

1. Counting petals may be cited as the easiest way to identify plants as monocots or dicots.
2. Answers will vary based on plants used in the investigation. Students should have at least one monocot and one dicot to identify.
3. All flowering plants have either one or two cotyledons. This is a physiological characteristic that clearly divides all flowering plants into two groups. Other traits, such as number of petals and vascular tissue arrangement, can vary greatly within the monocot and dicot classes.

INVESTIGATION

Investigating Medicinal Plants

Rain forests have great biodiversity, and botanists frequently discover new plants in these ecosystems. One important area of research involves testing the chemical properties of these plants for medical purposes. You have learned that chemicals from the Madagascar periwinkle are used to treat childhood leukemia and Hodgkin's disease. Chemicals from another plant, *Forsteronia refracta*, have been found to stop the growth of breast cancer cells. Each time a new plant is discovered, there is a possibility of finding a new treatment or cure.

SKILL Researching

PROBLEM What medicinal qualities can be found in rain forest plants?

RESEARCH

1. Find another example of a rain forest plant that is being used to produce pharmaceuticals.
2. Record the scientific and common names of the plant.
3. What disease or condition is this plant used to treat?
4. What chemical qualities of the plant make it an effective treatment?
5. Are there any problems associated with harvesting this plant?
6. Why do you think so many medicinal plants are discovered in the rain forests of the world, rather than in other biomes?

The Madagascar periwinkle contains two alkaloids, vinblastine and vincristine, which have been isolated and developed into anti-cancer drugs.

Online BIOLOGY CLASSZONE.COM

ANIMATED BIOLOGY

Plant and Pollinator Matching Game

What pollinates a saguaro cactus? Examine the adaptive features of flowers and animals, and use them as clues to determine which animal pollinates a particular plant.

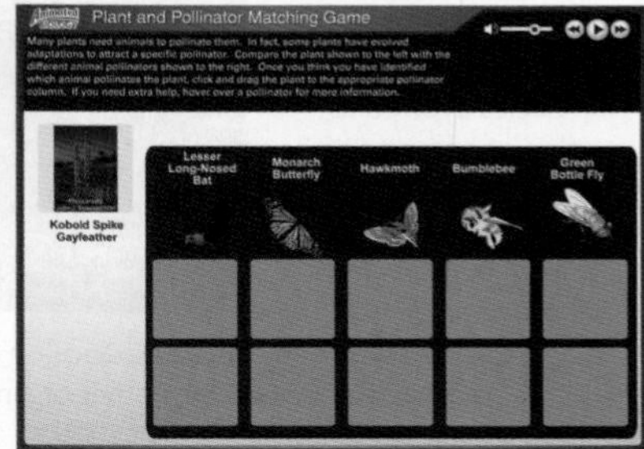

WEBQUEST

When you think of endangered species, you may think of animals. In this WebQuest, you will explore one of more than 700 plant species that are threatened or endangered in the United States. Learn about a plant in your state that is protected by the Endangered Species Act. Explore the threats to the plant and determine how to keep an essential producer from going extinct.

BIOZINE

Stories about plants—such as "Compound in Tropical Plant Used to Treat Cancer" and "Transgenic Corn Boasts Higher Yields, Greater Controversy"—are often in the headlines. Get the latest news about botany in the BioZine.

Online Biology ▼

ANIMATED BIOLOGY Use this interactive animation to reinforce the concepts in **Section 20.1.**

WEBQUEST The WebQuest takes one full class period. Students complete the activity online and will need access to a printer to print their answers. Sample answers, teacher notes, and alternative assessment ideas are available on **ClassZone.com.** Use with **Section 20.4.**

INVESTIGATION

Time 45 minutes	TEACHER TESTED ✔
Teacher Preparation	
Student Difficulty	
Lab Binder Plants, p. 7	

Purpose Research a rain-forest plant that has medicinal qualities.

POST-LAB DISCUSSION

Have students share their research with the class.

Answers

Research

1–3. Answers will vary, but should include the scientific name and common name of a rain-forest plant and the disease or condition this plant is used to treat. For example:

1. *Cinchona pubescens,* cinchona tree, quinine to treat malaria
2. *Physostigma venenosum,* calabar bean, glaucoma
3. *Erythroxylum coca,* coca plant, novocaine as an anesthetic

4–5. Answers will vary.

6. Rain forests have higher plant diversity than any other biome.

CHAPTER REVIEW

Interactive Review

Encourage students to go to **Classzone.com** for a detailed review of each section, including visuals and vocabulary practice.

Unit Resource Book, Vocabulary Practice, pp. 23–26

CHAPTER 20 Interactive Review @ CLASSZONE.COM

KEY CONCEPTS | Vocabulary Games | Concept Maps | Animated Biology | Online Quiz

20.1 Origins of Plant Life

Plant life began in the water and became adapted to land. The common ancestor of plants is an ancient species of green algae. Green algae called charophyceans are the closest living relatives to this common ancestor. Over time, the first true plant species evolved as they adapted to life on land. Land plants have evolved mechanisms to retain moisture, transport resources, grow upright, and reproduce on land. They have also coevolved with other organisms that inhabit dry land.

20.2 Classification of Plants

Plants can be classified into nine phyla. Mosses and their relatives make up three phyla of seedless nonvascular plants. These plants rely on water for reproduction and must grow low to the ground to absorb water and nutrients. Club mosses and ferns make up two phyla of seedless vascular plants. Vascular tissue allows these plants to grow higher above the ground. Seed plants, which include three phyla of cone-bearing plants and one phylum of flowering plants, do not rely on water for reproduction. Sperm of seed plants are produced by pollen grains. Seeds nourish and protect the embryos of these plants.

20.3 Diversity of Flowering Plants

The largest phylum in the plant kingdom is the flowering plants. Flowers and fruit are two adaptations that have allowed flowering plants to become the dominant plant group on Earth today. Flowers often allow for more efficient pollination by animals, while fruit can aid in seed dispersal. Botanists classify flowering plants into two groups based on the number of cotyledons inside the seed. Flowering plants can also be categorized based on stem type and lifespan.

20.4 Plants in Human Culture

Humans rely on plants in many ways. Plants are essential to human existence. All of the food that we eat comes either directly or indirectly from plant life. Agriculture provides stable food supplies for most people today. Many agricultural products are important economic resources on a global scale. Plants also provide us with clothing, paper, textiles, lumber, and medicines.

Synthesize Your Notes

Three-Column Chart Use a three-column chart to take notes about the nine divisions of plants. Use the columns to write the scientific names of each division, the common names, and details about the plants.

Scientific Name	Common Name	Details

Concept Map Use a concept map to review how flowering plants can be classified.

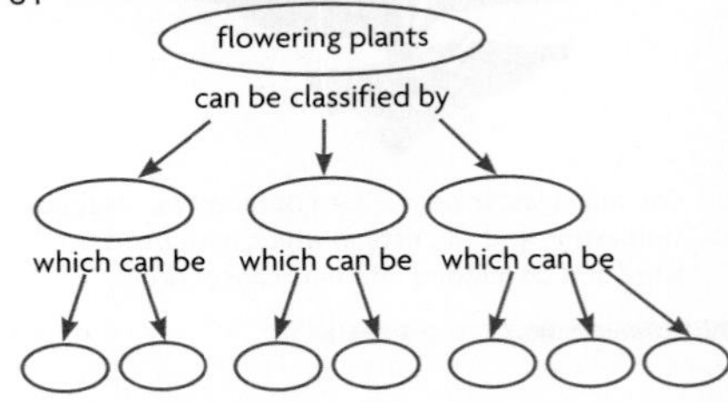

Reviewing Vocabulary

1. Wood is a fibrous material made up of dead plant cells whose cell walls contain high concentrations of lignin and cellulose.
2. Pollination occurs when a pollen grain meets the female reproductive parts of the same plant species.
3. Gymnosperms are cone-bearing seed plants.
4. Angiosperms are seed plants that produce flowers and fruit.
5. Monocots have one cotyledon, or seed leaf, whereas dicots have two.
6. Alkaloids are potent plant chemicals that are studied in pharmacology.
7. The cuticle of plants forms a protective outer layer, similar in function to the skin of animals.
8. Stoma are holes in the cuticle that allow for gas exchange; the mouths of animals are openings through which they exchange gas by breathing.
9. Pollen grains are two-celled structures that are released in large clouds that can resemble dust or flour.
10. The scales of cones can be wedge shaped.
11. Fruits are so-named because many of them are sweet or otherwise enjoyable as foods.
12. Monocots have one cotyledon, while dicots have two.

Chapter Assessment

Chapter Vocabulary

20.1	20.2	20.3
plant, p. 612	pollination, p. 620	cotyledon, p. 625
cuticle, p. 614	gymnosperm, p. 621	monocot, p. 626
stomata, p. 614	angiosperm, p. 621	dicot, p. 626
vascular system, p. 614	cone, p. 621	wood, p. 627
lignin, p. 614	flower, p. 622	**20.4** botany, p. 629
pollen grain, p. 614	fruit, p. 622	ethnobotany, p. 629
seed, p. 614		pharmacology, p. 631
		alkaloid, p. 631

Reviewing Vocabulary

Vocabulary Connections

For each group of words below, write a sentence or two to clearly explain how the terms are connected. For example, for the terms *cuticle* and *stomata*, you could write "Together, the cuticle and stomata prevent water loss while allowing for gas exchange."

1. lignin, wood
2. pollen grain, pollination
3. gymnosperm, seed, cone
4. angiosperm, seed, flower, fruit
5. cotyledon, monocot, dicot
6. pharmacology, alkaloid

Greek and Latin Word Origins

7. *Cuticula* is the Latin word for "skin." How does this meaning relate to the definition of *cuticle?*

8. In Greek, the word *stoma* means "mouth." How does this meaning relate to its botanical meaning?

9. In Latin, the word *pollen* means "dust" or "fine flour." How does this meaning relate to its botanical meaning?

10. *Conus* is a Latin word that means "wedge" or "peak." How does this meaning relate to the definition of *cone?*

11. *Fruī* is a Latin verb meaning "to enjoy." How does this meaning relate to the role that various fruits play in human culture?

12. The prefix *mono-* means "one" in Latin, while the prefix *di-* means "two." How do these meanings relate to the words *monocot* and *dicot?*

Reviewing MAIN IDEAS

13. Summarize the evidence supporting the statement that modern plants evolved from an ancient species of green algae. **B.8.3**

14. Discuss four major challenges that early plants faced while adapting to life on dry land.

15. The 30-centimeter tongue of the hawk moth is long enough to reach the nectar—and reproductive organs—of the night-blooming orchid. What can be concluded about the evolution of plants from these types of relationships? Explain.

16. Describe the structural features that limit the height of mosses and their relatives.

17. Explain why most seedless vascular plants live in moist environments.

18. What is the main difference between the seeds of cone-bearing plants and the seeds of flowering plants?

19. Summarize two of the adaptations of flowering plants that allow them to flourish in today's world.

20. Describe the system that botanists use to classify flowering plants into two main groups. **B.8.3**

21. Compare and contrast annual, biennial, and perennial lifespans.

22. What role does agriculture play in the stability and survival of modern human populations?

23. How can plants play a role in developing modern medicines, even if they are not used as ingredients?

CHAPTER REVIEW

Reviewing Main Ideas

13. Green algae and plants share many characteristics. Both are able to photosynthesize; they contain the same types of chlorophyll; both use starch as a storage product; and most green algae, as well as all plants, have cell walls containing cellulose. Genetic analysis reveals that charophyceans, green algae common in shallow fresh-water environments today, are the closest living relatives of plants.
14. retaining moisture, or not drying out; transporting resources that are obtained from below ground and above ground to various parts of the plant; growing upright without the support of water; reproducing without freestanding water
15. They have likely coevolved with their animal pollinators. The orchid evolved to rely on a moth with a long tongue to pollinate it, while the moth evolved to specialize in obtaining food from deep within the orchid.
16. They do not have a vascular system to carry resources to various parts of the plant. As a result, the plants' cells need to be close to water and nutrients on the ground, so height is limited.
17. They need freestanding water for reproduction; sperm must swim through water in order to reach and fertilize an egg.
18. The seeds of flowering plants are enclosed in fruit, and the seeds of cone-bearing plants are not.
19. Flowers can attract animal pollinators, and therefore allow for more efficient pollination. Fruit can protect seeds and aid in seed dispersal.
20. Monocots have one cotyledon within their seeds, and dicots have two cotyledons within their seeds.
21. Annuals mature from seed, produce flowers, and die all in one year. Biennials take two years to go through this cycle. Perennials live for more than two years.
22. Agriculture provides a more reliable source of food than hunting and gathering, and this food source can often support a growing population. Agriculture also allows for socially complex centers of human populations because people do not have to move around to find food.
23. The chemical structures of many synthetic drugs are based on the structures of plant compounds.

ITEM CORRELATIONS

Standard	Items
B.4.2	27
B.8.3	13, 20, 31, 32

CHAPTER REVIEW

Critical Thinking

24. They have limited access to sunlight because some of the light is filtered out by the water. Also, gas exchange (CO_2) may be more difficult underwater, and certain minerals are much less common in aquatic soils than in terrestrial soils.
25. The sperm of seed plants are derived from pollen grains. Pollen grains are carried from the male parts of flowers to the female parts, either by wind or animals; therefore, the sperm of seed plants do not need water to "swim" through to reach an egg.
26. Seedless plants disperse by way of their spores. Seed plants disperse with their seeds.
27. Economic resources, including potential medicines, will be lost. The rain forests are some of the most biodiverse ecosystems on Earth, so a tremendous amount of species may be lost.
28. They can guide animal pollinators to the pollen or nectar, and also to the plant's reproductive structures.
29. The fruit around dandelion seeds is a fluffy, parachute-like material that allows the seeds to be carried easily by wind. The seeds of pine trees are not enclosed in fruit and cannot be dispersed very far by wind.
30. Insecticides may cause a decline in insect populations, which means there are potentially fewer pollinators for certain plant species. If plants do not get pollinated, they cannot complete their reproductive cycle. Ultimately, this can result in declining plant populations.

Critical Thinking

24. Analyze Aquatic plants, which evolved from land plants, have adaptations that allow them to live in the water. Some aquatic plants grow completely submerged in water. What challenges might these plants face that do not apply to plants that live entirely on land?

25. Analyze The sperm of seedless plants are flagellated, while those of seed plants are not. How do the sperm of seed plants reach eggs without flagella?

26. Compare When a plant reproduces, it is important for its offspring to disperse so that they do not compete directly with the parent plant. Compare the structures that allow seedless plants and seed plants to disperse to new locations.

27. Synthesize Some experts predict that the Amazon rain forest will be completely destroyed due to human activities within the next century. What resources would potentially be lost along with this ecosystem? **B.4.2**

28. Infer Some types of flowers have special markings on their petals that act as guides to the pollen or nectar for their pollinators. How could such markings have evolved through natural selection?

29. Analyze What evolutionary advantage do the seeds of dandelions have over the seeds of pine trees?

30. Synthesize How might an increase in the use of insecticides affect flowering-plant populations in the area?

Interpreting Visuals

Use the illustration below to answer the next two questions.

31. Analyze What parts of this plant could you examine to determine whether it is a monocot or a dicot? **B.8.3**

32. Apply Is this plant likely a monocot or a dicot? Explain your reasoning. **B.8.3**

Analyzing Data

Valencia oranges, which likely originated in Spain or Portugal, are now the most widely planted orange variety in the world. Use the data below on the number of California Valencia oranges per tree to answer the next three questions.

CALIFORNIA VALENCIA ORANGES PER TREE
596, 402, 489, 708, 374, 548, 640, 585, 518, 450

Source: California Agricultural Statistics Service

33. Calculate What are the mean, median, and mode for this data set? Round the mean to the nearest whole number.

34. Analyze Does this data set contain outliers? Explain your answer.

35. Evaluate Which measure of central tendency best represents this data set? Explain your answer.

Connecting CONCEPTS

36. Write About Seeds From the viewpoint of a plant embryo, write about the importance of a seed. What does the seed provide for you? In what ways does it help you? What advantages do you have over nonseed plants?

37. Synthesize The flowering proteas of South Africa are adapted to a dry climate that receives as little as 600 mm of rain each year. However, plants must retain moisture in order for photosynthesis to occur. Describe the adaptations that allow these plants to retain moisture in their leaves while still allowing for air to move in and out.

636 Unit 7: Plants

Interpreting Visuals

31. From this illustration, you can examine the number of flower parts and the pattern of leaf veins to identify the plant as a monocot or a dicot.
32. It is likely a monocot because it has six petals (a multiple of 3) and parallel veins.

Analyzing Data

33. mean = 531, median = 533, mode = none
34. No outliers; the two extremes (374 and 708) do not seem different enough from the rest of the numbers to be considered outliers.
35. When there are no outliers, the mean usually best represents the data because all data points factor into it.

INDIANA ISTEP+ Test Prep

B.8.5, NOS.1, NOS.9

Test Practice
For more test practice, go to ClassZone.com.

1 In the 1940s, Barbara McClintock observed patterns of inheritance in corn plants that could not be explained by the current gene theory. The conclusions of her work were not widely accepted for many years until further supported by the work of other scientists. What does this scenario demonstrate about science?

A Data that are more than 50 years old should be discarded.
B Data that do not fit a scientific theory should be discarded.
C Theories may be modified as additional data lead to new conclusions.
D The repetition of results by many scientists is not necessary to validate a theory.

2 Many wind-pollinated flowers are small and green, with male reproductive structures that hang outside the flower where wind can easily pick up and carry the pollen. Which is likely to also be true for wind-pollinated flowers?

A Colorful petals would not be an advantage.
B Sweet-smelling petals would be an advantage.
C They produce less pollen than other flowers.
D They can thrive in any environment.

3

Tomato Plant Growth Per Week (cm)		
Plot	Condition	Average Growth
1	full sun	9 cm
2	part sun	7 cm
3	full shade	2 cm

Gardeners are testing three plots of land with similar soil to find out which is best for growing tomato plants. Which of the following conclusions is ***best*** supported by their data?

A Plot 1 received the most nutrients.
B Plot 3 did not receive enough water.
C Tomato plants grow best in full sun.
D Tomato plants cannot grow in the shade.

4 The sugar in corn is rapidly converted to starch after the corn has been picked. After picking, corn with the ***Sh2*** gene was found to have more sugar and less starch than corn without this gene. Which of the following statements is ***most*** likely to be true about corn with this gene?

A It cannot convert sugar to starch.
B It cannot photosynthesize.
C It has no chloroplasts.
D It has no chlorophyll.

THINK THROUGH THE QUESTION

Think about the process by which plants produce sugars. You can eliminate any answer choices that would result in plants with less sugar.

5 The beak shape shown here likely evolved through a process in which birds that could get food most efficiently

A died in the absence of long, tubular flowers.
B did not have time to find mates.
C shared food with other individuals.
D were more likely to survive and reproduce.

6 Scientists believe that the first plants on Earth were nonvascular aquatic plants. Fossil evidence indicates that a great period of time passed before land plants emerged. Why couldn't aquatic plants have just spread to land? What do land plants possess that aquatic plants do not?

CHAPTER REVIEW

Standards-Based Assessment

1. C	4. A
2. A	5. D
3. C	6. See Below

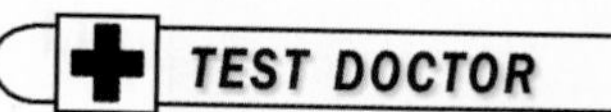

Question 2 Answer A is correct. Answer B is incorrect because sweet-smelling petals do not attract more wind. Answer C is incorrect because these flowers would likely produce more pollen since it is windborne, rather than being carried to other flowers by animal pollinators. Answer D is incorrect because these plants would not thrive in an environment that was not windy or where the plants were sheltered from wind.

Question 3 Answer C is correct. Answers A and B are incorrect because nutrients and water were not tested in this experiment, and these conclusions are not supported by the data. Answer D is incorrect because the tomato plants planted in the full shade grew 2 cm.

Question 4 Answer A is correct. Answer B is incorrect because plants need to carry out photosynthesis to grow and reproduce. Answers C and D are incorrect because plants need chloroplasts and chlorophyll to carry out photosynthesis.

Question 6 Most aquatic plants are nonvascular, meaning that they do not possess the internal vascular system necessary to transport water and nutrients from their roots to their stems and leaves. They must pull in water and nutrients from the environment directly surrounding them. Land plants are able to survive because they have vascular tissues that allows them to transport the nutrients and water they need to live from their roots to their stems and leaves.

Connecting Concepts

36. Students should write a clear response that reflects an understanding of the adaptive advantages of seeds. A seed coat protects an embryo. A food supply within the seed coat provides nourishment. Seeds help individual plants disperse to new areas, away from the parent plant. A major advantage that seed plants have over nonseed plants is that seed plants can reproduce without freestanding water.

37. The surfaces of many plants are covered with a cuticle, which is a waxy, waterproof layer that helps hold in moisture. Tiny holes in the cuticle, called stomata, allow air to move in and out of the plant surfaces.

ITEM CORRELATIONS

Standard	Items
B.8.5	2, 5, 6
NOS.1	3, 4
NOS.9	1

CHAPTER 21

Indiana Resource Preview

Print Resources

Plant Structure and Function

INDIANA STANDARDS		Sections	PAGES and PACING	UNIT RESOURCE BOOK
	21.1	**Plant Cells and Tissues** **KEY CONCEPT** Plants have specialized cells and tissue systems.	pp. 640–642 30 minutes	URB pages 27–30
	21.2	**The Vascular System** **KEY CONCEPT** The vascular system allows for the transport of water, minerals, and sugars.	pp. 643–646 30 minutes	URB pages 31–34
NOS.3		CHAPTER INVESTIGATION: Density of Stomata	p. 647 45 minutes	**Lab Binder** Plants pages 15–17
	21.3	**Roots and Stems** **KEY CONCEPT** Roots and stems form the support system of vascular plants.	pp. 648–651 45 minutes	URB pages 35–38
		DATA ANALYSIS: Identifying the Importance of Repeated Trials	p. 649 30 minutes	URB page 43
	21.4	**Leaves** **KEY CONCEPT** Leaves absorb light and carry out photosynthesis.	pp. 652–655 30 minutes	URB pages 39–42
NOS.1, NOS.3		OPTIONS FOR INQUIRY	pp. 656–657 45 minutes, 45 minutes	**Lab Binder** Plants pages 18–21
		Chapter Review	pp. 658–661	**Assessment Book** Chapter Tests A, B pp. 417–424

INDIANA STANDARDS

NOS.1 Develop explanations based on reproducible data and observations gathered during laboratory investigations.
NOS.3 Clearly communicate their ideas and results of investigations verbally and in written form using tables, graphs, diagrams, and photographs.

Labs

PUPIL EDITION LABS

Density of Stomata, p. 647 Students compare the density of stomata on upper and lower leaf surfaces. **Lab Binder** pp. 15–17	**Time:** 45 minutes **Materials:** tree leaf, clear fingernail polish, 5 cm clear tape, microscope slide, compound light microscope
Chlorophyll Fluorescence, Section 4, p. 654 Students observe fluorescence given off by chlorophyll that has been extracted from leaves and exposed to light. **Lab Binder** p. 22	**Time:** 30 minutes **Materials:** mortar, pestle, handful spinach leaves, 10 mL methanol, graduated cylinder, filter paper, funnel, beaker, eye dropper or pipette, test tube, test tube rack, flashlight

OPTIONS FOR INQUIRY

Photosynthesis and Red Leaves, p. 656 Students use chromatograms to compare the pigments of red leaves and green leaves. **Lab Binder** pp. 18–20	**Time:** 45 minutes **Materials:** 2 paper clips stretched into a wire, 2 rubber stoppers, 2 strips of chromatography paper, 2 large test tubes, test tube rack, green leaf, red leaf, coin, 10-mL graduated cylinder, 5 mL isopropyl alcohol
Connecting Form to Function, p. 657 Students connect the structures of plant organs to their functions. **Lab Binder** p. 21	**Time:** 45 minutes **Materials:** plant root, stem, and leaf; razor tool, 3 slides, 3 cover slips, eyedropper, water, compound microscope

LAB BINDER Unit 7 Plants

Additional Investigation: Comparing Plant Structures, pp. 23–26

Challenge Lab: Absorption Spectra of Plant Pigments, pp. 52–57

Virtual Lab Worksheet: Plant Transpiration, pp. 58–59

LAB GENERATOR

A searchable CD of all labs in the program in editable format, including forensic, probeware, and biotechnology labs.

Presentation Tools

POWER PRESENTATIONS

Presentation Chapter 21
Power Presentations for each section incorporate images and clips from the Media Gallery: Includes Note Navigator for each section.

MEDIA GALLERY

Contains the following images and video clips, as well as animations, simulations and forms of visuals from the book.

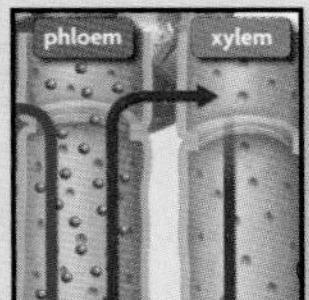

Pressure flow model

Dichotomous key

Tendril

Cactus spines

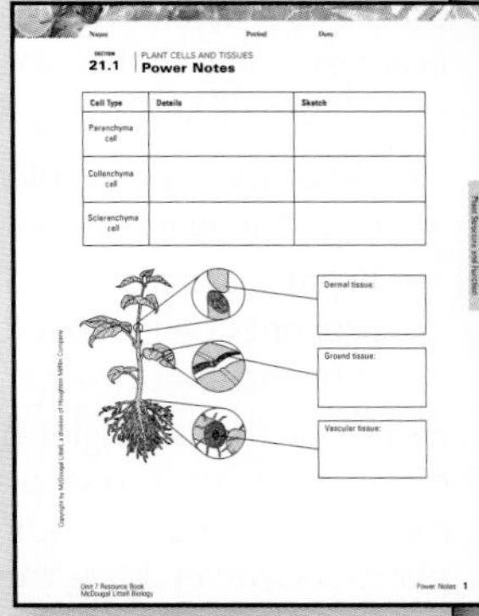

Power Notes

ANIMATED BIOLOGY

Movement Through a Plant

Name That Tree

TRANSPARENCIES

Plant Tissue Systems T88

Movement of Fluids through Xylem T89

Leaf Cross-Section T90

Online BIOLOGY CLASSZONE.COM

BioZine
Animated Biology
Interactive Review
SciLinks
Resource Centers

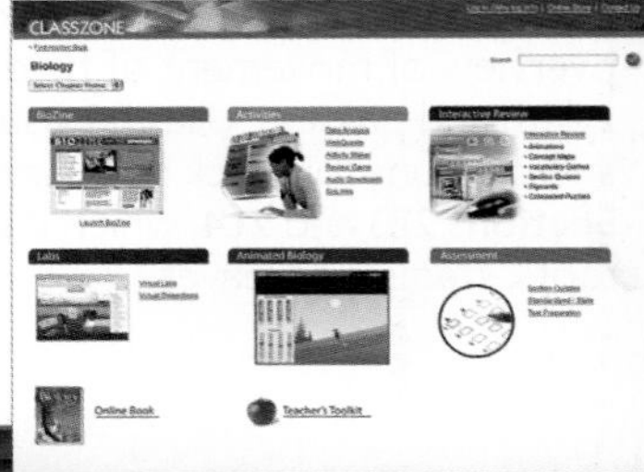

CHAPTER 21

Focus and Motivate

How would this tree compete with other species?

Students may answer that the tree competes with other species by growing over them or strangling them. **Ask**

- What part of this plant is growing over the walls? roots
- What do plants need that this plant prevents other species from getting? sunlight, space, water, nutrients

Point out that strangler figs have modified roots. Other plants have modified leaves or modified stems. All plants, however, have the same basic cell types and tissue systems, and the vascular systems, roots, stems, and leaves of plants have similar structures and functions.

BIOZINE ClassZone.com

Students can access BioZine at **ClassZone.com** to check out articles featured in "Strange Biology."

In a Hurry?

Students may be familiar with some of the material on roots, stems, and leaves. The critical material in this chapter is found in **Sections 21.1** and **21.2,** which cover the three basic cell types and tissue systems, as well as the movement of fluids through xylem and phloem. **FIGURE 21.4 (Section 21.2)** provides an overview of movement of fluids in the xylem and phloem. Use the visuals and captions for quick coverage of **Sections 21.3** and **21.4,** which discuss roots, stems, and leaves.

CHAPTER 21 Plant Structure and Function

KEY CONCEPTS

21.1 Plant Cells and Tissues
Plants have specialized cells and tissue systems.

21.2 The Vascular System
The vascular system allows for the transport of water, minerals, and sugars.

21.3 Roots and Stems
Roots and stems form the support system of vascular plants.

21.4 Leaves
Leaves absorb light and carry out photosynthesis.

Online BIOLOGY CLASSZONE.COM

Animated BIOLOGY
View animated chapter concepts.
- Movement Through a Plant
- Plant Transpiration
- Name That Tree

BIOZINE
Keep current with biology news.
- News feeds
- Strange Biology
- Polls

RESOURCE CENTER
Get more information on
- Plant Tissues
- Plant Systems
- Leaves

Student Activity

Purpose **Have students observe the roots, stems, and leaves of different plants.**

Materials (per nine students)

- whole carrot plant, small pine sapling, and small deciduous sapling, all in soil
- newspaper (for covering desks)
- water
- hand lens

Any three plant species can be used, but aim for a diversity of leaf, stem, and root types.

How would this tree compete with other species?

Connecting CONCEPTS

Fig trees (*Ficus*) have a unique way of growing. Many trees of this genus are called strangler figs because their aggressive growth actually strangles other trees. Strangler figs can also wrap around unmoving objects such as these temple walls. Their seeds germinate easily in tree branches or building cracks, and then snakelike roots grow down to the ground.

Competition Besides strangling their host trees, figs can kill by outcompeting other plants for sunlight. Many tropical figs develop aerial roots that extend through the air from the branches to the ground. These roots are commonly called prop roots, and they allow the tree to spread outward for long distances. In fact, the tree canopy of a great banyan fig in Calcutta, India, covers three acres and has 1775 prop roots.

Introduce Tell students that they are going to work in teams of three to come up with as many observations of the plants as they can in ten minutes. Plants should be passed around among three groups. Students can remove the plant from the soil to examine its roots, but they should put the plant back into the soil before passing the plant to the next group.

Discuss Have teams take turns reporting their other observations. **Ask**

- What plant parts did you observe? roots, stems, leaves
- Where did the plant seem to be growing? at the top
- Did you observe any differences among the roots, stems, and leaves? Students should observe the differences of shape and texture among woody and herbaceous stems, deciduous and coniferous leaves, and different root systems. Point out that all plants have the same basic structures, cells, tissues, and systems, but there is great diversity of form.

Activate Prior Knowledge

Direct students attention to the photograph. **Ask,** Have you ever seen a tree "move" a block of cement on the sidewalk or push through a fence? What does that suggest about the roots and stems of a woody plant? have a good degree of strength Remind students that a tree must have a system to support its own weight.

Preview Vocabulary

Greek and Latin Word Origins The word *vascular* comes from the Latin word *vas,* meaning "vessel." In humans, the vascular system contains the blood vessels. In plants, *vascular* refers to xylem and phloem vessels that carry water, nutrients, and sugars. In this chapter, *vascular* is used in several ways:

vascular tissue

vascular system

vascular cylinder

vascular bundles

Academic Vocabulary *Apical* and *lateral* are two keywords in this chapter. When used in the context of plant roots and stems, *apical* refers to an area of growth at the tip of a stem or root. *Lateral* refers to the side. Have students look for these words combined with *meristem* as they read and notice what kind of growth takes place.

English Learners Have students use the vocabulary strategy list-group-label (*Biology Toolkit,* p. D6) to learn the many new terms of this chapter. First, they skim through the chapter, focusing on the section titles and main-idea statements. Then they close their books and, as a class, create a list of the keywords they remember. Teams of three students group the words, explain their grouping system, and then label each word cluster according to relatedness. When students have finished, have them look again at the chapter to adjust their groupings.

Chapter 21: Plant Structure and Function **639**

SECTION 21.1

▼ Plan and Prepare

Objectives

- Describe the three cell types and three tissue types of plants.

Section Resources

Unit Resource Book
Study Guide pp. 27–28
Power Notes p. 29
Reinforcement p. 30

Interactive Reader Chapter 21
Spanish Study Guide pp. 215–216

Biology Toolkit pp. C19, C26, D6

Technology
Power Presentation 21.1
Media Gallery DVD
Online Quiz 21.1

Activate Prior Knowledge Have students think about how animals grow and develop and then compare that with how plants grow and develop. **Ask,** What is a major difference between the period of growth for an animal compared with that of a plant? Plants grow throughout their lifetime. Discuss how plants add height and girth in such a way as to maintain support but continue to provide nutrients and water.

▼ Teach

Vocabulary

Greek and Latin Word Origins The words for the three plant cell types—**parenchyma, collenchyma,** and **sclerenchyma**—come from Greek roots:

enchyma = cellular tissue
para = beside
coll = glue
scler- = hard

21.1 Plant Cells and Tissues

KEY CONCEPT Plants have specialized cells and tissue systems.

MAIN IDEAS

- Plant tissues are made of three basic cell types.
- Plant organs are made of three tissue systems.

VOCABULARY

parenchyma cell, p. 640
collenchyma cell, p. 640
sclerenchyma cell, p. 641
dermal tissue, p. 642
ground tissue, p. 642
vascular tissue, p. 642
xylem, p. 642
phloem, p. 642

Review
tissue, lignin, vascular system, cuticle

Connect You already know that besides roots, plants have stems, or trunks, and leaves. But did you know that these parts are considered the organs of the plant? Just like other organisms, plants have organs that are made of tissues, and tissues that are made of cells. It is easy to remember: plants have three main organs, made up of three tissue systems, mostly made up of three basic cell types.

MAIN IDEA

Plant tissues are made of three basic cell types.

Plant cells are quite different from animal cells. In addition to all of the structures that animal cells have, plant cells have cell walls, plastids, and a large vacuole. Just as with animals, plants are made up of many types of cells that are organized into tissues. Three basic types of plant cells, shown in **FIGURE 21.1,** are parenchyma cells, collenchyma cells, and sclerenchyma cells.

***Connecting* CONCEPTS**

Cells Recall from **Chapter 3** that plant cells differ from animal cells in having cell walls, chloroplasts, and large vacuoles. Like animals, plants have different cell types.

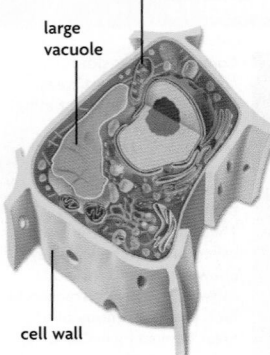

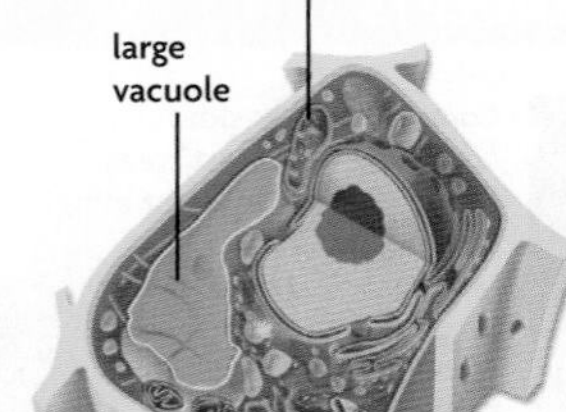

Parenchyma Cells

A **parenchyma cell** (puh-REHNG-kuh-muh)—the most common type of plant cell—stores starch, oils, and water for the plant. You can find parenchyma cells throughout a plant. These cells have thin walls and large water-filled vacuoles in the middle. Photosynthesis occurs in green chloroplasts within parenchyma cells in leaves. Both chloroplasts and colorless plastids in parenchyma cells within roots and stems store starch. The flesh of many fruits we eat is also made of parenchyma cells. Parenchyma cells are sometimes thought of as the least specialized of plant cells, but they have one very special trait. They have the ability to divide throughout their entire lives, so they are important in healing wounds to the plant and regenerating parts. For example, parenchyma cells let you place stem cuttings of many types of plants in water to grow into a complete, new plant.

Collenchyma Cells

A **collenchyma cell** (kuh-LEHNG-kuh-muh) has cell walls that range from thin to thick, providing support while still allowing the plant to grow. These cells are most common in the younger tissues of leaves and shoots. They often form into strands. For example, celery strings are strands of collenchyma cells.

Differentiated Instruction

BELOW LEVEL

Have students list and then group key vocabulary words listed on page 640. Students should differentiate between the groups by describing the type of information each set of terms provides. Tell students to group the three cell types, the three tissue types, and then group xylem and phloem with vascular tissue.

Biology Toolkit, List-Group-Label, p. D6

ENGLISH LEARNERS

Have students use Cornell notes to create an outline for the concepts and key vocabulary of the section. After reading the section, students should create a two-column chart with a standard outline in the second column that organizes the main points and concepts of the section. Then, in the first column, they can write in keywords alongside the corresponding part of the outline in the second column. In a bottom section overlapping both columns, students can write a brief chapter summary.

Biology Toolkit, Cornell Notes, p. C26

FIGURE 21.1 Basic Plant Cell Types

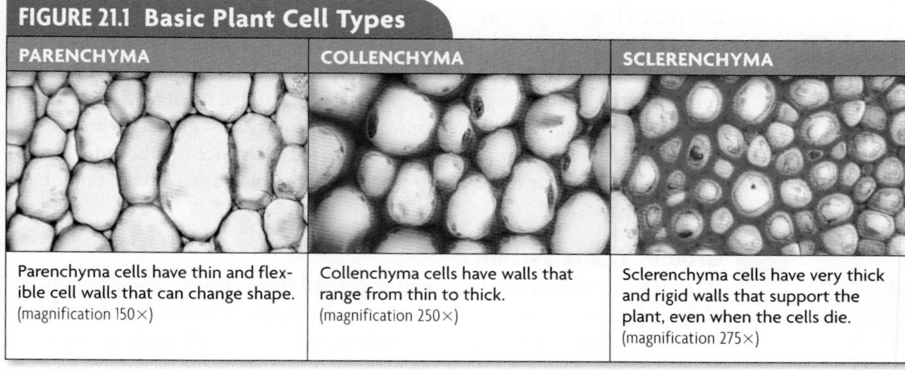

PARENCHYMA	COLLENCHYMA	SCLERENCHYMA
Parenchyma cells have thin and flexible cell walls that can change shape. (magnification 150×)	Collenchyma cells have walls that range from thin to thick. (magnification 250×)	Sclerenchyma cells have very thick and rigid walls that support the plant, even when the cells die. (magnification 275×)

The unique feature of collenchyma cells is that they are flexible. Their cell walls don't contain lignin, so they are stretchy and can change size. As a young leaf grows, collenchyma cells can elongate and still give the leaf structure.

Sclerenchyma Cells

Of the three basic plant cell types, a **sclerenchyma cell** (skluh-REHNG-kuh-muh) is the strongest. These cells have a second cell wall that is hardened by lignin, which makes these cells very tough and durable. But the lignin also makes these cells very rigid. Unlike collenchyma cells, they can't grow with the plant. Therefore, sclerenchyma cells are found in parts of the plant that aren't lengthening anymore. Many sclerenchyma cells, such as those within the vascular system, die when they reach maturity. The cytoplasm and organelles of these dead cells disintegrate, but the rigid cell walls are left behind as skeletal support for the water-conducting tissues or for the plant itself. Sclerenchyma cells form a major part of fruit pits and the hard outer shells of nuts. They are also found in stems and leaf veins and are responsible for the gritty texture of pears. Humans use sclerenchyma cell fibers to make linen and rope.

A Contrast **How are the cell walls of parenchyma, collenchyma, and sclerenchyma cells different from one another?**

TAKING NOTES

Make a three-column chart that organizes the relationship between plant cells, where they are found, and their function.

Cell Type	Where	Function
Parenchyma		

MAIN IDEA

Plant organs are made of three tissue systems.

Just as there are three basic types of plant cells, there are three groups of tissue systems in plants: dermal, ground, and vascular tissue systems. Recall from Chapter 5 that a tissue is a group of cells working together to perform a certain function. The tissue systems of plants may consist of simple tissues from the basic cell types: parenchyma, collenchyma, and sclerenchyma. They may also be made of complex tissues that have additional types of cells. Neighboring cells are often connected by plasmodesmata (PLAZ-muh-DEHZ-muh-tuh), strands of cytoplasm that pass through openings in cell walls and connect living cells. Through the plasmodesmata, cells of a plant tissue can share water, nutrients, and chemical signals.

PRE-AP

After students have read the section, have them write for five minutes about why the ground tissue system would need all three plant cell types. Students should discuss the properties and functions of each cell type, and how they relate to the functions of ground tissue.

Biology Toolkit, Quick-Write, p. C19

ONLINE BIOLOGY Go to the chapter Resource Center at **ClassZone.com** for additional resources and information on plant tissues and systems.

TEACH FROM VISUALS

FIGURE 21.1 Have students look at the three cell types to reinforce the main differences between them. **Ask**

- Which type of cell is the strongest? sclerenchyma
- Which type is most flexible and able to stretch? collenchyma
- Which type is likely to have the most water and sugar stored inside? parenchyma
- Which type composes the wood that we use for building houses and furniture? sclerenchyma

Vocabulary

Greek and Latin Word Origins Help students remember **plasmodesmata** by breaking it down into its Greek roots:

plassein = to mold
desma = bond

Plasmodesmata are strands of cytoplasm that pass through openings in cell walls of adjacent plant cells, thereby creating a bond. A single such strand is a *plasmodesma.* **Ask,** What do plasmodesmata allow cells to share? water, nutrients, chemical signals

Answers

A Contrast Parenchyma cell walls are thin and can grow with the plant. Collenchyma cells range from thin to thick, but still allow the plant to grow. Sclerenchyma cells have a second cell wall that contains lignin and is very tough, durable, and rigid. Sclerenchyma cells cannot grow with the plant.

▼ Teach *continued*

TEACH FROM VISUALS

FIGURE 21.2 Have students locate the dermal, ground, and vascular tissues in the plant's stem, leaf, and root. **Ask**

- What tissue system covers the outside of the plant? dermal
- What tissue system transports materials in the plant? vascular
- What tissue system makes up most of the inside of the plant? ground

Vocabulary

Greek and Latin Word Origins The words **xylem** and **phloem** are German words that come from Greek roots:

xulon = wood
phloios = bark

The xylem is found within the wood of a tree, while the phloem is usually near to or part of the bark.

Tell students that they can remember that xylem transports water by remembering *WXY: W*ater goes in *xy*lem.

Tell students that they can remember that phloem transports the products of photosynthesis by remembering: *Ph*loem is for *f*ood.

Answers

A Identify ground tissue system

▼ Assess and Reteach

Assess Use the Online Quiz or Section Quiz (*Assessment Book,* p. 413).

Reteach Create a cluster map to review the cell types, tissue types, and how they are related.

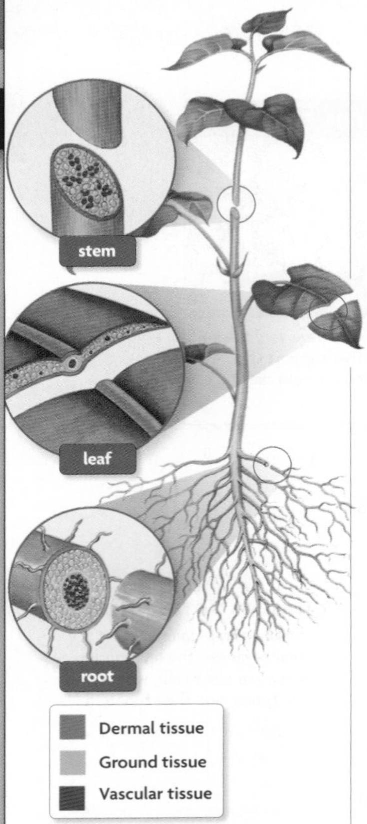

stem
leaf
root

Dermal tissue
Ground tissue
Vascular tissue

FIGURE 21.2 All three types of tissue systems are found throughout a plant.

Dermal Tissue System

Your body is covered with skin. Plants don't have skin, but they do have a system of **dermal tissue,** shown in **FIGURE 21.2**, that covers the outside of a plant and protects it in a variety of ways. Dermal tissue called epidermis is made up of live parenchyma cells in the nonwoody parts of plants. On leaves and some stems, epidermal cells may secrete a wax-coated substance that becomes the cuticle. Dermal tissue made of dead parenchyma cells makes up the outer bark of woody plants.

Ground Tissue System

Dermal tissue surrounds the system of **ground tissue,** which makes up much of the inside of a plant. Ground tissue provides support and stores materials in roots and stems. In leaves, ground tissue is packed with chloroplasts, where photosynthesis makes food for the plant. The ground tissue system consists of all three of the simple tissues—parenchyma tissue, collenchyma tissue, and sclerenchyma tissue—but parenchyma is by far the most common of the ground tissues. The ground tissue of cacti has many parenchyma cells that store water. However, the spines of cacti—which are actually modified leaves—contain mostly rigid sclerenchyma cells in their ground tissue.

Vascular Tissue System

Surrounded by ground tissue, the system of **vascular tissue** transports water, mineral nutrients, and organic compounds to all parts of the plant. Plants can transport necessary fluids and nutrients throughout their systems. A plant's vascular system is made up of two networks of hollow tubes somewhat like our veins and arteries. Each network consists of a different type of vascular tissue that works to move different resources throughout the plant. **Xylem** (ZY-luhm) is the vascular tissue that carries water and dissolved mineral nutrients up from the roots to the rest of the plant. **Phloem** (FLOH-EHM) is the vascular tissue that carries the products of photosynthesis through the plant. You will learn more about the vascular system in the next section.

A Identify What tissue system contains the most photosynthesizing cells?

21.1 ASSESSMENT

ONLINE QUIZ
ClassZone.com

REVIEWING MAIN IDEAS

1. Describe three basic types of cells found within plants.
2. List two functions for each type of tissue system found in plants.

CRITICAL THINKING

3. **Connect** The **dermal tissue** system has been compared to human skin. In what ways does this analogy hold true?
4. **Compare** What structures in the human body provide a function similar to that of **sclerenchyma cells** in plants? Explain.

***Connecting* CONCEPTS**

5. **Cell Biology** Plant cells have distinct differences from animal cells, such as cell walls, large vacuoles, and chloroplasts. How are these differences useful for a plant?

21.1 ASSESSMENT

1. Parenchyma cells: most common type, thin-walled, large vacuoles to store starch, oils, and water for the plant. Collenchyma cells: have variable cell walls, often form into strands, are flexible and can change size. Sclerenchyma cells: strongest of type, with a lignin-strengthened second cell wall that remains after cell death.
2. The dermal tissue protects the plant and can secrete a waxy cuticle. The ground tissue provides support and stores materials in roots and stems. In leaves, it is packed with chloroplasts which photosynthesize. The vascular tissue system transports water, mineral nutrients, and organic compounds throughout the plant.
3. Both cover and protect the bodies of these organisms. Both secrete things that are useful to the organism's health and prevent the loss of water.
4. The bones of a human body provide a function similar to that of sclerenchyma cells. Both are rigid and provide structure, allowing for growth of other tissues.
5. Cell walls provide structure and strength, parenchyma vacuoles allow for storage of sap and water, and chloroplasts allow the plant to make its own food.

21.2 The Vascular System

KEY CONCEPT The vascular system allows for the transport of water, minerals, and sugars.

MAIN IDEAS
- Water and dissolved minerals move through xylem.
- Phloem carries sugars from photosynthesis throughout the plant.

VOCABULARY

cohesion-tension theory, p. 643
transpiration, p. 645
pressure-flow model, p. 645

Review
hydrogen bond, cohesion, adhesion, osmosis

Connect As you read this, your heart is pumping blood, which carries nutrients to your cells and removes wastes from them. In the world outside, fluids are also moving from tree roots all the way up to the highest leaves. But a tree has no heart to act as a pump. How can it move water up to a height of two, three, even ten stories?

MAIN IDEA

Water and dissolved minerals move through xylem.

Recall that xylem is one of the two types of vascular tissue. Water and dissolved minerals move up from the roots to the rest of the plant through xylem. Xylem contains other types of cells besides the basic cell types. Because it contains other types of cells, xylem tissue is called a complex tissue.

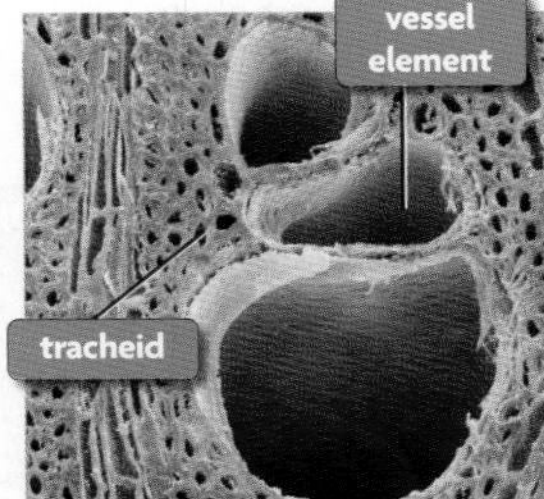

FIGURE 21.3 Xylem tissue consists of tracheids and vessel elements, conducting and supporting cells that lie end-to-end throughout xylem. Tracheid cells are narrow and long, while vessel elements are wider and shorter. (colored SEM; magnification unknown)

One type of specialized cell in xylem is called a tracheid (TRAY-kee-ihd). Tracheid cells, shown in **FIGURE 21.3,** are long and narrow. Water can flow from cell to cell in tracheids through openings in the thick cell walls. Some types of vascular plants, including most flowering plants, have an additional kind of xylem cell called a vessel element. Vessel elements are shorter and wider than tracheids. Both types of cells mature and die before water moves through them. When a vessel element dies, the cell wall disintegrates at both ends. The cells then connect end to end, forming long tubes.

Amazingly, plants don't use any metabolic energy to move water through xylem. So how do they do it? The **cohesion-tension theory** proposes that the physical properties of water allow the rise of water through a plant. This well-supported theory is based on the strong attraction of water molecules to one another and to other surfaces. The tendency of hydrogen bonds to form between water molecules creates a force called cohesion. However, water molecules are also attracted to the xylem wall due to adhesion, a force made by hydrogen bonds forming between water molecules and other substances. Cohesion and adhesion create tension that moves water upward in xylem.

***Connecting* CONCEPTS**

Hydrogen Bonding Recall from **Chapter 2** that a hydrogen bond is an attraction between a slightly positive hydrogen atom and a slightly negative atom. Hydrogen bonds between water molecules produce a force called cohesion that helps water move through a plant.

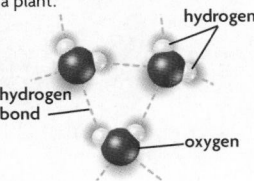

hydrogen
hydrogen bond
oxygen

Differentiated Instruction

HANDS-ON ACTIVITY

Students can observe both adhesion and cohesion by lowering a clear plastic straw into a container full of water. Have them observe what happens when they close off the top opening of the straw and draw the straw upwards out of the water. **Ask,** What does your finger create by plugging the end of the straw? a vacuum **Ask,** What force is pulling the water molecules down? gravity Explain that the vacuum works in part because the water molecules touching the inside of the straw are adhering to the plastic, and the other water molecules are bound to each other through cohesion.

Next, try the same thing using a larger cylinder. Students may discover that the vacuum and the cohesive and adhesive forces are not adequate to fight gravity. Tell them that the narrower the tube, the more adhesive the water is to the inner walls of the tube, and this is why plants have many small xylem vessels instead of a single wide xylem vessel.

SECTION 21.2

Plan and Prepare ▼

Objectives

- Describe how water and dissolved minerals move through xylem, and how sugars move through phloem.

Section Resources

Unit Resource Book
Study Guide pp. 31–32
Power Notes p. 33
Reinforcement p. 34

Interactive Reader Chapter 21
Spanish Study Guide pp. 217–218

Biology Toolkit pp. C20, C38

Technology
Power Presentation 21.2
Media Gallery DVD
Online Quiz 21.2

Activate Prior Knowledge Have students imagine a carrot growing in the ground. **Ask,** How does water needed for photosynthesis get from the root to the leaves? through the xylem of the vascular system **Ask,** Where does the sugar produced by photosynthesis end up, and how? in the root (carrot), via the phloem of the vascular system

Teach ▼

***Connecting* CONCEPTS**

Hydrogen bonding Students can witness the **cohesion** of water molecules simply by looking at a droplet of water on a flat surface. Point out that if the water molecules were not forming hydrogen bonds, they would all be pulled down against the surface by the force of gravity. A droplet of water would instead be a thin layer of water. A droplet of water on a vertical surface demonstrates **adhesion.** If the molecules of the droplet were not adhering to the surface, they would fall.

▼ Teach *continued*

History of Science

In 1686, the Italian anatomist and physiologist **Marcello Malpighi** conducted a classic experiment on the movement of fluids in plants. He removed a ring of bark from the trunk of a tree. Materials from the leaves accumulated in the area above the ring and caused the area to swell. The tree eventually died.

In 1928, **T. G. Mason** and **E. J. Maskell** studied this procedure, called girdling. They discovered that the leaves remain healthy for a period of time because the xylem is still transporting water and nutrients, but girdling damages the phloem, blocking the movement of sugars down to the roots. Mason and Maskell concluded that sugar is transported through the bark of a tree.

Integrating Entomology

Because of its high concentration of sugar, high osmotic pressure, and unbalanced composition of amino acids, very few animals use phloem sap as their main source of food. **Aphids** are an exception. These insects have symbiotic microorganisms in their bodies that provide them with the essential amino acids they need. Aphids have mouthparts called stylets that are inserted into a single phloem sieve element. The pressure forces the phloem sap into the aphid's body. Aphids use the sugar they need and convert the excess sugar into long-chain oligosaccharides that are excreted from the body as a substance called **honeydew.** Other animals then consume the honeydew. Scientists can study phloem sap by studying honeydew. To study phloem sap before it has been changed in any way, scientists can remove the aphid's body from its stylets and collect the phloem sap directly from the plant.

Answers

A Critical Viewing Transpiration; as water vapor evaporates from leaves, it acts as a vacuum on water farther down in the xylem, pulling it up through the plant.

FIGURE 21.4 Movement of Fluids Through Xylem

Forces responsible for the movement of fluids through xylem are transpiration, cohesion, adhesion, and absorption.

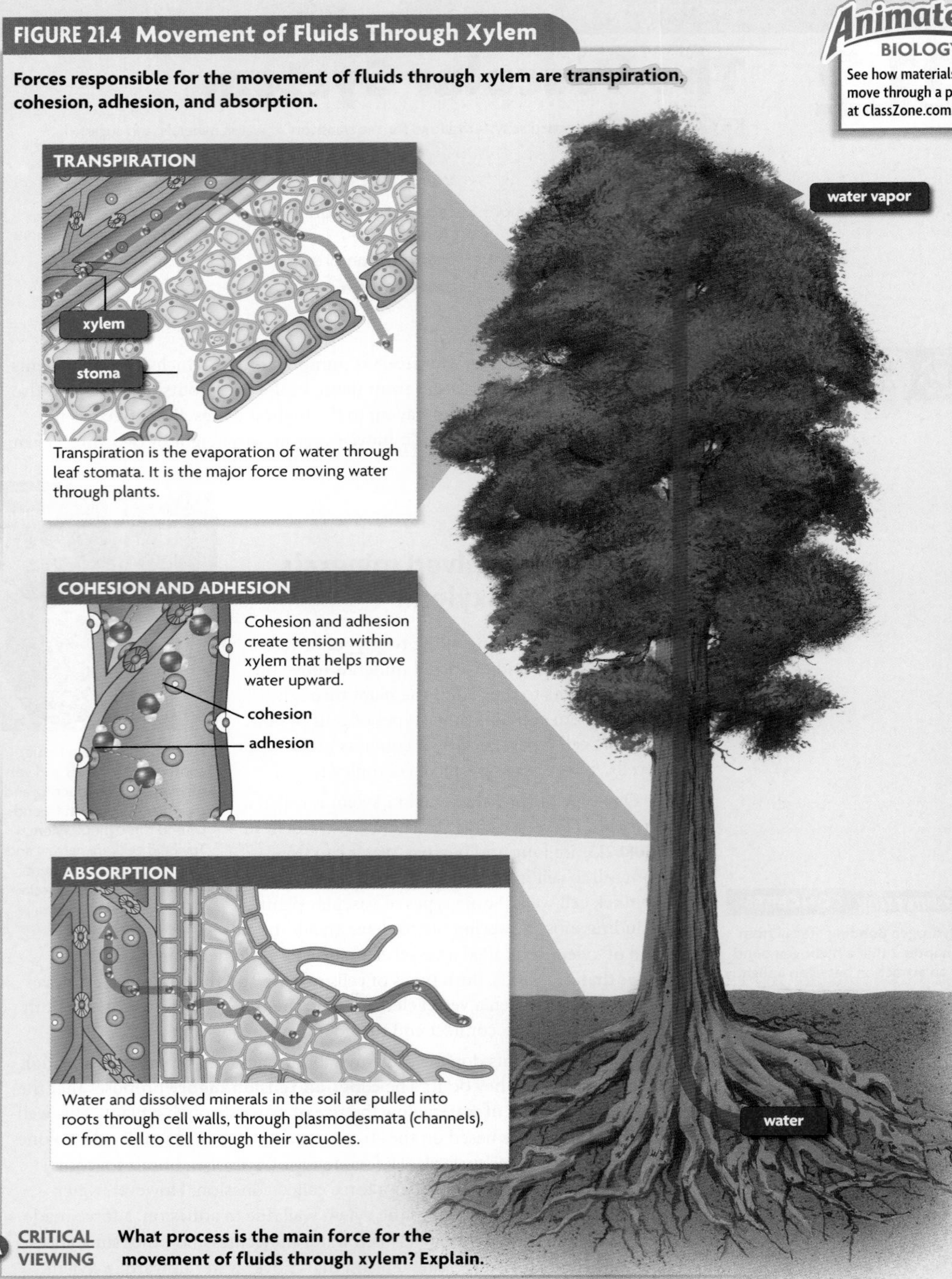
Animated BIOLOGY
See how materials move through a plant at ClassZone.com.
water vapor
TRANSPIRATION
xylem
stoma
Transpiration is the evaporation of water through leaf stomata. It is the major force moving water through plants.
COHESION AND ADHESION
Cohesion and adhesion create tension within xylem that helps move water upward.
cohesion
adhesion
ABSORPTION
Water and dissolved minerals in the soil are pulled into roots through cell walls, through plasmodesmata (channels), or from cell to cell through their vacuoles.
water

A CRITICAL VIEWING **What process is the main force for the movement of fluids through xylem? Explain.**

Differentiated Instruction

ENGLISH LEARNERS

Have students form pairs. Assign one student to create a sequence diagram for the movement of water and minerals through xylem, while the other student does the same for the movement of sugars through phloem. After students have drawn the full sequence, they should teach each other how their process works. Students can then copy each other's diagrams.

Biology Toolkit, Sequence Diagram, p. C38

To understand how cohesion and adhesion affect xylem flow, imagine you are inside the cylinder of a xylem vessel. In the middle, the water molecules float freely, attracted to each other. Toward the edges, though, the molecules are also drawn to the xylem wall. Where the water meets the wall, this attraction draws it upward a bit so that the actual shape of the water surface is slightly concave. You can see this shape if you fill a test tube with water. The tendency of water to rise in a hollow tube is known as capillary action. Capillary action causes water to rise above ground level in the xylem of plants.

For most plants, capillary action is not enough force to lift water to the top branches. Upward force is also provided by the evaporation of water from leaves. The loss of water vapor from plants is called **transpiration.** As leaves transpire, the outward flow of water lowers the pressure in the leaf xylem, creating a vacuum that pulls water upward. This force is responsible for most of the water flow in plants, including lifting water to the tops of trees. The movement of water through xylem is shown in **FIGURE 21.4.**

Apply **How does transpiration affect water movement through a plant?**

VOCABULARY

The term *cohesion* comes from the Latin prefix *co-*, which means "together," and the term *haerere*, which means "to cling."

MAIN IDEA

Phloem carries sugars from photosynthesis throughout the plant.

The second tissue in a plant's vascular system is phloem tissue, shown in **FIGURE 21.5.** Phloem carries plant nutrients, including minerals and sugars, throughout the plant. Phloem moves the products of photosynthesis out of the leaves to stems and roots. Minerals that travel up the xylem can also move into the phloem through specialized parenchyma transfer cells in the leaves.

Unlike xylem, phloem tissue is alive. Phloem is a complex tissue made mostly of cells called sieve tube elements. Their name comes from the small holes in the end walls of their cells. These holes let the phloem fluids, or sap, flow through the plant. As they form, sieve tube elements lose their nuclei and ribosomes. Nutrients can then move from cell to cell. Each sieve tube element is next to a companion cell, and the two cells are connected by many plasmodesmata, or small channels. Because the companion cells keep all their organelles, they perform some functions for the mature sieve tube cells. In some plants, the companion cells help load sugars into the sieve tube cells.

Recall that fluids in xylem always flow away from the roots toward the rest of the plant. In contrast, phloem sap can move in any direction, depending on the plant's need. The **pressure-flow model** is a well-supported theory that explains how food, or sap, moves through a plant. Phloem sap moves from a sugar source to a sugar sink. A source is any part of the plant that has a high concentration of sugars. Most commonly this source is the leaves, but it can also be a place where the sugars have been stored, such as the roots. A sink is a part of the plant using or storing the sugar, such as growing shoots and stems, a fruit, or even the storage roots that will be a sugar source later in the season. The locations of sugar sources and sinks in a plant can change as the plant grows and as the seasons change.

FIGURE 21.5 Fluids move from the roots to the rest of the tree through the xylem. Phloem carries the sugars produced by photosynthesis.

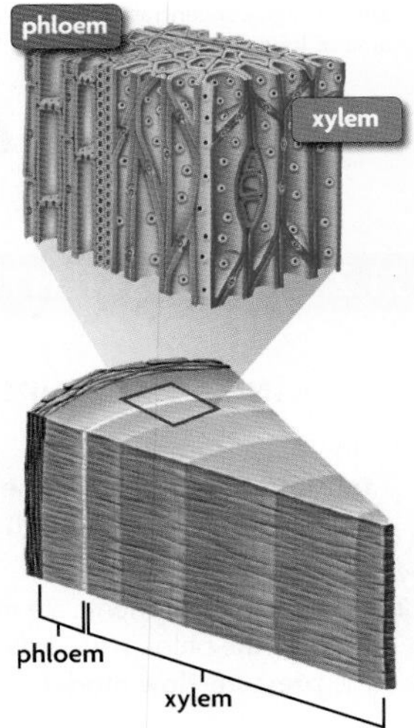

PRE-AP

Have students use a graphic organizer to compare the transport of water and sugars throughout a plant. To get students started, have them consider these questions:

- What structures transport the materials?
- What forces are involved?
- What energy is used, and what is its source?

Biology Toolkit, T-Chart, p. C20

ONLINE BIOLOGY Have students use the virtual lab on plant transpiration to determine how environmental conditions affect the rate of transpiration. See Options for Inquiry on page 657.

Integrating Earth Science

Transpiration is an important part of the **hydrologic cycle.** Water vapor that enters the atmosphere through plant transpiration and through evaporation from Earth's surface condenses and forms clouds. The water droplets in clouds become available to plants and animals when they fall to the ground as precipitation. The cycle continues as plants absorb water from the soil, xylem transports water through the plant, and water vapor enters the atmosphere through transpiration. Studies have shown that transpiration accounts for about 10 percent of the moisture in the atmosphere.

Take It Further

Numerous plant diseases affect the flow of materials through xylem or phloem. **Bacterial leaf scorch** affects a tree's xylem. Leaf beetles, or leafhoppers, transmit the bacteria to the plant when they feed from the xylem. After being introduced, the bacteria multiply and clog the xylem.

Vascular-tissue wilts also cause the xylem to become plugged. Wilts are caused by fungus and are usually introduced to the tree by insects.

Other diseases affect a tree's phloem. **Elm phloem necrosis** is caused by specialized bacteria that multiply in the sieve tubes and interfere with the transport of sugars. Diseases of the phloem can affect growth of the plant because it is through phloem that growth hormones are transported.

Answers

A **Apply** The evaporation of water through leaf stomata creates a vacuum that draws water up through the xylem. A higher rate of transpiration means more movement of water throughout the plant.

▼ Teach *continued*

Addressing Misconceptions

Common Misconception Students may expect the movement of sugars from leaves to roots to be passive and aided by gravity, while the movement of water up a plant's xylem must require energy because it is working against gravity.

Correcting the Misconception In fact, the movement within xylem requires no energy, whereas movement through phloem does. A tree can send water up to a height equal to several stories against the pull of gravity without expending any energy. However, loading and unloading sugars requires ATP.

Integrating Biotechnology

Various plants are harvested for the sugar they produce. Sugar cane and sugar beets account for the vast majority of sugar that is refined and consumed by humans. Today, some countries are responding to the growing fossil-fuel shortage by producing **biofuels** from sugar cane.

When sugars ferment, they produce an alcohol called ethanol. This can then be burned, like gasoline, in an automobile engine. Brazil is leading the way in ethanol production, taking advantage of its sugar cane industry. The United States would like to do the same with corn, but thus far, the potential energy yield from corn ethanol does not outweigh the energy needed for its production. As petroleum and other fossil fuels become more expensive, many countries are investing in technologies to make ethanol production more efficient.

Answers

Ⓐ **Apply** leaves and roots

▼ Assess and Reteach

Assess Use the Online Quiz or Section Quiz (*Assessment Book,* p. 414).

Reteach Draw a tree and its root system on the board. Have students describe how a plant transports materials, using the vocabulary on page 643.

FIGURE 21.6 Pressure-Flow Model

The pressure-flow model explains the movement of sugars through the phloem.

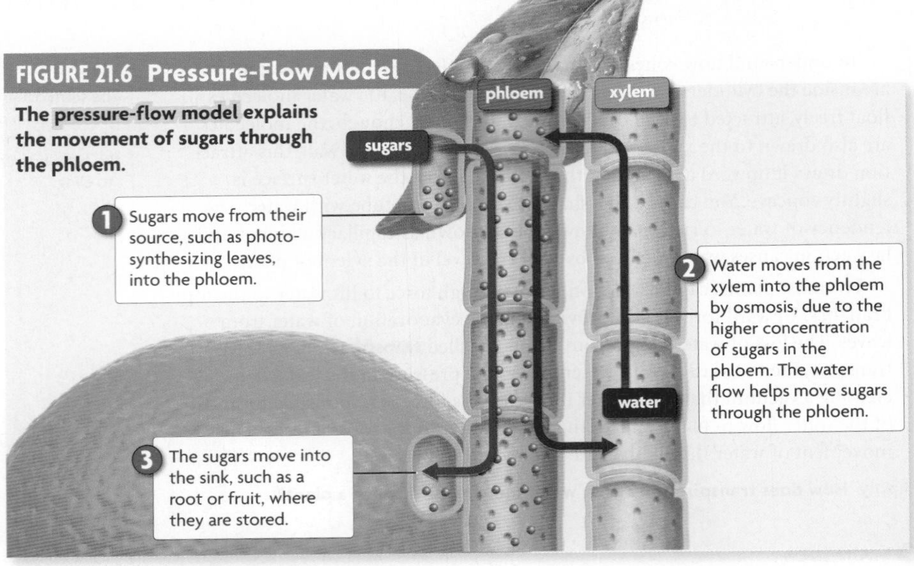

phloem
xylem
sugars
1 Sugars move from their source, such as photo-synthesizing leaves, into the phloem.
2 Water moves from the xylem into the phloem by osmosis, due to the higher concentration of sugars in the phloem. The water flow helps move sugars through the phloem.
water
3 The sugars move into the sink, such as a root or fruit, where they are stored.

The pressure changes between sugar sources and sinks, shown in **FIGURE 21.6**, keep nutrients moving through phloem. At a source, many plants use ATP to pump or load sugar into phloem at a high concentration. Therefore, at a source, there is a low concentration of water relative to sugars. Water then flows into the phloem through osmosis, due to the high concentration of sugars. Osmosis requires no energy on the part of the plant. This active loading of sugars and passive flow of water creates high pressure at the sugar source. At the same time, the sugar concentration of the sink end is lessened as sugar is unloaded into the sink. Unloading sugars also uses ATP from the plant. The overall result is higher pressure at the source end and lower pressure at the sink end. This difference in pressure keeps the sugary sap flowing in the direction of the sink.

***Connecting* CONCEPTS**

Osmosis Recall from **Chapter 3** that osmosis is the diffusion of water molecules across a semi-permeable membrane from an area of high concentration to an area of lower concentration.

Ⓐ **Apply What are two plant parts that can be sugar sources?**

21.2 ASSESSMENT

ONLINE QUIZ
ClassZone.com

REVIEWING ▶ MAIN IDEAS

1. How are absorption and **transpiration** involved in the movement of water through the xylem of a plant?
2. Describe how nutrients are moved through the phloem according to the **pressure-flow model.**

CRITICAL THINKING

3. **Infer** Suppose that xylem were located only in the roots and stems of a plant. Would fluids in the xylem still move? Why or why not?
4. **Analyze** How are the specialized cells of xylem and phloem suited for their functions?

***Connecting* CONCEPTS**

5. **Cell Function** Which process requires more energy from the plant, moving water up through the xylem or moving nutrients down through the phloem? Explain.

21.2 ASSESSMENT

1. Water and minerals in the soil are pulled into the roots by absorption. Water loss through transpiration creates a vacuum that pulls the water up through the xylem.
2. Plants pump sugar from a source into the phloem. The change in concentration causes water to follow sugars into the phloem, increasing the pressure. Meanwhile, the sugars are pushed though the phloem. Together, these phenomena result in the flow from the source to the sink.
3. No, if the leaves did not have xylem, transpiration would not take place and a vacuum that pulls water upward would not be created.
4. Cells within xylem are dead at maturity and become tubes that allow for the flow of fluids. Phloem cells are alive and use energy to load sugars into the phloem. Companion cells keep their organelles and help with the load; sieve tube elements lose many organelles and allow for the transport of the sugars.
5. Moving fluids through phloem relies on an initial pumping of sugars to a point of high concentration. Moving fluids through the xylem requires no energy.

MATERIALS

- tree leaf
- clear fingernail polish
- 5 cm clear tape
- microscope slide
- compound light microscope

PROCESS SKILLS

- **Observing**
- **Collecting Data**
- **Analyzing Data**

NOS.3 Clearly communicate their ideas and results of investigations verbally and in written form using tables, graphs, diagrams, and photographs.

Density of Stomata

In this lab, you will examine the upper and lower leaf surfaces from trees and determine the density of the stomata in the leaves.

PROBLEM How does the density of stomata vary among leaf surfaces?

PROCEDURE

1. Obtain a leaf of a known species.
2. Paint both the upper and lower surfaces of an area of leaf between two veins with clear fingernail polish. Allow the fingernail polish to dry completely.
3. Place a piece of clear tape over the dried nail polish on the lower surface of the leaf. Gently but firmly press the tape to the leaf.
4. Peel the tape from the leaf and place the tape onto the microscope slide. Examine the tape, which has an impression of the leaf cells, under low power and high power of the microscope.
5. Under high power, count the number of stomata in the field of view. Then count the number of epidermal cells in the same field of view. Record your data in a table like the one shown below.
6. Repeat steps 2–5 two more times, using a new leaf of the same species each time, and find the average number of stomata and the average number of cells of your three samples.
7. Repeat steps 3–6 using the upper surface of the leaf.

TABLE 1. STOMATA AND EPIDERMAL CELLS IN THE SURFACES OF A LEAF

	Lower Leaf Surface		Upper Leaf Surface	
Field of View	Number of Stomata (S)	Number of Epidermal Cells (E)	Number of Stomata (S)	Number of Epidermal Cells (E)
1				
2				
3				
TOTAL				

ANALYZE AND CONCLUDE

1. **Calculate** Find the density of stomata for the lower and upper leaf surfaces of each leaf using the following equation:

$$\textbf{Stomata Density} = \frac{S}{(S + E)} \times 100$$

where S = the average number of stomata and E = the average number of epidermal cells in one surface of the leaf.

2. **Analyze** What is the difference between the density of stomata on the lower surface of the leaf and on the upper surface of the leaf? Form a hypothesis that might explain this difference.
3. **Predict** How might the stomata density be different for a tree in the desert? in the rain forest?

Answers

Analyze and Conclude

1. Answers will vary.
2. Students should find that the density of stomata on the lower surface of the leaf is greater than that of the upper surface. Accept all reasonable hypotheses.
3. Desert plants often have a reduced number of stomata compared to temperate varieties, because they generally transpire less water. Rain-forest plants have greater access to water, so they may have a higher density of stomata.

Sample of Student Data

	Lower Leaf Surface		Upper Leaf Surface	
Field of View	# of Stomata	# of Epidermal Cells	# of Stomata	# of Epidermal Cells
1	6	160	3	110
2	6	150	4	120
3	5	120	3	100
Total	17	430	10	330
Density:	(17/447) × 100 = 3.8		(10/340) × 100 = 2.9	

INVESTIGATION

Time 45 minutes	TEACHER TESTED
Teacher Preparation	
Student Difficulty	
Lab Binder Plants, pp. 15–17	

Purpose Compare the density of stomata on upper and lower leaf surfaces.

Overview Students will prepare microscope slides with impressions of cells in upper and lower surfaces of three leaves. They will

- examine the cells under low and high power
- count the number of stomata and epidermal cells in the field of view for each impression
- calculate the density of stomata for the lower and upper leaf surfaces
- form a hypothesis that might explain different densities of stomata

LAB PREPARATION

- Be sure to use transparent tape.
- Provide good ventilation for preparing the leaves and slides.

LAB MANAGEMENT

- Tell students to randomly sample the leaf surfaces by moving the slides beneath the microscope lens and then looking through the eyepieces to be sure that the field is filled with the surface of the leaf.

Safety Caution students not to inhale any fumes and to wash their hands at the end of the lab. For students with allergies to leaves or the chemicals used to prepare the leaves, provide prepared slides.

POST-LAB DISCUSSION

Discuss results. **Ask,** How might the preparation of the leaves affect the results? Answers may include the idea that the tape must be pressed firmly enough to make an impression of all the cells and stomata, but not so hard that cells are damaged.

SECTION 21.3

▼ Plan and Prepare

Objectives

- Describe the forms and functions of plant roots and stems.

Section Resources

Unit Resource Book Study Guide pp. 35–36 Power Notes p. 37 Reinforcement p. 38 Pre-AP Activity pp. 45–46
Interactive Reader Chapter 21 **Spanish Study Guide** pp. 219–220
Biology Toolkit pp. C7, C34
Technology Power Presentation 21.3 Media Gallery DVD Online Quiz 21.3

Activate Prior Knowledge See if students have ever transplanted a plant, either from the ground or from a pot. **Ask**

- What is it like to uproot a well-established plant from the ground? Students will probably describe how the plant has to be torn from the ground because of the strength of its root system.
- What do you notice when you remove a houseplant from its pot? Students will probably describe mass of white hairlike roots that surround the base.

Discuss the root system in terms of its surface area.

▼ Teach

TEACH FROM VISUALS

FIGURE 21.7 Have students find the parts of the root in the root tip cross section. Point out that the root hairs shown in **FIGURE 21.8** are located just above the root tip. **Ask**

- What parts of a root absorb the most water? root hairs
- What part of a root transports water to the rest of the plant? vascular cylinder

21.3 Roots and Stems

KEY CONCEPT Roots and stems form the support system of vascular plants.

MAIN IDEAS

- Roots anchor plants and absorb mineral nutrients from soil.
- Stems support plants, transport materials, and provide storage.

VOCABULARY

vascular cylinder, p. 648
root hair, p. 648
root cap, p. 648
meristem, p. 648
fibrous root, p. 649
taproot, p. 649
primary growth, p. 651
secondary growth, p. 651

Connect Humans reach a certain height and stop growing. Plants, however, can continue growing their entire lives. Woody plants in particular can keep growing in both height and width. Each part of a plant grows in the direction that allows it to reach the resources the plant needs, and each part plays a role in the plant's survival.

MAIN IDEA

Roots anchor plants and absorb mineral nutrients from soil.

Why are roots important? Roots may make up over half of the body of a plant. They anchor the plant to the ground, and from the soil they absorb water and minerals the plant needs.

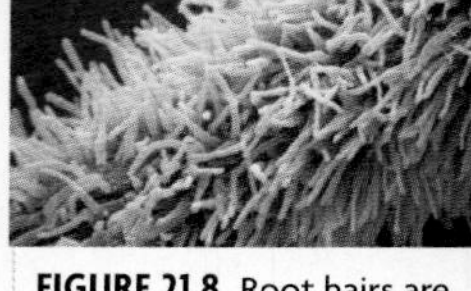

FIGURE 21.8 Root hairs are located above the root tip. (colored SEM; magnification 80×)

Parts of a Root

Roots support the plant and absorb, transport, and store nutrients. Like other plant parts, roots contain all three tissue systems—vascular, ground, and dermal. Parts of a root are shown in **FIGURE 21.7.**

FIGURE 21.7 This light micrograph of a root tip cross-section shows some of the parts of a root. (LM; magnification 35×)

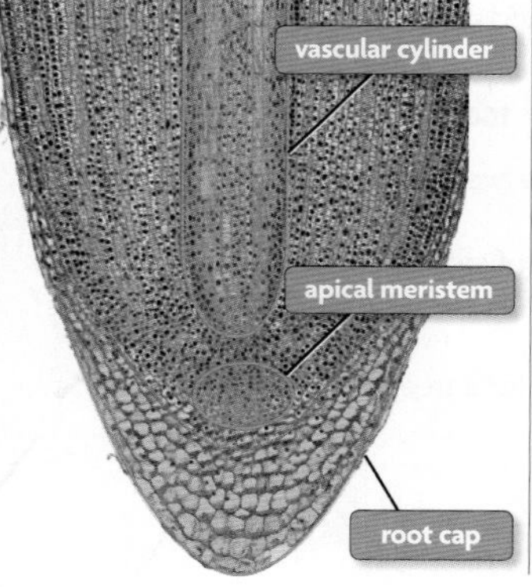

In the center of the root is the **vascular cylinder,** which is made of xylem and phloem tissues. The vascular cylinder is surrounded by ground tissue, covered by dermal tissue. A plant absorbs most of its water in the dermal tissue just above the root tips. These cells have tiny projections called **root hairs,** shown in **FIGURE 21.8.** Root hairs find their way through the spaces between soil particles, greatly adding to the surface area available to take up water. Covering the tip of the root is the **root cap,** a small cone of cells that protects the growing part of the root as it pushes through the soil.

Just behind the root cap is where most of the root's growth occurs. Groups of cells that are the source of new cells form tissue called **meristem.** Meristem cells aren't specialized, but when they divide, some of the new cells specialize into tissues. Areas of growth that lengthen the tips of roots and stems are called apical (AY-pik-kul) meristems. Lateral meristems, found all along woody roots and stems, increase the thickness of these plant parts.

Differentiated Instruction

BELOW LEVEL

Students can preview this section using this strategy:

- Predict what the section is about, using the headings.
- Locate key terms.
- Add details and definitions while reading.
- Note how the text supports the section's main ideas, writing a summary for each main idea.

Biology Toolkit, PLAN, p. C7

ENGLISH LEARNERS

Have students use a compare/contrast chart to visually reinforce the similarities and differences between stems and roots. In two boxes at the top of the chart, students should write the words *Roots* and *Stems.* Arrows from these boxes should point to a single box in which students write shared features. From this box, students should draw arrows leading right or left. These arrows lead to small boxes featuring differences between roots and stems.

Biology Toolkit, Compare/Contrast Chart, p. C34

Types of Roots

Roots take one of two basic forms, as shown in **FIGURE 21.9**. **Fibrous root** systems make fine branches in which most of the roots are the same size. These roots spread like a mat beneath the soil surface, and firmly anchor the plant to the ground. **Taproot** systems have a long, thick, vertical root with smaller branches. Long taproots allow plants to get water from deep in the ground. The thick taproot can also sometimes store food. Radishes, carrots, and beets are examples of taproots that we eat.

Water and Mineral Uptake

All plants require water and certain mineral nutrients for growth, development, and function. Their roots take up nutrients in a process that also results in water absorption. Mineral nutrients are usually dissolved in soil water as ions. For example, nitrogen is often taken up as NO_3^- ions, and iron can be taken up as Fe^{2+} ions. Plants use energy to transport nutrient ions into the roots through active transport. The increased concentration of ions within root cells also causes water to move into the root tip by osmosis.

Some minerals are needed in large amounts. Nitrogen, for example, is an essential mineral needed for nucleic acids, proteins, and chlorophyll. Other minerals serve mostly to catalyze reactions and are needed only in tiny amounts. Magnesium is a mineral involved in the production of chlorophyll. Even though only tiny amounts are needed, these minerals are also necessary for plant health.

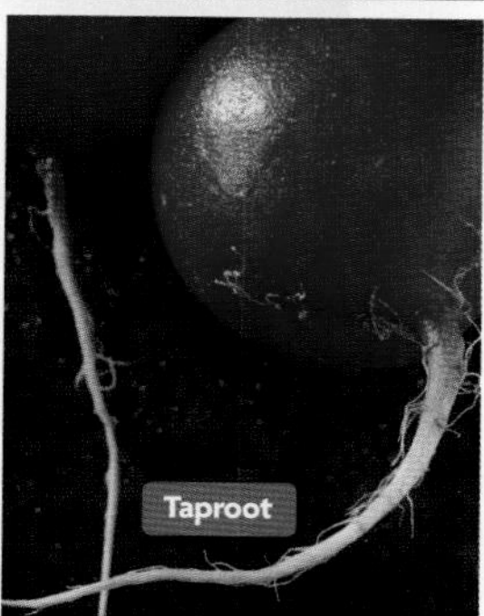

FIGURE 21.9 Corn plants have fibrous root systems. Radishes have one large taproot from which much smaller roots may branch.

(A) Explain **How do root hairs help roots absorb water?**

DATA ANALYSIS

IDENTIFYING THE IMPORTANCE OF REPEATED TRIALS

Scientists need to include repeated trials in experiments in order to draw reliable conclusions. One factor to consider when determining the number of trials in an experiment is how much variation there is among the organisms being tested.

A group of students collected data on the effect of water on the root densities of bean plants. They planted three bean seeds of the same species, each in the same size pot. They used the same type and amount of soil for each plant. Each plant received the same amount of sunlight.

- Plant A received 30 mL of water every day.
- Plant B received 30 mL of water every other day.
- Plant C received 30 mL of water once a week.

Root density, the number of roots per cm², was measured in all three plants after 30 days. The graph shows the results of the experiment. The students conclude that this species of bean plant should receive 30 mL of water every other day in order to produce the most roots.

1. **Analyze** Did the students reach a valid conclusion? Why or why not?
2. **Experimental Design** How would you change the experiment to improve the experimental design?

GRAPH 1. ROOT DENSITIES

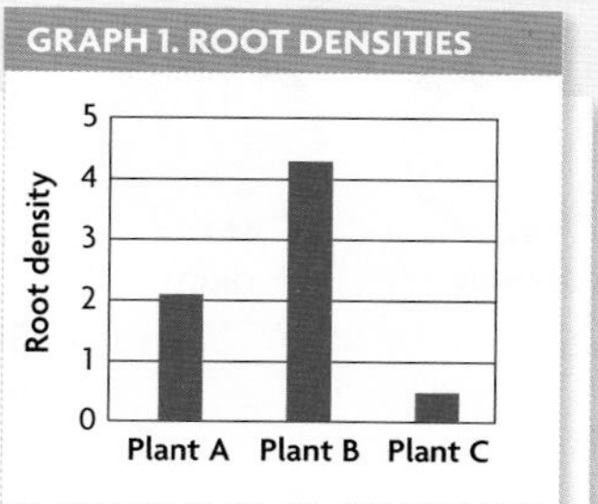

Take It Further

Of the 17 elements that a plant needs to survive, 9 are **macronutrients,** meaning plants need large amounts of them. Carbon, oxygen, hydrogen, nitrogen, phosphorus, sulfur, potassium, calcium, and magnesium are macronutrients. The other eight essential elements are known as **micronutrients,** because plants need only small amounts of them. Chlorine, iron, manganese, boron, zinc, copper, nickel, and molybdenum are micronutrients.

Answers

(A) Explain Root hairs greatly increase the surface area of the root, allowing for more absorption of water and dissolved minerals.

DATA ANALYSIS

Discuss

Have students read the data in the graph. **Ask**

- What is the root density of Plant A? about 2 roots per cm²
- What variable other than amount of water could have affected the results? health and genetics of the individual plants
- Do we have enough data to infer what the graph would look like if plant D had been given water every three days? No, it is possible that watering every three days would have yielded a higher, lower, or identical root density.

Answers

1. The conclusion is not valid because there was only one plant per treatment, and any variation in terms of growth could have been the result of that particular plant's genes or another factor.
2. Test many plants under each condition, and test more conditions. For example, water 50 plants every day, 50 others every other day, 50 others every 3 days, 50 others every 4 days, and so on.

Unit Resource Book, Data Analysis, p. 43

HANDS-ON ACTIVITY

Have students draw a root on a sheet of graph paper that is ten squares long by two squares wide. Have students calculate the surface area of this root, using a standard of 1 cm² per unit on the graph paper. The surface area is 22 cm² (10 + 2 + 10). Next, using a different colored pen or pencil, have them add ten root hairs to their roots, each one two squares long and one square wide. **Ask,** How do the root hairs change the surface area of the roots? up to 62 cm²

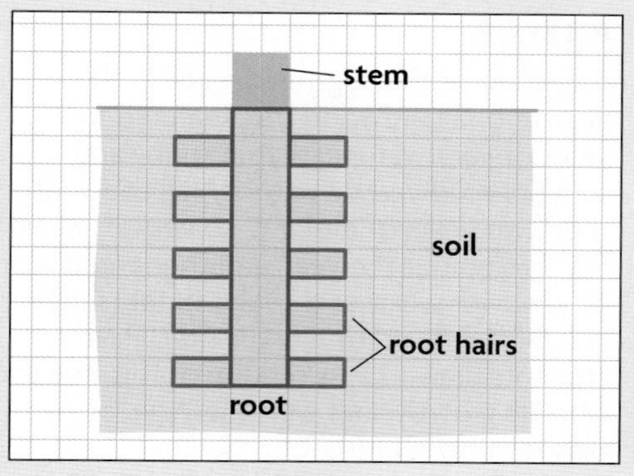

▼ Teach *continued*

Address Misconceptions

Common Misconception Students often think that as trees and other plants grow taller, this growth is occurring throughout their length, so that the lowermost branches of a tree will get higher off the ground over time.

Correcting the Misconception Growth in plant height is primary growth, which only takes place in apical meristems found at the ends of stems. Each stem or branch gets longer only at its tip. The lowermost branches of older trees often seem higher because they have already lost many branches. The knots that are visible in the bark or wood of trees indicate where a branch used to be.

Take It Further

In the angle between a leaf and a woody or herbaceous stem of a plant, you should see an **axillary bud.** Most axillary buds are dormant. At the tip of a stem is the **terminal bud,** which adds to the length of a stem. If a terminal bud is eaten by an animal, if the bud is pruned, or if leaves that are lower on the stem than the terminal bud get more sunlight, the once-dormant axillary buds start to grow and develop lateral branches, each one featuring a terminal bud, leaves, and more axillary buds. This is the reason gardeners prune the tips of their plants. Snipping off the terminal buds triggers the growth of the axillary buds, thereby creating a fuller, bushier plant that will yield more leaves and stems.

Vocabulary

Academic Vocabulary Tell students that an **herb** is any plant that does not have a woody stem and so generally dies back at the end of each growing season. This includes, but is not limited to, plants used for medicines and seasoning. **Ask,** What does this suggest about the consumers referred to as herbivores? They generally feed on the soft tissue of plants. Point out that the soft tissue may belong to a woody plant.

Strawberry stolons

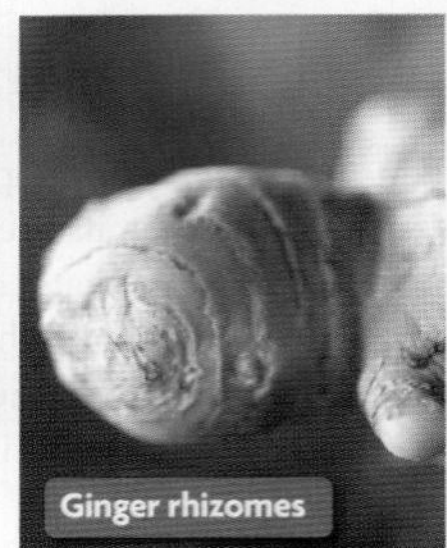

FIGURE 21.10 Stems take various forms. Baobab tree trunks store water, as do the fleshy stems of cacti; potato tubers store starch; ginger rhizomes are underground stems; and strawberry stolons, or runners, form new plants.

MAIN IDEA

Stems support plants, transport materials, and provide storage.

You may know that stems support flowers and leaves, giving them better access to pollinators and sunlight. But stems have other functions as well, as you can see in **FIGURE 21.10.** Stems often house a majority of the vascular system and can store food or water. The green stems of cacti, for example, can both photosynthesize and store water. Although most stems grow above ground, potatoes and ginger are examples of stems that can grow underground.

Some stems are herbaceous. Herbaceous plants produce little or no wood. They are usually soft because they do not have many rigid xylem cells. Herbaceous plants may be monocots, such as corn, or dicots, such as beans, and most do not grow taller than two meters. Herbaceous stems are often green and may conduct photosynthesis.

Stems can also be woody. Most plants with woody stems are dicots, such as many broadleaf trees or gymnosperms—pines or fir trees. Tree trunks are an example of woody stems. The oldest part of the xylem, the heartwood, is in the center of a tree trunk. Heartwood no longer conducts water but still provides structure. Sapwood, which is xylem and conducts water, surrounds the heartwood. Phloem produced near the outside of the trunk forms the inner layer of bark. An outer layer of bark provides a protective covering.

Connecting CONCEPTS

Monocots and Dicots Recall from **Chapter 20** that the pattern of vascular tissue in dicots differs from that in monocots. The cross-section of a monocot stem shows ground tissue with bundles of vascular tissue scattered through it. The cross-section of a herbaceous dicot shows vascular bundles forming a ring.

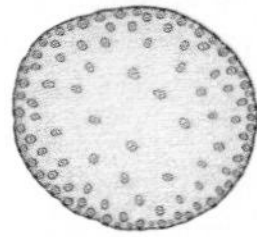
Monocot

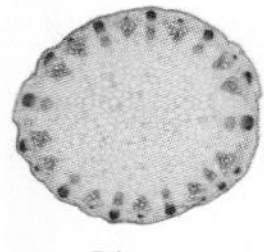
Dicot

Stem Growth

For as long as a plant survives, it is capable of growth. The continued growth of plants is possible because meristems are active throughout the life of the plant. Meristem cells divide to create more cells. Some of the divided cells remain meristem cells for future divisions, while the others become specialized and end up as part of the tissues and organs of a plant.

Differentiated Instruction

PRE-AP

Tell students that a given decade in the growth of a hardwood tree featured five years of very wet weather in spring and summer followed by very dry fall and winter; then two years of drought, so very little rain fell throughout the year; and then three years of very wet weather through spring, summer, and fall, followed by a dry winter. Have students draw a cross section of this tree and label its growth rings with the years or periods they represent.

The pattern of plant growth depends on the location of the meristems within the plant. Growth that increases a plant's length—makes stems grow taller or roots grow longer—is called **primary growth.** This type of growth takes place in apical meristems found at the ends of stems and roots. **Secondary growth** adds to the width in the stems and roots of woody plants. Dicot trees, such as oak and maple, produce a lot of secondary growth over their lifetimes. Secondary growth takes place in lateral meristems in the outer trunk layers.

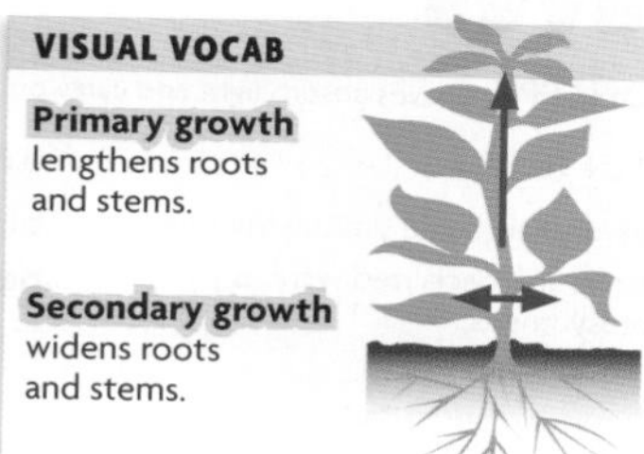

Tree Rings

Secondary growth is also responsible for the formation of tree rings, shown in **FIGURE 21.11.** Tree rings form due to uneven growth over the seasons. In spring, if water is plentiful, new xylem cells are wide and have thin walls. These cells appear light in color. When water becomes more limited in the following months, xylem cells are smaller and have thicker walls, so they appear darker in color.

The age of a tree can be determined by counting these annual rings. One ring represents one year of growth. Each ring includes both the larger, lighter cell bands of spring growth and the smaller, darker cell bands of later season growth. Climate, too, can be inferred from the rings since the rings will be thicker if there were good growing conditions. Some trees live thousands of years and can provide climate data that are not available from any other scientific records.

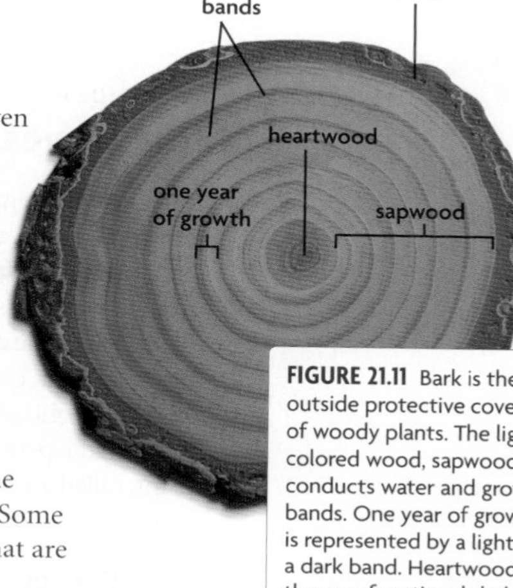

FIGURE 21.11 Bark is the outside protective covering of woody plants. The light-colored wood, sapwood, conducts water and grows in bands. One year of growth is represented by a light and a dark band. Heartwood is the non-functional dark-colored wood in the center.

A Summarize How are tree rings formed?

21.3 ASSESSMENT

ONLINE QUIZ ClassZone.com

REVIEWING MAIN IDEAS

1. Describe two major functions of roots. Explain why these functions are important to the plant.
2. How do the functions of stems differ from those of roots? How are they similar?

CRITICAL THINKING

3. **Analyze** Some stems, such as ginger rhizomes, grow underground. Why are they considered stems rather than roots?
4. **Apply** What effect could a cold winter with little precipitation have on the **primary growth** and **secondary growth** of a tree?

***Connecting* CONCEPTS**

5. **Earth's History** The principle of uniformitarianism states that processes that can be observed today can be used to explain events that occurred in the past, or "The present is the key to the past." How does this principle relate to tree ring dating?

21.3 ASSESSMENT

1. Answers should include two of the following functions of roots: anchoring plants, providing storage, and absorbing mineral nutrients and water from the soil. Anchoring a plant keeps it from being toppled by weather conditions or other forces. The ability to store food allows plants to endure periods of drought, poor sunlight, or other challenging conditions. Because plants typically do not change locations, it is important that they be able to extract water and nutrients from the ground.
2. Stems provide support for the plant's flowers and leaves, and roots anchor the plants in the soil. Both contain vascular tissues that transport water, minerals, and sugars. Both have a meristem, which allows for lateral and apical growth.
3. Roots and shoots will grow from rhizomes such as ginger.
4. Cold temperatures and low precipitation could slow or halt both primary and secondary growth.
5. Analysis of how climate and other conditions are correlated with growth rings in trees now can help scientists use older growth rings to infer climatic and other conditions in the past.

TEACH FROM VISUALS

FIGURE 21.11 Have students look at one year of growth. **Ask,** What causes new xylem cells to be lighter in the spring and darker in the fall? More water in spring means the xylem is wider and thin walled; less water in the fall means the xylem is narrowed and more tightly packed.

Integrating Climate Science

The science of analyzing tree-ring growth is known as **dendrochronology.** Dendrochronologists use a drill-like tool called an increment borer to remove a long, thin increment core from a tree trunk. This core is then used to determine what the climatic conditions were in any year of a tree's life. Dendrochronology can reveal how much rain fell, what temperatures were like, the quality of soil, and other aspects of life in and around a forest in ancient times.

Answers

A Summarize Tree rings form because of the secondary growth of plants, which increases the width of stems and roots of woody plants. Light bands form in the wet season when xylem cells are full of water and the cell walls are thin. In the dry or cold season, water is less plentiful and xylem cell walls need to be thicker, so the band marking this growth appears darker and more compacted.

Assess and Reteach ▼

Assess Use the Online Quiz or Section Quiz (*Assessment Book,* p. 415).

Reteach Using real examples or digital images of herbaceous plants and cross sections of hardwood trees, review primary and secondary growth and how plant structures are related to them.

SECTION 21.4

▼ Plan and Prepare

Objectives

- Describe the structures that are common to most leaves.
- Identify the adaptations that allow plants to photosynthesize and survive in various climates and regions.

Section Resources

Unit Resource Book
Study Guide pp. 39–40
Power Notes p. 41
Reinforcement p. 42
Pre-AP Activity pp. 47–48

Interactive Reader Chapter 21
Spanish Study Guide pp. 221–222

Biology Toolkit p. C3

Technology
Power Presentation 21.4
Media Gallery DVD
Online Quiz 21.4

Activate Prior Knowledge Remind students that deciduous trees typically lose their leaves with the onset of winter. **Ask,** How does a tree survive if the leaves it needs to produce sugars are gone? Students may compare this to a form of hibernation. Tell students that not only does losing leaves prepare a tree for winter, it also enables the tree to rid itself of older leaves, which are photosynthetically less efficient, and recycle mineral nutrients, such as nitrogen and phosphorous.

21.4 Leaves

KEY CONCEPT Leaves absorb light and carry out photosynthesis.

MAIN IDEAS
- Most leaves share some similar structures.
- Most leaves are specialized systems for photosynthesis.

VOCABULARY
blade, p. 652
petiole, p. 652
mesophyll, p. 652
guard cell, p. 653

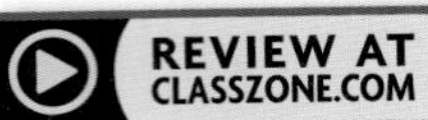

Connect "Leaves of three, let it be." This is a saying of many experienced hikers who know how to avoid poison ivy. Hikers can identify poisonous plants in the same way that people can identify many plants that are safe to eat—by the shapes of their leaves. Plant species have their own unique leaf shapes, specially adapted for light gathering and retaining water in their particular environment.

MAIN IDEA

Most leaves share some similar structures.

Leaves of different species don't all look the same, but most leaves do share some common parts. Leaves grow out from a plant's stem, and they are made up of a few basic parts. The **blade** is usually broad and flat, and it collects the sunlight for the plant. The blade connects to the stem by a thin stalk called the **petiole** (PEHT-ee-ohl). A bud that grows between the petiole and the stem of a plant, called an axillary bud, marks where a leaf ends.

VISUAL VOCAB

The **blade** of a leaf collects sunlight for photosynthesis. It connects to the plant's stem by a **petiole.**

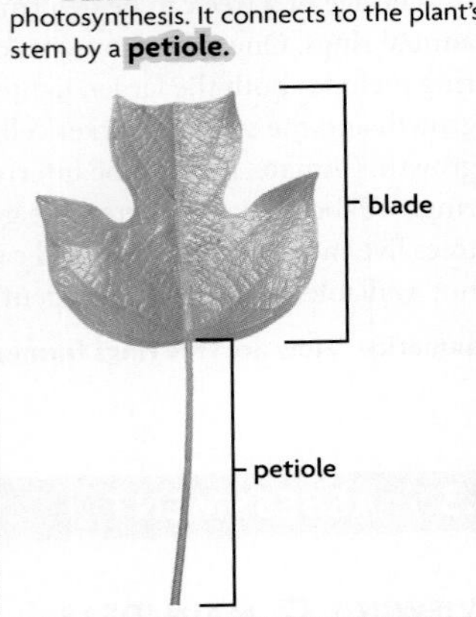

Leaf Tissues

Like roots and stems, leaves have an outer covering of dermal tissue and an internal system of vascular tissue surrounded by ground tissue. The dermal tissue of many leaves is covered by a waxy cuticle that forms a water resistant covering. The cuticle protects the inner tissues and limits evaporation from the plant. Between the two dermal layers of a leaf is parenchyma tissue called **mesophyll** (MEHZ-uh-FIHL). The vascular tissues of xylem and phloem make up the veins that run throughout the mesophyll.

Stomata and Guard Cells

In most plants, the top and undersides of leaves have different functions. The upper portion of the mesophyll has most of the chloroplasts and is where most photosynthesis takes place. The underside portion of a leaf has stomata and is the site of transpiration and gas exchange.

▼ Teach

Vocabulary

Greek and Latin Word Origins The Greek roots of **mesophyll** reveal where in the leaf this tissue is located:

mesos = middle
phullon = leaf

Differentiated Instruction

BELOW LEVEL

To test students' understanding, write five to ten statements about the main points of leaves. Focus on the shared structures of most leaves, the leaf characteristics used to identify plants, the cells and tissues in leaves, and leaf adaptations. Have students react to the statements as being true or false both before and after reading the section.

Biology Toolkit, Anticipation Guide, p. C3

TEACH WITH TECHNOLOGY

Assemble a digital slide show of leaf images. For each leaf shown, have students identify the type of margin, vein, and leaf type. Use a pointer to show specific parts of the leaves, such as the petioles and veins, when asking questions. As an alternative, you can gather leaves from local plants, attach them to index cards labeled numerically, and have students write down the leaf type, margin type, and vein type for each.

A pair of **guard cells,** shown in **FIGURE 21.12**, surround each stoma, and can open and close by changing shape. During the day, the stomata of most plants are open, allowing the carbon dioxide (CO_2) necessary for photosynthesis to enter. Potassium ions (K^+) from neighboring cells accumulate in the guard cells. A high concentration of K^+ causes water to flow into the guard cells as well. When the plant is full of water, the two guard cells plump up into a semicircle shape, opening the stoma.

When the stomata are open, water evaporates from the leaves. When the plant is losing water from transpiration faster than it is gaining water at its roots, the guard cells deflate and close the stomata. With the stomata closed, the plant may run low on CO_2 for photosynthesis. The stomata also close at night. Factors such as temperature, humidity, hormonal response, and the amount of CO_2 in the leaves signal the guard cells to open or close.

FIGURE 21.12 GUARD CELLS

Two guard cells help regulate water loss and photosynthesis by opening and closing the stoma. (colored SEMs; magnification 450×)

Open stoma | Closed stoma

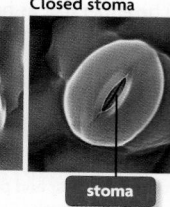

guard cells | stoma

Leaf Characteristics

It is not always obvious what part of a plant is actually a leaf. As shown in **FIGURE 21.13**, leaves may be simple, with just one blade connected to the petiole, or they may be compound, with many blades on one petiole. The multiple blades are called leaflets. All of the leaflets and their petiole together are actually a single leaf because the axillary bud is at the base of the petiole. There are no buds at the bases of the leaflets. Besides leaf shape, other traits of leaves used to identify plants include the pattern of veins and the leaf edge, or margin.

A Summarize **What is the function of the guard cells of a plant?**

FIGURE 21.13 Leaf Characteristics

Certain leaf characteristics—such as the leaf type, the vein pattern, and the shape of the leaf margin—can be used to identify plants.

LEAF TYPE

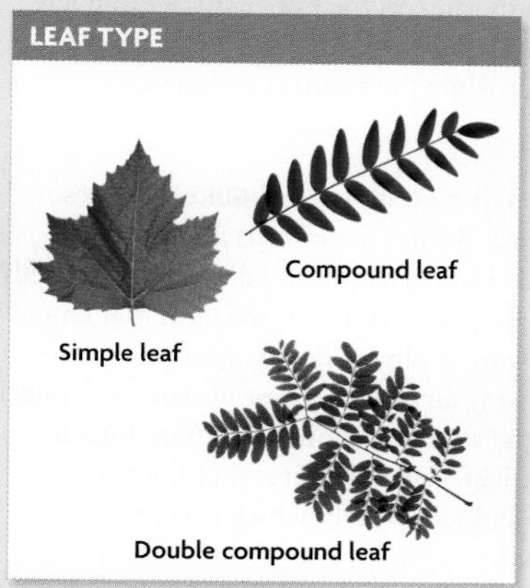

LEAF VEINS

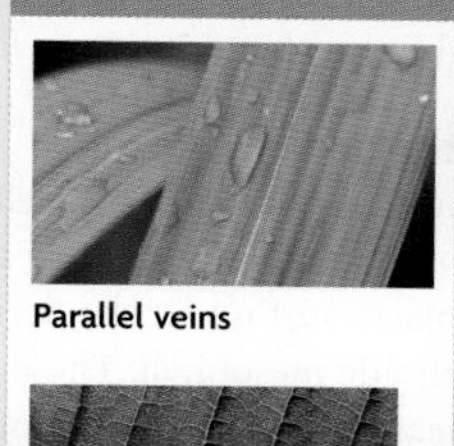

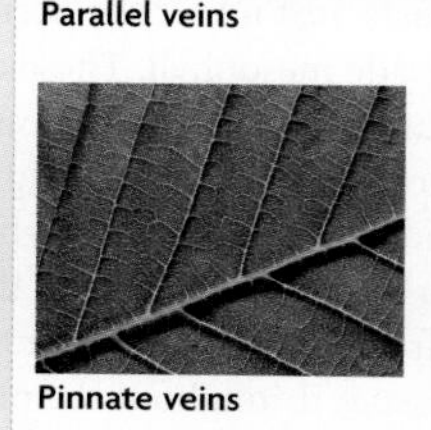

LEAF MARGIN

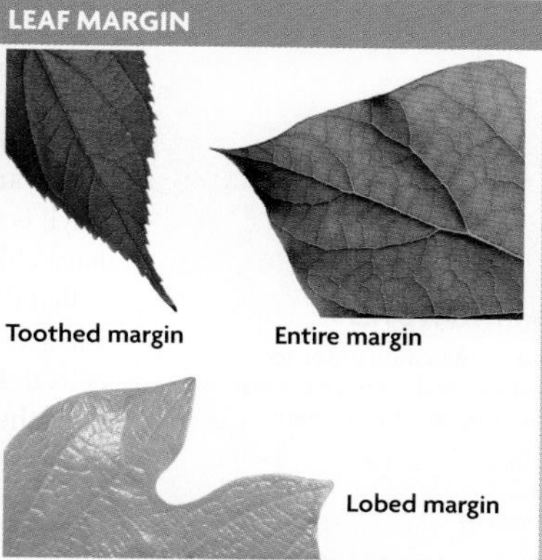

B Infer **How might compound leaves and leaves with lobed margins be well-suited to windy environments?**

INCLUSION

Provide a variety of tree leaves so that students who are visually impaired can feel the similarities and differences of margin, shape, and leaf pattern. Be sure to ask about plant allergies before allowing the leaves to be handled. Pair these students with partners who can review leaf features by telling what parts of a leaf or what characteristics are being touched.

ONLINE BIOLOGY Have students use an interactive dichotomous key to identify trees by their leaves. See Options for Inquiry on page 657.

Take It Further

Deciduous trees lose their leaves in the fall through a process of **abscission.** Changes in hormones cause a separation layer to develop between the petiole and the stem. A protective layer develops on the stem side of the separation layer. Leaves change color during this time because green chlorophyll breaks down, and pigments that were hidden by the green pigments become visible. Rain and wind provide enough force to make the leaves fall. Other plants, including evergreens, also lose leaves by abscission. Evergreen trees lose their leaves (needles) over a period of time, instead of all at one time.

Vocabulary

Academic Vocabulary Tell students that the process of trees losing their leaves is often referred to as **senescence,** which is quite simply the process of growing old, or *senescent*. The words share the same root as **senile,** which in a general sense means "having the characteristics of old age." Compare this to **obsolescence,** which is the process of passing out of usefulness, or becoming *obsolete*.

Answers

A Summarize The guard cells open and close the stomata, regulating gas exchange and water loss from the plant.

B Infer The lobed margins or compound form of some leaves allows wind to pass through or around them, so they are not torn from the tree during high winds.

▼ Teach *continued*

ONLINE BIOLOGY See the chapter Resource Center at **ClassZone.com** for additional information and resources on leaves.

QUICK LAB

Time 30 minutes	TEACHER TESTED
Lab Binder Plants, p. 22	

Purpose Observe fluorescence given off by chlorophyll that has been extracted from leaves and exposed to light.

LAB PREPARATION

- Review the concepts of light wavelengths, absorption of light, and excited electrons.
- The lab works even more effectively with an ultraviolet light source.

Teacher Note "I have the students use different leaves and a spectrophotometer to measure absorbance of different wavelengths."

LAB MANAGEMENT

A blender can be used in place of a mortar and pestle.

Safety Make sure students wear gloves and safety goggles, work in a well-ventilated area, avoid inhaling fumes, and avoid splashes and spills. Remind students to wash their hands after the lab.

Teacher Note "The students will see the significance of chlorophyll and its relation to light energy."

Answers

Analyze and Conclude

1. a dull red color
2. If the chlorophyll was not extracted, the light energy would be used for photosynthesis instead of being released.

QUICK LAB ANALYZING

Chlorophyll Fluorescence

If you remove chlorophyll molecules from their cells and then expose them to bright light, the energy absorbed from the excited electrons in the chlorophyll will be either lost as heat or released as a dull-colored light as the electrons return to their normal state. This is an example of fluorescence: the absorption of light at one wavelength, and its release at a longer—and lower-energy—wavelength.

PROBLEM How can fluorescence be used to study photosynthesis?

PROCEDURE

1. Use the mortar and pestle to crush a handful of spinach leaves, adding enough methanol to make 10 mL of extract. Use a graduated cylinder to collect and measure the extract.
2. Place the filter paper in the funnel, and hold the funnel over a beaker. A second person should pour the extract through the funnel to filter the extract.
3. Carefully transfer the extract to a test tube, and hold it in front of a lit flashlight. Observe the fluorescence that occurs at a 90-degree angle from the beam of light.

ANALYZE AND CONCLUDE

1. **Identify** What color does the fluorescence appear?
2. **Analyze** Why did the chlorophyll have to be extracted before the fluorescence could be observed?

MATERIALS

- mortar
- pestle
- handful spinach leaves
- 10 mL methanol
- graduated cylinder
- filter paper
- funnel
- beaker
- eyedropper or pipette
- test tube
- test tube rack
- flashlight

MAIN IDEA

Most leaves are specialized systems for photosynthesis.

The leaves of a plant are the main sites for photosynthesis. The broad, flat shape of many leaves allows for light gathering on the upper surface and gas exchange on the underside. Since the undersides of leaves are not exposed to direct sunlight, the plant loses less water while the stomata are open.

Photosynthetic Structures

There are two types of mesophyll cells in leaves, shown in **FIGURE 21.14.** Mesophyll is the photosynthetic tissue of a leaf. Both types of cells in mesophyll have chloroplasts. Just under the dermal layer is a layer of tall, rectangular cells called the palisade mesophyll. These cells absorb much of the light that enters the leaf. Beneath this layer is the spongy mesophyll. Spongy mesophyll has cells that are loosely packed, creating many air spaces. These air spaces connect with the outside of the plant through the stomata, allowing carbon dioxide and oxygen to diffuse in and out of the leaf. Carbohydrates that the plant makes move from mesophyll cells into phloem vessels, which carry the products to tissues throughout the plant.

TAKING NOTES

Use combination notes to describe and sketch each leaf structure mentioned here.

Notes	Sketch
stomata mesophyll	

Differentiated Instruction

TEACH WITH TECHNOLOGY

If you have a spectrophotometer available to you, you can have students use it to determine the absorption spectra of different plant pigments.

Leaf Adaptations

Not all leaves are "leafy." Leaves are adapted for photosynthesis in the plant's particular environment. For example, cacti leaves are actually the sharp spines that protect them from predators and help minimize water loss due to transpiration. Other desert plants, such as agave, store water in their leaves. The leaves and stems of many desert plants are protected by very thick cuticles, which minimize the loss of water from the plant.

Similar adaptations are common in coniferous trees in cold, dry climates. Pine needles, for example, are leaves with a small surface area and a thick, waxy epidermis that protects them from cold damage. Tiny sunken areas for the stomata help reduce water loss.

FIGURE 21.14 LEAF CROSS-SECTION

This cross-section of a leaf shows the cuticle, dermal tissue, leaf veins made up of xylem and phloem, and palisade and spongy mesophyll.

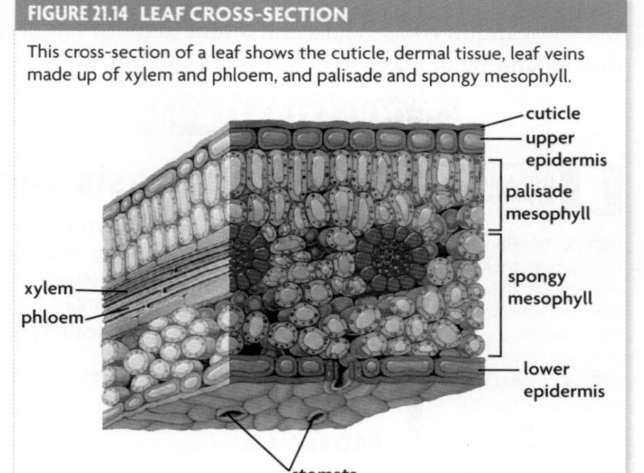

Water loss is not a problem for aquatic plants, however. The undersides of a water lily's leaves are below the water surface. To accommodate gas exchange in an aquatic environment, the water lily has stomata on the upper surface of its leaves. Many aquatic plants also have flexible petioles adapted to wave action.

Many tropical plants have very large, broad leaves. In the crowded rain forest, the challenge is to get enough light and space among all the other plants. Larger leaves mean more light-gathering surface.

A few plants are actually predators. The pitcher plant, for example, has tall, tubular leaves that help lure, trap, and digest insects. These insects provide extra nitrogen for the plant, which is needed because there is little of it in the soil where the plant grows.

For more information on plant adaptations, go to scilinks.org. Keycode: MLB021

A Infer Flower petals are also an adaptation of leaves. Their bright colors and fragrance attract animals and insects. Why is attracting other organisms important for some plants?

21.4 ASSESSMENT

ONLINE QUIZ ClassZone.com

REVIEWING MAIN IDEAS

1. Describe the functions of the **blade** and **petiole** in a leaf.
2. How do the palisade and spongy **mesophyll** layers help a leaf perform photosynthesis?

CRITICAL THINKING

3. **Infer** The leaves of aquatic plants that are completely underwater have few stomata. Why might this be so?
4. **Apply** Grass blades are leaves that are joined directly to the stem. What structure that is typical of many leaves is missing in grass?

***Connecting* CONCEPTS**

5. **Analogous Structures** The tendrils that allow pea plants to climb up an object are modified leaves, whereas the tendrils of grape vines are modified stems. Explain.

21.4 ASSESSMENT

1. The blade collects sunlight for the plant. The petiole connects the blade to the stem.
2. Palisade cells absorb light, and spongy mesophyll cells aid in gas diffusion. The air spaces between these cells connect to the outside of the plant through the stomata.
3. Totally submerged aquatic plants exchange dissolved gases with the water directly through their dermal tissues.
4. the petiole
5. Natural selection could have selected for pea plants and grape vines that are able to reach greater heights in order to maximize exposure to sunlight. Because both longer stems and longer leaves would achieve this, it makes sense that both could have evolved to climb in this way.

ONLINE BIOLOGY To describe the adaptations that a fictitious new plant has developed for its environment, use the WebQuest in Options for Inquiry on page 657.

TEACH FROM VISUALS

FIGURE 21.14 Have students find the two kinds of mesophyll in the cross section of the leaf. **Ask**

- Where does the most photosynthesis take place? in the palisade layer
- What is the importance of the spongy layer? creates air spaces and connects to outside

Take It Further

Insects can easily slide down the smooth, modified leaves of a **pitcher plant.** However, stiff "hairs" make it difficult for them to get out. The insects then drown in water that collects in the pitcher plant's tubular leaves. Bacteria and digestive enzymes from the plant break down the insects' bodies, and the leaves absorb needed nutrients. Other plants, such as the **sundew,** have modified leaves that produce a sticky substance that traps insects. Some plants, such as the **Venus flytrap,** have modified leaves that are hinged and fringed with toothlike hairs. When insects land within the "mouth" and brush against the hairs, the leaf snaps shut, trapping the insect inside.

Answers

A Infer Some plants need animals to act as pollinators, carrying sperm to the ovaries so fertilization can occur.

Assess and Reteach ▼

Assess Use the Online Quiz or Section Quiz (*Assessment Book,* p. 416).

Reteach Collect leaves to use in class to go over the basic structure of a leaf. Use **FIGURE 21.14** from the Media Gallery to relate cellular-level detail to one of the leaves.

OPTIONS FOR INQUIRY

INVESTIGATION

Time 45 minutes	TEACHER TESTED
Teacher Preparation	
Student Difficulty	
Lab Binder Plants, pp. 18–20	

Purpose Use chromatograms to compare the pigments of red leaves and green leaves.

Overview Students will rub lines of pigment from red leaves and green leaves on two separate strips of chromatography paper. They will

- hang the strips in test tubes with the bottom of the strips in alcohol
- remove the papers after the alcohol has traveled to the top of the papers
- dry the papers and compare the records of pigment patterns to a table of pigments
- identify and compare the separated pigments from the red leaves and green leaves

LAB MANAGEMENT

Tell students to make sure that the strips of paper do not touch the sides or bottoms of the test tubes.

Safety Caution students about not inhaling fumes, and remind them to wash their hands after the lab.

Teacher Note "The students all got good results with 2 to 4 different pigment separations."

POST-LAB DISCUSSION

Discuss the leaf pigments. **Ask,** What was the purpose of creating a chromatogram of the pigments of the green leaf? It was a control or normal leaf to compare the red leaf to.

Use these inquiry-based labs and online activities to deepen your understanding of plant structure and function.

NOS.1 Develop explanations based on reproducible data and observations gathered during laboratory investigations.
NOS.3 Clearly communicate their ideas and results of investigations verbally and in written form using tables, graphs, diagrams, and photographs.

INVESTIGATION

Photosynthesis and Red Leaves

How do plants with yellow, purple, or red leaves year-round carry out photosynthesis to produce the food they need to live? In this lab, you will investigate whether a red-leafed plant contains the same pigments for photosynthesis as a green-leafed plant.

SKILLS Observing, Interpreting Data, Drawing Conclusions

PROBLEM What pigments are found in plants that appear red?

MATERIALS

- 2 paper clips stretched into a wire
- 2 rubber stoppers
- 2 strips of chromatography paper
- 2 large test tubes
- test tube rack
- green leaf
- red leaf
- coin
- 10-mL graduated cylinder
- 5 mL isopropyl alcohol

PROCEDURE

1. Make a J-shaped hook out of each paper clip. Carefully push the straight end into the bottom of the rubber stoppers. Attach the strip of chromatography paper to the other end of each wire. **Caution:** Do not force the stopper.
2. Place the green leaf on one paper strip, about 2 cm from the bottom. Roll the coin over the leaf until you see a horizontal green line across the strip. Repeat with the red leaf on the other strip of paper.
3. Add alcohol to the test tubes so that the bottom edge of the chromatography paper will be submerged. Lower the papers into the test tubes, making sure that each horizontal line of pigments is NOT submerged in the alcohol.
4. Place the tests tubes in a holder and leave them undisturbed for 15–30 minutes. Record your observations.
5. After the alcohol has traveled to the top of the paper strips, remove the papers from the test tubes. Allow the papers to dry and compare the chromatograms, or records of pigment patterns, for the two leaves. Use the table provided by your teacher to identify the separated pigments.

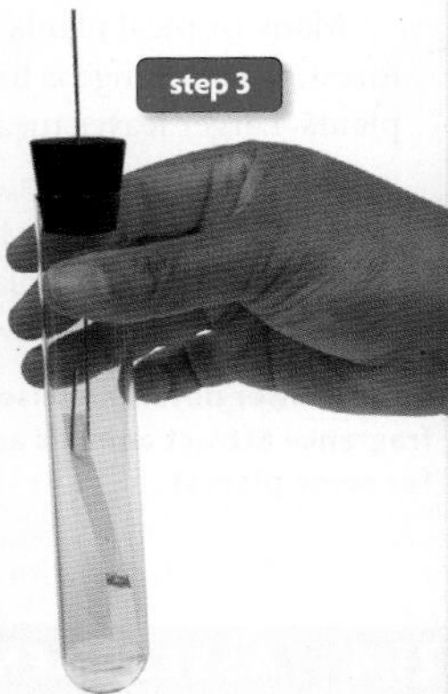

ANALYZE AND CONCLUDE

1. **Compare and Contrast** Describe the similarities and the differences between the two chromatograms.
2. **Apply** Based on your results, explain how a red-leafed plant photosynthesizes.
3. **Analyze** During the fall, some trees form a plug at the base of their leaf petioles, cutting off water to the leaf. This causes the leaf to stop photosynthesizing. Chlorophyll begins to break down, and the colors of the other pigments present in the leaf begin to show. How do you think a chromatogram of a healthy red leaf would compare with a chromatogram of a tree leaf that just turned red in autumn?

Answers

Analyze and Conclude

1. Both chromatograms should reveal green, yellow, and red pigments. The red leaf will also have brown (xanthophyll) pigments.
2. A red leaf photosynthesizes using chlorophyll in the same way that a green leaf does.
3. There will be less pigment overall in the leaf that changed colors for fall. In particular, there will be less green pigments.

656 Unit 7: Plants

INVESTIGATION

Connecting Form to Function

In this lab, you will examine a slice of the roots, stems, and leaves of a plant and describe how their structures relate to their functions.

SKILL Observing

PROBLEM How are plant structures related to their functions?

MATERIALS
- plant root, stem, and leaf
- razor tool
- 3 slides
- 3 cover slips
- eyedropper
- water
- compound microscope

PROCEDURE
1. Draw a table with three labeled columns: name of plant part, sketch, and function. Label three rows: root, stem, and leaf.
2. Carefully use the razor tool to cut a very thin slice from the root, stem, and leaf of the plant. You must be able to see light through the sliced sections.
3. Prepare a wet mount slide of a slice of each plant organ. Examine each slide under the microscope and sketch the structures that you see. Describe the function of each structure under the third column.

ANALYZE AND CONCLUDE
1. **Compare** What similarities did you observe among the slides of the three plant organs? Explain why these similarities may exist.
2. **Analyze** Which organ had the most vessels? Which organ had the most chloroplasts? Which organ had the most hairs? Is this what you would predict based on the function of these organs? Explain your answer.

Online BIOLOGY
CLASSZONE.COM

VIRTUAL LAB
Plant Transpiration
Is the rate of transpiration always the same? In this interactive lab, you will determine how different environmental conditions affect the rate of transpiration.

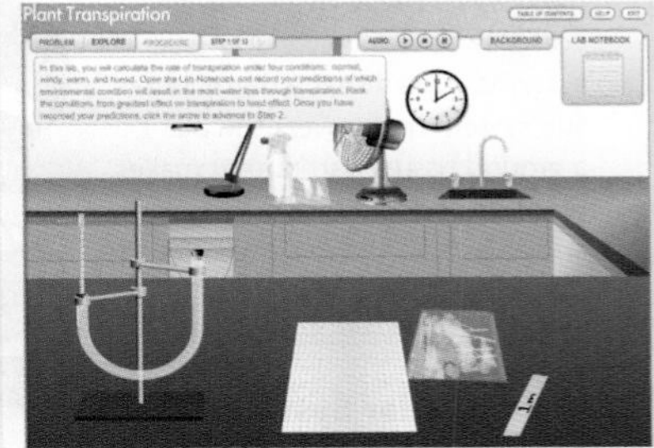

ANIMATED BIOLOGY
Name That Tree
Is that leaf from an oak or a hickory tree? Are those needles from a pine tree or spruce? Choose a mystery leaf, then identify the tree it came from with an interactive dichotomous key.

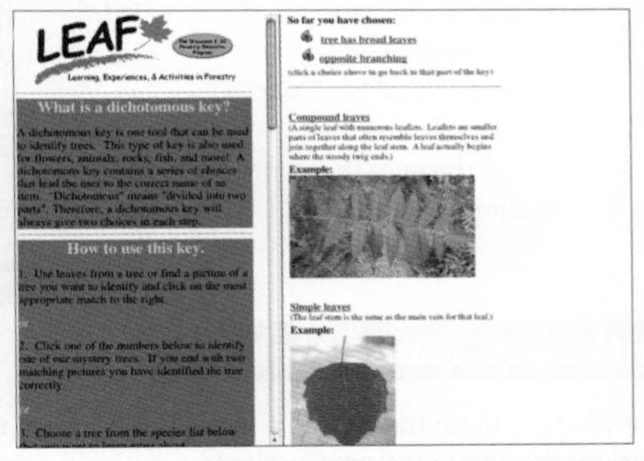

WEBQUEST
How have plants adapted to their surroundings? In this WebQuest, you will learn about various adaptations that plants have developed for specific environments. Then write a description of the adaptations found on a fictitious new plant.

Answers

Analyze and Conclude
1. Roots, stems, and leaves all have vessels for moving water and nutrients.
2. Roots had the most vessels and the most hairs. Leaves had the most chloroplasts. This is expected, because the roots absorb water and the leaves absorb sunlight.

Teacher Note "The students did a great job. Drawings were accurate."

Online Biology ▼

VIRTUAL LAB Students should find that the rate of transpiration goes up in windy and warmer conditions and down in humid conditions. Use with **Section 21.2.**

ANIMATED BIOLOGY Use this interactive animation to reinforce the concepts in **Section 21.4.**

WEBQUEST The WebQuest takes one full class period. Students complete the activity online and will need access to a printer to print their answers. Sample answers, teacher notes, and alternative assessment ideas are available on **ClassZone.com.** Use with **Section 21.4.**

INVESTIGATION TEACHER TESTED

Time	45 minutes
Teacher Preparation	(1 flask)
Student Difficulty	(1 flask)
Lab Binder	Plants, p. 21

Purpose Connect the structures of plant organs to their functions.

Overview Students will make thin slices of a plant's root, stem, and leaves, and observe their structures under a microscope.

LAB PREPARATION
- Obtain plants with roots, stems, and leaves. Clean the soil off the roots.
- Have prepared slides ready for students who cannot prepare them themselves.

LAB MANAGEMENT

Safety Remind students to always cut away from their bodies when using razor tools, and to wash their hands after completing the lab.

POST-LAB DISCUSSION

Discuss any problems students had making their slides and observing the structures.

CHAPTER REVIEW

Interactive Review

Encourage students to go to **ClassZone.com** for a detailed review of each section, including visuals and vocabulary practice.

Unit Resource Book, Vocabulary Practice, pp. 49–52

CHAPTER 21 Interactive Review @ CLASSZONE.COM

KEY CONCEPTS | Vocabulary Games | Concept Maps | Animated Biology | Online Quiz

21.1 Plant Cells and Tissues

Plants have specialized cells and tissue systems. There are three basic types of plant cells that differ in cell wall structure. Each of these cell types can make up simple tissues. These tissues, as well as complex tissues, make up tissue systems. A plant has a dermal tissue system that covers the plant, a ground tissue system that makes up most of the inside of the plant, and a vascular tissue system that transports fluids throughout the plant.

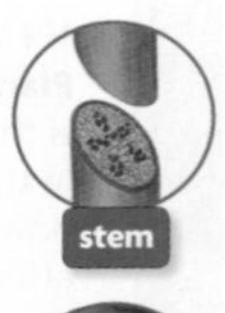

21.2 The Vascular System

The vascular system allows for the transport of water, minerals, and sugars. Xylem and phloem are the two main tissues of the vascular system. Water and dissolved minerals move through xylem from the roots of a plant up to the leaves, where it evaporates through leaf stomata. This process is called transpiration. The pressure-flow model is a hypothesis of how sugars from photosynthesis move through the plant within the phloem.

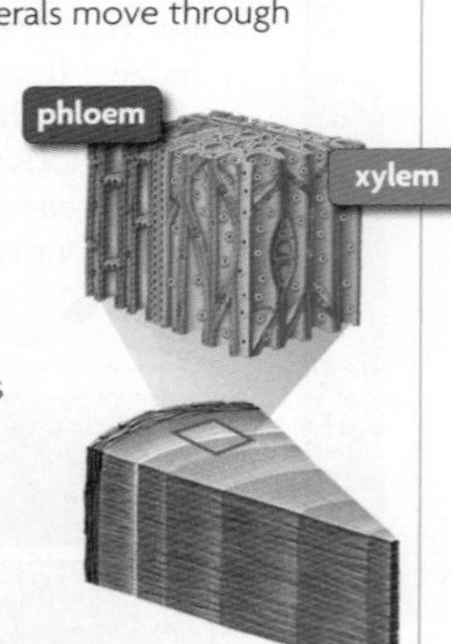

21.3 Roots and Stems

Roots and stems form the support system of vascular plants. Roots anchor plants in the soil and absorb water and mineral nutrients for the plant to use. There are two main types of roots: fibrous roots and taproots. Stems provide support for the plant, and house the vascular systems of the plant. They also give leaves and flowers better access to sunlight and to pollinators. Some stems can store food, while other stems are adapted to store water.

21.4 Leaves

Leaves absorb light and carry out photosynthesis. Most leaves are specialized for photosynthesis, with a broad shape, many chloroplasts, and stomata that allow carbon dioxide and oxygen to move into and out of the plant. Certain leaf characteristics, such as the vein pattern and the shape of the leaf, can be used to help identify plants. There are many adaptations of leaves, such as cactus spines, pine needles, and the tubular leaves of a pitcher plant that are used to lure and trap insects for food.

Synthesize Your Notes

Supporting Main Ideas Use a main idea diagram to outline the tissue systems in plants.

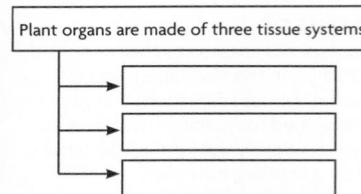

Plant organs are made of three tissue systems.

- →
- →
- →

Three-Column Chart Make a three-column chart to summarize the forces involved in the movement of fluids within xylem.

Force	Description	Where in Plant
Transpiration		
Cohesion and adhesion		
Absorption		

658 Unit 7: Plants

Reviewing Vocabulary

1. Both are types of plant cells. Parenchyma divide throughout their lives and are found throughout a plant's tissues. Sclerenchyma cells die at maturity and cannot grow with the plant.
2. Both are found throughout the plant and help support the plant. Ground tissue provides support and storage; vascular tissue enables movement of materials throughout the plant.
3. Both are tissues that are part of a plant's vascular system. Xylem transports water and nutrients from the roots to the rest of the plant. Phloem transports nutrients both up and down through the plant. Xylem is made of dead cells, and phloem is made of living cells.
4. Both support the plant and absorb, transport, and store nutrients. Fibrous roots are branched and spread beneath the soil. A taproot has one long, thick, vertical root with smaller branches extending from it.
5. Both help a plant increase in size. Primary growth makes a plant stem grow longer or roots grow longer. Secondary growth makes a plant grow wider.
6. Sclerenchyma is a plant tissue that is made up of hard, rigid cells.
7. Dermal tissue is like skin because it covers and protects the outside of plants.
8. Root growth happens in the meristem, where cells divide to form new cells.
9. Mesophyll is found in the middle of leaves, between two layers of dermal tissue.
10. Drawing should be of two water molecules with a hydrogen bond formed between them. Label: Cohesion is a force that attracts water molecules to one another.
11. Drawing should show a plant with an arrow (labeled "water" or "water vapor") leading from the roots up through the plant toward the sky. Label: Transpiration is the loss of water vapor from plants.
12. Drawing should be of a leaf with blade (main body of leaf) and petiole (leaf stalk) labeled. Label: Leaves are made up of blades and petioles.
13. Drawing should show an opening (stoma) with two cells (guard cells) surrounding it, one on each end of the opening. Label: A pair of guard cells surround each stoma.

Chapter Assessment

Chapter Vocabulary

21.1 parenchyma cell, p. 640
collenchyma cell, p. 640
sclerenchyma cell, p. 641
dermal tissue, p. 642
ground tissue, p. 642
vascular tissue, p. 642
xylem, p. 642
phloem, p. 642

21.2 cohesion-tension theory, p. 643
transpiration, p. 645
pressure-flow model, p. 645

21.3 vascular cylinder, p. 648
root hair, p. 648
root cap, p. 648
meristem, p. 648
fibrous root, p. 649
taproot, p. 649
primary growth, p. 651
secondary growth, p. 651

21.4 blade, p. 652
petiole, p. 652
mesophyll, p. 652
guard cell, p. 653

Reviewing Vocabulary

Compare and Contrast

Describe one similarity and one difference between the two terms in each of the following pairs.

1. parenchyma cell, sclerenchyma cell

2. ground tissue, vascular tissue

3. xylem, phloem

4. fibrous root, taproot

5. primary growth, secondary growth

Word Origins

6. The Greek word *skleros* means "hard" and the suffix *-enchyma* means "cellular tissue." Explain how these word parts relate to characteristics of sclerechyma.

7. *Derma* is a Greek word meaning "skin." How does this relate to the function of dermal tissue in plants?

8. The Greek verb *merizein* means "to divide." How does this relate to the function of a root's meristem?

9. *Meso-* is a prefix meaning "middle" and *-phyll* is a suffix meaning "leaf." Based on these word parts, explain where you would find a plant's mesophyll.

Visualize Vocabulary

For each word or pair of words below, use simple shapes, lines, or arrows to illustrate the meaning. Label each picture, and write a short caption.

10. cohesion

11. transpiration

12. blade, petiole

13. guard cell

Reviewing MAIN IDEAS

14. Name two roles of parenchyma cells, and briefly explain how these cells are specialized for these roles.

15. Both collenchyma and sclerenchyma cells provide support to a plant. But only one of these cell types can exist in plant parts that are still growing. Identify the cell type and explain the traits that make this so.

16. Describe one similarity and one difference between the dermal tissues in nonwoody and woody parts of a plant.

17. Some ground tissue contains many chloroplasts. Where is this tissue located and why does it contain so many chloroplasts?

18. How is the structure of vascular tissue related to its ability to transport materials in the plant?

19. What must happen to tracheids and vessel elements before they can function in xylem?

20. What processes are responsible for water flowing through xylem from the roots to the tips of leaves?

21. Name three substances that are transported by phloem.

22. What can taproots do that fibrous roots cannot do?

23. Describe similarities between herbaceous stems and woody stems.

24. How do the xylem and phloem in leaves help identify a plant species?

25. Photosynthesis requires carbon dioxide and produces oxygen. How does spongy mesophyll play a role in the diffusion of these gases into and out of the leaves?

CHAPTER REVIEW

Reviewing Main Ideas

14. Parenchyma cells perform photosynthesis by using chloroplasts. They can also heal wounds to the plant through their ability to divide throughout their entire lives.

15. Collenchyma cells; they do not contain lignin, so they are flexible and able to grow.

16. In both non-woody and woody parts of the plant, dermal tissue helps prevent water loss. In non-woody parts, the epidermis may secrete a waxy substance to do this.

17. Ground tissue containing many chloroplasts is found in leaves, the primary site of photosynthesis.

18. Vascular tissue consists of two networks of hollow tubes through which materials can flow.

19. Both cell types must mature and die before they can be used by the plant to transport water.

20. absorption, cohesion, adhesion, transpiration

21. minerals, sugars, complex organic compounds

22. store food

23. Both herbaceous stems and woody stems provide similar functions: supporting leaves and flowers, and housing the majority of the plant's vascular system.

24. The vascular tissues are bundled together and form visible veins in the leaves. The veins have different patterns, depending on the type of plant.

25. Spongy mesophyll has loosely packed cells with air spaces between them. These connect to the outside of the plant through the stomata.

Critical Thinking

26. Meristem cells are also unspecialized or undifferentiated cells that can become specialized plant cells.
27. During the first growing season, the root is first a sink, receiving sugars. As it stores the sugars it receives, it becomes a source for later use. The high concentration of sugar in the root causes water to flow into the root by osmosis. The root remains in this state all winter until the nutrients are needed in the spring for the stem, leaves, and flowers to develop.
28. Muir could have only determined the tree's age by counting the annual growth rings. More than 400 growth rings in a narrow tree means that very little growth occurred each year. This, plus the tree's lack of height, indicates that water and other things necessary for primary and secondary growth were in short supply.
29. If water remained on the leaves, transpiration might be blocked and the weight of the water could weaken and break the petioles.
30. The first water molecules to touch the paper towel will pull other water molecules along because they are bound by hydrogen bonds. This is cohesion. The water molecules are also attracted to additional areas of the paper towel because of hydrogen bonds. This is adhesion. Cohesion brings more water toward and into the paper towel, and more adhesion spreads the water to other areas of the paper towel.

Interpreting Visuals

31. The tree was approximately 8 years old when it was cut down.
32. Growth and climate were steady. The wide light-colored band suggests ample rain in spring and summer followed by a brief, dry fall and winter.
33. The next growth ring would have a narrower light-colored band than those of previous springs and a dark ring similar in width to those of previous summers. The lack of spring rain would mean less growth than in previous springs.

Critical Thinking

26. Compare In animals, the term *stem cells* refers to unspecialized or undifferentiated cells that give rise to specialized cells, such as a blood cell. How are meristem cells in plants similar to animal stem cells?

27. Analyze A sugar beet plant develops a large root in the first year of growth and stores sugar in it until the second growing season. But, besides sugar, as much as three-fourths of the root's weight can be water. Why is there so much water in the root?

28. Apply In 1894, naturalist John Muir wrote about white bark pines he saw at Yosemite National Park in California. At high elevations, where there was snow on the ground for six months each year, he studied a tree only three feet tall and six inches in diameter and determined it was 426 years old. How did he know how old the tree was? Why might it be so small when trees of the same species were much larger down the mountain?

29. Infer Many rain forest plants have leaves that taper to tips on the ends. Water from heavy rains drips off the tips of the leaves so that water doesn't collect on the leaves. Why might this be an adaptive advantage for the plant?

30. Synthesize Use what you know about cohesion and adhesion to explain why almost an entire sheet of paper towel can become wet even if only a corner of it is placed in water.

Interpreting Visuals

Use the photograph to answer the next three questions.

31. Apply About how many years old was this tree when it was cut down?

32. Infer What does the pattern of growth rings indicate about the climate and the rate of growth of this tree over the years?

33. Predict Imagine this tree were still growing. If the next year had a spring with much less rain than previous springs and then a summer with a lot of sunshine, what would the next growth ring look like? Explain.

Analyzing Data

An experiment was designed to test the effect of various environmental factors on the successful germination of grass seed. The control group of seeds was planted according to the directions on the seed packet. Each of three additional groups tested one variable. The experimental design and results are shown in the chart below. Use the chart to answer the next three questions.

ENVIRONMENTAL FACTORS THAT AFFECT GRASS SEED GERMINATION

Environmental Factor	Control Group	Group A	Group B	Group C
Hours daylight	12	6	12	12
Water	100%	100%	50%	100%
Temperature (°C)	24	24	24	12
Seeds planted/ seeds germinated	5/5	5/5	5/1	5/3

34. Infer What does the data suggest about the conditions under which grass seeds will or will not germinate?

35. Evaluate Do the results seem logical? Explain.

36. Analyze If you could change anything in this experimental design, what would it be? Give at least two reasons to support your response.

Connecting CONCEPTS

37. Write an Instruction Manual Imagine that you want to sell plant dissection kits. The kits will include instructions on where to find all of the structures of a plant, such as the different type of cells and tissues, roots, leaves, stomata, stems, phloem, and xylem. You need to write an instruction manual to help people dissect the plant. Write instructions to dissect the plant from the bottom up. Decide whether it is a woody or nonwoody plant.

38. Analyze Strangler figs were transplanted from the tropics to states such as Florida and California because of their unusual growth forms. Considering how they got their common name, why was this perhaps not a good idea?

Analyzing Data

34. The data on the chart implies that seeds are as likely to germinate if they get only half as much light as recommended, but they are less likely to germinate if given less water or are grown in a temperature less than what is recommended.
35. It is logical that an inadequate supply of water and low temperatures would decrease the chance of germination. Because seeds do not depend on sunlight for germination, the amount of daylight will not affect the plant until after the seed has sprouted aboveground.
36. Planting more seeds for each group would yield more reliable data. Factors other than the tested variables may have resulted in the failure of germination in groups B and C. Such a small number of seeds in the control group creates the false impression that every seed can be expected to germinate under ideal conditions.

660 Unit 7: Plants

INDIANA ISTEP+ Test Prep

B.2.1, B.3.1, NOS.1

Test Practice
For more test practice, go to ClassZone.com.

1

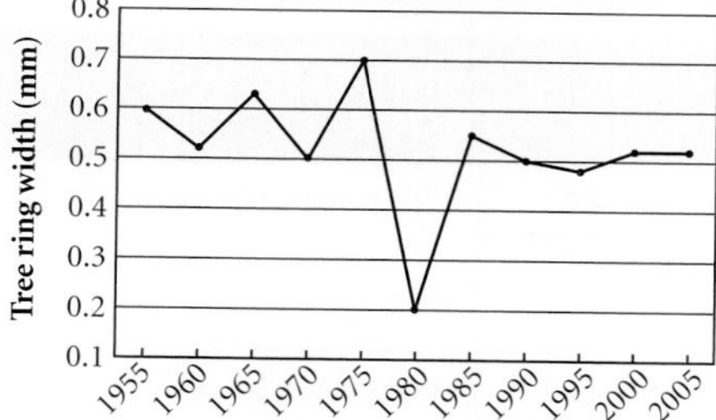

Suppose a tree farmer has collected data about tree ring growth for many years. During that time, only one major drought has occurred. Based on the graph, between which years did the drought most likely occur?

A 1955–1960
B 1965–1970
C 1975–1980
D 1990–1995

THINK THROUGH THE QUESTION

First, eliminate answer choices that list the years where there is no remarkable change in the graph. Then consider the remaining choices. Would drought have a negative or a positive effect on the width of a tree ring?

2 Plant tissues are made of three basic types of cells: parenchyma, collenchyma, and sclerenchyma. Which of the following statements is true about all plant cells?

A They do not have a nucleus.
B They do not have a cell membrane.
C They have a cell wall.
D They have the same function.

3 Plants capture radiant energy from sunlight and convert it into usable energy in the form of

A carbon dioxide.
B. protein.
C oxygen.
D sugar.

4 What two structures do plant cells have that animal cells do not have?

A ribosomes and mitochondria
B mitochondria and cell walls
C chloroplasts and cell walls
D chloroplasts and ribosomes

5 Which of the following characteristics is shared by both plant cells and photosynthetic bacteria?

A cell wall of lignin
B chlorophyll
C DNA enclosed in a nucleus
D vacuole for starch storage

6 Describe the structure of a chloroplast.

Standards-Based Assessment

1. C	4. C
2. C	5. B
3. D	6. See Below

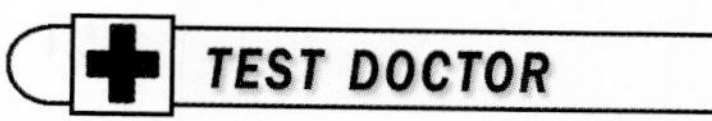

Question 1 Answer C is correct because tree ring width decreased from 0.7 mm in 1975 to 0.2 mm in 1980. Answer A is incorrect because ring width decreased by only about 0.09 mm. Answer B is incorrect because ring width decreased by only about 0.12 mm. Answer D is incorrect because ring width decreased by only about 0.02 mm.

Question 2 Answer C is correct. Answer A is incorrect because plant cells are eukaryotic and have a nucleus. Answer B is incorrect because all cells have a cell membrane. Answer D is incorrect because plants have specialized cells that carry out different functions.

Question 4 Answer C is correct. Answers A, B, and D are incorrect because both plant and animal cells have ribosomes for protein synthesis and mitochondria for energy conversion.

Question 6 A chloroplast is a membrane-bound organelle that contains stacks of compartments called thylakoids. Surrounding the thylakoids is the fluid-filled area called the stroma.

Connecting Concepts

37. Answers will vary slightly depending on the type of plant, but the manual should include the following parts: parenchyma, sclerenchyma, and collenchyma cells; dermal, ground, and vascular tissues; stems, leaves, mesophyll, petioles, blades, guard cells, stomata, roots, root hairs, vascular cylinder; xylem, phloem, tracheids, vessel elements, pores, sieve tube elements, and companion cells.

38. Strangler figs can out-compete and smother native plants, edging them out of an area. Eventually, the invasive nature of introduced plants, such as the strangler figs, can be a significant factor in loss of biodiversity on local, regional, and global levels.

ITEM CORRELATIONS

Standard	Items
B.2.1	2, 4, 5
B.3.1	3, 6
NOS.1	1

CHAPTER 22

Indiana Resource Preview

Print Resources

Plant Growth, Reproduction, and Response

INDIANA STANDARDS		Sections	PAGES and PACING	UNIT RESOURCE BOOK
	22.1	**Plant Life Cycles** **KEY CONCEPT** All plants alternate between two phases in their life cycles.	pp. 664–667 30 minutes	URB pages 53–56
	22.2	**Reproduction in Flowering Plants** **KEY CONCEPT** Reproduction of flowering plants takes place within flowers.	pp. 668–672 30 minutes	URB pages 57–60
	22.3	**Seed Dispersal and Germination** **KEY CONCEPT** Seeds disperse and begin to grow when conditions are favorable.	pp. 673–675 30 minutes	URB pages 61–64
		DATA ANALYSIS: Identifying Experimental Design Flaws	p. 674 30 minutes	URB page 73
NOS.5		CHAPTER INVESTIGATION: Seed Germination	pp. 676–677 30 minutes	**Lab Binder** Plants pages 27–30
	22.4	**Asexual Reproduction** **KEY CONCEPT** Plants can produce genetic clones of themselves through asexual reproduction.	pp. 678–679 30 minutes	URB pages 65–68
	22.5	**Plant Hormones and Responses** **KEY CONCEPT** Plant hormones guide plant growth and development.	pp. 680–683 30 minutes	URB pages 69–72
NOS.1		OPTIONS FOR INQUIRY	pp. 684–685 20 minutes, 45 minutes	**Lab Binder** Plants pages 31–34
		Chapter Review	pp. 686–689	**Assessment Book** Chapter Tests A, B pp. 437–444

INDIANA STANDARDS

NOS.1 Develop explanations based on reproducible data and observations gathered during laboratory investigations.
NOS.5 Apply standard techniques in laboratory investigations to measure physical quantities in appropriate units and convert known quantities to other units as necessary.

Labs

PUPIL EDITION LABS

A Closer Look at Flowers, Section 2, p. 669 Students explore floral structure by dissecting a flower. **Lab Binder** pp. 35–36	**Time:** 30 minutes **Materials:** flower, colored pencils, tweezers, magnifying glass
Seed Germination, pp. 676–677 Students observe how irradiating radish seeds affects their germination. **Lab Binder** pp. 27–30	**Time:** 30 minutes **Materials:** 2 plastic grids, 2 petri dishes, pencil, forceps, 7 nonirradiated radish seeds, 7 irradiated radish seeds, paper towel, small container to hold petri dishes, fluorescent light, hand lens, metric ruler

OPTIONS FOR INQUIRY

Investigating Plant Hormones, p. 684 Students explore the effects of ripened fruit on unripe fruit. **Lab Binder** pp. 31–32	**Time:** 20 minutes **Materials:** 3 unripe bananas from the same bunch, several pieces of various ripened fruit, 3 large resealable plastic bags
Fruit Dissection, p. 685 Students illustrate a fruit and its seeds accurately. **Lab Binder** pp. 33–34	**Time:** 30 minutes **Materials:** peapod, scalpel, dissecting tray, metric ruler, tweezers, paper towel, dissecting microscope

LAB BINDER Unit 7 Plants

Additional Investigation: Cotyledon Removal in Peanut Seeds, pp. 37–40

Biotechnology Lab: Plant Propagation and Asexual Reproduction, pp. 41–44

Challenge Lab: Monocot and Dicot Seed Structure, pp. 49–51

Virtual Lab Worksheet: Exploring Plant Responses, p. 60

LAB GENERATOR

A searchable CD of all labs in the program in editable format, including forensic, probeware, and biotechnology labs.

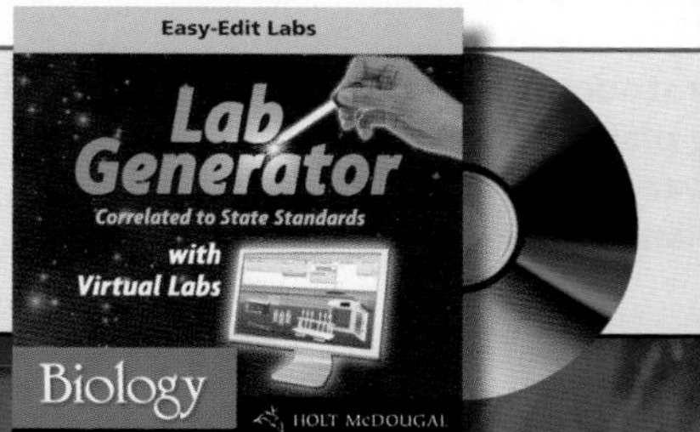

Presentation Tools

POWER PRESENTATIONS

Presentation Chapter 22
Power Presentations for each section incorporate images and clips from the Media Gallery: Includes Note Navigator for each section.

MEDIA GALLERY

Contains the following images and video clips, as well as animations, simulations and forms of visuals from the book.

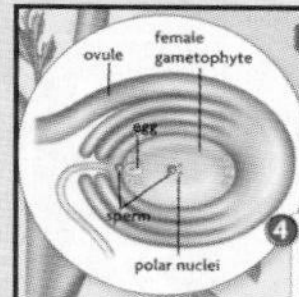

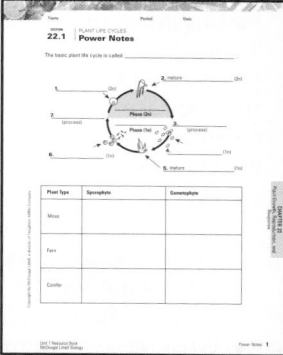

Flowering plant life cycle

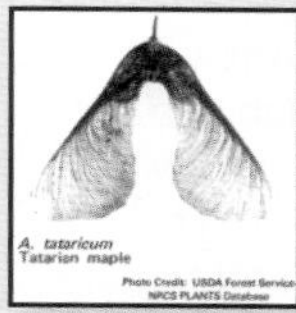

Seed dispersal

Power Notes

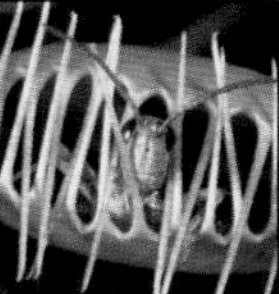
Venus flytrap

Butterfly pollinator

VIDEO

View a set of short video clips exploring different plant responses.

ANIMATED BIOLOGY

Seed Dispersal

TRANSPARENCIES

Alternation of Generations T91

Flower Anatomy T92

Online BIOLOGY CLASSZONE.COM

BioZine
Animated Biology
Interactive Review
SciLinks
Resource Centers

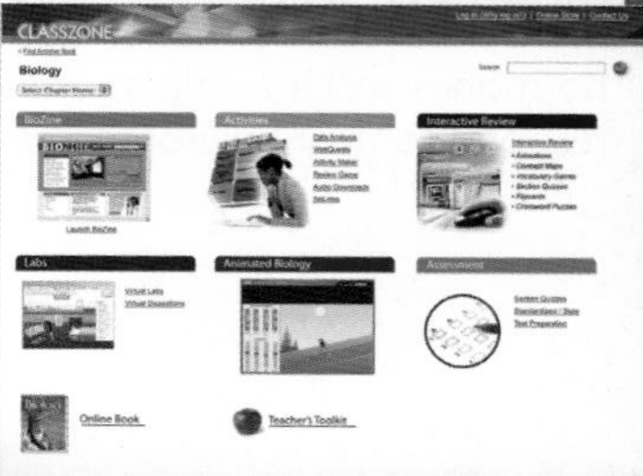

CHAPTER
22

▼ Focus and Motivate

How does a mothlike appearance help this plant?

Have students brainstorm possible reasons that orchids might benefit from looking like moths. *Sample Answer:* They attract real moths, which act as pollinators. Explain that many flowers that look like insects also give off chemicals that attract male and female insects. **Ask**

- How would looking like a moth and having an attractive scent increase the likelihood of pollination? Moths that cannot see the flower may still be drawn to it.
- What reward might the moth get by visiting the flower? food in the form of nectar, or another moth to mate with

BIOZINE ClassZone.com

Students can access BioZine at **ClassZone.com** to check the daily news feeds.

In a Hurry?

The critical material of the chapter is found in **Sections 22.1, 22.2,** and **22.3,** which cover plant life cycles, reproduction in flowering plants, and seed dispersal and germination. **Section 22.4** covers asexual reproduction in plants, which is a common method of propagating plants. **Section 22.5** contains more detailed information about plant hormones and how plants are able to respond to their environments.

CHAPTER 22

Plant Growth, Reproduction, and Response

KEY CONCEPTS

22.1 Plant Life Cycles
All plants alternate between two phases in their life cycles.

22.2 Reproduction in Flowering Plants
Reproduction of flowering plants takes place within flowers.

22.3 Seed Dispersal and Germination
Seeds disperse and begin to grow when conditions are favorable.

22.4 Asexual Reproduction
Plants can produce genetic clones of themselves through asexual reproduction.

22.5 Plant Hormones and Responses
Plant hormones guide plant growth and development.

Online BIOLOGY CLASSZONE.COM

Animated BIOLOGY
View animated chapter concepts.
- Exploring Plant Responses
- Seed Dispersal

BIOZINE
Keep current with biology news.
- Featured stories
- News feeds
- Strange Biology

RESOURCE CENTER
Get more information on
- Plant Life Cycles
- Plant Reproduction
- Seeds and Fruits

Teacher Demo

Eye Opener **Show students how the gamete-producing plants and spore-producing plants vary in size in different major groups of plants.**

Materials

- live specimens or models of a moss with sporophytes, a fern, and a flowering plant
- prepared slides or photomicrographs of the sporophytes and gametophytes of a moss, a fern, and a flowering plant
- projector

Demonstrate

- Show students live specimens or models of examples of the major plant groups.
- Tell students that both phases of the plant life cycle—a gamete-producing plant and a spore-producing plant—can be seen in the moss specimens. Have students speculate about which structures represent the different phases of the plant life cycle.
- Show students prepared slides or photomicrographs of the gametophytes and sporophytes of the three plant types.

How does a mothlike appearance help this plant?

Connecting CONCEPTS

Some pollinators are attracted to flowers that mimic insects. This orchid belongs to a genus commonly called "moth orchids." Moths may be drawn to this flower and be dusted with pollen grains. The pollen now has a free ticket to the next flower on the moth's route. When pollen comes into contact with the female parts of another flower, the reproductive cycle begins.

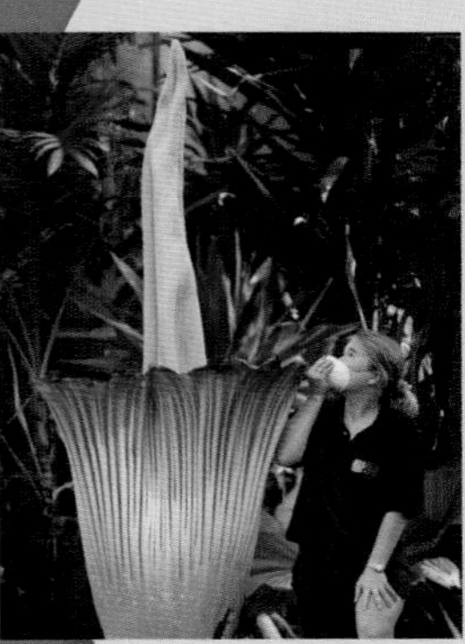

Ecology The titan arum plant, shown at left, produces a flower that smells like carrion, or rotting meat. Beetles that eat carrion are attracted by this odor and often wind up pollinating the flower. This ecological relationship is an example of commensalism. The plant benefits from being pollinated, but the beetles are neither helped nor harmed. Instead, they are tricked by the flower's smell, expecting to find a meal.

Discuss Point out the location of the gamete-producing generation and the spore-producing generation of each plant specimen.

- Help students recognize that the gamete-producing moss plant and the spore-producing moss plant are both readily visible, but that the "leafy" gamete-producing moss is the most familiar, most often seen, and largest form of a moss.
- Explain that the fronds of a fern are part of a spore-producing plant in the fern life cycle and that this plant grew from a flat gamete-producing plant smaller than a fingernail.
- Explain that the body of the flowering plant is the spore-producing plant in its life cycle and that the spores produced by the plant are not released.

Ask, Which phase of the flowering plant life cycle is microscopic? the gamete-producing plant

Activate Prior Knowledge

Direct students' attention to the chapter title. **Ask,** What are some of the reproductive structures of plants that you can find in a garden, on trees, floating in the breeze, or lying on the ground? flowers, cones, seeds, pollen, spores What are some examples of how plants respond to stimuli? *Sample Answer:* bending or growing toward light, wilting when dry, leaves changing color in fall

Preview Vocabulary

Greek and Latin Word Origins Tell students that they will see the suffix *-phyte,* from the Greek root meaning "to make grow," used to describe parts of a plant life cycle. The root is sometimes translated as "plant" but in this case it can describe just a portion of a plant. Most important is that students recognize that the terms *sporophyte* and *gametophyte* apply to the plant or structure that produces its namesake. A sporophyte produces spores (diploid to haploid) and a gametophyte produces gametes (haploid to diploid).

Academic Vocabulary The verb *generation* refers to the process of reproduction, or producing offspring. In plant biology, *alternation of generations* refers to a life cycle in which a stage that produces reproductive cells by meiosis alternates with a stage that produces reproductive cells by mitosis.

You might want to point out the difference in meaning between *alternate* and *alternative.*

alternate (v.), to proceed or act by turns

alternate (n.), a substitute or one who acts in place of another

alternative, the choice between two mutually exclusive possibilities

English Learners Draw an enlarged version of **FIGURE 22.1** on the board so you can refer to it as you go through the chapter. Students need to understand how meiosis and fertilization fit into the picture of the alternation of haploid and diploid generations. Use the diagram to clarify for students how different reproductive structures, such as spores, pollen, and seeds, fit into the larger picture.

SECTION 22.1

▼ Plan and Prepare

Objectives

- Summarize alternation of generations in plants.
- Compare and contrast the life cycles of mosses, ferns, and conifers.

Section Resources

Unit Resource Book
Study Guide pp. 53–54
Power Notes p. 55
Reinforcement p. 56

Interactive Reader Chapter 22
Spanish Study Guide pp. 223–224

Biology Toolkit pp. C13, C22, C25

Technology
Power Presentation 22.1
Media Gallery DVD
Online Quiz 22.1

Activate Prior Knowledge Review the concept of a life cycle. **Ask**

- What is a cycle? a repeating series of events
- What are the stages in the cycle of human life? conception, birth, infancy, childhood, adolescence, adulthood, reproduction

Tell students that in order for a plant to reach the stage at which it can produce gametes, it must first go through another stage.

▼ Teach

TEACH FROM VISUALS

FIGURE 22.1 Use the illustration to review mitosis, meiosis, diploid (2*n*), haploid (1*n*), spores, gametes, fertilization, and zygote.

Answers

A Analyze Gametophyte cells must divide by mitosis because they have only one copy of each chromosome.

22.1 Plant Life Cycles

KEY CONCEPTS All plants alternate between two phases in their life cycles.

MAIN IDEAS

- Plant life cycles alternate between producing spores and gametes.
- Life cycle phases look different among various plant groups.

VOCABULARY

alternation of generations, p. 664
sporophyte, p. 664
gametophyte, p. 664

Review
pollination, meiosis, diploid, haploid, zygote, mitosis, sporangia, flagella

Connect The moth orchid flower mimics the shape of its pollinators, which are attracted to what they think is a potential mate. Pollination is a part of sexual reproduction in seed plants. But how do seedless plants, such as moss, reproduce? And what are the common features of all plant life cycles?

MAIN IDEA

Plant life cycles alternate between producing spores and gametes.

Recall that animals produce gametes—sperm and eggs—through meiosis. When a sperm fertilizes an egg, a new diploid organism is produced. Plants also produce gametes, but their reproductive cycle includes a few extra steps. Plants complete their life cycle by alternating between two phases. Together, these phases allow plants to reproduce sexually and disperse to new areas. One phase involves a diploid plant body that produces spores. Remember, diploid cells have two copies of each chromosome (2*n*). The other phase involves a haploid plant body that produces gametes. Haploid cells have one copy of each chromosome (1*n*). This type of life cycle, which alternates between diploid and haploid phases, is called **alternation of generations.**

As shown in **FIGURE 22.1**, the diploid phase of a plant life cycle begins with a fertilized egg, called a zygote. A zygote divides by mitosis and grows into a mature **sporophyte** (SPAWR-uh-FYT), or spore-producing plant. A mature sporophyte has specialized cells that divide by meiosis to produce haploid spores. Recall that cell division by meiosis reduces the number of chromosomes in a cell by one-half.

A spore marks the beginning of the haploid phase of the plant life cycle. A spore divides by mitosis and grows into a mature **gametophyte** (guh-MEE-tuh-fyt), or gamete-producing plant. Specialized parts of a mature gametophyte produce gametes—sperm and eggs—through mitosis. When a sperm meets an egg, fertilization takes place, and the cycle continues with a new sporophyte.

FIGURE 22.1 ALTERNATION OF GENERATIONS

Plant life cycles alternate between a sporophyte phase, which produces spores, and a gametophyte stage, which produces gametes.

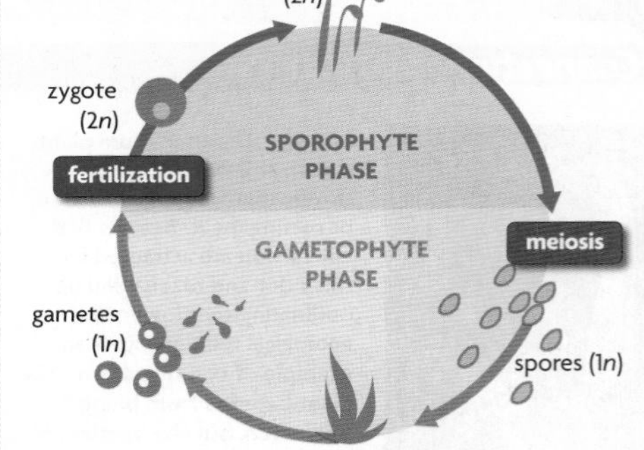

A Analyze Why must gametophyte cells divide by mitosis?

Differentiated Instruction

ENGLISH LEARNERS

Have pairs of students first outline the chapter using the standard format, except change the chapter title into a complete sentence: "Plants Grow, Reproduce, and Respond."

- Use Roman numerals to list the Key Concepts of the sections.
- Use capital letters for subsections, marked as Main Ideas.
- Use Arabic numerals for key ideas in each part, identified by large black lettering.

After students read the section, have them flesh out the corresponding parts of the outline. For example, under **1. Life Cycle of Nonvascular Plants: Moss,** they might list these key ideas:

a. Nonvascular plants, such as mosses, are the only plants in which the gametophyte phase is dominant.

b. A moss gametophyte produces gametes in special reproductive structures.

Have students use bullets for key vocabulary.

Biology Toolkit, Outline, C25

MAIN IDEA

Life cycle phases look different among various plant groups.

Different plant groups each have their own version of alternation of generations. The sporophyte and gametophyte generations look different for nonvascular plants, seedless vascular plants, and seed plants.

TAKING NOTES

Use combination notes to summarize the life cycles of nonvascular, seedless vascular, and seed plants.

type of plant	*life cycle*

Life Cycle of Nonvascular Plants: Moss

Nonvascular plants are the only plants in which the gametophyte phase is dominant. In other words, the green, carpetlike plants that you might recognize as moss are gametophytes. If you look very closely, sometimes you can see the moss sporophytes. Moss sporophytes are stalklike structures that grow up from the gametophyte. As you can see in **FIGURE 22.2**, the moss sporophyte looks like a brown stem topped with a tiny cup called a capsule.

The capsule at the tip of the moss sporophyte contains spore-producing sacs called sporangia. When the spores are mature, the capsule opens and releases them. Spores allow seedless plants to disperse to new areas. If a spore lands in a favorable spot for growing, it can grow into a gametophyte.

A moss gametophyte produces gametes in special reproductive structures. Each male structure produces hundreds of sperm with whiplike flagella, and each female structure produces a single egg. When water is present, sperm swim toward an egg. Once a sperm fertilizes an egg, the sporophyte phase begins once again.

VOCABULARY

The suffix *–phyte* comes from the Greek word *phuton*, meaning "plant."

FIGURE 22.2 MOSS LIFE CYCLE

The gametophyte of mosses is the carpet-like plant that may be familiar to you. The sporophyte grows up from the gametophyte. A tiny cup called a capsule forms at the tip of each moss sporophyte.

Spores form inside the capsule. When the spores are mature, the capsule opens and releases them. Spores can grow into new gametophytes when the environmental conditions are favorable.

***Connecting* CONCEPTS**

Life Cycles Refer to the **Appendix** for a detailed view of the moss life cycle.

Take It Further

Plants' gametes result from mitosis in structures called **gametangia.** Nonvascular plants produce two kinds of gametangia:

- vase-shaped *archegonia* produce eggs
- club-shaped *antheridia* produce sperm

A sperm from an antheridium swims through water to reach an egg in an archegonium. The zygote that results from fertilization in an archegonium develops into a new sporophyte, which sprouts from the leafy stalk of the gametophyte.

TEACH FROM VISUALS

FIGURE 22.2 Point out the gametophyte (leafy, green) and the sporophyte (stalk and capsule) generations of the moss in the photos. **Ask**

- What will happen to the spores released from the capsule of the moss sporophyte? They will grow into new moss gametophytes.
- What environmental conditions might be unfavorable for growth of new gametophytes? lack of moisture and freezing temperatures, because the sperm needs water to swim though to reach the egg

BELOW LEVEL

To help students understand that the moss sporophyte is a separate generation that grows from the body of a gametophyte, have students think of it as being analogous to a symbiotic relationship. Have students work together to relate the photographs of **FIGURE 22.2** to the diagram of **FIGURE 22.1.** Have them address the question of how the sporophyte generation of a moss is connected to the gametophyte generation.

Biology Toolkit, Think-Pair-Share, p. C13

▼ Teach *continued*

TEACH FROM VISUALS

FIGURE 22.3 Use the photos to discuss the two stages of the fern life cycle. Explain that like mosses, ferns exist as two different generations that together complete the fern life cycle. Point out the rows of sori, which are clusters of sporangia, on the lower side of the fern frond. **Ask**

- What happens when one of the spores falls to the ground? It can grow into a gametophyte called a prothallus.
- What side of the prothallus is shown in this photo? the lower side How do you know? because the rhizoids on it are what holds the plant in the ground

Point out the tiny knobs seen near the rhizoids. Tell students that these are antheridia, the sperm-producing gametangia of this fern gametophyte. The sperm from these antheridia can reach an egg only by swimming through water to a nearby archegonium.

Integrating Evolutionary Biology

Plants that produce two kinds of spores, and thus two kinds of gametophytes, have an evolutionary advantage over the seedless plants that produce only one kind of spore and one kind of gametophyte. First, the sperm, which form from male gametophytes, do not need water to reach eggs. Also, the pollen grains can be carried long distances on the wind, which promotes cross breeding and genetic diversity. This is why seed plants dominate many of Earth's landscapes.

FIGURE 22.3 FERN LIFE CYCLE

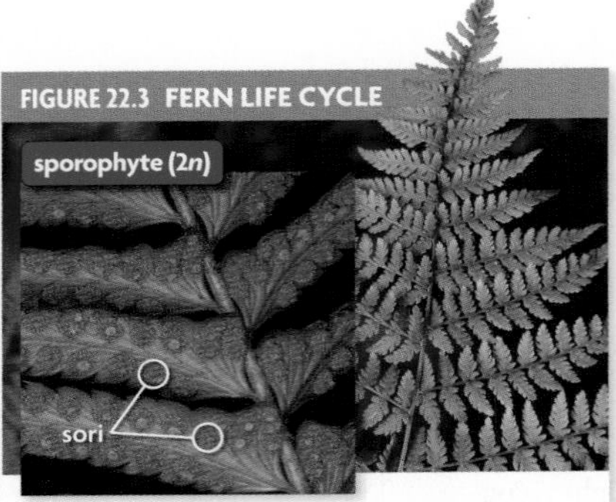

The fern sporophyte is the leafy plant that you may be familiar with. Clusters of spore-holding sacs called sori grow on the underside of each fern leaf, or frond.

A fern spore can grow into a fern gametophyte, called a prothallus. The prothallus is about the size of your little fingernail. Structures that produce sperm and eggs are located on the bottom of the prothallus.

Life Cycle of Seedless Vascular Plants: Ferns

The sporophyte is the dominant phase for all vascular plants, including seedless vascular plants such as ferns. This means that the plants you recognize as ferns are sporophytes. If you look at the underside of a fern leaf, called a frond, you might see sori. Sori are clusters of sporangia, which are spore-producing sacs. As shown in **FIGURE 22.3,** sori look like brown dots on the fern frond. Spores are released from the sporangia when they are mature. If a spore lands in a favorable spot for growing, it can develop into a gametophyte.

A fern gametophyte is often called a prothallus. As you can see in **FIGURE 22.3**, a prothallus is a plant body about the size of your little fingernail. It anchors itself to the soil with tiny threadlike structures called rhizoids. The prothallus contains special reproductive structures that produce sperm and eggs.

When free-standing water is present, male structures release sperm. Sperm then swim toward an egg. When a sperm fertilizes an egg, a zygote forms on the prothallus. Remember that the zygote is the beginning of the sporophyte generation. The zygote grows above the prothallus, which eventually rots away. The mature sporophyte is the familiar fern plant. Newly forming fronds are called fiddleheads, and they slowly uncurl as they grow. Eventually, the sporophyte will produce spores on the underside of each frond, and the cycle will begin again.

Life Cycle of Seed Plants: Conifers

The sporophyte is the familiar form for all seed plants. Unlike most seedless plants, seed plants produce two types of spores that develop into male and female gametophytes. Another difference between most seedless plants and seed plants is that the gametophytes of seed plants are microscopic.

Connecting CONCEPTS

Life Cycles Refer to the **Appendix** for detailed views of fern and conifer life cycles.

A pine tree is a typical conifer sporophyte. If you look closely at a branch of a pine tree, you may notice two different types of cones. This is because cone-bearing plants have male and female cones. Female cones are usually larger and more scaly than male cones. They live and grow for several years. Each scale of a female pine cone has two ovules that produce spores. One spore in each ovule can develop into a microscopic female gametophyte, and the rest will die. Male spores are produced inside of male cones, which only live for a few weeks. Male spores develop into pollen grains, which are the very tiny male gametophytes of seed plants.

As shown in **FIGURE 22.4,** male cones release clouds of pollen in the spring. When a pollen grain lands on a female cone, it sticks. Pollination occurs in a cone-bearing plant when a pollen grain reaches the small opening of an ovule. After pollination, eggs are produced inside the ovule and a pollen tube begins to grow from the pollen grain toward an egg. In pine species, it takes a year for the pollen tube to reach the egg, which is only several millimeters away.

Differentiated Instruction

PRE-AP

Have students construct a table that compares the life cycles of the three plant groups discussed in this section. Have them compare the sporophyte and gametophyte phases, including which is dominant, the numbers and types of spores produced, and how those spores function in the life cycle. After students have completed their tables, ask questions about plant life cycles and have students consult their tables to find the answers.

Biology Toolkit, Content Frame, p. C22

HANDS-ON ACTIVITY

Place clumps of mosses—which can be found in areas that stay moist, such as shady forests and greenhouses—in terrariums made from clear plastic storage containers with lids. Place the moss terrariums where they will receive bright light. Allow the clumps of moss to dry before showing them to students. Then have students add water to some of the terrariums. **Ask,** What happens when water comes in contact with the dry mosses? The mosses become bright green and get larger. Have students keep some of the mosses moist for several days. Students may be able to observe the growth of sporophytes.

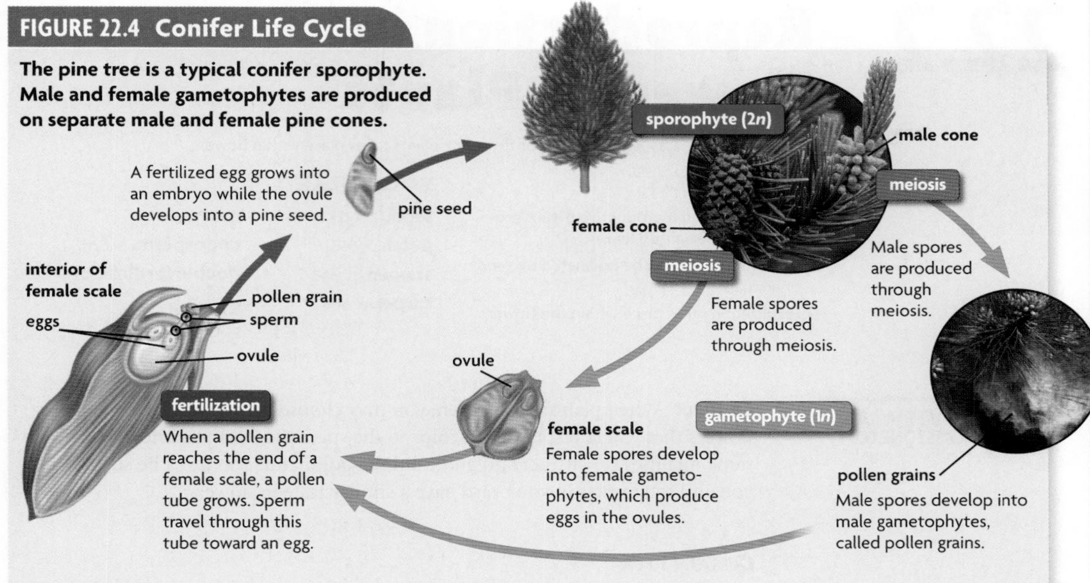

FIGURE 22.4 Conifer Life Cycle

The pine tree is a typical conifer sporophyte. Male and female gametophytes are produced on separate male and female pine cones.

Two sperm also develop inside the pollen grain during this time. Eventually, these sperm travel down the pollen tube toward the egg. The sperm of seed plants do not have flagella, since they do not need to swim through water to reach an egg. One sperm may fertilize an egg, forming a zygote, which will develop into an embryo. Meanwhile, the ovule develops into a protective pine seed. Each scale of a female pine cone can be home to two developing pine seeds. Once the seeds are mature, the scales open up and release them. The life cycle then begins again with a new sporophyte—a pine tree seedling.

A **Contrast What is the difference between how seedless plants and seed plants disperse to new areas?**

22.1 ASSESSMENT

ONLINE QUIZ ClassZone.com

REVIEWING  MAIN IDEAS

1. What is the main difference between the two types of plant bodies involved in the **alternation of generations**?
2. What is the main difference between the **gametophytes** of nonvascular plants and those of seed plants?

CRITICAL THINKING

3. **Apply** Why do seedless plants require free-standing water for sexual reproduction, while seed plants do not?
4. **Infer** The scales of female pine cones produce a sticky substance. What function might this serve?

Connecting CONCEPTS

5. **Genetics** Draw a diagram to show how cellular division through meiosis results in the haploid spores of plants.

ONLINE BIOLOGY Go to the chapter Resource Center at **ClassZone.com** for additional resources and information on plant life cycles.

TEACH FROM VISUALS

FIGURE 22.4 Lead students through each part of the conifer life cycle, starting with the pine seed. **Ask**

- What stage is the pine seed a part of? the sporophyte
- Where do the spores made by this stage form? male and female cones
- What structure does a spore in a male cone become? a pollen grain
- What is the chromosome number of the male and female gametophytes? haploid, or 1*n*
- Where does fertilization occur? ovule in a scale of a female cone
- What is the chromosome number of the cells in the embryo of a pine seed? diploid, or 2*n*

Answers

A **Contrast** Seedless plants disperse through spores, and seed plants disperse through seeds.

Assess and Reteach ▼

Assess Use the Online Quiz or Section Quiz (*Assessment Book,* p. 431).

Reteach Create a table that compares the life cycles of the three plant types in this section. Have students use their own notes to help you fill it in.

22.1 ASSESSMENT

1. The gametophyte is haploid. Haploid cells divide by mitosis to produce gametes that will ultimately result in fertilization, which gives rise to the sporophyte. The sporophyte is diploid and produces haploid spores through meiosis.
2. The gametophyte of nonvascular plants is the dominant phase; gametophytes of seed plants are microscopic.
3. Seedless plants' sperm must travel through water in order to reach and fertilize an egg. The sperm of seed plants are carried to female reproductive structures by pollen, which can be carried by wind or animals.
4. Pollen grains stick to this substance, allowing for germination and, ultimately, fertilization.
5. Students' illustration should show the process by which a single parent diploid cell (with both homologous chromosomes) divides to produce four daughter haploid cells. The illustration should show two rounds of cell division.

SECTION 22.2

▼ Plan and Prepare

Objectives

- Describe the reproductive organs and fertilization of flowering plants.
- Compare and contrast pollination by animals and by wind.

Section Resources

Unit Resource Book
Study Guide pp. 57–58
Power Notes p. 59
Reinforcement p. 60
Interactive Reader Chapter 22
Spanish Study Guide pp. 225–226
Biology Toolkit pp. C19, C38, D6
Technology
Power Presentation 22.2
Media Gallery DVD
Online Quiz 22.2

Activate Prior Knowledge Discuss the diversity of flowers. **Ask,** In what ways do different species of flowering plants differ from each other? Size, shape, color and number of petals; method of pollination (wind, animal); number of seeds produced; some flowers last a long time, while others bloom once and then wither; some smell good, others smell bad or seem odorless; some are poisonous, while others are edible. Tell students that the flowers of all flowering plants have evolved to become functioning reproductive organs.

▼ Teach

Vocabulary

Greek and Latin Word Origins Tell students that **carpel** is from the Greek *karpos,* which means "fruit." Explain that the ovary of a carpel is where plant embryos develop and the mature ovary is what we call **fruit.**

Answers

A Compare male cones

22.2 Reproduction in Flowering Plants

KEY CONCEPTS Reproduction of flowering plants takes place within flowers.

MAIN IDEAS

- Flowers contain reproductive organs protected by specialized leaves.
- Flowering plants can be pollinated by wind or animals.
- Fertilization takes place within the flower.

VOCABULARY

sepal, p. 668
petal, p. 668
stamen, p. 668
carpel, p. 668
ovary, p. 668
endosperm, p. 670
double fertilization, p. 670

Review
cotyledon, fruit

Connect When planning a garden, you may choose plants with sweet-smelling flowers that will add splashes of color to the space. But did you know that these same qualities can attract and guide animal pollinators? So don't be surprised if you and the insects in your yard have a similar taste in flowers.

MAIN IDEA

Flowers contain reproductive organs protected by specialized leaves.

Look at a bouquet of flowers in various stages of bloom, and you will likely notice that different flower parts are arranged in layers. The outermost layer of a flower is made up of sepals. **Sepals** are modified leaves that protect the developing flower. They are often green but can also be brightly colored. The layer just inside of the sepals is made of up **petals,** which are also modified leaves. Their bright colors often help to attract animal pollinators. Monocot flowers, such as lilies, have sepals and petals that look the same. These structures are often called tepals. Flowering plants that are not pollinated by animals usually have very small sepals and petals, or they have none at all.

Some species have flowers with only male or only female structures, but the flowers of most species have both. A typical flower is illustrated in **FIGURE 22.5.** A **stamen** is the male structure of a flower. Each stamen has a stalk called a filament that supports an anther. Anthers produce pollen grains, the male gametophytes. The innermost layer of a flower is made up of the female structure, called a **carpel.** Most flowers have several carpels fused together, forming a structure called a pistil. Each carpel is made of three parts. The tip, called the stigma, is often covered with a sticky substance that holds pollen grains when they land there. The style is a tube that leads from the stigma to the ovary. Female gametophytes are produced inside the **ovary,** which is found at the base of a flower.

FIGURE 22.5 This lily has both male and female structures. In lilies and other monocots, sepals and petals look similar and are often called "tepals."

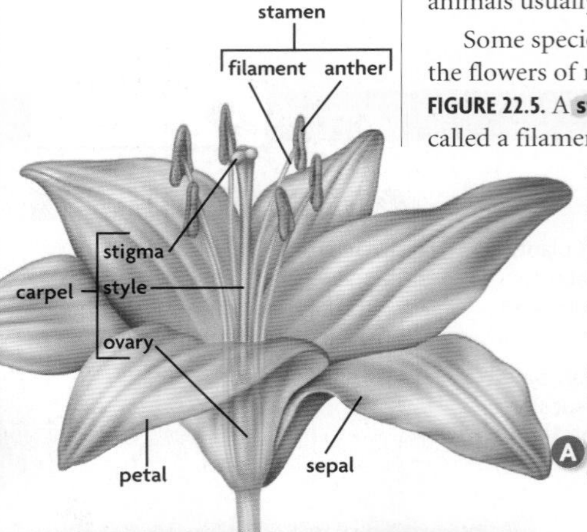

A Compare What parts of conifers have functions similar to stamens?

Differentiated Instruction

HANDS-ON ACTIVITY

To reinforce the concept that two or more carpels are fused together in the female part of most flowers, provide students with fresh or pickled cucumbers and plastic knives. Have students cut the cucumber, which is the fruit of the cucumber plant, into several circular slices. Students will be able to see three to five pie-shaped sections in the slices, each containing seeds. Each of these sections is an ovary of a different carpel.

MAIN IDEA

Flowering plants can be pollinated by wind or animals.

When a pollen grain reaches the stigma of the same plant species, that flower has been pollinated. Pollination is a necessary step of sexual reproduction in flowering plants. You can often tell how a flowering plant is pollinated by looking at its flowers. Wind-pollinated species usually have small or inconspicuous flowers and produce large amounts of pollen. A lot of energy is required to produce so much pollen.

Many flowering plants are pollinated when insects, birds, or other animals visit flowers to collect pollen or nectar as a food source. In the process of feeding, an animal is dusted with pollen grains, as shown in **FIGURE 22.6.** As the animal searches for food in another flower, pollen from the first flower may brush against the stigma of the other flower. Because animal pollinators transfer pollen in this reliable way, pollination by an animal is more efficient than wind pollination. Animal pollinators are important factors in the success and diversity of flowering plants.

FIGURE 22.6 This honeybee has many tiny hairs on its body (right). When a bee moves around inside of a flower, gathering pollen or nectar, pollen grains stick to these hairs (left). (colored SEM; magnification unknown)

A Infer **Why is pollination more reliable by animals than by wind?**

QUICK LAB **DISSECTING** NOS.1

A Closer Look at Flowers

Dissect a flower to discover how its various structures aid in reproduction.

PROBLEM How do the parts of a flower aid in reproduction?

PROCEDURE

1. Locate the outermost layer of flower parts. These are the sepals. Draw and label the sepals to begin your flower diagram. Carefully remove the sepals.
2. Petals form the next layer of flower parts. Draw and label the petals in your drawing. Carefully remove each petal.
3. Now the stamens, the male flower parts, should be exposed. Add the stamens to your drawing and label them. Label an anther and a filament in your drawing. Remove the stamens.
4. The female flower part remains. Most flowers have several carpels fused together, forming a structure called a pistil. Add the carpel or pistil to your drawing. Label the carpel or pistil, stigma, style, and ovary.

MATERIALS

- flower
- colored pencils
- tweezers
- magnifying glass

ANALYZE AND CONCLUDE

1. **Identify** Write the function of the following structures next to their labels in your drawing: sepals, petals, anther, filament, stigma, style, and ovary.
2. **Infer** Do flowers usually contain more stamens or carpels? Why do you think this is?
3. **Infer** What does the position of the anthers relative to the position of the stigmas suggest about how this flower is pollinated?

PRE-AP

Have students write a five-minute essay that identifies the type of symbiosis exhibited by some different pollinators and flowering plants. Ask them to include an example of both mutualism and commensalism and to consider why parasitism does not figure into these types of interactions.

Biology Toolkit, Quick-Write, p. C19

BELOW LEVEL

Have students list and then group keywords in this section: *stamen-anther-filament, carpel-stigma-style-ovary,* and *petals-sepals.* Have students differentiate between the groups by describing what they relate to. Example: the anther and filament are part of the stamen, the male reproductive structure of a flower.

Biology Toolkit, List-Group-Label, p. D6

Answers

A Infer Animals move methodically from flower to flower in search of food and transfer pollen in the process, but wind scatters pollen randomly, so a lot of it does not land on flowers of the same species.

QUICK LAB

Time 30 minutes 

Lab Binder Plants, pp. 35–36

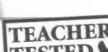

Purpose Explore floral structure by dissecting a flower.

LAB PREPARATION

- Use large flowers such as lilies, tulips, daylilies, gladioli, and irises.

LAB MANAGEMENT

- Use **FIGURE 22.5** to point out that sepals are not always green and may closely resemble petals. Also, point out that some flowers can have a superior ovary, such as the lily flower pictured, but that others (for example, iris and gladiolus) have an inferior ovary, found below the point of attachment of petals and sepals.

Teacher Note "Students took their time in completing the drawing, leaving little time for the functions."

Safety Some people are allergic to pollen. Caution students not to hold flowers near their faces. Have them wear gloves or wash their hands thoroughly after handling flowers.

Answers

Analyze and Conclude

1. sepals: protect a developing flower; petals: attract pollinators; anther: produces pollen; filament: supports anther; stigma: receives pollen; style: connects stigma to ovary; ovary: produces and houses eggs
2. more stamens, increases the odds that more flowers will be pollinated
3. If the anthers are below the stigmas, a flower is less likely to be self-pollinated than if the anthers are above the stigmas.

▼ Teach *continued*

The Inside Story

Charles Darwin was fascinated by the variation in flower structure he observed among orchids, and he wrote essays on the subject. In his writings, he hypothesized that the structures of orchid flowers were adaptations to the physiology and behavior of specific pollinators. Darwin wrote about one orchid native to Madagascar, *Angraecum sesquipedale,* whose nectar is found at the bottom of a floral tube that is 30 centimeters long. He wrote that a moth with a proboscis long enough to reach the orchid's nectar must also live in the area, but he never saw it.

More than 40 years after Darwin's death, a hawk moth with a 30-centimeter proboscis was observed pollinating the orchid. When not feeding, the proboscis coils up. Tell students to see page 616 of Chapter 20 for a photo of the moth and orchid.

Answers

A Summarize One sperm fertilizes the egg; the other unites with the polar nuclei to form the endosperm.

MAIN IDEA

Fertilization takes place within the flower.

In flowering plants, as in all vascular plants, the sporophyte is the dominant phase. The parts of a flower that you have just learned about are all part of the sporophyte, while the gametophytes of flowering plants are tiny and enclosed within flower parts. **FIGURE 22.7** illustrates the life cycle of flowering plants.

***Connecting* CONCEPTS**

Meiosis Recall from **Chapter 6** that meiosis is the form of cellular division needed for sexual reproduction. Gametes—sperm and eggs—are haploid, containing half as many chromosomes as somatic cells do.

Production of Male Gametophytes

Recall that anthers produce pollen grains, which are the male gametophytes of seed plants. Cells within the anthers divide by meiosis to produce four male spores. Each spore divides again, by mitosis, producing two haploid cells. These two cells, together with a thick wall that protects them, form a single pollen grain. Wind-pollinated plants have light, fine pollen grains that can be carried far by the wind. Pollen from wind-pollinated plants, such as ragweed, is the source of some outdoor allergies.

Production of Female Gametophytes

One female gametophyte can form in each ovule of a flower's ovary. One cell in the ovule divides by meiosis to produce four female spores. In most flowering plants, three of these spores die. The nucleus of the last spore grows, dividing by mitosis three times, resulting in one spore with eight nuclei. Membranes grow between the nuclei to form seven cells. Together, these seven cells make up the female gametophyte, which is sometimes called an embryo sac. One large, central cell has two haploid nuclei, called polar nuclei. One of the other cells develops into an egg.

Double Fertilization

After pollination, one cell in the pollen grain grows into a pollen tube. This tube extends down the style toward the ovule. The other cell in the pollen grain divides by mitosis, producing two sperm. Both sperm travel down the pollen tube. One sperm fertilizes the egg. The other sperm combines with the polar nuclei in the embryo sac. This cell now has a triploid ($3n$) nucleus. It will become the **endosperm,** a food supply for the developing plant embryo. The process in which one sperm fertilizes an egg and the other forms a triploid cell is called **double fertilization.** Double fertilization only happens in flowering plants and gives them an advantage over cone-bearing plants. Cone-bearing plants produce a food supply for each egg before fertilization. However, if the egg of a flowering plant is not fertilized, the plant does not waste energy making an unneeded food supply.

VISUAL VOCAB

The **endosperm** nourishes the developing plant embryo inside of the seed coat. The prefix *endo-* means "inside," and *sperm* comes from the Greek word *sperma,* which means "seed."

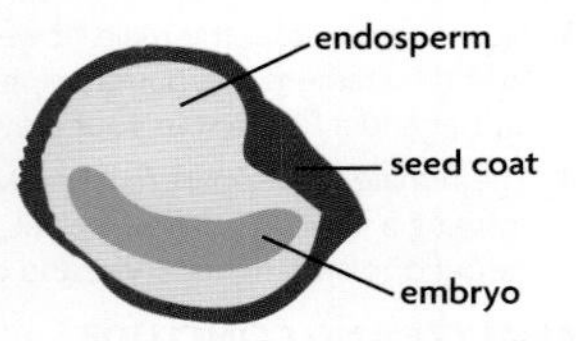

 **Summarize** **What is the function of each sperm during double fertilization?**

Differentiated Instruction

INCLUSION

To help students who will have a hard time processing the information in the text above and relating it to **FIGURE 22.7,** model how you read and interpret the material for understanding. You can also have students model double fertilization with yarn (or string) and marbles (or gumdrops).

The yarn or string can be used to form the outlines of a carpel with an ovule inside. Different colors and sizes of marbles or gumdrops can represent pollen grains, sperm cells, egg cells, and the polar nuclei. Explain that each marble or gumdrop carries one set of chromosomes. Have students show pollination, transfer of a pollen grain to a stigma, two sperm moving down the style, one sperm joining the egg to make a diploid ($2n$) nucleus, and one sperm joining with the polar nuclei to make a triploid ($3n$) nucleus.

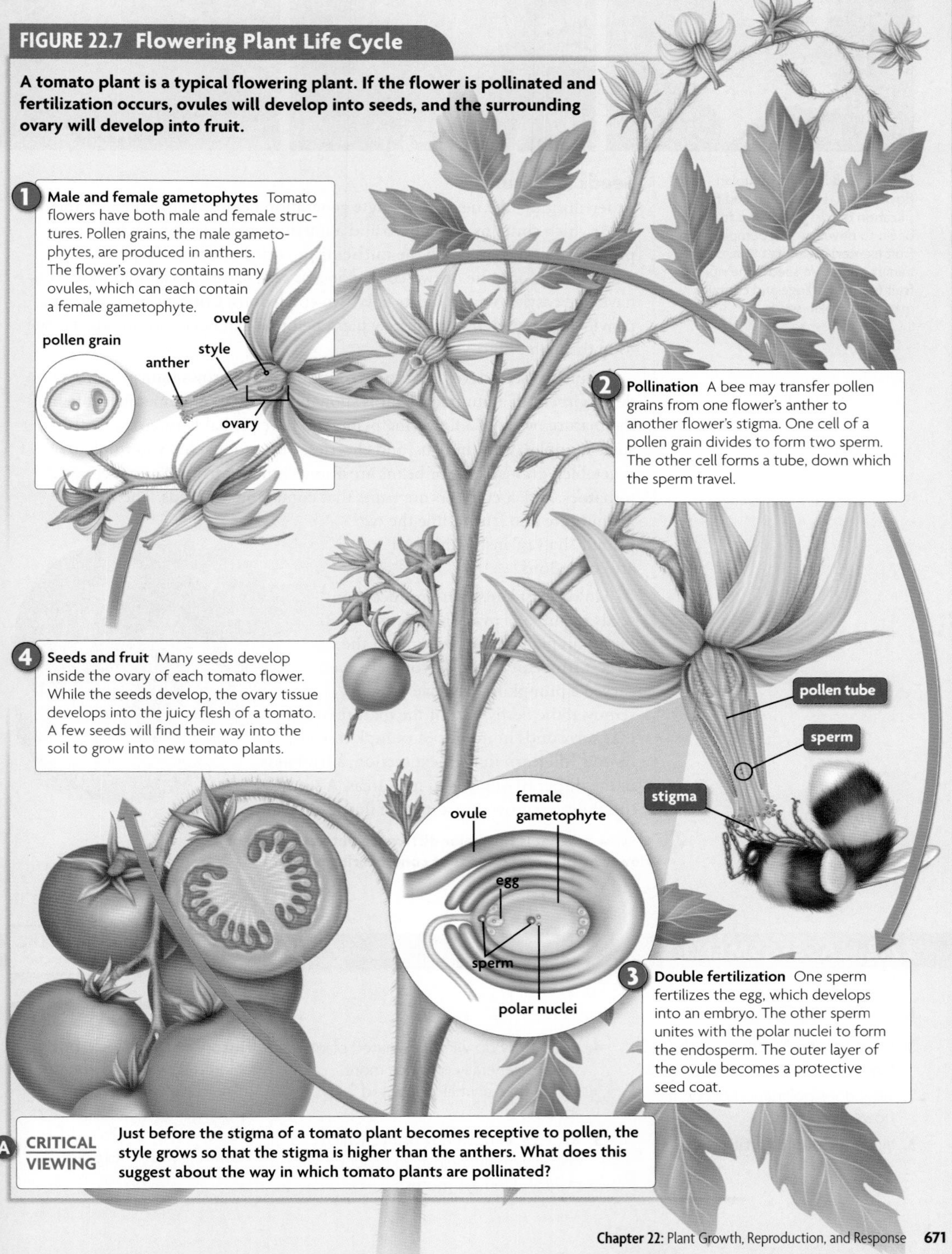

FIGURE 22.7 Flowering Plant Life Cycle
A tomato plant is a typical flowering plant. If the flower is pollinated and fertilization occurs, ovules will develop into seeds, and the surrounding ovary will develop into fruit.
1 Male and female gametophytes Tomato flowers have both male and female structures. Pollen grains, the male gametophytes, are produced in anthers. The flower's ovary contains many ovules, which can each contain a female gametophyte.
pollen grain
anther
style
ovule
ovary
2 Pollination A bee may transfer pollen grains from one flower's anther to another flower's stigma. One cell of a pollen grain divides to form two sperm. The other cell forms a tube, down which the sperm travel.
pollen tube
sperm
stigma
female gametophyte
ovule
egg
sperm
polar nuclei
3 Double fertilization One sperm fertilizes the egg, which develops into an embryo. The other sperm unites with the polar nuclei to form the endosperm. The outer layer of the ovule becomes a protective seed coat.
4 Seeds and fruit Many seeds develop inside the ovary of each tomato flower. While the seeds develop, the ovary tissue develops into the juicy flesh of a tomato. A few seeds will find their way into the soil to grow into new tomato plants.

A CRITICAL VIEWING Just before the stigma of a tomato plant becomes receptive to pollen, the style grows so that the stigma is higher than the anthers. What does this suggest about the way in which tomato plants are pollinated?

ONLINE BIOLOGY Go to the chapter Resource Center at **ClassZone.com** for additional resources and information on plant reproduction.

TEACH FROM VISUALS

FIGURE 22.7 Walk students through each step of the diagram of a tomato plant. **Ask,** How many cells appear to be inside the pollen grain shown in step 1? two Explain that the larger of these structures divides to form the sperm. The other structure is called a tube nucleus, which is responsible for forming a pollen tube through the style. **Ask,** How many pollen grains must fall on the stigma in order to ensure that many seeds are formed? many

Take It Further

Tomatoes are a popular garden plant that can be grown from seed. Seedlings emerge about three to five days after seeds are planted, and the plants begin to flower in about two to three weeks. The plants are able to self-pollinate. The vibrations given off by bees that land on the flowers loosen some of the pollen and allow it to pollinate the nearby stigma.

Answers

A **Critical Viewing** The fact that the stigma extends beyond the anthers suggests that tomatoes are cross pollinated.

BELOW LEVEL

Have students translate **FIGURE 22.7** into a sequence diagram, starting with the male and female gametophyte production in step 1. Tell them to label each part of the diagram with whichever stage, gametophyte or sporophyte, the life cycle is in.

Biology Toolkit, Sequence Diagram, p. C38

▼ Teach *continued*

ONLINE BIOLOGY Go to the chapter Resource Center at **ClassZone.com** for additional resources and information on seeds and fruits.

TEACH FROM VISUALS

FIGURE 22.8 Use these photos to review the relationship between flowers, fruits, and seeds in flowering plants. **Ask**

- How do you think the fruit is able to grow in size? Sugars produced by photosynthesis in the leaves and water absorbed from the soil move through the stems and are stored in the fruit.
- How do you know that sugars are stored in a fruit such as this pumpkin? It tastes sweet.

Answers

A Contrast The seeds of flowering plants are enclosed in fruit.

▼ Assess and Reteach

Assess Use the Online Quiz or Section Quiz (*Assessment Book,* p. 432).

Reteach Have students come to the board and, person by person, contribute to a drawing of how a flowering plant goes through a complete cycle of reproduction.

FIGURE 22.8 After a pumpkin flower (left) is pollinated and fertilization occurs, seeds and fruit begin to develop. The pumpkin fruit (center) is green at first, containing immature seeds. The ripe fruit (right) is orange and contains mature pumpkin seeds.

Seeds and Fruit

At fertilization, the next sporophyte generation begins. The ovule becomes a seed, which contains an embryo and a nutritious endosperm enclosed by a protective seed coat. Using the nutrients provided by the endosperm, the embryo develops one or two cotyledons, or seed leaves. Recall that monocots have one cotyledon and dicots have two cotyledons. Cotyledons sometimes provide nourishment for the new plant before it can begin producing its own food through photosynthesis.

While the seed develops, the surrounding ovary grows into a fruit. The development of a pumpkin fruit is shown in **FIGURE 22.8.** Remember, a fruit is the mature ovary of a flowering plant. You have probably eaten many fruits, such as apples, watermelons, and cherries. Many foods that you think of as vegetables, grains, nuts, or beans are also technically fruits. Sweet peppers, tomatoes, and cucumbers are fruits that contain many seeds. The shells of peanuts are also fruit, while the two peanut "halves" inside the shell are cotyledons.

Flowering plants that produce many seeds within one ovary have larger fruit. Pumpkin plants produce some of the largest fruits on record. If you have ever carved a pumpkin, you have actually removed the fleshy part of the mature ovary that surrounds hundreds of pumpkin seeds. As you will learn in the next section, a fruit aids in the dispersal of seeds to new areas. A seed has the ability to grow into a mature flowering plant.

A Contrast What is the major difference between seeds of flowering plants and seeds of cone-bearing plants?

22.2 ASSESSMENT

ONLINE QUIZ ClassZone.com

REVIEWING MAIN IDEAS

1. What are the functions of the four basic parts found in most flowers?
2. How does pollination occur in flowering plants?
3. What is **double fertilization**?

CRITICAL THINKING

4. **Infer** Why do wind-pollinated plant species generally produce more pollen than animal-pollinated species?
5. **Analyze** In flowering plants, which cells divide by meiosis to produce male and female spores?

***Connecting* CONCEPTS**

6. **History of Life** Would brightly colored flowers and sweet, juicy fruits have been as beneficial to the earliest land plants as they are to modern flowering plants? Explain.

22.2 ASSESSMENT

1. Sepals protect the developing flower, petals attract pollinators, stamens have the male reproductive organs, and carpels have the female organs.
2. Wind or animals transfer pollen to a flower's stigma.
3. Double fertilization is a process that occurs in flowering plants in which one sperm fertilizes an egg and another combines with the polar nuclei to form the endosperm, which nourishes the developing embryo.
4. Wind pollination is less targeted and efficient than pollination by animals. By producing a lot of pollen, wind-pollinated plants improve their odds of pollination.
5. Cells in the anthers divide by meiosis to produce male spores; one cell in each ovule divides by meiosis to produce female spores.
6. No, because at the time of the earliest flowering plants, there were far fewer animal species; therefore, there would have been few animal pollinators. Brightly colored flowers and edible fruits would not be advantageous to plants.

22.3 Seed Dispersal and Germination

KEY CONCEPT Seeds disperse and begin to grow when conditions are favorable.

MAIN IDEAS
- Animals, wind, and water can spread seeds.
- Seeds begin to grow when environmental conditions are favorable.

VOCABULARY
dormancy, p. 674
germination, p. 675

Connect It's lunchtime—how about a burrito stuffed with seeds and fruit? This burrito may not sound too appetizing; that is, unless you know that white rice and beans are seeds and tomatoes are fruits. Although burritos are cooked, many seeds and fruits we eat are not. Animals eat seeds and fruits for their nutritional benefits, and plants benefit by getting their seeds dispersed.

MAIN IDEA

Animals, wind, and water can spread seeds.

You have learned that cone-bearing plants do not bear fruit, and their seeds are often spread by wind and gravity. The function of fruit in flowering plants is to help disperse seeds. Seed dispersal is important because a plant that grows right next to its parent may compete with it for space, sunlight, water, and nutrients. As shown in **FIGURE 22.9,** fruits come in a variety of different shapes and sizes, each of which is adapted to spread seeds to new areas.

Fleshy fruits, such as apples and berries, attract animals with their fragrant, nutritious offerings. When an animal eats the fruit, it digests the flesh. But the seeds, covered with a tough protective coat, pass through. Eventually, the animal eliminates the seeds from its digestive tract, along with a supply of fecal fertilizer that serves as a sprouting ground for the seedling. Some plants have fruits that can hitchhike a ride with an animal that is passing by. Burrs, for example, can cling to a passing animal and fall off later in a new area.

Seeds dispersed by wind often have fruits that act like parachutes or wings. Clumps of cotton from cottonwood trees are actually fruits with a seed attached. Some plants that grow near water produce fruits that float. Coconuts can travel thousands of miles across oceans and arrive on different islands.

VOCABULARY

The word *disperse* means "to scatter apart." The prefix *dis-* means "apart", and *sperse* comes from the Latin verb *spargere,* which means "to scatter."

A Analyze Why is it important for a fruit to ripen when its seeds are mature?

FIGURE 22.9 Fruits can take many forms, including burrs, parachute-like structures such as cypselae, and winglike structures such as samaras.

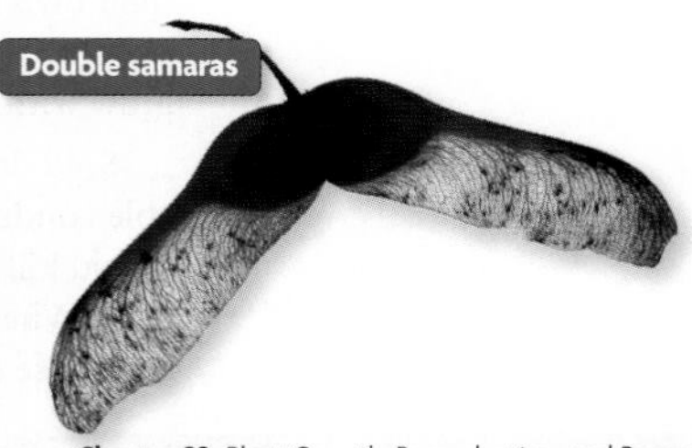

Differentiated Instruction

ENGLISH LEARNERS

Have groups of three or four students create a sequence diagram titled "How Seeds Germinate." Provide some of the events:

- A parent plant releases seeds.
- The seeds may lie dormant for a time.
- Water activates enzymes inside the seed.
- Leaves develop and begin to make food for the seedling through photosynthesis.

Tell students to fill in the gaps in the diagram.

Biology Toolkit, Sequence Diagram, p. C38

PRE-AP

Tell students that a new island has formed near an underwater volcanic eruption. It has a long, flat shoreline sloping upwards to the rim of a crater, which eventually becomes dormant and cool. Have students spend five minutes writing about how plants from nearby islands might colonize this new island. How might seeds arrive on the island? How might they reach the inside of the crater? When might animals arrive?

Biology Toolkit, Quick-Write, p. C19

Plan and Prepare

Objectives

- Compare methods of seed dispersal by animals, gravity, wind, and water.
- Summarize the events in seed germination and its requirements.

Section Resources

Unit Resource Book	
Study Guide	pp. 61–62
Power Notes	p. 63
Reinforcement	p. 64
Pre-AP Activity	pp. 75–76
Interactive Reader	Chapter 22
Spanish Study Guide	pp. 227–228
Biology Toolkit	pp. C19, C38
Technology	
Power Presentation	22.3
Media Gallery DVD	
Online Quiz	22.3

Activate Prior Knowledge Tell students that if they have ever pulled burrs off of their socks or jeans, they have helped a plant disperse its seeds. **Ask**

- Which of the fruits shown in **FIGURE 22.9** would not travel far in a dense forest? Cypselae probably would not get very far because they would land on trees soon after taking flight; wind would be limited.
- What kind of habitat do you think plants with cypselae are best adapted to? open fields, prairies, meadows

Teach

Answers

A Analyze If fruit is not ripe when seeds are mature, then animals are less likely to eat them and disperse the seeds. If fruit ripens before the seeds mature, the animal may disperse the seeds before they are able to withstand exposure to various conditions of the environment.

▼ Teach *continued*

DATA ANALYSIS

Discuss

If students have difficulty identifying design flaws in the Data Analysis activity, have them list all the variables in the experiment. **Ask**

- How many independent variables should a scientific experiment have? one
- What are the two possible independent variables in this experiment? amounts of water and sunlight Point out that because of the way the pots are lined up, it is likely that Pot C will get the least amount of sunlight, Pot B the second least, and Pot A the most.
- What other factors have not been controlled? In addition to distance from the window, the variety of radish seeds used and the depth at which they are planted have not been defined.

Answers

1. The distances between the pots and the window are different. This means that each set of seeds may receive a different amount of sunlight, which adds another variable to the experiment. If germination data differ between the pots, students will have no way of knowing if these differences are due to the variable they were trying to test (water) or the different levels of exposure to sunlight. Also, two radish seeds per pot is a very small sample size, and students should plant all seeds at the same depth in the soil.
2. Line up the pots so that each is equally close to the window (light source). Increase the sample size to five or ten seeds per pot.

Unit Resource Book, Data Analysis, p. 73

DATA ANALYSIS

IDENTIFYING EXPERIMENTAL DESIGN FLAWS

Recall that a good experimental design is necessary to obtain valid results. In the experiment described below, a group of students collected data about the effect of water on germination.

- Students planted 2 radish seeds in each of 3 flower pots.
- Each pot contained the same amount and type of soil.
- The pots were placed close to a window, as shown at the right.
- Pot A was given 200 mL of water each day, Pot B was given 100 mL of water each day, and Pot C was given no water. This watering pattern was continued for one full week.
- Every day, students recorded the seeds' progress.
- The students made conclusions about the amount of water that is best for radish seed germination.

1. **Analyze** Which parts of the experimental design are flawed?
2. **Design** How would you change the experimental design to collect valid results?

MAIN IDEA

Seeds begin to grow when environmental conditions are favorable.

After a parent plant releases seeds, it may be days, months, or years until the seeds begin to grow into new plants. In fact, scientists recently found a 2000-year-old seed from a now-extinct species of date palm tree in Israel. After they placed it in the conditions the tree needs to grow, the seed sprouted. How can the living embryo inside a seed last years without food or water?

Dormancy

For 2000 years, the embryo inside the date palm seed was in a state of **dormancy.** When a seed is dormant, the embryo has stopped growing. For some plant species, proper temperature, moisture, oxygen, and light levels are enough to end dormancy.

Other plant species have seeds that stay dormant even during good growing conditions. For example, strawberry seeds remain dormant until their seed coats are weakened in the digestive tract of an animal. This way, the seeds are not only carried far from the parent plant but they are also deposited with their own batch of fertilizer. Other seeds have waterproof seed coats that can only be cracked by winter ice. Then, in the spring, the embryo can begin to grow with less chance of freezing than if it had begun to grow in the fall.

Seed dormancy allows the next generation of plants to grow under favorable conditions. Inside the seed coat, an embryo can withstand extremes that would kill a young seedling. Gardeners contend with seed dormancy all the time. When soil is turned over before planting a garden, fresh air and sunlight can cause the buried seeds of unexpected plants to come out of dormancy.

Differentiated Instruction

TEACH WITH TECHNOLOGY

Create a digital slide show of seed dispersers. Include dispersers from different classes and environments, such as the following:

- pinyon jay (*Gymnorhinus cyanocephalus*), a bird of the southwest United States that feeds on and disperses pinyon pine seeds, which we know as pine nuts and pignoles
- tambaqui (*Colossoma macropomum*), a large fish of the Amazon and Orinoco river basins that disperses rain forest tree seeds
- Eastern gray squirrel (*Sciurus carolinensis*), a small rodent that feeds on and disperses various nuts and acorns of North American forests
- flying fox *(Pteropus spp.)*, also known as a fruit bat; this flying mammal disperses seeds and also acts as a pollinator

Go to **ClassZone.com** for links to Internet sources of images and information on these species.

FIGURE 22.10 The embryonic root emerges from the seed.

As the root continues to emerge, root hairs can be seen.

The embryonic shoot and the cotyledons are revealed.

The young plant is completely free of its seed coat.

Germination

Many types of seeds begin to grow when there are certain changes in temperature, moisture, or light levels. During **germination,** the embryo breaks out of the seed coat and begins to grow into a seedling, as shown in **FIGURE 22.10.** Germination begins when the embryo starts to take up water. Water causes the seed to swell and crack the seed coat. As the embryo grows, the embryonic root, called a radicle, breaks through the cracks. Water also activates enzymes inside the seed. Recall that enzymes are proteins that need specific conditions to speed up chemical reactions. These enzymes help to break down material in the endosperm into sugars, which are moved to the growing embryo.

As the embryo continues to grow, a young shoot called the plumule eventually breaks through the surface of the soil. In most monocots, the cotyledon stays underground while the shoot grows upwards. Some species of dicots have cotyledons that stay below ground, but the cotyledons of other dicots emerge above ground with the growing shoot. When leaves emerge from the shoot, they begin to make food through photosynthesis. Once photosynthesis begins, the young plant is called a seedling.

Connecting CONCEPTS

Enzymes Recall from **Chapter 2** that enzymes are catalysts for chemical reactions in living things. Enzymes allow chemical reactions to take place under controlled conditions.

A Sequence **Which emerges first from a seed, a root or a shoot?**

22.3 ASSESSMENT

ONLINE QUIZ
ClassZone.com

REVIEWING MAIN IDEAS

1. What are three ways that seeds of flowering plants can be dispersed?
2. What is the advantage of most seeds going through a stage of **dormancy** before **germination**?

CRITICAL THINKING

3. **Analyze** How are enzymes involved in the process of germination?
4. **Infer** What is the adaptive advantage to water uptake causing a seed coat to crack?

Connecting CONCEPTS

5. **Adaptations** Some tropical plant species have fruits with air cavities that allow them to float. How might natural selection have led to this adaptation?

22.3 ASSESSMENT

1. wind, water, animals
2. Seeds can "wait out" unfavorable conditions that a seedling would not be able to withstand, such as freezing temperatures.
3. Enzymes inside a seed help to break down material in the endosperm into sugars. These sugars are used by the growing embryo.
4. A developing seedling needs water to grow. If the seed coat cracks during dry conditions, the seedling may not survive.
5. Through a random mutation, the seeds of an individual plant may have formed with air cavities. If these seeds fell into water and the air cavities allowed them to float, the water may have dispersed the seeds into new areas, enabling these plants to get established and increase in number.

Address Misconceptions

Common Misconception All mature seeds have stored food in endosperm.

Correcting the Misconception Most monocot seeds have endosperm, but the endosperm has been used up in a mature dicot seed. Even orchids, which are monocots, have such tiny seeds that they have almost no stored nutrients. Symbiotic fungi help them get nutrients for germination and growth.

Take It Further

In the wild, **seed dormancy** is usually overcome as a seed spends time in the ground through the winter, and frost and weathering action soften the hard seed coat. Then the embryo is able to take up water, which allows it to grow and eventually crack the seed coat.

Answers

A Sequence the root, or radicle

Assess and Reteach ▼

Assess Use the Online Quiz or Section Quiz (*Assessment Book,* p. 433).

Reteach Review the animation of seed dispersal at **ClassZone.com** and have students help you create a sequence diagram of seed germination.

INVESTIGATION

Time 30 minutes TEACHER TESTED
Teacher Preparation
Student Difficulty
Lab Binder Plants, pp. 27–30

Purpose Observe how irradiating radish seeds affects their germination.

Overview Students will germinate irradiated and nonirradiated radish seeds. They will

- observe the seeds each day and record any changes in each seed
- measure the size of seedling structures after five days
- compare the germination rate of irradiated and nonirradiated seeds and their seedling structures

LAB PREPARATION

- Set up an area in the lab where seeds can be kept under a fluorescent light or indoor gardening light.
- Before beginning the experiment, discuss with students the reason the radish seeds are irradiated. Explain that radish seeds are germinated to produce fresh sprouts, as are alfalfa seeds. Outbreaks of illness caused by *Salmonella* and *Escherichia coli* bacteria have been traced to fresh produce, including sprouts. The sources of the infections spread by eating fresh sprouts have been found to be contaminated seeds. Irradiation is a method of sterilizing the seeds, which kills the disease-causing bacteria they may carry.

MATERIALS

- 2 plastic grids
- 2 petri dishes
- pencil
- forceps
- 7 nonirradiated radish seeds
- 7 irradiated radish seeds
- paper towel
- small container to hold petri dishes
- fluorescent light
- hand lens
- metric ruler

PROCESS SKILLS

- **Observing**
- **Measuring**
- **Collecting**
- **Interpreting Data**

NOS.5 Apply standard techniques in laboratory investigations to measure physical quantities in appropriate units and convert known quantities to other units as necessary.

Seed Germination

Germination is the process in which a seed develops into a plant. During this lab, you will observe the emergence of different seedling parts and track their growth. As a class, you will test the effect that different levels of radiation have on the process of germination. Irradiated seeds have been treated with specific levels of radiation; nonirradiated seeds have not been exposed to radiation.

PROBLEM What effect does radiation have on the process of seed germination?

PROCEDURE

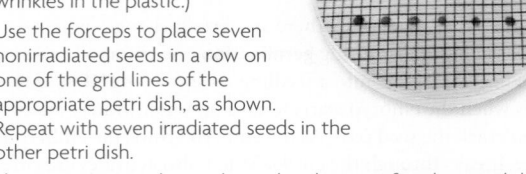

1. Label two plastic grids with your initials, date, and level of radiation. Place one grid in the top of each petri dish. (You may want to put a bit of water between the petri dish and the plastic grid to hold it in place. Make sure you smooth out any air pockets or wrinkles in the plastic.)
2. Use the forceps to place seven nonirradiated seeds in a row on one of the grid lines of the appropriate petri dish, as shown. Repeat with seven irradiated seeds in the other petri dish.
3. Place a paper towel over the grid in the top of each petri dish. Wet the paper towel thoroughly and cover each dish with its bottom half.
4. Put the petri dishes in a small container. Rest the petri dishes at a slight angle against the side of the container, as shown. Add water to the container to a depth of 2 cm.
5. Place the container holding the petri dishes under a fluorescent light or close to a window.
6. Beginning on the day after you set up the experiment (Day 1), observe the process of seed germination for each seed. Use a hand lens to examine each seed closely. Using two tables similar to Table 1 (one for control and one for irradiated seeds), record the day that these events occur for each seed:
   - the embryo splits from its seed coat
   - the radicle emerges
   - the plumule emerges
   - the cotyledons emerge

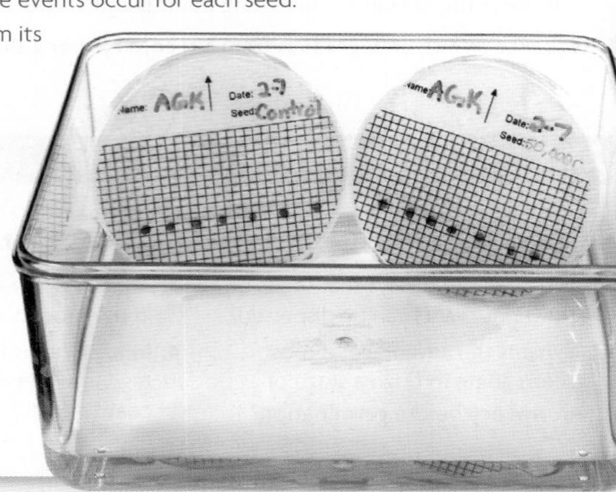

Answers

Expected Results

Students should have found that seeds that were irradiated germinated at a lower rate than nonirradiated seeds did. Students may also find that growth of seedlings is slower or less successful.

Analyze and Conclude

1. Order of structure emergence should always be the same.
2. Size differences of the same structures could be due to when the seeds first germinated and when structures first emerged from the seed coat. In general, structures of irradiated seeds' seedlings may be smaller than those of the nonirradiated group.
3. Calculations should reflect a lower frequency of germination in the irradiated group of seeds.
4. Students should conclude that radiation had a negative effect on germination.

TABLE 1. SEED GERMINATION AND EMERGENCE OF SEEDLING PARTS

	Newly Split Seed Coats	Newly Emerged Radicles	Newly Emerged Plumules	Newly Emerged Cotyledons
Day 1				
Day 2				
Day 3				
Day 4				

7. Observe the germinating seeds for four days. Be sure to keep the paper towel moist by adding water to the container, as necessary, up to 2 cm deep.
8. On the last day of your experiment, randomly pick three of the germinated seedlings from each dish. Use a ruler to measure the radicle/root length, plumule/stem length, and cotyledon/leaf length of each of these seedlings. Record this data for both sets of seedlings in your notebook.

ANALYZE AND CONCLUDE

1. **Analyze** Did the seedling structures emerge in the same order in all of your germinating seeds? Describe any variation that you observed.
2. **Analyze** When you measured seedling structures on the last day of the experiment, did the size of the same structures differ from one seedling to another? If so, what would account for this difference?
3. **Calculate** What percentage of your nonirradiated seeds germinated? What percentage of your irradiated seeds germinated?
4. **Analyze** Pool your class data for percent germination (question 3) by finding the average percent germination for level of radiation. What effect did level of radiation have on seed germination?
5. **Compare** Compare your measurements with the measurements of seedlings that were exposed to a different level of radiation. Did the level of radiation affect the growth rate of the seedlings?
6. **Infer** You may have noticed that the seeds that germinated increased in size before the seed coats cracked open. What likely caused this increase in size?
7. **Infer** At what point in the germination process would photosynthesis begin to provide energy for further seedling growth?

EXTEND YOUR INVESTIGATION

Plant the seedlings from each petri dish into two flower plots. Track their development as they grow into mature radish plants.

During germination, the embryo emerges from its seed coat and begins to grow into a seedling.

INVESTIGATION

LAB MANAGEMENT

- Instead of petri dishes, resealable plastic bags can be used as containers for germinating seeds. The bags can be hung on string under a light.
- Allow students 10–15 minutes each day for four days in order to observe seedlings and record data.
- Before students begin to collect data, go over the information in the data table. Emphasize that students must prepare two data tables, one for the irradiated seeds and one for the control, or nonirradiated seeds. Also, explain that the columns in the data table list events of seed germination in the order in which they occur, from left to right. Emphasize that once an event has been recorded as occurring on a particular day, that seed should not be counted for that event again.

POST-LAB DISCUSSION

Have student groups record their results in a class data table on the board or an overhead projector. Then have them discuss the results as a class. **Ask,** What is a possible drawback to using radiation to sterilize seeds, such as radish seeds, to be germinated for sprout production? Based on results, students should realize that radiation also reduces the germination rate of seeds, and may result in deformed or stunted seedlings.

Explain that radiation damages the chromosomes in the cells and that this can cause mutations or disrupt the process of mitosis, both of which can lead to abnormal cells and possibly cell death.

5. Seedlings that were exposed to more radiation as seeds may exhibit less growth.
6. The embryo takes up water, causing the seed to swell.
7. when the cotyledons emerge

Extend Your Investigation

In the field, radishes grow from seed to plants with roots ready for harvest in three to six weeks. Growing times may be longer for radishes grown indoors. Spring varieties mature more quickly that winter varieties. Spring varieties should be planted 1/2 to 1 inch apart. Winter varieties should be planted 2 to 4 inches apart. A slow-release fertilizer should be mixed with potting soil before the radish seedlings are planted. Radishes should be watered regularly. Harvesting of radishes normally begins just before the roots reach 1 inch in diameter. Radish roots thicken in response to short days; plants should not be exposed to more than eight to ten hours of light per day.

SECTION 22.4

Plan and Prepare

Objectives

- Survey vegetative reproduction in plants.
- Identify methods and advantages of vegetative propagation of plants.

Section Resources

Unit Resource Book	
Study Guide	pp. 65–66
Power Notes	p. 67
Reinforcement	p. 68
Interactive Reader	Chapter 22
Spanish Study Guide	pp. 229–230
Biology Toolkit	p. D9
Technology	
Power Presentation	22.4
Media Gallery DVD	
Online Quiz	22.4

Activate Prior Knowledge Have students share experiences they have had with growing plants from bulbs or pieces of tubers. **Ask,** What plants have you observed growing from parts other than seeds? *Sample Answer:* potato plants sprouting from a potato's eye; plantlets on a kalanchoe; runners in lawn grass, strawberries, or mint

Teach

Science Trivia

- The world's smallest flowering plant, *Wolffia microscopica,* is also one of the fastest reproducers. It can reproduce itself vegetatively by budding every 30 hours.
- One of the oldest living things in the United States also owes its record-making existence to vegetative reproduction. A Mojave Desert creosote bush, *Larrea tridentata,* that exists as a ring of shrubs 15 meters (50 ft) in diameter, is estimated to have started from a seed that germinated 12,000 years ago.

22.4 Asexual Reproduction

KEY CONCEPTS Plants can produce genetic clones of themselves through asexual reproduction.

MAIN IDEAS
- Plants can reproduce asexually with stems, leaves, or roots.
- Humans can produce plants with desirable traits using vegetative structures.

VOCABULARY
regeneration, p. 678
vegetative reproduction, p. 678
Review
asexual reproduction

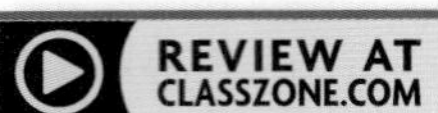

Connect Have you ever noticed that some plants, such as grasses and irises, grow in clumps? If you try to pull up a single iris, you'll likely find that it is connected to others by underground stems. These clumps are often made up of clones, or genetically identical copies, of one individual parent plant.

MAIN IDEA

Plants can reproduce asexually with stems, leaves, or roots.

Connecting CONCEPTS

Asexual Reproduction Recall from **Chapter 5** that asexual reproduction is the production of offspring from a single parent. These offspring are produced through mitosis and are genetically identical to the parent.

A combination of sexual and asexual reproduction helps plants to populate a variety of environments. Sexual reproduction gives rise to genetic diversity, which allows a population to adapt to changing conditions. Asexual reproduction allows a well-adapted plant to make many copies of itself. Most plants have a way of cloning themselves through asexual reproduction.

Plants that can grow a new individual from a fragment of a stem, leaf, or root are reproducing by **regeneration.** For example, the prickly pear cactus shown in **FIGURE 22.11** has a jointed stem that looks like teardrop-shaped pads stuck together. If one of these "pads" falls off, it can take root and a new plant will grow.

Vegetative reproduction is a type of asexual reproduction in which stems, leaves, or roots attached to the parent plant produce new individuals. One stunning example of vegetative reproduction is a forest of aspen trees in Utah that would almost cover 100 football fields. The forest is actually 47,000 trunks growing from the roots of one parent plant.

FIGURE 22.11 The jointed stem of this prickly pear cactus is made of teardrop-shaped pads. A pad that falls to the ground can grow into a full-size plant.

Many plants have structures that are specifically adapted for vegetative reproduction.

- **Stolons** Some plants send out stems that grow horizontally along the ground. These stems are called runners, or stolons. At certain points on a stolon, roots and leaves are produced, and a new plant can grow. Strawberries reproduce almost exclusively in this way.
- **Rhizomes** Other plants, such as irises, can reproduce using horizontal underground stems called rhizomes. New plants grow from buds in the rhizome's joints, even if separated from the parent plant.

Differentiated Instruction

ENGLISH LEARNERS

Have students learn about asexual reproduction by creating an analogies chart that might read like this:

Strawberries	are to	stolons	as
Irises	are to	rhizomes	as
Potatoes	are to	tubers	as
Daffodils	are to	bulbs	

Have students use the chart as a memory aid. Have them explain what happens in each case. For example, they can talk about how strawberries reproduce by sending out long stems that grow along the ground. At certain points on a stolon, roots and leaves are produced and a new plant grows. You may wish to do this as a team competition, in which you can also ask, "Strawberries are to stolons as irises are to what? Explain."

Biology Toolkit, Analogies, p. D9

- **Tubers** A potato is actually a tuber, an underground stem modified for storage. The "eyes" of a potato are buds that can sprout new plants, as shown in **FIGURE 22.12.**
- **Bulbs** Tulips, daffodils, and onion plants can all reproduce asexually with bulbs. Bulbs are underground stems surrounded by modified leaves adapted for storage, covered with a protective, papery skin. In favorable conditions, bulbs can divide to produce new plants.

A Analyze **What distinguishes regeneration from vegetative reproduction?**

FIGURE 22.12 New potato plants are growing from the "eyes" of this potato tuber.

MAIN IDEA

Humans can produce plants with desirable traits using vegetative structures.

Plant growers use a process called vegetative propagation to grow plants with desirable qualities, such as seedless fruits or tolerance to frost. Vegetative propagation takes advantage of a plant's ability to grow new individuals from fragments of a parent plant. For example, most apples and oranges that we eat come from propagated branches rather than trees grown from seeds.

Vegetative propagation can be achieved by a few common methods. Many houseplants, including African violets, are reproduced using cuttings from stems or leaves. If the cutting is buried in soil or placed in water, it will produce new roots, as shown in **FIGURE 22.13.** Cuttings are an easy way for horticulturists to produce new houseplants for sale to nurseries.

Fruit and nut tree growers usually use trees that have been produced by grafting, or joining vegetative structures from two or more plants together. Grafting involves making an incision in the bark of one tree and attaching to it either a branch or a bud from another tree. Growers can graft a bud from a tree that produces the desired fruit or nut onto the trunk of a tree that has other desired qualities, such as disease resistance.

FIGURE 22.13 This plant cutting has grown roots after being placed in water for several weeks. Many types of houseplants can be propagated in this way.

B Analyze **What is a benefit of producing houseplants through asexual reproduction?**

22.4 ASSESSMENT

ONLINE QUIZ ClassZone.com

REVIEWING MAIN IDEAS

1. How can a combination of sexual and asexual reproduction be beneficial for plant populations?
2. How do humans use plants' ability to reproduce asexually?

CRITICAL THINKING

3. **Compare and Contrast** What are the differences and similarities between stolons and rhizomes?
4. **Infer** What is a benefit of using propagated branches to grow fruits?

Connecting CONCEPTS

5. **Genetics** How does the genotype of an offspring produced through asexual reproduction compare with the parent plant's genotype?

22.4 ASSESSMENT

1. Sexual reproduction can lead to genetic variation, which allows populations to adapt to their environment; asexual reproduction allows well-adapted individuals to make many copies of themselves.
2. Humans can graft propagated branches or buds that will yield good fruit to trees that are healthy and already established. A potato can be cut up and replanted to grow more potatoes. Plants with stolons can be cut up and replanted elsewhere.
3. Stolons are aboveground stems, and rhizomes are underground stems. New plants grow (asexually) from both.
4. Propagated branches can be grown from fruit trees or bushes that produce fruits of known quality with preferred characteristics.
5. They are identical.

Integrating Agricultural Science

Nearly all commercial varieties of fruits and nuts are harvested from branches that resulted from **grafting.** Using different techniques, commercial varieties are grafted onto rootstocks that are adapted to the area in which the crop is to be grown. The primary reasons for this practice are to produce fruits and nuts with uniformity and the most desired traits, and to prevent soil-borne diseases and unfavorable environmental conditions from killing commercial plantings.

Answers

A Analyze In regeneration, new individuals grow independently (or unattached) from the parent plant. In vegetative reproduction, new individuals grow from structures that are attached to the parent plant.

B Analyze It is faster than growing a new plant from seed, and you will get a plant that is identical to the parent.

Assess and Reteach ▼

Assess Use the Online Quiz or Section Quiz (*Assessment Book,* p. 434).

Reteach Have students help you create a concept map that summarizes asexual reproduction in plants and includes the terms *regeneration, vegetative reproduction, propagation, stolons, rhizomes, tubers, bulbs, cuttings,* and *grafting.* Make sure the concept map distinguishes natural vegetative reproduction by plants from vegetative propagation by humans.

SECTION 22.5

▼ Plan and Prepare

Objectives

- Identify several plant hormones and their effects on plants.
- Explain how plants respond to environmental stimuli.

Section Resources

Unit Resource Book Study Guide pp. 69–70 Power Notes p. 71 Reinforcement p. 72 Pre-AP Activity pp. 77–78
Interactive Reader Chapter 22 **Spanish Study Guide** pp. 231–232
Biology Toolkit pp. C19, D1
Technology Power Presentation 22.5 Media Gallery DVD Online Quiz 22.5

Activate Prior Knowledge Discuss whether students have ever seen a plant move on its own. **Ask,** Have you ever seen signs of movement in a plant? If so, what? Students may mention plants bending toward the light. Some may have seen how sunflowers change position relative to the sun or may have witnessed a Venus flytrap in action. Mention that some movements are the result of changes in growth patterns, but others are not.

▼ Teach

Vocabulary

Greek and Latin Word Origins Tell students that **hormone** comes from the Greek word *hormon,* meaning "to urge on." In biology, the term *hormone* refers to chemicals that stimulate responses in animals and in plants.

22.5 Plant Hormones and Responses

KEY CONCEPT Plant hormones guide plant growth and development.

MAIN IDEAS

- Plant hormones regulate plant functions.
- Plants can respond to light, touch, gravity, and seasonal changes.

VOCABULARY

hormone, p. 680
gibberellin, p. 680
ethylene, p. 681
cytokinin, p. 681
auxin, p. 681
tropism, p. 681
phototropism, p. 682
thigmotropism, p. 682
gravitropism, p. 682
photoperiodism, p. 683

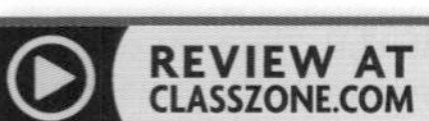

Connect If you have houseplants, you've seen how they grow toward the sunlight streaming through the window. But without eyes, how do plants know where the light is? Plant hormones are involved in this process, which is only one of many ways that plants can respond to their environment.

MAIN IDEA

Plant hormones regulate plant functions.

A **hormone** is a chemical messenger produced in one part of an organism that stimulates or suppresses the activity of cells in another part. In humans and other animals, hormones control functions vital to survival and reproduction. Hormones direct and regulate many of the same functions in plants. However, most plant hormones are very different chemicals from those in animals.

Some plant hormones are released in response to normal changes in the environment where the plant grows. Other hormones are released due to internal changes, as part of a plant's life cycle. Hormones have an influence when they move from the cells that secrete them to the cells for which they are targeted. Target cells have receptors that recognize the hormone. Most plant cells have receptors for many different hormones. When a hormone meets the right receptor, it triggers a response. Plant hormones are divided into several different groups based on their functions and chemical properties.

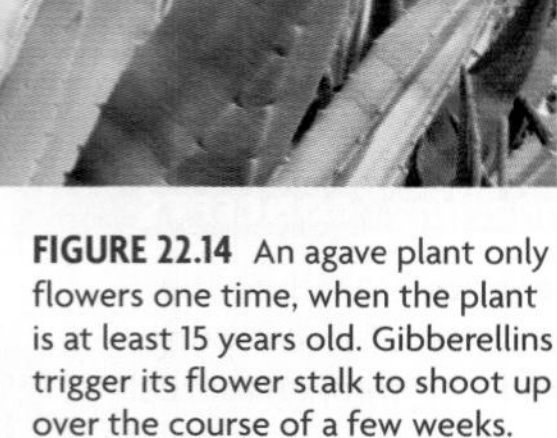

FIGURE 22.14 An agave plant only flowers one time, when the plant is at least 15 years old. Gibberellins trigger its flower stalk to shoot up over the course of a few weeks.

Gibberellins

Gibberellins (jihb-uh-REHL-ihnz) are plant hormones that produce dramatic increases in size. They are involved in ending seed dormancy, starting germination, and promoting the rapid growth of young seedlings. Gibberellins are also responsible for the large size of many fruits and the rapid upward growth of some flower stalks. For example, the agave shown in **FIGURE 22.14** can send a flowering stalk up to 12 meters (40 ft) tall in a few weeks. Grape growers often spray their vines with a gibberellin solution, which makes the fruits grow larger and elongates the stems in the bunches, making room for more grapes.

Differentiated Instruction

ENGLISH LEARNERS

Do a word splash with the ten new vocabulary words, as well as others from the section such as *secrete, elongate, receptor, dormancy, germination, seedling, cytokinesis, lateral growth, environmental stimulus, tendril, shoot, predator, deciduous, chlorophyll,* and *stunt.* Write all the words on the board or on a transparency. Have students arrange the words into categories and give reasons for their choices.

Biology Toolkit, Word Splash, p. D1

Ethylene

Put an apple in an airtight container for a day, and it will get soft and start to look rotten. The apple is being ripened abnormally fast by its own production of **ethylene** (EHTH-uh-LEEN), a plant hormone that causes ripening and is naturally produced by fruits. Commercial growers can use ethylene to their advantage. Fruits such as apples that are shipped long distances must be kept in rooms where the ethylene is filtered out, or they may become overripe during the journey. Some fruits, such as the tomatoes in **FIGURE 22.5**, are picked before they are ripe. Once they reach their destination, they are exposed to ethylene gas, which makes them turn a ripe-tomato red. They may not taste so ripe, though, because this artificial ripening process does not bring out the same sugars that a vine-ripened tomato has.

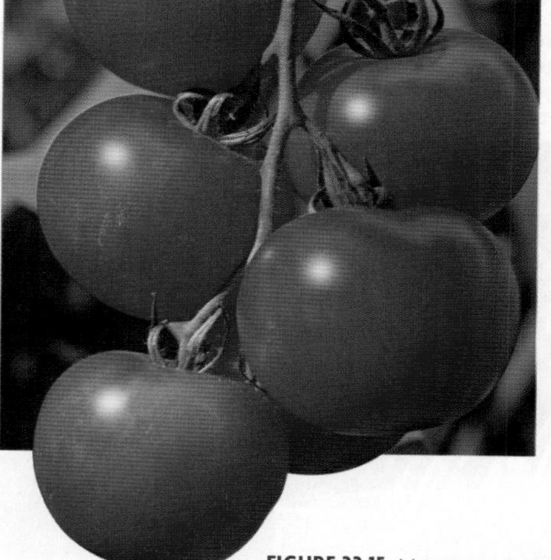

FIGURE 22.15 Many tomatoes are picked before they are ripe and treated with ethylene before they are sold at grocery stores. These tomatoes may not taste as sweet as vine-ripened tomatoes.

Cytokinins

Cytokinins (SY-tuh-KY-nihnz) are plant hormones that stimulate cytokinesis, which is the final stage of cell division. They are produced in growing roots and developing seeds and fruits. They are also involved in the growth of side branches. This sideways growth is called lateral growth. Commercial florists make use of another property of cytokinins—they slow the aging process of some plant organs. For example, leaves dipped in a cytokinin solution stay green much longer than normal.

Auxins

Auxins (AWK-sihnz) are plant hormones involved in the lengthening of plant cells produced in the apical meristem, or growing tip. Auxins stimulate growth of the primary stem, preventing growth of new branches. Gardeners can use this property of auxins to control branching patterns by cutting off the tip of a growing stem. With no growing tip, there is less auxin in the stem, and side branches are encouraged to grow. Conversely, high concentrations of auxins can prevent plant growth altogether, particularly in the roots. For this reason, auxins are a common ingredient in herbicides, chemicals used to kill unwanted plants.

The lengthening of cells triggered by auxins also controls some forms of **tropism,** the movement of a plant in response to an environmental stimulus. For example, if a stimulus such as light hits one side of a stem, auxins will build up in the cells on the shaded side of the stem. These cells then elongate, or grow longer, causing the stem to bend toward the light. As you will soon learn, auxins have different effects in the cells of different plant organs.

TAKING NOTES

Use a main idea web to take notes about four major plant hormones.

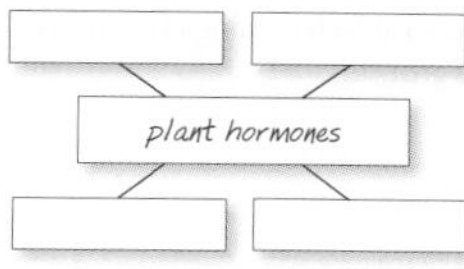

A **Apply If you started your own plant nursery, explain two ways in which you could use different plant hormones to your advantage.**

Take It Further

Many people know that they can speed up the ripening process of fruits by placing them together in a closed container or bag. With the exception of the banana, it can be very hard to tell if a piece of fruit really is ripe. Millions of pieces of fruit are discarded every year because they turn out to be too ripe by the time someone is ready to buy or eat them.

To reduce this waste, scientists are working on a small, coin-sized sticker that will turn from white to blue when the fruit it is placed on has ripened. Such stickers can be placed on fruit at the point of harvest or in supermarkets, allowing sellers or buyers to know whether or not a fruit is ready to be eaten.

Vocabulary

Academic Vocabulary Point out to students that with the words **stimulus** and **response,** one word is used to define the other.

stimulus, an agent, action, or condition that elicits an activity or response

response, a reaction to a specific stimulus

Answers

A Apply You could control growth patterns by snipping growing tips, where auxins are produced, to produce bushier plants; using cytokinin solution to help keep leaves green; applying solutions that contain gibberellins to stimulate germination or make plants grow taller.

BELOW LEVEL

Remind students that mnemonic devices, or memory aids, can help with recall. For example, to remember the basic kinds of plant hormones, ask students to come up with an expression that uses the first letter of each hormone. Example: Good eating causes alertness. To help students remember the functions of each hormone, have them develop their own mnemonic devices. Example: If the banana is green, it needs ethylene; gibberellin is for giants; auxin activates apical meristems.

▼ Teach continued

ONLINE BIOLOGY Students can explore plant response mechanisms further in a WebQuest or virtual lab. See Options for Inquiry on page 685.

History of Science

In 1880, **Charles Darwin** published *The Power of Movement in Plants.* In the book, he described experiments that he and his son, **Francis Darwin,** had conducted on plant responses to light. These are among the earliest known scientific experiments on plant responses. Almost 50 years later, **Fritz Went,** a graduate student from Holland, confirmed the role of auxin in plant phototropism by performing experiments that were very similar to the earlier work of Charles Darwin and Francis Darwin.

Vocabulary

Greek and Latin Word Origins Explain that the root word of **tropism** is *trope* from the Greek word *tropos,* meaning "turning" or "a turn."

phototropism = a turning caused by light

thigmotropism = a turning caused by touch

gravitropism = a turning caused by gravity

Tell students that plant tropisms are responses that occur in a direction that is based on the direction from which a stimulus comes. Then explain that the words *positive* and *negative* are used as adjectives to describe the direction in which a plant turns in relation to where the stimulus is located.

MAIN IDEA

Plants can respond to light, touch, gravity, and seasonal changes.

If you've ever touched a hot pan in the kitchen, you likely responded by pulling your hand away quickly. And if you've ever been outside on a very hot summer day, you may have responded by moving to a shady spot. While plants cannot uproot themselves and change locations, they have other ways of responding to their environment.

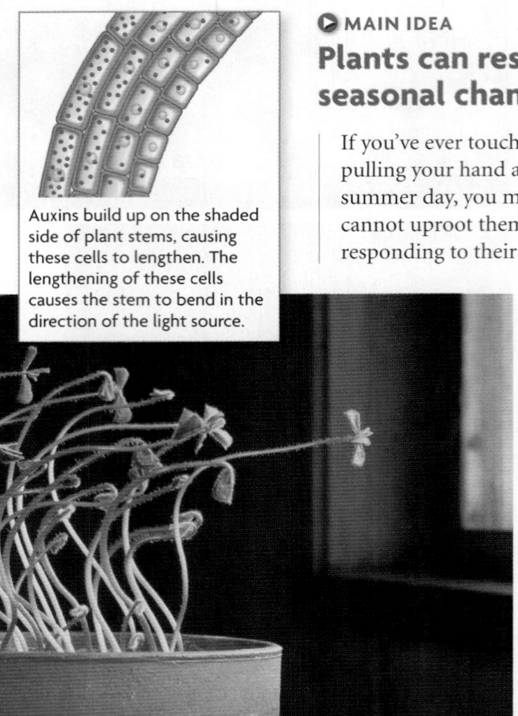

Auxins build up on the shaded side of plant stems, causing these cells to lengthen. The lengthening of these cells causes the stem to bend in the direction of the light source.

FIGURE 22.16 Phototropism is the process in which plants grow toward a light source. Here, the stems and leaves of a houseplant bend toward a nearby window.

Phototropism

When light hits a plant stem, it causes auxins to build up on the shaded side. Remember that in a stem, auxins cause cell elongation. As described earlier, cell lengthening on the shaded side of a stem causes the stem to bend toward the light. This tendency of a plant to grow toward light is called **phototropism.** If you grow a plant in a space with only one small light source, that plant will lean toward the light through the process of phototropism, as shown in **FIGURE 22.16.** Let's say you turn that plant around so that it's pointing away from the light. If you come back in a few days, you will likely find the plant growing in the direction of the light again.

Thigmotropism

Many plants also have a response to touch, called **thigmotropism.** This quality is apparent in climbing plants and vines. Tendrils emerge from the leaf base of these plants and grow in coils around anything they touch. In these curling "fingers," contact with an object triggers the same sort of cell growth that is found with other tropisms. Plants are sensitive to many kinds of touchlike stimuli. For example, a plant regularly exposed to winds on a hillside will grow as if it is being pushed in the direction of the wind. Repeatedly touching a young plant can even stunt its growth.

Connecting CONCEPTS

Physical Science Recall that gravity is the force that objects exert on each other because of their mass. Gravity is the force responsible for things falling to the ground.

Gravitropism

When a seed germinates underground, the root grows downward into the soil, and the shoot grows upward toward the soil surface. This up-and-down growth of a plant is called **gravitropism,** because the plant is responding to Earth's gravitational pull. Downward growth is positive gravitropism because the growth is in the direction that gravity pulls. Upward growth is negative gravitropism because it is growth against the force of gravity.

Auxins play a part in gravitropism, which is more complex than phototropism. Root growth is stimulated by low levels of auxin, but is slowed down by high levels of auxin. Auxins build up on the lower side of horizontally growing roots so that the upper side grows faster and the root grows downward. At the same time, high levels of auxin, which stimulate shoot growth, build up in the lower side of the stem. This buildup causes the stem to grow upward.

Differentiated Instruction

PRE-AP

Tell students to imagine a grove of tall coconut palm trees on a beach in the Pacific islands. All of them are leaning to the west, the direction that the prevailing winds are blowing. When cyclone season arrives, the trees are still leaning this way, despite the fact that cyclones tend to come from the west and blow eastward. After a cyclone, some of the trees have been toppled or stripped of their fronds, but those that are still standing are still leaning towards the west. Have students spend five minutes writing about what advantage such trees have by being thigmotropic, and why they do not bend the other way during cyclone season. Students should speculate that leaning away from the wind reduces the friction that trees experience in strong winds, thereby improving their chances of survival. The reason a single cyclone will not cause a palm's growth to bend the tree in the other direction is that the cyclone event is relatively brief, whereas the prevailing winds blow for much of the year.

Biology Toolkit, Quick-Write, p. C19

Rapid Responses

Some plants have very rapid responses that do not involve growth. These rapid responses are often adaptations that help to protect plants from predators. For example, the mimosa, or sensitive plant, quickly folds its leaves together a few seconds after being touched. A few plants are quick enough to capture insects for a meal. The Venus flytrap shown in **FIGURE 22.17** can close its leaves on an unsuspecting insect in less than a second. Scientists recently discovered that when the leaves are touched, water rushes to the cells at their bases, changing their curvature and snapping the trap shut.

FIGURE 22.17 When the leaves of a Venus flytrap are touched, water rushes to the cells of the leaf bases, causing the leaves to rapidly bend inward.

Photoperiodism

What triggers a shrub to flower or a tree to drop its leaves? Plants take signals from the changing lengths of day and night throughout the year, in a response called **photoperiodism.** Some plants keep very accurate clocks when it comes to the amount of daylight or darkness in a 24-hour period. In fact, some plants that flower while the days are short, such as poinsettias, will not bloom if there is one extra minute of light in the evening.

Shorter days and longer nights during the fall help trigger the leaves of many deciduous trees to change color. This response is part of the preparation for winter, when these trees enter a stage of dormancy. Winter dormancy in plants is functionally similar to the hibernation of many animals during the winter months. With less rainfall and less direct sunlight, it is more energy-efficient for these plants to shut down and rely on reserved sugars than it is for them to photosynthesize. Leaves therefore begin to die in the fall. Chlorophyll, the pigment that gives leaves their green color, breaks down. Once the chlorophyll is gone, the remaining leaf pigments become visible and new pigments are produced. Water and nutrients are drawn out of the leaves for the rest of the tree to use during the winter, and the leaves eventually fall off of the tree.

To learn more about plant responses, visit scilinks.org.
Keycode: MLB022

A Apply What stimulus causes each of the following tropisms: phototropism, gravitropism, thigmotropism?

22.5 ASSESSMENT

ONLINE QUIZ
ClassZone.com

REVIEWING MAIN IDEAS

1. Describe two plant **hormones** that regulate plant growth and development.
2. Name and describe five ways in which plants can respond to their environment.

CRITICAL THINKING

3. **Apply** A vine grows sideways, twisting along a railing. What type of **tropism** is this plant exhibiting?
4. **Apply** If you want full, bushy plants, which part of the plant would you trim to control **auxin** production in your favor?

Connecting CONCEPTS

5. **Adaptations** Many trees in temperate climates lose their leaves before the long, cold winter. How is this ability an adaptation for these trees?

22.5 ASSESSMENT

1. Any two plant hormones discussed in the text (gibberellins, ethylene, cytokinins, and auxins) can be described.
2. phototropism: stem and leaves bend towards light; gravitropism: roots grow down into soil, and stems generally grow up out of soil; thigmotropism: response in which growth is influenced by "touching" another object, as in vines that wind around an upright object; rapid response: quick responses not involving growth, triggered by touch; photoperiodism: response to changing amounts of daylight through the year
3. thigmotropism
4. growing stem tips, where auxins are produced
5. During the winter in temperate climates, light levels are low, so photosynthetic rates drop. For some trees, it is more energy efficient to lose their leaves and go through a period of dormancy during these months.

TEACH FROM VISUALS

FIGURE 22.17 Rapid movements of plants that are based on changes in cell turgor pressure are called **nastic movements.** Such movements occur in response to stimuli, but, in contrast to tropisms, the response is unrelated to the direction from which the stimulus comes.

Take It Further

Another kind of tropism exhibited by some species in the plant kingdom is **heliotropism,** or turning in response to the movement of the Sun. A heliotropic flower, for example, may begin the day leaning eastward, where the Sun rises, then straighten as the Sun ascends in the sky, and finally lean westward as dusk approaches. This allows the plant to maximize its direct exposure to sunlight. The bending of heliotropic plants is controlled by motor cells at the base of the stem, which pump potassium ions into the shady side, thereby temporarily lengthening it. Point out that the bend or turning of the plant is temporary, not true growth.

Answers

A Apply light, gravity, touch

Assess and Reteach ▼

Assess Use the Online Quiz or Section Quiz (*Assessment Book,* p. 435).

Reteach Create two tables on the board: one comparing the different plant hormones and their functions, the other comparing the various plant responses. Involve students by asking questions such as "Under which hormone should I write *involved in gravitropism*?"

OPTIONS FOR INQUIRY

INVESTIGATION

Time 20 minutes	TEACHER TESTED
Teacher Preparation	
Student Difficulty	
Lab Binder Plants, pp. 31–32	

Purpose Explore the effects of ripened fruit on unripe fruit.

Overview Students will design an experiment to test how a hormone affects fruit ripening. They will

- write an experimental procedure that describes how they will test their independent variable
- make observations and compare results
- evaluate their experimental designs

LAB PREPARATION

- Provide bunches of green bananas and pieces of ripe fruits such as apples, pears, peaches, and plums.

Teacher Note "You may need to call stores for greenest bananas."

LAB MANAGEMENT

- Set aside 10 minutes each day over the course of a week so students can observe and record change in the bananas.

POST-LAB DISCUSSION

Discuss the results with the class. **Ask,** What changes could be made in the experimental design to improve the results? Larger pieces of fruits or a chemical that contains ethylene could be used to speed ripening or get more even ripening. **Ask,** What kinds of fruits were most helpful in ripening bananas? Answers will vary, depending on the fruits used, the level of ripeness of those fruits, and the size of the pieces used.

Use these inquiry-based labs and online activities to deepen your understanding of seeds and fruit.

INDIANA STANDARDS

NOS.1 Develop explanations based on reproducible data and observations gathered during laboratory investigations.

DESIGN YOUR OWN INVESTIGATION

Investigating Plant Hormones

Ethylene is a plant hormone that is released by the cells of ripening fruit. As ethylene is released, new pigments are revealed as chlorophyll is broken down, causing the fruit skin to change color. The cell walls begin to break down, making the fruit softer. Finally, complex sugars break down into simple sugars, which make the fruit smell and taste sweet. These properties make fruit more appealing to eat. In this activity, you will design an experiment to determine the effects that ethylene produced by ripe fruit can have on unripe fruit.

MATERIALS

- 3 unripe bananas from the same bunch
- several pieces of various ripened fruit (apple, pear, peach, and so on)
- 3 large resealable plastic bags

SKILL Observing

PROBLEM How can hormones produced by ripened fruit affect unripe fruit?

PROCEDURE

1. Using the materials provided, design a procedure that will test the effect of ripened fruit on unripe bananas. Be sure to include a control group in your design.
2. Have your experimental design checked by your teacher.
3. Record observations, such as color, texture, firmness, and smell, over a five-day period.
4. Compare your results with the results of other classmates.

ANALYZE AND CONCLUDE

1. **Summarize** What changes took place in each plastic bag over the five-day period?
2. **Analyze** Draw conclusions about the production of ethylene based on your results.
3. **Experimental Design** Why was it important that the bananas in your experiment were from the same bunch?
4. **Experimental Design** Identify some possible sources of unavoidable experimental error in your design.
5. **Infer** Why is fruit ripening an important phase in the reproduction of flowering plants?

EXTEND YOUR INVESTIGATION

Do some research to find out what kinds of fruit are often harvested before they are ripe.

Answers

Analyze and Conclude

1. Bananas in bags with ripe fruit should ripen faster than those in bags without ripe fruit. As bananas ripen, the color should change from green to yellow to brown. They should also get softer and start to smell sweet.
2. The slices of ripened fruit release ethylene, which induces ripening in bananas.
3. It ensures that the bananas were comparably ripe (or unripe).
4. *Sample Answer:* Some of the ripe fruits provided as sources of ethylene were riper than others, and therefore released more ethylene and ripened the bananas faster.
5. Ripened fruits are eaten by animals, which then disperse the seeds.

Extend Your Investigation

In addition to bananas, fruits that are harvested before they are ripe include include apples, peaches, nectarines, some plums, and apricots, among others.

INVESTIGATION

Fruit Dissection

In this lab, you will accurately represent the inside of a fruit and its seeds with a scientific illustration.

SKILL Illustrating

PROBLEM How can you represent the sizes and proportions of structures in a scientific illustration?

MATERIALS
- pea pod
- scalpel
- dissecting tray
- metric ruler
- tweezers
- paper towel
- dissecting microscope

PROCEDURE

1. Carefully open the pea pod with a scalpel. **Caution:** Always cut away from your body.
2. Draw and label the inside of the pea pod so that the size of the peas (seeds) relative to the size of the pod (fruit) is accurate.
3. Use tweezers to remove one pea from the pod. Use a paper towel to clean the outside of the pea. Carefully cut the pea in half lengthwise.
4. Examine the inside of the pea under the microscope.
5. Draw a cross-section of the pea. Label the seed parts that are visible under the microscope.

ANALYZE AND CONCLUDE

1. **Analyze** What accounts for genetic differences between peas in the same pod?
2. **Analyze** How many eggs were likely fertilized in the ovary that developed into your pea pod?
3. **Infer** Pods burst at the seam when they are mature. What function might this bursting serve?
4. **Synthesize** Why is it important for scientific illustrations to be drawn with correct proportions?

Online BIOLOGY
CLASSZONE.COM

VIRTUAL LAB
Exploring Plant Responses
How do plants respond to different stimuli? In this interactive lab, you will test for plant reactions to light, gravity, and touch.

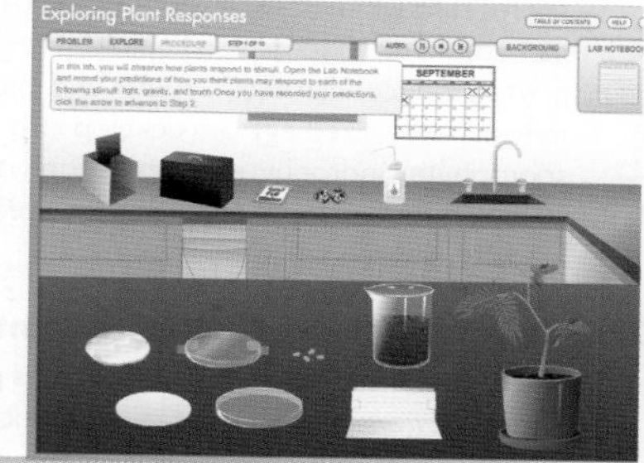

ANIMATED BIOLOGY
Seed Dispersal
Some glide through the air and others drop straight to the ground. Plants have adapted many methods to get their seeds from one place to another. Use physical characteristics to determine how seeds are spread.

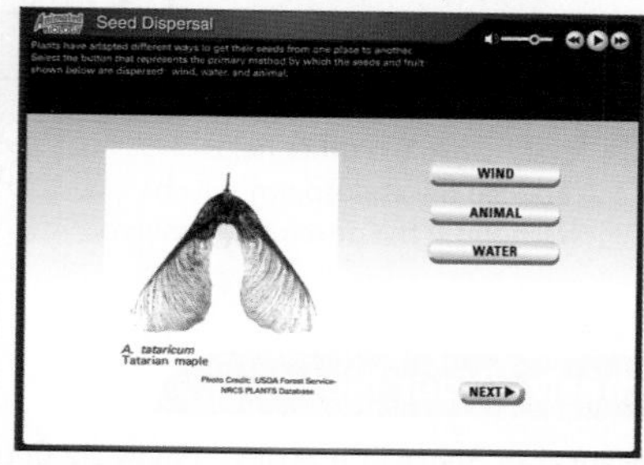

WEBQUEST
We often take for granted that shoots grow up and roots grow down. But what would happen if you took a plant into space? Complete this WebQuest to find out. Learn how plants respond to conditions in outer space and why these experiments are important to the future of space exploration.

Answers

Analyze and Conclude

1. Each pea developed from a different egg that was fertilized by a different sperm.
2. The number of fertilized eggs should equal the number of peas.
3. The peas are then scattered as they fall to the ground, dispersing the peas slightly so that seedlings will not grow too close together.
4. Scientific illustrations should accurately represent the real object, as they are used as learning tools and for reference. An illustration that is reduced in size compared to the actual size should be proportionally accurate.

Online Biology ▼

VIRTUAL LAB Use this lab on plant reactions to reinforce the concepts of **Section 22.5.**

ANIMATED BIOLOGY Use this interactive animation on seed dispersal to reinforce the concepts of **Section 22.3.**

WEBQUEST The WebQuest takes one full class period. Students complete the activity online and will need access to a printer to print their answers. Sample answers, teacher notes, and alternative assessment ideas are available on **ClassZone.com.** Use with **Section 22.5.**

INVESTIGATION

TEACHER TESTED

Time	30 minutes
Teacher Preparation	1 flask
Student Difficulty	1 flask
Lab Binder	Plants, pp. 33–34

Purpose Illustrate a fruit and its seeds accurately.

Overview Students will examine and represent the external and internal structure of a fruit. They will
- dissect a pea pod and one of its peas
- draw and label the parts of the pea pod and pea

LAB MANAGEMENT

Explain that peas in a pod may differ in appearance due to genetic traits, such as cotyledon color and smooth or wrinkled texture—two traits that Mendel studied in garden peas.

POST-LAB DISCUSSION

Discuss results. **Ask,** How can the peas in the same pod look different? Each one represents a new plant, which inherited its traits from two parents. In this way, peas in the same pod are similar to fraternal twins.

CHAPTER REVIEW

Interactive Review

Encourage students to go to **ClassZone.com** for a detailed review of each section, including visuals and vocabulary practice.

Unit Resource Book, Vocabulary Practice, pp. 79–82

CHAPTER 22 Interactive Review @ CLASSZONE.COM

KEY CONCEPTS | Vocabulary Games | Concept Maps | Animated Biology | Online Quiz

22.1 Plant Life Cycles

All plants alternate between two phases in their life cycles. This type of life cycle is called alternation of generations, and it involves a diploid (2*n*) and a haploid (1*n*) phase. The diploid phase, called the sporophyte, produces haploid spores through meiosis. A spore develops into a gametophyte, which is also haploid. The gametophyte produces gametes—sperm and eggs—by mitosis. A fertilized egg can develop into a new sporophyte. Sporophyte and gametophyte phases look different among nonvascular, seedless vascular, and seed plants.

22.2 Reproduction in Flowering Plants

Reproduction of flowering plants takes place within flowers. Flowers contain reproductive organs surrounded by specialized leaves called sepals and petals. Brightly colored petals can attract animal pollinators. A flower is pollinated when a pollen grain reaches the tip of the female reproductive structure. One cell in the pollen grain grows into a pollen tube and the other cell divides to form two sperm. In a process called double fertilization, one sperm fertilizes an egg, produced in the flower's ovary, while the other helps produce the endosperm, which will nourish the developing embryo.

22.3 Seed Dispersal and Germination

Seeds disperse and begin to grow when conditions are favorable. The function of fruit in flowering plants is to help disperse seeds. Many seeds go through a stage of dormancy, or nongrowth, until environmental conditions are favorable for growing. Germination is the process by which the embryo breaks out of the seed coat and begins to grow into a seedling.

22.4 Asexual Reproduction

Plants can produce genetic clones of themselves through asexual reproduction. Some plants can grow a new individual from a fragment of a stem, a leaf, or a root in a process called regeneration. Vegetative reproduction involves new individuals growing from a stem, a leaf, or a root attached to the parent plant. Humans can produce plants with desirable traits by propagating plants asexually.

22.5 Plant Hormones and Responses

Plant hormones guide plant growth and development. Four major groups of plant hormones are gibberellins, ethylene, cytokinins, and auxins. Auxins are involved with the lengthening of plant cells that controls several forms of tropism, including responses to light and gravity. Some types of plants can also respond to touch and seasonal changes in the lengths of day and night.

Synthesize Your Notes

Concept Map Summarize what you know about plant responses using a concept map.

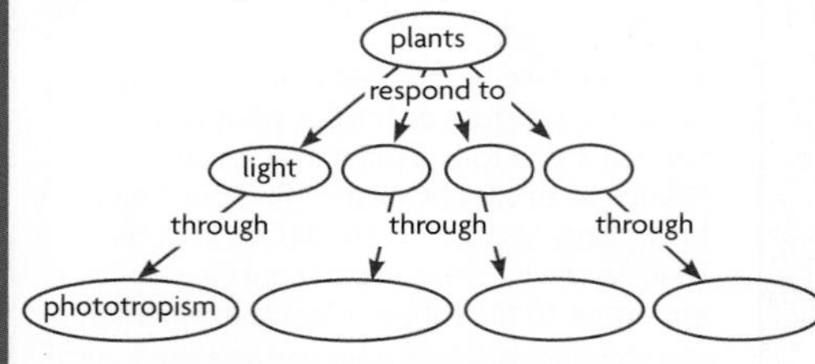

Cycle Diagram Draw a cycle diagram to show the alternation of generations in flowering plants. Include sketches of the sporophyte and gametophytes, using labels specific to flowering plants.

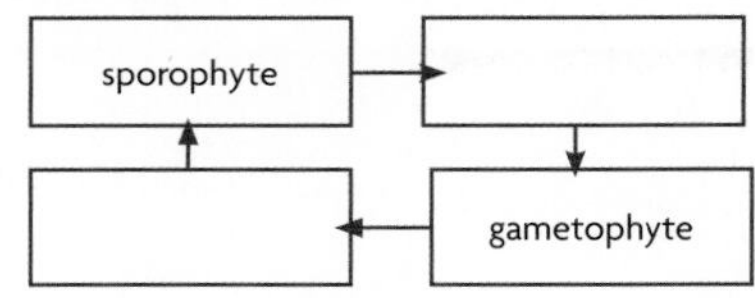

686 Unit 7: Plants

Reviewing Vocabulary

1. carpel
2. stamen
3. sepal
4. ovary
5. petal
6. The endosperm provides nourishment to the embryo inside the seed coat.
7. Dormancy is a stage of little activity, similar to sleep, when a plant or plant embryo does not grow.
8. In germination of a seed, the embryonic shoot sprouts up above the soil.
9. Phototropism and gravitropism both involve a type of bending, or turning, of plant parts in response to stimuli.
10. phototropism
11. thigmotropism
12. gravitropism
13. photoperiodism

Chapter Assessment

Chapter Vocabulary

22.1 alternation of generations, p. 664
sporophyte, p. 664
gametophyte, p. 664

22.2 sepal, p. 668
petal, p. 668
stamen, p. 668
carpel, p. 668
ovary, p. 668
endosperm, p. 670
double fertilization, p. 670

22.3 dormancy, p. 674
germination, p. 675

22.4 regeneration, p. 678
vegetative reproduction, p. 678

22.5 hormone, p. 680
gibberellin, p. 680
ethylene, p. 681
cytokinin, p. 681
auxin, p. 681
tropism, p. 681
phototropism, p. 682
thigmotropism, p. 682
gravitropism, p. 682
photoperiodism, p. 683

Reviewing Vocabulary

Label Diagrams

In your notebook, write the vocabulary term that matches each item that is pointed out below.

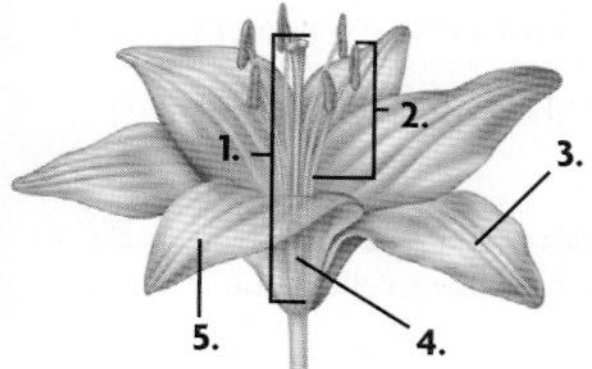

Word Origins

6. The prefix *endo-* means "inside," and the Greek word *sperma* means "seed." How do these meanings relate to the word *endosperm?*

7. How does the word *dormancy* relate to the French verb *dormir,* which means "to sleep"?

8. How does the Latin verb *germinare,* which means "to sprout," relate to the meaning of *germination?*

9. The prefix *trop-* means "a turning." How does this relate to the meaning of the word *tropism?*

Category Clues

For each clue, list the appropriate vocabulary term from the chapter.

Category: Plant Responses

10. response to light

11. response to touch

12. response to gravity

13. response to amount of daylight or darkness

Reviewing MAIN IDEAS

14. What types of cellular division are involved in the alternation of generations?

15. What is a major difference between the gametophyte generations of moss and pine trees?

16. How can brightly colored petals aid in the reproduction of flowering plants?

17. What characteristic might be a clue that a flower is wind-pollinated? Explain your answer.

18. Name the two structures in the female gametophyte that are fertilized in the process of double fertilization.

19. How does seed dispersal aid in the survival of plant offspring?

20. People may enjoy a spring season with relatively little rain. How might this type of spring weather affect seeds that were dispersed during the previous fall?

21. Discuss the role of enzymes in the development of an embryo during germination.

22. How can the ability to produce both sexually and asexually allow plant species to populate a variety of environments?

23. Why is plant propagation an efficient way for people to produce new plants?

24. A well-known disease of rice plants causes rice seedlings to grow to several times their normal size and then die. Which of the major plant hormones is likely involved in this disease? Explain your answer.

25. Name four types of stimuli to which plants are capable of responding.

Reviewing Main Ideas

14. meiosis and mitosis

15. The gametophyte generation is the dominant phase of nonvascular plants (moss); gametophytes of vascular plants (pine trees) are microscopic.

16. They can attract animal pollinators.

17. lots of inconspicuous or very small flowers on a single plant; need to produce a lot of pollen to have better odds of some landing on another flower's stigma

18. egg and polar nuclei

19. gets seeds farther away from parent plants to avoid direct competition and, potentially, colonize new locations and take advantage of its resources

20. For many types of seeds, water triggers germination. If there is little rain in the spring, these seeds may germinate late or, possibly, not until the following spring.

21. During germination, water uptake activates enzymes that help break down materials in the endosperm into sugars. These sugars are then transported to the developing embryo for nourishment.

22. Sexual reproduction gives rise to genetic variation, which allows a population to adapt to new environments. If certain individuals are well-adapted to a new environment, asexual reproduction allows these individuals to make copies of themselves, populating this new environment.

23. New plants can be propagated relatively quickly from individuals with desired qualities. That way, the new individuals will have the same desirable qualities.

24. gibberellins, which are involved in dramatic increases in size

25. light, touch, gravity, changes in amount of daylight/darkness

CHAPTER REVIEW

Critical Thinking

26. Both have alternation of generations, which includes a sporophyte and a gametophyte. The gametophyte of seedless plants, such as moss, is the dominant phase. The sporophyte is the dominant phase of seed plants. Seed plants have two types of gametophytes—male and female—and they are very tiny.
27. Cones open when they are receptive to pollen for pollination; they close once they have been pollinated, while the embryos/seeds are developing; they open again to release the mature seeds.
28. A potato left on a kitchen counter for a while will sprout. Eyes in the potato are actually buds from which new potato plants can grow.
29. Seeds that will germinate faster have likely been treated with gibberellins, because these hormones are involved in dramatic increases in growth and ending seed dormancy.
30. Ethylene produced by the ripening apple affected the kiwi, causing it to ripen more quickly.
31. photoperiodism; the opening and closing is associated with the duration of daylight/darkness.

Interpreting Visuals

32. pollination
33. As bees gather pollen for food, some pollen grains stick to their bodies. When they land on a different flower, some pollen grains from a previously visited flower may be brushed off onto the stigma/female structure of the new flower, thereby pollinating it.

Critical Thinking

26. **Compare and Contrast** What are some differences and similarities between the life cycle of a seedless plant and that of a seed plant, such as a conifer?

27. **Infer** Female pine cones have scales that open, close, and then open again. These three phases correspond with three specific events in the conifer reproductive cycle. What three events might trigger these phases in female cones?

28. **Predict** Most people cook potatoes soon after they buy them at the store. What will happen to a potato that is left sitting on the kitchen counter for a few weeks? Explain your answer.

29. **Infer** A homeowner is planting a new garden and buys some plant seeds. The plant shop owner offers to sell her regular seeds or specially treated seeds that will germinate faster. How may these special seeds have been treated?

30. **Analyze** A kiwi fruit was purchased at the store, but it was not ripe enough to eat. It was placed in a sealed container along with an apple. Several days later, the kiwi was ripe. Explain how this likely happened.

31. **Analyze** Four-o'clock flowers bloom late in the day, as their name suggests. The flowers stay open all night and close the following morning. What type of response is the flower demonstrating? Explain your answer.

Interpreting Visuals

Use this cartoon to answer the next two questions.

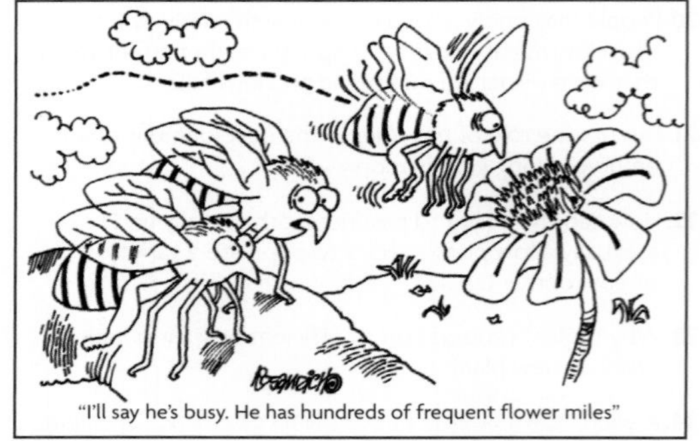

"I'll say he's busy. He has hundreds of frequent flower miles"

source: www.CartoonStock.com

32. **Apply** Name the process that these bees have carried out for flowering plants.

33. **Summarize** Describe how this process occurs as bees fly from flower to flower.

Analyzing Data

Students are testing the effect of light on the germination of millet seeds. The setup for their experiment is shown in the table below. Students observe and track seed development for one week. Use the data to answer the next four questions.

MILLET SEED EXPERIMENT SETUP

	Tray A	Tray B
Seeds	50	50
Water	25 mL per day	25 mL per day
Location	on a shelf beneath a grow light	on a shelf in a dark refrigerator

34. **Analyze** What are the dependent and independent variables in this experiment?

35. **Analyze** What is the control in this experiment?

36. **Evaluate** Which part of the experimental design is flawed?

37. **Experimental Design** What changes would you make to the experimental design to collect valid results?

Connecting CONCEPTS

38. **Write a Blog** Imagine that you are a seed that is about to come out of dormancy. Write a blog describing your experiences as you germinate. Be sure to include the following terms: *dormancy, germinate, seed coat, radicle, plumule, cotyledons,* and *seedling.*

39. **Analyze** Look at the moth orchid shown in the chapter opener on page 663. Does this photograph show the gametophyte or sporophyte generation? Explain your answer.

Analyzing Data

34. dependent: germination rate; independent: light
35. tray of seeds put in the refrigerator, where there is no light
36. The control tray of seeds was put into a dark refrigerator where the low temperature can also affect germination.
37. Place the control seeds in an opaque container and the experimental seeds in a transparent container.

688 Unit 7: Plants

INDIANA ISTEP+ Test Prep

B.6.4; B.6.5; B.8.5; NOS.1; NOS.4

Test Practice For more test practice, go to ClassZone.com.

1 A strawberry grower divides a large field into three sections: the first bordering a grove of trees, the second in the middle, and the third bordering an interstate. Each section is treated with a different insecticide to determine effectiveness. Which of the following is not a design flaw of this experiment?

A No part of the field was used as a control.
B Fumes from the interstate might kill pests in the third section.
C The same type of strawberries were grown in each section.
D The trees might harbor animals that eat pests in the first section.

2 Which of the following scenarios is using sexual reproduction to increase genetic variation?

A A researcher grafts the branch of a pear tree onto a drought-resistant apple tree.
B A gardener slices the "eyes" off of potatoes and plants them to yield a new crop.
C A flower lover cuts the leaves from a violet and plants them in soil to grow more violets.
D A farmer uses pollen from tall pea plants to fertilize short pea plants.

3

Enzyme Activity at Different Temperatures	
Temperature (°C)	Enzyme Activity (units/μL)
25	6
20	8
15	14
10	27
5	36
0	30

Suppose that scientists are studying the activity of enzymes that are involved in ending seed dormancy. Which statement is best supported by their data?

A The enzyme is ineffective below 0°C.
B Temperature does not affect enzyme activity.
C Enzyme activity peaks at around 5°C.
D The enzyme is most active in warm weather.

4 The plant life cycle involves a diploid sporophyte stage that produces haploid spores. Which of the following statements is true?

A Haploid spores are produced through meiosis.
B Haploid spores are produced through mitosis.
C Diploid spores are produced through meiosis.
D Diploid spores are produced through mitosis.

5

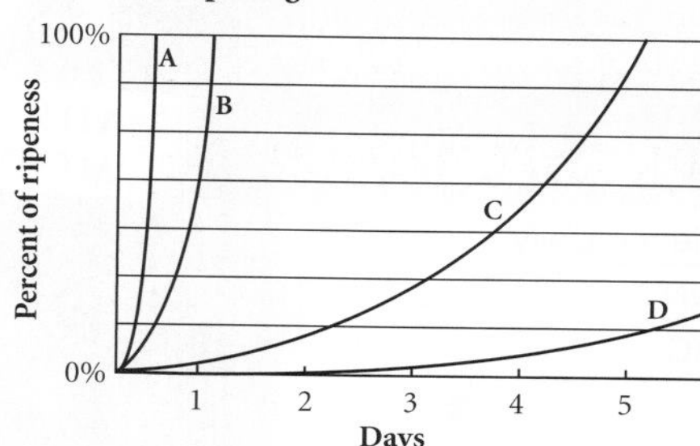

Scientists are developing a molecule that will slow down the rate of fruit ripening to a few days. Based on the graph, which molecule do you think they would choose?

A A
B B
C C
D D

6 Flowers may be pollinated by wind or by animals. Describe the characteristics that make animal-pollinated and wind-pollinated flowers distinctive.

Standards-Based Assessment

1. C	4. A
2. D	5. C
3. C	6. See Below

Question 2 Answer D is correct because pollen contains plants' male sex cells. Answers A, B, and C are incorrect because they are all examples of asexual propagation.

Question 4 Answer A is correct because meiosis produces haploid spores from a diploid sporophyte. Answer B is incorrect because mitosis produces genetically identical daughter cells; diploid sporophytes undergoing mitosis would make diploid spores. Answer C is incorrect because meiosis reduces chromosome number by half; diploid sporophytes undergoing meiosis would make haploid spores. Answer D is incorrect because although diploid sporophytes undergoing mitosis would make diploid spores, the question states that haploid spores are produced, not diploid spores.

Question 5 Answer C is correct. Answer A is incorrect because molecule A causes fruit to ripen within half a day. Answer B is incorrect because molecule B causes fruit to ripen within a day. Answer D is incorrect because molecule D slows down fruit ripening too much; only about 14% of fruit has ripened by day 5.

Question 6 Wind-pollinated flowers often have small flowers with great quantities of pollen. Animal-pollinated flowers have pollen-bearing parts that touch or catch on animals as they visit or brush by the flower. Animal-pollinated flowers also tend to be larger and more colorful to attract visitors.

Connecting Concepts

38. Blogs will vary, but should be written from the perspective of a germinating seed, and should include references to the terms *dormancy, germinate, seed coat, radicle, plumule, cotyledons,* and *seedling.*

39. The chapter-opener image is a sporophyte. The sporophyte is the dominant phase for all vascular plants, including flowering plants. The gametophytes of this plant—pollen grains and embryo sacs—are microscopic.

ITEM CORRELATIONS

Standard	Items
B.6.4	4
B.6.5	2
B.8.5	6
NOS.1	3, 5
NOS.4	1

UNIT 7

Introduce

Tell students that scientists make or recommend decisions based on a scientific process. This process, known as **risk analysis,** is used when studying the risks versus the benefits of genetically modified (GM) foods in order to protect human health and the environment. Risk analysis is made up of three parts:

Risk assessment is the scientific evaluation of known or potential adverse effects on health. This evaluation consists of different steps, which include identifying and evaluating the adverse effects and estimating if the hazards are likely to occur in a given population.

Risk management weighs policy alternatives to accept or reduce risks and to select and implement appropriate options. This process also consists of different steps, which include an evaluation of risk management options, making a decision about managing the risk, implementing the decision, and monitoring and reviewing the effectiveness of the decision.

Risk communication is the exchange of information about the risk assessment and the risk management decisions. Information is shared among risk assessors, risk managers, consumers, the food industry, and the academic community. Risk communication takes place throughout the risk analysis process and includes the perception of risks that may or may not exist.

Discuss the process of risk analysis with students. **Ask**

- Why is risk analysis of GM foods important? It guides policy that protects people's health and the environment.
- What are some ways that risk communication is important to the food industry and to consumers? The food industry needs to know about food policies and how to communicate risk to consumers; consumers need to be informed about food content and what is considered safe.

UNIT 7: PLANTS

BIOZINE at CLASSZONE.COM

INTERNET MAGAZINE

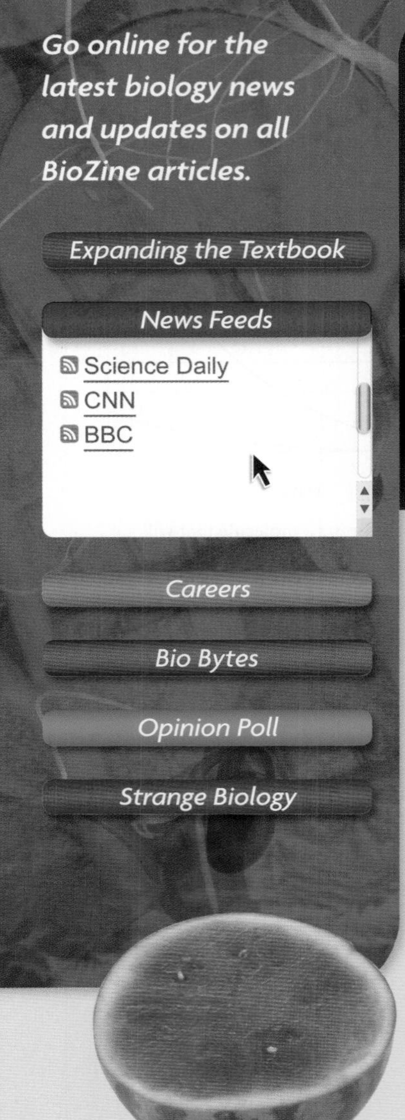

Although these tomatoes are labeled, genetically modified foods are not required to be labeled in the United States. However, they must meet the same standards of safety as traditionally grown foods.

Genetically Modified Foods—Do Potential Problems Outweigh Benefits?

There is a food fight going on, and you may need to choose a side. Genetically modified (GM) foods have been on the market since the early 1990s, and today most foods in U.S. grocery stores have GM ingredients. But the wide availability of GM food also raises concerns on topics ranging from health to the environment. Should you be worried about eating GM foods?

Current News

Have students use a computer with Internet access to check the Current News section of BioZine at **ClassZone.com.** Have students consider these questions:

- What topics in science involve possible risks to human health or the environment?
- What do the stories communicate about risks and risk management?
- How do people's perceptions of risk vary?

Opinion Poll

Have students take the online poll and report the outcome to the class. Discuss with students whether they have ever taken a poll that dealt with health risks. **Ask**

- How are risks typically described?
- How do you react to the description of a health risk that is related in quantitative terms?

New Technology, Old Idea

GM plants have genes that have been genetically engineered, or artificially introduced into the plant's genome. This technology gives plants a new characteristic. For instance, many crop plants are commonly engineered for disease resistance. Some examples of crops that have GM varieties on the market are wheat, rice, corn, soybeans, potatoes, squash, papayas, tomatoes, and cantaloupes.

Genetic engineering is a fairly new process, but plants have been modified through careful breeding for thousands of years. Many people knowledgeable about genetics argue that genetic engineering of crops is just a faster and more precise method of selective breeding.

The Green Revolution

In the 1960s, scientist Norman Borlaug and a team of researchers used cross-breeding techniques to develop a new strain of wheat. The new strain produced two to three times as much wheat as traditional varieties, and resisted many types of insects and diseases. Widely planted, these new varieties changed Mexico from an importer of wheat to an exporter within 20 years. Borlaug and his team began shipping the new strain of wheat to India and Pakistan, and both countries quickly doubled their wheat production. Known as the Green Revolution, this scientific advance improved crop yields drastically worldwide. For his work, Borlaug received the Nobel Prize in 1970. Today, Borlaug and many others view genetic engineering of crops as the next wave of the Green Revolution.

Plants can be genetically modified to produce larger fruits.

Benefits of GM crops

One benefit of GM crops is the potential of improved nutrition. For example, half of the world's population relies on rice as the main part of their diet. Rice lacks vitamin A, however, and vitamin A deficiency can cause blindness and sometimes death. Researchers developed a new strain of rice, called "golden rice." Unlike regular rice, golden rice is high in vitamin A. Golden rice could prevent millions of deaths of young children in developing countries every year.

TECHNOLOGY

Gene Gun

Genetic engineers use various ways to insert new genes into host cells. For plant cells, which have thick cell walls, one of the best ways to put foreign DNA into the cell is to actually shoot it through the plant tissue using a gene gun.

1. A researcher coats gold or tungsten particles with DNA and places them on the end of a microscopic plastic bullet.
2. The plastic bullet is placed in the gene gun and directed toward the target plant tissue.
3. A burst of helium propels the bullet to the end of the gun. The gold particles containing the DNA are released while the bullet remains in the gun.
4. Particles enter the cytoplasm of some of the cells in the target tissue. DNA is released from the gold particles and moves into the plant cell's nucleus, where it ultimately combines with the cell's DNA.

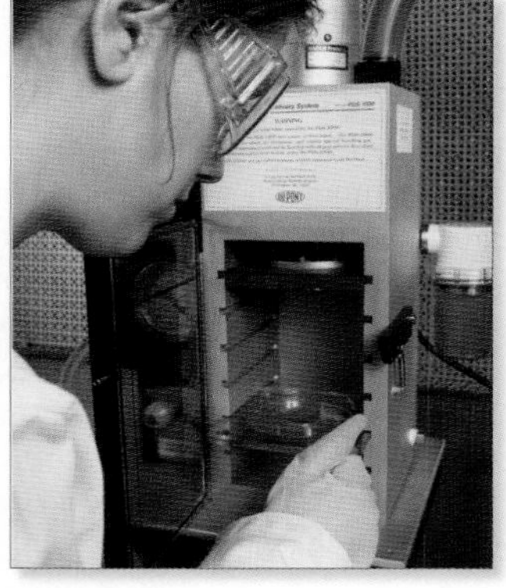

Read More >> at CLASSZONE.COM

Expanding the Textbook

Have students go the BioZine at **ClassZone.com** to read more about genetically modified foods. Students should come to class prepared to discuss what crops are genetically modified, what organisms the genes are from, and the advantages of each GM crop. Have students identify common foods that contain GM crops.

You could extend the discussion to include concerns different people have about the safety risks of GM foods. Have students identify risks that are more likely not real risks, risks that can be more easily addressed and controlled, and risks that are more difficult to control.

You could also divide the class into teams to debate the issue of genetically modifying crops. Have each team research the topic to gather information and evidence that supports their position. Have students debate the issue in class while you act as the moderator.

Vocabulary of Genetically Modified Foods

Students may be unfamiliar with some of the terms used to discuss genetically modified foods.

genetically modified (GM) food—food from an organism in which the genetic material has been altered by biotechnology. A GM organism contains genetic material from another organism, often from a different species. GM seeds are used to grow GM food crops, such as corn and soybeans, which are used to make GM food products.

***Bacillus thuringiensis* (Bt)**—a bacteria that contains a gene for toxin production. The toxin is currently used as an insecticide. Some GM crops contain the Bt gene for toxin production and require less use of insecticides since they produce the toxin for themselves.

herbicide—a chemical substance used to destroy or inhibit the growth of plants, especially weeds.

herbicide tolerance—a resistance to some herbicides. Some GM crops contain a gene from a bacterium that resists herbicides. Weeds growing in the crop fields can be killed without damaging the crop.

allergenicity—the tendency to cause an allergic reaction. A concern for human health is that GM foods could cause allergic reactions in some people. Genes from foods known to cause allergies usually are not transferred into other crops.

gene transfer—the movement of a gene from one organism to another organism. Gene transfer from GM foods is a debated issue. Human health could be affected if an antibiotic-resistance gene from a GM food were transferred to cells in the body and then to bacteria in the digestive system. The bacteria would acquire the gene, making it more difficult to treat diseases.

outcrossing—the movement of genes from GM plants to conventional crops or to plants in the wild. Outcrossing also refers to the human error of mixing GM seeds with conventional seeds.

UNIT

7

Take It Further

In the United States, genetically modified foods are regulated by the following three federal agencies:

- The U.S. Department of Agriculture's Animal and Plant Health Inspection Service (APHIS)
- The U.S. Environmental Protection Agency (EPA)
- The Department of Health and Human Services' Food and Drug Administration (FDA)

Not every country regulates GM foods, but at an international level, the Codex Alimentarius Commission is the body responsible for establishing international standards on foods. It is comprised of two United Nations organizations, the Food and Agriculture Organization (FAO) and the World Health Organization (WHO).

CAREERS

Research Engineer in Action

DR. TONG-JEN FU

TITLE Research Engineer, Food and Drug Administration

EDUCATION Ph. D., Chemical Engineering, Pennsylvania State University

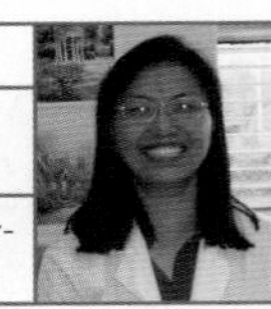

Dr. Tong-Jen Fu is a research engineer with the U.S. Food and Drug Administration (FDA), where she evaluates the methods currently used by scientists to determine the allergic potential of GM foods. She and other researchers are trying to understand exactly what makes substances in food cause allergic reactions.

One of the concerns of GM food is its potential to increase allergies in humans. Many proteins can potentially be an allergen—that is, cause an allergic reaction in some people. Since genetic engineering introduces new proteins into crops, concerns have been raised that unexpected allergies may arise. GM foods could trigger allergies by including proteins already known to cause a reaction, or by introducing completely new allergy-causing proteins—such as those from bacteria—into the food supply.

Researchers use extensive safety tests to determine whether a genetically modified food is likely to cause an allergic reaction. If any of these tests has a positive reaction, the GM food is not likely to be commercially produced. These tests include checking the amino acid sequences of introduced proteins against those of known allergens and testing whether the introduced proteins are resistant to digestion.

Read More >> at CLASSZONE.COM

Other promising uses of genetic engineering include growing fruits and vegetables that produce vaccines in their tissues. This would make shipment, storage, and administration of medicine easier worldwide.

Some benefits of GM crops are well established. They include benefits to farmers, such as crops that take less time, water, and land to grow, and plants that can withstand drought, cold temperature, insect damage, or that grow in poor soils.

There are also benefits to the environment, such as crops that lessen the need for pesticide, herbicide, or fertilizer applications. Even the consumer benefits with GM produce that stays fresh longer.

Potential Hidden Costs of GM Crops

Not everyone is enthusiastic about genetically modified foods. Opponents argue that it is impossible to predict exactly how the new crops—sometimes called "Frankenfoods"—will affect ecosystems. For example, the bacterial gene *Bt* is commonly inserted into GM plants. It produces an insecticidal toxin that is harmless to people. But will insects become resistant to *Bt*? Insect-repelling GM plants may speed the evolution of pesticide-resistant pests.

Another concern is that weeds can become stronger by cross-breeding with GM crops. When herbicide-resistant genes are inserted into crop plants, the weed are easily killed by herbicides while the crops remain unaffected. But pollen from plants can be carried by the wind for long distances, and seeds from GM crop could be accidentally dispersed outside their intended locations, causing the rise of "superweeds."

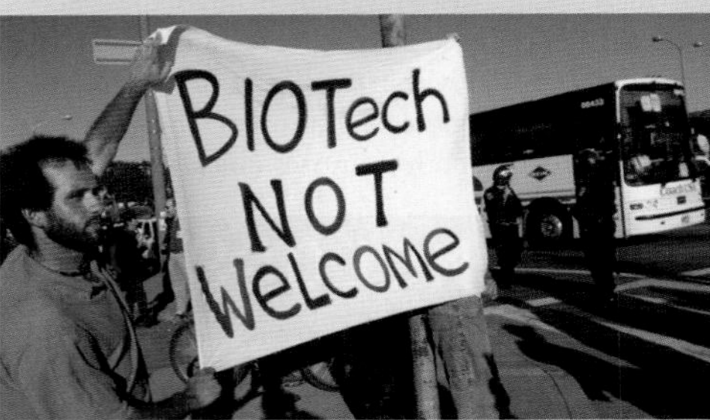

Unanswered Questions

Genetically modified crops are no longer considered new, but some questions about them remain. Many of the most important research questions concern the long-term effects of GM crops on human health and the environment. Specific questions include

- Will the levels of various vitamins in genetically modified crops differ from those found in their traditionally grown relatives?
- Could GM crops, such as those engineered to produce medicines, have adverse effects on wildlife

Read More >> at CLASSZONE.COM

Careers

Have students go to BioZine at **ClassZone.com** to learn about careers in biology. As students check out the careers, have them determine which careers involve plants. Have students identify careers that belong to the biotechnology industry. Ask them to consider how requirements for jobs in the biotechnology sector differ from those in more traditional fields.

UNIT 8

Animals

CHAPTER 23
Invertebrate Diversity 694

CHAPTER 24
A Closer Look at Arthropods 728

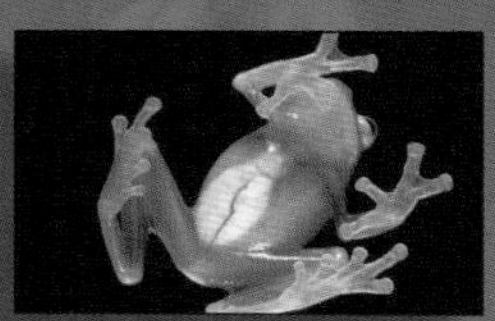

CHAPTER 25
Vertebrate Diversity 756

CHAPTER 26
A Closer Look at Amniotes 786

CHAPTER 27
Animal Behavior 816

INTERNET MAGAZINE
The Loss of Biodiversity 846

TECHNOLOGY Bioremediation

CAREER Conservation Biologist

Unit Project

Purpose **Explore and compare organ system anatomy and functions of representative organisms from each of the nine major animal phyla.**

Overview Students investigate five organ systems for a representative organism in each of the animal phyla. Students will

- search Internet, textbook, and/or library resources to obtain information about each organism
- take careful notes on note cards
- create a display for each organism in each of the major animal phyla that includes descriptions for five organ system functions and the structures involved

Preparation Make a copy of the project description and rubric for each student (*Unit Resource Book,* pp. 151–152). Tell students that their projects will be evaluated for organization and completeness.

Project Management Allow three weeks for the completion of the project. Have students check in weekly to monitor progress.

Unit Resource Book Unit 8 Project, pp. 151–153

CHAPTER 23

Indiana Resource Preview

Print Resources

Invertebrate Diversity

INDIANA STANDARDS		Sections	PAGES and PACING	UNIT RESOURCE BOOK
B.8.2	23.1	**Animal Characteristics** **KEY CONCEPT** Animals are diverse but share common characteristics.	pp. 696–698 30 minutes	URB pages 1–4
B.8.2	23.2	**Animal Diversity** **KEY CONCEPT** More than 95 percent of all animal species are invertebrates.	pp. 699–704 30 minutes	URB pages 5–8
	23.3	**Sponges and Cnidarians** **KEY CONCEPT** Sponges and cnidarians are the simplest animals.	pp. 705–708 30 minutes	URB pages 9–12
NOS.1		CHAPTER INVESTIGATION: Feeding *Hydra*	p. 709 45 minutes	**Lab Binder** Animals pages 1–4
	23.4	**Flatworms, Mollusks, and Annelids** **KEY CONCEPT** Flatworms, mollusks, and annelids belong to closely related phyla.	pp. 710–715 30 minutes	URB pages 13–16
	23.5	**Roundworms** **KEY CONCEPT** Roundworms have bilateral symmetry and shed their outer skeleton to grow.	pp. 716–717 30 minutes	URB pages 17–20
	23.6	**Echinoderms** **KEY CONCEPT** Echinoderms are on the same evolutionary branch as vertebrates.	pp. 718–720 30 minutes	URB pages 21–24
NOS.1		DATA ANALYSIS: Analyzing Scatterplots Correlations Among Invertebrate Data	p. 721 30 minutes	URB page 25
NOS.3		OPTIONS FOR INQUIRY	pp. 722–723 60 minutes, 45 minutes	**Lab Binder** Animals pages 5–9
		Chapter Review	pp. 724–727	**Assessment Book** Chapter Tests A, B pp. 459–466

INDIANA STANDARDS

B.8.2 Explain how organisms are classified and named based on their evolutionary relationships into taxonomic categories.
NOS.1 Develop explanations based on reproducible data and observations gathered during laboratory investigations.
NOS.3 Clearly communicate their ideas and results of investigations verbally and in written form using tables, graphs, diagrams, and photographs.

Labs

PUPIL EDITION LABS

Feeding Hydra, p. 709 Students observe *Hydra* behaviors. **Lab Binder** pp. 1–4	**Time:** 45 minutes **Materials:** 2 large eyedroppers, culture of *Hydra*, petri dish, drop of bottled spring water, hand lens or dissecting microscope, toothpick, culture of *Daphnia magna*
Anatomy of a Clam, Section 4, p. 714 Students observe the soft body of a clam to identify different systems. **Lab Binder** pp. 10–12	**Time:** 60 minutes **Materials:** preserved clam specimen, dissecting tray, Anatomical Clam Drawing, screwdriver, scalpel, probe, scissors, forceps, 12 dissecting pins, hand lens, paper towels

OPTIONS FOR INQUIRY

Anatomy of a Sea Star, p. 722 Students observe the internal anatomy of a sea star. **Lab Binder** pp. 5–7	**Time:** 60 minutes **Materials:** preserved sea star specimen, dissecting tray, scissors, forceps, dissecting needle, 12 dissecting pins, hand lens or dissecting microscope, paper towels, Anatomical Sea Star Drawing
Anatomy of a Annelid, p. 723 Students observe the anatomy of an annelid. **Lab Binder** p. 9	**Time:** 45 minutes **Materials:** 6–10 filter paper disks, forceps, petri dish, 10 mL spring water, California blackworm, eyedropper, dissecting microscope

LAB BINDER Unit 8 Animals

Additional Investigation: Evolution of the Coelom, pp. 13–16

Challenge Lab: Cardiovascular System of Mudworms, pp. 92–96

LAB GENERATOR

A searchable CD of all labs in the program in editable format, including forensic, probeware, and biotechnology labs.

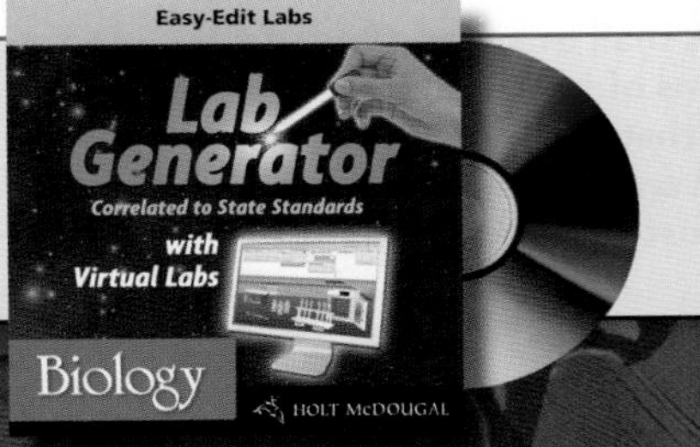

Presentation Tools

POWER PRESENTATIONS

Presentation Chapter 23
Power Presentations for each section incorporate images and clips from the Media Gallery: Includes Note Navigator for each section.

MEDIA GALLERY

Contains the following images and video clips, as well as animations, simulations and forms of visuals from the book.

Body plan symmetry

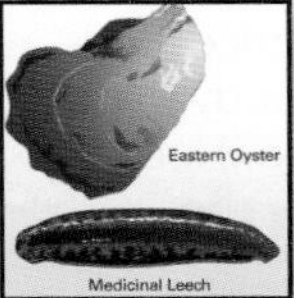

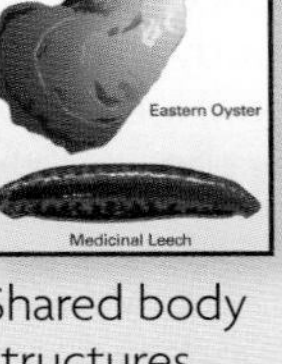

Shared body structures

Lion's mane jellyfish

Flamingo tongue snail

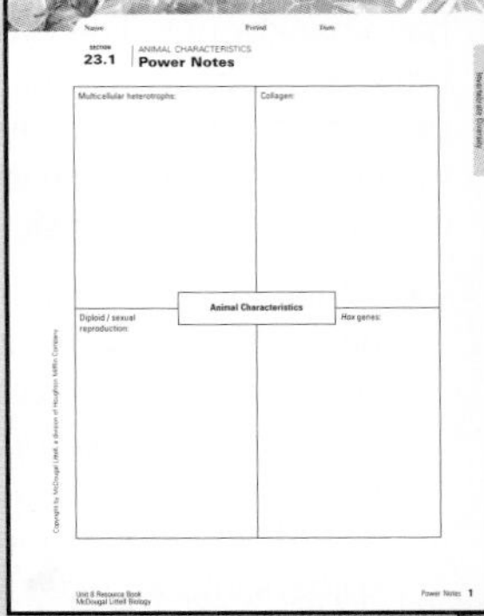

Power Notes

VIDEO

Short video clips explore the diversity of invertebrates.

ANIMATED BIOLOGY

Digestive Tract Formation
Shared Body Structures

TRANSPARENCIES

Hox Gene Expression T93
Protostome and Deuterostome Development T94
Phylogeny of Animals T95
Sponge Anatomy T96
Cnidarian Anatomy T97
Flatworm Anatomy T98
Mollusk Anatomy T99
Annelid Anatomy T100
Roundworm Anatomy T101
Echinoderm Anatomy T102

Online BIOLOGY CLASSZONE.COM

BioZine
Animated Biology
Interactive Review
SciLinks
Resource Centers

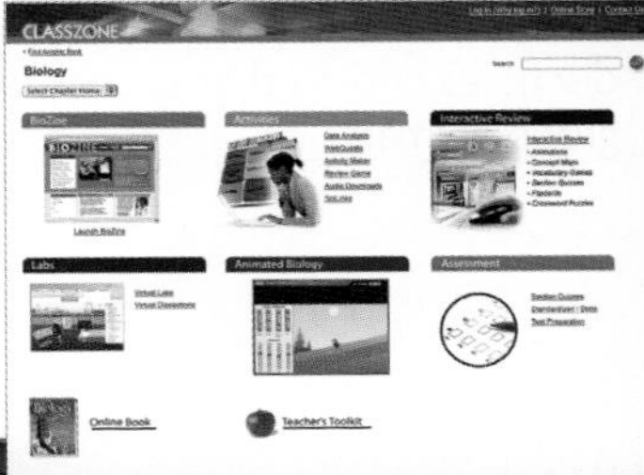

CHAPTER
23

▼ Focus and Motivate

How is this sea slug similar to a spider?

They are both invertebrates; they do not have backbones. The differences between the two animals (body make-up, habitat, diet, reproduction) are indicative of the diversity of the invertebrate group. **Ask**

- What are some invertebrates you have contact with in your daily activities? Answers may include seafoods such as shrimp, crab, lobster, and clams; natural sponges used for cleaning and bathing; spiders, mosquitoes, and houseflies
- What are some ways that invertebrates impact human life? parasitism, disease transmission, crop pests, sources of food

BIOZINE ClassZone.com

Students can access BioZine at **ClassZone.com** to check out articles featured in "Strange Biology."

In a Hurry?

The critical material of the chapter is found in **Sections 23.3, 23.4, 23.5,** and **23.6,** which cover the characteristics of sponges and cnidarians; flatworms, mollusks, and annelids; roundworms; and echinoderms, respectively. A quick reading of the heads in **Section 23.1** will introduce students to the characteristics that all animals share. **Section 23.2** discusses criteria that scientists use to group animals.

CHAPTER
23 Invertebrate Diversity

KEY CONCEPTS

23.1 Animal Characteristics
Animals are diverse but share common characteristics.

23.2 Animal Diversity
More than 95 percent of all animal species are invertebrates.

23.3 Sponges and Cnidarians
Sponges and cnidarians are the simplest animals.

23.4 Flatworms, Mollusks, and Annelids
Flatworms, mollusks, and annelids belong to closely related phyla.

23.5 Roundworms
Roundworms have bilateral symmetry and shed their outer skeleton to grow.

23.6 Echinoderms
Echinoderms are on the same evolutionary branch as vertebrates.

BIOLOGY CLASSZONE.COM

View animated chapter concepts.
- Digestive Tract Formation
- Shared Body Structures

BIOZINE
Keep current with biology news.
- News feeds
- Bio Bytes
- Polls

RESOURCE CENTER
Get more information on
- Sponges and Cnidarians
- Worms
- Mollusks

Teacher Demonstration

Eye Opener **Use a snail as an example of the diverse adaptations of invertebrates. Students will see that snails absorb gases through their skin and through an organ called the pneumostome on their right side.**

Materials
- snail, preferably a terrestrial species
- paper towels
- cotton swabs
- small container of white vinegar

How is this sea slug similar to a spider?

Connecting CONCEPTS

Both sea slugs and spiders are invertebrates. Invertebrates, which are animals without backbones, account for the vast majority of animals on Earth. You are surrounded by invertebrates on a daily basis, whether you are aware of them or not. Invertebrates exist in a wide variety of shapes and sizes and live in many different habitats—including your body!

Adaptation Because adult sea slugs do not have shells, they must use other methods to avoid being eaten. Some sea slugs eat sponges. Sponges (left) have chemicals that make them taste bad. Sea slugs have the ability to overcome the foul taste and are able to incorporate the chemicals into their body. These chemicals, in turn, give the sea slugs a bad taste, helping them to avoid predation.

Demonstrate

- Place a snail on a moist paper towel.
- Dip a cotton swab into vinegar, then hold the tip of the swab close to the snail's head, sides, and tail without touching it.

Discuss Have students compare how the snail reacted when the vinegar was held near different parts of its body. **Ask,** Do snails have a nose? no Point out the following:

- Snails breathe and detect smells through their skin and through a pore on their right side called the pneumostome, which connects directly to the snail's single lung.
- The layer of mucus covering the snail's skin makes it easier for the snail to exchange gases with the environment.

Activate Prior Knowledge

Direct students' attention to the chapter title. **Ask,** What is meant by the term *diversity* as it relates to organisms? number of different types of organisms or species Remind students that diversity is only possible because of natural selection and evolution. **Ask,** What allows such a wide variety of forms and organisms to exist and thrive on Earth? There are innumerable niches to be filled.

Preview Vocabulary

Greek and Latin Word Origins Have students watch for the application of these prefixes here and in the later chapters of this unit:

meso- = middle
endo- = inner
ecto- or *exo-* = outer

Academic Vocabulary It might be useful to have students think again about classification. Early scientists organized the living world into a *hierarchy,* a ranking of organisms based on human notions of complexity. Human beings were placed at the top, with all organisms being subordinate. The word *hierarchy* implies a ranking based on the degree of power, ability, or status an individual has.

With the great diversity and number of invertebrates, such an idea loses its power. Suggest that students think in ecological terms when learning about the different invertebrate phyla and the different niches the organisms fill.

English Learners In this chapter, students are introduced to terms that describe distinguishing characteristics of animals:

invertebrate	*vertebrate*
protostome	*deuterostome*
bilateral	*radial*

You can help students get a sense of how and when such words are used by setting up a word wall. Write the terms on individual cards and post them on the board as you introduce them. Remember to review the words periodically.

SECTION 23.1

▼ Plan and Prepare

Objectives

- Describe how animals comprise a diverse kingdom.
- Identify the defining characteristics of animals.

Section Resources

Unit Resource Book Study Guide pp. 1–2 Power Notes p. 3 Reinforcement p. 4
Interactive Reader Chapter 23 **Spanish Study Guide** pp. 233–234
Biology Toolkit pp. C3, C19, C28
Technology Power Presentation 23.1 Media Gallery DVD Online Quiz 23.1

Activate Prior Knowledge Have students look at the animal diversity reflected in the photographs on the page. **Ask**

- Where would you start? If no one had gone before you, how would you begin to classify the life forms shown on this page? Answers will vary, but may be based on outward appearance, perceived size, or habitat.
- Knowing these are all animals, what can you state about these organisms with certainty? made up of eukaryotic cells, heterotrophic, consumers, require oxygen

Suggest to students that the best way to think about animal diversity is to think about all the ecological niches to be filled.

▼ Teach

TEACH FROM VISUALS

FIGURE 23.1 Have students attempt to classify the animals shown as far as they can. **Ask,** Which of the animals are vertebrates? blue whale, giraffe, Steller's jay

23.1 Animal Characteristics

KEY CONCEPT Animals are diverse but share common characteristics.

MAIN IDEAS

- Animals are the most physically diverse kingdom of organisms.
- All animals share a set of characteristics.

VOCABULARY

collagen, p. 697
homeotic, p. 698
homeobox, p. 698

B.8.2 Explain how organisms are classified and named based on their evolutionary relationships into taxonomic categories.

Connect We are animals. So are jellyfish, squid, cockroaches, tapeworms, sea stars, and the family dog. Animals live in nearly every environment on Earth, from high in the atmosphere to the deepest sea trench. While they come in a huge variety of shapes and sizes, they all share a common ancestry and a set of common physical and genetic characteristics.

MAIN IDEA

Animals are the most physically diverse kingdom of organisms.

More than 1 million species of animals have been described so far, and scientists predict that tens of millions more have yet to be discovered. Animals are a remarkably diverse group of organisms. They range in size from blue whales twice the length of a school bus to rotifers smaller than the period at the end of this sentence. As shown in **FIGURE 23.1**, some look like soft tubes, and others have muscular bodies inside hard shells, or soft tissues over hard internal skeletons. Some animals have many specialized tissues and organs, and others have no distinct tissues at all.

FIGURE 23.1 Animal body plans vary widely in shape and size, from microscopic rotifers (colored SEM; magnification 170×) to blue whales 24 meters in length.

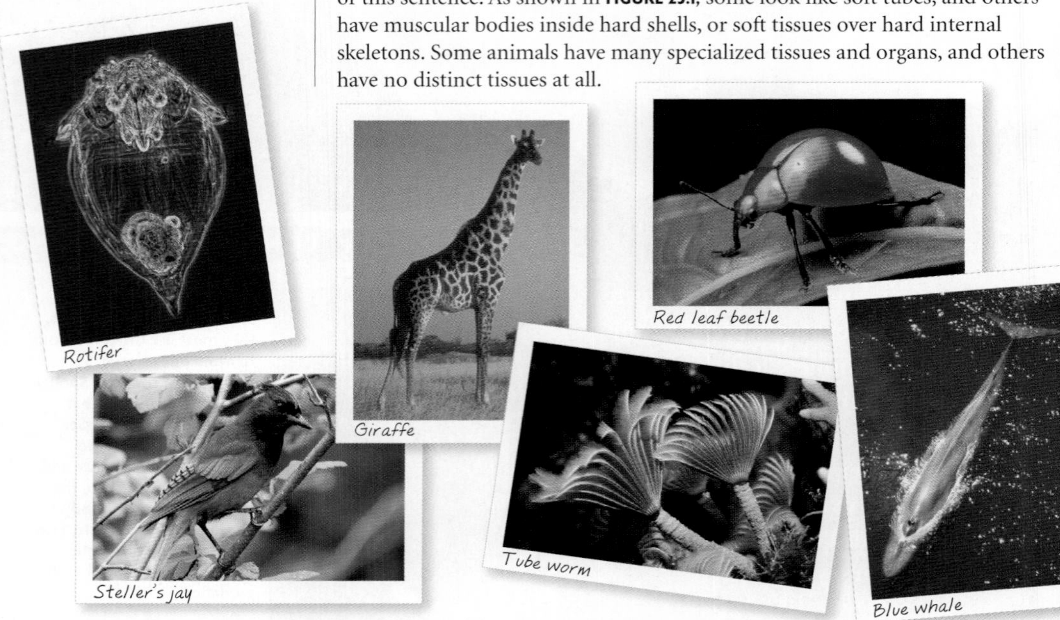

Differentiated Instruction

ENGLISH LEARNERS

Have students create a mind map to serve as a study guide for this section. They can begin with the Main Idea on page 697, "All animals share a set of characteristics." From this they can branch off to the four headings with details and notes beneath each. Have students focus on the main ideas of each paragraph and record brief definitions of key terms such as *Hox* genes, collagen, heterotroph, and diploid.

Biology Toolkit, Mind Map, p. C28

BELOW LEVEL

Prepare a list of true/false statements to test students' knowledge of animal characteristics and animal diversity. Include obvious statements, such as "All animals are multicellular." But also have students think about points of differentiation, as in "Multicellular organization means all animals have tissues, organs, and organ systems" or "All animals have blood to transport oxygen and nutrients."

Biology Toolkit, Anticipation Guide, p. C3

Animals are found nearly everywhere on Earth, including places where plants and fungi do not live. They are the dominant herbivores, predators, and detritivores in most ecosystems. Some walk, burrow, swim, fly, or slide along on mucus trails in search of food. Others spend their whole adult lives fixed to a single spot, endlessly straining water to collect microscopic particles of food.

A Connect What ecological factors determine where certain animals are found?

Connecting **CONCEPTS**

Niches Recall from **Chapter 14** that an ecological niche includes all of the factors a species needs to survive, thrive, and reproduce.

MAIN IDEA

All animals share a set of characteristics.

Given the huge physical diversity among animals, what characteristics distinguish animals from other organisms? All animals share a set of derived characters, or heritable features, that set them apart from other eukaryotes. These characteristics suggest that all animals are the descendants of a single common ancestor.

TAKING NOTES

Use a diagram to take notes on the unique characteristics of animals.

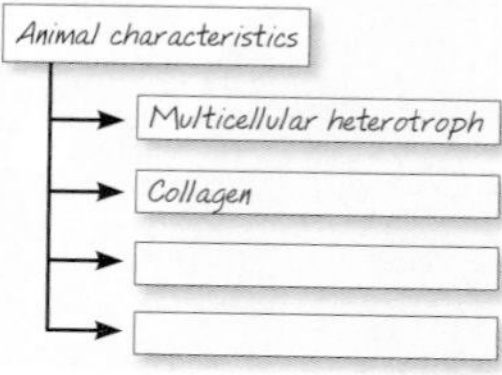

All Animals Are Multicellular Heterotrophs

Animals must eat. Their cells lack the chloroplasts that let photosynthetic organisms make their own food. All animals are heterotrophs, meaning they eat other organisms to gain the nutrients they need to survive. Any organic compound an animal uses in cellular respiration has to come from an outside source. Single-celled protists also eat other organisms. But because even the simplest animal is built of many specialized cells, all animals can ingest and process larger food particles than a single cell can engulf.

Animals are not the only eukaryotes that are both heterotrophic and multicellular. Fungi are also multicellular and use organisms for food. But cells of fungi do not have the same diversity of functions that animal cells have. Although animals and fungi share heterotrophic ancestors, it is likely that they evolved the trait of multicellularity independently.

Animal Cells Are Supported by Collagen

Unlike the cells of plants and fungi, animal cells lack rigid cell walls. Therefore, animals are the only multicellular organisms with no cellular structure to support their cells. What component carries out these functions in animals?

Collagen (KAHL-uh-juhn), shown in **FIGURE 23.2**, is a three-stranded protein unique to animals. Animal body parts that contain collagen include skin, bone, ligaments, fingernails, and hair. Individual collagen proteins combine with one another to form ropelike fibers that are both strong and flexible. These fibers form an extracellular network that many animal cells use for support. Unlike a cell wall, the collagen network does not glue cells in place, so it is possible for cells to move within the animal's body. Collagen also forms an integral part of the jointed skeleton that many animals use to move their entire bodies.

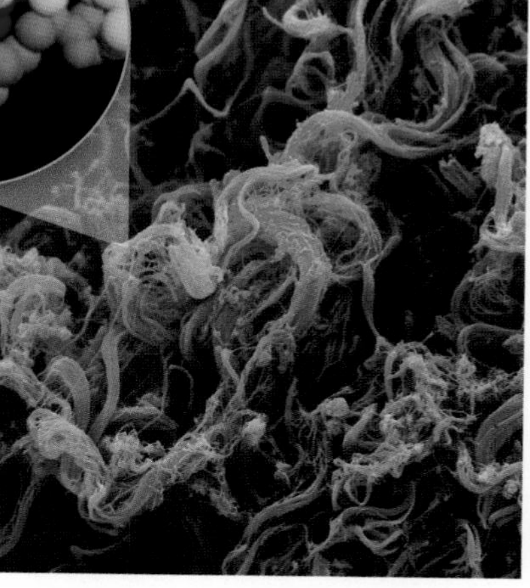

FIGURE 23.2 This molecular model and SEM show the triple-stranded structure of collagen, a strong and flexible protein that is unique to animals. (colored SEM; magnification 3000×)

Vocabulary

Greek and Latin Word Origins Remind students of the meanings of the roots of **heterotroph:**

hetero- = different
trophos = feeder

The opposite of a heterotroph is an **autotroph,** which produces its own food, usually through photosynthesis. Discuss with students what the implications are for an organism that gets food from its environment. Animals must have the means to do the following:

- capture and take in food
- break down food and absorb nutrients
- move nutrients throughout the body
- capture energy from nutrients
- get rid of unused materials

Science Trivia

- The word *collagen* is derived from the Greek word *colla,* meaning "glue."
- Collagen was used by ancient Egyptians to make glue.
- Gelatin is made from collagen. Gelatin is used in various foods such as Jell-O, marshmallows, gummy candies, soups, and cream cheese.
- The collagen used to make gelatin and glue is processed from the bones, hooves, and connective tissues of cows, pigs, and horses.
- Collagen from cows is also used in cosmetic surgery to make humans' lips fuller or temporarily remove the appearance of wrinkles in the skin. Because this collagen comes from a different species, allergic reactions are possible.

PRE-AP

Give students five minutes to write about these questions: What are the characteristics of all living things, and how would you expect those characteristics to be reflected in the different body systems of an animal? Remind students to keep writing for the full five minutes, even if they just list every animal they can think of and the body systems they have. Discuss what students come up with and look for commonalities as well as characteristics that would help distinguish different phyla.

Biology Toolkit, Quick-Write, p. C19

Answers

A Connect Answers may include climate and availability of food and other resources.

▼ Teach *continued*

Vocabulary

homeotic, homeobox The roots *homo-* and *homeo-* are variations of the same Greek root, meaning "like" or "similar." Students have seen these roots before in *homeostasis* and *homogeneous.* **Homeosis** refers to a situation in which one structure gets transformed into the "likeness" of another, as with the antennae that become legs in the fly shown in **FIGURE 23.3.**

Answers

A Analyze Each homeotic gene has a sequence of 180 nucleotides called *Hox* genes that defines the head-to-tail pattern of development in animal embryos.

▼ Assess and Reteach

Assess Use the Online Quiz or Section Quiz (*Assessment Book,* p. 453).

Reteach Create a graphic organizer like the one on page 697. Ask students to summarize the common characteristics of animals and how animals are distinguished from other living things.

FIGURE 23.3 In the wildtype fly (top), the antennae develop normally. In the mutant fly (bottom), a mutation causes legs to form in place of the antennae.
(SEMs; magnification 70×)

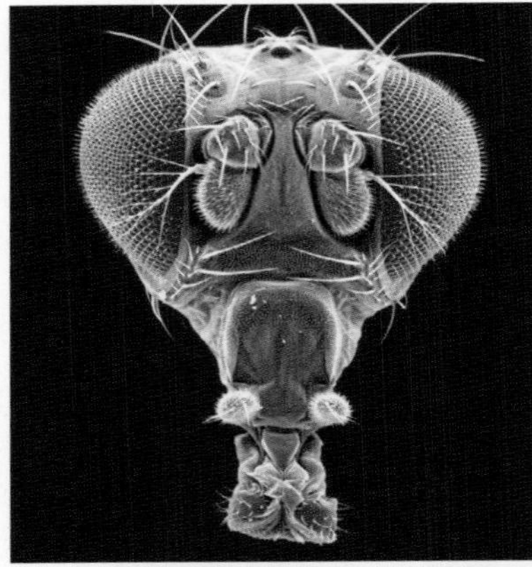

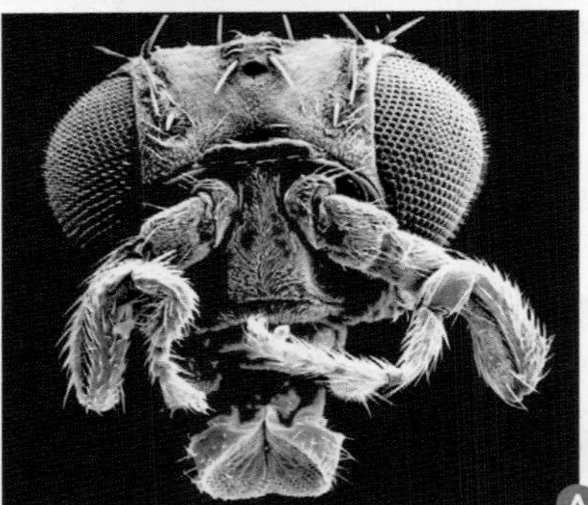

Animals Are Diploid and Usually Reproduce Sexually

Animals are the only multicellular organisms that do not alternate between free-living diploid and haploid stages. In all animal species, the individuals that reproduce are diploid (meaning they have one set of chromosomes from each parent), and they produce offspring that are also diploid. Some kinds of animals can reproduce both asexually and sexually. For example, a *Hydra* can clone itself by budding. These species have male and female sexual organs and also reproduce sexually. A few animals have become completely asexual. All whiptail lizards, for example, are females, and all their offspring are clones of the mother. But these animals evolved from sexual species, and their asexual habits are derived characters.

Most Animals Have *Hox* Genes

Most of the animals that scientists have studied so far share a group of genes called homeotic genes. **Homeotic** (HOH-mee-AH-tihk) genes are a class of genes that control early development in animals. Every homeotic gene has a specific sequence of 180 nucleotides called **homeobox** (HOH-mee-uh-BAHKS), or *Hox,* genes. *Hox* genes define the head-to-tail pattern of development in animal embryos. Homeotic genes create segments in a larva or embryo that develop into specific organs and tissues. The *Hox* genes within these segments determine the position of cell differentiation and development by switching certain genes "on" or "off."

A mutation in a homeotic gene leads to the development of a body structure in the wrong position. For example, the effect of a mutation in a homeotic gene, *Antennapedia,* determines whether an insect body segment will grow antennae or legs. As shown in **FIGURE 23.3,** in the wildtype fly (top), antennae develop normally. In the fly with a mutation in its homeotic genes (bottom), legs develop where the antennae should be. However, the rest of the fly develops normally. Although the misplaced legs look normal in structure, they are not functional for the fly. Flies with homeotic mutations usually do not live very long.

A Analyze How are homeotic and *Hox* genes related?

23.1 ASSESSMENT

ONLINE QUIZ ClassZone.com

B.8.2

REVIEWING ▶ MAIN IDEAS

1. In what ways are animals physically diverse? Give three examples.
2. List and describe the derived characters that all animals share.

CRITICAL THINKING

3. **Apply** How does the structure of animal cells allow animals to move?
4. **Hypothesize** Animals are heterotrophs. How might this have contributed to such great animal diversity?

***Connecting* CONCEPTS**

5. **Genetics** How does the genome of an offspring resulting from sexual reproduction differ from that of an offspring resulting from asexual reproduction?

23.1 ASSESSMENT

1. Animals differ in size, shape, and body composition. (Some have specialized tissues and organs, others do not.)
2. All animals are multicellular heterotrophs; they need to get their nutrients from other organisms. Collagen is a strong, triple-stranded, but flexible protein that supports animal cells. Animals are diploid—one set of chromosomes from each parents. Most animals reproduce sexually and have homeotic genes, which regulate embryonic development.
3. The absence of cell walls and the flexibility of collagen allows animals to move.
4. Competition for resources such as food leads to diversification. The interactions of animals with one another and with autotrophs and the environment function as selective pressure that can select for or against traits that arise naturally through genetic mutation.
5. The genome of a sexually produced offspring is diploid—contains DNA from both parents. An asexually produced offspring has DNA from just one parent.

23.2 Animal Diversity

KEY CONCEPT More than 95 percent of all animal species are invertebrates.

MAIN IDEAS

- Each animal phylum has a unique body plan.
- Animals are grouped using a variety of criteria.
- A comparison of structure and genetics reveals the evolutionary history of animals.

VOCABULARY

vertebrate, p. 699
invertebrate, p. 699
phylum, p. 699
bilateral symmetry, p. 701
radial symmetry, p. 701
protostome, p. 702
deuterostome, p. 702

B.8.2 Explain how organisms are classified and named based on their evolutionary relationships into taxonomic categories.

Connect When you think of an animal, something familiar such as a dog or a snake probably comes to mind. Both of these animals are vertebrates, a group that represents one small subset of animals. However, most animals are invertebrates and look nothing like your mental picture. To understand the vast diversity of animal life, biologists look for unique characteristics that help them sort animals into distinct groups and arrange those groups into a family tree.

MAIN IDEA

Each animal phylum has a unique body plan.

A **vertebrate** (VUR-tuh-briht) is an animal with an internal segmented backbone. Vertebrates are the most obvious animals around us, and we are vertebrates, too. But vertebrates make up less than five percent of all known animal species. All other animals are invertebrates. **Invertebrates** (ihn-VUR-tuh-brihts) are animals without backbones. Early animal classifications divided all animals into vertebrates and invertebrates. But because invertebrates are not defined by a set of shared derived characters, the division is considered outdated. Many invertebrates are not closely related to one another.

***Connecting* CONCEPTS**

Classification Recall from **Chapter 17** that in the Linnaean system of classification, phylum is the first level below kingdom. As you learned earlier, all animals are classified in the kingdom Animalia.

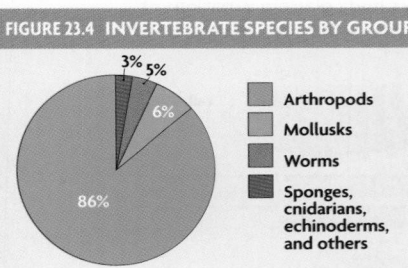

FIGURE 23.4 INVERTEBRATE SPECIES BY GROUP

3% 5% 6% 86%

Arthropods
Mollusks
Worms
Sponges, cnidarians, echinoderms, and others

Animal Phyla

Scientists now use shared characters to divide animals into more than 30 major groups. Each group, or **phylum** (FY-luhm) (plural, *phyla*), of animals is defined by structural and functional characteristics that are different from every other animal group. Each animal phylum has a unique body plan and represents a different way that a multicellular animal is put together.

Every animal phylum has a unique set of anatomical characteristics. These unique characteristics are true of both the largest and smallest phyla. Some phyla, such as mollusks, have tens of thousands of species, ranging from land snails to marine octopuses. Others are much less diverse. Phyla such as Arthropoda contain species that look very different from one another. In other phyla, such as Nematoda, all of the species look very similar. The relative amount of invertebrate species per group is shown in **FIGURE 23.4.**

Differentiated Instruction

BELOW LEVEL

Have students work in small groups to preview the section by looking at the different characteristics that can be used to classify groups of animals. Suggest they start with a circle containing "All Animals" and then use a cluster diagram to look for way to organize the information. Suggest they think of the vocabulary terms as different ways to characterize body plans.

Biology Toolkit, Think-Pair-Share, p. C13; Cluster Diagram, p. C30

ENGLISH LEARNERS

Have students prepare word squares to compare and contrast pairs of terms to describe different body characteristics:

invertebrate	*vertebrate*
bilateral symmetry	*radial symmetry*
anterior	*posterior*
ventral	*dorsal*
protostome	*deuterostome*

Remind students that highlighted vocabulary appears in the *Multilanguage Glossary.*

Biology Toolkit, Word Squares, p. D4

SECTION 23.2

Plan and Prepare ▼

Objectives

- Describe the unique body plans of the animal phyla.
- Describe the criteria used to group animals.
- Explain how genetics reveals the evolutionary history of animals.

Section Resources

Unit Resource Book
Study Guide pp. 5–6
Power Notes p. 7
Reinforcement p. 8

Interactive Reader Chapter 23
Spanish Study Guide pp. 235–236

Biology Toolkit pp. C13, C17, C19, C30, D4

Technology
Power Presentation 23.2
Media Gallery DVD
Online Quiz 23.2

Activate Prior Knowledge Have students consider whether symmetry in body shape is a characteristic of all animals. **Ask**

- How would you describe the symmetry of your body? bilateral symmetry
- How would you describe the symmetry of a starfish? radial symmetry
- How would you describe the symmetry of a sponge? variable

Explain that symmetry in animals relates to their development and affects the way they interact with the environment.

Teach ▼

TEACH FROM VISUALS

FIGURE 23.4 Point out the enormity of the arthropod group. **Ask,** Do you expect that the arthropods also dominate the invertebrate group in terms of numbers of animals? Students may say yes, because many arthropods are very small and numerous. Remind students that diversity is measured in species, not in numbers of individuals.

▼ Teach *continued*

ONLINE BIOLOGY For a comparison of four different invertebrates, see Animated Biology in Options for Inquiry on page 723.

Take It Further

The relationship between *Hox* genes and **birth defects** is an active area of research. Several studies have demonstrated a connection between **retinoic acid** (a derivative of vitamin A) and *Hox* genes controlling head and facial development. The link between retinoic acid and birth defects was first made in the 1930s, when researchers noticed that pregnant animals with either excessive or deficient levels of vitamin A produced offspring with severely malformed heads, limbs, hearts, lungs, and central nervous systems.

A spike in human birth defects in the 1980s was connected with the release of several acne and skin medications containing high levels of retinoic acid. Recent studies in mice and humans have shown that high doses of retinoic acid taken during pregnancy interfere with the expression of *Hox* genes in the embryo, leading to an increased incidence of miscarriage, cleft palate, abnormal brain development, and other anomalies.

Answers

A Analyze Because *Hox* genes regulate the formation of segments or parts of a body, a mutation of such a gene could cause dramatic variation of body plan. Over time, these forms could be selected for, leading to diversification and speciation.

B Analyze The order of the genes corresponds to the segments or tissues in each body plan in a linear, head-to-tail way.

Homeobox Genes and Body Plans

If you take a look at the animals that you might see on a walk through the park, you may notice how different their body plans are. The swimming fish in a park pond have sets of fins, the flying birds have pairs of wings, and the squirrels chasing one another have four legs.

Differences in body plans result from differences in the expression of homeobox genes. As shown in **FIGURE 23.5,** homeobox genes tell embryonic cells which part of the body they are going to become, such as the head, middle, or tail. These instructions start a chain reaction that turns on all other genes that define the adult form—where limbs go, how many eyes will develop, the location of the gut, and so on. For this reason, a mutation in a *Hox* gene can change an animal's entire body plan. Scientists think that mutations in these genes led to the vast diversity of animal species.

All the animal phyla now known first appeared during the Cambrian explosion. How did so many unique body plans appear in such a short time? The trigger may have been an increase in oxygen levels in the atmosphere that began about 700 million years ago. As oxygen levels rose, eukaryotic organisms could become more active and begin to occupy different niches within more complex ecosystems.

The Cambrian explosion was only possible because animals had already evolved *Hox* genes. These genes became a toolkit that changed animal bodies through duplication and loss. For example, a sponge is a simple animal that has at least one *Hox* gene, while an arthropod has eight. This difference suggests that over time, mutations have caused the original *Hox* gene to be copied repeatedly, forming a series of similar genes along a chromosome. Every time a gene is duplicated, one of the copies can keep doing its original job in the organism, leaving the other free to mutate and take on new roles.

A Analyze How are *Hox* genes related to the diversity of body plans?

FIGURE 23.5 *Hox* Gene Expression

The genes that determine a fruit fly's body plan are variations of the same genes that determine a human's, but they are expressed in different patterns.

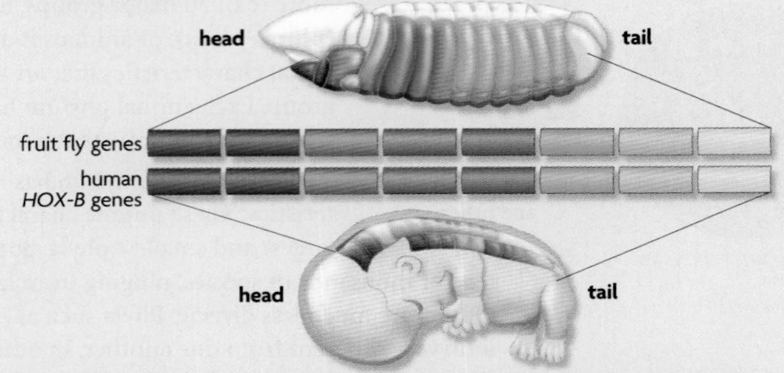

B Analyze In both fruit flies and humans, *Hox* genes occur in a similar order on chromosomes. How does the illustration emphasize this point?

Differentiated Instruction

TEACH WITH TECHNOLOGY

Collect images of closely related animals that share similar features but are phenotypically quite different. For example, compare insects such as dragonflies, butterflies, and houseflies, and point out differences in wing number and shape, eye structure and placement, antennae and mouthparts. Looking at **FIGURE 23.5,** discuss with students the implications of homeobox genes that can "turn off or on" different body parts as different species evolved and occupied different niches or habitats.

MAIN IDEA

Animals are grouped using a variety of criteria.

Like other organisms, animals are placed in separate groups based on certain characteristics. Three criteria used to categorize animals are body plan symmetry, number of tissue layers, and developmental patterns.

Body Plan Symmetry

Symmetry refers to how similar an object is across a central axis. For example, if you draw a line down the middle of a square, both sides are equal in shape and size. An object is asymmetrical if the two sides are not mirror images of one another. Most animal body plans fall into one of two types of symmetry.

- Animals with **bilateral symmetry** can be divided equally along only one plane, which splits an animal into mirror-image sides.
- Animals with **radial symmetry** have body parts arranged in a circle around a central axis.

Bilateral animals have distinct heads and tails, which are called the anterior (head) and posterior (tail) ends. These animals also have distinct backs and bellies, which are called the dorsal (back) and ventral (belly) surfaces. Each of these regions can become specialized. For example, structures that an animal uses to move, such as legs, are usually found on its ventral surface. Active hunters that often travel in one direction in search of food have a head region with a concentration of nervous tissue that forms a brain and with sensory organs such as eyes.

VISUAL VOCAB

Animals with **bilateral symmetry** can be divided equally along only one plane, which splits an animal into mirror-image sides.

Animals with **radial symmetry** have body parts arranged in a circle around a central axis.

TAKING NOTES

Draw a simple sketch of an animal in your notes. Mark its symmetry, then label its anterior, posterior, dorsal, and ventral sides.

Tissue Layers

Bilateral animals have three distinct layers of tissue. Animals with three tissue layers are triploblastic. These layers are the ectoderm, endoderm, and mesoderm. The ectoderm is the outer layer that develops into both the skin and the brain and nervous system. The endoderm is an inner layer that lines the animal's gut. The mesoderm is a middle layer that develops into internal tissues and organs. Complex organ systems resulted from the evolution of this third tissue layer.

Most radial animals have only two distinct layers of tissue. These layers are an inner endoderm and an outer ectoderm. Radial animals do not have a mesoderm layer, and therefore they lack the complex internal tissues and organs found in triploblastic animals.

VOCABULARY

The following Greek word parts can help you remember the names of tissue layers.

- *-derm* comes from a word meaning "skin"
- *ecto-* means "outer"
- *endo-* means "inner"
- *meso-* means "middle"

Vocabulary

Academic Vocabulary Students are probably familiar with the language of geometry used in this section.

plane, flat or level surface

axis, a straight line about which a body rotates

Point out that the term *plane* applies to both bilateral and radial symmetries. In bilateral symmetry, a plane not only divides an animal's body into two sides *(bilateral),* but also head and tail *(anterior, posterior)* and back and belly *(dorsal, ventral).*

In radial symmetry, any plane that passes through the central axis produces two mirror-image sides. The terms *anterior, posterior, dorsal,* and *ventral* are not used to describe radial symmetry. However, radially symmetrical animals do have two distinct ends oriented around the central axis, with one end defined by the location of the mouth.

Take It Further

An animal can be bilaterally symmetrical without its two sides displaying perfect mirror images of each other. Male **fiddler crabs,** for example, have one very large claw on one side and a much smaller one on the other. Another arthropod, the American **lobster,** *Homarus americanus,* possesses one claw that is heavy and armed with molar-like "teeth" that are good for crushing, and another that is lighter and armed with smaller, sharper teeth for slicing and cutting.

INCLUSION

Use plastic models of animals to discuss body symmetry with students who are visually impaired. Discuss the implications of body shape on how animals move and how they capture food. For example, compare a jellyfish filtering food from the water with a highly maneuverable predator such as a shark.

PRE-AP

Have students take five minutes to write about how body shape affects movement and food capture for animals that are radially symmetric compared to those that are bilaterally symmetric. Also, have them consider the implications of the two dermal layers typical of radially symmetric animals compared to the three layers in bilaterally symmetric animals. Suggest that students compare a jellyfish to a shark.

Biology Toolkit, Quick-Write, p. C19

▼ Teach continued

Vocabulary

Greek and Latin Word Origins Students have seen the Greek root *stoma* that is used in **protostome** and **deuterostome.** *Stoma* means "mouth"; *stomata* are the mouthlike openings in leaves that enable gases to pass in and out. *Stoma* is also found in the word *stomach.* Add the prefix *proto-*, which means "first," or *deutero-*, which means "second," and students will see how descriptive each term is.

Integrating Embryology

The process during which embryonic cells differentiate into distinct tissue layers is called **gastrulation.** Following fertilization and cleavage, the rapidly dividing embryo is a simple ball of undifferentiated cells called a blastula. During gastrulation, the cells migrate to different parts of the embryo and begin to differentiate into the three (or two) distinct tissue types.

Answers

A Connect bilateral

B Contrast protostome: spiral cleavage pattern, and the first opening of the digestive cavity (blastopore) becomes the mouth; deuterostome: radial cleavage pattern, and the first opening in the gut becomes the anus.

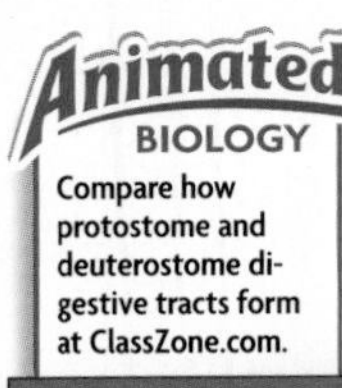

Animated
BIOLOGY
Compare how protostome and deuterostome digestive tracts form at ClassZone.com.

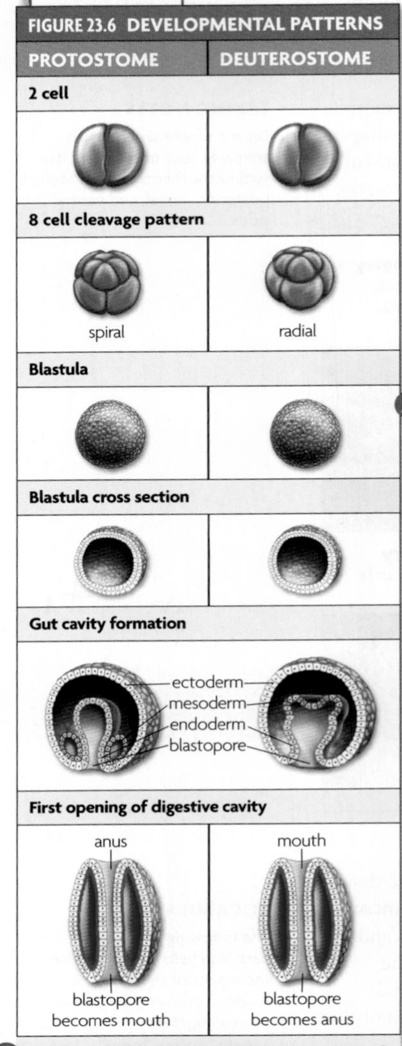

B Contrast How does the development of protostomes and deuterstomes differ?

Developmental Patterns

Animals are separated into two major divisions: the protostomes and the deuterostomes. As shown in **FIGURE 23.6**, protostome and deuterostome development differs in a number of ways:

- **First opening of the digestive cavity** The major difference between protostomes and deuterostomes is the structure that develops from the first opening of the digestive cavity. In **protostomes** (PROH-tuh-STOHMZ), the mouth is formed first, and the anus second. In **deuterostomes** (DOO-tuh-roh-STOHMZ), the first opening forms the anus, and the mouth is formed second.
- **Gut cavity formation** In protostomes, the gut cavity is formed from separations in the mesoderm. In deuterostomes, the gut cavity forms from pouches created by the folds in the gut tube.
- **Cleavage pattern** In most protostomes, early cell divisions lead to an eight-celled embryo in a twisted arrangement called spiral cleavage. In deuterostomes, cells divide into eight-celled embryos with cells that are lined up one atop the other in an arrangement called radial cleavage.

A Connect Is the symmetry of the human body bilateral or radial?

MAIN IDEA

A comparison of structure and genetics reveals the evolutionary history of animals.

Work by the American zoologist Libbie Hyman in the mid-1900s provided the basis for scientists' understanding of the relationships between invertebrate species. Hyman based her phylogeny, or evolutionary history, on major events in development. The ability to compare ribosomal DNA and *Hox* genes has helped to both confirm and rearrange some relationships among invertebrate animal groups.

The presence of tissues is one characteristic that separates one animal group from another. Sponges, which lack tissues, are the simplest members of the animal kingdom, followed by animals with two tissue layers, such as jellyfish and corals. Whether an animal has radial or bilateral symmetry is another defining characteristic. As shown in **FIGURE 23.7**, the two major radiations, or phylogenetic branches, are the protostomes and the deuterostomes.

Protostomes Protostomes are further divided into the Lophotrochozoa (flatworms, annelids, and mollusks) and Ecdysozoa (roundworms and arthropods). All members of the Lophotrochozoa have either a specialized feeding structure made of hollow tentacles or a free-swimming ciliated larval form. Members of the Ecdysozoa must shed their outer skin to grow.

Deuterostomes Deuterostomes include members of the Echinodermata (such as sea stars and sand dollars) and the Chordata (such as birds, mammals, and all other vertebrates). As a member of the Chordata, you are a deuterostome.

Differentiated Instruction

BELOW LEVEL

Have students consider what they learned in preceding chapters about how prokaryotes, protists, fungi, and plants get the materials they need to support life. Then ask them to write for five minutes on why, in studying animals, there is so much emphasis on the development of a digestive system.

Biology Toolkit, Quick-Write, p. C19

FIGURE 23.7 Phylogeny of Animals

Comparisons of genetic sequences were used to modify the phylogenetic tree of animals.

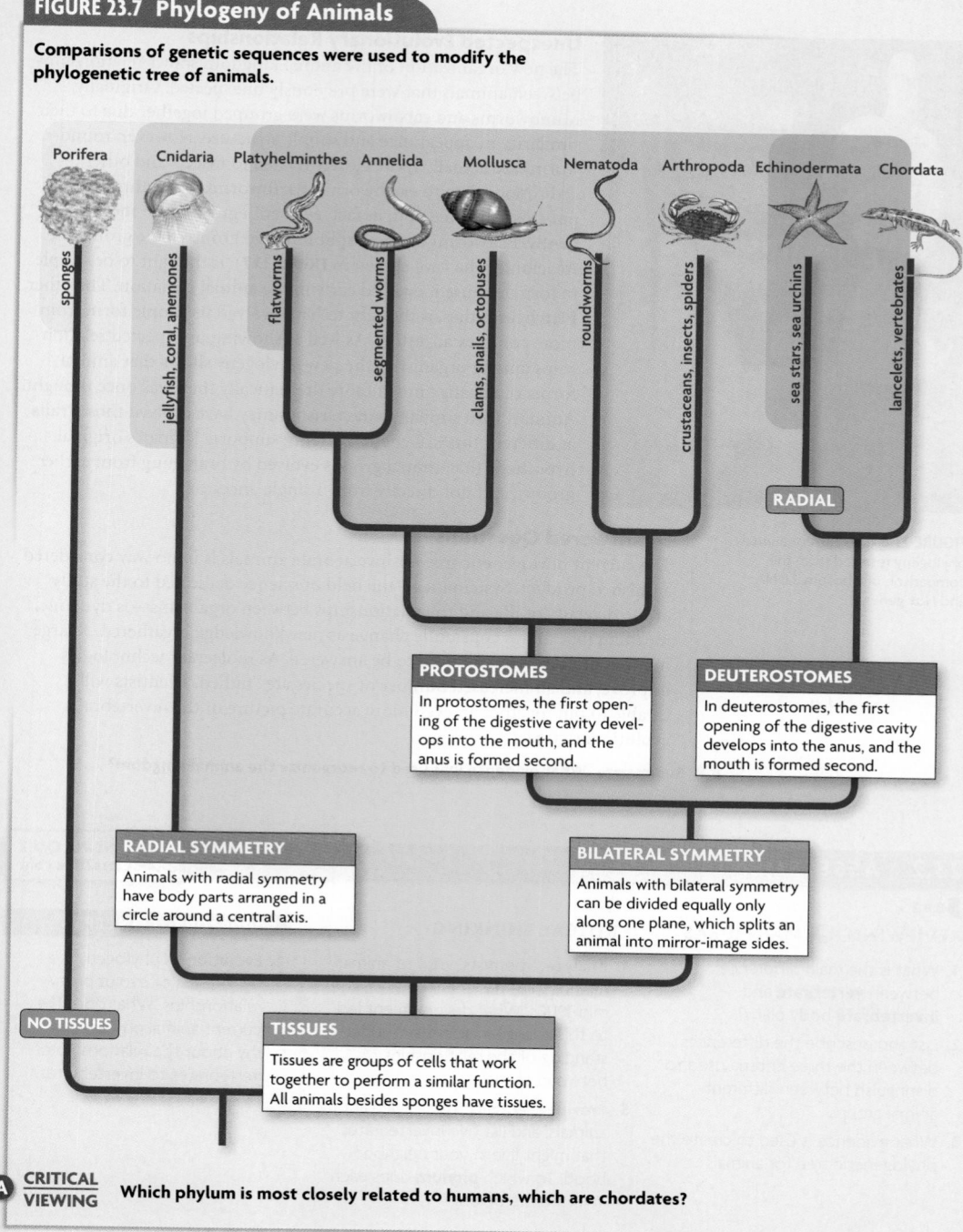

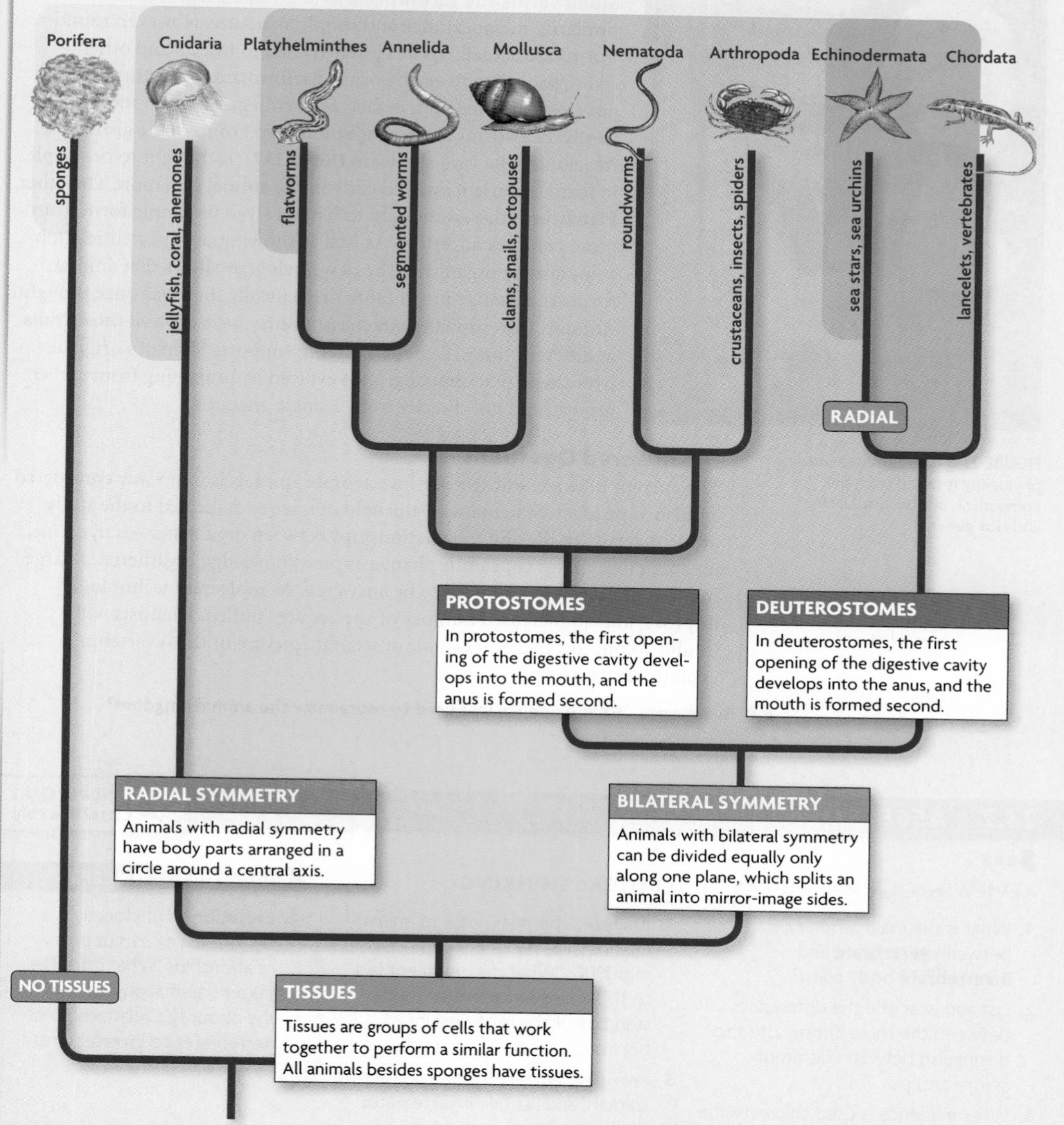

Porifera — sponges

Cnidaria — jellyfish, coral, anemones

Platyhelminthes — flatworms

Annelida — segmented worms

Mollusca — clams, snails, octopuses

Nematoda — roundworms

Arthropoda — crustaceans, insects, spiders

Echinodermata — sea stars, sea urchins

Chordata — lancelets, vertebrates

RADIAL

PROTOSTOMES
In protostomes, the first opening of the digestive cavity develops into the mouth, and the anus is formed second.

DEUTEROSTOMES
In deuterostomes, the first opening of the digestive cavity develops into the anus, and the mouth is formed second.

RADIAL SYMMETRY
Animals with radial symmetry have body parts arranged in a circle around a central axis.

BILATERAL SYMMETRY
Animals with bilateral symmetry can be divided equally only along one plane, which splits an animal into mirror-image sides.

NO TISSUES

TISSUES
Tissues are groups of cells that work together to perform a similar function. All animals besides sponges have tissues.

(A) **CRITICAL VIEWING** **Which phylum is most closely related to humans, which are chordates?**

Take It Further

Point out that the **larvae** of many species in the invertebrate phyla have very different body plans, behaviors, means of movement, and other characteristics when compared to adults of the same species. In the case of **echinoderms,** even the symmetry is different. Adults are radial; larvae are bilateral. This is why Echinodermata appears among other bilateral phyla in **FIGURE 23.7.**

The Inside Story

In 1801, **Jean-Baptiste Lamarck** published the first authoritative book on invertebrates. Few scientists before him had studied these animals. It was Lamarck, the professor of "insects and worms" at the Museum d'Histoire Naturelle, who first coined the term *invertebrate.* It had been the custom to classify all animals lacking backbones as insects and worms. Or as Lamarck put it: "The celebrated Linnaeus, and almost all other naturalists up to now, have divided the entire series of invertebrate animals into only two classes: insects and worms. As a consequence, anything that could not be called an insect must belong, without exception, to the class of worms." Lamarck was the first to distinguish crustaceans, arachnids, and annelids as groups different from both insects and worms.

To appreciate the awesome task of classifying invertebrates, skip ahead to the 20th century. **Libbie Hyman** spent a good part of her life working to compile *The Invertebrates,* published in six volumes from 1940 to 1968. Hyman, who earned her living working as a writer of lab manuals, was given a lab at the American Museum of Natural History, though never a salary. She suffered from Parkinson's disease toward the end of her life, and so was unable to produce volumes on arthropods or mollusks.

ENGLISH LEARNERS

Use **FIGURE 23.7** to show students how the different terms they learned for the section relate to one another. Ask questions about each branching of the diagram. Relate the information contained in the label boxes to the images of the animal phyla shown above.

Biology Toolkit, Connect to Content through Visuals, p. C17

PRE-AP

Suggest students devise a way to remember the phyla. One mnemonic that covers them in the order shown in **FIGURE 23.7** is Proper cooks prepare a meal near an electric cooker.

Answers

(A) **Critical Viewing** Echinodermata

▼ Teach *continued*

Take It Further

In some cases, analysis of molecular and genetic evidence is the only way to correctly classify organisms and determine relationships. Two organisms may appear to be closely related—or even identical—and then DNA evidence suggests otherwise.

In 2006, a new species of hammerhead shark was discovered off the coast of South Carolina. This shark, as of yet unnamed, is visually indistinguishable from the scalloped hammerhead, *Sphyrna lewini,* but DNA analysis reveals a distinct genetic signature. It is thought that this population may breed only in certain estuaries and bays of South Carolina, and that this may have led to genetic isolation from the scalloped hammerhead over time.

Answers

A Summarize comparisons of ribosomal DNA and *Hox* genes

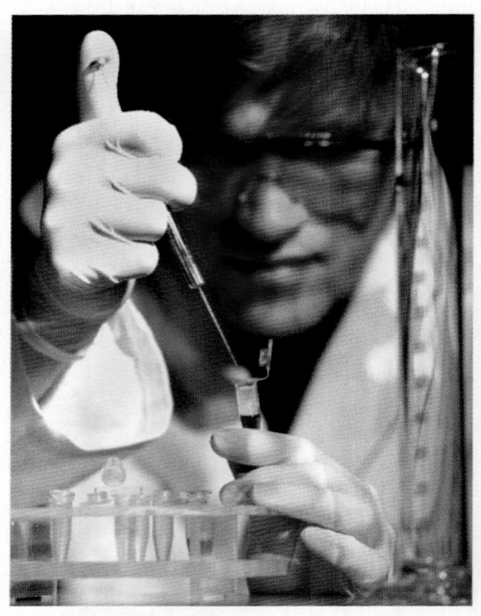

FIGURE 23.8 The current animal phylogeny resulted from the comparison of ribosomal DNA and *Hox* genes.

Unexpected Evolutionary Relationships

The new organization of the animal kingdom shows relationships between animals that were previously unexpected. Originally, roundworms and earthworms were grouped together due to their similarity in appearance and simple structure. However, roundworms are actually more closely related to insects and other arthropods than to earthworms. Earthworms and arthropods are not closely related and, in fact, evolved segmentation independently. Flatworms are now split into two groups. One group, the Acoelomorpha (not shown in **FIGURE 23.7**), is thought to be simple in form because it evolved early in the animal radiation. The other, Platyhelminthes, is thought to have evolved its simple form from more complex ancestors. As well as showing unexpected relationships among organisms, the new phylogeny shows that animal forms can change much more dramatically than was once thought. Animals with similar characteristics may have evolved those traits at different times. Genetic evidence supports Hyman's original hypothesis that animal groups evolved by branching from earlier groups, and not directly from a single ancestor.

Unanswered Questions

The current phylogenetic tree for invertebrate animals is in no way considered a finished product. Systematics—the field of science dedicated to the study of the diversity of life and the relationships between organisms—is dynamic, meaning that things constantly change as new knowledge is gathered. A large number of questions still need to be answered. As molecular technologies improve, and an increased number of species are studied, scientists will be able to put together an even more accurate picture of the invertebrate evolutionary tree.

A Summarize **What evidence was used to reorganize the animal kingdom?**

▼ Assess and Reteach

Assess Use the Online Quiz or Section Quiz (*Assessment Book,* p. 454).

Reteach Start a concept map on the board with the term *animal diversity.* Have students add to the map by identifying the different ways animals are distinguished from one another. Have them think about whether a certain characteristic is a subset of another.

23.2 ASSESSMENT

ONLINE QUIZ
ClassZone.com

B.8.2

REVIEWING ▶ MAIN IDEAS

1. What is the main difference between **vertebrate** and **invertebrate** body plans?
2. List and describe the differences between the three criteria used to distinguish between different animal groups.
3. What evidence is used to create the phylogenetic tree for animals?

CRITICAL THINKING

4. **Analyze** Scientists' view of animal relationships has changed since the mid-1900s. What development led to this change in scientists' understanding of the relationships between animals?
5. **Provide Examples** Think again about animals, and list five invertebrates that might live in your neighborhood. To which **phylum** does each invertebrate belong?

***Connecting* CONCEPTS**

6. **Evolution** A phylogeny is a hypothesis of evolutionary relationships. What does the current animal phylogeny say about the relationship of vertebrates to invertebrates?

23.2 ASSESSMENT

1. Invertebrates have no backbone; vertebrates do.
2. Bilateral versus radial symmetry: body is symmetrical along the length of the animal or body plan is arranged in a circle around a central axis; two tissue layers versus three; deuterostome versus protostome development: first opening of digestive cavity becomes anus; first opening becomes mouth.
3. Evidence includes comparative anatomy, developmental patterns, and analysis of ribosomal DNA and *Hox* genes.
4. Advances in molecular studies let scientists take a closer look at the relationships between phyla by comparing ribosomal DNA and *Hox* genes.
5. Answers may include insects and spiders (Arthropoda), earthworms (Annelida), and snails and slugs (Mollusca).
6. Vertebrates evolved from invertebrate species.

23.3 Sponges and Cnidarians

KEY CONCEPT Sponges and cnidarians are the simplest animals.

MAIN IDEAS

- Sponges have specialized cells but no tissues.
- Cnidarians are the oldest existing animals that have specialized tissues.

VOCABULARY

sessile, p. 705
filter feeder, p. 706
polyp, p. 707
medusa, p. 707
mesoglea, p. 707
nematocyst, p. 707
gastrovascular cavity, p. 708

REVIEW AT CLASSZONE.COM

Connect Imagine you are snorkeling beneath the clear blue waters surrounding Australia's Great Barrier Reef. In addition to schools of tropical fish and sharks, covering the ocean floor are brightly colored sponge and coral species. Sponges and corals are members of two of the simplest animal phyla, the Porifera and the Cnidaria.

MAIN IDEA

Sponges have specialized cells but no tissues.

VOCABULARY

Sessile comes from a Latin word meaning "to sit." The opposite of sessile is mobile. *Mobile* comes from a Latin word meaning "to move."

Sponges have long been considered the most primitive animals on Earth because their body plan is much like what scientists would expect for an early multicellular organism. Two lines of recent evidence have strengthened this hypothesis.

- Sponge fossils more than 570 million years old were found in Australia, making sponges one of the most ancient groups of known animals.
- Molecular evidence confirms that sponges are closely related to a group of protists called choanoflagellates. Choanoflagellates are very similar in size and shape to certain cells found within a sponge. These protists are considered the most likely ancestors of all animals.

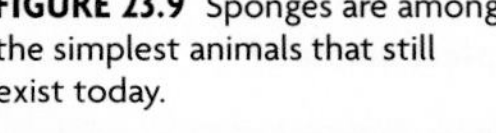

FIGURE 23.9 Sponges are among the simplest animals that still exist today.

Sponge Characteristics

Sponges lack muscle and nerve cells. So not surprisingly, they are **sessile,** meaning they are unable to move from where they are attached. As **FIGURE 23.9** shows, sponges attach to hard surfaces. They secrete toxic substances that prevent other sponges from growing into their area and also protect them from hungry predators and parasites. Some of these chemicals have been used in the development of medicines to treat forms of cancer such as lymphoma.

Sponge Reproduction

Sponges reproduce both sexually and asexually. In sexual reproduction, some species release eggs and sperm into the water, and fertilization occurs there. In other species, sperm is released into the water, and the egg is fertilized within the female sponge. The fertilized egg develops into a free-swimming larva that attaches to a surface, where it remains and develops into its adult form.

Differentiated Instruction

PRE-AP

As students go through the animal phyla in this and later chapters, they will need to organize their notes in a way that will enable them to make comparisons among the phyla. You can suggest students use index cards much like baseball cards, drawing some representative examples on the front, with the pertinent statistics on the back. See the chapter resources at **ClassZone.com** for a file of the prepared card plus additional online resources. Remind students of the Classification tables on pages R15–R31.

Phyla Porifera
Common Name(s) sponges
Cells pinacocytes, choanocytes, amoebocytes
Tissues none
Organ/Organ Systems none
Other Details most ancient phylum
Body Shape asymmetrical
Body Support framework of spicules, covered by two layers of cells
Life Cycle Stages (as applicable) free-swimming larva, sessile as adult
Reproduction sexual reproduction with free-swimming sperm; asexual reproduction by budding
Food Source/Feeding filter feeding

Plan and Prepare

Objectives

- Describe the characteristics and anatomy of sponges and cnidarians.

Section Resources

Unit Resource Book
Study Guide pp. 9–10
Power Notes p. 11
Reinforcement p. 12
Pre-AP Activity pp. 27–28

Interactive Reader Chapter 23
Spanish Study Guide pp. 237–238

Biology Toolkit pp. C8, C22, C34

Technology
Power Presentation 23.3
Media Gallery DVD
Online Quiz 23.3

Activate Prior Knowledge Sponges are so simple and vegetable-like in appearance that students may be surprised to learn that sponges are animals, not plants. **Ask,** What characteristics must sponges have to be included in the animal kingdom? multicellular, heterotrophic, have collagen, able to move, diploid Explain that sponges are free-swimming as larvae.

Teach

Vocabulary

Academic Vocabulary Two ideas are associated with the word **primitive:**

- not derived from something else, primary
- characterized by simplicity

Both meanings apply to sponges.

Take It Further

Many of the toxic substances secreted by **sponges** are being studied to determine their potential for **fighting diseases.** Extracts of the Chesapeake Bay sponge *Microciona prolifera* have been shown to inhibit the growth of tuberculosis bacteria.

▼ Teach *continued*

Science Trivia

- The loofa, a common bath accessory, is not a true sponge. It is derived from a gourdlike fruit that, after being dried and peeled, reveals a spongy fibrous skeleton.
- Most household sponges are synthetic and are made from rubber, cellulose, or plastic.
- The demand for natural sponges has led to sponge farming. Sponge farmers grow sponges from cuttings that are attached to growing lines suspended in the ocean.

Vocabulary

Greek and Latin Word Origins Cytology is the study of cells, and *-cyte* is often used as a foundation for naming types of cells. The roots of the prefixes used to name the cells in this section are descriptive of each cell's function and shape:

pina- = board or plank

choanē = funnel

amoibē- = changing form, associated with movement

cnida- = sea nettle, nettles being plants with stinging hairs

Answers

A Summarize Sponges do not have tissues and lack muscle and nerve cells.

Some sponges reproduce asexually by budding. Buds break off from the adult sponge and float in the water until they attach to an underwater surface, where they grow into their adult form.

Connecting CONCEPTS

Symbiosis Recall from **Chapter 14** that symbiosis is a close relationship between two or more species living in close contact. Sponges form symbiotic relationships with many different animals. Shrimps, crabs, and worms have been found living within the cavities of a sponge.

Sponge Anatomy

Sponges do not have mouths. As you can see in **FIGURE 23.10**, their cells are arranged around a network of channels that let water flow directly through the sponge's body. Water is pulled into the sponge though tiny pores in its body wall, and used water is ejected from a larger hole at the top of the sponge called the osculum. Of the thousands of known species of sponges, most are marine filter feeders. **Filter feeders** eat by straining particles from the water.

Sponges can be found in many colors and shapes. Some sponges are shaped like tubes, while others lie flat against the ocean floor. Regardless of their shape, all sponge bodies are made up of two layers of cells that cover a framework of collagen-like fibers, called spongin. The skeleton is usually reinforced with hard calcium- or silicon-based crystals called spicules. While sponges do not have tissues, they do have several types of specialized cells.

- **Pinacocytes** These thin and leathery cells form the sponge's outer layer.
- **Choanocytes** These cells, also called "collar cells," form the inner layer of the sponge. Each has a long flagellum surrounded by a collar of tiny hairlike structures called microvilli. These cells pull water through the sponge by beating their flagella. As the water passes the choanocytes, tiny food particles are trapped in the mucus on the microvilli.
- **Amoebocytes** These are mobile cells found in the jellylike material sandwiched between the two cell layers. Amoebocytes absorb and digest the food particles caught by the choanocytes and move the nutrients to other parts of the sponge. They also transport oxygen and wastes in the sponge. Because of their mobility, amoebocytes are important to a sponge's growth and repair of injuries.

A Summarize What characteristics make sponges the simplest animals?

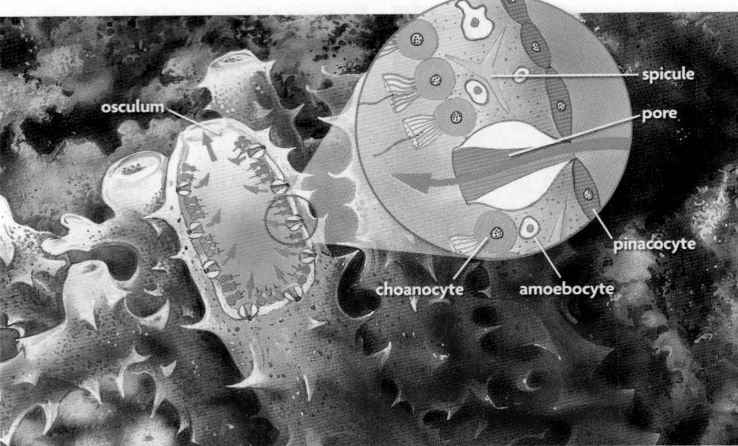

FIGURE 23.10 Sponges are animals that have specialized cells but lack tissues. This cutaway shows the internal organization of the sponge.

Differentiated Instruction

ENGLISH LEARNERS

Divide the class into two groups. Have one group review the material on sponges, and the other review cnidarians. Each group then prepares questions about their phylum, letting the vocabulary terms and heading guide them. Students then use the text to prepare answers. The two groups can then present their questions and answers to each other. This exercise could also be done with pairs of students.

Biology Toolkit, SQ3R, p. C8

PRE-AP

Have students compare and contrast the reproductive strategy of sponges to that of plants. They should consider whether sponges have the best of both worlds: the ability of a sessile organism to sexually reproduce free-swimming larvae, as well the benefits of asexual reproduction.

Biology Toolkit, Compare/Contrast Chart, p. C34

MAIN IDEA

Cidarians are the oldest existing animals that have specialized tissues.

In contrast to sponges, cnidarians (ny-DAIR-ee-uhnz) can move. A jellyfish pulsing through the water and an anemone waving its tentacles make deliberate movements using simple nerves and muscles.

Cnidarian Characteristics

Cnidarians have two body forms: the polyp and the medusa, both of which are shown in **FIGURE 23.11. Polyps** (PAHL-ihps) are cylindrical tubes with mouth and tentacles facing upward. This form is characteristic of cnidarians such as corals. **Medusas** are umbrella-shaped, with their mouth and tentacles on the underside. This form is characteristic of free-swimming cnidarians such as the jellyfish. Many cnidarian species alternate between the two forms during their life cycle. Both polyps and medusas have radial symmetry, a characteristic of all cnidarians.

FIGURE 23.11 In the polyp form of a coral (top), the tentacles and mouth face upward. In the medusa form of a jellyfish (bottom), the tentacles and mouth face downward.

Cnidarian Reproduction

A cnidarian may reproduce both asexually and sexually during its life cycle. Polyps reproduce asexually by budding. This method produces genetically identical offspring. In the medusa form, cnidarians reproduce sexually by releasing gametes into the water. The fertilized egg develops into a free-swimming larva, called a planula. The planula then develops into the polyp stage.

Cnidarian Anatomy

Cnidarian bodies have two tissue layers separated by a non-cellular jellylike material called **mesoglea** (MEHZ-uh-GLEE-uh). The outer layer of tissue is made up of three types of cells.

- **Contracting cells** Contracting cells cover the surface of the cnidarian and contain muscle fibers.
- **Nerve cells** Nerve cells interconnect and form a network over the entire animal. They send sensory information around the animal and coordinate muscular contractions. Cnidarians do not have brains.
- **Cnidocytes** (NY-duh-SYTS) Cnidocytes are specialized cells that contain stinging structures used for defense and capturing prey. They are unique to cnidarians. Cnidocytes are found all over a cnidarian's body, but most of them are on the tentacles.

One type of stinging structure found in both sea anemones and jellyfish is the nematocyst. A **nematocyst** (NEHM-uh-tuh-SIHST) is a capsule containing a thin, coiled, harpoon-shaped tubule with a poisonous barb at one end.

BELOW LEVEL

Have students make a two-column chart that lists the types and functions of specialized cells found in sponges and cnidarians. They should also include other structures, such as spicules and nematocysts.

Biology Toolkit, Content Frame, p. C22

TEACH FROM VISUALS

FIGURE 23.11 Have students compare the coral and jellyfish. **Ask**

- What type of symmetry is displayed by the coral and jellyfish? radial
- What is the main structural difference between the coral polyp and the jellyfish medusa? coral: tentacles and mouth face upward; jellyfish: tentacles and mouth face downward

Take It Further

Just as there are bilaterally symmetrical animals that have features that make them appear asymmetrical, there are medusas that at first glance appear to be hydras or even something entirely different. The **upside-down jellyfish,** *Cassiopea xamachana,* is a medusa that lives upside down on the sea floor in the tropics. This species uses the rhythmic pulsations of its "bell" to circulate water through its gills and trap food in its arms, which also hold photosynthetic algae. These algae use sunlight to produce food for the jellyfish. By positioning itself upside down, this species gives the algae maximum exposure to sunlight. When disturbed, this jellyfish is able to swim away.

Science Trivia

Many cnidarians are dangerous to humans. The box jellyfish, *Chironex fleckeri,* found along the northeast coast of Australia from October through April, is perhaps the worst.

- This species has tentacles up to 10 feet long, each armed with up to 5000 nematocysts.
- The venom is strong enough to kill a person within minutes, but quick treatment of the affected area with a large amount of vinegar can neutralize the venom and save a life.

▼ Teach *continued*

ONLINE BIOLOGY Have students go to the chapter Resource Center at **ClassZone.com** for additional resources and information on sponges and cnidarians.

Science Trivia

- The Portuguese man-of-war is actually a colony of four types of polyps. The man-of-war is so named because the uppermost polyp features a gas-filled bladder that floats atop the water, functioning as a sail to propel the colony through the water like a ship.
- The man-of-war has tentacles up to 50 meters (165 ft) in length, with nematocysts that deliver a neurotoxin nearly as powerful as that of the cobra.

Answers

A Contrast A polyp is a cylindrical tube topped with a mouth and tentacles. A medusa is umbrella shaped, with the mouth and tentacles on the underside.

▼ Assess and Reteach

Assess Use the Online Quiz or Section Quiz (*Assessment Book*, p. 455).

Reteach Assemble images of cnidarians and sponges into a digital slide show to review their characteristics, diversity, habitats, and reproductive strategies.

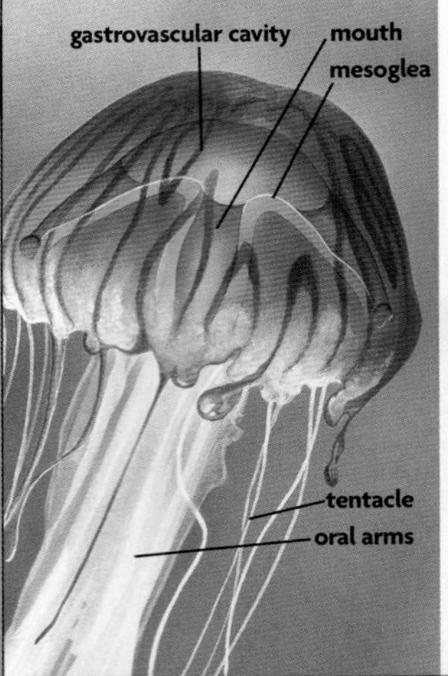

NEMATOCYST STRUCTURE

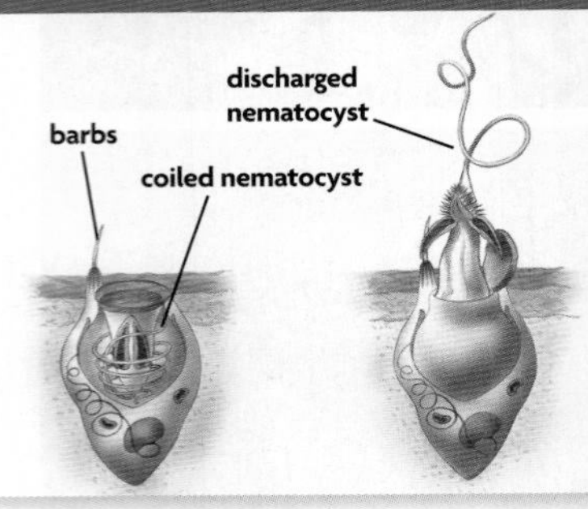

FIGURE 23.12 Cnidarians such as this jellyfish use nematocysts, a type of stinging structure found on their tentacles, to both capture prey and defend themselves against predators.

Nematocysts, shown in **FIGURE 23.12**, usually do not fire on contact unless a chemical signals the presence of prey or a predator. When they fire, nematocysts uncoil rapidly to spear and poison prey. Prey captured by nematocysts on the tentacles are stuffed through the animal's mouth into a saclike digestive space called the **gastrovascular cavity.** The cavity is lined with the cnidarian's inner tissue layer, which has cells that secrete digestive enzymes and absorb nutrients. Cnidarians do not have an anus, which in other animals is a separate exit for wastes. In cnidarians, wastes are pushed out through the mouth.

The gastrovascular cavity also moves oxygenated water to internal cells. When the animal's mouth is closed, water in the cavity becomes pressurized and provides skeletal support to the tissue, similar to a balloon full of water. Muscular contractions can work against the pressurized fluid and change the animal's shape.

Cnidarian Classes

There are four major groups, or classes, of cnidarians. Each class is defined in part by which body form is dominant during the animals' lives.

- **Anthozoa** (AN-thuh-ZOH-uh) include sea anemones and corals. The polyp form is dominant in these animals. There is no medusa stage.
- **Hydrozoa** (HY-druh-ZOH-uh) include fire corals, the Portuguese man-of-war, and hydras. These animals alternate between polyp and medusa forms. Medusas reproduce sexually, producing gametes that fuse to produce larvae. Larvae settle to the seafloor and grow into polyps. Most polyps are asexual.
- **Scyphozoa** (SY-fuh-ZOH-uh) are jellyfish. The medusa form is dominant in these animals. Some species have either a very short polyp stage or none at all.
- **Cubozoa** (KYOO-buh-ZOH-uh) include the tropical box jellyfish and sea wasps. These animals also have a dominant medusa form. Unlike the Scyphozoa, they have a cube-shaped body and well-developed eyes with retinas, corneas, and lenses—though how an animal with no brain interprets visual data is still unknown.

A Contrast How do the polyp and medusa forms differ?

23.3 ASSESSMENT

ONLINE QUIZ ClassZone.com

REVIEWING ▶ MAIN IDEAS

1. What is the main function of each of the three types of cells that make up a sponge's body?
2. What are the functions of the inner and outer tissue layers in a cnidarian?

CRITICAL THINKING

3. **Infer** What are the advantages of a **gastrovascular cavity** to the body functions of a cnidarian?
4. **Contrast** How do sponges and cnidarians defend themselves against predators? What is different about the methods used by each?

***Connecting* CONCEPTS**

5. **Evolution** Some sponges have the remarkable ability to reassemble themselves after they are experimentally broken down into individual cells. What might this suggest about the origin of multicellularity in animals?

23.3 ASSESSMENT

1. Pinacocytes form the outer layer of the sponge; choanocytes form the inner layer and capture food particles. Amoebocytes are mobile cells between the sponge's two layers. They absorb and digest food particles, transport oxygen and wastes, and aid in growth and injury repair.
2. The inner layer of tissue is specialized for digestion, the outer layer for protection.
3. The gastrovascular cavity allows cnidarians to engulf and digest large prey and also helps to transport oxygen to the inner tissue layer.
4. Sponges contain toxic substances to defend passively against predators. Cnidarians have stinging cells called cnidocytes that are used actively to strike predators and prey.
5. Multicellular animals can exist only if cells recognize each other as being the same or related. The sponges' ability to reassemble themselves suggests that early animals may have evolved from unicellular organisms that were able to recognize one another and form clumps or colonies.

MATERIALS

- 2 large eyedroppers
- culture of *Hydra*
- petri dish
- drop of bottled spring water
- hand lens or dissecting microscope
- toothpick
- culture of *Daphnia magna*

PROCESS SKILLS

- **Observing**
- **Collecting Data**

NOS.1 Develop explanations based on reproducible data and observations gathered during laboratory investigations.

Feeding *Hydra*

Hydra belong to the phylum Cnidaria, which includes jellyfish and coral. These animals have thin body walls that are only a few cells thick. They eat small groups of microorganisms, called plankton, that include single-celled animals and protists. In this investigation, you will observe the *Hydra's* anatomy, responses to touch, and feeding behavior.

Hydra (LM; magnification 20×)

PROBLEM What are the behaviors of a *Hydra*?

PROCEDURE

1. Using the eyedropper, place a drop of water from the culture containing a *Hydra* into a petri dish. Be careful not to damage the *Hydra*. Cover the *Hydra* with spring water.
2. Observe the *Hydra* using a hand lens or dissecting microscope. Draw the *Hydra* and label its parts.
3. Using a toothpick, gently touch the side of the *Hydra* and note its response. Record your observations in your lab notebook.
4. Using a toothpick, gently touch the tentacles of the *Hydra* and note its response. Record your observations in your lab notebook.
5. Using a new eyedropper, transfer a drop of water containing *Daphnia* to the petri dish with the *Hydra*. Note all the events that happen as the *Hydra* catches and eats the *Daphnia*. Write all of your observations in your lab notebook. Wash your hands when you are finished with your work.

ANALYZE AND CONCLUDE

1. **Analyze** Did the *Hydra* have a head or tail end? If so, explain how you could tell the difference.
2. **Describe** Where was the *Hydra's* mouth?
3. **Infer** How do you think a *Hydra* removes wastes from its body? Explain your answer.
4. **Analyze** What was the most sensitive part of the *Hydra*? Why do you think this part was sensitive?
5. **Analyze** Describe the feeding behavior of the *Hydra*. How did it react to the presence of *Daphnia*?
6. **Apply** From your observations of the *Hydra's* feeding behavior, what do you think the small, rounded cells on the *Hydra's* tentacles do? Explain your answer.

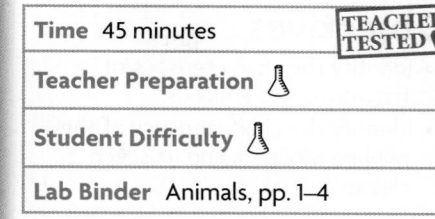

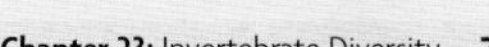

INVESTIGATION

Time 45 minutes	TEACHER TESTED
Teacher Preparation	
Student Difficulty	
Lab Binder Animals, pp. 1–4	

Purpose Observe *Hydra* behaviors.

Overview Students will study the response of a *Hydra* to external stimuli, including touch and the presence of prey.

LAB MANAGEMENT

- Tell students to use the low-power objective to find the *Hydra*.
- Suggest students compare how the *Hydra* reacts to the touch of the toothpick on different parts of the body, not just the tentacles.

Safety Remind students to wipe down the microscope eyepieces with alcohol wipes after using them and wash their hands.

POST-LAB DISCUSSION

Discuss students' results with the class.
Ask

- As a sessile organism, how can a *Hydra* be an effective predator? It uses its tentacles and nematocysts to capture prey swimming within reach.
- Given that a *Hydra* does not have a brain, how would you characterize its actions? reflexive

Discuss whether the *Hydra* reacted differently to the toothpick than to the *Daphnia*.

Answers

1. The *Hydra* does not have a distinct head or tail because it has only one opening to its body cavity. Most students will respond that the end with the tentacles and mouth is the anterior, while the other end is the posterior.
2. The *Hydra's* mouth is at the base of its tentacles.
3. Food is taken in through the mouth, and wastes are expelled from the mouth.
4. The tentacles are the most sensitive part. They respond to touch by striking and seizing prey.
5. Students should mention the *Hydra* using its nematocysts to strike the *Daphnia* and using its tentacles to bring the *Daphnia* to its mouth.
6. The small, rounded cells on the tentacles have nematocysts armed with a harpoon-like venomous barb that shoots into prey to kill or immobilize it.

SECTION 23.4

▼ Plan and Prepare

Objectives

- Identify the characteristics of flatworms and annelids.
- Identify the characteristics of the phylum Mollusca and its seven classes.

Section Resources

Unit Resource Book
Study Guide pp. 13–14
Power Notes p. 15
Reinforcement p. 16
Pre-AP Activity pp. 29–30

Interactive Reader Chapter 23
Spanish Study Guide pp. 239–240

Biology Toolkit pp. C10, C14

Technology
Power Presentation 23.4
Media Gallery DVD
Online Quiz 23.4

Activate Prior Knowledge Students should already be familiar with mollusks and annelids. **Ask**

- What are some examples of mollusks? clams, mussels, squid, octopus, snails, slugs
- What common annelid can you dig up in a yard or garden? earthworm
- What kind of symmetry do these animals exhibit? bilateral

▼ Teach

Take It Further

The ability of **planarians** to **regenerate** body tissues and structures is widely known. What often goes unrecognized is the strong sense of head and tail, or anterior and posterior polarity, in these animals. If a planarian is cut crosswise into two pieces, the head end generates a new tail, and the tail end generates a new head. If the middle is cut out, it will grow both a head and a tail.

23.4 Flatworms, Mollusks, and Annelids

KEY CONCEPT Flatworms, mollusks, and annelids belong to closely related phyla.

MAIN IDEAS

- Flatworms are simple bilateral animals.
- Mollusks are diverse animals.
- Annelids have segmented bodies.

VOCABULARY

complete digestive tract, p. 712
radula, p. 712
hemocoel, p. 712
segmentation, p. 714
coelom, p. 714

Connect Imagine if you had no stomach or lungs. Just like a flatworm, you would have to be rather flat and thin in order to get the oxygen and food you need to survive. While some flatworms can grow up to 20 meters long, they are never more than a few millimeters thick.

MAIN IDEA

Flatworms are simple bilateral animals.

Based on molecular studies, most flatworms, mollusks, and annelids are classified together as members of the Lophotrochozoa. These animals have either a feeding structure made of hollow tentacles called a lophophore, or a distinctive free-swimming ciliated larva called a trochophore. The name Lophotrochozoa is taken from these two anatomical features.

Flatworms have a solid body and an incomplete or absent gut. A flatworm's shape is the direct result of having no circulatory system. Flatworms can only move oxygen to their cells by diffusion, so all their cells must be close to the outside environment. Complex characters such as gut tubes were probably lost at a later stage of evolution, often as the flatworms became parasitic on other animals. The three classes of flatworms include the planarians, flukes, and tapeworms.

FIGURE 23.13 Planarians, such as this zebra flatworm, have a solid body that lacks a complete gut.

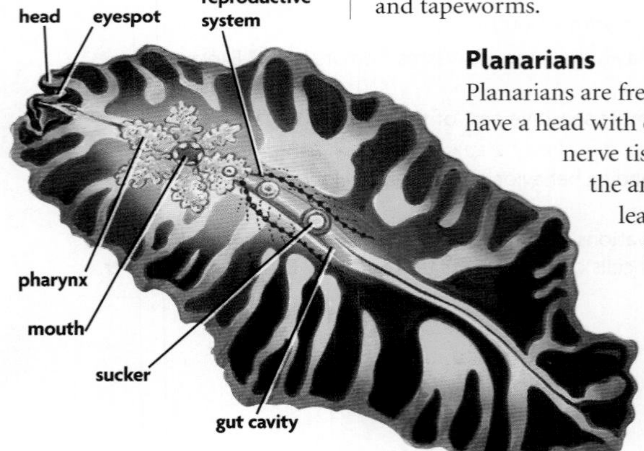

Planarians

Planarians are free-living, nonparasitic flatworms. Planarian worms have a head with eyespots and a simple brain built of a cluster of nerve tissue. As shown in **FIGURE 23.13,** the mouth is found on the animal's ventral surface rather than in its head, and it leads to a gut cavity. A muscular tube called the pharynx extends from the mouth to collect food. These worms actively hunt for food using chemoreceptors to detect odors in the water or in the air. They usually move using the cilia on their ventral surface, but they also have bands of muscle that let them twist their bodies.

Differentiated Instruction

ENGLISH LEARNERS

Before reading this section, review the four strategies for reciprocal teaching: predict, question, clarify, and summarize. Divide the class into three groups to focus on the three animal phyla in this section. Have each group divide their portion of the section so that each student has a paragraph or an idea to focus on. When all the students have read their material, have the groups teach one another the material.

Biology Toolkit, Reciprocal Teaching, p. C14

PRE-AP

Have students prepare a biological profile card for each phylum introduced, as described on page 705. Remind students that flatworms belong to the phylum Platyhelminthes.

Adult fluke The larva eventually settles in the human intestine, where it matures into an adult. (LM; magnification 40×)
Human The fluke larva penetrates through a human's bare skin into the blood vessels.
Snail After hatching from eggs in the water, the young flukes infect their intermediate host, an aquatic snail. Inside the snail, the flukes develop into tadpolelike larvae.
Egg An egg is passed in human feces back into local waters. (LM; magnification 400×)

FIGURE 23.14 Life Cycle of a Parasitic Fluke

The fluke *Schistosoma* can infect humans and cause a serious disease called schistosomiasis.

Flukes

Flukes are parasites that feed on the body fluids of other animals. Flukes have a mouth with a pharynx that opens into a gut cavity. They are found in both invertebrate and vertebrate hosts. Many species of flukes have life cycles that involve more than one host. **FIGURE 23.14** shows the life cycle of one fluke, *Schistosoma* (SHIHS-tuh-SOHM-uh), which can infect humans and cause a serious disease called schistosomiasis. This disease affects about 200 million people in areas such as Africa and Southeast Asia. The disease is contracted by wading in or drinking fresh water contaminated with fluke larvae. Symptoms of the disease include the onset of fever and muscle pain within one to two months of infection. The disease is treated by an anti-parasitic medicine.

Tapeworms

Tapeworms are parasites that live in vertebrate guts. They have a small head with suckers or hooks used to attach to the host. Their long ribbonlike body has no gut. Instead of swallowing food, these animals absorb nutrients from the digested food in which they live. An adult tapeworm's body is made up of segments containing both male and female sexual organs. When these segments fill with fertilized eggs, they break off and are excreted with the host's feces.

Many tapeworms have complex life cycles involving multiple hosts. The life cycle of a dog tapeworm begins when an egg is passed with a dog's feces. A flea eats the egg, and the egg develops into a larva within the flea's body. The tapeworm infects another dog when it accidentally eats the infected flea while licking its fur. The tapeworm develops into an adult within the dog's intestines, and the cycle begins again.

Connecting CONCEPTS

Structure and Function The simple structure of a tapeworm reflects that as an adult it does not have to move or digest food. The lack of complex internal systems allows for a simpler body plan.

A Contrast How are planarians different from flukes and tapeworms?

HANDS-ON ACTIVITY

The crossed "eyes" of a planarian are actually highly sensitive photoreceptors. Many organisms respond to light by moving toward it, a behavior called phototaxis. Movement away from light is called negative phototaxis. Divide students into small groups and give each a petri dish filled with fresh water, a medicine dropper, gloves, a culture of planarians, white construction paper, and a small flashlight.

Dim the classroom lights or draw the shades. Have students place the petri dish on top of the construction paper and transfer a planarian from the culture to the dish. Tell them to observe and record the planarian's movement for a moment, then shine the flashlight toward the dish from different angles and record the planarian's responses. Have students return the planarian to the culture and wash their hands. **Ask**

- How did the planarian respond to light? moved away from it
- Based on your observations, where would you expect to find these worms in nature? darker areas of aquatic habitats, such as under rocks or in muck

ONLINE BIOLOGY Students can learn about the life cycle of a tapeworm and the role humans play. Go to the WebQuest in Options for Inquiry on page 723.

Integrating Epidemiology

The cycle of **tapeworm infection** described is not unique to canines. Humans also are prone to parasitic infections transmitted by accidentally ingesting parasite eggs. Some infections occur through eating undercooked pork or beef infected with the eggs or cysts of a parasite. However, many infections result from contact with contaminated fecal matter. Epidemiologists have a formal name for this route of transmission: fecal-oral. Touching hands to mouth after gardening or scooping a pet's feces are common routes of fecal-oral infection. Vigorous hand-washing is the single most effective method of preventing transmission of parasites or other infectious organisms passed by this method.

Take It Further

Despite popular belief, most of the fish that is used to make **sushi** and sashimi in the United States is frozen at some point prior to consumption. This is done in large part to kill any parasites that may be living in the flesh, but also to preserve the flesh of the fish until it is ready to be consumed.

Answers

A Contrast Planarians are free-living, nonparasitic flatworms. Both flukes and tapeworms are parasites. Flukes feed on body fluids of other animals; tapeworms live in guts of invertebrates.

▼ Teach *continued*

Vocabulary

Academic Vocabulary Point out that **gut** refers to the area where food is held and digested. It is typically used for animals with simple digestive systems, ones not having separate organs for digestion. For more complex systems, the terms **digestive tract** or **alimentary canal** are used. *Gut* is not particularly useful in describing human anatomy despite slang expressions about "having the guts to act" or having a "gut feeling."

Take It Further

Snails called **naticids** are capable of boring through the hard shells of bivalves by using the **radula** in combination with a gland located at the tip of the **proboscis.** The proboscis is a long, muscular extension of the snail's mouth containing the radula and the esophagus. The gland secretes acid that dissolves the shell and then the radula drills. These two organs take turns working on the shell until it is penetrated about eight hours later. The proboscis then enters the bivalve, and the radula tears out chunks of the soft tissues within and delivers them to the esophagus for ingestion.

TEACH FROM VISUALS

FIGURE 23.15 Use the figure to review the digestive anatomy of mollusks. **Ask**

- What feature of the snail's gut distinguishes it from the flatworm's gut? an anus at the opposite end of the gut from the mouth
- What advantage does this feature provide? Food moves in one direction, allowing the animal to feed continuously.

Discuss the level of specialization shown in the snail's digestive system, including a crop for mechanical digestion and salivary and digestive glands for chemical digestion.

MAIN IDEA

Mollusks are diverse animals.

While flatworms have a digestive sac with only one opening, mollusks and all other bilateral animals have a complete digestive tract. A **complete digestive tract** consists of two openings—a mouth and an anus—at opposite ends of a continuous tube. Because food moves one way through the gut, animals with complete digestive tracts can turn their guts into disassembly lines for food. As food moves down the gut, it travels through areas that are specialized for digestion or absorption. Animals with complete digestive tracts can eat continuously. This efficient and frequent digestion allows animals to be more active.

Mollusk Anatomy

Mollusks include animals as different-looking as oysters, garden snails, and giant squid. Mollusks may be sessile filter feeders, herbivores that graze on algae, or predators. Despite this variety of form and lifestyle, all mollusks share at least one of three features, shown in **FIGURE 23.15.**

- **Radula** The **radula** is a filelike feeding organ. Mollusks eat by scraping the radula over their food. The hard teeth of the radula pick up tiny particles that the animal swallows.
- **Mantle** The mantle is an area of tissue covering the internal organs. In most mollusks, the mantle secretes a hard calcium-based shell that protects the animal from predators.
- **Ctenidia** (tih-NIHD-ee-uh) The ctenidia are flat gills found in a pocket of the mantle tissue called the mantle cavity. The gills absorb oxygen from water that enters this cavity. In the land-dwelling snail shown below, the gills have been lost, and oxygen is absorbed from air rather than from water in the cavity.

While the gills contain blood vessels, blood is also pumped through the hemocoel. The **hemocoel** (HEE-muh-SEEL) consists of spaces between cells within the animal's tissues. This circulatory system extends into a large muscular foot. Snails and slugs crawl on the foot, while clams and scallops dig with the foot. In cephalopods, such as squids and octopuses, the foot forms a muscular siphon, parts of the tentacles, and head.

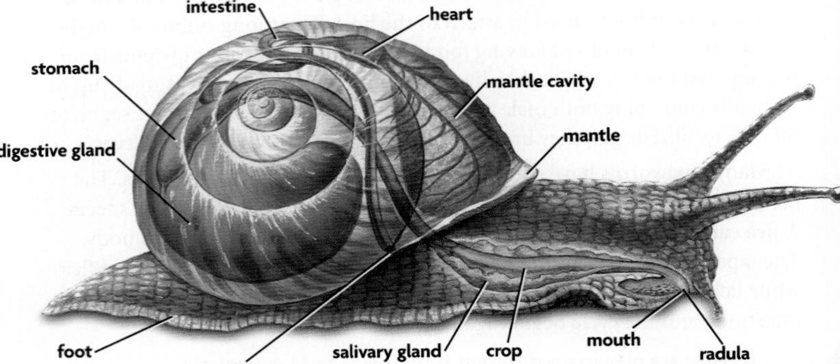

FIGURE 23.15 The anatomy of a common garden snail includes a radula and a mantle, both of which are features shared by most mollusks.

Differentiated Instruction

TEACH WITH TECHNOLOGY

Assemble a digital slide show of images that convey the wide range of form and function of the three mollusk features described in the text. For example, show photographs of the long, streamlined mantle of the giant squid, the colorful, zooxanthellae-filled mantle of the giant clams (genus *Tridacna*), and the edible mantles of blue mussels and quahogs. After running through a series of comparative images and pointing out these features, test students by showing new images and seeing if they can spot the radula, mantle, and ctenidia.

Classes of Mollusks

There are seven classes of mollusks. The majority of species, however, are found within three classes: the gastropods, pelecypods (bivalves), and cephalopods.

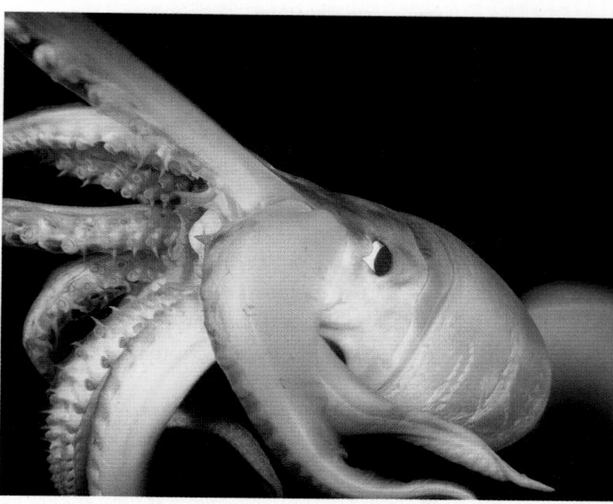

FIGURE 23.16 The Humboldt, or jumbo, squid may grow to nearly 2 meters (6 ft) in length.

- **Gastropoda** This class includes snails, nudibranchs, abalones, and limpets. This class includes over half of the species found in the Mollusk phylum. Gastropods live in both land and aquatic ecosystems. This class includes species that are herbivores, carnivores, and scavengers.
- **Pelecypoda** This class includes clams, oysters, mussels, and scallops. Pelecypods, which are also called bivalves, have a soft body that is protected by two hard shells that are hinged together. Most bivalves are filter feeders that live in marine ecosystems.
- **Cephalopoda** This class includes squid, as shown in **FIGURE 23.16**, octopuses, nautiluses, and cuttlefish. Among the mollusks, the nervous system and eye of the cephalopod are the most well-developed. Cephalopods are carnivores that eat animals such as crustaceans, fish, and other mollusks.
- **Scaphopoda** This class is also called the tusk shells, so named because their shells resemble the shape of an elephant's tusks. These mollusks live at the bottom of water bodies, where they feed on detritus.
- **Polyplacophora** This class is also called the chitons, which are animals that have a shell with overlapping plates. These marine mollusks spend most of their lifetime clinging to rocks, where they feed by using their radula to scrape algae and plant matter from the rocks.
- **Aplacophora** This class includes small wormlike animals that, unlike most mollusks, do not have shells. These mollusks live in deep water. Some feed on small marine invertebrates, while others are parasites of coral.
- **Tryblidia** This class of mollusks was once believed to be extinct, but they were rediscovered in 1952. Little is known about these marine mollusks that live in deep water.

Connecting CONCEPTS

Convergent Evolution Much like the human eye, the cephalopod eye is made up of a lens, retina, iris, and pupil. However, the evolution of cephalopod and human eyes occurred independently. Recall from **Chapter 11** that convergent evolution is the evolution of similar structures in unrelated species.

Mollusk Reproduction

Mollusks use a variety of reproductive strategies. Garden snails, for example, are hermaphrodites. Hermaphrodites are organisms that have both male and female reproductive organs. Reproduction usually involves cross-fertilization. Just before mating, the impregnating snail fires a "love dart" into the other. This calcium-rich, mucus-covered dart causes the recipient snail's reproductive system to store more sperm. During mating, a packet of sperm is transferred into the recipient snail. This packet of sperm is used to fertilize the eggs. These eggs are laid in underground nests. After a period of two to four weeks, juvenile snails hatch from the eggs.

A Summarize What common features are shared by mollusks?

ONLINE BIOLOGY Students can go to the chapter Resource Center at **ClassZone.com** for additional resources and information on mollusks.

Vocabulary

Greek and Latin Word Origins Remind students that roots often contain clues about a word's meaning. For example, *gastropod* means "stomach foot," a fair description of an animal whose stomach is situated atop its muscular foot. Another example is *cephalopod,* which translates to "head foot." Cephalopods are so-named because their "feet," or tentacles, are attached to their head.

The Inside Story

In the age of wooden ships, one particular type of bivalve posed a serious threat to ocean exploration. Species of the Teredinidae family, known commonly as **shipworms,** use their specialized valves to bore into wood. The wood provided shelter and allowed the animals to strain the seawater for food. Because half of the volume of a ship's timbers could be removed by the boring bivalves before the crew even noticed the problem, numerous ships were far more vulnerable to impacts from rocks, reefs, and cannonballs.

The British navy dealt with the problem in the late 18th century by sheathing the hulls of ships in a layer of copper. This process was expensive, but it kept the bivalve out and allowed ships such as Captain James Cook's *Endeavour* and William Bligh's *Bounty* to sail for years without disintegrating.

PRE-AP

Choose a topic covered in this section, such as "Mollusk Anatomy" or "Common Characteristics of Annelids." Ask each student to state an example or known fact about the topic without repeating what has already been said. Repeat for each topic of the section. After each topic has been exhausted, you can have students spend two minutes writing down as many facts as they can recall.

Biology Toolkit, Round Robin, p. C10

Answers

A Summarize complete digestive tract; a radula (file-like feeding organ), mantle (area of tissue covering the internal organs), and ctenidia (flat gills found in the pocket of the mantle tissue)

▼ Teach *continued*

QUICK LAB

Time 60 minutes TEACHER TESTED

Lab Binder Animals, pp. 10–12

Purpose Observe the soft body of a clam to identify different systems.

LAB MANAGEMENT

- Make copies of the datasheet for students (*Lab Binder*, pp. 11–12).
- Remind students not to touch their mouths while handling clams.

Safety Students should wash their hands thoroughly after handling the clams and before writing their analyses.

Answers

Analyze and Conclude

1. The clam draws water in through one of its siphons, passes the water over the ctenidia for gas exchange, and pumps the water out through the other siphon.
2. Water containing food particles enters the mouth from the mantle cavity. The water passes through the digestive system where the food particles are digested and absorbed. The wastes exit through the anus into the mantle cavity and get pumped out through the siphon.
3. The clam has an open circulatory system, which pumps blood to spaces around the tissues and drains blood back to the heart. This system is a lower pressure system than the closed system found in mammals, birds, and reptiles.

Teacher Note "I've never taught this before, and it was a lot easier than I thought it would be."

Vocabulary

Academic Vocabulary The branch of physics that studies the effects of fluids under pressure or at rest is **hydrostatics.** **Hydraulics** is the technology that uses liquid under pressure, typically water, to produce force or motion.

QUICK LAB OBSERVING

Anatomy of a Clam

A clam is a bivalve mollusk. In this lab, you will explore the parts and systems of a clam.

PROBLEM What are the internal organs and systems of a clam?

PROCEDURE

1. Place the clam in the dissecting tray and follow the instructions on the drawing to carefully open the shell.
2. Look for the gills, and use your probe to study them.
3. Observe and note the shape of the foot. Locate the palps.
4. Follow the instructions to peel away the muscle layer to see the internal organs.
5. Locate the reproductive organs, and then find the digestive system.
6. Dispose of your specimen as instructed by your teacher.

ANALYZE AND CONCLUDE

1. **Infer** What organ does the clam use to breathe?
2. **Infer** The clam is a filter feeder. Based on your observations of the digestive system, how does the clam eat?
3. **Infer** The arteries and veins are not attached to each other. How might the circulatory system work?

MATERIALS

- preserved clam specimen
- dissecting tray
- Anatomical Clam Drawing
- screwdriver
- scalpel
- probe
- scissors
- forceps
- 12 dissecting pins
- hand lens
- paper towels

MAIN IDEA

Annelids have segmented bodies.

All annelids share more similarities in their body plans than mollusks do. Three groups of annelids—earthworms, marine worms, and leeches—are characterized by segmentation. **Segmentation** refers to the repeated sections of an annelid's long body that contain a complex set of body structures.

Annelid Anatomy

The features of an annelid's segmented body are shown in **FIGURE 23.17.** A typical annelid segment contains part of the digestive tract, nerve cord, and blood vessels that carry blood to the worm's tissues. Annelids have a closed circulatory system, where blood travels in a closed circuit inside blood vessels. Each body segment also contains organs that collect and excrete wastes, bands of longitudinal and circular muscle, and a coelom.

VOCABULARY
Coelom comes from a Greek word meaning "cavity." *Septum* comes from a Latin word meaning "partition."

The **coelom** (SEE-luhm) is a fluid-filled space that is completely surrounded by muscle. The coelom is divided by partitions called septa (singular, *septum*). The fluid inside the coelom acts as a hydrostatic skeleton. To understand how a hydrostatic skeleton works, think of a water balloon. When you squeeze one end, the water moves to the opposite end. An annelid uses its hydrostatic skeleton in a similar way to move from one place to another. When the longitudinal muscles contract, the segment shortens. When circular muscles contract, the segment lengthens. Alternating waves of contractions move from head to tail, producing the worm's characteristic crawling motion.

Differentiated Instruction

HANDS-ON ACTIVITY

Provide students with a hand lens and an earthworm in a petri dish. Have them locate the earthworm's segments, mouth, and anus and observe its crawling motion. Students can use the eraser end of a pencil to prod the earthworm gently. Remind students to wash their hands after handling the earthworm.

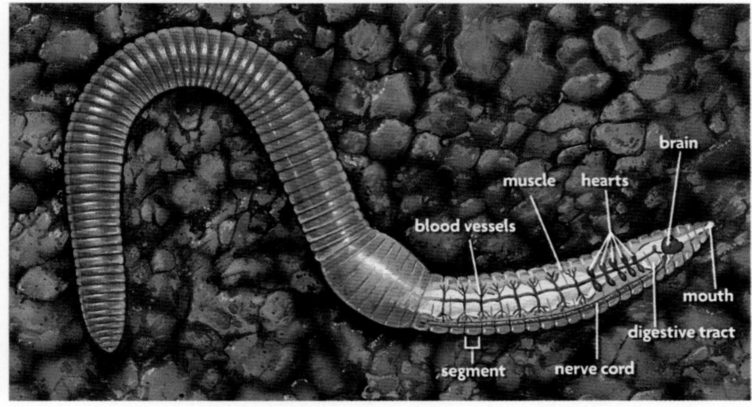

FIGURE 23.17 Annelids, such as earthworms, have similar body plans, characterized by segmentation.

Annelid Diet

Earthworms and marine worms eat organic waste material. Earthworms excrete digested material, called castings, into the soil. Castings help maintain a nutrient-rich soil. While most people think of leeches as blood-feeders, a number of leech species are actually predators that feed on invertebrates such as snails and aquatic insect larvae.

Annelid Reproduction

Annelid reproduction may be either asexual or sexual. Asexual reproduction results from fragmentation. In this method, a portion of the posterior end of the annelid breaks off and forms a new individual. Some annelids, such as earthworms, are hermaphrodites. Just as in land snails, reproduction occurs by cross-fertilization. Other annelids, such as marine worms, have separate males and females. Fertilized eggs of marine annelids initially develop into free-swimming larvae. Larvae grow in size by the formation of new segments.

A **Contrast** **In what ways are annelids different from mollusks?**

23.4 ASSESSMENT

ONLINE QUIZ ClassZone.com

REVIEWING MAIN IDEAS

1. Describe the characteristics that separate the three groups of flatworms.
2. What is the function of a mollusk's **radula**?
3. What are the three groups of annelids? Describe their body plan, using the word **coelom.**

CRITICAL THINKING

4. **Apply** How might a community prevent *Schistosoma* infections?
5. **Infer** What adaptations might mollusks without shells use to defend against predators?

***Connecting* CONCEPTS**

6. **Evolution** Free-living flatworms have pairs of sensory organs in their heads. What might make two sense organs set on either side of the head more adaptive than a single central organ?

23.4 ASSESSMENT

1. Flukes and tapeworms are both parasitic; planarians are not. Tapeworms feed on food within the host's digestive tract; flukes feed on the host's body fluids.
2. scrape off food particles to eat
3. Earthworms, marine worms, and leeches; all have segmented bodies with organs that collect and excrete wastes, bands of muscle, and a coelom, which is a fluid-filled space completely surrounded by muscle. The fluid-filled coelom helps the annelid move.
4. Sewage treatment could prevent larvae excreted by infected people from getting back into the water supply. Water treatment could kill larvae.
5. *Sample Answers:* chemical defenses (inedible), camouflage, rapid escape mechanisms (jet propulsion)
6. Pairs of organs help animals determine the direction of a stimulus through comparison of the stimulus' strength from one organ to the other.

TEACH FROM VISUALS

FIGURE 23.17 Have students study the external and internal anatomy of the earthworm. Point out that the earthworm is segmented both externally and internally. **Ask**

- What organs make up the earthworm's circulatory system? hearts and blood vessels
- Is the circulatory system open or closed? closed

Take It Further

The **palolo worm,** *Palola viridis,* is a marine annelid that is considered a delicacy by the people of Samoa. This species reproduces by producing a long chain of segments at its tail end that is filled with gametes. Once a year, usually around a full moon in spring, the worms rise to the surface and release the reproductive sections, which burst open so that sperm and eggs can mix and fertilize. This **swarming** allows for a much greater chance of fertilization, but it also makes these animals vulnerable to predators, such as humans, who have learned to show up at the right place and right time for a palolo feast.

Answers

A **Contrast** Annelids have closed circulatory systems, coeloms, and segmented bodies. There is greater diversity of body plan in the mollusks than in the annelids.

Assess and Reteach ▼

Assess Use the Online Quiz or Section Quiz (*Assessment Book,* p. 456).

Reteach Create a crossword puzzle featuring important terms from the section.

SECTION 23.5

Plan and Prepare

Objectives

- Identify characteristics of roundworms.
- Recognize the role of roundworms as parasites.

Section Resources

Unit Resource Book
Study Guide pp. 17–18
Power Notes p. 19
Reinforcement p. 20

Interactive Reader Chapter 23
Spanish Study Guide pp. 241–242

Technology
Power Presentation 23.5
Media Gallery DVD
Online Quiz 23.5

Activate Prior Knowledge Students with pets may be familiar with one particular type of roundworm. **Ask,** What is the common name of the parasite that can infect dogs? heartworm This roundworm species is carried by mosquitoes and infects various canines and felines.

Teach

Vocabulary

Greek and Latin Word Origins

The root of **cuticle** is the Latin word *cutis,* which means "skin."

The words **chiton,** a type of mollusk mentioned in **Section 23.4,** and **chitin** both come from the Greek *khitōn,* a word for the tunic worn by both men and women in ancient Greece. Students can describe the cuticle of roundworms or the exoskeleton of arthropods as **chitinous.**

In the phylum name Nematoda, *nema-* comes from a Greek word meaning "thread."

23.5 Roundworms

KEY CONCEPT Roundworms have bilateral symmetry and shed their outer skeleton to grow.

MAIN IDEAS
- Roundworms shed their stiff outer skeleton as they grow.
- Many roundworms are parasites.

VOCABULARY
cuticle, p. 716
pseudocoelom, p. 716

Connect Imagine grabbing a handful of soil. In that single handful, there may be thousands of roundworms. These animals are found in nearly every ecosystem on Earth, including mountaintops and deep ocean trenches. They are also found within extreme environments such as hot springs and Arctic ice.

MAIN IDEA

Roundworms shed their stiff outer skeleton as they grow.

Roundworms, also called nematodes, are one of the most numerous kinds of animals, in terms both of numbers and of species diversity. The more than 15,000 species of roundworms vary in size from less than a millimeter to over 10 meters in length.

Roundworms are part of the group Ecdysozoa, which also includes arthropods—crustaceans, spiders, and insects. Like mollusks and annelids, members of the Ecdysozoa are protostomes and have bilateral symmetry. All Ecdysozoans have a tough exoskeleton called a cuticle. The **cuticle** (KYOO-tih-kuhl) is made of chitin, and must be shed whenever the animal grows larger. When the animal sheds its cuticle, its soft body is exposed to predators until its new skeleton hardens.

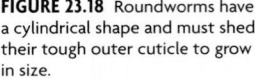

FIGURE 23.18 Roundworms have a cylindrical shape and must shed their tough outer cuticle to grow in size.

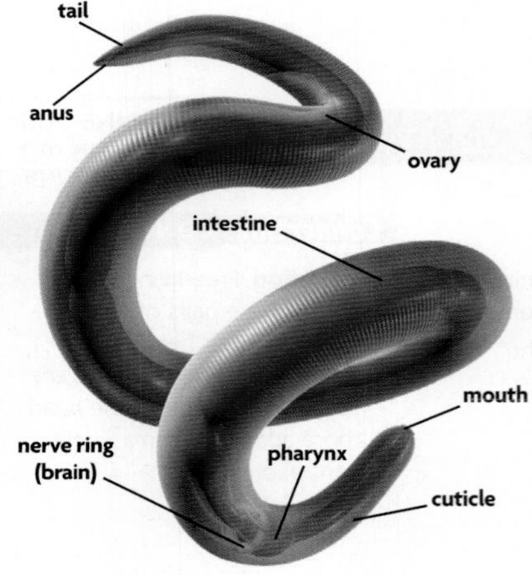

Roundworm Anatomy

As shown in **FIGURE 23.18,** a roundworm is cylindrical, with a blunt head and tapered tail. It is covered with a tough cuticle that lies over a layer of muscle. Muscle in the roundworm is laid out lengthwise. This arrangement means that a roundworm moves by bending its body side-to-side. Rather than crawling like other types of worms, a roundworm's movement is more whiplike.

Muscle within the roundworm is separated from the central gut tube by a fluid-filled space. This fluid-filled space is called a **pseudocoelom** (soo-duh-SEE-luhm) because it is not completely lined by muscle. (The prefix *pseudo-* means "false.") Roundworms do not have circulatory or respiratory systems. However, they do have a digestive system, which includes a mouth, pharynx, intestine, and anus. Food that is eaten, such as plant matter, algae, or bacteria, travels the length of the roundworm, from the mouth at one end to the anus at the other.

Differentiated Instruction

PRE-AP

Have students continue with the practice of preparing a biological profile card for each phylum, this time for the phylum Nematoda.

Roundworm Reproduction

Most roundworms reproduce sexually. In some cases, female roundworms bear live young after eggs hatch within the female's reproductive tract. In most cases, however, larvae develop from eggs laid by the female. Roundworms grow into their adult form by molting.

A Contrast How does growth differ in a roundworm and in a human?

MAIN IDEA

Many roundworms are parasites.

Roundworms are parasites of nearly every plant and animal species. These animals cause a lot of damage to the crop species they infect. Such a widespread loss of crops can seriously harm the economy of farming communities. Other roundworms infect humans. These roundworms include hookworms, pinworms, and Guinea worms.

- **Hookworms** A hookworm is found within the digestive tract of its host. This parasite feeds on its host's blood. A hookworm infects its human host when a person walks barefoot over contaminated soil. Over 1 billion people are infected with hookworms. Such infections are common in the tropics and subtropics.
- **Pinworms** A pinworm is found in the gut of its host. Pinworm infections often occur when the host accidentally swallows eggs picked up from contaminated surfaces.
- **Guinea worms** Guinea worms are found in the guts and connective tissues of their hosts. Guinea worm infections occur when a person drinks contaminated water. Work by global health organizations has helped to eliminate this disease from most of the world.

"So much for being the early bird, you've got worms."

Source: CartoonStock.com

B Infer Why might most parasitic roundworms live in the gut of their host?

23.5 ASSESSMENT

ONLINE QUIZ ClassZone.com

REVIEWING MAIN IDEAS

1. Why do roundworms molt? Use the term **cuticle** in your answer.
2. What are three parasitic roundworms that infect human hosts?

CRITICAL THINKING

3. **Contrast** How are earthworm and roundworm body cavities different?
4. **Apply** How might Guinea worm infections be prevented?

***Connecting* CONCEPTS**

5. **Parasitism** Many species of roundworms are parasites of plants and animals. How is a roundworm's body plan related to its function as a parasite?

ONLINE BIOLOGY Students can go to the chapter Resource Center at **ClassZone.com** for additional resources and information on roundworms.

Integrating Epidemiology

The heartworm that affects dogs is one type of **filarial worm,** which can be very harmful to humans. The worm *Onchocerca volvulus* is transmitted to humans through black flies, and can cause a disease commonly known as **river blindness.** Flies deliver larval worms into a human's blood. These worms can grow and infest the eyes and other tissues. Nearly 18 million people have this disease, and close to one million people are blind or visually impaired as a result. This disease is especially prevalent in rural African villages near fast-moving streams, but it is also known in parts of Central and South America.

Answers

A Contrast Roundworms must shed their cuticle (exoskeleton) in order to grow. Humans have an endoskeleton that grows in size to accommodate growth of other tissues.

B Infer The gut provides a stable environment with few or no predators and plenty of available nutrients.

23.4 ASSESSMENT

1. A roundworm's cuticle (or exoskeleton) is made of nonliving material and cannot grow as the roundworm gets bigger.
2. hookworms, pinworms, Guinea worms
3. Earthworms have coeloms; roundworms have pseudocoeloms. Functionally, the roundworm's pseudocoelom is used for circulation, whereas the earthworm's coelom is used for locomotion.
4. *Sample Answers:* avoiding contaminated water supplies and drinking only treated or filtered water
5. The roundworm's body plan is very simple, consisting of a mouth, gut tube, and anus. Because roundworms spend most of their lifetime within their host, they do not need to have a complex body plan suited for locomotion.

Assess and Reteach

Assess Use the Online Quiz or Section Quiz (*Assessment Book,* p. 457).

Reteach Set up a three-column chart on the board with the following column headings: Roundworms, Segmented Worms, Flatworms. Give students examples such as leeches, tapeworms, pinworms, and earthworms and ask them to indicate in which column each should be placed. Have students compare and contrast the phyla.

SECTION 23.6

▼ Plan and Prepare

Objectives

- Describe the symmetry of echinoderms.
- Identify the five classes of echinoderms and describe some of their characteristics.

Section Resources

Unit Resource Book Study Guide pp. 21–22 Power Notes p. 23 Reinforcement p. 24
Interactive Reader Chapter 23 **Spanish Study Guide** pp. 243–244
Biology Toolkit pp. C19, C38
Technology Power Presentation 23.6 Media Gallery DVD Online Quiz 23.6

Activate Prior Knowledge Students who have been to a beach may know at least one type of echinoderm. **Ask,** What type of animal found in tide pools is radially symmetric? sea stars, or "starfish" Introduce these as just one of five major types of echinoderms. **Ask,** What other invertebrate phylum in this chapter has radial symmetry? Cnidaria

▼ Teach

TEACH FROM VISUALS

FIGURE 23.19 Have students find the structures that make up the sea star's water vascular system. Explain that the bulblike structures extending from the radial canals are connected to the external tube feet. The tube feet extend when water from the bulbs is pushed into the tube feet. The tube feet retract when the bulbs relax.

23.6 Echinoderms

KEY CONCEPT Echinoderms are on the same evolutionary branch as vertebrates.

MAIN IDEAS
- Echinoderms have radial symmetry.
- There are five classes of Echinoderms.

VOCABULARY
ossicle, p. 718
water vascular system, p. 718

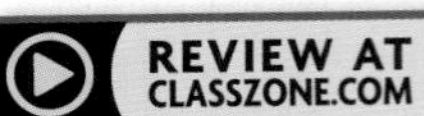

Connect If you have ever seen a tide pool, you may have noticed several creatures clinging to the pool's rocky bottom and sides. Brightly colored sea stars and spiky sea urchins are just two of the echinoderms that are often found in these habitats.

MAIN IDEA

Echinoderms have radial symmetry.

Adult echinoderms are slow-moving marine animals that have radial symmetry. In contrast, echinoderm larvae have bilateral symmetry. This difference suggests that echinoderms had bilateral ancestors and that radial symmetry is a derived character.

Echinoderm Anatomy

The anatomy of a sea star is shown in **FIGURE 23.19.** Note that each arm of a sea star contains both digestive glands and reproductive glands. For clarity, they are shown separately in different arms in the illustration.

All echinoderms have an internal skeleton made up of many tiny interlocking calcium-based plates called **ossicles.** These ossicles are embedded within the skin. The plates are joined together by a unique catch connective tissue with adjustable stiffness. Catch connective tissue allows echinoderms to change their consistency, going from very flexible to very stiff in a matter of seconds. The combination of a firm skeleton and a surface covered with spiny projections (often poisonous) helps to fend off predators.

FIGURE 23.19 Echinoderms, such as sea stars, are radially symmetrical animals with an internal skeleton made of interlocking plates embedded under the skin. Three arms of this sea star have been "cut away" to show internal anatomy.

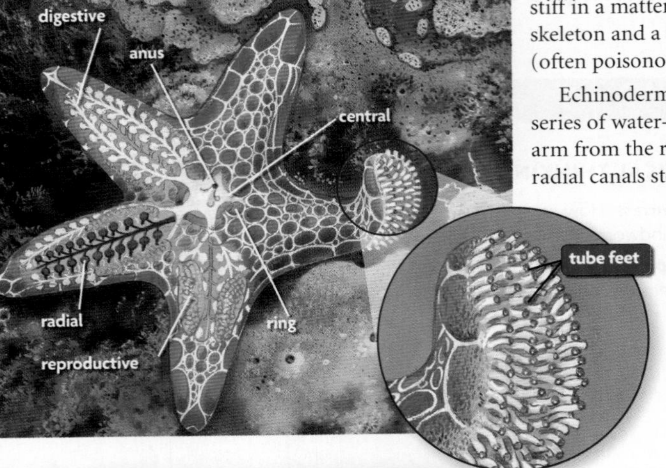

Echinoderms have a **water vascular system,** which is a series of water-filled radial canals that extend along each arm from the ring canal surrounding the central disk. The radial canals store water that is used for circulation and for filling tiny suckerlike appendages along the arms called tube feet. Changes in water pressure extend and retract the tube feet. On its own, a tube foot is small, but many of them working together can exert large forces. Tube feet are used to grab objects and to move around.

Differentiated Instruction

BELOW LEVEL

Have students consider the material in this section and previous sections. Ask them to write for five minutes on the different functions water performs in marine animals. Have them think about which of the animals they studied have blood.

Biology Toolkit, Quick-Write, p. C19

PRE-AP

Have students prepare a biological profile card for the phylum Echinodermata and its five classes.

A sea star has a complete digestive system made up of a mouth, stomach, a small length of intestine, and an anus. To eat a clam, a sea star grabs hold of the clam with its tube feet and uses pressure to pull apart the clam's shell. Sea stars are able to push their stomach out of their mouths. The stomach enters the narrow space between the two shells of a clam, and digestive juices from the digestive glands dissolve the clam's body. The clam is completely digested in the stomach. Waste material exits out the anus.

Echinoderms such as sea stars can regenerate, or regrow, their limbs, as shown in **FIGURE 23.20.** Sea cucumbers can regenerate a portion of their digestive system, which they sometimes eject when disturbed. For regeneration to occur, certain body parts, such as a portion of a sea star's central disk, must still remain.

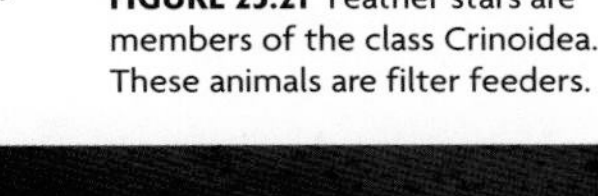

FIGURE 23.20 Sea stars and other echinoderms are able to regenerate, or regrow, limbs.

Echinoderm Reproduction

Most echinoderms reproduce sexually. Adult sea stars, for example, release sperm and eggs from the reproductive glands in their arms into the water. The fusion of these gametes results in fertilization of the egg. The fertilized egg develops into a free-floating, planktonic larva that matures in the water. As it matures, an echinoderm undergoes a complex series of changes into its adult form. The left side of its body begins to form the tube feet, while the right side forms the ossicle plates that will protect its outer surface. Eventually, the echinoderm settles onto the ocean floor, where it develops into an adult.

Connect A sea star specimen has bilateral symmetry. Is it an adult or a larva? Why?

MAIN IDEA

There are five classes of Echinoderms.

Echinoderms have a variety of body plans, ranging from the spiny round sea urchin to the oblong and the well-named sea cucumber.

Feather Stars and Sea Lilies

Feather stars and sea lilies are members of the class Crinoidea (kry-NOY-dee-uh). A feather star, shown in **FIGURE 23.21,** can move with its arms, but it is usually attached to a surface. Sea lilies are sessile. They are attached to the ocean bottom by a stalk on one side of their bodies. These animals filter feed by using the tube foot–like extensions covering their arms to collect and transfer food to the mouth.

FIGURE 23.21 Feather stars are members of the class Crinoidea. These animals are filter feeders.

Sea Stars

Sea stars are members of the class Asteroidea (AS-tuh-ROY-dee-uh). Some sea stars are filter feeders, while others are opportunistic feeders, meaning that they will eat whatever food source they happen to come upon. Other sea stars are carnivorous predators.

Vocabulary

Greek and Latin Word Origins The word **echinoderm** comes from the Greek roots *echino-*, meaning "hedgehog" (a spiny mammal) and *-derm* meaning "skin."

Integrating Ecology

The sea star *Pisaster ochraceus* is a **keystone species** in rocky intertidal communities of the northeast Pacific Ocean. Experiments conducted in the 1960s demonstrated that if *Pisaster* individuals were removed from their communities, the community structure quickly fell into disarray, mostly through the opportunistic niche-grab of the mussel *Mytilus californicus,* a key prey of the sea star. The experimental removal of the sea star took away the predation pressure on mussel population, which quickly multiplied, outcompeting other species for both food and space and ultimately driving down biodiversity in the community. When the sea star was reintroduced into these communities, it quickly decreased the mussel population through efficient predation.

Answers

A Connect The specimen is a larva. Sea stars have bilateral symmetry as larvae and radial symmetry as adults.

ENGLISH LEARNERS

Refer students to the first paragraph on page 719, which describes a sea star's method of eating. Have them make a sequence diagram that summarizes the sequence of steps described in the paragraph.

Biology Toolkit, Sequence Diagram, p. C38

INCLUSION

Provide dried or live specimens of echinoderms for students who are visually impaired. Some sea urchin species have spines that are blunt and safe to touch. Sea stars will apply their tube feet to a hand, allowing students to feel how the sea star moves and attaches itself to prey and to the seafloor. Sea cucumbers can be handled as well, but be sure to tell students to handle them gently. Students should wash their hands after the activity.

▼ Teach *continued*

Integrating Ecology

The **crown-of-thorns sea star,** *Acanthaster planci,* eats corals on tropical reefs throughout the South Pacific Ocean. Scientists believe that periodic surges in the populations of this species may be the result of human influences on the coral reef ecosystem. One theory suggests that the removal of the sea star's predators is to blame. The giant triton snail, humphead Maori wrasse, sweetlip emperor fish, and starry puffer fish all are known predators of the crown-of-thorns, and all have been heavily fished on various reefs in the Pacific. Another theory is that **nutrient runoff** from coastal land results in phytoplankton blooms that in turn support the larvae of the crown-of-thorns.

Answers

A Contrast Sea stars are voracious predators of clams and other organisms, while sea cucumbers are sediment feeders.

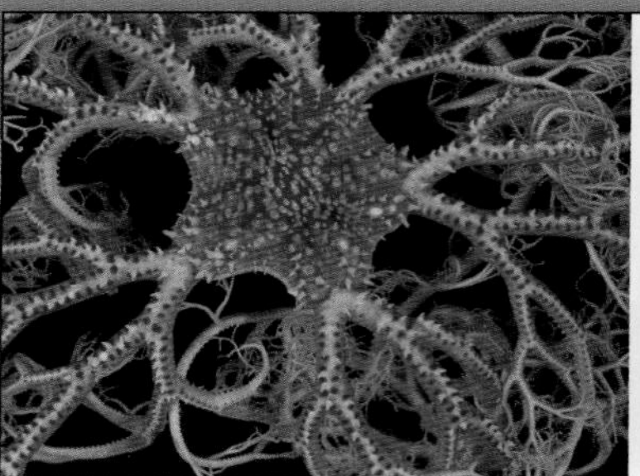

FIGURE 23.22 Basket stars (left) use their long, branched arms to capture plankton. Sea urchins (middle) are covered in long, sharp spines that protect them from predators. Sea cucumbers (right) are fleshy animals that live on the ocean floor.

Brittle Stars and Basket Stars

Brittle stars and basket stars are both members of the class Ophiuroidea (AHF-ee-yuh-ROY-dee-uh). Brittle stars have long spindly arms and are fast movers. Because their tube feet lack suckers, brittle stars use their arms to move. Some brittle stars are scavengers that feed on detritus on the ocean floor. Others are predators. Basket stars, shown in **FIGURE 23.22**, also have long arms, although with many branches. Basket stars filter feed by capturing plankton with their arms.

Sea Urchins, Sea Biscuits, and Sand Dollars

Sea urchins, sea biscuits, and sand dollars are all members of the class Echinoidea (EHK-uh-NOY-dee-uh). The bodies of sea biscuits and sand dollars are covered with tiny projections, which the animals use for movement and for burrowing on the ocean floor. Sea urchins, which do not burrow, do not have these projections. Instead, these animals are covered in long, sharp spines. Burrowing animals feed on waste matter on the ocean floor. Most sea urchins graze on algae by trapping it on sticky tentacles found on their ventral side.

Sea Cucumbers

Sea cucumbers are the only members of the class Holothuroidea (HAHL-uh-thu-ROY-dee-uh). Sea cucumbers are fleshy animals that have a long, bilateral shape. Instead of arms, sea cucumbers have thick, fleshy tentacles. These tentacles are used to capture particles of food, which the animal eats by pulling its tentacles through its mouth. Sea cucumbers, which live on the ocean floor, are also sediment feeders. These animals absorb food items in their digestive tract, and eject nonfood particles through their anus.

For more information on echinoderms, visit scilinks.org. Keycode: MLB023

A Contrast How do feeding behaviors differ between sea stars and sea cucumbers?

▼ Assess and Reteach

Assess Use the Online Quiz or Section Quiz (*Assessment Book,* p. 458).

Reteach Work with students to create a compare/contrast chart that summarizes the information provided in this section about the five classes of echinoderms. The chart should address the echinoderms' mobility, methods of feeding, and body types.

23.6 ASSESSMENT

ONLINE QUIZ ClassZone.com

REVIEWING MAIN IDEAS

1. How does the **water vascular system** enable echinoderms to move?
2. Describe the differences in body plans between the five classes of echinoderms.

CRITICAL THINKING

3. **Contrast** How do the feeding habits of sessile echinoderms differ from those that are mobile?
4. **Infer** How does an echinoderm benefit from the ability to regenerate limbs?

Connecting CONCEPTS

5. **Bioindicators** Sea urchins live on rock- and sand-covered areas of the ocean floor. What changes in an ocean ecosystem might be indicated by an increase in the sea urchin population?

23.6 ASSESSMENT

1. The water vascular system allows echinoderms to move their tube feet by forcing water in and out of them.
2. Asteroidea: move with tube feet, regenerate limbs; Ophiuroidea: tube feet lack suckers, use long arms to move: Echinoidea: covered with spines or small projections used for movement; Holothuroidea: long bilateral shape with fleshy tentacles; Crinoidea: immobile stalk topped with feathery arms
3. Sessile echinoderms tend to be filter feeders; mobile echinoderms tend to be active predators or sediment feeders.
4. Echinoderms can survive extensive damage to their bodies and can regain functions.
5. decrease in marine plant life or populations of other bottom-dwelling organisms that cover sand or rock; could also indicate an abundance of the algae on which urchins feed

NOS.1

DATA ANALYSIS ClassZone.com

Correlations Among Invertebrate Data

A **scatterplot** is a type of graph used to identify a trend or a correlation between two variables.

- The independent variable is usually graphed on the *x*-axis.
- The dependent variable is usually graphed on the *y*-axis.
- The data points are plotted but not connected.

Three types of correlations between variables can be shown on a scatterplot.

- Positive—as one variable increases or decreases, the other variable increases or decreases respectively.
- Negative (inverse)—as one variable increases, the other decreases.
- No correlation—there is no change in one variable as the other variable either increases or decreases.

EXAMPLE

Graph 1, a scatterplot of butter clam shell length and width, shows that as the width of the clam's shell increases, the length of the shell increases as well. This is a positive correlation, because as width increases, length increases. If it were an inverse correlation, one of the variables would increase as the other decreased.

Graph 2, a scatterplot of zooplankton feeding rates, shows no correlation between the feeding rates of zooplankton and the concentration of dinoflagellates. You can infer that there is no correlation from the graph, because the data is scattered across the graph and does not form a pattern.

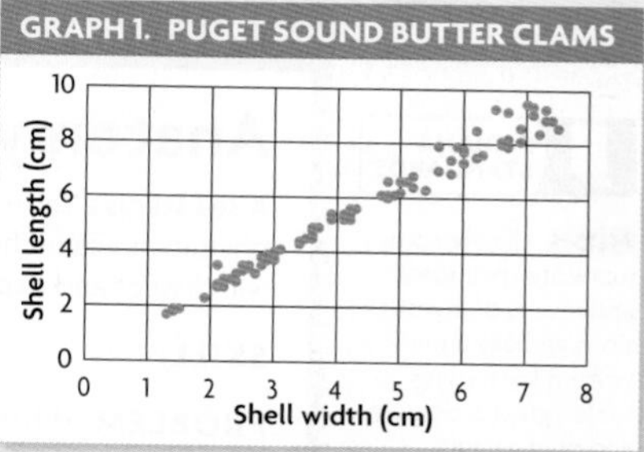

Source: Seattle Central Community College

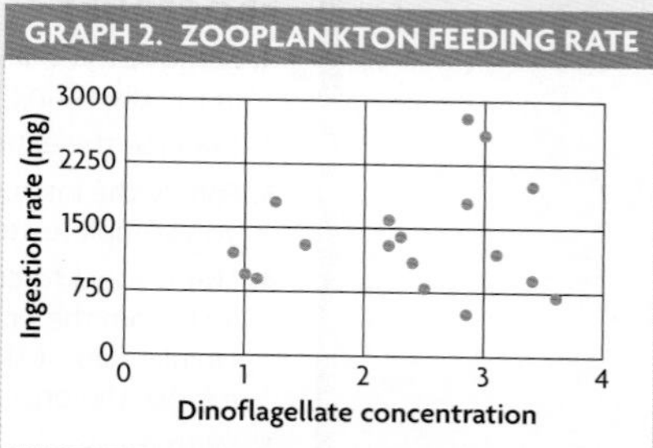

Source: Calbet, A. et al. *Journal of Aquatic Microbial Ecology 26*

ANALYZE A SCATTERPLOT

Scientists measured the heart rate and shell diameter of snails. These data are shown in the graph at the right. Use the graph to answer the following three questions.

1. **Analyze** Describe the correlation between the shell diameter and the heart rate in this species of snail.
2. **Predict** If a snail shell were to grow past 14 mm, what do you think would happen to the snail's heart rate?
3. **Infer** Suggest a possible explanation for the correlation between heart rate and shell diameter.

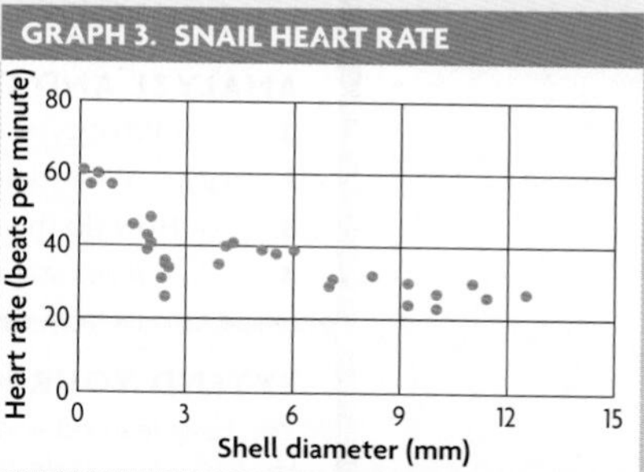

Source: Iowa State University

Answers

1. There is an negative relationship between shell diameter and heart rate. As the shell diameter increases, the heart rate decreases.
2. The heart rate could slow a little or remain the same as the 13-mm snail.
3. A larger snail has a larger heart. A larger heart can pump a larger volume of blood than a small heart can, meaning it does not need to beat as often in order to deliver oxygen and other nutrients to the snail's tissues.

DATA ANALYSIS

Introduce

A scatterplot illustrates the relationship between two variables. This relationship may be viewed as positive, negative, or nonexistent.

Discuss

Ask students for examples of other pairs of variables that show positive, negative, or no relationship. Have them draw on the board what a scatterplot for each pair of variables would look like.

Discuss the gradual flattening of the slope of the plotted data on graph 3. Point out that such a trend is common when there are physiological or physical limitations at play. For example, if we plotted human population over the last thousand years, it would show remarkable growth, especially in the last century. **Ask**

- Does this mean that in another hundred years the population will have doubled again? not necessarily; many populations reach a point or a capacity at which their rate of growth can no longer be supported by the resources. Relate this to the trend in graph 3 and to other trends in nature.
- Why might the heart rate decrease very little or not at all if a snail continues to grow beyond 14 mm in shell diameter? The heart may have a limit in terms of how much volume it can pump or how large it can grow, even if the snail continues to grow.

Unit Resource Book, Data Analysis, p. 25

OPTIONS FOR INQUIRY

INVESTIGATION

Time 60 minutes	TEACHER TESTED
Teacher Preparation	
Student Difficulty	
Lab Binder Animals, pp. 5–7	

Purpose Observe the internal anatomy of a sea star.

Overview Students will observe the external anatomy of a sea star and then dissect it to study its internal anatomy.

LAB PREPARATION

Make copies of the datasheet for students (*Lab Binder*, p. 7).

Safety Remind students to dispose of the sea stars properly and to wash their hands thoroughly before leaving the lab. If microscopes are used, remind students to clean the eyepieces with alcohol wipes after using them.

POST-LAB DISCUSSION

Discuss students' findings with the class. **Ask**

- How are fluids circulated in the sea star? through the coelom and canals running through each ray
- What characteristics of a sea star adapt it for life on rocks? Tube feet allow it to grip the surfaces of rocks and other substrata.

Use these inquiry-based labs and online activities to deepen your understanding of invertebrates.

NOS.3 Clearly communicate their ideas and results of investigations verbally and in written form using tables, graphs, diagrams, and photographs.

INVESTIGATION

Anatomy of a Sea Star

A sea star is a saltwater echinoderm in the same phylum as sea urchins and sand dollars. In this lab, you will dissect and explore the parts of a sea star.

SKILL Observing

PROBLEM What organs and systems are inside a sea star?

MATERIALS

- preserved sea star specimen
- dissecting tray
- scissors
- forceps
- dissecting needle
- 12 dissecting pins
- hand lens or dissecting microscope
- paper towels
- Anatomical Sea Star Drawing

PROCEDURE

1. Remove the sea star from its container and place it in the dissecting tray.
2. Examine the external anatomy of the sea star.
3. Follow the instructions on the sea star drawing as you complete steps 4–8.
4. Use scissors to cut off the end of one ray about one inch from the tip. Use the scissors to cut a long circular flap of skin along the length of one ray to expose the organs underneath. Look closely in the ray on either side of the groove.
5. With forceps and scissors, lift and cut the skin closer to the center (within half an inch). There, on either side of the groove, you will see the gonads, or reproductive organs, of the sea star.
6. The water-filled space in each ray is called the coelom. Notice that the sea star has no heart or circulatory system.
7. When finished, dispose of your sea star according to instructions from your teacher. Be sure to wash your hands thoroughly before leaving the lab.

ANALYZE AND CONCLUDE

1. **Apply** What type of symmetry does the sea star have?
2. **Analyze** What type of texture does the dorsal surface have? What is it covered with?
3. **Infer** How do the eyespots compare with eyes of other animals?
4. **Predict** A sea star does not have teeth. How does it eat?

EXTEND YOUR INVESTIGATION

You have learned about the different structures and their functions within a sea star. How would you design an experiment to determine what food items sea stars prefer? Use the library or Internet to research which food items sea stars eat, and then design your experiment. Include in your experimental design your control, independent variables, and dependent variables.

Answers

Analyze and Conclude

1. radial symmetry
2. rough; covered with small projections
3. The eyespots are less complex than eyes. They merely distinguish light from dark.
4. The sea star pushes its stomach outside its body into or around the edible tissues of its prey. The stomach releases digestive enzymes, and the mouth absorbs the digested material and sends it through the stomach and ducts to the digestive glands of each ray. Undigested material is excreted through the anus.

Extend Your Investigation

Students' experimental designs should include offering one or more sea stars several different types of prey, such as bivalves, gastropods, carrion (dead fish or other animal), crustaceans, and annelids. Students can offer different sizes of the same species of food to see if size makes a difference, or they can experiment with water temperature or currents to see if the sea star's ability to detect its prey is affected.

INVESTIGATION

Anatomy of an Annelid

The California blackworm (*Lumbriculus variegatus*) lives in sediments and organic debris on the edges of freshwater ponds, marshes, and lakes. In this investigation, you will observe a blackworm's anatomy and behavior, and observe and measure blood flow.

SKILL Observing

PROBLEM What are the features of an annelid?

MATERIALS
- 6–10 filter paper disks
- forceps
- petri dish
- 10 mL spring water
- California blackworm
- eyedropper
- dissecting microscope

PROCEDURE
1. Place a filter paper disk in the petri dish and moisten it with water at room temperature.
2. Carefully transfer a blackworm to the petri dish using the eyedropper.
3. Observe the blackworm at low (40×) and high (400×) powers with the microscope.
4. Draw what you see. What structures can you identify? How many segments does the blackworm have? Can you see the large blood vessels running along the worm? Draw them.
5. Observe the blood vessels more closely. Do they change over time? If so, what happens?

ANALYZE AND CONCLUDE
1. **Analyze** Does the worm have a head end and tail end? Explain.
2. **Infer** What causes blood to flow in the worm?
3. **Experimental Design** Write a procedure to measure the blood flow using a ruler and a watch.

Online BIOLOGY CLASSZONE.COM

ANIMATED BIOLOGY
Shared Body Structures
Animals that look very different can have similar body structures. Compare structures and organs of four different invertebrates to explore shared characteristics.

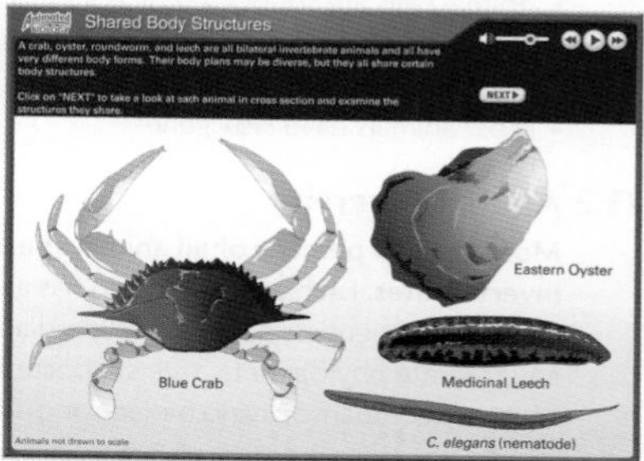

WEBQUEST
Parasites. Just the word can make your skin crawl. In this WebQuest, you will explore one parasite, the tapeworm. You will learn about its lifecycle and how to keep from becoming a host yourself! (colored SEM; magnification 40×)

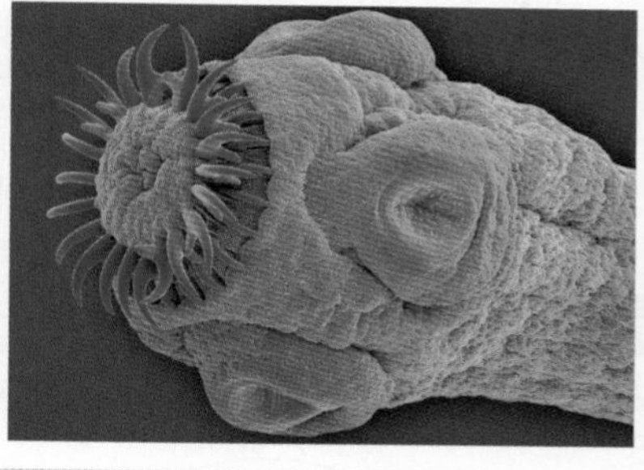

BIOZINE
Stories about invertebrates—such as "Sea Snails' Slime Holds Healing Properties" and "Designer Dogs: Get the Mix You Want"—are often in the headlines. Read the latest news about animals in the BioZine.

Answers

Analyze and Conclude

1. Yes, the worm's segments contract in a tail-to-head direction, forcing the worm forward and indicating the head end.
2. Wavelike, pulsing muscular contractions around the blood vessel walls push blood along from the tail to the head.
3. Students' experiments should include observing the rate of blood flow by recording the pulse (contractions/minute). If the effect of temperature is tested, the worm's pulse should increase until room temperature or slightly higher. Thereafter, it should decrease.

Online Biology ▼

ANIMATED BIOLOGY Use this interactive animation to reinforce the concepts of **Section 23.2.**

WEBQUEST The WebQuest takes one full class period. Students complete the activity online and will need access to a printer to print their answers. Sample answers, teacher notes, and alternative assessment ideas are available on **ClassZone.com.** Use with **Section 23.4.**

INVESTIGATION TEACHER TESTED

Time	45 minutes
Teacher Preparation	1
Student Difficulty	1
Lab Binder	Animals, p. 9

Purpose Observe the anatomy of an annelid.

Overview Students will observe a California blackworm. They will
- observe the blackworm's external anatomy
- observe changes in the blackworm's blood vessels

LAB MANAGEMENT

Safety Remind students to wipe down the microscope eyepieces with alcohol wipes after using them and to wash their hands.

POST-LAB DISCUSSION

Discuss students' results. **Ask**
- What structures were the most visible? Answers will vary, but students should be able to see the head, tail, and blood vessels.
- What changes did you expect to see in the blood vessels over time? Did your observations match your predictions? Answers will vary.

Teacher Note "It's nice because it enables observations and inferences to be made through inquiry."

CHAPTER REVIEW

Interactive Review

Encourage students to go to **ClassZone.com** for a detailed review of each section, including visuals and vocabulary practice.

Unit Resource Book, Vocabulary Practice, pp. 31–34

CHAPTER 23 Interactive Review @ CLASSZONE.COM

KEY CONCEPTS | Vocabulary Games | Concept Maps | Animated Biology | Online Quiz

23.1 Animal Characteristics

Animals are diverse but share common characteristics. Animals are the most physically diverse kingdom of organisms. All animals share a set of characteristics.

- All animals are multicellular heterotrophs.
- Animal cells are supported by collagen.
- Animals that reproduce are diploid and usually reproduce sexually.
- Most animals have *Hox* genes.

23.2 Animal Diversity

More than 95 percent of all animal species are invertebrates. Each animal phylum has a unique body plan. Scientists have constructed an invertebrate phylogenetic tree supported by anatomy comparisons and molecular evidence.

Bilateral symmetry **Radial symmetry**

23.3 Sponges and Cnidarians

Sponges and cnidarians are the simplest animals. Sponges are aquatic animals that have specialized cells but lack tissues. These animals were among the first to evolve during the Cambrian explosion. Cnidarians, which include jellyfish, corals, and sea anemones, are the most primitive animals still in existence today with specialized tissues.

23.4 Flatworms, Mollusks, and Annelids

Flatworms, mollusks, and annelids belong to closely related phyla. Flatworms are simple bilateral animals. They include planarians, flukes, and tapeworms. Mollusks share at least one feature in common: a radula, a mantle, or ctenidia. Common mollusks include snails, bivalves such as clams, and squid. Annelids have segmented bodies and include earthworms, leeches, and marine polychaete worms.

23.5 Roundworms

Roundworms have bilateral symmetry and shed their outer skeleton to grow. Roundworms are cylindrical, with a blunt head and tapered tail. They are covered with a tough cuticle that lies over a layer of muscle. Roundworms may be free-living or parasitic. Common human parasites include hookworms, pinworms, and Guinea worms.

23.6 Echinoderms

Echinoderms are on the same evolutionary branch as vertebrates. Echinoderms and vertebrates are both deuterostomes. Like cnidarians, echinoderms have radial symmetry. These animals have body parts arranged in a circle around a central axis and use a water vascular system to move and transport nutrients. Some echinoderms can regenerate portions of their body, and sometimes they use regeneration as a way to produce offspring.

Synthesize Your Notes

Concept Map Use a concept map to summarize what you know about animal phylogeny.

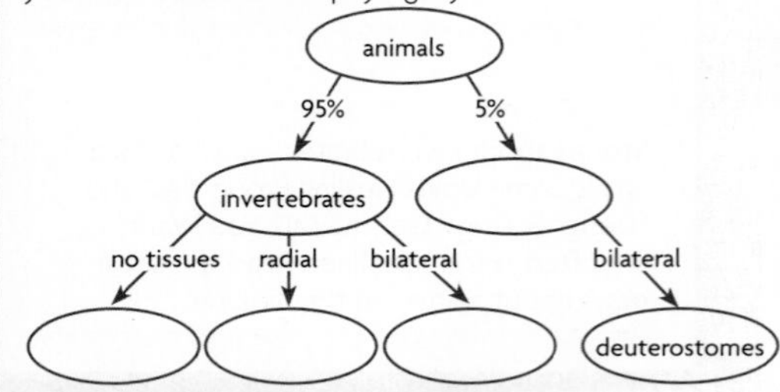

Content Frame Use a table to synthesize notes on the characteristics of the different invertebrate phyla.

Phyla	Features	Symmetry	Examples
Cnidaria	Tissues	Radial	Jellyfish, coral
Flatworms			

724 Unit 8: Animals

Reviewing Vocabulary

1. Drawing should be of three-stranded protein. Label: Collagen is a three-stranded protein.
2. Drawing should be of worm with segments. Label: Segmentation is the repetition of an annelid's body segments, each one containing a complex set of body structures.
3. Drawing should be of jellyfish with two layers separated by middle layer. Label: Mesoglea is a noncellular jellylike material that separates a cnidarian's two tissue layers.
4. Drawing should be of simple oval within a larger oval. Label: Digestive enzymes in the gastrovascular cavity absorb nutrients from food.
5. Drawing should be of umbrella-like medusa and polyp of opposite shape. Label: Polyps are cylindrical tubes with mouth and tentacles facing upward. Medusas are umbrella-shaped with downward-facing mouth and tentacles.
6. Drawing should be of radial animal such as adult echinoderm, bilateral animal such as human. Label: Radial animals have body parts arranged in a circle around a central axis. Bilateral animals can be divided equally along one plane.
7. Drawing should be of tonguelike organ. Label: The radula is a filelike feeding organ.
8. Drawing of a cavity with thick layer marked on one side. Label: The hemocoel is an open circulatory system made up of open spaces between mollusk tissue cells.
9. A phylum is a group of organisms classified by their shared characteristics and evolutionary relationships.
10. Sessile animals do not move from where they are attached, as if they are sitting in one place.
11. Segmented animals appear to be nearly cut into multiple parts.
12. Snails use their radula to scrape up food items to eat.
13. The pseudocoelom is a hollow cavity partially lined by muscle. It is a false coelom because it is only partially lined by muscle, while a true coelom is completely lined by muscle.

Chapter Assessment

CHAPTER REVIEW

Chapter Vocabulary

23.1 collagen, p. 697
homeotic, p. 698
homeobox, p. 698

23.2 vertebrate, p. 699
invertebrate, p. 699
phylum, p. 699
bilateral symmetry, p. 701
radial symmetry, p. 701
protostome, p. 702
deuterostome, p. 702

23.3 sessile, p. 705
filter feeder, p. 706
polyp, p. 707
medusa, p. 707
mesoglea, p. 707
nematocyst, p. 707
gastrovascular cavity, p. 708

23.4 complete digestive tract, p. 712
radula, p. 712
hemocoel, p. 712
segmentation, p. 714
coelom, p. 714

23.5 cuticle, p. 716
pseudocoelom, p. 716

23.6 ossicle, p. 718
water vascular system, p. 718

Reviewing Vocabulary

Visualize Vocabulary

For each word or word pair below, use simple shapes, lines, or arrows to illustrate the meaning. Label each picture, and write a short caption.

1. collagen
2. segmentation
3. mesoglea
4. gastrovascular cavity
5. polyp, medusa
6. radial symmetry, bilateral symmetry
7. radula
8. hemocoel

Greek and Latin Word Origins

Using the Greek or Latin word origins of the terms below, explain how the meaning of the root relates to the definition of the term.

9. The word *phylum* comes from the Greek word *phūlon*, which means "class."

10. The word *sessile* comes from the Latin word *sedere*, which means "to sit."

11. The word *segment*, as in *segmentation*, comes from *segmentum*, from the Latin word *secāre*, which means "to cut."

12. The word *radula* comes from the Latin word *radere*, which means "to scrape."

13. The word *pseudocoelom* comes from the Greek words *pseudes*, which means "false," and *koilos*, which means "hollow."

Reviewing MAIN IDEAS

14. What four characteristics are common to members of the animal kingdom? **B.8.3**

15. What is the difference between an invertebrate and a vertebrate? **B.8.3**

16. Describe three different criteria used to classify animals into groups. **B.8.3**

17. What types of evidence are used to put together the evolutionary history of the animal kingdom? **B.8.3**

18. What characteristic makes sponges the simplest animals?

19. Describe the two general body forms of cnidarians, which include jellyfish and corals.

20. What are the three types of flatworms? Describe the main features of each.

21. Mollusks have a complete digestive tract. What is one benefit of having this feature?

22. Describe what a segmented body plan looks like. Which phylum includes animals with segmented bodies?

23. Why must roundworms shed their outer skeleton?

24. Several species of roundworms are parasites with human hosts. Name one and explain how it affects human health.

25. What is the function of an echinoderm's water vascular system?

26. How does the ability to regenerate help an echinoderm escape from predators?

Reviewing Main Ideas

14. multicellular heterotrophs, cells supported by collagen, diploid and usually reproduce sexually, most have *Hox* genes
15. A vertebrate has an internal segmented backbone; an invertebrate does not.
16. body symmetry (radial or bilateral), number of tissue layers, developmental patterns
17. genetic evidence from mitochondrial DNA and *Hox* genes, along with comparisons of anatomy
18. Sponges lack tissues.
19. medusa: umbrella-shaped with mouth and tentacles pointing downward; polyp: cylindrical with mouth and tentacles pointing upward
20. planarian: free-living, nonparasitic flatworm; fluke: parasitic, feeds on body fluids; tapeworm: parasitic, feeds on food in gut of host
21. Animals with a complete digestive tract can eat continuously; food absorption is more efficient.
22. A segmented body plan has repeated sections. This is a feature of phylum Annelida.
23. In order to grow, the nongrowing cuticle must be shed.
24. *Sample Answer:* Pinworms are found in the human gut. Infection occurs when a person accidentally swallows an egg from a contaminated surface.
25. The water vascular system is used in movement, to grab objects, and for circulation.
26. A part of an echinoderm, such as an arm, can be damaged or eaten without killing the animal. Later, the part can grow back.

ITEM CORRELATIONS

Standard	Items
B.8.3	14-17
B.8.4	31, 36

CHAPTER REVIEW

Critical Thinking

27. Mutation or duplication of *Hox* genes led to the development of body parts in different locations than normal. Over time, this leads to a variety of different body plans and characteristics.

28. Echinoderm: deuterostome; radial cleavage; gut cavity forms from pouches created by folds in the gut tube; gut opening becomes anus.

    Mollusk: protostome; spiral cleavage; gut cavity forms from separations in the mesoderm; gut opening becomes mouth.

29. Tissues allow for the development of complex systems of organs through the specialization of different tissues.

30. Secreting toxic substances is the only method a sponge has to defend itself, because it is unable to move.

31. Molecular studies have both confirmed and rearranged relationships within and between animal phyla.

32. Each segment contains part of the central gut tube, nerve cord, and blood vessels.

33. Catch connective tissue is used to change the consistency of an echinoderm's body as a defense against predators.

34. An advantage of having a gastrovascular cavity is that digestion is a simple process compared to digestion in an animal with a complete digestive tract. A disadvantage of having a gastrovascular cavity is that the animal can digest only one thing at a time.

Interpreting Visuals

35. *Hox* genes define the head-to-tail development pattern in animal embryos and are laid out in a corresponding sequence on the chromosome.

36. The sequential layout of *Hox* genes on a chromosome and how they are expressed on the body is the same in a wide range of animals, suggesting a common origin.

Critical Thinking

27. Analyze How are the functions of *Hox* genes related to the diversity of body plans and characteristics within the animal kingdom?

28. Contrast How is development different for an echinoderm and a mollusk? Use a table to summarize their different development patterns.

29. Infer While both sponges and cnidarians are simple animals, cnidarians have specialized tissues. What might be some advantages of having specialized tissues?

30. Infer Why is the ability to secrete toxic substances important to the survival of a sponge?

31. Synthesize How has molecular biology played a critical role in our understanding of animal relationships and phylogeny? **B.8.4**

32. Infer Even when an annelid is cut in half, it can often still survive. What anatomical feature enables an annelid to remain alive when half of its body is gone?

33. Apply What is the function of an echinoderm's catch connective tissue?

34. Compare and Contrast Animals exhibit variety in their digestive systems. What do you think are the advantages and disadvantages of having a gastrovascular cavity compared with a complete digestive tract?

Interpreting Visuals

Use the *Hox* gene diagram below to answer the next two questions.

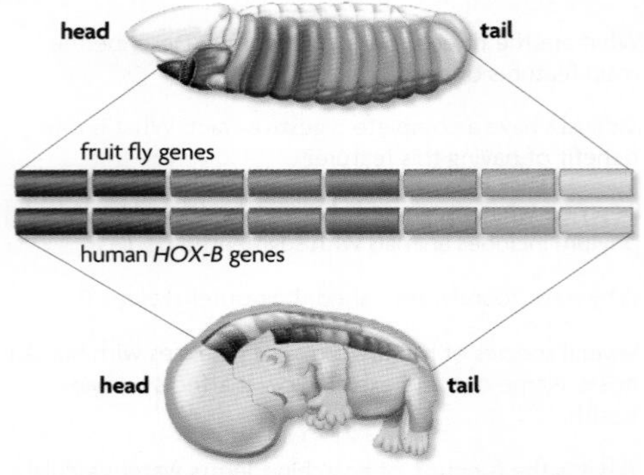

35. Apply How do the two organisms above display the pattern seen in all *Hox* genes?

36. Synthesize How does the diagram support the idea that all animals share a common ancestor? **B.8.4**

Analyzing Data

Scientists measured the depth and velocity of water in the Columbia River in Washington. These data are shown on the scatterplot graph below. Use the graph to answer the next three questions.

COLUMBIA RIVER DEPTH AND VELOCITY

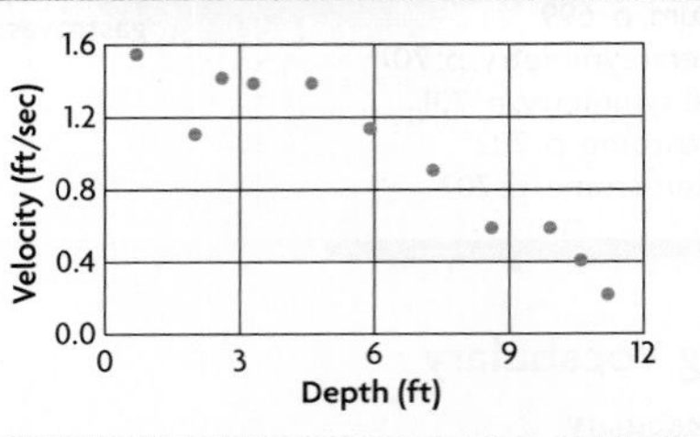

Source: USGS

37. Analyze What type of relationship exists between the depth and the velocity of the water? Explain your answer.

38. Predict Make a prediction about the velocity of the water if the depth were 14 feet.

39. Infer In what way might a species adapted to living at lower depths differ from a species adapted to living in shallow water?

***Connecting* CONCEPTS**

40. Write a Travel Brochure Imagine you are an advertising director for a travel agency. Choose an invertebrate from this chapter, and create a brochure to entice your chosen invertebrate to visit a vacation spot. Remember that each invertebrate species has specific requirements for survival. In your brochure, include a description of the location (and why it is the perfect place for your invertebrate), the menu of local restaurants, and other features that would make your chosen invertebrate feel at home.

41. Connect In addition to storing poisonous chemicals from their food, nudibranchs also are very colorful. In other colorful animals, such as birds, fish, and insects, colors are important for a variety of reasons. What might be the adaptive advantage of a nudibranch's bright coloration?

726 Unit 8: Animals

Analyzing Data

37. negative; as depth increases, velocity decreases

38. between 0.2 and 0.0 ft/sec

39. Species living in shallow, fast-moving water might have a streamlined shape and adaptations to help it grip surfaces. A species in deeper water might be less streamlined, slower, and have adaptations for burrowing in soft sediment.

INDIANA ISTEP+ Test Prep

B.5.1; B.6.4; B.8.3; B.8.6; NOS.2; NOS.9

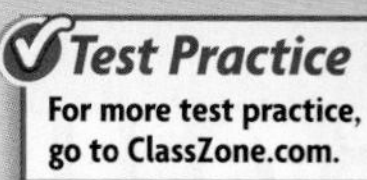

Test Practice
For more test practice, go to ClassZone.com.

1 The earliest classification system divided all animals into two main groups. Linnaeus' original classification scheme used six major groups of animals. Now, based on hundreds of years of scientific research, over 30 animal groups, or phyla, are recognized. This progression supports the idea that scientific evidence

A changes frequently.
B should be disregarded after 100 years.
C is cumulative.
D is often incorrect.

2

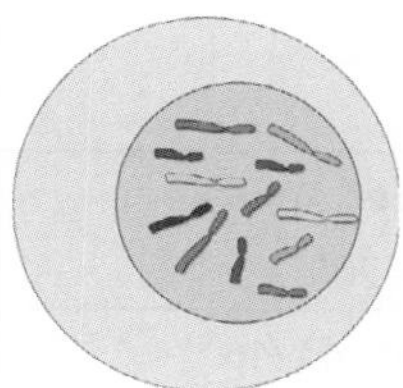

This illustration shows the chromosomes within the egg cell of a snail. If this egg cell unites with a sperm cell of the same snail species, the offspring will have

A 6 chromosomes from each parent.
B 6 pairs of chromosomes from each parent.
C 12 chromosomes from each parent.
D 12 pairs of chromosomes from each parent.

THINK THROUGH THE QUESTION

Recall that each egg and sperm cell has a single set of chromosomes.

3 Two roundworms mate and produce offspring. Which of the following most directly accounts for each offspring receiving half of its DNA from each parent?

A mutation
B maturation
C mitosis
D meiosis

4

Appearance of Early Animals in Fossil Record

Organism Type	Appearance in Fossil Record
Sponges	570 million years ago
Mollusks	545 million years ago
Echinoderms	500 million years ago

Choanoflagellates are animal-like protists that do not leave behind fossil evidence. They are considered the most likely ancestors to sponges and all other animals. Given this information, when did choanoflagellates likely evolve?

A less than 500 million years ago
B between 545 and 500 million years ago
C between 570 and 545 million years ago
D more than 570 million years ago

5 Over one million species of animals have been described by scientists. Which of the following ***best*** accounts for the incredible diversity in the animal kingdom, given that all animals are thought to be descendants of a common ancestor?

A The DNA of the common animal ancestor had no mutations.
B New mutations are constantly generated in the gene pools of animal populations.
C Collagen has allowed animal populations to diversify rapidly.
D Heterotrophs are able to diversify more rapidly than autotrophs.

6 What are the two types of symmetry found in invertebrates. Give an example of each.

Standards-Based Assessment

1. C	4. D
2. C	5. B
3. D	6. See Below

TEST DOCTOR

Question 2 Answer C is correct. Answer A is incorrect because the egg cell alone has 12 chromosomes. Answers B and D are incorrect because reproductive cells do not have paired chromosomes; the cells have undergone meiosis, so each parent cannot contribute "pairs" of chromosomes to the offspring.

Question 3 Answer D is correct because meiosis produces sex cells with half the original number of chromosomes, thus each parent contributes half the DNA to its offspring. Answer A is incorrect because mutations introduce genetic diversity. Answer B is incorrect because maturation is the process of becoming able to reproduce sexually. Answer C is incorrect because mitosis results in genetically identical daughter cells and is used by the body for growth and repair.

Question 4 Answer D is correct. Answers A, B, and C are incorrect because the choanoflagellates are possible ancestors of sponges, which means that they would have evolved before the sponges appear in the fossil record.

Question 6 Some invertebrates exhibit bilateral symmetry, meaning that two sides of their bodies are symmetrical, like spiders. The other type of symmetry exhibited by invertebrates is radial symmetry. Starfish are a classic example of this type of symmetry, which involves a repeating body pattern around a central point.

Connecting Concepts

40. Brochures should include the name of the invertebrate, features of its habitat, its prey items, and feeding habits.

41. The bright color announces to potential predators that the nudibranch is poisonous. If a predator eats a brightly colored nudibranch and gets sick, it may avoid similarly colored prey in the future. Predators also may have evolved to avoid prey of such coloration. Bright coloration may also help the nudibranch blend in with its coral reef surroundings.

ITEM CORRELATIONS

Standard	Items
B.5.1	2
B.6.4	3
B.8.3	6
B.8.6	5
NOS.2	4
NOS.9	1

CHAPTER 24

Indiana Resource Preview

Print Resources

A Closer Look at Arthropods

INDIANA STANDARDS		Sections	PAGES and PACING	UNIT RESOURCE BOOK
B.8.3	24.1	**Arthropod Diversity** **KEY CONCEPT** Arthropods are the most diverse of all animals.	pp. 730–734 30 minutes	URB pages 35–38
	24.2	**Crustaceans** **KEY CONCEPT** Crustaceans are a diverse group of ancient arthropods.	pp. 735–738 30 minutes	URB pages 39–42
NOS.3		CHAPTER INVESTIGATION: **Design Your Own** Hatching Brine Shrimp	p. 739 45 minutes	**Lab Binder** Animals pages 17–20
	24.3	**Arachnids** **KEY CONCEPT** Arachnids include spiders and their relatives.	pp. 740–742 30 minutes	URB pages 43–46
NOS.3		DATA ANALYSIS: Constructing Scatterplots	p. 742 45 minutes	URB page 55
	24.4	**Insect Adaptations** **KEY CONCEPT** Insects show an amazing range of adaptations	pp. 743–746 30 minutes	URB pages 47–50
	24.5	**Arthropods and Humans** **KEY CONCEPT** Arthropods and humans interact in many ways.	pp. 747–749 30 minutes	URB pages 51–54
NOS.1, NOS.3		OPTIONS FOR INQUIRY	pp. 750–751 45 minutes, 45 minutes	**Lab Binder** Animals pages 21–25
		Chapter Review	pp. 752–755	**Assessment Book** Chapter Tests A, B pp. 479–486

INDIANA STANDARDS

B.8.3 Use anatomical and molecular evidence to establish evolutionary relationships between organisms.
NOS.1 Develop explanations based on reproducible data and observations gathered during laboratory investigations.
NOS.3 Clearly communicate their ideas and results of investigations verbally and in written form using tables, graphs, diagrams, and photographs.

Labs

PUPIL EDITION LABS	
Comparing Arthropods, Section 1, p. 733 Students compare the structural features of several arthropod groups. **Lab Binder** p. 26	**Time:** 20 minutes **Materials:** slide of tick, slide of mite, slide of spider, slide of mosquito, microscope
Hatching Brine Shrimp, p. 739 Students test the effect of environmental conditions on hatching success of brine shrimp eggs. **Lab Binder** pp. 17–20	**Time:** 45 minutes **Materials:** clear plastic cups, 100-mL graduated cylinder, 2 100 mL sea salt solution, 0.1 g brine shrimp eggs, plastic spoon, balance, clear plastic wrap, aluminum foil, clear plastic bottles with lids, vinegar, baking soda, pH duo-test paper, 2 eyedroppers, 10 petri dishes, hand lens or dissecting microscope, lamp

OPTIONS FOR INQUIRY	
***Daphnia* and Heart Rate,** p. 750 Students observe the effect of an environmental change on the heart rate of *Daphnia*. **Lab Binder** pp. 21–23	**Time:** 45 minutes **Materials:** cotton swab, tissues, petroleum jelly, microscope slide, culture of *Daphnia magna*, 2 eyedroppers, cover slip, stopwatch, microscope, hydrogen peroxide solutions
Inside a Crayfish, p. 751 Students relate structure to function in crayfish. **Lab Binder** pp. 24–25	**Time:** 45 minutes **Materials:** dissecting tray, scissors, forceps, dissecting needle, 12 dissecting pins, preserved crayfish specimen, hand lens or dissecting microscope, paper towels, paper and pencil, Anatomical Crayfish Drawing

LAB BINDER Unit 8 Animals

Additional Investigation: Identifying Arthropods in a Decomposer System, pp. 27–31

Forensics Lab: Determining Time of Death Using Entomology, pp. 84–87

Virtual Lab Worksheet: Insect and Crime Scene Analysis, p. 101

LAB GENERATOR

A searchable CD of all labs in the program in editable format, including forensic, probeware, and biotechnology labs.

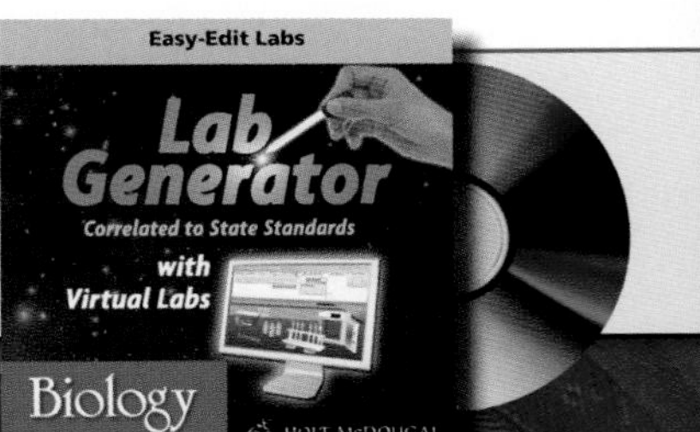

Presentation Tools

POWER PRESENTATIONS

Presentation Chapter 24
Power Presentations for each section incorporate images and clips from the Media Gallery: Includes Note Navigator for each section.

MEDIA GALLERY

Contains the following images and video clips, as well as animations, simulations and forms of visuals from the book.

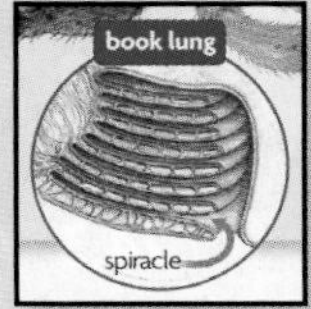

Arachnid anatomy

Arthropod types

Reef lobster

Praying mantis

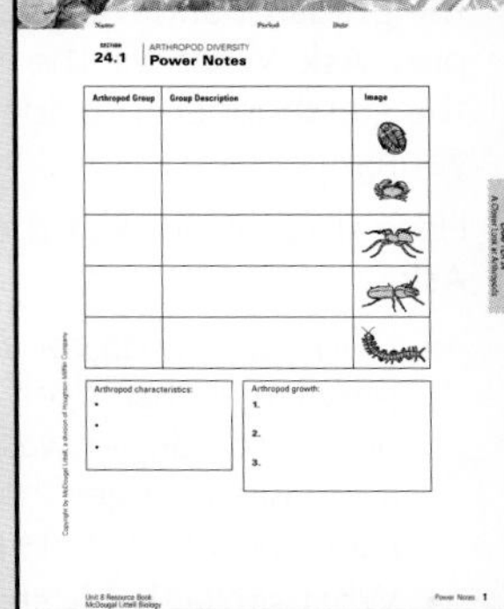

Power Notes

VIDEO

Check out a set of short video clips on the evolution and importance of arthropods.

ANIMATED BIOLOGY

Molting Cicada
Insect Metamorphosis
What Type of Arthropod?

TRANSPARENCIES

Crustacean Anatomy T103
Arachnid Anatomy T104
Complete Metamorphosis of a Monarch Butterfly T105

Online BIOLOGY CLASSZONE.COM

BioZine
Animated Biology
Interactive Review
SciLinks
Resource Centers

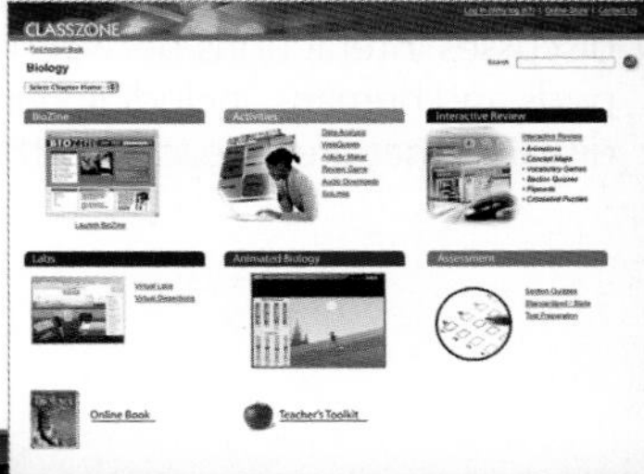

CHAPTER 24

▼ Focus and Motivate

What is the relationship between these two insects?

Students may suggest that the wasp is the predator and the grasshopper is the prey. **Ask,** What will the wasp do with the grasshopper? provide a meal for its young

Have students look at the picture again. **Ask**

- How can this digger wasp capture prey larger than itself? Like other wasps, the digger wasp has an abdominal stinger that it uses to inject venom into its prey.
- What similar body structures are found in the wasp and the grasshopper? Both have six legs, three body sections, wings, compound eyes, and antennae.

BIOZINE ClassZone.com

Students can access BioZine at **ClassZone.com** to receive updates to featured topics in the book.

In a Hurry?

Many students will be familiar with some of the material in this chapter. For quick coverage, review arthropod adaptations and diversity in **Section 24.1,** crustacean anatomy in **FIGURE 24.8 (Section 24.2),** arachnid anatomy in **FIGURE 24.13 (Section 24.3),** and insect adaptations in **Section 24.4. Section 24.5** discusses interactions between arthropods and humans, including human diseases that are spread by arthropods.

CHAPTER 24 A Closer Look at Arthropods

KEY CONCEPTS

24.1 Arthropod Diversity
Arthropods are the most diverse of all animals.

24.2 Crustaceans
Crustaceans are a diverse group of ancient arthropods.

24.3 Arachnids
Arachnids include spiders and their relatives.

24.4 Insect Adaptations
Insects show an amazing range of adaptations.

24.5 Arthropods and Humans
Arthropods and humans interact in many ways.

Online BIOLOGY CLASSZONE.COM

Animated BIOLOGY
View animated chapter concepts.
- Molting Cicada
- Insect Metamorphosis
- Insect and Crime Scene Analysis
- What Type of Arthropod?

BIOZINE
Keep current with biology news.
- Featured stories
- News feeds
- Strange Biology

RESOURCE CENTER
Get more information on
- Ancient Arthropods
- Crustaceans
- Insects

Student Activity

Purpose Classify various arthropods by placing photos of arthropods into their respective groups.

Materials (per team)

Each team will need pictures of various arthropods, including crustaceans, arachnids, and insects. Examples:

- crustaceans—lobster, crab, crayfish, shrimp
- arachnids—spiders, mites, ticks, scorpions
- insects—moths, butterflies, flies, honeybees

What is the relationship between these two insects?

Connecting CONCEPTS

Arthropod predators such as this digger wasp help to keep an important balance among Earth's invertebrates. This digger wasp has captured a meal not for itself but for its young. The wasp will deposit the live, but paralyzed, grasshopper into a burrow she has constructed. She will then lay a single egg next to the grasshopper so when the egg hatches the larva will have a fresh meal.

Animal Behavior Unlike the solitary digger wasp, many insects live in large social colonies. This paper wasp nest has been carefully constructed of wood pulp mixed with the insects' saliva. Within the colony, all insects are related to one another. A single queen lays eggs, which are raised by workers. Wasps will aggressively defend their nests from predators to ensure that the colony survives.

Introduce Describe the general features of each group. For example, crustaceans have a carapace, arachnids have two body sections, and insects have three body sections.

Discuss Have teams discuss which characteristics they used to group their photos. **Ask**

- What do all these arthropods have in common? They are small and have several pairs of legs, an exoskeleton, and body sections (segmentation).
- How are the arthropods in the various groups different? Some have wings that are large relative to their body size, some have tiny wings, and some have no wings. They have different numbers of legs, body sections, and antennae.

Tell students that scientists use these kinds of structural features as well as behavioral adaptations and reproductive adaptations to classify arthropods.

Activate Prior Knowledge

Have students look at the section titles and the descriptions beneath the titles and note the number of times the words *diverse* and *diversity* are used. **Ask,** In what ways do you think arthropods are diverse? Arthropods vary in size, body structure, habitat, and behavior.

Preview Vocabulary

Greek and Latin Word Origins Many Greek and Latin word parts are used throughout the chapter. Among the most prominent is Greek *skeletos,* which means "dried up." Tell students that in a figurative sense one can understand its relationship to *skeleton,* given that bones remain long after soft tissue has decayed. Some word parts are more useful, such as the Greek *pod-,* which means "foot." Remind students that their books contain a table of common Greek and Latin word parts on pages R18–R19.

Academic Vocabulary Tell students there are different ways to describe the general regions of a body, for instance, *head, trunk,* and *tail.* Such words aren't particularly helpful when considering the variety of shapes found in different animals. Introduce students to these terms:

thorax, region of the body between the head and the abdomen—in humans corresponds to the chest

abdomen, region below the thorax—in humans sometimes referred to as the belly

appendage, extension such as an arm, leg, tail, or fin, that is attached to the central parts of a body

English Learners Suggest students use the strategy of new word analysis for the vocabulary in this chapter. Have them create and list the key vocabulary in the first column, then add their own predictions for what the words mean in the second column. As students read the chapter, they should record the correct definitions in the third column and compare those to their own predictions.

SECTION 24.1

▼ Plan and Prepare

Objectives

- Describe the adaptive features of arthropods, including the exoskeleton.
- Recognize that arthropod diversity evolved over millions of years.

Section Resources

Unit Resource Book
Study Guide pp. 35–36
Power Notes p. 37
Reinforcement p. 38

Interactive Reader Chapter 24
Spanish Study Guide pp. 245–246

Biology Toolkit pp. C3, C19, C23

Technology
Power Presentation 24.1
Media Gallery DVD
Online Quiz 24.1

Activate Prior Knowledge Have students discuss different arthropods they have seen, reminding them to not overlook those that live in the ocean. **Ask**

- What arthropods can you hear in summertime? crickets, cicadas, grasshoppers
- What arthropods can you order from a menu at a seafood restaurant? crustaceans such lobster, shrimp, crab
- What arthropods have you been bitten by? mosquitoes, flies, spiders, ticks

▼ Teach

Vocabulary

Greek and Latin Word Origins
Students may confuse the meanings of the prefixes *anthropo-* and *arthro-*. *Arthro-* comes from the Greek *arthron*, meaning "joint"; *anthropo-* is Greek for "human being."

arthropod, an animal with jointed appendages

arthritis, an inflammation of the joints

anthropomorphic, having human form or characteristics

24.1 Arthropod Diversity

KEY CONCEPT Arthropods are the most diverse of all animals.

MAIN IDEAS
- Arthropod features are highly adapted.
- Arthropod exoskeletons serve a variety of functions.
- Arthropod diversity evolved over millions of years.

VOCABULARY
arthropod, p. 730
exoskeleton, p. 730
chitin, p. 730
appendage, p. 730
segmentation, p. 730

Review
cuticle

B.8.3 Use anatomical and molecular evidence to establish evolutionary relationships between organisms.

Connect Earth is truly ruled by bug-eyed monsters. In just about every way, arthropods are the most successful animal phylum on Earth. More than three-fourths of all known animals—more than 1 million species—are arthropods. They play an important role in every ecosystem on the planet. What makes this phylum so interesting? Arthropods are as diverse in shape and size as any life form on Earth, and are the result of millions of years of adaptation.

MAIN IDEA

Arthropod features are highly adapted.

Without knowing it, almost everywhere you go, you are interacting with arthropods. They can be found in the carpet you walk on and in the bed where you sleep. An **arthropod** is an invertebrate animal with an exoskeleton made of chitin; a series of paired, jointed appendages; and segmented body parts.

Arthropod Characteristics

The entire surface of an arthropod's body is covered by a protective exoskeleton. An **exoskeleton** is an external skeleton that supports the animal's tissues against gravity. Arthropods, such as the rhino beetle in **FIGURE 24.1**, have exoskeletons made of proteins and chitin. **Chitin** (KYT-uhn) is a long organic molecule made of sugars—similar to plant cellulose—that is arranged in layers. In each layer, fibers are laid out parallel to one another. But fibers in different layers point in different directions, forming a biological "plywood" that is very tough and strong. Like armor, chitin also protects the animal from predators.

FIGURE 24.1 The hard exoskeleton of this rhino beetle is constructed of layers of chitin that help protect it from predators.

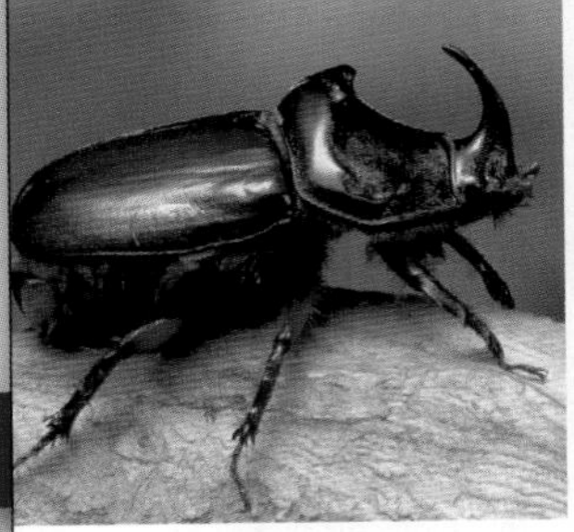

Jointed appendages were an important adaptation during the evolution of arthropods. An **appendage** is an extension of an organism's body. It can be used for walking, swimming, sensing, manipulating food, or chewing. Arthropods can have six, eight, ten, or even hundreds of appendages. The appendages can be shaped like rakes, tweezers, nutcrackers, hammers, or paddles.

Arthropods have an incredible variety of body forms. Some are microscopic, while others are quite large. For example, some tropical stick insects and millipedes can reach 30 centimeters (1 ft) in length, and spider crabs can have an arm span of 3.6 meters (12 ft). But all arthropod bodies are segmented for specific functions. **Segmentation** describes how an arthropod's body parts are divided into similar sections that have each evolved for a different function.

Differentiated Instruction

ENGLISH LEARNERS

Assess students' understanding of the material by providing students with five to ten true/false statements before they read the section. For example, "Spiders and ticks are eight-legged insects."; "All arthropods have an exoskeleton, even flying ones." Pay special attention to misconceptions about which arthropods are insects. Then have students review their answers after reading the section.

Biology Toolkit, Anticipation Guide, p. C3

Arthropod Groups

Classifying animals with so many differences might seem difficult, but most fossil and living arthropod species can be placed into one of five groups.

- **Trilobites** Trilobites are now extinct but were an important part of Paleozoic marine ecosystems for nearly 300 million years. As you can see in **FIGURE 24.2**, their bodies were divided into three long vertical sections, or lobes. A central body and outgrowths of shell on each side covered their many delicate legs. Most of the 4000 known species were bottom feeders, sucking up muck, algae, or soft animals from the sea floor.
- **Crustaceans** Among the most familiar arthropods, crustaceans (kruh-STAY-shuhnz) are found in all of the oceans, freshwater streams, and even on land. Crustaceans are a diverse group that includes huge king crabs and lobsters, microscopic copepods, oysterlike barnacles, and armored pill bugs.
- **Chelicerates** The group known as chelicerates (kih-LIHS-uh-RAYTS) includes horseshoe crabs, scorpions, spiders, mites, ticks, and the extinct sea scorpions. These animals share a set of specialized daggerlike mouthparts that are used for tearing their food.
- **Insects** Insects account for 80 percent of all known animal species. Familiar animals such as ants, bees, butterflies, moths, cockroaches, flies, and mosquitoes are all insects. Though this group is very diverse, most insects are terrestrial and have six legs.
- **Myriapods** The most commonly known myriapods (MIHR-ee-uh-PAHDS) are centipedes and millipedes. Their long bodies and many pairs of legs are the most distinctive characteristics of the myriapods. The largest species can grow up to a foot long. They generally live in humid environments, such as leaf litter, decaying wood, or moist soil. The first pair of legs in centipedes bear poisonous fangs for capturing prey.

A Infer How did the evolution of jointed appendages lead to the wide variety of arthropods we see today?

FIGURE 24.2 Trilobite fossils such as this one show the exoskeleton, segmentation, and jointed appendages. These features led scientists to suggest that trilobites were one of the first marine arthropods.

TAKING NOTES

Use a main idea diagram to outline the unique features of each arthropod group.

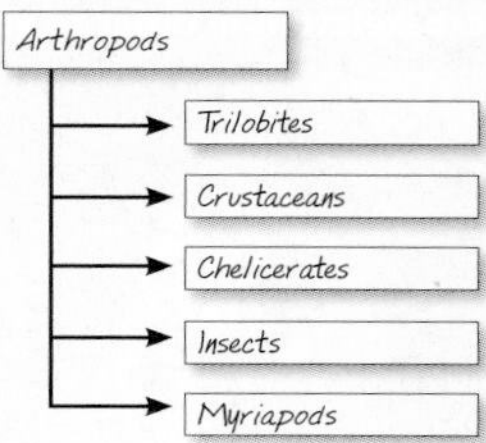

FIGURE 24.3 Arthropod Diversity

Arthropods are a diverse group of animals. Millions of years of evolution has led to many different body forms and functions.

CRUSTACEANS

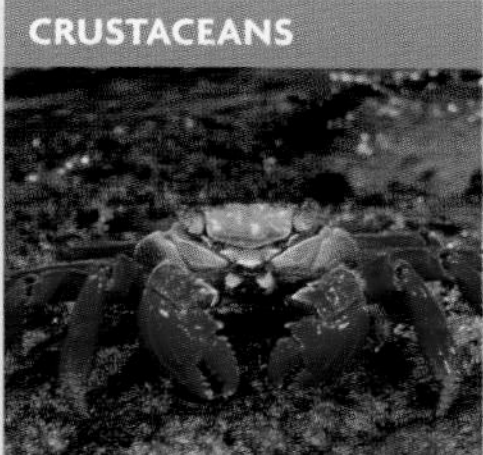

Crab As aquatic arthropods, crabs have appendages adapted for both swimming and walking.

CHELICERATES

Scorpion The carnivorous scorpions have sharp appendages for tearing apart their prey.

INSECTS

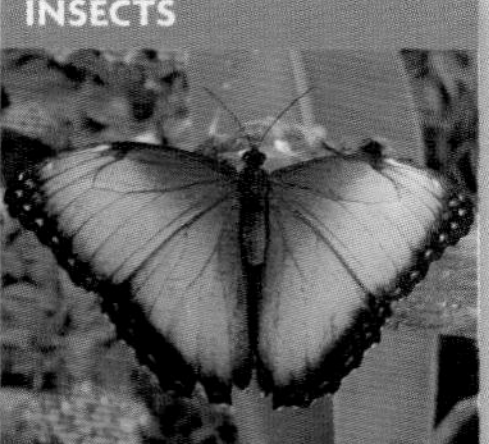

Butterfly Insects have three pairs of jointed appendages that are used for many different functions.

MYRIAPODS

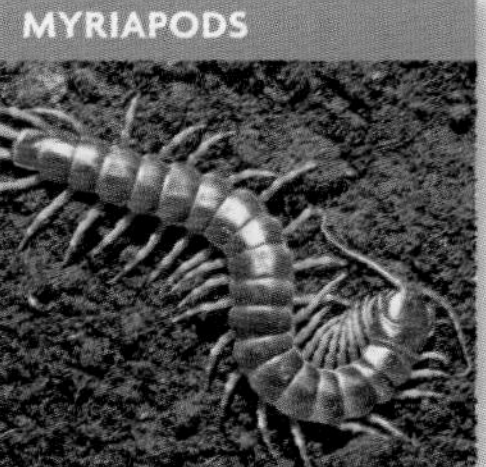

Centipede Many pairs of legs make centipedes suited to a wide variety of biomes.

ONLINE BIOLOGY Students can research arthropods living in their area and develop a field guide to the arthropods. Or have students categorize arthropods based on their characteristics using an interactive animation. See Options for Inquiry on page 751.

Integrating Evolutionary Biology

In studying the evolution of arthropod mouthparts, scientists have found a genetic relationship between mouthparts and appendages. The gene that controls the addition of segments to the end of an appendage is expressed in the chelicerate jaw, but not in the jaws of insects and crustaceans. The crushing jaws of insects and crustaceans evolved from the base of a long, ancestral appendage.

Science Trivia

- In terms of body size, the largest known arthropod is the Japanese spider crab, *Macrocheira kaempferi,* which can grow to more than 3.7 m (12 ft) wide from leg tip to leg tip and weigh as much as 18 kg (40 lb). This crustacean lives in the Pacific Ocean at depths of 45 to 300 m (147 to 984 ft).
- The heaviest arthropod, just barely outweighing the spider crab, is the American lobster, *Homarus americanus.* The largest lobster ever caught weighed 20 kg (44 lb).
- The smallest known arthropod is the parasitic mite, *Demodex.* It lives in hair follicles and is only 0.1 mm (0.004 in.) in length.

BELOW LEVEL

As students read this section, have them keep a running list in their notebook of the arthropod features described in the text. After each groups' features are described, have students sketch what they think these animals look like. As they read about each type in more detail in the chapter, have them revisit their sketches to add details or start over again.

Biology Toolkit, Combination Notes, p. C23

PRE-AP

Have students continue to fill out cards detailing biological profiles, as they did for the phyla in Chapter 23. Tell students to refer to page R30 for a quick summary of arthropods. They should include cards for the subphyla and classes listed there.

Answers

A Infer Specialized jointed appendages enabled arthropods to radiate out into many ecological niches.

▼ Teach continued

Connecting CONCEPTS

Chemistry of Life Remind students that cellulose, found in plants, is a linear polysaccharide and that it is the most abundant polysaccharide on Earth. Chitin also is a polysaccharide. Chitin is found in fungi as well as arthropods and is the second most abundant polysaccharide on Earth. The beaks of cephalopods contain chitin.

TEACH FROM VISUALS

FIGURE 24.4 Have students study the changes the arthropod undergoes as it grows. **Ask**

- At what point does the arthropod secrete a new layer of cuticle? before molting
- What happens to the old cuticle? Enzymes digest and weaken it, and the animal crawls out of it.
- What happens after the arthropod sheds the old cuticle? The new exoskeleton fills with fluid and then hardens.

Answers

A Apply Advantage: molting allows arthropods to grow despite their exoskeleton; disadvantage: during molting, arthropods are more vulnerable to predators.

MAIN IDEA

Arthropod exoskeletons serve a variety of functions.

Connecting CONCEPTS

Chemistry of Life Recall that in **Chapter 2**, you learned about the plant structure cellulose. The molecular structure of chitin forms a polymer similar to plant cellulose. This rigid structure contributes to the strength of an insect's exoskeleton.

All arthropods have an exoskeleton and its structure determines how an arthropod lives. Recall that an exoskeleton is made of many layers of chitin. Chitin is not living tissue, and having a living body crammed into a hard exoskeleton is similar to how a medieval knight would wear a suit of armor. Despite the protective benefits, an exoskeleton makes important functions, such as movement, growth, and maintaining internal and external equilibrium, difficult. Over millions of years, arthropods have developed ways of managing normal functions that are both efficient and effective.

Movement and Growth

Movement Two types of cuticle plates assist in movement. Stiff cuticle plates of the exoskeleton are separated by sections of more flexible cuticle that form joints in the hard armor. When muscles stretching across exoskeleton joints contract, they bend the joint so the arthropod can move. The cuticle supporting arthropod legs acts as a spring, efficiently storing and releasing energy as the animal moves.

Molting Arthropod cuticle cannot grow along with the animal, so an arthropod must shed its exoskeleton in a process called molting. This process of shedding and reforming a new exoskeleton is illustrated in **FIGURE 24.4.**

1. Before molting, the animal secretes a new layer of cuticle underneath its exoskeleton. The new cuticle layer will actually be larger than the layer of cuticle covering it.
2. The animal secretes enzymes that begin to digest and weaken the old cuticle, allowing the exoskeleton to split open and the animal to crawl out of it. This is as extreme as it sounds—the animal must shed every surface of its body, including the entire lining of its gut and tracheae. Some animals die in the process.
3. The new exoskeleton is filled with fluid while it is still soft, making the animal larger than it was before the molt. However, the exoskeleton takes time to harden. During this time, the animal is very vulnerable to predators.

FIGURE 24.4 Molting

Arthropods must molt their old exoskeletons in order to grow.

Animated BIOLOGY
Watch a cicada molt at ClassZone.com.

1 Under the old exoskeleton, fluids are secreted that will form the new exoskeleton.

2 The insect sheds the old exoskeleton in a process called ecdysis.

3 Once the arthropod crawls out of the old exoskeleton, the new exoskeleton will begin to harden.

A Apply What are the advantages and disadvantages of going through the process of molting?

Differentiated Instruction

HANDS-ON ACTIVITY

Provide pairs of students with one or more insect molts. Exoskeletons from cicadas are frequently large and intact, and the parts are easily viewed. Have students examine the detail present in the exoskeleton. **Ask,** Which body parts undergo molting? all body parts, including the eyes

Managing Internal and External Functions

Circulation Arthropods have an open circulatory system, in which blood is pumped through a tubelike heart and out into the body cavity. In comparison, vertebrates have a closed circulatory system, in which blood is contained inside a system of arteries, veins, capillaries, and a heart. In an open circulatory system, blood is pumped through the heart and into the body, where it comes in direct contact with organs and tissues. The stiff exoskeleton of arthropods also helps control blood pressure. Because an exoskeleton does not change shape, when the heart pumps blood out into the body, the exoskeleton keeps the blood contained, while body movements keep it circulating.

Senses Most arthropod sensory organs, including antennae, are made of modified cuticle. Hard cuticle would otherwise block environmental stimuli. Antennae and body hairs allow an arthropod to sense its surrounding environment, including temperature, touch, sound, and smell.

Most arthropods also have compound eyes. Unlike mammalian eyes, which have a single lens that collects all visual information, arthropod eyes have thousands of tiny individual lenses that interpret only a small portion of the field of view. The image in **FIGURE 24.5** gives an idea of how many individual eyes form a single compound eye. When all of these individual images come together, they form a rough mosaic of an object that resembles a newspaper or magazine image.

FIGURE 24.5 The compound eye of this fruit fly contains 800 individual eye units. These eyes are highly sensitive to movement and can also determine colors.

A Summarize How does an exoskeleton make functions such as movement and growth difficult?

QUICK LAB **COMPARING**

Comparing Arthropods

In this lab you will examine and compare the structures of different arthropods.

PROBLEM How do arthropods differ from one another?

PROCEDURE

1. Choose one of the four arthropod slides. Observe one organism under low power. Switch to high power and draw and label the structures of each organism.
2. Repeat the process with a second slide and compare features such as appendages, antennae, and body segments between the two organisms.
3. Find another group who viewed different specimens. View and note any differences between their specimens and yours.

MATERIALS

- slide of tick
- slide of mite
- slide of spider
- slide of mosquito
- microscope

ANALYZE AND CONCLUDE

1. **Observe** What unique structures did you notice on the slide specimens? Predict what uses these structures may have for the survival of each organism.
2. **Evaluate** What similar features do the organisms share? Based on your observations, how closely related do you think the specimens are?

Take It Further

Lobsters' keen sense of smell can be attributed to extremely sensitive chemical sensors on their long antennae. These sensors, called **aesthetascs,** coupled with the lobster's brain, allow these crustaceans to recognize one another by smell. This allows lobsters who have already fought each other to remember which one is more dominant, so they do not waste time and energy repeating a battle that has already been fought.

Answers

A Summarize Stiff cuticle plates limit movement to the joints, so arthropods are not particularly flexible. Chitinous exoskeletons are not living tissue and do not grow; therefore, as an arthropod grows, it must shed its exoskeleton and make a larger one.

QUICK LAB

Time 20 minutes	TEACHER TESTED
Lab Binder Animals, p. 26	

Purpose Compare the structural features of several arthropod groups.

LAB MANAGEMENT

Safety Remind students to handle the slides with care and wipe down the eyepieces of the microscope with alcohol after using them.

Answers

Analyze and Conclude

1. Students should notice features such as jointed appendages, wings, exoskeleton, and mouthparts.
2. All have exoskeletons and jointed appendages. Mosquitoes have six walking legs; the other specimens have eight walking legs. Ticks, mites, and spiders have two body sections; whereas mosquitoes have three. In ticks and mites, the body sections are fused together so that it appears as if they have one body section. Based on these observations, ticks and mites are the most closely related. Ticks and mites are also more closely related to spiders than they are to mosquitoes.

PRE-AP

Read students the Take It Further above, on lobsters' recognition of each other by scent and how that modifies their behavior. Have students write for five minutes on the adaptive advantage of this behavior. Ask them to consider whether this constitutes learning and, if so, if that means lobsters exhibit a type of intelligence.

Biology Toolkit, Quick-Write, p. C19

▼ Teach continued

ONLINE BIOLOGY Go to the chapter Resource Center at **ClassZone.com** for additional resources and information on ancient arthropods.

Integrating Earth Science

Paleontologists use **trilobites** as **index fossils,** which are used to date rock layers. Like other organisms that are used as index fossils, trilobites were widespread, are abundantly preserved in rocks, and evolved rapidly, resulting in many short-lived species. Because the species existed for relatively short, known periods of time, they are useful in identifying the specific ages of the rock layers in which they are found. The briefer the existence of the species, the more precisely the rock layer can be dated.

Answers

A Analyze Ancient arthropod fossils may show characteristics similar to those of modern arthropods. These similarities may help scientists better understand the evolutionary history of modern arthropods.

▼ Assess and Reteach

Assess Use the Online Quiz or Section Quiz (*Assessment Book*, p. 473).

Reteach Project photographs from the Media Gallery, or your own, and have students compare and contrast the different arthropod groups. Tell students to use all the vocabulary of this section.

MAIN IDEA

Arthropod diversity evolved over millions of years.

FIGURE 24.6 The velvet worm (top) and the water bear (below) belong to two phyla thought to be the closest relatives of arthropods. (colored SEM water bear; magnification 200×)

All of the major arthropod groups are incredibly old. The oldest arthropod fossils are trilobites from the early Cambrian period, about 540 million years ago. The oldest known chelicerates and crustaceans appeared a few million years later, during the Cambrian explosion. The oldest known myriapod fossils are younger—about 415 million years old—but trace fossils from rocks in Pennsylvania suggest myriapods are older than this. During the next 100 million years, rapid diversification of arthropod species resulted in the appearance of all the major groups of arthropods. Many of today's arthropods are very similar to the arthropods that lived hundreds of millions of years ago. Because the major groups of arthropods appeared so long ago, relationships between them are difficult to determine, and many questions about classification still exist.

Based on similarities in body structures, some scientists think that arthropods are most closely related to annelid worms. Because both groups have segmented bodies, some scientists hypothesize they share a similar ancestry. Recent molecular evidence indicates that annelids and arthropods may have evolved segmentation independently. Two other members of the Ecdysozoa, velvet worms and water bears, are thought to be the closest living relatives of the arthropods. You can see these animals in **FIGURE 24.6.**

- **Velvet worms** (phylum Onchyophora) are soft-bodied carnivorous invertebrates that can grow up to 10 centimeters in length and are covered with a thin cuticle layer. They roam about the tropical forest floor on many unjointed legs, hunting for termites and small mollusks.
- **Water bears** (phylum Tardigradia) are microscopic invertebrates, less than one millimeter in length. Water bears are commonly found in the mud of marine, freshwater, and terrestrial environments. They are omnivores, feeding on plants, algae, dead organic matter, and other organisms.

A Analyze **Explain how ancient fossils can be used to determine relationships between modern arthropods.**

24.1 ASSESSMENT

ONLINE QUIZ ClassZone.com

B.8.3

REVIEWING MAIN IDEAS

1. What are the five main groups of **arthropods**?
2. What characteristics make the phylum Arthropoda unique?
3. Why are the relationships between arthropod families so difficult to determine?

CRITICAL THINKING

4. **Contrast** How are the structures used for supporting organs different in arthropods and humans?
5. **Synthesize** Fossils reveal that arthropods have been walking the planet for nearly 500 million years. How have arthropods survived for so long? What features have allowed them to be so successful?

***Connecting* CONCEPTS**

6. **Anatomy** In contrast to arthropods, humans have an internal skeleton. What advantages and disadvantages does this type of support system have, as compared with an **exoskeleton**?

24.1 ASSESSMENT

1. trilobites, crustaceans, chelicerates, insects, myriapods
2. the combination of jointed appendages, segmented body parts, and an exoskeleton
3. All of the major groups of Arthropoda appeared several hundred million years ago in a very rapid diversification, and existing species are very similar to those from that time.
4. Arthropods have an external skeleton to which muscles and tissues attach from the inside. A human's body is built on an internal skeleton, with muscles and tissues surrounding these structures.
5. The radiation of arthropods into so many ecological niches, yielding a great diversity of species and forms, meant that it was more likely that some populations would withstand changes to the global environment.
6. An endoskeleton allows us to grow without molting, but it does not provide as much outer protection as an exoskeleton would.

24.2 Crustaceans

KEY CONCEPT Crustaceans are a diverse group of ancient arthropods.

MAIN IDEAS
- Crustaceans evolved as marine arthropods.
- Crustacean appendages can take many forms.
- There are many different types of crustaceans.

VOCABULARY
crustacean, p. 735
cephalothorax, p. 735
abdomen, p. 735
carapace, p. 735
mandible, p. 737

Review
filter feeding, sessile

Connect If you have ever eaten a shrimp, you may have an idea of what a crustacean looks like. But this large group of arthropods is surprisingly diverse. Shrimp and lobsters are crustaceans, but so are the tiny brine shrimp better known as "sea monkeys." Tadpolelike copepods, oysterlike barnacles, and the pill bugs that live under damp rocks in your garden are also crustaceans.

MAIN IDEA
Crustaceans evolved as marine arthropods.

Crustaceans are a group of arthropods that have two distinct body sections, a hard exoskeleton, two pairs of antennae, and one pair of appendages per segment. Crustaceans evolved in the oceans, and today most crustaceans still live in saltwater environments. But there are also many freshwater species, and a few have evolved to survive on land.

Crustaceans come in a variety of shapes and sizes. They are vital to the stability of aquatic ecosystems. Some species, such as the violet-spotted reef lobster in **FIGURE 24.7**, are predators of marine fish, mollusks, and worms, while others scavenge dead animals and plants. Most importantly, crustaceans are a significant food source for larger animals. Large crustaceans such as shrimp, lobsters, and crabs are a primary food source for fish, birds, seals, and even humans. But there are also numerous species of microscopic crustaceans. Zooplankton, krill, and copepods are very small as adults but are so abundant that they constitute an important food source for fish, whales, and many species of filter-feeding crustaceans.

FIGURE 24.7 Crustaceans such as this violet-spotted reef lobster can be found in all of Earth's oceans. They play an integral role in marine ecosystems.

Crustacean bodies are made up of two distinct body sections, a cephalothorax and an abdomen. The **cephalothorax** (SEHF-uh-luh-THAWR-aks) is the region of an organism in which the head and trunk region are combined into one long section. The **abdomen** refers to the rear portion of the organism. The cephalothorax is covered by a shieldlike section of cuticle called the carapace. The **carapace** (KAR-uh-PAYS) covers the sides of the body and protects the gills. The largest crustaceans have a cuticle layer with calcium deposits that make the carapace a hard shell.

(A) **Connect** **Describe how a decrease in marine crustacean populations could affect an ocean ecosystem.**

Differentiated Instruction

BELOW LEVEL

Ask students to write down what they know about crustaceans. They may be familiar with crustaceans served as food, such as shrimp and lobster. Help them recall what they may have observed about these animals. For example, if they have ever cracked a lobster, they know these animals have a hard exoskeleton. Then have them write what they want to know. At the end of the section, ask them to write down what they have learned.

Biology Toolkit, KWL, p. C5

Plan and Prepare

Objectives
- Explain the ecological significance of marine crustaceans.
- Describe crustacean appendages and the main crustacean groups.

Section Resources

Unit Resource Book Study Guide pp. 39–40 Power Notes p. 41 Reinforcement p. 42 Pre-AP Activity pp. 57–58
Interactive Reader Chapter 24 **Spanish Study Guide** pp. 247–248
Biology Toolkit pp. C5, C19, C22
Technology Power Presentation 24.2 Media Gallery DVD Online Quiz 24.2

Activate Prior Knowledge Students might be familiar with some crustaceans from their dining experiences. **Ask,** What are some crustaceans that you have eaten? lobster, crab, shrimp, crayfish **Ask,** When you eat crustaceans, what are the two body parts that you get most of the meat from? legs (claws), tail

Tell students that the United States imported more than 500,000 tons of shrimp in 2005, valued at $3.6 billion.

Teach

Integrating Climate Science

Adult blue whales eat about five tons of krill, a planktonic crustacean, each day during their high feeding season in the Antarctic Ocean. Scientists speculate that global climate change is reducing the available biomass of krill and that some blue whales will starve.

Answers

(A) **Connect** Loss of planktonic crustaceans would remove a huge lower trophic level, affecting the entire marine food chain.

▼ Teach *continued*

ONLINE BIOLOGY Go to the chapter Resource Center at **ClassZone.com** for additional resources and information on crustaceans.

Vocabulary

Greek and Latin Word Origins The term **cephalothorax** refers to the fused head and thorax of a crustacean. The prefix *cephalo-* comes from a Greek word meaning "head," and "thorax" comes from a Greek word meaning "chest." In Latin, the word *thōrāx* meant "breastplate."

Take It Further

The large chelipeds of the American lobster are actually two different types that are specialized for specific behaviors. One cheliped is slightly longer, more slender, and armed with sharp toothlike projections. This claw is called the **cutter,** because it is used for cutting and tearing. The other cheliped is more massive and powerful, and its toothlike projections are more like molars. This is the **crusher** claw. It is strong enough to crack open hard-shell clams and other mollusks. In especially large lobsters, the crusher claw's shell can be so dense that a chef needs a large mallet or hammer to crack it open to get at the meat inside.

FIGURE 24.8 Crustacean Anatomy

The anatomy of a crustacean is well suited to its underwater habitat. Crustacean appendages are adapted for many different purposes.

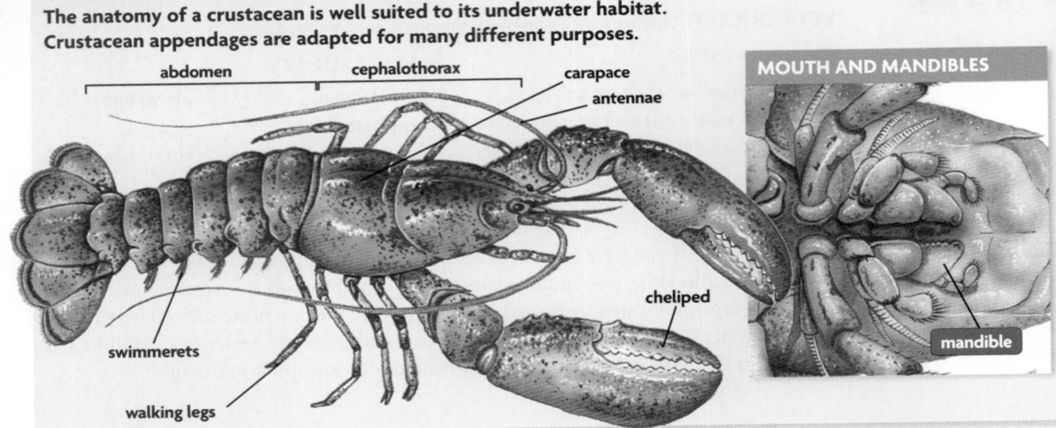

MAIN IDEA

Crustacean appendages can take many forms.

All crustacean appendages are homologous structures. Anatomical structures are homologous when they share a common origin. For example, your arm is homologous to a bat wing because long ago, humans and bats shared a common ancestor. As the ancestors of bats and humans evolved, different uses for the same appendage structures developed. In bats, the appendage evolved into a winglike structure, while in humans, the appendage evolved into the arm structure we have today.

Long ago, crustacean appendages probably all looked the same. Today, crustacean appendages have been modified for a variety of different functions. Crustacean appendages are used for sensing the environment, defending against predators, walking, feeding, and even attracting mates.

FIGURE 24.9 The mantis shrimp is a crustacean that spends most of its time scavenging for food. Many species of shrimp and prawn inhabit the coastlines of every continent.

Crustacean appendages are adapted to an underwater habitat and are essential for survival. The illustration in **FIGURE 24.8** shows many of the different types of crustacean appendages. Probably the best known of crustacean appendages are the large claws that are found on many species of crabs and lobsters. Lobsters' claws, or chelipeds (KEE-luh-PEHDZ), are used for collecting and manipulating food. But chelipeds can be specialized for other jobs. Male fiddler crabs have large claws that are used to attract females. Some hermit crabs use their claws to block the entrance to the shells in which they live. There are also some mantis shrimp, such as the one shown in **FIGURE 24.9,** that have hunting claws shaped like clubs. The clubs are attached to spring-loaded limbs that can strike at more than 22 meters per second (50 mph), letting the shrimp break through snail shells to feed.

Differentiated Instruction

PRE-AP

Tell students that lobsters can live out of water for several days as long as they keep cool and moist. Yet lobsters, unlike crabs, will have a difficult time moving and gathering food on land. Have students write for five minutes on what this suggests about the ecological niche of each and the abiotic factors that affect how each lives. For example, students might consider how buoyancy affects a lobster's ability to survive.

Biology Toolkit, Quick-Write, p. C19

BELOW LEVEL

Have students examine the anatomy of the lobster in **FIGURE 24.8.** Have students write for five minutes about how the parts of the body and its appendages are suited to the tasks they perform. Have students consider the question of how form relates to function in crustacean anatomy.

Biology Toolkit, Quick-Write, p. C19

All crustaceans have two pairs of antennae on their head. These appendages have a covering of tiny hairs packed with chemical sensors. As antennae flick through the water, crustaceans use these appendages to smell food, locate mates, and avoid predators. Some crustaceans, such as the tiny water flea *Daphnia,* use the hairy antennae as oars to move around. Many species of spiny lobsters rub antennae against their cephalothorax to make loud calls that are thought to startle predators.

Crustaceans, like other arthropods, have mouths composed of a pair of hard appendages called mandibles. **Mandibles** are highly adapted appendages that crush and bite food before ingestion. Other appendages near the mouth can act as additional jaws and tear food into bits. In copepods, they can collect food from the water and push it toward the animal's mouth.

Appendages such as walking legs allow a crustacean to move along the ocean floor as it scavenges for food. Swimming requires additional specialized appendages called swimmerets, which move in wavelike motions to propel the crustacean through the water.

As their appendages changed shape over time, crustaceans were able to use them for more than movement. This diversification of appendages allowed crustaceans to specialize and move into different ecological niches. The speciation of crustaceans through changes to their appendages is a good illustration of the process of natural selection.

A Summarize **Give three examples of crustacean appendages and how they are used.**

TAKING NOTES

Use a main idea web to describe the many ways arthropods use jointed appendages.

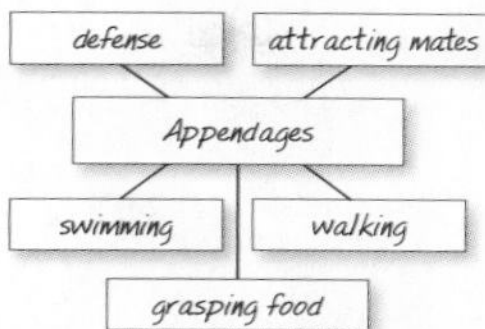

MAIN IDEA

There are many different types of crustaceans.

Crustaceans vary in both anatomy and structure. However, they are all similar in how they develop into the adult form.

Decapods

When you think of a crustacean, you are probably thinking of a decapod. This familiar group includes lobsters, crabs, and shrimp, as well as hermit crabs, their cousins the king crabs, and many others. Decapods live primarily in saltwater environments, but species such as crayfish have invaded fresh water. Some crabs, such as the coconut crab shown in **FIGURE 24.10,** even venture onto land to look for food.

Decapods have characteristic features that distinguish them from other crustaceans. The name *decapod* means "ten legs," so all decapods have five pairs of jointed appendages that are used for many different purposes. Decapods also have fused body segments that contain two regions, the cephalothorax and abdomen.

FIGURE 24.10 This coconut crab is the largest terrestrial arthropod in the world, and can have a leg span of almost 1 meter. Primarily a nocturnal creature, this arthropod feeds on coconuts it cracks open using a powerful cheliped.

ENGLISH LEARNERS

Have students make a four-column chart that lists the four groups of crustaceans, their habitats, characteristic features, and examples within each group.

Biology Toolkit, Content Frame, p. C22

Take It Further

While American lobsters use their sense of smell to identify one another, the Caribbean spiny lobster, *Panulirus argus,* has the additional ability of detecting lobsters that are diseased. Scientists studying the effects of a disease called PaV1, which strikes spiny lobsters, observed that diseased lobsters seemed to be isolated in their own dens despite the species' habit of communal living.

The scientists set up an experiment in which diseased and healthy lobsters could choose to enter a den containing a healthy or diseased lobster. The scientists found that healthy lobsters avoided the dens containing diseased lobsters, while diseased lobsters did not discriminate. The ability to avoid infected lobsters, and thereby avoid infection, has a clear adaptive advantage for individuals as well as the population as a whole. It is likely that PaV1's rate of infection would be much higher if the lobsters did not effectively quarantine the sick individuals.

Science Trivia

U.S. lobster fisheries are among the most lucrative.

- In 2005, the United States exported 303 metric tons of spiny or rock lobster, valued at $4.5 million.
- U.S. exports of American lobsters in 2005 were more than 25,000 metric tons, valued at over $335 million.

Answers

A **Summarize** *Sample Answers:* Claws, or chelipeds, are used for grasping and manipulating food. Antennae allow crustaceans to gather sensory information from their environment. Mandibles allow crustaceans to crush food items. Walking legs are used for movement and respiration.

▼ Teach *continued*

TEACH FROM VISUALS

FIGURE 24.11 Have students study the enlargement showing the structures of a barnacle. **Ask**

- If an adult barnacle is sessile, what is the function of its legs? to sweep food into its mouth
- What do you think is the function of the barnacle's cement gland? It produces a cementlike substance that attaches the barnacle to a whale, rock, or other object.

Answers

Ⓐ **Analyze** Scientists discovered that the larvae of both tongue worms and barnacles are of the nauplius form, which is characteristic only of crustaceans.

▼ Assess and Reteach

Assess Use the Online Quiz or Section Quiz (*Assessment Book,* p. 474).

Reteach Have students form groups, and ask a student from each group to state a fact about crustaceans. Go around the room until every group has participated and major ideas concerning crustaceans have been covered.

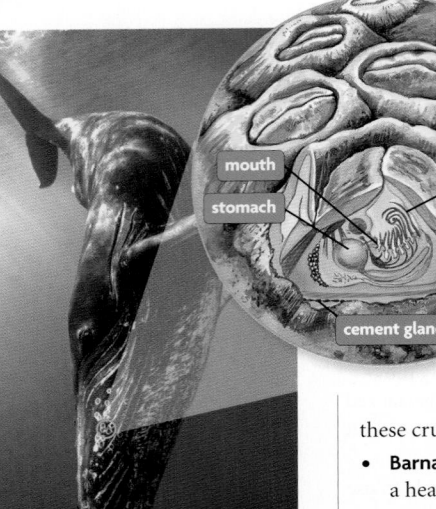

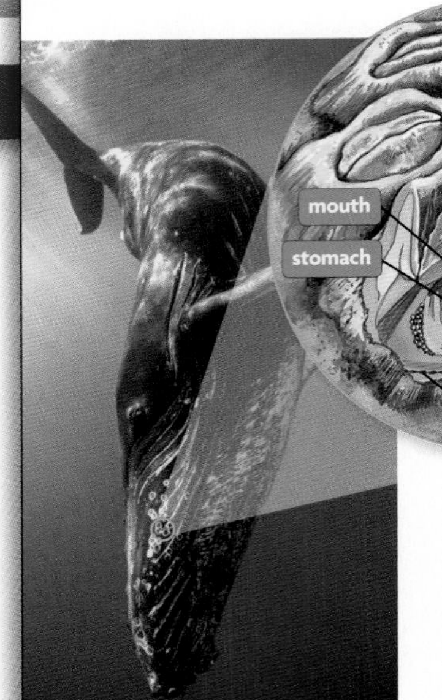

FIGURE 24.11 Attached to the skin of this humpback whale, thousands of barnacles use the whale's constant movement through the water to filter food from the water.

Barnacles, Isopods, and Tongue Worms

Other species of crustaceans look nothing like a "typical" decapod. Although these species are different in structure from other crustaceans, scientists discovered from developmental evidence that most crustaceans pass through similar phases as they grow into adults. Almost all juvenile crustaceans pass through a free-swimming planktonic larval stage. The most common of these larva forms is the nauplius larva. A nauplius larva has a carapace and six long, feathery limbs. When scientists looked at newly hatched barnacles and tongue worms, they found nauplius larvae. Only crustaceans have nauplius larvae, so both groups are recognized as crustaceans. But as they grow into their adult form, these crustaceans look very different from any other crustacean.

- **Barnacles** Barnacles are sessile, or nonmoving, filter feeders wrapped in a heavily calcified shell. They live attached to the surface of rocks, boats, sea turtle shells, and even the skin of humpback whales, such as the one shown in **FIGURE 24.11.** Barnacles have turned their carapace into a saclike "mantle" (similar to that found in a mollusk) that secretes a calcium shell. Inside the shell, the animal sits on its head and sweeps food into its mouth with its legs.
- **Isopods** Isopods have flattened bodies and seven pairs of legs. Most species are marine and freshwater scavengers. Pill bugs and wood lice belong to a group of isopods that have become completely terrestrial. These animals usually live in damp habitats and eat rotting plants.
- **Tongue worms** Tongue worms are parasites that live in the lungs and nasal passages of vertebrates. They have no eyes, mandibles, or antennae, and they have lost most of their limbs. Despite this, molecular evidence shows tongue worms to be most closely related to crustaceans.

Ⓐ Analyze **What evidence helped scientists to classify barnacles and tongue worms as crustaceans?**

24.2 ASSESSMENT

ONLINE QUIZ ClassZone.com

REVIEWING ▶ MAIN IDEAS

1. What characteristics make **crustaceans** different from other arthropods?
2. What are some of the different functions of arthropod appendages?

CRITICAL THINKING

3. **Summarize** Draw a food web that includes at least three different types of arthropods.
4. **Infer** How did the discovery of nauplius larvae allow scientists to categorize barnacles and tongue worms as crustaceans?

Connecting CONCEPTS

5. **Evolution** Lobster claws can grow extremely large. What selective pressures may have led to the evolution of such large appendages?

24.2 ASSESSMENT

1. Crustaceans are primarily aquatic and have a cephalothorax, an abdomen, and two pairs of antennae.
2. grasping, sensing by touch and smell, eating, walking, swimming, respiring
3. Drawings should include three types of arthropods.
4. Both barnacles and tongue worms go through the nauplius larval stage. Because only crustaceans go through such a stage, both animals are classified as crustaceans.
5. Larger claws could have been selected for because they are advantageous in competing for mates and food, handling food, defense against predators, and capturing prey.

MATERIALS

- clear plastic cups
- 100-mL graduated cylinder
- 400 mL sea salt solution
- 0.1 g brine shrimp eggs
- plastic spoon
- balance
- clear plastic wrap
- aluminum foil
- clear plastic bottles with lids
- vinegar
- baking soda
- pH duo-test paper
- 2 eyedroppers
- 10 petri dishes
- hand lens or dissecting microscope
- lamp

PROCESS SKILLS

- **Designing Experiments**
- **Collecting Data**
- **Analyzing**
- **Predicting**

NOS.3 Clearly communicate their ideas and results of investigations verbally and in written form using tables, graphs, diagrams, and photographs.

Hatching Brine Shrimp

Brine shrimp are small arthropods found in oceans, salt lakes, estuaries, and tidal ponds. Brine shrimp are used primarily for fish food, especially on fish farms where natural food sources are unavailable. Their eggs can be harvested and hatched under controlled conditions by biologists working in an aquaculture facility. In this investigation, you will design an experiment to determine the best conditions for hatching brine shrimp eggs.

PROBLEM What are the best conditions for hatching brine shrimp eggs?

PROCEDURE

1. Choose one factor to investigate. Some factors to consider are the presence or absence of light, aeration (open container versus air-tight container), and pH (6–8). Make a hypothesis about that factor, and design an experiment to test your hypothesis. Have your teacher approve your design.
2. The conditions of the hatching (temperature, pH, light conditions, and so on) will depend upon your independent variable. If you are testing pH, use vinegar to adjust the pH of the sea salt solution to pH 6.0 or baking soda to adjust the pH to 8.0 as measured with the pH test paper.
3. Determine the number of cups of brine shrimp needed based on your experimental design. Be sure to include a control. Hatch the brine shrimp eggs by filling each cup with 200 mL sea salt solution and 0.1 g brine shrimp eggs. Cover the cups with plastic wrap or aluminum foil depending upon your experiment. If you are testing aeration, use bottles with lids instead of cups.
4. Once you have set up your cups or bottles, remove 5 mL from each with an eyedropper and place each volume in a separate clean petri dish.
5. Examine each dish with a hand lens or microscope. Count the number of eggs and the number of hatched brine shrimp. Note these numbers.
6. Repeat steps 4 and 5 each day for five days and note the numbers of hatched shrimp and eggs each day.

step 4

ANALYZE AND CONCLUDE

1. **Analyze** Graph the data with the number of shrimp hatching or number of shrimp hatching rate (shrimp hatching divided by number of eggs) on the y-axis and the days on the x-axis.
2. **Analyze** On what day did you observe the most shrimp hatching? Was this day consistent with the findings of other members of your group? List possible reasons for inconsistent results.
3. **Experimental Design** Identify possible sources of error in your experiment and give reasons why they might have occurred.
4. **Analyze** How did your factor affect the hatching of brine shrimp?
5. **Infer** Compare your team's result with other teams in your group. Identify conditions that had the most positive effect on the hatching of brine shrimp.
6. **Experimental Design** Explain why it was important to have a control in your experiment.

INVESTIGATION

Time	45 minutes — TEACHER TESTED
Teacher Preparation	⚗
Student Difficulty	⚗⚗
Lab Binder	Animals, pp. 17–20

Purpose Test the effect of environmental conditions on hatching success of brine shrimp eggs.

Overview Students will vary one condition to test its effect on brine shrimp eggs. They will

- write an experimental procedure to test their independent variable
- count the number of hatched brine shrimp every day for five days

LAB PREPARATION

- To make 3 L of sea salt solution (20 ppt), dissolve 60 g of sea salt in 3 L of spring water; let sit overnight.
- Plastic cups and bottles should be 200-mL capacity.

LAB MANAGEMENT

Independent variables may include:

- Light—wrap the experimental cup in aluminum foil and place both cups under a lamp.
- Temperature—leave the control cup at room temperature and place the experimental cup in the refrigerator.
- Aeration—leave the control cup open and place a lid on the experimental cup.
- pH—keep the control cup at the pH of the sea salt solution; add vinegar to make a second cup acidic; add baking soda to make a third cup basic.

Allow five minutes each day to count how many shrimp have hatched.

POST-LAB DISCUSSION

Results suggest the best conditions for hatching and survival include relatively warm temperatures and a source of light and aeration. **Ask,** Where would you find these conditions? tidal ponds, estuaries, not deep-sea habitats

Answers

Sample Data

Difference between the control groups and the following experimental groups:

- pH of 6.2 (acidic): 66% fewer hatched
- absence of light: 62% fewer hatched
- non-aerated: 20% fewer hatched
- refrigerated: 49% fewer hatched

Analyze and Conclude

1. Control groups show an increase until day 5; experimental groups increase until day 3.
2. Hatching should have peaked on day 4 for the control group; day 3 for the experimental.
3. *Sample Answer:* inconsistent controls, differences in viability of brine shrimp eggs
4. acidic solution, low light, low temperature, lack of aeration yield fewer hatched eggs
5. presence of light; pH of 8.0 or higher; room temperature, aeration
6. control provides basis of comparison for experimental results

SECTION 24.3

Plan and Prepare

Objectives

- Describe the adaptations and diversity of arachnids.

Section Resources

Unit Resource Book Study Guide pp. 43–44 Power Notes p. 45 Reinforcement p. 46
Interactive Reader Chapter 24 **Spanish Study Guide** pp. 249–250
Biology Toolkit pp. C19, C23
Technology Power Presentation 24.3 Media Gallery DVD Online Quiz 24.3

Activate Prior Knowledge Of all arthropods, arachnids probably elicit the most fear among humans. **Ask,** What is the term for the condition of being afraid of spiders? arachnophobia Tell students that spiders are just one group within the arachnids. **Ask,** What eight-legged, clawed arachnid is known for its poison-barbed tail? scorpion Tell students that ticks, mites, chiggers, and other animals are also among the arachnids.

Teach

TEACH FROM VISUALS

FIGURE 24.12 Have students recall what they learned about flowering plants and pollinators in Chapter 22. **Ask,** What might an insect mistake the spiny spider for? a flower Discuss how this spider, its mimicry of a flower, and the response of pollinating insects provide an example of coevolution.

24.3 Arachnids

KEY CONCEPT Arachnids include spiders and their relatives.

MAIN IDEAS

- Arachnids are the largest group of chelicerates.
- Arachnids have evolved into a diverse group.

VOCABULARY

chelicerate, p. 740
arachnid, p. 740
book lung, p. 740
spiracle, p. 741
trachea, p. 741

Connect At first, the bump on Emily's back looked like an insect bite. But soon the rash grew into a bulls-eye that was six inches wide. Emily began complaining of aches, and her temperature shot up to 102 degrees. A trip to the doctor gave her parents a startling surprise—Emily had Lyme disease. This disease is caused by bacteria that is carried and spread by a tiny arachnid called a deer tick.

MAIN IDEA

Arachnids are the largest group of chelicerates.

Deer ticks are chelicerates—arthropods without mandibles. **Chelicerates** (kih-LIHS-ur-AYTS) are arthropods that lack antennae and have six pairs of appendages, which include four pairs of walking legs. One set of highly modified appendages form fanglike mouthparts called chelicerae, which are used to mash up food and shove it into a holelike mouth. A second set of appendages, called pedipalps, are used to grasp and subdue prey. Chelicerate bodies have two sections: a cephalothorax and an abdomen.

There are three main groups of chelicerates. The horseshoe crabs and sea spiders are two of these groups. Arachnids are the third group, representing more than 80 percent of all chelicerate species. **Arachnids,** such as the spiny spider shown in **FIGURE 24.12,** are a terrestrial group of chelicerates characterized by eight legs, fanglike pincers that inject venom, and the ability to produce silk.

FIGURE 24.12 The bright coloration of the spiny spider actually attracts insects to the spider's web, where they are trapped and made into an easy meal.

Evidence from fossils nearly 400 million years old suggests that arachnids evolved adaptations that allowed them to conserve water and live on land. Arachnids have four different adaptations that reduce water loss.

- **Waterproof cuticle** An arachnid's cuticle is waterproof, so water cannot evaporate across the skin.
- **Book lungs** Some arachnids have specialized respiratory structures called book lungs that allow them to breathe air. **Book lungs** are structures built of many thin, hollow sheets of tissue that look like the pages of a book. They provide a large surface for gas exchange but also create a very large surface for water loss. To prevent water loss, book lungs are enclosed in a humid chamber covered by a plate of abdominal cuticle.
- **Malpighian tubules** Excretory structures called Malpighian (mal-PIHG-ee-uhn) tubules allow spiders to minimize loss of water while excreting metabolic wastes.

Differentiated Instruction

BELOW LEVEL

Have students consider how millions of years of evolution may have made a fear of spiders a natural response in humans, including those who have never seen or heard of a spider before. Students should write a paragraph describing how such a response could have evolved in humans.

Biology Toolkit, Quick-Write, p. C19

ENGLISH LEARNERS

Have students use a drawing similar to **FIGURE 24.13** around which to organize their notes for the section.

Biology Toolkit, Combination Notes, p. C23

FIGURE 24.13 Arachnid Anatomy

Arachnids have many unique adaptations for catching and consuming their prey.

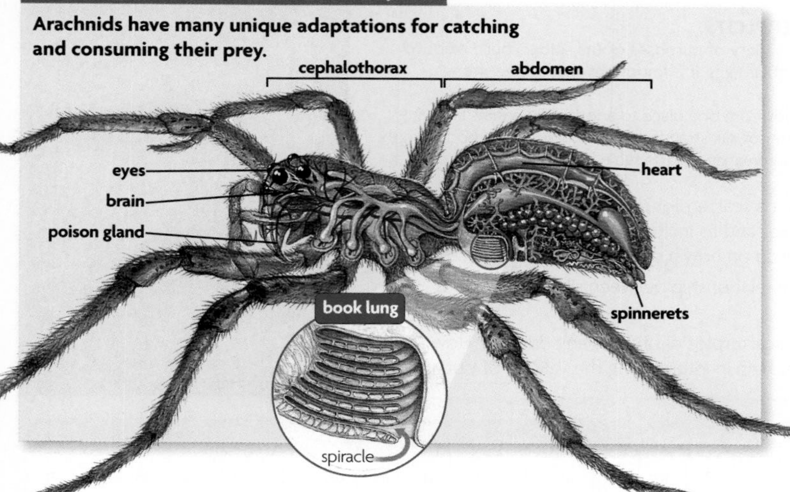

- **Spiracles** Some species of arachnid use spiracles to breathe. **Spiracles** are tiny holes on the abdomen that open and close to allow oxygen to enter. Oxygen flows through a series of tubes called tracheae. **Tracheae** (singular, *trachea*) carry oxygen directly to the arachnid's tissues.

A Explain **How do the features of an arachnid allow it to live on land?**

VOCABULARY

The word *spiracle* comes from the Latin word *spirare* meaning "to breathe."

MAIN IDEA

Arachnids have evolved into a diverse group.

Spiders make up half of the more than 60,000 known arachnid species. They are predators that hunt or trap their prey. All spiders have the ability to make silk and produce venom. Silk is made by glands in the spider's abdomen and released by modified appendages called spinnerets. Spiders use silk for building webs, wrapping prey and egg cases, building shelters, and producing drag lines that anchor the animal like a climber's safety line.

All spiders produce venom. Spiders inject venom into their prey through modified chelicerae. Neurotoxic proteins paralyze the victim by attacking the central nervous system, and digestive enzymes in the venom begin to dissolve the prey from the inside. Among North American spiders, only the black widow and brown recluse spiders have venom that can affect a human, but many species around the world have venom that can paralyze or even kill humans.

Mites, ticks, and chiggers are a large group of very small arachnids. Some species are less than 0.25 millimeters long. Many are parasites of plants and animals, sucking up sap or blood through their needlelike mouthparts. Scorpions are arachnids with huge pincers for grabbing their prey after it has been injected with venom from a stinger at the end of their tail. Scorpions hunt at night by feeling the vibrations made as their prey moves.

***Connecting* CONCEPTS**

Neurotransmitters Neurotoxins in the venom of spiders disrupt neurotransmitter function and lead to paralysis of a victim. You will learn more about the nervous system and neurotransmitters in **Chapter 29.**

PRE-AP

Have students compare **FIGURE 24.13** to **FIGURE 24.8** on page 736. Have students note how the appendages of a spider compare to those of a crustacean. Have students describe the differences in these adaptations and how they relate to the way in each of these predators hunt their prey.

Biology Toolkit, Combination Notes, p. C23

Science Trivia

- Spiders are found everywhere, except in the ocean and on the continent of Antarctica.
- When spiders spin their webs, they coat most of the strands with a sticky substance that traps prey. But spiders leave some strands uncoated so that they themselves do not become stuck. Spiders also have oily secretions on their feet that keep them from sticking to the web.

Address Misconceptions

Common Misconception Tarantulas are the deadliest spiders on Earth.

Correcting the Misconception While tarantulas are some of the largest species of spiders, their venom causes only minor swelling and pain lasting a few hours. Allergic reactions to specific proteins in the venom pose more of a threat than the actual venom's effects.

Vocabulary

Word Origins The word **arachnid** has an origin in Greek mythology. The goddess Athena challenged a talented but boastful weaver named **Arachne** to a contest of weaving skill. Arachne won, but Athena ended up turning her into a spider.

Answers

A Explain The waterproof cuticle prevents water loss. Book lungs provide a large surface for gas exchange to take place internally. Malpighian tubules minimize the loss of water while excreting metabolic wastes. Spiracles and tracheae provide a system for moving oxygen throughout the body.

▼ Teach *continued*

DATA ANALYSIS

Discuss

Discuss dependent and independent variables. **Ask**

- What is the independent variable in this study? body length
- What is the dependent variable? silk diameter

Have students construct their scatterplots accordingly, with the independent variable on the *x*-axis and the dependent variable on the *y*-axis.

Answers

1. Scatterplots should suggest a positive correlation between spider length and silk diameter. For a sample graph, go to page R107.
2. The longer the spider, the larger is the silk diameter.
3. Yes, a larger data set might make it more obvious what data are outliers.

Unit Resource Book, Data Analysis, p. 55

Answers

A Infer Because arachnids are such an important arthropod predator, their prey, including many insects, would experience great population growth.

▼ Assess and Reteach

Assess Use the Online Quiz or Section Quiz (*Assessment Book,* p. 475).

Reteach Project the image of **FIGURE 24.13** (Arachnid Anatomy) from the Media Gallery. Have students make a T-chart that lists in the left-hand column, the arachnid's adaptations for living on land and in the right-hand column, the adaptations for capturing and consuming prey.

DATA ANALYSIS NOS.3

CONSTRUCTING SCATTERPLOTS

Spiders produce silk for a wide variety of purposes. Some spiders build webs to capture prey, or to safely wrap their eggs. It is important that silk be strong enough to support the spider as it moves from one place to another. Scientists studying spider silk measured the diameter of silk strands in relationship to the body length of the spider. Their results are summarized in the table below.

1. **Graph Data** Construct a scatterplot using the data from the table. Be sure to label the axes and to include a title for your graph. Refer to page 721 in Chapter 23 on how a scatterplot is constructed.
2. **Interpret** What is the relationship between silk diameter and spider length?
3. **Interpret** Does your scatterplot data show any outliers? How might a larger data set help in interpreting the validity of outliers?

TABLE 1. SPIDER LENGTH AND SILK DIAMETER

Body length (mm)	7	8	10	11	12	15	16	17	18	20	25	26	26	35	40	45
Silk diameter (mm)	.02	.03	.03	.04	.04	.06	.05	.08	.06	.05	.08	.09	.10	.18	.14	.15

Most scorpions eat insects, spiders, and other scorpions, while some of the largest species eat lizards and small rodents.

Arachnids are important prey species for vertebrates, but they are even more important as predators. Spiders are some of the most widespread predators on the planet and play an important role in most terrestrial food webs. The mass of the insects they eat each year is larger than the combined mass of all human beings. Mites and ticks also have a major impact on ecosystems. Spider mites are serious pests of fruit trees, cotton, and other crops. Ticks can transmit serious human diseases such as Rocky Mountain spotted fever and Lyme disease.

To find out more about arachnids, go to scilinks.org.
Keycode: MLB024

 **Infer How might the loss of many arachnid species affect an ecosystem?**

24.3 ASSESSMENT

ONLINE QUIZ ClassZone.com

REVIEWING MAIN IDEAS

1. What unique features do all **arachnids** share?
2. What four adaptations do arachnids have for conserving water?
3. Why are spiders such an important part of an ecosystem?

CRITICAL THINKING

4. **Summarize** How do **book lungs** help arachnids to reduce water loss?
5. **Infer** Spiders use different kinds of silk for different purposes. What might a spider build with sticky silk?

***Connecting* CONCEPTS**

6. **Ecology** Describe a situation in which spiders would be a secondary consumer. What species might prey on a spider? Draw a simple food web to illustrate your answer.

24.3 ASSESSMENT

1. four pairs of walking legs; two pairs of modified appendages called chelicerae and pedipalps; fanglike pincers that inject venom; the ability to produce silk
2. waterproof cuticle, book lungs, Malpighian tubules, spiracles
3. Spiders are important predators of insects and other animals, and are themselves a food source for some animals.
4. Book lungs seal off the gas exchange mechanism from the outside, keeping the gases in a humid chamber. Their large surface area allows for more gas exchange to occur.
5. webs for catching prey
6. *Sample Answer:* Fruit is eaten by a fruit fly, which is in turn eaten by a spider, which is in turn eaten by a bird.

24.4 Insect Adaptations

KEY CONCEPTS Insects show an amazing range of adaptations.

MAIN IDEAS
- Insects are the dominant terrestrial arthropods.
- Insects undergo metamorphosis.
- Insects have adapted to life on land.

VOCABULARY

incomplete metamorphosis, p. 744
complete metamorphosis, p. 744
pupa, p. 744

Connect Everywhere you turn, there are more of them. They are under your feet, flying over your head, nestled in your clothing fibers, and waiting for you to go to bed. Insects are virtually everywhere, and many times you may not even know it. With more than 900,000 known species, insects are the single largest and most diverse group of animals on the planet.

MAIN IDEA

Insects are the dominant terrestrial arthropods.

Insects are an incredible success story. Like the arachnids, they invaded land around 400 million years ago. They have many of the same adaptations for terrestrial life as arachnids do. Insects have moved into virtually every ecological niche, which has helped them diversify into the largest group of animals.

Insects can be found in the most extreme places, including hot sulphur springs and the soil of Antarctica. They are also found in streams and ponds. Though some species live in the marine intertidal zone, they are largely absent in the seas, where crustaceans are the dominant arthropods. Due to such a wide distribution, scientists are discovering new species of insects each day.

All insects have a body with three parts: a head, a central region called the thorax (THAWR-AKS), and an abdomen, as shown in **FIGURE 24.14.** The thorax has three pairs of legs, and most adult insects also have two pairs of wings. Insects usually have one pair of antennae and one pair of compound eyes. Many have mandibles that they use to chew up their food, but others have modified mouthparts for more specialized feeding behaviors.

FIGURE 24.14 This potter wasp illustrates the three-part body structure of all insects: head, thorax, and abdomen.

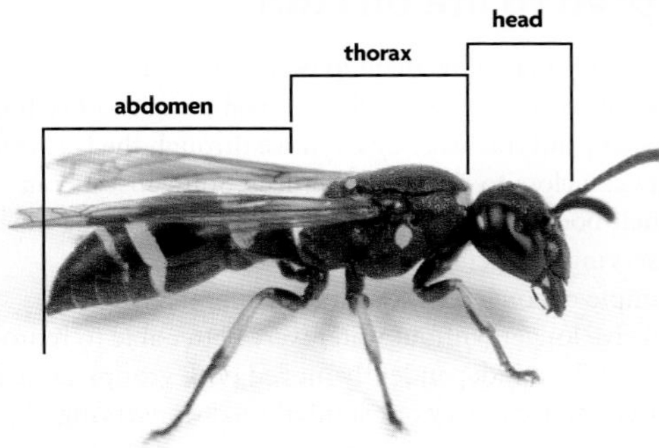

Some insect species live in colonies of hundreds or thousands of individuals. Within these colonies, complex social structures exist. Individuals perform specific jobs that help the colony be successful. Scientists believe that an insect's genetic code determines what role it will play in a colony.

A Compare and Contrast **How are insects similar to and different from crustaceans and arachnids?**

Differentiated Instruction

HANDS-ON ACTIVITY

Purchase a butterfly kit so that students can observe complete metamorphosis. Painted lady butterflies are readily available. The butterflies come in the egg stage and hatch into larvae within a few days. The larvae feed on the provided material and grow for several days, until they pupate. Students will be able to see slight movement coming from the pupae. If students are vigilant, they may be able to see butterflies emerging. Students can release the butterflies, or keep them and try to hatch more.

Plan and Prepare ▼

Objectives

- Contrast incomplete metamorphosis and complete metamorphosis.
- Describe how insects are adapted to life on land.

Section Resources

Unit Resource Book
Study Guide pp. 47–48
Power Notes p. 49
Reinforcement p. 50

Interactive Reader Chapter 24
Spanish Study Guide pp. 251–252

Biology Toolkit pp. C19, C32, C38

Technology
Power Presentation 24.4
Media Gallery DVD
Online Quiz 24.4

Activate Prior Knowledge Discuss insects that students have seen inside or outside of their homes. **Ask**

- Which insects are able to fly? butterflies, moths, bees, wasps, flies, mosquitoes, mayflies, gnats
- Of the flying insects, which ones begin their lives as wormlike caterpillars? moths, butterflies
- What do we call the transition from caterpillar to adult butterfly or moth? metamorphosis

Tell students that many other insects go through true metamorphosis. For example, beetles begin life as grubs, and flies start out as maggots. Other insects undergo a gradual or incomplete metamorphosis.

Teach ▼

Answers

A **Compare and Contrast** All arthropods have exoskeletons, jointed appendages, and segmented bodies. Insects' bodies have a head, a thorax, and an abdomen. The thorax has three pairs of legs and, in most insects, two sets of wings.

▼ Teach *continued*

ONLINE BIOLOGY Go to the chapter Resource Center at **ClassZone.com** for additional resources and information on insects.

Integrating Ecology

The gypsy moth, *Lymantria dispar,* was brought to the United States in 1869 in a failed attempt to start a silk industry. The caterpillars of this moth proved devastating to the deciduous trees of the Northeast. These caterpillars feed voraciously on the leaves of oak trees, but they will also feed on conifers.

Eggs typically hatch in May, and the caterpillars feed and grow through June, when they pupate and become moths that do not feed. In years when the gypsy moth caterpillar population is very large, humans have combated them with applications of *Bacillus thuringiensis,* a bacterium known as B.t.; chemical pesticides; and a fungus, *Entomophaga maimaiga,* all of which can kill the caterpillars.

Answers

A Connect Incomplete metamorphosis most closely resembles human development. When humans are born, they have the same body parts as they will have when they are fully mature.

MAIN IDEA

Insects undergo metamorphosis.

VOCABULARY

The word *metamorphosis* comes from the Greek word *metamorphoun,* which means "to transform."

Insects do not develop the same way you do. When you were first born, you had all of the same body parts as an adult. The same is not true of most insects. Some insects, such as butterflies and mosquitoes, go through dramatic physical changes between their immature and mature forms.

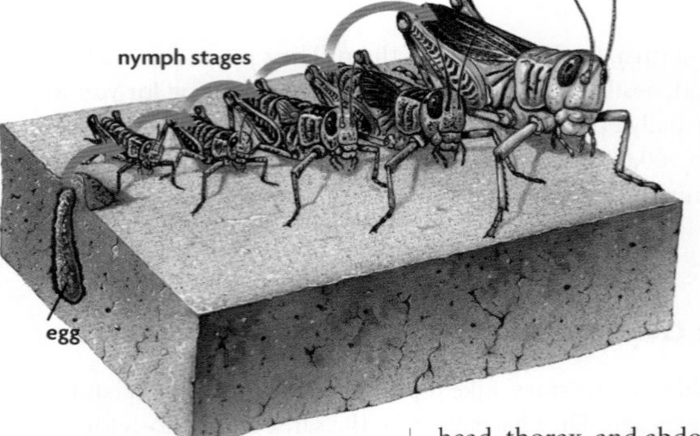

FIGURE 24.15 In the process of incomplete metamorphosis, a nymph appears to be a miniature copy of the adult insect. But on closer inspection, these immature insects lack important features such as wings and sex organs.

Some insects, such as grasshoppers and cockroaches, look like miniature adults when they hatch. This pattern of development, illustrated in **FIGURE 24.15,** is **incomplete metamorphosis** (MEHT-uh-MAWR-fuh-sihs), or direct development. These immature insects are often called nymphs. They have six legs and a head, thorax, and abdomen, but they do not have wings or sex organs. Nymphs get larger with each molt, but only grow wings and sexual organs during the later molting stages.

In the process of **complete metamorphosis**, illustrated in **FIGURE 24.16,** young insects do not look like adults but molt and change their form as they mature. Young insects hatch out of eggs as wormlike larvae whose bodies are not clearly divided into a head, thorax, and abdomen, and they often lack legs or antennae. As they grow, larvae pass through several molts, getting bigger each time, until they molt into an inactive form called a **pupa.** Inside the pupa, some tissues are broken down for energy and others are reorganized to produce a completely new body form. When the adult insect emerges from the pupa, it looks very different from a larva. It has wings, legs, and compound eyes, and is ready to fly away and begin its search for a mate.

A Connect Which type of metamorphosis more closely resembles human development? Explain.

MAIN IDEA

Insects have adapted to life on land.

***Connecting* CONCEPTS**

Plants Recall from **Chapter 21** that stomata are holes in the leaves of plants that open and close to control transpiration and gas exchange. Many arthropods use spiracles in the same way, opening and closing them to control water and gas exchange.

Insects have several adaptations that allow them to be successful terrestrial species. Just like arachnids, insects retain water for survival using exoskeletons, Malpighian tubules, spiracles, and tracheae. Gases move through the tracheae by diffusion, and spiracles can close to prevent water loss. Some insects can also pump air through their bodies by rapidly squeezing and expanding the tracheae. The water-conserving characteristics that are shared by insects and arachnids are an example of convergent evolution. In both groups, individuals that could survive longer without water were better able to reproduce. In this way, natural selection independently moved both groups toward similar features that allowed them to carry out similar water-conserving functions.

Differentiated Instruction

ENGLISH LEARNERS

After they have read the section and studied **FIGURES 24.15** and **24.16,** have students create a Y diagram to compare incomplete and complete metamorphosis. Tell students to begin their diagram by writing in the characteristics of both types of metamorphosis in the two branches of the Y. Then have students write in the shared characteristics, such as "hatch from eggs," in the stem of the Y, crossing off the shared terms from the upper parts of the diagram.

Biology Toolkit, Y Diagram, p. C32

PRE-AP

Have students consider how seasons vary across the yearly life cycle of an insect, such as a butterfly. Have them write for five minutes on the question of how a butterfly's varying forms are adaptive to the cyclical changes in its environment.

Biology Toolkit, Quick-Write, p. C19

FIGURE 24.16 Complete Metamorphosis of a Monarch Butterfly

The complete metamorphosis of an insect involves two completely different forms: a juvenile form and an adult form. This prevents adults and juveniles from competing for the same resources.

Animated BIOLOGY
See a butterfly go through metamorphosis at ClassZone.com.

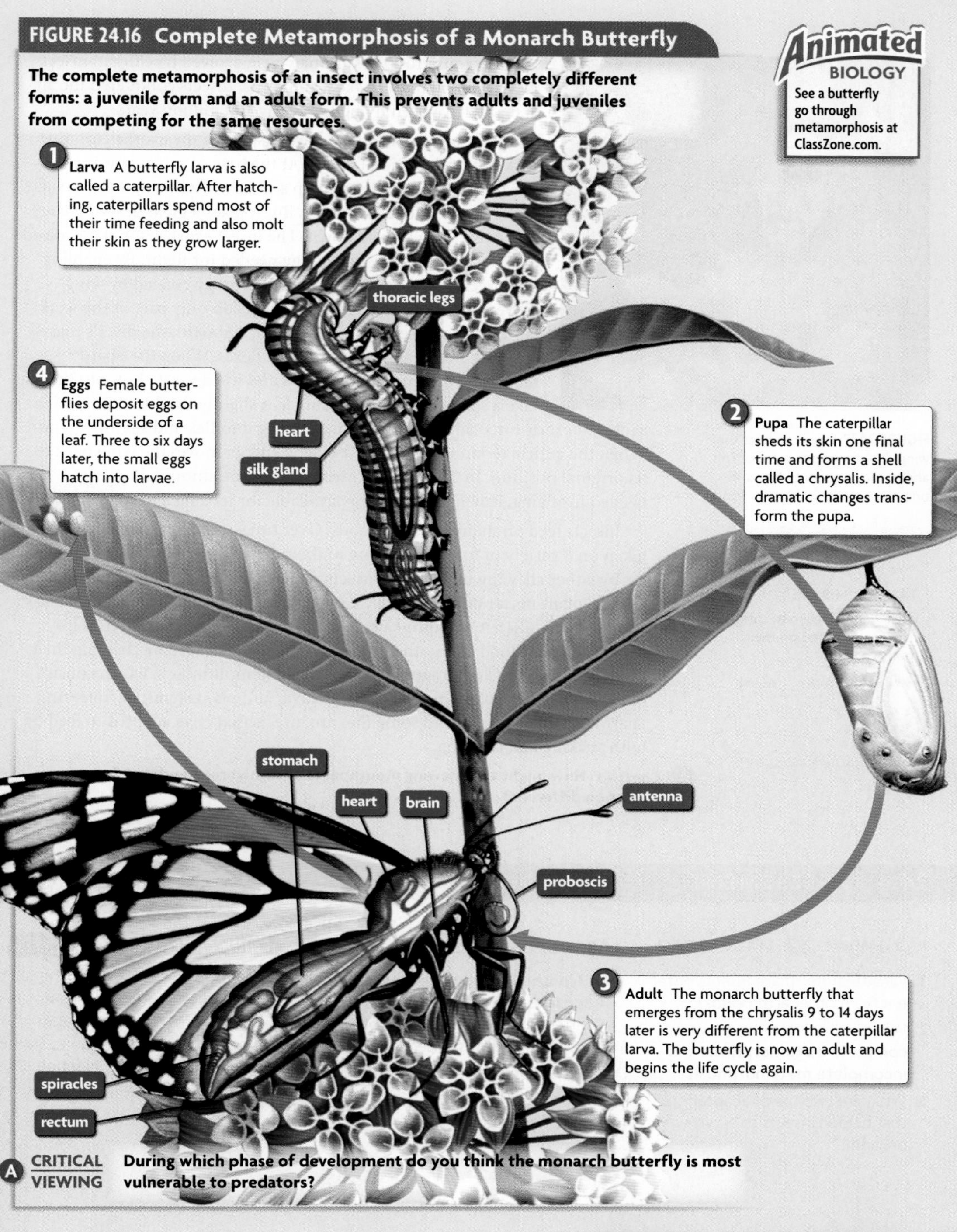

1 **Larva** A butterfly larva is also called a caterpillar. After hatching, caterpillars spend most of their time feeding and also molt their skin as they grow larger.

2 **Pupa** The caterpillar sheds its skin one final time and forms a shell called a chrysalis. Inside, dramatic changes transform the pupa.

3 **Adult** The monarch butterfly that emerges from the chrysalis 9 to 14 days later is very different from the caterpillar larva. The butterfly is now an adult and begins the life cycle again.

4 **Eggs** Female butterflies deposit eggs on the underside of a leaf. Three to six days later, the small eggs hatch into larvae.

A CRITICAL VIEWING **During which phase of development do you think the monarch butterfly is most vulnerable to predators?**

BELOW LEVEL

Have students translate the metamorphosis shown in **FIGURE 24.16** into a sequence diagram that is easier for them to follow. Have them note which features remain, disappear, or change in the transition between caterpillar and butterfly.

Biology Toolkit, Sequence Diagram, p. C38

ONLINE BIOLOGY Students learn how to use insects to help solve a crime in the virtual lab in Options for Inquiry on page 751.

Integrating Forensic Science

Forensic entomologists are scientists who use insects and their arthropod relatives as evidence in investigations. **Forensic entomology** covers three broad areas: homicide investigations, food contamination, and urban aspects. The last area deals with how insects affect humans and their immediate environment. For example, a forensic entomologist may be asked to provide information in civil suits involving insect infestations and resultant structural damages to buildings.

Blowflies and beetles are two kinds of insects frequently observed in homicide investigations; both undergo complete metamorphosis. The forensic entomologist can estimate a person's time of death from a number of criteria, including the stages of metamorphosis of any insects found on the corpse, succession of various insect species, larval weights, and larval lengths. Some species of insects prefer to lay their eggs indoors, outdoors, in the shade, or in sunlight. Thus, a forensic entomologist can determine if a corpse has been moved based on the species present or its developmental stage.

Answers

A Critical Viewing The monarch butterfly is most vulnerable during the developmental stages. Caterpillars are especially vulnerable when they are forming a chrysalis.

Chapter 24: A Closer Look at Arthropods 745

▼ Teach continued

Take It Further

Insects that feed on the blood of other organisms have a proboscis that is adapted for finding blood vessels, cutting into tissue, and sucking up blood. The proboscises of mosquitoes, black flies, horseflies, deer flies, and midges (no-see-ums, sand flies) are composed of a long pair of lips that form a tube. At the ends of these lips are receptors that detect where the best spot is for the insect to bite. Within the lips are five cutting tools called **stylets.** Two of the five tools are mandibles that have serrated edges for cutting open the skin; two are maxillae that have barbs that help draw the styles deeper into the host; and the fifth is a hypopharynx that injects a saliva that prevents the blood from clotting. Blood is then drawn up through the proboscis like water through a straw.

Answers

A Contrast Mouthparts of carnivorous insects might be adapted for tearing and crushing the chitin exoskeletons of other insects. Mouthparts of herbivorous insects might be adapted for cutting through plant tissues and chewing cellulose.

▼ Assess and Reteach

Assess Use the Online Quiz or Section Quiz (*Assessment Book,* p. 476).

Reteach Project the **ClassZone.com** animation of complete metamorphosis onto a screen for review of this process. After running through the animation once, replay it with the sound turned off, and ask students to narrate.

FIGURE 24.17 Bees can beat their wings 200 times per second. This ability allows them to hover in one place while looking for food.

Only four groups of animals have evolved true flight: insects, the extinct pterosaurs, bats, and birds. Insects conquered the air first and have been flying for nearly 400 million years.

Insect wings are long, flat extensions of the exoskeleton that stick out of the animal's back. At the base of each wing are muscles that move the wing up and down, allowing insects, such as the bee in **FIGURE 24.17**, to fly. But it takes a great deal of energy to move a wing up and down. The insect exoskeleton has evolved in ways that conserve the energy needed for flight. By enabling the insect to reuse the stored kinetic energy created by wing movement, muscles attached to wings do only part of the work. For example, when a diver uses a springboard, the diver's mass creates kinetic energy as the board flexes. When the board rebounds, this energy is released and the diver is shot into the air. Like a springboard, insect cuticle is slightly flexible. As the wing moves, it exerts force on the exoskeleton, causing it to flex and slightly deform. When the cuticle rebounds, the stored kinetic energy moves the wing back to its original position. In this way, an insect reduces the amount of energy needed for flying, leaving more energy available for feeding and reproduction.

TAKING NOTES

Use a Venn diagram to categorize insects based on their mouth parts.

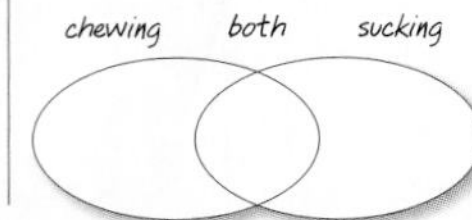

Insects feed on many different foods. Over time, insect mouth shapes have taken on a variety of forms according to their diets. Generally speaking, insects eat by either chewing or sucking. Insects such as butterflies and moths that feed on plant nectar and fruits have a long, strawlike mouth called a proboscis (proh-BAHS-sihs). A mosquito also has a proboscis, but instead it uses its mouth to suck blood from other animals. Other insects feed by chewing their food. Ants, beetles, and dragonflies have chewing mouthparts, which consist of mandibles adapted either to crushing leaves and plant stems, or to tearing apart flesh. Bees, wasps, and some flies are insects that have adapted to feed by both sucking and chewing.

A Contrast How might the chewing mouthparts of carnivorous and herbivorous insects be different?

24.4 ASSESSMENT

ONLINE QUIZ ClassZone.com

REVIEWING MAIN IDEAS

1. What features make insects different from other arthropods?
2. What is the difference between **complete metamorphosis** and **incomplete metamorphosis**?
3. What are two major adaptations that helped insects to survive on land?

CRITICAL THINKING

4. **Hypothesize** How might the spiracles of a desert insect be different from the spiracles of a tropical rain forest insect?
5. **Infer** Give two reasons why flight has enabled insects to be so successful.

Connecting CONCEPTS

6. **Evolution** Hundreds of millions of years ago, spiders began to use silk around the same time insects began to fly. Explain how natural selection affected these changes.

24.4 ASSESSMENT

1. Insects have three distinct body parts—head, thorax, and abdomen—and three pairs of thoracic legs, along with paired wings (usually).
2. Insects that undergo incomplete metamorphosis look like miniature adults when they are young; they develop wings and sex organs during their final molt. Insects that undergo complete metamorphosis have distinct larva, pupa, and adult stages that look very different from one another.
3. Answers should include two of the following: exoskeleton, Malpighian tubules, spiracles, and tracheae.
4. A desert insect would have spiracles that remained closed most of the time, whereas a tropical rain-forest insect would have spiracles that stay open longer.
5. Insects were able to move into new areas, exploit different resources, and occupy new niches. Wings offer another means of escaping predation.
6. Wings allowed insects to avoid predators such as spiders, but spiders that made webs were able to catch flying insects.

24.5 Arthropods and Humans

KEY CONCEPT Arthropods and humans interact in many ways.

MAIN IDEAS
- Arthropods and humans share many of the same resources.
- Some arthropods can spread human diseases.

VOCABULARY
insecticide, p. 747
vector, p. 748

Review
biomagnification

Connect People have a love-hate relationship with arthropods. Some arthropods are important pollinators that fertilize human crops. Others are pests that destroy crops and infest our homes. Still others are predators that eat pests. Insect species are used for food and fibers in many human cultures, but other insect species spread human diseases. Over time, the unavoidable interactions between arthropods and humans have created many conflicts.

MAIN IDEA

Arthropods and humans share many of the same resources.

Many arthropods are herbivores, and many of them eat the same plants people use for food, textiles, and building materials. These arthropods compete with humans for the same resources. Competition is stiff, because there are far more arthropods than people. For example, when you look under the leaves of apple trees or pepper plants, you may see clusters of tiny bumps. These bumps are insects called aphids. Aphids, shown in **FIGURE 24.18,** use their needlelike mouthparts to pierce the cell walls of a plant and suck up the sugary liquid inside. A single aphid is small and cannot do much damage on its own. But aphids live in large colonies. Hundreds of aphids on a plant can remove enough sap to damage or kill the plant.

FIGURE 24.18 Aphids devour plant tissues, often killing the host plant. Arthropod pest species can cause damage to crops, forests, and even homes.

Each year, arthropods cause millions of dollars in damage to crops such as corn, wheat, and cotton. To prevent costly infestations, farmers use insecticides to control arthropod populations. An **insecticide** is a chemical compound that kills insects and other arthropods. But spraying toxic chemicals on plants can have unwanted side effects. Many insecticides are toxic to other animals, including people. Some, such as chlordane and DDT, do not break down quickly. They can accumulate in predator species through the process of biomagnification. Arthropods can also become resistant to insecticides through natural selection. This resistance causes humans to use even larger doses of the toxin.

To avoid the potential hazards of using insecticides, scientists have discovered ways to use the unique characteristics of arthropods to find safer ways of controlling pest populations.

Differentiated Instruction

PRE-AP

Have students use a fishbone diagram to compare the benefits of insect control to the risks. Suggest students list the benefits in the upper half of the diagram and the risks in the lower half. In the "head" of the fish have students write "pest management."

Biology Toolkit, Fishbone Diagram, p. C37

Plan and Prepare

Objectives

- Summarize the shared resources and interactions of arthropods and humans, including transmission of diseases.

Section Resources

Unit Resource Book
Study Guide pp. 51–52
Power Notes p. 53
Reinforcement p. 54
Pre-AP Activity pp. 59–60

Interactive Reader Chapter 24
Spanish Study Guide pp. 253–254

Biology Toolkit pp. C13, C36, C37

Technology
Power Presentation 24.5
Media Gallery DVD
Online Quiz 24.5

Activate Prior Knowledge Discuss interactions between humans and arthropods. **Ask**
- What resources might caterpillars and humans compete for? trees and crops
- How do humans depend on arthropods to help crop plants reproduce? Flowering plants often need pollinators.
- What diseases do you know of that are transmitted by insects? malaria, West Nile virus, Lyme disease, viruses that cause encephalitis

Point out that we interact with arthropods as predator, host, competitor, and other ways that affect each other's survival.

Teach

Vocabulary

Greek and Latin Word Origins The suffix *-cide* in **insecticide** comes from the Latin word *caedere,* meaning "to kill." The suffix is found in the words *fungicide, matricide,* and *suicide,* among others.

▼ Teach continued

Integrating Biochemistry

The protein genetically engineered into **Bt corn** attacks the corn borer by binding to its gut membrane. The protein damages the gut lining and leads to paralysis of the gut. The insect stops feeding and dies. The protein is effective on species of insects with a specific gut pH. In addition, the insect must be at a stage of development that is susceptible to the protein, such as the caterpillar stage of the corn borer. Bt genes have been inserted into several important crops, including cotton, tomatoes, and potatoes.

Vocabulary

Academic Vocabulary The word **vector** comes from the Latin word *vehere*, which means "to carry." Students may be familiar with vectors used in mathematics and some of their applications. A vector in mathematics represents a quantity that has magnitude and direction. An example of an application is airplane flight. Compass and associated navigational readings are based on vectors. **Ask,** What do vectors in disease transmission and in mathematics have in common? They signify movement from one place to another.

Answers

A Infer The predator may prey on non-target species.

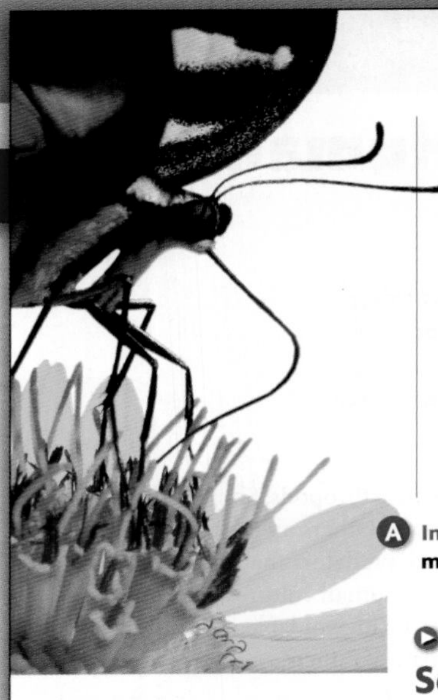

FIGURE 24.19 Many arthropods are important pollinators. In addition to getting a nectar meal, this Eastern tiger swallowtail butterfly helps to pollinate flowers by carrying pollen from one flower to another.

- Insecticides can be developed to be specific to arthropods. One example is a neurotoxin that blocks a particular receptor that is common in arthropod nerves but not found in other animal nerves.
- Integrated pest management, or IPM, reduces the number of insect pests on a plant crop by managing their ecology. By using a variety of other methods including insect traps, physical barriers, and introduced predators such as ladybugs and parasitic wasps, IPM helps to control pest species.
- Genetically modified plants can be made to resist particular pest species. For example, Bt corn has been engineered to include a gene from a soil bacterium, *Bacillus thuringiensis,* artificially inserted into its DNA. The gene makes a protein that kills caterpillar pests such as the European corn borer but is harmless to most other animals.

A Infer **What would be a disadvantage to introducing a predator insect for pest management?**

MAIN IDEA

Some arthropods can spread human diseases.

Humans are a source of food to arthropods such as mosquitoes, biting flies, fleas, and ticks. **FIGURE 24.20** shows how arthropods can also be vectors that carry diseases. A **vector** is an organism that carries a disease from one host to another.

Diseases spread by arthropods can have serious effects on human populations. Many methods for controlling arthropod vectors have been developed. Vaccinations have been developed to protect individuals from many types of diseases by delivering small doses of the pathogen to the immune system, which can then fight off future pathogen invasions. The use of pesticides targeted to specific arthropods can also help slow the spread of disease.

TAKING NOTES

Use a main idea diagram to list the diseases carried by arthropod vectors.

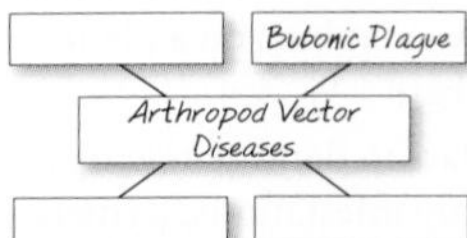

- **Bubonic plague** is caused by a bacterium carried by a flea. The disease normally affects rodents such as prairie dogs, squirrels, and rats. Human infections occur when a flea that has fed on an infected rat feeds on a human. Outbreaks of bubonic plague devastated European cities between the 1300s and the 1600s. The largest of these epidemics, between 1347 and 1350, killed between one-third and one-half of the people living in Europe. Today, bubonic plague is controlled by antibiotics and improved hygiene.
- **Yellow fever** is caused by a virus and normally affects monkeys, but it can be carried to humans by mosquitoes. The virus causes fever and bleeding. It was common in the United States until the early part of the 1900s and is still common in Africa and South America. Yellow fever epidemics killed nearly 20,000 people during the construction of the Panama canal before mosquito eradication programs brought the disease under control.
- **Malaria** is caused by a protozoan parasite carried by mosquitoes. The parasites enter red blood cells to breed, periodically emerging and destroying them. Like yellow fever, malaria was once common in the United States and Europe. Malaria was largely eliminated in temperate countries during the 1950s by a program of DDT spraying. It is still common in tropical regions of Africa, Asia, and Central and South America.

Differentiated Instruction

HANDS-ON ACTIVITY

Have students develop a Green Schools Checklist for pest management. Suggest that students solicit suggestions from staff, faculty, and other students. A checklist might include the following items: caulking and sealing structural cracks; fixing moisture problems; keeping lockers and buildings clean and dry; using non-chemical pest-control methods, such as traps or barriers.

For more information regarding Green Schools and integrated pest management, visit **ClassZone.com.**

BELOW LEVEL

Have students work in small groups to create cause and effect chains to diagram the conditions under which different diseases spread. Looking at the diagrams, have students highlight points of intervention that would help stop the spread of the diseases.

Biology Toolkit, Think-Pair-Share, p. C13; Cause and Effect Chain, p. C36

FIGURE 24.20 Arthropod Vectors

Arthropods are vectors for carrying diseases such as Lyme disease.

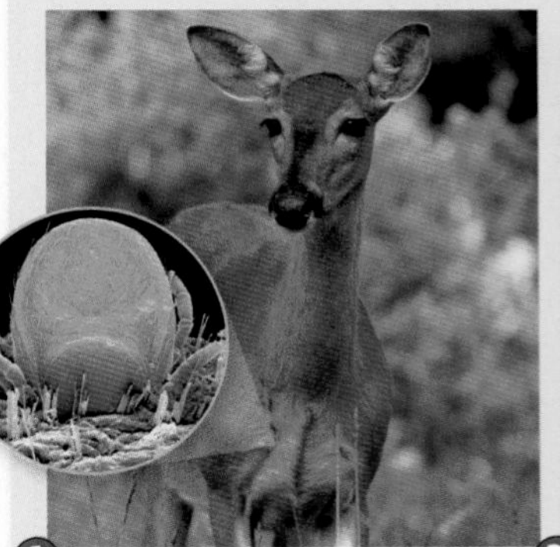

1 As the tick feeds on the host's blood, microscopic pathogens pass from deer to tick. (colored SEM tick; magnification 15×)

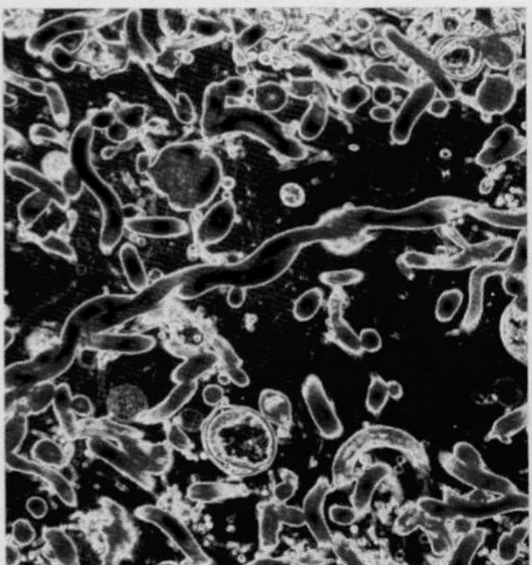

2 Inside the tick, the pathogens are stable and do not affect the tick. (LM; magnification 4000×)

3 When the tick feeds on another host, pathogens are passed from the tick to the new host.

A **Analyze** **Though vectors can bring disease into human populations, explain why diseases carried by arthropods spread more quickly through the populations of other animals.**

- **West Nile virus** is contracted from mosquito carriers that have previously fed on birds infected with the virus. Originally discovered in Africa, West Asia, and the Middle East, the virus has spread throughout the world and has been identified in 46 of the United States. Fever, headache, and skin rashes are some of the minor symptoms, but the virus can lead to meningitis or encephalitis, potentially fatal diseases. Scientists are currently working to control the spread of the virus.

B **Infer** **Explain how an organism other than an arthropod could be a vector.**

Connecting CONCEPTS

Immune System Vaccines can only work to prevent a disease; they cannot cure a person who is already sick. The human immune system has specifically designed cells which work to fight diseases in your body.

24.5 ASSESSMENT

ONLINE QUIZ ClassZone.com

REVIEWING MAIN IDEAS

1. What are three effective ways of managing insect pest populations?
2. How does a **vector** spread a disease such as malaria?

CRITICAL THINKING

3. **Analyze** What are the potential costs and benefits of using an introduced predator to control a pest population?
4. **Connect** What effect, if any, would the development of a vaccine against a tick-borne disease have on the tick population? Explain.

Connecting CONCEPTS

5. **Natural Selection** Describe a situation in which natural selection could lead to an arthropod population that is resistant to pesticides.

TEACH FROM VISUALS

FIGURE 24.20 Use the figure to discuss the spread of Lyme disease to humans. Symptoms of Lyme disease in its early stages include a bull's-eye patterned rash and flulike symptoms, such as headache, fever, and aching joints. In the later stages of the disease, an infected person may experience arthritis, facial paralysis, and memory loss. **Ask,** Although the pathogen does not affect the tick, how might the transmission of Lyme disease to humans ultimately affect the deer tick species? Humans could reduce the deer tick population through various controls in order to reduce the chance of Lyme disease transmission.

Answers

A **Analyze** Wild animals are exposed to arthropods much more frequently than humans are.

B **Infer** Any organism that is a parasite on multiple species could function as a vector for a pathogen. For example, the vampire bat, a mammal that drinks blood from other animals, could carry a disease from the blood of one animal and transmit it to the blood of another.

Assess and Reteach ▼

Assess Use the Online Quiz or Section Quiz (*Assessment Book,* p. 477).

Reteach Work with students to create a cluster diagram that examines the interaction of arthropods and humans. Have students consider how human technology factors into the interactions, in both good and bad ways.

24.5 ASSESSMENT

1. insecticides, integrated pest management (IPM), genetically modified plants
2. A disease is picked up by an arthropod vector, such as a mosquito, from an infected organism. The disease remains stable in the arthropod, but when it feeds on another host, the pathogens it carries are passed to the new host.
3. The predatory species may become too abundant and begin to feed on non-target species. A benefit might be that using a predatory species rather than a wide-scale pesticide can be a less expensive, less polluting, but effective way of dealing with a pest.
4. There would be no direct effect, because the tick is not affected by the virus it carries. However, if vaccination meant that humans would no longer find it necessary to avoid ticks or control their population, the tick population could grow as a result of more exposure to humans (food) and less effort to control them.
5. A mutation could render an individual arthropod resistant to the toxin in a pesticide. Because other arthropods would be killed, this resistant individual would have a much better chance of passing on its genes. Over the course of generations, the gene for pesticide resistance would become more prevalent in the population if the pesticide remained in use.

INVESTIGATION

Time 45 minutes	TEACHER TESTED
Teacher Preparation	
Student Difficulty	
Lab Binder Animals, pp. 21–23	

Purpose Observe the effect of an environmental change on the heart rate of *Daphnia.*

Overview Students will predict the effect of adding hydrogen peroxide to the environment of *Daphnia.* They will

- calculate *Daphnia* heart rate before and after adding hydrogen peroxide
- compare heart rate data for different concentrations of hydrogen peroxide

LAB PREPARATION

- Make a 30 mg/L stock solution of hydrogen peroxide by adding 1 mL of 3% hydrogen peroxide to 999 mL of spring water. Use this solution to make solutions of the concentrations listed on page R107.

LAB MANAGEMENT

Safety Make sure students wash their hands after the lab.

POST-LAB DISCUSSION

Review how environmental changes affect populations and, consequently, food chains. **Ask**

- How could you apply the results observed in this lab to a freshwater population of *Daphnia*? Changes to the water could have a detrimental effect on *Daphnia* and cause a decline in the population. Organisms that are part of the same food chain as *Daphnia* would be affected.
- Is there any concentration at which hydrogen peroxide may be considered safe? Concentrations below 1 mg/L should be safe in the environment.

Use these inquiry-based labs and online activities to deepen your understanding of arthropods.

INDIANA STANDARDS

NOS.1 Develop explanations based on reproducible data and observations gathered during laboratory investigations.

NOS.3 Clearly communicate their ideas and results of investigations verbally and in written form using tables, graphs, diagrams, and photographs.

INVESTIGATION

Daphnia and Heart Rate

The water flea, or *Daphnia,* is a tiny crustacean that lives in fresh water. Biologists often use *Daphnia* to study the effects of various chemicals, such as hydrogen peroxide, on freshwater ecosystems.

SKILLS Collecting Data, Graphing, Analyzing

PROBLEM How does hydrogen peroxide affect *Daphnia* heart rate?

MATERIALS

- cotton swab
- tissues
- petroleum jelly
- microscope slide
- culture of *Daphnia magna*
- 2 eyedroppers
- cover slip
- stopwatch
- microscope
- hydrogen peroxide solutions

PROCEDURE

1. Make a ring of petroleum jelly on a slide and make wet mount with a *Daphnia* sample.
2. Observe the *Daphnia* under low and high power.
3. Looking through the microscope, measure the heart rate of the *Daphnia* by tapping a pencil on the desk once for each heartbeat. Your partner should count the number of taps in 15 seconds. Calculate the number of beats per minute by multiplying this number by 4. Take the average of three trials, and record the data in a data table.
4. Predict the effect of adding hydrogen peroxide to the *Daphnia* environment, and record it in your notebook.
5. Place two drops of one of the hydrogen peroxide solutions on one side of the wet mount. Draw the liquid under the cover slip by placing the edge of a tissue on the opposite edge of the cover slip.
6. Repeat step 3 to measure the *Daphnia* heart rate.
7. Calculate the change in heart rate by subtracting the average heart rate observed after adding hydrogen peroxide from the average heart rate observed in water.
8. Collect average heart rate data from other groups who used different hydrogen peroxide concentrations.

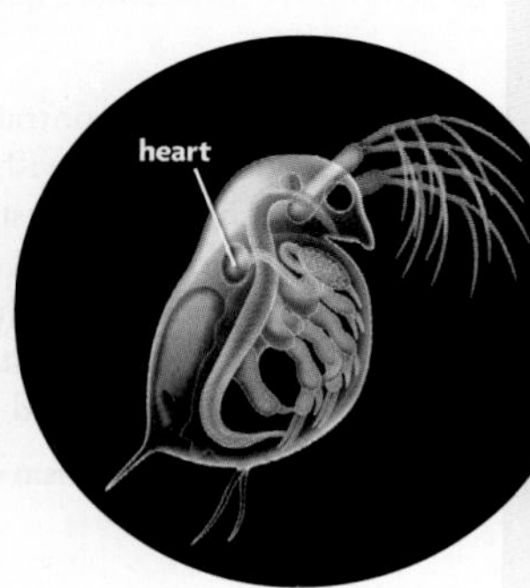

Daphnia

ANALYZE AND CONCLUDE

1. **Analyze** Using your own data and the data collected by your classmates using different hydrogen peroxide concentrations, construct a graph with the change in heart rate on the *y*-axis versus hydrogen peroxide concentration on the *x*-axis.
2. **Interpret** How did hydrogen peroxide affect the heart rate of *Daphnia*? At what concentration was the effect greatest?
3. **Experimental Design** What are possible reasons for error in the experimental design?

Answers

Expected Results

Students should find a decrease in heart rate when hydrogen peroxide concentrations are above 1.3 mg/L.

Analyze and Conclude

1. Graphs will show a decrease in heart rate as hydrogen peroxide concentration increases; thus, graphs will go down from left to right.
2. Hydrogen peroxide decreases the heart rate of *Daphnia.* Actual results will vary somewhat; if concentration is high enough, the heart stops beating and the *Daphnia* dies.
3. errors in heart rate calculations, rounding errors, and individual differences among *Daphnia*

INVESTIGATION

Inside a Crayfish

A crayfish is a freshwater crustacean similar to shrimp, crabs, and lobsters. In this lab, you will dissect and examine the parts of a crayfish.

SKILL Observing

PROBLEM How do the form and function of crayfish organs help it survive in a marine environment?

MATERIALS
- dissecting tray
- scissors
- forceps
- dissecting needle
- 12 dissecting pins
- preserved crayfish specimen
- hand lens or dissecting microscope
- paper towels
- paper and pencil
- Anatomical Crayfish Drawings

PROCEDURE
1. Examine the external anatomy of the crayfish. Draw and label a picture of the crayfish anatomy, using illustrations in your handout. Label the structures listed on the drawing.
2. Turn the crayfish on its side and remove the legs below the carapace.
3. Using the forceps and scissors, lift and cut the carapace to expose the featherlike gills.
4. Carefully remove the gills and the joints. Cut the remaining plates from the top (dorsal) midline to the base of each leg to expose the internal organs. Examine the inside of the crayfish and identify as many internal organs as you can.

ANALYZE AND CONCLUDE
1. **Infer** What do you think the antennae and antennules do?
2. **Analyze** How does the feathery structure of the gills help with their function?
3. **Infer** Why do you think the gills are attached to the legs?

Online BIOLOGY
CLASSZONE.COM

VIRTUAL LAB
Insects and Crime Scene Analysis
How can bugs help solve a crime? In this interactive lab, you will examine insects found on a corpse to determine how long the body was lying in a field.

ANIMATED BIOLOGY
What Type of Arthropod?
Can you tell what group an arthropod belongs to just by looking at it? Examine a series of arthropod images and try to categorize them. Be careful—looks can be very deceiving!

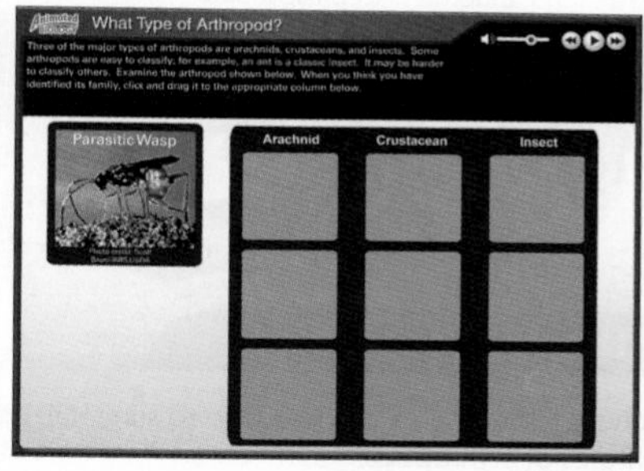

WEBQUEST
Arthropods live in almost any environment. As a class, develop a field guide of arthropods in your area. Research and report on each arthropod's habitat, feeding habits, life cycle and evolutionary history.

Answers

Analyze and Conclude
1. Antennae and antennules are used for sensing the surrounding environment.
2. The feathery structure increases the surface area, allowing for more gas exchange.
3. Movement of the legs may help with movement of water across the gills, allowing for more gas exchange.

Online Biology ▼

VIRTUAL LAB Students use insect molts found on a corpse to determine time of death. Use this lab to reinforce the concepts in **Section 24.4.**

ANIMATED BIOLOGY Students categorize arthropods by examining their features. Use this interactive animation to reinforce the concepts in **Section 24.1.**

WEBQUEST The WebQuest takes one full class period. Students complete the activity online and will need access to a printer to print their answers. Sample answers, teacher notes, and alternative assessment ideas are available on **ClassZone.com.** Use with **Sections 24.1–24.4.**

INVESTIGATION

TEACHER TESTED

Time	45 minutes
Teacher Preparation	⚗
Student Difficulty	⚗
Lab Binder	Animals, pp. 24–25

Purpose Relate structure to function in crayfish.

Overview Students will dissect a crayfish and identify internal and external structures.

LAB PREPARATION
- Copy and distribute the Anatomical Crayfish Drawings (*Lab Binder*, p. 25).

LAB MANAGEMENT

Safety Make sure students wash their hands after the lab. Students who are allergic to preservative should observe without handling the specimen.

POST-LAB DISCUSSION

Discuss the feeding behavior of crayfish. Ask students to describe the appendages that crayfish use to capture, manipulate, and bite their food.

CHAPTER REVIEW

Interactive Review

Encourage students to go to **ClassZone.com** for a detailed review of each section, including visuals and vocabulary practice.

Unit Resource Book, Vocabulary Practice, pp. 61–64

CHAPTER 24 Interactive Review @ CLASSZONE.COM

KEY CONCEPTS | Vocabulary Games | Concept Maps | Animated Biology | Online Quiz

24.1 Arthropod Diversity

Arthropods are the most diverse of all animals. The five major groups of arthropods are trilobites, crustaceans, chelicerates, insects, and myriapods. Each group has unique features that have evolved over millions of years, but all share features—including an exoskeleton made of chitin, and jointed appendages.

24.2 Crustaceans

Crustaceans are a diverse group of ancient arthropods. Most crustaceans are aquatic arthropods with segmented bodies, a hard exoskeleton, two pairs of antennae, and one pair of appendages per segment that set crustaceans apart from other arthropods. The recognizable decapods have two major body segments: a cephalothorax and an abdomen. Isopods, barnacles, and tongue worms appear very different but share the same characteristic features. The appendages of crustaceans are highly adapted to each species' habitat and niche.

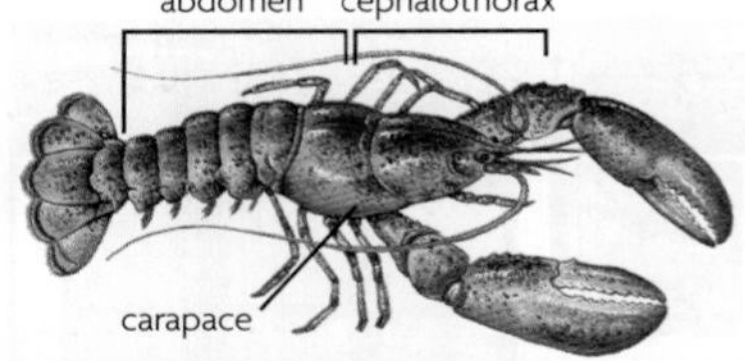

24.3 Arachnids

Arachnids include spiders and their relatives. Chelicerates are arthropods that are distinguished by four pairs of walking appendages and two pairs of modified appendages used for feeding. The arachnids are terrestrial chelicerates that have evolved book lungs and other adaptations for survival on land. The most common arachnids are spiders, but mites, ticks, chiggers and scorpions are also members of this family. They play an important ecological role as invertebrate predators.

24.4 Insect Adaptations

Insects show an amazing range of adaptations. Insects are the dominant terrestrial arthropods and are found in all of Earth's biomes. All insects have three body segments—a head, thorax, and abdomen—as well as wings, compound eyes, and three pairs of legs. Insects grow through either complete or incomplete metamorphosis. Breathing through a system of tracheae and spiracles helps insects to conserve water.

24.5 Arthropods and Humans

Arthropods and humans interact in many ways. Humans and arthropods often compete for the same resources. Pesticides are a common way in which humans control arthropod populations. Arthropods are also vectors for many different diseases, carrying viruses and bacteria from one species and infecting another.

Synthesize Your Notes

Concept Map Use a concept map to summarize the features of arthropods.

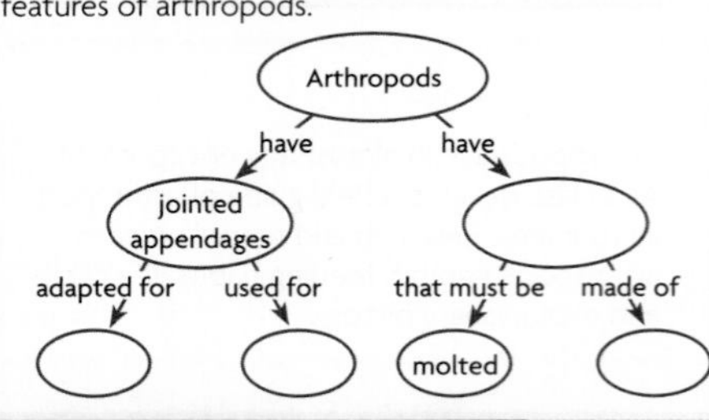

Process Diagram Use a process diagram to explain arthropod vectors.

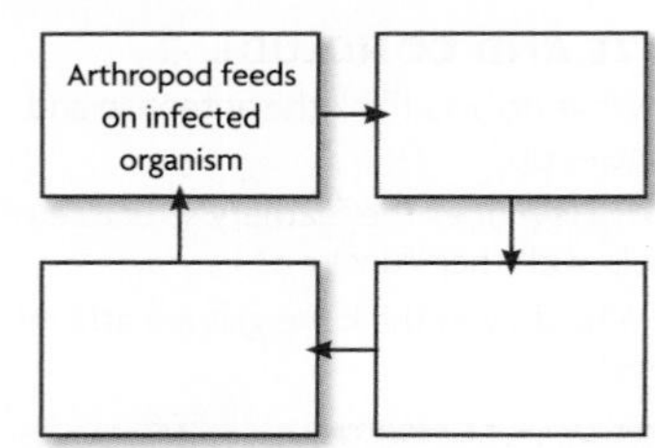

752 Unit 8: Animals

Reviewing Vocabulary

1. The pupa phase is the part of complete metamorphosis in which an insect develops from a larva into an adult.
2. In crustaceans, the cephalothorax is covered by the carapace, a protective covering of the gills and abdomen.
3. An arthropod's exoskeleton is made of chitin.
4. Mandibles are appendages used by insects and other arthropods to feed; chelicerae are fanglike appendages used by chelicerates for feeding.
5. distinct body sections
6. fanglike mouthparts
7. humid breathing chamber
8. insects growing from young to adult
9. breathing holes
10. An appendage is a part of an arthropod that extends outward from the central body region.
11. The carapace is an outer coating that helps cover internal structures of crustaceans, similar to how a tortoise shell protects the vital organs of the tortoise.

Chapter Assessment

Chapter Vocabulary

24.1 arthropod, p. 730
exoskeleton, p. 730
chitin, p. 730
appendage, p. 730
segmentation, p. 730

24.2 crustacean, p. 735
cephalothorax, p. 735
abdomen, p. 735
carapace, p. 735
mandible, p. 737

24.3 chelicerate, p. 740
arachnid, p. 740
book lung, p. 740
spiracle, p. 741
trachea, p. 741

24.4 incomplete metamorphosis, p. 744
complete metamorphosis, p. 744
pupa, p. 744

24.5 insecticide, p. 747
vector, p. 748

Reviewing Vocabulary

Vocabulary Connections

For each pair of words below, write a sentence or two that clearly shows how the terms are connected. For example, for *appendage* and *chelipeds*, you could write, "A cheliped is a type of appendage that looks like a large claw."

1. pupa, metamorphosis
2. cephalothorax, carapace
3. chitin, exoskeleton
4. mandible, chelicerae

Keep It Short

Write a short, precise phrase that defines each vocabulary term below. For example, a short phrase to describe *exoskeleton* could be "hard, outer covering."

5. segmentation
6. chelicerae
7. book lung
8. metamorphosis
9. spiracle

Word Origins

10. The term *appendage* comes from the Latin word *appendere*, which means "to cause to hang (from something)." Explain how this meaning relates to what an appendage is.

11. The term *carapace* is a French word that means "tortoise shell." Explain how this meaning relates to what a carapace is.

Reviewing MAIN IDEAS

12. Each of the thousands of known arthropod species can be placed into one of five groups. What features do arthropods in all five groups have in common?

13. Your skeleton is inside your body, and it grows along with you. How does an arthropod's exoskeleton differ in both its location and its response to growth?

14. Explain how scientists can determine relationships between ancient arthropods that lived 500 million years ago and arthropods of today.

15. Crustaceans, such as crabs and shrimp, are found in nearly all aquatic food chains. Describe the significance of crustaceans to these ecosystems.

16. Arachnids were some of the first land animals. How did the development of methods for conserving water allow them to colonize land?

17. What important function do arachnids serve in an ecosystem?

18. What features set insects apart from other arthropods?

19. What stages does a butterfly go through during metamorphosis?

20. Insects evolved from ancestors that lived in water. What adaptations did insects develop that allowed them to live on land?

21. Insects and humans interact in many ways. Give two ways in which insects are beneficial to humans, and two ways in which they are harmful to human societies.

CHAPTER REVIEW

Reviewing Main Ideas

12. jointed appendages, exoskeleton, segmented bodies
13. An arthropod's skeleton surrounds its body. It must be shed and replaced in order for the arthropod to grow.
14. Scientists can compare body structures of fossilized arthropods with the structures of modern arthropods.
15. Crustaceans are important consumers at various levels of the food chain. Krill and other planktonic crustaceans make up much of the primary consumer level, and other crustaceans are important predators, prey items, and scavengers.
16. Because they were not reliant on nearby sources of water, arachnids could move into new habitats and niches.
17. Arachnids are important predators of insects and are themselves prey of various animals.
18. All insects have a head, a thorax, and an abdomen; two antennae; and three pairs of thoracic legs.
19. An egg hatches into a larva, also called a caterpillar. The caterpillar molts and forms a pupa inside a chrysalis. Inside the chrysalis, dramatic restructuring leads to the development of the full-grown adult butterfly, which then emerges from the pupa.
20. spiracles, tracheae
21. Many insects are natural pollinators of plants we consume, and others are predators of pest species. Insect pests consume our crops, and others are vectors for pathogens that infect humans.

Critical Thinking

22. Myriapods; They probably eat other insects.
23. When the barnacles are nauplius larvae, they are able to come into contact with whales and settle onto their skin.
24. Advantage: if some tracheae are blocked, others can still take in air for gas exchange; disadvantage: in some insects, tracheae depend on diffusion of oxygen into the body, so the insect cannot alternate the source as a human can.
25. application of insecticides, integrated pest management
26. *Sample Answers:* The ability of the exoskeleton and jointed appendages to bear weight may limit the spider's size. The dependence of the spiracles and tracheae on passive diffusion of oxygen would mean that the air would have to have much more oxygen in order for the spider to grow any larger.

Interpreting Visuals

27. complete metamorphosis
28. egg—developing embryo; larva—wormlike grub with thoracic legs; pupa—chrysalis in which the larval form becomes an adult; adult—beetle with six legs, antennae, and wings. The adaptive advantage is that the pupa stage can take place in periods of drought or food shortage, when other organisms struggle to survive.

Critical Thinking

22. Classify You turn over a rock and several long, thin animals with many sets of legs scurry away into the leaves. To what group of arthropods do they likely belong? What do they likely eat?

23. Apply If you walk along a rocky shoreline, you will likely see many barnacles attached to rocks. But barnacles can also be found attached to large whales that never swim up on the shore. How do these barnacles get onto whales?

24. Compare and Contrast The tracheae of insects branch out throughout the body. Humans can only breathe through their mouth or nose. What are the advantages and disadvantages of having tracheae instead of a mouth or nose?

25. Apply Termites are a pest species that feed on the cellulose found in wood. They live in large colonies and can destroy houses over the course of a few years if left untreated. What are some ways in which a homeowner might eliminate a termite colony?

26. Infer The world's largest spider is the goliath bird-eating spider of South America, which can be as large as a dinner plate. What anatomical features may prevent spiders from growing any larger than this?

Interpreting Visuals

Use the diagram to answer the next two questions.

27. Apply What type of metamorphosis is illustrated in the diagram?

28. Identify Name and describe each phase of metamorphosis shown above. What adaptive advantage does this type of metamorphosis give this species?

Analyzing Data

Use the data below to answer the next three questions.

Crab nets have to be designed to capture crabs of varying lengths. The data below show the efficiency of crab nets at capturing crabs of varying carapace length.

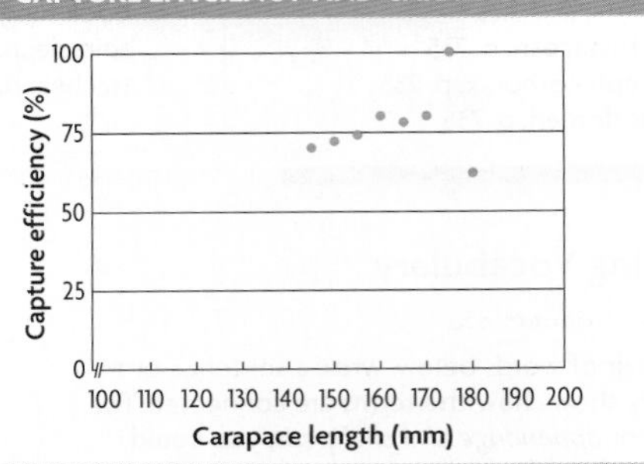

29. Interpret What is the relationship between capturing efficiency and carapace length?

30. Interpret Does the scatterplot have any outliers? If so, what explanation might explain the outlier?

Connecting CONCEPTS

31. Write Science Fiction Create your own species of arthropod. Imagine that you are sampling arthropod species 1 million years into the future. Arthropods are very different than they are today. Draw and label the appendages and other features of this new species. Write a brief description of the species, and include your hypothesis on its ancestors, what environmental pressures selected for its features, and describe its habitat, food, and lifestyle.

32. Compare and Contrast Insect predators such as the potter wasp hunt numerous species of arthropods. In what ways are the hunting styles of arachnids and wasps similar and different?

Analyzing Data

29. For crabs within a size range of 145 to 175 millimeters, the larger the carapace length, the higher is the capture efficiency.
30. The data point corresponding to the 180-millimeter crab(s) is an outlier. Students may hypothesize that the sample size of crabs of this size may have been very small. For example, maybe three out of five 180-millimeter crabs were caught. Other answers may apply.

Connecting Concepts

31. Answers will vary.
32. Most arachnids build nests to trap their prey or ambush prey from burrows, while wasps actively hunt their prey by flying. Both arachnids and wasps use venom to kill or paralyze their prey. Arachnids' venom is delivered via fangs; wasps' venom is delivered by stingers.

INDIANA ISTEP+ Test Prep

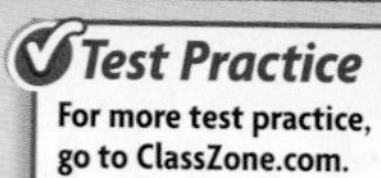
B.3.5; B.4.1; B.8.5; NOS.1; NOS.2

Test Practice
For more test practice, go to ClassZone.com.

1

Set Up for Daphnia Experiment	
Daphnia	**Treatment**
Group A	flashes of light from above
Group B	flashes of light from below
Group C	no light

Two students observed how a species of daphnia, a microscopic crustacean, responds to light. They divided their daphnia into three groups with each receiving a different light treatment. Based on their experimental design shown above, which group served as a control?

A Group A
B Group B
C Group C
D no control group in this experiment

2 In one chain of a soil food web, dead plant material is decomposed by fungi. The fungi are eaten by tiny insects called springtails, which are in turn eaten by centipedes. At each link in this chain, about 90 percent of the energy

A stays with the primary producer.
B is stored in body structures of the consumer.
C is lost to the environment as heat.
D is transferred to the decomposers.

3 Sowbugs and pillbugs are terrestrial crustaceans that feed primarily on decaying organic matter. They are important to the stability of ecosystems in part due to their role as

A producers.
B predators.
C decomposers.
D autotrophs.

4 Walking sticks are insects that look like parts of a plant. They are eaten by birds, lizards, and other predators. Over many generations, natural selection has ***most*** likely favored individual walking sticks that

A cannot be easily seen by predators.
B look the most frightening to predators.
C stand out the most to predators.
D do not have any predators.

THINK THROUGH THE QUESTION

Remember that natural selection favors individuals with adaptations that allow them to survive and reproduce.

5

Trilobite Abundance in the Fossil Record	
Millions of Years Ago (MYA)	**Fossil Record**
540 MYA	trilobite fossils appear
500 MYA	peak of trilobite diversity
450 MYA	trilobite diversity drops
300 MYA	trilobites uncommon
245 MYA to Present	no trilobites

Scientists have generated the above data based on hundreds of thousands of trilobite fossils that have been identified and dated in the fossil record. What conclusion can be drawn from these data?

A Scientists must look longer for trilobite fossils.
B Trilobite fossils began to decay 300 MYA.
C Trilobite speciation peaked about 300 MYA.
D Trilobites went extinct about 245 MYA.

6 One of the physical characteristics that make arthropods distinct is the exoskeleton. How might having an exoskeleton be both advantageous and disadvantageous?

Standards-Based Assessment

1. C	4. A
2. C	5. D
3. C	6. See Below

Question 2 Answer C is correct. Answers A, B, and D are incorrect because the energy is lost as heat, therefore it is not stored with the producer, the consumer, or the decomposer.

Question 3 Answer C is correct because they break down organic matter into simpler compounds, thereby returning nutrients into an ecosystem. Answer A is incorrect because a producer obtains its energy from light or inorganic chemicals, not from biotic sources. Answer B is incorrect because predators hunt and kill other organisms for food. Answer D is incorrect because autotrophs, another name for producers, obtain their energy from light or inorganic chemicals.

Question 4 Answer A is correct. Answer B is incorrect because walking sticks blend in with their surroundings, which is counter to the idea of trying to look frightening. Answer C is incorrect because those that stand out are most likely to be eaten. Answer D is incorrect because walking sticks continue to have predators.

Question 6 Exoskeletons serve as a protective barrier. However, because they are made of a rigid chitinous wall, they can make movement and growth difficult.

ITEM CORRELATIONS

Standard	Items
B.3.5	2
B.4.1	3
B.8.5	4, 6
NOS.1	1
NOS.2	5

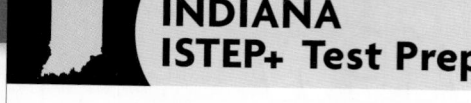

CHAPTER 25

Indiana Resource Preview

Print Resources

Vertebrate Diversity

INDIANA STANDARDS		Sections	PAGES and PACING	UNIT RESOURCE BOOK
B.8.3	25.1	**Vertebrate Origins** **KEY CONCEPT** All vertebrates share common characteristics.	pp. 758–762 30 minutes	URB pages 65–68
	25.2	**Fish Diversity** **KEY CONCEPT** The dominant aquatic vertebrates are fish.	pp. 763–767 30 minutes	URB pages 69–72
	25.3	**A Closer Look at Bony Fish** **KEY CONCEPT** Bony fish include ray-finned and lobe-finned fish.	pp. 768–771 30 minutes	URB pages 73–76
NOS.3		DATA ANALYSIS: Constructing Scatterplots	p. 770 45 minutes	URB page 85
NOS.1, NOS.3		CHAPTER INVESTIGATION: Fish Reproduction	p. 772 30 minutes	**Lab Binder** Animals pages 33–36
	25.4	**Amphibians** **KEY CONCEPT** Amphibians evolved from the lobe-finned fish.	pp. 773–777 30 minutes	URB pages 77–80
	25.5	**Vertebrates on Land** **KEY CONCEPT** Reptiles, birds, and mammals are adapted for life on land.	pp. 778–779 30 minutes	URB pages 81–84
NOS.1		OPTIONS FOR INQUIRY	pp. 780–781 45 minutes, 30 minutes	**Lab Binder** Animals pages 37–42
		Chapter Review	pp. 782–785	**Assessment Book** Chapter Tests A, B pp. 499–506

INDIANA STANDARDS

B.8.3 Use anatomical and molecular evidence to establish evolutionary relationships between organisms.
NOS.1 Develop explanations based on reproducible data and observations gathered during laboratory investigations.
NOS.3 Clearly communicate their ideas and results of investigations verbally and in written form using tables, graphs, diagrams, and photographs.

Labs

PUPIL EDITION LABS

Fish Reproduction, p. 772 Students investigate external fertilization in fish reproduction. **Lab Binder** pp. 33–36	**Time:** 30 minutes **Materials:** 20 colored beads, 1 large bowl, 100 clear beads, graph paper, ruler, calculator
Frog Development, Section 4, p. 776 Students observe and describe the stages of development of a frog from embryo to adult. **Lab Binder** pp. 43–44	**Time:** 30 minutes **Materials:** preserved specimens of frog embryos and tadpoles, petri dish, spatula, hand lens or dissecting microscope

OPTIONS FOR INQUIRY

Anatomy of a Bony Fish, p. 780 Students observe the organs and systems of a bony fish. **Lab Binder** pp. 37–40	**Time:** 45 minutes **Materials:** dissecting tray, preserved perch specimen, Anatomical Perch Drawings, hand lens, scalpel, scissors, forceps, dissecting needle, 12 dissecting pins, paper towels
Vanishing Amphibian—an Indicator Species, p. 781 Students will conduct research on the role of amphibians as ecological indicators. **Lab Binder** pp. 41–42	**Time:** 30 minutes **Materials:** map of the United States, colored pencils

LAB BINDER Unit 8 Animals

Additional Investigation: Homologies in Vertebrate Skeletons, pp. 45–49

Challenge Lab: Examining Zebrafish Development, pp. 88–91

LAB GENERATOR

A searchable CD of all labs in the program in editable format, including forensic, probeware, and biotechnology labs.

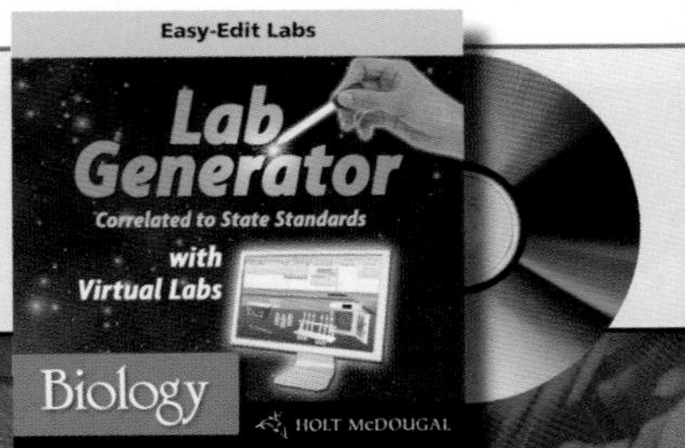

Presentation Tools

POWER PRESENTATIONS

Presentation Chapter 25
Power Presentations for each section incorporate images and clips from the Media Gallery: Includes Note Navigator for each section.

MEDIA GALLERY

Contains the following images and video clips, as well as animations, simulations and forms of visuals from the book.

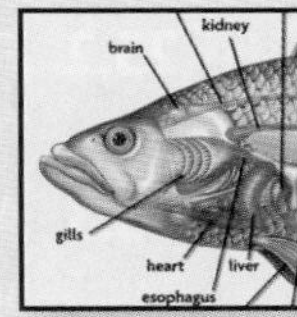

Bony fish anatomy

Fish types

Axolotl

Lionfish

Power Notes

VIDEO

Explore a set of short video clips on vertebrate evolution and diversity.

ANIMATED BIOLOGY

Gas Exchange in Gills
What Type of Fish Is It?
Frog Metamorphosis

TRANSPARENCIES

Chordate Anatomy T106
Vertebrate Phylogeny T107
Bony Fish Anatomy T108
Amphibian Anatomy T109

Online BIOLOGY CLASSZONE.COM

BioZine
Animated Biology
Interactive Review
SciLinks
Resource Centers

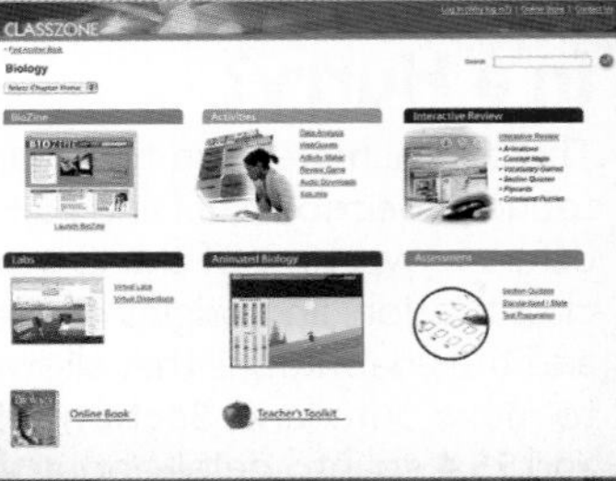

CHAPTER 25

▼ Focus and Motivate

Why is this frog see-through?

Tell students that the Fleischmann's glass frog is see-through because there is no pigment in the skin of its underbelly. **Ask,** What advantage does the frog have by being transparent when viewed from below and green when viewed from above? camouflage Tell students that transparency is one of the few forms of camouflage used by organisms that live near the surface of water. **Ask,** How might this camouflage be effective? Above water, the green blends in with leaves and water plants; from below, the frog's transparency reduces its silhouette against the light sky.

Tell students that this frog is only about 20 mm long and is classified as follows:

Kingdom: Animalia

Phylum: Chordata

Class: Amphibia

Order: Anura

Family: Centrolenidae

Genus: *Hyalinobatrachium*

Species: *fleischmanni*

In this chapter, students will learn about Chordata.

BIOZINE ClassZone.com

Students can access BioZine at **ClassZone.com** to check out articles featured in "Strange Biology."

In a Hurry?

The critical material in this chapter is found in **Sections 25.1** and **25.5,** which offer an overview of the characteristics, classification, and origins of vertebrates; and the adaptations that allowed them to move onto land. **Sections 25.2, 25.3,** and **25.4** go into detail about the anatomy and characteristics of fish and amphibians.

CHAPTER 25 Vertebrate Diversity

KEY CONCEPTS

25.1 Vertebrate Origins
All vertebrates share common characteristics.

25.2 Fish Diversity
The dominant aquatic vertebrates are fish.

25.3 A Closer Look at Bony Fish
Bony fish include ray-finned and lobe-finned fish.

25.4 Amphibians
Amphibians evolved from lobe-finned fish.

25.5 Vertebrates on Land
Reptiles, birds, and mammals are adapted for life on land.

Online BIOLOGY CLASSZONE.COM

Animated BIOLOGY
View animated chapter concepts.
- Gas Exchange in Gills
- What Type of Fish Is It?
- Frog Metamorphosis

BIOZINE
Keep current with biology news.
- News feeds
- Careers
- Polls

RESOURCE CENTER
Get more information on
- Chordates
- Fish
- Amphibians

Student Activity

Purpose **Have students compare exoskeletons to external structures of animals with endoskeletons.**

Materials
- crustacean exoskeleton
- insect molt
- fish scales
- lizard or snake skin
- hand lenses or microscopes

Set up the molts and skins at viewing stations.

Why is this frog see-through?

Connecting CONCEPTS

The Fleischmann's glass frog is one of several members of the family Centrolenidae. Glass frogs lack pigment on their undersides, making their skin transparent. The skin on the top portion of their body has a pigment that reflects the same wavelength of light as plants, helping them to blend in with the green leaves on which they live.

Reproduction In some species of glass frogs, the male protects the eggs from predators. Seahorses, such as the one shown at left, also exhibit male parental care. The seahorse's role is even more extreme than that of the glass frog. A female deposits eggs into the male's brood patch, where they are fertilized and left to develop. After two to four weeks, the male seahorse gives birth to live young.

Introduce Tell students that for most motile animals, the outer covering of their bodies must not only protect internal structures but also provide for movement. Explain that the students are to rotate through the stations in small groups and compare a selection of invertebrate exoskeletons (molts) with the skins of certain vertebrates.

Discuss Point out that the specimens are not living tissue, however one can still make inferences about how an outer covering affects the motility—ability to move—of an organism. **Ask**

- As a body covering, how do the scales of a snake or lizard skin compare to a segmented exoskeleton? skin more flexible, surface covered by many overlapping scales, not a single unit
- What do the differences suggest about how the different animals move? exoskeleton: movement limited to joints between segments; vertebrates: whole body can flex
- What do the differences suggest about the protection offered? The exoskeleton offers more protection.

Activate Prior Knowledge

Have students call out the names of as many aquatic animals as they can think of. List them on the board. *Sample Answers:* whale, shark, fish, octopus, dolphin, shrimp **Ask**

- Which of these has no backbone? octopus, shrimp, and others depending on the list Cross these off the list. Explain that the remaining organisms are vertebrates.
- How does a shark differ from a trout? It has a cartilaginous skeleton; a trout has a skeleton of bone.
- How do dolphins and whales differ from fish? They are mammals.
- How do frogs and salamanders differ from fish? They can live on land.

Tell students that these are some of the things they will study in this chapter.

Preview Vocabulary

Greek and Latin Word Origins Tell students that typically the animals most familiar to people belong to the phylum Chordata. The Latin word *chorda* means "cord," and one characteristic that all these animals share is not a backbone, but a "back cord," a notochord. The Greek word *nōton* means "back."

Academic Vocabulary Tell students that they will be introduced to different classes of vertebrates in this chapter: *Agnatha, Chondrichthyes, Osteichthyes, Amphibia, Reptilia, Aves, Mammalia.* Some of the parts of these names are found in everyday language, for example:

osteoporosis, disease characterized by fragile bones, osteon = bone

amphibious, able to operate on land or in water

aviator, one who operates an aircraft

reptilian, when not used to describe a reptile, means despicable or treacherous

English Learners Suggest students use a word square called a Frayer Model (*Biology Toolkit,* p. D5) for organizing the different groups of animals in this chapter. The squares include boxes for a definition, characteristics, examples, and for the fourth box suggest that students include a small drawing.

SECTION 25.1

▼ Plan and Prepare

Objectives

- Identify and give examples of the three groups of organisms in the phylum Chordata.
- Describe the characteristics and origins of vertebrates.

Section Resources

Unit Resource Book
Study Guide pp. 65–66
Power Notes p. 67
Reinforcement p. 68

Interactive Reader Chapter 25
Spanish Study Guide pp. 255–256

Biology Toolkit pp. C2, C17, C31, C34, D1

Technology
Power Presentation 25.1
Media Gallery DVD
Online Quiz 25.1

Activate Prior Knowledge Tell students that an earthworm is an invertebrate and a snake is a vertebrate. **Ask,** In what obvious way is a snake different from a worm? A snake has a backbone; a worm does not. Have students discuss what advantages a backbone and internal skeleton provide an animal, not just in mobility but also in size. Point out that the only really large invertebrates are found in the oceans, where the water provides buoyancy.

▼ Teach

Vocabulary

Academic Vocabulary Students may wonder what the difference is between the words **cord** and **chord.** In anatomy, *chord* is a variant of *cord,* which is how it appears in *chordate* and *notochord.* When used in a musical context, the word *chord* derives from the strings of a musical instrument, which produce the sound.

25.1 Vertebrate Origins

KEY CONCEPT All vertebrates share common characteristics.

MAIN IDEAS
- The phylum Chordata contains all vertebrates and some invertebrates.
- All vertebrates share common features.
- Fossil evidence sheds light on the origins of vertebrates.

VOCABULARY
chordate, p. 758
notochord, p. 758
endoskeleton, p. 759

B.8.3 Use anatomical and molecular evidence to establish evolutionary relationships between organisms.

Connect Just like the glass frog, you too are a vertebrate. So are birds, tigers, lizards, and squirrels. While the vertebrates you most often see are those that live on land like us, the group first evolved in the ocean. The first vertebrates were fish, and even today the vast majority of vertebrates are still fish.

MAIN IDEA

The phylum Chordata contains all vertebrates and some invertebrates.

The phylum Chordata is made up of three groups. One group includes all vertebrates. Vertebrates are large, active animals that have a well-developed brain encased in a hard skull. The other two groups are the tunicates and lancelets, which are both invertebrates. Tunicates, or the urochordates, include both free-swimming and sessile animals such as sea squirts. Lancelets, or the cephalochordates (SEHF-uh-luh-KAWR-DAYTS), are small eel-like animals that are commonly found in shallow tropical oceans. Although lancelets can swim, they spend most of their lives buried in sand, filtering water for food particles.

Despite their enormous differences in body plans and ways of life, all **chordates** share the four features illustrated in **FIGURE 25.1** at some stage of their development.

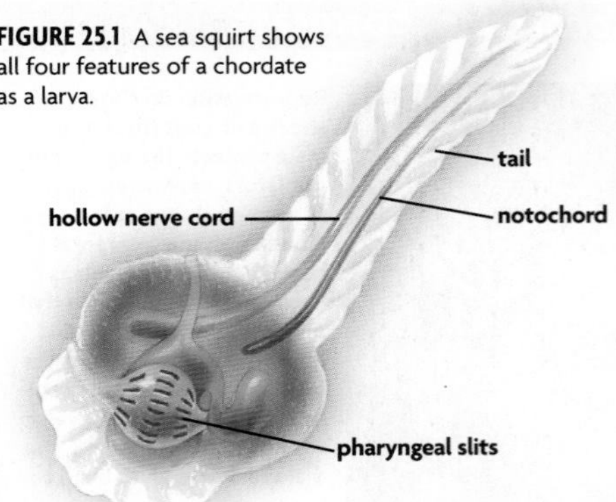

FIGURE 25.1 A sea squirt shows all four features of a chordate as a larva.

- **Notochord** A **notochord** is a flexible skeletal support rod embedded in the animal's back.
- **Hollow nerve cord** A hollow nerve cord runs along the animal's back. The nerve cord forms from a section of the ectoderm that rolls up during development.
- **Pharyngeal slits** Pharyngeal (fuh-RIHN-jee-uhl) slits are slits through the body wall in the pharynx, the part of the gut immediately beyond the mouth. Water can enter the mouth and leave the animal through these slits without passing through the entire digestive system.
- **Tail** A tail extends beyond the anal opening. The tail, as well as the rest of the animal, contains segments of muscle tissue used for movement.

Differentiated Instruction

BELOW LEVEL

Have students preview the section by preparing an outline. Tell them to look at the introductory paragraph, headings, topic sentences, and the concluding paragraph to write their outlines. Have students leave some space between entries. Then have them fill in their outline with notes as they read, focusing on the characteristics of members of the Chordata and the Vertebrata.

Biology Toolkit, Section Preview, p. C2

ENGLISH LEARNERS

To help students see how far along they are in their study of animals, have them turn back to **FIGURE 23.7** on page 703. Remind them that while the distinction between invertebrate and vertebrate is important, it is not a good basis for classification.

Biology Toolkit, Connect to Content through Visuals, p. C17

Most chordate groups lose some or all of these characteristics in adulthood, but they are present in their larvae and embryos. For example, the larval form of sea squirts have all four chordate characteristics. However, an adult sea squirt, shown in **FIGURE 25.2**, retains only one chordate characteristic, the pharyngeal slits. Adult sea squirts use the pharyngeal slits for filter feeding. Similarly, vertebrate embryos have a notochord that is for the most part replaced by the vertebrae during later development. The fluid-filled disks between adjacent vertebrae are remnants of the notochord.

A Compare and Contrast How are humans similar to sea squirts? How are they different?

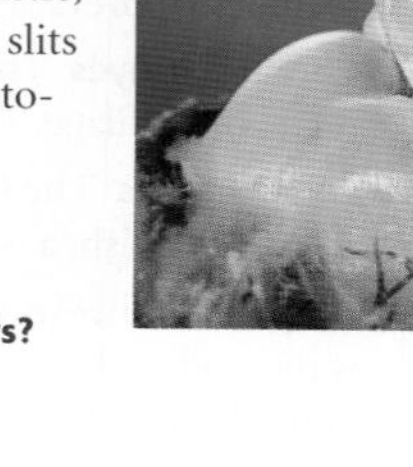

FIGURE 25.2 In its adult form, the only chordate feature a sea squirt retains is the presence of pharyngeal slits (located within the sea squirt's body).

MAIN IDEA

All vertebrates share common features.

Vertebrates tend to be large, active animals. Even the smallest living vertebrate, an Indonesian carp smaller than a fingernail, is larger than most invertebrates.

Vertebrate Endoskeleton

One characteristic that allows vertebrates to grow to large sizes is the endoskeleton. An **endoskeleton** is an internal skeleton built of bone or cartilage. Bone and cartilage are both dense connective tissues. Each tissue is made of collagen fibers that are embedded in a matrix, or combination, of harder materials.

Vertebrate endoskeletons can be divided into distinct parts. Some of these parts are shown on the ape skeleton in **FIGURE 25.3**.

- **Braincase** A braincase or cranium protects the brain.
- **Vertebrae** A series of short, stiff vertebrae are separated by joints. This internal backbone protects the spinal cord. It also replaces the notochord with harder material that can resist forces produced by large muscles. Joints between the vertebrae let the backbone bend as the animal moves.
- **Bones** Bones support and protect the body's soft tissues and provide points for muscle attachment.
- **Gill arches** Gill arches, found in the pharynx of fish and some amphibians, support the gills.

The endoskeleton forms a framework that supports muscles and protects internal organs. It contains cells that can actively break down skeletal material and rebuild it. This characteristic means a vertebrate endoskeleton can slowly change size and shape. It can grow as a vertebrate changes size, unlike arthropod exoskeletons, which must be shed as the animal grows. It can also change shape in response to forces on a vertebrate's body. Bones subjected to large forces get thicker.

FIGURE 25.3 Every vertebrate has an endoskeleton, such as the one you see in this x-ray of a small ape.

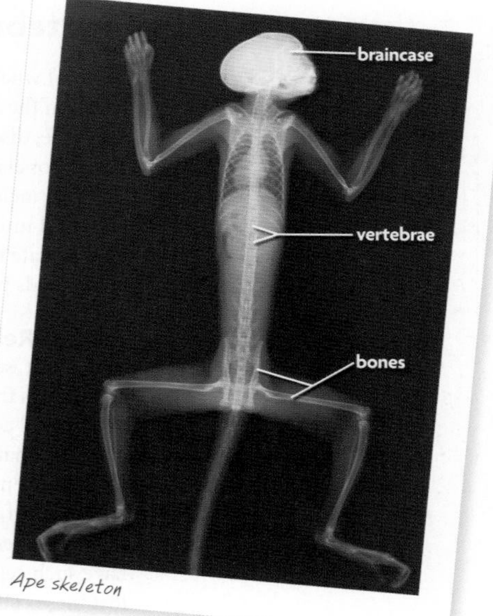

ONLINE BIOLOGY Go to the chapter Resource Center at **ClassZone.com** for additional resources and information on chordates.

Integrating Forensic Anthropology

The branch of anatomy that deals with the study of the structure and function of bones is called **osteology.** This knowledge is applied by a **forensic anthropologist** to the study of human skeletal remains for the purpose of identification. For example, unidentified remains from a crime scene can provide information about gender, age, stature, race, and time and cause of death. The first thing a forensic anthropologist will do when only bone fragments are found is to determine if they are human. Bone density and thickness of human bone, especially of the leg and arm, can even give clues about a person's lifestyle.

Answers

A Compare and Contrast Sometime during development, humans and sea squirts have a notochord, a hollow nerve cord, pharyngeal slits, and a tail. In humans, the notochord is replaced with the vertebrae, and the pharyngeal slits and tail disappear. Sea squirts retain the pharyngeal slits, but none of the other characteristics as adults.

PRE-AP

Have students compare and contrast an endoskeleton with an exoskeleton. Have them include not just structural differences but also how each type of skeleton has an impact on behaviors as well as affects potential for ecological niches.

Biology Toolkit, Compare/Contrast Chart, p. C34

▼ Teach *continued*

Take It Further

Some students may not be familiar with the cartilaginous fish called **chimera** (kye MEER ah). They are named after a creature from Greek mythology that was a mixture of a lion, a snake, and a goat. These fish have been described as a creature assembled by a committee that couldn't agree. They have a huge head, well-developed eyes, and an odd, rodentlike mouth with grinding teeth. The tail is very thin and streamerlike, so the chimera propels itself through the water by flapping its winglike pectoral fins. Plownose chimeras, including the elephant fish and ghost shark, can grow to about one meter in length and are commercially fished. Other types of chimera include the ratfish, rabbit fish, and spookfish.

History of Science

Fossil fish helped to establish the reputation of **Jean Louis Rodolphe Agassiz.** Between the years 1833 and 1843, he published five volumes on the fossil record of fish, *Poissons Fossiles.* He became a professor of zoology at Harvard University in 1848. Eleven years later, he founded the Museum of Comparative Zoology and was a founding member of the National Academy of Sciences.

Agassiz's greatest lasting insight was the realization that paleontology, embryology, ecology, and biogeography all were necessary for any classification scheme that claimed to be based on the relationships of organisms. Yet, he was a lifelong opponent of Darwin's theory of evolution. Ironically, his greatest works have provided evolutionary biologists with tremendous insights and made lasting contributions to evolutionary biology and systematics.

Answers

A Contrast An endoskeleton grows along with the animal, while an exoskeleton must be shed in order for the animal to grow.

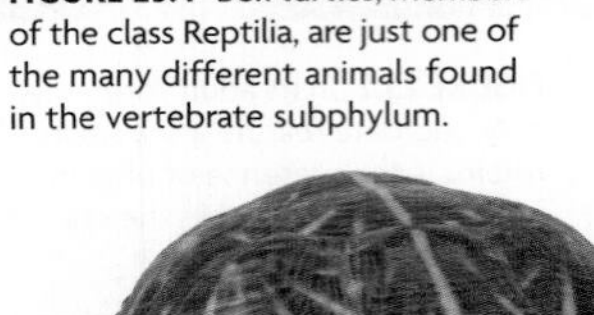

FIGURE 25.4 Box turtles, members of the class Reptilia, are just one of the many different animals found in the vertebrate subphylum.

Vertebrate Classes

The phylogenetic tree shown in **FIGURE 25.5** shows the probable evolutionary relationships among the seven classes of vertebrates.

Agnatha The Agnatha are the oldest class of vertebrates. These jawless animals include lampreys, a type of fish.

Chondrichthyes The Chondrichthyes, or cartilaginous fish, have skeletons made of cartilage. These animals include sharks, rays, and chimeras.

Osteichthyes The Osteichthyes, or bony fish, have skeletons made of bone. Ray-finned fish, a type of bony fish, are the most diverse group of vertebrates.

Amphibia The Amphibia were the first vertebrates adapted to live both in water and on land, although they reproduce in water or on moist land. These animals include salamanders, frogs (including toads), and caecilians.

Reptilia The Reptilia are able to retain moisture, which lets them live exclusively on land. Reptiles produce eggs that do not have to develop in water. Reptiles include snakes, lizards, crocodiles, alligators, and turtles.

Aves The Aves are birds. Aves are distinguished by the presence of feathers, along with other features.

Mammalia The Mammalia are animals that have hair, mammary glands, and three middle ear bones.

A Contrast How does growth differ between an animal with an endoskeleton and an animal with an exoskeleton?

MAIN IDEA

Fossil evidence sheds light on the origins of vertebrates.

TAKING NOTES

Use a main idea web to take notes on the origin of vertebrates.

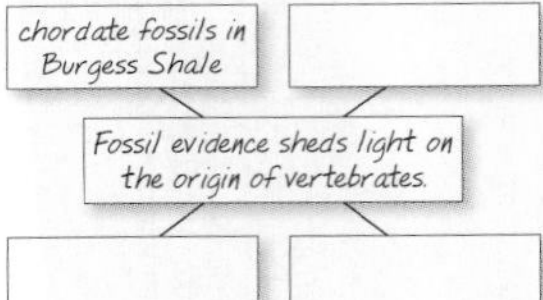
chordate fossils in Burgess Shale
Fossil evidence sheds light on the origin of vertebrates.

Much of what we know about early vertebrates comes from fossil evidence found in the Burgess Shale located in the Canadian Rocky Mountains. This fossil site, discovered in the early 1900s, was not fully explored until the late 1960s. Fossils found within the Burgess Shale date from the Cambrian explosion and include preserved exoskeletons, limbs, and in some cases, gut contents and muscles. Fossils of sponges, worms, and arthropods are among the invertebrate remains found at the quarry site. Other fossils with traces of notochords provide evidence of the earliest chordates.

Closest Relatives of Vertebrates

In the past, scientists thought that lancelets were more closely related to vertebrates than tunicates were. They based this on fossil evidence, along with anatomical comparisons and molecular evidence. However, recent research indicates that tunicates may actually be the closest relatives of vertebrates. All vertebrate embryos have strips of cells called the neural crest, which develops into parts of the nervous system, head, bone, and teeth. Scientists have found that tunicates have cells that resemble the neural crest, but lancelets do not have such cells. This evidence could indicate that either lancelets secondarily lost these cells, or tunicates are indeed the closest relatives to vertebrates.

Differentiated Instruction

ENGLISH LEARNERS

Work with students to compile cards of the seven vertebrate classes, with examples and, if available, images of each. Include cards with information on the distinguishing features of each class. Then use these cards to organize and display this information for the class.

Biology Toolkit, Word Sort/Word Splash, p. D1

TEACH WITH TECHNOLOGY

Once students are comfortable with the seven class names and their distinguishing characteristics, assemble a digital slide show of unlabeled images of various vertebrates from all seven classes. Go through the slides, asking students to name the class to which each animal belongs and, if appropriate, the common name for that type of animal. For example, show an image of a stingray, let students call out *Chondrichthyes* and *ray,* and have them explain what characteristics identified it as such.

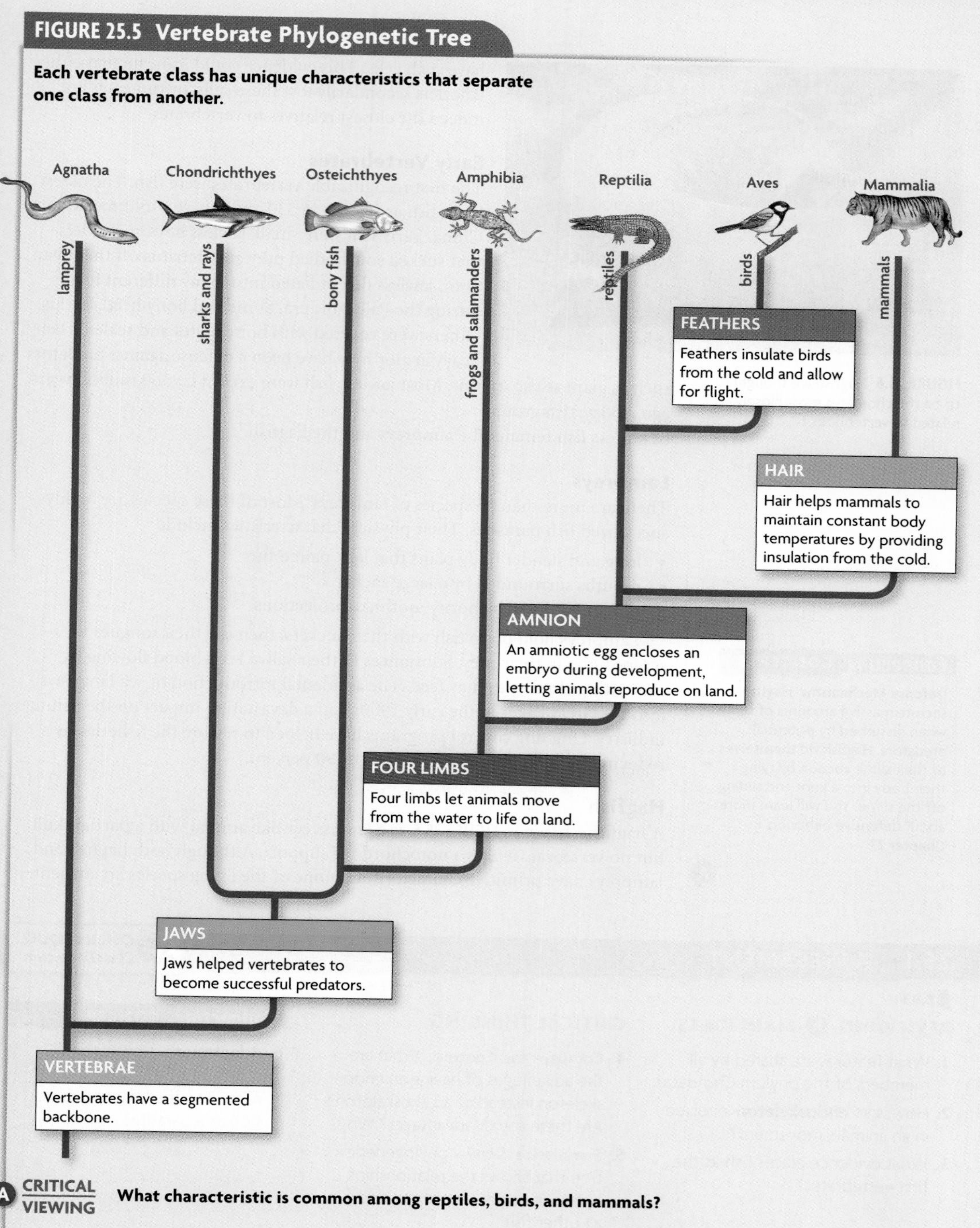
FIGURE 25.5 Vertebrate Phylogenetic Tree
Each vertebrate class has unique characteristics that separate one class from another.
Agnatha
Chondrichthyes
Osteichthyes
Amphibia
Reptilia
Aves
Mammalia
lamprey
sharks and rays
bony fish
frogs and salamanders
reptiles
birds
mammals
FEATHERS
Feathers insulate birds from the cold and allow for flight.
HAIR
Hair helps mammals to maintain constant body temperatures by providing insulation from the cold.
AMNION
An amniotic egg encloses an embryo during development, letting animals reproduce on land.
FOUR LIMBS
Four limbs let animals move from the water to life on land.
JAWS
Jaws helped vertebrates to become successful predators.
VERTEBRAE
Vertebrates have a segmented backbone.

A CRITICAL VIEWING What characteristic is common among reptiles, birds, and mammals?

PRE-AP

Have students convert the phylogenetic tree in **FIGURE 25.5** into a timeline. They should do it in such a way that they can give a somewhat accurate sense of scale. For example, they might use a spiral rather than a straight line. Provide them with the following information or refer them to **FIGURE 12.6** on page 366.

- Jawless fish (agnathan fish) appeared and diversified during the Ordovician period (505–440 mya).
- Fossils representing most major lineages of fish and the earliest amphibians existed before the Devonian period (410–360 mya).
- Reptiles appeared during the Carboniferous period (360–286 mya).
- Mammals appeared before the end of the Triassic (248–213 mya).
- Birds appeared before the end of the Jurassic (213–145 mya).

Biology Toolkit, Timeline, p. C31

Integrating Evolutionary Biology

Students may wonder how or why vertebrates managed to make their way onto land, especially when the ocean is so vast and offers so many niches. It is likely that some ancient vertebrates were inhabitants of shallow water. These low water levels would have posed a problem for animals unable to support their own body weight or get oxygen in the absence of water.

Over time, beneficial variations among individuals led to the evolution of short, stout legs instead of fins; lungs instead of the swim bladder and gills; and tough, waterproof skin instead of soft, permeable skin. These adaptations allowed these vertebrates to survive and temporarily take advantage of an otherwise unused resource: an assortment of dry land habitats. Millions of years later, the amniotic egg evolved, enabling some vertebrates to leave the water permanently and radiate out into the biomes.

Vocabulary

amnion Tell students that the first terrestrial animals, once separated from the seas, had to have a means to protect and support an embryo as it grew. An *amnion* is a fluid-filled sac that encloses an embryo, providing it with its own self-contained aquatic environment. Tell students they will learn more about amniotes in **Section 25.5** and Chapter 26.

Answers

A Critical Viewing All develop from an amniotic egg.

▼ Teach *continued*

Take It Further

Point out to students the very simple body plan of the **hagfish.** They have no backbone, no fins except a primitive tail fin, and reduced eyes. Newly hatched hagfish look just like the adults, except they have both male and female sex organs. They will eventually be either male or female, but retain the ability to change gender if their population structure requires it. Hagfish feed on dead animals such as whales and fish that sink to the bottom of the ocean. They will also feed on fish that have died after being caught by fishing gear set on or near the sea floor.

The hagfish's skin is processed into "eelskin" boots, wallets, and other products in South Korea. Fishers catch hagfish—which they call slime eels because of their defensive secretion of slippery slime—by sinking large barrels to the sea floor. The barrels have holes punched through their sides, allowing hagfish to swim inside to feed on bait held within.

Answers

A Summarize Evidence indicates that tunicates may be more closely related to vertebrates than to lancelets.

▼ Assess and Reteach

Assess Use the Online Quiz or Section Quiz (*Assessment Book,* p. 493).

Reteach Create a number of profiles of unknown animals that students will analyze in order to classify them. Include invertebrates so that students will distinguish between them and chordates. For each vertebrate class described in the section, offer at least one profile.

FIGURE 25.6 Hagfish are thought to be the chordates most closely related to vertebrates.

have such cells. This evidence could indicate that either lancelets secondarily lost these cells, or tunicates are indeed the closest relatives to vertebrates.

Early Vertebrates

The first recognizable vertebrates were fish. The oldest fossil fish are found in 530-million-year-old rocks from China. Early fish were small, jawless bottom-feeders that sucked soft-bodied prey and detritus off the ocean floor. Jawless fish radiated into many different forms during the Paleozoic era. Some had bony head shields. Others were covered with bony plates and scales. Their heavy armor may have been a defense against predators such as giant sea scorpions. Most jawless fish were extinct by 360 million years ago. Today, two groups of jawless fish remain: the lampreys and the hagfish.

Lampreys

There are more than 35 species of lampreys. Most of these species are highly specialized fish parasites. Their physical characteristics include

- long and slender body plans that lack paired fins
- mouths surrounded by a large sucker
- tongues covered by horny toothlike projections

Lampreys hold on to fish with their suckers, then use their tongues to scrape holes in their prey. Substances in their saliva keep blood flowing by preventing clotting as they feed. The accidental introduction of sea lampreys into the Great Lakes in the early 1900s had a devastating impact on the fishing industry. Ongoing control programs have helped to restore the fisheries by reducing the sea lamprey population by 90 percent.

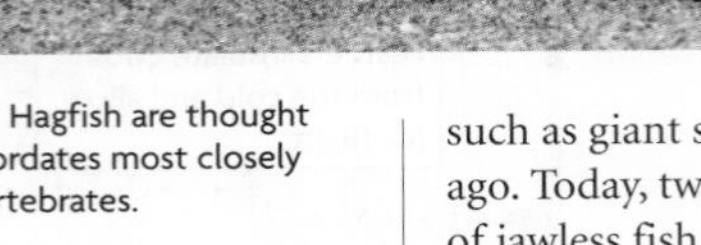

***Connecting* CONCEPTS**

Defense Mechanisms Hagfish secrete massive amounts of slime when disturbed by potential predators. Hagfish rid themselves of their slime cocoon by tying their body into a knot and sliding off the slime. You will learn more about defensive behaviors in Chapter 27.

Hagfish

A hagfish, shown in **FIGURE 25.6,** is a jawless eel-like animal with a partial skull but no vertebrae. It uses a notochord for support. Although both hagfish and lampreys have primitive characteristics, none of the living species are ancient. (A)

25.1 ASSESSMENT

ONLINE QUIZ ClassZone.com

B.8.3

REVIEWING MAIN IDEAS

1. What features are shared by all members of the phylum Chordata?
2. How is an **endoskeleton** involved in an animal's movement?
3. What evidence places fish as the first vertebrates?

CRITICAL THINKING

4. **Compare and Contrast** What are the advantages of having an endoskeleton instead of an exoskeleton? Are there any disadvantages? Why?
5. **Summarize** Draw a phylogenetic tree that shows the relationships between hagfish, lampreys, and all other fish.

***Connecting* CONCEPTS**

6. **Adaptations** How is the structure of a lamprey's body related to the lamprey's function as a parasite?

25.1 ASSESSMENT

1. notochord, hollow nerve cord, pharyngeal slits, tail
2. The endoskeleton forms a framework that supports a vertebrate's muscles.
3. fossil evidence in 530-million-year-old rocks from China
4. Advantages: Vertebrates don't have to shed their skeleton in order to grow. An endoskeleton can change shape in response to forces on the animal's body. Disadvantages: An endoskeleton is less protective to an animal's body than is a hard exoskeleton.
5. Tree should show hagfish and lampreys diverging from a common ancestor, and jawed fishes diverging from the lamprey branch.
6. The structure of a lamprey's body is simple—long and slender, allowing its body to trail from its host like a tail on a kite. The mouth is modified as a sucker to attach to its host, with a horny tongue that scrapes a hole through which blood can be sucked out.

25.2 Fish Diversity

KEY CONCEPT The dominant aquatic vertebrates are fish.

MAIN IDEAS
- Fish are vertebrates with gills and paired fins.
- Jaws evolved from gill supports.
- Only two groups of jawed fish still exist.

VOCABULARY
gill, p. 763
countercurrent flow, p. 764
lateral line, p. 767
operculum, p. 767

Connect In order to move in a swimming pool, you need to push your body through a thick, heavy blanket of water. Swimming for a long time is tiring. Long-distance swimming requires endurance and a lot of energy. Fish spend their entire lives moving through water, but adaptations to an aquatic environment make their movements through water much more energy-efficient than yours.

MAIN IDEA
Fish are vertebrates with gills and paired fins.

You get the oxygen you need by breathing in the air that surrounds you. Because fish live underwater, the way that they get oxygen is completely different from the way you breathe. Fish use specialized organs called gills to take in the oxygen dissolved in water. **Gills** are large sheets of thin frilly tissue filled with capillaries that take in dissolved oxygen from the water and release carbon dioxide. As shown in **FIGURE 25.7**, gills have a very large surface area, which increases the amount of gases they can exchange with the water. Muscles in the body wall expand and contract, creating a current of water that brings a steady supply of oxygen to the blood.

Just like you, fish have body systems that provide their cells with oxygen and nutrients and also remove waste products. Fish circulatory systems pump blood in a single circulatory loop through a heart with two main chambers. An atrium collects blood returning from the body and moves it into the ventricle. The ventricle pumps blood through the gills, where carbon dioxide is released and oxygen is picked up by the blood. The blood then carries the oxygen directly to the tissues and picks up more carbon dioxide. The blood returns to the heart, and the process begins again.

Animated BIOLOGY Explore oxygen and carbon dioxide exchange in gills at ClassZone.com.

FIGURE 25.7 Fish use the large surface area of their gills to exchange carbon dioxide and oxygen with the water in which they live.

Differentiated Instruction

HANDS-ON ACTIVITY

Bring in several whole fish from a supermarket. Lay each fish out on a dissecting tray for viewing. Have students form groups around each tray. Instruct students to look at the fish, but not touch them. Pass through each station and, using a dissecting tweezers, lift the operculum to reveal the gills for students to observe. Have students sketch the fish and label the following (if present): eye, mouth, jaw, dorsal fin, caudal fin, anal fin, pectoral fin, pelvic fin, gills, operculum, lateral line, scales. **Ask**

- What is the advantage of having a gill covering? protection from injury and parasites, help in breathing
- What are the functions of fins? stability and motion in the water

If you have supplied different types of fish, have students discuss their differences and speculate on what types of habitat they live in and what they may feed on.

Plan and Prepare

Objectives

- Identify the characteristics of the two classes of jawed fish.
- Describe the evolution and advantage of jaws.

Section Resources

Unit Resource Book
Study Guide pp. 69–70
Power Notes p. 71
Reinforcement p. 72
Pre-AP Activity pp. 87–88

Interactive Reader Chapter 25
Spanish Study Guide pp. 257–258

Biology Toolkit pp. C20, C39

Technology
Power Presentation 25.2
Media Gallery DVD
Online Quiz 25.2

Activate Prior Knowledge Have students think about aquatic habitats and the conditions that fish must cope with. **Ask,** If you dive into a cold lake without scuba gear or a wetsuit, and you remain underwater and motionless for a few moments, what problems will you have? cannot breathe (get oxygen from your surroundings), could sink to the bottom if you do not move, lose too much heat from your body (hypothermia), cannot see very well Tell students that fish have features that allow them to cope with these and other challenging conditions of aquatic environments.

Teach

TEACH FROM VISUALS

FIGURE 25.7 Point out that oxygenated blood is shown in red and deoxygenated blood in blue. **Ask,** What is different about the flow of oxygen in a fish, compared to a human? Oxygen is dissolved in water and moves in one opening (mouth) and out another (gills); in humans oxygen is carried by air, and is inhaled and exhaled through the same openings.

▼ Teach *continued*

ONLINE BIOLOGY Students can use an interactive animation to help classify fish in Options for Inquiry on page 781.

Vocabulary

Academic Vocabulary The branch of zoology that focuses on the study of fish is **ichthyology,** and its practitioners are called *ichthyologists.*

Integrating Physics

Most bony fish depend on a swim bladder for adjusting or maintaining **buoyancy.** Freshwater fish require a larger gas bladder than do marine fish to keep from sinking, because fresh water is less dense than seawater. Most fish fill and deflate the swim bladder by diffusing gas in and out of the blood. Some deflate the bladder by pushing gas into the gullet and gills. Some simply gulp air at the surface to fill the bladder.

Answers

A Summarize The more a fish moves through the water, the more oxygen it needs. Because of the countercurrent flow of blood and water in the gills, faster movement through the water means that the supply of oxygen to the blood will keep up with the demand.

Connecting **CONCEPTS**

Diffusion Recall from **Chapter 3** that diffusion is the movement of dissolved molecules in a fluid from a region of higher concentration to a region of lower concentration.

TAKING NOTES

Draw a simple picture of a fish in your notes and label the five kinds of fins found on most fish.

Countercurrent Flow

Arteries in the gills carry blood to the exchange surfaces. The arteries are arranged so that blood flows in the opposite direction of the current of water entering the gills. **Countercurrent flow** is the opposite movement of water against the flow of blood in the fish's gills. Because oxygen dissolved in the water is at a greater concentration than the oxygen in the fish's blood, countercurrent flow maximizes the amount of oxygen the fish can pull from the water by diffusion. In countercurrent flow, blood is always passing by water that contains more oxygen than it does. Both well-aerated water entering the gills and depleted water leaving the gills pass by blood with an even lower oxygen load. Oxygen diffuses into the blood along the entire length of the gill.

VISUAL VOCAB

Countercurrent flow maximizes the amount of oxygen the fish can pull from the water.

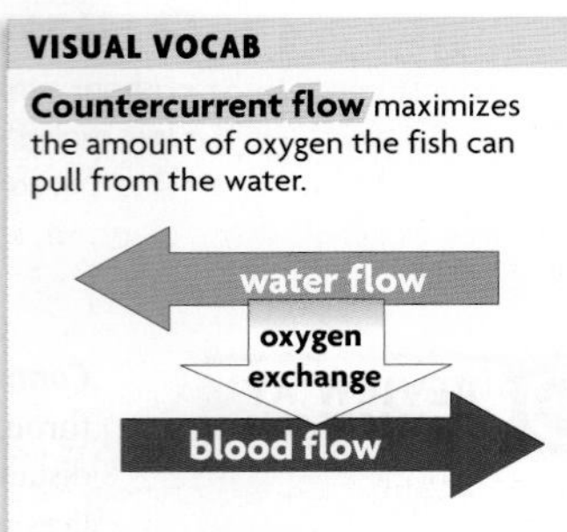

Swimming and Maneuvering

Most fish swim by contracting large segmented muscles on either side of their vertebral column from the head to the tail. These muscle segments power the contractions that produce a series of S-shaped waves that move down the fish's body and push it through the water. These waves also tend to nudge the fish from side to side. Such horizontal movements waste energy, so fish counteract them with their fins.

As you can see in **FIGURE 25.8**, fins are surfaces that project from a fish's body. Most fish have dorsal fins on their backs and anal fins on their bellies. Most fish also have two sets of lateral paired fins. One set, the pectoral fins, are found just behind the head. The other set, the pelvic fins, are often found near the middle of the belly. The caudal fin is another name for the tail fin. Fin tissue is supported by part of the endoskeleton, and its associated muscles let fish actively move their fins as they swim.

FIGURE 25.8 This clown anemone fish shows the main types of fins commonly found in fish.

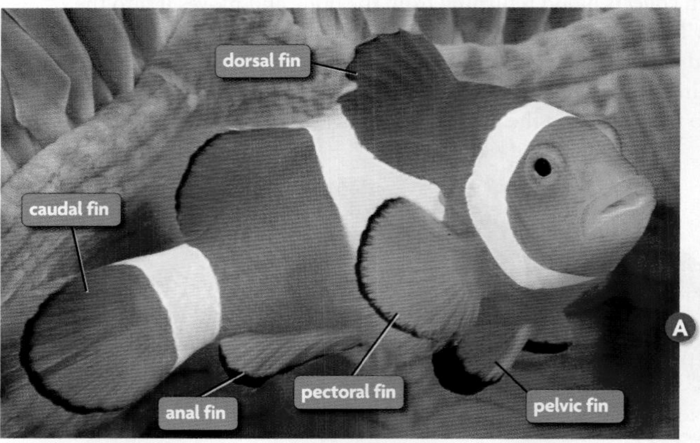

Fins keep fish stable. Their movements redirect water around the fish as it swims, producing forces that keep it from rolling, pitching up and down, and moving from side to side. The dorsal and anal fins keep the fish from rolling over. The caudal fin moves the fish in a forward direction. The pectoral and pelvic paired fins help the fish to maneuver, stop, and hover in the water.

A Summarize What is the connection between countercurrent flow and a fish's movement in the water?

Differentiated Instruction

ENGLISH LEARNERS

Draw a cycle diagram on the board that shows how oxygen and carbon dioxide are carried through a fish's body. Have students review the last paragraph on page 763 and call out the events as you go through the diagram. Once you have gone through the cycle as a class, have students close their books and write a paragraph in their notebooks describing the circulatory cycle.

Biology Toolkit, Cycle Diagram, p. C39

TEACH WITH TECHNOLOGY

Assemble images for a digital slide show of fish. Show a variety of fin shapes and differences in the placement and number of fins. For example, show a thresher shark's long caudal fin, a spiny dogfish (no anal fin; spiny dorsal fins), a whale shark (large first dorsal fin set way back on body), an Atlantic cod (three dorsal fins), a sailfish (enormous dorsal fin), and an anglerfish (dorsal fin used as fishing pole). Have students identify each fin. Point out how the fins of some fish are movable and powerful, while in others, the same fins are immobile or not as specialized.

MAIN IDEA

Jaws evolved from gill supports.

Jaws evolved from gill arches. Located on both sides of the pharynx, gill arches are structures made of bone or cartilage that function as a support for a fish's gills. As shown in **FIGURE 25.9**, jaws developed from gill arches near the mouth, which fused to the cranium. The upper section of the third gill arch attached to the cranium, forming the upper jaw. Because the gill arches are jointed, the bottom part of the gill arch could bend to open and close the mouth, forming the lower jaw.

In most fish, the fourth set of gill arches are also fused to the cranium. In these animals, the upper part of the gill arch reinforces the jaws. The gill arch's lower part supports the tissue inside the floor of the mouth. Most jawed vertebrates have teeth on their upper and lower jaws. Teeth are used to capture and process food. They evolved from the armored scales that covered early jawless fish.

As a result of natural selection, jaws gave vertebrates a huge advantage as predators and quickly pushed them to the top of the food chain. But the original function of jaws may not have been to help fish capture food. Evidence suggests that the earliest jaws prevented backflow as a fish pumped water over its gills. Clamping the front pair of arches together prevented oxygen-rich water from escaping through the mouth, ensuring that it all flowed over the gills. The fact that they also kept prey from escaping was a happy accident.

A Compare **What advantages are provided to an animal that has jaws, compared with an animal that does not have jaws?**

FIGURE 25.9 JAW EVOLUTION

Evidence from animal development studies supports the idea that jaws evolved from gill arches.

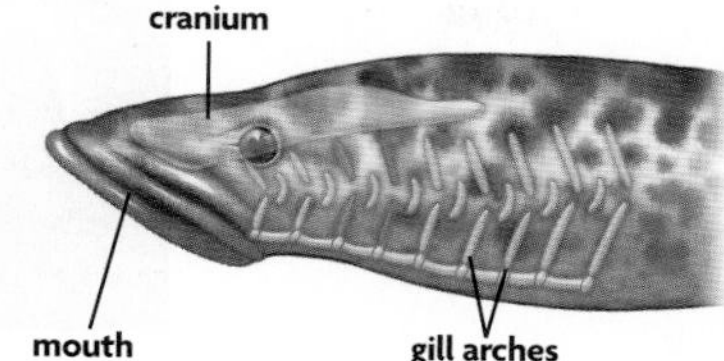

Agnatha Jawless fish such as lampreys evolved from filter-feeding ancestors. In jawless fish, the filters were modified to function as gills.

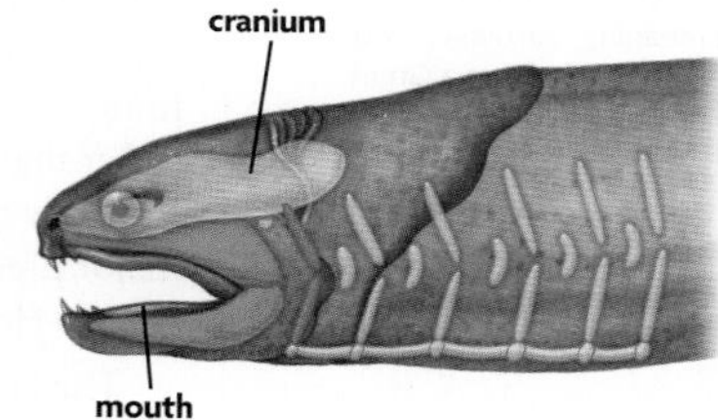

Placoderms Jaws developed from what was the third gill arch in Agnatha.

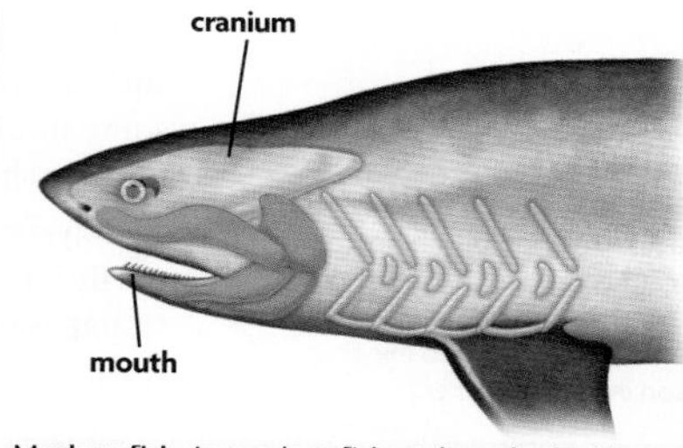

Modern fish In modern fish such as sharks, the fourth set of gill arches fused to the cranium.

MAIN IDEA

Only two groups of jawed fish still exist.

Jawed fish diversified very quickly after their first appearance about 440 million years ago. Four groups of fish appeared at this time.

- **Acanthodians** Acanthodians were fish covered with spines. They became extinct about 250 million years ago.
- **Placoderms** Placoderms were heavily armored with huge bony plates. They became extinct about 350 million years ago.
- **Cartilaginous fish** Cartilaginous fish are one of the two groups of fish that survive today. The cartilaginous fish include sharks, rays, and chimeras.
- **Bony fish** Bony fish are the group that includes all other living fish, and is the other group of fish still in existence.

Integrating Evolutionary Biology

Scientists think that **placoderms** were the first vertebrates to live in fresh water and the open ocean. Their heavy, bony armor was usually on the head and neck, sometimes with a joint in between the head and neck plates that may have allowed the fish to open its mouth very wide.

Dunkleosteus, a marine placoderm from the Devonian period, grew to lengths of at least 6 meters (19.5 ft) and had a heavily armored skull that was 1.2 meters (4 ft) wide. The bony plates of the jaws of placoderms like *Dunkleosteus* had sharp edges that functioned like shears to slice through prey. In 1997, a placoderm fossil found in Antarctica revealed preserved pigment cells. The belly of this fish was iridescent silver; the dorsal surface was red. Placoderms became extinct at the end of the Devonian period, 360 million years ago.

Science Trivia

Over the course of hundreds of millions of years, jaws have evolved to function in a wide variety of ways.

- The Atlantic wolffish is an eel-like fish armed with large canines, heavy molars, and very powerful jaws. It eats sea urchins, mollusks, and crustaceans.
- The foremost part of the upper jaw of various billfish is like a long, sharp sword or spear that is used to slash through schools of fish.
- The jaws of the aptly named cookiecutter shark allow it to gouge out small scoops of flesh from large marine animals, such as whales, dolphins, and large bony fish. Often the victim of this shark is relatively unharmed, meaning this species is more of a parasite.

HANDS-ON ACTIVITY

Objects in water can be described as positively, negatively, or neutrally buoyant. For any organism that swims through the water column, the ability to achieve neutral buoyancy—whether through a physical adaptation or a behavior—is advantageous because the organism will not be expending energy trying to descend or ascend using only its muscle power. Scuba divers achieve neutral buoyancy by adjusting the amount of air in an inflatable vest worn around their torsos. Bony fish use their swim bladders to adjust their buoyancy. Cartilaginous fish get much of their buoyancy from their high-volume livers.

Demonstrate how a small volume of oil can change a negatively or neutrally buoyant object to a positively buoyant one. Fill one balloon with 1/2 L of water. Fill another with 3/4 L of water and 1/4 L of cooking oil. Place both balloons in a container of water. **Ask,** If both balloons have the same volume, why does the one with oil float more than the one filled with water? The oil is less dense with water, so as a whole, the object that contains it is more positively buoyant.

Answers

A Compare Jawed animals are able to be more effective predators, allowing them to occupy a variety of niches and move up in the food chain.

▼ Teach *continued*

Take It Further

Shark teeth are arranged in rows; when one tooth is damaged or lost, it is replaced by another that emerges from the soft gum tissue behind the visible teeth. Most sharks have about five rows of teeth, and many will go through thousands of teeth in a lifetime.

The skin of sharks is essentially a layer of tiny teeth called **dermal denticles** or placoid scales. These denticles have the same structure as a tooth: an outer layer of enamel, dentine, and a central pulp cavity. The denticles point backwards toward the tail, making the shark hydrodynamic in the forward direction while offering a tough protective hide. Some cultures used sharkskin like sandpaper, and others still process sharkskin into a very durable leather used for making wallets, jackets, and other clothes or accessories.

TEACH FROM VISUALS

FIGURE 25.11 Call attention to the fin structure, body shape, and mouth and eye positions of the ray in the photograph. **Ask,** How do these adaptations help the ray to live successfully in its habitat? The eyes are placed at the top of the heads so it can see while flat on the ocean floor. The body is flattened, allowing it to hide on the bottom, bury itself in sand, and glide through the water. The mouth is located on the bottom, where it can grab prey from the sea floor. The bold coloration may function as a warning to potential predators.

FIGURE 25.10 The grey reef shark is found in the tropical waters surrounding coral reefs. When pursuing prey, some shark species may swim at speeds up to 48 km/h (30 mph).

VOCABULARY

In the word *Chondrichthyes, chondr-* comes from a Greek word meaning "cartilage," and *-ichthyes* comes from a Greek word meaning "fish."

Cartilaginous Fish

Members of the class Chondrichthyes, or cartilaginous fish, have skeletons made of cartilage, while their ancestors had skeletons made of bone. This characteristic means that their cartilaginous skeleton is not a primitive trait. These fish have lost the ability to make bone. In fact, the type of cartilage found in their skeletons is unique. It contains calcium deposits that make it stiffer than the squishy stuff found in human joints. Even though they have relatively flexible skeletons, cartilaginous fish have a strong bite, and they are major predators in every ocean. There are two groups within the Chondrichthyes—Holocephali and Elasmobranchs.

The Holocephali include chimeras, or ratfish. Chimeras are a small group of deep-sea fish with platelike grinding teeth. They feed on crustaceans and other invertebrates.

The Elasmobranchs include sharks, rays, and skates. There are more than 300 species of sharks and nearly 400 species of rays and skates. Most sharks, such as the grey reef shark shown in **FIGURE 25.10,** hunt other fish, although some species eat seals and sea lions. The biggest sharks, the whale sharks and basking sharks, are both filter feeders that eat plankton.

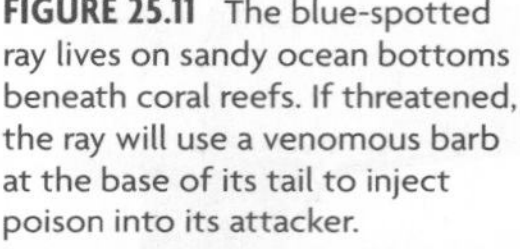

FIGURE 25.11 The blue-spotted ray lives on sandy ocean bottoms beneath coral reefs. If threatened, the ray will use a venomous barb at the base of its tail to inject poison into its attacker.

Rays and skates have flattened bodies and large pectoral fins that they use to "fly" through the water. Most rays, such as the blue-spotted ray shown in **FIGURE 25.11,** crush invertebrates such as crustaceans for food. Others, such as the huge manta rays, are planktonic filter-feeders. Most rays have poisonous venom in their barbed tails, which they use to defend themselves against predators. Skates do not have poisonous venom, but instead use thorny projections on their backs to fight off attackers.

While the cartilaginous fish as a group may be ancient, they have many advanced features. They have internal fertilization, and many species give birth to live young. They are actually denser than water, but oil stored in their livers provides buoyancy that keeps them from sinking.

Cartilaginous fish are incredibly efficient hunters. They are powerful swimmers with good eyesight and an excellent sense of smell. They can also sense their prey's movements at a distance with a sensory system called the lateral line.

Differentiated Instruction

BELOW LEVEL

Ask students to make a two-column chart titled "Characteristics of Fish." Tell them to list the following in the left column: gills, heart, movement, jaws, skeleton, and sensory organs. In the right column, have them describe each of these features in two or three sentences.

Biology Toolkit, T-Chart, p. C20

All fish have a **lateral line** system, which is a series of shallow canals on the sides of the fish made up of cells that are sensitive to small changes in water movement. The lateral line gives fish a sense of "distant touch," letting them feel the movements in the water currents created by more distant animals as they swim.

Many fish also have sensory organs that detect the electrical currents made by muscular contractions in other animals. These sensory organs are called electroreceptive cells because they receive electric signals. In cartilaginous fish, the electroreceptive cells are clustered on the snout, and they are extremely sensitive. In experiments in which all other senses are blocked, a shark can still detect the electric currents generated by the heartbeat of a hiding animal.

Bony Fish

All other living fish have skeletons made of bone. These bony fish are called the Osteichthyes (*oste-* comes from a Greek word meaning "bone"). There are more than 20,000 species of bony fish living in nearly every aquatic environment on Earth, including tropical freshwater streams, Antarctic oceans, and deep-sea trenches. Some have become parasites of other fish. One group of bony fish can even spend short periods of time on land.

The gills of all bony fish are in a chamber covered by a protective plate called the **operculum** (oh-PUR-kyuh-luhm), shown in **FIGURE 25.12.** Movements of the operculum help bony fish move water over their gills by creating a low-pressure area just outside the gills. Water flows from the high-pressure area in the mouth through the gills toward the low-pressure area by the operculum.

Some of these characteristics have been modified or lost in some species of bony fish. In Section 25.3, Osteichthyes will be examined in more detail.

A Contrast **What is the difference between cartilaginous and bony fish?**

FIGURE 25.12 The operculum is a protective plate that covers a fish's gills, as shown on this white margate, a bony fish.

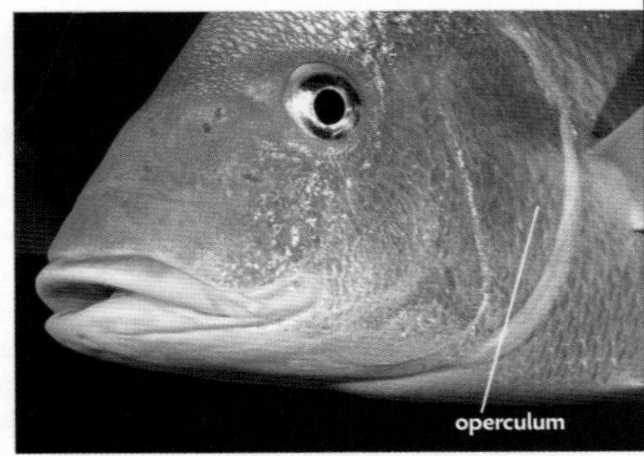

To learn more about jaw evolution, visit scilinks.org.
Keycode: MLB025

Science Trivia

While it is not unreasonable to think about whether or not you may be swimming in an area populated by sharks, we ought to be far more concerned about dogs, snakes, and lightning.

- From 2001 to 2005, there were 10 fatal shark attacks and 113 fatal dog attacks in the United States.
- In the 1990s, snakes killed an average of 15 people per year in the United States. Sharks killed 0.4 people per year.
- From 1959 to 2004, there were 22 fatal shark attacks and 1863 fatal lightning strikes in the United States.

Answers

A Contrast Cartilaginous fish have skeletons made of cartilage; bony fish have skeletons made of bone.

25.2 ASSESSMENT

ONLINE QUIZ ClassZone.com

REVIEWING MAIN IDEAS

1. What is the function of **countercurrent flow** in a fish's **gills**?
2. What key changes took place in the evolution of fish jaws?
3. Name the four groups of jawed fish that evolved during the Paleozoic. Which groups are still alive today?

CRITICAL THINKING

4. **Infer** How might fin shape differ in a fish with a torpedo-shaped cylindrical body and a fish with a flattened body?
5. **Analyze** How would you expect the **lateral line** system to differ in fish that live in rivers with strong currents?

Connecting CONCEPTS

6. **Evolution** A shark's jaw is lined with several rows of teeth. How is this adaptation related to a shark's effectiveness as a predator?

Assess and Reteach

Assess Use the Online Quiz or Section Quiz (*Assessment Book,* p. 494).

Reteach Display images of bony fish and cartilaginous fish. Point to their features (fins, organs, and so on) and have students identify and describe their functions. Provide them with simple outlines of a bony fish and a shark, and have them fill in as much detail as they can recall from the section.

25.2 ASSESSMENT

1. Countercurrent flow is the opposite movement of water against the flow of blood in the fish's gills. This process allows blood to efficiently release carbon dioxide into the water and absorb oxygen from the water.
2. Jaws developed from gill arches near the mouth that fused to the skull. The upper section of the first gill arch attached to the skull, forming the upper jaw. The bottom part of the jointed gill arch, able to open and close the mouth, formed the lower jaw.
3. Ancanthodians, placoderms, cartilaginous fish, and bony fish; cartilaginous fish and bony fish are still alive today.
4. A fish with a cylindrical body would most likely have fairly rigid fins that allow it to swim and maneuver with great speed. A fish with a flattened body is likely to have small, flexible fins that allow the fish to burrow in sediment. In some flat fish, such as the rays and skates, the fins are part of the flattened shape of the body and flap like wings to propel the fish forward.
5. Fish that live in fast-moving waters may have a lateral line that is less sensitive to the movement of water.
6. Sharks can afford to be very aggressive when feeding, because broken or lost teeth will be replaced.

▼ Plan and Prepare

Objectives

- Differentiate between the fins of ray-finned fish and lobe-finned fish.
- Describe the diversity of body plans of bony fish.
- Explain the origin and function of a fish's swim bladder.

Section Resources

Unit Resource Book Study Guide pp. 73–74 Power Notes p. 75 Reinforcement p. 76
Interactive Reader Chapter 25 **Spanish Study Guide** pp. 259–260
Biology Toolkit pp. C13, C19, C24, C33
Technology Power Presentation 25.3 Media Gallery DVD Online Quiz 25.3

Activate Prior Knowledge Have students call out the common names of various fish. Write them on the board. Remind students that some marine animals, such as jellyfish, are called "fish" but they are invertebrates or members of other non-fish classes. **Ask,** Which of the true fish you have named are bony fish? *All species that are not sharks, skates, or rays should be cited.* Tell students that there are tens of thousands of bony fish known to science.

25.3 A Closer Look at Bony Fish

KEY CONCEPT Bony fish include ray-finned and lobe-finned fish.

MAIN IDEAS

- Ray-finned fish have a fan of bones in their fins.
- Lobe-finned fish have paired rounded fins supported by a single bone.

VOCABULARY

ray-fin, p. 768
swim bladder, p. 769
lobe-fin, p. 770

Connect Most of the fish you are familiar with are bony fish. Perhaps you won a goldfish at a carnival or ate a tuna fish sandwich for lunch. Or maybe you fish at a local lake for trout or bass. All of these fishes are examples of bony fish.

MAIN IDEA

Ray-finned fish have a fan of bones in their fins.

All ray-finned fish, such as goldfish and tuna, have fins supported by a fan-shaped array of bones called a **ray-fin.** Ray-fins are embedded in a thin layer of skin and connective tissue. The muscles that move the bones are found in the fish's body wall. This arrangement of bones and muscles makes the fin light, collapsible, and easy to move. Ray-finned fish can quickly change a fin's shape, making the fish more maneuverable in the water. But the fins' maneuverability also means that they are thin and too weak to provide support out of water. They would buckle under the fish's weight. It would be like trying to stand on a few soda straws. Some ray-finned fish such as mudskippers have thickened ray-fins that let them shuffle around slowly on land.

Diversity of Body Plans

The ray-finned fish are the most diverse group of living vertebrates, making up nearly half of all vertebrate species. Most familiar species, such as tuna, have streamlined torpedo-shaped bodies that make it easier to swim through the water. But others can look quite different. As a result of natural selection, the bodies of bony fish are specialized for specific swimming and feeding strategies.

FIGURE 25.13 A barracuda's torpedo-shaped body is adapted for quick swimming and ambushing prey.

- Long, torpedo-shaped fish, such as the barracuda shown in **FIGURE 25.13,** are ambush predators that can accelerate quickly and surprise their prey.
- Fish that are flattened from side to side, such as butterflyfish, cannot swim quickly but are very maneuverable. They are usually found on coral reefs, in dense algae beds, or in large schools of their own species.
- Fish that feed on the surface of the water, such as some killifish, have flattened heads and mouths that point up. This body plan allows them to slurp up invertebrates from the surface while avoiding being seen by predators lurking above the surface.

▼ Teach

TEACH FROM VISUALS

FIGURE 25.13 Point out to students that they have already encountered the torpedo-like body shape in the sharks. **Ask,** What other things can you think of that are shaped similarly, and what function do they have in common? *Sample Answers:* Submarines, boat hulls, bullets, airplanes, missiles; all of these are shaped in a way that allows them to move through a medium with less resistance.

Differentiated Instruction

ENGLISH LEARNERS

After reading the section, have small groups of students practice summarizing by first looking at individual structural cues such as headings, boldface vocabulary, figures, and assessment questions. Students should then write down what they think are the most important concepts of the section. The groups should compare notes and come up with a list of points that they agree are the main ideas.

Biology Toolkit, Summarizing, p. C24

BELOW LEVEL

Have students prepare a Venn diagram of bony and cartilaginous fish. They can begin by filling in the characteristics of the cartilaginous fish, which they learned about in **Section 23.2.** As they read, they should fill in the characteristics of bony fish. When both fishes' characteristics are listed, students can merge the shared characteristics into the center field.

Biology Toolkit, Venn Diagram, p. C33

- Flatfish, such as the plaice shown in **FIGURE 25.14**, are flat-shaped and lie on the sea floor waiting for their prey to swim by. During development into its adult form, one eye migrates to the top of its head as its body flattens out.
- Some slow-swimming fish use camouflage to hide from predators or prey. For example, a leafy sea dragon has dozens of fleshy flaps on its body that make it look like the seaweed it lives in.

FIGURE 25.14 A plaice's flat-shaped body helps it to blend in with the sea floor, where it lies and waits for prey to swim by.

Staying Afloat

Most ray-finned fish have lungs modified into a buoyancy organ called a **swim bladder.** The swim bladder, shown in **FIGURE 25.15**, helps a fish float higher or lower in the water. The swim bladder lets the fish save energy, because a neutrally buoyant fish does not have to swim to keep from sinking or floating toward the surface. But if the fish changes depth, it must either add or remove air from the swim bladder to maintain neutral buoyancy. Adding oxygen from the bloodstream increases buoyancy the same way inflating a life vest makes you more buoyant. Reabsorbing oxygen into the bloodstream reduces buoyancy. Some species' swim bladders are adapted for use as an amplifier, picking up sound waves and transmitting them to the inner ear through a series of bones. A few fish even use the swim bladder to make sounds by vibrating it like a loudspeaker.

Some ray-finned fish still have lungs. One example is the bichir, which lives in stagnant streams in West Africa. These fish have gills, but can also breathe air and survive out of water for several hours at a time.

Connecting CONCEPTS

Buoyancy You may recall from physical science that buoyancy is the upward force that a fluid exerts on an object. To rise to the surface, a fish fills its swim bladder with oxygen, increasing its volume but not its mass, causing it to float upwards.

A Explain What is a swim bladder, and how does it work?

FIGURE 25.15 Bony Fish Anatomy

The unique features of the anatomy of a bony fish include a swim bladder that maintains buoyancy and gills used to breathe.

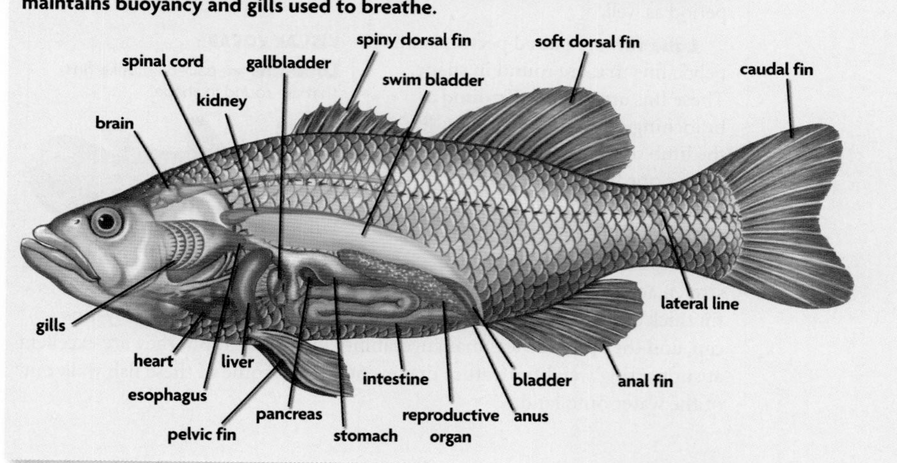

Take It Further

Most bony-fish species have a larval stage. The **winter flounder** *(Pseudopleuronectes americanus)*, a member of the same family as the plaice, starts out as a planktonic larva that swims and feeds in the water column. Once grown to 6 mm, the left eye begins to migrate towards the right side. At 8 mm, the fins are fully formed, and the left eye moves some more. At 9 mm, the pigment on the left side fades to white, both eyes are on the right side, and the fish swims to the bottom where it will swim on its left side for the rest of its life, reaching a size of approximately 0.6 m (2 ft), weighing 3.6 kg (8 lbs).

Science Trivia

Some species in both the cartilaginous and bony fish classes have evolved with functional electric organs that can be used as both defensive and offensive weapons.

- The electric eel (*Electrophorus electricus*), which lives in freshwater swamps and creeks in the tropics and grows to over 7 feet, is able to emit an electrical charge of 300–650 volts.
- The Atlantic torpedo ray (*Torpedo nobiliana*), which grows to 6 feet long and 200 pounds, uses a charge of 220 volts to stun its prey.
- The Pacific electric ray (*Torpedo californica*), which is smaller than its Atlantic counterpart, has a charge of about 50 volts.

PRE-AP

Tell students that when some bony fish are hooked and reeled to the surface, their swim bladders are so full of air that they protrude from the fish's mouth. If the fish were thrown back into the water, it would be difficult for the fish to get back down to its preferred depth. Have students write an explanation for why the fish's swim bladder would be so full of air if the fish is not trying to ascend to the surface.

Have students focus on what happened to the fish upon being hooked. They should realize that the forced and rapid ascent of the fish immediately reduces the pressure surrounding it. The gas that is in the fish's swim bladder expands much faster than it can be dissolved into the fish's bloodstream.

Biology Toolkit, Quick-Write, p. C19

Answers

A Explain A swim bladder is a buoyancy organ that helps fish float higher or lower in the water. Adding or removing air from the swim bladder allows the fish to change the depth at which it swims by increasing or decreasing the fish's density relative to the surrounding water.

DATA ANALYSIS

Discuss

Scatterplots are similar to line graphs in that they use horizontal and vertical axes to plot data points. The difference is that with a scatterplot, the individual points are not connected directly together with a line, but instead express a trend. This trend can be seen by calculating and plotting a line of best fit. A line of best fit is a straight line that best represents the data on a scatterplot. This line may pass through some of the points, none of the points, or all of the points. **Ask,** What is the general trend in these data? The larger the fish is, the older it is.

Answers

1. The plotted data should suggest a positive slope, but students should not actually draw a line of best fit.

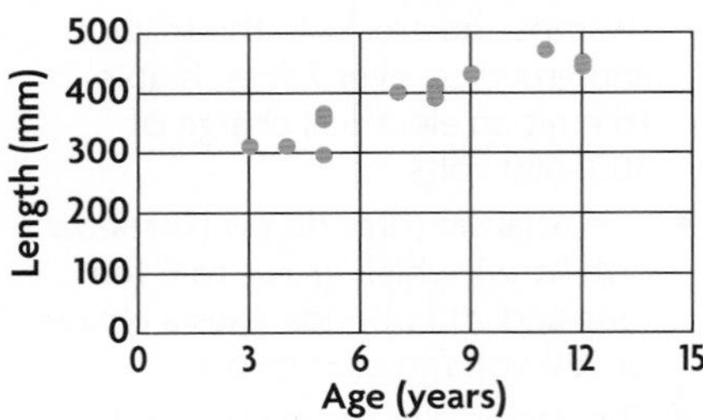

2. It is a positive correlation. As the age increases, the length increases.
3. Judging by the general trend of the data, the fish is probably less than three years old.

Unit Resource Book, Data Analysis, p. 85

ONLINE BIOLOGY Have students look at fish diversity relative to depth in the Data Analysis in Options for Inquiry on page 781. Or they can explore the current state of fisheries in the WebQuest.

DATA ANALYSIS

NOS.3

CONSTRUCTING SCATTERPLOTS

In order to analyze the relationship between two variables, scientists graph their data. The table below contains data about the length and age of largemouth bass in two lakes in Washington state.

1. **Graph** Construct a graph of the data in the table. Remember, for scatterplots you do not connect the data points.
2. **Analyze** What is the relationship between length and age in largemouth bass?
3. **Infer** An additional fish is measured with a length of 250 millimeters. What might be the age of this fish? Explain your answer.

TABLE 1. LARGEMOUTH BASS LENGTH AND AGE

Length (mm)	295	310	310	355	365	405	390	400	410	430	470	450	442
Age (years)	5	4	3	5	5	8	8	7	8	9	11	12	12

Source: Washington State Department of Ecology

MAIN IDEA

Lobe-finned fish have paired rounded fins supported by a single bone.

The lobe-finned fish include the ancestors of all terrestrial vertebrates. But most species of lobe-finned fish are extinct. Only seven species remain today. These fish first appeared about 400 million years ago in the Devonian period. Despite their early presence in the fossil record, the lobe-finned fish have never been as diverse as the ray-finned fish, which first appeared in the Devonian period as well.

Lobe-fins are paired pectoral and pelvic fins that are round in shape. These fins are arranged around a branching series of bony struts, like the limb of a land vertebrate. There is always one bone at the base of the fin. It is attached to a pair of bones, which are attached to a fan of smaller bones. Muscles extend into the fin and stretch across the bones, making the fin thick and fleshy. Lobe-fins cannot change shape as quickly as ray-fins can, and they provide less maneuverability in the water. But they are excellent at supporting weight, a feature that eventually let some of these fish walk out of the water onto land.

VISUAL VOCAB

Lobe-fins are paired limblike fins that are round in shape.

Differentiated Instruction

BELOW LEVEL

Write the following question on the board: *Why would a fish without a swim bladder probably have to eat more than a fish that has a swim bladder?* It would use more energy swimming without the aid of buoyancy. Have students think about the question, and then form pairs to discuss and prepare their answers. Have students share their answers with the class.

Biology Toolkit, Think-Pair-Share, p. C13

PRE-AP

Have students work in pairs to design a simple dichotomous key that would enable someone to determine if a fish belongs to the cartilaginous, ray-finned, or lobe-finned class of fish. Tell students to define any key terms (such as *operculum, fin rays, swim bladder,* and *dorsal fin*) so that anyone who was fishing from the shore and caught an unfamiliar fish would be able to determine which class it belongs to.

Coelacanths

Coelacanths (SEE-luh-KANTHS) are distinctive-looking fish with thick, fleshy fins and a tail with three lobes. They breathe with gills. Their swim bladders are filled with fat and provide buoyancy. There are two species of coelacanth. Both live in deep water in the Indian Ocean.

Coelacanths were first known from fossils. They are found in freshwater and shallow marine deposits from the Devonian until the late Cretaceous periods (410 to 65 million years ago), and then completely disappear from the fossil record. Before 1938, scientists assumed that they had gone extinct at the same time as the dinosaurs. In 1938, a modern coelacanth was caught off the coast of South Africa. Another was discovered near Indonesia in 1997.

VOCABULARY

The name *coelacanth* comes from the combination of the Greek word *koilos*, which means "hollow," and the Greek word *akantha*, which means "spine."

Lungfish

Lungfish, such as the one shown in **FIGURE 25.16**, live in streams and swamps in Australia, South America, and Africa. They can breathe with either gills or lungs. This characteristic means that they can live in stagnant, oxygen-poor water that other fish cannot tolerate. Lungs even keep some species alive when their ponds dry up. They make burrows in the mud, which hardens as the water dries up. Then they breathe air until the next rain refills their pond.

FIGURE 25.16 Lungfish are lobe-finned fish that are able to breathe with either gills or lungs.

The relationships between lungfish, coelacanths, and the terrestrial vertebrates are controversial. Recent studies of mitochondrial DNA suggest that lungfish are the closest living relatives of terrestrial vertebrates. Anatomical evidence also supports this idea. For example, lungfish and terrestrial vertebrates are the only animals with separate blood circuits for the lungs and the rest of the body. However, this characteristic does not mean that modern lungfish are the direct ancestors of terrestrial vertebrates. Both groups are descended from ancient lungfish, and they have changed in different ways over time.

A Infer How are lobe-fins related to vertebrate evolution?

25.3 ASSESSMENT

ONLINE QUIZ ClassZone.com

REVIEWING MAIN IDEAS

1. How are the bones arranged in a **ray-fin**? How is the arrangement related to the fin's function?
2. What are two examples of living **lobe-finned** fish? How are lobe-finned fish different from ray-finned fish?

CRITICAL THINKING

3. **Infer** You are looking at a long, torpedo-shaped fish with a flat head and a mouth that points upward. What do you predict about the hunting style of this fish?
4. **Predict** Any animal that is underwater is under pressure. Diving exposes animals to higher pressures. How would this affect a fish's **swim bladder**?

***Connecting* CONCEPTS**

5. **Genetics** Early coelacanth fossils have a single dorsal and a single anal fin. Second sets of dorsal and anal fins appear suddenly in the fossil record and persist in modern species. Explain how *Hox* genes could be responsible for the sudden appearance of this novel feature.

25.3 ASSESSMENT

1. Ray-finned fish have fins supported by a fan-shaped array of bones. The arrangement of bones and muscles makes the fin easy to maneuver.
2. Coelacanths and lungfish; lobe-fins are paired, fleshy limblike fins that are round in shape, less maneuverable, and able to support more weight.
3. The fish is probably an ambush predator that feeds at the surface.
4. The air in the swim bladder would get compressed as the fish descended, resulting in a decrease in the volume of the swim bladder.
5. *Hox* gene duplication could create a second set of instructions for fins farther down the animal's body.

The Inside Story

In 1938, the curator of the local natural history museum in East London, South Africa, received a telephone call that would change her life and rewrite some biological history. **Marjorie Courtenay-Latimer** had made it known to the local fishermen that she was interested in seeing any unusual specimens that she might add to the museum's collection. Buried in the catch of Hendrik Goosen's fishing boat was a fish that fit the bill. Courtenay-Latimer described it this way: "It was five foot long, a pale mauvy blue with faint flecks of whitish spots; it had an iridescent silver-blue-green sheen all over. It was covered in hard scales, and it had four limb-like fins and a strange puppy dog tail." She put the fish into the trunk of a taxi and took it back to the museum for examination.

It took two months and the help of taxidermists to preserve the fish to have the specimen identified. It was a **coelacanth**—a fish that was thought to have been extinct for 80 million years. In her honor, the fish was given the scientific name *Latimeria chalumnae*, the Chalumna River being the place where it was found. Have students go to the chapter resources at **ClassZone.com** for more on the story of this unusual find.

Answers

A Infer Lobe-fins are excellent at supporting weight, a feature that allowed some vertebrates to move onto land. Some lobe-fins have lungs, suggesting a possible common origin with terrestrial vertebrates.

Assess and Reteach ▼

Assess Use the Online Quiz or Section Quiz (*Assessment Book*, p. 495).

Reteach Create a two-column chart on the board, labeled *Bony Fish Adaptations* and *Function*. One by one, fill in the function side and ask students to call out what feature or adaptation you are describing. Have students copy the chart as you complete it.

INVESTIGATION

Time 30 minutes	TEACHER TESTED
Teacher Preparation	
Student Difficulty	
Lab Binder Animals, pp. 33–36	

Purpose Investigate external fertilization in fish reproduction.

Overview Students simulate spawning to investigate the advantage of a large number of eggs with external fertilization.

LAB MANAGEMENT

- Tell students to assume that there are many sperm for every egg that is laid and that this is why the males choose as many beads in each trial as there are eggs available.

POST-LAB DISCUSSION

Students should understand that this exercise asks them to estimate the chances that an egg (any egg) of one female fish will be fertilized. **Ask**

- What might the clear beads represent? Answers should include the eggs of other females of the same species or, more simply, the water. A female fish's egg can be thought of as a bull's-eye on a dart board, and the sperm are like darts. The larger the bull's-eye (the more eggs there are), the more likely it is that at least one will get hit by a dart (sperm). In some species, the bull's-eye is small because the female lays her eggs in a confined nest, and the sperm are released over them. In other species, the bull's-eye is large—the volume of water in which eggs and sperm mingle is vast.
- What needs to be true in order to improve the chances of more than one egg getting fertilized? The male(s) must release many sperm.
- Why might it be advantageous for a mating pair of fish to fertilize thousands or millions of eggs? Few larval fish will survive to adulthood. A larger number of larvae improves the odds that some of them will survive and pass on the parents' genes.

MATERIALS

- 20 colored beads
- 1 large bowl
- 100 clear beads
- graph paper
- ruler
- calculator

PROCESS SKILL

Modeling

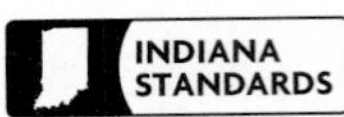

NOS.1 Develop explanations based on reproducible data and observations gathered during laboratory investigations.

NOS.3 Clearly communicate their ideas and results of investigations verbally and in written form using tables, graphs, diagrams, and photographs.

Fish Reproduction

For many species of fish, reproduction usually occurs outside the body. Male and female fish must come together in one place where the females lay eggs and the males release sperm to fertilize the eggs. Some female fish lay as many as 9 million eggs at a time. In this lab, you will model the reproduction method of egg-laying fish.

PROBLEM Why must fish produce so much eggs and sperm?

PROCEDURE

1. With your lab partner, decide who will represent the male fish and who will represent the female fish.
2. If you represent the female obtain beads of a single color. Each bead represents an egg released by the female.
3. Obtain a bowl with 100 clear beads. If you are the female fish, place one bead into the bowl and mix them up.
4. If you are the male, draw one bead from the bowl without looking. If you draw a colored bead, then you have had a successful fertilization. Record whether the attempt was successful. Replace the bead and repeat this step four more times.
5. If you represent the female, add four more eggs to the bowl (total = 5).
6. If you are the male fish, choose five beads from the bowl without looking. Record the number of successful fertilizations. Replace the beads and repeat this step four more times.
7. If you represent the female, add five more eggs to the bowl.
8. If you are the male fish, choose ten beads from the bowl, for a total of five trials.
9. If you represent the female, add ten more eggs to the bowl.
10. If you are the male fish, choose twenty beads from the bowl. Repeat for a total of five trials.

CALCULATE

1. Calculate the average number of successful fertilizations for each condition (1, 5, 10, and 20 eggs released).

ANALYZE AND CONCLUDE

1. **Graph Data** Plot the average successful fertilizations versus the number of eggs released.
2. **Analyze** What were the chances of a single egg becoming fertilized?
3. **Analyze** How might the chances of an egg becoming fertilized change as a male produces more sperm?
4. **Infer** What might be the connection between the production of a large number of eggs and the survivorship of hatched fish?
5. **Hypothesize** How might the situation change if fertilization occurred internally?

772 Unit 8: Animals

Answers

Calculate

The average number of successful fertilizations should increase in each condition.

Analyze and Conclude

1. Graphs should reflect the increase in average number of fertilizations in each condition.
2. chances of fertilization in the following conditions: 1 egg: 1/101; 5 eggs: 5/105 (1/21); 10 eggs: 10/110 (1/11); 20 eggs: 20/120 (1/6)
3. The chances increase.
4. In general, the chances of fertilization go up with an increase in the number of eggs, provided that there is also an increase in sperm available to fertilize these eggs.
5. The sheltered, confined space of the inside of the female would improve the chances of successful fertilization, provided that sperm and eggs have room to come into contact.

25.4 Amphibians

KEY CONCEPT Amphibians evolved from lobe-finned fish.

MAIN IDEAS

- Amphibians were the first animals with four limbs.
- Amphibians return to the water to reproduce.
- Modern amphibians can be divided into three groups.

VOCABULARY

tetrapod, p. 773
amphibian, p. 773
tadpole, p. 774

Connect What would it really be like to be a "fish out of water"? On shore, the air does not support your body. Gravity pulls on you and makes it hard to move. Your lateral line does not work. You are deaf, because your body absorbs sound waves before they reach your ear. The air is too thin to let you suck food into your mouth, and it is so dry that you start losing water through your skin. These are just a few of the conditions animals faced when they first moved onto land.

MAIN IDEA

Amphibians were the first animals with four limbs.

Connecting **CONCEPTS**

History of Life In 2006, scientists uncovered the fossil remains of a transitional species between fish and tetrapods. *Tiktaalik roseae* has fins and scales like a fish. However, it also has the beginnings of limbs, including digits, proto-wrists, elbows, and shoulders along with a functional neck and ribs similar to a tetrapod's.

One of the oldest known fossils of a four-limbed vertebrate was found in 360-million-year-old rocks from Greenland. We know that *Acanthostega* had lungs and eight-toed legs. But it also had gills and a lateral line system, neither of which work in air. These features suggest that the earliest animals with four limbs were aquatic and used their limbs to paddle underwater.

All of the vertebrates that live on land, as well as their descendants that have returned to aquatic environments, are tetrapods. A **tetrapod** is a vertebrate that has four limbs. Each limb evolved from a lobe-fin. Tetrapod legs contain bones arranged in the same branching pattern as lobe-fins, except that the fan of bones at the end of the fin is replaced by a set of jointed fingers, wings, or toes. Animals such as snakes, which do not have four limbs, are still considered to be tetrapods because they evolved from limbed ancestors.

Limbs and lungs were features that made these animals successful in an oxygen-poor, debris-filled underwater environment. But, over time, these adaptations let tetrapods climb out of the water to search for food or escape predators. These animals gave rise to the first amphibians. **Amphibians** are animals that can live both on land and in water. In the word *amphibian,* the root *amphi* comes from a Greek word meaning "on both sides," while the suffix *-bian* comes from a Greek word meaning "life."

A number of adaptations help amphibians to live on land. Large shoulder and hip bones help support more weight, while interlocking projections on the vertebrae help keep the backbone from twisting and sagging. A mobile, muscular tongue allows amphibians to capture and manipulate food. Development of a middle ear helps some amphibians to hear out of the water.

Differentiated Instruction

BELOW LEVEL

Before students read this section, have them prepare a three-column table with the headings *Statement, My Answer,* and *Text Answer.* Provide five to ten statements and have students answer whether they are true or false, both before and after reading the section. Examples:

1. Amphibians can breathe with skin, gills, or lungs. T
2. All amphibians lay their eggs in water. F
3. Salamanders are herbivorous. F
4. Frogs are the largest group of amphibians. T

Have students record explanatory statements or details in the Text Answer column.

Biology Toolkit, Anticipation Guide, p. C3

SECTION 25.4

Plan and Prepare

Objectives

- Describe the adaptations of amphibians that help them live on land.
- Summarize the reproduction and development of amphibians.
- Distinguish among the three groups of modern amphibians.

Section Resources

Unit Resource Book
Study Guide pp. 77–78
Power Notes p. 79
Reinforcement p. 80
Pre-AP Activity pp. 89–90

Interactive Reader Chapter 25
Spanish Study Guide pp. 261–262

Biology Toolkit pp. C3, C19, C23, C39

Technology
Power Presentation 25.4
Media Gallery DVD
Online Quiz 25.4

Activate Prior Knowledge Students may confuse reptiles with amphibians. **Ask,** Of the following animals, which are amphibians: frog, turtle, snake, alligator, toad, salamander, iguana? frog, toad, salamander Tell students that while some reptiles and amphibians may occupy the same habitats and share some characteristics, amphibian eggs require moisture in order to develop and hatch; the other animals listed, all of which are reptiles, lay eggs that do not require moisture.

Teach

Vocabulary

tetrapod The word *tetrapod,* which comes from Greek, means "four feet." A similar word, *quadruped,* is used in zoology to describe a tetrapod that moves by using all four limbs. A *biped* moves on two feet. Bipeds and quadrupeds are tetrapods, but not all tetrapods are bipeds or quadrupeds. Snakes, for example, are tetrapods that have no feet.

▼ Teach *continued*

The Inside Story

In the mid-1700s, the Swedish botanist **Carolus Linnaeus** established the system for naming species that is still in use today. The great man had something of an attitude where amphibians were concerned. "These foul and loathsome animals are abhorrent because of their cold body, pale color, filthy skin, fierce aspect, calculating eye, offensive smell, harsh voice, squalid habitation, and terrible venom; and so their Creator has not exerted his powers to make many of them." Linnaeus was wrong: there are at least 5743 known amphibian species, and they number in the billions.

Address Misconceptions

Common Misconception Handling toads will give a person warts.

Correcting the Misconception Toads do not give people warts. Some amphibians do secrete a substance from the skin that can be very irritating if it comes into contact with the eyes, nose, or mouth, but human warts are caused by a virus, not by handling amphibians.

Vocabulary

Word Origins The word **tadpole** comes from Middle English roots:

tadde = toad
pol = head

Answers

A Analyze Large shoulder and hip bones helped to support more weight; mobile, muscular tongue let amphibians capture and manipulate food; middle ear development let amphibians hear outside of water.

Some amphibians can hear sound due to the development of a tympanic membrane attached to a bone called the stapes. The stapes evolved from the top part of the second gill arch. Sound waves moving through the air vibrate the tympanic membrane, or eardrum, which transfers the sound waves further into the ear cavity to the middle and inner ear.

Depending on the species, amphibians breathe through their skin or with the use of gills or lungs. The balloonlike lungs of an amphibian are simple in structure. An amphibian uses its lungs to breathe by changing the amount and pressure of air in its mouth. Unlike fish, which have a two-chambered heart, amphibians have a three-chambered heart. An amphibian heart is made up of two atria and one ventricle. Oxygenated and deoxygenated blood are partially separated by the two atria. Blood is pumped through the heart on a double circuit. Blood pumped through the pulmonary circuit goes to the skin and lungs. Blood pumped through the systemic circuit brings oxygen-rich blood to the organs, and returns oxygen-poor blood to the heart.

Over time, amphibian species evolved with adaptations that allowed them to live on land. But they did not evolve ways to keep themselves or their eggs from drying out in the air.

A Analyze What adaptations helped amphibians move from water to live on land?

MAIN IDEA

Amphibians return to the water to reproduce.

An amphibian's skin is thin and wet. Water constantly evaporates from it, and amphibians risk drying out if they move too far from a source of water. This need for moisture is why you rarely find an amphibian in arid habitats. A few species live in deserts, where they burrow underground, emerging only during the brief rainy season. Desert-living species can absorb large amounts of water through their skin when it is available and store it for the dry season.

FIGURE 25.17 This female pygmy marsupial frog keeps her eggs moist by tucking them into a pouch under the skin of her back.

Reproduction Strategies

Amphibians need a source of water to reproduce. Their eggs do not have a shell, and the embryos will dry out and die without a source of moisture. Amphibians use many strategies to keep their eggs wet, including

- laying eggs directly in water
- laying eggs on moist ground
- wrapping eggs in leaves
- brooding eggs in pockets on the female's back, as shown in **FIGURE 25.17.**

Some frogs start their lives as tadpoles. **Tadpoles** are aquatic larvae of frogs. Tadpoles have gills and a broad-finned tail, and swim by wiggling their limbless bodies like fish. They typically eat algae, but some may eat small invertebrates or even other tadpoles.

Differentiated Instruction

PRE-AP

Have students write for five minutes about how amphibians are adapted to the following challenges posed by terrestrial life:

- absence of support for body weight
- inability to suck in prey from the air
- inability of vibrations to travel as well in air as in water
- scarcity of water for acquiring oxygen

Write these challenges on the board or read them aloud so students can copy them into their notebooks. Answers should include the size of the shoulder and hip bones and the interlocking projections on the vertebrae as means of supporting the body; the muscular tongue as a means of capturing food; middle ear or eardrum for hearing; specialized skin, lungs, and three-chambered heart for acquiring and distributing oxygen to the body.

Biology Toolkit, Quick-Write, p. C19

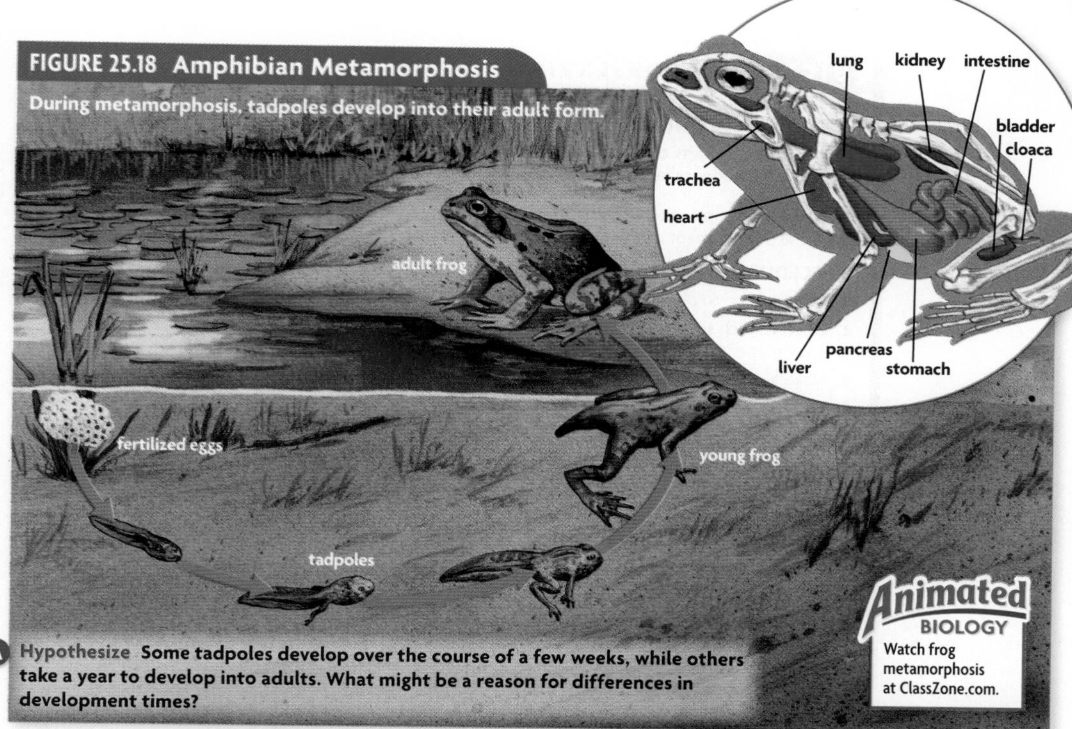

FIGURE 25.18 Amphibian Metamorphosis

During metamorphosis, tadpoles develop into their adult form.

A Hypothesize Some tadpoles develop over the course of a few weeks, while others take a year to develop into adults. What might be a reason for differences in development times?

Amphibian Metamorphosis

To grow into terrestrial adults, tadpoles must undergo metamorphosis. Recall from Chapter 24 that metamorphosis is the change in form and habits of an animal. Similar to the metamorphosis of a butterfly, the metamorphosis of a tadpole into an adult frog affects nearly every organ in the tadpole's body. It produces enormous changes in the animal's body form, physiology, and behavior. The stages of amphibian metamorphosis, in which a tadpole transforms into its adult form, are shown in **FIGURE 25.18.**

During metamorphosis, the tadpole undergoes many changes. The gills are reabsorbed and lungs develop, shifting the frog from a water-breathing to an air-breathing mode of life. The circulatory system is reorganized to send blood to the lungs. The tail fin (if not the entire tail) is reabsorbed. The body grows limbs and completely reorganizes its skeleton, muscles, and parts of the nervous system. The digestive system is rebuilt to handle a carnivorous diet. In the adult amphibian, digestion occurs in the animal's stomach, and wastes are expelled through the cloaca. The cloaca is also a part of the reproductive system.

Many amphibians do not undergo metamorphosis. Adult females lay eggs on the ground or keep them in their bodies, and the young develop directly into their terrestrial forms.

B Infer **Describe the stages of amphibian metamorphosis.**

TAKING NOTES

Draw a simple diagram of amphibian metamorphosis in your notes. At each step, label the changes that occur as the amphibian changes from an egg to its adult form.

ENGLISH LEARNERS

Have students sketch the stages of amphibian metamorphosis in a cycle diagram. Tell students to sketch all the stages in a series of boxes arranged in a circle. Tell them to label each box and explain the characteristics of each stage of development.

Biology Toolkit, Cycle Diagram, p. C39

HANDS-ON ACTIVITY

Collect tadpoles from a local source or obtain them from a biological supply company. Place them in an aquarium in the classroom. Have students observe the tadpoles daily and record any changes they see. Tell them to make sketches at regular intervals so they can see how the tadpoles are changing. Only if the tadpoles were obtained from the local environment should the adults be released into the wild.

TEACH FROM VISUALS

FIGURE 25.18 Go through the stages of metamorphosis with students. **Ask**

- At which stage is a frog most like a fish? freshly hatched tadpole
- How can you relate the characteristics of the tadpole and the adult frog to the meaning of the word *amphibian,* or "living on both sides"? Tadpoles have the characteristics of fish: gills and fins. Adult frogs have lungs and limbs. Tadpoles are herbivores, and frogs are carnivores.

Science Trivia

- The world's largest frog is the West African goliath frog, *Conraua goliath.* Its upper body can be more than 30 centimeters (1 ft) long; with its back legs extended, it is often more than 75 centimeters (2.5 ft) long.
- The goliath frog eats insects, crustaceans, fish, and amphibians, and may also eat aquatic birds and small mammals.

Answers

A Hypothesize Answers may include environmental differences, such as dry seasons or winter seasons causing a period of dormancy or quickening the time of development (such as in eggs that develop in short-lived puddles).

B Infer Egg—tadpole—frog; when developing into a frog, a tadpole reabsorbs its gills and develops its lungs, goes through a reorganization of its circulatory system to send blood to the lungs, absorbs its tail fin, grows limbs, and develops a digestive system suited for eating other animals.

▼ Teach *continued*

QUICK LAB

Time 30 minutes	TEACHER TESTED
Lab Binder Animals, pp. 43–44	

Purpose Observe and describe the stages of development of a frog from embryo to adult.

LAB MANAGEMENT

As an alternative, the lab could be done with photographs of the various stages from textbooks or the Internet.

Safety Remind students to wipe down the microscopes' eyepieces with alcohol wipes after using them. Make sure they wash their hands before leaving the lab.

Answers

Analyze and Conclude

1. The embryo's tail bud stages through the latter stages of the tadpole's metamorphosis (just before legs bud) resemble a fish.
2. The tadpole has gills. During metamorphosis, gills are absorbed and lungs develop.
3. The circulatory system is reorganized to send blood to the body's lungs.
4. Students will identify various stages of frog development from embryo to adult. Answers depend on the specimens observed, but typically follow a sequence such as this: **a.** 1-cell, fertilized egg; **b.** 4-cell; **c.** 8-cell; **d.** Morula: 4 hours; **e.** Blastula: 6 to 20 hours; **f.** Mid-gastrula: 10 to 40 hours; **g.** Late gastrula; **h.** Early neurula; **i.** Neurula: 19 to 80 hours; **j.** Late neurula; **k.** Tailbud: 32 to 100 hours; **l.** Late tailbud; **m.** Tadpole: 110 to 180 hours, Gills, Rear leg buds, Rear legs (tail), Front legs (tail), Four legs (no tail); **n.** Adult: 5 weeks.

QUICK LAB OBSERVING NOS.3

Frog Development

Every vertebrate starts off as a fertilized egg or zygote. In this lab, you will identify and sequence the various stages of development of a frog from embryo to adult.

PROBLEM In what order should the specimens be placed to trace the development of the frog?

PROCEDURE

1. Use a spatula to place each coded specimen in a petri dish.
2. Observe each specimen with either a hand lens or a dissecting microscope.
3. Make a drawing of each specimen.
4. When finished, return the specimens to the coded jar.
5. Label your drawings, and put them in the proper sequence.

ANALYZE AND CONCLUDE

1. **Analyze** What stage of development most resembles a fish?
2. **Analyze** Explain how the breathing mechanism changes during frog development.
3. **Identify** What change occurs in the circulatory system to accommodate the change in the breathing mechanism?
4. **Infer** What is the correct sequence of your drawings from the earliest to the latest stages of development?

MATERIALS

- preserved specimens of frog embryos and tadpoles
- petri dish
- spatula
- hand lens or dissecting microscope

MAIN IDEA

Modern amphibians can be divided into three groups.

The three groups of modern amphibians are salamanders, frogs, and caecilians. The body plans of the amphibians in each of these groups is adapted to the feeding habits and requirements of the habitats in which they live.

Salamanders

There are more than 300 species of salamanders. As shown in **FIGURE 25.19**, salamanders have a long body, four walking limbs, and a tail. They walk with a side-to-side movement biologists think is similar to the way ancient tetrapods probably walked. But appearances can be deceiving. Salamanders have a number of adaptations specific to their way of life. Some salamander species, such as the axolotl (AK-suh-LAHT-uhl), retain some juvenile features as they mature, growing into aquatic adults that look like giant tadpoles with legs. Members of the largest family of salamanders do not have lungs and exchange gases through the lining of their skin and mouth.

Salamander larvae and adults are carnivorous. They eat invertebrates such as insects, worms, and snails. Large species eat smaller vertebrates such as fish and frogs. Salamander larvae and some aquatic adults suck food into their mouths as fish do. On land, a salamander hunts by flinging its sticky tongue at its prey and pulling it back into its mouth.

FIGURE 25.19 The mud salamander lives in swamps, bogs, springs, and streams of the southeastern United States.

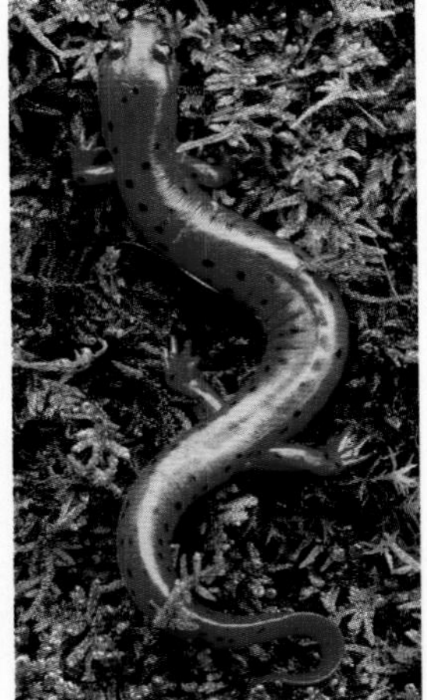

Differentiated Instruction

BELOW LEVEL

Have students use a combination of notes and drawings to learn the characteristics of the three groups of amphibians. In this section, with visuals available, students may wish to first re-create the salamander, frog, and caecilian shown in **FIGURES 25.19, 25.20,** and **25.21,** and then label the drawings with descriptions of external and internal characteristics.

Biology Toolkit, Combination Notes, p. C23

Frogs

Frogs make up the largest group of living amphibians, with more than 3000 species. Adult frogs are physically distinctive, with tailless bodies, long muscular hind limbs, webbed feet, exposed eardrums, and bulging eyes. Their bodies are adapted for jumping. Elongated bones in their hips, legs, and feet increase their speed and power. Their hind legs have fused bones that absorb the shock of landing.

Toads are actually one family of frogs. They have rougher and bumpier skin than do other frogs, as well as relatively shorter legs that make them poor jumpers. Glands in the bumpy skin of toads and the smooth skin of tropical frogs make toxins that protect the animals from predators. Many species of these poisonous frogs and toads have bright coloration that warns predators that they are deadly.

Frogs live in every environment on Earth except at the poles and in the driest deserts. Although most tadpoles eat algae, adult frogs are predators and will eat any animal they can catch.

FIGURE 25.20 The Wallace's flying frog is able to glide up to 15 meters (50 ft) using its webbed feet and skin folds as mini-sails to float through the air.

FIGURE 25.21 Caecilians, common to South America, are legless amphibians that live in underground burrows.

Caecilians

Caecilians (suh-SIHL-yuhnz), such as the one shown in **FIGURE 25.21**, are legless, burrowing amphibians that live in the tropics. There are 160 species, ranging in length from about 10 centimeters (4 in.) to 1.5 meters (5 ft). Caecilians have banded bodies that make them look like giant earthworms, and they are specialized for a life burrowing through the soil.

Like other amphibians, caecilians are predators. They burrow through the soil searching for earthworms and grubs. Because they have no legs, they cannot dig through the soil the way a mole would. Instead, like an earthworm, a caecilian uses a hydrostatic skeleton to stiffen its body and drive its head forward like a battering ram.

Contrast **How are caecilians different from other amphibians?**

25.4 ASSESSMENT

ONLINE QUIZ ClassZone.com

REVIEWING MAIN IDEAS

1. What evidence suggests that the first **tetrapods** were **amphibians**?
2. List two reasons why amphibians must live in moist environments.
3. In what ways are the three groups of amphibians similar? different?

CRITICAL THINKING

4. **Connect** Like poisonous dart frogs, monarch butterflies are brightly colored. What might be the adaptive advantage of bright coloration?
5. **Apply** Amphibians are very sensitive to changes in their environment. Why might this be?

Connecting CONCEPTS

6. **Evolution** Caecilians have no legs. Neither do snakes or whales. Why, then, do we call them all tetrapods? (**Hint:** consider their evolutionary histories.)

25.4 ASSESSMENT

1. The oldest known tetrapod fossils had lungs, legs with toes, gills, and a lateral line—characteristics shared with amphibians.
2. Amphibian skin is very thin and will dry out—thereby drying out the animal—if the environment is not moist. The same problem faces an amphibian's shell-less eggs.
3. All amphibians are tetrapods with three-chambered hearts, and all are dependent on moisture for survival and reproduction. Frogs go through metamorphosis, salamanders move using a side-to-side shuffling of limbs, and caecilians lack limbs.
4. Bright coloration may alert potential predators that the frog is poisonous, thereby protecting the frog from predation.
5. The skin of an amphibian is very thin in order to absorb moisture (and, in some species, oxygen) from their environment. This also means that other substances, such as pollutants, may be absorbed as well.
6. Caecilians, snakes, and whales all descended from four-limbed ancestors.

ONLINE BIOLOGY Go to the chapter Resource Center at **ClassZone.com** for additional resources and information on amphibians.

Integrating Ecology

Although amphibians have radiated out into most of Earth's biomes, their populations have been declining dramatically all over the world in recent years. Habitat destruction contributes to some of the decline, but scientists infer from evidence that the thinning of the ozone layer and global climate change are playing roles too. Many amphibians lay their eggs in shallow water where they are exposed to ultraviolet radiation from the Sun. Because UV rays are known to cause genetic damage, and more UV radiation is reaching Earth as a result of the thinning ozone layer, this could explain why frog eggs frequently fail to develop and hatch. Other research suggests that global climate change is making conditions ideal for a fungus that is fatal in many amphibian species.

Answers

A Contrast Caecilians are limbless and use a hydrostatic skeleton to burrow.

Assess and Reteach ▼

Assess Use the Online Quiz or Section Quiz (*Assessment Book*, p. 496).

Reteach Assemble a digital slide show of amphibians. Ask students to identify which group the animal belongs to and explain their reasoning. Include images of fish, reptiles, and worms to see if students can tell them apart from tadpoles, salamanders, and caecilians.

SECTION 25.5

▼ Plan and Prepare

Objectives

- Describe two important characteristics of amniotes that help them retain water.
- Explain the evolutionary importance of the amniotic egg.

Section Resources

Unit Resource Book Study Guide pp. 81–82 Power Notes p. 83 Reinforcement p. 84
Interactive Reader Chapter 25 **Spanish Study Guide** pp. 263–264
Biology Toolkit p. D5
Technology Power Presentation 25.5 Media Gallery DVD Online Quiz 25.5

Activate Prior Knowledge Hold a chicken egg behind you. Tell students, "In my hand I'm holding an example of the adaptation that allows terrestrial vertebrates to occupy some of the most extreme biomes." **Ask,** What is this powerful adaptation? the amniotic egg Show students the chicken egg. **Ask,** Why was this so important? Because their eggs would not dry out, amniotes were able to radiate out into deserts, mountains, and other biomes where water was not always available.

▼ Teach

Take It Further

Tell students that human embryos are encapsulated in an **amnion,** and that it is this tough, membranous sac that defines the amniotes, not the hard shell characteristic of some amniotic eggs.

Answers

A Connect Keratin; it prevents loss of water from our tissues, so we can live in drier environments.

25.5 Vertebrates on Land

KEY CONCEPT Reptiles, birds, and mammals are adapted for life on land.

MAIN IDEAS

- Amniotes can retain moisture.
- Amniotes do not need to return to water to reproduce.

VOCABULARY

amniote, p. 778
keratin, p. 778
amniotic egg, p. 779
placenta, p. 779

Connect Around 350 million years ago, one group of ancient amphibians evolved traits that let them walk away from the water forever. Over time, they diversified into the types of vertebrates you are most familiar with, including reptiles, birds, and mammals—the class that includes you.

MAIN IDEA

Amniotes can retain moisture.

An **amniote** is a vertebrate that has a thin, tough, membranous sac that encloses the embryo or fetus. Amniotes first appeared as small, lizardlike creatures in the late Carboniferous period. Since that time, amniotes have evolved into thousands of different forms and have invaded nearly every ecosystem on Earth. They have become predators in the tropics, the most arid deserts, the Arctic, and in any number of freshwater and marine environments. They have become burrowers, sprinters, sit-and-wait predators, and slow trackers. Some species never leave the trees. Some specialize in eating plants and have evolved symbiotic relationships with bacteria that can break down cellulose. Some have also developed powered flight.

When you look at the phylogenetic tree of amniotes, it is clear that many of the species we see today are survivors of larger radiations that have gone extinct. Mammals are survivors of a huge line of animals that went extinct about 245 million years ago. Birds are survivors of the dinosaur radiation and extinction. You will learn more about amniote diversity in Chapter 26.

***Connecting* CONCEPTS**

Extinction Recall from **Chapter 11** that a mass extinction is an intense period of extinction that occurs on a global scale. In the Permian-Triassic extinction, 95 percent of all species and over 50 percent of all families disappeared.

All amniotes share a set of characteristics that prevent water loss. Skin cells are waterproofed with keratin. **Keratin** is a protein that binds to lipids inside the cell, forming a hydrophobic—or water repellent—layer that keeps the water inside the animal from reaching the skin. The presence of this hydrophobic layer means that amniotes lose less water to evaporation than amphibians do. Waterproofing also means that amniotes cannot exchange gases across their skin. They rely on their lungs for respiration.

Kidneys and large intestines are bigger in amniotes than in amphibians. These organs contain tissues that reabsorb water. The increased surface area of these tissues enables amniotes to absorb more water internally, so they lose less to excretion than do amphibians.

A Connect What makes your skin cells waterproof? Why is this important?

Differentiated Instruction

ENGLISH LEARNERS

Tell students that the key vocabulary in this section is important to Chapter 26. Have students create Frayer model charts for these terms. They should include a definition, characteristics, examples, and a drawing.

Biology Toolkit, Frayer Model, p. D5

MAIN IDEA

Amniotes do not need to return to water to reproduce.

With adaptations that limit water loss, amniote adults could move into drier environments on land. But it was the evolution of the amniotic egg that let them stay there. The **amniotic egg** is an almost completely waterproof container that keeps the embryo from drying out as it develops. After it evolved, amniotes did not have to return to a wet environment to reproduce.

An amniotic egg, shown in **FIGURE 25.22**, is essentially a private pool that the mother builds for her embryo. Like any swimming pool, the egg is expensive. In egg-laying amniotes, the mother must make enough yolk and white to feed the embryo until it hatches, then build the shell around the fertilized egg. Each egg represents a large investment of energy. For example, a bird may lose 5 to 30 percent of its body weight as it makes an egg.

FIGURE 25.22 Amniotes, such as this gecko, develop within an amniotic egg.

Other amniotes, such as rattlesnakes and garter snakes, make eggs but do not lay them. Instead, they keep their eggs in their oviduct until they hatch. Retaining eggs protects them from predators. Some amniotes have evolved the ability to give birth to living, well-developed young.

Most mammal embryos develop inside of the mother's reproductive tract. Their eggs have no shells, but their embryos make the same series of membranes found in a typical amniotic egg. The **placenta** is a membranous organ that develops in female mammals during pregnancy. It lines the uterine wall and partially envelops the fetus. The placenta carries nutrients from the mother to the embryo and also removes metabolic wastes from the embryo.

A **Summarize** **How is an amniotic egg protected from water loss?**

Take It Further

The **placenta** used by mammals to feed their embryonic young can be considered an example of **convergent evolution.** About 70 percent of shark species give birth to live young, and about 30 percent of these employ a placenta to nourish their young. The difference between the placenta of these sharks and that of many mammals is that it actually develops from the yolk sac and yolk stalk from which the embryo first gets its nutrients. Specifically, the stalk forms the umbilical cord, and the sac becomes the placenta. Placental sharks, including the bull shark and hammerheads, are born with the umbilical cord still attached. The cord detaches, leaving the shark pup with an umbilical scar that is analogous to the human navel, or "bellybutton."

Answers

A **Summarize** A tough membrane prevents water loss. In some amniotes, the eggs have a hard shell.

25.5 ASSESSMENT

ONLINE QUIZ ClassZone.com

REVIEWING MAIN IDEAS

1. What characteristics help an **amniote** retain moisture?
2. Why don't amniotes need to return to water to reproduce?

CRITICAL THINKING

3. **Infer** If eggshells were thicker, the egg would lose even less water to the environment. Why are eggshells thin?
4. **Infer** What is an advantage of giving birth to live young, rather than having young that hatch from eggs?

***Connecting* CONCEPTS**

5. **Evolution** Most mammals and at least some lizards and snakes have evolved live birth by keeping the eggs inside the mother until they hatch. However, no bird species has ever retained its eggs. Suggest a possible explanation for this fact.

Assess and Reteach ▼

Assess Use the Online Quiz or Section Quiz (*Assessment Book,* p. 497).

Reteach Show images of the eggs of amniotes in various environments. For example, show the eggs of a sea turtle as they are laid into a nest on a sandy tropical beach; the single eggs of king penguins in Antarctica; and the early embryo of a human. Discuss the adaptations of the amniotes (keratin in skin) and their eggs (waterproof amnion) that prevent water loss.

25.5 ASSESSMENT

1. Keratin waterproofs skin cells. Larger kidneys and intestines maximize the absorption and retention of water.
2. The amniotic egg protects the embryo inside from drying out.
3. The shell must be thin enough to allow for gas exchange.
4. Live young may be better able to avoid predation. Eggs that are laid cannot defend themselves or escape predators; they depend on parental care. For the mother, carrying embryos until they are born may mean they are free to move, migrate, and find food; some species that lay eggs have to protect their eggs at all times until they hatch.
5. Birds that fly would have a difficult time doing so if they had to carry the weight of their eggs.

OPTIONS FOR INQUIRY

INVESTIGATION

Time 45 minutes	TEACHER TESTED
Teacher Preparation	
Student Difficulty	
Lab Binder Animals, pp. 37–40	

Purpose Observe the organs and systems of a bony fish.

Overview Students will dissect a preserved specimen of fish. They will

- examine the external and internal anatomy of the fish
- examine a scale and count the rings to determine the approximate age of the fish

LAB PREPARATION

- Distribute copies of the Anatomical Perch Drawing datasheet (*Lab Binder*, pp. 39–40).

LAB MANAGEMENT

- Group students so that students with physical disabilities will have assistance with this lab.

Safety

- Have students wear safety goggles, gloves, and aprons when handling the preserved specimens.
- Be sure that students dissect in a well-ventilated area to avoid prolonged exposure to the preservative.
- Remind students to be careful with scissors, needles, and scalpels.
- Remind students to wash their hands thoroughly before leaving the lab.

POST-LAB DISCUSSION

Discuss the results of the dissection. **Ask**

- How does counting the rings on the scale of a fish tell you the age of the fish? Fish scales grow as the fish grows. Scales show a ring for every year of age.
- What adaptations for life in the water did you observe in the perch? gills, swim bladder, scales, lateral line, fins

Use these inquiry-based labs and online activities to deepen your understanding of vertebrate diversity.

NOS.1 Develop explanations based on reproducible data and observations gathered during laboratory investigations.

INVESTIGATION

Anatomy of a Bony Fish

A perch is a bony fish. There are several freshwater species and a saltwater species of perch. In this lab, you will dissect and explore the anatomy of a perch.

SKILL Observing

PROBLEM What is the relationship between the structure and functions of the organ systems of a fish?

MATERIALS

- dissecting tray
- preserved perch specimen
- Anatomical Perch Drawing
- hand lens
- scalpel
- scissors
- forceps
- dissecting needle
- 12 dissecting pins
- paper towels

PROCEDURE

1. Place the perch in the dissecting tray.
2. Examine the external anatomy of the fish. Use the Anatomical Perch Drawing to explore the fish's external anatomy.
3. Use the scalpel to make a cut from the anal opening forward 2 centimeters. Take the scissors and cut through the body wall along the underside to the pelvic fin. Use the scissors to cut vertically from the anal region to the lateral line. Use the scalpel to make a cut along the lateral line toward the operculum. Use the scissors to cut vertically from the pelvic fin to the lateral line (you may remove the pelvic fins).
4. Look in the body cavity at the internal organs. Follow the handout instructions to explore the fish's internal anatomy.
5. Cut a small flap of skin from the rear dorsal fin down to the lateral line to expose the underlying muscles. The muscles are arranged in groups called myotomes.
6. When finished, dispose of your perch according to instructions from your teacher. Be sure to clean and dry your instruments and tray. Wash your hands thoroughly.

ANALYZE AND CONCLUDE

1. **Analyze** What type of symmetry does the fish have?
2. **Analyze** What is the function of the operculum?
3. **Analyze** How many gill arches does the perch have? Would you expect a lamprey to have more or fewer gill arches? Explain.
4. **Infer** Which structure did you observe that allows fish to sense prey in the distance? Describe it.
5. **Analyze** What organ in humans is homologous to the swim bladder?
6. **Apply** If the fish's swim bladder was damaged and could not hold air, would the fish sink or float? Explain.
7. **Infer** How does the shape of the perch's body help it to maneuver through the water?

Answers

Analyze and Conclude

1. bilateral
2. When extended out, the operculum creates a low-pressure area just outside the gills, which draws water in through the mouth and over the gills. It also serves as protection for the gills.
3. Four pairs of gill arches; because the jaws of jawed fish evolved from gill arches, we should expect the jawless lamprey to have more gill arches than the perch has.
4. Lateral line; it looks like a linear series of scales that are darker in color than the other scales, running from behind the operculum to the tail.
5. the lungs
6. The fish would sink because the absence of air in its swim bladder would give it a lower volume and therefore a higher density. Fish are negatively buoyant if the liver or swim bladder is removed.
7. The compressed, streamlined shape of the fish helps it to slice through the water.

INVESTIGATION

Vanishing Amphibian—an Indicator Species

Indicator species are species that can be used as a measure, or indicator, of the overall health of an ecosystem. In this activity, using the Internet and other resources, you will research the role of amphibians as ecological indicators.

SKILL Researching

MATERIALS
- map of the United States
- colored pencils

PROBLEM What characteristics make amphibians a good choice as ecological indicators?

RESEARCH
1. **Apply** Why are amphibians good indicators of ecological health?
2. **Analyze** Are populations of amphibians increasing or decreasing?
3. **Analyze** What are the reasons for the change in amphibian populations?
4. **Apply** On the map, shade in areas of the United States where changes in amphibian populations are occurring, and cite specific examples and possible reasons for the changes in populations.

Online BIOLOGY CLASSZONE.COM

ANIMATED BIOLOGY
What Type of Fish Is It?
Can you tell a ray-finned fish from a cartilaginous fish? Use physical characteristics to categorize a set of jawed fish.

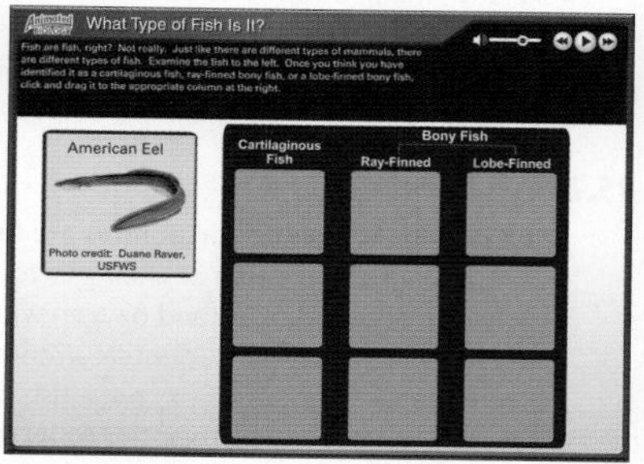

WEBQUEST
Worldwide, more than 70 percent of marine fisheries have been fished to their sustainable limits or overfished. At the same time, an increasing number of people depend on fish for food. In this WebQuest, you will explore the problems facing fisheries and what is being done to save them.

DATA ANALYSIS ONLINE
Lake Malawi in Africa has a great diversity of fish. However, the fish aren't distributed evenly throughout the lake. One factor that determines where fish can live is availability of oxygen. Graph the number of species and the amount of dissolved oxygen at specific depths and determine the relationship.

Answers

1. Amphibians such as frogs and salamanders are good indicators of the environment because their skin is permeable to substances in the environment such as toxins, pollutants, and other chemicals. Because they live in both aquatic and terrestrial environments, they indicate the health of a wide range of habitats. By following the amphibian populations, as well as the incidences of birth and developmental defects in these animals, scientists can determine the extent of environmental changes and impacts of pollution.
2. In the United States, frog populations are declining in the West (California, Rocky Mountains), Southwest, and in Puerto Rico.
3. The reasons vary from airborne pollutants to habitat losses and introductions of nonnative predators.
4. Students' maps should reflect the regions and possible causes described above.

Online Biology ▼

ANIMATED BIOLOGY Use this interactive animation to reinforce the concepts of **Section 25.2.**

WEBQUEST The WebQuest takes one full class period. Students complete the activity online and will need access to a printer to print their answers. Sample answers, teacher notes, and alternative assessment ideas are available on **ClassZone.com.** Use with **Section 25.3.**

DATA ANALYSIS ONLINE
Students will see that as the depth increases in the lake, the amount of dissolved oxygen falls, as well as the number of species. Fewer species have adapted to conditions of low oxygen. Use with **Section 25.3.**

INVESTIGATION

TEACHER TESTED

Time	30 minutes
Teacher Preparation	(1 flask)
Student Difficulty	(1 flask)
Lab Binder	Animals, pp. 41–42

Purpose Students will conduct research on the role of amphibians as ecological indicators.

Overview Students will conduct research on the Internet to answer the questions.

LAB PREPARATION

- Distribute copies of U.S. Map (*Lab Binder,* p. 42).

CHAPTER REVIEW

Interactive Review

Encourage students to go to **ClassZone.com** for a detailed review of each section, including visuals and vocabulary practice.

Unit Resource Book, Vocabulary Practice, pp. 91–94

CHAPTER 25 Interactive Review @ CLASSZONE.COM

KEY CONCEPTS | Vocabulary Games | Concept Maps | Animated Biology | Online Quiz

25.1 Vertebrate Origins

All vertebrates share common characteristics. At some point during development, all chordates have a notochord, a hollow nerve cord, pharyngeal slits, and a tail. All vertebrates have an endoskeleton made of bone or cartilage. The first recognizable vertebrates were fish. Lampreys and hagfish are two primitive jawless fish still in existence today.

25.2 Fish Diversity

The dominant aquatic vertebrates are fish. Fish use the large surface area of their gills to exchange carbon dioxide and oxygen with the water in which they live. Countercurrent flow maximizes the amount of oxygen a fish can pull from the water. Fish use their fins to move around in the water. Cartilaginous fish include sharks, rays, and chimeras. All other living fish are categorized as bony fish.

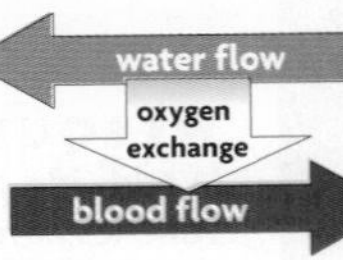

25.3 A Closer Look at Bony Fish

Bony fish include ray-finned and lobe-finned fish. Ray-finned fish have a fan of bones in their fins. Most ray-finned fish use an organ called a swim bladder to stay neutrally buoyant, which means they neither sink nor float in the water. Lobe-finned fish have a series of bones in their fins. Lobe-finned fish include the ancestors of all land vertebrates. Coelacanths and lungfish are two types of lobe-finned fish.

25.4 Amphibians

Amphibians evolved from lobe-finned fish. Amphibians were the first vertebrates with four limbs. Amphibians can live both on land and in water. However, they must live in moist environments, as they need a source of water to reproduce. Modern amphibian groups include salamanders, frogs, and caecilians.

25.5 Vertebrates on Land

Reptiles, birds, and mammals are adapted for life on land. During embryonic or fetal development, an amniote is enclosed within a thin, tough, membranous sac. This waterproof container allows amniotes to reproduce outside of water. Some amniotes give birth to live young, while others lay hard-shelled eggs.

Synthesize Your Notes

Concept Map Use a concept map like the one below to summarize what you know about fish diversity.

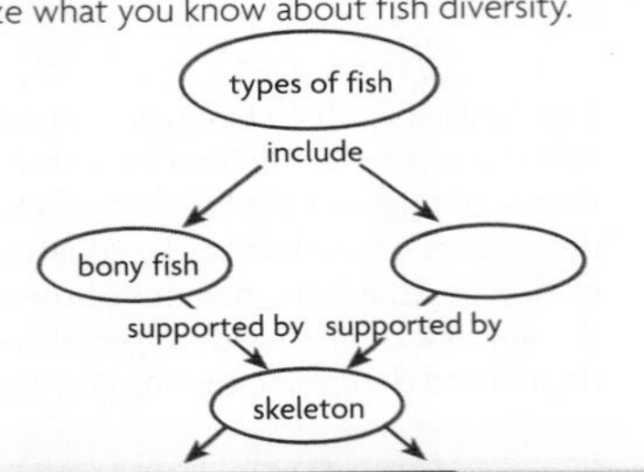

Process Diagram Use a process diagram like the one below to make a detailed summary of the steps that occur during amphibian metamorphosis.

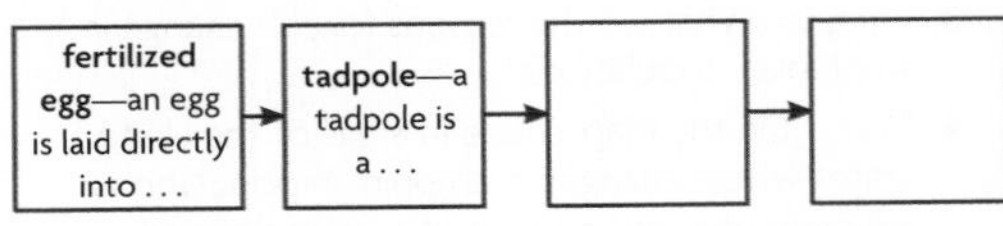

Reviewing Vocabulary

1. Both are types of animals. A vertebrate has an internal segmented backbone; an invertebrate does not.
2. Both provide support for the animals. An endoskeleton is internal; an exoskeleton is external.
3. Both are organs used for gas exchange. Gills exchange gas between an animal and water; lungs exchange gas between an animal and air.
4. Both help fish move through the water. Ray-fins are thin, have a fan-shaped array of bones, and are controlled by muscles embedded in the fish's body; lobe-fins are rounded and fleshy, have bony struts for support, and contain muscles.
5. Tetrapods are vertebrates with four limbs, such as amphibians, mammals, birds, and reptiles.
6. Both are reproductive adaptations of amniotes, but not all amniotes use a placenta. The placenta provides nutrients from the mother to the embryo; the amniotic egg is the container that protects the developing embryo.
7. The operculum covers the gills of a bony fish.
8. Caecilians live underground in the dark.
9. The notochord is a lengthy support rod (similar to a length of string) that is embedded in an animal's back.
10. Tetrapods have four limbs.
11. A shark has a skeleton made of cartilage.
12. The illustration should show two arrows pointing in opposite directions—one marked *water flow,* the other marked *blood flow.* Between the two large arrows could be smaller arrows indicating the exchange of gases. The caption could read "Countercurrent flow maximizes the amount of oxygen a fish can get from water."
13. The illustration should show a simple illustration of a fish with the lateral line marked on its body. The caption could read "The lateral line system gives fish a sense of distant touch, letting them feel the movements in the water created by animal and currents."

Chapter Assessment

Chapter Vocabulary

25.1 chordate, p. 758
notochord, p. 758
endoskeleton, p. 759

25.2 gill, p. 763
countercurrent flow, p. 764
lateral line, p. 767
operculum, p. 767

25.3 ray-fin, p. 768
swim bladder, p. 769
lobe-fin, p. 770

25.4 tetrapod, p. 773
amphibian, p. 773
tadpole, p. 774

25.5 amniote, p. 778
keratin, p. 778
amniotic egg, p. 779
placenta, p. 779

Reviewing Vocabulary

Compare and Contrast

Describe one similarity and one difference between the two terms in each of the following pairs.

1. invertebrate, vertebrate
2. endoskeleton, exoskeleton
3. gill, lung
4. ray-fin, lobe-fin
5. tetrapod, amphibian
6. amniotic egg, placenta

Greek and Latin Word Origins

Using the Greek or Latin word origins of the terms below, explain how the meaning of the root relates to the definition of the term.

7. The word *operculum* comes from the Latin word *operire,* which means "to cover."
8. The term *caecilian* comes from the Latin word *caecus,* meaning "blind." (**Hint:** Consider where a caecilian lives.)
9. The word *notochord* comes from a combination of the Greek words meaning "back" and "gut or string."
10. In the term *tetrapod,* the prefix *tetra* means "four."
11. In the term *chondrichthyes,* the word part *chondr-* comes from a Greek word meaning "cartilage." Why is a shark a member of the group Chondrichthyes?

Visualize Vocabulary

For each term below, use simple shapes, lines, or arrows to illustrate their meaning. Below each picture, write a short caption. Here's an example for *operculum.*

An operculum is a protective plate that covers the gills of a bony fish.

12. countercurrent flow
13. lateral line

Reviewing MAIN IDEAS

14. Sea squirts and dogs are both chordates, but they are very different kinds of animals. What four features do these animals share at some point in their development?
15. All vertebrates have an endoskeleton. What are the main parts of an endoskeleton?
16. What are the seven classes of living vertebrates?
17. How does countercurrent flow contribute to the function of a fish's gills?
18. What evidence indicates that jaws were once gill arches?
19. Barracuda and flatfish have very different body shapes and methods of finding food, yet both have ray-fins. How does the structure of their fins help them to survive?
20. What is the function of the swim bladder in a ray-finned fish?
21. What feature of a lobe-fin fish makes it the closest relative to terrestrial vertebrates?
22. List two adaptations of amphibians and briefly describe why each is important for life on land.
23. Why does amphibian reproduction require a moist environment?
24. What are the three types of modern amphibians?
25. How does the presence of keratin in skin cells affect where an amniote can live?
26. Mammals and birds have very different methods of reproduction, but both are able to reproduce on land. Explain why amniotes do not need to return to water to reproduce.

CHAPTER REVIEW

Reviewing Main Ideas

14. notochord, pharyngeal slits, hollow nerve cord, tail
15. braincase, vertebrae, bones, gill arches
16. Agnatha (jawless fish); Chondrichthyes (cartilaginous fish); Osteichthyes (bony fish); Amphibia (amphibians); Reptilia (reptiles); Aves (birds); Mammalia (mammals)
17. Countercurrent flow ensures that water is always flowing past blood that has a lower oxygen concentration and a higher carbon dioxide concentration than the water. This means oxygen is constantly diffusing into the bloodstream, and carbon dioxide is constantly diffusing out.
18. The third gill arch evolved into the upper and lower jaws of modern fish. The fourth arch also fused to the cranium, adding support to the jaws.
19. A ray-fin is embedded in a thin layer of skin that is light and flexible and allows the fin to change shape quickly, so the fish can maneuver in order to hunt prey or elude predators. Fins also function as stabilizers and, in some species, protection.
20. The swim bladder is a buoyancy organ that a ray-finned fish uses to adjust its depth in the water.
21. the lobe-fins themselves, which contain strutlike bones wrapped in muscle, like the limbs of a terrestrial vertebrate
22. *Sample Answers:* larger shoulder and hip bones that can support more weight; interlocking projections on the vertebrae to support the backbone; ears that can detect vibrations in the air to permit hearing; a muscular tongue to catch food
23. Amphibian eggs develop outside the animal's body and do not have a waterproof shell to protect the embryo and retain nutrients.
24. salamander, frog, caecilian
25. Keratin prevents water loss, so amniotes do not have to live in moist environments.
26. Mammals retain their embryos inside their bodies, providing nutrients and water through a placenta. Birds lay waterproof eggs that keep the embryo from drying out.

Chapter 25: Vertebrate Diversity 783

Critical Thinking

27. Both the notochord and the internal backbone provide support. The notochord is flexible. The backbone is much stiffer because it is composed of short, stiff vertebrae, but it can bend because there are joints between vertebrae. The internal backbone is made of cartilage or bone.
28. *Sample Answer:* At the first station, at the front of the gill, the relative concentrations of dissolved oxygen and carbon dioxide in the incoming water are 80% and 20%, respectively. The countercurrent bloodstream at this station has already been offloading carbon dioxide and taking up oxygen, but the concentrations of these gases are still such (75% O_2 and 25% CO_2) that oxygen diffuses into the blood and carbon dioxide diffuses out. At the next station, the same thing occurs, but the concentrations of the gases in the water might be more like 75% O2 and 25% CO_2, and 70% O_2 and 30% CO_2 in the blood. This pattern of diffusion continues through the other three stations. (Concentrations of gases in blood and water are essentially changing in opposite directions.)
29. To rise, a submarine forces compressed air into a water-filled chamber. The water is forced out and replaced by the air, thereby making the submarine less dense than the water. To descend, the sub vents the air out of the chamber, allowing water to flood back in and make the sub more dense than water.
30. Webbed feet help them swim when they are in water and also help them move through soft mud. Another species' webbed feet allow it to fly.
31. The large kidneys of amniotes allow for reabsorption of water, so less is excreted.

Critical Thinking

27. Analyze Describe the structure and function of the notochord and the internal backbone of an endoskeleton.

28. Analyze Gas exchange in fish occurs in the gills using a countercurrent flow. Imagine that there are five stations in a gill at which gas exchange takes place. Describe what happens and why as the water and blood pass each other at each station.

29. Apply Submarines rise and sink using a mechanical system that works much like a swim bladder. Use your knowledge of how a swim bladder works to explain how submarines use these systems to rise and descend in the water.

30. Infer Frogs have bodies that are specialized for jumping, yet they have webbed feet. How are webbed feet beneficial for frogs?

31. Connect How would your kidneys help you survive for a couple of days without water better than the type of kidneys that frogs have?

Interpreting Visuals

Use the image below to answer the next three questions.

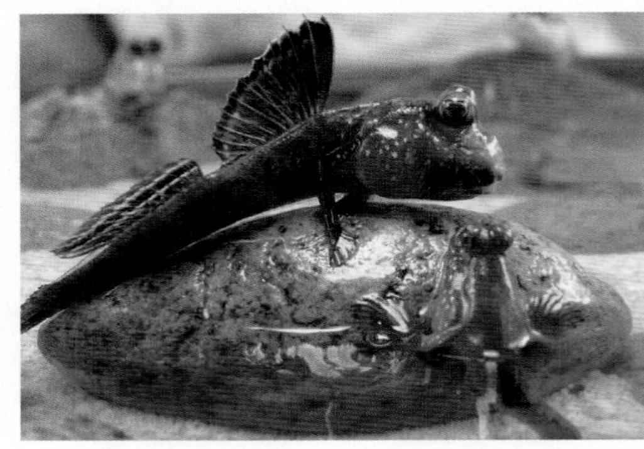

32. Classify This mudskipper has climbed out of the water and is resting on a rock. Based on the physical characteristics of the mudskipper's fin shape, to which group of fish does the mudskipper belong? Explain your reasoning.

33. Analyze When it is out of the water, how might the lungless mudskipper breathe?

34. Apply If mudskippers were to evolve into a terrestrial animal, what body part might function as a limb?

Analyzing Data

Use the data below to answer the next three questions. The calling activity, body size, and body temperature were recorded for a population of Fowler's toads. Below is a scatterplot that shows the relationship between a male toad's body temperature and calling effort, measured as the number of seconds the male called per minute of time.

BODY TEMPERATURE AND CALLING EFFORT

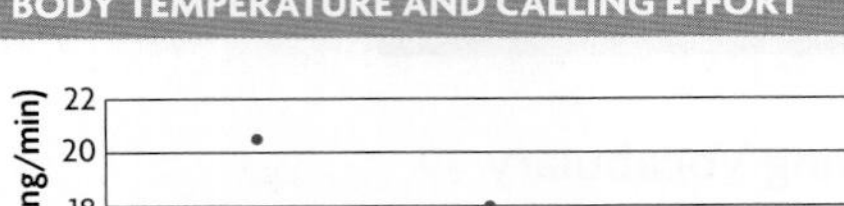

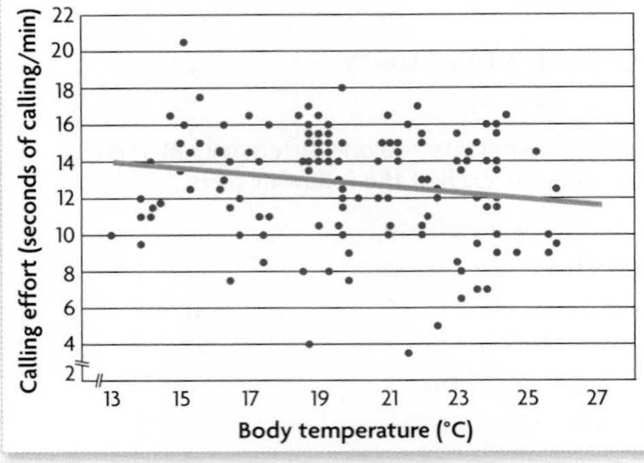

Source: Given, M. *Copeia* 2002:04.

35. Analyze What is the relationship between the body temperature of the Fowler's toad and calling efforts?

36. Analyze Is this data an example of positive correlation, negative correlation, or no relationship?

37. Predict Would you expect a toad with a body temperature of 15° Celsius to have a higher or lower calling effort than a toad with a body temperature of 21° Celsius? Explain.

Connecting CONCEPTS

38. Write a Letter Imagine you are a green frog, adapted to life both in water and on land, and one of your best friends is a fish that lives in a nearby lake. Write a letter to the fish, explaining what adaptations he would need to survive outside of the water on land. In the letter, be sure to compare any similar characteristics and contrast differing characteristics.

39. Connect Take another look at the glass frog on page 757. Its translucent skin helps it to blend in with the green leaves on which it lives. How could natural selection have played a role in the development of this trait common among all glass frogs?

784 Unit 8: Animals

Interpreting Visuals

32. It is a bony, ray-finned fish. Mudskippers' thickened ray-fins allow them to shuffle onto land. Its fins are not fleshy or rounded like lobe-fins are.
33. The mudskipper must have some adaptation to its gills that allows it to exchange gases with the air. (Mudskippers do not have lungs. Their gill cavities are enlarged and filled with a mixture of air and water when on land. As long as the gills remain moist, they can exchange gases with air.)
34. pectoral fins or pelvic fins

Analyzing Data

35. As body temperature increases, calling effort decreases.
36. negative correlation
37. The colder toad should have a higher calling effort than the warmer toad. Judging by the line of best fit, the colder toad would call at a rate of about 14 seconds of calling per minute; the warmer toad would call at less than 13.

INDIANA ISTEP+ Test Prep

B.8.2; B.8.3; NOS.1; NOS.3; NOS.8

Test Practice
For more test practice, go to ClassZone.com.

1 A scientist discovers a new type of organism in the deep ocean. Because this organism was found in the water, the scientist suspects it may be related to fish. This idea ***most*** closely resembles a scientific

A theory.
B hypothesis.
C suggestion.
D experiment.

2 Fossils found in New Zealand suggest that as many as 2000 frog species lived there in the past. Today, there are fewer than 300 frog species. What conclusion can you draw from this information?

A The climate conditions in New Zealand have changed over time.
B The species alive today are more specialized to a particular niche than the species of the past.
C Biological diversity of frogs in New Zealand has decreased.
D There are fewer frog species today because a mass extinction occurred.

3

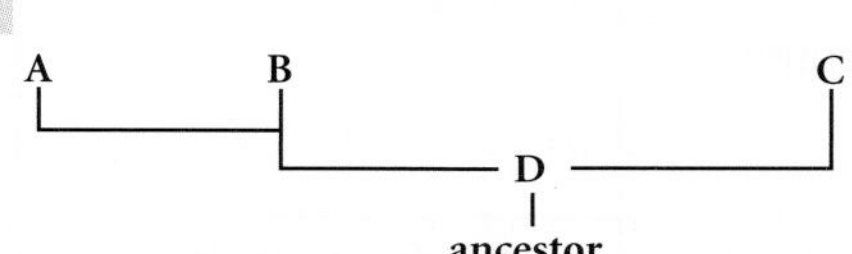

After studying fossils of prehistoric fish in one region, scientists developed this family tree to describe how the various species they found are related. Which of the following is true with regard to this diagram?

A The Ancestor species has gone extinct.
B Species A and Species C are not related.
C Species D evolved before Species A, B, and C.
D Species C evolved before Species A and B.

4

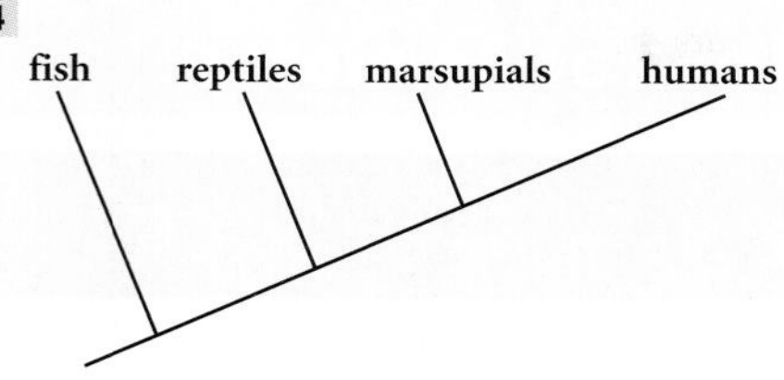

According to this cladogram, which of the following statements is true?

A Fish are more closely related to humans than reptiles.
B Reptiles are more closely related to marsupials than fish.
C Marsupials and fish do not share a common ancestor.
D Marsupials and humans share a common ancestor.

THINK THROUGH THE QUESTION
Recall that cladograms are based on common ancestory, and they are read from left to right.

5 Countercurrent flow in a fish's gills allows blood to efficiently release carbon dioxide into the water and absorb oxygen from the water. This maintenance of oxygen levels in the fish's body is an example of

A homeostasis.
B bioregulation.
C nutrient cycling.
D biomagnification.

6 Despite their aquatic habitat, whales are classified as mammals. Which characteristics of whales make them more like mammals than fish?

Standards-Based Assessment

1. B	4. D
2. C	5. A
3. C	6. See Below

TEST DOCTOR

Question 2 Answer C is correct. Answers A and D are incorrect because the decrease in the number of frog species cannot be attributed to climate change or to mass extinction based on the given information. Answer B is incorrect because it cannot be determined that the species alive today are more specialized to a particular niche based on the given information.

Question 3 Answer C is correct. Answers A and D are incorrect because they cannot be determined from the family tree. Answer B is incorrect because all of the species shown in the diagram are related to each other.

Question 6 Whales give birth to live young and must breathe oxygen to live. They do not have gills. Whales also have bony skeletons, not cartilaginous skeletons like some fish.

Connecting Concepts

38. Students should mention that the fish would need large shoulder and hip bones to support more weight; mobile, muscular tongue to capture food; middle ear to hear; lungs for respiration; modified fins or true limbs to get around; three-chambered heart; way to either protect its eggs from drying out or ensure that they are in a moist environment.

39. Frogs that blend in better with their surroundings are less likely to be killed by predators, so their traits—including their coloration—are more likely to be passed on than those of frogs who do not avoid predation.

ITEM CORRELATIONS

Standard	Items
B.8.2	4
B.8.3	6
NOS.1	2
NOS.3	3
NOS.8	1

CHAPTER 26

Indiana Resource Preview

Print Resources

A Closer Look at Amniotes

INDIANA STANDARDS		Sections	PAGES and PACING	UNIT RESOURCE BOOK
	26.1	**Amniotes** **KEY CONCEPT** Reptiles, birds, and mammals are amniotes.	pp. 788–792 30 minutes	URB pages 95–98
NOS.3		DATA ANALYSIS: Choosing Graphs	p. 792 30 minutes	URB page 111
B.8.3	26.2	**Reptiles** **KEY CONCEPT** Reptiles were the first amniotes.	pp. 793–797 30 minutes	URB pages 99–102
	26.3	**Birds** **KEY CONCEPT** Birds have many adaptations for flight.	pp. 798–803 45 minutes	URB pages 103–106
NOS.5		CHAPTER INVESTIGATION: A Bird's Airframe	p. 804 60 minutes	**Lab Binder** Animals pages 51–54
	26.4	**Mammals** **KEY CONCEPT** Evolutionary adaptations allowed mammals to succeed dinosaurs as a dominant terrestrial vertebrate.	pp. 805–809 30 minutes	URB pages 107–110
NOS.3		OPTIONS FOR INQUIRY	pp. 810–811 30 minutes, 30 minutes	**Lab Binder** Animals pages 55–59
		Chapter Review	pp. 812–815	**Assessment Book** Chapter Tests A, B pp. 517–524

INDIANA STANDARDS

B.8.3 Use anatomical and molecular evidence to establish evolutionary relationships between organisms.
NOS.3 Clearly communicate their ideas and results of investigations verbally and in written form using tables, graphs, diagrams, and photographs.
NOS.5 Apply standard techniques in laboratory investigations to measure physical quantities in appropriate units and convert known quantities to other units as necessary.

Labs

PUPIL EDITION LABS

Comparing Feathers, Section 3, p. 802 Students observe and describe the characteristics of bird feathers. **Lab Binder** pp. 60–61	**Time:** 10 minutes **Materials:** purchased quill feather, purchased contour feather, purchased down feather
A Bird's Airframe, p. 804 Students investigate the density of different types of bones. **Lab Binder** pp. 51–54	**Time:** 60 minutes **Materials:** balance, 100 mL graduated cylinder, 50 mL water, boiled chicken bone (flightless bird), boiled duck or turkey bone (flying bird), boiled cow bone (mammal), hammer, hand lens

OPTIONS FOR INQUIRY

The Parts of an Egg, p. 810 Students examine the parts of an egg. **Lab Binder** pp. 55–57	**Time:** 30 minutes **Materials:** chicken egg, dissecting tray, Egg Drawing, colored pencils, fine scissors, dissecting needle, dissecting forceps, hand lens
Migration and Range, p. 811 Students read and research selected topics about bird migration. **Lab Binder** pp. 58–59	**Time:** 30 minutes **Materials:** pencil, North America map

LAB BINDER Unit 8 Animals

Additional Investigation: Form and Function of Teeth, pp. 62–65

Forensics Lab: Identifying Features: Hair, pp. 80–83

Vernier Probeware Lab: The Effect of Temperature on Ectotherms, pp. 96–100

LAB GENERATOR

A searchable CD of all labs in the program in editable format, including forensic, probeware, and biotechnology labs.

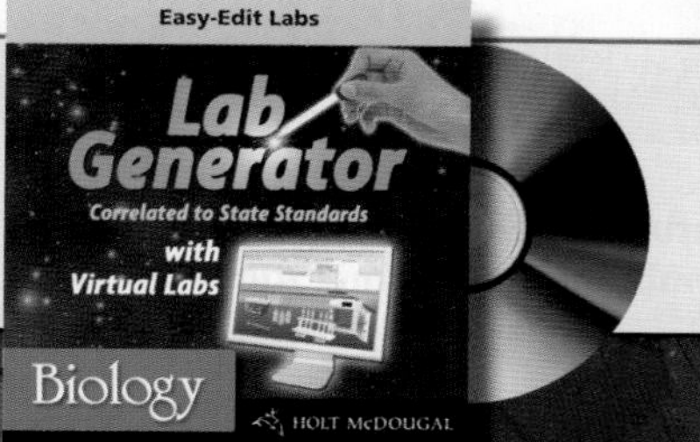

Presentation Tools

POWER PRESENTATIONS

Presentation Chapter 26
Power Presentations for each section incorporate images and clips from the Media Gallery: Includes Note Navigator for each section.

MEDIA GALLERY

Contains the following images and video clips, as well as animations, simulations and forms of visuals from the book.

Phylogenetic tree of reptiles

Beak shape and diet

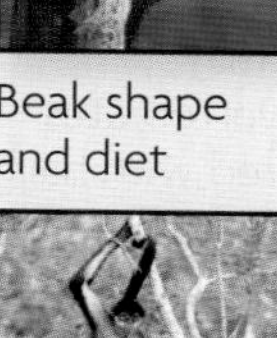

Spider monkey

Pelican

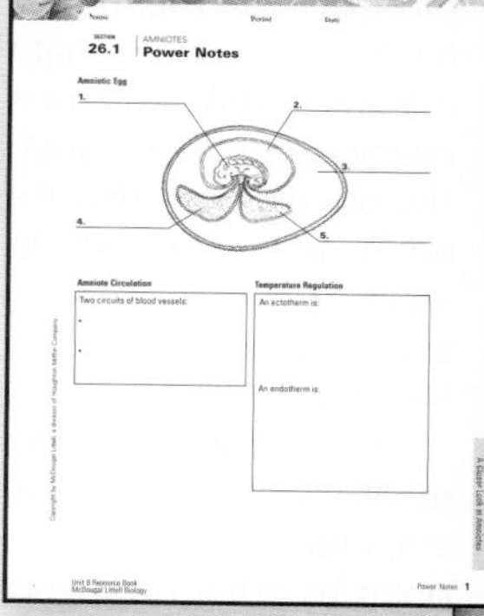

Power Notes

VIDEO

Find a set of short video clips on the adaptations and success of amniotes.

ANIMATED BIOLOGY

Bird Flight

Beak Shape and Diet

TRANSPARENCIES

Reptile Phylogeny T110

Reptile Anatomy T111

Bird Anatomy T112

Online BIOLOGY CLASSZONE.COM

BioZine
Animated Biology
Interactive Review
SciLinks
Resource Centers

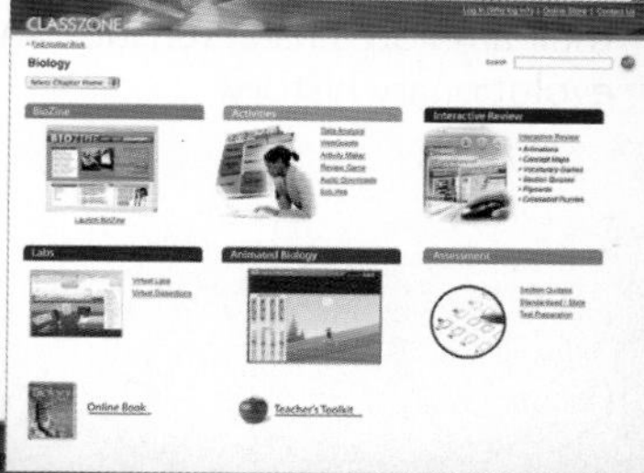

CHAPTER 26

▼ Focus and Motivate

Is this a monkey or a mouse?

The correct answer to the question asked is "neither"; however, as a primate, the tarsier is closer in lineage to the monkey than the mouse. What all three have in common is that they are mammals. **Ask,** What are some common characteristics of mammals? Other than the obvious fact that the young are nourished by milk, students may mention that mammals are vertebrates and most have a body covered with hair. Remind students of the animals they studied in earlier chapters, such as mollusks, crustaceans, insects, and amphibians. With those animals in mind, point to other distinguishing characteristics of mammals, such as two jaws with teeth, movable eyelids, fleshy external ears, four limbs, and a respiratory system that includes lungs and a voice box.

BIOZINE ClassZone.com

Students can access BioZine at **ClassZone.com** to check the daily news feeds.

In a Hurry?

The critical material in this chapter is found in **Sections 26.1** and **26.4,** which describe the defining characteristics of amniotes and how mammals became Earth's dominant amniotes. **Sections 26.2** and **26.3** provide detailed information about reptiles and birds, their amniote characteristics, and their evolutionary history.

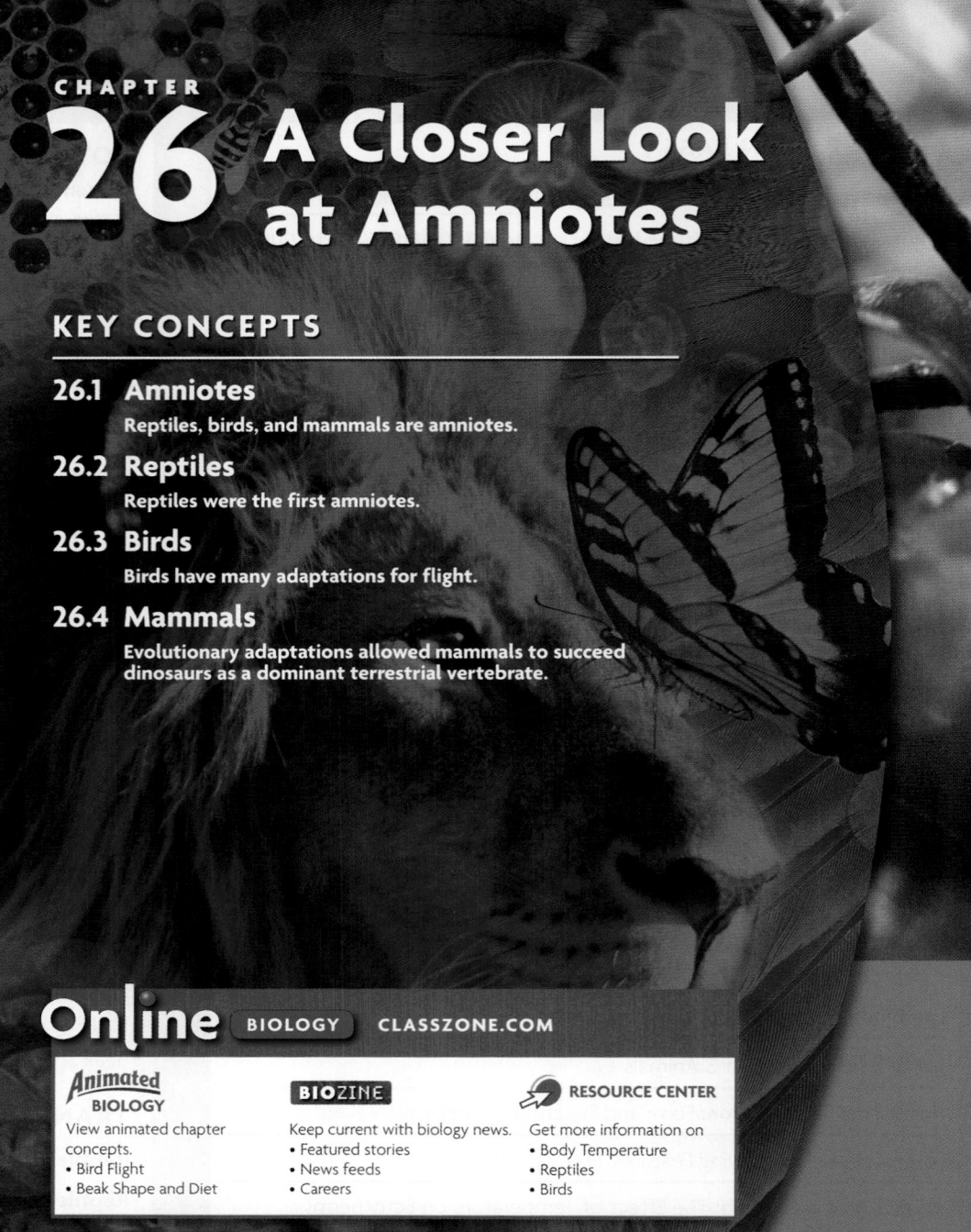

CHAPTER

26 A Closer Look at Amniotes

KEY CONCEPTS

26.1 Amniotes
Reptiles, birds, and mammals are amniotes.

26.2 Reptiles
Reptiles were the first amniotes.

26.3 Birds
Birds have many adaptations for flight.

26.4 Mammals
Evolutionary adaptations allowed mammals to succeed dinosaurs as a dominant terrestrial vertebrate.

Online BIOLOGY CLASSZONE.COM

Animated BIOLOGY
View animated chapter concepts.
- Bird Flight
- Beak Shape and Diet

BIOZINE
Keep current with biology news.
- Featured stories
- News feeds
- Careers

RESOURCE CENTER
Get more information on
- Body Temperature
- Reptiles
- Birds

Teacher Demo

Eye Opener Give students an opportunity to examine the membranes of an amniotic egg.

Materials

- a fresh raw egg that has been soaked in vinegar overnight to dissolve the shell
- a fresh raw egg with shell intact
- a boiled egg with shell intact
- tray or dissecting pan

Demonstrate Show students a diagram of an amniotic egg while you demonstrate. Use fertile chicken eggs if they are available. Carefully peel one of the boiled eggs. Point out to students the membrane just below the shell that tends to hold the shell together. This is the shell membrane that is formed around the albumen. Carefully lift the egg from the vinegar solution and place it on the pan. Show students the pliable shell membrane. This membrane allows gas exchange, but does not keep water in or out.

Is this a monkey or a mouse?

The large eyes and ears of this eastern tarsier make it an excellent nocturnal hunter. These unusual mammals are primates and are closely related to modern monkeys. About the same size as a kitten, a tarsier has strong hind legs similar to those of frogs. The tarsier's eyes cannot move but it has a full range of view because it can rotate its head almost 360 degrees.

Connecting CONCEPTS

Biomes Tarsiers are exceptional climbers that live only in the tropical rain forests of southeastern Asia. Deep within these jungles are areas of the highest biodiversity on Earth. High above the ground, an entire community of species have adapted to become arboreal. They live almost their entire lives in the treetops, or forest canopy, very rarely setting foot on the dense forest floor.

Carefully break the fresh raw egg. Show students the thin liquid that spreads farthest. **Ask,** What is this material? albumen Then point out the clear somewhat mounded material outside the yolk. This material is held in place by the chorion. Allow students to look but not touch. **Ask,** What purpose does the chorion serve? allows oxygen in and carbon dioxide out Peel away the albumen (the white) of the boiled egg and carefully pop out the yolk. **Ask,** Where would you find the developing embryo? surrounded by amnion and attached to the yolk and allantois **Ask,** What purpose is served by the yolk? nutrient supply

Tell students that the self-contained water supply is inside the amnion and is called amniotic fluid. The allantois will be visible only if a zygote is present. Students will learn more about the characteristics of the amniotic egg in **Section 26.1.** Wash your hands when you are finished.

Activate Prior Knowledge

Remind students that they were introduced to amniotes at the end of the last chapter. The feature that gives them their name is the amniotic egg. **Ask,** What did the evolution of the amniotic egg enable amniotic species to do? Students should recall that it freed amniotes from being near a source of water for the purpose of reproduction. **Ask,** How does such an evolutionary development affect animal life on Earth? greatly increases its range

Preview Vocabulary

Greek and Latin Word Origins There are many words in this chapter that have been constructed from Greek and Latin word parts to describe different groups of animals or their characteristics. These include

endo- = inner *ecto-* = outer
-therm = heat
ovi- = egg *vivi-* = alive
-parous = to give birth to

Have students use these word parts to come up with their own definitions for the words *endotherm, ectotherm, oviparous,* and *viviparous.*

Academic Vocabulary Students will be introduced to species of animals in this chapter, some of which are considered *ancient* and some of which are considered *modern.* Explain to students that when describing the history of life, *modern* is a relative term meaning "recently evolved." In this context, many species considered modern evolved tens of millions of years ago.

English Learners Write the words *amniote, reptile, bird,* and *mammal* on cards. Ask students what the relationship is between the words and arrange the cards on the board accordingly. Then have students supply their own words to describe features or examples of reptiles, birds, and mammals. Add these to the board and then continue to have students add more words as you go through the chapter.

SECTION 26.1

▼ Plan and Prepare

Objectives

- Describe the amniotic egg and its evolutionary significance.
- Summarize key anatomical and circulatory differences among amniotes.
- Explain two strategies for regulating body temperature.

Section Resources

Unit Resource Book
Study Guide pp. 95–96
Power Notes p. 97
Reinforcement p. 98
Pre-AP Activity pp. 113–114

Interactive Reader Chapter 26
Spanish Study Guide pp. 265–266

Biology Toolkit pp. C2, C20, C33

Technology
Power Presentation 26.1
Media Gallery DVD
Online Quiz 26.1

Activate Prior Knowledge Poll students to see what types of pets they have. **Ask,** What do you have to do to keep a lizard as a pet? maintain stable temperature Have students describe the different ways their pets cope with variations in temperature, then help them categorize their pets as ectotherms or endotherms.

26.1 Amniotes

KEY CONCEPT Reptiles, birds, and mammals are amniotes.

MAIN IDEAS
- Amniote embryos develop in a fluid-filled sac.
- Anatomy and circulation differ among amniotes.
- Amniotes can be ectothermic or endothermic.

VOCABULARY
pulmonary circuit, p. 789
systemic circuit, p. 789
ectotherm, p. 791
endotherm, p. 791

REVIEW AT
CLASSZONE.COM

Connect When you were about nine weeks into your development, you had a mass of about 2 grams and measured about 18 millimeters long, roughly the size of a dime. Over the next seven months, you grew and developed while living safely inside a fluid-filled membrane, or amniotic sac. There are many different types of amniotes, but each of them, like you, begins life inside an amniotic sac.

MAIN IDEA

Amniote embryos develop in a fluid-filled sac.

Reptiles, birds, and mammals are all amniotes. Recall from Chapter 25 that amniotes develop in a sac inside the mother's abdomen. This sac contains everything an embryonic vertebrate needs to grow and prepare for the world outside. In some amniotes, the sac is contained inside the mother's body. In other amniotes, a tough outer shell protects embryos as they develop outside of the mother. This shell is semipermeable, which means that it allows gases such as oxygen and carbon dioxide to pass through but prevents the embryo from drying out by holding water inside.

FIGURE 26.1 Amniotic Egg

Inside the shell of an amniotic egg, four membranes perform specific functions during development of the embryo.

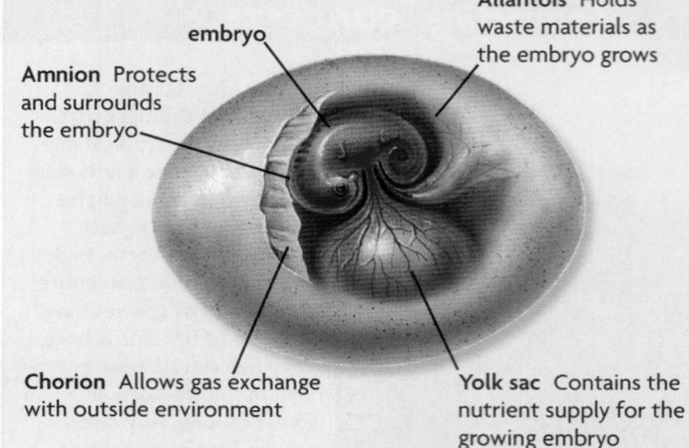
embryo
Allantois Holds waste materials as the embryo grows
Amnion Protects and surrounds the embryo
Chorion Allows gas exchange with outside environment
Yolk sac Contains the nutrient supply for the growing embryo

An egg is a completely self-sustaining container that provides enough energy and nutrients to enable the embryo to mature. The illustration in **FIGURE 26.1** shows the different membranes found inside an amniotic egg. The egg you may have eaten for breakfast this morning was formed with all of the necessary membranes and nutrient stores to support a chicken embryo. But because the egg was never fertilized, the genetic composition of the egg remained haploid and did not develop into an embryo.

The development of the amniotic egg was an important adaptation because it allowed vertebrates to reproduce on land. Without the self-contained source of energy and water, an egg needed to develop in water or else the embryo would dry out.

(A) **Predict What happens when all of the resources that are stored inside the egg are used?**

▼ Teach

TEACH FROM VISUALS

FIGURE 26.1 Point out each labeled structure. **Ask,** What is the role of the network of capillaries that connects the allantois and the yolk sac to the embryo? Capillaries deliver wastes to the allantois and nutrients from the yolk to the blood. **Ask,** Can you infer which came first—internal fertilization or the hard-shelled egg? Yes, the egg must be fertilized before the shell is formed.

Answers

(A) **Predict** The egg will hatch.

Differentiated Instruction

BELOW LEVEL

Have students survey this section by completing the following tasks:

- Read the key concept and main ideas.
- Note how the subheadings relate to the main ideas.
- Locate the vocabulary words within the chapter and write them in their notebooks.
- Relate how the figures and illustrations relate to the main-idea headings.

Biology Toolkit, Section Preview, p. C2

ENGLISH LEARNERS

Suggest that students take notes using the two-column note-taking method shown on page 789. Tell them to use the first column to record key characteristics of amniotes, particularly anatomical features; the second column can be used to compare features among different amniote groups.

Biology Toolkit, Two-Column Notes, p. C20

MAIN IDEA

Anatomy and circulation differ among amniotes.

Over time, amniotes have evolved many different body shapes and sizes, resulting in many differences in anatomy and blood circulation.

Anatomy

The first amniotes walked in a sprawl similar to that of the lizard in **FIGURE 26.2.** A lizard's legs stick out on either side of its body. It walks with its elbows and knees bent. Muscles around the ribs help propel the body forward, and their contractions make the lizard's body sway from side to side with each step. Because these same muscles also inflate the lungs, many animals with a sprawling stance cannot run and breathe at the same time. However, some reptiles have adaptations that allow them to breathe while running.

Amniotes such as mammals, dinosaurs, and birds evolved a more upright stance. The cat in **FIGURE 26.2** has straighter limbs than the lizard. Its legs are underneath its body and hold it far away from the ground. When it walks, its legs swing back and forth like pendulums, and its body does not wiggle from side to side. An upright stance uses less energy than a sprawling one. It also separates the muscles the animal uses to breathe from the muscles it uses to walk and run. The evolution of the diaphragm, an independent muscle used to expand the chest cavity and force air into the lungs, separated the muscles needed for walking and breathing. A diaphragm enables amniotes with an upright stance to run and breathe at the same time.

FIGURE 26.2 The sprawling walking style illustrated by this Komodo dragon is very different from the upright stance of a cat. Anatomical features make breathing easier and more efficient for upright walkers.

Circulation

As amniotes evolved, their bodies required more energy for movement and growth. To get this energy, their tissues demanded more energy and needed highly efficient ways of delivering this oxygen. This need led to the development of many different types of circulatory systems. All amniotes have a centralized heart that moves blood through a complex system of blood vessels to deliver nutrients to tissues and organs.

All amniotes have two circuits of blood vessels. Because the circuits are separate, amniotes can conserve energy more effectively. The two circuits of blood vessels are the pulmonary and systemic circuits.

- The **pulmonary circuit** moves oxygen-poor blood from the heart to the lungs, and oxygen-rich blood back to the heart.
- The **systemic circuit** moves oxygen-rich blood from the heart to the rest of the body.

The differences in amniote circulatory systems evolved over millions of years. As you will see, these differences affect the efficiency of an organism's everyday functions and behavior.

TAKING NOTES

Use a two-column chart to take notes on the pulmonary and systemic blood circuits.

Pulmonary Circuit	Systemic Circuit

PRE-AP

Have students compare the amniotic egg in **FIGURE 26.1** to the seed diagram on page 670 of Chapter 22. Have them draw a diagram of each and note similarities and differences. Have them consider in what sense each embryo is alive and ready to develop.

Take It Further

The **Komodo dragon** is largest lizard species alive today. They are an endangered species, with only an estimated 5000 left. Unlike most lizards, the Komodo dragon is a meat eater. Despite its size, it can run fast enough to prey upon deer, wild horses, and wild boar. The Komodo dragon has a long tongue that can pick up the smell of its prey a mile away.

Komodos live mainly on the Indonesian islands of Komodo, Rintja, Padar, and Flores. The islands of Padar and Rintja are official nature reserves dedicated to protecting the lizard and its prey.

Integrating Paleontology

Scientists can compare footprints of modern animals with those of extinct animals to gain insight into how the animals moved. In one such investigation, a Komodo dragon was enticed with a juicy dead rat to make footprints in clay for researchers. The footprints were used to reconstruct a theoretical skeleton and to assess gait and breathing mode as well as to interpret posture and the motion of the body while walking. These results were compared with fossilized footprints to make inferences about the bodies and behaviors of extinct amniotes.

Vocabulary

Academic Vocabulary Tell students that the words **systemic** and **pulmonary** are being used as complementary terms. The word *pulmonary* comes from the Latin *plumōn-*, meaning "lungs." The heart pumps blood into the lungs, which make up the center of the circuit, and then moves oxygenated blood to the extremities, through a system of vessels. The circuit is completed when deoxygenated blood returns to the heart.

▼ Teach *continued*

Take It Further

Crocodiles have an odd mix of features. They are **ectothermic reptiles,** but unlike lizards and snakes, they have a four-chambered heart like humans and birds. Some researchers say they inherited a four-chambered heart from a more active, endothermic ancestor. The debate continues, but it is interesting to imagine that the giant crocodile of the Cretaceous was an endotherm, hungry all the time, and had the fast-moving metabolism of modern mammals and birds.

TEACH FROM VISUALS

FIGURE 26.3 Discuss both illustrations with students, tracing the pathway of blood flow through the hearts. Point out where oxygen-rich blood crosses paths with oxygen-poor blood in the three-chambered heart. **Ask,** Why would a three-chambered heart be inefficient for most mammals? It does not oxygenate the tissues enough to allow for endothermy and the increased metabolism and energy use by mammals.

Answers

A Infer Reptiles cannot run and breathe at the same time. By being an ambush predator, a reptile can conserve energy it may need to make a kill.

B Contrast The open septum of the three-chambered heart means the single ventricle pumps blood to the lungs and body. When the lungs are not in use, the ventricle can divert blood flow away from them, maximizing blood flow to tissues that need oxygen. In the four-chambered heart, the septum separates the systemic and pulmonary blood flows, meaning flow is constant to both the lungs and the body.

Connecting CONCEPTS

Circulatory System The heart is a muscle for pumping blood through the body. It is made of two different types of chambers. The right and left atria collect blood from the body and lungs, and the right and left ventricles pump blood to the lungs and body. You will learn more about the heart in **Chapter 30**.

Like amphibians, reptiles have a three-chambered heart. A reptile's heart has two atria and one ventricle, as shown in **FIGURE 26.3.** One atrium collects oxygen-poor blood from the body. The other collects oxygen-rich blood from the lungs. Both atria send blood into the ventricle, which pumps blood into the pulmonary and systemic circuits. This unique anatomy lets these animals temporarily "turn off" their lungs. Like amphibians, amniotes such as lizards and turtles do not breathe continuously. Remember that sprawling amniotes stop breathing when they run. Others spend a lot of time under water. In either case, a single ventricle can divert blood away from the lungs when the animal is not using them. This strategy lets these animals adjust blood flow in response to their oxygen needs.

Mammals and birds have a four-chambered heart. As you can see in **FIGURE 26.3,** four-chambered hearts have two atria and two ventricles. This anatomy keeps oxygen-poor and oxygen-rich blood separate, but it cannot shift blood away from the lungs when the animal is not breathing. Keeping oxygen-rich and oxygen-poor blood separate effectively increases the flow of oxygen-rich blood to tissues. This adaptation gives these active animals a large and constant supply of oxygen. The development of the four-chambered heart allowed for an increase in energy use and eventually gave organisms increased control over their body temperature.

A Infer Many reptiles are ambush predators, hiding and waiting for prey to come to them as opposed to actively hunting. Explain how this behavior may be related to their circulatory system.

FIGURE 26.3 Amniote Hearts

The heart, the pump that moves blood around an organism's body, has developed differently in reptiles and mammals.

Oxygen-poor blood
Oxygen-rich blood

THREE-CHAMBERED HEART

Reptile hearts have three chambers. A septum that only partially divides the heart helps direct oxygen-rich and oxygen-poor blood.

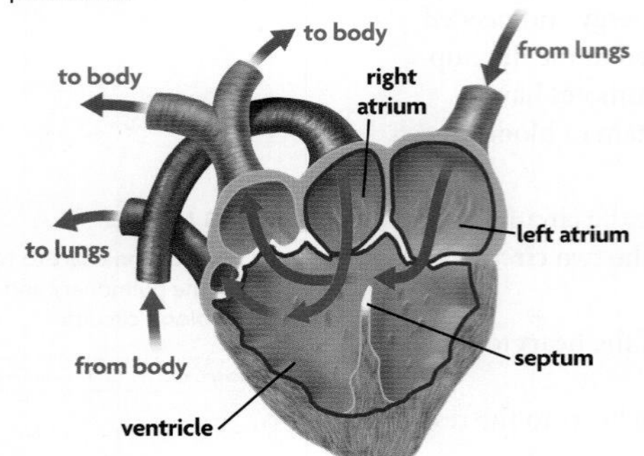

FOUR-CHAMBERED HEART

Birds and mammals have a heart divided into four chambers, which keeps oxygen-rich and oxygen-poor blood separate.

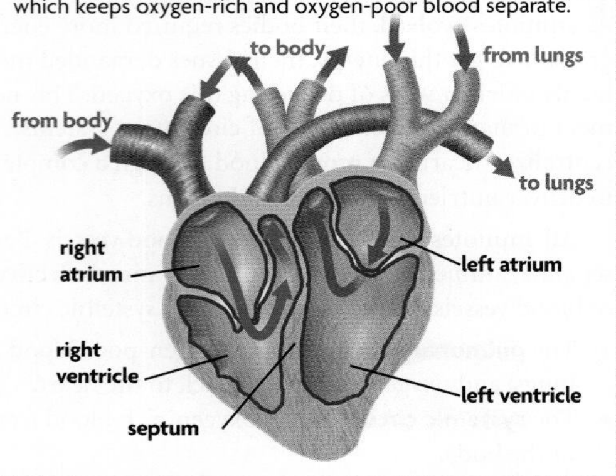

B Contrast How do differences in the septum affect blood flow in these hearts?

Differentiated Instruction

BELOW LEVEL

Have students draw two overlapping circles, with one circle representing a three-chambered heart and the other representing a four-chambered heart. Then have students list the characteristics for each type of heart in the appropriate circle. In the area where the two circles intersect, key similarities should be listed.

Biology Toolkit, Venn Diagram, p. C33

MAIN IDEA

Amniotes can be ectothermic or endothermic.

Like all organisms, amniotes are more active when they are warm. Enzymes that speed up the chemical reactions inside cells are more active at higher temperatures. A warm amniote digests food faster and can send more nutrients to its tissues. It can also move faster because its muscles contract more quickly and more often. All living organisms absorb heat from the environment and release heat as a byproduct of metabolism. But all animals manage heat in different ways.

You may have heard the term "cold-blooded" to describe a snake or a lizard. This term does not accurately describe reptiles and amphibians, because their blood is not actually cold. Instead, scientists use the term **ectotherms** to refer to organisms whose body temperatures are determined by their surrounding environment. These organisms' body temperature fluctuates with the temperature of their environment. They have higher body temperatures in a warm environment than in a cool one.

Ectotherms regulate their body temperature through their behavior. For example, many reptiles, such as the chameleon in **FIGURE 26.4**, bask in sunny places to warm their tissues when they are cold. Similarly, desert lizards move into shady burrows when outside temperatures climb too high. Large animals have a harder time shedding heat than small animals. If an ectothermic animal is massive enough, it will take a long time to cool down. Large ectotherms, such as crocodiles, can stay warm even when the environment is relatively cool.

On the other hand, you have probably heard humans and other mammals described as "warm-blooded." But to describe these organisms more accurately, scientists use the term *endotherm.* **Endotherms** are organisms that use their own metabolic heat to keep their tissues warm. More specifically, endotherms regulate their metabolic activity in ways that keep their body temperature relatively constant all of the time. They may shiver when they get too cold, contracting their muscles to generate extra heat. If they get too hot, they may cool down by sweating or panting. Many endotherms, such as the polar bear in **FIGURE 26.4**, are covered with insulation in the form of hair, fat cells, or feathers, which helps them control heat loss.

FIGURE 26.4 As an ectotherm, a chameleon increases its body temperature by basking in sunlight. Endotherms such as this polar bear can maintain a relatively constant body temperature even in cold environments.

You can think of endotherms and ectotherms as having two different strategies for managing energy use. There is a trade-off between an animal's body temperature and the amount of energy it uses. Warm tissues work quickly and require more ATP, which requires an animal to eat more. For example, lions and crocodiles are both large predators, but a crocodile can survive on much less meat than a lion can. In short, ectotherms are less active when it is cold but can survive on less food than endotherms. Endotherms are active all the time but must eat more than ectotherms eat.

ONLINE BIOLOGY Students can compare body temperatures of different amniotes in Data Analysis Online; see Options for Inquiry on page 811. For additional resources and information on body temperature, go to the chapter Resource Center at **ClassZone.com.**

The Inside Story

Were dinosaurs sluggish and stupid or were they intelligent and quick? The debate began when a young paleontologist, **Robert T. Bakker,** wrote an article in 1968 titled *The Superiority of Dinosaurs.* In the article, Bakker describes dinosaurs as "fast, agile, energetic creatures." He maintains that dinosaurs were endothermic and cites several points of evidence:

- They were anatomically built to move quickly.
- They evolved alongside mammals and were superior competitors.
- They had erect posture.
- They had a large brain size for reptiles.
- Their fossils have been found at high, cold latitudes, indicating endothermy.

Opponents of Bakker's theory cite equally logical arguments. Some say that dinosaurs were simple ectotherms enjoying the warmer Mesozoic climate. However, it was Bakker who was hired by director Steven Spielberg to be one of the technical consultants for the movie ***Jurassic Park.*** The image many people have of dinosaurs is not one of a languid oversized lizard but rather that of a *Tyrannosaur* overtaking a sport utility vehicle and a *Velociraptor* opening a door.

HANDS-ON ACTIVITY

Students know that there is some mixing of oxygen-rich blood and oxygen-poor blood in the three-chambered heart. To demonstrate how these two differently oxygenated bloodstreams keep from completely mixing in the reptilian ventricle, demonstrate how liquids of different densities stay separated. Pour about 50 mL of heavy corn syrup into a 100-mL graduated cylinder. **Ask,** What will happen if I pour colored water on top of the syrup? Will the solutions mix? No, they have different densities.

Slowly fill the rest of the cylinder with colored water. The syrup will stay on the bottom, and the water will stay on the top. With another 100-mL cylinder, reverse the order of additions. The syrup will sink to the bottom. **Ask,** What helps oxygen-rich and oxygen-poor blood stay separated in the reptilian ventricle? There is a slight difference in density.

Vocabulary

Academic Vocabulary Unlike the complementary terms *pulmonary* and *systemic* that describe different parts of an amniote's circulatory system, the terms **endotherm** and **ectotherm** describe alternative mechanisms for regulating body temperature: either from the inside, *endo-* meaning "inner," or from the outside, *ecto-*, meaning "outer."

▼ Teach *continued*

DATA ANALYSIS

Discuss

Tell students that one of the first things to consider when determining how to present data is to look at the type of data collected. Data presented as percentages can often be effectively displayed in a circle graph. A bar graph is effective for displaying data points that represent separate or discrete events or data entries. Continuous data, which chart a change in condition over time, are typically displayed as a line graph.

Answers

1. For a sample graph, go to page R107.
2. Endotherms must eat more food to fuel the metabolism that keeps their body temperature at an appropriate level. Ectotherms do not need as much food because the environment regulates their body temperature.

Unit Resource Book, Data Analysis, p. 111

Answers

A Analyze Because ectotherms rely on their environment as a source of heat, the conditions in colder latitudes are inhospitable. Because endotherms can maintain their body temperature in a wider range of climates, they can withstand conditions in colder latitudes.

▼ Assess and Reteach

Assess Use the Online Quiz or Section Quiz (*Assessment Book,* p. 513).

Reteach Hold up pictures of amniotes with which students are familiar. Have volunteers tell you its name, what kind of animal it is (reptile, bird, mammal), whether it is endothermic or ectothermic, if it lays eggs or gives birth to live young, and how it is adapted to land. You can find images in the Media Gallery.

DATA ANALYSIS

NOS.3

CHOOSING GRAPHS

Choosing an appropriate type of graph to represent data collected in an experiment is an important part of the scientific process.

The table to the right contains data that show the differences in energy requirements for endotherms and ectotherms. Despite having similar sizes, endotherms and ectotherms use energy in different ways and therefore require different amounts of food.

TABLE 1. BODY MASS AND FOOD INTAKE

Organism	Mass (kg)	Food Intake (kg/yr)
Nile crocodile	150	750
Grey kangaroo	45	1108
Komodo dragon	45	250
Koala	8	252
Monitor lizard	8	93

Source: Nagy, K.A. *Nutrition Abstracts and Reviews* Series B:71.

1. **Graph** Choose and construct one graph that can represent both sets of data.
2. **Analyze** Explain why there is a difference in energy requirements between endotherms and ectotherms.

The ability to regulate their own temperature served as an important function in the early stages of endotherm evolution. This adaptation gave endotherms a distinct advantage over ectotherms as Earth's climate changed millions of years ago. Because they could stay warm in colder weather, endotherms were able to exploit resources that the ectotherms could not. Many scientists believe that the ability to regulate their own body temperature allowed endotherms to survive the catastrophic events that led to the extinction of dinosaurs.

A Analyze As you move away from Earth's equator into colder latitudes, why are there fewer ectotherms and more endotherms?

26.1 ASSESSMENT

ONLINE QUIZ ClassZone.com

REVIEWING MAIN IDEAS

1. How did the development of an amniotic egg allow vertebrates to reproduce on land?
2. How does anatomy and circulation differ among amniotes?
3. What is the difference between an **endotherm** and an **ectotherm**?

CRITICAL THINKING

4. **Infer** A 30-gram shrew will die if it cannot eat for a few hours. A 30-gram gecko thrives on a few crickets every other day. Why might shrews need food more often?
5. **Compare** Illustrate the path of blood through a three-chambered heart when the animal is breathing. Show how the pathway changes when the animal is not breathing.

Connecting CONCEPTS

6. **Survivorship** When eggs are laid by a species of reptile or bird, they generally stay in a nest that is closely guarded by a mother. How does this behavior affect the chances for offspring to survive to adulthood? What type of survivorship strategy does this represent?

26.1 ASSESSMENT

1. prevented the embryo from drying out
2. reptiles: sprawling stance, legs project out, bent limbs, cannot breathe and run at the same time due to use of the same muscles, three-chambered heart; birds and mammals: upright stance, straight limbs, a diaphragm that allows them to breathe and run at the same time, four-chambered heart
3. Endotherms regulate body temperature internally, and ectotherms use the surrounding environment as a source of heat.
4. Shrews are endotherms, requiring more food to maintain a high metabolism.
5. Students' drawings should show the septum diverting blood to the body and away from the lungs.
6. It increases the chances of offspring survival by guarding against predators and keeping the eggs safe and warm; Type I survivorship strategy.

26.2 Reptiles

KEY CONCEPT Reptiles were the first amniotes.

MAIN IDEAS
- Reptiles are a diverse group of amniotes.
- Reptiles have been evolving for millions of years.
- There are four modern groups of reptiles.

VOCABULARY
reptile, p. 793
oviparous, p. 793
viviparous, p. 793

INDIANA STANDARDS

B.8.3 Use anatomical and molecular evidence to establish evolutionary relationships between organisms.

Connect Basking on the sunny banks of the river, the lizard may look slow, but it has a top speed of almost 20 kilometers per hour, and strong jaws filled with sharp teeth. It is a daunting predator. The eastern water dragon may only grow to 80 centimeters in length and may never compare to a crocodile as a threat to humans, but it hunts, kills, and eats its prey in the same way that its larger cousins do. What makes reptiles unique?

MAIN IDEA

Reptiles are a diverse group of amniotes.

About 200 million years ago, a mass extinction resulted in the loss of many of Earth's plant and animal species. One group of organisms that survived—the reptiles—have thrived for millions of years. **Reptiles** are ectotherms that are covered with dry scales or plates and reproduce by laying amniotic eggs covered with a tough outer shell.

VOCABULARY
The name *reptile* comes from the Latin word, *reptilis,* which means "creeping."

Unlike amphibians, reptiles produce a completely self-sustaining, amniotic egg that allows an embryonic reptile to develop fully before it is born. There are two ways that reptile eggs develop.

- **Oviparous** reptiles deposit their eggs into an external nest, and the eggs develop completely independent of the adult reptile.
- **Viviparous** reptiles hold the eggs inside their body through the duration of development and give birth to live offspring.

FIGURE 26.5 As a reptile, this eastern water dragon must use energy from sunlight to maintain its body temperature. From its perch atop a rock, it can also spot predators or look for prey.

The shapes and sizes of modern reptiles vary widely. Some reptiles have no legs. Other reptiles run swiftly on land or spend much of their time in the water. The oddly shaped turtles and tortoises carry their homes on their backs. Each reptile group has adapted different features that allow it to be successful. But despite these differences, all reptiles share a few similarities.

All living reptiles are ectotherms. Recall that an ectotherm's body temperature changes based on the surrounding environment. Similar to the eastern water dragon in **FIGURE 26.5,** many reptiles spend a great deal of time basking, or sunbathing, to absorb energy from sunlight. In addition, reptiles have dry scales or plates that absorb energy and help contain heat needed to maintain normal body functions.

(A) Analyze What advantages does a self-sustaining egg give reptiles?

SECTION 26.2

Plan and Prepare ▼

Objectives

- Describe the diversity and evolution of reptiles.
- Differentiate among the four groups of modern reptiles.

Section Resources

Unit Resource Book
Study Guide pp. 99–100
Power Notes p. 101
Reinforcement p. 102

Interactive Reader Chapter 26
Spanish Study Guide pp. 267–268

Biology Toolkit pp. C13, C17, C19, D7

Technology
Power Presentation 26.2
Media Gallery DVD
Online Quiz 26.2

Activate Prior Knowledge For students who have a pet reptile, have them describe the animal's behavior. **Ask,** How would you describe the level of activity? typically a low level of activity Have them describe the feel of the animal's skin.

Teach ▼

Take It Further

There are different types of **viviparity.** Many fish and lizards are **ovoviviparous.** They give birth to live young that are nourished by and hatch from eggs while still inside the mother. Mammals are **placental** animals. Fertilized eggs develop in a uterus. The young get their nourishment directly from the mother through the walls of the uterus.

Answers

(A) Analyze allows reproduction on land

Differentiated Instruction

HANDS-ON ACTIVITY

Ask students what they have heard or believe about snakes. List their responses on the board. Some students may say that they are cold and slimy or that all snakes are poisonous. Show students a living snake, such as a garter snake. Allow students to carefully touch the snake and observe its movements. Discuss with students how misconceptions can contribute to the common fear of snakes.

BELOW LEVEL

Display a map of the United States including Alaska and Hawaii. **Ask,** If you want to see the most diversity and numbers of reptiles, where would you go? south **Ask,** Where would you see the fewest reptiles? north Have students write for five minutes on why they would see a greater number of reptiles in the warmer regions of the United States, and why reptiles are not found in very cold climates.

Biology Toolkit, Quick-Write, p. C19

▼ Teach continued

ONLINE BIOLOGY Go to the chapter Resource Center at **ClassZone.com** for additional resources and information on reptiles.

Vocabulary

Greek and Latin Word Origins The terms **anapsid, diapsid,** and **synapsid** are more meaningful if broken down into their roots.

an- = without
di- = two
syn- = together

The word part *apse* is Greek for "arch." When these types of skulls were named, scientists were interested in the arches of bone below the various openings. In a synapsid skull, the opening was once erroneously thought to have come from the fusion of two openings.

History of Science

Paul Sereno is a geologist and paleontologist who teaches at the University of Chicago. While in Argentina in 1988, his team discovered fossils of what are believed to be the first dinosaurs to roam Earth—*Herrerasaurus* and *Eoraptor*. Throughout the early 1990s, Serano and his team discovered and named six new dinosaurs found in Niger and Morocco: *Afrovenator, Jobaria, Suchomimus, Nigersaurus, Deltadromeus,* and *Carcharodontosaurus*. In 2000, in the Sahara, Sereno's team discovered the fossil nicknamed **"SuperCroc,"** a 12-meter long, 10-ton *Sarcosuchus imperator* that 110 million years ago inhabited the swampy rivers of what is now desert.

MAIN IDEA

Reptiles have been evolving for millions of years.

Fossil evidence suggests that reptiles began to emerge from the water during the late Paleozoic era, almost 350 million years ago. They became the dominant vertebrate during the Mesozoic era.

FIGURE 26.6 Turtles and tortoises are anapsids. Aside from the holes for eyes and nose, this skull of a modern turtle has no temporal holes.

Synapsids, Anapsids, and Diapsids

Scientists discovered that, over time, amniotes evolved into three different groups. This discovery was based on temporal holes that are found on the sides of the amniote skull.

Synapsids Reptiles that had one hole in each temporal region were synapsids. The synapsids eventually gave rise to modern mammals.

Anapsids Reptiles that have skulls with no temporal holes are anapsids. Scientists do not know why anapsids have no skull holes. Some think that they may still have the same skull anatomy as the first amniotes or that they may have lost skull holes through natural selection. The anapsids of today are turtles and tortoises, with skulls similar to the one shown in **FIGURE 26.6.**

AMNIOTE SKULL TYPES

SKULL TYPE	PAIRS OF TEMPORAL HOLES	EXAMPLE
Anapsid	0	turtles
Synapsid	1	mammals
Diapsid	2	birds, lizards, crocodilians

Diapsids Reptiles that have two holes in each temporal region, one above the other, are diapsids. Diapsid skulls came about as reptiles began to colonize land. For the next 200 million years, diapsid reptiles ruled Earth. Eventually, this group gave rise to many of the modern reptiles and birds of today.

Skull holes may have started out as a weight-reducing adaptation. Less bone would have made the skull lighter and easier to move and given more space for muscle attachments, allowing jaw muscles to get larger. The phylogenetic tree in **FIGURE 26.7** shows how the ancient and now extinct groups of reptiles may have evolved.

Diversity of Extinct Amniotes

Pelycosaurs were synapsids that first appeared during the late Carboniferous period. This group included both carnivores and herbivores. Some pelycosaurs had a distinctive "sail-back" made of elongated vertebral spines. Most pelycosaurs died in a mass extinction 245 million years ago, but some of their descendants later gave rise to the mammals.

Ichthyosaurs were some of the first diapsid reptiles. An ichthyosaur's sleek body, flipper-shaped limbs, and fleshy dorsal fin were similar to those of the modern day dolphin. Ichthyosaurs swam by beating their fishlike tails back and forth in the water, and their peglike teeth suggest that they ate fish. Fossil evidence indicates that ichthyosaurs first appeared about 250 million years ago and went extinct about 90 million years ago.

Plesiosaurs were some of the strangest prehistoric marine reptiles. They "flew" through the water like sea lions, using four limbs like elongated flippers. Some plesiosaurs had small heads and very long necks, which were likely used to help them catch fish. Others had short necks and long heads and probably chased down larger prey. Fossils show the plesiosaurs first appeared around 220 million years ago and then died out around 80 million years ago.

Differentiated Instruction

PRE-AP

Tell students that fossils of extinct reptiles have been found in some very unexpected places, including Canada and Alaska. Have students research the reptiles of Pangaea in an earth science book or on the Internet. Ask them to demonstrate, using a current world map, how the ancient reptiles *Cynognathus, Mesosaurus,* and *Lystrosaurus* helped scientists sort out the early history of Earth's continents. Information is also provided in the chapter resources at **ClassZone.com.**

FIGURE 26.7 Phylogenetic Tree of Reptiles

The diversification of ancient reptiles eventually led to the evolution of modern animals.

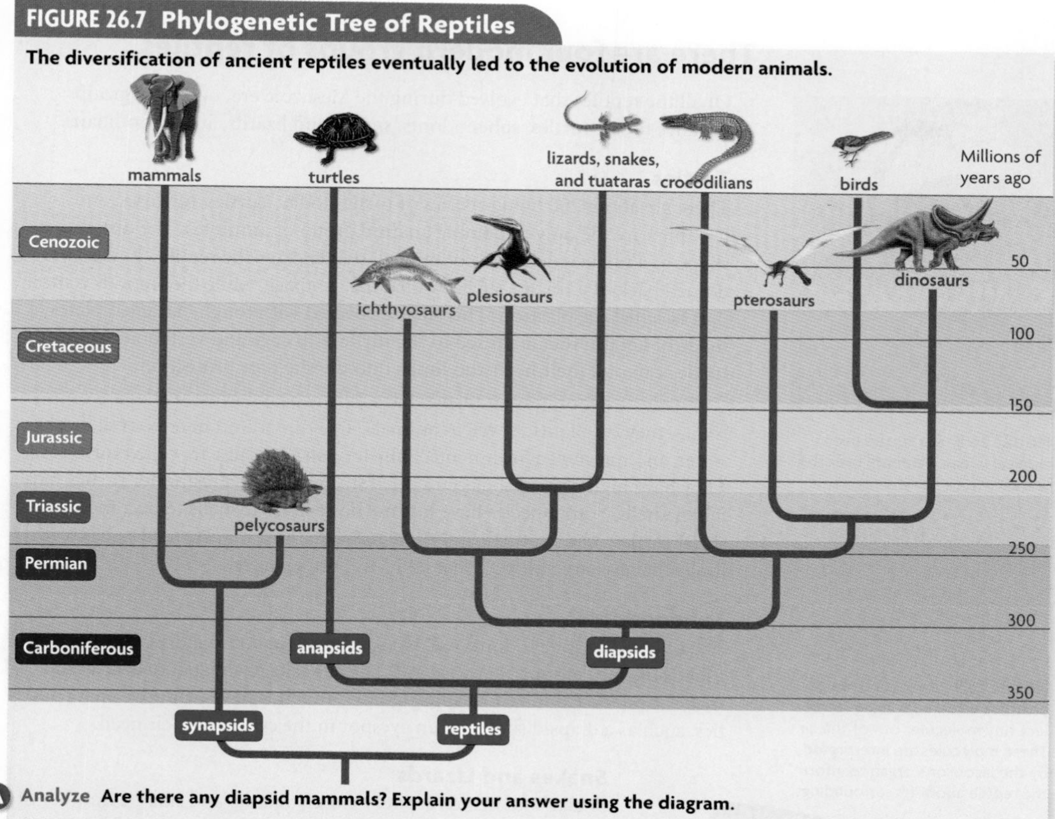

A Analyze **Are there any diapsid mammals? Explain your answer using the diagram.**

Dinosaurs were the second great radiation of the amniote family. They appeared 230 million years ago and were the dominant land vertebrates for the next 150 million years. Many kinds of dinosaurs evolved during that time. Herbivorous species included huge sauropods, tanklike ceratopsians, and duck-billed dinosaurs. They were hunted by carnivorous theropod dinosaurs, which eventually gave rise to birds. All of the nonavian, or walking, dinosaurs went extinct 65 million years ago.

Pterosaurs were the first vertebrates to evolve powered flight. Their wings consisted of skin supported by an extremely elongated fourth finger. The earliest species, from the end of the Triassic, were small animals with long tails. Later species, such as *Pteranodon* lost their tails and grew as large as small airplanes. Recent fossils show that pterosaurs may have been covered with hair, suggesting that they were endothermic. They went extinct at the end of the Cretaceous along with the dinosaurs.

B Apply **How did the discovery of temporal skull holes help scientists determine phylogeny of amniotes?**

***Connecting* CONCEPTS**

Phylogeny Recall from **Chapter 17** that a phylogeny is a type of evolutionary tree that illustrates how different species are related to each other. The relationships between modern animals and ancient reptiles help scientists understand evolution.

BELOW LEVEL

Have students use **FIGURE 26.7** to make a large, unlined index card for each of the example animals shown. On each card, students should write the name of the animal or glue a picture of the animal, and then list its characteristics on the back. The characteristics should include its skull type, the age in which it lived (or lives), how it was (or is) adapted to land, and other important information from the text. Have students use these as flash cards to quiz each other.

INCLUSION

For students who have difficulty processing graphic displays of information, "walk through" the periods of **FIGURE 26.7** with them. Tell them the significance of the end points of different branches. Also mention that humans, as mammals, are represented by the elephant.

Biology Toolkit, Connect to Content through Visuals, p. C17

Address Misconceptions

Common Misconception The pterosaurs were the ancestors of modern birds.

Correcting the Misconception Use Figure 26.7 to show students that the pterosaurs became extinct before the end of the Mesozoic, and they were an evolutionary dead end. Most scientists believe that birds evolved from the carnivorous bipedal dinosaurs called theropods, of which the *Tyrannosaurs* and *Velociraptors* were members.

TEACH FROM VISUALS

FIGURE 26.7 Review the phylogenetic tree with students. **Ask,** Were there ever any synapsid reptiles? No, synapsids diverged from reptiles more than 350 million years ago. **Ask,** Which group experienced the greatest diversification during the Mesozoic era (Triassic, Jurassic, and Cretaceous periods)? reptiles Tell students that the Mesozoic era is often called the Age of Reptiles, characterized by the development of flying reptiles, birds, and flowering plants, and the extinction of the dinosaurs and flying reptiles at the end of the Cretaceous.

Answers

A Analyze No, mammals are evolved from synapsids that diverged from reptilian anapsids and diapsids more than 350 mya.

B Apply It showed how ancient or extinct reptiles diverged and evolved into the organisms of today.

▼ Teach *continued*

Take It Further

Of the seven species of **sea turtles,** all are listed as threatened or endangered. Humans are the main threat to sea turtles from accidental catches in fishing gear, human predation of the eggs, and commercial development on nesting beaches. Of all the sea turtles, the leatherback sea turtle grows the largest, dives the deepest, and travels the farthest to nest.

The leatherback is listed as endangered all over the world, but one place their numbers are increasing is on the central and southeastern coast of Florida. For more on the plight of sea turtles, have students do the WebQuest in Options for Inquiry on page 811.

Integrating Paleontology

A snake fossil discovered in Argentina has provided evidence that snakes once had legs. The snake, *Najash rionegrina,* is one of the most primitive, fully terrestrial snakes known. The fossil clearly shows hip vertebrae, a sacrum, a pelvis, and hind legs. This information has led some scientists to infer that snakes evolved on land, but later lost their limbs.

Vocabulary

Academic Vocabulary The branch of zoology that deals with reptiles—and amphibians—is called **herpetology.** The Greek word *herpein* means "to creep." This is the same root found in the word **herpes,** which is a viral disease that can cause blisterlike vesicles reminiscent of scales.

Reptiles tend to evoke negative feelings in people. The adjective **reptilian** is used to describe a treacherous person, which is also the meaning associated with the expression "a snake in the grass." Attributing human movitations or characteristics to animals is a form of **anthropomorphism.**

MAIN IDEA

There are four modern groups of reptiles.

Of all the reptiles that evolved during the Mesozoic era, only four groups are alive today: turtles, sphenodonts, snakes and lizards, and crocodilians.

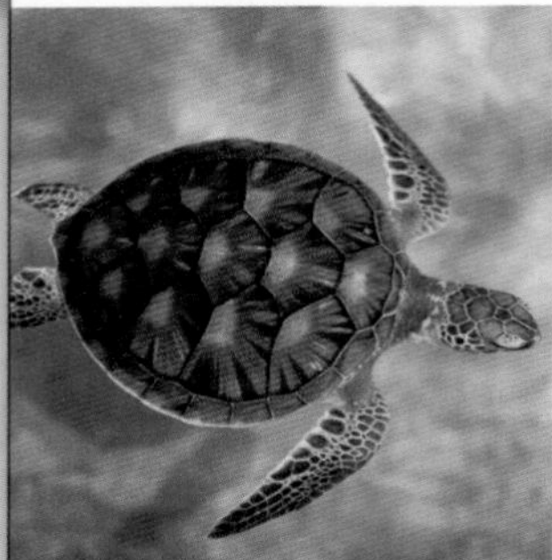

FIGURE 26.8 Sea turtles live in tropical ocean waters all over the world.

Turtles

There are about 200 living species of turtles today. Turtles, tortoises, and terrapins are the only remaining anapsid group of amniotes. The distinctive shape of a turtle is actually a bony shell that encases the reptile's body. The domed back of a turtle's shell is called the carapace, while the smooth ventral part is called the plastron. This shell is covered with tough, flattened plates made of keratin that are fused to the turtle's rib cage and vertebrae. Many turtles can pull their head and limbs into the shell for protection.

Turtles are toothless and have sharp, horny beaks. Most turtles are omnivorous—they eat plants as well as animals. They are found in terrestrial, freshwater, and marine environments. Fully terrestrial turtles are called tortoises. They have high domed shells and thick stumpy limbs. Freshwater turtles have flatter shells. Some species have lost the bone in their shells to become "soft shell" turtles. The sea turtle in **FIGURE 26.8,** like most marine turtles, has forelimbs that are large flippers that let it "fly" underwater.

Sphenodonts

The only living sphenodonts are two species of tuatara that live on a few small islands off the coast of New Zealand. They are closely related to lizards and snakes, and look similar to a spiny iguana. Tuataras have primitive characteristics, such as a diapsid skull and an eyespot in the center of their head.

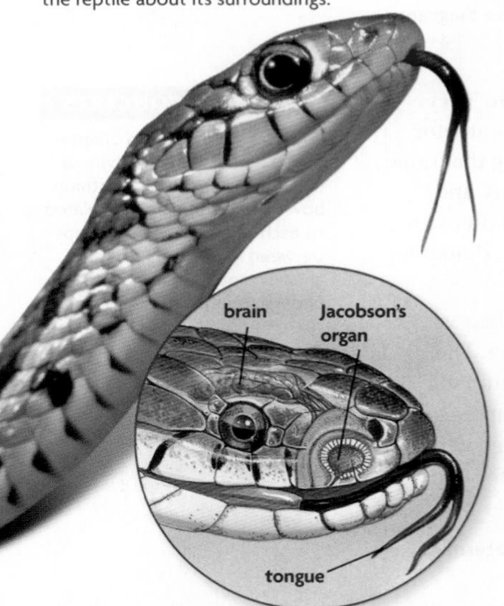

FIGURE 26.9 Snakes and lizards protrude a forked tongue to collect tiny molecules out of the air. These molecules are interpreted by the Jacobson's organ to inform the reptile about its surroundings.

Snakes and Lizards

Snakes and lizards are very closely related and share a number of features. Snakes and lizards all shed their skin at regular intervals. They also have flexible skulls that let them capture and swallow prey larger than their head. All snakes and lizards use a highly developed organ that allows them to "taste" the air. As shown in **FIGURE 26.9,** when a snake or lizard flicks its forked tongue out of its mouth, the tongue collects particles out of the air. Particles are interpreted by a sensory receptor called the Jacobson's organ, which is found in the top of the reptile's mouth. This organ allows lizards and snakes to locate prey and avoid predators.

Most lizards are carnivorous. Small species hunt insects, but large species such as the Komodo dragon prey on mammals. Some species, such as iguanas, are strict herbivores. Snakes are a group of legless lizards. All snakes are predators. Some snakes kill their prey by constriction, wrapping their body around their prey and squeezing. Others use poisons that are injected into their prey through modified teeth.

Differentiated Instruction

ENGLISH LEARNERS

Have small groups of students work together to compare the four modern groups of reptiles: turtles, tortoises, and terrapins; sphenodonts; snakes and lizards; and crocodilians. Each group decides which features to compare. When they finish, have the groups copy their work onto the board. Then help them prepare a table that compiles all the information into a matrix.

Biology Toolkit, Think-Pair-Share, p. C13; Semantic Feature Analysis, p. D7

FIGURE 26.10 Reptile Anatomy

The unique features of reptiles include a three-chambered heart and a single reproductive and excretory opening called a cloaca.

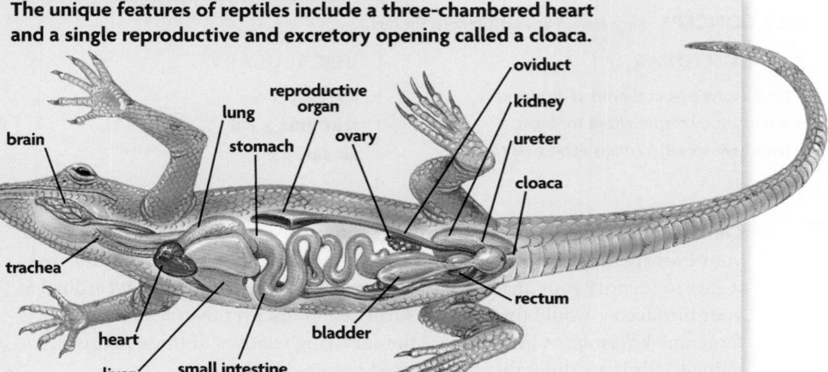

A Apply How does reptile anatomy prevent the organism from running and breathing at the same time?

Crocodilians

There are 23 species of crocodilians, including alligators, crocodiles, and caimans. They are all semiaquatic predators that live in swamps and rivers in the tropics and subtropics. They are ambush predators, waiting underwater to surprise other animals. Their sprawling resting posture makes them look slow, but they are capable of lifting up their bodies and running at up to 27 kilometers per hour (17 mph).

Crocodilians are one of two groups of archosaurs that survived the mass reptile extinction 65 million years ago. Archosaurs were a large group of reptiles that included crocodiles, dinosaurs, and modern-day birds. Based on fossil evidence, crocodilians are actually more closely related to birds than they are to lizards and snakes. Many of the body shapes and structures of ancient crocodilians are similar to the features of modern crocodilians.

B Summarize What features do all reptiles share?

26.2 ASSESSMENT

ONLINE QUIZ ClassZone.com

B.8.3

REVIEWING MAIN IDEAS

1. How is a **viviparous** reptile different from an **oviparous** reptile?
2. What are the major groups of extinct **reptiles**?
3. What features do modern reptiles share?

CRITICAL THINKING

4. **Classify** You find a fossil of a reptile that has a long neck and four long flippers for limbs. It is in marine sediments. To which group of ancient reptiles could it belong?
5. **Infer** Explain why there are no reptiles found in the Arctic.

Connecting CONCEPTS

6. **Amphibians** Amniotes emerge from their shell fully developed. Amphibians must go through metamorphosis to reach their adult form. What is the advantage of direct development for amniotes?

Take It Further

Most reptiles leave their eggs to hatch and be on their own. **Crocodiles,** however, invest time and energy in the care of their young. Mother crocodiles guard the eggs until they hatch. She will hear them calling and will help uncover them. She will then carry several at a time in her mouth to the water until all are in a creche (small nursery group) together. For several weeks or months, she viciously guards her new hatchlings from predators until they are mature enough to disperse on their own. Some studies suggest that parental care behavior declines when the population is healthy, but increases when population numbers decline.

Answers

A Apply The same muscles are used for breathing and walking, so it cannot do both at the same time.

B Summarize They are ectotherms, have dry outer shells or scales, and reproduce with an amniotic egg with a tough outer coating.

Assess and Reteach ▼

Assess Use the Online Quiz or Section Quiz (*Assessment Book*, p. 514).

Reteach Have students volunteer facts they have learned about reptiles. Then have them suggest how to organize the information into a cluster diagram.

26.2 ASSESSMENT

1. An oviparous reptile lays eggs in a nest, outside of its body, whereas a viviparous reptile holds eggs internally until they hatch, giving birth to live offspring.
2. ichthyosaurs, plesiosaurs, dinosaurs, and pterosaurs
3. ectothermic, dry outer shells or scales, and all reproduce with an amniotic egg covered by a tough outer coating
4. plesiosaur
5. Temperatures in the Arctic are not warm enough to be conducive to the ectothermic lifestyle of a reptile.
6. Direct development allows amniotes to become independent sooner by learning the skills they need to survive after birth, such as hunting for food and avoiding predation.

SECTION 26.3

▼ Plan and Prepare

Objectives

- Describe the relationship between modern birds and extinct theropod dinosaurs.
- Explain flight adaptations in birds.
- Relate adaptations to ecological niches.

Section Resources

Unit Resource Book
Study Guide pp. 103–104
Power Notes p. 105
Reinforcement p. 106
Interactive Reader Chapter 26
Spanish Study Guide pp. 269–270
Biology Toolkit p. C18
Technology
Power Presentation 26.3
Media Gallery DVD
Online Quiz 26.3

Activate Prior Knowledge Have students examine **FIGURE 26.11.** Explain that it is an ancient animal halfway between a bird and a dinosaur. **Ask**

- What characteristics do birds have? feathers, beak, flight, two legs, wings, scaly legs, lay eggs, claws or talons
- What are some characteristics of dinosaurs? teeth, talons or claws, scaly legs, two legs, lay eggs, long tail
- What are the similarities between the two? two legs, scaly legs, lay eggs, claws or talons

▼ Teach

TEACH FROM VISUALS

FIGURE 26.11 The *Archaeopteryx* had a bony tail and a flattened furcula. Because the furcula is the wide area of the breastbone where flight muscles attach, most scientists speculate that it was a weak flier and glided through the air from tree to tree. **Ask,** Why would a flattened furcula indicate that a bird is a weak flier? an insufficient site for muscle attachment

26.3 Birds

KEY CONCEPT Birds have many adaptations for flight.

MAIN IDEAS

- Birds evolved from theropod dinosaurs.
- A bird's body is specialized for flight.
- Birds have spread to many ecological niches.

VOCABULARY

airfoil, p. 799
sternum, p. 801
air sac, p. 801

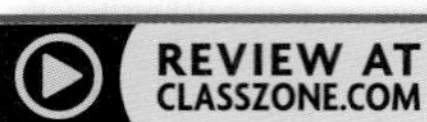

Connect You may share certain features with your parents or siblings. Perhaps your eyes are the same color or your nose is the same shape. Certain traits make it easy to identify your ancestors. Birds have a bit more trouble. That cardinal at your bird feeder would probably be surprised to discover that it is related to a ferocious *Velociraptor,* but birds are the surviving relatives of those prehistoric animals. Birds are dinosaurs that evolved powered flight.

MAIN IDEA

Birds evolved from theropod dinosaurs.

Most paleontologists agree that birds are the descendants of one group of theropod dinosaurs. Theropods were bipedal, or two-legged, dinosaurs that evolved during the Triassic period of the Mesozoic era. Most were carnivorous, and some, such as *Allosaurus* and *Tyrannosaurus,* were enormous. Theropod fossils support the hypothesis that these dinosaurs are closely related to birds. They show that birds and many theropods share anatomical features, including

- hollow bones
- fused collarbones that form a V-shaped wishbone, or furcula
- rearranged muscles in the hips and legs that improve bipedal movement
- "hands" that have lost their fourth and fifth fingers
- feathers

FIGURE 26.11 Fossil evidence of *Archaeopteryx* shows features such as feathers and a beaklike structure not seen in dinosaurs. *Archaeopteryx* is an important link between dinosaurs and modern-day birds.

In the 1990s scientists discovered theropod fossils with feathers. This important discovery showed that feathers did not originate as an adaptation for flight. These theropods were covered with feathers, but they did not have wings. They were running animals. This means that feathers originally had another function in the theropods. They may have been insulation that trapped air to keep the animals warm. Or they may have been used in courtship or territorial displays. As birds evolved, they used the feathers they had inherited from their theropod ancestors to form wings.

The oldest undisputed fossil bird is shown in **FIGURE 26.11.** *Archaeopteryx* was a chicken-sized animal that lived about 150 million years ago. Like all modern birds, it had feathered wings and a furcula. But it also had many reptilian features, including clawed fingers, a long tail, and teeth. Because of its features, *Archaeopteryx* was classified as a dinosaur. However, its feathers made it an important link between flightless dinosaurs and avian, or flying, dinosaurs, as well as the birds of today.

Differentiated Instruction

HANDS-ON ACTIVITY

Tell students to place their index and middle fingers on the opposite wrist just below the fleshy part of the thumb, count the number of pulse beats in 15 seconds, and then multiply by 4. This is the pulse rate per minute. Have students write their pulse rate on the board. Determine the class average; it will probably be 70–80 beats per minute. Ask students to predict whether their pulse rate will be faster or slower than that of a bird. Then provide the following information:

Bird	Pulse Rate/Minute
chicken	300
canary	514
hummingbird	1000
sparrow	800

Discuss why a bird's pulse rate is so much faster than a human's. **Ask,** What general trend do you see in the data? The smaller the animal is, the faster the heartbeat.

Scientists have two hypotheses for the origin of flight in birds. The "trees-down" hypothesis suggests that birds evolved from animals that used their feathers to glide down to the forest floor. In contrast, the "ground-up" hypothesis suggests that birds evolved from running animals that used their feathered arms for balance.

The fossil evidence showing a close relationship between theropods and birds tends to support the "ground-up" hypothesis. Many theropods were bipedal carnivores that hunted by running down their prey. Scientists still do not know how these dinosaurs moved from running and grabbing to flapping and flying. Some recent research suggests that small theropods could have flapped their feathered arms to run up trees and escape predators. Whether they also used those feathered arms to glide back down to the ground is unknown, but future fossil discoveries may provide an answer.

FIGURE 26.12 The broad wings of an eagle owl are adapted for silent flight, making this nocturnal bird a quiet and deadly predator.

A Infer How might hollow bones have helped theropods move more efficiently?

MAIN IDEA

A bird's body is specialized for flight.

Birds such as the eagle owl in **FIGURE 26.12** have many specialized adaptations for powered flight. Some of them are modifications of features inherited from their theropod ancestors. Others are unique to birds. These adaptations include

- wings that produce flight
- strong flight muscles that move the wings
- an active metabolism that provides energy to the muscles
- hollow bone structure that minimizes weight
- reproductive adaptations

Wings

Wings are structures that enable birds to fly. Bird wings are curved similar to the shape of an airplane wing. This kind of curved surface is called an airfoil. An **airfoil** is curved down on the top (convex) and curved up on the bottom (concave). The curved shape makes air move faster over the top of the airfoil than underneath it. The difference in air speed above and below the airfoil produces a pressure difference that lifts the wing up. In birds, the airfoil is constructed of limbs that are homologous to human arms and covered by large feathers.

VISUAL VOCAB

An **airfoil** is convex on the top and concave on the bottom. Differences in air pressure above and below the airfoil create lift.

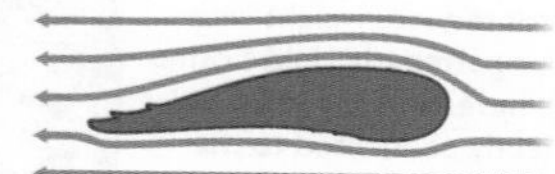

Vocabulary

Greek and Latin Word Origins Write these word parts on the board:

archaeo- = ancient
dino- = terrible
ichthyo- = fish
-pod = foot
-ptery = feathered wing
-saurus = lizard
thero- = beast
tyranno- = tyrant

Take It Further

Theropods first appeared during the late Triassic, about 220 million years ago. These dinosaurs were some of the largest terrestrial carnivores ever. The movie *Jurassic Park* featured a number of theropods: *Velociraptor, Tyrannosaurus rex,* and *Deinonychus.* Today, theropods are represented by some 10,000 living species of birds, which evolved in the late Jurassic.

Integrating Physics

Aerodynamic forces, such as **lift** and **drag,** affect flight. When in flight, a bird holds its wing at a slight angle to the air current. This makes the air move faster over the top of the wing than below the wing, creating less pressure above the wing than below it, which causes lift. To slow, the bird tilts its wing or tips its tail down in back, which creates drag. The tail also acts like a rudder, balancing and steering the bird in flight.

Answers

A Infer They were lighter, allowing theropods to move more quickly and save energy.

ENGLISH LEARNERS

Review material with students as you go through the section. Every few minutes ask a question that can be answered with a short phrase or identifier. Have students write their response on a piece of paper and hold it up for you to see.

Biology Toolkit, Card Responses, p. C18

▼ Teach *continued*

TEACH FROM VISUALS

FIGURE 26.13 Explain that some of the structures, such as the keeled sternum, are drawn see-through so the organs can be seen beneath it. Review the illustration with students by pointing out structures.

1. Have a student read aloud the caption about feathers. Explain that all birds have at least two types of feathers—contour and down. Contour feathers are long and aid in flight. Down feathers are short and fluffy and provide insulation. **Ask,** Where would you most likely find the down feathers? next to the body

2. Have a student read aloud the caption on bones. Discuss the structure of birds' bones, and state that it is similar to dinosaur bones and steel bridge structures. **Ask,** How are birds' bones like steel bridges? Struts provide strength without increasing mass.

3. Have students examine the feet and legs. **Ask,** How are the bird's legs similar to the legs and feet of their dinosaur ancestors? They are scaled, the digits are adapted for grasping, and they have talons.

4. Tell students that birds have no teeth. They have a crop that stores food and a gizzard that grinds food. **Ask,** What advantage is a food-grinding organ like the gizzard? It enables the bird to eat seeds, nuts, and other solid foods without using teeth.

5. Though not shown, tell students that air sacs are attached to each lung. When birds inhale, fresh air enters the lungs and pushes air in the lungs to the air sacs. When birds exhale, fresh air enters the lungs from the air sacs, meaning the bird has a steady supply of oxygen. **Ask,** What advantage is this adaptation with regard to the energy available to the bird? Oxygen is constantly available for cellular respiration, providing the bird with energy for flight.

Answers

Ⓐ Critical Viewing Penguins are adept swimmers and use their wings and feet to "fly" through the water. Feathers help insulate their bodies in the cold water.

FIGURE 26.13 Bird Anatomy

Bird anatomy is highly adapted, with unique features that help to conserve energy and allow flight.

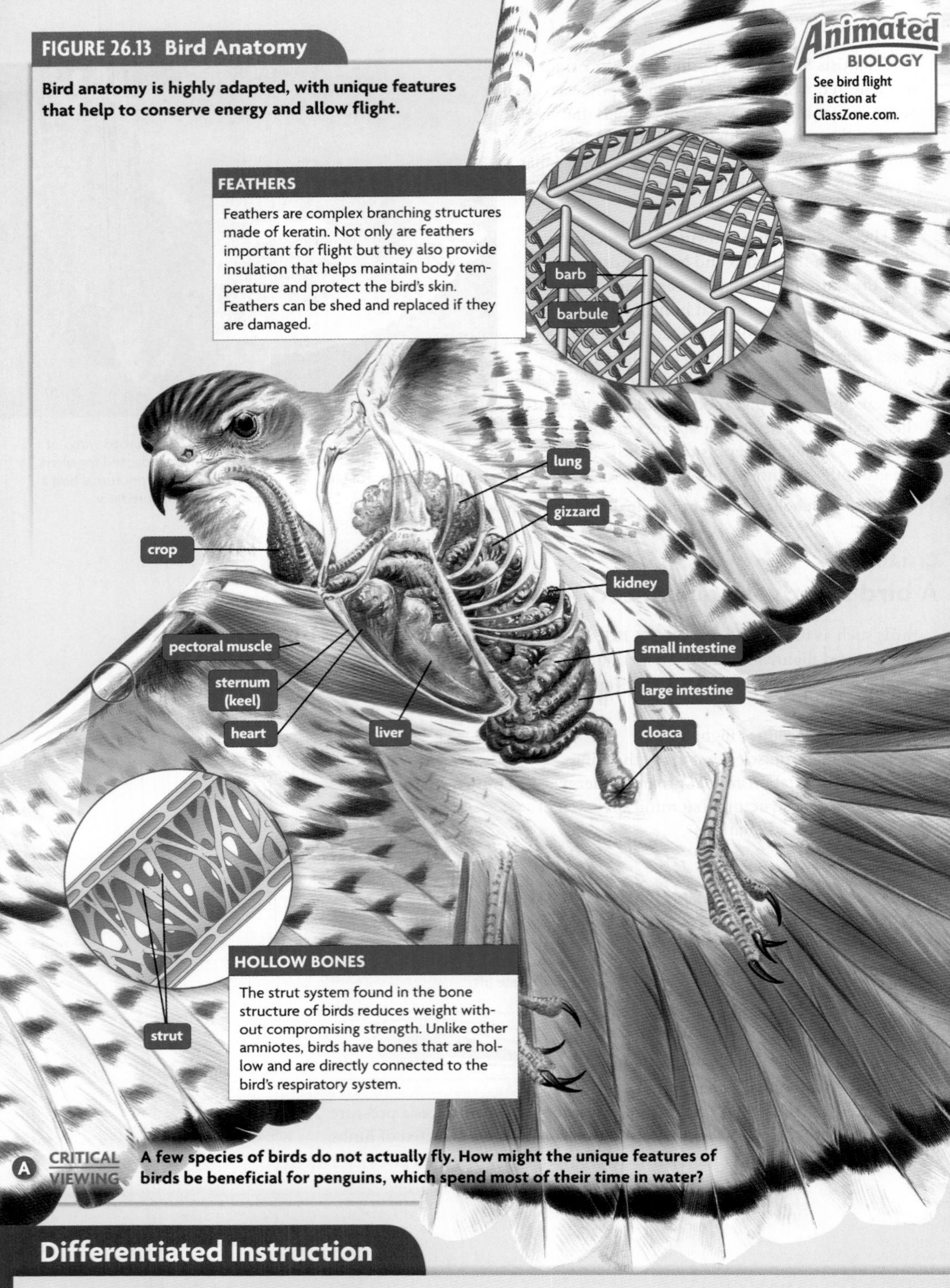

Animated
BIOLOGY
See bird flight in action at ClassZone.com.
FEATHERS
Feathers are complex branching structures made of keratin. Not only are feathers important for flight but they also provide insulation that helps maintain body temperature and protect the bird's skin. Feathers can be shed and replaced if they are damaged.
barb
barbule
lung
gizzard
crop
kidney
pectoral muscle
sternum (keel)
heart
liver
small intestine
large intestine
cloaca
HOLLOW BONES
The strut system found in the bone structure of birds reduces weight without compromising strength. Unlike other amniotes, birds have bones that are hollow and are directly connected to the bird's respiratory system.
strut

Ⓐ CRITICAL VIEWING **A few species of birds do not actually fly. How might the unique features of birds be beneficial for penguins, which spend most of their time in water?**

Differentiated Instruction

TEACH WITH TECHNOLOGY

Take a field trip to observe, record, videotape, and photograph local birds and their behaviors. Create a Web page field guide to local birds. Have students study a specific bird, give a class presentation on it, and then post their research on the Internet.

Muscles

A bird's chest muscles provide the power for flight. In almost all vertebrates, chest muscles attach to the arms and the breastbone, or **sternum.** But anyone who has carved a chicken knows that a bird's chest muscles are enormous. They are so large that the sternum has evolved a large keel, or ridge, that supports the muscles. The keel provides a large attachment surface for the chest muscles, and serves as an anchor that they can pull against to flap the wings.

When birds fly, their chest muscles contract to pull their wings backward and down. The downstroke moves the wings to produce lift and propel the animal forward. Deeper chest muscles contract during the upstroke, moving the wings forward and up until the bird starts another downstroke.

TAKING NOTES

Use a main idea diagram to take notes on how the features of birds help them to achieve flight.

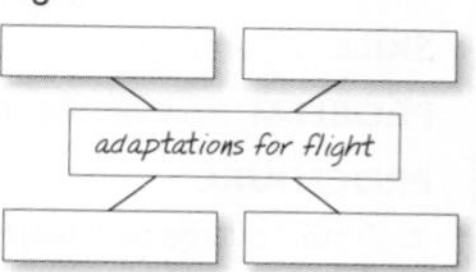

Metabolism

Flying takes a lot of energy. Birds are endotherms and have active metabolisms that can produce large amounts of ATP for the flight muscles. But maintaining an active metabolism during flight requires an enormous amount of oxygen. Birds meet this challenge with a respiratory system that increases the amount of oxygen they can take out of the air.

A bird's body is filled with a series of **air sacs** that connect to the lungs. Air sacs store air as the bird breathes. During flight, movements of the furcula help push air through the air sacs and lungs. Inhaled air travels through the lungs and air sacs in such a way that oxygen-rich air is always available. In other vertebrates, oxygen-rich air mixes with oxygen-poor air inside the lungs during respiration. But because only oxygen-rich air flows through a bird's lungs, the amount of oxygen that can be absorbed into the bloodstream is dramatically increased and maximizes a bird's metabolism.

AIR SAC

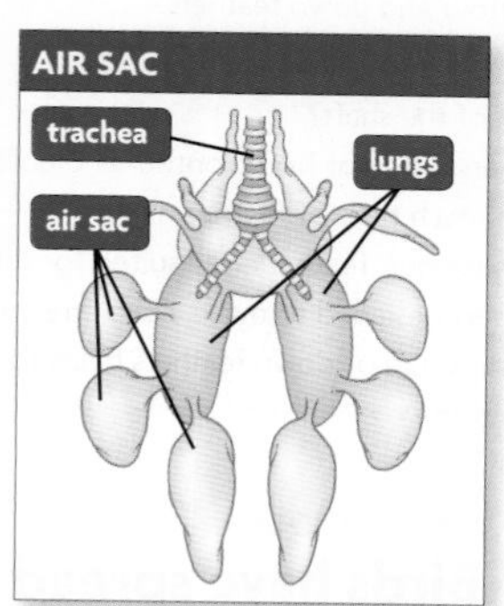

Connecting CONCEPTS

Cellular Respiration Birds require large amounts of ATP to provide the energy needed for flight. Recall from **Chapter 4** that cellular respiration needs oxygen and glucose to produce ATP. Air sacs provide a great deal of oxygen, but birds must also consume large amounts of food to support their active metabolism.

Bone Structure

The structure of a bird's skeletal system is different than that of other amniotes. Birds have evolved bones that are hollow. As you can see in **FIGURE 26.13**, inside bird bones, a system of struts and support structures maintain the bird's bones to meet the demanding requirements of flight. In all birds, many bones are connected to the air sacs, and air fills the cavities in the bone, aiding in flight. This adaption further increases the amount of air in a bird's body, and makes flying easier. It also helps to decrease the mass of the bird. In fact, a bird's skeleton makes up only five percent of its overall body mass.

Reproductive Adaptations

The reproductive organs of both male and female birds are only active for the two to three months of the mating season. During the rest of the year, the unused organs shrink to reduce the mass of the bird. This weight-reducing adaptation serves to decrease the amount of energy needed for flight.

A Summarize **How are bird bodies adapted to flying?**

Science Trivia

Here are some facts about hummingbirds:

- There are 343 species, all of which are found only in the Western Hemisphere.
- Muscles used for flight account for about 30 percent of the bird's total weight.
- The brain makes up about 4 percent of the hummingbird's total weight, making it proportionally the largest brain in the bird class.
- They rotate their wings in a circle; fly forwards, backwards, sideways, up, down; and hover in the air.
- They fly at 25–30 mph, but can speed up to 60 mph in a dive.
- Their wings beat about 60 to 80 times a second; 200 times per second when diving.
- Their hearts beat up to 1260 times per minute.
- They weigh no more than a nickel and eat half their body weight in sugar each day.
- They can fly up to 845 kilometers (525 mi) nonstop.

Vocabulary

Academic Vocabulary The branch of zoology that deals with the study of birds is **ornithology;** the adjective that describes birdlike characteristics is **ornithic.** An **ornithopter** is an aircraft that is held up and propelled by wings. A **birder** is one who watches, breeds, or hunts birds.

Answers

A Summarize They have hollow bones, strong pectoral muscles, appendages adapted to create lift, feathers that are light and strong, as well as circulatory systems that are efficient for carrying oxygen to muscles.

PRE-AP

Have students visit the Audubon website to look up their state bird. The link is provided in the chapter resources at **ClassZone.com.** Have students summarize what John James Audubon wrote about the bird, listing interesting facts about its physical characteristics, habitat, range, feeding habits, songs, and ecological niche.

▼ Teach *continued*

QUICK LAB

Time 10 minutes	TEACHER TESTED
Lab Binder Animals, pp. 60–61	

Purpose Observe and describe the characteristics of bird feathers.

Answers

Analyze and Conclude

1. provides a strong base for the vanes of the feather to attach
2. softer and more flexible
3. down feathers: undercoat that provides warmth; contour feathers: outer coat that protects the skin from sun and rain; quill feathers: important for flight
4. long, broad, and very rigid
5. short and pliable
6. can be tightly packed into a single area to prevent heat from escaping

Take It Further

Some birds, such as cowbirds, are **brood parasites** that lay their eggs in the nests of another bird species (the host). The advantages for the cowbird are that it does not have to build its own nest or invest time and energy in mothering. The mother cowbird watches a smaller bird build a nest and lay its eggs and then under the cover of darkness, when the other mother is away, it sneaks in and lays her single egg among the other eggs. The host bird feeds and protects the cowbird chick like her own, and sometimes the larger cowbird chick out-competes the host bird's actual offspring for food.

QUICK LAB **OBSERVING**

Comparing Feathers

Feathers are features that allow birds to adapt to a unique way of life. In this lab, you will examine three different types of feathers.

SKILL Observing

PROBLEM How do the structures and functions of different feathers compare?

MATERIALS
- purchased quill feather
- purchased contour feather
- purchased down feather

PROCEDURE

1. Obtain a large quill feather and study its overall shape, structure and weight. Draw the features.
2. Examine the central shaft of the feather. Hold the end of the shaft with one hand. With your other hand, gently try to bend the upper third of the feather without breaking it.
3. Observe the vane, the flat part of the feather on either side of the shaft. Separate some of the barbs of a vane. Join them again with your fingers.
4. Hold the end of the shaft and wave the feather so that it catches the air. Note the resistance you feel as you move the feather through the air.
5. Repeat steps 1–4 with the contour and down feathers.

ANALYZE AND CONCLUDE

1. **Analyze** What is the function of the shaft?
2. **Analyze** How are down feathers different from contour and quill feathers?
3. **Infer** Describe the function of each type of feather.
4. **Apply** What characteristics make quill feathers well suited for their function?
5. **Apply** How are contour feathers designed to make a bird streamlined?
6. **Infer** How do you think the structure of down feathers helps to insulate a bird?

MAIN IDEA

Birds have spread to many ecological niches.

Birds first evolved during the Mesozoic era, but most Mesozoic bird species went extinct with the dinosaurs. All modern birds are the descendants of the one group that survived the mass extinction. This group diversified into the more than 9000 species of bird we see today. Through natural selection, birds have adapted to many different habitats and methods of feeding. This has led to visible physical differences in the shapes of the wings, beaks, and feet.

Differences in Wing Shape

The shape of a bird's wing reflects the way it flies. Most birds have short, broad wings that allow them to maneuver very easily. In contrast, albatrosses and gulls, such as the blue-footed booby in **FIGURE 26.14**, have long, narrow wings specialized for soaring long distances over water. Hawks, eagles, and condors have wide, broad wings specialized for soaring at low speeds over land. Many types of songbirds, including woodpeckers, finches, and robins, have stout, tapered wings that help them to maneuver through tight spaces. Penguins have short wings adapted to "fly" in water. Flightless birds, such as ostriches and emus, have wings that are too small to let them fly at all.

Differentiated Instruction

TEACH WITH TECHNOLOGY

Tell students that in the spring of 2005, scientists announced a sighting of the ivory-billed woodpecker, the largest North American woodpecker, which everyone had long thought to be extinct. Visit the Cornell ornithology website to view the evidence used to identify this elusive bird and check in on the current state of the search. A link is provided in the chapter resources at **ClassZone.com.** Cornell also invites public participation in its research in a program called Citizen Science.

Differences in Beak Shape

The shape of a bird's beak reflects how it eats. A bird's beak is a sheath of keratin that covers the jaw bones. As Charles Darwin observed in the many finch species of the Galapagos Islands, beak shapes are adapted for many different functions. For example, the blue-footed booby uses its long, spearlike beak to capture fish on the bird's dives into the ocean. The beak of the bald eagle is hooked to tear flesh from its prey. Birds that catch insects often have thin, pointed bills. Woodpeckers have beaks like chisels to pry insects out of trees. Other birds, such as hummingbirds, have long, thin beaks that can reach deep into flowers for nectar. Pelicans have large pouches of skin attached to their beaks for scooping fish out of the water. Parrots use their thick, strong beaks for ripping open fruits and cracking nuts.

Differences in Foot Shape

With few exceptions, bird feet have four toes. But as **FIGURE 26.14** shows, their feet can look very different. The blue-footed booby and other aquatic birds have webbed feet, with skin connecting the toes to form paddles. Predatory birds such as the bald eagle have heavy claws that they use to capture and kill prey. Birds that live in trees have feet that can grab onto branches and tree bark. Woodpeckers, for example, have two toes pointing forward and two pointing backward, which lets them cling to vertical tree trunks. Sparrows and crows have three toes pointing forward and one pointing backward, which lets them perch on horizontal tree limbs.

A Infer **Where would you expect to find a bird with webbed feet and very long and narrow wings?**

FIGURE 26.14 Birds' features are specifically adapted to their habitat and niche. Natural selection has led to a wide array of wings, beaks, and feet.

ONLINE BIOLOGY Students can use an interactive animation to compare a bird's beak shape with its diet; see Options for Inquiry on page 811. You can also find additional resources and information on birds in the chapter Resource Center at **ClassZone.com.**

Address Misconceptions

Common Misconception Baby birds or nests that have been handled by a human will be abandoned by the mother bird.

Correcting the Misconception Birds, songbirds especially, have a poor sense of smell, and will return to the nest as soon as they are certain the human is gone. It is important to return a baby bird to its nest if it has fallen out. It is difficult to take care of a baby bird, and the mother bird is the best one to do it.

Answers

A Infer soaring near water where it can swim

26.3 ASSESSMENT

ONLINE QUIZ ClassZone.com

REVIEWING MAIN IDEAS

1. What are three anatomical features that birds share with their theropod ancestors?
2. What adaptations do birds have that help them with flight?
3. Describe how the wings, beak, and feet of an eagle are well adapted to its niche.

CRITICAL THINKING

4. **Analyze** The red-headed woodpecker has an unusually long tongue and a stout, pointed beak. How are these features related to the woodpecker's feeding habits?
5. **Connect** Reptiles and birds are closely related. Why is the evolution from being an ectotherm to being an endotherm so important for bird evolution?

***Connecting* CONCEPTS**

6. **Selection** Male cardinals have bright red feathers, whereas females have dull brown feathers. What type of selection likely caused these differences?

26.3 ASSESSMENT

1. hollow bones, fused collarbones that form a furcula, feathers
2. wings, strong flight muscles, an active metabolism, hollow bone structure, reproductive adaptations
3. An eagle's broad wings enable it to spend time hunting for food. Its beak is sharp to tear apart its food once it catches it, and sharp talons are used to grasp and subdue its prey.
4. The woodpecker feeds on ants and other insects it finds in trees. To reach its prey, it pecks away at the hard bark of the tree, and the tongue allows it to reach the insects inside.
5. allowed birds to move into niches that were uninhabitable for reptiles
6. Sexual selection for mates with bright feathers indicates a strong ability to provide and survive.

Assess and Reteach ▼

Assess Use the Online Quiz or Section Quiz (*Assessment Book,* p. 515).

Reteach Organize students into small cooperative learning groups. Provide them with field guides and have each group identify three birds that have the same or similar habitats. Students should observe and record the differences in their three birds with regard to beaks, feet, and behavior. Have each group present to the class what they have learned about how birds are adapted to take advantage of different resources within the same habitat.

INVESTIGATION

Time 60 minutes	TEACHER TESTED
Teacher Preparation	
Student Difficulty	
Lab Binder Animals, pp. 51–54	

Purpose Investigate the density of different types of bones.

Overview Students will find the density of the bones and make inferences about flight adaptations based on those data.

LAB PREPARATION

- Collect and boil bones ahead of time and refrigerate until used.
- Use bones that are small enough in size to be completely submerged in a graduated cylinder.

LAB MANAGEMENT

- Have students work in small groups.
- Lab can be done in two sessions. Day 1: observe and mass bone structures; Day 2: calculate volume and density, and make conclusions.
- Make sure the bones are not stuck and are completely submerged in the graduated cylinder when measuring volume.

Safety Caution students to handle the hammer carefully. Remind them not to put any of the bones in their mouths, to dispose of materials properly, and to wash their hands afterwards.

POST-LAB DISCUSSION

Have students discuss their data and their conclusions. **Ask,** If the bone densities of flying birds and flightless birds are approximately the same, what causes the flightless bird to be unable to fly? The breast muscles may not be developed enough, or the furcula or the wing structure may be reduced.

A Bird's Airframe

Wings were an important adaptation for birds. The structure of wings gave birds the ability to fly and move great distances in search of resources. But for some birds, flight was not necessary for survival. In this lab, you will investigate the differences and similarities between flying and flightless birds, and compare them with mammals.

MATERIALS
- balance
- 100 mL graduated cylinder
- 50 mL water
- boiled chicken bone (flightless bird)
- boiled duck or turkey bone (flying bird)
- boiled cow bone (mammal)
- hammer
- hand lens

PROCESS SKILLS
- **Observing**
- **Measuring**
- **Analyzing**

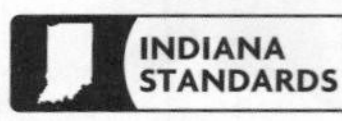

NOS.5 Apply standard techniques in laboratory investigations to measure physical quantities in appropriate units and convert known quantities to other units as necessary.

PROBLEM Besides wings, what major adaptation is beneficial for flight?

PROCEDURE
1. Measure the mass of each bone (chicken, duck, cow) using the balance. Record the mass for each.
2. Pour the water in the graduated cylinder and note the volume. Add one of the bones to the cylinder and record the volume again. To find the volume of the bone, subtract the original volume from the second reading.
3. Repeat step 2 for each bone used.
4. Attempt to break the bone by hand and note how easy or difficult it is. (If you can't break the bone by hand, it is okay.)

   Caution: Wearing your safety goggles, carefully break each experimental bone with the hammer (watch out for flying pieces).
5. Examine the internal structure of each bone with the hand lens. Make a labeled drawing for each bone.

ANALYZE AND CONCLUDE
1. **Predict** Which bone do you think has the greatest density? Which bone is the least dense?
2. **Calculate** Calculate the densities for each bone (density = $\frac{\text{mass}}{\text{volume}}$).
3. **Apply** What can you conclude about bone density and the ability to fly?
4. **Observe** How does the structure of the flightless bird bone compare with that of the flying bird bone? with the cow bone?
5. **Infer** What bones are easier to break by hand than others? Explain why you think this is true.
6. **Analyze** What features of the bird bones might be adaptations for flight?
7. **Contrast** Were there any significant differences between bones from flying birds and those from flightless birds? Why might one bird be able to fly while another cannot fly?

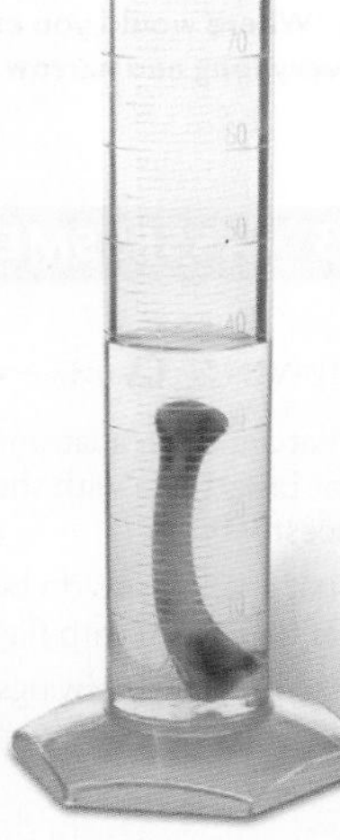

100 mL graduated cylinder

Answers

Expected Results

Students should observe similar densities in both birds' bones and find that the cow bone is more dense: 1.49–1.96 g/cm^3 for beef, 1.08–1.34 g/cm^3 for duck, and 1.13–1.19 g/cm^3 for chicken.

Analyze and Conclude

1. Answers should be consistent with students' measurements.
2. Answers should be consistent with the sample data.
3. Less dense bones are strong but lightweight, enabling birds to fly.
4. The flightless bird's hollow bone structure is the same as the flying bird's and different from the cow's solid bone.
5. bird bones, because they are hollow
6. hollow, light, strong, low-density
7. No, their bones are the same, but each bird has evolved to fill a different niche in which some birds do not need to fly.

26.4 Mammals

KEY CONCEPT Evolutionary adaptations allowed mammals to succeed dinosaurs as a dominant terrestrial vertebrate.

MAIN IDEAS
- All mammals share several common characteristics.
- Modern mammals are divided into three main groups.

VOCABULARY
mammal, p. 805
mammary gland, p. 806
monotreme, p. 807
marsupial, p. 808
eutherian, p. 809

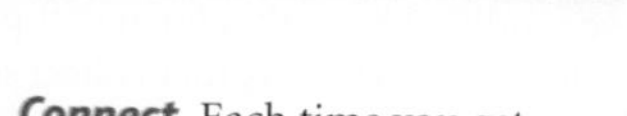

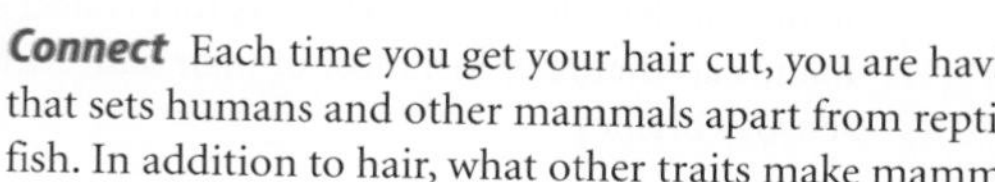

REVIEW AT CLASSZONE.COM

Connect Each time you get your hair cut, you are having a feature clipped off that sets humans and other mammals apart from reptiles, birds, amphibians, and fish. In addition to hair, what other traits make mammals unique?

MAIN IDEA

All mammals share several common characteristics.

All **mammals** are active, large-brained, endothermic animals with complex social, feeding, and reproductive behaviors. Modern mammals—such as the bat in **FIGURE 26.15**—come in many shapes, but they share a set of four anatomical characteristics.

- hair
- mammary glands
- a middle ear containing three bones
- a jaw that lets them chew their food

FIGURE 26.15 This Yuma myotis bat has all of the basic mammalian features. Bats are the only mammals that can fly.

Mammals are as ancient as dinosaurs and are the only group of synapsids alive today. They are descended from a group of carnivorous synapsids. Many of the characteristics we now see only in mammals were actually inherited from these reptilian ancestors. Earth's first mammals appeared more than 200 million years ago, when dinosaurs were already on their way to becoming the top predators and herbivores on the planet. During the Cretaceous period, while *Tyrannosaurus rex* was hunting *Triceratops,* tiny rodentlike mammals had found a niche as nocturnal insect eaters.

Fossil evidence suggests that early mammals had long noses and short legs. They may have looked similar to modern-day shrews. They probably lived underground, reproduced by laying eggs, and nursed their young on nutrient-rich milk produced by highly adapted glands. The ability to regulate their own body temperature was an important adaptation that gave mammals a distinct advantage over reptiles. When the dinosaurs went extinct, mammals survived and filled their vacant ecological niches. In time, mammals succeeded dinosaurs as a dominant terrestrial life form.

Differentiated Instruction

BELOW LEVEL

Suggest students use an outline to structure their notes for this section. Remind them to start with the Key Concept at the top of the page. Then as they take notes, have them consider mammalian features in the context of how these features are advantageous to mammals' success in their habitats. Remind students of the concept of ecological niches.

Biology Toolkit, Outline, p. C25

PRE-AP

Write the following quotation from Robert T. Bakker on the board: *Dinosaurs suppressed the evolutionary potential of mammals, not the other way around.* Have students write for five minutes to explain what they think he meant. Some people think that mammals survived the extinction 65 million years ago because they are superior animals. Bakker implies that mammals survived only because the dinosaurs became extinct and left niches open that the mammals could occupy.

Biology Toolkit, Quick-Write, p. C19

SECTION 26.4

Plan and Prepare

Objectives

- Identify the characteristics of mammals.
- Describe the three groups of modern mammals.

Section Resources

Unit Resource Book
Study Guide pp. 107–108
Power Notes p. 109
Reinforcement p. 110
Pre-AP Activity pp. 115–116

Interactive Reader Chapter 26
Spanish Study Guide pp. 271–272

Biology Toolkit pp. C14, C19, C25, C40

Technology
Power Presentation 26.4
Media Gallery DVD
Online Quiz 26.4

Activate Prior Knowledge Have students think about the fact that mammals have many distinctive adaptations that relate to their skin, not just hair. **Ask,** Beyond their characteristic covering of hair, what other adaptations do various mammal have that are part of their outer covering? nails, claws, hooves, feathers, antlers, and various types of glands including mammary glands Discuss how these adaptations relate to the variety of habitats mammals can occupy.

Teach

TEACH FROM VISUALS

FIGURE 26.15 Tell students that a bat has all the usual mammalian characteristics. **Ask,** What visible characteristics distinguish a bat from a bird? A bat has hair, not down; the wing is made of skin, not feathers; it has teeth, not a beak.

▼ Teach *continued*

Connecting CONCEPTS

Natural Selection Whales, dolphins, and porpoises lose their sparse hair as adults, but for warmth, they have evolved a layer of blubber under the skin. These mammals give birth in the sea. Other aquatic mammals, such as seals, walruses, and sea lions have retained their hair, because they are still tied to the land for reproduction. These animals still need their hair for insulation from the cold while they care for their young that are born on land.

History of Science

New species of organisms are being discovered every day, but it is rare for a previously undescribed mammalian species to be found. A new species of **tree kangaroo** was sighted in New Guinea in 1981 by **Jared Diamond,** an evolutionary biologist, biogeographer, writer, and professor at UCLA. But it was not until 1990 that it was sighted again, captured alive, described and named *Dendrolagus pulcherrimus.* The word *pulcherrimus* means "most beautiful." It has a pink face, sepia eyes, white ears, golden shoulders, white rings on its tail, and a rich burgundy back.

Integrating Evolutionary Biology

Pelycosaur comes from the Greek *pelyx,* meaning "bowl" and *sauros,* meaning "lizard." The pelycosaurs were synapsid reptiles that reached their main dominance in the early Permian. They had tall sails on their backs, which were probably used for thermoregulation. The pelycosaurs represent a direct ancestral link to mammals.

Connecting CONCEPTS

Natural Selection All mammals have hair or, more accurately, hair follicles. Whales are mammals, but most adult whales do not have hair. Recall from **Chapter 10** that natural selection favors traits that increase the fitness of individuals. In the underwater environment of whales, hair causes resistance and may be obstructions in catching prey, thus making them less likely to survive and reproduce.

Hair

Mammals are furry. Most species are covered with a layer of hair that helps them retain heat. Each hair is a long, thin shaft of dead, keratinized cells that grows out of a follicle in the skin. The hair traps a layer of air next to the skin, which insulates the animal, much like a down vest insulates you. When mammals get cold, muscles around the follicles pull the hair upright. When you get "goose bumps," your insulating air layer is thickening to help keep you warm.

Hair also has other functions. Anyone who has watched a frightened cat fluff up knows that mammals can use hair for behavioral displays. Patterns of pigmented hairs provide camouflage for many mammals. Porcupines and hedgehogs have modified hairs that form stiff protective quills. And many mammals have long, stiff whiskers that collect sensory information. Even mammals that have lost most of their hair, such as whales, retain some sensory bristles.

FIGURE 26.16 Mammals produce milk in mammary glands to provide nutrients to their offspring. These piglets will nurse from their mother for three to eight weeks.

Mammary Glands

All mammals take care of their babies after they are born. Females feed them a specialized fluid called milk. **Mammary glands** are specialized glands that produce milk. Milk contains water, sugars, protein, fats, minerals, and antibodies that help young animals grow and develop.

Mammary glands are unique to mammals. They are present in both males and females but produce milk only in females. Some mammals, such as pigs or dogs, have a series of glands along the belly. Other mammals have glands only in specific areas, such as udders in a cow's groin or the pair of glands on a primate's chest. Mammary glands contain masses of milk-producing tissues that are connected to a series of ducts. The ducts bring milk to the surface of the skin. In most mammals, the ducts empty into nipples or teats that young mammals, such as the piglets in **FIGURE 26.16,** can hold in the mouth and suckle.

Middle Ear

Mammals have three small bones in their middle ear. One of the bones, the stapes, is also found in other tetrapods. The other two, the malleus and incus, are unique to mammals. They were derived from reptilian jaw bones.

The top part of the hyoid arch became modified to form the stapes in early tetrapods. Bones that supported the jaws in fish became bones that transferred vibrations to the inner ear in tetrapods. A similar shift, illustrated in **FIGURE 26.17,** occurred as mammals evolved from their reptilian ancestors.

Synapsids such as the pelycosaur had jaws that were made of many bones fused together. The middle ear of these reptiles contained only one bone, the stapes, which transmitted sound to the inner ear, where it was converted to nerve impulses and interpreted by the brain. This is the same configuration of bones we see in reptiles today.

Differentiated Instruction

ENGLISH LEARNERS

Assign students to small groups, and tell them to each choose a topic within the section to become an expert on and teach to the rest of the group. Remind them that a good teacher will preview the text, ask questions, and clarify information. Once this is accomplished the "expert" should be able to summarize the main points for the group.

Biology Toolkit, Reciprocal Teaching, p. C14

Over time, the formation of these bones changed. Two bones, the quadrate and the articular bones, once formed the joint between the jaws of reptiles. These bones evolved to serve a different function—hearing. In mammals, the quadrate and articular bones are now tiny and are incorporated into the middle ear as the malleus and the incus. Sounds collected in the ear canal vibrate the eardrum. These vibrations are transferred through the malleus and incus bones to the stapes. These tiny vibrations are converted into nerve impulses in the inner ear and then interpreted by the brain. The ability to detect small vibrations allowed mammals to hear higher-pitched sounds.

FIGURE 26.17 As mammals evolved, the structures of the inner ear changed. The incus and malleus bones that were once part of reptilian jaw structures evolved in ways that enhanced hearing.

Chewing

Mammals developed the ability to chew their food. Amphibians, reptiles, and birds usually bite off large chunks of food or swallow it whole. Most of their mechanical processing occurs inside their digestive tract. Mammals, in contrast, start to break up their food as soon as it enters the mouth.

A set of adaptations in the mammalian jaw makes chewing possible. While food is in the mouth, a secondary palate separates the nasal and oral cavities. It keeps the passages for air and food separate, so mammals can chew and breathe at the same time. In addition, complex muscles can move the jaw from side to side.

A Infer **Hair was an important adaptation for mammals. How might hair and other adaptations have enabled mammals to survive where reptiles could not?**

MAIN IDEA

Modern mammals are divided into three main groups.

More than 4500 species of mammal are alive today. They can be classified into three groups: monotremes, marsupials, and eutherian mammals.

Monotremes

The **monotremes** are mammals that lay eggs. They are remnants of an ancient group of mammals that have characteristics of both mammals and reptiles. The group split off from the line that led to the other living mammals sometime during the Mesozoic. Their fossils suggest that they once lived throughout the Southern Hemisphere. But today only three species of monotreme survive. The duck-billed platypus is found only in Australia and Tasmania. Two types of echidna live in Australia, Tasmania, and New Guinea.

VOCABULARY

The name *monotreme* comes from a Greek word that means "single opening," referring to the cloaca opening, which these mammals have in common with birds and reptiles.

TEACH FROM VISUALS

FIGURE 26.17 Call students' attention to the large, visible part of the mammal's ear. Tell students that the dishlike structure is called the pinna. It can be tilted and turned by some mammals, such as a fox, to gather soundwaves from specific directions, thereby providing valuable information about the source of a sound. The human ear has a pinna, but we cannot move ours as well as mammals such as the fox in the figure. **Ask,** In terms of the physics of sound, what does an extra large pinna do? funnels more sound into the ear canal

Take It Further

Animal bones or fossils are often identified by the number, arrangement, and kinds of teeth they have. Scientists hypothesize that an animal's eating habits and anatomy evolved at the same time. Thus, much can be inferred about an extinct animal's lifestyle just by analyzing its teeth. Meat eaters have jaws and teeth designed for tearing and crushing. The **canine teeth** are large, and the **molars** have sharp cusps. Plant eaters usually have large **incisors** for cropping and cutting plants. Their broad molars are adapted for grinding tough plant fibers. **Ask,** Which kind of teeth do humans have? both

Answers

A Infer Mammals are endotherms. Hair helped them to keep body heat longer.

HANDS-ON ACTIVITY

This activity will help students identify the characteristics of mammalian skulls. Students will examine dentition and infer they type of diet the mammal has. Ideally, real skulls or skull casts of animals such as a cat, human, horse, beaver, and rabbit should be used so that students can handle them. If these are not available, locate the following images and download them from the Internet: skulls of a horse, beaver, lion, gorilla, and rabbit.

Have students form cooperative groups. Assign each group a skull or an illustration. Students should discuss the shape of the skull; the number, kind, and arrangement of the teeth, and infer what kind of food this animal eats. Then students should try to decide the name of the animal, based on its inferred lifestyle. Group members should agree and then defend their decision based on evidence they see in the teeth and skull shape.

Chapter 26: A Closer Look at Amniotes **807**

▼ Teach *continued*

Integrating Comparative Anatomy

Although a mammal, a **platypus** has traits common to reptiles and birds. To show students how difficult a platypus is to classify, have them set up a three-column chart with the headings "Reptilian," "Avian," and "Mammalian." Then have them place the following traits in appropriate column:

- lays eggs
- hair
- no teats
- produces milk
- young have teeth
- provides parental care
- ducklike bill
- beaverlike tail
- birdlike skull
- splayed pectoral girdle
- small number of offspring
- leathery eggs
- semiaquatic
- endothermic
- cloaca
- no external ears
- four legs
- bony plates instead of teeth (adults)
- produces venom (males only)

Take It Further

Opossums are marsupials. The young develop in a pouch. Opossums have only 13 teats in their pouches, and the embryos develop for only 13 days in the mother's uterus. This may seem unlucky, and for some of the embryos, it is. As many as 20 embryos may be born within a few minutes. **Ask,** What happens if more than 13 embryos are born? They will die. Marsupials invest a lot of time caring for their young, but if one of the embryos falls off in its climb toward the pouch, the mother will not pick it up.

FIGURE 26.18 The shovel-like bill of the duck-billed platypus is tightly packed with nerve endings. The platypus uses this bill to scrape the bottom of rivers and lakes in search of food.

Monotremes such as the platypus in **FIGURE 26.18** have a mix of ancestral mammalian and reptilian features. Monotremes have retained reptilian characteristics such as

- a sprawling posture
- a single external opening, called the cloaca, for their urinary, digestive, and reproductive tracts
- amniotic eggs with leathery shells that develop outside the body

Monotremes also have characteristic mammalian features, including mammary glands. When monotreme babies hatch, their mothers feed them milk. But monotremes do not have nipples. Their babies lick milk from pools on their mother's belly.

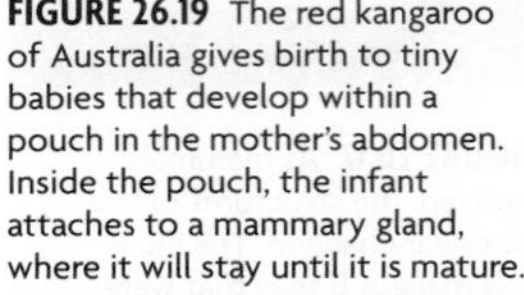

FIGURE 26.19 The red kangaroo of Australia gives birth to tiny babies that develop within a pouch in the mother's abdomen. Inside the pouch, the infant attaches to a mammary gland, where it will stay until it is mature.

Marsupials

Kangaroos, wombats, koalas, and opossums are a few of the 282 living species of marsupial. **Marsupials** are mammals that give birth to immature, underdeveloped live young that grow to maturity inside a marsupium, or pouch. After fertilization, marsupial embryos begin to develop internally, attached to a placenta that exchanges nutrients and wastes with the mother. But the amount of time the embryo develops inside the mother is very short. Most marsupial species give birth only a few weeks after fertilization. The immature babies, such as the one seen in **FIGURE 26.19**, attach themselves to a nipple inside the marsupium and nurse for up to six months before emerging from their mother's pouch.

Fossil evidence shows marsupials once lived all over the world. They have gone extinct over most of their former range. Most living species are found only in Australia and New Guinea. A few live in South America. One species, the Virginia opossum, lives in North America. Australian marsupials have diversified into many forms, and there are many examples of convergent evolution between these marsupials and eutherian mammals. In each case, the animals share similar ecological roles. For example, Australia is home to mouselike, molelike, anteating, and gliding marsupials that are physically similar to unrelated mice, moles, anteaters, and flying squirrels.

Differentiated Instruction

PRE-AP

Have students go back to **FIGURE 26.7** on page 795 and use the diagram as the basis for an upside-down concept map that follows the evolution of different traits among reptiles, birds, and mammals.

Biology Toolkit, Concept Map, p. C40

Eutherian Mammals

All the mammals most familiar to you are eutherians. **Eutherian** mammals give birth to live young that have completed fetal development. Eutherian mammals are commonly called placental mammals, but this term is misleading because most marsupials also use a placenta during embryo development. In most eutherian development, an embryo is attached to the mother's uterine wall. The connection between the fetus and the mother forms an organ called the placenta. Through the placenta, the mother delivers oxygen and nutrients to the embryo and removes waste products. The placenta only forms during gestation and leaves the mother's body following birth. The placenta is the only example of a disposable organ.

Eutherian gestation lasts longer than in marsupials—often months—and the babies are born at a more advanced stage of development. In some species, including the Bengal tiger in **FIGURE 26.20**, newborns are still relatively helpless and need extensive parental care until they can survive on their own. In others, such as deer or horses, the time shortly after birth is when the newborn is most vulnerable to predators, so it is important that they are able to get up and run within hours of birth.

After the extinction of the dinosaurs, eutherians quickly filled vacant ecological niches, and the modern groups of mammals appeared quickly. Rodents and carnivores appeared about 55 million years ago, and the first known species of bat, elephant, manatee, and horse appeared soon afterwards. Modern eutherians include fast carnivores such as cheetahs, and massive herbivores such as elephants. Three groups of aquatic eutherians—whales, manatees, and seals—evolved from land-dwelling mammals. Bats evolved powered flight. And one group of primates, the humans, evolved the ability to think about their ancestors.

FIGURE 26.20 The cubs of this Bengal tiger will stay with their mother for up to 18 months until they are able to hunt on their own. Many eutherian mammals care for their young after birth.

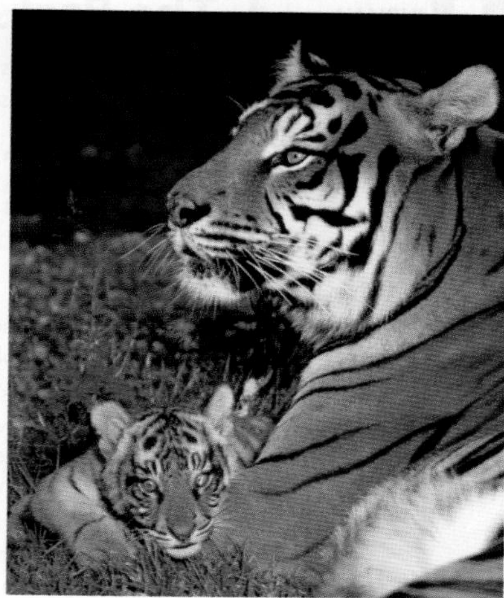

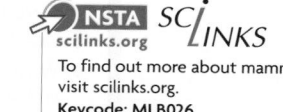

To find out more about mammals, visit scilinks.org.
Keycode: MLB026

Compare and Contrast **Compare and contrast the advantages and disadvantages of marsupial and eutherian mammal reproduction.**

26.4 ASSESSMENT

ONLINE QUIZ
ClassZone.com

REVIEWING MAIN IDEAS

1. What features make **mammals** different from reptiles?
2. How does fetal development differ among the three living groups of mammals?

CRITICAL THINKING

3. **Summarize** How did the mass extinction that ended the reptile reign help lead to today's mammal diversity?
4. **Classify** **Monotremes** were confusing to early scientists because they had both reptilian and mammalian features. How might scientists have classified monotremes differently?

Connecting CONCEPTS

5. **Ecology** A sea turtle may lay up to 200 eggs in a nest, then leave and return to the ocean. When the young turtles hatch they must fend for themselves. How do mammals differ in the number of offspring produced and in the role of parental care of offspring?

26.4 ASSESSMENT

1. hair, mammary glands, middle ear with three bones, a jaw to chew with
2. Monotremes lay eggs; marsupials are born at a very early age, but are kept in a pouch until maturity; eutherians have long gestation periods, but give birth to young that are fully developed.
3. Mammals were able to regulate their body temperature internally and filled in the ecological niches that were left by the extinction of the reptiles.
4. They could have been classified as reptiles.
5. Mammals do not produce as many offspring and tend to care for their young after birth.

Take It Further

The period between conception and birth is called the **gestation period.** The **elephant** has the longest gestation period—as long as 22 months. Usually one calf is born and is nursed for up to 4 years or until the mother is pregnant again. Calves are cared for by the entire herd and receive attentive parental care for at least 5 years. Mother elephants have been observed to cry and grieve if their babies are lost or killed by predators. An elephant can live up to 70 years.

In comparison, a common house **mouse** lives about a year, has a gestation period of about 19 days, has a litter of up to 8 pups, and nurses them only about 3 to 4 weeks, after which they are on their own. A mouse can give birth several times in a year. **Ask,** How does lifespan relate to the length of maternal care? Longer lifespans mean longer maternal care.

Answers

A Compare and Contrast Marsupials do not dedicate as much bodily fluid to the infant; they just provide milk and warmth. Eutherians must share oxygen, blood, and nutrients directly with the growing fetus. Eutherian gestation lasts longer than in marsupials.

Assess and Reteach ▼

Assess Use the Online Quiz or Section Quiz (*Assessment Book,* p. 516).

Reteach List the mammalian characteristics on the board and have students tell which one they believe is most important for survival. Write their responses on the board and have students defend their opinion.

OPTIONS FOR INQUIRY

INVESTIGATION

Time 30 minutes	TEACHER TESTED
Teacher Preparation	
Student Difficulty	
Lab Binder Animals, pp. 55–57	

Purpose Examine the parts of an egg.

Overview Students will dissect an egg to examine the parts. Students will

- observe the shell, membranes, and structures of the egg (fertilized or unfertilized)
- draw and label their observations

LAB PREPARATION

- Distribute copies of the Egg Drawing datasheet (*Lab Binder,* p. 57).

LAB MANAGEMENT

- Have extra eggs available in case the shell membrane is broken early on.

Safety Tell students to exercise great caution with the sharp dissection tools. Have them dispose of their lab materials in a designated container. Remind students to wash their hands with soap and warm water before leaving.

Teacher Note "I like this lab. Students are familiar with eggs and can use relevant information, preconceptions, and experiences to perform this activity."

Inclusion Group students so that students with physical disabilities will have assistance.

POST-LAB DISCUSSION

Discuss students' observations and form conclusions. Tell students that raw chickens and eggs can carry a type of bacteria, salmonella, that can make them sick. This is usually due to fecal contamination during commercial processing.

Use these inquiry-based labs and online activities to deepen your understanding of amniotes.

NOS.3 Clearly communicate their ideas and results of investigations verbally and in written form using tables, graphs, diagrams, and photographs.

INVESTIGATION

The Parts of an Egg

Birds, some reptiles, and even a few mammals lay eggs. In this lab, you will dissect and identify the parts of an egg.

SKILL Observing

PROBLEM What are the parts of an egg, and what are their functions?

MATERIALS

- chicken egg
- dissecting tray
- Egg Drawing
- colored pencils
- fine scissors
- dissecting needle
- dissecting forceps
- hand lens

PROCEDURE

1. Use colored pencils to illustrate and label the structures you observe.
2. With the various dissecting tools, carefully chip away at the eggshell without breaking the delicate membranes beneath the shell or the yolk. Make observations with the hand lens and record them.
3. In an unfertilized egg, you will find several structures, including the vitelline membrane, which surrounds the yolk; a white spot on the yolk called the germinal disk; and two cordlike strands on either side of the yolk, called chalazae.
4. In a fertilized egg, you may find an embryo attached to the yolk and two additional membranes within the yolk: the amnion and the allantois. Surrounding the yolk is chorion.
5. Use the Egg Drawing to identify and illustrate additional structures.
6. When you have identified all structures and investigated both fertilized and unfertilized eggs, dispose of the eggs and wash your hands.

ANALYZE AND CONCLUDE

1. **Infer** What do you think would happen to the yolk if the egg were to become fertilized?
2. **Infer** What is the function of the vitelline membrane and the albumen? Explain.

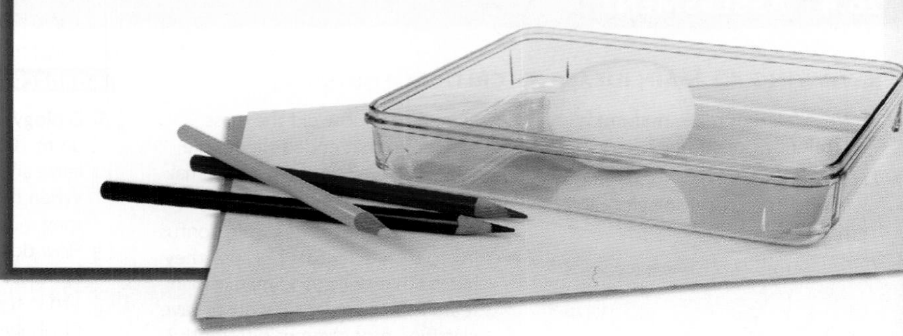

Answers

Analyze and Conclude

1. It would gradually shrink as the embryo grew and developed.
2. It carries nutrients to the developing embryo.

INVESTIGATION

Migration and Range

Each year, when the days begin to get shorter and the temperature begins to drop, you may notice flocks of birds flying across the sky. The seasonal movement of birds is called migration. Birds use a great deal of energy to migrate.

Tiny ruby-throated hummingbirds, for example, spend much of the spring and summer in the eastern United States and Canada. But each year, they make an incredible migration, flying south around the Gulf of Mexico to Central America, and some go as far south as Panama. Compare this to the Arctic tern, which travels over 32,000 kilometers (20,000 mi) per year.

In this activity, you will research aspects of bird migration.

SKILL Researching

MATERIALS
- pencil
- North America map

PROBLEM Why do birds migrate?

PROCEDURE

Choose three of the following questions to research and help explain bird migration.

1. Why do birds migrate?
2. How do birds know when to start migrating?
3. How do migrating birds navigate?
4. What methods do scientists use to monitor bird migration?
5. What problems do migrating birds face?
6. What are the major routes of bird migrations in North America? On the attached map, shade in areas of major flyways over the United States.

Online BIOLOGY CLASSZONE.COM

ANIMATED BIOLOGY

Beak Shape and Diet

The shape of a bird's beak allows it to take advantage of specific food sources. Examine a set of bird images and use the shape of each beak as a clue to identify the food source.

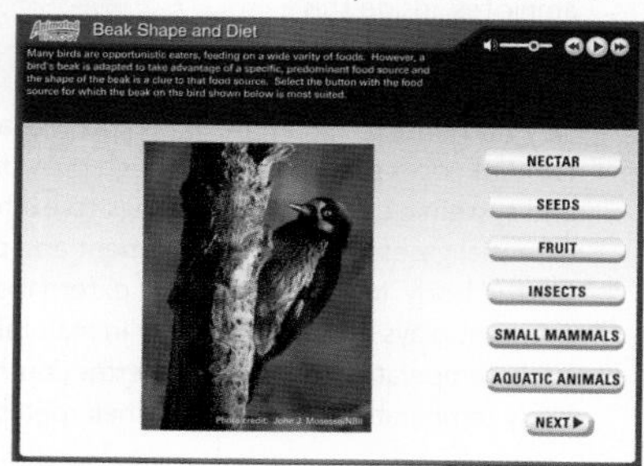

WEBQUEST

There are seven species of sea turtles on Earth; all are endangered or threatened. In this WebQuest, you will explore the threats sea turtles face and the actions people are taking to save them. Find out if we can reverse the sea turtles' paths to extinction.

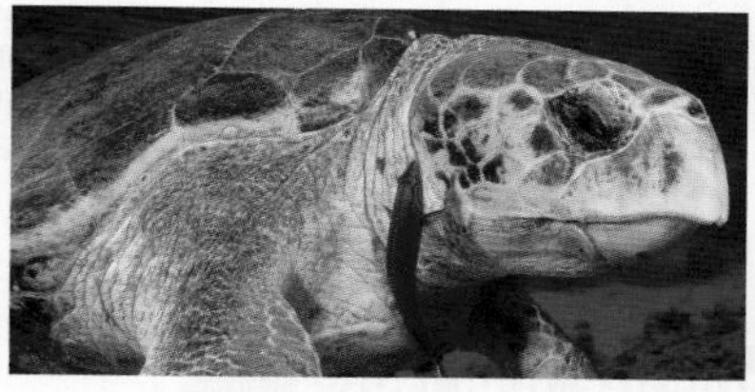

DATA ANALYSIS ONLINE

Internal body temperature can provide information about an unknown amniote. Graph and compare body temperatures of four hypothetical animals over a range of environmental temperatures. Use data in the graphs to make inferences about the animals.

Answers

1. to find food, water, protective cover, and a protected place to nest and breed
2. When days get shorter, food supplies diminish, or the weather changes.
3. sighting landmarks, monitoring Earth's magnetic field, observing the stars and the Sun, smell, following parents and members of their flock
4. mapping migration routes, reports of observers along the way, banding individuals, satellite imaging of wetlands
5. severe weather, predators, hunters, habitat loss, pollution
6. Pacific Flyway, Central Flyway, Mississippi Flyway, Atlantic Flyway

Online Biology ▼

ANIMATED BIOLOGY Use this interactive animation to reinforce the concepts in **Section 26.3.**

WEBQUEST The WebQuest takes one full class period. Students complete the activity online and will need access to a printer to print their answers. Sample answers, teacher notes, and alternative assessment ideas are available on **ClassZone.com.** Use with **Section 26.2.**

DATA ANALYSIS ONLINE

This activity can be done in class or as a homework project. Students should use line graphs to display the body temperature data for the six different animals. Use with **Section 26.1.**

INVESTIGATION

TEACHER TESTED

Time	30 minutes
Teacher Preparation	(1 flask)
Student Difficulty	(1 flask)
Lab Binder	Animals, pp. 58–59

Purpose Read and research selected topics about bird migration.

Overview Students will do research in the library or on the Internet about bird migrations, answer the questions, and trace migration routes on a map of North America.

LAB PREPARATION

- Distribute copies of the map of North America before students begin their research (*Lab Binder*, p. 59).

CHAPTER REVIEW

Interactive Review

Encourage students to go to **ClassZone.com** for a detailed review of each section, including visuals and vocabulary practice.

Unit Resource Book, Vocabulary Practice, pp. 117–120

CHAPTER 26 Interactive Review @ CLASSZONE.COM

KEY CONCEPTS | Vocabulary Games | Concept Maps | Animated Biology | Online Quiz

26.1 Amniotes

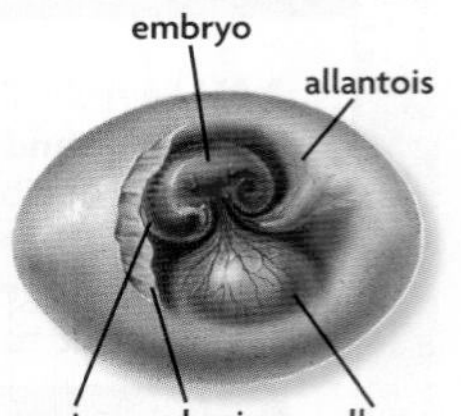

Reptiles, birds, and mammals are amniotes. Organisms that develop inside an amniotic sac are called amniotes. Inside this sac, an embryo is provided with the necessary nutrients to help it develop and prepare for life. Amniotes pump blood through pulmonary and systemic circuits and use lungs to exchange essential gases with the environment and provide for the body. In ectotherms, the external environment plays an important role in maintaining body temperature, while endotherms control their body temperature by regulating their metabolism.

26.2 Reptiles

Reptiles were the first amniotes. Reptiles come in many shapes and sizes, but all have a three-chambered heart and are ectotherms. Oviparous reptiles lay eggs externally, and viviparous reptiles retain eggs internally to full development. Scientists have traced the ancestors of modern reptiles based on skull anatomy and have determined how modern birds, reptiles, and mammals are descended from ancient reptiles. Today, turtles, sphenodonts, snakes and lizards, and crocodilians are the major reptile groups.

26.3 Birds

Birds have many adaptations for flight. All birds share unique features such as hollow bones, a highly modified circulatory system, and feathers. Bird wings have a convex curved shape, called an airfoil, to enable flight. Their strong chest muscles are attached to a large sternum, or keel. Birds have a very high metabolism and a unique one-way breathing system that is highly efficient. Birds are directly descended from dinosaurs. Birds come in many shapes and sizes, and features such as wings, beak, and feet are highly adapted to each species' niche.

26.4 Mammals

Evolutionary adaptations allowed mammals to succeed dinosaurs as a dominant terrestrial vertebrate. Mammals evolved while dinosaurs were walking Earth. After the dinosaurs went extinct, many new species of mammals evolved and filled the vacant niches. Mammals share four features—hair, mammary glands, a modified middle ear, and a jaw that lets them chew food. Mammals are endotherms, and hair plays an important role in keeping their body temperature stable. Mammary glands produce nutrient-rich milk, which is the primary food source for growing infant mammals. There are three major groups of mammals: monotremes, marsupials, and eutherians.

Synthesize Your Notes

Concept Map Use a concept map like the one below to summarize distinctive amniote characteristics.

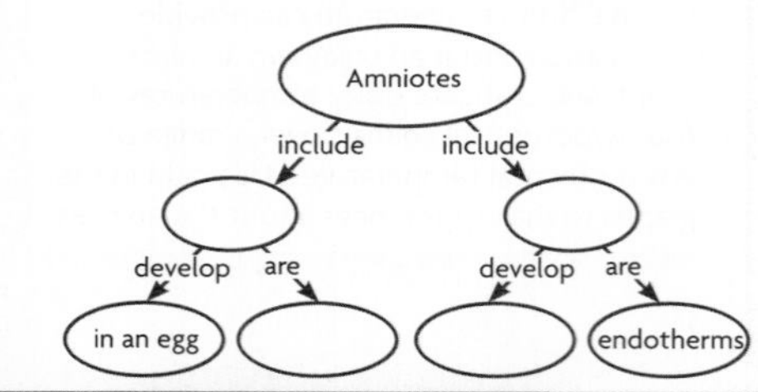

Main Idea Web Use a main idea web like the one below to summarize the features of mammals, birds, and reptiles.

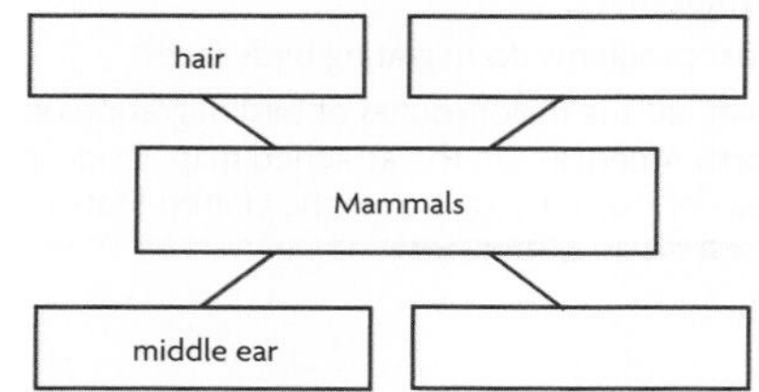

Reviewing Vocabulary

1. Mammals are one type of endotherm.
2. Viviparous reptiles hold their eggs inside their bodies until they are mature enough to hatch.
3. Both marsupials and eutherians have placentas. But the placenta in an eutherian is embedded in the uterine tissue, and gestation lasts longer than in a marsupial.
4. Blood flows to the lungs to pick up oxygen.
5. The temperature of birds and mammals is regulated internally.
6. Oviparous organisms give birth by laying eggs.
7. Both circuits move blood. The pulmonary circuit moves blood between the heart and the lungs, while the systemic circuit moves blood between the heart and the rest of the body.
8. Both are ways that reptiles reproduce. In viviparous reptiles, eggs are held internally until they are mature, while oviparous reptiles lay eggs externally.
9. Both are ways that organisms regulate body temperature. Ectotherms use the external environment to regulate body temperature, while endotherms regulate body temperature internally.

Reviewing Main Ideas

10. The amnion is the fluid-filled sac that protects the embryo. The chorion is a membrane that allows gas exchange. The yolk sac contains the food supply for the growing embryo. The allantois holds waste material from the embryo.

Chapter Assessment

Chapter Vocabulary

26.1 pulmonary circuit, p. 789
systemic circuit, p. 789
ectotherm, p. 791
endotherm, p. 791

26.2 reptile, p. 793
oviparous, p. 793
viviparous, p. 793

26.3 airfoil, p. 799
sternum, p. 801
air sac, p. 801

26.4 mammal, p. 805
mammary gland, p. 806
monotreme, p. 807
marsupial, p. 808
eutherian, p. 809

Reviewing Vocabulary

Vocabulary Connections

Write a sentence or two to clearly explain how the vocabulary terms in this chapter are connected. For example, for the terms *mammal* and *mammary gland,* you could write, "The mammary gland is one of the unique characteristics of a mammal."

1. endotherm, mammal
2. reptile, viviparous
3. marsupial, eutherian

Greek and Latin Word Origins

Use the definitions of the word parts to answer the following questions.

Part	Meaning
pulmo-	lung
endo-	inner
-parous	to give birth

4. Explain why the prefix *pulmo-* is used to describe blood circuits.
5. Why is the prefix *endo-* used to describe the temperature regulation strategy of mammals and birds?
6. How is the meaning of the suffix *-parous* related to its use in the word *oviparous*?

Compare and Contrast

Describe one similarity and one difference between the two terms in each of the following pairs.

7. pulmonary circuit, systemic circuit
8. oviparous, viviparous
9. endotherm, ectotherm

Reviewing MAIN IDEAS

10. Name the four membranes found in an amniotic egg and explain the function of each.

11. Describe one similarity and one difference between the functions of a three-chambered heart and those of a four-chambered heart.

12. The desert tortoise, an ectotherm, spends as much as 95 percent of its time in underground burrows. Even in a predator-free environment, why might it have to do this?

13. Birds live in hot deserts and in Antarctica. How is it possible for birds to live in hot and frigid environments where reptiles cannot survive?

14. What are two ways that reptiles can reproduce?

15. Summarize the relationships between modern birds, reptiles, and mammals and their ancient ancestors.

16. Compare how snakes and lizards find prey with how crocodiles find prey.

17. What five pieces of evidence indicate that birds evolved from theropod dinosaurs?

18. What is the sternum? How does it help make flight possible for birds?

19. How is the reproductive system of a bird adapted for flight?

20. What three parts of a bird's body can indicate what ecological niche the bird fills?

21. How is the mammalian middle ear different from that of reptiles?

22. How does development differ among the three groups of mammals?

11. Both types of hearts process oxygenated and deoxygenated blood separately. With a three-chambered heart, an animal can temporarily close off its lungs based on its need for more oxygen or less oxygen. This is helpful when the animal is running. In a four-chambered heart, the system works continually. This provides a constant and increased supply of oxygen to the animal under all circumstances.

12. Desert tortoises burrow to keep cool because they cannot regulate their body temperatures. A tortoise that spent too much time in the hot sun of a desert would overheat and probably die.

13. Birds can regulate their body temperatures using metabolic heat. They can also shiver to generate extra heat. Feathers provide insulation.

14. Oviparous reptiles lay eggs in an external nest, and the eggs develop independent of the adult. Viviparous reptiles keep their eggs inside their bodies during development and give birth to live young.

15. Modern birds, reptiles, and mammals have similar skull structures.

16. Snake and lizards use their tongues to pick up particles in the air that are interpreted by the Jacobsen's organ at the top of their mouths. This allows them to sense whether a prey animal is close by. Crocodiles are ambush predators. They wait underwater to surprise an animal that comes by.

17. hollow bones; fused collarbones; different arrangement of muscles in the hips and legs that improve bipedal movement; no fourth or fifth fingers on the hands; feathers

18. The sternum in birds is a large, bony ridge called the keel. It provides a place for large chest muscles to attach. These chest muscles are necessary for flight.

19. In both male and female birds, the reproductive organs shrink after mating and egg laying have occurred. This reduces the amount of weight the bird has to carry and saves energy.

20. Wing shape can indicate the type of habitat a bird lives in, for example, deep forest or open water. The shape of the bill gives clues about what it eats. Foot shape also gives clues about habitats, for example, webbed feet in an aquatic habitat.

21. The stapes is found in all tetrapods. But as mammals evolved from reptilian ancestors, the quadrate and articular bones of the jaw became smaller and were incorporated into the middle ear as the incus and malleus.

22. In monotremes, the babies hatch from eggs and lick milk from pools on their mother's belly. In marsupials, the babies are not fully developed when they are born. They attach to a nipple inside a pouch on their mother's belly and nurse as they finish developing. In eutherians, the babies are born at an advanced stage of development. However, all three types of young are somewhat helpless and need to be cared for.

Critical Thinking

23. People are endotherms and can generate heat from their metabolic processes. Running and other forms of exercise generate metabolic heat. Even though the outside temperature has not changed, the person's body is making more heat.
24. This animal is a reptile, a lizard. It is viviparous and capable of swallowing prey larger than its head.
25. Ectotherms cannot survive in cold climates for a long time, because they require a specific body temperature to maintain bodily functions.
26. Feathers have more surface area than hair does and in this way help a bird to carry its own body weight.
27. Leopards need to hide so they can approach their prey. Their fur coats provide camouflage. Large animals such as elephants must be careful not to overheat because it would take a long time for them to cool down. Because hair can retain heat, having less of it can help an animal stay cool.
28. A secondary palate separates the nasal and mouth cavities while a mammal eats, allowing for breathing while eating. Breathing is necessary for speaking.

Interpreting Visuals

29. 2, left atrium
30. 3, ventricle
31. This is a three-chambered heart. You can see the incomplete division of the ventricle. This heart has two atria and one ventricle.

Critical Thinking

23. Analyze A person goes out for a jog wearing a jacket because the morning is cool. After about 15 minutes, the person feels very warm and has to take off the jacket, even though the temperature hasn't changed. Explain what is happening.

24. Classify Imagine that a new animal has been discovered in the rain forest. It has four limbs and a tail. Scientists observe that it can swallow prey larger than its head. It gives birth to live young. Based on this information, how would you classify this animal? Explain your answer.

25. Apply Explain why the number of native reptile species decreases as you move away from Earth's equator.

26. Analyze Feathers are one of the most important adaptations for birds. Why are feathers a more useful adaptation for flying than hair?

27. Infer Elephants and leopards both live in Africa, where it is hot. But elephants have very little hair, and leopards have a full coat of hair. Explain why this might be.

28. Analyze Though it is bad manners, why is it possible for a person to talk while chewing a mouthful of food?

Interpreting Visuals

Use the following illustration to answer the next three questions.

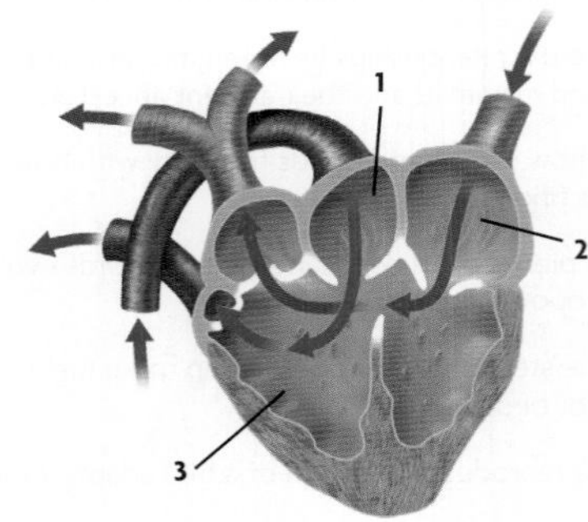

29. Analyze Blood coming from the lungs enters which part of this heart? Give the number and identify the part.

30. Analyze Blood going to the body comes from which part of the heart? Give the number and identify the part.

31. Synthesize Is this a three-chambered heart or a four-chambered heart? Explain how you know.

Analyzing Data

The table below shows the weight loss of two box turtles during hibernation. A box turtle should lose only about 1 percent of its body weight during each month of hibernation and no more than 5 percent during the entire hibernating period. Use the data to answer the next two questions.

WEIGHT LOSS DURING HIBERNATION

Turtle	Nov	Dec	Jan	Feb	Mar
No. 1	600g	594g	588g	582g	576g
No. 2	600g	590g	585g	580g	576g

32. Graph Which type of graph would best represent both sets of data in the table? Why?

33. Evaluate Based on the differences in mass over the course of hibernation, which turtle will be healthier at the end of hibernation? Explain your reasoning.

Connecting CONCEPTS

34. Write a Script Birds, reptiles, and mammals coexist in many environments on Earth. But many times their paths cross and confrontations occur. Perhaps while a lion is feeding, a vulture may fly down to try and get a bite to eat, or maybe a bird's nest is being invaded by a reptile. Choose a place where two very different amniotes might interact, and write a script of their conversation. Using what you have learned about birds, reptiles, and mammals and how they function, have them discuss advantages and disadvantages of each other's lifestyles and how their conflict could be resolved.

35. Apply Look again at the picture of the tarsier on page 787 and read the description. Despite body parts that might remind you of other types of animals, why are scientists sure that the tarsier is a mammal?

Analyzing Data

32. A line graph would be best because line graphs are best for showing change over time.
33. Students should recognize that neither turtle lost more than it should have over five months of hibernation. It is true that turtle #2 lost more than 1 percent between November and December, but it made up for this loss by losing less than 1 percent during later months.

INDIANA ISTEP+ Test Prep

B.1.2; B.8.3; B.8.5; NOS.1

Test Practice For more test practice, go to ClassZone.com.

1

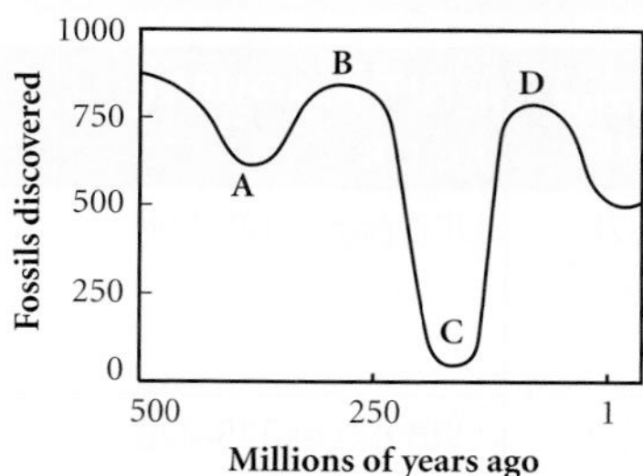

This graph shows the number of fossils found at a hypothetical site from each time period over the past 500 million years. Which of these statements is ***best*** supported by the data?

A Many speciation events occurred at Node A.
B Nodes B and D indicate a lack of biodiversity.
C Species diversity increased after Node D.
D A possible mass extinction occurred at Node C.

2 During the summer, the arctic fox produces enzymes that cause its fur to become reddish brown. These enzymes do not function during the winter, causing the fox's fur to become white and blend in with the snow. Which of the following statements is ***most*** likely true?

A The genes in arctic fox populations are unstable.
B Reddish brown fur during the fall is likely not selected for in arctic fox populations.
C White fur during the winter is a trait that was selected for in arctic fox populations.
D The enzyme that controls fur color is not affected by temperature.

3 Amniotes are multicellular animals whose embryos develop in an enclosed membrane. What else must be true of ***all*** amniotes?

A They can only reproduce asexually.
B Fertilization is always external.
C They lay eggs during their life cycle.
D Half of their DNA comes from each parent.

THINK THROUGH THE QUESTION

First, think about what an embryo is. Can an embryo be produced asexually? Next, eliminate answer choices that could be true for some amniotes, but may not be true for all amniotes.

4 During chewing, digestive enzymes in the mouths of mammals begin breaking down food particles. Which is true about enzymes?

A Without enzymes, certain chemical reactions would require more energy input.
B Once enzymes react, new ones must replace those that were changed during the reaction.
C Enzymes work faster at high temperatures.
D Enzymes bond to substrates, forming new molecules.

5

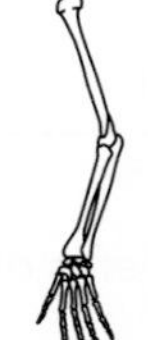

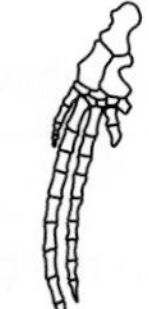

These illustrations show the bones of the forelimbs of three organisms. The similarities in bone arrangement supports the hypothesis that these organisms

A are members of one species.
B descended from a common ancestor.
C have adaptations for similar environments.
D have the same genetic information.

6 Theropods were a group of two-legged dinosaurs that are similar to birds. They had hollow bones, feathers, hip muscles that aided two-legged movement, and a fused collarbone called a furcula.

A. Why might scientists think theropods were the ancestors of ancient birds?
B. What kind of evidence supports this theory?

Standards-Based Assessment

1. D	4. A
2. C	5. B
3. D	6. See Below

Question 1 Answer D is correct. Answers A, B, and C are incorrect because the graph tells only the number of fossils discovered, not the number of different species represented by the fossils.

Question 3 Answer D is correct. Answer A is incorrect because amniotes reproduce sexually. Answer B is incorrect because amniotes reproduce via internal fertilization. Answer C is incorrect because not all amniotes lay eggs during their life cycle; marsupials and eutherians give birth to live young.

Question 4 Answer A is correct. Answer B is incorrect because enzymes are not used up during a chemical reaction. Answer C is incorrect because different enzymes work optimally under a variety of different conditions. Answer D is incorrect because enzymes are not directly involved in the chemical reactions that they catalyze.

Question 6 The two groups share many structural features. Fossil evidence supports this theory and was the reason that scientists could examine an organism that no longer exists on Earth.

Connecting Concepts

34. Answers will vary, depending on whether students chose to be mammals, birds, or reptiles. Answers should accurately reflect the body shape, body covering, type of heart, type of respiratory system, and reproductive body parts needed by the type of animal students choose.

35. The photo shows that the tarsier is covered with fur. Tarsiers may be different from other members of the primate group, but they still have the same basic characteristics shared by all mammals. One of these characteristics is hair or fur.

ITEM CORRELATIONS

Standard	Items
B.1.2	4
B.8.3	5, 6
B.8.5	2
NOS.1	1

CHAPTER 27

Indiana Resource Preview

Print Resources

Animal Behavior

INDIANA STANDARDS		Sections	PAGES and PACING	UNIT RESOURCE BOOK
	27.1	**Adaptive Value of Behavior** **KEY CONCEPT** Behavior lets organisms respond rapidly and adaptively to their environment.	pp. 818–821 30 minutes	URB pages 121–124
	27.2	**Instinct and Learning** **KEY CONCEPT** Both genes and environment affect an animal's behavior.	pp. 822–826 30 minutes	URB pages 125–128
	27.3	**Evolution of Behavior** **KEY CONCEPT** Every behavior has costs and benefits.	p p. 827–829 30 minutes	URB pages 129–132
NOS.3		CHAPTER INVESTIGATION: Using an Ethogram to Describe Animal Behavior	p. 830 60 minutes	**Lab Binder** Animals pages 67–69
	27.4	**Social Behavior** **KEY CONCEPT** Social behaviors enhance the benefits of living in a group.	pp. 831–836 30 minutes	URB pages 133–136
NOS.3		DATA ANALYSIS: Constructing Bar Graphs	p. 836 30 minutes	URB page 141
	27.5	**Animal Cognition** **KEY CONCEPT** Some animals other than humans exhibit behaviors requiring complex cognitive abilities.	pp. 837–839 30 minutes	URB pages 137–140
NOS.1, NOS.3		OPTIONS FOR INQUIRY	pp. 840–841 45 minutes, 30 minutes	**Lab Binder** Animals pages 71–74
		Chapter Review	pp. 842–845	**Assessment Book** Chapter Tests A, B pp. 537–544

INDIANA STANDARDS

NOS.1 Develop explanations based on reproducible data and observations gathered during laboratory investigations.
NOS.3 Clearly communicate their ideas and results of investigations verbally and in written form using tables, graphs, diagrams, and photographs.

Labs

PUPIL EDITION LABS

Human Behavior, Section 2, p. 824 Students observe and collect data on a selected human behavior. **Lab Binder** pp. 75–76	**Time:** 15 minutes **Materials:** paper, pencil
Using an Ethogram to Describe Animal Behavior, p. 830 Students develop an ethogram. **Lab Binder** pp. 67–69	**Time:** 60 minutes **Materials:** pet or classroom animal, watch, calculator, graph paper, ruler

OPTIONS FOR INQUIRY

Pill Bug Behavior, p. 840 Students test the behavioral response of pill bugs to environmental changes. **Lab Binder** pp. 71–73	**Time:** 45 minutes **Materials:** shoebox lid, marker, 12 pill bugs, 25 cm piece of foil, light source, 10-mL graduated cylinder, 10 mL water, 4 paper towels, sheet dark-colored paper, sheet light-colored paper
Animal Cognition, p. 841 Students research animal cognition studies. **Lab Binder** p. 74	**Time:** 30 minutes **Materials:** computer with Internet access

LAB BINDER Unit 8 Animals

Additional Investigation: Investigating Behavior, pp. 77–79

Virtual Lab Worksheet: Interpreting Bird Response, p. 102

LAB GENERATOR

A searchable CD of all labs in the program in editable format, including forensic, probeware, and biotechnology labs.

Presentation Tools

POWER PRESENTATIONS

Presentation Chapter 27
Power Presentations for each section incorporate images and clips from the Media Gallery: Includes Note Navigator for each section.

MEDIA GALLERY

Contains the following images and video clips, as well as animations, simulations and forms of visuals from the book.

Animal

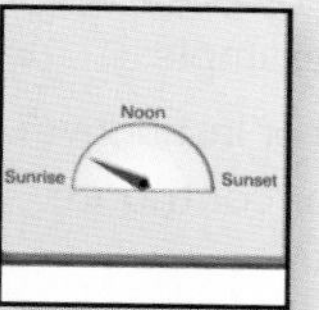

Behavioral costs and benefits

Preventing imprinting

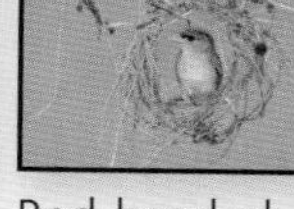
Red-headed weaver nest

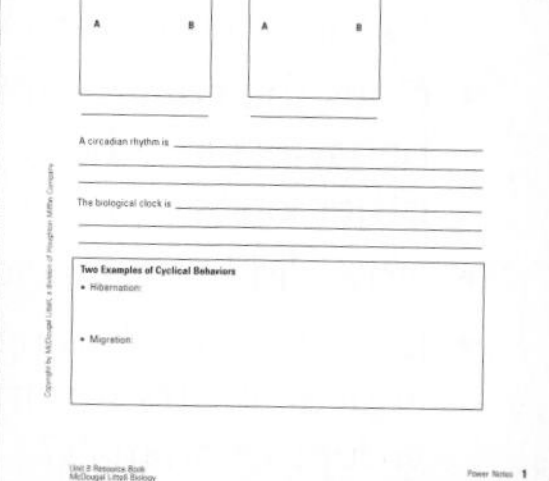

Power Notes

VIDEO

View as set of short video clips exploring instances of animal cognition and behavior.

ANIMATED BIOLOGY

Spider Mating Habits
Animal Cognition
Behavioral Costs and Benefits

Online BIOLOGY CLASSZONE.COM

BioZine
Animated Biology
Interactive Review
SciLinks
Resource Centers

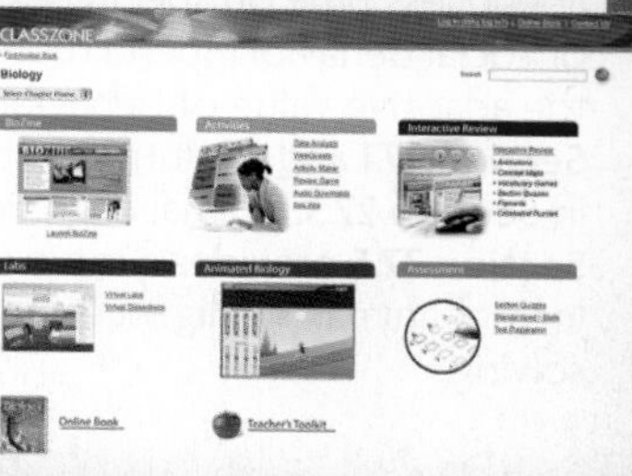

CHAPTER

27

▼ Focus and Motivate

What can be learned from this chimpanzee's behavior?

Students may come up with a variety of things that can be learned by observing the chimp's behavior. For example:

- Is the behavior learned or instinctive?
- How does the behavior contribute to the chimp's survival?
- Does the chimp exhibit similar behaviors in other contexts or with other kinds of tools?
- How did the behavior evolve?
- Do similar tool-using behaviors appear in other primates or other groups of animals?

Ask, What is the adaptive advantage of using a leaf to drink? The chimp can more easily scoop up water to drink.

Discuss the behavior in terms of efficiency and reducing energy spent.

BIOZINE ClassZone.com

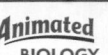

Students can access BioZine at **ClassZone.com** to receive updates to featured topics in the book.

In a Hurry?

Students may be familiar with some of the material in this chapter. For quick coverage, briefly define instinct and innate behavior. Discuss the benefits versus the costs of social behavior. Spend less time on specific examples of social behavior. Spend more time on the adaptive value of behavior in **Section 27.1** and evolution of behavior in **Section 27.3.** Animal cognition in **Section 27.5** provides a more in-depth look at animal intelligence and problem solving.

CHAPTER

27 Animal Behavior

KEY CONCEPTS

27.1 Adaptive Value of Behavior
Behavior lets organisms respond rapidly and adaptively to their environment.

27.2 Instinct and Learning
Both genes and environment affect an animal's behavior.

27.3 Evolution of Behavior
Every behavior has costs and benefits.

27.4 Social Behavior
Social behaviors enhance the benefits of living in a group.

27.5 Animal Cognition
Some animals other than humans exhibit behaviors requiring complex cognitive abilities.

Online BIOLOGY CLASSZONE.COM

Animated BIOLOGY
View animated chapter concepts.
- Spider Mating Habits
- Animal Cognition
- Interpreting Bird Response
- Behavioral Costs and Benefits

BIOZINE
Keep current with biology news.
- News feeds
- Strange Biology
- Bio Bytes

RESOURCE CENTER
Get more information on
- Courtship Behaviors
- Animal Tools

Student Activity

Purpose **Have students make careful observations and classify types of behavior visible with birds at a bird feeder.**

Materials (for the class)

- birdseed
- platform bird feeder

Place the feeder in an area where bird behavior can be observed from the classroom. You may want to do this a few days ahead to allow the birds to habituate to the circumstances.

What can be learned from this chimpanzee's behavior?

Connecting CONCEPTS

This chimpanzee is using a leaf to drink water. Chimpanzees use a variety of tools. Bunched up leaves might serve as a sponge to sop up water for drinking or for cleaning themselves. Some chimpanzees also use twigs to dig termites out of their mounds and rocks to crack open hard-shelled nuts or fruits. Tool use is considered an example of complex behavior.

Scientific Methods Modern animal behavior studies are conducted with the aid of a variety of tools, including computers. For example, a keyboard that allows for speech synthesis was developed for language acquisition studies with bonobos. Data from these experiments have helped scientists to understand the cognitive abilities of primates, such as their ability to understand spoken words.

Introduce Remind students that part of what scientists do is to record observations and take measurements of natural phenomena. Behavior is a natural phenomenon, and animals display a wide variety of behaviors that are characteristic of their species.

Have students think about how to classify behaviors, for example whether the behavior is submissive or aggressive. Does the size of a bird seem to have an effect on its level of aggressiveness? What can be measured? Have them consider what stimuli the birds respond to. Tell students to distinguish between intraspecies behaviors and interspecies behaviors.

Discuss Have students discuss their observations. **Ask**

- What behaviors did you observe? vocalizing, flapping wings, ruffling feathers, thrusting beaks, chasing other birds
- How did the birds interact with each other? some species or individuals may be more aggressive than others, and there may be a hierarchy or pecking order

Activate Prior Knowledge

Remind students that they have many of the same physical traits as other members of their family. **Ask,** Are there also certain mannerisms or behavioral traits you share with members of your family? What sorts of things are they? Students will probably mention simple behaviors. **Ask,** Are the behaviors learned behaviors or instinctive? Most students will probably suggest that as young children they learned the behaviors by mimicking parents or older siblings. Tell students that they will be learning about complex behaviors in other animals in this chapter and that not all complex behaviors are learned.

Preview Vocabulary

Greek and Latin Word Origins Tell students that they will be studying learned and instinctive behaviors in this chapter. Point out that the word *instinct* shares the same root as the word *impulse,* a root meaning "to incite." This suggests that the behavior is immediate, unplanned, and not learned. By comparison, a learned behavior implies a degree of awareness or cognition. The word *cognition* derives from roots meaning "to learn" or "to know."

Academic Vocabulary Have students think about the relationship between the following words and which can be applied to the behavior of animals:

perception, the act of becoming aware of something directly through a sensory experience

knowledge, familiarity, awareness, or understanding gained through experience or study

intelligence, the capacity to acquire and apply knowledge

learning, modification of behavior by experience

English Learners Have students prepare word squares for some of the words that appear in the section titles: *behavior, instinct, social, learning,* and *cognition.* Square 1: translate the word into their home language. Square 2: draw an image that captures the idea. Square 3: students write their own definition, then preview the chapter and rewrite the definition to fit with how the word is used in the context of animal behavior. Square 4: students use the word in a sentence.

SECTION 27.1

▼ Plan and Prepare

Objectives

- Explain why responding to stimuli is adaptive.
- Describe how internal and external stimuli trigger behavior.
- Discuss how biological clocks influence behavior.

Section Resources

Unit Resource Book
Study Guide pp. 121–122 Power Notes p. 123 Reinforcement p. 124
Interactive Reader Chapter 27 **Spanish Study Guide** pp. 273–274
Biology Toolkit pp. C12, C19
Technology Power Presentation 27.1 Media Gallery DVD Online Quiz 27.1

Activate Prior Knowledge Discuss with students some of the behaviors they have observed in common organisms such as cats, dogs, fish, birds, and people. Make a list on the board of some of their responses. **Ask,** Why do you think organisms have certain behaviors? *Sample Answers:* to get attention from a potential mate, to obtain food, to play, or for defense and protection

▼ Teach

Vocabulary

Academic Vocabulary The word **stimulus** is used in contexts other than biology. A stimulus can be anything that incites activity. For example, an economic stimulus might be the lowering of interest rates to stimulate spending and thus economic growth. Ask students to give some other examples of stimuli in nonbiological contexts.

27.1 Adaptive Value of Behavior

KEY CONCEPT Behavior lets organisms respond rapidly and adaptively to their environment.

MAIN IDEAS

- Behavioral responses to stimuli may be adaptive.
- Internal and external stimuli usually interact to trigger specific behaviors.
- Some behaviors occur in cycles.

VOCABULARY

stimulus, p. 818
kinesis, p. 819
taxis, p. 819
circadian rhythm, p. 820
biological clock, p. 820

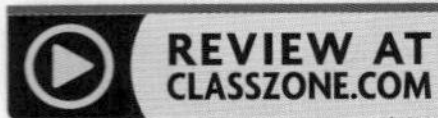

Connect Animal behavior can be simple, such as a moth flying toward a light, or it can be complex, such as a chimpanzee using a leaf as a tool to drink water from a stream. At its most basic level, however, every animal behavior demonstrates the adaptive advantage of an organism's ability to detect and respond to stimuli.

MAIN IDEA

Behavioral responses to stimuli may be adaptive.

TAKING NOTES

Use a cause-and-effect diagram to take notes on stimuli.

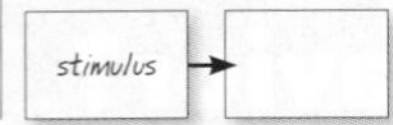

A houseplant bends its leaves toward a sunny window. A lizard moves into the shade on a hot day. A pufferfish inflates when threatened by a predator, as shown in **FIGURE 27.1.** Your cat comes running when it hears a can opener. What do these four observations have in common? They are all examples of organisms responding to stimuli in a beneficial way. A plant can only bend toward light by growing in its direction, but organisms such as the lizard, the pufferfish, or your cat have mechanisms that let them gather and actively respond to information. Behavior can be quite complex, especially in animals with complex nervous systems, but the adaptive nature of behavior can be seen in the relationship between a stimulus and a response.

FIGURE 27.1 When threatened, a pufferfish responds by inflating itself with water until its spines stick out from its rounded body.

Stimulus and Response

A **stimulus** (plural, *stimuli*) is a type of information that has the potential to make an organism change its behavior. Internal stimuli tell an animal what is occurring in its own body. For example,

- Hunger signals a need for more energy and causes an animal to search for food.
- Thirst signals a loss of internal fluid and causes an animal to look for water.
- Pain warns an animal that some part of its body may be subject to injury and causes it to take some action to avoid injury.

External stimuli give an animal information about its surroundings. For example,

- The sound of a predator can cause an animal to hide or run away to avoid being caught.
- The sight of a potential mate can trigger courtship behaviors.
- Changes in day length can trigger reproductive behaviors or migration.

Differentiated Instruction

ENGLISH LEARNERS

Tell students that once they've read the section, they will be asked to collect their thoughts on four questions:

- In what way are behavioral responses adaptive?
- What is the function of behavior?
- What are factors that contribute to behavioral responses?
- What function do cyclical behaviors serve?

Place chart paper at four stations around the room. When ready, divide students into four groups, and assign each group to a station. They will have five minutes to discuss and write answers to the question before rotating to the next station. As they rotate, tell them they can check off answers with which they agree, comment on answers with which they do not, and add new answers. When groups are finished, discuss the answers.

Biology Toolkit, Carousel Review, p. C12

Animals detect sensory information with specialized cells that are sensitive to changes in specific kinds of physical or chemical stimuli. These sensory cells may detect things such as light, sound, or chemicals. They transfer information to an animal's nervous system. The nervous system, in turn, may activate other systems in the animal's body that generate a response to the stimulus. For example, a stimulus may cause a gland to increase or decrease its production of a hormone. When you are startled or scared, your adrenal glands release a hormone called epinephrine that causes many other systems in your body to react in what is known as the "fight-or-flight" response. The most obvious organs activated in response to nervous activity are muscles. An animal's ability to move is what lets it behave in response to stimuli.

FIGURE 27.2 The attack by a lioness activates the "flight" response in this kudu, helping it try to evade its predator.

The Function of Behavior

One way to look at an animal's behavior is to consider it as a kind of high-level homeostatic mechanism. Recall that homeostasis refers to the maintenance of constant internal conditions. Many animal behaviors are responses to stimuli—both internal and external—that affect an individual's well-being. For example, temperature receptors cause a lizard to move to a sunnier spot if it is too cold, or to a shadier spot if it becomes too warm. The lizard's body has an ideal temperature, and when its actual temperature differs from its ideal temperature, the lizard behaves in a way that returns its body to its ideal temperature.

VISUAL VOCAB

Kinesis is an increase in random movement.

Like a taxi that takes you directly from one location to another, **taxis** is a movement in a particular direction induced by a stimulus.

Kinesis and taxis are two simple types of movement-related behaviors that illustrate behavior's adaptive nature. Both behaviors cause an animal to go from a less desirable location to a more desirable location. **Kinesis** is an increase in random movement that lasts until a favorable environment is reached. For example, when a pill bug begins to dry out, its activity increases until it happens upon a moist area, after which its activity decreases again. **Taxis** is a movement in a specific direction, either toward or away from a stimulus. For example, *Euglena* are light-sensitive and will move toward a light source.

Like any trait, the way an animal behaves can vary from individual to individual. A kudu that waits too long to run may wind up being a lion's dinner, as shown in **FIGURE 27.2**. A male mockingbird with a weak repertoire of songs may not attract a mate. Animals with more successful behaviors tend to have more offspring. If the behaviors are heritable, their offspring will likely behave in similar ways. Just like any of an animal's characteristics, behaviors can evolve by natural selection.

Ⓐ **Analyze How is taxis or kinesis an example of the adaptive nature of behavior?**

***Connecting* CONCEPTS**

Plant Biology Plants also react to stimuli. Recall from **Chapter 22** that tropism is the movement of a plant in response to an environmental stimulus.

***Connecting* CONCEPTS**

Plant Biology Tropic responses in plants include those to light, gravity, and touch. Some plants can make rapid responses to stimuli, as does a Venus flytrap to the presence of an insect. Tell students that plants also exhibit taxis. Remind them of the sperm cells that must "swim" or make their way to an egg cell to fertilize it. That response has direction.

Vocabulary

Greek and Latin Word Origins Mention to students that the word **kinesis** is derived from the Greek word *kinein,* meaning "to move." Students may be familiar with the term in the context of **kinetic energy,** which is the energy of motion. Remind students that atoms generally move in a random manner.

Taxis, based on the Greek word *tassein,* means "arrangement." Taxis can be thought of as movement in an arranged direction in response to a stimulus. **Taxonomy,** the arrangement of organisms, and **taxidermy,** the arrangement of animal skin, are also based on *tassein.*

Answers

Ⓐ **Analyze** Both behaviors cause an animal to move from a less desirable location to a more desirable location, thus helping to maintain constant internal conditions. If such movements were not made, the animal might not survive.

BELOW LEVEL

Help students visualize the difference between kinesis and taxis. Tell them to imagine they are thirsty, but they are in a new school and do not know where the water fountains are located. Their search is similar to kinesis because they would follow a somewhat random path until they find the water fountain. Then tell students to imagine they are going to the refrigerator at home for a drink. Their movement is similar to taxis because they would move in a specific direction, toward the refrigerator.

PRE-AP

Have students address the question of whether behavior requires some form of nervous system to recognize a stimulus and produce a response. Ask students whether plants and sponges are capable of behavior.

Biology Toolkit, Quick-Write, p. C19

▼ Teach *continued*

ONLINE BIOLOGY To determine how male song sparrows respond to other males, use the virtual lab in Options for Inquiry on page 841.

Take It Further

Cyclic behavior is often complex and may involve the coordination of circadian rhythms with annual cycles. **White-crowned sparrows,** for example, migrate annually to their breeding grounds in the northern United States and Canada from their wintering grounds in the southern United States and Mexico. This migratory pattern is determined by the birds' sensitivity to day length.

The white-crowned sparrow's internal clock responds to photosensitive receptors in the brain, not in the eyes. Scientists learned this when blindfolding the birds did not disturb the birds' circadian rhythm. By altering the birds' light and dark cycles, the scientists further discovered that the birds have a **photosensitive period,** during which the brain must receive light for hormones to be released and gonads to develop properly.

In birds, the energy needed to carry the extra weight of reproductive structures year-round is too costly, so gonad development starts when day length starts to change. At the same time the gonads are developing, the birds become increasingly restless and gain as much as one-third of their body weight in fat. All of these events depend on the release of hormones, which is in turn mediated by the hypothalamus.

Answers

A Connect internal: biological clock, hunger; external: alarm clock, awakened by parent or sibling, sunlight

MAIN IDEA

Internal and external stimuli usually interact to trigger specific behaviors.

Some behaviors can be triggered by a single stimulus, but most behaviors occur in response to a variety of internal and external stimuli. For example, an external signal, such as a change in day length, might cause an animal to secrete specific hormones. These hormones act as internal signals that cause other physiological changes. These changes, in turn, make the animal more likely to respond to another external stimulus, such as the mating display of an individual of the opposite sex. This kind of interaction can be seen in the reproductive behavior of green anoles.

Green anoles are small lizards that live in the woodlands of the southeastern United States. During most of the year, female anoles ignore males. However, their behavior changes each spring, when males begin to aggressively guard territories and court females. Two external stimuli trigger the females' change in behavior. First, females must be exposed to long days and short nights. Females must also see reproductively active males.

To court females, males that are ready to mate bob their bodies up and down while extending their dewlap. The dewlap, shown in **FIGURE 27.3**, is a flap of bright red skin under the lizard's chin. Seeing the red dewlap during the spring makes females release sex hormones into their bloodstream. Sex hormones are an internal signal that make females reproductively receptive.

FIGURE 27.3 The extended red dewlap of this male green anole announces to females that it is ready to mate. The dewlap is also used in territorial defense as a "keep out" signal to other males.

Experiments with female anoles have shown that their reproductive behavior depends on the presence of both external and internal signals. Females that do not have sex hormones do not respond to courtship. And hormones are not released unless females are exposed to both external stimuli.

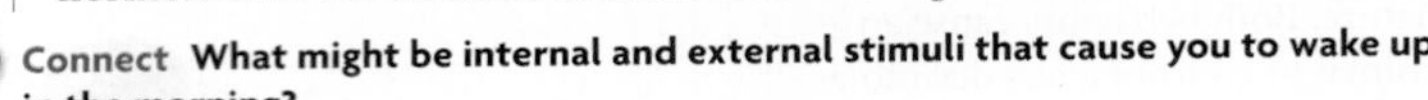

A Connect What might be internal and external stimuli that cause you to wake up in the morning?

MAIN IDEA

Some behaviors occur in cycles.

VOCABULARY

The term *circadian* comes from a combination of the Latin words *circa,* meaning "around," and *dies,* meaning "day."

Many environmental changes are predictable, especially those that occur on a daily, monthly, or yearly basis. Animals often use cues such as differences in day length to keep track of these changes, triggering adaptive changes in their behavior. For example, in order to be active during the day, your body requires a period of sleep every night. This daily pattern of activity and sleep is an example of a circadian rhythm. A **circadian rhythm** (suhr-KAY-dee-uhn) is the daily cycle of activity that occurs over a 24-hour period of time.

These activity patterns are controlled by an internal mechanism called a **biological clock.** Evidence indicates that an organism's biological clock is run by a combination of melatonin secretions by the pineal gland in the brain and proteins in the body that can detect changes in light.

Differentiated Instruction

TEACH WITH TECHNOLOGY

Students can access various online resources to follow the migrations of several species, such as monarch butterflies, sandhill cranes, Canada geese, or right whales. For more information on resources for migratory studies, visit **ClassZone.com.**

HANDS-ON ACTIVITY

Ask students to monitor their own circadian rhythms for several days. Tell them to record what time they wake up and go to bed, and times when they are most energetic, least energetic, most hungry, and least hungry. Have students compile their observations to see if a particular pattern emerges more often. For example, is there a particular time of day when most people experience high energy levels?

Hibernation

Hibernation is a behavior in which an animal avoids cold winter temperatures by entering into a dormant state. During hibernation, an animal, such as the dormouse shown in **FIGURE 27.4**, has a lower body temperature, reduced heartbeat, and a slowed breathing rate. Hibernating animals prepare for the winter by eating large amounts of food and storing it as fat. This layer of fat not only provides a food source for the animal but also provides additional insulation from the cold.

External factors such as light intensity and temperature determine when an animal enters and leaves hibernation. Shorter days and cooler temperatures cause animals to enter hibernation in the fall. In the spring, increasing day length and warmer temperatures cause the secretion of hormones that awaken the animal out of its dormant state.

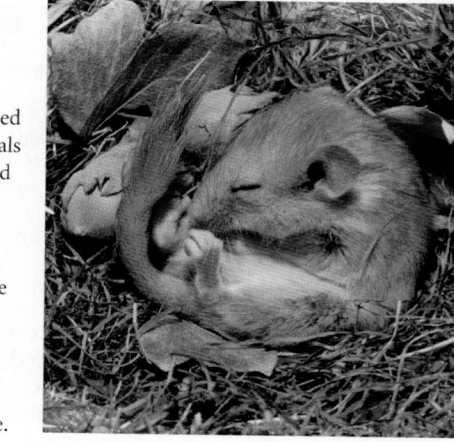

FIGURE 27.4 During hibernation, the dormouse's blood temperature drops from 36°C (97°F) to just above 0°C (32°F).

Migration

Many kinds of animals migrate, but you are probably most familiar with bird migration. If you've ever seen—or heard—a flock of geese flying southward during the fall, you've seen bird migration in action. Migratory Canada geese typically spend the spring and summer in Canada and the northern United States. They spend the winter in the southern United States and northern portions of Mexico. Like hibernation, migratory behavior allows animals to avoid harsh conditions in their home range for a part of the year.

Migration is set in motion by a variety of internal and external stimuli. A change in day length during the spring and fall stimulates a change in the portion of the bird's brain that controls hunger. This change causes birds to gain weight. An increase in fat storage is needed to fuel the bird's long-distance migration.

A Infer **How might climate change affect animal migration patterns?**

27.1 ASSESSMENT

ONLINE QUIZ ClassZone.com

REVIEWING MAIN IDEAS

1. Why are behavioral responses to **stimuli** considered to be adaptive?
2. What internal and external stimuli might signal to Alaskan caribou that it is time to migrate?
3. What is the connection between a **circadian rhythm** and the **biological clock**?

CRITICAL THINKING

4. **Analyze** What is the relationship between an animal's behavior and homeostasis?
5. **Predict** How might an animal's behavior be affected if its pineal gland is destroyed?

Connecting CONCEPTS

6. **Sexual Selection** A peacock uses its colorful train of feathers to attract a mate. What factors might control how large a peacock's train of feathers may grow to be?

27.1 ASSESSMENT

1. If a behavior necessary for survival does not result from a certain stimulus, the animal may not survive. Animals that do respond correctly to a stimulus have a greater chance of survival.
2. internal: hormonal changes; external: changes in day length or temperature
3. Circadian rhythms are the daily cycles of activity controlled by an internal mechanism, the biological clock.
4. An animal performs behaviors that maintain homeostasis.
5. Behaviors dependent on the changes in light would not be performed properly.
6. Factors may include how the size of the tail affects the male bird's fitness or movement. The female's preference for tail size is another factor.

Take It Further

Bears such as the **American black bear** (*Ursus americanus*) hibernate through the winter. Bears can go without food or water for more than three months and do not defecate, urinate, or exercise during this time. Nutrients are supplied by the breaking down of fat tissue that releases water and up to 4000 calories per day, and by muscle and organ tissues that supply protein. Bears sleep rolled into a tight ball, with their heads under their paws, and their backs to the cold. This keeps their head and torso warm, which allows them to wake up when disturbed.

The **Arctic ground squirrel** (*Spermophilus parryii*) is the only known mammal that can lower its body temperature below freezing when hibernating. These squirrels hibernate between seven to eight months a year and can lower their body temperature to as much as −3°C (27°F). With temperatures so low, they are said to be in a supercooled state. Every two to three weeks however, without waking up, the squirrels shiver in order to raise their body temperature back up to 36°C (98°F).

Answers

A Infer Colder temperatures might cause migration to begin earlier in the year.

Assess and Reteach

Assess Use the Online Quiz or Section Quiz (*Assessment Book*, p. 531).

Reteach Write the words *internal stimuli* and *external stimuli* on the board. Have students name as quickly as possible examples of each as you write them under the appropriate heading.

SECTION 27.2

▼ Plan and Prepare

Objectives

- Explain how internal and external stimuli trigger innate behaviors.
- Describe various behaviors that have both innate and learned components.
- Explain how various kinds of associative learning are adaptive.

Section Resources

Unit Resource Book Study Guide pp. 125–126 Power Notes p. 127 Reinforcement p. 128 Pre-AP Activity pp. 143–144
Interactive Reader Chapter 27 **Spanish Study Guide** pp. 275–276
Biology Toolkit pp. C3, C17, C20, C30, C33, C36
Technology Power Presentation 27.2 Media Gallery DVD Online Quiz 27.2

Activate Prior Knowledge Have students think about the behaviors they demonstrate in the course of an average day. **Ask,** What are some behaviors you have learned, and how are they adaptive? *Sample Answer:* learning to read and write, which enable you to get food (grocery shop or read a menu), have a job (to obtain food and shelter), or read a medicine label Discuss whether students think they have any instinctive behaviors.

27.2 Instinct and Learning

KEY CONCEPT Both genes and environment affect an animal's behavior.

MAIN IDEAS

- Innate behaviors are triggered by specific internal and external stimuli.
- Many behaviors have both innate and learned components.
- Learning is adaptive.

VOCABULARY

instinct, p. 822
innate, p. 822
releaser, p. 822
habituation, p. 823
imprinting, p. 824
imitation, p. 825
classical conditioning, p. 826
operant conditioning, p. 826

Connect Why are some families filled with good athletes? Is athleticism passed on from parent to child? Or are younger generations repeating behaviors they watched while they were growing up? You may have heard this "nature versus nurture" debate about many human behaviors, including musical ability, addiction, and thrill seeking. But research shows that genetic and environmental factors interact in most behaviors. "Nature versus nurture" is a false division. Most behaviors represent a mixture of both nature *and* nurture.

MAIN IDEA

Innate behaviors are triggered by specific internal and external stimuli.

Nothing teaches a spider to build a web. It builds it correctly the first time it tries. This kind of complex inborn behavior is called an **instinct.** Instinctive behavior is characterized as being innate and relatively inflexible. An **innate** behavior is performed correctly the first time an animal tries it, even when the animal has never been exposed to the stimulus that triggers the behavior. An inflexible behavior is performed in a similar way each time.

FIGURE 27.5 After hatching from its egg, a leatherback sea turtle hatchling instinctively makes its way to the ocean, where it will remain until maturity.

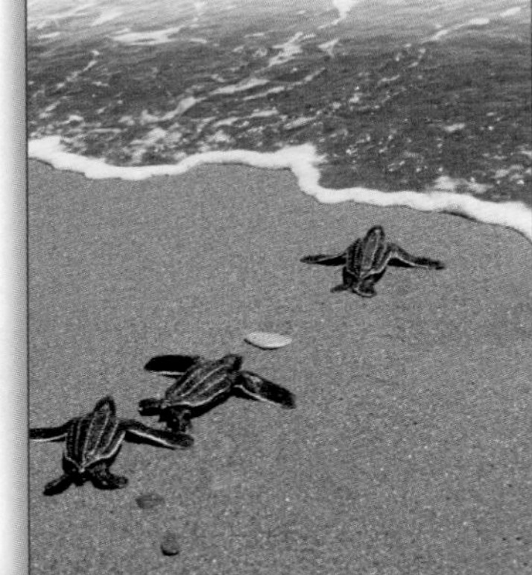

Instinctive behaviors are typically found where mistakes can have severe consequences. Baby mammals that do not suckle die of starvation. Newly hatched sea turtles, such as those shown in **FIGURE 27.5,** that do not race to the ocean will be eaten by predators. By having set reactions to particular stimuli, animals can automatically respond correctly in a life-or-death situation.

Instinctive behavior is especially important in newborns, who have had no time to learn any behaviors. Performing certain innate behaviors is key to both the animal's survival and its ability to pass its genes on to future generations. Animals that do not perform a necessary innate behavior will likely die.

Many innate behaviors are triggered by a simple signal. The signal is called a **releaser** because it makes the animal run through a behavior. Releasers can be any kind of stimulus: a visual sign, a sound, a scent, or a touch. When a releaser signal has been detected, the animal's nervous system triggers the expression of a specific behavior. Sometimes the triggered behavior is fixed, and the animal runs through a set sequence of movements each time the behavior is performed.

▼ Teach

Vocabulary

innate The literal translation of the word *innate* is "to be born in." Synonyms for the word include *hereditary* and *inborn*. In the text on page 823, the term *hard-wired* is used, which suggests that innate behaviors are "part of the equipment."

Differentiated Instruction

ENGLISH LEARNERS

Have small groups of students create a cause and effect chain showing how innate behaviors in animals are triggered by specific stimuli. It should include the following points: (1) A stimulus is presented. (2) The animal detects the releaser. (3) A sensory message is sent to the animal's brain. (4) The brain activates motor neurons that move the animal's muscles in a predictable pattern. Have students diagram three examples of cause and effect chains.

Biology Toolkit, Cause and Effect Chain, p. C36

PRE-AP

Provide students a list of statements before they read the section, and have them indicate whether they are true of false. Then have them reassess their responses once they have read the material. For example: (1) Humans do not rely on instinctive behaviors. F (2) Innate behaviors are inherited. T (3) Habituation results from imprinting. F (4) Imprinting is an instinctive behavior. T (5) Conditioning is not considered learning because an animal is forced to make an association. F

Biology Toolkit, Anticipation Guide, p. C3

Dutch zoologist Niko Tinbergen's experiments with herring gulls showed how simple releasers can be. Hungry herring gull chicks will peck at a red spot at the tip of a parent's bill. The parent usually responds by coughing up a bit of half-digested fish for the chick to eat. Very young chicks do not actually recognize their parent when they beg for food. Instead, the behavior is triggered simply by the sight of a long bill with a red dot near its tip. The chicks will beg from any long object with a red dot, including cardboard cutouts of a herring gull head and the end of a painted stick. Other gull species, such as the lesser black-backed gull shown in **FIGURE 27.6**, also have red-dotted bills.

FIGURE 27.6 Some gull species, such as this lesser black-backed gull, have a red-dotted bill. The red dot is the releaser that causes the gull chick to beg for food.

Biologists think that innate behaviors are hard-wired into an animal's nervous system, but they have studied the details for only a few invertebrate species. Innate behaviors are heritable and are strongly affected by gene expression. But they can also be changed by environmental factors. For example, during its lifetime, a honeybee moves through a sequence of innate behaviors that help to maintain the hive. The behaviors are regulated by different sets of genes. As a bee ages, its brain cells express different genes and its behavior changes. But gene expression is also affected by the hive's social environment. If a hive has few older foragers, some of the younger bees will mature faster. Even the bill-pecking behavior of gulls has been shown to improve with age, as young herring gulls become more accurate in their ability to aim their pecks at the red spot on their parent's bill.

A **Apply** **Why is behavior considered to be a mixture of both nature and nurture?**

MAIN IDEA

Many behaviors have both innate and learned components.

Animals often change their behavior as they gain real-world experience. In other words, animals learn. Learning takes many forms, ranging from simple changes in an innate behavior to problem-solving in new situations. In each case, learning involves the strengthening of nerve pathways. Most animal behaviors are not simple reactions to stimuli using preset pathways in the animal's brain. Instead, they represent a combination of innate tendencies influenced by learning and experience.

Connecting **CONCEPTS**

Brain Chemistry Research indicates that during learning, some neurons undergo structural and molecular changes that allow for the easier flow of information. You will learn more about the structure and function of neurons in **Chapter 29**.

Habituation

Garden shops sell plastic owls that are supposed to frighten away birds. But a gardener who doesn't move the owls every few days may soon see birds sitting on top of them. This is an example of habituation. **Habituation** occurs when an animal's behavioral response decreases due to a repeated stimulus, even if it has features that trigger innate behaviors. The habit of seeing owls in the exact same place in the garden every day causes the birds to get used to, and basically ignore, the stimulus.

The Inside Story

In his autobiography, zoologist **Nikolaas Tinbergen** shares with humor the story of his early days wandering the shores of his native Holland. He recounts his boyhood preference for camping and bird watching over academics. He developed a keen ability to observe detail by watching the behavior of sticklebacks in a backyard aquarium. Tinbergen scraped through school, married, and started a family. He met Konrad Lorenz at a 1936 symposium on instinct and says in his autobiography, "We clicked at once." Shortly thereafter, Tinbergen became Lorenz's student.

They developed a lifelong friendship and collaboration on animal behavior. Tinbergen published numerous books and scholarly articles on behavior, including *The Herring Gull's World* in 1953. He was awarded the Nobel Prize in 1973 along with his colleagues Karl von Frisch and Konrad Lorenz. The three men were acknowledged as the principal architects of a new science, called **ethology,** which is the systematic study of the behavior of animals in their natural habitats.

BELOW LEVEL

Write the words *instinct* and *learning* on the board. Have students call out as many of the terms that relate to these concepts as they can while you construct a cluster diagram. Have students refer to the cluster diagram as they read the section together in groups.

Biology Toolkit, Cluster Diagram, p. C30

Take It Further

Gull colonies are noisy places that can contain thousands of breeding pairs and their chicks. Nests may be only a few inches apart. It is incumbent upon the chicks to remain close to their own nest, as gulls are extremely aggressive when breeding and are known to kill chicks that wander. Chicks recognize their parents by their vocalizations, which include several kinds of calls. Parents raise the chicks together, taking turns to bring back fish, which they regurgitate for the chicks. As one parent lands at the nest when returning from a fishing expedition, it emits several calls. The other parent takes off, and the chicks run toward the sound of their parent's voice for the meal they know has arrived.

Answers

A **Apply** Both genetic and environmental factors interact in most behaviors.

▼ Teach *continued*

QUICK LAB

Time 15 minutes TEACHER TESTED

Lab Binder Animals, pp. 75–76

Purpose Observe and collect data on a selected human behavior.

LAB MANAGEMENT

- You may wish to give students a few minutes during class to collect data.

Answers

Analyze and Conclude

1. Answers will vary, but should be quantitative. For the suggested study, people may sit in evenly spaced clumps.
2. Answers will vary, but hypotheses should be testable. Possible hypothesis: If people establish territories, they will sit a certain distance apart and in a certain place.
3. Answers will vary, but should include clearly defined dependent and independent variables and a way to measure them.

The Inside Story

In his autobiography, **Konrad Lorenz** recalls a favorite childhood story about the adventures of Nils Holgersson who travels all over Sweden on the back of a goose. Lorenz wanted a goose of his own, but instead settled for pet ducks. Lorenz says, "I discovered imprinting and was imprinted myself." Lorenz wanted to study zoology, but his father convinced him to study medicine.

During World War II, Lorenz served as a psychiatrist in the German army. He was captured by the Russians and began writing a book on epistemology (study of knowledge) to pass the time. After he was released, he received an unsalaried position at a research station in his native Austria. Eventually, Lorenz went to work at the Max Planck Institute in Germany, where he did ethological research until his retirement from the institute in 1973, the same year he won the Nobel Prize.

QUICK LAB **OBSERVING**

Human Behavior

Have you ever wondered what might explain a particular kind of behavior you observe in people? In this lab, you will observe some aspect of human behavior and form a hypothesis that explains the behavior.

PROBLEM What is the behavior of people in certain situations?

MATERIALS
- paper
- pencil

PROCEDURE

1. Choose a question that you have about human behavior that can be answered by observing people. For instance, you could ask, "Where do people sit in a cafeteria?"
2. Determine which behavior you will observe.
3. Determine how you will quantitatively measure the behavior. For example, you may record how many people are in the cafeteria, where people are sitting, and the number of full, partially full, and empty tables.
4. Make your observations and record your data.

ANALYZE AND CONCLUDE

1. **Analyze** Present your results in a table or graph. What can you conclude?
2. **Hypothesize** Form a hypothesis that could explain the behavior pattern you saw.
3. **Extend** Create an experiment to test your hypothesis.

Imprinting

Imprinting is a rapid and irreversible learning process that only occurs during a short time in an animal's life. During this critical period the animal may, for example, learn to identify its parents, its siblings, its offspring, characteristics of its own species, or the place it was born.

Austrian zoologist Konrad Lorenz's studies with graylag geese are among the most famous studies of imprinting. Newly hatched graylag geese normally imprint on their mother during the first two days after hatching. After this period, the goslings will follow their mother and eventually grow up to mate with other graylag geese. Lorenz divided a clutch of goose eggs in half, leaving some with the mother and raising the rest himself. The goslings that stayed with their mother behaved normally. Their siblings, which stayed with Lorenz during their critical period, did not recognize other geese as members of their own species. They followed Lorenz as goslings, and tried to mate with humans when they matured. This experiment showed that imprinting is an innate and automatic process, even though the behavior's stimulus is learned.

FIGURE 27.7 To avoid having cranes imprint on their human handlers, biologists use puppets painted to resemble the head of an adult crane to feed young birds raised in captivity.

When working to reintroduce species into the wild, it is important to avoid having the animals imprint on their human handlers. For example, when working with endangered wattled cranes, scientists try to minimize the birds' contact with humans. When humans need to interact with the cranes, they wear costumes that cover their entire bodies. They use puppets painted to look like adult cranes to feed the young, as shown in **FIGURE 27.7**.

Differentiated Instruction

PRE-AP

Have students summarize the experimental evidence for imprinting using a two-column chart labeled *Hypothesis-Experiment*. In the left column, have them formulate the hypothesis. In the right column, have them identify the variables and controls as well as the researcher's observations on which the conclusion was based.

Biology Toolkit, Two-Column Notes, p. C20

ENGLISH LEARNERS

Ask students to illustrate Lorenz's experiments on imprinting in a cartoon format. Have them include several frames in their cartoons. For example, the first frame could show a goose sitting on a nest. The second frame could show an egg hatching. The third frame could show the gosling seeing a human, and so on.

Biology Toolkit, Connect to Content through Visuals, p. C17

Imitation

In **imitation,** animals learn by observing the behaviors of other animals. The initial behavior becomes a model that the other animals try to copy. Young male songbirds learn to sing by listening to adult males and trying to repeat what they hear. By trial and error, over time they begin to sing the species-specific song they heard from adults. Human babies also imitate adults in a number of ways, such as when they learn to speak their native language.

Not all imitative behaviors are passed from adult to younger animals, however. For example, consider the potato washing behavior among Japanese macaques, or snow monkeys, shown in **FIGURE 27.8.** A juvenile female monkey, named Imo by researchers, discovered that it was easier to wash sand off a potato by dipping it in water rather than by brushing it off with her hands. At first, only her brothers and sisters imitated the behavior, followed by her mother. Over a period of time, a number of individuals in the troop adopted the potato washing behavior.

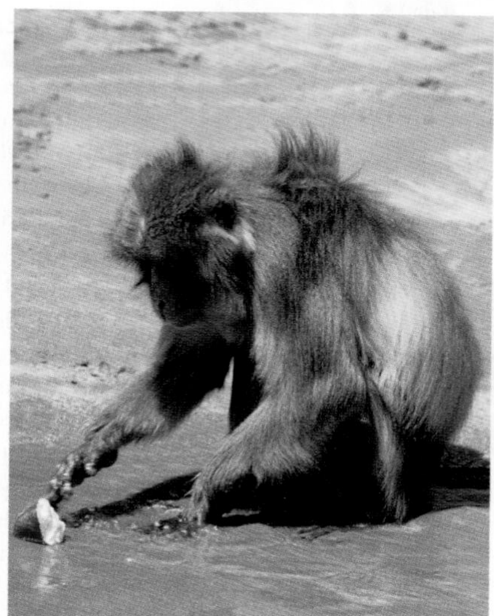

FIGURE 27.8 Snow monkeys learn to wash their potatoes before eating them by imitating the behavior of other individuals.

A Infer What would be the harm of having a captive animal intended for release imprint on its human handlers?

MAIN IDEA

Learning is adaptive.

Animals that are able to learn can modify, or change, their behavior to better adapt to new situations. This ability to learn can give animals an edge in survival and reproduction, allowing them to pass their genes on to future generations.

Associative Learning

In associative learning, an animal learns to associate a specific action with its consequences. For example, an experiment with young blue jays showed that the birds do not identify prey instinctively. Instead, they ate every new insect that was offered to them. Insects that tasted good, such as grasshoppers, they ate again and again. But it only took one experience with a bad-tasting monarch butterfly to make the jays avoid them for the rest of their lives. The jays learned to associate the monarch's distinctive orange and black markings with its bad taste. Such trial-and-error learning can help animals to survive within their environments.

One type of associative learning studied by animal behavior scientists is conditioning. Conditioning is a way to modify an animal's behavior in response to certain stimuli. When teaching an animal by conditioning, two stimuli are paired together, and an animal is conditioned to give a specific response to these stimuli. The two main types of conditioning are called classical conditioning and operant conditioning.

History of Science

The study of **animal behavior** has a long history.

- Aristotle's anecdotal observations led him to conclude that nonhuman animals are motivated by things such as revenge.
- Charles Darwin in 1859 revolutionized the study of behavior when he proposed that natural selection acts on heritable behaviors; that is, animals already possessing the behavior pass along that behavior to their offspring.
- C. L. Morgan in 1903 stated that we cannot attribute higher-order thinking to a behavior if a more basic explanation will suffice.
- Ivan Pavlov in 1903 presented his paper on the conditioned response.
- Edward Thorndike in 1905 studied animal behavior by using a systematic, empirical methodology.
- Karl von Frisch is best known for his study of bees. He found that bees perform round dances and waggle dances to communicate the presence, distance, and direction of food.
- B. F. Skinner in 1938 published *The Behavior of Organisms* and developed his theory of operant conditioning.

Answers

A Infer A captive animal would not recognize members of its same species upon release, mating would be affected, and the animal would be dependent on humans for food and other resources.

BELOW LEVEL

Have student make Venn diagrams to compare classical and operant conditioning. Their diagrams could include the following:

- classical—original stimulus, neutral stimulus, conditioned response to neutral stimulus
- operant—random behavior, positive or negative reinforcement, reinforced behavior
- area of overlap—associative learning, behavior modified by associating stimuli with response

Biology Toolkit, Venn Diagram, p. C33

HANDS-ON ACTIVITY

If you have an aquarium, you can do a simple experiment in classical conditioning. Before you feed the fish, gently tap on the glass. After several trials, you should be able to tap on the glass and have the fish respond by swimming to the surface to be fed. **Ask**

- What is the neutral stimulus? tapping on the glass
- What is the conditioned response? swimming to the surface when you tap on the glass

▼ Teach *continued*

The Inside Story

While **Ivan Pavlov** is credited with the process of classical conditioning, it was not originally his idea. **Aristotle** came up with the idea first, except that he focused on thoughts instead of observable behaviors. Pavlov was not even the first to conduct research on classical conditioning. In 1902, **E. B. Twitmeyer,** a graduate student at the University of Pennsylvania, wrote his dissertation on the conditioning of a reflexive response. Since Twitmeyer was not yet a prominent scientist, other scientists were not interested in his research.

Answers

A Apply When the dog correctly performs the trick, a treat such as a food reward could be given to the dog so that it associates something positive with the behavior.

"AND THEN INSTEAD OF FEEDING ME HE WOULD RING A LITTLE BELL."
Source: CartoonStock.com

FIGURE 27.9 Teaching a pet a trick, such as how to shake, often involves giving it a reward after it performs the correct behavior.

Classical Conditioning

Classical conditioning is a process in which an animal learns to associate a previously neutral stimulus with a behavior that was once triggered by a different stimulus. Ivan Pavlov, a Russian physiologist, was studying digestion in dogs when he realized that salivation, or drooling, is an automatic behavior. Pavlov created an experiment to determine if external stimuli are involved in this behavior.

- Normally, the presence of food makes a dog salivate.
- A bell is rung when food is presented to the dog.
- The dog salivates because of the presence of the food.
- After constantly being presented with both food and the ringing bell at the same time, when only the bell is rung, the dog salivates even though the food is not present.

In this experiment, the ringing bell is initially a neutral stimulus. The response in which the dog salivates upon hearing the ringing bell is the conditioned response. Because the dog was given food at the same time the bell rang, the dog has been conditioned to salivate when the bell is rung because it also expects to be given food.

Operant Conditioning

Operant conditioning is a process in which the likelihood of a specific behavior is increased by reinforcement. In positive reinforcement, such as a food reward as shown in **FIGURE 27.9,** a reward is given to increase a behavior. Negative reinforcement is the removal of a negative or aversive stimulus to increase a behavior.

B. F. Skinner, an American psychologist, created "Skinner boxes" to study operant conditioning. A Skinner box is a cage that has a bar or pedal on one wall. When an animal such as a rat pushes down on the bar, a food pellet pops out. The rat then associates the behavior of pressing the bar with the food reward, even if not rewarded every time. If the behavior is no longer rewarded, the rat will, over time, stop performing it.

A Apply How might you train a dog to do a trick using positive reinforcement?

▼ Assess and Reteach

Assess Use the Online Quiz or Section Quiz (*Assessment Book*, p. 532).

Reteach Write the vocabulary terms for the section on the board. Have student groups brainstorm as many examples for each term as they can in five minutes and then share their responses with the class.

27.2 ASSESSMENT

ONLINE QUIZ ClassZone.com

REVIEWING MAIN IDEAS

1. What is the difference between an **instinct** and a learned behavior?
2. Describe a behavior that you learned by **imitation.**
3. Using either **classical** or **operant conditioning** as an example, explain how learning can be adaptive.

CRITICAL THINKING

4. **Apply** Ducklings that are shown a paper silhouette of a hawk initially freeze and cower. After repeated exposure to the silhouette they stop responding. What is this lack of response called?
5. **Summarize** What is the connection between neurons in the brain and learning?

***Connecting* CONCEPTS**

6. **Evolution** Monarch butterflies are toxic. Viceroy butterflies, which look like monarch butterflies, are not toxic, but birds avoid them anyway. Explain how the bird behavior described in this section could have influenced the evolution of viceroys.

27.2 ASSESSMENT

1. A learned behavior is a behavior the animal must be taught how to complete. An instinct is innate. It is a behavior the animal is able to complete on its own without being taught how to do it.
2. Answers may include tying shoes, learning to speak, and learning a sport.
3. Animals that can learn are able to modify their behavior in order to adapt to new situations. In operant conditioning, the animal learns to perform a certain behavior in order to receive a reward or avoid punishment.
4. habituation
5. Research indicates that during learning, some neurons undergo structural and molecular changes that allow for the easier flow of information.
6. When a bird eats an unpalatable insect, it learns to associate the insect's appearance with the bad taste. Palatable insects that look like the bad-tasting one will also be avoided. This behavior selects for insects that mimic the appearance of the poisonous insect.

27.3 Evolution of Behavior

KEY CONCEPT Every behavior has costs and benefits.

MAIN IDEAS
- Even beneficial behaviors have associated costs.
- Animals perform behaviors whose benefits outweigh their costs.

VOCABULARY
survivorship, p. 827
territoriality, p. 828
optimal foraging, p. 829

Connect The zebra was very thirsty. It flicked his ears to and fro as it walked toward the water hole, listening carefully for any sign of a hungry lioness. Nothing looked out of the ordinary. But as it neared the edge of the water, it saw a crocodile lurking in the shallows. The zebra quickly retreated and trotted back to its herd. It needed water, but the risk to its life was too great.

MAIN IDEA

Even beneficial behaviors have associated costs.

Every behavior has benefits and costs. Shorebirds travel thousands of miles during their spring and fall migrations, burning through an enormous amount of energy in the process. But migration increases a bird's chances of survival by escaping from cold seasonal temperatures to warmer locations.

Benefits of Behavior

From an evolutionary standpoint, the most important benefits of a behavior include increased survivorship and reproduction rates. **Survivorship** refers to the number of individuals that survive from one year to the next. Certain behaviors reduce the chance that an animal will die in a given time period. Similarly, some behaviors increase the number of offspring that an animal will have during its lifetime.

Behaviors that increase an individual's survival or reproduction are behaviors that increase its fitness. These behaviors will be favored by natural selection, but they still have associated costs. For instance, when a sea star touches a sea anemone called *Stomphia,* the anemone stops feeding, wrenches free of the sea bottom, and swims away. Escape behaviors such as this are expensive in terms of energy in the short term. The animal stops eating and uses up stored energy. But dead animals cannot reproduce. The long-term benefit of the behavior is the increase in the animal's survival and reproduction rates.

FIGURE 27.10 These male Siberian tigers are very territorial. Fights over territory can lead to serious injury or even death.

Costs of Behavior

Behavioral costs can be broken down into three basic categories.

Energy costs Every animal behavior, such as running away from a predator, uses up ATP. When an animal uses metabolic energy for one behavior, such as searching for a mate, that energy is not available for other needs, such as searching for food.

Differentiated Instruction

ENGLISH LEARNERS

Before reading the section, have students do a think-pair-share activity. Ask a question, give individual students a chance to think about it, have students pair up to compare their answers, and ask them to share a final answer with the whole class. Possible questions: What are the three categories of behavior costs? What is territoriality and its consequences? What is optimal foraging?

Biology Toolkit, Think-Pair-Share, p. C13

Plan and Prepare

Objectives

- Explain what is meant by the costs and benefits of behavior.
- Describe several behaviors in terms of their costs and benefits.

Section Resources

Unit Resource Book
Study Guide pp. 129–130 Power Notes p. 131 Reinforcement p. 132
Interactive Reader Chapter 27 **Spanish Study Guide** pp. 277–278
Biology Toolkit pp. C13, C20
Technology Power Presentation 27.3 Media Gallery DVD Online Quiz 27.3

Activate Prior Knowledge Have students participate in cost-benefit analysis. **Ask**
- Is it worth spending $1000 for a used CD? Most students will say no.
- Is it worth spending $1000 for a used car? Many students will say yes.

Discuss the difference between the two examples. Point out that biologists consider cost-benefit analysis to be an important tool in determining why animals engage in certain behaviors.

Teach

ONLINE BIOLOGY To evaluate the energy costs of certain behaviors, use the Animated Biology in Options for Inquiry on page 841.

Vocabulary

Academic Vocabulary The technique of **cost-benefit analysis** is used in business to compare the total expected costs of given activities against the total expected benefits. The goal is to choose the best or most profitable option.

▼ Teach *continued*

TEACH FROM VISUALS

FIGURE 27.11 Draw students' attention to the size disparity between the male and female spider. It is not uncommon for males and females of a species to be different sizes. **Ask,** What is an advantage of a female being larger than the male? It allows her to produce large numbers of eggs. Other examples in which females are larger than males include many species of turtles, birds, and insects.

Take It Further

The size and distribution of **territories** vary greatly among species. For example, song sparrows have relatively small territories with no overlap. The birds have access to lookout posts and can patrol the territory by flying quickly from post to post. Mammals, on the other hand, are larger and less mobile. So it is energetically more costly for them to patrol an area, and they tend to have overlapping home ranges.

In addition to benefiting the individual that controls the territory, territoriality benefits populations. When resources are scarce, individuals that are less fit, and therefore less successful at competing for the resources, will die. Thus, territoriality serves to cull the population and keep it healthy.

Answers

A Analyze Answers will vary. Possible benefits: escape harsh conditions of one habitat for another, more temperate location; provides access to greater genetic diversity. Possible costs: migration can lead to death due to predation along the migratory path; high energy cost in flying to another location.

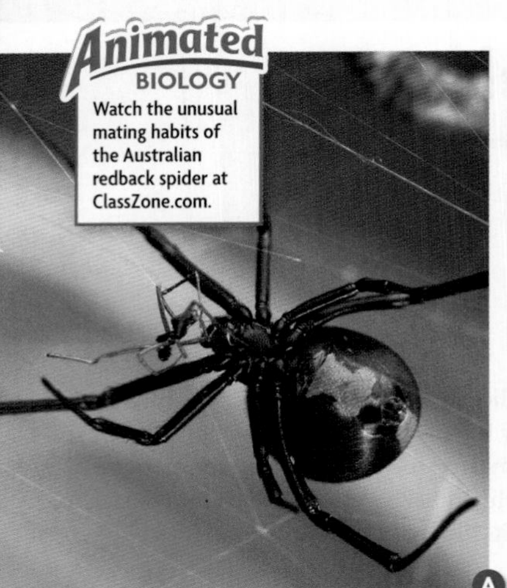

Animated BIOLOGY
Watch the unusual mating habits of the Australian redback spider at ClassZone.com.

FIGURE 27.11 While mating with the female, the smaller male Australian redback spider somersaults directly over the female's mouth, offering himself as her next meal.

Opportunity costs Every animal behavior takes time. When an animal spends time doing one behavior, it loses the opportunity to do a different behavior. For example, when a songbird defends its territory from rivals, it is using time that could have been spent eating or mating.

Risk costs Many behaviors expose an individual to possible injury or death. All animals have to look for food, but foraging also increases the chance that an animal will meet a predator. In many species, males risk injury by fighting for access to females during the breeding season.

Some behaviors that seem harmful may have surprising benefits for an animal. For example, while most male spiders go to great lengths to avoid getting eaten by their mates, a male Australian redback spider deliberately flips his abdomen over the female's mouth, as shown in **FIGURE 27.11.** As they mate, she literally eats him alive. His behavior clearly does not increase his survival. But because it lets him fertilize more of her eggs, it has the benefit of increasing his reproductive success.

A Analyze **What is the benefit of bird migration? The cost?**

MAIN IDEA

Animals perform behaviors whose benefits outweigh their costs.

It is difficult to determine if animals make conscious decisions about their actions. Whether behavioral responses are automatic or reflect more complex cognitive processes, they evolve only if they improve the fitness of those individuals that perform them. Territoriality and optimal foraging are just two examples that demonstrate how animal behaviors are expressed if their benefits outweigh their costs.

Connecting CONCEPTS

Competition Recall from **Chapter 14** that competition occurs when two organisms fight for the same limited resources. Interspecific competition occurs when members of different species fight for access to resources. Intraspecific competition is the fight for resources between members of the same species.

Territoriality

Territoriality refers to the control of a specific area—or territory—by one or more individuals of an animal species. The benefit of territorial behavior is the ability to control the resources within the animal's territory, such as food or access to potential mates. The costs associated with territorial behavior include the energy and time that could have been used for feeding or mating. That time is instead spent protecting territory from invasion by other animals.

Consider the territorial behavior of the Hawaiian honeycreeper. This bird feeds on the nectar of flowers, and it defends a territory that has the flowers from which it feeds. The benefit of holding a territory can be measured in the amount of nectar the bird can get from the flowers located in its territory. An individual should only defend a territory if that territory holds enough flowers to provide the food it needs to at least offset the energy cost of defense. Studies of honeycreeper behavior have shown that individuals stop defending territories when the number of flowers falls below a certain minimum or exceeds a certain maximum number. Individuals only defend a territory in which there is a benefit from excluding other individuals, and in which the energy benefit from the nectar outweighs the energy cost of the defensive behavior.

Differentiated Instruction

PRE-AP

Ask students to select a behavior and do a cost-benefit analysis. For example, they could analyze the costs and benefits to a mixed flock of birds at a feeder. Possible costs include competition for the food at the feeder or being more visible to predators. Possible benefits include more eyes to search for predators or access to a concentrated food source.

Biology Toolkit, T-Chart, p. C20

TEACH WITH TECHNOLOGY

If you have GPS equipment, students can map bird territories. Select a bird that is visible, easy to follow, and has a territory on or near the school grounds. Have students follow the bird as it moves from singing post to singing post. Tell students to enter the coordinates at each post. When students are done, they can use their coordinates to estimate the size of the territory. With enough data, students may be able to compare territories of different individuals and species.

Optimal Foraging

When animals search for food, they must make decisions about what they should eat. The benefits of foraging are measured in the amount of energy gained. The costs of foraging include the energy used to search for, catch, and eat food; the risk of capture by a predator while foraging; and the loss of time to spend on other activities. The theory of **optimal foraging** states that natural selection should favor behaviors that get animals the most, or optimal amount of, calories for the cost.

The foraging methods of oystercatchers, a type of shorebird shown in **FIGURE 27.12**, have been the subject of many studies. As the birds' name suggests, they eat bivalves such as oysters and mussels. Some birds sneak up on relaxed bivalves and quickly stab out the meat. Others use their chisel-shaped beak to hammer a hole through the shells.

FIGURE 27.12 The oystercatcher uses its long, sharp beak to break open the shells of bivalves such as oysters.

Hammering oystercatchers get a benefit from eating the mollusks, but at the cost of the time and energy it takes to break open their shells. Small mussels are easy to open, but don't contain much meat. Larger mussels are meatier but harder to open. Scientists first hypothesized that oystercatchers would prefer to eat the largest mussels they could find. These mussels contained the most meat for the time the birds spent opening them.

When the biologists observed oystercatchers in the wild, they found that the birds did not eat the largest mussels they could find. Their experiment showed that there was another cost to eating mussels. Their first model assumed that the birds could open any mussel given enough time. However, their experiment showed them that the birds also faced a "handling cost" when they hunted. Birds that picked very large mussels lost time handling bivalves they could not open. They actually got less meat on average than birds that ate smaller mussels. Oystercatchers that learn to hunt medium-sized mussels get the most food for their efforts. Better-fed birds have higher survivorship and their chicks, in turn, learn this behavior.

A Apply **How does optimal foraging improve an individual's overall fitness?**

27.3 ASSESSMENT

ONLINE QUIZ ClassZone.com

REVIEWING MAIN IDEAS

1. Compare the three categories of behavior costs.
2. Any animal behavior has a cost and a benefit. Explain this statement using **optimal foraging** as an example.

CRITICAL THINKING

3. **Infer** What might be a stimulus that triggers a songbird's **territorial** behaviors?
4. **Analyze** Some species of cichlid fish hold their fertilized eggs inside their mouths until they hatch. What might be the costs and benefits of this behavior?

***Connecting* CONCEPTS**

5. **Scientific Process** Some spiders build webs that include visible zigzag lines of silk. But more visible webs catch fewer insects than do less visible webs. Hypothesize what benefits the spider gets by building such a visible web.

TEACH FROM VISUALS

FIGURE 27.12 Have students examine the oystercatcher's beak. **Ask,** How is the shape of the beak adapted for opening bivalves? It is long, thin, and sharp, which allows it to break the shells and pry them open.

Vocabulary

Word Origins The Indo-European prefix *op-* is associated with wealth, as in **opulent.** In the words **optimum** and **optimal,** the meaning changes to one of favorable or most desirable outcomes.

Answers

A **Apply** Optimal foraging improves an individual's overall fitness by ensuring that the animal gets the most calories for the least amount of energy spent in obtaining the food item.

Assess and Reteach ▼

Assess Use the Online Quiz or Section Quiz (*Assessment Book,* p. 533).

Reteach Have student groups each write three quiz questions for the section. Then have students switch with another group and answer the questions each has written. Continue until all groups have quizzed one another.

27.3 ASSESSMENT

1. Energy costs are those that use up metabolic energy that cannot be regained. Opportunity costs refer to the time the animal loses in performing a certain behavior over another. Risk costs refer to the harm to which an animal may expose itself in conducting a certain behavior.
2. *Sample Answer:* A groundhog leaves its burrow to forage. Benefit of the behavior is energy gained from food. Cost of the behavior is exposure to predators and lost opportunity to pursue other behaviors.
3. The sight of another songbird or hearing another songbird's song.
4. They cannot eat while they are brooding eggs, so the behavior has an energetic cost. A benefit of the behavior is that the eggs are protected from predation, so there is a greater chance that the parent's genes will be passed on to future generations.
5. Possible hypotheses: Webs are an enormous investment in protein. The visible lines keep larger animals from crashing into the web and destroying it. The lines help hide the spider from potential predators.

INVESTIGATION

Time 60 minutes TEACHER TESTED
Teacher Preparation
Student Difficulty
Lab Binder Animals, pp. 67–69

Purpose Develop an ethogram.

Overview Students will observe an animal's behavior for one hour. They will

- record the order in which behaviors occur, the number of times a behavior occurs, and the duration of the behavior each time it occurs
- make a bar graph of behaviors
- analyze the behaviors

LAB PREPARATION

- A video of an animal provides an alternative to watching a live animal.

LAB MANAGEMENT

- Because observations take at least one hour and students can choose an animal to observe, you may need to assign the observational portion of this lab as homework.

Teacher Note "The lab produces excellent data and graphs."

POST-LAB DISCUSSION

Discuss results. **Ask**

- What variables could affect the results you observed? species, animal's age, time of day
- How would you expect these variables to affect behavior? Species will affect what behaviors the animal performs. For example, cats may use scratching posts, while dogs may gnaw on rawhide. Age will affect how much an animal eats, sleeps, and plays. Time of day will affect sleeping behavior.

MATERIALS

- pet or classroom animal
- watch
- calculator
- graph paper
- ruler

PROCESS SKILLS

- **Observing**
- **Graphing Data**

NOS.3 Clearly communicate their ideas and results of investigations verbally and in written form using tables, graphs, diagrams, and photographs.

Using an Ethogram to Describe Animal Behavior

An ethogram is a catalog of the types of behaviors an animal may perform. For example, in a 24-hour period, male and female chimpanzees may display behaviors such as hunting, eating, sleeping, grooming, caring for young, and defending territory. After making initial observations, a scientist might make further observations and collect data to create a time budget of the observed behaviors. The time budget shows how much time individuals spend in each type of behavior. Among other uses, data from a time budget can be used to compare behavior patterns between males and females of the same species or members of different species. In this investigation, you will create an ethogram by observing an animal of your choice.

Jane Goodall's studies with chimpanzees involved many long hours in the field observing behavior.

PROBLEM How much time do animals spend on specific behaviors?

PROCEDURE

1. Decide which animal you are going to study.
2. You must be able to observe active animal behavior for at least one hour. Conceal yourself so your presence does not influence its behaviors. For example, your family pet may respond to your presence and want attention.
3. Predict what types of behaviors the animal will engage in, and create a table to record your data. For example, behaviors might include sleeping, eating, or playing.
4. Observe your animal for at least one hour. Record the specific behaviors of the animal, the order in which the animal carries out those behaviors, the number of times the behavior occurs, and the length of time of each behavior. **Caution:** If the animal you are observing becomes agitated, stop observing it.

ANALYZE AND CONCLUDE

1. **Categorize** Make a list of the most common behaviors that your animal carried out. Was each behavior isolated, or were some behaviors carried out in a specific order? Explain.
2. **Graph Data** Determine the percentage of the total time spent in each behavior. Make a bar graph from the data.
3. **Analyze** Use your bar graph to determine which behavior was the most frequent. Which behavior was least frequent? Explain.

830 Unit 8: Animals

Answers

Expected Results

Each student should produce a log, written description of behaviors, and a bar graph of the frequency of behaviors. Answers to each question will vary depending on the animal chosen. For sample data, go to page R107.

Analyze and Conclude

1. Answers will vary. The most common behavior may be sleeping/resting. Students may find that some behaviors are carried out in a specific order; for example, cats groom after they eat.
2. Answers will vary. Make sure students calculate percents by using the time for each behavior divided by total time. The total should add up to 100 percent. Bar graphs should show percent of time spent in each behavior, with behaviors on the x-axis and time in percents on the y-axis.
3. Answers will vary. The most frequent behavior may be sleeping/resting. The least frequent may be eating, urinating, or defecating.

27.4 Social Behavior

KEY CONCEPT Social behaviors enhance the benefits of living in a group.

MAIN IDEAS

- Living in groups also has benefits and costs.
- Social behaviors are interactions between members of the same or different species.
- Some behaviors benefit other group members at a cost to the individual performing them.
- Eusocial behavior is an example of extreme altruism.

VOCABULARY

pheromone, p. 832
altruism, p. 833
inclusive fitness, p. 834
kin selection, p. 834
eusocial, p. 834

Connect Many factors determine if a species lives alone or in a group. Even closely related species have different living patterns. Such is the case with marmots. Woodchucks (*Marmota monax*), found in the eastern United States, live alone. Yellow-bellied marmots (*Marmota flaviventris*), which live out west, live in colonies.

MAIN IDEA

Living in groups also has benefits and costs.

TAKING NOTES

Use a two-column chart to take notes on the costs and benefits of social behavior.

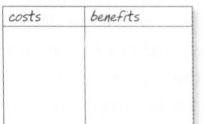

costs	benefits

Some species, such as the emperor penguins shown in **FIGURE 27.13**, live together in groups. These groups may have a definite social structure or they may have a constantly changing membership. Social behaviors evolve in species in which the benefits of group living outweigh its costs.

Benefits of Social Behavior

Living in a social group provides significant benefits to individuals within the group. Living in a group may lead to improved foraging, as an individual can follow other members of the group to good feeding sites. Immature or nonreproductive members of the group can provide assistance to those who do reproduce by helping to gather food for or protecting newborn members. Living in a group can lead to a reduced chance of predation. Having more eyes and ears in the group helps in detecting predators. Although groups of animals are easier for predators to spot, a predator can usually capture only one member of a group in any attack, letting the others escape.

FIGURE 27.13 During the breeding season, emperor penguins live in huge colonies made up of between 200 and 50,000 pairs.

Costs of Social Behavior

Living in a group also comes at some cost to an individual. Living together in large groups leads to increased visibility. A group of animals cannot hide from predators as easily as an individual can. Group living also leads to increased competition. A limited amount of resources, such as food or mates, can lead to conflicts between group members. Animals that live together in groups also have an increased chance of contracting diseases or passing parasites to each other. As group size increases, so does the risk.

A Connect What is the benefit of doing group work in class? Are there any drawbacks?

Differentiated Instruction

ENGLISH LEARNERS

Have students form into small groups and have students number off. Ask them questions about the different types of social behavior, and its costs and benefits. After each question, give groups time to develop their answer. Then call out a number to identify a spokesperson to answer the question for the group.

Biology Toolkit, Numbered Heads Together, p. C16

Plan and Prepare

Objectives

- Analyze the costs and benefits of living in social groups.
- Describe types of social behavior.
- Explain how cooperative social behaviors could have evolved.

Section Resources

Unit Resource Book
Study Guide pp. 133–134
Power Notes p. 135
Reinforcement p. 136
Pre-AP Activity pp. 145–146

Interactive Reader Chapter 27
Spanish Study Guide pp. 279–280

Biology Toolkit pp. C13, C16, C27, D2, D6

Technology
Power Presentation 27.4
Media Gallery DVD
Online Quiz 27.4

Activate Prior Knowledge Discuss with students how aspects of social behavior are closely associated with learning. For example, an animal's ability to identify members of its social group may be based on visual, vocal, or chemical cues. Failure to learn or respond to the appropriate cues or associate them with the appropriate individuals could mean death. **Ask,** What were the consequences of greylag geese imprinting on a human rather than on other geese? As adults, they failed to recognize their own species, which reduced their reproductive success. Ask students to think of examples of social behavior and learning seen in high school.

Teach

Answers

A Connect Benefits include combining knowledge of the group and ability to have different people accomplish different tasks. Drawbacks include some people doing more or less than their share of the work.

▼ Teach *continued*

ONLINE BIOLOGY Go to the chapter Resource Center at **ClassZone.com** for additional resources and information on courtship behaviors.

Science Trivia

- Auditory communication can be observed in grasshoppers when they rub their hind legs against their front wings.
- The number of call types in birds varies from about 5 to 23 depending on the species.
- The pheromone released by the female silkworm moth, bombykol, is so concentrated that it takes only one molecule to attract a male. It is theoretically estimated that 1.5 micrograms is enough to attract more than 1 billion males.
- Scents carried both externally and in the bee's stomach provide information on the type of flower available as a food source. When scouts share the scent by regurgitating their stomach contents, their hive mates will fly only to the same species of flower.

Answers

A Infer In large groups, not all individuals need to be vigilant at all times to avoid predators. Some individuals can keep watch while other individuals perform other behaviors, such as eating. The larger number also means that each individual is less likely to be killed by a predator because there are many more individuals from which to choose. Smaller groups would require animals to be vigilant constantly, reducing the time for other behaviors such as eating, and would also increase the risk of individuals being killed.

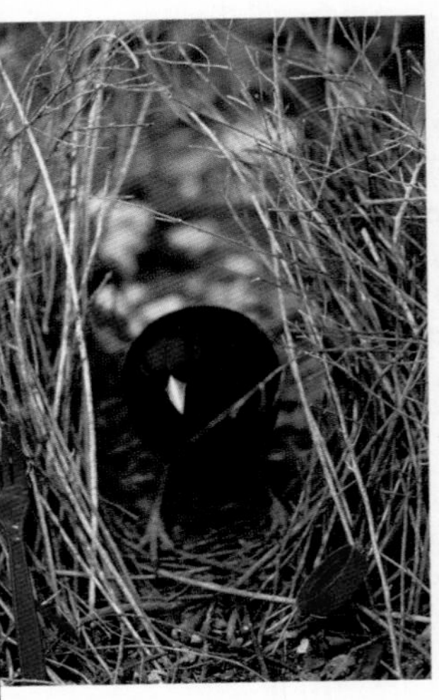

FIGURE 27.14 Male satin bowerbirds decorate their bowers with shiny and brightly colored objects (including human-made items) to attract a mate.

***Connecting* CONCEPTS**

Evolution Recall from **Chapter 11** that sexual selection is a factor that violates Hardy-Weinberg equilibrium. When certain traits improve mating success, alleles for these traits increase in frequency within a population, causing the population to evolve over time.

MAIN IDEA

Social behaviors are interactions between members of the same or different species.

Social behaviors are behaviors animals use when interacting with members of their own or other species. These behaviors help to make interactions such as mate selection easier, and they often involve specialized signals.

Communication

Animals use communication as a way to keep in contact with one another, raise alarm in the presence of danger, and attract a mate.

Visual Gestures or postures, such as the submissive posture of a dog with its tail between its legs, may help to identify an animal's status in the group.

Sound Animals often use calls to identify offspring, such as the specific call shared between a young penguin and its parents. Alarm calls and distress calls alert others to the presence of a threat. Mating calls are also used to advertise an animal's readiness to mate.

Touch Bees use their antennae, for example, to interpret the waggle dance performed by a scout bee in order to locate a food source outside the hive.

Chemical Some animals communicate by using pheromones. **Pheromones** are chemicals released by an animal that affect the behavior of other individuals of the same species. Often, these chemicals announce an animal's readiness to mate. Odors are also used to identify group members and mark territory.

Mate Selection

Courtship displays are behaviors most often used by male members of a species to attract females. Scientists theorize that females use courtship displays to judge the condition of their potential mate or the quality of his genes. By being choosy about a mate, a female can help ensure that her offspring have the best chance of survival. While some behaviors may be simple in nature, such as the leg-waving dance display of the jumping spider, other behaviors are more elaborate. For example, as shown in **FIGURE 27.14,** the male satin bowerbird of Australia constructs a nest site, called a bower, that is decorated with brightly colored and shiny objects. Females inspect the bowers when choosing a mate.

Defense

Defensive behaviors include aggressive actions to protect both the individual and the group. For example, when threatened, an elephant herd will form a protective circle surrounding the younger members of the family group. Another defensive behavior is mobbing by birds. When a predator is spotted, flocks of birds, often of the same species, will join together to harass the intruder to force it to leave. Keeping watch is another defense tactic. For example, while foraging, one or more members of a giraffe herd will serve as a lookout for the group. While vigilant individuals forage less, they also benefit themselves and other members of their group by keeping an eye out for predators.

A Infer How might the size of a group affect its defense?

Differentiated Instruction

BELOW LEVEL

Have students use a main idea web to take notes on the different types of social behavior. Remind them that communication supports all social behaviors, whether the behavior involves parents taking care of their young, adults mating, or a group mobbing a predator.

Biology Toolkit, Main Idea Web, p. C27

MAIN IDEA

Some behaviors benefit other group members at a cost to the individual performing them.

Individuals that live in a social group often help one another. They may share food or warmth or warn others about an approaching predator. But remember that animals typically perform behaviors that aid their own fitness. In some cases, however, social behaviors seem to reduce the fitness of the individuals that perform them. How could such behaviors evolve?

Types of Helpful Social Behavior

Most social interactions between animals improve the survival and reproduction of both individuals. The three kinds of helpful social behavior are cooperation, reciprocity, and altruism.

Cooperation involves behaviors that improve the fitness of both individuals. For example, lionesses hunt in a group and share the prey they catch, even though only one member of the pride may have made the kill.

Reciprocity involves behaviors in which individuals help other group members with the expectation that they will be helped in return. For example, vampire bats form feeding relationships with one another. Bats that have fed will regurgitate blood for other bats that are hungry. The cost to the donor bat is small. But there is a large benefit for the hungry bat, because vampire bats starve if they do not eat every few nights. By giving up some food, the donor ensures that it will be fed when it is hungry.

Altruism is a kind of behavior in which an animal reduces its own fitness to help other members of its social group. In other words, the animal appears to sacrifice itself for the good of the group. Consider the behavior of Belding's ground squirrels. A Belding's ground squirrel, shown in **FIGURE 27.15,** is a small rodent that lives in large colonies on the open grasslands such as the alpine grasslands surrounding the Sierra Nevada mountains in California. When ground squirrels are active during the late spring and summer, they are hunted by predators from the air and on the ground. When an individual spots a predator, it may give an alarm call to alert the rest of the colony. But alarm calls are costly. A calling ground squirrel is twice as likely to be killed as a ground squirrel that does not call. Calling benefits other colony members because it gives them time to escape, but it is harmful to the caller.

Evolution of Altruism

How can we explain the evolution of altruism if behavior is supposed to increase fitness? British evolutionary biologist William Hamilton addressed this puzzle by asking how alleles involved in altruistic behavior could spread through a population. He realized that alleles can be transmitted and therefore spread in a population two ways, either directly from an individual to its offspring or indirectly by helping close relatives survive.

VOCABULARY

Reciprocity can be thought of in a "You scratch my back, I'll scratch yours" kind of way. Each animal performing the behavior will eventually benefit when another animal performs it in return.

FIGURE 27.15 An adult female Belding's ground squirrel gives an alarm call to alert her relatives to the presence of a predator.

BELOW LEVEL

Describe for students different examples of social behaviors. Ask them to characterize the behaviors in terms of costs and benefits for both individual and populations. Then have students determine the type of social behavior for each example.

Biology Toolkit, List-Group-Label, p. D6

Address Misconceptions

Common Misconception Students may think that animals that live in social groups are not territorial or are less territorial than animals who do not live in social groups.

Correcting the Misconception Although they exhibit altruism, female Belding's ground squirrels are also known to exhibit territoriality. Females share territories with closely related females, but chase others away. Animals that live in other kinds of social groups also may be highly territorial. For example, gulls are not altruistic, but nest in large colonies. Adults aggressively defend their nest and the small space surrounding it from all intruders, including chicks that may wander in.

Vocabulary

Academic Vocabulary The words **cooperation** and **reciprocity** are used in the same way in everyday language as they are in biology. However, the word **altruism** takes on a different connotation in biology. *Altruism,* in an everyday sense, is the unselfish concern for the welfare of others. In biology, altruistic behavior comes at a cost to the individual.

Take It Further

Belding's ground squirrels engage in what appears to be kissing. In reality, they are sniffing secretions from facial scent glands to identify who are family members and who are not. A Cornell scientist conducted recognition studies by putting scent gland samples on plastic cubes and placing the cubes at the entrances of burrows that housed previously tagged individuals. The scientist timed how long squirrels spent sniffing scents from closely related individuals and compared the results with time spent sniffing scents from distantly related and unrelated individuals. The shorter the sniff, the more related was the individual. Squirrels were able to identify individuals of varying degrees of relatedness with great precision.

▼ Teach *continued*

Science Trivia

Here are some unique ways to which some animal groups are referred:

- a *gang* of elk
- a *business* of ferrets
- a *prickle* of porcupines
- a *crash* of rhinoceros
- a *tribe* of goats
- a *tower* of giraffes
- a *streak* of tigers
- a *barrel* of monkeys
- a *parliament* of owls
- a *murder* of crows
- a *party* of jays
- an *army* of frogs
- an *intrusion* of cockroaches
- a *shiver* of sharks

Answers

A Infer While the group benefits, the individual who performs the altruistic behavior may be killed as a result.

Integrating Genetics

Sister wasps of the genus ***Polistes*** can share as much as 100 percent of their genes. A female wasp may mate with only one male and store the sperm. Because the male is haploid, the sperm are all genetically identical. The female's eggs are not genetically identical because she is diploid. Her eggs will have about 50 percent of their genes in common.

When egg and sperm unite, the resulting offspring (daughters) will have about 75 percent of their genes in common. (100 percent from father + 50 percent from mother/2 = 75 percent) If a mother's eggs have identical genotypes, which is possible, then sisters will share 100 percent of their genes. **Ask,** How would you expect the genotypes of sisters to compare with the genotypes of mothers and daughters? Sisters are more genetically similar (75 percent). Mothers and daughters share only about half of the same genes.

When an animal reproduces, its offspring gets half of its alleles. But its relatives also share some of the same alleles, in the following proportions:

- Parents and siblings share 50 percent of the animal's alleles.
- Nephews and nieces share 25 percent of its alleles.
- First cousins share 12.5 percent of its alleles.

The total number of genes an animal and its relatives contribute to the next generation is called its **inclusive fitness.** It includes both direct fitness from reproduction and indirect fitness from helping kin survive. When natural selection acts on alleles that favor the survival of close relatives, it is called **kin selection.**

If kin selection explains the squirrels' altruism, callers should be closely related to others in the group. Ground squirrel colonies are made up of closely related females and unrelated males. Males do not call much. Nor do adult females foraging alone. The ones that risk their lives are adult females foraging near their daughters, siblings, and nieces. They are warning their relatives.

A Infer Why is altruistic behavior not very common?

MAIN IDEA

Eusocial behavior is an example of extreme altruism.

VOCABULARY

The term *eusocial* comes from the Greek prefix *eu-*, which means "good, well, or true" and the Latin word *socius*, which means "companion."

Relationships within populations of some social animals are very specialized. **Eusocial** species live in large groups made up of many individuals, most of whom are members of nonreproductive castes such as workers or soldiers. All of the young in the colony are the offspring of one female, called the queen. Other adults look for food, defend the colony, care for the queen, and raise her offspring. Eusocial behaviors likely evolve by kin selection.

Social Insects

Many social insects, such as bees, ants, and wasps, are haplodiploid, which means their sex is determined by the number of chromosome sets in an individual. Males are haploid and females are diploid. Female social insects produce daughters through eggs fertilized by sperm. Unfertilized eggs produce sons. In these animals, daughters share half of their mother's alleles but all of their father's alleles. Sisters therefore share up to 75 percent of their alleles overall with one another, compared with 50 percent in humans and most other animals. The very close relationship between sisters in a colony may influence the evolution of eusociality in these insects.

As shown in **FIGURE 27.16**, weaver ants are one example of a eusocial insect species. The three main castes of this species are a queen, major workers, and minor workers. The worker ants work together to weave their nests from leaves that hang from branches throughout one tree or several trees located next to one another. The ants communicate by secreting pheromones. For example, the queen secretes pheromones that induce workers to groom or feed her. If threatened, major worker ants may release pheromones to call in reinforcements to help protect the nest.

Differentiated Instruction

PRE-AP

Ask students to explain how the percentages for allele sharing (at the top of the page) were derived. Assign each bulleted statement to a different group of students. Encourage students to use diagrams of meiosis to support their explanations. Invite them to present their explanations to the class. (Remind students that the percentages given are averages.)

Biology Toolkit, Think-Pair-Share, p. C13

BELOW LEVEL

Help students with the term *haplodiploid* by having them break down the word. *Haplodiploid* becomes *haplo* (haploid males) and *diploid* (females).

Biology Toolkit, New Word Analysis, p. D2

COOPERATION
ANT CASTES
Queen The queen lays eggs inside the nest.
Minor worker The smaller minor worker spends most of its time within the nest tending the larvae and egg chambers.
Major worker The larger major worker defends the territory surrounding the nest, tends the queen, and forages for food.
Chapter 27: Animal Behavior 835
FIGURE 27.16 Social Behavior of Ants

Ants live together in colonies. Each ant has an important part to play within the colony.

After pulling together two leaves, weaver ants attach one leaf to another by using their mandibles to gently squeeze a larva, which produces a silk that glues the leaf edges to each other.

A CRITICAL VIEWING What genetic benefit does a worker ant receive by taking care of its siblings?

HANDS-ON ACTIVITY

If you have access to an ant farm or a beehive with a glass viewing panel, let student groups take turns observing the insects and taking notes on their behaviors. Students may be able to identify queens and the different kinds of workers by their activities. Students will probably be able to see the bees dance.

TEACH FROM VISUALS

FIGURE 27.16 Point out the three castes of the weaver ant shown in the figure. Tell students that after mating, the queen sheds her wings and seals herself into the nest, where she begins egg laying. She will lay eggs for the rest of her life.

Take It Further

Army ants (*Eciton burchellii*) are found in tropical and subtropical regions of Central and South America. Colonies may contain up to two million individuals. Army ants are carnivorous swarm feeders that must migrate daily to find enough food. The lead workers leave a chemical signal on the trail for the colony to follow, because army ants are blind. They can travel at a speed of up to 20 meters per hour. On a given day, army ants can devastate an area larger than 1800 square yards (1500 m^2) and eat up to 100,000 animals. Army ants have been known to eat other ants, lizards, chickens, goats, pigs, and scorpions.

A temporary camp, called a **bivouac,** is set up each night to protect the queen. Between 150,000 and 700,000 ants work cooperatively to join their bodies together with their mandibles to make the bivuac, which can be up to a meter across. The ants also show other cooperative behaviors when crossing a stream (forming bridges by interlocking their legs and bodies) and when caught in a flood (sticking together to form a floating ball).

Answers

A Critical Viewing Because ants are haplodiploid, a worker ant is helping its close relatives when it takes care of its siblings.

▼ Teach *continued*

DATA ANALYSIS

Discuss

Have students describe the type of data given here. **Ask,** Why would you use a bar graph to depict the data shown here? The data are not continuous; each behavior is independent of the others.

Answers

1. Active perching = 41.2%; Hunting flight = 49.4%; Cruising flight = 1.1%; Other flight = 1.8%; Feeding nestlings = 6.6%. Behavior should be on the *x*-axis, and Time (%) on the *y*-axis. For a completed bar graph, go to page R108.
2. Kites spent the most time in hunting flight in order to consume enough prey to meet their energy needs.

Answers

A Apply Eusocial species are highly related to one another, which ensures that similar genetic material continues to be passed on to future generations.

Unit Resource Book, Data Analysis, p. 141

▼ Assess and Reteach

Assess Use the Online Quiz or Section Quiz (*Assessment Book,* p. 534).

Reteach Conduct a rapid-fire question and answer session on the costs and benefits of different social behaviors.

DATA ANALYSIS NOS.3

CONSTRUCTING BAR GRAPHS

As you learned earlier in this chapter, an ethogram is a catalogue of the types of behaviors an animal may perform. A time budget shows how much time organisms spend engaged in each type of behavior. Scientists can use these time budgets to compare patterns of behavior between different species, or between different sexes or age groups of the same species.

TABLE 1. KITE BEHAVIOR

Behavior	Time (min)
Active perching	162
Hunting flight	194
Cruising flight	4
Other flight	7
Feeding nestlings	26

Source: Jaksic et al. *The Condor* 89:4.

Table 1 contains data that were recorded through observations of male and female black-shouldered kites, a type of hawk, during the summer.

1. **Graph Data** Construct a time budget that shows the percent of time (per 24-hour period) the hawks spent in each behavior. (**Hint:** Remember to convert the amount of time to a percent before graphing.)
2. **Analyze** What behavior did the hawks spend the most time engaged in? Why do you think this behavior was most common?

Other Eusocial Animals

Eusocial termites, snapping shrimp, and naked mole rats are all normal, diploid animals. But their colonies are still made up of closely related animals. These animals often live in areas where it is difficult for individuals to survive on their own. For example, naked mole rats live in colonies of 70 to 80 individuals dominated by a single queen and a few fertile male "kings." Most of the colony are the queen's siblings or offspring. Nonreproducing adults are either soldiers or workers. Soldiers defend the colony, while workers work together as a chain gang to dig through the soil to find edible tubers. This eusocial behavior may have evolved due to the amount of work needed to find food. If leaving the colony leads to starvation, kin selection may favor staying in the burrow to work together as a group instead.

NSTA scilinks.org SCILINKS
To learn more about animal communication, go to scilinks.org.
Keycode: MLB027

A Apply How are eusocial behavior and a species' level of relatedness connected?

27.4 ASSESSMENT

ONLINE QUIZ ClassZone.com

REVIEWING MAIN IDEAS

1. Outline the costs and benefits of living in a group.
2. Use an example to explain what social behavior is.
3. What are the three types of helpful behavior?
4. What characteristic makes a social group **eusocial**?

CRITICAL THINKING

5. **Connect** Give an example of reciprocal behavior from everyday life.
6. **Analyze** Why might a juvenile scrub jay help its parents raise a new brood of chicks instead of building its own nest?

***Connecting* CONCEPTS**

7. **Genetics** How is a haplodiploid species different from a diploid species?

27.4 ASSESSMENT

1. *Sample Answer:* Cost—predators can spot large groups more easily; benefit—the predator is less likely to catch a particular individual.
2. Social behaviors are interactions among members of the same species. For example, giraffes often browse together, and one or more individuals may serve as lookouts for predators while other individuals feed.
3. cooperation, reciprocity, altruism
4. Most members of the group do not reproduce; only one (or a few) females in the group have offspring.
5. In the student's example, both parties must benefit, but one party receives a delayed benefit.
6. An animal shares the same number of genes with its siblings and its offspring. If young adults are unlikely to successfully raise their own chicks, helping to raise their siblings gives them the same inclusive fitness.
7. In haplodiploid species, males result from unfertilized eggs (haploid) and females result from fertilized eggs (diploid). In diploid species, both sexes result from fertilized eggs and have two sets of chromosomes (one from each parent).

27.5 Animal Cognition

KEY CONCEPT Some animals other than humans exhibit behaviors requiring complex cognitive abilities.

MAIN IDEAS
- Animal intelligence is difficult to define.
- Some animals can solve problems.
- Cognitive ability may provide an adaptive advantage for living in social groups.

VOCABULARY
- **cognition,** p. 837
- **insight,** p. 838
- **cultural behavior,** p. 839

Connect No one would deny that humans are intelligent animals. We surround ourselves with invented objects, from the clothes we wear to the buildings in which we live. But from where did human cognition come? And do other animals share aspects of this ability to think about the world?

MAIN IDEA

Animal intelligence is difficult to define.

In the first half of the 20th century, the focus of many animal intelligence studies was determining whether a certain animal was "intelligent" according to human standards. Today, learning how an animal's level of intelligence compares with a human's is no longer a focus of research. Instead, as shown in **FIGURE 27.17,** scientists study an animal's cognitive abilities. **Cognition** is the mental process of knowing through perception or reasoning. Cognitive behavior also includes awareness and the ability to judge. Animals with a higher level of cognition can solve more complex problems.

FIGURE 27.17 While considered to have fewer cognitive abilities than other primates, studies have shown that lemurs have the ability to remember long sequences of images and can place images in the correct order.

In contrast to intelligence, which is difficult to define and measure, cognitive abilities can be more objectively described and measured. However, even an animal's cognitive abilities can be difficult to distinguish from other factors that might be affecting an animal's behavior.

For example, in the early 1900s, a horse in Germany nicknamed Clever Hans seemed to be able to solve math questions by using its hoof to tap out the correct answer. However, upon closer inspection it was found that the horse's ability to tap out the correct answer had nothing to do with mathematical skills. Instead, it was relying on changes in the posture or facial expressions of its trainer. The horse was able to perceive the increased tension in its trainer when it neared the correct answer, and would stop tapping its hoof. This example illustrates how difficult it can be to determine the cognitive abilities of animals. While the horse was unable to solve mathematical problems, it can be argued that its ability to perceive changes in its trainer's posture is an example of cognition on a different level.

(A) Analyze **Why do scientists focus on an animal's cognitive abilities rather than its "intelligence" when studying animal behavior?**

Differentiated Instruction

ENGLISH LEARNERS

Have students create a two-column notes chart with the column headings *Main Ideas* and *Details.* In the first column, list the following: main ideas, concepts, issues, and/or people. In the second column, have students give details. One way to fill in the chart is to use the blue main idea headings for the *Main Ideas* column. For example, "Animal intelligence is difficult to define." Details could be "intelligence is subjective" and "cognition can be described and measured."

Biology Toolkit, Two-Column Notes, p. C20

Plan and Prepare

Objectives

- Discuss the difference between intelligence and cognition.
- Describe problem-solving behaviors in animals.
- Explain the role of cognition for animals living in social groups.

Section Resources

Unit Resource Book Study Guide pp. 137–138 Power Notes p. 139 Reinforcement p. 140
Interactive Reader Chapter 27 **Spanish Study Guide** pp. 281–282
Biology Toolkit pp. C19, C20
Technology Power Presentation 27.5 Media Gallery DVD Online Quiz 27.5

Activate Prior Knowledge Discuss with students how they learned to perform a task such as tying their shoe. **Ask,** How did you learn to do new things as a child? *Sample Answer:* taught by an adult, imitation, trial and error Tell students that other animals think, problem solve, and learn in similar ways. Remind students that these behaviors have adaptive value, allowing them to survive an enormous variety of situations.

Teach

Vocabulary

Academic Vocabulary When studying animal cognition, students will encounter many terms used to describe it. Have students look up the definitions of the following words.

perception	*reasoning*
comprehension	*thinking*
learning	*knowledge*

Answers

(A) **Analyze** Intelligence is subjective, while cognitive abilities can be objectively defined and measured.

▼ Teach *continued*

ONLINE BIOLOGY To learn how scientists study cognition in dolphins, birds, and chimps, have students do the WebQuest in Options for Inquiry on page 841.

Take It Further

Off the coast of Australia, bottlenose dolphins have been observed carrying sponges on their snouts. Scientists infer that the dolphins use the sponges as a fishing tool to probe the sea floor for fish and protect themselves from being stung by a stonefish. It appears that mothers teach this behavior to their daughters. Scientists reasoned that if the behavior were genetic, they would see males engaging in the behavior. But, they do not.

Other **cultural behaviors** in cetaceans include these amazing observations:

- Bottlenose dolphins in Laguna, Brazil, herd schools of fish toward the beach and signal people fishing along the shore to cast their nets. Fish that escape the nets are then caught by the dolphins. This has been occurring since 1847.
- Female killer whales in Argentina take their young on practice seal hunts. The mothers rush toward the beach with their offspring, even if seals are not in sight, to teach them how to hunt.
- Male humpback whales that are spread out across entire oceans change their songs at almost the same time.

Answers

A Contrast Associative learning is trial-and-error learning, while insight is the ability to solve a problem mentally without repeated trial and error.

MAIN IDEA

Some animals can solve problems.

Scientists sometimes study how animals think by giving them problems to solve. If cognition involves the ability to invent new behaviors in new situations, then animals with cognitive abilities should be able to solve problems they have never encountered before. Different species react to new situations with varying amounts of success.

Problem-Solving Behavior

Researchers have observed extremely complex problem-solving behavior in primates, dolphins, and the corvids—a group of birds that includes crows, ravens, and jays. In one classic study, a chimpanzee was placed in a room containing boxes, sticks, and a banana hung out of reach. At first, the chimp sat around and did nothing. But after a while it suddenly piled up the boxes and climbed up to knock down the fruit with a stick. This ability to solve a problem mentally without repeated trial and error is called **insight.**

Tool Use

Tools are inanimate objects that help an animal accomplish a task, such as collecting hard-to-reach foods. A number of different animals use tools. For example, Australian bottlenose dolphins use pieces of sponge to cover their snouts when foraging. Not only does this method protect them from being stung on their noses by stonefish but it also helps to scare up fish from the ocean floor. Some primates and New Caledonian crows have been observed making tools. Chimpanzees trim sticks to make termite probes. As shown in **FIGURE 27.18**, brown capuchin monkeys use rocks to crack open palm nuts. In one experiment, crows given straight wires bent the wire to make a hook, then used it to fish food out of a tube. Tool use itself is not a sign of cognitive ability. But making tools suggests that an animal can understand cause and effect, and can make predictions about its own behavior.

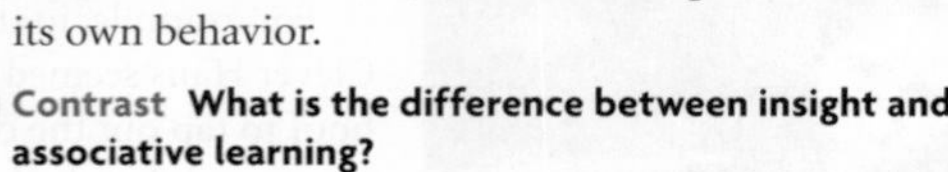

A Contrast What is the difference between insight and associative learning?

FIGURE 27.18 Brown capuchin monkeys use a rock to crack open the hard shells of palm nuts.

MAIN IDEA

Cognitive ability may provide an adaptive advantage for living in social groups.

Animals we recognize as the most "intelligent" often have two things in common. They have relatively large brains for their body size, and they live in complex social groups. More neurons may mean more interconnections and greater opportunities for complex behaviors to emerge. But evidence suggests that it is just as important to live in a group with a complex social system.

Differentiated Instruction

PRE-AP

The Think Tank exhibit at the Smithsonian National Zoological Park asks visitors several questions to get them to think about the nature of tools and their use.

- Can a tool be alive?
- Can a tool be a part of the user's body?
- Must the user hold or carry the tool?
- Must the user manipulate the tool?

Have students select one of these questions and write an argument for or against it. Encourage students to give specific examples to support their postion. The chapter Resource Center at **ClassZone.com** has additional information on tool use in animals.

Biology Toolkit, Quick-Write, p. C19

Animated BIOLOGY Watch instances of animal cognition at ClassZone.com.

FIGURE 27.19 Elephants are social animals that form close bonds within their group.

Animals that live in large groups with a definite social structure, such as the elephants shown in **FIGURE 27.19**, are surrounded by politics. Surviving and reproducing depends on remembering and being able to use a vast amount of information to the individual's advantage. These animals must be able to

- identify other individuals in the group
- remember which individuals are their allies and rivals
- keep track of the constantly changing state of affairs among individuals
- use this information to their own advantage

Cultural behavior is behavior that is spread through a population by learning, rather than by selection. The key to cultural behavior is that the behavior is taught to one generation by another. The development of cultural behavior does not require living in complex societies. For example, some scientists would argue that the transmission of birdsong is an example of cultural behavior. However, living close together in social groups may help to enhance the transmission and expression of cultural behaviors.

A Connect **What is an example of cultural behavior from your life?**

History of Science

The primatologist **Jane Goodall** has been studying the chimpanzees of Gombe National Park in Tanzania since 1960. Her observations have provided invaluable information toward understanding chimpanzee behavior and culture. In 1960, Goodall observed chimpanzees using sticks as a tool to fish termites out of the ground. This observation challenged the idea that humans were the only toolmakers. She went on to document chimpanzees using various other objects such as stems, twigs, rocks, and leaves to perform tasks associated with eating, drinking, investigating, defense, and personal hygiene.

Goodall also observed similarities between chimpanzees and humans in regards to development, facial expressions, child rearing, and diet. Goodall's observations led her to conclude that chimpanzees have distinct personalities, emotions, and family relationships, just like humans have. Goodall also documented that chimpanzee behavior for tool usage, grooming, and courtship varies between populations of chimpanzees. The only other documented animal species that has such a wide variety of cultural behaviors is humans.

27.5 ASSESSMENT

ONLINE QUIZ ClassZone.com

REVIEWING MAIN IDEAS

1. Why is animal intelligence difficult to define?
2. Use an example to explain what solving a problem by using **insight** means.
3. Explain how living in a complex social group might select for increased cognitive abilities.

CRITICAL THINKING

4. **Apply** In Section 27.2, you learned about the potato-washing behavior of snow monkeys. Is this an example of **cultural behavior**? Explain your reasoning.
5. **Analyze** There are three keys on a table. How might you use insight to determine which key opens a nearby door?

Connecting CONCEPTS

6. **Scientific Process** Why are scientists so interested in studying primate behavior? What might scientists learn about human behavior?

Answers

A Connect *Sample Answer:* learning language or ethnic customs, such as dances or songs from previous generations

Assess and Reteach

Assess Use the Online Quiz or Section Quiz (*Assessment Book*, p. 535).

Reteach Have students provide examples of cognition in animals as you write them on the board. Provide feedback for any incorrect examples that students name.

27.5 ASSESSMENT

1. Intelligence is subjective, which makes it difficult to define.
2. Insight is the ability to solve a problem mentally without repeated trial and error. For example, a crow will often choose a stick of the right length on its first try when trying to dislodge food from a tree.
3. Navigating the social hierarchy depends on remembering and manipulating a lot of information.
4. Yes; the behavior was passed between members of the group by imitation, a type of learning.
5. Insight could be used by inspecting the keyhole and comparing it to the key shape and size.
6. Primates (the mammalian order that also includes humans) are our closest relatives. Studying primate behavior might give insight into the evolution of human behavior.

OPTIONS FOR INQUIRY

INVESTIGATION

Time 45 minutes	TEACHER TESTED
Teacher Preparation	
Student Difficulty	
Lab Binder Animals, pp. 71–73	

Purpose Test the behavioral response of pill bugs to environmental changes.

Overview Students will design an experiment to test a variable. They will

- choose a variable to test response
- conduct multiple trials to collect data
- evaluate their hypotheses
- evaluate their experimental design

LAB PREPARATION

- You can substitute petri dishes or shallow containers for shoebox lids.

LAB MANAGEMENT

- Allow enough time for three trials.
- Review *dependent* and *independent* with students.
- Make sure students include a control.

Possible experimental setups for independent variables include the following:

- Light—Cover half of the lid with black paper.
- Moisture—Place a dampened paper towel in half of a lid lined with foil.

Safety Caution students to handle pill bugs with care and as little as possible.

POST-LAB DISCUSSION

Review the habitat of pill bugs. **Ask**

- Where would you look to find pill bugs in nature? under rocks, logs, in damp soil
- Why do pill bugs prefer moist, dark environmental conditions? breathe through gills, feed on decaying matter, avoid predators

Use these inquiry-based labs and online activities to deepen your understanding of animal behavior.

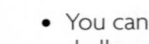

INDIANA STANDARDS

NOS.1 Develop explanations based on reproducible data and observations gathered during laboratory investigations.

NOS.3 Clearly communicate their ideas and results of investigations verbally and in written form using tables, graphs, diagrams, and photographs.

DESIGN YOUR OWN INVESTIGATION

Pill Bug Behavior

Pill bugs (*Armadillidium vulgare*) are terrestrial crustaceans that feed on decaying plant and animal matter. As scavengers and composters, they even eat their exoskeleton when it sheds, to recycle the calcium. As crustaceans, they have two pairs of antennae, breathe through gills, and have seven pairs of legs on their abdomen and thorax. In this investigation, you will design an experiment to determine how manipulating a variable changes the behavior of pill bugs.

MATERIALS

- shoebox lid
- marker
- 12 pill bugs
- 25 cm piece of foil
- light source
- 10-mL graduated cylinder
- 10 mL water
- 4 paper towels
- sheet dark-colored paper
- sheet light-colored paper

PROBLEM How does the behavior pattern of pill bugs change when their environment is manipulated?

1. Formulate a question to ask about pill bug behavior by looking at the materials list and determining how you can manipulate their environment.
2. Determine a control setting. Create a data table to record your observations of 12 pill bugs in the control setting.
3. Choose a variable to manipulate. Create a data table to record your observations of pill bug behavior in the manipulated environment. Remember to treat all living things carefully.
4. Make a list of all the conditions you will hold constant in your experiment.
5. Formulate a hypothesis to your question.
6. Have your teacher approve your experimental design.
7. Conduct your experiment.
8. If time permits, conduct three trials, using a new set of pill bugs for each trial.
9. Wash your hands when you are done.

ANALYZE AND CONCLUDE

1. **Analyze** Compare your data to your hypothesis. Explain whether your data supported your hypothesis or not.
2. **Conclude** What effect did manipulating the environment have on pill bug behavior?
3. **Experimental Design** Identify possible sources of unavoidable experimental error in your design.
4. **Experimental Design** List possible reasons for inconsistent results you may have observed.
5. **Predict** How might pill bug behavior be different in a more natural environment? Why might this occur?

Answers

Analyze and Conclude

1. Students who hypothesized that pill bugs prefer dark or moist environments should be able to indicate that their data supported their hypotheses.
2. Pill bugs tended to seek out environments that resembled their natural habitat.
3. *Sample Answer:* natural variation in pill bug behavior; experiment conducted in an unnatural environment; pill bugs responded to heat as opposed to light from the light source
4. *Sample Answer:* inconsistent amount of time allowed for pill bugs to respond; dampened paper towels too wet or dry; distance and angle of light source; sample size too small
5. A more realistic environment would allow the pill bugs to act in a more natural manner. The foreign material used in the chambers (cardboard or plastic) plus any stress from transport to the lab could impact behavior.

INVESTIGATION

Animal Cognition

With technology such as remote-controlled cameras, scientists can observe the behavior of animals in their natural environment. This allows them to learn more about how animals communicate with each other, their mating rituals, how they compete with each other, and problem-solving skills they may have.

SKILL Researching

PROBLEM What are scientists learning about animal cognition?

RESEARCH

1. Choose an animal to research in the field of animal cognition, such as the African elephant, the New Caledonian crow, the Australian bottlenose dolphin, the octopus, the humpback whale, or the chimpanzee.
2. Investigate, using library and/or Internet resources, what research is being done to learn more about the cognitive abilities of the animal. Include
   - methods for data collection
   - data obtained
   - conclusions drawn

EXTEND YOUR INVESTIGATION

Based on information from your research, form a hypothesis that is relevant to the topic of animal intelligence and design an experiment to test the hypothesis.

Online BIOLOGY CLASSZONE.COM

VIRTUAL LAB
Interpreting Bird Response
Does a male song sparrow react to other song sparrows in the same way? In this interactive lab, you will determine how male song sparrows respond to the songs of local and foreign song sparrows.

WEBQUEST
How smart is a dolphin? In this WebQuest, you will learn about the study of animal cognition. Explore examples of animal cognition as well as experiments used to test the mental capabilities of animals.

ANIMATED BIOLOGY
Behavioral Costs and Benefits
Can you balance the energy costs and benefits of behaviors? Have a hummingbird use optimal foraging and defensive strategies to maximize its limited energy supply.

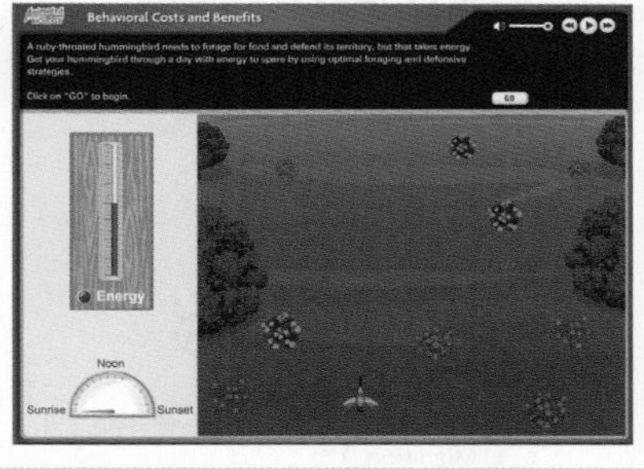

Answers

Research

1. Studies on African elephants have focused on memory, use of tools, and infrasonic vocalizations. Octopuses have long been the subject of visual discrimination studies to understand their ability to learn visual cues.
2. Students should present a detailed summary of the current research, including methods for data collection, data obtained, and conclusions drawn.

Extend Your Investigation

Students should present a testable hypothesis and a realistic experimental design.

Online Biology ▼

VIRTUAL LAB Male sparrows identify the song of a local male as belonging to a competitor more than that of a foreign male. Use this lab to reinforce the concepts in **Section 27.1.**

WEBQUEST The WebQuest takes one full class period. Students complete the activity online and will need access to a printer to print their answers. Sample answers, teacher notes, and alternative assessment ideas are available on **ClassZone.com.** Use with **Section 27.5.**

ANIMATED BIOLOGY Use this simulation to reinforce the concepts in **Section 27.3.**

INVESTIGATION

TEACHER TESTED ✓

Time 30 minutes	
Teacher Preparation	1 flask
Student Difficulty	1 flask
Lab Binder Animals, p. 74	

Purpose Research animal cognition studies.

Overview Students will research cognition studies for a chosen animal.

LAB PREPARATION

- You may wish to conduct advance research in order to assist students.

LAB MANAGEMENT

- Use Internet search terms such as the animal's name and *cognition studies.*

POST-LAB DISCUSSION

Discuss types of research and the advantages and disadvantages of each.

CHAPTER REVIEW

Interactive Review

Encourage students to go to **ClassZone.com** for a detailed review of each section, including visuals and vocabulary practice.

Unit Resource Book, Vocabulary Practice, pp. 147–150

CHAPTER 27 Interactive Review @ CLASSZONE.COM

KEY CONCEPTS | Vocabulary Games | Concept Maps | Animated Biology | Online Quiz

27.1 Adaptive Value of Behavior

Behavior lets organisms respond rapidly and adaptively to their environment. A stimulus is a type of information that has the potential to make an organism change its behavior. An animal's behavior can be considered as a way of maintaining homeostasis. Many animal behaviors are responses to stimuli that affect an individual's well-being. Internal and external stimuli interact to trigger specific behaviors. Some behaviors occur in cycles. Hibernation and migration are two behaviors that are controlled by an animal's biological clock.

27.2 Instinct and Learning

Both genes and environment affect an animal's behavior. Innate behaviors are inborn instinctive behaviors. Many behaviors have both innate and learned components. Animals that are able to learn can modify their behavior to adapt to new situations. Classical conditioning and operant conditioning are two examples of associative learning.

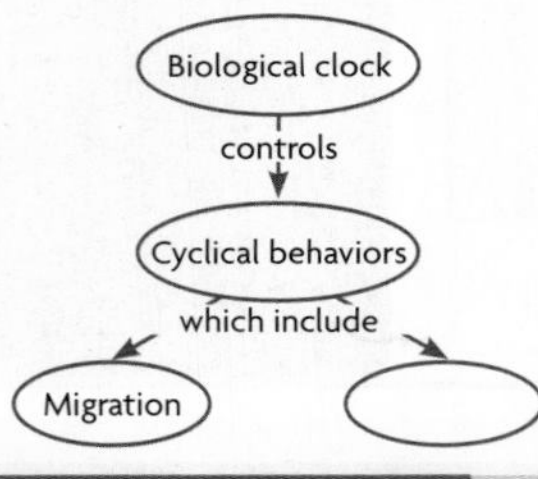

27.3 Evolution of Behavior

Every behavior has costs and benefits. Benefits of certain behaviors include increased survivorship and rates of reproduction. Three categories of behavioral costs include energy costs, opportunity costs, and risk costs. Animals perform behaviors for which the benefits outweigh the costs.

27.4 Social Behavior

Social behaviors enhance the benefits of living in a group. Social behaviors are interactions between members of the same species. Altruistic behaviors benefit other group members at the cost to the individual performing them. Eusocial behaviors are an example of extreme altruism.

27.5 Animal Cognition

Some animals other than humans exhibit behaviors requiring complex cognitive abilities. Animal intelligence is difficult to define, but animal behavior scientists are able to study the cognitive abilities of animals. Characteristics of animal cognition include awareness, perception, reasoning, and judgment. Some animals can solve problems through the use of insight. Cultural behavior is behavior that is spread through a population by learning rather than by selection.

Synthesize Your Notes

Concept Map Use a concept map like the one below to summarize your notes on cyclical behaviors.

Process Diagram Use a process diagram like the one below to summarize your notes on an animal's response to a stimulus.

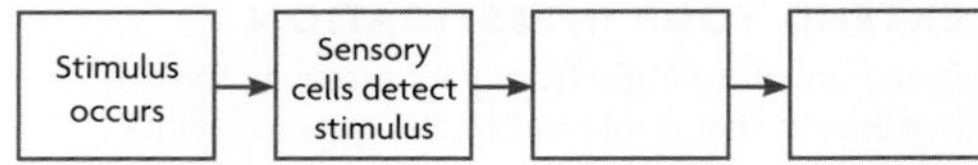

Reviewing Vocabulary

1. Both classical conditioning and operant conditioning are types of associative learning. In classical conditioning, an animal learns to associate a previously neutral stimulus with a behavior that is already being triggered by some other stimulus. In operant conditioning, an animal learns to associate an arbitrary behavior with a positive or negative outcome of performing the behavior.
2. Cultural behavior spreads through a population by learning, rather than by natural selection. Cultural behavior may be learned by imitation, in which animals learn by observing the behaviors of other animals.
3. Territoriality and optimal foraging are two behaviors in which the benefits outweigh the costs. Territoriality refers to the control of a specific area by one or more individuals of a species. Optimal foraging is a theory that states that natural selection should favor behaviors that get animals the most, or optimal amount, of calories for the cost.
4. A taxis is a movement in a particular direction, either toward or away from a stimulus.
5. Protecting the resources within a territory through territoriality may help to increase a species' survivorship, or chance of surviving to the next year.
6. Altruism is a kind of behavior in which an animal reduces its own fitness to help other members of its social group. Eusocial behavior is an example of extreme altruism, in which a species lives in large social groups where the majority of individuals do not reproduce.
7. An instinct is a complex inborn behavior. Instinctive behavior is characterized as being innate and relatively inflexible. An innate behavior is performed correctly the first time an animal tries it, even when the animal has never been exposed to the stimulus that triggers the behavior.
8. A stimulus causes, or prods, an animal to perform a certain behavior.
9. Habituation occurs when an animal becomes used to, or conditioned, to a certain stimulus and no longer reacts to it.
10. Pheromones are chemicals that carry a signal, or an impulse, that affects the behavior of other animals.
11. An altruistic behavior is one that benefits other individuals, while putting the animal that is performing the behavior at risk.
12. Kinesis is a random movement that results from an increase in activity levels due to a stimulus.

Chapter Assessment

Chapter Vocabulary

27.1 stimulus, p. 818
kinesis, p. 819
taxis, p. 819
circadian rhythm, p. 820
biological clock, p. 820

27.2 instinct, p. 822
innate, p. 822
releaser, p. 822
habituation, p. 823
imprinting, p. 824
imitation, p. 825
classical conditioning, p. 826
operant conditioning, p. 826

27.3 survivorship, p. 827
territoriality, p. 828
optimal foraging, p. 829

27.4 pheromone, p. 832
altruism, p. 833
inclusive fitness, p. 834
kin selection, p. 834
eusocial, p. 834

27.5 cognition, p. 837
insight, p. 838
cultural behavior, p. 839

Reviewing Vocabulary

Compare and Contrast

Describe one similarity and one difference between the two terms in each of the following pairs.

1. classical conditioning, operant conditioning

2. cultural behavior, imitation

3. territoriality, optimal foraging

Vocabulary Connections

The vocabulary terms in this chapter are related to each other in various ways. For each group of words below, write a sentence or two to clearly explain how the terms are connected.

4. stimulus, taxis

5. survivorship, territoriality

6. altruism, eusocial

7. instinct, innate

Greek and Latin Word Origins

8. The term *stimulus* comes from a Latin word, *stimulare*, which means "to goad, prod, or urge." Explain how this meaning relates to *stimulus.*

9. The term *habituation* comes from the Latin word *habitus*, which means "condition or habit." Explain how this meaning relates to *habituation.*

10. The term *pheromone* comes from a combination of the Greek words *pherein*, meaning "to carry," and *horme*, meaning "impulse." How do these words relate to the meaning of *pheromone*?

11. The term *altruism* comes from the Latin word *alter*, meaning "other." How is this meaning related to the definition of an altruistic individual?

12. The term *kinesis* comes from the Greek word *kinein*, meaning "to move." Explain this connection.

Reviewing MAIN IDEAS

13. What is the role of the nervous system in an animal's response to a stimulus?

14. Identify the internal and external factors that are likely to lead to migration in songbirds.

15. What are some of the characteristics of innate behaviors?

16. When does habituation occur?

17. How is the ability to adapt behaviors to new situations important to an animal's survival?

18. Describe the benefits and costs of migratory behavior.

19. The territory of a pack of gray wolves can be more than 3000 square kilometers. The alpha male marks the boundaries of the territory with urine. Explain why a wolf would engage in this time-consuming behavior.

20. Groups of small songbirds will often mob an owl or a hawk. They fly around it and call loudly. What is the cost and benefit of this behavior to the songbirds? Explain your answer.

21. Arctic ground squirrels live in groups and forage for food during daylight. What is the cost of foraging in a group?

22. What information might be provided to potential mates by a courtship display such as the competitive performances of sage grouses?

23. In the meerkat group, one animal always stands guard and sounds an alarm call if a bird of prey is sighted. Why is this an altruistic behavior?

24. What are the characteristics of eusocial behavior?

25. What is the connection between cognitive ability and insight?

CHAPTER REVIEW

Reviewing Main Ideas

13. The nervous system generates a response to the stimulus.
14. internal: amount of fat stored in the body; external: the time of year, which brings with it certain temperatures and day lengths
15. Innate behaviors are instinctive and relatively inflexible.
16. when an animal learns to ignore a repeated stimulus, even if it may trigger an innate response
17. If an animal cannot learn from a negative experience and modify its behavior to avoid repeating that experience, it might be injured or killed.
18. The benefit is finding food. The costs are energy and putting safety at risk. It takes energy to migrate, and there are dangers along the way.
19. Territory is important to secure a food supply. Without adequate prey, it would be difficult to supply enough food for growing pups and the adults in the pack.
20. The benefit is that it alerts all the birds to the presence of a predator and makes it harder for the predator to surprise its prey. The cost would be energy involved in performing the behavior.
21. The cost is that the group of ground squirrels is more visible to predators than is a single ground squirrel.
22. Courtship displays help to determine a potential mate's condition and gene quality. A particular posture can also communicate an animal's status within the group.
23. The guard meerkat is risking its own life to save the other members of the group. The bird of prey may hear and see the guard meerkat while the others escape.
24. caste system, sterile individuals, high level of relatedness
25. Animals with increased cognitive abilities are often able to solve problems by insight, so they can solve a problem mentally without repeated trial and error.

Critical Thinking

26. Alarm clock sound is external; the hunger that makes you take another slice of toast is internal; outside temperature is external; feeling the need for a lighter weight jacket is internal because the heavier jacket made you feel too warm.
27. The zookeeper could provide the otter with a food reward each time it is on the scale. This would condition the otter to associate being on the scale with a positive reinforcement.
28. Chasing down prey requires energy and involves the risk of an injury. The benefits are that an older, weaker animal is easier to catch and minimizes both the energy spent on hunting and the risk of injury. A group of animals might have a better chance of catching prey than an individual, and this increases survivorship. Because all adults help feed the pups, this increases reproductive success.
29. Since the male and female perform the call together, it is important to mate selection. Because it is loud enough for other cranes to hear it, the call is also important for territorial defense.
30. This behavior was insight. The bag was opened successfully without having to try out other methods. There was no repeated trial and error.

Interpreting Visuals

31. The adults are protecting the baby.
32. The benefit for the baby is protection from predators. The cost to the adults is being more exposed to predators.
33. The benefit to the baby outweighs the cost to the adults. Protecting the baby helps ensure reproductive success for the elephant family. Adult elephants are so big and strong that the risk of being hurt by a predator is not very great.

Critical Thinking

26. Connect Your alarm clock wakes you up and you get ready for school. You eat breakfast but then eat one more slice of toast. After stepping outside, you go back in to get a lighter jacket. Identify all the stimuli in this scene and whether they are internal or external.

27. Apply A zookeeper needs to use a scale to measure the weight of an otter. How might she use operant conditioning to get the otter onto the scale?

28. Analyze Gray wolves live in packs with about 6 to 15 members. Young pups remain behind while the older animals hunt for prey as a group. They often seek out old, sick, and slower prey animals. All of the adults regurgitate food for the pups. Suggest two costs and two benefits of gray wolf feeding behavior.

29. Infer The unison call is performed by a pair of whooping cranes. The male and female each have their own notes and perform this call often when they arrive at their nesting area. Suggest some reasons why the birds perform this call.

30. Apply You buy a bag of raisins. There are no directions how to open the bag. There is no tab to pull. You do not have a scissors to cut the bag open. You examine the bag for a few seconds and then pull the seams of the sealed top apart to open it. What type of problem-solving behavior did you demonstrate? Explain your answer.

Interpreting Visuals

Use the photograph to answer the next three questions.

31. Infer Why do you think the baby elephants are traveling between the adults?

32. Analyze For which elephants might there be a benefit for this type of behavior and for which elephants might there be a cost?

33. Evaluate If there is a benefit, does it outweigh the cost? Explain your answer.

Analyzing Data

The graph below shows a time budget for different behaviors exhibited by grizzly bears in a national park in the Yukon Territory, Canada. Use the data to answer the next three questions.

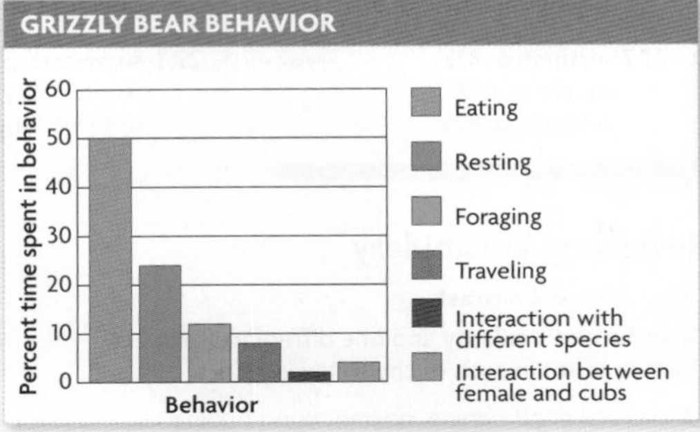

Source: MacHutchon *Ursus* 12:2001.

34. Analyze What behavior did the bears engage in most of the time?

35. Analyze Do the bears interact more often with other bears or with other species in this park?

36. Infer What can you infer about the habitat based on the data for foraging and eating?

***Connecting* CONCEPTS**

37. Write a Fable You may remember reading Aesop's fables as a child. A fable is a story that ends with a moral, or lesson, such as "the early bird gets the worm." This chapter described reasons for animal behaviors, various types of responses, and the situations in which behaviors might occur. Write a short fable about an animal's behavior, in which the moral of the story illustrates the adaptive value of the behavior.

38. Analyze Consider again the chimpanzee shown on page 817. Why might scientists be interested in studying tool use in primates such as chimpanzees?

Analyzing Data

34. eating
35. with other bears
36. Because they spend only a small amount of time looking for food compared to the time they spend eating the food, it is likely that when they do find a location with food, there is a lot of it. They do not have to spend too much time looking for food.

INDIANA ISTEP+ Test Prep

B.3.5; B.7.1; B.8.5; NOS.8

Test Practice
For more test practice, go to ClassZone.com.

1 Students plan an experiment to determine whether fish exhibit different feeding behaviors when presented with food flakes of different colors. The students predict that fish will be able to see brightly colored flakes more easily and will therefore eat more of these flakes. This prediction ***most*** closely resembles a scientific

A theory.
B hypothesis.
C conclusion.
D law.

2 A female ground squirrel may send out a call warning her offspring that a predator is near. Often, the mother sacrifices her own life since the predator can more easily locate her from the call. Even though this behavior results in death, it is beneficial to her in that

A half of her alleles are preserved in each offspring.
B all of her alleles are preserved in each offspring.
C the predator may be less likely to attack the population again.
D the alleles that caused her behavior will no longer be in the gene pool.

3

This action illustrated above will ***most*** likely result in a response produced by the

A nervous system.
B respiratory system.
C endocrine system.
D immune system.

4 When a frog hunts, it catches its prey with one flick of its long, sticky tongue. Energy obtained from eating the insect that is ***not*** stored in newly made body structures is

A lost to the environment as heat.
B converted into sugars.
C passed on to offspring.
D recycled within the frog.

THINK THROUGH THE QUESTION
Consider the flow of energy though an energy pyramid. In which directions does energy flow?

5 Which of the following ***best*** illustrates natural selection?

A Primates that don't use a tool to get more food are less likely to be eaten by predators.
B Primates that don't use a tool to get more food have more time to breed.
C Primates that use a tool to get more food are more likely to survive and reproduce.
D Primates that use a tool to get more food are more likely to eat too much.

6

Alleles for Rabbit Fur Color

Allele	Trait
F	gray fur
f	brown fur

In a hypothetical rabbit species, females prefer to mate with brown males over gray males. Fur color is a trait controlled by one gene that can occur in a dominant form (*F*) or a recessive form (*f*). A gray female (*Ff*) mates with a gray male (*Ff*), and they produce a brown male offspring. How is this possible?

Standards-Based Assessment

1. B	4. A
2. A	5. C
3. A	6. See Below

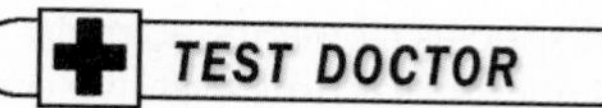

Question 1 Answer B is correct. Answer A is incorrect because a theory is a proposed explanation for a wide variety of observations and experimental results. Answer C is incorrect because the students have not determined an answer from data; they've simply made an educated guess. Answer D is incorrect because a law, similar to a theory, is a widely accepted, proposed explanation for a wide variety of observations and experimental results.

Question 2 Answer A is correct. Answer B is incorrect because only half of her alleles are passed to (and thus preserved in) each offspring. Answer C is incorrect because it does not explain how this change in behavior would increase the likelihood of the female ground squirrel passing on her alleles. Answer D is incorrect because half of her alleles are present in her offspring.

Question 6 A new combination of alleles (ff) formed in the offspring during fertilization.

Connecting Concepts

37. Stories should include plausible animal behaviors, and morals of story should illustrate adaptive nature of behavior (for example, an early bird gets the worm, behavior leads to survival of bird).

38. Learning about tool use in primates may provide researchers with clues as to how tool use developed in humans.

ITEM CORRELATIONS

Standard	Items
B.3.5	4
B.7.1	6
B.8.5	5
NOS.8	1

UNIT

8

Introduce

Tell students that of the 10 million to 100 million species of plants, animals, fungi, and microorganisms that live on Earth, only about 1.75 million species have been identified. In recent years, scientists have begun to add information about these species to databases of biodiversity. However, many different databases exist—all of the existing databases are not available to everyone, and not all of the identified species are in a database.

In the United States, the Biological Resources Division of the U.S. Geological Survey (USGS) works with partners to develop, maintain, and update the National Biological Information Infrastructure (NBII). The NBII is an information system that makes biodiversity information available to everyone. The website also provides links to many of the other available electronic biodiversity databases.

On an international level, organizations and companies are working to make biodiversity data easily accessible. For example, the Global Biodiversity Information Facility is an organization that makes biodiversity data from sources around the world available in an electronic form. The data include information about biodiversity from natural history collections, library materials, and existing databases.

Discuss the availability of biodiversity databases with students. **Ask**

- Why do you think one large database with all identified species does not exist? *Sample Answers:* The number of species is too large; the species are located all over the world; not all the data is electronic.
- Why are databases of biodiversity important? Databases make information available to everyone, people can view more complete records and information, and information can be more readily shared.

UNIT 8: ANIMALS

BIOZINE at CLASSZONE.COM

INTERNET MAGAZINE

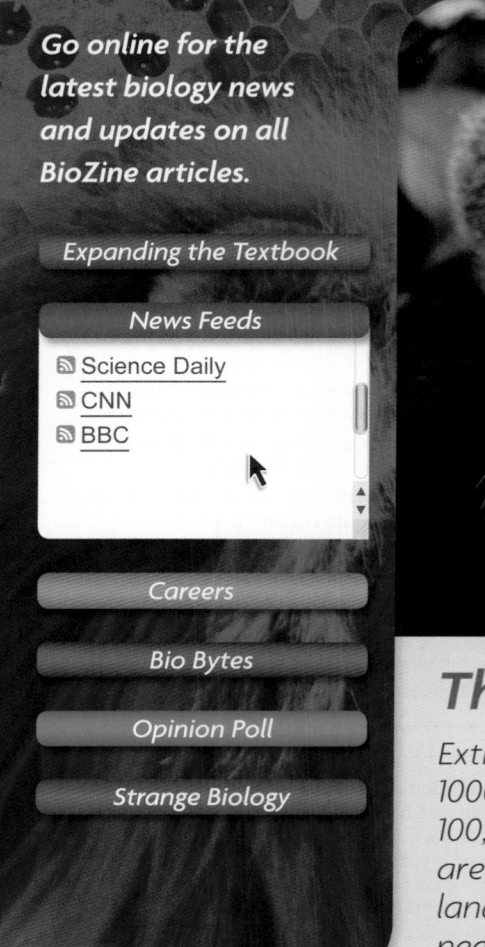

Go online for the latest biology news and updates on all BioZine articles.

Expanding the Textbook

News Feeds

Science Daily
CNN
BBC

Careers

Bio Bytes

Opinion Poll

Strange Biology

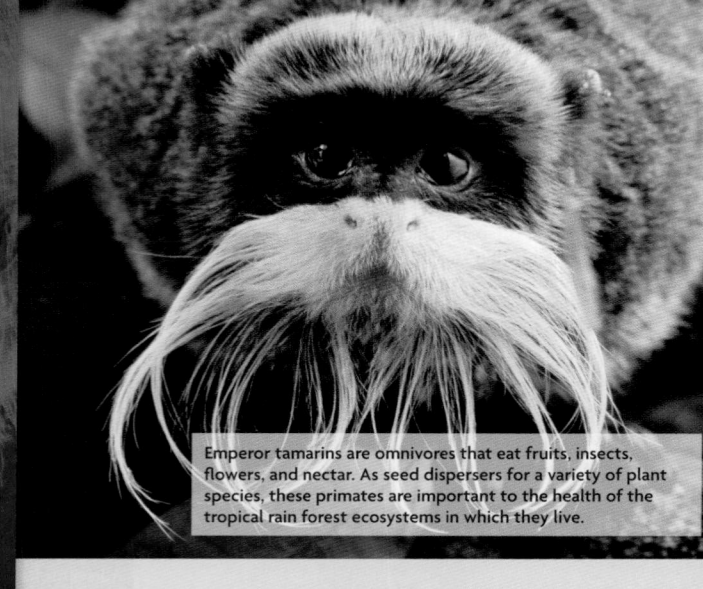

Emperor tamarins are omnivores that eat fruits, insects, flowers, and nectar. As seed dispersers for a variety of plant species, these primates are important to the health of the tropical rain forest ecosystems in which they live.

The Loss of Biodiversity

Extinction is occurring at a rate that is 1000 times faster than any time in the past 100,000 years. Wide swathes of rain forest are being destroyed as humans develop the land for agriculture and other human needs. Because rain forests are areas with high biodiversity, each time an acre of land is lost, species that once lived there may be lost as well. Why is biodiversity important? How does its loss affect you?

Current News

Have students look for stories about species loss and extinction in the Current News section of BioZine at **ClassZone.com.** Have students consider these questions:

- Is there any pattern to which organisms seem to get the most attention?
- Are animals much more likely to get attention than other kingdoms of organisms?
- How many of the stories involve the issue of biodiversity, and how is it defined?

Did You Know?

Of the 45 species of bats found in the continental United States, six are listed as endangered, with another 20 species considered to be a special concern. Have students go to BioZine to read the "Did you know?" of the day. Have students discuss what makes the information interesting or surprising.

Biodiversity at Risk

At present, we are losing more species than we are finding. Across the globe, animal species that are known to be threatened with extinction include

- 12 percent of all birds
- 30 percent of all fishes
- 24 percent of all mammals
- 20 percent of all amphibians

Biologists think that there are least 10 million, and possibly as many as 100 million, species of living organisms. At current rates of extinction, over half of these species will be gone by the end of this century. Extinction is a natural process and is always occurring. Using evidence from the fossil record, the background extinction rate is calculated to be between 10 and 100 species per year. However, the current rate of extinction greatly exceeds that number. Hundreds of thousands of species will disappear before we are even aware of their existence.

Does Biodiversity Really Matter?

Some people might suggest that biodiversity belongs in a zoo and the rest of the world belongs to humans to develop. Arguments in favor of development include the following:

- The rise and fall of species is part of nature. No species lives forever. New species replace old ones.
- Economic development provides jobs to people who are living in poverty.
- Land set aside as wilderness could be better used as farmland to provide more food for a rapidly increasing human population.

Conservation biologists view the pro-development arguments as shortsighted. Their view is that the Earth must be maintained for future generations, not simply harvested to provide for the needs of its current population. In fact, they argue that biodiversity plays an important part in ecosystem stability.

TECHNOLOGY

Bioremediation

Microorganisms can be used to clean up wastes that are spilled. Some bacteria can eat substances that would be fatal to humans and most other animals. Using microorganisms to clean up a polluted environment is called bioremediation.

1. Toxic waste, such as crude oil, is spilled on soil or in water.
2. The waste kills most bacteria, but a few survive and adapt.
3. Surviving bacteria feed on the toxins that were spilled and break them down. They may change the toxin to another form that is not dangerous, break the compound into smaller parts, or completely degrade it into inorganic molecules such as carbon dioxide and water.
4. Oxygen and nutrients are added so that more bacteria will survive to help break down the toxins.
5. When the spill has been completely broken down, bacteria die because they have run out of food.

Sometimes the needed microbes do not naturally occur in the contaminated site. When this is the case, the clean-up crew adds the specialized microbes to the site to break down the toxins.

Read More >> at CLASSZONE.COM

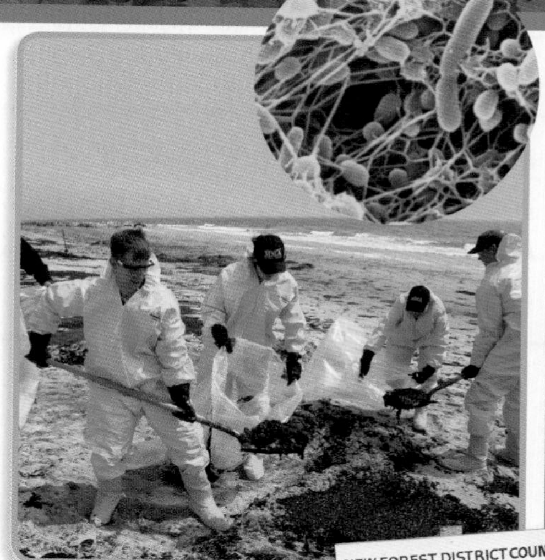

Clean-up crews use the *Pseudomonas putida* bacteria (inset) to decontaminate soil polluted by oil spills. (colored SEM; magnification 300×)

Vocabulary of Biodiversity

Students may need clarification of some of the terms used in the study of biodiversity.

endangered species—a species that is in danger of extinction throughout all or a significant portion of its range.

threatened species—a species that is likely to become endangered in the foreseeable future.

biodiversity—the variety of plants, animals, and other living things on Earth and the natural patterns it forms. Biodiversity is important because species interact and depend on one another. Biodiversity has three components: species diversity, ecosystem diversity, and genetic diversity.

species richness—the total number of different species in a community. Species richness is one part of species diversity in a community. The other part is the proportion of the total number of individuals that each species represents. A rain forest has much more species richness than an apple orchard does.

genetic diversity—the variation in the genetic composition of individuals within or among species.

conservation biology—the branch of biology that strives to preserve genetic diversity in plants and animals and also to determine the effect humans have on biodiversity.

biodiversity hot spots—areas that are the most rich in plant and animal species but the most threatened by human activities. Madagascar, the Philippines, the Caribbean, and parts of Brazil are a few of the 34 biodiversity hot spots that have been identified.

Expanding the Textbook

Have students go to BioZine at **ClassZone.com** to read more about animal species biodiversity. You could extend the discussion by having students research species diversity of animals that live in their state. **Ask**

- In what biome do you live?
- How does climate affect biodiversity?
- Which ecosystems in the state have the most biodiversity?
- Which species are endangered? threatened?

Have students calculate the percentages for the number of endangered and threatened species in their state.

UNIT

8

Take It Further

Scientists track biodiversity loss. As a result of tracking, lists are developed that identify plants and animals as being endangered of becoming extinct. Then steps are taken to try to prevent their extinction.

The World Conservation Union, also known as the International Union for the Conservation of Nature and Natural Resources (IUCN), is the world's largest conservation network. The Union forms a network made up of countries, government agencies, non-government organizations, and scientists. One function of the Union is to create and make available IUCN Red Lists, which include all the threatened species throughout the world. These lists are widely recognized as the most comprehensive lists for evaluating the status of species.

In addition to the Red Lists, some individual countries and states have their own lists for species in their areas. In the United States, the U.S. Fish and Wildlife Service is responsible for a list of threatened and endangered species. Once a species is listed, it is protected under the Endangered Species Act.

Individuals can contribute to tracking species by joining various organizations and volunteering. For example, the Audubon Society has a program called Citizen Science that provides opportunities for individuals to collect data on birds.

The Value of Biodiversity

Ecosystems provide human communities with a number of services free of charge, including air and water purification, flood and drought control, pollination of crops and other vegetation, dispersal of seeds, and nutrient cycling. These services have an economic value. If it were possible for humans to pay for ecosystem services based on their market value, biologists estimate that the cost would be approximately $33 trillion annually.

In general, the more species that live in an ecosystem, the more efficient and stable that ecosystem will be. For example, a rain forest can produce much more oxygen than an orchard full of apple trees. Also, many plants, including 75 percent of the world's staple crop plants, need animal pollinators such as birds and insects to help them reproduce.

In addition, 40 percent of all medicines are derived from plants, animals, and microbes. For example, biologists are developing a painkiller based on an extract from the skin of an Ecuadorian frog. The painkiller is 200 times stronger than morphine, but is not addictive. Every time a plant, animal, or microbe becomes extinct, biologists lose whatever knowledge they might have been able to gain by studying it.

In general, the more species that live in an ecosystem, the more efficient and stable that ecosystem will be.

By the mid-1970s, peregrine falcon populations had declined between 80 and 90 percent. Today, their numbers have rebounded. They were taken off the endangered species list in 1999.

Unanswered Questions

As you have learned, biodiversity is very valuable. Yet questions remain about how best to protect biodiversity. Two of these unanswered questions include

- How can we slow down the current extinction rate?
- Some of the areas with the highest amount of biodiversity are located in developing countries. How can biodiversity be preserved without harming the country's economic growth?

Read More >> at CLASSZONE.COM

CAREERS

Conservation Biologist in Action

ANGEL MONTOYA
TITLE Senior Field Biologist, The Peregrine Fund
EDUCATION M.S., Wildlife Science, New Mexico State University

In 1990 Angel Montoya was a student intern working at Laguna Atascosa National Wildlife Refuge in Texas. He became interested in the Aplomado falcon, a bird of prey that disappeared from the southwestern United States during the first half of the 20th century. Montoya decided to go looking for the raptors, and he found a previously unknown population of Aplomados in Chihuahua, Mexico. His work helped to make it possible for the falcons to be reintroduced to an area near El Paso, Texas.

Restoration of the Aplomado falcon became Montoya's life work. He has monitored and researched the falcon since 1992. He helps release falcons that have been raised in captivity back into the wild, and monitors falcons that have already been released. It isn't easy to keep tabs on a falcon, however. "Their first year they are pretty vulnerable because they haven't had parents," Montoya says. "Just like juveniles, they're always getting into trouble. But I think they will do just fine."

Read More >> at CLASSZONE.COM

BIOZINE ClassZone.com

Have students use the resources available in the Unit 8 BioZine at **ClassZone.com** to report about recent discoveries of new species, the threat to a known species, or the loss of a species. In addition to the BioZine sources, have students work with a librarian to locate other sources. **Ask**

- Where are the species you read about found?
- Why is the species you read about important?

Careers

Have students go to BioZine to learn about careers that involve animals. Have them consider the following questions as they read about the careers:

- What careers involve research and the collection of data about species of animals?
- What type of field work does the scientist do?
- What role do scientists in different careers have in conservation and slowing the loss of biodiversity?

UNIT 9

Human Biology

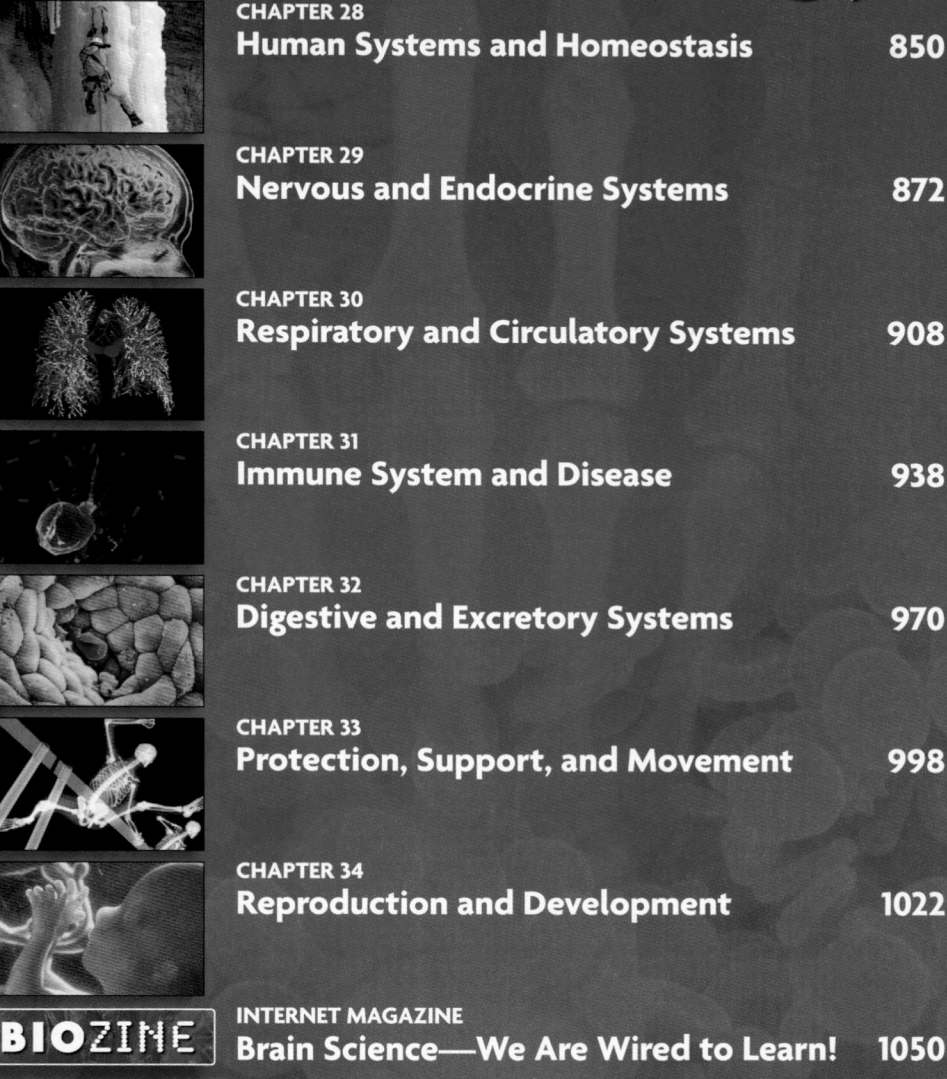

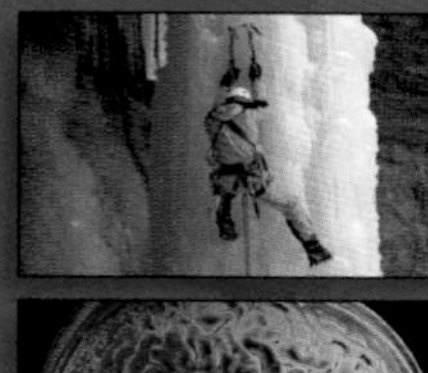
CHAPTER 28
Human Systems and Homeostasis 850

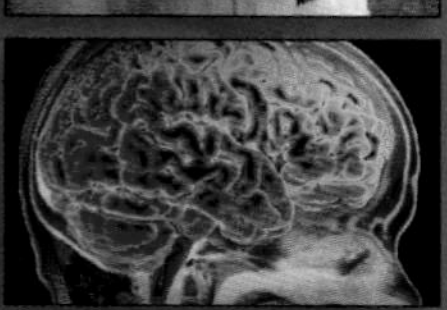
CHAPTER 29
Nervous and Endocrine Systems 872

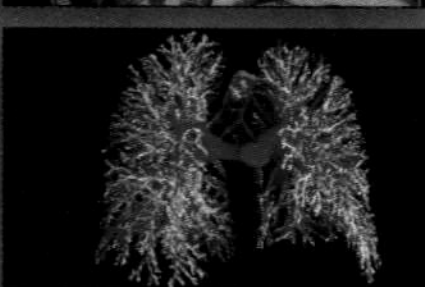
CHAPTER 30
Respiratory and Circulatory Systems 908

CHAPTER 31
Immune System and Disease 938

CHAPTER 32
Digestive and Excretory Systems 970

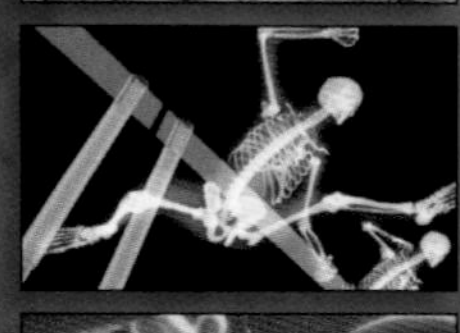
CHAPTER 33
Protection, Support, and Movement 998

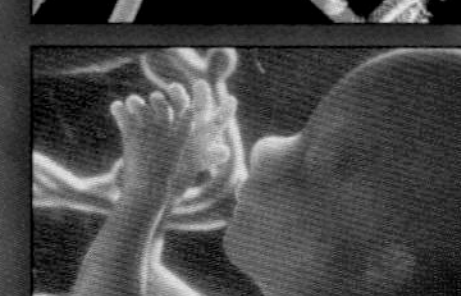
CHAPTER 34
Reproduction and Development 1022

INTERNET MAGAZINE
Brain Science—We Are Wired to Learn! 1050
TECHNOLOGY Scanning the Brain
CAREER Neuroscientist

Unit Project

Purpose Examine personal food choices, relate diet to nutrition, and understand the relationship between balanced nutrition and healthy body functions.

Overview Students analyze two food guide pyramids and compare them to the USDA food guide pyramid. Students will

- analyze and compare two food guide pyramids to the USDA food guide pyramid
- consider some of the scientific community's objections to the USDA food guide pyramid
- use food guide resources to plan a healthful diet for one week
- write an essay that explains why personal food choices are important to health and well-being

Preparation Make a copy of the project description and rubric for each student (*Unit Resource Book,* pp. 199–200).

Project Management Allow three weeks for the completion of the project. Have students check in weekly to monitor progress.

Unit Resource Book Unit 9 Project, pp. 199–201

CHAPTER 28

Indiana Resource Preview

Print Resources

Human Systems and Homeostasis

INDIANA STANDARDS		Sections	PAGES and PACING	UNIT RESOURCE BOOK
B.6.3	28.1	**Levels of Organization** **KEY CONCEPT** The human body has five levels of organization.	pp. 852–856 30 minutes	URB pages 1–4
NOS.3		CHAPTER INVESTIGATION: Homeostasis and Exercise	p. 857 45 minutes	**Lab Binder** Human Bio pages 1–4
	28.2	**Mechanisms of Homeostasis** **KEY CONCEPT** Homeostasis is the regulation and maintenance of the internal environment.	pp. 858–861 30 minutes	URB pages 5–8
	28.3	**Interactions Among Systems** **KEY CONCEPT** Systems interact to maintain homeostasis.	pp. 862–865 30 minutes	URB pages 9–12
NOS.1		DATA ANALYSIS: Interpreting Inverse Relationships	p. 865 30 minutes	URB page 13
NOS.3		OPTIONS FOR INQUIRY	pp. 866–867 45 minutes, 45 minutes	**Lab Binder** Human Bio pages 5–7
		Chapter Review	pp. 868–871	**Assessment Book** Chapter Tests A, B pp. 557–564

INDIANA STANDARDS

B.6.3 Explain that in multicellular organisms the zygote produced during fertilization undergoes a series of cell divisions that lead to clusters of cells that go on to specialize and become the organism's tissues and organs.
NOS.1 Develop explanations based on reproducible data and observations gathered during laboratory investigations.
NOS.3 Clearly communicate their ideas and results of investigations verbally and in written form using tables, graphs, diagrams, and photographs.

Labs

PUPIL EDITION LABS

Homeostasis and Exercise, p. 857 Students measure the effects of exercise on body systems. **Lab Binder** pp. 1–4	**Time:** 45 minutes **Materials:** jump rope, stop watch
Negative Feedback Loop, Section 2, p. 861 Students model a negative feedback loop. **Lab Binder** p. 8	**Time:** 5 minutes **Materials:** hardcover book at least 6" × 9"

OPTIONS FOR INQUIRY

Examining Human Cells, p. 866 Students observe cells and relate structure to function. **Lab Binder** pp. 5–6	**Time:** 45 minutes **Materials:** slide of skeletal-muscle cells, slide of bone cells, slide of nerve cells, microscope
Hormones and Homeostasis, p. 867 Students research the effects of an endocrine disorder on homeostasis. **Lab Binder** p. 7	**Time:** 45 minutes **Material:** Computer with Internet access

LAB BINDER Unit 9 Human Biology

Additional Investigation: Negative and Positive Feedback, pp. 9–14

LAB GENERATOR

A searchable CD of all labs in the program in editable format, including forensic, probeware, and biotechnology labs.

Presentation Tools

POWER PRESENTATIONS

Presentation Chapter 28
Power Presentations for each section incorporate images and clips from the Media Gallery: Includes Note Navigator for each section.

MEDIA GALLERY

Contains the following images and video clips, as well as animations, simulations and forms of visuals from the book.

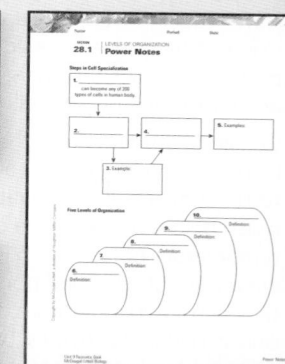

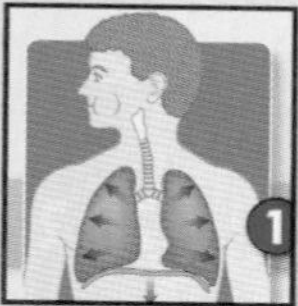
Negative feedback

Homeostasis

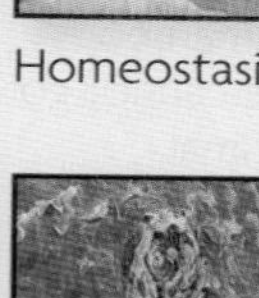
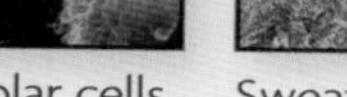
Alveolar cells

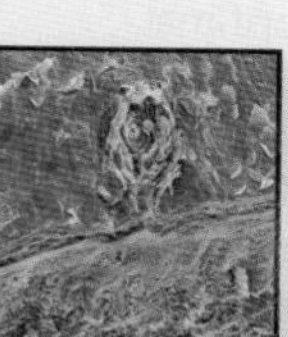

Sweat pore

Power Notes

VIDEO

View a set of short video clips exploring how the body maintains homeostasis.

ANIMATED BIOLOGY

Human Organ Systems

Keep an Athlete Running

TRANSPARENCIES

Levels of Organization in the Human Body T11

Online BIOLOGY CLASSZONE.COM

BioZine

Animated Biology

Interactive Review

SciLinks

Resource Centers

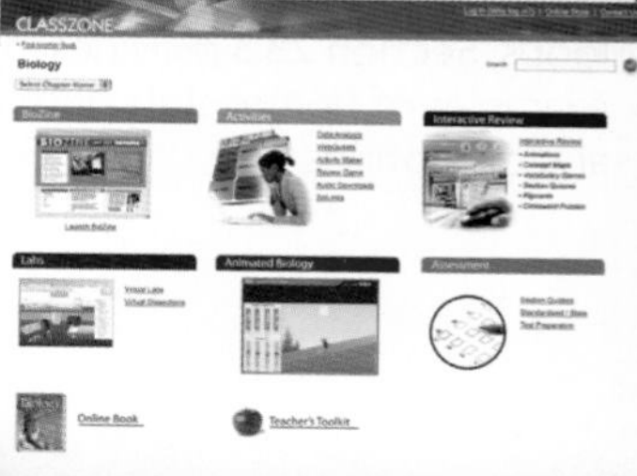

CHAPTER 28

▼ Focus and Motivate

How does this ice climber hang on to his body temperature?

Have students read the caption under Connecting Concepts. **Ask,** What cell process provides the energy and heat necessary for survival? cellular respiration

Explain to students that the body does its own balancing act. For a human body to function, body temperature cannot go much below or above the optimal temperature of 37°C (98.6°F), no matter what the outside conditions are. Maintaining body temperature depends not only on cellular activities, but also on different body systems working together. In particular, the endocrine and nervous systems interact to stabilize body temperature. Point out that the heat given off during cellular respiration helps to maintain internal body temperature.

BIOZINE ClassZone.com

Students can access BioZine at **ClassZone.com** to learn about some of the latest research in the biological sciences.

In a Hurry?

Levels of organization can be reviewed using the headings and **FIGURES 28.3** and **28.4** in **Section 28.1.** Focus on **Section 28.2** to make sure students understand homeostasis and feedback loops. **Section 28.3** provides in-depth examples of homeostatic interactions and disruptions.

CHAPTER 28 Human Systems and Homeostasis

KEY CONCEPTS

28.1 Levels of Organization
The human body has five levels of organization.

28.2 Mechanisms of Homeostasis
Homeostasis is the regulation and maintenance of the internal environment.

28.3 Interactions Among Systems
Systems interact to maintain homeostasis.

Online BIOLOGY CLASSZONE.COM

Animated BIOLOGY
View animated chapter concepts.
- Human Organ Systems
- Keep an Athlete Running

BIOZINE
Keep current with biology news.
- Featured stories
- News feeds
- Careers

RESOURCE CENTER
Get more information on
- Levels of Organization
- Organ System Interactions

Teacher Demo

Model Demonstrate the effectiveness of water as a cooling agent, modeling the effect of sweat on cooling the body.

Materials
- 2 test tubes in test-tube rack
- hot tap water in plastic-foam cup
- dropper
- timer
- 2 thermometers
- paper towels
- 2 rubber bands

Safety Wear safety goggles and heat-resistant gloves.

How does this ice climber hang on to his body temperature?

This climber has to concentrate on every move—one slip could mean serious injury or even death. His body is working just as hard on the inside to provide energy and to maintain a stable body temperature. The climber's clothes help prevent heat loss, while his body's internal systems increase his body heat.

Connecting CONCEPTS

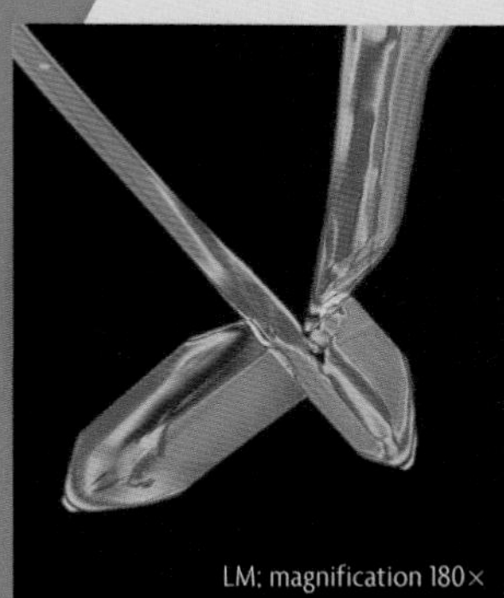

Biochemistry Recall that the metabolic processes in cells release energy stored in nutrients. The thyroid gland produces hormones that regulate cell metabolism. One hormone, thyroxine (shown here under polarized light), stimulates cells to produce more energy when needed. In this chapter, you will learn about the body's organ systems and the control mechanisms that maintain homeostasis.

Demonstrate

- Wrap a dry paper towel around one test tube and a wet paper towel around the other. Secure each towel with a rubber band.
- Use the dropper to fill the two test tubes with hot water.
- Place a thermometer into each test tube. Note the temperature of the water on the board, then make a temperature reading of the water in each tube every minute for ten minutes.

After ten minutes, the data should show that the water in the "wet" tube has cooled at a rate faster than that in the "dry" tube.

Discuss The water in the "wet" tube returns to equilibrium (room temperature) faster than the water in the "dry" tube. When body temperature rises, the hypothalamus activates the sweat glands. **Ask**

- What effect do you think sweating has on body temperature? Sweating helps decrease body temperature through the cooling effect of evaporation.
- Why it is that on a humid day, no amount of sweating seems to help? For sweat to cool the body, it must evaporate from the skin. Moisture in the air limits evaporation.

Activate Prior Knowledge

Direct students' attention to the photograph of the ice climber. **Ask,** How quickly do you think this climber will reach the top of the ice wall? It will take a long time. For the climber to move even a short distance requires careful coordination and planning at each step.

Discuss with students their experience of activities that require a high degree of attention and coordination, for example, skateboarding or ballet. **Ask,** What would it be like for you if you had to concentrate on every step you took or every movement of your hands? would be hard to do anything

Discuss that the human body maintains coordination between cells, tissues, and systems that goes well beyond anything a human can experience at a conscious level. Tell students that in this chapter, they will see how body systems must work together to maintain life.

Preview Vocabulary

Academic Vocabulary In this chapter, students will see some familiar words linked and used in a new context:

determination, fixing of the quantity, quality, position, or character of something

commit, to bind or obligate

differentiate, to become specialized; to acquire a different character

Cells in a developing zygote undergo a process of *determination* that *commits* them to *differentiate* into a particular type of cell.

English Learners Students have seen the words *structure* and *function* in their study of cells and organelles. Tell them that in this chapter, they will be looking at levels of organization or structure that starts with the cell.

cell → tissue → organ → organ system → organism

The structure of cells and the tissues and organs they form enable a certain *function,* or job, to be done. Have students watch for words in the text that are "function" words: *support, protect, transmit, receive, move, regulate, absorb, secrete.* Students should approach this chapter with these questions in mind: What job does a structure do, and how does it do it?

Chapter 28: Human Systems and Homeostasis **851**

SECTION 28.1

▼ Plan and Prepare

Objectives

- Describe cell specialization and levels of organization.
- Identify how levels of organization work together in an organism.

Section Resources

Unit Resource Book Study Guide pp. 1–2 Power Notes p. 3 Reinforcement p. 4 Pre-AP Activity pp. 15–16
Interactive Reader Chapter 28 **Spanish Study Guide** pp. 283–284
Biology Toolkit pp. C6, C19, D3, D9
Technology Power Presentation 28.1 Media Gallery DVD Online Quiz 28.1

Activate Prior Knowledge Have students think about the way employees in a large company are organized. **Ask,** How would you describe the relationship between different jobs, divisions, and levels of responsibility in a company? Every part of the company is dependent on every other part functioning properly and efficiently. Tell students that in this section, they will learn about how the body levels of organization work together.

▼ Teach

TEACH FROM VISUALS

FIGURE 28.1 Have students observe the differences in appearance of the cells. **Ask**

- In what way are all the cells in the body alike? have the same DNA
- What accounts for the differences in these two cells? Different genes are turned off and on depending on cell type.

Remind students of the Hox genes they learned about in genetics.

28.1 Levels of Organization

KEY CONCEPT The human body has five levels of organization.

MAIN IDEAS

- Specialized cells develop from a single zygote.
- Specialized cells function together in tissues, organs, organ systems, and the whole organism.

VOCABULARY

determination, p. 852
differentiation, p. 853
tissue, p. 854
organ, p. 854
organ system, p. 854

Review
cell, stem cell, zygote

INDIANA STANDARDS

B.6.3 Explain that in multicellular organisms the zygote produced during fertilization undergoes a series of cell divisions that lead to clusters of cells that go on to specialize and become the organism's tissues and organs.

Connect Climbing a wall of ice requires careful interaction among all parts of the body. You probably know that the brain and muscles work together to coordinate the climber's movements. The heart and lungs also have to work together to help provide energy for the climb. Yet every human body starts out as a single cell, a fertilized zygote. How does a single cell give rise to all the different types of cells, tissues, and organs in the human body? Further, how do such different parts coordinate their activities to keep the body functioning?

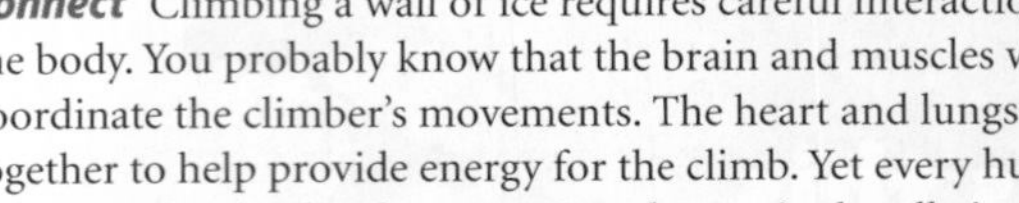

MAIN IDEA

Specialized cells develop from a single zygote.

If you were to watch an emergency medical team in action, you would quickly notice that each person has a special job. One keeps in radio contact with the main hospital. Another monitors the patient's vital signs. Still others perform life-saving procedures. All emergency teams are made up of people, but each person within the group has a different job.

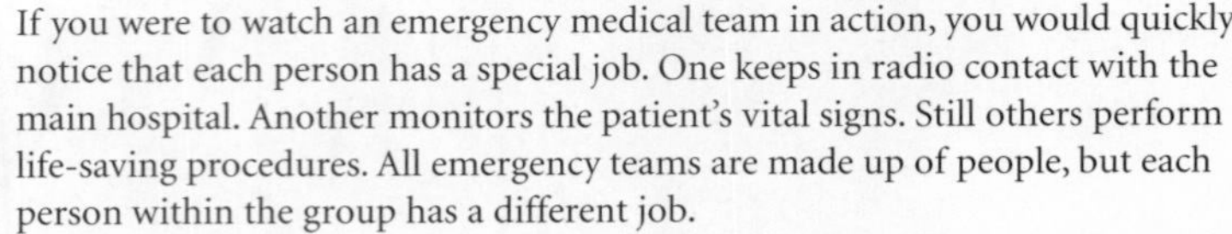

FIGURE 28.1 The disk-shaped red blood cells (top) carry oxygen to all parts of the body. The neuron (bottom), through its extensions, receives and transmits messages from and to other neurons. (colored SEMs; magnifications: blood cells 2800×; neuron about 1600×)

Likewise, multicellular organisms are made up of cells, but different cells in the organism have different functions. Take a moment to study the images of the blood cells and nerve cells, or neurons, in **FIGURE 28.1.** You will notice that the red blood cells are round with a concave center. This structure gives them more surface area to help deliver oxygen to all parts of the body. In contrast, neurons develop extensions that transmit and receive messages from other neurons.

Humans, like almost all multicellular organisms, are collections of specialized cells that work together. These cells arise from a single cell, the zygote, which is formed by the union of an egg and sperm. The zygote divides and differentiates into more than 200 different types of human cells. These cells allow you to do everything from lifting a glass, to learning people's names, to maintaining your body temperature on a cold day. Cell specialization involves two main steps: determination and differentiation.

Determination

The cells produced during the first few divisions of the zygote are known as embryonic stem cells. These cells have the potential to become any type of specialized cell in the body. Within a few weeks, however, a process called **determination** occurs in which most stem cells become committed to develop

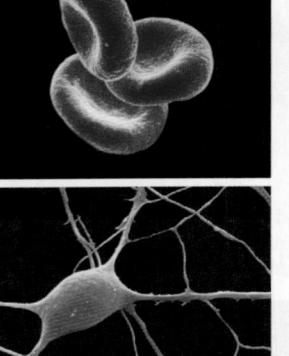

Differentiated Instruction

ENGLISH LEARNERS

Have students preview the chapter by having them look at headings, illustrations, and key terms. Ask them to predict what will be important and why they think so. Set up a four-column table with the headings: *What I Know I Know, What I Think I Know, What I Think I'll Learn, What I Learned.* Have students fill in the first three columns, leaving the last column empty until they complete the chapter.

Biology Toolkit, DRTA, p. C6

into only one type of cell. For instance, a stem cell might become a cardiac muscle cell or a spinal neuron. These committed cells still retain all of the genetic information needed to build an entire organism. However, during determination, they lose their ability to express some of this information.

Once a cell is committed to becoming a specialized cell, it will develop into only that type of cell. For instance, a cell that will become a neuron can only be a neuron, even if it is transplanted into another part of the body. During normal development, determination cannot be reversed.

TAKING NOTES

Use a supporting main ideas strategy to take notes about processes such as cell specialization.

Specialized cells develop from embryonic stem cells.
- *determination—cells are committed to be one type of cell*
- *differentiation*
- *supporting detail*

Differentiation

Differentiation is the process by which committed cells acquire the structures and functions of highly specialized cells. Differentiation occurs because specific genes in each cell are turned on and off in a complex, regulated pattern. The different structures of these specialized cells, such as those shown in **FIGURE 28.2**, allow them to perform specific functions within the body.

The function of muscle cells, for example, is to produce movement by contracting and relaxing. However, skeletal muscle and smooth muscle cells have different structures. Skeletal muscle cells align in bands of orderly rows and contain many nuclei. They are responsible for nearly all voluntary muscle movements, such as lifting your foot to kick a ball. In contrast, smooth muscle cells are shorter and have only one nucleus. They perform involuntary movements, such as raising the hairs on your arms and legs.

Other cells have even more specialized structures and functions. Sperm cells, for instance, develop whiplike tails that enable them to swim. Cells lining the gut are elongated and tightly packed to provide more surface area for the absorption of nutrients.

Not all cells continue to develop into specialized cells. The process of programmed cell death, called apoptosis (AP-uhp-TOH-sihs), is also a normal part of development. For example, when your hands first formed, your fingers resembled a mitten. The death of cells between the fingers allowed individual fingers to develop.

FIGURE 28.2 Cell Differentiation

Cells develop specialized structures and functions during differentiation.

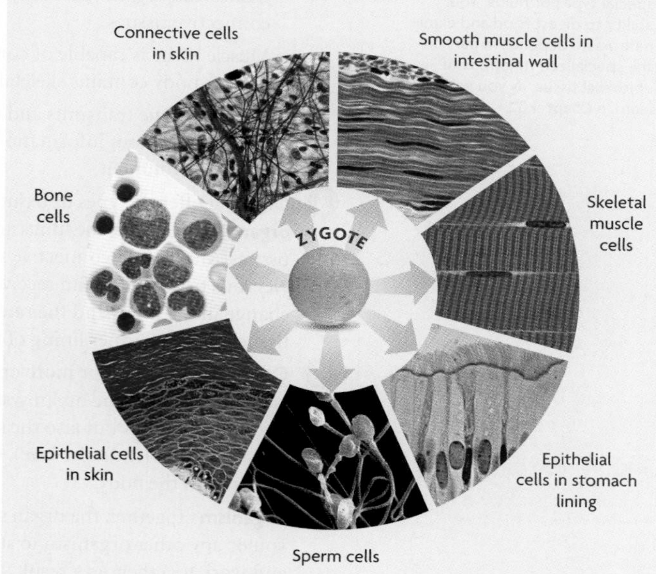

A **Analyze** **What are some of the reasons that multicellular organisms need specialized cells?**

B **Contrast** **How do the structures of sperm cells and epithelial cells in the stomach differ?**

Vocabulary

Greek and Latin Word Origins Students know the word **species,** which shares the same Latin root as the word *special,* meaning "of a certain kind." Tell students that it is possible to think of **specialized** cells as belonging to a species. A "species" of muscle cell is distinct from a "species" of skin cell, in a similar sense that one species of bird is different, yet similar, to another.

The Inside Story

What does it mean that you are 16 or 17 years old if your cells regularly replace themselves? **Dr. Jonas Frisén,** a stem-cell biologist at the Karolinska Institute in Stockholm, has developed a way to estimate the ages of human cells. He developed a scale for converting the carbon-14 in tissues into calendar dates. Using this dating technique, Dr. Frisén estimates the average age of all the cells in an adult's body may be seven to ten years.

A hotly debated topic is whether the brain generates new neurons. Using his technique, Dr. Frisén has shown that cells from the visual cortex in the brain are the same age as the individual. These are the cells that enable you to see and interpret what you see. Still to be determined are whether the cells associated with the cerebral cortex, involved with memories and consciousness, are also as old as you are.

BELOW LEVEL

Have students note how key vocabulary are used in the text. In their notebooks, have them write what each word means based on their reading of the text. Have them check the definition in the Glossary. Then have students use the word in a sentence and draw a picture that will help them remember the meaning.

Biology Toolkit, Student Vocabulary, p. D3

PRE-AP

Tell students that there are about 25 trillion red blood cells in the human body, each with a life span of about 100–120 days. Red blood cells that are worn out and die are replaced by new cells produced in the bone marrow and stored in the spleen. Have students calculate the number of blood cells the human body loses due to natural cell death each second. 25 trillion cells ÷ 10.4 million seconds = 2.4 million cells per second This is about half the number of red blood cells in one cubic millimeter of blood.

Answers

A **Analyze** Multicellular organisms need specialized cells to build specialized tissues and organs that carry out functions such as respiration, digestion, and elimination. Specialization also allows multicellular species to become much larger than unicellular species can.

B **Contrast** Sperm have a head and a long tail that enables them to move. Epithelial cells are elongated, are tightly packed, and have hairlike cilia at the surface to move materials.

▼ Teach *continued*

ONLINE BIOLOGY Go to the chapter Resource Center at **ClassZone.com** for additional resources and information on levels of organization.

Science Trivia

- Skin is the largest organ of the human body.
- Unlike other organs that are distinct and separate structures, skin covers the entire body.
- Adults have about 1.7 square meters (20 ft^2) of skin.
- Skin makes up about 15–20 percent of a person's body weight.
- Every minute approximately 30,000–40,000 dead skin cells are removed from the body.
- In a person's lifetime, he or she will lose around 18 kilograms (40 lb) of dead skin.
- Your body will produce an entirely new layer of skin in one month's time.

MAIN IDEA

Specialized cells function together in tissues, organs, organ systems, and the whole organism.

Specialized, or differentiated, cells are only the first level of organization in a multicellular organism. Scientists organize multicellular structures into five basic levels, beginning with cells and moving to increasingly complex levels—tissues, organs, organ systems, and the whole organism. These five levels in the human body are shown in **FIGURE 28.3**.

1. **Cells** Each type of specialized cell has a particular structure and a chemical makeup that enable it to perform a specific task. Some cells in the lungs, for instance, are involved in the exchange of gases. Others secrete mucus that helps to trap foreign particles and to protect the lungs from pathogens, such as bacteria and viruses.
2. **Tissues** Groups of similar cells that work together to perform a specialized function are known as **tissues.** The human body is made up of four general types of tissues.
   - Epithelial tissue consists of protective sheets of tightly packed cells connected by special junctions. The skin and the membranes that line the stomach, the lungs, and other organs are epithelial tissues.
   - Connective tissue serves to support, bind together, and protect other tissues and organs. Tendons, ligaments, bone, and cartilage are all connective tissues.
   - Muscle tissue is capable of contracting to produce movement. The human body contains skeletal, cardiac, and smooth muscle tissues.
   - Nervous tissue transmits and receives impulses in response to stimuli, processes information, and regulates the body's response to its environment.
3. **Organs** Different types of tissue that function together form an **organ.** For example, the lungs are organs composed of all four types of tissues. Muscle and connective tissues expand and contract the lungs. Nervous tissue sends and receives messages that help regulate gas exchange in the lungs and the rate at which a person breathes. Epithelial tissue forms the inner lining of the lungs.
4. **Organ systems** Two or more organs working in a coordinated way form an **organ system.** The organ system that allows you to breathe includes not only the lungs but also the sinuses, the nasal passages, the pharynx, and the larynx (the voice box). Organ systems perform the most complex activities in the body.
5. **Organism** Together, the organ systems make up the entire organism. For you or any other organism to stay alive, all of the systems must interact and work together. As a result, anything that harms one organ or organ system will affect the health of the entire body.

***Connecting* CONCEPTS**

Digestion and Elimination In addition to serving as a protective layer, epithelial tissue can absorb materials and secrete special types of fluids. Your ability to digest food and eliminate waste depends in part on the specialized functions of epithelial tissue, as you will learn in **Chapter 32.**

Differentiated Instruction

TEACH WITH TECHNOLOGY

Students might enjoy viewing a portion of the 1966 film *Fantastic Voyage.* In this science fiction film, a miniaturized medical team is inserted into the human bloodstream with the goal of removing a blood clot in the brain of an important scientist. The film was made long before the advent of computer animation yet provides an entertaining realization of the body.

PRE-AP

The human body, with its five levels of organization, can be compared to the structure of an ecosystem with its different levels of organization. Have students explore this analogy by developing a visual presentation that illustrates their interpretation of this idea. Students should provide a written explanation of the thinking behind their interpretation.

Biology Toolkit, Analogies, p. D9

FIGURE 28.3 Five Levels of Organization

All levels of organization interact and work together to maintain the body's health.

Animated BIOLOGY
Explore the human organ systems at ClassZone.com.

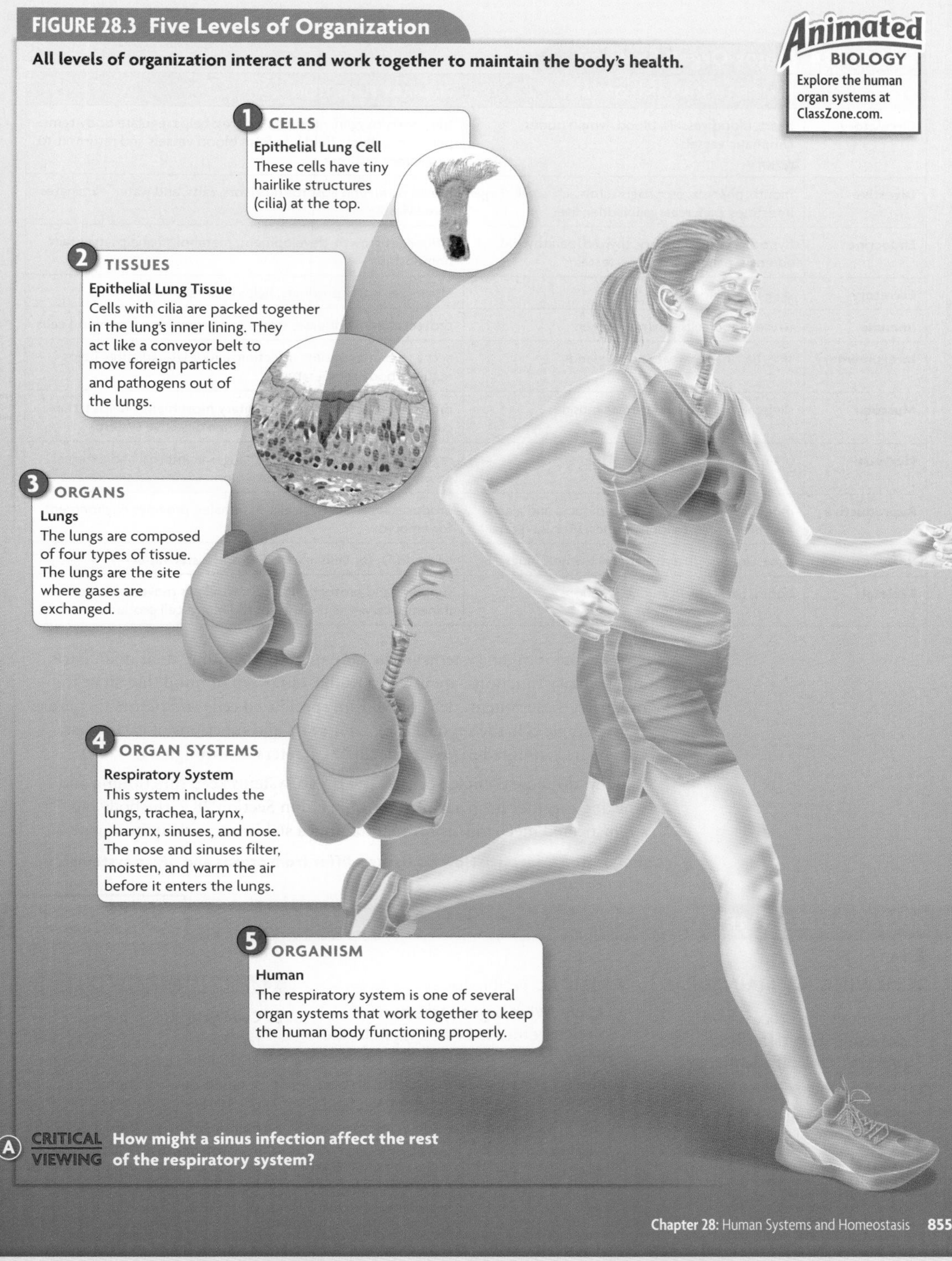

1 CELLS
Epithelial Lung Cell
These cells have tiny hairlike structures (cilia) at the top.
2 TISSUES
Epithelial Lung Tissue
Cells with cilia are packed together in the lung's inner lining. They act like a conveyor belt to move foreign particles and pathogens out of the lungs.
3 ORGANS
Lungs
The lungs are composed of four types of tissue. The lungs are the site where gases are exchanged.
4 ORGAN SYSTEMS
Respiratory System
This system includes the lungs, trachea, larynx, pharynx, sinuses, and nose. The nose and sinuses filter, moisten, and warm the air before it enters the lungs.
5 ORGANISM
Human
The respiratory system is one of several organ systems that work together to keep the human body functioning properly.

(A) CRITICAL VIEWING **How might a sinus infection affect the rest of the respiratory system?**

BELOW LEVEL

Have students look at the full list of systems in **FIGURE 28.4.** Point out that the first letter of each system can be used to make the words *miners* and *cider.* After reviewing the information, have students close their books. Give them five minutes to write down as many systems as they can remember and a function for each. To help them remember, remind them that *miners* like *cider.*

Biology Toolkit, Quick-Write, p. C19

TEACH FROM VISUALS

FIGURE 28.3 Point out to students that the numbers in the diagram correspond to the numbered list on page 854. **Ask**

- What cells are featured in the figure, and what system do they belong to? epithelial cells of the lung and respiratory system
- Looking at the drawing of the girl and the organs identified in caption 4, what parts of the respiratory system lead from the nose to the lungs? nose leads to pharynx and larynx, then to trachea and into lungs
- What is the primary function of the respiratory system? exchange of gases, supply oxygen needed to release energy, remove waste carbon dioxide

Science Trivia

- The size of an average human body cell is ten micrometers.
- It would take over 39 million cells to cover the floor of a high school basketball court.
- It would take 6000 cells to cover a sheet of notebook paper.
- Roughly 1000 cells would be needed to cover a dollar bill.

Answers

(A) Critical Viewing Air first enters through the nose and sinuses, where it is filtered, moistened, and warmed. If the sinuses were blocked by infection, the person would have to breathe through the mouth and there would be a greater chance of harmful pathogens or foreign matter entering the lungs. Drainage from the sinuses could also spread pathogens to the airways, producing a lower respiratory infection.

▼ Teach *continued*

Take It Further

In 1989, the National Library of Medicine set out to create a digital atlas of the human body called the **Visible Human Project.** The University of Colorado Heath Sciences Center created the atlas by combining CT and MRI images of cross sections of a male and a female cadaver. Both bodies, from a 39-year-old male and a 59-year-old female, had been donated to science. The Visible Human Project provides medical, research, and educational communities with the unique opportunity to see organs and systems in relation to one another, along the entire length of the human body.

Answers

A Compare and Contrast Tissues are composed of one specific type of differentiated cell. Organs consist of two or more types of tissues. Organ systems are composed of two or more organs working in a coordinated fashion. Organs and organ systems perform more complex activities than tissues do.

FIGURE 28.4 Major Organ Systems

SYSTEM	MAJOR TISSUES AND ORGANS	PRIMARY FUNCTION
Circulatory	heart, blood vessels, blood, lymph nodes, lymphatic vessels	transports oxygen, nutrients, wastes; helps regulate body temperature; collects fluid lost from blood vessels and returns it to circulatory system
Digestive	mouth, pharynx, esophagus, stomach, small/large intestines, pancreas, gallbladder, liver	breaks down and absorbs nutrients, salts, and water; eliminates some wastes
Endocrine	hypothalamus, pituitary, thyroid, parathyroid, adrenals, pancreas, ovaries, testes	influences growth, development, metabolism; helps maintain homeostasis
Excretory	skin, lungs, kidneys, bladder	eliminates waste products; helps maintain homeostasis
Immune	white blood cells, thymus, spleen	protects against disease; stores and generates white blood cells
Integumentary	skin, hair, nails, sweat and oil glands	acts as a barrier against infection, injury, UV radiation; helps regulate body temperature
Muscular	skeletal, smooth, and cardiac muscles	produces voluntary and involuntary movements; helps to circulate blood and move food through digestive system
Nervous	brain, spinal cord, peripheral nerves	regulates body's response to changes in internal and external environment; processes information
Reproductive	*male:* testes, penis, associated ducts and glands *female:* ovaries, fallopian tubes, uterus, vagina	produces reproductive cells; in females, provides environment for embryo
Respiratory	nose, sinuses, pharynx, larynx, trachea, lungs	brings in O_2 for cells; expels CO_2 and water vapor
Skeletal	bones, cartilage, ligaments, tendons	supports and protects vital organs; allows movement; stores minerals; serves as the site for red blood cell production

The major organ systems in the human body, including their main parts and primary functions, are listed in **FIGURE 28.4**. Keep in mind that all of the organs in these systems developed from specialized cells and tissues that arose from a single cell, the zygote. The major parts and functions of each organ system are examined in greater detail in Chapters 29 through 34.

How do these complex organs and organ systems keep functioning and working together properly? As you will read in Section 28.2, the body has sophisticated mechanisms for maintaining a stable internal environment.

A Compare and Contrast How do tissues differ from organs and organ systems?

▼ Assess and Reteach

Assess Use the Online Quiz or Section Quiz (*Assessment Book,* p. 553).

Reteach Have students make a graphic organizer that shows the hierarchical relationships among cells, tissues, organs, organ systems, and organism.

28.1 ASSESSMENT

ONLINE QUIZ ClassZone.com

B.6.3

REVIEWING MAIN IDEAS

1. How does the process of cell **determination** differ from the process of cell **differentiation**?
2. Briefly define and give an example of each of the five levels of organization in multicellular organisms.

CRITICAL THINKING

3. **Apply** What **organ systems** must work together to bring oxygen to the body's cells?
4. **Predict** A cell has undergone determination to become an endocrine gland cell. If it is transplanted to a leg muscle, what do you think will happen to this cell?

***Connecting* CONCEPTS**

5. **Cell Cycle** In the spring, tadpoles lose their tails as part of their life cycle. At a certain stage in development, the human fetus acquires individual fingers and toes. What occurs in some cells of both species to explain these changes?

28.1 ASSESSMENT

1. In cell determination, stem cells commit to becoming a certain type of cell, such as a muscle cell. In cell differentiation, cells develop the actual structures and functions that make them specialized cells.
2. A cell is the smallest unit of life (example: neuron). A tissue is a group of similar cells that work together to perform a specialized function (example: nerve tissue). Organs consist of two or more types of tissues that function together (example: brain). Organ systems consist of two or more organs working together (example: brain and spinal cord).
3. The respiratory system brings oxygen into the body. Part of the muscular system coordinates the movement of the lungs. The circulatory system picks up oxygen from the lungs and delivers it to body cells.
4. Because determination is usually not reversible, the cell and its daughter cells will continue to develop as endocrine cells.
5. Both are examples of programmed cell death, or apoptosis.

MATERIALS
- jump rope
- stop watch

PROCESS SKILLS
- Observing
- Collecting data

NOS.3 Clearly communicate their ideas and results of investigations verbally and in written form using tables, graphs, diagrams, and photographs.

Homeostasis and Exercise

Your body's temperature, heart rate, and blood pressure need to remain within certain set ranges. In this lab, you will work in groups to examine the effects of exercise on the circulatory and respiratory systems and on perspiration level.

PROBLEM How does exercise affect a person's heart rate, breathing rate, and perspiration level?

PROCEDURE

1. Choose one person to jump rope. Measure the person's heart rate by taking his or her pulse for 15 seconds. Multiply this number by four to calculate beats per minute. (**Caution:** If the person exercising feels discomfort at any time, stop the experiment and inform your teacher.)
2. Measure the person's breathing rate by counting the number of breaths taken in 15 seconds. Multiply this number by four to calculate breaths per minute.
3. Rate the person's perspiration level from 1 to 5 (1 = none; 5 = droplets dripping down the face).
4. Design a data table like the one shown below. Write a hypothesis about the effect of exercise on the dependent variables that you are measuring.
5. Have the person jump rope for 2 minutes. When the person stops, measure heart rate, breathing rate, and perspiration level and record the data. Repeat step 5 three more times and record your data at each point.
6. After the final recording of the dependent variables, wait 1 minute and measure all of the variables again.

TABLE 1. EFFECTS OF EXERCISE

Time (Min)	Heart Rate (Beats/Minute)	Breathing Rate (Breaths/Minute)	Perspiration Level
0			
2			
4			
6			
8			
9			

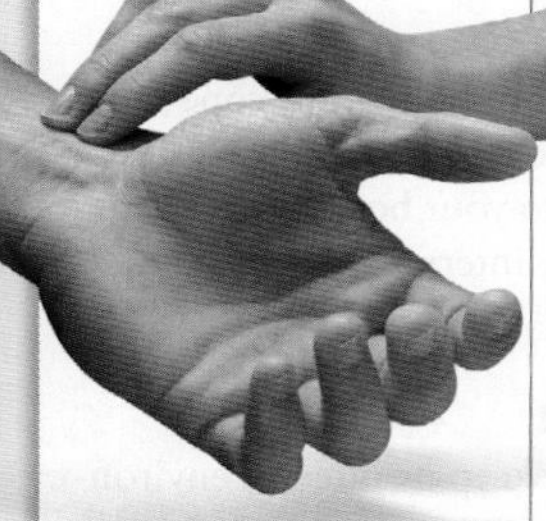

ANALYZE AND CONCLUDE

1. **Identify Variables** What is the independent variable in this experiment?
2. **Organize Data** Graph the relationship between the independent and dependent variables. You may choose one graph to display all of your data, or you may use separate graphs for each of the dependent variables. Explain your graph choice.
3. **Summarize** What are the effects of exercise over time on the circulatory and respiratory systems and on perspiration level?
4. **Synthesize** What other processes could you have measured to determine the external and internal effects of exercise on the body?
5. **Infer** How is perspiration level related to body temperature? How is perspiration related to homeostasis?

Answers

Sample Data

For a sample of student graphs from this lab, go to page R108.

Analyze and Conclude

1. amount of time spent exercising
2. Graphs can be line graphs, bar graphs, or a combination of both. Heart and breathing rates can be placed on one y-axis with perspiration level on a second.
3. Exercise leads to increased heart rate, breathing rate, and perspiration level.
4. *Sample Answer:* blood pressure and body temperature
5. Higher perspiration level indicates higher body temperature. Perspiration is one way the body cools itself to maintain a fairly constant body temperature.

INVESTIGATION

Time 45 minutes TEACHER TESTED
Teacher Preparation
Student Difficulty
Lab Binder Human Bio, pp. 1–4

Purpose Measure the effects of exercise on body systems.

Overview Student teams will test the effect of exercise on the circulatory, respiratory, and integumentary systems. They will
- predict the effect of exercise on heart rate, breathing rate, and perspiration level
- graph the relationships between the independent and dependent variables, using the data collected

LAB PREPARATION

Move furniture to create an open space.

LAB MANAGEMENT

Ask for one or two volunteers to jump rope for the experiment.

Extend the readings at the end of the investigation to see how long it takes to return to the resting rates.

Safety Caution students to stop jumping if they feel uncomfortable and to inform you right away. Any student who has a health problem that could be exacerbated by physical activity should not be allowed to jump rope.

POST-LAB DISCUSSION

Relate the variables tested to homeostasis. **Ask,** Why do heart rate and breathing rate increase with exercise? During exercise, muscle cells demand more energy. More oxygen must be taken in for cellular respiration to produce energy, so the breathing rate increases. The heart rate increases so that the blood can quickly deliver oxygen to the muscles.

Teacher Note "Students are able to make connections beyond homeostasis and inquire about relationships between breathing and heart rate."

SECTION 28.2

▼ Plan and Prepare

Objectives

- Relate homeostasis to the internal environment of the body.
- Explain how negative and positive feedback loops maintain homeostasis.

Section Resources

Unit Resource Book Study Guide pp. 5–6 Power Notes p. 7 Reinforcement p. 8 Pre-AP Activity pp. 17–18
Interactive Reader Chapter 28 **Spanish Study Guide** pp. 285–286
Biology Toolkit pp. C18, C39, D8
Technology Power Presentation 28.2 Media Gallery DVD Online Quiz 28.2

Activate Prior Knowledge Have students think about what it would be like to live in an environment that constantly hovers at 38°C (100°F). **Ask,** If you had to live your life constantly at one temperature setting, what would it be? Answers will vary, but most students will probably choose moderate temperatures. Discuss that the normal core body temperature is 37°C (98.6°F).

▼ Teach

ONLINE BIOLOGY Have students look at how a runner maintains homeostasis. See the simulation in Options for Inquiry on page 867.

Vocabulary

Academic Vocabulary Students may wonder if the word **homeopathy** relates to *homeostasis.* Homeopathy is a nonmedical approach to treating illness by using minute amounts of the *same* substance believed to be the cause. The principle is to "cure like with like" by stimulating the body's defenses. There are no conclusive scientific studies as to its effectiveness.

28.2 Mechanisms of Homeostasis

KEY CONCEPT Homeostasis is the regulation and maintenance of the internal environment.

MAIN IDEAS
- Conditions within the body must remain within a narrow range.
- Negative feedback loops are necessary for homeostasis.

VOCABULARY
homeostasis, p. 858
feedback, p. 859
negative feedback, p. 860
positive feedback, p. 861

Review
tissue, organ, organ system

Connect The complex tissues, organs, and organ systems in your body must respond to a wide variety of conditions. For instance, during the summer, you might walk out of a cold, air-conditioned store into a stifling hot summer day. Your body temperature has to remain the same under both conditions in order for you to survive. In fact, your life depends on your body's ability to maintain the delicate balance of your internal chemistry.

MAIN IDEA

Conditions within the body must remain within a narrow range.

During every moment of your life, trillions of chemical reactions are taking place in your body. The enzymes that control these reactions work best within a narrow range of conditions. One of these conditions is your internal body temperature, which should remain between 36.7°C and 37.1°C (98.2°F and 98.8°F). If it rises only a few degrees, you could easily die from overheating. At temperatures over 41°C (106°F), many enzymes stop functioning. If your internal temperature falls below 27°C (80°F), your heart may fail.

Likewise, the levels of trace minerals in your body must stay within strict limits. For instance, if calcium levels are too high, you can slip into a coma. If they are too low, your heartbeat becomes irregular.

You live in a constantly changing environment. Your body must cope not only with temperature changes but also with pollution, infection, stress, and many other conditions. Every change is a challenge to your body. What keeps the human body from breaking down every time the internal or external environment changes?

Homeostasis and the Internal Environment

Fortunately, the body has many control systems that keep its internal environment stable. Together, these control systems are responsible for maintaining homeostasis. **Homeostasis** (HO-mee-oh-STAY-sihs) is the regulation and maintenance of the internal environment—temperature, fluids, salts, pH, nutrients, and gases—within the narrow ranges that support human life. Your internal control systems respond quickly to change, whether from outside conditions or internal ones, as shown in **FIGURE 28.5.**

VOCABULARY
The word *homeostasis* is formed from two Greek words: *homos,* meaning "similar," and *stasis,* meaning "standing" or "stopping."

Differentiated Instruction

ENGLISH LEARNERS
Check on students' comprehension as you go through the material describing various control systems in the body. You can use simple signals, such as thumbs up or thumbs down for understanding. Or ask questions in which students write responses on a sheet of paper or an index card.

Biology Toolkit, Signals, p. C18; Card Responses, p. C18

Control Systems in the Body

Internal control systems require sensors, a control center, communication systems, and targets.

Sensors Sensors, also called receptors, gather information about conditions inside and outside of the body. In cold or hot weather, for instance, sensors in your skin and nasal passages gather data about air temperatures. The body has thousands of internal sensors and other specialized sensors that detect changes in the outside world.

Control center A control center, often the brain, receives information from the sensors. It then compares this information to the set points, or ideal values, at which the body functions best. When conditions move above or below a set point, the control center responds by sending messages through a communication system.

Communication systems Communication is controlled by the nervous system and the endocrine system, which carry messages to all parts of the body. These messages, in the form of nerve impulses or hormones, tell targets in the body how to respond to internal or external changes.

Targets A target is any organ, tissue, or cell that changes its level of activity in response to a message. For instance, in a cold environment, a message might cause the muscles to start shivering to generate more body heat.

FIGURE 28.5 Homeostasis and Change

Control systems in the skin help reduce or conserve body heat.

hot temperature
pore
sweat gland
Blood flow to the skin increases. Tiny muscles expand the pores. Sweat glands release water to cool the body.
normal temperature
hair follicle muscle
Pores and muscles are relaxed. Blood flow to the skin is normal. Sweat glands are not active.
cold temperature
goose bump
Blood flow to the skin decreases. Tiny muscles contract the pores and the skin around body hairs to conserve heat.

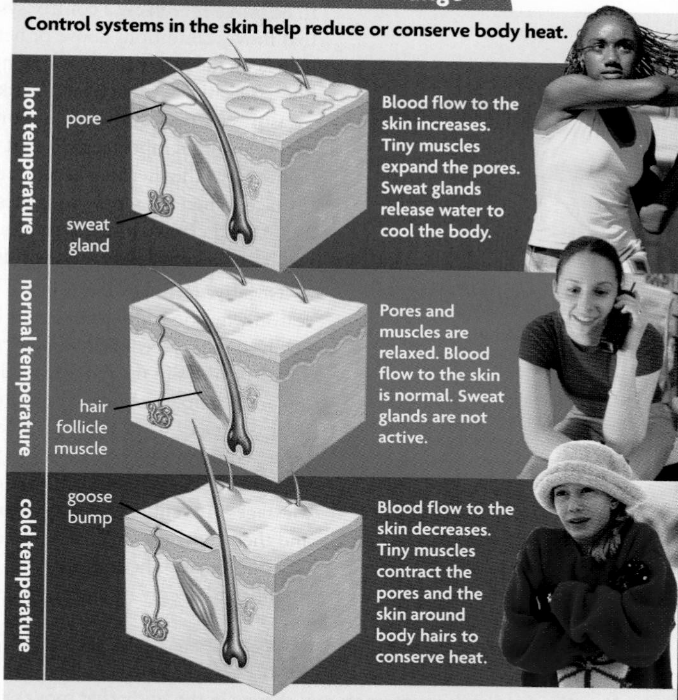

Ⓐ Apply **If the girl in cold temperature starts jogging, how would the control mechanisms in her skin respond as she runs?**

Ⓑ Draw Conclusions **Why is it so important to maintain homeostasis within the body?**

MAIN IDEA

Negative feedback loops are necessary for homeostasis.

Sensors, control centers, communication systems, and targets work together in what is known as a feedback loop. **Feedback** is information from sensors that allows a control center to compare current conditions to a set of ideal values. In a feedback loop, information moves continuously among sensors, a control center, and a target. Most functions in the body are regulated by negative feedback loops.

BELOW LEVEL

Have students relate homeostasis to feedback loops by using a graphic organizer, such as a concept definition map. A concept definition map starts with a general category, in this case, how a body regulates its internal environment. A particular concept is identified, either negative or positive feedback. Then students include separate boxes to list properties and examples of each concept. Students should also compare one to the other.

Biology Toolkit, Concept Definition Map, p. D8

TEACH FROM VISUALS

FIGURE 28.5 Explain the figure in terms of the four body control systems. Tell students that the control center for regulating body temperature is located in the hypothalamus region of the brain.

Ask

- What sensors are involved? temperature sensors in the skin
- What are the targets? sweat glands, blood vessels, and muscles in the skin
- What kinds of messages are involved in this communication system? nerve impulses and hormones

Answers

Ⓐ **Apply** Her skin would respond the way it does in hot temperatures: pores would open, and sweat glands would release water to cool the body.

Ⓑ **Draw Conclusions** The processes necessary for life work best within a narrow range of conditions. To maintain these ranges, the internal environment of the body must remain stable.

Vocabulary

Academic Vocabulary Point out to students how the words associated with a mechanical system are applied to a living system.

mechanism a system of parts that operate or interact like those of a machine

control an instrument used to operate, regulate, or guide a machine

sensor a device that receives and responds to a signal

set point the point at which a circuit is either activated or deactivated

target something aimed or fired at

feedback return of a portion of the output of a system to the input, used to maintain performance or control

loop a closed circuit

Chapter 28: Human Systems and Homeostasis 859

▼ Teach *continued*

Connecting CONCEPTS

Biochemistry Oxygen is used by the cell in the breakdown of glucose and the accompanying release of energy in the form of ATP. A lack of oxygen can lead to cell death because ATP production stops, and as a result, there is no energy for cell activities.

History of Science

The physiologist **Walter Bradford Cannon** coined the term **homeostasis,** which he described for the general public in 1932. In his book *The Wisdom of the Body,* he proposed these four general features of homeostasis:

1. The body, being an open system and subject to change, requires mechanisms to maintain constancy and a steady state.
2. Steady-state conditions require that any tendency toward change be met with resistance.
3. Homeostasis must be maintained by a regulating system that consists of a number of cooperating mechanisms acting simultaneously or in sequence.
4. Homeostasis does not occur by chance but is the result of organized self-government.

Answers

A Infer Sensors would detect too much oxygen and too little carbon dioxide in the blood. Your breathing would stop or slow down for a short time until the gases returned to their set points, then normal breathing would resume.

Negative Feedback

In **negative feedback,** a control system counteracts any change in the body that moves conditions above or below a set point. Negative feedback loops help keep the internal environment stable. A thermostat is a good example of how a negative feedback loop works. A sensor in the thermostat continuously measures air temperature in a room. A control mechanism then compares the current room temperature to a set point, say 21°C. When the temperature falls below 21°C, the thermostat sends an electronic message that turns on the furnace. When the sensor indicates the air temperature is at or just above 21°C, the thermostat sends another message that turns off the furnace. As a result, the room always stays within a few degrees of the desired temperature.

Negative feedback loops in the body work in a similar way. They are the reason why you cannot hold your breath for a long time. The control systems involved in this feedback loop are shown in **FIGURE 28.6.** As you hold your breath, sensors in the circulatory and respiratory systems send information to the brain stem, the body's respiratory control center. Sensors signal a gradual increase in carbon dioxide (CO_2) and a decrease in oxygen (O_2). The control center compares this information with the set points for these gases. When the change becomes too great, the control center takes steps to counteract it. Messages are sent to the muscles of the diaphragm and the rib cage to relax and then contract, forcing you to exhale and then inhale deeply. At this point, you cannot stop these muscles from moving. You will continue to breathe rapidly and deeply until the gas levels return to their set points.

Connecting CONCEPTS

Biochemistry As you read in **Chapter 4,** cells require a constant supply of oxygen to maintain cell metabolism. Oxygen is not stored in the human body in any great amounts. Once oxygen reserves have been used up, the body must have a fresh supply of oxygen to prevent cell death.

FIGURE 28.6 Negative Feedback Loop

Negative feedback counteracts any change in the body that moves conditions away from a set point.

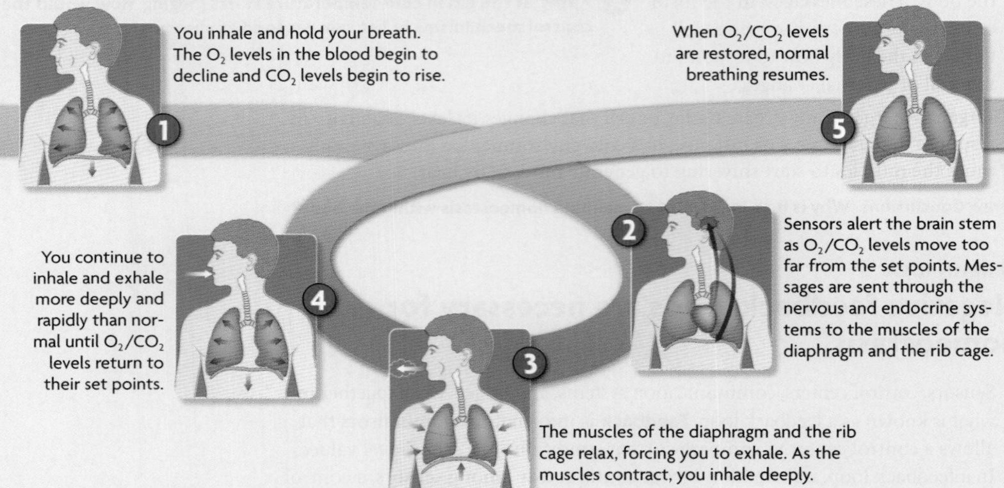

1 You inhale and hold your breath. The O_2 levels in the blood begin to decline and CO_2 levels begin to rise.
2 Sensors alert the brain stem as O_2/CO_2 levels move too far from the set points. Messages are sent through the nervous and endocrine systems to the muscles of the diaphragm and the rib cage.
3 The muscles of the diaphragm and the rib cage relax, forcing you to exhale. As the muscles contract, you inhale deeply.
4 You continue to inhale and exhale more deeply and rapidly than normal until O_2/CO_2 levels return to their set points.
5 When O_2/CO_2 levels are restored, normal breathing resumes.

A Infer If you continued to breathe rapidly and deeply for too long in step 4, how would this affect the negative feedback loop?

Differentiated Instruction

ENGLISH LEARNERS

Have students work with the analogy used in the text, comparing a negative feedback system in the body to a thermostat. Have students read the text and create two cycle diagrams. The first should show how a thermostat regulates temperature. The second can detail the negative feedback loop shown in **FIGURE 28.6.** Tell students to incorporate the terms *control system, sensor, set point, target, communicate,* and *feedback.*

Biology Toolkit, Cycle Diagram, p. C39

PRE-AP

Have students set up a cycle diagram that shows a fever as a combination of positive and negative feedback mechanisms. Tell students that the body raises its temperature in response to pathogens invading the body. Once the pathogens have been destroyed by heat, negative feedback brings the body temperature back down. Have students think about the experience of having a fever and relate physiological responses, such as shivering and sweating, to what is happening in the bloodstream.

Biology Toolkit, Cycle Diagram, p. C39

QUICK LAB MODELING

Negative Feedback Loop

You can experience a negative feedback loop by doing a simple demonstration.

MATERIALS
hardcover book at least 6" × 9"

PROBLEM How does a negative feedback loop work?

PROCEDURE

1. Balance the hardcover book on your head.
2. Walk 3 meters forward and backward—once with eyes open, then with eyes closed.

ANALYZE AND CONCLUDE

1. **Analyze** Describe the negative feedback loop that helped keep the book balanced on your head. How did closing your eyes affect your ability to balance the book?
2. **Connect** Think of another example of a negative feedback loop that you might observe in your everyday life. Explain how you think this loop works.

Positive Feedback

Negative feedback loops maintain homeostasis by counteracting, or reversing, change to return conditions to their set points. In some cases, however, the body actually needs change to accomplish a specific task. In **positive feedback,** a control center uses information from sensors to increase the rate of change away from the set points. Though not as common in the body, this type of feedback is important whenever rapid change is needed.

For example, if you cut your finger, positive feedback mechanisms increase the rate of change in clotting factors in the blood until the wound is sealed. Once the injury heals, another positive feedback loop occurs as chemicals are released to dissolve the clot. Positive feedback also occurs in the release of certain growth hormones during puberty. Your body needs higher levels of these hormones to accomplish all of the changes that take place at this time.

A Infer Why are most of the functions of the body regulated by negative, rather than by positive, feedback mechanisms?

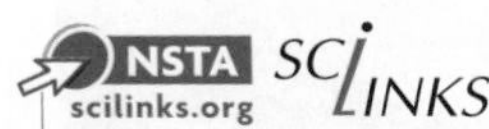

To find out more about homeostasis, go to scilinks.org.
Keycode: MLB028

28.2 ASSESSMENT

ONLINE QUIZ ClassZone.com

REVIEWING MAIN IDEAS

1. A system to maintain **homeostasis** must have at least four parts that function together. Name these parts and briefly explain what each one does.
2. What is the main difference between the way **negative feedback** and **positive feedback** mechanisms regulate change in the body?

CRITICAL THINKING

3. **Predict** When a newborn baby nurses, the mother's body is stimulated to produce milk. What would happen to the milk supply if the mother chose to bottle feed rather than breast feed? Why?
4. **Sequence** Suppose you go on a long hike in hot weather. Describe a possible negative feedback loop that would keep your body from overheating.

Connecting CONCEPTS

5. **Zoology** Reptiles regulate their body temperature by changing their environment. A snake, for instance, must lie in sunlight to warm its body. Mammals, on the other hand, can regulate their internal environment to gain or lose heat. How might this ability give mammals an advantage over reptiles?

28.2 ASSESSMENT

1. Sensors gather information. A control center analyzes and compares the information to the desired values. Communication systems send messages from the control center to regulate the change. Targets receive and respond to the messages.
2. Negative feedback loops counteract change to return to a set point, while positive feedback loops accelerate change away from a set point.
3. A baby nursing creates a positive feedback loop that causes the mother's body to lactate. Bottle feeding eliminates the stimulus.
4. Sensors would detect a rise in body temperature, increasing blood flow to the skin, activating sweat glands, and increasing heart and breathing rates.
5. Mammals can live in a wider range of habitats and tolerate rapid changes in external conditions.

QUICK LAB

Time 5 minutes
Lab Binder Human Bio, p. 8

Purpose Model a negative feedback loop.

LAB MANAGEMENT

Use books that are not too heavy.

Answers

Analyze and Conclude

1. As sensors in the scalp detect changes in the book's position, they send messages to control sensors in the brain, which then send messages to the muscles. Students may have adjusted their speed, shifted their head or body, or grabbed the book with their hands. When students closed their eyes, they lost sensory information about body position relative to their surroundings, which may have made the balancing task more difficult.
2. Other feedback systems include cooling systems in a car engine; thermostats that control air conditioners or furnaces; and the body's signals for hunger and thirst. All these feedback loops involve preset values and information about changing conditions that are relayed to control centers, which then send messages to targets to counteract changes and restore conditions to the preset values.

Answers

A Infer Negative feedback is the means by which the body maintains homeostasis. Positive feedback occurs only in situations in which a change away from set values is needed.

Assess and Reteach ▼

Assess Use the Online Quiz or Section Quiz (*Assessment Book,* p. 554).

Reteach Write the following headings on the board: Sensors, Control Center, Communication Systems, Targets. Have students tell you what to list beneath the headings for the respiratory control system shown in **FIGURE 28.6.**

SECTION 28.3

▼ Plan and Prepare

Objectives

- Describe the interaction between organ systems in terms of homeostasis.
- Describe the effect of disruption of homeostasis.

Section Resources

Unit Resource Book
Study Guide pp. 9–10
Power Notes p. 11
Reinforcement p. 12

Interactive Reader Chapter 28
Spanish Study Guide pp. 287–288

Biology Toolkit pp. C19, C20, C36, C38, C39

Technology
Power Presentation 28.3
Media Gallery DVD
Online Quiz 28.3

Activate Prior Knowledge Relate homeostasis to the idea of balance. **Ask,** What is it like to be on a balance beam or walking across a log bridge, and your weight shifts? Typically you move back and forth to reestablish balance; if you do not, you fall. Discuss how when one body system is out of balance, it affects others.

▼ Teach

TEACH FROM VISUALS

FIGURE 28.7 Have students observe what the members of the pit crew are doing. **Ask**

- What differentiates one member of the crew from another? Each has a specific job: refuel, check tires, check engine.
- What happens if a member of the crew is missing or does not do his job right? The car will not perform as it should, and could endanger the life of the driver.

Relate the analogy of the pit crew to the interaction of different systems in the body.

28.3 Interactions Among Systems

KEY CONCEPT Systems interact to maintain homeostasis.

MAIN IDEAS

- Each organ system affects other organ systems.
- A disruption of homeostasis can be harmful.

VOCABULARY

thermoregulation, p. 863

Review
homeostasis, feedback, negative feedback

Connect The moment a race car pulls in for a pit stop, the pit crew springs into action. Each person has a special role that must be coordinated with the efforts of the team. As one member jacks up the car, others are changing the tires, putting in fuel, and checking the engine. If anyone fails to do a job properly, it affects the entire team and places the driver at serious risk.

MAIN IDEA

Each organ system affects other organ systems.

At its most basic level, the body is a community of specialized cells that interact with one another. On a larger scale, all of the organ systems form a type of community regulated by feedback mechanisms. This interaction among organ systems means that what affects a single organ system affects the entire body.

Like highly trained crew members, each organ system in your body must do its own special job. But for you to remain healthy, each system also must coordinate with other organ systems through chemical messages and nerve impulses. The relationship among your organs and organ systems is not always obvious—for example, when the body produces a substance such as vitamin D. In other cases, you are more aware that some organs are affecting others, as in the regulation of your body temperature in hot or cold weather.

FIGURE 28.7 Precision teamwork is the secret to a pit crew's success. Likewise, your life depends on every organ system doing its job at the right time and in the right order.

Vitamin D Production

You may know that sunlight plays a part in the production of vitamin D in your body. You may not know that the liver, kidneys, circulatory system, and endocrine system are necessary for this process as well. The skin contains a substance that in the presence of ultraviolet light is changed into an inactive form of vitamin D. As **FIGURE 28.8** shows, this form enters the blood and is carried to the liver. The liver changes the inactive form of vitamin D into another compound, which is then carried to the kidneys. Here, this compound is converted into active vitamin D.

The blood transports active vitamin D throughout the body, where it interacts with hormones that regulate the amount of calcium and phosphorus in the body. These two minerals are essential for building strong bones. If any organ along this path fails to do its job, the level of vitamin D in the body decreases. Without enough vitamin D, children's bones do not develop normally. Adults lose bone mass, which means their bones break more easily.

Differentiated Instruction

BELOW LEVEL

Model for students how to interpret the text describing vitamin D production on page 862. Work with students to come up with a sequence diagram of the events described and the body systems involved. Students can refer to the **FIGURE 28.4** on page 856 for a summary of the body systems. Then suggest students do the same for thermoregulation on page 863.

Biology Toolkit, Sequence Diagram, p. C38

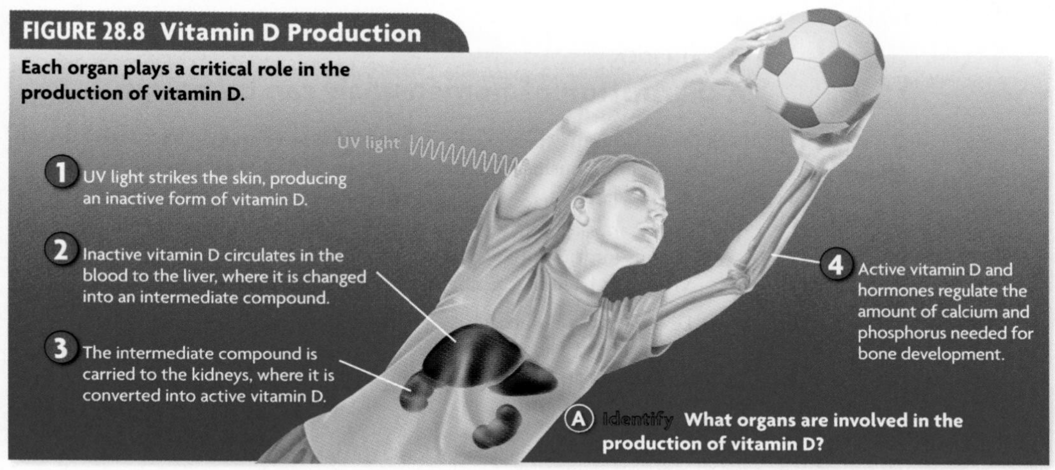

UV light
1 UV light strikes the skin, producing an inactive form of vitamin D.
2 Inactive vitamin D circulates in the blood to the liver, where it is changed into an intermediate compound.
3 The intermediate compound is carried to the kidneys, where it is converted into active vitamin D.
4 Active vitamin D and hormones regulate the amount of calcium and phosphorus needed for bone development.

FIGURE 28.8 Vitamin D Production

Each organ plays a critical role in the production of vitamin D.

(A) Identify **What organs are involved in the production of vitamin D?**

Regulation of Body Temperature

The process of maintaining a steady body temperature under a variety of conditions is known as **thermoregulation** (THUR-moh-REHG-yoo-LAY-shuhn). The most obvious organ systems involved in maintaining body temperature are the skin and muscles. You sweat in hot weather and shiver when you are cold. However, far more is going on than what you can see on the surface. Thermoregulation requires the close interaction of the respiratory, circulatory, nervous, and endocrine systems.

VISUAL VOCAB

Thermoregulation maintains a stable body temperature under a variety of conditions, just as a thermostat regulates a furnace. Both mechanisms use feedback to keep temperatures within set ranges.

control — THERMOSTAT — messages — FURNACE — target — info to control

Connecting **CONCEPTS**

Animals In **Chapter 26** you learned that animals have many ways of regulating their body temperatures. For example, some animals stay cool by panting, by being active only at night, or by getting rid of excess heat through their body structures, such as large ears or thin skins.

Sensors in the skin and blood vessels provide information about body temperature to a control center in the brain called the hypothalamus. The hypothalamus protects the body's internal organs by monitoring temperature. When the hypothalamus receives information that the temperature of the blood is rising, it sends messages through the nervous and endocrine systems. These messages activate the sweat glands, dilate blood vessels in the skin, and increase both heart and breathing rates. All of these activities carry heat away from the center of the body to the surface, where excess heat can escape.

When the temperature of the blood falls too low, the hypothalamus sends another set of signals to the skin and to the muscular, respiratory, and circulatory systems. Blood vessels in the skin constrict, reducing blood flow to prevent loss of heat. Muscles in the skin contract around the pores, reducing their size. Rapid, small contractions of skeletal muscles cause shivering. The thyroid gland releases hormones that increase metabolism. All of these activities increase body heat and reduce the loss of heat to the environment.

(B) Infer **If a person's circulatory system does not function well, how might thermoregulation in his or her body be affected?**

PRE-AP

Present this scenario: You and your friends have spent the day hiking on a cool fall day and are about to drive home. You see another hiker coming off the trail who is soaked and shivering. The hiker mentions having fallen into a stream. You are concerned that the hiker may be suffering from mild hypothermia, a lowered body temperature. Describe the steps you would take to assist this hiker en route to the local hospital.

Biology Toolkit, Quick-Write, p. C19

ONLINE BIOLOGY For more on thermoregulation and hypothermia, see the WebQuest in Options for Inquiry on page 867.

Integrating Physics

Thermoregulation is a balancing act between systems in the body that produce heat and those that lose heat.

All body tissues produce heat as a product of **metabolism**—as bonds break and new ones form. Tissues that are the most active metabolically produce the most heat. When at rest, most of the body's heat is produced by the liver, heart, brain, and endocrine glands. When in motion, the body's skeletal muscles produce 30–40 times the heat generated by the rest of the body.

Most heat loss occurs in the body by four different mechanisms. Any object that is warmer than its surrounding environment radiates heat into that environment. Under normal conditions, the body loses 25–40 percent of its heat by **radiation.** Direct contact with a cool object also causes the body to lose heat by **conduction. Convection** occurs as cool air replaces the warm air released by the body, creating more opportunity for heat loss. Conduction and convection account for 15–20 percent of the body's heat loss. **Evaporation** from the lungs, mouth, and skin remove substantial amounts of body heat. Water absorbs heat and, once it has gained enough energy, vaporizes.

Answers

(A) **Identify** The organs involved in vitamin D production are the skin, liver, and kidneys.

(B) **Infer** A person with an impaired circulatory system would be less able to lose heat in hot conditions and conserve heat in cold conditions.

▼ Teach continued

ONLINE BIOLOGY Go to the chapter Resource Center at **ClassZone.com** for additional resources and information on organ system interactions.

Integrating Medical Science

Type 2 diabetes, once thought to be an adult disease, is becoming more common in young people in the United States. The Centers for Disease Control and Prevention estimates that 206,000 people under the age of 20 have some form of diabetes.

A significant risk factor for Type 2 diabetes is being overweight or obese. The American diet has become loaded with processed foods that are high in fat and sugar. These factors along with a lack of exercise have put people at greater risk of increased weight and Type 2 diabetes. The percentage of children under the age of 19 who are overweight has increased from about 4.5 percent to about 15.5 percent in the last 40 years.

Take It Further

Diabetes is linked to **diabetic retinopathy,** which causes blindness. This condition develops as a result of the reaction between excess glucose in the blood and proteins in the body. Glucose and proteins react to form a complex in which the proteins lose their flexibility. As these proteins accumulate, they cause the walls of blood vessels to thicken and lose their elasticity. The weakened blood vessels bulge and eventually leak. Any amount of blood that leaks from blood vessels in the retina can obscure vision. Laser treatments can slow the leakage of fluid and reduce the amount of retinal fluid. Similar damage occurs in other parts of the body, but it is not as readily detectable as in the eye.

Answers

A Apply Muscle cells depend on glucose for energy. The less glucose available, the more difficult it is for muscles to perform work, repair injuries, or increase mass.

MAIN IDEA

A disruption of homeostasis can be harmful.

Some changes may be too great or too rapid for your body to control through feedback mechanisms. Homeostasis can be disrupted for several reasons.

- Sensors fail to detect changes in the internal or external environment.
- Wrong messages may be sent or the correct ones fail to reach their targets.
- Serious injuries can overwhelm the homeostatic mechanisms.
- Viruses or bacteria can change the body's internal chemistry.

Disruption of homeostasis can begin in one organ or organ system and result in a chain reaction that affects other organs and organ systems. These effects can be harmful to your body over the short or long term.

Short-Term Effects

Short-term effects usually last a few days or weeks. For example, when a cold virus first enters your body, your immune system may not be able to prevent the virus from multiplying. As a result, you develop a sore throat, runny nose, and dry cough, and your muscles and joints become inflamed. However, within a few days, your body's immune system begins to kill the virus and to restore homeostasis. Usually, there is no lasting harm to your body.

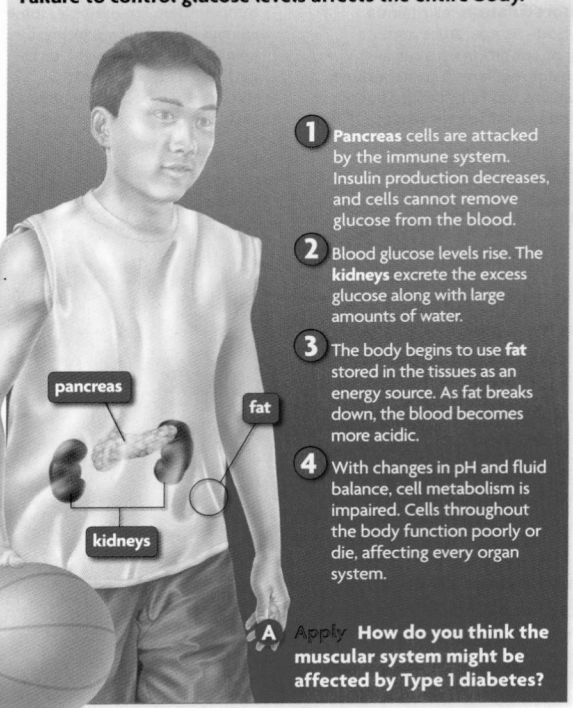

FIGURE 28.9 Type 1 Diabetes

Failure to control glucose levels affects the entire body.

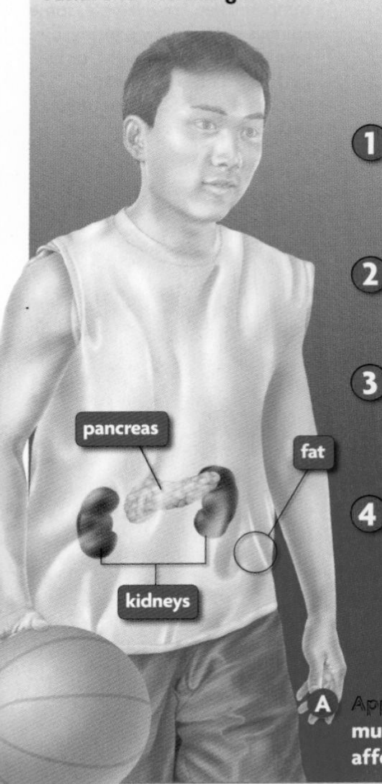

1. **Pancreas** cells are attacked by the immune system. Insulin production decreases, and cells cannot remove glucose from the blood.
2. Blood glucose levels rise. The **kidneys** excrete the excess glucose along with large amounts of water.
3. The body begins to use **fat** stored in the tissues as an energy source. As fat breaks down, the blood becomes more acidic.
4. With changes in pH and fluid balance, cell metabolism is impaired. Cells throughout the body function poorly or die, affecting every organ system.

A Apply **How do you think the muscular system might be affected by Type 1 diabetes?**

Long-Term Effects

A long-term disruption of homeostasis, as in the case of diabetes, can cause more damage. Diabetes occurs when the body fails to control the amount of glucose circulating in the blood.

Normal glucose control Glucose levels are controlled by two hormones—insulin and glucagon—which are released by the pancreas. When glucose in the blood rises above a set point, beta cells in the pancreas release insulin. Insulin causes cells to take in more glucose from the blood and causes the liver to store glucose as glycogen. When blood glucose levels fall below the set point, alpha cells in the pancreas release glucagon. This hormone stimulates the liver to break down stored glycogen into glucose and release it until levels in the blood rise to the set point.

Type 1 and Type 2 diabetes What if the pancreas fails to do its job? The result can be diabetes mellitus, a condition in which the body can no longer regulate glucose levels. There are two types of diabetes. Type 1 occurs when the body's immune system destroys the ability of beta cells to produce insulin. Type 2 is caused when insulin production decreases or when insulin cannot move glucose into cells.

Differentiated Instruction

ENGLISH LEARNERS

Point out the similarities among the names of one of the hormones and the sugar and fat involved in glucose regulation on page 864. Have student set up a T-chart in their notes with a category for hormones (insulin, glucagon) and stimulants (glucose, glycogen). The chart should include a description of the function of each.

Biology Toolkit, T-Chart, p. C20

BELOW LEVEL

Point out the example of diabetes described in the text on page 864. The text first describes the normal interaction of insulin and glucagon to control glucose levels. Have students represent this with a cycle diagram. Then, in contrast, have students create two cause and effect chains, one each for Type 1 and Type 2 diabetes. Have them compare this to the cycle diagram that represents normal homeostatic control of glucose.

Biology Toolkit, Cycle Diagram, p. C39; Cause and Effect Chain, p. C36

DATA ANALYSIS

NOS.1

INTERPRETING INVERSE RELATIONSHIPS

Two variables are inversely related if an increase in the value of one variable is associated with a decrease in the value of the other variable. For example, the level of insulin decreases the longer a person exercises. Therefore, insulin levels have an inverse relationship with exercise time. The graphs at right show the levels of insulin, glucose, and glucagon during moderate exercise over 250 minutes. Use the graphs to answer the questions.

GRAPH 1. INSULIN LEVELS

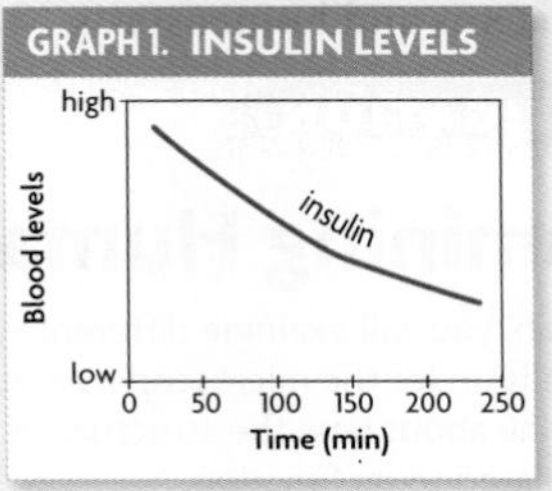

GRAPH 2. GLUCOSE LEVELS

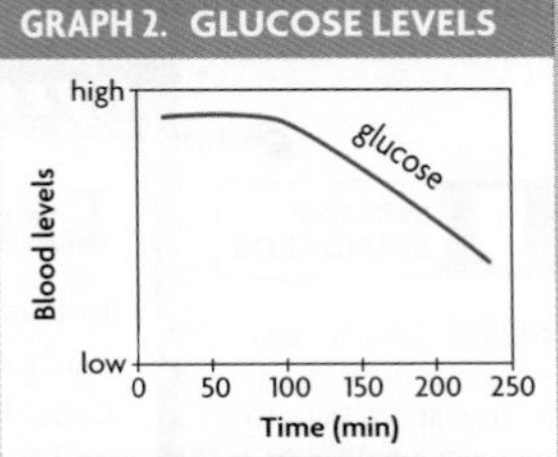

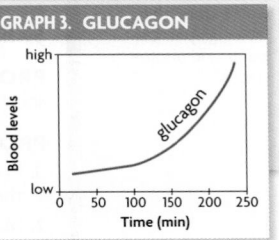

GRAPH 3. GLUCAGON

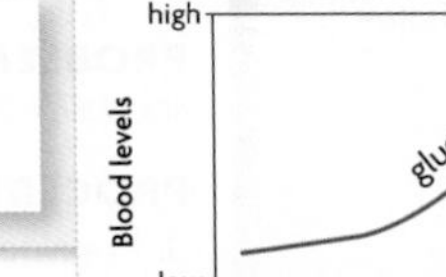

1. **Analyze** Which variable(s) has/have an inverse relationship with time?
2. **Conclude** What relationship exists between glucagon and the other two variables (insulin and glucose)? Explain.

In Type 1 diabetes, the failure of the pancreas sets up a destructive chain reaction in other organ systems, as shown in **FIGURE 28.9.** As glucose builds up in the blood, the kidneys must remove it along with large amounts of water. Also, since the body is unable to use glucose as an energy source, it must use stored fat instead. As the fat breaks down, the blood becomes more acidic. This altered pH disrupts the metabolism of the cells in every organ and every system in the body. The long-term effects can result in heart disease, blindness, nerve damage, kidney damage, and even coma and death.

In Type 2 diabetes, the pancreas cannot produce enough insulin, or the insulin cannot be used to move glucose into the cells. As a result, blood glucose levels rise, and the cells starve. Risk factors for developing Type 2 diabetes include chronic obesity, a family history of diabetes, and aging.

A Connect **Why might diabetes be a particular problem for an athlete?**

28.3 ASSESSMENT

ONLINE QUIZ ClassZone.com

REVIEWING MAIN IDEAS

1. Why do the organ systems in the body need to work so closely together?
2. Explain why a long-term disruption of homeostasis can often be more damaging to the body than a short-term disruption is.

CRITICAL THINKING

3. **Analyze** Why would giving synthetic insulin to people with Type 1 diabetes restore their glucose homeostasis?
4. **Predict** If you lived in Alaska for the whole year, what changes might occur in your calcium and phosphorus levels during the winter versus the summer? Explain.

***Connecting* CONCEPTS**

5. **Evolution** Some animals can store more glucose—in the form of glycogen—in their bodies than can other animals. What might be the evolutionary advantage of having these extra energy stores?

DATA ANALYSIS

Discuss

Make sure students understand that the graphs relate to the same event. **Ask,** Which hormone is released when the glucose level is high? insulin when the glucose level is low? glucagon

Answers

1. Glucose and insulin levels have inverse relationships with time.
2. inverse relationship; a high value of glucagon is associated with low values of insulin and glucose.

Unit Resource Book, Data Analysis, p. 13

Answers

A **Connect** Athletes require large amounts of energy to perform. If there is not enough glucose taken into the body's cells, the athlete will not have enough energy to maintain his or her performance.

Assess and Reteach

Assess Use the Online Quiz or Section Quiz (*Assessment Book,* p. 555).

Reteach Use the terms from **Section 28.2** that describe control systems and apply them to one of the examples in this section. Have students identify at what point homeostasis can be disrupted.

28.3 ASSESSMENT

1. All body systems contribute to maintenance of homeostasis. What happens in one system may require response from another.
2. Long-term disruption can produce a type of chain reaction in which more and more organ systems are affected over time. The result can be permanent damage to organs and possibly death.
3. In Type 1 diabetes, no insulin is made. When synthetic insulin is given to people with Type 1 diabetes, glucose can enter cells, so blood glucose levels return to normal.
4. During winter months, because there is little sunlight and your skin is fully covered with clothing, you would be exposed to very little UV light. As a result, you would produce less vitamin D, and calcium and phosphorous levels in your body would decrease. In summer, your skin would be exposed to sunlight far more often. The increase in vitamin D production would result in an increase in calcium and phosphorous levels.
5. Answers may include the development of more efficient cellular metabolism, the ability to survive on an irregular food supply, or the ability to mobilize extra glucose rapidly to provide energy in fight-or-flight situations.

OPTIONS FOR INQUIRY

INVESTIGATION

Time 45 minutes	TEACHER TESTED ✓
Teacher Preparation	
Student Difficulty	
Lab Binder Human Bio, pp. 5–6	

Purpose Observe cells and relate structure to function.

Overview Students will observe prepared slides of muscle, bone, and nerve cells. They will

- draw and label cells as they appear under high power

LAB MANAGEMENT

Safety Remind students to wipe down the eyepieces with alcohol wipes after using them.

Teacher Note "I use a camera-projector on the microscope and look at the cells in a certain order to make it easier for students to follow along. It also makes the lab easier to grade."

POST-LAB DISCUSSION

Review cellular differentiation and discuss the relationship between structure and function of cells.

Use these inquiry-based labs and online activities to deepen your understanding of human systems and homeostasis.

NOS.3 Clearly communicate their ideas and results of investigations verbally and in written form using tables, graphs, diagrams, and photographs.

INVESTIGATION

Examining Human Cells

In this lab, you will examine different types of human body cells under the microscope. As you study the cells, think about how the structure of each type of cell is related to its function.

MATERIALS
- slide of skeletal-muscle cells
- slide of bone cells
- slide of nerve cells
- microscope

SKILL Observing

PROBLEM How can you identify different types of specialized cells?

PROCEDURE
1. Examine the first slide under low power and high power on the microscope.
2. Make a data sheet to draw and label one cell and its structures.
3. Repeat steps 1 and 2 for the remaining slides.

ANALYZE AND CONCLUDE
1. **Describe** What is the general shape of a muscle cell? How does this shape differ from the shape of a bone cell or a nerve cell?
2. **Evaluate** How can the differences in the shapes of cells be explained?
3. **Compare** What structures do all of the cells viewed have in common?
4. **Apply** Sometimes, due to inherited disorders, nerve cells in the muscular system do not function properly. What problems might a person have if he or she had one of these disorders?
5. **Infer** Find a diagram on the Internet showing bone cells embedded within bone tissue. Explain how nutrients and oxygen might reach bone cells that are surrounded by hardened bone tissue.

EXTEND YOUR INVESTIGATION

Find examples on the Internet of muscle cells or bone cells that have been damaged by disease or injury or that did not develop properly. How do these changes affect the cells' structure and function? What effect might these cells have on the tissues they are part of?

Answers

Sample Data

For a sample of student work from this lab, go to page R109.

Analyze and Conclude

1. Muscle cells are long and usually bundled. Bone cells are round and have a central canal. Neurons have a cell body with several extensions.
2. The genes that are expressed during determination are coded to produce a particular type of cell. During differentiation, the cell develops the structure associated with its particular type.
3. They all have a nucleus, a cell membrane, organelles, and genetic material.
4. The person would have limited ability or inability to move the affected body part.
5. Answers should include the idea that the canals within the bone tissue allow materials to diffuse into the cells.

Extend Your Investigation

Students' answers will vary.

INVESTIGATION

Hormones and Homeostasis

Endocrine glands release chemical messengers (hormones) that help regulate functions throughout the body. Sometimes these glands fail to respond to normal feedback loops, resulting in a disruption of homeostasis. For example, the pituitary gland, located in the brain, secretes human growth hormone. If cells in the gland produce too much of this hormone, a person will continue to grow far above average height. The result is a condition known as gigantism, as shown in the photograph.

If the cells produce too little of the hormone, a person will grow to far less than average height. This condition is known as dwarfism.

Robert Wadlow stands 2.6 meters (8 ft 9 in.) in this 1938 photo. The two people next to him are average size.

SKILL Researching

PROBLEM How does the disorder of a particular endocrine gland affect the rest of the body?

RESEARCH

Choose one of the glands below and one of the disorders listed under it.

Thyroid Gland
- hypothyroidism
- Graves' disease
- myxedema

Adrenal Gland
- Cushing's syndrome
- Addison's disease

1. Describe the function of the gland and the hormones it releases.
2. What happens to the functioning of the gland in the disorder that you have chosen?
3. How does the disorder affect the rest of the body?
4. How is the disorder diagnosed? What treatments or lifestyle changes are necessary?
5. What are the long-term health effects if the disorder remains untreated?

Online BIOLOGY
CLASSZONE.COM

ANIMATED BIOLOGY
Keep an Athlete Running
Regulate a runner's homeostasis to get her to the end of a course in the best time without stopping.

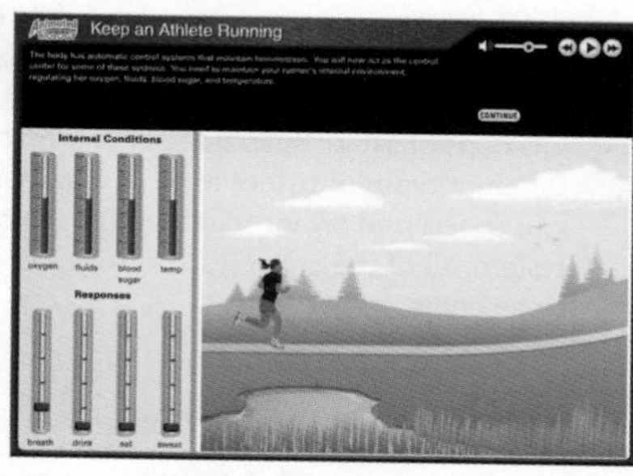

WEBQUEST
When you are cold, the systems in your body respond in ways that maintain your body temperature. In this WebQuest, you will learn about hypothermia and its potentially life-threatening consequences. Find out what happens when you get so cold that homeostasis breaks down.

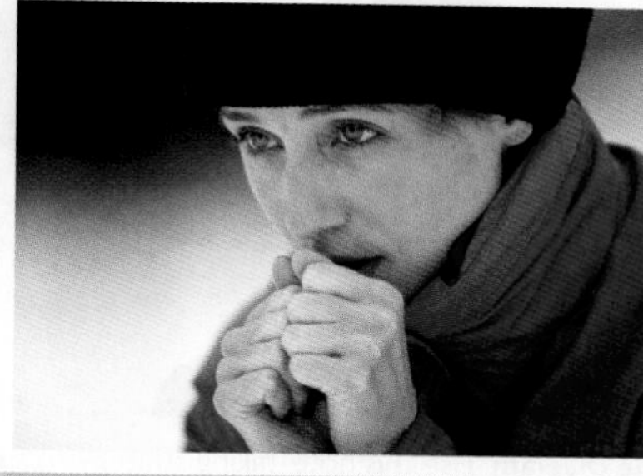

BIOZINE
Stories about human biology—such as "Researchers Test Vaccine for Emerging Flu Virus" and "Obesity a Growing Problem for Kids and Teens"—are often in the headlines. Catch the latest news about human biology in the BioZine.

Answers

1. Thyroid gland releases hormones that regulate metabolic rate; adrenal gland releases steroid hormones.

2–3. Hypothyroidism: undersecretion of thyroid hormones during fetal development or infancy affects skeletal growth, brain development; cretinism or dwarfism can result.

Graves' disease: oversecretion of thyroid hormones; enlarged thyroid gland, weight loss, increased appetite, protruding eyes.

myxedema: reduced output of thyroid hormones lowers heart rate and body temperature; results in sensitivity to cold, weight gain, and fatigue.

Cushing's syndrome: oversecretion of cortisol changes storage of body fat, resulting in thin legs and arms, rounded face, large abdomen, a hump on the back, weakness, and weight gain.

Addison's disease: too little cortisol, produces weight loss, vomiting, weakness, low blood pressure, and dehydration. If left untreated, a heart attack can result.

4–5. Answers will vary.

Online Biology ▼

ANIMATED BIOLOGY Students will maintain a runner's homeostasis—regulating oxygen, fluids, blood sugar, and body temperature—by controlling her rates of breathing, drinking, eating, and sweating. Use with **Section 28.2.**

WEBQUEST The WebQuest takes one full class period. Students complete the activity online and will need access to a printer to print their answers. Sample answers, teacher notes, and alternative assessment ideas are available on **ClassZone.com.** Use with **Section 28.3.**

INVESTIGATION

Time 45 minutes (TEACHER TESTED)
Teacher Preparation
Student Difficulty
Lab Binder Human Bio, p. 7

Purpose Research the effects of an endocrine disorder on homeostasis.

Overview Students will use Internet and library resources to research one endocrine disorder and describe its effect on the body.

LAB MANAGEMENT

- Make sure each disorder is researched by at least one student.
- An excellent resource is the National Institutes of Health Medline Plus Encyclopedia, available on the Internet.

POST-LAB DISCUSSION

Have one student researcher introduce each of the disorders to the class. Discuss social stigmas that can be associated with disorders that affect appearance and behavior.

CHAPTER REVIEW

Interactive Review

Encourage students to go to **ClassZone.com** for a detailed review of each section, including visuals and vocabulary practice.

Unit Resource Book, Vocabulary Practice, pp. 19–22

CHAPTER 28 Interactive Review @ CLASSZONE.COM

KEY CONCEPTS | Vocabulary Games | Concept Maps | Animated Biology | Online Quiz

28.1 Levels of Organization

The human body has five levels of organization. Specialized cells in multicellular organisms arise from the zygote. Most embryonic stem cells go through determination, during which they are committed to becoming specialized cells. During differentiation, cells develop their specialized structures and functions.

Groups of similar specialized cells form tissue. Different types of tissues form an organ, and various specialized organs together form an organ system. All of the organ systems together make up an entire organism.

Differentiated Cells

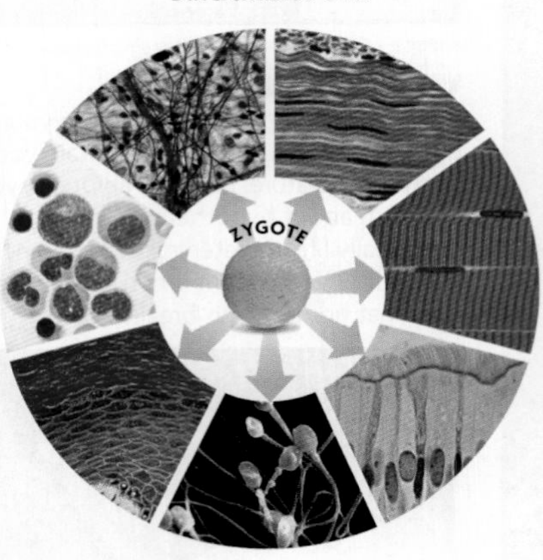

28.2 Mechanisms of Homeostasis

Homeostasis is the regulation and maintenance of the internal environment. Conditions within the body must remain within the narrow ranges that support human life. Homeostasis is maintained by internal control systems composed of sensors, a control center, communication systems, and target tissues or organs. The control centers use feedback to keep the internal environment stable. In a negative feedback loop, control systems counteract change to maintain conditions within a narrow range. In a positive feedback loop, control systems increase change away from set points.

28.3 Interactions Among Systems

Systems interact to maintain homeostasis. Each organ system affects other organ systems. For example, thermoregulation depends on the interaction of the circulatory, respiratory, endocrine, and skin systems. If one organ system fails, it can affect other systems in a chain reaction. Long-term disruptions of homeostasis, as in diabetes, are more serious than temporary short-term disruptions because more organ systems can be damaged over time.

Synthesize Your Notes

Cycle Diagram Use this note-taking strategy to summarize what you know about how control systems work to maintain homeostasis.

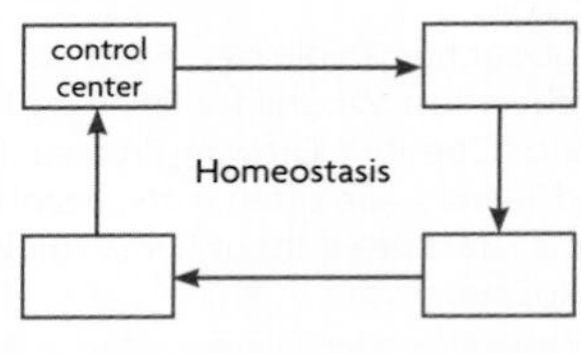

Concept Map Draw a concept map to help you remember the developmental steps of cells.

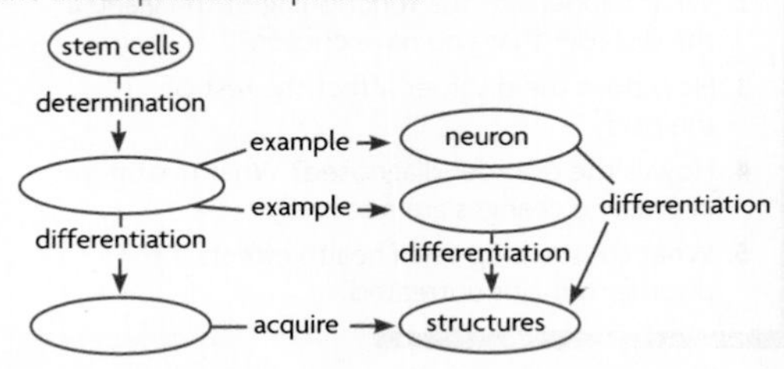

868 Unit 9: Human Biology

Reviewing Vocabulary

1. one type of specialized cells working together
2. different tissues working together
3. different organs working together
4. process of stem cells committing to become specific types of cells
5. process of committed cells acquiring structures and functions of specific cells
6. counteracts change away from set points
7. increases change away from set points
8. process of maintaining a stable body temperature
9. An organ is an instrument or implement that is built to carry out specific functions in the body.
10. Homeostasis means keeping or maintaining something so it remains the same.
11. Thermoregulation is the process of managing or regulating the temperature of a body or an environment to keep it within set values.
12. The electrical signal returns to its source, just as sensors in a biological source send out information to a control center that sends messages back to the biological source to make changes.

Chapter Assessment

Chapter Vocabulary

28.1 determination, p. 852
differentiation, p. 853
tissue, p. 854
organ, p. 854
organ system, p. 854

28.2 homeostasis, p. 858
feedback, p. 859
negative feedback, p. 860
positive feedback, p. 861

28.3 thermoregulation, p. 863

Reviewing Vocabulary

Keep It Short

For each vocabulary word that follows, write a short phrase that defines its meaning. For example: *cell—the basic unit of life.*

1. tissue
2. organ
3. organ system
4. determination
5. differentiation
6. negative feedback
7. positive feedback
8. thermoregulation

Word Origins

9. The word *organ* comes from the Latin word *organum*, meaning "instrument" or "implement." Describe how this meaning relates to the definition of a living organ.
10. *Homeostasis* can be broken into two parts: *homos*, meaning "similar," and *stasis*, meaning "standing" or "stopping." Write a brief definition of *homeostasis* based on the meaning of these two parts.
11. A thermos is a container for keeping liquids hot. The word comes from the Greek *thermos*, which means "hot" or "warm." How does this meaning relate to the term *thermoregulation?*
12. The word *feedback* originally comes from the field of electrical engineering. Feedback occurs when part of a signal put out by an amplifier returns to its source. It's that loud squeal you sometimes hear when someone is using a microphone. Explain how this meaning of feedback relates to what happens in a feedback loop.

Reviewing MAIN IDEAS

13. Embryonic stem cells have the potential to become any type of cell in the body. What happens to these cells during the process of determination? **B.6.3**
14. Once a cell goes through the process of determination, what happens next as the cells develop in the embryo? **B.6.3**
15. Briefly explain how cell differentiation and cell death are both needed to develop such structures as human hands and feet.
16. A human being is composed of five levels of organization. Name each of the levels of organization and give an example of each one.
17. Organs have many specialized cells and tissues that enable them to carry out their functions. Describe two specialized cells in the respiratory system that enable the lungs to function well. **B.6.3**
18. Your body has control systems that keep its internal conditions within the narrow ranges that support life. On a hot day, how do your body's control center and sensors work together to help you stay cool?
19. Your body has many feedback loops to help maintain homeostasis. Explain the difference between a negative feedback loop and a positive feedback loop.
20. Explain how the failure of one organ can lead to the failure of other organs or of an entire organ system.
21. When glucose levels in the blood rise above a set point, hormones are released that cause the glucose levels to decline. Is this process an example of a positive or a negative feedback loop? Explain your answer.
22. Give two example of what can happen to a person if the body's homeostasis is not maintained.

CHAPTER REVIEW

Reviewing Main Ideas

13. In determination, committed cells acquire the unique structures and functions they need to function as specialized cells.
14. Differentiation occurs as cells acquire specialized structures and functions.
15. Cell differentiation creates cells that form specific structures, such as hands and feet. Cell death is needed to separate parts of the hands and feet into individual fingers and toes.
16. cells (sperm, neuron), tissues (muscle, epithelial, nervous), organs (lungs, heart, liver), organ systems (respiratory, circulatory), and the organism (human being)
17. Cilia, hairlike cells, help to move foreign particles out of the lungs. Epithelial cells line the inner surface of the lungs to keep it moist.
18. Sensors in the blood and skin relay information to the brain and endocrine systems. Messages from these centers cause blood vessels to dilate, sweat glands to release fluid, and heart and breathing rate to increase to let excess body heat escape.
19. Negative feedback loop counteracts change away from set points. Positive feedback loop increases change away from set points.
20. The organs in the body all work together, like a well-coordinated team. If one organ fails, it affects the organ that depends on it. In time, the second organ will also fail, affecting more organs in the system. The longer the problem remains, the more organs are affected.
21. Negative feedback loop; the body acts to counteract an increase away from a set point.
22. If people's fluid homeostasis is not maintained, they become dehydrated. If their glucose homeostasis is not maintained, they become diabetic. If oxygen/carbon dioxide homeostasis is not maintained, they might die within a matter of minutes.

ITEM CORRELATIONS

Standard	Items
B.6.2	24
B.6.3	13, 14, 17

Critical Thinking

23. A house is made up of wood, metal, plastic, glass, cloth, and other specialized materials. Each material has a particular shape and function. Likewise, different cells in the body have specialized structures and functions that make up an entire organism.
24. Embryonic stem cells have the potential to become any one of over 200 different types of cells in the human body.
25. The circulatory and immune systems both contain lymph nodes and lymphatic vessels.
26. Circulatory, respiratory, integumentary, digestive, excretory, nervous, endocrine, and muscular systems would all likely be involved. Before and during the presentation, the person might be breathing faster, sweating, have an upset stomach or have to go to the bathroom more often, shiver or shake, and have a racing heart. After the presentation, all the symptoms would likely disappear and conditions return to normal.
27. Nerve cells have extensions that reach out and lay on top of muscle cells. At these points, the two different cells can exchange ions and transmit and receive information.
28. Positive feedback increases the rate of change. Therefore, only negative feedback loops could be used to counteract change and keep conditions within the ranges that support life.
29. A weak or damaged heart means that the circulatory system cannot work as well to cool or warm the blood in the body and either conserve heat or let excess heat escape.

Critical Thinking

23. Compare Explain how the cells in the human body might be similar to various building materials in a house.

24. Infer Scientists are investigating methods to use embryonic stem cells to repair any tissue in the human body. What characteristic of embryonic stem cells could make this type of treatment possible? **B.6.2**

25. Analyze Review the chart of organ systems on page 856. Identify some interconnections between the immune system and the circulatory system.

26. Apply Describe which organ systems you think would be involved in maintaining homeostasis when a person gives a major speech or presentation. Include what may be happening within the person just before, during, and after the speech.

27. Synthesize For various specialized cells to work together, they must communicate with one another. Use the information you learned in Chapter 3 about cell parts to describe how you think a neuron might communicate with a muscle cell.

28. Compare and Contrast Explain how the difference between negative and positive feedback makes negative feedback more effective in maintaining homeostasis in the body.

29. Infer People with weak or damaged hearts often have trouble regulating their body temperatures in a hot or a cold environment. Explain why an impaired heart might make a person less able to maintain homeostasis.

Analyzing Visuals

Use the diagram of the digestive system to answer the next three questions.

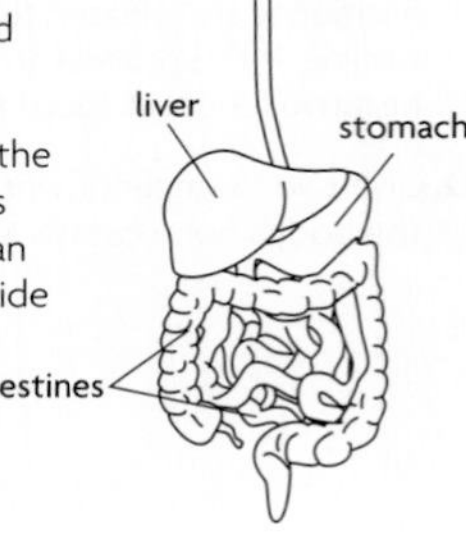

30. Analyze Why is this considered an organ system?

31. Infer How do you think the nutrients released from food leave the digestive system and travel throughout the body?

32. Predict When a person has the flu and is vomiting, how does this condition affect the organ system and its ability to provide nutrients to the body?

Analyzing Data

The graph below shows the relationship between different types of energy yield during exercise. Use the graph to answer the next three questions.

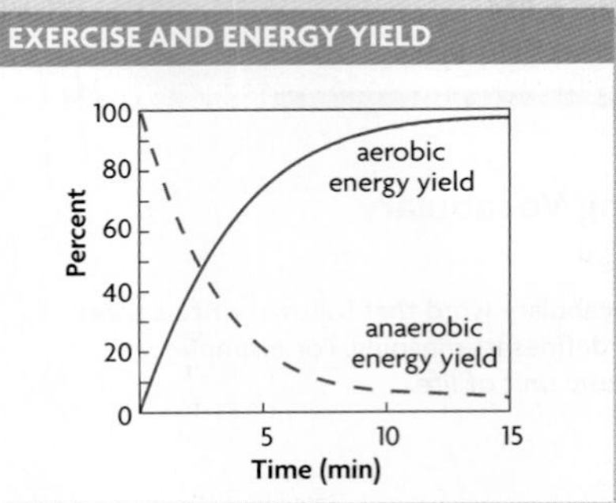

33. Compare and Contrast Within what time period does the greatest amount of change occur in both variables?

34. Analyze Which variable is inversely related to time? Explain.

35. Conclude What relationship do the two variables have to each other at the beginning and at the end of the exercise period?

Connecting CONCEPTS

36. Blog Your Morning Wake-Up Call Blogs have become a popular form of communicating personal experiences online. Think about the changes that occur in your body when you wake up in the morning—changes in your heart rate, in your breathing, and in the movements of your arms and legs. Describe in a blog entry some of the environmental and physical changes that you experience. Which organ systems seem to be involved? What feedback loops might be working to make sure such changes do not become too great?

37. Apply Extreme sports test the limits of the human body. Describe one extreme condition, other than temperature, facing the ice climber in the photograph on page 851. Explain how feedback mechanisms in the climber's body can maintain homeostasis under the extreme condition you choose to describe.

Analyzing Visuals

30. It consists of several organs working together.
31. Nutrients can only reach other parts of the body by traveling through the circulatory system. Therefore, there must be a connection from the digestive organs to the blood—probably through diffusion into capillaries.
32. Vomiting prevents a person from digesting food and absorbing water. Therefore, the digestive tract would be unable to provide many nutrients or fluids to the rest of the body.

Analyzing Data

33. in the first five minutes
34. Anaerobic energy yield; it declines as the length of time increases.
35. Inverse relationships at both beginning and end; one is rising, while the other is falling.

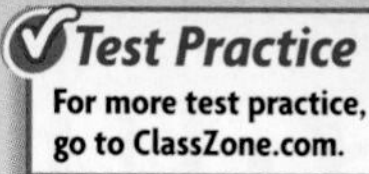

INDIANA ISTEP+ Test Prep

NOS.5

Test Practice
For more test practice, go to ClassZone.com.

1 A group of scientists investigates how the blood pressure of students changes while taking an exam. To properly control their experiment, the scientists must first measure the

A number of questions on the exam.
B students' grade point averages.
C temperature and humidity of the exam room.
D students' blood pressure before the exam.

2 The hormone glucagon increases blood sugar levels while the hormone insulin reduces blood sugar levels. When blood sugar becomes too high, what is most likely to happen to insulin and glucagon levels for the body to maintain homeostasis?

A Insulin levels increase and glucagon levels decrease.
B Insulin and glucagon levels remain the same.
C Glucagon levels increase and insulin levels decrease.
D Insulin and glucagon levels decrease.

3 Why is it important that oxygen and carbon dioxide levels be closely regulated in the human body?

A Both gases are needed for the proper functioning of cell processes.
B Oxygen is needed for cell processes and carbon dioxide is a waste product.
C Both gases are waste products that need to be removed from cells.
D The carbon and oxygen from the gases are needed to build new molecules.

4 No matter what the temperature is outside, your body temperature stays relatively constant at about 98.6°F. This is part of your body's ability to maintain

A osmoregulation.
B homeostasis.
C negative feedback loops.
D positive feedback loops.

5 The kidneys filter wastes and excess salts from the blood. If salt concentrations are low, negative feedback mechanisms would most likely

A decrease the amount of salts removed.
B increase the amount of salts removed.
C slow down overall kidney function.
D increase the rate of kidney function.

THINK THROUGH THE QUESTION

Think about what the body needs to do to maintain homeostasis in this situation. Remember, the feedback mechanism should affect only salt concentration.

6 Individuals with diabetes lack the ability to produce insulin in response to rising blood sugar. Is this a problem with a negative feedback loop or a positive feedback loop?

Standards-Based Assessment

1. D	4. B
2. A	5. A
3. B	6. See Below

TEST DOCTOR

Question 2 Answer A is correct. Answer B is incorrect because insulin and glucagon levels are affected by—and affect—blood sugar levels. Answer C is incorrect because it would further increase the blood sugar levels. Answer D is incorrect because while decreased glucagon should help by not further increasing blood sugar level, decreased insulin would not help to lower the blood sugar level.

Question 4 Answer B is correct. Answer A is incorrect because osmoregulation is the maintenance of osmotic pressure within certain limits in organisms. Answer C is incorrect because a negative feedback loop is a control system that counteracts changes in the body. Answer D is incorrect because positive feedback increases the rate of change from a set point.

Question 5 Answer A is correct. Answer B is incorrect because increased salt removal would lower the salt concentration even further. Answers C and D are incorrect because salt concentration is unrelated to the rate of kidney function.

Question 6 Negative feedback loops help to control the internal body environment. They do so by triggering responses within the body when certain levels move away from norms. An example of this would be blood sugar. In a normal person's body, the increase in blood sugar would trigger a release of insulin. In the body of a person with diabetes, this does not happen.

Connecting Concepts

36. Answers will vary. Students would probably notice as they wake up that their heart beats slightly faster, their breathing rate increases, and their legs and arms move and stretch. They might sneeze or cough on waking. They might also notice the air temperature of the room is warmer or cooler than under the covers. They may notice they are hungry or need to go to the bathroom. Nearly all the organ systems would be involved. Feedback loops working to maintain homeostasis might include those in the circulatory, respiratory, endocrine, and nervous systems.

37. *Sample Answer:* Conditions: extreme cold, extreme muscular exertion, extreme oxygen requirements, extreme energy (glucose) requirements. Feedback mechanisms: maintaining body temperature, blood glucose levels, oxygen levels, and activity in the brain to coordinate movements and be aware of surroundings

ITEM CORRELATIONS

Standard	Items
NOS.5	1

CHAPTER 29

Indiana Resource Preview

Print Resources

Nervous and Endocrine Systems

INDIANA STANDARDS		Sections	PAGES and PACING	UNIT RESOURCE BOOK
	29.1	**How Organ Systems Communicate** **KEY CONCEPT** The nervous system and the endocrine system provide the means by which organ systems communicate.	pp. 874–875 30 minutes	URB pages 23–26
	29.2	**Neurons** **KEY CONCEPT** The nervous system is composed of highly specialized cells.	pp. 876–879 45 minutes	URB pages 27–30
	29.3	**The Senses** **KEY CONCEPT** The senses detect the internal and external environments.	pp. 880–883 30 minutes	URB pages 31–34
NOS.1		CHAPTER INVESTIGATION: The Stroop Effect	p. 884 45 minutes	**Lab Binder** Human Bio pages 15–17
	29.4	**Central and Peripheral Nervous Systems** **KEY CONCEPT** The central nervous system interprets information, and the peripheral nervous system gathers and transmits information.	pp. 885–890 30 minutes	URB pages 35–38
	29.5	**Brain Function and Chemistry** **KEY CONCEPT** Scientists study the functions and chemistry of the brain.	pp. 891–894 30 minutes	URB pages 39–42
NOS.1		DATA ANALYSIS: Correlation or Causation Relationships Between Variables	p. 895 30 minutes	URB page 47
	29.6	**The Endocrine System and Hormones** **KEY CONCEPT** The endocrine system produces hormones that affect growth, development, and homeostasis.	pp. 896–901 30 minutes	URB pages 43–46
NOS.1, NOS.3		OPTIONS FOR INQUIRY	pp. 902–903 45 minutes, 30 minutes	**Lab Binder** Human Bio pages 18–21
		Chapter Review	pp. 904–907	**Assessment Book** Chapter Tests A, B pp. 577–584

INDIANA STANDARDS

NOS.1 Develop explanations based on reproducible data and observations gathered during laboratory investigations.
NOS.3 Clearly communicate their ideas and results of investigations verbally and in written form using tables, graphs, diagrams, and photographs.

Labs

PUPIL EDITION LABS

The Stroop Effect, p. 884 Students investigate how interference (conflicting information) affects the completion of a task. **Lab Binder** pp. 15–17	**Time:** 20 minutes **Materials:** watch with second hand
The Primary Sensory Cortex, Section 4, p. 886 Students compare the relative amounts of space given to touch reception in a fingertip and a forearm. **Lab Binder** p. 22	**Time:** 5 minutes **Materials:** 3 toothpicks, soft blindfold/bandana

OPTIONS FOR INQUIRY

Reaction Time, p. 902 Students observe how a distraction affects task completion. **Lab Binder** pp. 18–20	**Time:** 45 minutes **Materials:** deck of cards
Brain-Based Disorders, p. 903 Students research a brain-based disorder. **Lab Binder** p. 21	**Time:** 30 minutes **Material:** Computer with Internet access

LAB BINDER Unit 9 Human Biology

Additional Investigation: Smell and Olfactory Fatigue, pp. 23–26

Challenge Lab: Investigating the Photic Sneeze Reflex, pp. 96–99; Investigating Eye Anatomy, pp. 100–102

LAB GENERATOR

A searchable CD of all labs in the program in editable format, including forensic, probeware, and biotechnology labs.

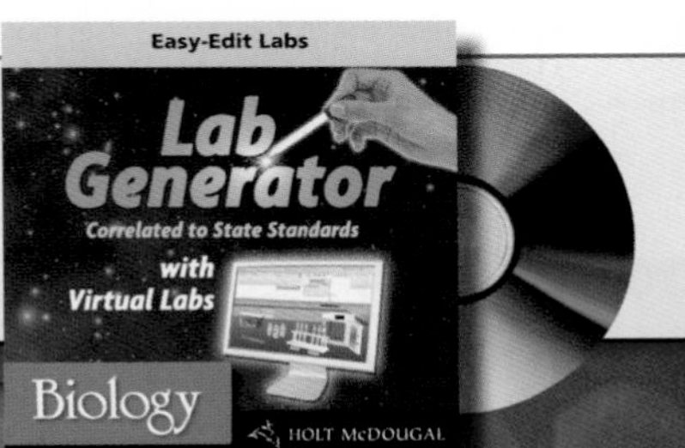

Presentation Tools

POWER PRESENTATIONS

Presentation Chapter 29
Power Presentations for each section incorporate images and clips from the Media Gallery: Includes Note Navigator for each section.

MEDIA GALLERY

Contains the following images and video clips, as well as animations, simulations and forms of visuals from the book.

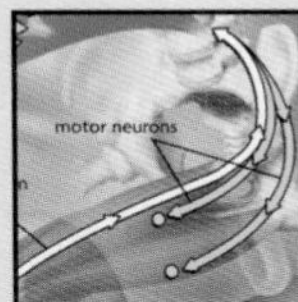

Reflex arc

Hormonal disorders

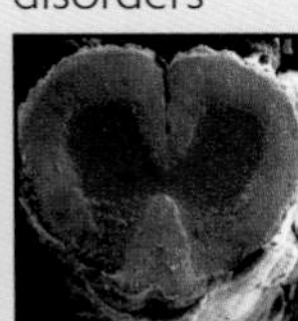

Brain function scan

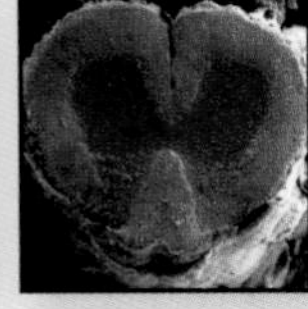
Cross-section of spinal cord

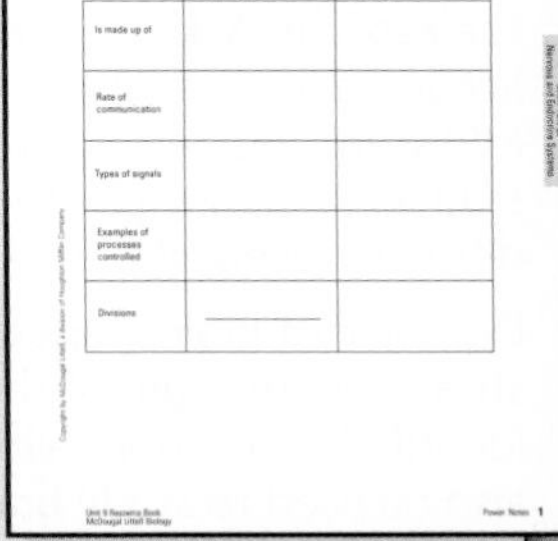

Power Notes

VIDEO

Explore a set of short video clips on the function of nerves and hormones.

ANIMATED BIOLOGY

Nerve Impulse Transmission
Diagnose a Hormone Disorder
Reflex Arc

TRANSPARENCIES

Nervous and Endocrine System T114
Structure of a Neuron T115
Synapse T116
Vision T117
Hearing T118
Touch T119
The Stroop Effect T120
Central and Peripheral Nervous System T121
Lobes of the Brain T122
Glands of the Body T123

Online BIOLOGY CLASSZONE.COM

BioZine
Animated Biology
Interactive Review
SciLinks
Resource Centers

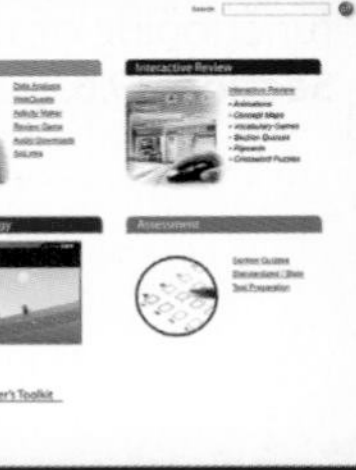

CHAPTER 29

▼ Focus and Motivate

What happens when you think?

Have students speculate on what happens inside their brain when they think. Direct their attention to the MRI scan of the brain and have them read the caption. **Ask,** What do you think accounts for the different colors in the MRI scan? Answers will vary, but students may suggest they represent different levels of brain activity.

Discuss that brain scans are used to study the structure of the brain and to identify brain abnormalities. Scans can also be used to study brain activity, including activity associated with thinking, which occurs in the front part of the brain. **Ask,** What are some activities that are associated with thinking? remembering, learning, understanding, recognition

BIOZINE ClassZone.com

Students can access BioZine at **ClassZone.com** to look for topics suitable for research reports, writing assignments, or classroom debates.

In a Hurry?

Students will already have an understanding of general aspects of the nervous and endocrine systems. More detailed information on the functioning of the nervous system and neurons is presented in **Section 29.2** and on the functioning of the endocrine system in **Section 29.6.**

CHAPTER 29 Nervous and Endocrine Systems

KEY CONCEPTS

29.1 How Organ Systems Communicate
The nervous system and the endocrine system provide the means by which organ systems communicate.

29.2 Neurons
The nervous system is composed of highly specialized cells.

29.3 The Senses
The senses detect the internal and external environments.

29.4 Central and Peripheral Nervous Systems
The central nervous system interprets information, and the peripheral nervous system gathers and transmits information.

29.5 Brain Function and Chemistry
Scientists study the functions and chemistry of the brain.

29.6 Endocrine System and Hormones
The endocrine system produces hormones that affect growth, development, and homeostasis.

Online BIOLOGY CLASSZONE.COM

Animated BIOLOGY
View animated chapter concepts.
- Nerve Impulse Transmission
- Reflex Arc
- Diagnose a Hormone Disorder

BIOZINE
Keep current with biology news.
- Featured stories
- News feeds
- Bio Bytes

RESOURCE CENTER
Get more information on
- Senses
- Nervous System

Student Activity

Purpose Demonstrate how experience affects memory.

Materials
- black marker
- poster board, cut in half

On each piece of the poster board, write a set of color words.

Set 1: red, blue, white, green, yellow, orange, brown, black

Set 2: magenta, opal, aquamarine, violet, cyan, taupe, ebony, teal

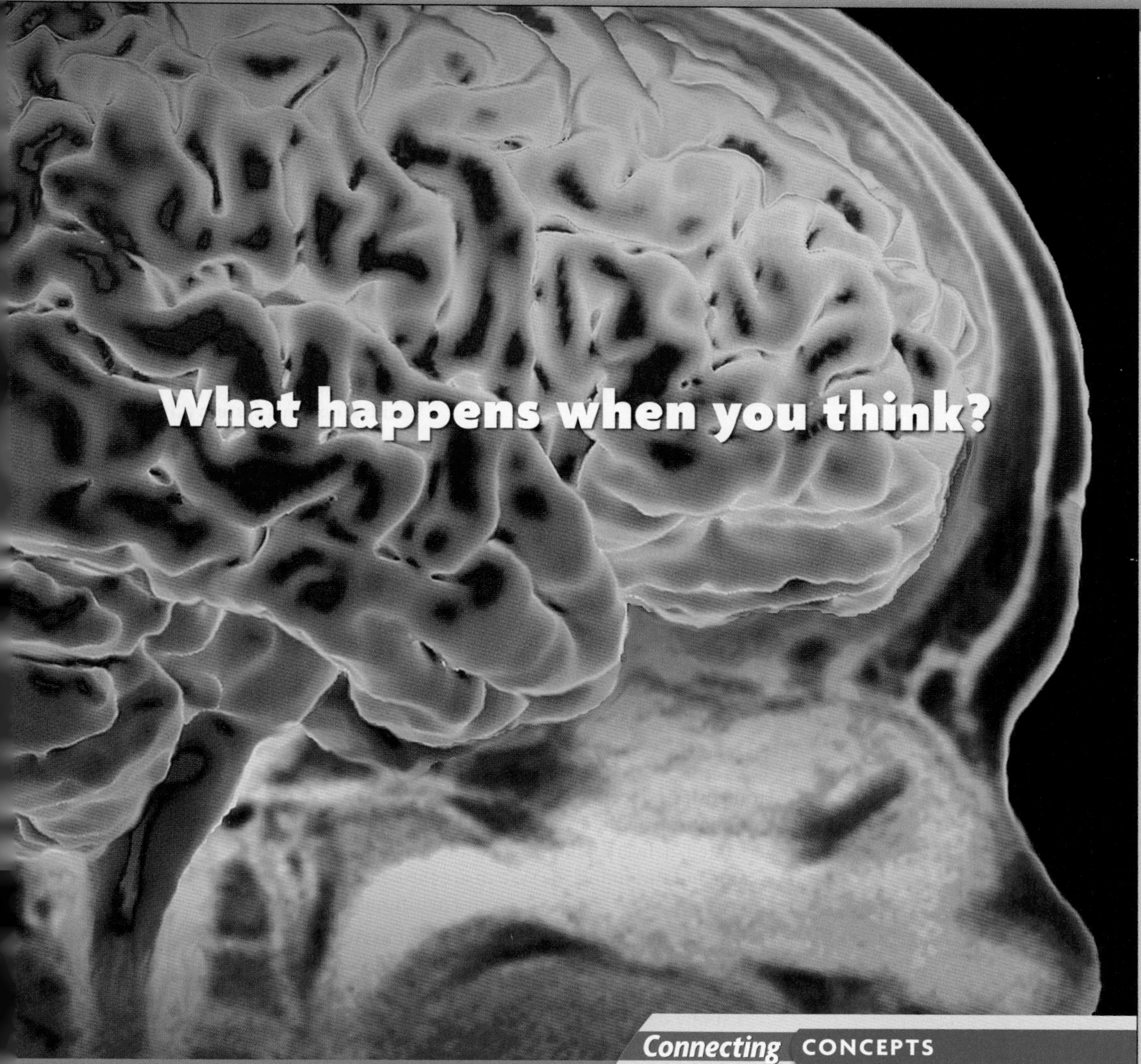

What happens when you think?

Connecting CONCEPTS

Some technology allows researchers to look into the body of a living person. As recently as the 1970s, there was no way for doctors and scientists to see inside of the body without putting a patient through surgery. Today, researchers and others use magnets and computer technology, such as the MRI scan above, to look at the internal organs of live patients.

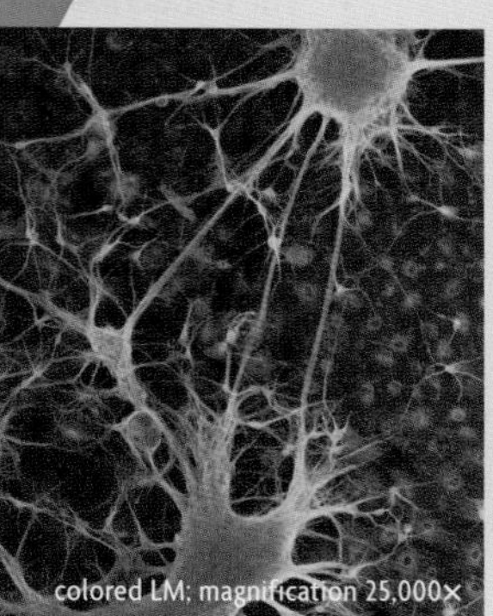
colored LM; magnification 25,000×

Animals Although only vertebrates have a spinal column, most animals have neurons. Neurons are specialized cells that send signals to different organ systems throughout the body. Neurons connect the brain to muscles and other tissues, and some neurons send such fast signals that they can make a person blink in less than one one-hundreth of a second.

Introduce Show students the poster with the Set 1 words. Allow them to memorize the list for exactly one minute, and then take the list away. Have students write down as many of the words as they can remember in one minute. Repeat the exercise, using the Set 2 words.
Ask

- Which list were you able to recall better? Most students will say the first list.
- Why? The words on the first list were more familiar.

Discuss Help students recognize that learning involves memory. We remember things because our brain creates pathways to store information. If a pathway is used more often, the information is more easily remembered. **Ask,** Why was the first list more familiar? We use or see those color words more often.

Every time we use or see a particular word, the information moves along a particular pathway, thus reinforcing the information in our brain.

Activate Prior Knowledge

Tell students that a characteristic of both the nervous and endocrine systems is the ability for their organs to communicate. **Ask,** How do you communicate? speech, written language, body language, touch Discuss with students how the body communicates through hormones, chemicals, and nerve impulses. Tell them that as they sit there, billions and billions of signals are moving through their bodies each minute.

Preview Vocabulary

Academic Vocabulary In this chapter, students will see words they are familiar with used in a different context: *stimulus, stimulant,* and *stimulating.* Mention to students that what all these words have in common is the idea of a signal and response.

English Learners Tell students to watch for words relating to *communication,* for example, *message, delivery, network,* and *signal.* In this chapter, they will learn how parts of the body communicate with one another. Suggest they pay attention to where the message starts, how it moves, and what happens when it gets there.

Integrating Medical Science

Radiology is the medical specialty of imaging technology, such as the MRI (Magnetic Resonance Imaging) technology that produced the scan on this page. Radiology allows doctors to examine the body without having to perform surgery. To make an MRI scan, a patient is placed inside a strong magnetic field, and a radio wave is passed through the body. A receiver is set to detect signals from hydrogen atoms in water. Varying amounts of water in the tissues produce a clear image of the tissues, as shown in the brain scan. An MRI scan can detect differences between the different types of tissue and any abnormalities that may be present.

▼ Plan and Prepare

Objectives

- Explain how the nervous and endocrine systems help maintain homeostasis.
- Contrast the nervous and endocrine systems' methods of communication.

Section Resources

Unit Resource Book Study Guide pp. 23–24 Power Notes p. 25 Reinforcement p. 26
Interactive Reader Chapter 29 **Spanish Study Guide** pp. 289–290
Biology Toolkit pp. C9, D9
Technology Power Presentation 29.1 Media Gallery DVD Online Quiz 29.1

Activate Prior Knowledge Have students think of a sports team playing a big game. If the team wants to win, they have to run plays that will put them in the best scoring position. **Ask,** How are all the players going to know what play to run? The coach or player communicates the play to other team members. Tell students that the body has two major modes of internal communication, through the nervous and endocrine systems. The types of signals they send are very different.

▼ Teach

TEACH FROM VISUALS

FIGURE 29.1 Point out that the organs of the endocrine system are not physically connected. They communicate with the body by way of the chemical signals they produce that travel through the bloodstream.

Answers

A Analyze Elevated body temperature causes the body to sweat. Bright light causes the pupils to shrink.

29.1 How Organ Systems Communicate

KEY CONCEPT The nervous system and the endocrine system provide the means by which organ systems communicate.

MAIN IDEAS

- The body's communication systems help maintain homeostasis.
- The nervous and endocrine systems have different methods and rates of communication.

VOCABULARY

nervous system, p. 874
endocrine system, p. 874
stimulus, p. 874
central nervous system (CNS), p. 875
peripheral nervous system (PNS), p. 875

Connect Scientists try to find new ways, such as MRI scans, to study the brain because the brain is so important. Your brain lets you think and move. It controls digestion, heart rate, and body temperature. Your brain does these things with help from the endocrine system and the rest of the nervous system.

MAIN IDEA

The body's communication systems help maintain homeostasis.

Homeostasis depends on the ability of different systems in your body to communicate with one another. To maintain homeostasis, messages must be generated, delivered, interpreted, and acted upon by your body. The nervous system and the endocrine system are the communication networks that allow you to respond to changes in your environment countless times each day.

- The **nervous system** is a physically connected network of cells, tissues, and organs that controls thoughts, movements, and simpler life processes such as swallowing. For example, when you walk outside without sunglasses on a sunny day, your nervous system senses the bright light coming into your eyes. It sends a message that tells your pupils to shrink and let in less light.
- The **endocrine system** (EHN-duh-krihn) is a collection of physically disconnected organs that helps to control growth, development, and responses to your environment, such as body temperature. For example, when you are outside on a hot day or you exercise, your body starts to feel warm. Your endocrine system responds by producing messages that tell your body to sweat more so that you can cool down.

Both of these systems, which are shown in **FIGURE 29.1**, let you respond to a stimulus in your environment and maintain homeostasis. A **stimulus** (STIHM-yuh-luhs) is defined most broadly as something that causes a response. In living systems, a stimulus is anything that triggers a change in an organism. Changes can be chemical, cellular, or behavioral.

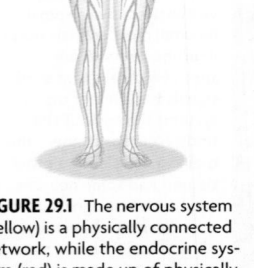

FIGURE 29.1 The nervous system (yellow) is a physically connected network, while the endocrine system (red) is made up of physically separated organs.

Analyze **What stimuli cause you to sweat and cause your pupils to shrink?**

Differentiated Instruction

BELOW LEVEL

Encourage students to write one or two potential test questions for each of the paragraphs that they read in this section. Tell them to write the answer to each question immediately. Explain that this is a method of reinforcing learning by building memory pathways by two different routes—reading and writing.

Biology Toolkit, QAR (Question-Answer Relationships), p. C9

ENGLISH LEARNERS

Some students may not understand the analogy on page 875 comparing the endocrine system to satellite television and the nervous system to cable television. You may need to explain the differences between standard, satellite, and cable television for students to grasp this concept.

Biology Toolkit, Analogies, p. D9

MAIN IDEA

The nervous and endocrine systems have different methods and rates of communication.

You can think about your endocrine system as working like a satellite television system. A satellite sends signals in all directions, but only televisions that have special receivers can get those signals. Your endocrine system's chemical signals are carried by the bloodstream throughout the body, and only cells with certain receptors can receive the signals. On the other hand, your nervous system is like cable television. A physical wire connects your television to the cable provider. Similarly, your nervous system sends its signals through a network of specialized tissues.

The nervous and endocrine systems also have different rates of communication. Your endocrine system works slowly and controls processes that occur over long periods of time, such as hair growth, aging, and sleep patterns. The endocrine system also helps regulate homeostatic functions such as body temperature and blood chemistry. For example, as the day gradually warms, your endocrine system responds by releasing chemicals that stimulate sweat glands. The change in the temperature over the course of a day is slow so you do not need a rapid response from your body.

Your nervous system works quickly and controls immediate processes, such as heart rate and breathing. If you touch your hand to a hot stove, an immediate response from the nervous system causes you to jerk your hand away. Without a quick reaction, your hand would be badly burned.

Signals move from the skin on your hand to the muscles in your arm by passing through the two parts of the nervous system: the central and the peripheral. The **central nervous system (CNS)** includes the brain and spinal cord. The CNS interprets messages from other nerves in the body and stores some of these messages for later use. The **peripheral nervous system (PNS)** is a network of nerves that transmits messages to the CNS and from the CNS to other organs in the body. You can see some of the nerves of the PNS extending from the spinal cord toward the neck and shoulders in **FIGURE 29.2.**

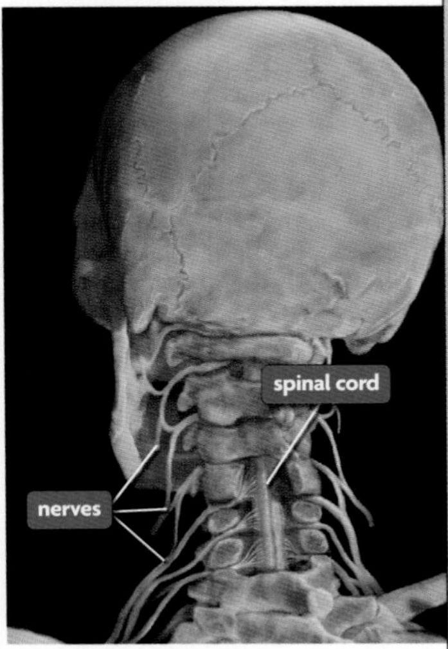

FIGURE 29.2 This medical illustration shows how the spinal cord connects the brain to the nerves that run throughout the body.

A **Infer Which system controls the rate at which your fingernails grow?**

29.1 ASSESSMENT

ONLINE QUIZ ClassZone.com

REVIEWING MAIN IDEAS

1. Why does your body need a communication system?
2. What are three differences between the ways in which the **endocrine system** and the **nervous system** work?

CRITICAL THINKING

3. **Apply** Which system, the endocrine or the nervous, controls the rate at which you blink? Explain.
4. **Predict** How might a clogged blood vessel affect the nervous system's and the endocrine system's abilities to deliver signals?

***Connecting* CONCEPTS**

5. **Cell Structure** What structures on a cell membrane might ensure that the endocrine system's signals only affect the cells for which they are intended?

TEACH FROM VISUALS

FIGURE 29.2 Have students refer to the photograph of the nervous system to distinguish the central and peripheral nervous systems. **Ask**

- Based upon the location of the structures, which one do you think belongs to the central nervous system? the spinal cord
- The peripheral nervous system? the nerves

Vocabulary

Academic Vocabulary Two terms important to this chapter are **central** and **peripheral.** Students may be familiar with these words used in the context of computers. The computer is the *central processing unit* (CPU), which interprets and executes instructions. The *peripherals*—scanners, printers, sound and video equipment—collect data as well as produce the desired end product.

Answers

A **Infer** endocrine system

Assess and Reteach

Assess Use the Online Quiz or Section Quiz (*Assessment Book,* p. 571).

Reteach Have students create a Venn diagram, comparing and contrasting the nervous and endocrine systems.

29.1 ASSESSMENT

1. A communication system allows the body to respond to its environment and maintain homeostasis.
2. The nervous system sends signals through specialized tissues, works quickly, and controls immediate processes. The endocrine system sends signals through the bloodstream, works slowly, and controls processes that occur over long periods of time.
3. The nervous system controls the rate of blinking because the nervous system controls fast processes.
4. A clogged blood vessel might slow the delivery of signals by the endocrine system but not by the nervous system.
5. Students' responses should discuss membrane proteins such as gated channels, transport proteins, and protein receptors.

SECTION 29.2

▼ Plan and Prepare

Objectives

- Describe neurons as specialized cells.
- Explain how neurons transmit and receive signals.

Section Resources

Unit Resource Book Study Guide pp. 27–28 Power Notes p. 29 Reinforcement p. 30 Pre-AP Activity pp. 49–50
Interactive Reader Chapter 29 **Spanish Study Guide** pp. 291–292
Biology Toolkit pp. C8, C17, C36
Technology Power Presentation 29.2 Media Gallery DVD Online Quiz 29.2

Activate Prior Knowledge Explain that a phobia is a fear of a specific thing that usually elicits an immediate response. Have students think of what they fear the most and how it makes them feel.
Ask

- How do you respond to your fear? Students may suggest screaming, jumping back, increased heart and breathing rates, or sweating.
- What body system makes immediate reactions possible? nervous system

▼ Teach

Vocabulary

dendrite Tell students that the prefix of *dendrite* has two meanings: *dendro-* from the Greek *dendron,* meaning "tree," or *dendr-,* meaning "earlier." Relate this to dendrite structure. A dendrite branches like a tree; it is also where an impulse enters a neuron—its "earliest" point.

Answers

A Infer Having more than one dendrite enables a neuron to receive signals from multiple neurons.

29.2 Neurons

KEY CONCEPT The nervous system is composed of highly specialized cells.

MAIN IDEAS

- Neurons are highly specialized cells.
- Neurons receive and transmit signals.

VOCABULARY

neuron, p. 876
dendrite, p. 876
axon, p. 876
resting potential, p. 877
sodium-potassium pump, p. 877
action potential, p. 878
synapse, p. 879
terminal, p. 879
neurotransmitter, p. 879

Connect When you eat a snack, you might flick crumbs off of your fingers without giving it much thought. The specialized cells of your nervous system, however, are hard at work carrying the messages between your fingers and your brain.

MAIN IDEA

Neurons are highly specialized cells.

A **neuron** is a specialized cell that stores information and carries messages within the nervous system and between other body systems. Most neurons have three main parts, as shown in **FIGURE 29.3.**

1. The cell body is the part of the neuron that contains the nucleus and organelles.
2. **Dendrites** are branchlike extensions of the cytoplasm and the cell membrane that receive messages from neighboring cells. Neurons can have more than one dendrite, and each dendrite can have many branches.
3. Each neuron has one axon. An **axon** is a long extension that carries electrical messages away from the cell body and passes them to other cells.

FIGURE 29.3 Structure of a Neuron

A neuron is a specialized cell of the nervous system that produces and transmits signals.

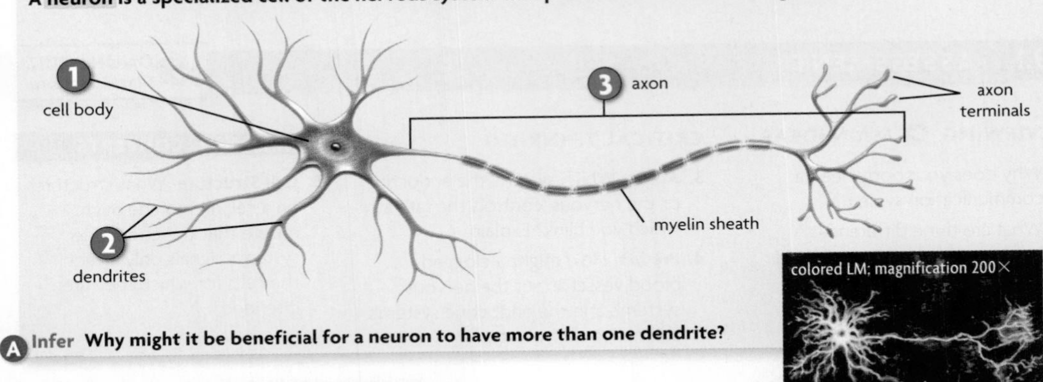

A Infer Why might it be beneficial for a neuron to have more than one dendrite?

Differentiated Instruction

HANDS-ON ACTIVITY

To demonstrate how a nerve impulse travels along the axon of a neuron, give each group of students eight dominoes. Have students set the dominoes on end, about three-quarters of a domino's length away from one another, in a straight line. Then have them flick the first domino in the line. **Ask,** How is the action of the dominoes like a nerve impulse? requires a stimulus, moves one way at a set speed Discuss the need for a network to move a message any distance and the fact that the original condition must be reinstated before a new signal can be sent.

PRE-AP

For this section, suggest students use the Survey/Question/Read/Recite/Review strategy. First they preview the section by surveying the material and developing questions. As they read, they will answer the questions, clarify the answers, and then use these to review what they have learned.

Biology Toolkit, SQ3R, p. C8

There are three types of neurons: (1) sensory neurons, (2) interneurons, and (3) motor neurons. Sensory neurons detect stimuli and transmit signals to the brain and the spinal cord, which are both made up of interneurons. Interneurons receive signals from sensory neurons and relay them within the brain and the spinal cord. They process information and pass signals to motor neurons. Motor neurons pass messages from the nervous system to other tissues in the body, such as muscles.

The nervous system also relies on specialized support cells. For example, Schwann cells cover axons. A collection of Schwann cells, called the myelin sheath, insulates neurons' axons and helps them to send messages.

Analyze How does a neuron's shape allow it to send signals across long distances?

TAKING NOTES

Use a flow chart to organize your notes on how a neuron transmits a signal.

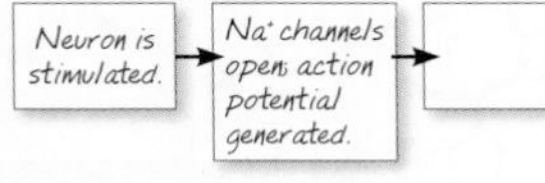

MAIN IDEA

Neurons receive and transmit signals.

When your alarm clock buzzes in the morning, the sound stimulates neurons in your ear. The neurons send signals to your brain, which prompt you to either get out of bed or hit the snooze button. Neurons transmit information in the form of electrical and chemical impulses. When a neuron is stimulated, it produces an electrical impulse that travels only within that neuron. Before the signal can move to the next cell, it changes into a chemical signal.

Before a Neuron Is Stimulated

When a neuron is not transmitting a signal, it is said to be "at rest." However, this does not mean that the neuron is inactive. Neurons work to maintain a charge difference across their membranes, which keeps them ready to transmit impulses when they become stimulated.

While a neuron is at rest, the inside of its cell membrane is more negatively charged than the outside. The difference in charge across the membrane is called the **resting potential,** because it contains the potential energy needed to transmit an impulse. The resting potential occurs because there are unequal concentrations of ions inside and outside the neuron.

Two types of ions—sodium ions (Na^+) and potassium ions (K^+)—cause the resting potential. More Na^+ ions are present outside the cell than inside it. On the other hand, there are fewer K^+ ions outside the cell than inside it. Notice that both ions are positively charged. The neuron is negative compared with its surroundings because there are fewer positive ions inside the neuron.

Proteins in the cell membrane of the neuron maintain the resting potential. Some are protein channels that allow ions to diffuse across the membrane—Na^+ ions diffuse into the cell and K^+ ions diffuse out. However, the membrane has many more channels for K^+ than for Na^+, so positive charges leave the cell much faster than they enter. This unequal diffusion of ions is the main reason for the resting potential. In addition, the membrane also has a protein called the **sodium-potassium pump,** which uses energy to actively transport Na^+ ions out of the cell and bring K^+ ions into the cell. This process also helps maintain the resting potential.

Connecting CONCEPTS

Active Transport Recall from **Chapter 3** that energy and specialized membrane proteins are required to move molecules and ions against the concentration gradient.

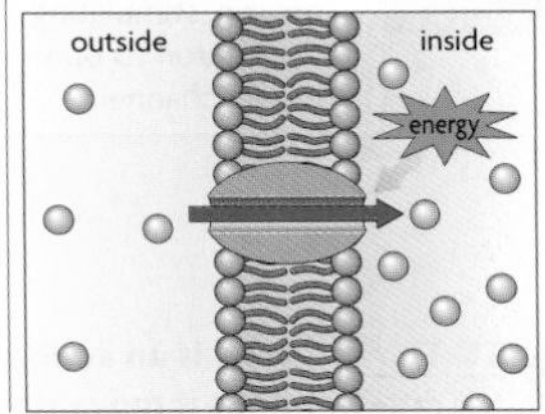

Answers

A Analyze A neuron has a long axon that carries signals long distances.

Take It Further

In a cell membrane, there are many openings, or channels, formed by proteins that extend through to both sides of the membrane. There are at least three types of protein channels in a neuron's membrane:

ion channels These channels are always open and allow tiny quantities of ions to enter and leave the cell by diffusion. This normally helps create a balance inside and outside the cell.

Na^+–K^+ pump These channels use active transport to maintain a negative charge, or resting potential, inside the neuron.

gated channels When a dendrite is stimulated by a neurotransmitter, gated channels in the dendrite open to allow Na^+ to enter the cell at that site. If the number of ions that enter crosses a threshold, the site becomes depolarized, which causes other gated channels to open sequentially down the axon.

Vocabulary

Academic Vocabulary The words *potent* and *potential* have the same root, meaning "to be able":

potent, capable of exerting a strong effect

potential, capable of being but not yet in existence

Students may have seen the word used in physics: potential energy versus kinetic energy. There is a similar use here: *resting potential* versus *action potential.*

Connecting CONCEPTS

Active Transport It is important for students to understand that active transport is not involved in the propagation of a nerve impulse through the axon. It is active transport that maintains resting potential via the sodium-potassium pump.

ENGLISH LEARNERS

Use **FIGURE 29.4** as a prereading stimulus for a picture-imaging activity. As background, choose points from pages 877 and 879, "Neurons receive and transmit signals." Ask questions using *what, where, when; size, color, number, shape, sound; movement, direction, pattern, background, perspective.* Students provide details about the diagram and then compare the description to pages 877 and 879.

Biology Toolkit, Connect to Content through Visuals, p. C17

BELOW LEVEL

Have students use a graphic organizer, such as a cause and effect chain, to interpret and remember the details of a nerve impulse. Have students work with the text on page 877 as well as **FIGURE 29.4.**

Biology Toolkit, Cause and Effect Chain, p. C36

▼ Teach *continued*

TEACH FROM VISUALS

FIGURE 29.4 Have students study the illustration and walk them through each step. **Ask**

- When a neuron is at rest, what is the charge of its inner cell membrane? negative
- What causes an area of the inner membrane to become positively charged? How does this happen? a stimulus; Na^+ channels open, allowing Na^+ ions to rush into the cell.
- How does an area of positive charge, or impulse, move down the axon of a neuron? The Na^+ channels along the axon open in sequence, allowing an area of positive charge to move down the axon.
- How is the negative charge of the axon's inner membrane restored? K^+ channels open, causing K^+ to move out of the cell.
- What happens when the impulse reaches the axon terminal? Vesicles inside the terminal release neurotransmitters into the synapse.
- How do the neurotransmitters generate an impulse in an adjacent neuron? The neurotransmitters bind to receptors on the adjacent neuron, causing Na^+ channels in that neuron to open.

Answers

A Critical Viewing An action potential is generated when a neuron is stimulated and a portion of the inner membrane becomes positively charged. The action potential moves down the axon as portions of the inner membrane down the axon become positively charged in sequence.

FIGURE 29.4 Transmission Through and Between Neurons

Once a neuron is stimulated, a portion of the inner membrane becomes positively charged. This electrical impulse, or action potential, moves down the axon. Before it can move to the next neuron, it must become a chemical signal.

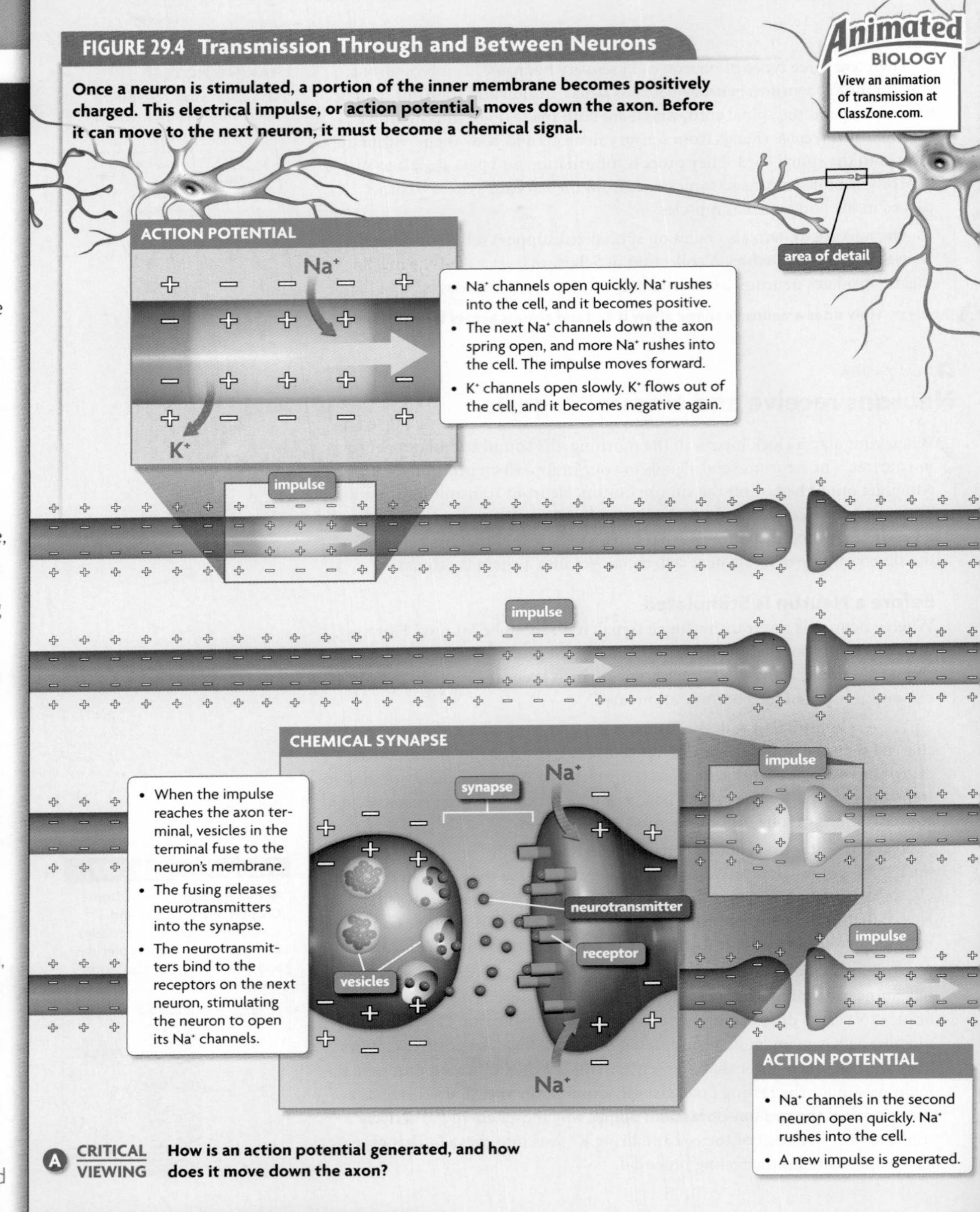

Animated BIOLOGY
View an animation of transmission at ClassZone.com.
area of detail
ACTION POTENTIAL
Na⁺
K⁺
• Na⁺ channels open quickly. Na⁺ rushes into the cell, and it becomes positive.
• The next Na⁺ channels down the axon spring open, and more Na⁺ rushes into the cell. The impulse moves forward.
• K⁺ channels open slowly. K⁺ flows out of the cell, and it becomes negative again.
impulse
impulse
CHEMICAL SYNAPSE
• When the impulse reaches the axon terminal, vesicles in the terminal fuse to the neuron's membrane.
• The fusing releases neurotransmitters into the synapse.
• The neurotransmitters bind to the receptors on the next neuron, stimulating the neuron to open its Na⁺ channels.
synapse
Na⁺
neurotransmitter
receptor
vesicles
Na⁺
impulse
impulse
ACTION POTENTIAL
• Na⁺ channels in the second neuron open quickly. Na⁺ rushes into the cell.
• A new impulse is generated.

A CRITICAL VIEWING **How is an action potential generated, and how does it move down the axon?**

Differentiated Instruction

HANDS-ON ACTIVITY

Students can make their own animation of an action potential moving down an axon. Give each group of students six index cards. Tell them to draw two lines along the length of one of the cards, with a series of ten evenly spaced negatives on the inside of each line and a series of matching positives on the outside of each line, as shown here.

+ + + + + + + + + +
– – – – – – – – – –
– – – – – – – – – –
+ + + + + + + + + +

On a second card, have students draw a reversal of the first two pairs of positives and negatives along each line. On a third card, they should draw a reversal of the second two pairs of positives and negatives along each line, restoring the first two pairs. They should continue reversing two pairs of negatives and positives on each subsequent card until the last two pairs are reversed on the last card. Tell students to stack the cards in the order in which they were made and to flip through them to watch the action potential move.

Transmission Within a Neuron

As you tap your finger on a desk, pressure receptors in your fingers stretch. The stretching causes a change in charge distribution that triggers a moving electrical impulse called an **action potential,** shown in **FIGURE 29.4.**

An action potential requires ion channels in the membrane that have gates that open and close. When a neuron is stimulated, gated channels for Na^+ open quickly, and Na^+ ions rush into the cell. This stimulates adjacent Na^+ channels down the axon to spring open. Na^+ ions rush into the cell, and then those ion channels snap shut. In this way, the area of positively charged membrane moves down the axon.

At the same time Na^+ channels are springing open and snapping shut, K^+ ion channels are opening and closing more slowly. K^+ ions diffuse out of the axon and cause part of the membrane to return to resting potential. Because K^+ channels are slow to respond to the change in axon's charge, they appear to open and close behind the moving impulse.

Transmission Between Neurons

Before an action potential moves into the next neuron, it crosses a tiny gap between the neurons called a **synapse.** The axon **terminal,** the part of the axon through which the impulse leaves that neuron, contains chemical-filled vesicles. When an impulse reaches the terminal, vesicles bind to the terminal's membrane and release their chemicals into the synapse. **Neurotransmitters** (NUR-oh-TRANS-miht-urz) are the chemical signals of the nervous system. They bind to receptor proteins on the adjacent neuron and cause Na^+ channels in that neuron to open, generating an action potential.

Typically, many synapses connect neurons. Before the adjacent neuron generates an action potential, it usually needs to be stimulated at more than one synapse. The amount a neuron needs to be stimulated before it produces an action potential is called a threshold.

Once neurotransmitters have triggered a new action potential, they must be removed from the synapse so that ion channels on the second neuron will close again. These neurotransmitters will be broken down by enzymes in the synapse, or they are transported back into the terminal that released them.

Contrast **How does signal transmission within and between neurons differ?**

29.2 ASSESSMENT

ONLINE QUIZ ClassZone.com

REVIEWING MAIN IDEAS

1. What are the roles of the three types of **neurons**?
2. Draw a picture to illustrate **resting potential,** and explain how it helps transmit signals in neurons.

CRITICAL THINKING

3. **Infer** How does a threshold prevent a neuron from generating too many **action potentials**?
4. **Predict** What might happen if a drug blocked **neurotransmitter** receptors?

Connecting CONCEPTS

5. **Cell Chemistry** Hyponatremia occurs when people have very low amounts of sodium in their body. How might the nervous system be affected if a person had this condition?

History of Science

In 1952, a series of papers was published summarizing the work of **Alan Hodgkin** and **Andrew Huxley** on neural **action potential.** Their work contributed to our current understanding of how an action potential is generated. Working at Cambridge University, Hodgkin and Huxley chose an unusual subject for their studies—the squid. A squid has an axon that is about 1 millimeter (0.04 in.) in diameter, enabling them to work a wire down its axis. In 1963, Hodgkin and Huxley won a Nobel Prize for their work.

Answers

A Contrast Signal transmission within a neuron is electrical. Signal transmission between neurons is chemical.

Assess and Reteach ▼

Assess Use the Online Quiz or Section Quiz (*Assessment Book,* p. 572).

Reteach Have students view nerve impulse transmission at **ClassZone.com.** Then have them draw and label their own diagrams to illustrate impulse transmission.

29.2 ASSESSMENT

1. Sensory neurons detect stimuli and transmit signals to interneurons in the brain and spinal cord. Interneurons relay the signals within the brain and spinal cord, process information, and pass signals to motor neurons. Motor neurons pass signals from the brain and spinal cord to other parts of the body, such as muscles.
2. Drawings should show more Na^+ outside the neuron and more K^+ inside the neuron. The resting potential sets up the ion gradient necessary so that Na^+ will move into the cell and K^+ will move out of the cell.
3. A threshold ensures that action potentials are not produced unless the neuron has received enough stimulation.
4. Neurotransmitters would not be able to bind with the receptors and initiate impulses in the neurons.
5. Students' responses should discuss the importance of sodium ions in generating action potentials and conclude that low amounts of sodium would make neurons less able to transmit signals.

SECTION 29.3

▼ Plan and Prepare

Objectives

- Explain how senses help maintain homeostasis.
- Explain how the senses detect physical and chemical stimuli.

Section Resources

Unit Resource Book
Study Guide pp. 31–32
Power Notes p. 33
Reinforcement p. 34

Interactive Reader Chapter 29
Spanish Study Guide pp. 293–294

Biology Toolkit pp. C22, C36, C40

Technology
Power Presentation 29.3
Media Gallery DVD
Online Quiz 29.3

Activate Prior Knowledge Discuss sensory compensation with students. **Ask,** If I were to blindfold you and place you at the back of the room, how would you reach the door? using other senses Discuss the adaptive advantages of having multiple senses.

▼ Teach

Take It Further

The constriction of the **pupil** in response to bright light is called the pupillary reflex, which involves **cranial nerves** and the **brain.** In a medical emergency, a doctor may shine light onto a patient's pupils. Normal pupils constrict equally. If pupils do not react or respond abnormally, this could indicate damage to the brain or to the optic or oculomotor nerves. It is also an indicator for an individual who is on depressant drugs.

Answers

Ⓐ **Summarize** Sensory organs monitor the internal and external environment and respond to specific situations that may cause injury or even death.

29.3 The Senses

KEY CONCEPT The senses detect the internal and external environments.

MAIN IDEAS
- The senses help to maintain homeostasis.
- The senses detect physical and chemical stimuli.

VOCABULARY
rod cell, p. 881
cone cell, p. 881
hair cell, p. 882

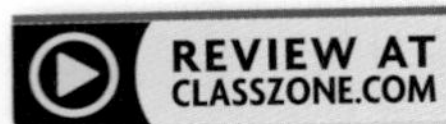

Connect You may think that you hear sounds with your ear, smell with your nose, or taste with your tongue, but that is not true. Your sensory organs only collect stimuli and send signals to your brain. Your brain interprets these signals. Together, your sensory organs and your brain allow you to perceive stimuli as various sounds, sights, smells, tastes, and so forth.

MAIN IDEA
The senses help to maintain homeostasis.

You rely on your sensory organs to collect information about the world around you. Once your brain has information from sensory organs, it triggers a response that will maintain homeostasis. For example, eyes adjust to bright and dim light by changing the size of your pupils, as shown in **FIGURE 29.5**. If your skin feels cold, you might shiver. You might get goose bumps, or your arm hairs might stand up, trapping the heat that would otherwise escape from your skin.

Your sensory organs also influence your behavior. Although homeostasis is strictly defined as the regulation and maintenance of the body's internal condition, you could also think of behaviors that prevent death or injury as a kind of homeostatic mechanism.

Imagine that you are getting ready to cross a street, and you look both ways to see if it is safe. Light enters your eyes and the light receptors in your eyes are stimulated to produce impulses. The impulses travel down bundles of axons to your brain. Your brain filters these impulses and forwards some of them to the specific area of your brain that interprets visual information. Your brain then combines this information with that from your other sense organs. Your brain interprets the light that entered your eyes as a large truck speeding your way. With the help of your eyes, you will wait for the truck to pass before walking into the street.

Your senses influence many other behaviors that help protect your tissues from damage. For example, if automatic responses such as shivering and goose bumps don't warm you up, you might decide to put on a jacket. If the sun is too bright, you might decide to put on sunglasses. If a room is too dark, you might decide to turn on a light.

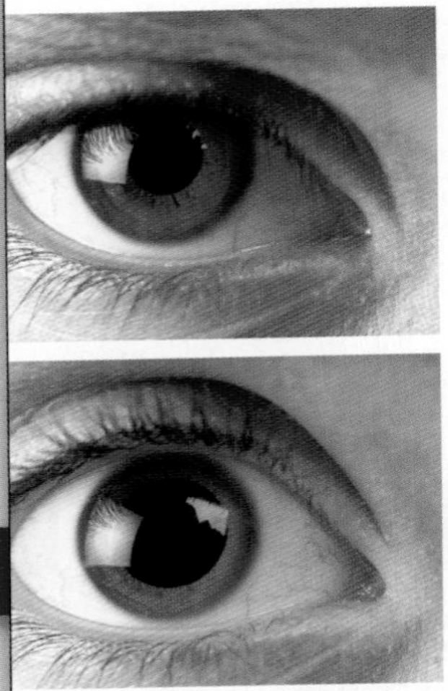

FIGURE 29.5 The size of your pupil changes depending on the amount of light around you. In bright light, your pupil constricts. In dim light, the pupil expands.

Ⓐ Summarize **How do your sensory organs help you to maintain homeostasis?**

Differentiated Instruction

ENGLISH LEARNERS

Have students organize material in this section according to sensory organs. Have them include information on the types of sensory receptors involved.

Biology Toolkit, Content Frame, p. C22

BELOW LEVEL

Have students use a concept map to organize material in this section. Have them organize material according to types of sensory receptors, as listed on page 881.

Biology Toolkit, Concept Map, p. C40

MAIN IDEA
The senses detect physical and chemical stimuli.

Humans have specialized sensory organs that detect external stimuli. The information these organs collect helps to make up the five senses: vision, hearing, touch, taste, and smell. Five different types of sensory receptors help humans to detect different stimuli.

- Photoreceptors sense light.
- Mechanoreceptors respond to pressure, movement, and tension.
- Thermoreceptors monitor temperature.
- Chemoreceptors detect chemicals that are dissolved in fluid.
- Pain receptors respond to extreme heat, cold, and pressure, and to chemicals that are released by damaged tissues.

VOCABULARY

You can remember what kind of stimuli each receptor receives by remembering what their prefixes mean:
photo- = light
mechano- = machine, movement
thermo- = heat
chemo- = chemical

Vision

Humans rely on vision more than any of the other senses. In fact, the eye contains about 70 percent of all the sensory receptors in the body. Most of these are photoreceptors on the back inside wall of the eye. This layer of tissue, called the retina, is shown in **FIGURE 29.6.** Specialized cells called rods and cones are the photoreceptors. **Rod cells** detect light intensity and are used in black and white vision. **Cone cells** detect color. Rod cells are sensitive to low amounts of light, and cone cells need bright light to function. This is why you have difficulty seeing color when it is dark.

Because sight depends on the amount of light available, the eye must have a way to limit the amount of light from a bright source or allow more light to enter from a dim light source. Muscles around the iris—the colored part of the eye—control the size of the hole at its center, the pupil. The eye adjusts the amount of light that enters it by changing the size of the pupil. The larger the pupil, the more light that can enter.

Before light can stimulate the rod and cone cells in the retina, it must pass through structures at the front of the eye. Light enters the eye through a protective transparent layer called the cornea and moves through the pupil. After the pupil, light passes through the lens. The lens is behind the iris, and it focuses the light onto the retina. The light stimulates the rod and cone cells, which generate nerve impulses. The impulses travel along the bundle of axons that form the optic nerve. The nerve carries the impulses to the brain, where they are interpreted as images.

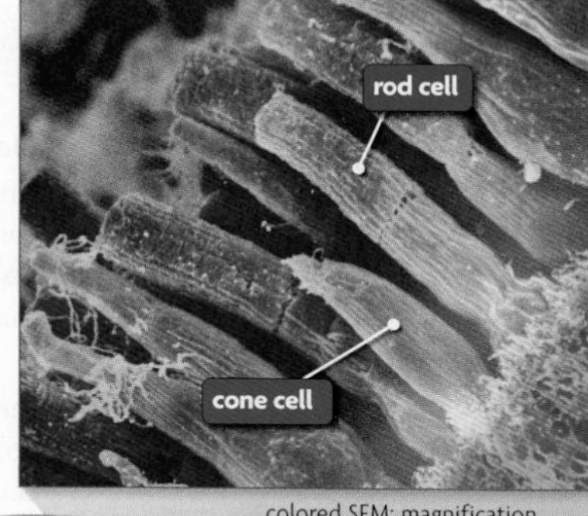

colored SEM; magnification about 5000×

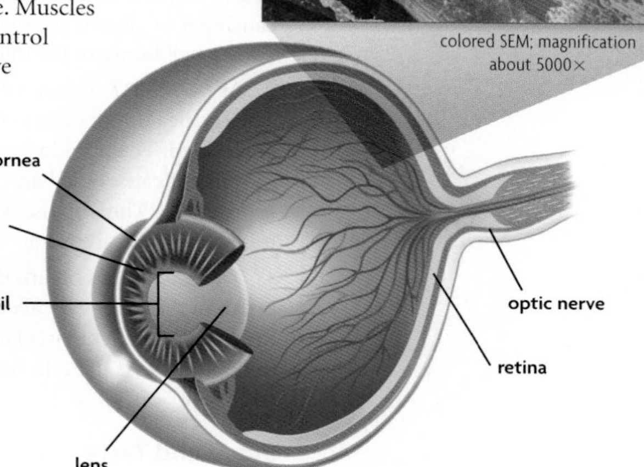

FIGURE 29.6 Light is focused by the lens onto the retina, where rod and cone cells generate impulses. These impulses travel through your optic nerve to your brain, where they are interpreted as images.

TEACH WITH TECHNOLOGY

Use a digital camera to capture a scene familiar to all students. The image should not include people or temporary objects. Project the image and have students write a list of things that they had not noticed before. **Ask,** Why don't you notice these objects on a daily basis? Is there some selective advantage to that? We see with our eyes, but we perceive with our brains. We need to distinguish between things that are not important to our interaction with the environment and those that are.

ONLINE BIOLOGY Go to the chapter Resource Center at **ClassZone.com** for additional resources and information on the senses.

Science Trivia

- There are 3500 inner and 12,000 outer hair cells in the cochlea that contain mechanoreceptors for hearing.
- Each taste bud contains between 50–150 chemoreceptors.
- There are 12 million human olfactory chemoreceptors.
- The eye has 5–6 million cones and 120–140 million rods that are retinal photoreceptors.
- The hand has 17,000 mechano-receptors.

Address Misconceptions

Common Misconception People who are visually impaired live in a world of total darkness.

Correcting the Misconception More than 80 percent of people with vision impairment retain some ability to see. A person with profound vision loss may be able to see outlines of objects, the presence or absence of light, and the direction from which light is coming.

▼ Teach *continued*

TEACH FROM VISUALS

FIGURE 29.7 Direct students' attention to the semicircular canals in the illustration and point out that each canal lies in a different plane—vertical, sideways, and horizontal. **Ask,** What does the orientation of the semicircular canals suggest about how they function in maintaining balance? They provide information of the body's orientation in three dimensions.

Integrating Physics

The intensity of sound waves is measured in units called **decibels** (dB). The decibel scale is based on powers of 10. The level 0 dB (10^0) represents the softest sound a human ear can detect. **Ask,** How many times greater in intensity is a whisper at 20 dB (10^2 dB) than the threshold of hearing at 0 dB? 100 times; 20 dB = 10^2 dB = 100×10^0 (1) Tell students that loud rock music can be 130 dB (10^{13} dB)—the threshold of pain. A jet plane takeoff is 140 dB. An eardrum will burst at 160 dB.

Take It Further

With the increasing popularity of **portable music players** comes the increased risk of hearing loss. Most portable music players can reach 91 to 121 dB. Any prolonged exposure to noise over 85 dB (such as a lawn mower running) can cause hearing loss.

France and other European countries have capped the sound limit for portable music players at 100 dB, while the United States has no set limit. According to an article in *The Journal of Pediatrics,* an estimated 12.5 percent of children from ages 6 to 19 have noise-induced hearing loss. To reduce the chances of hearing loss, volume should not exceed 65 to 70 dB, which is the level of normal conversation.

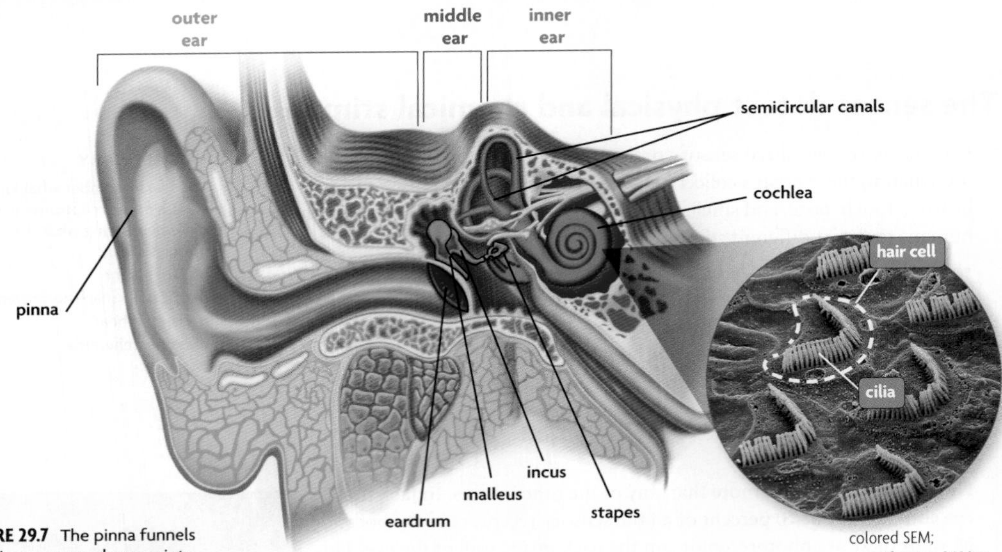

FIGURE 29.7 The pinna funnels vibrations, or sound waves, into the ear. Hair cells convert vibrations into impulses that are sent to the brain for interpretation.

***Connecting* CONCEPTS**

Animal Behavior Sensory organs collect stimuli that influence human and animal behavior, as you read in **Chapter 27.**

Hearing

The ear collects vibrations—sound waves—from the air, amplifies them, and converts them into nerve impulses that are interpreted in the brain as sounds. **Hair cells** are specialized cells in the inner ear that contain mechanoreceptors that detect vibrations. Hair cells produce action potentials when they are bent.

Sound waves enter the body through the outer ear. The pinna, the part of the ear you can see, collects sound and funnels it into the auditory canal. Sound waves in the auditory canal hit the eardrum, or tympanic membrane, causing it to vibrate like the head of a drum. The vibrations are amplified by three small bones in the middle ear—the malleus, the incus, and the stapes.

As **FIGURE 29.7** shows, the amplified vibrations are transferred to the cochlea. The cochlea is a structure of fluid-filled canals in the inner ear where hair cells are located. The fluid in the cochlea moves in response to vibrations. This movement causes the hair cells to bend. When the hair cells bend, an impulse is produced. The impulse is carried by the auditory nerve to the brain, where it is perceived as a sound.

The ear also has organs that regulate balance. Balance is controlled by an organ in the inner ear called the semicircular canals. When your head moves, fluid inside the semicircular canals moves. The movement bends the hair cells in the canals. As the cells bend, they generate impulses that are transmitted to the brain.

Smell and Taste

You may have noticed that food seems to have less flavor when you have a cold. If you haven't, you can try holding your nose the next time you eat. It will have a similar effect. Your sense of taste is less sensitive when your nose is stuffed up because your smell and taste senses are closely related. Both the nose, which senses odors, and the tongue, which senses flavors, have chemoreceptors. These receptors detect molecules that are dissolved in liquid.

Differentiated Instruction

INCLUSION

Have students who are literal thinkers work out each category of sensory information using the analogy of an input-output device. Suggest they use the list of receptor types on page 881 as input. Then they can use a cause and effect chain that leads to the output—the type of information sent to the brain.

Biology Toolkit, Cause and Effect Chain, p. C36

In smell, small airborne chemicals enter the nose. These chemicals dissolve in mucus in the nose, and they are detected by olfactory cells, which generate impulses. The olfactory nerve takes impulses to the brain.

Taste buds are chemoreceptors that detect tastes. They are found in bumps on the tongue called papillae. As in the nose, chemicals must be dissolved before they can be detected. The chemoreceptors generate impulses that are sent to the brain. Although your tongue can only detect five basic tastes—sweet, sour, salty, bitter, and savory—your brain interprets combinations of these as complex flavors.

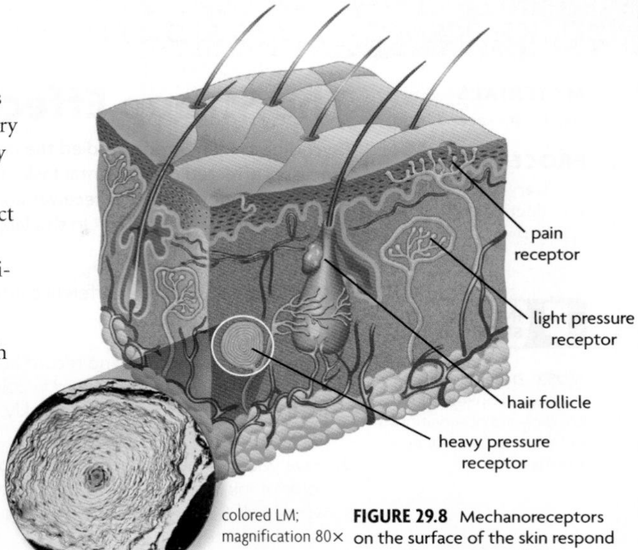

FIGURE 29.8 Mechanoreceptors on the surface of the skin respond to gentle pressure, and those deep in the skin respond to hard pressure. Pain receptors are close to the skin's surface.

Touch, Temperature, and Pain

Your skin contains receptors that sense touch, temperature, and pain. Touch is sensed by mechanoreceptors that detect pressure, movement, and tension. The skin has two general types of mechanoreceptors. Mechanoreceptors that detect gentle touch are located in the upper layer of the skin. Some of these are wrapped around hair follicles. They help you feel when these hairs move, as they might when a small fly lands on your arm. Mechanoreceptors that recognize heavy pressure are found deeper within the skin, as you can see in **FIGURE 29.8.**

Temperature and pain are sensed by thermoreceptors and pain receptors. Thermoreceptors detect heat and cold. Pain receptors detect chemicals that are released by damaged cells. Some pain receptors detect sharp pains, such as the pain you would feel by stepping on a nail. Other pain receptors sense blunt or throbbing pain, such as that caused by a bruise.

A **Summarize** **To which senses do mechanoreceptors contribute?**

TEACH FROM VISUALS

FIGURE 29.8 Have students count the number of hairs shown in the section of skin. Explain that this is a good indicator of the number of light pressure receptors in that section. **Ask,** Does the skin on different areas of the body have the same distribution of light pressure receptors? No, areas of the body that need to be more sensitive to touch have a greater concentration of light pressure receptors.

Tell students that there are about 100 times more light-pressure receptors per square centimeter (645 per square inch) on their fingertips than on the backs of their hands.

Answers

A **Summarize** Mechanoreceptors contribute to hearing, balance, and touch.

29.3 ASSESSMENT

ONLINE QUIZ ClassZone.com

REVIEWING MAIN IDEAS

1. How do your sensory organs work with your brain to help you perceive the world around you?
2. What kinds of receptors are **hair cells, rod cells,** and **cone cells,** and to which of your senses do these cells contribute?

CRITICAL THINKING

3. **Connect** Why do you think that you can perceive some sounds as loud and others as very soft?
4. **Predict** In the human eye, there are 20 rod cells for every 1 cone cell. How would your vision be different if you had 5 rod cells for every 20 cone cells?

Connecting CONCEPTS

5. **Evolution** For some invertebrates that live in water, the sense of taste and the sense of smell are identical. Why do you think separate organs for taste and smell might have evolved in animals that live on land but not in some animals that live exclusively in water?

Assess and Reteach

Assess Use the Online Quiz or Section Quiz (*Assessment Book,* p. 573).

Reteach Create a table on the board, listing the sense organs. Have students provide information on the types of receptors found in each organ and the kinds of stimuli the receptors detect.

29.3 ASSESSMENT

1. Sensory organs gather stimuli and send impulses to the brain, which interprets and forms responses.
2. Hair cells are mechanoreceptors in the ear that detect movement and allow a person to hear and maintain balance. In the eye, rod cells are photoreceptors that detect light intensity, and cone cells detect colors.
3. A sound is perceived as loud or soft depending on the extent to which the eardrum vibrates and hair cells bend. The greater the vibration and bending, the louder is the perceived sound.
4. More cone cells might enable a wider variation of colors to be perceived. However, fewer rod cells might mean less contrast between brightness and darkness; colors might be muted.
5. Taste and smell both depend on chemoreceptors that detect substances dissolved in fluid. In water invertebrates, there is no need to detect substances carried in air, only in water, so a single sense is all that is necessary. As animals became air breathers, they developed a new sense—smell—that detected chemicals in air.

INVESTIGATION

Time 20 minutes TEACHER TESTED
Teacher Preparation
Student Difficulty
Lab Binder Human Bio, pp. 15–17

Purpose Investigate how interference (conflicting information) affects the completion of a task.

Overview Students will demonstrate the Stroop Effect. They will

- time the completion of a task while reading consistent information and record the number of incorrect responses made during the task
- time the completion of a task while reading conflicting information and record the number of incorrect responses made during the task
- compare the times and numbers of incorrect responses and explain any differences

LAB PREPARATION

- Each group should have a watch with a second hand or a stopwatch.

LAB MANAGEMENT

- Students who have color-vision impairment should work with two other students.
- Tell students to respond as quickly as possible.

Teacher Note "This lab could be extended by having students do research to discover why the Stroop Effect occurs, based on the chemistry and physiology of the brain."

POST-LAB DISCUSSION

Students immediately realize the "confusion" of words and colors in the second column. Most understand that they read the word before recognizing that the color is not the same as the word. **Ask,** What would happen if you took more time? The brain would have more time to resolve the interference so they would more likely give correct responses.

The Stroop Effect

MATERIALS
watch with second hand

PROCESS SKILLS
- Observing
- Collecting Data
- Inferring

NOS.1 Develop explanations based on reproducible data and observations gathered during laboratory investigations.

Psychologist John Stroop studied the processing of words and how these thought processes affected other mental tasks. He found that the brain must override an automatic response when it receives conflicting information, or interference. This is now called the Stroop Effect. In this lab, you will complete a task that demonstrates the Stroop Effect.

PROBLEM How does interference affect the completion of a task?

PROCEDURE

1. Have your partner time and record how long it takes for you to say aloud the color of ink in which each word in column 1 is printed (say the color, not the word itself). Give your responses as quickly as possible. Also record the number of incorrect responses.
2. Have your partner time and record how long it takes for you to say aloud the color of ink in which each word in column 2 is printed (say the color, not the word itself). Give your responses as quickly as possible. Also record the number of incorrect responses.
3. Switch roles and repeat steps 1 and 2.

TABLE 1. STROOP EFFECT COLOR TEST

COLUMN 1	COLUMN 2
blue	red
yellow	gray
red	orange
green	blue
black	black
purple	yellow
gray	green
orange	purple

ANALYZE AND CONCLUDE

1. **Analyze** Compare the times for naming the ink colors in both column 1 and column 2. Was there a difference between the two times? Explain why this difference exists.
2. **Infer** How many incorrect responses did you give for column 1? for column 2? Explain why incorrect responses might have occurred.
3. **Experimental Design** Design your own Stroop Effect test. For example, you could draw outlines of animals and write the name of a different animal in the drawing and test if interference occurs.

Answers

Analyze and Conclude

1. Students should report that it took longer for them to complete the task for column 2. The interference of conflicting information—the color that a word indicates and the color of the ink in which the word is printed—means that the brain requires more processing, which delays response time.
2. More incorrect responses should have been given for column 2. Incorrect responses occurred because the color of ink conflicted with the color indicated by the word.
3. Students' responses will vary. One example is to draw different geometric shapes, such as triangles, circles, squares, and rectangles, and write the word for a different shape inside each drawing (for example, draw a triangle and write the word *circle* inside the triangle).

29.4 Central and Peripheral Nervous Systems

KEY CONCEPT The central nervous system interprets information, and the peripheral nervous system gathers and transmits information.

MAIN IDEAS
- The nervous system's two parts work together.
- The CNS processes information.
- The PNS links the CNS to muscles and other organs.

VOCABULARY
- **cerebrum,** p. 886
- **cerebral cortex,** p. 887
- **cerebellum,** p. 888
- **brain stem,** p. 888
- **reflex arc,** p. 889
- **somatic nervous system,** p. 889
- **autonomic nervous system,** p. 890
- **sympathetic nervous system,** p. 890
- **parasympathetic nervous system,** p. 890

Review
central nervous system (CNS), peripheral nervous system (PNS)

Connect Imagine that you're watching television, and you want to turn up the volume. Without taking your eyes off the screen, you reach for the remote control on a table next to you. When you touch a glass of water or your homework that is sitting on the table, you will not pick it up because you know that it does not feel like the remote. Your brain is interpreting the stimuli gathered by your sense of touch. If you had no way to interpret each stimulus, you might pick up every item on the table before finding the remote.

MAIN IDEA

The nervous system's two parts work together.

Earlier in this chapter you read that your nervous system is divided into two parts—the central nervous system and the peripheral nervous system—which are shown in **FIGURE 29.9.**

- The central nervous system (CNS) includes the brain and spinal cord. The CNS is composed of interneurons that interact with other nerves in the body. The CNS receives, interprets, and sends signals to the PNS.
- The peripheral nervous system (PNS) is the collection of nerves that connects the CNS to all of your organ systems. The PNS uses sensory neurons to detect stimuli from inside and outside your body, and it uses motor neurons to carry signals from the CNS to other parts of the body and stimulate your muscles or other target organs.

Both the CNS and the PNS are made of several smaller parts. For example, the brain has several areas that control different functions. Divisions of the PNS influence voluntary responses, such as muscle contractions that occur while you walk, and involuntary responses, such as those that occur during digestion.

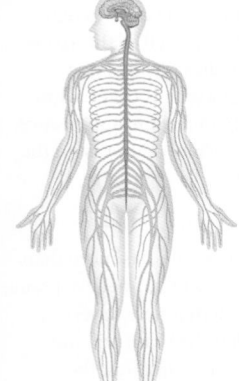

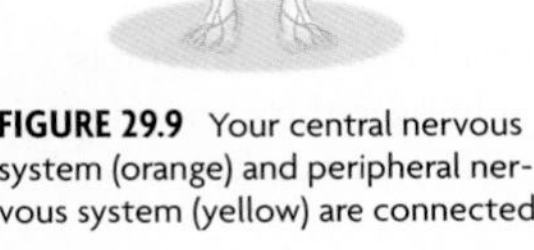

FIGURE 29.9 Your central nervous system (orange) and peripheral nervous system (yellow) are connected.

(A) **Summarize How do the neurons of the CNS and PNS work together to produce responses to stimuli?**

Differentiated Instruction

PRE-AP
Have students use Cornell notes to organize the material in this section.

Biology Toolkit, Cornell Notes, p. C26

BELOW LEVEL
Suggest that students use a T-chart to organize definitions for the chapter under CNS and PNS. Have students think in terms of structure and function when organizing the definitions.

Biology Toolkit, T-Chart, p. C20

SECTION 29.4

Plan and Prepare

Objectives
- Explain how the two parts of the nervous system work together.
- Describe the structure and function of the central nervous system.
- Describe the structure and function of the peripheral nervous system.

Section Resources

Unit Resource Book
Study Guide pp. 35–36
Power Notes p. 37
Reinforcement p. 38

Interactive Reader Chapter 29
Spanish Study Guide pp. 295–296

Biology Toolkit pp. C11, C20, C26, C39, D8

Technology
Power Presentation 29.4
Media Gallery DVD
Online Quiz 29.4

Activate Prior Knowledge Remind students that the body has many functions that occur simultaneously. **Ask,** Can you walk and chew gum at the same time? yes Explain that cooperation between the central and peripheral nervous systems enables processing of many forms of sensory input.

Teach

Vocabulary

Academic Vocabulary The prefix *peri-* in **peripheral** comes from a root meaning "to carry around." The related words *periphery* and *perimeter* refer to an outer boundary. Discuss how this description matches with the peripheral nervous system shown in **FIGURE 29.9.**

Answers

(A) **Summarize** The PNS sensory neurons pick up signals from all parts of the body and transmit them to the CNS, which interprets those signals. The CNS relays a response to motor neurons of the PNS, which stimulate a response.

▼ Teach *continued*

QUICK LAB

Time 5 minutes	TEACHER TESTED
Lab Binder Human Bio, p. 22	

Purpose Compare the relative amounts of space given to touch reception in a fingertip and a forearm.

Teacher Note "It's a fun, interactive, and relevant activity for the classroom."

LAB MANAGEMENT

- Use toothpicks with pointed ends.
- Straightened paper clips can be used instead of toothpicks.

Answers

Sample Data

Area Tested	Number of Toothpicks	
	Used	Reported
fingertip	1	1
fingertip	2	2
fingertip	1	1
forearm	2	1
forearm	2	1
forearm	1	1

Teacher Note "A lot of students believe there is less "meat" in the finger than the forearm and therefore this affects results."

Analyze and Conclude

1. Students should observe that the fingertip received more sensory information. The number of toothpicks reported and the number of toothpicks used were the same in more instances when the fingertip was tested than when the forearm was tested.
2. The fingertip has more space devoted to it in the primary sensory cortex.

QUICK LAB DESIGN YOUR OWN

NOS.1

The Primary Sensory Cortex

The primary sensory cortex is the part of your cerebrum that receives information about your sense of touch from different parts of your body. Each body part sends information to a different place in your primary sensory cortex. In this lab, you will determine the relationship between different body parts and the amount of space the brain devotes to receiving touch information from those body parts.

MATERIALS
- 3 toothpicks
- soft blindfold/bandana

PROBLEM Does your finger or your forearm have more space devoted to it in the primary sensory cortex?

PROCEDURE

1. Hypothesize which area will be more sensitive. Make a data table to record the information you gather during the lab.
2. Have your partner close his or her eyes. Gently, touch the tip of your partner's index finger with the tip(s) of one, two, or three toothpicks at the same time.
3. Ask your partner how many points he or she feels. Write down the number your partner says next to the number of toothpicks you used. Repeat three more times, varying the number of toothpicks used.
4. Repeat steps 2 and 3 on your partner's forearm.

TABLE 1. PRIMARY SENSORY CORTEX DATA

Area Tested	Number of Toothpicks	
	Used	Reported

ANALYZE AND CONCLUDE

1. **Analyze** Did your partner's finger or forearm receive more sensory information? Do your data support your hypothesis? Why or why not?
2. **Infer** Which area likely has more space in the primary sensory cortex?

TAKING NOTES

Use a main idea diagram to study the parts of the brain.

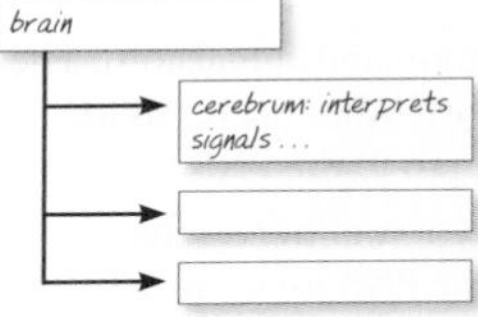

MAIN IDEA

The CNS processes information.

The interneurons of the brain and spinal cord are arranged in a particular way. All of the neuron cell bodies are clustered together, and all of the axons are clustered together. The collection of neuron cell bodies is called gray matter because of its dark gray color. The collection of axons is called white matter because the myelin sheath on the axons give them a white appearance. In the brain, the gray matter is on the outside, and the white matter is on the inside. The spinal cord has the opposite arrangement.

The Brain

The entire brain weighs about half as much as a textbook and has more than 100 billion neurons. The brain is protected by three layers of connective tissue, called meninges (muh-NIHN-jeez), that surround it. Between the layers of meninges is a fluid. The fluid cushions the brain so that the brain will not bang up against the skull. The brain itself has three main structures: the cerebrum, the cerebellum, and the brainstem.

The **cerebrum** (SEHR-uh-bruhm) is the part of the brain that interprets signals from your body and forms responses such as hunger, thirst, emotions, motion, and pain. The cerebrum has right and left halves, or hemispheres.

Differentiated Instruction

ENGLISH LEARNERS

Suggest students use a five-column chart for all new and review vocabulary. They will make four associations with each word; tell them to write *NI* if there is no information for a category. For example:

***Word:* cerebrum**

1. *Category* (type of thing it is): part of CNS
2. *Properties:* interprets signals from the body; forms responses such as hunger, thirst, emotions; has right and left hemispheres
3. *Examples:* NI
4. *Comparisons* (other ways to categorize it): one of the main structures of the brain

Biology Toolkit, Concept Definition Map, p. D8

Each hemisphere controls the opposite side of the body. For example, the right hemisphere of your brain processes all of the stimuli received by your left hand. Similarly, the left side of your brain controls the muscles that kick your right leg. When the spinal cord brings a signal from the body, the signal crosses over to the opposite hemisphere in the corpus callosum. The corpus callosum is a thick band of nerves that connects the two hemispheres.

The outer layer of the cerebrum, called the **cerebral cortex,** interprets information from your sensory organs and generates responses. The cerebral cortex is about as thick as a pencil. Yet its size is deceptive because its folds give it a larger surface area than you might expect. If the cerebral cortex were unfolded, it would cover a typical classroom desk. This surface area is large enough to hold more than 10 billion neurons.

The neurons in the cerebral cortex are arranged in groups that work together to perform specific tasks. For example, movement is initiated by an area of the brain called the motor cortex, and the sense of touch is received by the sensory cortex. Scientists divide the cerebral cortex into different areas, or lobes, based on function. Each hemisphere of the human brain can be divided into four lobes—frontal, parietal, occipital, and temporal. The lobes and the cortical areas they contain are shown in **FIGURE 29.10.**

FIGURE 29.10 Lobes of the Brain

The various areas of the cerebral cortex process different types of information.

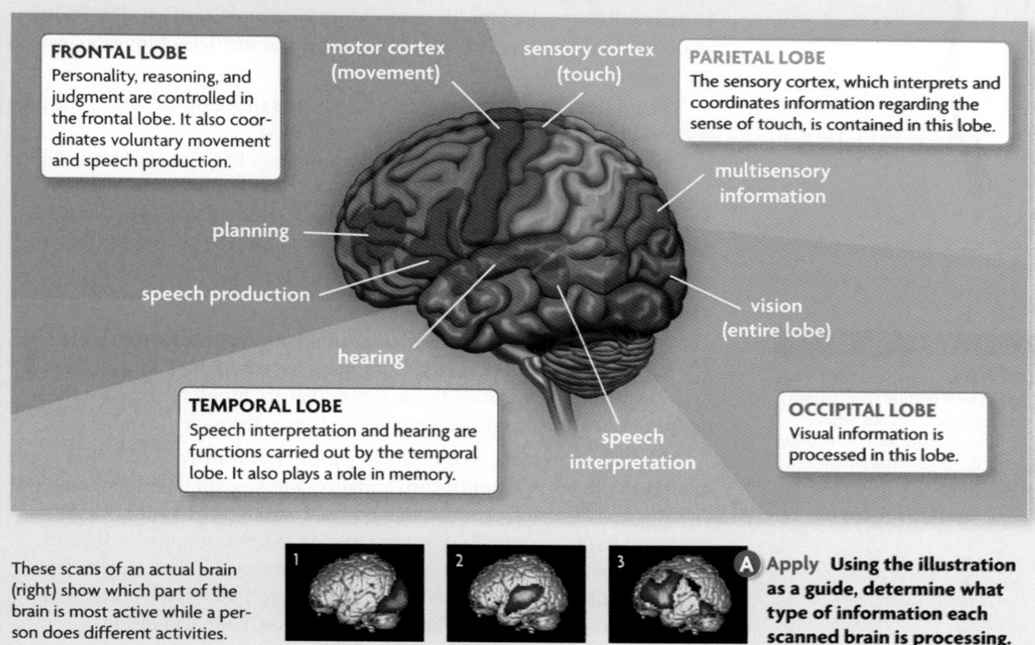
FRONTAL LOBE
Personality, reasoning, and judgment are controlled in the frontal lobe. It also coordinates voluntary movement and speech production.
motor cortex (movement)
sensory cortex (touch)
PARIETAL LOBE
The sensory cortex, which interprets and coordinates information regarding the sense of touch, is contained in this lobe.
multisensory information
planning
speech production
vision (entire lobe)
hearing
TEMPORAL LOBE
Speech interpretation and hearing are functions carried out by the temporal lobe. It also plays a role in memory.
speech interpretation
OCCIPITAL LOBE
Visual information is processed in this lobe.
1
2
3

These scans of an actual brain (right) show which part of the brain is most active while a person does different activities.

A Apply Using the illustration as a guide, determine what type of information each scanned brain is processing.

The Inside Story

In 1848, **Phineas Gage** was a young foreman of a railroad crew whose job was to use explosives to clear ground for laying tracks. On September 13, an accidental explosion blew an iron rod, more than 1 meter (1 yd) long, completely through his head. The rod entered Gage's face below the cheekbone, traveled behind his eye, and exited the top of his head. He recovered, but the once capable foreman became obstinate, fitful, and vulgar. He lost his job.

The extensive injury to the frontal lobe of his brain and his subsequent change in behavior enabled the medical world to make a connection between the **frontal lobe** and psychological processes involved in emotion, personality, and problem-solving. Gage lived his life generally out of the public eye, yet stories abounded of him exhibiting himself in fairgrounds and circuses around the country. All sorts of characteristics were attributed to him, such as drunkenness, slovenliness, and being sexually uninhibited, though there is little evidence to support any of it. He died in 1860 after suffering a seizure. The iron rod went to the grave with him.

Vocabulary

Word Origins The roots of the words **lobe** and **cortex** both come from the language of botany. *Lobe* comes from a root meaning "hull" or "pod," and describes a structure that projects outward, as does an ear lobe. *Cortex* comes from a root meaning "bark" and refers to an outer layer.

HANDS-ON ACTIVITY

Help students understand how the brain's folds and wrinkles increase its surface area. Bring to class a small container, such as a food-storage container or shoebox. Have students measure the six sides of the container and find the surface area. (Add the areas of the top, bottom, and all four sides.)

Tell students to wad sheets of newspaper and fill the container. Then have them remove the paper, flatten the sheets, measure the area of each sheet, and add the area of each sheet to the container's surface area. **Ask**

- How much did the total surface area increase by adding the wadded sheets to the container? Students should note a large increase.
- How does the increased surface area produced by the folding of the brain affect sensory perception and response? It provides more space for information processing in the cerebral cortex.

Answers

A Apply (1) vision; (2) hearing, speech; (3) reasoning, speech, movement

▼ Teach *continued*

ONLINE BIOLOGY Go to the chapter Resource Center at **ClassZone.com** for additional resources and information on the nervous system.

Science Trivia

- The brain of an adult human weighs between 1300 and 1400 grams.
- The brain of a bottle-nosed dolphin weighs about 1600 grams, an elephant's about 6000 grams.
- The brain of a cat weighs about 30 grams, a dog's about 70 grams.
- The brain of a hamster weighs about 1.4 grams, a goldfish's 0.097 gram.

Vocabulary

hypothalamus The prefix *hypo-* comes from the Greek word *hypo,* meaning "under." The hypothalamus is the part of the brain under the thalamus.

Take It Further

Researchers have tried to define the biological basis for **intelligence** for decades. Many attempts have been made to correlate IQ, a measure of intelligence known as the **intelligence quotient**, to brain size. A recent study by Richard Haier at the University of California in Irvine suggests that there may be some connection.

A study of MRI brain scans showed that people with high test scores had significantly more **gray matter** in 24 regions of the brain than did people with lower scores. Haier thinks that different types of intelligence may correlate to the amount of gray matter in a particular part of the brain. Still the study showed that only about 6 percent of total gray matter in the brain is related to IQ.

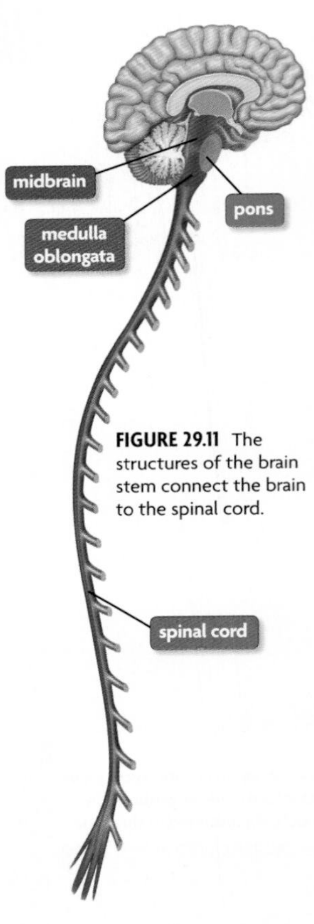

FIGURE 29.11 The structures of the brain stem connect the brain to the spinal cord.

***Connecting* CONCEPTS**

Chordates The spinal cord is one anatomical feature that defines the phylum Chordata, which includes humans and many other animals. You can read more about chordates in **Chapter 25**.

Underneath the cerebral cortex are many smaller areas with different functions. The limbic system, for example, is involved in learning and emotions and includes the hippocampus and the amygdala. The thalamus sorts information from your sensory organs and passes signals between the spinal cord and other parts of the brain. The hypothalamus gathers information about body temperature, hunger, and thirst. Then it sends signals that help the body adjust and maintain homeostasis, as you will see in Section 29.6.

The **cerebellum** (sehr-uh-BEHL-uhm) is the part of the brain that coordinates your movements. It helps you maintain your posture and balance, and it automatically adjusts your body to help you move smoothly. For example, when you brush your teeth, your cerebellum gets information about where your arm is positioned compared with the rest of your body. Your cerebellum plans how much your arm would need to move in order to brush your teeth. It sends this information to the motor cortex in your cerebrum, which signals your arm to move.

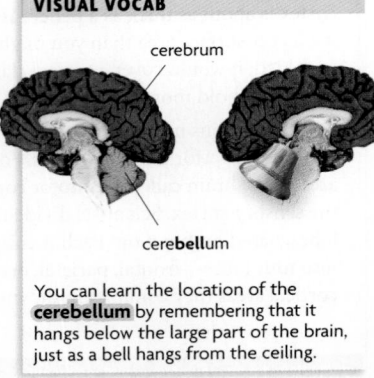

VISUAL VOCAB

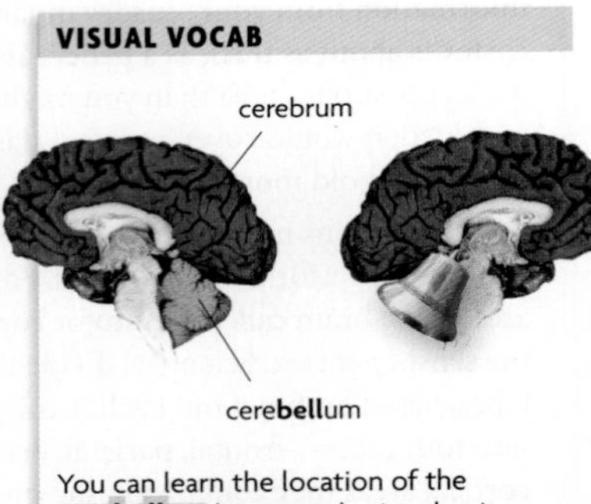

You can learn the location of the **cerebellum** by remembering that it hangs below the large part of the brain, just as a bell hangs from the ceiling.

The **brain stem** connects the brain to the spinal cord and controls the most basic activities required for life, such as breathing and heartbeat. The brain stem has three major parts—midbrain, pons, and medulla oblongata—which are shown in **FIGURE 29.11.**

- The midbrain controls some reflexes, such as changing the size of the pupil to control the amount of light entering the eye.
- The pons regulates breathing and passes signals between the brain and the spinal cord.
- The medulla oblongata connects the brain to the spinal cord. It controls basic life-sustaining functions, such as heart function, vomiting, swallowing, and coughing.

The Spinal Cord

The spinal column consists of vertebrae, fluid, meninges, and the spinal cord. The spinal cord is a ropelike bundle of neurons that is about as wide as your thumb. It connects the brain to the nerves that are found throughout the body. All signals that go to or from the brain pass through the spinal cord.

Although movement is controlled by your cerebrum and cerebellum, your brain depends on your spinal cord to deliver messages to the proper muscles. When you are brushing your teeth, and you want to move your arm, the cerebrum sends an impulse down the spinal cord. The impulse is directed by an interneuron to the motor neuron that connects to the arm muscles. The motor neuron then carries the impulse to receptors in the arm muscle. When the receptors are stimulated by the impulse, your arm moves.

Differentiated Instruction

HANDS-ON ACTIVITY

Have students observe the pupillary reflex. Ask several students to volunteer to be blindfolded for a few minutes. Provide hand lenses for the other students, having them form small groups around each volunteer. Ask the volunteers to remove their blindfolds and open their eyes. Direct the observers to look at the volunteers' pupils and record their observations. Suggest they time the response. Discuss the nature of the stimuli and the response. **Ask,** Is the action voluntary or involuntary? involuntary

BELOW LEVEL

Suggest that students think of a reflex as a circle. For example, a knee-jerk reflex begins with a stimulus at the knee and ends with a response at the knee. Have students draw the sequence of events in a reflex arc. Before they begin, have them view the animation of a reflex arc at **ClassZone.com.**

Biology Toolkit, Cycle Diagram, p. C39

If the spinal cord is damaged, messages cannot move between the brain and the rest of the body. This results in paralysis.

The spinal cord also controls involuntary movements called reflexes. **Reflex arcs,** as shown in **FIGURE 29.12,** are nerve pathways that need to cross only two synapses before producing a response. Because the signal never has to travel up the spinal cord to the brain, you react quickly.

For example, when the doctor taps your knee, tissues that connect your kneecap to your leg muscles stretch and stimulate a sensory neuron in your leg. The sensory neuron sends an impulse to your spinal cord. An interneuron in the spinal cord directs the impulse into motor neurons that cause your leg to jerk.

Reflex arcs play an important role in protecting your body from injury. When you put your hand on a hot stove, for example, you will jerk your hand away before you even have the chance to say "Ouch!" You do not feel the pain until moments after you jerk your hand away. If you did not have reflex arcs, your hand would remain on the stove until your brain interpreted the heat detected by thermoreceptors in your skin. Your hand would be badly burned before you ever reacted.

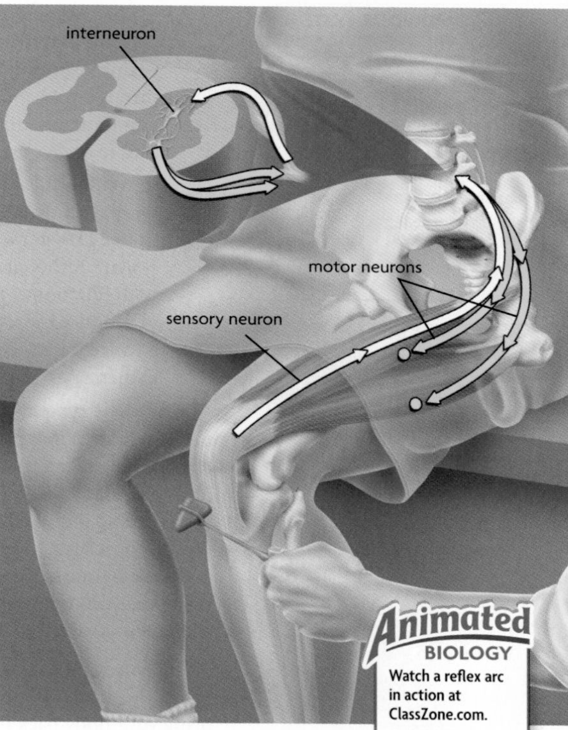

FIGURE 29.12 Reflex arcs allow your body to respond quickly and without thinking, as when your leg jerks after your doctor taps your knee with a mallet.

A Summarize How is a muscle movement caused by a reflex arc different from a voluntary muscle movement?

MAIN IDEA

The PNS links the CNS to muscles and other organs.

The peripheral nervous system (PNS) includes 12 pairs of nerves in the head, such as the facial and olfactory nerves, and 31 pairs of spinal nerves. Most nerves contain axons from both sensory and motor neurons that carry information to and from the CNS. In general, the PNS is made up of a sensory system and a motor system. The system of sensory nerves collects information about the body and its surroundings. The system of motor nerves triggers voluntary and involuntary responses within the body.

When you are running, walking, or even sitting, you rely on your somatic nervous system to stimulate your muscles to maintain your movement, posture, and balance. The **somatic nervous system** is the division of the PNS that regulates all of the movements over which you have voluntary control. It connects the CNS to target organs.

Integrating Genetics

CIPA, **Congenital Insensitivity to Pain with Anhydrosis,** is a rare genetic disorder that affects the nervous system. It is caused by mutations on the neurotrophic tyrosine kinase receptor gene (NTRK) and prevents the formation of nerve cells that transmit signals to the brain registering pain and temperature. People who suffer from CIPA are unable to feel pain, detect temperature, or even sweat. Their other senses are intact, however.

If a person suffering from CIPA were to inadvertently place their hand on a hot stove, they would not be able to detect the heat or feel any pain. No impulse would cause them to remove their hand. Instead they would first need to recognize the danger, then respond. Individuals with CIPA commonly suffer from injuries to the arms and legs, mouth, lips, tongue, and gums. Because of their inability to sweat, they commonly suffer fevers, and even hyperthermia. There is no treatment for this disorder.

Answers

A Summarize Unlike a voluntary muscle movement, a muscle movement caused by a reflex arc does not involve the brain.

PRE-AP

Remind students that all behaviors and traits of living things can potentially be considered adaptations for survival. Have students work in groups to brainstorm survival advantages of a reflex arc related to the fight-or-flight response in animals. Some examples are a skunk spraying, a squid squirting ink, the diving reflex of marine mammals, and a porcupine raising its quills.

Biology Toolkit, Brainstorming, p. C11

▼ Teach *continued*

Take It Further

Today, our **fight-or-flight** mechanism is oftentimes activated not because there is a threat to our lives but rather because we are experiencing a stressful situation. Our inability to fight or flee from stresses can lead to stress-related illnesses, such as heart disease, high blood pressure, migraines, and insomnia.

Answers

A Analyze Reflex arcs are part of the autonomic nervous system because they produce involuntary muscle movement.

▼ Assess and Reteach

Assess Use the Online Quiz or Section Quiz (*Assessment Book*, p. 574).

Reteach Have students work in groups to construct crossword puzzles using the vocabulary words and other important words in this section. Have groups exchange puzzles and fill them out.

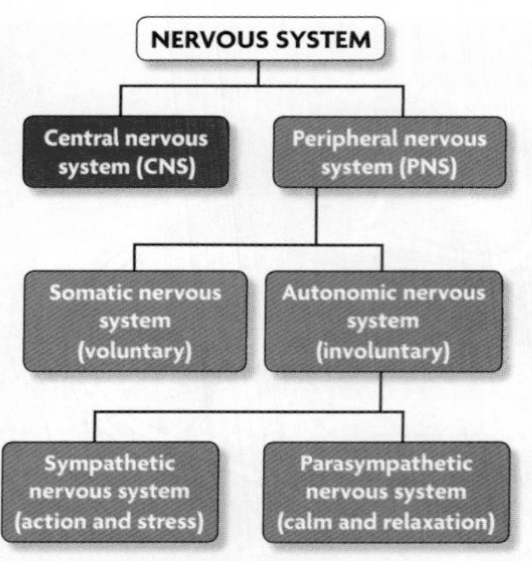

FIGURE 29.13 The nervous system can be divided into subsystems based on their functions.

The **autonomic nervous system** is the division of the PNS that controls automatic functions that you do not have to think about. For example, involuntary muscles help you to digest food by pushing it through your intestines. The autonomic nervous system is also important in maintaining homeostasis. It takes messages from the hypothalamus to organs in the circulatory, digestive, and endocrine systems.

Within the autonomic nervous system are two subdivisions: the sympathetic nervous system and the parasympathetic nervous system. **FIGURE 29.13** shows how these two systems relate to the rest of the nervous system. Although the two systems have opposite effects on the body, they both function continuously. If something happens to cause one system to produce more signals, the other system will become more active to balance the effects of the first. Together, the sympathetic and parasympathetic nervous systems help your body to maintain homeostasis.

The **sympathetic nervous system** is the part of the autonomic nervous system that prepares the body for action and stress. This is called the "fight or flight" response. When you become frightened or you are preparing to compete in a sport, your sympathetic nervous system is stimulated. Blood vessels going to the skin and internal organs contract, which reduces blood flow to those areas. Meanwhile, blood vessels going to the heart, brain, lungs, and skeletal muscles expand, increasing the blood supply in those areas. Heart rate increases. Airways enlarge, and breathing becomes more efficient. These changes improve your physical abilities and allow you to think quickly.

If something frightens you, your sympathetic nervous system activates. When the danger passes, the parasympathetic nervous system takes over to bring your body back to normal. The **parasympathetic nervous system** is the division of the autonomic nervous system that calms the body and helps the body to conserve energy. It does this by lowering blood pressure and heart rate. It is active when the body is relaxed.

 **Analyze Are reflex arcs part of the somatic or autonomic nervous system? Explain.**

29.4 ASSESSMENT

ONLINE QUIZ ClassZone.com

REVIEWING MAIN IDEAS

1. How do the types of neurons found in the CNS and PNS differ in their functions?
2. How does the **cerebral cortex** differ from the rest of the **cerebrum**?
3. What are some similarities and differences between the **somatic nervous system** and **autonomic nervous system**?

CRITICAL THINKING

4. **Apply** Why might a person with a brain injury be able to understand the speech of others but not be able to speak?
5. **Synthesize** You step on a sharp rock, your leg jerks upward, and a moment later you feel pain in your foot. Use the words *motor neuron*, *sensory neuron*, and *interneuron* to explain what happened.

Connecting CONCEPTS

6. **Evolution** Which part of the brain—the cerebrum, **cerebellum**, or **brain stem**—probably evolved first? (**Hint**: Consider which part is most important for basic life processes.)

29.4 ASSESSMENT

1. The interneurons of the CNS interpret signals and store information. The sensory and motor neurons of the PNS transmit signals.
2. The cerebral cortex is the outer layer of the cerebrum and has different areas that contribute to different functions. The cerebrum includes two hemispheres and all of the neuron cell bodies found beneath the cerebral cortex.
3. Both the somatic and autonomic nervous systems connect the CNS to the rest of the body. The somatic nervous system controls muscles under voluntary control; the autonomic nervous system regulates internal organs under involuntary control.
4. Because different functions are controlled by different parts of the brain, an injury to one part only affects the processes that are controlled by that region.
5. *Sample Answer:* The sensory neuron in the foot sends an impulse to the interneuron in the spinal cord and then back to the motor neuron in the leg. Later, when the signal reaches the brain, it is interpreted as pain.
6. The brain stem probably evolved first because it controls homeostatic functions such as heartbeat and breathing.

29.5 Brain Function and Chemistry

KEY CONCEPT Scientists study the functions and chemistry of the brain.

MAIN IDEAS
- New techniques improve our understanding of the brain.
- Changes in brain chemistry can cause illness.
- Drugs alter brain chemistry.

VOCABULARY

addiction, p. 893
desensitization, p. 893
tolerance, p. 893
sensitization, p. 893
stimulant, p. 894
depressant, p. 894

Review
neurotransmitter,
action potential

Connect When you take medicine for a headache, the drug alters your brain's chemistry. Aspirin, for example, stops your brain from making certain chemicals. In small amounts, it is beneficial to your health. However, even nonprescription drugs can cause permanent damage to your nervous system if taken incorrectly.

MAIN IDEA

New techniques improve our understanding of the brain.

For many years, the only way scientists could study brain function was by observing changes that occurred in people who had accidental brain injuries or by dissecting the brains of people who had died. A live patient would have to undergo surgery in order for scientists to learn about brain function.

Today, scientists use imaging technologies such as CT, MRI, and PET scans to study the brain in living patients without the need for surgery. These methods use x-rays, magnetic fields, or radioactive sensors and computer programs to form images of the brain, as shown in **FIGURE 29.14.**

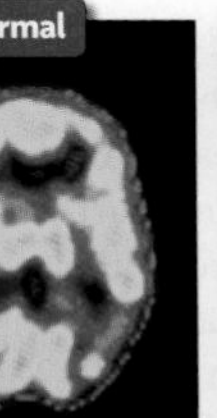

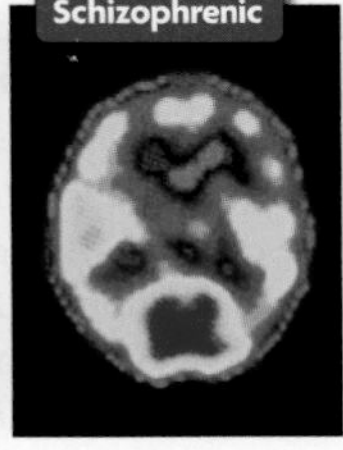

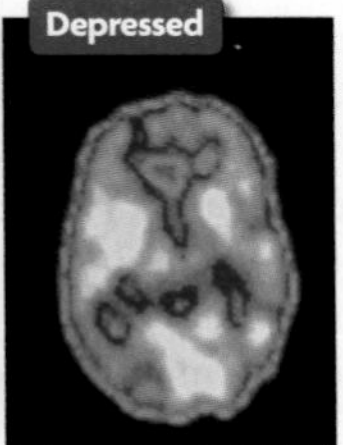

FIGURE 29.14 Modern technologies use computers and sensing devices to observe the brain without the need for surgery.

Computerized tomography (CT) scans use x-rays to view the brain. Magnetic resonance imaging (MRI) uses magnetic fields and radio waves. Both CT and MRI scans make images that show the structure of the brain. These scans are used to examine the brain's physical condition.

Positron emission tomography (PET) scans show which areas of the brain are most active. During PET scans, a person is injected with radioactive glucose. Recall from Chapter 4 that cells use glucose for energy. By measuring where the radioactive glucose collects in the brain, scientists can see which areas of the brain are using the most energy. In the image shown above, the bright red and yellow areas are the most active, and the dark blue areas are the least active.

A Infer **Why are modern technologies for studying the brain safer for the patients being studied?**

Differentiated Instruction

BELOW LEVEL

Have students list and group key terms in this section and label each by common features. Here are five such groupings.

CT, MRI, PET: technologies to study the brain

acetylcholine, dopamine, serotonin, glutamate, gamma amino butyric acid: types of neurotransmitters

Parkinson's disease, schizophrenia, depression: illnesses caused by changes in brain chemistry

addiction, desensitization, tolerance, sensitization: effects of drugs

stimulants, depressants: types of drugs

Biology Toolkit, List-Group-Label, p. D6

SECTION 29.5

Plan and Prepare ▼

Objectives

- Describe modern technologies used to study the human brain.
- Describe how an imbalance of neurotransmitters can cause illness.
- Explain how drugs change brain chemistry.

Section Resources

Unit Resource Book
Study Guide pp. 39–40
Power Notes p. 41
Reinforcement p. 42

Interactive Reader Chapter 29
Spanish Study Guide pp. 297–298

Biology Toolkit pp. C15, D3, D6

Technology
Power Presentation 29.5
Media Gallery DVD
Online Quiz 29.5

Activate Prior Knowledge Tell students that some of the most common types of over-the-counter medications (OTCs) are pain relievers (such as aspirin and acetaminophen), depressants (such as sleeping pills), and stimulants (such as decongestants). **Ask,** Knowing what you do about the nervous system, how do you think these drugs produce their effects? Students should suggest that these drugs affect the way nerve impulses are transmitted. Tell students that drugs affect the chemistry of the brain.

Teach ▼

Vocabulary

tomography The prefix *tomo-* comes from the Greek *tomos,* meaning "section." Tomography is an imaging technique that shows a thin cross section of tissue. A CT scan is shown on the left in **FIGURE 29.14.**

Answers

A Infer Modern technologies do not require surgery.

▼ Teach *continued*

History of Science

In 1973, neurochemist **Solomon H. Snyder** was among the first to identify the neurotransmitters that relieve pain. These opiate-like neurotransmitters are called **endorphins.** When a person exercises strenuously, the brain produces increased levels of endorphins. In distance runners, endorphins can produce the phenomenon known as a "runner's high." A runner suddenly feels energized after experiencing intense fatigue.

Integrating Medical Science

SAD, **Seasonal Affective Disorder,** is a type of depression that is caused by the body's response to seasonal variations of sunlight. When days are short and there is little sunlight, the pineal gland in the brain secretes more **melatonin,** a sleep-related hormone. Increased amounts of melatonin can cause depression. Common symptoms of SAD are an increase in appetite, weight gain, lack of energy, and excessive sleeping. Light therapy, which causes the body to produce less melatonin, and daily exercise, which increases endorphins in the body, are two ways to treat SAD.

Answers

A Summarize The treatments for neurological illnesses change the activity of neurotransmitters in the brain.

MAIN IDEA

Changes in brain chemistry can cause illness.

Connecting CONCEPTS

Enzymes In **Chapter 2** you read that enzymes are like locks because only certain shaped molecules can fit into them. Neurotransmitters only affect certain areas of the brain because they are like keys that can only fit into certain neurons' receptors.

In Section 29.2, you learned that your nervous system cannot work without neurotransmitters. These chemicals regulate different functions in different areas of the brain. Neurotransmitters are specific to some areas of the brain because, like hormones, they only affect cells that have specific receptors. The function of neurotransmitters relates to the functions of the cells they stimulate.

- Acetylcholine is involved in learning and memory.
- Dopamine primarily influences your emotional behavior, but it also plays some role in stress and voluntary muscles.
- Serotonin is mainly found in the hypothalamus and midbrain. It also influences mood, some muscle functions, and hunger.
- Glutamate affects learning, memory, and brain development.
- Gamma amino butyric acid (GABA) is found throughout the brain. Unlike other neurotransmitters, when GABA binds to a neuron's membrane, it prevents the neuron from generating an impulse.

When your brain produces the correct amount of these neurotransmitters, homeostasis is maintained. If your body produces too much or too little of a neurotransmitter, the areas of your brain that are targeted by that chemical will be more or less active than normal. Because all of the areas of your brain work together, abnormal activity in one part of the brain can affect the whole brain and change the way you move, behave, and think. **FIGURE 29.15** shows that the brain activity of a healthy patient differs from that of patients with depression or schizophrenia, which are associated with chemical imbalances in the brain.

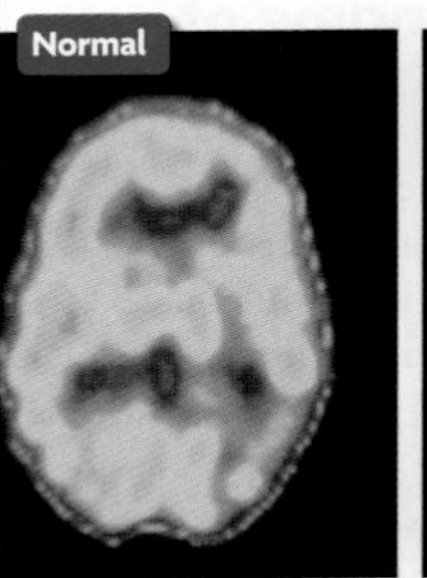

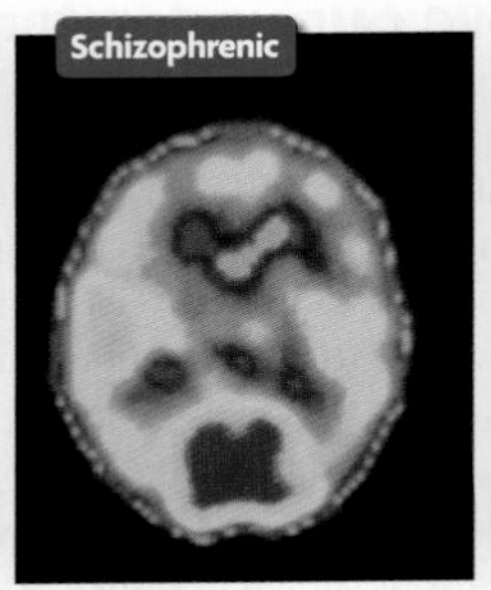

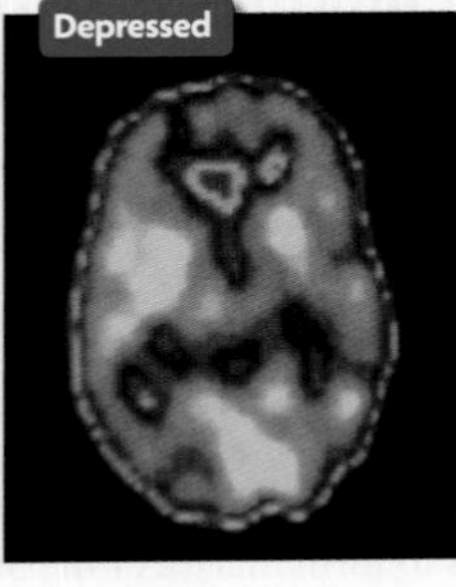

FIGURE 29.15 These PET images show the activity of a normal, a schizophrenic, and a depressed brain. Blue and green areas have low activity, and red areas are the most active.

Illnesses such as Parkinson's disease and schizophrenia are linked to abnormal amounts of dopamine. Parkinson's disease is caused by low amounts of dopamine in certain areas of the brain. People with Parkinson's disease have difficulty controlling their movements, maintaining their balance, and starting movements. Many patients with Parkinson's take drugs that increase the amount of dopamine in the brain. On the other hand, schizophrenia sometimes occurs when a person has too much dopamine. Schizophrenia is a mental disorder that causes hallucinations, irrational behavior, and illogical speech. It is treated with drugs that block dopamine receptors in the brain.

Depression is linked to low amounts of serotonin in parts of the brain. Depression causes extended periods of intense sadness, inability to sleep, and feelings of helplessness. One treatment for clinical depression uses drugs that extend the time that serotonin remains active in nerve synapses.

A Summarize How do treatments for neurological illnesses alter brain chemistry?

Differentiated Instruction

PRE-AP

Have students compare the PET scan images in **FIGURE 29.15** to parts of the brain in **FIGURE 29.10** on page 887. In their science notebooks, have students note which brain functions may be affected. Discuss students' observations in class.

ENGLISH LEARNERS

Divide students into home groups of three, and have them number off from 1 to 3. Then, by number, have students form into expert groups. Each of the groups is assigned one of the section's main ideas and a question to answer relating to that main idea. After becoming experts on the topic, students share their knowledge in their home groups.

Biology Toolkit, Jigsaw Reading, p. C15

MAIN IDEA

Drugs alter brain chemistry.

You may have noticed that some medicines come with warnings that say they may cause drowsiness so they should only be taken at night. People who use prescription, illegal, or other types of drugs can experience behavioral changes, such as changes in appetite, aggression, or sleep cycles. Drugs also cause changes in coordination or sensitivity to pain. Drugs might return one system in the body to homeostasis while pushing another system further out of balance. These changes occur because drugs change the way the brain works.

Many drugs affect the amount of neurotransmitter in synapses. Remember from Section 29.2 that a certain amount of neurotransmitter must be in the synapse before the threshold is reached and an action potential is generated. If a drug increases the amount of neurotransmitter released, impulses are more likely to occur. If a drug decreases the amount of neurotransmitter, action potentials are less likely to occur.

Some Drugs Cause Addiction

Many illegal, recreational, and prescription drugs can lead to addiction. **Addiction** is the physiological need for a substance. Through feedback loops, a person becomes addicted to a substance when the body changes the way it works so that it needs the drug in order to function normally. The brain adapts to drug exposure so that neurons will generate normal amounts of impulses despite abnormal levels of neurotransmitter.

Brain cells undergo **desensitization** when there is more neurotransmitter present in the synapse than usual. When a drug increases the amount of neurotransmitter in the synapses, the neuron generates more impulses than normal. The neuron responds by reducing the number of receptors on its cell membrane, as shown in **FIGURE 29.16**. With fewer receptors, less neurotransmitter can bind to the cell membrane and impulses are less likely to generate. Desensitization builds a person's tolerance. When someone has a **tolerance,** it takes larger doses of the drug to produce the same effect.

Sensitization occurs when low amounts of a neurotransmitter are in the synapses. When drugs lower the amount of a neurotransmitter, fewer action potentials are generated than normal. With less neurotransmitter than normal, brain cells adapt by increasing the number of receptors for them, also shown in **FIGURE 29.16.** By producing more receptors, cells increase the amount of neurotransmitter that bind to the cell. This causes the cell to generate more action potentials, just as if the normal amount of neurotransmitter were in the synapse.

FIGURE 29.16 Neurons Adapt

When the amount of neurotransmitter becomes abnormal, the adjacent neuron adapts.

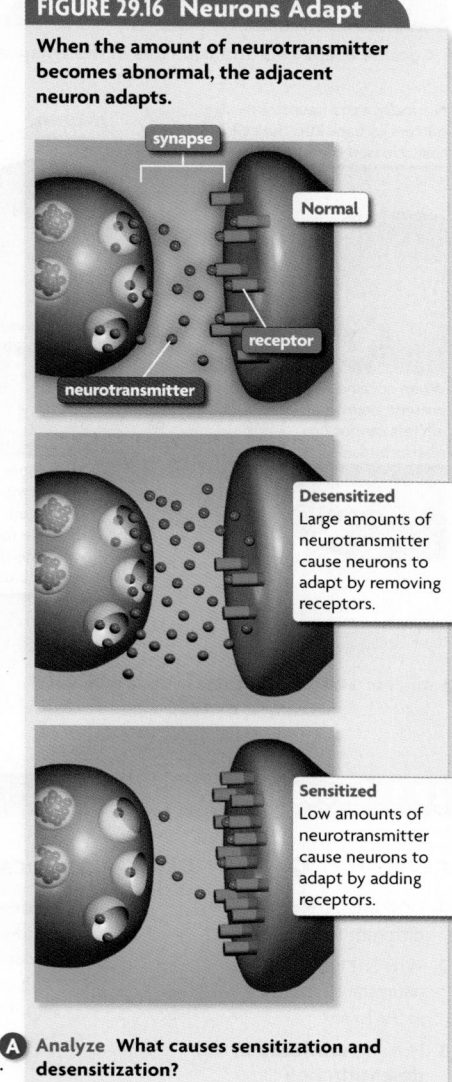

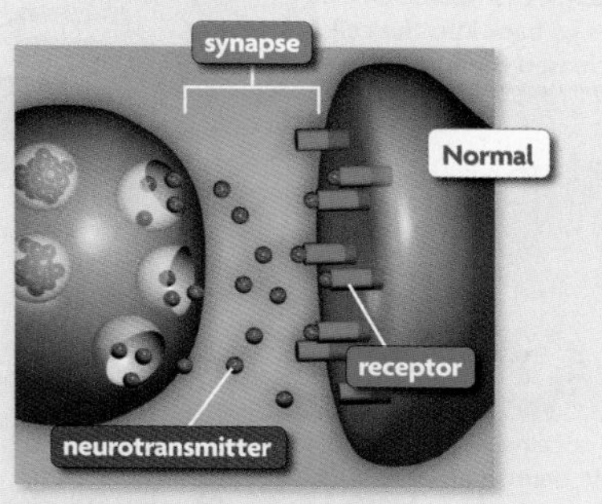

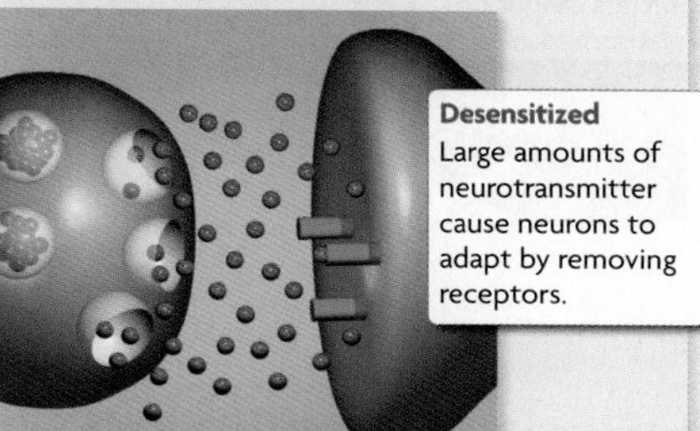

Desensitized
Large amounts of neurotransmitter cause neurons to adapt by removing receptors.

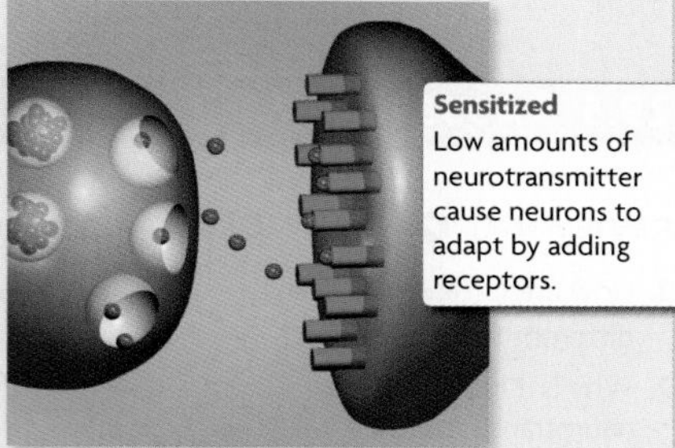

Sensitized
Low amounts of neurotransmitter cause neurons to adapt by adding receptors.

(A) Analyze **What causes sensitization and desensitization?**

ONLINE BIOLOGY For more on the effects of addiction on the brain, have students do the WebQuest in Options for Inquiry on page 903.

TEACH FROM VISUALS

FIGURE 29.16 Have students compare the three diagrams. **Ask,** How is the change in the number of receptors an example of homeostasis? The change in the number of receptors allows neurons to generate normal amounts of impulses even when the levels of neurotransmitters are abnormal.

Take It Further

Cocaine is one of the most highly addictive drugs. It directly affects the hypothalamus, resulting in intense feelings of joy and pleasure. The hypothalamus is a major component of the limbic system, which is thought to be the memory site of emotions. That is why, even after a long period of abstinence, just the memory of a person's first cocaine use often brings back intense cravings for the drug.

Answers

(A) **Analyze** Sensitization occurs when there is less neurotransmitter in synapses than usual. Desensitization occurs when there is more neurotransmitter in synapses than usual.

BELOW LEVEL

Have students use context clues to help them learn the key vocabulary of this section. They should write their own definitions and draw a picture to illustrate the term. Then have the student look up the definition in the Glossary.

Biology Toolkit, Student Vocabulary, p. D3

▼ Teach *continued*

Answers

A Analyze Cocaine prevents the reabsorption of neurotransmitters in a synapse. This causes increased stimulation of the next neuron and increases the number of action potentials the neuron generates.

B Analyze Stimulants increase a neuron's ability to generate impulses; depressants do the opposite.

▼ Assess and Reteach

Assess Use the Online Quiz or Section Quiz (*Assessment Book*, p. 575).

Reteach Review the material using **FIGURES 29.16** and **29.17.** Have students relate the key vocabulary to these figures. Ask them to consider how the PET images of the brain relate to what is happening in the neurotransmitters.

How Drugs Work

In order for drugs to have an effect on your behavior, they must change the number of action potentials your neurons generate.

Some drugs make a person feel happy, energetic, and alert. **Stimulants** are drugs that increase the number of action potentials that neurons generate by increasing the amounts of neurotransmitter in the synapses. Methamphetamine, for example, causes neurons to produce and release more neurotransmitters, especially serotonin and dopamine. However, there are other ways that stimulants can increase the amount of neurotransmitter.

FIGURE 29.17 How Cocaine Works

Cocaine keeps neurotransmitters in the synapse.

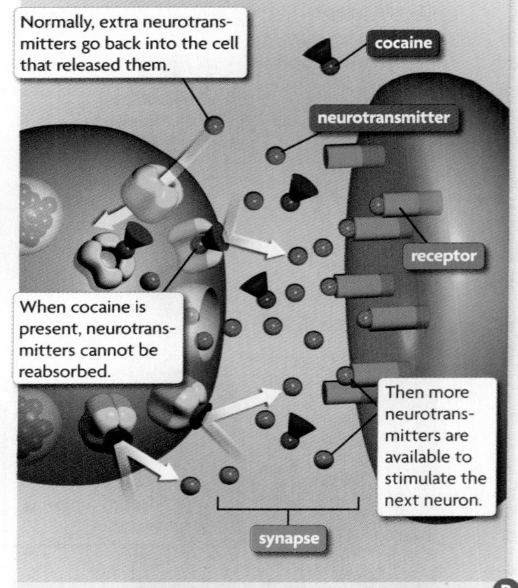
Normally, extra neurotransmitters go back into the cell that released them.
cocaine
neurotransmitter
receptor
When cocaine is present, neurotransmitters cannot be reabsorbed.
Then more neurotransmitters are available to stimulate the next neuron.
synapse

A Analyze How does cocaine act as a stimulant?

Some drugs have almost the same chemistry as neurotransmitters, and they bind directly to the receptors on neuron membranes. Other drugs slow the removal of neurotransmitters from the synapses. These drugs can bind to enzymes that break down the neurotransmitters and make them unable to work. Drugs such as cocaine, however, bind to transport proteins on the axon terminal, as shown in **FIGURE 29.17.** Normally, these proteins would allow neurotransmitters to flow back into the cell that released them. If a drug is blocking the protein, the neurotransmitter remains in the synapse and an action potential is more likely to occur.

Depressants are drugs that make a person feel relaxed and tired. The person may react slowly or seem out of touch with the world around them. Depressants reduce the ability of neurons to generate impulses. Some depressants block neuron receptors so that neurotransmitters cannot produce an impulse. Other depressants, such as methaqualone, can make a person feel relaxed or sleepy by increasing in the synapses the amount of GABA, which prevents neurons from generating impulses.

B Analyze How do stimulants and depressants affect a neuron's ability to generate impulses?

29.5 ASSESSMENT

ONLINE QUIZ ClassZone.com

REVIEWING MAIN IDEAS

1. How are CT and MRI scans different from PET scans?
2. Why is it important that neurotransmitters are balanced in the brain?
3. How do **sensitization** and **desensitization** differ?

CRITICAL THINKING

4. **Synthesize** Draw before and after pictures to explain why a person whose neurons were sensitized by drug use experiences opposite symptoms when they quit.
5. **Analyze** How does desensitization relate to drug **tolerance**?

***Connecting* CONCEPTS**

6. **Feedback Loops** What kind of feedback loops are sensitization and desensitization? Explain. (**Hint:** What causes these processes to begin and end?)

29.5 ASSESSMENT

1. CTs and MRIs show brain structure; PETs show areas of activity.
2. If neurotransmitters are not balanced, the neurons might generate too many or too few action potentials.
3. sensitization—low levels of neurotransmitter cause neurons to adjust by creating more receptors; desensitization—high levels of neurotransmitter cause neurons to adjust by removing some receptors
4. First drawing should show neuron with many receptors and very little neurotransmitter in the synapse. Second drawing should show neuron with many receptors and a lot of neurotransmitter in the synapse. With more neurotransmitter, more impulses are generated than when the person was on drugs.
5. Desensitization leads to drug tolerance. The decrease in receptors requires larger doses of the drug to generate the same level of nerve impulses that was generated prior to desensitization.
6. negative feedback loops, because both sensitization and desensitization are processes that try to bring the body back to homeostasis by generating normal numbers of nerve impulses

NOS.1

DATA ANALYSIS ClassZone.com

Relationships Between Variables

When scientists analyze their data, they must remember that just because two variables are related, it does not mean that one caused the other to change. A **causation** occurs when a change in one variable was caused by the other. Sometimes the cause of change in a variable may be the result of a third, unknown variable. A **correlation** occurs when scientists find that two variables are closely related, but the change in one variable did not definitely cause the change in the other. When a strong correlation exists between two variables, scientists will conduct other experiments to discover exactly how the variables are related.

EXAMPLE

Scientists studied the memory of people who regularly used the illegal drug ecstasy. They found that ecstasy users were more forgetful than people who didn't use ecstasy. Therefore, ecstasy use and memory loss are correlated. However, scientists do not know that ecstasy *causes* forgetfulness. It could be that people who are forgetful use ecstasy.

GRAPH 1. ECSTASY AND MEMORY

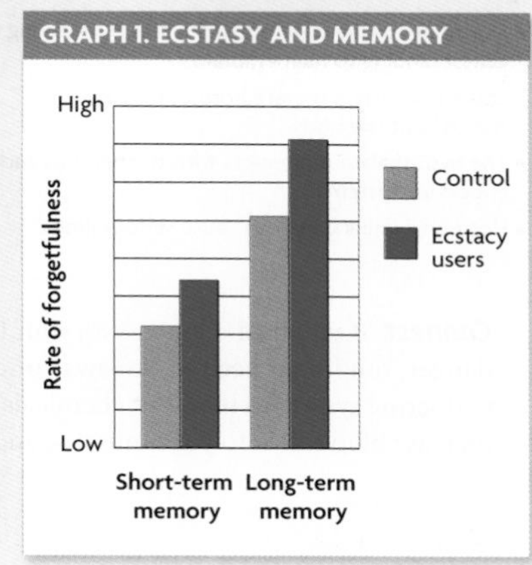

Source: T. M. Heffernan, et al., *Human Psychopharmacol Clinical Experiments* 2001:16.

DETERMINE CORRELATION OR CAUSATION

A panic attack is characterized by a sudden increase in pulse and anxiety. The graph on the right shows hypothetical data for the incidence of panic attacks in the general population and in a population of people who have a disorder called mitral valve prolapse, in which a heart valve does not work properly.

1. **Analyze** Does a correlation or a causation exist between mitral valve prolapse and panic attacks? How do you know?
2. **Evaluate** Can you conclude that mitral valve prolapse causes panic attacks? Why or why not?

GRAPH 2. MITRAL VALVE PROLAPSE AND PANIC ATTACKS

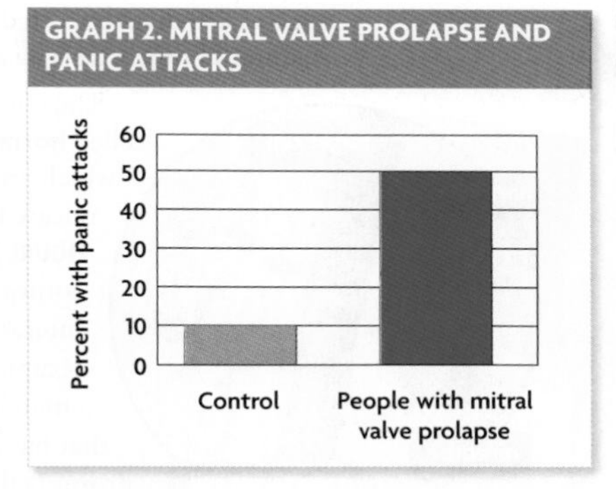

Answers

1. There is a correlation between having mitral valve prolapse and having panic attacks. According to the graph, 50 percent of people who have mitral valve prolapse also have panic attacks. In contrast, only 10 percent of the general population have panic attacks. We know there is some relationship because otherwise both populations would have equal rates of panic attacks.
2. No, there is no information on the graph to indicate that mitral valve prolapse causes panic attacks. Additional research is needed before causation can be proved.

DATA ANALYSIS

Introduce

Give students another example of the correlation/causation problem. For example, say, "Three houses on my street are painted white. The people who live in all three houses have red hair." **Ask,** Why can't we conclude that red hair causes people to paint their houses white? White is a popular color for houses, and people without red hair also paint their houses white.

Discuss

Tell students that observable phenomena as well as experimental data sometimes have a very high degree of correlation. **Ask,** To discover causal relationships between variables with a high correlation, what needs to be done? Each variable needs to be manipulated one at a time to determine whether there are other possible causes or other distinct correlations.

Vocabulary

Academic Vocabulary Have students suggest their own examples for these words:

correlation, a complementary or parallel relationship; in statistics, the simultaneous change in the value of two random variables:

causation, act of producing an effect, result, or consequence

relationship, a connection or association

Unit Resource Book, Data Analysis, p. 47

SECTION 29.6

▼ Plan and Prepare

Objectives

- Describe how hormones influence the activities of a cell.
- Describe the major endocrine glands and the hormones they produce.
- Explain the role of the hypothalamus.
- Identify some endocrine diseases, their causes, and effects.

Section Resources

Unit Resource Book
Study Guide pp. 43–44
Power Notes p. 45
Reinforcement p. 46
Pre-AP Activity pp. 51–52

Interactive Reader Chapter 29
Spanish Study Guide pp. 299–300

Biology Toolkit pp. C6, C13, C19, C38, C39

Technology
Power Presentation 29.6
Media Gallery DVD
Online Quiz 29.6

Activate Prior Knowledge Have students think about how their bodies have changed over the past ten years. **Ask,** What is the main cause of the changes associated with young adults? hormones Tell students that in this section they will be learning about the endocrine system, which is responsible for releasing those hormones.

▼ Teach

Vocabulary

Greek and Latin Word Origins The root of the word **hormone** is the Greek *hormon,* meaning "to urge on."

29.6 The Endocrine System and Hormones

KEY CONCEPT The endocrine system produces hormones that affect growth, development, and homeostasis.

MAIN IDEAS

- Hormones influence a cell's activities by entering the cell or binding to its membrane.
- Endocrine glands secrete hormones that act throughout the body.
- The hypothalamus interacts with the nervous and endocrine systems.
- Hormonal imbalances can cause serious illness.

VOCABULARY

hormone, p. 896
gland, p. 896
hypothalamus, p. 898
pituitary gland, p. 898
releasing hormones, p. 900

Connect If you hear a loud BANG, your brain tells your body that you could be in danger. You might need to run away or defend yourself. Your brain alerts your endocrine system to send out chemicals that will speed up your heart rate, increase blood flow to your muscles, and get you ready for action.

MAIN IDEA

Hormones influence a cell's activities by entering the cell or binding to its membrane.

The endocrine system makes chemical signals that help the body grow, develop, and maintain homeostasis. Some of these chemicals control processes such as cell division, cell death, and sexual development. Others help you maintain homeostasis by affecting body temperature, alertness, or salt levels.

The chemical signals made by the endocrine system are called **hormones.** Hormones are made in organs called **glands,** which are found in many different areas of the body. Glands release hormones into the bloodstream, as shown in **FIGURE 29.18.** As a hormone moves through the body, it comes into contact with many different cells. But it will interact only with a cell that has specific membrane receptors. If the hormone touches a cell that does not have a matching receptor, nothing happens. If it touches a cell that has the correct receptors, it binds to the cell and prompts the cell to make certain proteins or enzymes. Cells that have receptors for a hormone are called the target cells of that hormone.

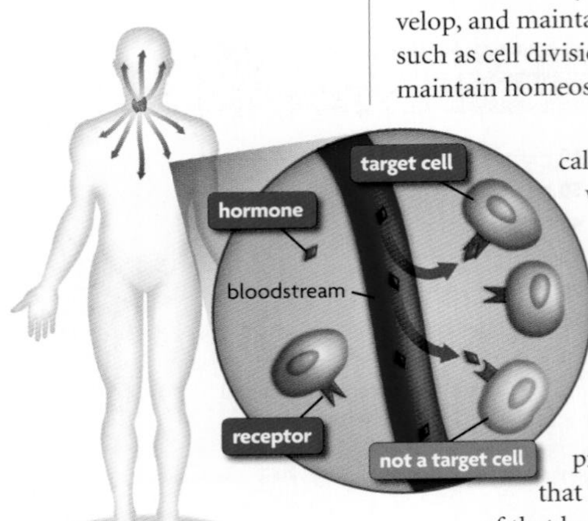

FIGURE 29.18 Glands release hormones into the bloodstream, but hormones will only affect cells that have receptors for those hormones.

All hormones belong to one of two categories: steroid hormones and nonsteroid hormones. All steroid hormones are made of cholesterol, a type of lipid. On the other hand, there are three types of nonsteroid hormones that are made up of one or more amino acids.

Differentiated Instruction

BELOW LEVEL

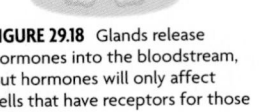

Have students use the Directed Reading-Thinking Activity for this section. Students skim the text to preview the material and then use a four-column chart to list what they know, what they think they know, what they need to find out, and what was learned.

Biology Toolkit, DRTA, p. C6

As **FIGURE 29.19** shows, steroid hormones and nonsteroid hormones influence cells' activities in different ways. A steroid hormone can enter its target cells by diffusing through the cell membrane. Once inside, the steroid hormone attaches to a receptor protein, which transports the protein into the nucleus. After it is inside, the steroid hormone binds to the cell's DNA. This binding causes the cell to produce the proteins that are coded by that portion of DNA.

Nonsteroid hormones do not enter their target cells. These hormones bind to protein receptors on a cell's membrane and cause chemical reactions to take place inside the cell. When nonsteroid hormones bind to receptors, the receptors change chemically. This change activates molecules inside the cell. These molecules, called second messengers, react with still other molecules inside the cell. The products of these reactions might initiate other chemical reactions in the cell or activate a gene in the nucleus.

Connecting CONCEPTS

Cell Membrane Recall from **Chapter 3** that cell membranes are made of a phospholipid bilayer. Only some molecules, such as steroid hormones, can diffuse through it.

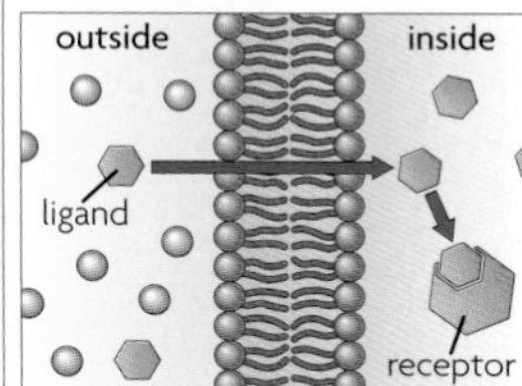
outside
inside
ligand
receptor

A Apply **Why do hormones only affect some cells?**

FIGURE 29.19 Hormone Action

Steroid hormones enter the cell, but nonsteroid hormones do not.

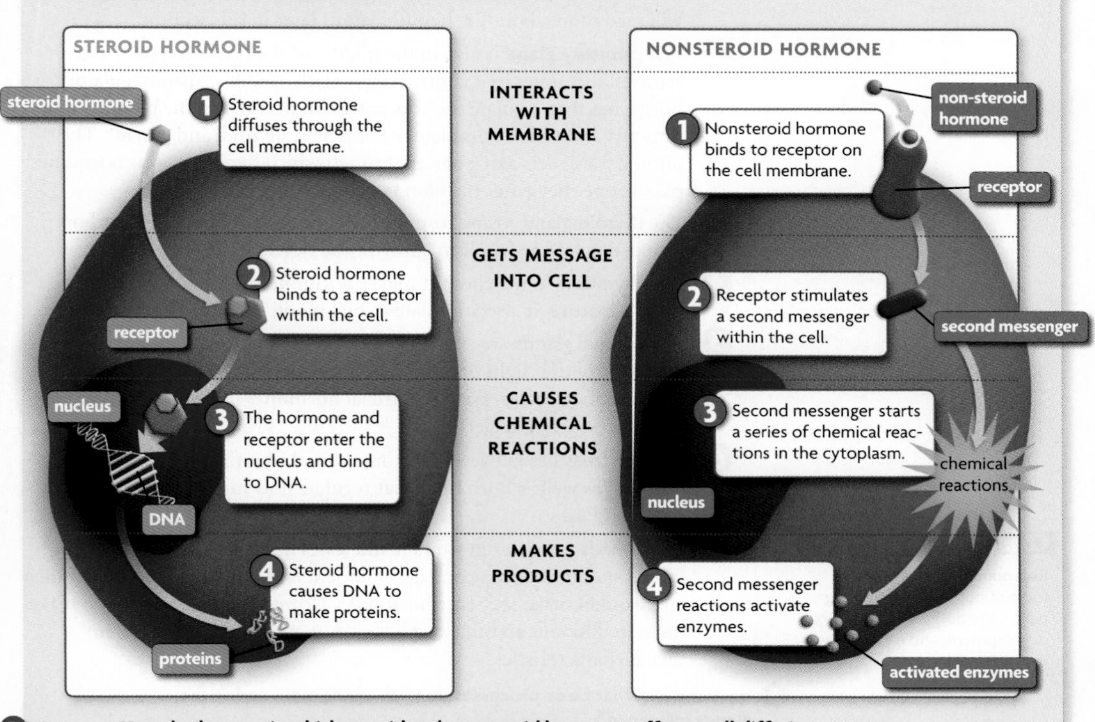
STEROID HORMONE
NONSTEROID HORMONE
steroid hormone
1 Steroid hormone diffuses through the cell membrane.
INTERACTS WITH MEMBRANE
non-steroid hormone
1 Nonsteroid hormone binds to receptor on the cell membrane.
receptor
GETS MESSAGE INTO CELL
2 Steroid hormone binds to a receptor within the cell.
receptor
2 Receptor stimulates a second messenger within the cell.
second messenger
nucleus
3 The hormone and receptor enter the nucleus and bind to DNA.
CAUSES CHEMICAL REACTIONS
3 Second messenger starts a series of chemical reactions in the cytoplasm.
chemical reactions
DNA
nucleus
MAKES PRODUCTS
4 Steroid hormone causes DNA to make proteins.
4 Second messenger reactions activate enzymes.
proteins
activated enzymes

B Contrast **How do the ways in which steroid and nonsteroid hormones affect a cell differ?**

PRE-AP

Tell students that the hormone commonly referred to as adrenaline (epinephrine) is a nonsteroid hormone. Adrenaline moves quickly into the bloodstream to contribute to the body's response when a person feels threatened or frightened. Have students take five minutes to write about whether there is a selective advantage in having a hormone associated with the fight-or-flight response be nonsteroidal.

Biology Toolkit, Quick-Write, p. C19

ENGLISH LEARNERS

Use the diagrams in **FIGURE 29.19** to help students visualize what is happening at each numbered step. Use questions to help bring out the detail of the diagrams. Then suggest students reformat each half of the diagram as a sequence diagram, placing one diagram above the other to make an easier comparison.

Biology Toolkit, Sequence Diagram, p. C38

Connecting CONCEPTS

Cell Membrane The phospholipid molecules of a cell membrane have their nonpolar heads facing the outside and inside surfaces of the cell membrane, with their polar tails hidden inside the membrane. Nonpolar substances such as steroid hormones are not repelled by the nonpolar cell membrane, so they can enter the cell.

TEACH FROM VISUALS

FIGURE 29.19 Have students compare both sides of the figure and point out the alignment of one side to the other.

Ask

- Where does the steroid hormone meet a receptor? within the cell the nonsteroid hormone? outside the cell
- How does the reaction caused by the steroid hormone differ from the nonsteroid hormone? Steroid hormone acts on DNA to produce its product; nonsteroid hormone produces a chemical reaction in the cytoplasm.
- Which type of hormone is more likely to produce an immediate effect and why? nonsteroid hormone, one that does not require DNA to go through protein synthesis

Answers

A Apply Hormones will affect only cells with matching receptors.

B Contrast Steroid hormones enter cells and bind with receptors inside the cells. The hormones and receptors then enter the nucleus, causing DNA to make proteins. Nonsteroid hormones bind with receptors on the cells' surface, causing chemical reactions in the cells, which activate enzymes.

▼ Teach *continued*

Vocabulary

Academic Vocabulary The words **secretion** and **secrete** are distinct in meaning from the words **excretion** and **excrete.**

secretion, a substance produced and used within the body

excretion, a product of bodily activity released as waste

Both words come from similar roots, meaning "to set aside" or "separate."

Take It Further

Hormones are especially potent chemicals that can produce significant effects, even when in low concentrations in the bloodstream. This is advantageous given that many hormones have only a short time in which to act. Most are quickly removed from the blood by the kidneys or liver. The time a hormone spends in the bloodstream is brief, from 1 to 30 minutes. In contrast, the time it takes for the hormone's effects to be felt can vary widely—anywhere from minutes to hours or days.

Answers

A Summarize Hypothalamus influences growth, reproduction, and body temperature. Pituitary influences water balance and growth. Thyroid influences metabolism, growth, and development. Thymus influences the immune system. Adrenal influences blood pressure and breathing rate. Pancreas influences digestion and blood glucose levels. Gonads influence sexual development and functions.

MAIN IDEA

Endocrine glands secrete hormones that act throughout the body.

Unlike the nervous system, the endocrine system does not have its own connected network of tissues. However, its chemical messages can still travel where they need to go. Hormones travel in the bloodstream to all areas of the body to find target cells.

The endocrine system has many glands. Each gland makes hormones that have target cells in many areas of the body. Some of these glands make hormones that prompt other endocrine glands to make and release their hormones. Other glands affect different body systems. Their hormones prompt cells to divide or to take up nutrients. Other hormones keep the body's blood pressure within a set limit. Some of the major glands, along with a few of the hormones that they make, are described below and in **FIGURE 29.20.**

1. The **hypothalamus** is a small area of the middle of the brain, as you might recall from Section 29.4. It makes hormones that stimulate the pituitary gland to release hormones. It also stimulates the production of hormones that control growth, reproduction, and body temperature. You will read more about the hypothalamus later in this section.
2. The **pituitary gland** is also in the middle of the brain. It makes and releases hormones that control cell growth as well as osmoregulatory hormones that regulate the concentration of water in the blood. Some pituitary hormones stimulate the adrenals, thyroid, and gonads. The pituitary also acts as a gateway through which hypothalamus hormones pass before they enter the bloodstream.
3. The **thyroid gland** wraps around the windpipe on three sides. Its hormones regulate metabolism, growth, and development.
4. The **thymus** is in the chest. It makes hormones that cause white blood cells to mature. It also stimulates white blood cells to fight off infection.
5. The **adrenal glands** are above the kidneys. The adrenals secrete hormones that control the "fight or flight" response when stimulated by the parasympathetic nervous system. Adrenal hormones increase breathing rate, blood pressure, and alertness.
6. The **pancreas** lies between the stomach and intestines. It makes digestive enzymes as well as hormones that regulate how much glucose the body stores and uses.
7. The **gonads**—ovaries in women and testes in men—make steroid hormones that influence sexual development and functions. Gonads of men and women make the same hormones. However, men and women make them in different amounts, which gives men and women different sexual characteristics.

Connecting CONCEPTS

Reproduction You can read more about how chemical signals in the body affect growth, development, and reproduction in **Chapter 34.**

A Summarize What body processes do each of the main endocrine glands influence?

Differentiated Instruction

BELOW LEVEL

Have students form pairs to think through and answer the following questions:

- What would happen if an action potential generated a response in the wrong motor cell? The wrong part of the body would respond.
- What would happen if a hormone's signal went to the wrong cell and why? Nothing would happen because the cell lacks the receptor.
- How is a message sent along a neuron different from one sent by a hormone? The neuron sends a chemical signal that runs along a specific pathway; the hormone sends a signal that goes wherever blood flows.

Biology Toolkit, Think-Pair-Share, p. C13

FIGURE 29.20 Glands and Some of the Major Hormones

Endocrine glands are found throughout the body, and they influence whole-body processes. Some of the hormones they make are listed here.

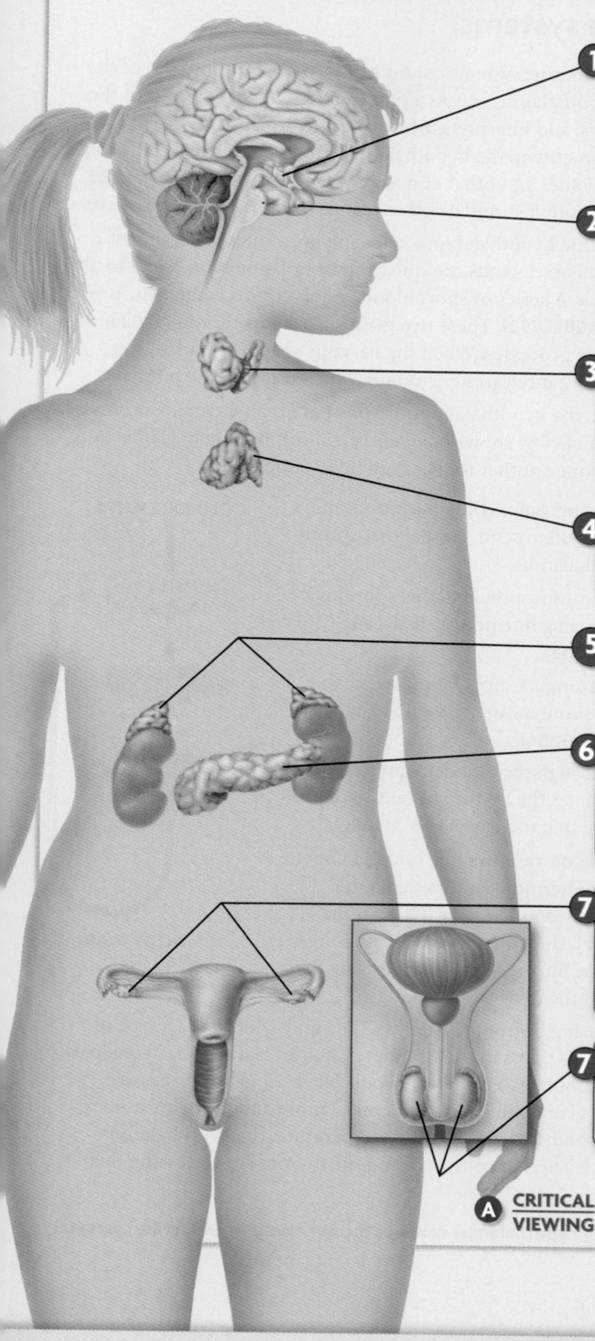

1 HYPOTHALAMUS
- **Growth hormone-releasing hormone (GHRH)** causes the pituitary to release growth hormone.
- **Gonadotropin-releasing hormone (GnRH)** causes gonads to release hormones that control the reproductive system.

2 PITUITARY
- **Growth hormone (GH)** stimulates cell division, protein synthesis, and bone growth in multiple tissues.
- **Antidiuretic hormone (ADH)** causes the blood to absorb water from the kidneys.

3 THYROID
- **Thyroxin (T4)** and **Triiodothyronine (T3)** increase metabolism, digestion, and a person's energy levels.
- **Calcitonin** causes the body to remove calcium from the blood and increase bone formation.

4 THYMUS
- **Thymosin** causes white blood cells to reproduce and mature.

5 ADRENAL GLANDS
- **Epinephrine** causes the heart to increase its strength and number of contractions, circulating blood more quickly.

6 PANCREAS
- **Insulin** removes sugar from the bloodstream and increases sugar metabolism.
- **Glucagon** increases sugar production and adds sugar to the bloodstream.

7 FEMALE GONADS: OVARIES
- **Estrogen** causes sexual maturation, including egg production, and influences female characteristics, such as fat distribution and widening of the hips.
- **Progesterone** causes menstruation.

7 MALE GONADS: TESTES
- **Testosterone** causes sexual maturation, including sperm production, and male characteristics, such as facial hair and a deep voice.

A CRITICAL VIEWING **Why is the bloodstream a good means for transporting hormones such as growth hormone and calcitonin?**

ONLINE BIOLOGY Students can graph cortisol levels and see how they relate to time of day in Data Analysis in Options for Inquiry on page 903.

Integrating Medical Science

In 1988, while training for the Olympics in Seoul, South Korea, American hurdler **Gail Devers** began to have migraines, sleeplessness, fainting spells, and vision loss. She was diagnosed with **Graves' disease,** a chronic disorder in which the thyroid gland produces too much thyroxin. When there is an increase in the amount of thyroid hormone, a person's metabolism rate can be increased by 60–100 percent.

As a result, Devers's feet became swollen, blistered, cracked, and painful. Doctors thought her feet might have to be amputated. However, with proper treatment and determination, Devers went on to win the Olympic gold for the 100-meter dash in 1992, and again in 1996.

Take It Further

Tell students not to confuse the steroid hormones that the body makes naturally with **anabolic-androgenic steroids** that some athletes use to enhance performance. Anabolic-androgenic steroids are synthetic substances related to male sex hormones. They are sometimes prescribed medically to treat delayed puberty and to prevent wasting in patients with AIDS. However, abuse of these steroids can lead to liver disease, blood clots, aggression, and irritability.

PRE-AP

Have students study **FIGURE 29.20,** then close their books. Ask them to draw a rough outline of the human body in their science notebook. Have them locate and identify as many endocrine glands as they can. Ask students if they see any parallels between the general placements of the endocrine system and that of the central nervous system. centralized location along the main axis of body, close to most major organs

INCLUSION

Provide students who are visually impaired with a cutout of the human body. Have them work with another student to add sticker dots where the endocrine glands are located. The pair should identify the glands, the hormones they secrete, and the effects of those hormones.

Answers

A Critical Viewing Growth hormone and calcitonin affect cells that are found throughout the body. Because the bloodstream reaches all parts of the body, it can get hormones to their target cells.

▼ Teach *continued*

TEACH FROM VISUALS

FIGURE 29.21 Point out that the hypothalamus connects the nervous and endocrine systems. **Ask**

- What system is the hypothalamus part of? both the endocrine and central nervous systems
- What is the function of the hypothalamus in the CNS? It receives and sorts impulses to other areas of the brain.
- What type of signals does the hypothalamus send? It produces releasing hormones that then activate other glands, such as the pituitary, to release their hormones.

Take It Further

Prostaglandins are hormonelike lipids that regulate cell activities. Unlike hormones, they are not produced by specific endocrine glands. Instead, they are produced by many cells throughout the body and act locally. Prostaglandins help regulate blood pressure, childbirth, blood clotting, and the body's inflammatory response to infection.

Answers

Ⓐ **Analyze** The hypothalamus receives nerve impulses from the brain and other parts of the body. It also releases regulating hormones, which cause other endocrine glands to release hormones.

ONLINE BIOLOGY The interactive animation in Options for Inquiry, page 903, examines what happens when an imbalance occurs in a hormone feedback loop.

pituitary gland

hypothalamus

blood flow

pituitary gland

FIGURE 29.21 The hypothalamus stimulates the pituitary to secrete hormones into the bloodstream.

MAIN IDEA

The hypothalamus interacts with the nervous and endocrine systems.

The nervous and endocrine systems connect to each other at the base of the brain, where the hypothalamus acts as a part of both systems. As part of the CNS, it receives, sorts, and interprets information from sensory organs. As part of the endocrine system, the hypothalamus produces releasing hormones that affect tissues and other endocrine glands. **Releasing hormones** are hormones that stimulate other glands to release their hormones.

Many of the hypothalamus's releasing hormones affect the pituitary gland. These glands can quickly pass hormones back and forth to each other. A series of short blood vessels connects the two, as you can see in **FIGURE 29.21.** These two glands work together to regulate various body processes. When the nervous system stimulates the hypothalamus, it releases hormones, which travel to the pituitary.

Together, the hypothalamus and pituitary regulate many processes. The diagram below shows how releasing hormones help glands to "talk with" one another to maintain body temperature.

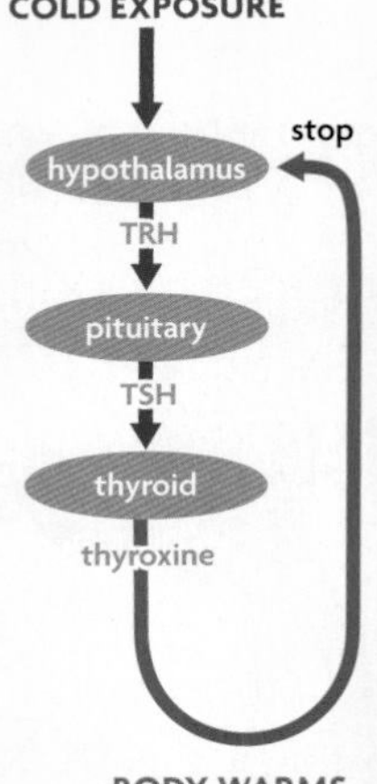

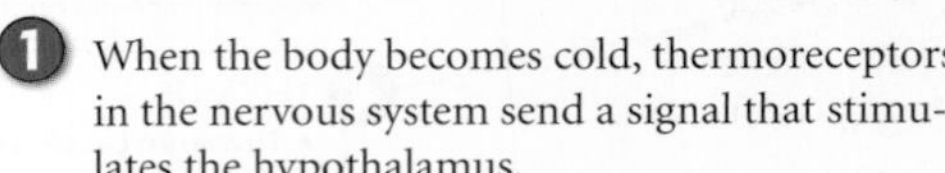

1. When the body becomes cold, thermoreceptors in the nervous system send a signal that stimulates the hypothalamus.

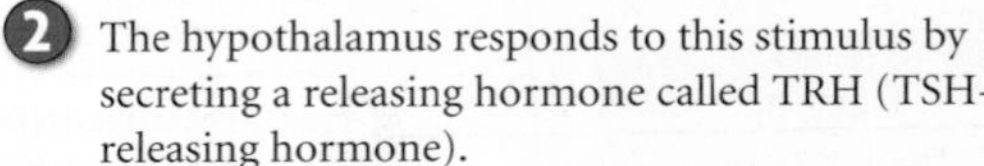

2. The hypothalamus responds to this stimulus by secreting a releasing hormone called TRH (TSH-releasing hormone).

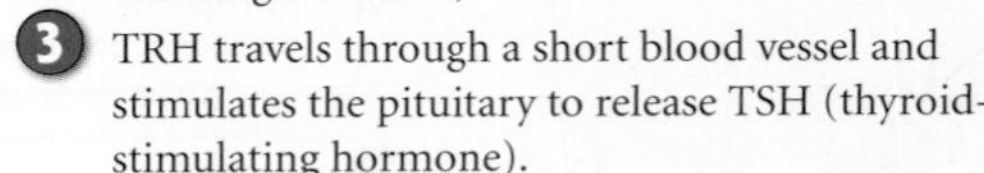

3. TRH travels through a short blood vessel and stimulates the pituitary to release TSH (thyroid-stimulating hormone).
4. TSH travels through the bloodstream to the neck, where it stimulates the thyroid to release thyroxine, a hormone that increases cells' activity.
5. As cells become more active, the body's temperature increases. Thermoreceptors signal the hypothalamus to stop releasing TRH. In the absence of TRH, the other glands are no longer stimulated. One by one, they stop releasing their hormones, and the cycle is turned off.

Notice that releasing hormones, such as TRH and TSH, act as a type of feedback on the glands they target. In Chapter 28, you learned that a feedback is something that stimulates a change. As long as releasing hormones are present, each target gland will continue to make more and more hormones. However, when the body reaches its ideal temperature, the hypothalamus stops releasing TRH. Then the pituitary and the thyroid stop releasing their hormones too.

Ⓐ Analyze **How does the hypothalamus connect the nervous and endocrine systems?**

Differentiated Instruction

BELOW LEVEL

Have students create a cycle diagram for the feedback loop shown on page 900. Suggest they overlay the diagram onto an outline of the human body, placing the hypothalamus, pituitary, and thyroid in their approximate locations.

Biology Toolkit, Cycle Diagram, p. C39

MAIN IDEA

Hormonal imbalances can cause severe illness.

Because hormones play an important role in maintaining homeostasis, too much or too little of a hormone will affect the entire body. In Chapter 28, you learned that diabetes occurs when the pancreas does not make the right amounts of insulin and glucagon, hormones that regulate sugar concentration in the blood. When other glands do not function properly, a person may get other diseases. For example, if the thyroid does not make enough hormones, a person will develop hypothyroidism. In children, this condition slows growth and mental development. In adults, hypothyroidism causes weakness, sensitivity to cold, weight gain, and depression. Hyperthyroidism, or the condition of having too many thyroid hormones, produces opposite symptoms.

The wrong amount of adrenal hormones also affects the entire body. Cortisol is an adrenal hormone that helps the body break down and use sugars and control blood flow and pressure. If the adrenal glands produce too much cortisol, the body cannot metabolize sugars properly, and a person can develop Cushing's syndrome. This syndrome causes obesity, high blood pressure, diabetes, and muscle weakness. It occurs when the pituitary, which releases hormones that stimulate the adrenal glands, is not working the way it should. Steroids, a pituitary tumor, or some prescription drugs can make the pituitary overactive and indirectly cause Cushing's syndrome.

On the other hand, in Addison's disease the adrenal glands do not make enough cortisol. Usually, Addison's disease occurs because the immune system attacks the adrenal glands. The disease causes loss of appetite, weight loss, and low blood pressure. Although hormonal imbalances can cause serious illnesses and may even be fatal, many hormonal imbalances can be treated with surgery or medicine.

To learn more about the endocrine system, visit scilinks.org.
Keycode: MLB029

A Infer Why might a problem with a person's pituitary gland lead to problems in other body systems?

History of Science

Cushing's syndrome is named after **Dr. Harvey Williams Cushing,** an early pioneer in neurosurgery. The syndrome is a disorder of the adrenal cortex, caused by a pituitary tumor. Cushing was among the first to treat such disorders surgically. He used surgery to treat **acromegaly,** a disease in which the pituitary gland releases too much growth hormone, producing enlarged bone structures of the face, hands, and feet.

Answers

A Infer The pituitary gland releases hormones that stimulate organs that are part of other body systems.

29.6 ASSESSMENT

ONLINE QUIZ ClassZone.com

REVIEWING MAIN IDEAS

1. What determines whether a particular **hormone** will act on a target cell?
2. What two main hormones does the **pituitary gland** produce?
3. How do **releasing hormones** of the **hypothalamus** connect the nervous and endocrine systems?
4. Why do hormonal imbalances affect the entire body?

CRITICAL THINKING

5. **Predict** How might your body be affected if a certain **gland** made too much releasing hormone that stimulates the thyroid? What if it made too little releasing hormone?
6. **Apply** What two body systems does the endocrine system rely on to generate and transport signals?

Connecting CONCEPTS

7. **Cell Biology** Steroid hormones are made of cholesterol, which is a type of lipid. Using what you know about cell membranes, why do you think steroids can diffuse into a cell, while nonsteroid hormones cannot?

Assess and Reteach

Assess Use the Online Quiz or Section Quiz (*Assessment Book,* p. 576).

Reteach Make a three-column chart on the board. Title the first column *Glands,* the second *Hormones,* and the third *Function.* Have students supply the information for the chart, copying it into their notebooks.

29.6 ASSESSMENT

1. A hormone will act on a cell only if the cell has the proper receptor.
2. growth hormone and osmoregulatory hormones
3. Releasing hormones are the chemical messages that the hypothalamus releases in response to the impulses it receives from the nervous system.
4. Hormones play an important role in maintaining homeostasis.
5. Too little of the releasing hormone would result in too little thyroid activity, which leads to weakness, sensitivity to cold, weight gain, depression, and memory loss. Too much of the releasing hormone would produce opposite effects.
6. nervous and circulatory systems
7. Because the cell membrane is a lipid-bilayer, lipid molecules, such as steroid hormones, can pass through the membrane. Nonlipid molecules, such as nonsteroid hormones, cannot pass through the membrane.

OPTIONS FOR INQUIRY

INVESTIGATION

Time 45 minutes	TEACHER TESTED
Teacher Preparation	
Student Difficulty	
Lab Binder Human Bio, pp. 18–20	

Purpose Observe how a distraction affects task completion.

Overview Students will design an experiment to time the completion of tasks with and without a distraction. They will

- perform four tasks and record the time needed to complete each task
- repeat the activity while being exposed to a distraction
- graph the two sets of data and make comparisons

LAB PREPARATION

- You will need four decks of playing cards.

LAB MANAGEMENT

- You may wish to provide a list of distractions from which students can choose, for example, having subjects recite the alphabet or list their relatives.

Teacher Note "Some students did not get expected results because they chose distractors such as stomping their feet or just making noise."

Inclusion Group students so that students with physical disabilities will have assistance with this lab.

POST-LAB DISCUSSION

Learning could affect results when a task is repeated. **Ask**

- How could you control for learning? Use different items for each task.
- How would the results of your experiment apply to a homework situation? Concentration and the ability to do a task are easier and take less time when there are fewer distractions.

Use these inquiry-based labs and online activities to deepen your understanding of nervous and endocrine systems.

INDIANA STANDARDS

NOS.1 Develop explanations based on reproducible data and observations gathered during laboratory investigations.

NOS.3 Clearly communicate their ideas and results of investigations verbally and in written form using tables, graphs, diagrams, and photographs.

DESIGN YOUR OWN INVESTIGATION

Reaction Time

In this lab you will test reaction time during the completion of simple sorting tasks. You will first find a baseline, or "normal" level, of time needed to complete the tasks. Then you will repeat the tasks when distracting stimuli are also present.

MATERIALS
deck of cards

SKILLS Collecting Data, Analyzing Data, Graphing Data

PROBLEM How does a distraction affect task completion?

PROCEDURE

1. Measure and record the amount of time it takes to finish each of the following tasks. The deck of cards should be shuffled before the beginning of each task.
   a. Separate a deck of cards into two even piles.
   b. Sort a deck of cards into two piles, with one pile for each card color.
   c. Separate a deck of cards into four even piles.
   d. Sort a deck of cards into four piles, with one pile for each suit of cards.
2. Design your own experiment to test how a distraction will change the amount of time needed to complete a task. Distractions could include listening to music or a video in the background, tapping a ruler on the desktop, talking to the person, or having the person say the alphabet aloud while completing the task.
3. Determine what the independent variable is in your experiment. Form a hypothesis about how manipulating your independent variable may affect reaction time. Create a data table in which to record your data. One possible data table is shown below.

TABLE 1. TIME TAKEN TO COMPLETE TASK

Task	Baseline Time (sec)	Time with Distractor (sec)
Two even piles		
Two piles (by color)		
Four even piles		
Four piles (by suit)		

4. Have your teacher approve your procedure. Conduct your experiment.

ANALYZE AND CONCLUDE

1. **Analyze** Draw a graph to present your data.
2. **Analyze** What are the trends in your data regarding the completion of tasks without a distraction? What effect did the distraction have on reaction time?
3. **Experimental Design** What are some possible sources of unavoidable experimental data in your design?

Answers

Sample Data

For a table and graph of student data, go to page R109. Some students may have consistently lower scores if the distractor is not effective in offsetting any learning of the task.

Analyze and Conclude

1. *Task* on the *x*-axis and *Time (sec)* on the *y*-axis, plotting both sets of data on the same graph
2. The greater the difficulty of a task, the more time is needed to complete the task. Distraction will increase completion time for a given task.
3. Answers will vary, but most likely will indicate that the distraction was not constant or there were multiple distractions. Some students may say the distraction used was more of an additional task than a distraction.

INVESTIGATION

Brain-Based Disorders

Scientists do not always know what causes many brain-based diseases or disorders because the scientific study of the brain is relatively new. Sometimes doctors find that drug treatments are effective, but they do not understand exactly how or why these treatments work.

SKILL Researching

PROBLEM Choose one of the following disorders or diseases to research: Autism, Tourette syndrome, obsessive-compulsive disorder, or migraine headaches.

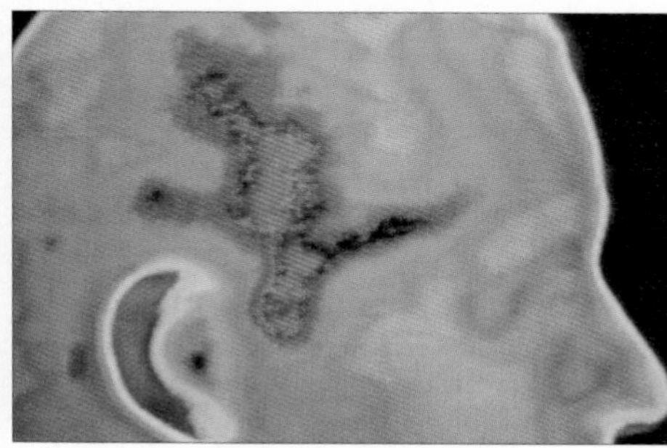

This PET scan shows a person who is experiencing a migraine headache.

RESEARCH

1. What are the symptoms of this disorder?
2. What do scientists believe causes this disorder?
3. How is the disorder treated?
4. What are the trends in diagnosis of the disorder over the past 10 to 15 years?
5. What could explain the trends?
6. What new discoveries and discussions have been in the news over the past year that indicate how scientists' understanding of this disorder is changing?

Online BIOLOGY CLASSZONE.COM

ANIMATED BIOLOGY

Diagnose a Hormone Disorder

Can you diagnose and correct a hormone imbalance? Review three patient histories and compare each to a set of hormone disorders. Diagnose the patients' disorders to get them, and their hormones, back on track.

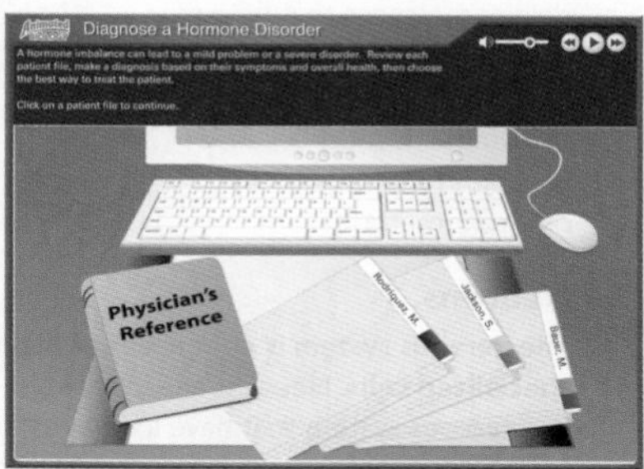

WEBQUEST

A drug addiction is not just life-altering—it alters the brain as well. In this WebQuest, you will learn about the biology of addiction. Find out how different drugs affect neurons and neurotransmitters, creating dependency.

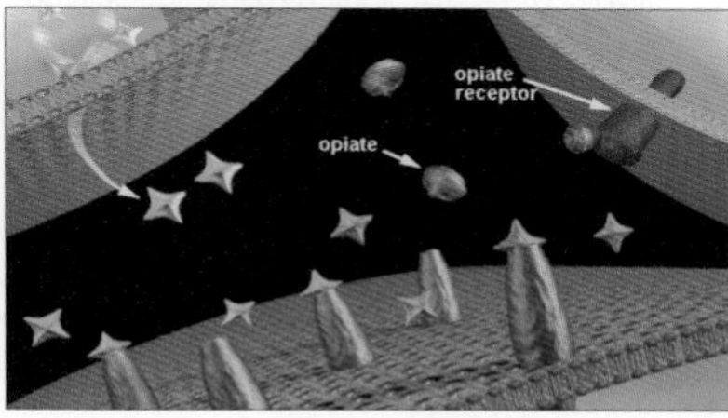

DATA ANALYSIS ONLINE

Cortisol is powerful hormone. Its many actions include metabolizing fats and proteins and managing stress. Graph cortisol levels in the body throughout the day and hypothesize why the body needs high amounts of cortisol at a specific time.

Answers

Sample Answers

1. **Autism:** disturbances in the rate of appearance of physical, social, and language skills

   Obsessive-compulsive disorder: Obsessions are thoughts, images, or impulses that occur over and over again. Compulsions are acts the person performs over and over again, often according to certain "rules."

   Tourette syndrome (TS): a neurological disorder characterized by repetitive, stereotyped, involuntary movements and vocalizations called tics

   Migraine: changes in mood or sensation, visual or auditory disturbances, nausea, light and sound sensitivity

2–6. Answers will vary.

Online Biology ▼

ANIMATED BIOLOGY Use this animation to reinforce the concepts in **Section 29.6.**

WEBQUEST The WebQuest takes one full class period. Students complete the activity online and will need access to a printer to print their answers. Sample answers, teacher notes, and alternative assessment ideas are available on **ClassZone.com.** Use with **Section 29.5.**

DATA ANALYSIS Students' graphs should show a peak around 7–8 A.M., a decline throughout the day, and then an increase between midnight and 7–8 A.M. Students may hypothesize that the cortisol levels are high in the morning because we are diurnal creatures and our systems have evolved to deal with the stress that we encounter during the daytime. Use with **Section 29.6.**

INVESTIGATION TEACHER TESTED

Time	30 minutes
Teacher Preparation	1 flask
Student Difficulty	1 flask
Lab Binder	Human Bio, p. 21

Purpose Students will learn about specific brain-based disorders or diseases.

Overview Students will conduct research in the library or on the Internet to answer the questions.

POST-LAB DISCUSSION

Discuss with students whether any of the disorders could be classified simply as behavioral or emotional, or if they inevitably involve some degree of both components.

CHAPTER REVIEW

Interactive Review

Encourage students to go to **ClassZone.com** for a detailed review of each section, including visuals and vocabulary practice.

Unit Resource Book, Vocabulary Practice, pp. 53–56

CHAPTER 29 Interactive Review @ CLASSZONE.COM

KEY CONCEPTS | Vocabulary Games | Concept Maps | Animated Biology | Online Quiz

29.1 How Organ Systems Communicate

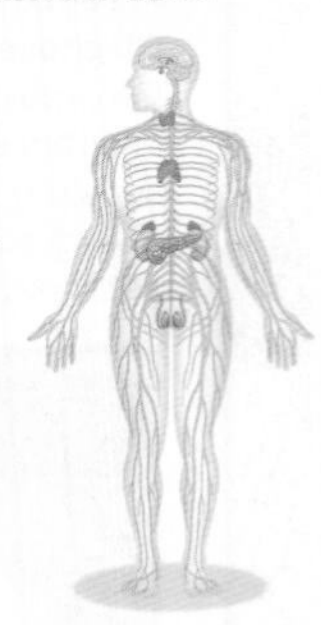

The nervous system and the endocrine system provide the means by which organ systems communicate. The body's nervous system and endocrine system generate, interpret, and deliver messages that help to maintain homeostasis. The two systems have different rates of communication because they send their signals by different methods.

29.2 Neurons

The nervous system is composed of highly specialized cells. Neurons are specialized cells of the nervous system that have long extensions for transmitting signals over long distances. These cells produce, receive, and transmit impulses called action potentials.

29.3 The Senses

The senses detect the internal and external environments. The senses gather information about the body's internal and external environments. The senses use five types of receptors and many specialized cells, including rod, cone, and hair cells, that detect physical and chemical stimuli.

29.4 Central and Peripheral Nervous Systems

The central nervous system interprets information, and the peripheral nervous system gathers and transmits information. The CNS and PNS work together. In the CNS, the cerebrum controls conscious thought and interprets sensory signals from throughout the body. The PNS delivers messages from the body toward and away from the CNS.

29.5 Brain Function and Chemistry

Scientists study the function and chemistry of the brain. Imaging techniques allow scientists to look at the brain without having to have a patient undergo surgery. This technology can show chemical and physical changes in brains that have severe illnesses. Both prescription drugs and illegal drugs alter brain chemistry and neuron structure.

29.6 Endocrine System and Hormones

The endocrine system produces hormones that affect growth, development, and homeostasis. The glands of the endocrine system produce chemical signals called hormones that act throughout the body. The hypothalamus is a gland that interacts with the nervous and endocrine systems. Hormone imbalances can cause severe illnesses, such as hypothyroidism, diabetes, and Addison's disease.

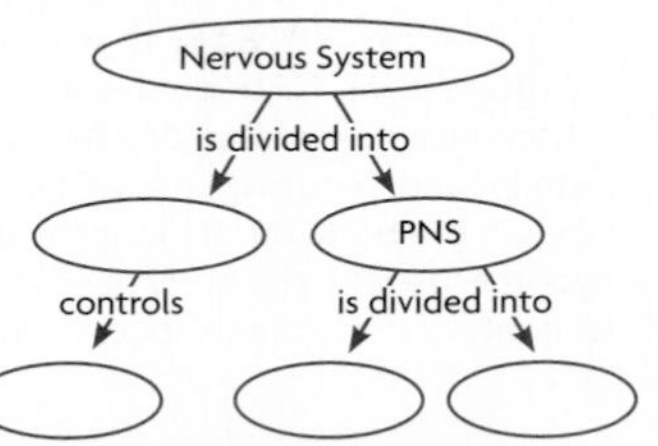

Synthesize Your Notes

Concept Map Summarize your notes about the nervous system by drawing a concept map.

Nervous System — is divided into → [blank] and PNS; [blank] controls → [blank]; PNS is divided into → [blank], [blank]

Three-Column Chart Make a chart to organize the information you learned about the senses.

Sense	Receptor Type	Receptor Name
sight	photoreceptor	

Reviewing Vocabulary

1. Both are part of the PNS, but the somatic nervous system controls voluntary responses, and the autonomic nervous system controls involuntary responses
2. Both are photoreceptors, but cone cells detect color, and rod cells detect light levels.
3. Both are ways the nervous system regulates the number of impulses a neuron generates, but in sensitization receptors are added and in desensitization receptors are removed.
4. Dendrites branch out of the cell body, in a way similar to that of branches spreading out from a tree.
5. Addiction is a dependence that suggest having given in to something.
6. Endocrine glands are separated from that which they affect; they work at a distance.
7. moving electrical impulse
8. quick response
9. chemical signal
10. long extension

Chapter Assessment

CHAPTER REVIEW

15. Your CNS passes a signal to a motor neuron in your PNS causing you to raise your hand.
16. Occipital lobe: vision; temporal lobe: hearing
17. sympathetic: prepares the body for action and stress; parasympathetic: calms the body
18. PET shows levels of activity in different areas of the brain. This information helps connect specific neurotransmitters to the parts of the brain they affect.
19. Hormones only act on cells that have a matching receptor.
20. Releasing hormones are those that stimulate other glands to produce and release their hormones.
21. A target cell will be overstimulated.

Chapter Vocabulary

29.1 nervous system, p. 874
endocrine system, p. 874
stimulus, p. 874
central nervous system (CNS), p. 875
peripheral nervous system (PNS), p. 875

29.2 neuron, p .876
dendrite, p. 876
axon, p. 876
resting potential, p. 877
sodium-potassium pump, p. 877
action potential, p. 878
synapse, p. 879
terminal, p. 879
neurotransmitter, p. 879

29.3 rod cell, p. 881
cone cell, p. 881
hair cell, p. 882

29.4 cerebrum, p. 886
cerebral cortex, p. 887
cerebellum, p. 888
brain stem, p. 888
reflex arc, p. 889
somatic nervous system, p. 889
autonomic nervous system, p. 890
sympathetic nervous system, p. 890
parasympathetic nervous system, p. 890

29.5 addiction, p. 893
desensitization, p. 893
tolerance, p. 893
sensitization, p. 893
stimulant, p. 894
depressant, p. 894

29.6 hormone, p. 896
gland, p. 896
hypothalamus, p. 898
pituitary gland, p. 898
releasing hormones, p. 900

Reviewing Vocabulary

Compare and Contrast

Describe one similarity and one difference between the two terms in each of the following pairs.

1. somatic nervous system, autonomic nervous system
2. rod cell, cone cell
3. sensitization, desensitization

Greek and Latin Word Origins

4. *Dendrite* comes from the Greek word *dendron,* which means "tree." Explain how the root word relates to the meaning of *dendrite.*

5. *Addiction* comes from the Latin word *addicere,* which means "deliver, yield, devote." How does this meaning relate to addiction?

6. *Endocrine* comes from the Greek word *krinein,* which means "to distinguish, separate." Explain how the root word relates to the meaning of *endocrine.*

Keep It Short

For each vocabulary term below, write a short, precise phrase that describes its meaning. For example, a short phrase to describe *stimulus* could be "causes change."

7. action potential
8. reflex arc
9. hormone
10. axon

Reviewing MAIN IDEAS

11. Name two differences between the way in which the nervous and endocrine systems communicate.

12. How does the structure of a neuron make it effective in carrying out the functions of the nervous system?

13. Draw pictures to show how Na^+ ions, K^+ ions, and electrical charges are distributed across a neuron's membrane during resting and action potential.

14. What type of receptor do each of your five senses have?

15. If you have a question, you will raise your hand to ask it. How do your CNS and PNS work together to allow you to raise your hand?

16. What types of information do the occipital lobe and the temporal lobe process?

17. What are the differences between the sympathetic and the parasympathetic nervous systems?

18. How can a PET scan give clues about the activity of different neurotransmitters in the brain?

19. Why do hormones act only on some cells?

20. How do releasing hormones help glands to communicate with one another?

21. How are a target cell's activities changed if a gland produces too much of a particular hormone?

Reviewing Main Ideas

11. The nervous system is quick working, interconnected, and uses electrical impulses. The endocrine system is slow working, not connected, and uses chemical signals.
12. Neurons have long extensions called axons, which allow messages to be carried long distances without having to pass the signal to another cell.
13. Students' drawings should show that during resting potential, there is more Na^+ outside of the cell and K^+ inside. The action potential should show Na^+ moving into the cell and K^+ moving out.
14. vision: photoreceptor; hearing: mechanoreceptor; taste and smell: chemoreceptor; touch: pain receptor, mechanoreceptor, and thermoreceptor

CHAPTER REVIEW

Critical Thinking

22. Light enters the eye, and the optic nerve sends a signal to the brain. The brain interprets the signal and determines that too much light is entering the eye. The brain sends a signal to the muscles around the iris to cause the pupil to shrink.
23. dendrites; because these are the structures that receive stimuli
24. The inside of the neuron becomes positively charged because there are more Na^+ molecules moving in than K^+ and the charge is relative.
25. If photoreceptors are damaged, the eye will send fewer signals to the brain.
26. Both are chemicals; both are specific to matching receptors; both stimulate a response.
27. It is beneficial because your hands are what you use to grasp and touch things.

Interpreting Visuals

28. terminal, vesicles, neurotransmitters, receptors
29. Botox is affecting the ability of the nervous system to release neurotransmitter into the synapse.

Critical Thinking

22. Apply You wake up at night and turn on the light next to your bed. The light seems very bright at first, but soon your eyes adjust. Describe how your senses and your brain interact to let your eyes adjust to the light level.

23. Infer Research on babies shows that a certain part of a neuron gets longer as the babies interact with more stimuli. Which part do you think it is? Why?

24. Analyze How does the inside of a neuron become positively charged during an action potential, even though both potassium (K^+) and sodium (Na^+) ions are positively charged?

25. Predict An eye disease called macular degeneration damages the light-sensitive cells in the eye. How might this disease affect the ability of the eye to communicate with the brain?

26. Compare What are three similarities between neurotransmitters, used in the nervous system, and hormones, which are used in the endocrine system?

27. Apply The part of your brain that processes touch devotes more space to interpreting signals from your hands than from other parts of your body. Why might this be beneficial?

Interpreting Visuals

The toxin in the diagram is commonly known as Botox. It is a cosmetic treatment used on the muscles under skin to reduce wrinkles. Use the diagram below to answer the next two questions.

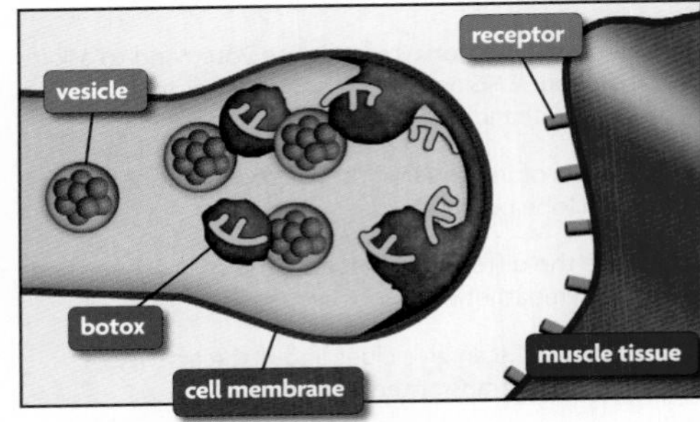

28. Apply What structures of the nervous system are being shown in the diagram?

29. Analyze Botox affects the normal functioning of nerve cells. According to the diagram, what part of the normal process is Botox affecting?

Analyzing Data

Cataracts can impair a person's vision, making objects appear fuzzy. Cataracts occur when the lens in a person's eye becomes cloudy, or less transparent. This happens when the proteins that make up the lens clump. Use the graph below to answer the next three questions.

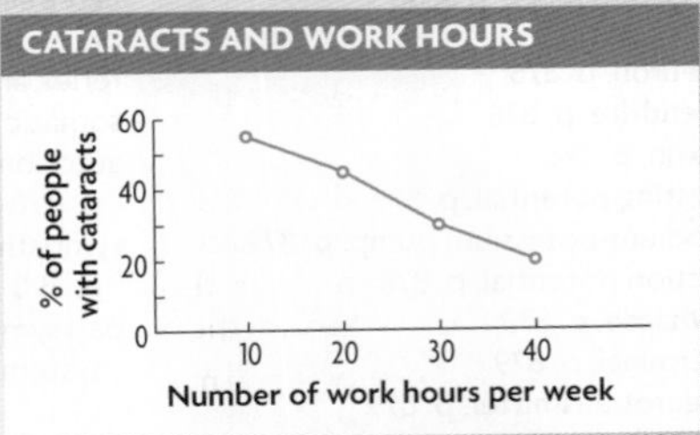

30. Analyze Does a correlation exist between incidents of cataracts and work hours? Explain.

31. Evaluate Can you conclude for sure that the number of hours worked causes cataracts? Explain your reasoning.

32. Infer If a correlation exists between cataracts and work hours, what might explain it?

Connecting CONCEPTS

33. Write a Script Imagine you have a friend who wanted to try drugs, and you wanted to tell your friend about the effects that drugs have on the nervous system. Write a conversation that you could have about addiction and the negative effects of drug use.

34. Connect The image on page 873 shows some of a person's internal organs. Write a paragraph that discusses which division of the nervous system is shown in this picture. Also, discuss how the cells of this body system allow you to rapidly pull your hand off of a hot pan before your hand is burned.

Analyzing Data

30. Yes, there is a correlation because a definite relationship exists.
31. No, there is not enough information to conclude that the number of hours worked causes cataracts.
32. As people get older, they retire and work less. Cataracts are a condition of age, and not work hours.

INDIANA ISTEP+ Test Prep

NOS.4

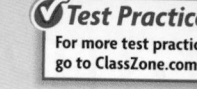

Test Practice
For more test practice, go to ClassZone.com.

1 A scientist investigates the toxic effects of a chemical on the brain. Which of the following experimental design elements would ***most*** likely lead to inconsistent results?

- **A** using the same method to measure toxicity
- **B** having a sample size that is very large
- **C** keeping the chemical at a constant temperature
- **D** running the tests in different locations

2 Negative feedback loops allow the body to maintain homeostasis as internal conditions change. Which of the following is the ***best*** example of negative feedback in the body?

- **A** increasing cells' activity to warm the body when it is cold
- **B** keeping large amounts of carbon available in the blood
- **C** stimulating muscle contractions to move the arm
- **D** releasing chemicals that will thin the blood

3 The hypothalamus releases antidiuretic hormone, which causes the kidneys to release less water from the body. Under which condition might the hypothalamus produce more antidiuretic hormone?

- **A** having high levels of antidiuretic hormone
- **B** having excess water in the body
- **C** drinking a bottle of juice
- **D** sweating due to exercise

THINK THROUGH THE QUESTION

Think carefully about each answer choice. Under which condition would the body respond by conserving water?

4 Anabolic steroids are drugs that mimic specific hormones in the body. As athletes abuse anabolic steroids in hopes of becoming stronger, their bodies produce less natural hormone. This effect can be best described as a(n)

- **A** form of negative feedback.
- **B** reflex arc.
- **C** conditioned response.
- **D** osmoregulatory response.

5 Nerve cells are essential to an animal because they directly provide

- **A** regulation of reproductive rates within other cells
- **B** transport of nutrients to various cells
- **C** communication between cells
- **D** an exchange of gases within the body

6 How do the nervous and endocrine systems work together?

CHAPTER REVIEW

Standards-Based Assessment

1. D	4. A
2. A	5. C
3. D	6. See Below

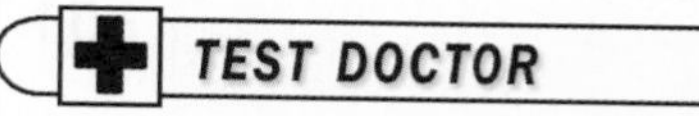

Question 1 Answer D is correct. Answers A, B, and C are incorrect because using similar methodology between test and control groups, testing a large sample size, and maintaining key constants would most likely lead to consistent results.

Question 3 Answer D is correct. Answer A is incorrect because high levels of antidiuretic hormone would likely decrease the amount produced by the hypothalamus via negative feedback. Answers B and C are incorrect because excess water or fluid intake would diminish the body's need to conserve water and thus decrease the amount of antidiuretic hormone produced.

Question 4 Answer A is correct. Answer B is incorrect because a reflex arc is the neural path of a reflex. Answer C is incorrect because a conditioned response is a learned response to a stimulus that was previously neutral. Answer D is incorrect because an osmoregulatory response relates to the maintenance of osmotic pressure within certain limits in organisms.

Question 6 The nervous and endocrine systems communicate with each other through the hypothalamus in the brain. The hypothalamus receives and sorts information from sense organs. It may signal another part of the brain or release hormones that stimulate the pituitary gland, which is part of the endocrine system.

Connecting Concepts

33. Students' answers should discuss addiction, tolerance, sensitization, and desensitization. Students should indicate these things make quitting a drug very difficult.

34. Students should indicate that the image is of the brain, part of the CNS. Students' answers should discuss reflex arcs and clearly demonstrate the knowledge that reflex arcs do not require processing by the brain, which is why the person can react quickly before becoming too badly burned.

ITEM CORRELATIONS

Standard	Items
NOS.4	1

CHAPTER 30

Indiana Resource Preview

Print Resources

Respiratory and Circulatory Systems

INDIANA STANDARDS		Sections	PAGES and PACING	UNIT RESOURCE BOOK
	30.1	**Respiratory and Circulatory Functions** **KEY CONCEPT** The respiratory and circulatory systems bring oxygen and nutrients to the cells.	pp. 910–913 30 minutes	URB pages 57–60
	30.2	**Respiration and Gas Exchange** **KEY CONCEPT** The respiratory system exchanges oxygen and carbon dioxide.	pp. 914–916 30 minutes	URB pages 61–64
	30.3	**The Heart and Circulation** **KEY CONCEPT** The heart is a muscular pump that moves the blood through two pathways.	pp. 917–920 30 minutes	URB pages 65–68
NOS.3		CHAPTER INVESTIGATION: Carbon Dioxide and Exercise	p. 921 45 minutes	**Lab Binder** Human Bio pages 27–29
	30.4	**Blood Vessels and Transport** **KEY CONCEPT** The circulatory system transports materials throughout the body.	pp. 922–924 30 minutes	URB pages 69–72
		DATA ANALYSIS: Forming a Null Hypothesis Age Group and Disease	p. 925 30 minutes	URB page 81
	30.5	**Blood** **KEY CONCEPT** Blood is a complex tissue that transports materials.	pp. 926–929 30 minutes	URB pages 73–76
	30.6	**Lymphatic System** **KEY CONCEPT** The lymphatic system provides another type of circulation in the body.	pp. 930–931 30 minutes	URB pages 77–80
NOS.1, NOS.3		OPTIONS FOR INQUIRY	pp. 932–933 45 minutes, 45 minutes	**Lab Binder** Human Bio pages 30–34
		Chapter Review	pp. 934–937	**Assessment Book** Chapter Tests A, B pp. 597–604

INDIANA STANDARDS

NOS.1 Develop explanations based on reproducible data and observations gathered during laboratory investigations.

NOS.3 Clearly communicate their ideas and results of investigations verbally and in written form using tables, graphs, diagrams, and photographs.

Labs

PUPIL EDITION LABS

Carbon Dioxide and Exercise, p. 921 Students investigate how exercise affects the release of carbon dioxide from the lungs. **Lab Binder** pp. 27–29	**Time:** 45 minutes **Materials:** 100-mL graduated cylinder, 250-mL beaker, 800 mL water, eyedropper, bromothymol blue, straw, 50 mL 0.4% sodium hydroxide solution, clock with second hand
Blood Cells, Section 5, p. 928 Students observe characteristics of different types of blood cells. **Lab Binder** p. 35	**Time:** 20 minutes **Materials:** slide of blood cells, microscope

OPTIONS FOR INQUIRY

Making and Using a Respirometer, p. 932 Students determine whether lung capacity changes with exercise. **Lab Binder** pp. 30–32	**Time:** 45 minutes **Materials:** 1 liter bottle with a hole in the bottom, scissors, white paper, marker, metric ruler, 15 cm clear tape, small paper cup, plastic straw that bends, clock with a second hand
Stimuli and Heart Rate, p. 933 Students determine the effects of different stimuli on heart rate. **Lab Binder** pp. 33–34	**Time:** 45 minutes **Materials:** CD player; VCR or DVD player; videos, DVDs or CDs; clock with a second hand (or stopwatch)

LAB BINDER Unit 9 Human Biology

Additional Investigation: Determining Blood Type, pp. 36–38

Vernier Probeware Lab: Monitoring EKG, pp. 104–107; Ventilation and Heart Rate, pp. 108–110

Virtual Lab Worksheet: Blood Typing, p. 111

LAB GENERATOR

A searchable CD of all labs in the program in editable format, including forensic, probeware, and biotechnology labs.

Presentation Tools

POWER PRESENTATIONS

Presentation Chapter 30
Power Presentations for each section incorporate images and clips from the Media Gallery: Includes Note Navigator for each section.

MEDIA GALLERY

Contains the following images and video clips, as well as animations, simulations and forms of visuals from the book.

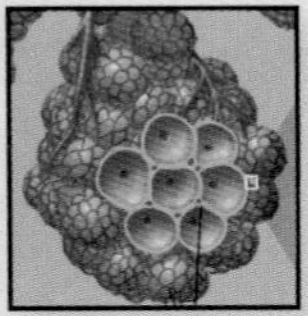
Gas exchange in alveoli

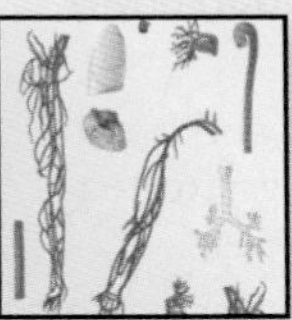
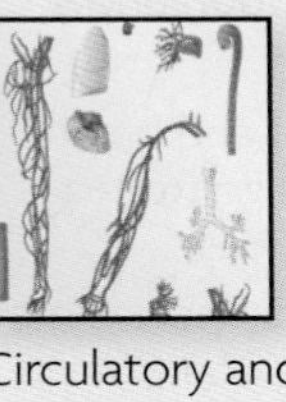
Circulatory and respiratory systems

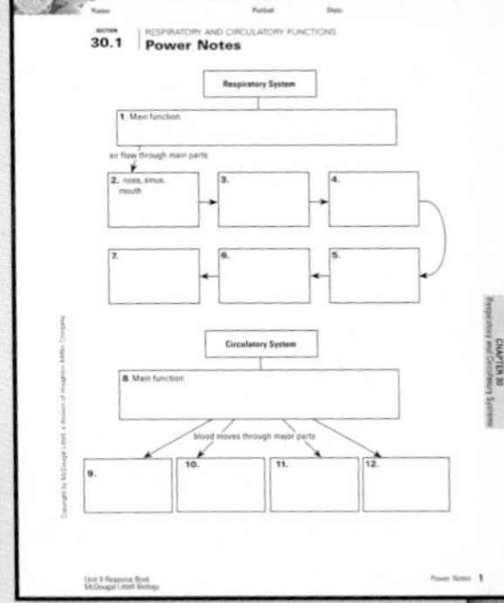
Power Notes

Artery with red blood cells

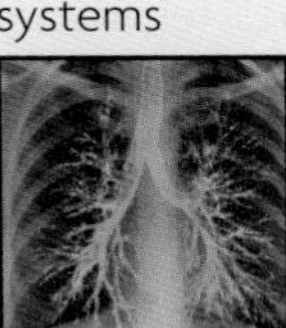
Bronchi and bronchioles

VIDEO

Check out a set of short video clips on circulation, the heart, and heart health.

ANIMATED BIOLOGY

How You Breathe
How the Heart Pumps Blood
Build the Circulatory and Respiratory Systems

TRANSPARENCIES

Respiratory Organs and Tissues T124
Circulatory System T125
Gas Exchange T126
Blood Flow in the Heart T127
Lymphatic System T128

Online BIOLOGY CLASSZONE.COM

BioZine
Animated Biology
Interactive Review
SciLinks
Resource Centers

CHAPTER 30

▼ Focus and Motivate

What can take your breath away?

Have students read the caption under Connecting Concepts. **Ask**

- How do your heartbeat and breathing rates change as you go from a walk to a run? They increase.
- In your experience, what factors may have interfered, making your breathing more difficult? being out of shape, asthma, allergies, respiratory infection, second-hand smoke, pollution, chemical fumes, blow to the solar plexus, disease

BIOZINE ClassZone.com

Students can access BioZine at **ClassZone.com** to learn about some of the latest biological research.

In a Hurry?

The critical material in this chapter is found in **Sections 30.2, 30.3,** and **30.5.** To focus on gas exchange, use **FIGURE 30.5 (Section 30.2).** Use **FIGURE 30.9 (Section 30.3)** to teach the pathway of blood flow through the heart. **Section 30.1** is an overview of the respiratory and circulatory systems. **Section 30.4** compares the different types of blood vessels and discusses the effects of lifestyle on the circulatory system. **Section 30.6** covers the lymphatic system, which will lead into the study of the immune system in Chapter 31.

CHAPTER 30

Respiratory and Circulatory Systems

KEY CONCEPTS

30.1 Respiratory and Circulatory Functions
The respiratory and circulatory systems bring oxygen and nutrients to the cells.

30.2 Respiration and Gas Exchange
The respiratory system exchanges oxygen and carbon dioxide.

30.3 The Heart and Circulation
The heart is a muscular pump that moves the blood through two pathways.

30.4 Blood Vessels and Transport
The circulatory system transports materials throughout the body.

30.5 Blood
Blood is a complex tissue that transports materials.

30.6 Lymphatic System
The lymphatic system provides another type of circulation in the body.

Online BIOLOGY CLASSZONE.COM

Animated BIOLOGY
View animated chapter concepts.
- How You Breathe
- How the Heart Pumps Blood
- Blood Typing
- Build the Circulatory and Respiratory Systems

BIOZINE
Keep current with biology news.
- News feeds
- Strange Biology
- Careers

RESOURCE CENTER
Get more information on
- Circulatory System
- Blood
- Lymphatic System

Student Activity

Purpose **Model vocal cords to explore a function of breathing not involved with gas exchange.**

Materials (per team)
- 3 different-sized boxes with lids
- 3 equal-sized rubber bands
- scissors

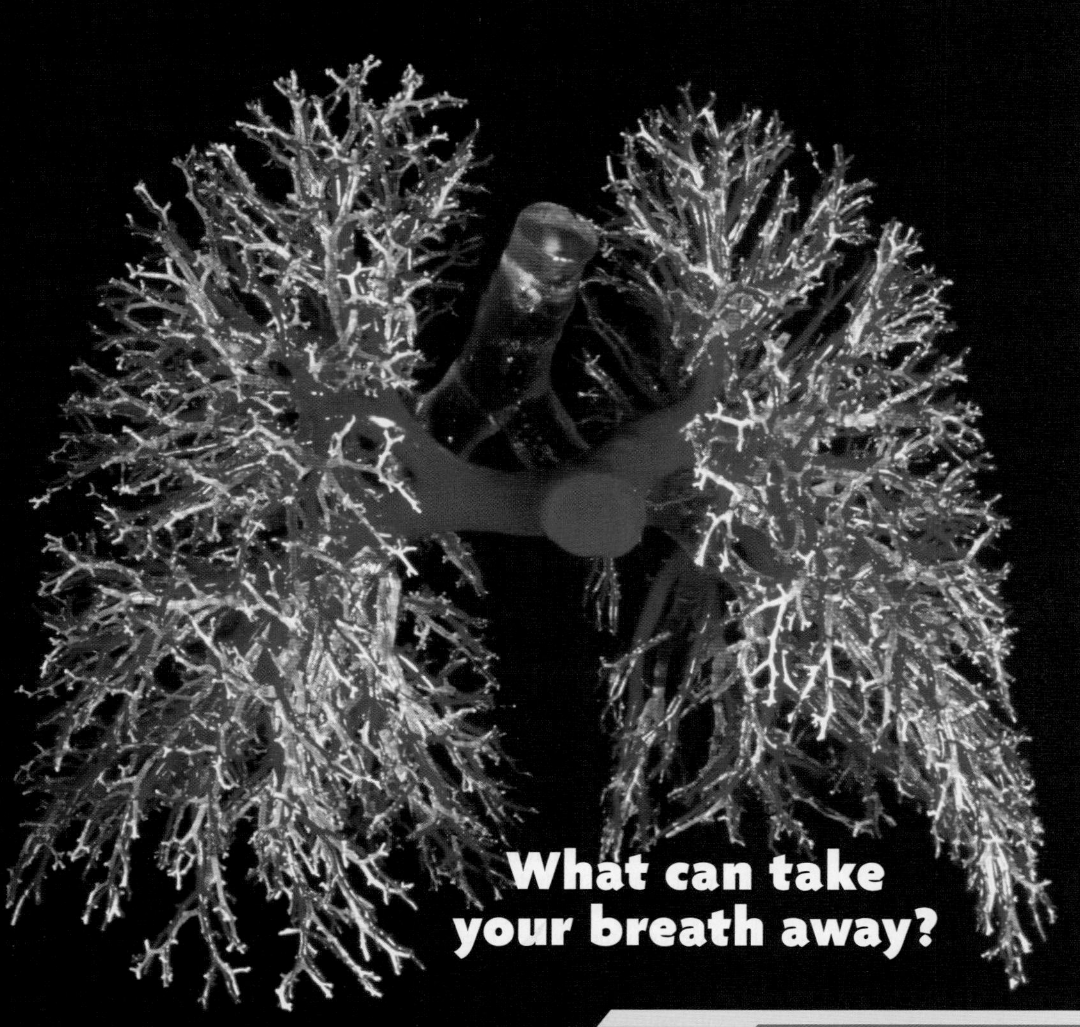
What can take your breath away?

This photograph shows a resin cast of the thousands of vessels that supply blood and air to your lungs. As you take a breath every three to five seconds, this network takes in oxygen and expels carbon dioxide. Pollution, disease, or injury can damage this intricate network, literally taking your breath away.

Connecting CONCEPTS

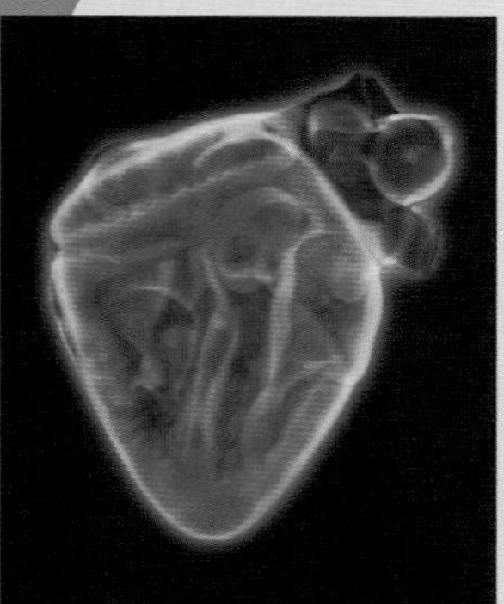

Nervous System The heart shown to the left is a model that has been x-rayed to reveal the inner chambers. Your heart is a muscular pump that moves blood through your body, bringing carbon dioxide to the lungs and picking up oxygen. When your body's needs for oxygen change, signals from the nervous system speed up or slow down your heartbeat and breathing rate.

Introduce Have students cut out a rectangle from each box lid. The openings should be the same proportionally for each lid. Tell students to stretch a rubber band around the length of each box so that the band passes over the cutout in the lid. Have students compare the degrees to which the rubber bands are stretched. Then direct them to pluck each rubber band and compare the sounds produced. **Ask,** Which rubber band produced the highest pitched sound when it vibrated? the one that was stretched the most

Discuss Tell students that the vocal cords are two ligaments that are flexible enough to vibrate and have enough elasticity that pitch can be varied as they are stretched. **Ask,** How do you think the vocal cords produce sound? During exhalation, the force of the air from the lungs rushes past the vocal cords, causing them to vibrate, generating sound. Explain to students that when they begin to speak or make sounds, muscles in the throat stretch the vocal cords, allowing for different-pitched sounds. Usually no sound is made when breathing, because the throat muscles are relaxed.

Activate Prior Knowledge

Have students think about how their chest feels after running or exercising strenuously and then discuss their experiences. Students may say that they feel a tightness in their chests, their hearts are beating faster, and they need to catch their breaths. Explain that these reactions are due to the body's need for energy. **Ask,** What process provides the body with energy? cellular respiration **Ask,** What key material is needed for cellular respiration? oxygen Tell students that increased heart and breathing rates are the body's way of getting oxygen to the parts of the body that need more energy.

Preview Vocabulary

Greek and Latin Word Origins There are numerous vocabulary words in this chapter that have been adopted into the English language either directly or with a slight variation in spelling from Greek or Latin.

trachea, Greek *tracheia,* "rough"

alveoli, Latin *alveus,* "hollow"

atrium, Latin *atrium,* "hall"

ventricle, Latin *ventriculus,* "belly"

lymph, Latin *lympha,* "spring water"

Academic Vocabulary In this chapter, there are several familiar words that relate to the movement of particles in a fluid:

circulate, to move in or flow through a circle or circuit

transport, to carry from one place to another

exchange, to give in return for something received

Blood is *circulated* and *transported* to all parts of the body to allow for the *exchange* of carbon dioxide and oxygen.

English Learners Write the key vocabulary for the chapter on cards. Give students a few minutes to skim the chapter and then have them identify words as belonging to the respiratory or circulatory systems. Arrange the words on the board and come back to them periodically as you go through new material. Suggest students develop cluster diagrams that incorporate these words.

SECTION 30.1

Plan and Prepare

Objectives

- Describe the respiratory system and its functions.
- Describe the circulatory system and its functions.

Section Resources

Unit Resource Book Study Guide pp. 57–58 Power Notes p. 59 Reinforcement p. 60 Pre-AP Activity pp. 83–84
Interactive Reader Chapter 30 **Spanish Study Guide** pp. 301–302
Biology Toolkit p. C34
Technology Power Presentation 30.1 Media Gallery DVD Online Quiz 30.1

Activate Prior Knowledge Remind students that they need a constant supply of oxygen. **Ask,** What is it like to hold your breath for any length of time? difficult to fight the impulse to take a gulp of air Tell students that breathing is the result of the close coordination of the respiratory and circulatory systems.

Teach

Take It Further

The record for holding one's breath, a state called **apnea,** is close to nine minutes. To achieve this, one has to slow the heartbeat considerably. Apnea leads to low levels of oxygen, which can produce **hypoxia.** The body diverts oxygen from the hands and feet to vital organs, usually causing a person to lose consciousness.

Answers

A **Apply** As activity level increases, the breathing and heart rates also increase in order to provide enough energy.

30.1 Respiratory and Circulatory Functions

KEY CONCEPT The respiratory and circulatory systems bring oxygen and nutrients to the cells.

MAIN IDEAS

- The respiratory and circulatory systems work together to maintain homeostasis.
- The respiratory system moves gases into and out of the blood.
- The circulatory system moves blood to all parts of the body.

VOCABULARY

circulatory system, p. 910
respiratory system, p. 910
trachea, p. 911
lung, p. 911
alveoli, p. 911
diaphragm, p. 912
heart, p. 912
artery, p. 913
vein, p. 913
capillary, p. 913

Connect You have thousands of kilometers of blood vessels in your body and several hundred *million* tiny air sacs in your lungs. Blood circulates constantly through the vessels, while air continually fills and empties from the tiny air sacs. Your heart keeps beating and your lungs keep working 24 hours a day, every day of your life. Even more amazing, everything works without your having to think about it.

MAIN IDEA

The respiratory and circulatory systems work together to maintain homeostasis.

Every cell in your body needs nutrients and oxygen to function and needs to get rid of its waste products. The **circulatory system** is the body system that transports blood and other materials. It brings vital supplies to the cells and carries away their wastes. The blood vessels of the circulatory system also keep oxygen-poor blood from mixing with oxygen-rich blood. The **respiratory system** is the body system in which gas exchange takes place. You can think of your respiratory system as a major supply depot where the blood can pick up oxygen (O_2) and deposit excess carbon dioxide (CO_2). The lungs of the respiratory system are the only place in your body where gases in the blood are exchanged with gases from the atmosphere.

The respiratory and circulatory systems work closely together to maintain homeostasis in the face of constant change. Every time you exercise, lie down to rest, or simply stand up, you change your needs for oxygen and nutrients. As a result, your heart speeds up or slows down and you breathe faster or slower, depending on your activity. This section gives you an overview of the major structures of the respiratory and circulatory systems and their functions. Sections 30.2 to 30.5 provide a closer look at the organs of each system, how they work, and what can damage them.

TAKING NOTES

Use a supporting main ideas strategy to help you remember the respiratory and circulatory structures and their functions.

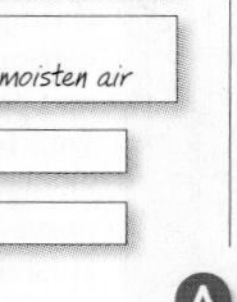

A Apply **When you stand up after lying down, why do your heart rate and breathing rate increase?**

Differentiated Instruction

ENGLISH LEARNERS

Have students create a chart to compare the respiratory and circulatory systems. For each system, students should include boxes labeled *Functions, Organs,* and *Structures.*

Biology Toolkit, Compare/Contrast Chart, p. C34

FIGURE 30.1 Respiratory Organs and Tissues

Specialized structures move air into and out of the body.

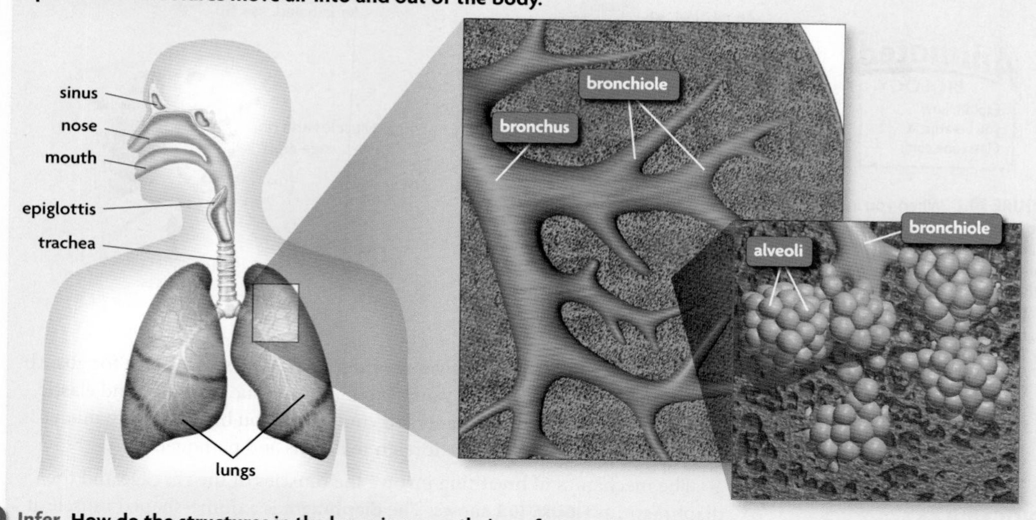

A Infer How do the structures in the lungs increase their surface area?

MAIN IDEA

The respiratory system moves gases into and out of the blood.

The function of the respiratory system is to bring O_2 into the body and to expel CO_2 and water vapor. The structures of this system bring the gases in close contact with the blood, which absorbs O_2. The circulatory system then carries O_2 to all of the body's cells and transports CO_2 from the rest of the body to the lungs, where it is exhaled.

The specialized structures of the respiratory system are shown in **FIGURE 30.1.** The nose and mouth are the entry points to the system. When air enters the nose, mucus that lines the nasal passages warms and moistens the air. The mucus and tiny hairs called cilia help filter dust and pathogens from the air. At the back of the throat, a small piece of tissue, the epiglottis, regulates airflow into the trachea, or windpipe. The **trachea** (TRAY-kee-uh) is a long structure made of soft tissue reinforced with C-shaped rings of cartilage. It resembles the hose of a vacuum cleaner. When you swallow, the epiglottis closes the entrance to the trachea to keep food or saliva from entering the airways. The trachea divides into the two bronchi, with one branch going to each lung.

The **lungs** are the organs that absorb O_2 from the air you inhale. Inside the lungs, the bronchi divide into smaller and smaller branches that resemble the limbs and twigs of a tree. The smallest branches, the bronchioles, end in clusters of tiny air sacs called **alveoli** (al-VEE-uh-LY). One air sac is called an alveolus. The lungs have a huge number of alveoli—from 300 to 600 million.

Connecting CONCEPTS

Cellular Respiration You learned in **Chapter 4** that eukaryotic cells require a constant supply of oxygen to produce ATP, which is the main energy source for cells.

HANDS-ON ACTIVITY

Have students locate their voice box, or larynx, by placing their fingertips on the front of their throats while humming. Point out that they should feel the vibrations caused by air passing over the vocal cords in the larynx. Next, have students place their palms gently over their throats below their chins while swallowing. **Ask,** What movement did you feel? The larynx moved up and down. Explain that the movement of the larynx when swallowing food causes the epiglottis to cover the opening of the trachea, thereby preventing food from entering the trachea.

Ask students to hum a note while pressing gently on the larynx with fingertips at the front of the throat. **Ask,** What did you notice about the note you were humming? The pitch went down. Explain that when they pressed on the larynx, the effect was to shorten the vocal cords, which changes the pitch.

Vocabulary

Greek and Latin Word Origins The **glottis,** which is Greek for "tongue," is the opening of the trachea. The **epiglottis** is a triangular flap of cartilage that covers the opening, the Greek prefix *epi-,* meaning "above."

The word **trachea** in Greek translates as "rough." The reference is to its being a rough vessel when compared to the smooth vessels that carry blood.

Take It Further

The act of **yawning** is commonly thought to be an involuntary action that occurs when the brain stem detects a lack of oxygen and an excess of carbon dioxide in the body. The body responds by opening the mouth wide and deeply inhaling. Dogs, cats, rats, snakes, fish, birds, and humans all yawn. However, the exact cause of a yawn is unknown.

One theory is that the higher the level of neurotransmitters, such as serotonin and dopamine, in the brain, the more we yawn. Whereas the more opiate neurotransmitters present, such as endorphins, the less we yawn.

Some theorize that yawning may be as much a sociological response as a physiological one. People who observe the behavior of apes note when an ape yawns it seems to be communicating to the rest of its group the desire to do something different. Other apes may respond by also yawning, which can result in the apes moving to a different location or engaging in different behaviors.

Answers

A Infer The millions of tiny alveoli provide more surface area for gas exchange to take place.

▼ Teach *continued*

TEACH FROM VISUALS

FIGURE 30.2 Describe the diagrams.

Left diagram: Muscles of the rib cage contract. This pulls the rib cage up and out. At the same time, the diaphragm contracts and flattens out. **Ask,** What is the effect of these movements on the chest cavity and lungs? The chest cavity increases in size. Air pressure is greater outside the body than inside the chest; therefore, air flows into the lungs.

Right diagram: Diaphragm relaxes and resumes its domelike shape. Muscles of the rib cage relax. This pulls the rib cage down and in. **Ask,** What is the effect of these movements on the chest cavity and lungs? The chest cavity decreases in size; pressure is greater inside the chest, forcing air out of the lungs. Point out that the level of activity influences how much the rib cage muscles have to work. At rest, the diaphragm does most of the work.

History of Science

In 1628, **William Harvey** published *An Anatomical Study of the Motion of the Heart and of the Blood in Animal.* He was the first person to demonstrate the function of the **heart** and the complete **circulation** of the blood. Harvey performed animal dissections and experiments that confirmed that arteries carry blood away from the heart, and veins carry blood to the heart. When he tied off an artery, he noticed that the bulge that resulted was always located between the heart and the blockage. When he tied off a vein, the bulge was always on the side farthest from the heart.

Answers

A Predict Oxygen levels might decrease because alveoli are the main sites of gas exchange in the body.

Animated
BIOLOGY
Explore how you breathe at ClassZone.com.

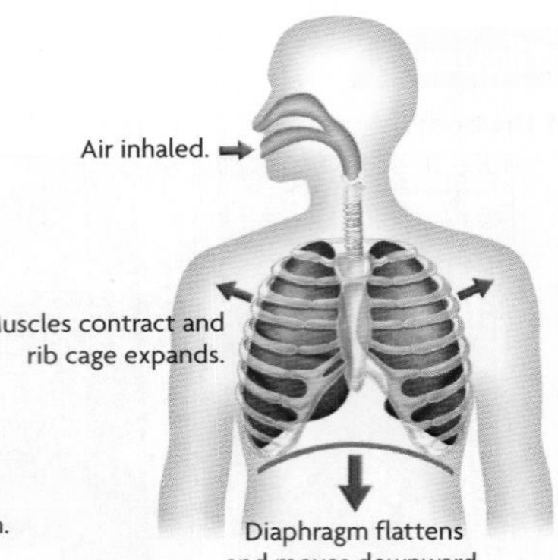

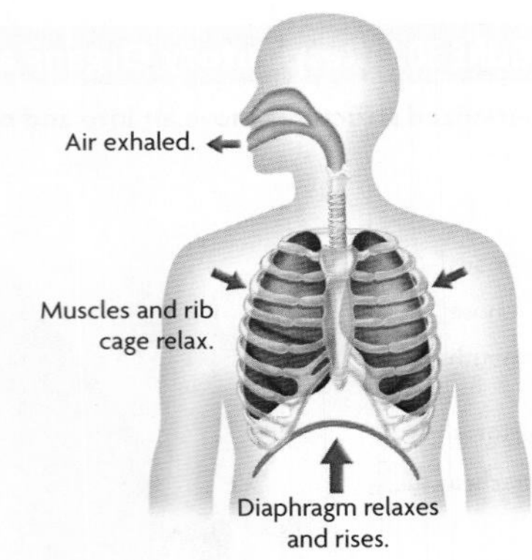

Air inhaled.
Muscles contract and rib cage expands.

FIGURE 30.2 When you inhale, movements of the rib cage and diaphragm produce lower pressure in the lungs, and air flows in. When you exhale, rib cage and diaphragm movements produce higher pressure in the lungs, and air flows out.

This huge number of alveoli gives the lungs a massive surface area for absorbing O_2 and releasing CO_2 and water vapor. Lung tissue is spongy and elastic, which allows the lungs to expand and contract as you breathe. Lung mucus and cilia help trap and remove foreign materials and pathogens.

The mechanics of breathing involve the muscles of the rib cage and the diaphragm, as **FIGURE 30.2** shows. The **diaphragm** is a dome-shaped muscle at the base of the rib cage. When you inhale, the muscles of the rib cage contract, causing the rib cage to expand. The diaphragm then flattens and moves downward. The volume of your lungs increases, and the air pressure decreases, falling below the air pressure outside your body. Gases move from areas of greater pressure to areas of lower pressure, so air flows into the lungs.

VOCABULARY

The word *diaphragm* is based on the Latin *diaphragma,* which means "midriff." The midriff extends from below the breast to the waist. The diaphragm is located in this area.

When you exhale, the rib cage muscles relax, and the rib cage becomes smaller. The diaphragm also relaxes, causing it to rise and regain its domelike shape. Now the air pressure inside your lungs is greater than the air pressure outside your body, so air flows out.

A Predict How might damaged alveoli affect the oxygen level in the blood?

MAIN IDEA

The circulatory system moves blood to all parts of the body.

The function of the circulatory system is to transport O_2 and nutrients to body cells and to carry oxygen-poor blood and CO_2 back to the heart and lungs. To do its job, the system must keep blood constantly circulating.

The main parts of the circulatory system are the heart, the blood, and the blood vessels. The **heart** is a muscular pump, about the size of your fist, that keeps the blood moving to every part of the body. The blood circulates through a closed system—that is, blood in the circulatory system stays inside the vessels. The average adult body contains about 5 liters (more than 5 qt) of blood. On average, your blood circulates from your heart, throughout your body, and back to your heart about every 60 seconds.

Differentiated Instruction

BELOW LEVEL

Model the role of air pressure in inhalation and exhalation. Use a balloon and a clear-plastic, dish-detergent bottle with a flip-lid cap. While a volunteer squeezes the bottle, insert the balloon into the bottle and pull the open end of the balloon over the rim and screw the cap in place, flip lid open. Tell the volunteer to stop squeezing the bottle. When the bottle is released, air pressure inside the bottle decreases, and the balloon fills with air.

The circulatory system has three types of blood vessels: arteries, veins, and capillaries. **Arteries** are blood vessels that carry blood away from the heart to the rest of the body. **Veins** are blood vessels that carry blood from the rest of the body back to the heart. As illustrated in **FIGURE 30.3**, arteries carry oxygen-rich blood (red) and veins carry oxygen-poor blood (blue). Blue is used for illustration purposes only. In your body, oxygen-poor blood is not actually blue but a darker red color. You can think of arteries and veins as a system of roads. Large arteries and veins are like major highways. Smaller arteries and veins are like streets that route traffic through local neighborhoods.

Arteries and veins are connected by a system of capillaries. **Capillaries** are the tiny blood vessels that transport blood to and from the cells of the body. These vessels are so small that blood cells must move through them in single file. The walls of these tiny blood vessels are only one cell thick. Materials can easily diffuse into and out of them.

In addition to transporting vital supplies to the cells, the circulatory system performs two other important functions that maintain homeostasis.

- The circulatory system collects waste materials produced by digestion and cell metabolism, and delivers them to the liver and kidneys to be filtered out of the body. For example, muscle cell activity produces a waste product known as urea. As blood moves past the muscle cells, urea is moved into the bloodstream and carried to the kidneys to be excreted.
- The circulatory system helps maintain body temperature by distributing the heat that cells produce in the muscles and internal organs. When you are active, your organs and muscles produce more heat. The heart pumps harder, and the blood vessels dilate to bring excess heat to the skin, where it can escape. In cold weather, the blood vessels constrict to conserve heat.

The heart, the blood vessels, and the blood are described in more detail in Sections 30.3 to 30.5.

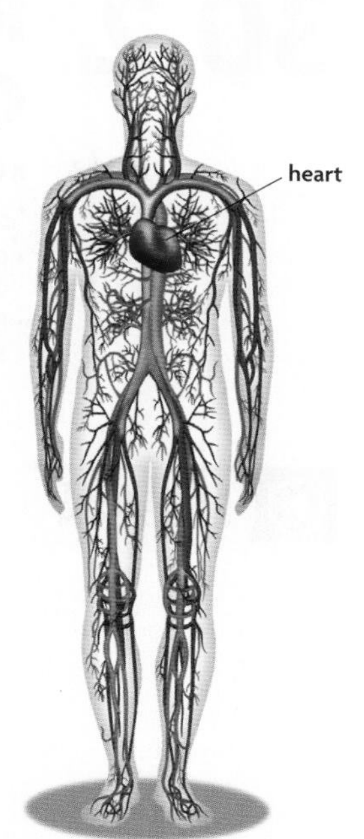

FIGURE 30.3 The circulatory system is composed of the heart, arteries carrying oxygen-rich blood (red), veins carrying oxygen-poor blood (blue), and capillaries.

A Infer If a person has a weak heart, how might his or her ability to maintain a stable body temperature be affected?

ONLINE BIOLOGY Have students view an interactive animation on the circulatory and respiratory systems. See Options for Inquiry on page 933.

Science Trivia

- The total length of all the capillaries in an adult human is approximately 40,000 km (about 25,000 mi).
- Blood vessels in a blue whale are so wide that a full-grown trout could swim through them.

Answers

A Infer Blood may not circulate efficiently in the body and would be less able to carry excess heat to the skin or to keep arms and legs warm in cold weather.

30.1 ASSESSMENT

ONLINE QUIZ ClassZone.com

REVIEWING MAIN IDEAS

1. How do the **respiratory** and **circulatory systems** help maintain homeostasis in the body?
2. List the main parts and functions of the respiratory system.
3. Describe the basic parts and functions of the circulatory system.

CRITICAL THINKING

4. **Apply** Why can't you breathe through the mouth while you are swallowing food? What would happen if you could do this?
5. **Infer** **Arteries** and **veins** are equally distributed throughout the body. How does this arrangement help to maintain the functions of each cell?

***Connecting* CONCEPTS**

6. **Science and Technology** A mechanical ventilator breathes for a paralyzed person. During inhalation, the machine forces air under pressure into the **lungs.** During exhalation, the pressure drops and air moves out of the lungs. How does this machine compare with natural breathing?

Assess and Reteach ▼

Assess Use the Online Quiz or Section Quiz (*Assessment Book*, p. 591).

Reteach List on the board the main structures of the respiratory and circulatory systems. Have students tell you what to write for the function of each.

30.1 ASSESSMENT

1. Changes in activity level are matched by an increase or decrease in heart and breathing rates to maintain homeostasis.
2. The nose and mouth are entry points; epiglottis protects the trachea from accidental blockage by food; trachea is the major airway to the lungs; lungs are paired organs that absorb oxygen and exhale carbon dioxide; bronchi and bronchioles are smaller airways; alveoli are main sites of gas exchange.
3. The heart is a muscular pump; arteries move blood from the heart; veins move blood to the heart; capillaries transport materials to and from the larger blood vessels to supply the cells.
4. Breathing is prevented by the epiglottis closing off the trachea when you swallow. Otherwise, food could block the airway or be inhaled into the lungs.
5. It allows the circulatory system to carry nutrients and oxygen to each cell and carry away carbon dioxide and waste products to maintain cell function.
6. The machine's pressure changes are the opposite of natural breathing. During inhalation, the machine creates positive pressure to push air into the lungs. In natural breathing, the chest expands, creating lower pressure. During exhalation, the machine stops, pressure drops, and air flows out of the lungs. In natural breathing, the chest relaxes, increasing pressure in the lungs, and air flows out.

SECTION 30.2

▼ Plan and Prepare

Objectives

- Summarize gas exchange in the lungs.
- Describe how respiratory diseases interfere with gas exchange.

Section Resources

Unit Resource Book
Study Guide pp. 61–62
Power Notes p. 63
Reinforcement p. 64

Interactive Reader Chapter 30
Spanish Study Guide pp. 303–304

Biology Toolkit pp. C23, C39, C40

Technology
Power Presentation 30.2
Media Gallery DVD
Online Quiz 30.2

Activate Prior Knowledge Have students visualize a crowded bus stop and what happens when an empty bus pulls up. **Ask**

- How does the concentration of people at a crowded bus stop compare to an almost empty bus? high concentration; low concentration
- When the bus doors open, how do the people respond? move from an area of high to low concentration
- What scientific term could you use to describe this action? diffusion

▼ Teach

TEACH FROM VISUALS

FIGURE 30.4 Direct students' attention to the numerous alveoli surrounding the single bronchiole. Remind students that the lungs contain more than 300–600 million alveoli. If the surface of the lungs were laid out flat, it would cover a tennis court. **Ask,** Why are a large number of alveoli an advantage? The alveoli provide a tremendous surface area for gas exchange, which allows a constant, adequate supply of oxygen to get to the body cells.

30.2 Respiration and Gas Exchange

KEY CONCEPT The respiratory system exchanges oxygen and carbon dioxide.

MAIN IDEAS

- Gas exchange occurs in the alveoli of the lungs.
- Respiratory diseases interfere with gas exchange.

VOCABULARY

red blood cell, p. 915
hemoglobin, p. 915
emphysema, p. 916
asthma, p. 916

Review
alveoli, lung, capillary, diffusion

Connect Nearly every winter, newspapers carry stories of people killed by carbon monoxide (CO) gas in their homes. This colorless, odorless gas escapes from leaks in furnaces that burn fossil fuels. What makes CO so deadly? Your body readily absorbs it into the blood, which means less O_2 is absorbed. Within a short time, your cells become oxygen starved. You must quickly get to an area where you can breathe fresh air.

MAIN IDEA

Gas exchange occurs in the alveoli of the lungs.

Recall that the cells in your body carry out cellular respiration, which requires O_2 and produces CO_2 as a waste product. Thus, every cell in the body needs O_2 and must get rid of CO_2. However, the alveoli and their capillaries are the only places where gas exchange with the atmosphere occurs. The lungs bring in a steady supply of O_2 and expel excess CO_2. Gas exchange in the lungs is based on three principles:

- O_2 and CO_2 are carried by the blood.
- Gases move by diffusion—that is, they move from an area of higher concentration to an area of lower concentration.
- The lining of the alveoli must be moist to help gases diffuse.

FIGURE 30.4 This micrograph shows a bronchiole and several alveoli. Alveoli walls are about one cell thick, which allows O_2 and CO_2 to diffuse easily across them. (colored SEM; magnification 150×)

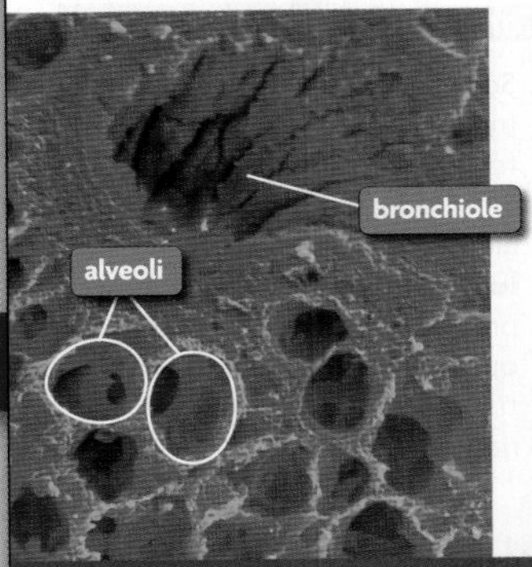

Diffusion of O_2 and CO_2

In the alveoli, the respiratory and circulatory systems come together in the process of gas exchange. When you inhale, air flows from the bronchi to the bronchioles and finally to the alveoli. A cross-section of a bronchiole and several alveoli is shown in **FIGURE 30.4.** Each alveolus is about the size of a grain of sand, but all of the alveoli together give the lungs a surface area of about 100 square meters. Without this huge area for gas exchange, the lungs would be unable to extract enough O_2 from the air to keep you alive.

A complex network of capillaries surrounds and penetrates the alveoli, as shown in **FIGURE 30.5.** Blood entering these capillaries contains a lower concentration of O_2 than does the air in the alveoli. As a result, the O_2 diffuses from an area of high concentration in the alveoli to an area of low concentration in

Differentiated Instruction

BELOW LEVEL

To help students review the movement of oxygen from the environment to the lungs and the movement of carbon dioxide from the lungs to the environment, have them draw a cycle diagram and then annotate it with notes, including the following:

- inhalation (nose and mouth)
- air containing oxygen (trachea, bronchi, bronchioles)
- oxygen exchanged for carbon dioxide (alveoli)
- carbon dioxide (bronchioles, bronchi, trachea)
- exhalation (nose and mouth)

Biology Toolkit, Cycle Diagram, p. C39; Combination Notes, p. C23

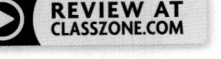

FIGURE 30.5 Gas Exchange in the Alveoli

Diffusion of gases into and out of the alveoli maintains O_2 and CO_2 homeostasis.

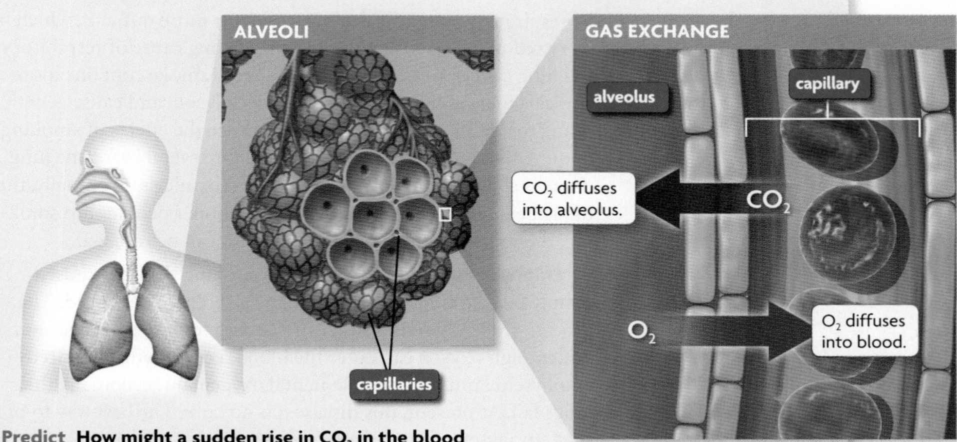

A Predict How might a sudden rise in CO_2 in the blood affect the gas exchange process?

the capillaries. The blood in the capillaries contain **red blood cells,** a type of cell that picks up oxygen in the lungs and delivers it to all of the body's cells. In red blood cells, most of the O_2 molecules bind to an iron-rich protein called **hemoglobin** (HEE-muh-GLOH-bihn). Each molecule of hemoglobin binds with four O_2 molecules. The iron in hemoglobin is what gives blood its reddish color. Blood becomes bright red only when it absorbs oxygen. The blood leaving the alveoli carries almost three times the amount of O_2 that it had coming into the lungs.

In contrast, CO_2 concentrations are higher in the blood than in the alveoli. As a result, CO_2 diffuses into the alveoli. The higher concentration of CO_2 in the blood is due to the fact that every cell produces CO_2 and water as waste products. The CO_2 and water combine in the blood to form the compound carbonic acid. The more carbonic acid there is in the blood, the more acidic the blood becomes. When carbonic acid diffuses into the alveoli, the compound separates into CO_2 and water, which are exhaled.

Gas Exchange and the Nervous System

Gas exchange is so critical to the body that it is an autonomic function regulated by the medulla and pons in the brain stem. These centers monitor dissolved gases in the blood, particularly CO_2 concentrations. As you become more active, CO_2 levels increase and the blood becomes more acidic. Sensors in the respiratory and circulatory systems signal this change to the brain stem. The medulla sends messages through the nervous and endocrine systems that stimulate the diaphragm and rib cage muscles to work harder. The medulla regulates how often and how deeply you breathe based on your activity.

B Analyze How does the alveoli's structure relate to the function of gas exchange?

Connecting **CONCEPTS**

Nervous System As you read in **Chapter 29**, the brain stem is located at the base of the brain. The brain stem is involved in regulating breathing and other autonomic functions that help maintain homeostasis.

PRE-AP

Have students make a concept map to compare the functions of the circulatory, respiratory, and nervous systems in gas exchange. To get students started, have them consider these questions:

- How is breathing initiated?
- How is respiration rate regulated?
- Which system is responsible for delivering oxygen to cells?
- How does exercise affect the function of each system?

Biology Toolkit, Concept Map, p. C40

TEACH FROM VISUALS

FIGURE 30.5 Refer students to the diagram showing gas exchange in the lungs. **Ask,** Why does oxygen diffuse from the alveolus into the capillary? Why does carbon dioxide diffuse in the opposite direction? Oxygen concentration is higher in the alveolus than in the capillary; carbon dioxide concentration is greater in the capillary than in the alveolus.

The Inside Story

Garrett A. Morgan was the son of former slaves whose formal education never went beyond elementary school. With hard work and an inventive mind, he went on to become an inventor and businessman. In 1914, Morgan invented the **gas mask.** The mask consisted of a hood with two attached tubes. One tube extended to the ground and was plugged with an absorbent material that filtered the inhaled air. Exhaled air was released through the second tube.

In 1916, an explosion in an underground tunnel below Lake Erie trapped 32 men in debris, dust, and smoke. Morgan and some volunteers used his gas mask to rescue the men. Morgan's gas mask was refined for use by the U.S. Army during World War I and saved hundreds of American soldiers.

Answers

A Predict The rate of gas exchange would increase to bring more oxygen into the alveoli.

B Analyze Being surrounded by capillaries and only one cell thick allows for easy diffusion between the alveoli and capillaries.

▼ Teach continued

ONLINE BIOLOGY To have students learn more about the causes of asthma, have them do the WebQuest in Options for Inquiry on page 933.

Integrating Medical Science

The rewards for **quitting smoking** are immediate. After the last cigarette, the following happens to the body:
20 minutes after: Blood pressure, heart rate, body temperature drop to normal.
8 hours after: Carbon monoxide and oxygen levels in blood return to normal.
24 hours after: Chance of heart attack decreases.
48 hours after: Nerve endings start to regrow.
72 hours after: Bronchial tubes relax, and lung volume increases.
2 weeks to 3 months after: Circulation improves, walking is easier, and lung function increases up to 30 percent.
1 to 9 months after: Cilia in lungs begin to heal, reducing infection.
5 years after: Lung cancer death rate for an average smoker drops almost as low as the rate of a nonsmoker.

Answers

A Synthesize Chemicals from tobacco smoke damage alveoli, reducing surface area and decreasing the lungs' ability to absorb oxygen and expel carbon dioxide.

▼ Assess and Reteach

Assess Use the Online Quiz or Section Quiz (*Assessment Book,* p. 592).

Reteach Assign students to groups of four. Have each group make a word-search puzzle using words related to the content of this section. Distribute the puzzles to the other groups to solve.

MAIN IDEA

Respiratory diseases interfere with gas exchange.

FIGURE 30.6 Healthy lung tissue is free of any deposits. When a person smokes for several years, black tar deposits first invade and then choke the tissue, and greatly reduce gas exchange. (LM; magnification 250×)

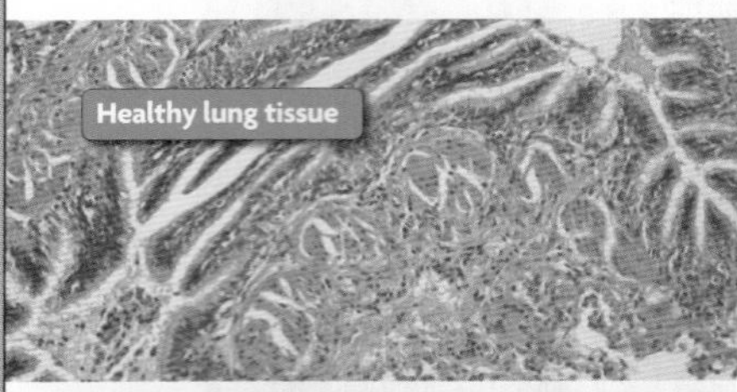

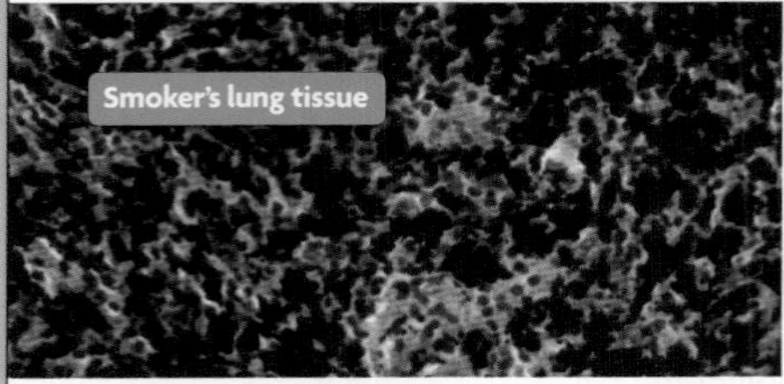

NSTA SCILINKS scilinks.org
For more information on the respiratory system, go to scilinks.org.
Keycode: MLB030

Damage to the respiratory system makes gas exchange more difficult, which in turn affects every cell in the body. Smoking is the leading cause of respiratory diseases such as lung cancer and emphysema. Tobacco smoke contains more than 4800 chemicals that can paralyze cilia, damage alveoli, and cause genetic mutations leading to cancer. In **FIGURE 30.6,** you can see the effects of smoking on lung tissue. When a person smokes for several years, the lung tissue is slowly coated by tars and other chemicals. Eventually, the tissue becomes almost solid black. The sooner people stop smoking, the sooner such damage to the lungs can be reversed.

Emphysema (EHM-fih-SEE-muh) is a lung disorder caused mainly by smoking. Over time, many alveoli are destroyed. This process gradually reduces the surface area for gas exchange, and not enough oxygen can enter the blood. People with advanced emphysema must use supplemental oxygen, but eventually their lungs fail. At present, this disease has no cure. The best way to prevent emphysema is to refrain from smoking.

Asthma (AZ-muh) causes the bronchioles to constrict due to muscle spasms. This condition makes it hard to move air in and out of the lungs. A person having a severe asthma attack can die from lack of oxygen. Attacks may be triggered by allergies, stress, exposure to smoke and chemicals, or exercise. The attacks can be relieved by drugs that relax the bronchioles.

Cystic fibrosis (CF) is a genetic disease that causes the lungs to produce a thick, sticky mucus. This mucus blocks the airways and allows microorganisms to thrive in the lungs. People with CF have frequent, sometimes fatal, lung infections. Treatments focus on preventing the mucus from building up.

A Synthesize How does smoking affect gas exchange?

30.2 ASSESSMENT

ONLINE QUIZ ClassZone.com

REVIEWING MAIN IDEAS

1. Explain how diffusion allows gases to move into and out of the alveoli of the lungs. Use the term **red blood cell** in your explanation.
2. In what ways can respiratory diseases reduce the level of O_2 in the blood?

CRITICAL THINKING

3. **Synthesize** Explain how your breathing rate would change if your blood became more acidic.
4. **Apply** People poisoned by CO are often given 100 percent O_2 in a room with two to three times normal atmospheric pressure. Explain why more oxygen would enter their blood under these conditions.

Connecting CONCEPTS

5. **Forensic Science** When police find a body in a lake or river, they must determine if the person was drowned or was killed in some other way and then thrown into the water. How would examining the lungs of the person help them to solve the mystery?

30.2 ASSESSMENT

1. As carbon dioxide concentration increases in the capillaries, the gas diffuses into the alveoli. As oxygen concentration increases in the alveoli, the gas diffuses into the capillaries, where oxygen molecules bind to hemoglobin in the red blood cells.
2. Respiratory diseases can damage the alveoli, constrict airways to prevent airflow, and block airways with mucus.
3. When carbon dioxide levels increase and carbonic acid forms in the blood, the nervous system signals the circulatory and respiratory systems to increase breathing and heart rates to bring more oxygen into the body and expel carbon dioxide faster.
4. First, 100 percent oxygen gas makes far more oxygen available in the lungs for diffusion. Second, the more pressure a gas is under, the more of it dissolves in fluid. As a result, more oxygen would be forced into the blood.
5. People who die by drowning always have water in their lungs. People can hold their breath underwater for a few minutes, but then begin breathing again, inhaling water instead of air.

30.3 The Heart and Circulation

KEY CONCEPT The heart is a muscular pump that moves the blood through two pathways.

MAIN IDEAS
- The tissues and structures of the heart make it an efficient pump.
- The heart pumps blood through two main pathways.

VOCABULARY
atrium, p. 917
ventricle, p. 917
valve, p. 917
pacemaker, p. 918
pulmonary circulation, p. 920
systemic circulation, p. 920

Review
heart, artery, vein

Connect *Lub-dub, lub-dub.* This is the sound of your heart beating. The *lub* sound occurs when the valves between the upper and lower chambers of the heart snap shut. The *dub* sound is made by valves closing the two arteries that carry blood out of the heart. If a valve does not close properly and allows blood to leak backward, the sound of the heart changes. A heart with a leaky valve might sound like this: *Lub-dub-shhh, lub-dub-shhh.* The sounds your heart makes can tell a physician a great deal about how it is performing.

MAIN IDEA

The tissues and structures of the heart make it an efficient pump.

Each day your heart beats about 100,000 times, circulating blood through nearly 96,000 kilometers of blood vessels—roughly one-quarter of the distance to the moon. Over 70 years, your heart will beat about 2.5 *billion* times. How can it keep going? One reason is that cardiac muscle tissue, unlike skeletal muscle tissue, can work continuously without becoming tired. Also, the structures of the heart make this organ an efficient pump.

FIGURE 30.7 HEART CHAMBERS AND VALVES

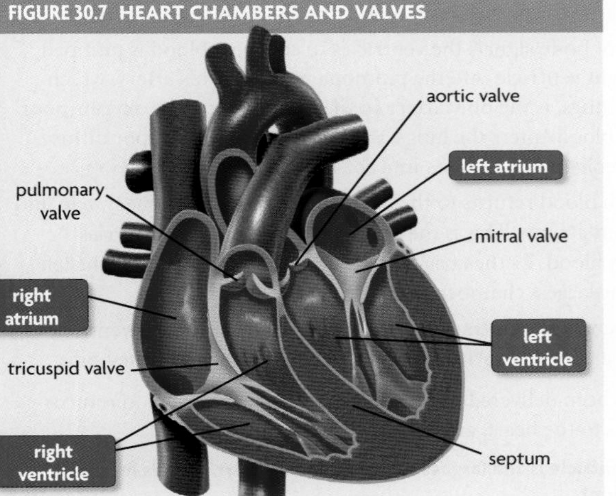

Structures of the Heart

The largest structures in your heart are the four chambers. As shown in **FIGURE 30.7**, the two smaller chambers are the right **atrium** and left atrium (plural, *atria*), and the two larger chambers are the right and left **ventricles.** The ventricles are separated by the septum, a thick wall of tissue. The heart **valves** are flaps of tissue that prevent blood from flowing backward. They open when the atria or ventricles contract, and close when the atria or ventricles relax.

After blood fills a chamber, the cardiac muscle contracts and pumps the blood out of the chamber. The heart is an amazingly powerful pump.

Plan and Prepare

Objectives
- Describe the structure and function of the heart.
- Contrast pulmonary and systemic circulation.

Section Resources

Unit Resource Book
Study Guide pp. 65–66
Power Notes p. 67
Reinforcement p. 68

Interactive Reader Chapter 30
Spanish Study Guide pp. 305–306

Biology Toolkit pp. C7, C17, C39, D5

Technology
Power Presentation 30.3
Media Gallery DVD
Online Quiz 30.3

Activate Prior Knowledge Explain to students that there are two types of circulatory systems—open and closed. Explain that in an open circulatory system, the heart would pump blood or a nutrient fluid into body cavities, directly to cells. In a closed circulatory system, the heart pumps blood through a continuous system of vessels in close contact with cells. **Ask,** Why is a closed system required for vertebrates, such as humans? The large size of the organisms requires a more efficient way to transport materials to and from cells.

Teach

TEACH FROM VISUALS

FIGURE 30.7 Have students compare the thicknesses of the walls of the atria and ventricles. **Ask,** How can the muscle layer in the chamber walls provide a clue as to which chamber of the heart pumps blood with the most force? left ventricle, because its muscular walls are thicker

Differentiated Instruction

ENGLISH LEARNERS

Suggest students use word squares for the structures discussed in this section. The vocabulary term is placed at the center of a 2 × 2 matrix. The first two cells should include a definition and characteristics. For the third square have students include the system involved, and, for the fourth, describe what might happen if the structure malfunctioned.

Biology Toolkit, Frayer Model, p. D5

BELOW LEVEL

Have students use the PLAN strategy to organize the material in this section:

- Predict what each subsection covers, focusing on the main ideas.
- Locate key vocabulary.
- Add details and definitions while reading.
- Note how the text supports the main ideas.

Biology Toolkit, PLAN, p. C7

▼ Teach *continued*

Integrating Medical Science

A defect in the heart can cause an irregular heart rhythm, or **arrhythmia.** In some cases, the atrial and ventricular contractions get badly out of sync. Any uncoordinated contraction of muscle fibers that prevents the smooth contraction of a muscle is called **fibrillation.** With the contractions of the heart muscles out of phase, the heart can no longer pump blood, circulation stops, and brain death occurs. By exposing the heart to a strong electric shock, the heart can in effect "reboot" and reestablish a normal rhythm. This process is called **defibrillation.**

An **artificial pacemaker** can be permanently implanted into the heart if a person's SA node is damaged. This small, battery-operated device helps the heart maintain regular contractions. An electrode is placed next to the heart wall, and small electrical charges travel through a wire to the heart. Most pacemakers are **demand pacemakers.** They have a sensing device that delivers impulses only when the SA node is not properly transmitting on its own. **Rate-responsive pacemakers** are capable of increasing the heart rate during periods of exercise.

Answers

A Analyze The larger volume and more muscle tissue exert enough force to propel blood throughout the body.

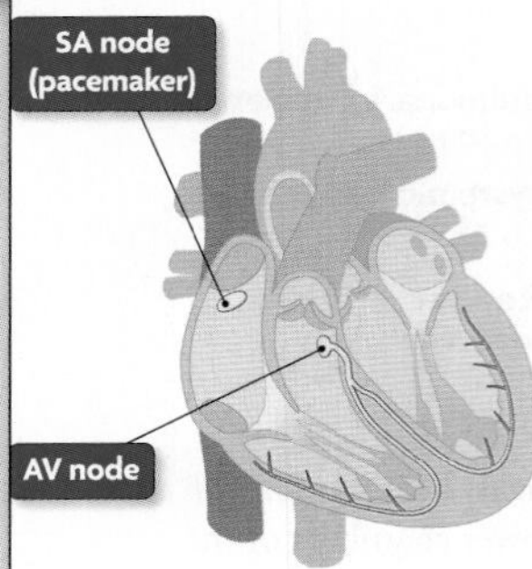

FIGURE 30.8 An electrical signal from the SA node causes both atria to contract. The AV node then picks up the signal and transmits it to both ventricles, causing them to contract.

The reason has to do with the small size of the heart, which allows the strong cardiac muscles to exert a great deal of force on the chamber. The combination of small size and large force results in a powerful pumping action. The heart is also an efficient, self-regulating pump. It can respond to signals from the nervous system to change the speed and force of its pumping action. For example, if you increase your level of activity, your heart will pump faster.

The Heartbeat

The heartbeat consists of two contractions: the first takes place in the atria and the second in the ventricles. The contractions occur partly because the cardiac muscle fibers of the chambers have a unique property. Whenever one fiber is stimulated to contract, all of the fibers contract at the same time.

The first contraction of the heart begins in the right atrium at a signal from the sinoatrial (SA) node, shown in **FIGURE 30.8.** The SA node is known as the heart's **pacemaker** because the cells in this node generate an electrical signal that starts the wave of contractions. Once the atria have contracted, the electrical signal spreads through conducting fibers to the atrioventricular (AV) node, located in the wall of the right ventricle. The AV signal stimulates both ventricles to contract at the same time.

If the SA node is seriously damaged by injury or disease, it can be replaced with an artificial pacemaker that is implanted into the heart. This device, like the SA node, sends electrical signals to the muscle fibers of the atria.

Blood Flow in the Heart

Once you know the basic structures and actions of the heart, you can follow how oxygen-rich and oxygen-poor blood flow through this organ. Study **FIGURE 30.9,** which illustrates this pathway. Notice that blood always enters the heart through an atrium and leaves the heart through a ventricle. The contractions of the atria and then of the ventricles keep blood moving in this sequence.

1. Oxygen-poor blood from the body enters the right atrium. The SA node signals the atria to contract, and blood flows into the right ventricle.
2. When the AV node signals the ventricles to contract, blood is pumped from the right ventricle into the pulmonary artery. This artery, which goes to the lungs, is the only artery in the body that carries oxygen-poor blood. The blood enters the lungs, where CO_2 and water vapor diffuse into the alveoli and O_2 diffuses into the blood.
3. Oxygen-rich blood returns to the heart through the pulmonary vein and enters the left atrium. This is the only vein in the body that carries oxygen-rich blood. As the atria contract, blood is pumped into the left ventricle, the largest chamber in the heart.
4. When the ventricles contract, blood is pumped from the left ventricle into a large artery, the aorta, and is circulated to the rest of the body.

After oxygen has been delivered to the cells, the oxygen-poor blood returns through the veins to the heart, and the sequence begins again.

A Analyze The left ventricle is the largest chamber of the heart. How is its size related to its function?

VOCABULARY

The word *pulmonary* comes from the Latin root *pulmo*, meaning "lung." The suffix *-ary* means "belonging to or connected with." Therefore, *pulmonary* means something "belonging to or connected with the lung."

Differentiated Instruction

TEACH WITH TECHNOLOGY

Display the electrocardiogram of a healthy heart. A normal electrocardiogram shows three waves. Explain that the first wave, called the *P wave,* indicates the sinoatrial node firing. The second wave, called the *QRS wave,* indicates the atrioventricular node firing. The third wave, called the *T wave,* represents relaxation of the ventricles. The *Lab Binder* includes a probeware lab on monitoring an EKG, Human Bio, pp. 104–107.

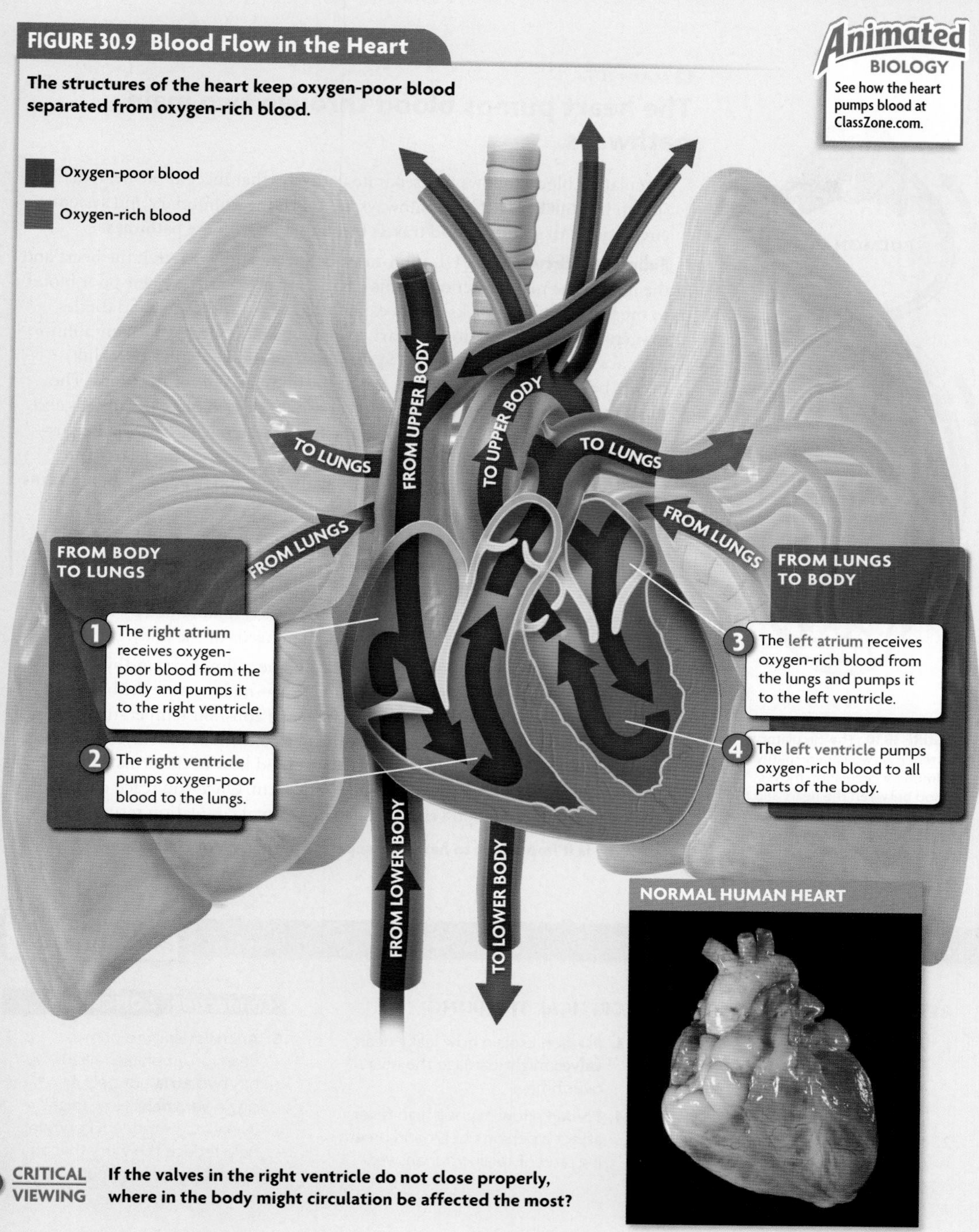
Animated BIOLOGY
See how the heart pumps blood at ClassZone.com.
Oxygen-poor blood
Oxygen-rich blood
TO LUNGS
FROM LUNGS
FROM UPPER BODY
TO UPPER BODY
TO LUNGS
FROM LUNGS
FROM BODY TO LUNGS
1 The right atrium receives oxygen-poor blood from the body and pumps it to the right ventricle.
2 The right ventricle pumps oxygen-poor blood to the lungs.
FROM LUNGS TO BODY
3 The left atrium receives oxygen-rich blood from the lungs and pumps it to the left ventricle.
4 The left ventricle pumps oxygen-rich blood to all parts of the body.
FROM LOWER BODY
TO LOWER BODY
NORMAL HUMAN HEART

FIGURE 30.9 Blood Flow in the Heart

The structures of the heart keep oxygen-poor blood separated from oxygen-rich blood.

A **CRITICAL VIEWING** **If the valves in the right ventricle do not close properly, where in the body might circulation be affected the most?**

Take It Further

Blood moves in the body from an area of highest pressure when it leaves the ventricles to an area of lowest pressure when it empties into the atria. **Blood pressure** is determined by heart rate, volume of blood, and resistance to the flow of blood in the blood vessels. If any of these factors increases, blood pressure increases.

Science Trivia

- The first heartbeat in a human embryo occurs about four to five weeks after conception.
- The diameter of the aorta is almost the same as that of the average garden hose.
- The heart can perform enough work in an hour to lift 3000 pounds (a small car) one foot off the ground.
- The leading cause of death in the United States is heart disease.

Answers

A **Critical Viewing** If the pulmonary valve does not close properly, then circulation to the lungs would be affected the most.

PRE-AP

Using the heart diagram at the center of **FIGURE 30.9** as a guide, have students draw the cardiac cycle, a series of four diagrams showing blood flow through the heart. Diagrams should show the position of the valves and the location and movement of blood in the four chambers. Tell students to follow the list shown on page 918.

Biology Toolkit, Cycle Diagram, p. C39

ENGLISH LEARNERS

Walk students through the cycle shown in **FIGURE 30.9,** helping them visualize the steps shown. Have them think about what they would see, feel, and hear as the heart's chambers contract and relax, and valves open and close.

Biology Toolkit, Connect to Content through Visuals, p. C17

▼ Teach *continued*

TEACH FROM VISUALS

FIGURE 30.10 Emphasize to students that the heart has its own supply of blood vessels that provide the heart with nutrients and oxygen and remove wastes. The heart has arteries, veins, and capillaries within the heart muscle.

Answers

A Infer Having two separate pathways prevents the oxygen-poor blood of the pulmonary system from mixing with the oxygen-rich blood of the systemic system.

▼ Assess and Reteach

Assess Use the Online Quiz or Section Quiz (*Assessment Book,* p. 593).

Reteach Provide pairs of students with a cross section of a heart, and red and blue markers or colored pencils. Have students draw arrows to show the pathway of blood into, within, and out of the heart, using blue for oxygen-poor blood and red for oxygen-rich blood. Students should also label the heart's atria, valves, and ventricles.

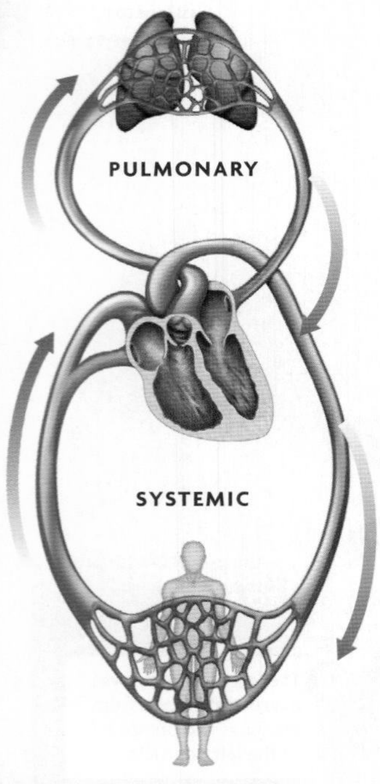

FIGURE 30.10 The circulatory system has two general pathways. Pulmonary circulation moves blood between the heart and the lungs. Systemic circulation moves blood between the heart and the rest of the body.

MAIN IDEA

The heart pumps blood through two main pathways.

Circulating blood follows two separate pathways that meet at the heart, as shown in **FIGURE 30.10.** These pathways are called the pulmonary and systemic circulation. All of your blood travels through both of these pathways.

Pulmonary circulation (PUL-muh-NEHR-ee) occurs only between the heart and the lungs. The main function of this circulation is to carry oxygen-poor blood to the lungs, where it picks up O_2, expels excess CO_2 and water, and carries oxygen-rich blood back to the heart. Each lung is supplied by its own pulmonary artery and pulmonary vein. **Systemic circulation** (sihs-STEHM-ihk) occurs between the heart and the rest of the body, except for the lungs. The main function of this circulation is to carry oxygen-rich blood to all cells and transport oxygen-poor blood back to the heart. Systemic circulation begins when blood leaves the left ventricle, the largest chamber of the heart. The blood then circulates through the torso, arms, legs, and head, and then returns to the heart.

As the body's need for oxygen changes, sensors in the walls of major arteries in the pulmonary and systemic pathways send information to the medulla in the brain stem. The medulla coordinates this information with signals from the respiratory system. Homeostasis is maintained by matching heart rate and respiration rate with the oxygen needs of the body.

In extreme conditions, such as severe cold, the pulmonary and systemic circulation systems serve another vital function—making sure the body's brain, heart, and other major organs remain at a constant temperature. When the body is exposed for any length of time to a cold environment, blood vessels to the arms and legs begin to constrict. The blood flow to the arms and legs is reduced in order to keep the torso and head warm. Once you reach a warmer environment, these blood vessels dilate and normal circulation resumes.

A Infer Why is it important to have two separate pathways for circulation?

30.3 ASSESSMENT

ONLINE QUIZ ClassZone.com

REVIEWING MAIN IDEAS

1. What structures make the heart an efficient pump? In your answer, describe the direction of blood flow into and out of the heart.
2. Briefly describe the **pulmonary** and **systemic circulation** pathways.

CRITICAL THINKING

3. **Predict** Explain how leaky heart **valves** might damage the heart over time.
4. **Predict** How might a high fever affect a person's heart and breathing rates? Explain your answer.

Connecting CONCEPTS

5. **Animals** Unlike a human heart, an amphibian heart has two **atria** but only a single **ventricle.** How might living in a watery environment help reduce the work that an amphibian heart needs to do?

30.3 ASSESSMENT

1. Structures of an efficient pump: system of chambers and valves, which keeps blood flowing in one direction; cardiac muscle fibers that contract together; ability to self-regulate. Blood enters the right atrium, which contracts at a signal by the SA node. Blood is then pushed into the right ventricle, which contracts at a signal from the AV node. Blood is pumped to the lungs. Blood returning from the lungs enters the left atrium, which contracts to push the blood into the left ventricle. When the left ventricle contracts, blood is pumped to the rest of the body.
2. Pulmonary circulation occurs only between the heart and the lungs. Systemic circulation occurs between the heart and the rest of the body.
3. A leaky valve would allow blood to flow backward into an atrium or a ventricle. This prevents the chambers of the heart from emptying completely, which reduces the efficiency of the heart and makes it work harder. Over time, the cardiac muscle may become weakened.
4. Students should be able to reason that a high fever means the body is producing more heat. In order to maintain homeostasis, the heart rate and breathing rate would increase as the body attempted to get rid of excess heat.
5. Water helps to support body weight, so the heart would not have to work as hard against gravity to move the blood throughout the body.

Carbon Dioxide and Exercise

MATERIALS
- 100-mL graduated cylinder
- 250-mL beaker
- 800 mL water
- eyedropper
- bromothymol blue solution
- straw
- 50 mL 0.4% sodium hydroxide solution
- clock with second hand

PROCESS SKILLS
- **Observing**
- **Measuring**
- **Analyzing**

NOS.3 Clearly communicate their ideas and results of investigations verbally and in written form using tables, graphs, diagrams, and photographs.

In this lab you will examine the effects of exercise on how much carbon dioxide is released by your respiratory system. Bromothymol blue turns yellow in the presence of carbon dioxide when sodium hydroxide is added to the solution. The more sodium hydroxide that needs to be added to turn the bromothymol blue solution yellow, the more carbon dioxide there is in the solution.

PROBLEM How does exercise affect the release of carbon dioxide from the lungs?

PROCEDURE
1. Fill the graduated cylinder with 100 mL of water and pour the water into a beaker.
2. Add four drops of bromothymol blue solution to the water.
3. Place one end of the straw in the water and blow into the water for one minute. **Caution:** Do not inhale from the straw.
4. Add one drop at a time of the sodium hydroxide solution to the water. Swirl the water while adding the drops. Count the number of drops needed for the solution in the cylinder to turn yellow and remain yellow for one minute.
5. Record your data in a table similar to the one below.
6. Empty the beaker. Repeat steps 1 and 2.
7. Perform three types of exercise during your experiment: one that is low impact, such as walking; one that is medium impact, such as running in place; and one that is high impact, such as jumping jacks.
8. Perform each type of exercise for two minutes. At the end of each two-minute exercise period, repeat steps 3 through 6.

TABLE 1. THE EFFECT OF EXERCISE ON CARBON DIOXIDE RELEASE

Exercise	Number of 0.4% Sodium Hydroxide Solution Drops
Rest	
Exercise 1 (walking)	
Exercise 2 (running in place)	
Exercise 3 (jumping jacks)	

ANALYZE AND CONCLUDE
1. **Graph Data** Construct a graph that represents your data.
2. **Analyze** How does the amount of carbon dioxide exhaled change with different types of exercise? What mechanisms in the body explain these results?
3. **Hypothesize** Suppose you had subjects exercise for 15 minutes, and every 5 minutes they increased their rate of exertion. If you measured the amount of carbon dioxide exhaled every 5 minutes, what results would you expect? Explain your answer.

Answers

Sample Data
Rest: 4 drops; Exercise 1: 5 drops; Exercise 2: 7 drops; Exercise 3: 9 drops

Analyze and Conclude
1. See sample graph below.

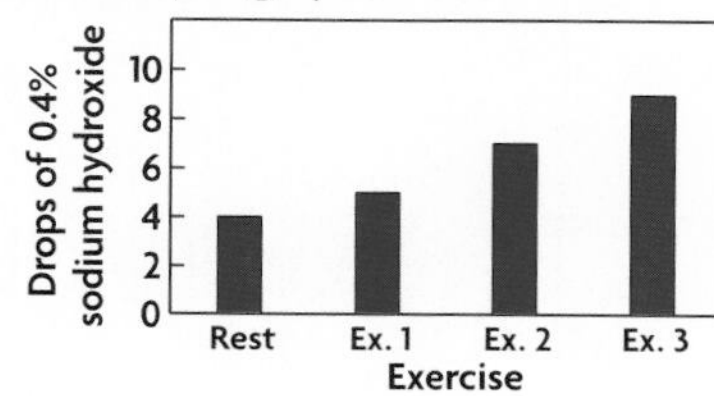

2. The amount of carbon dioxide increases with more vigorous exercise. As cellular activity increases, the need for oxygen increases, and the amount of carbon dioxide increases. To maintain homeostasis, the breathing rate increases to release the carbon dioxide.
3. The rate of carbon dioxide released may increase every five minutes. This would be due to increased levels of muscular activity, or cellular respiration, which would increase the amount of carbon dioxide.

INVESTIGATION

Time 45 minutes	TEACHER TESTED
Teacher Preparation	
Student Difficulty	
Lab Binder Human Bio, pp. 27–29	

Purpose Investigate how exercise affects the release of carbon dioxide from the lungs.

Overview Students will measure their output of carbon dioxide after performing exercises of increasing difficulty. They will
- blow into a bromthymol solution when at rest and after exercising
- add drops of sodium hydroxide solution to the bromthymol, counting the number of drops required to turn the solution yellow
- prepare a graph of their results

LAB PREPARATION
- Have a watch with a second hand available for students' use.

LAB MANAGEMENT
- Have students work in pairs.
- If students cannot blow into the straw continually for one minute, they should take a breath, exhale into the straw, take the straw out of their mouths and repeat the process.
- Have students rinse the graduated cylinders after each trial.
- Provide students with graph paper.

Safety
- Have students handle the sodium hydroxide solution carefully following all lab safety rules.
- Students should never inhale while the straws are in their mouths.
- Remind students to wash their hands before leaving the lab.

POST-LAB DISCUSSION
More carbon dioxide is produced during exercise, and its production increases with increased exertion. Discuss any results that differ from the expected results.

▼ Plan and Prepare

Objectives

- Describe the structures and functions of different blood vessels.
- Differentiate between systolic and diastolic blood pressure.
- Describe the effect of lifestyle on the circulatory system.

Section Resources

Unit Resource Book Study Guide pp. 69–70 Power Notes p. 71 Reinforcement p. 72
Interactive Reader Chapter 30 **Spanish Study Guide** pp. 307–308
Biology Toolkit p. C19
Technology Power Presentation 30.4 Media Gallery DVD Online Quiz 30.4

Activate Prior Knowledge Discuss how different types of roads, streets, and highways handle different types of traffic. **Ask,** How is traffic on a highway different from that on an unpaved road? Highways handle more cars at faster speeds; unpaved roads handle fewer at slower speeds. Compare this to the different types of blood vessels that transport blood.

▼ Teach

Vocabulary

Greek and Latin Word Origins The word **artery** derives from the ancient Greek *artēriā,* which means "windpipe." The word originally applied to any vessel coming from the chest cavity. This included arteries, veins, and bronchial tubes such as the trachea. The vessels examined were in cadavers and appeared empty. Hence they were assumed to carry air.

30.4 Blood Vessels and Transport

KEY CONCEPT The circulatory system transports materials throughout the body.

MAIN IDEAS
- Arteries, veins, and capillaries transport blood to all parts of the body.
- Lifestyle plays a key role in circulatory diseases.

VOCABULARY
blood pressure, p. 923
systolic pressure, p. 923
diastolic pressure, p. 923

Review
artery, vein, capillary, ventricle

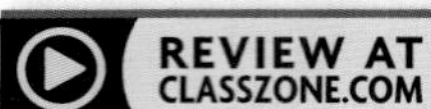

Connect In the 1600s, most scientists thought that the lungs, not the heart, moved the blood, and that blood was consumed and produced by the internal organs. William Harvey, court physician to the king of England, challenged these ideas. He showed that the heart was the true pump for the blood and that blood circulated in two pathways: one between the heart and the lungs, and another between the heart and the rest of the body. Harvey's work on circulation is regarded as one of the greatest advances in the history of medicine.

MAIN IDEA

Arteries, veins, and capillaries transport blood to all parts of the body.

As you read in Section 30.1, the circulatory system includes three types of blood vessels—arteries, veins, and capillaries—that act as transportation networks for the blood. Each of the three vessels has its own structure and function, as illustrated in **FIGURE 30.11.**

TAKING NOTES
A two-column chart can help you organize your notes about different blood vessels and circulatory pathways.

arteries	- Thicker, more muscular than veins - Blood under greater pressure

Arteries

Arteries need to be strong and flexible because the blood they carry from the heart is under great pressure. An artery's thick wall is composed of three layers. The innermost layer consists of endothelium coated with a protein that prevents blood from clotting. The middle layer is a thick band of smooth muscle and elastic fibers. The outer layer consists of connective tissue and elastic fibers. The elastic fibers allow the arterial walls to expand and contract to help move blood through the arteries. Arterioles, or smaller arteries, contain the same three layers, but the outer and middle layers are much thinner.

Veins

The structures of veins reflect the fact that blood is under much less pressure when it is returning to the heart. Veins have larger diameters and thinner walls than do arteries and contain valves that prevent blood from flowing backwards. Veins do not have a thick layer that expands and contracts to keep blood moving. Instead, they need the activity of skeletal muscles to help maintain circulation. For example, as you walk, skeletal muscles in your legs push against the veins. The valves open, and blood moves toward the heart. If you sit for too long, the lack of exercise makes it harder for the blood to move upward. Venules are small veins that join larger veins to capillaries.

Differentiated Instruction

TEACH WITH TECHNOLOGY

Set up microscopes with prepared slides of an artery, a vein, and a capillary. Have students take turns viewing the slides and comparing the images with the descriptions of the blood vessels in this section.

FIGURE 30.11 Three Types of Blood Vessels

Arteries, veins, and capillaries transport the blood to every cell.

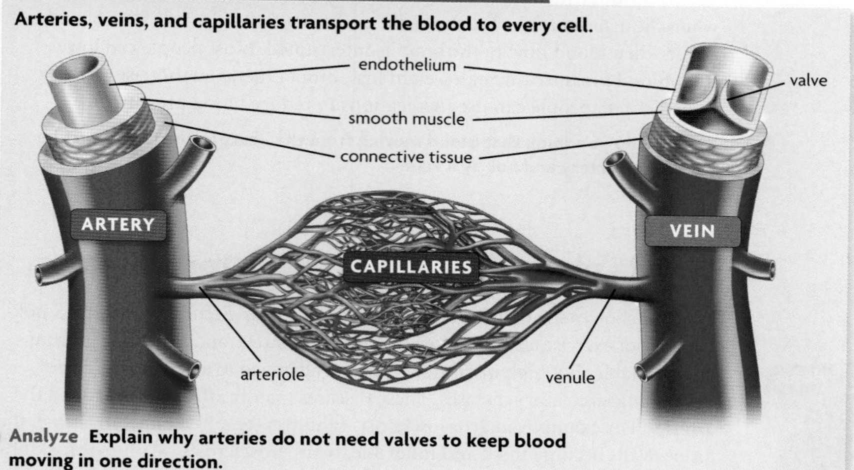

A Analyze Explain why arteries do not need valves to keep blood moving in one direction.

Capillaries

Capillary walls are made of epithelium, but they contain no muscle cells or elastic fibers. The thinness of capillary walls allows materials to diffuse into and out of the blood quickly and easily. In areas of high metabolic activity, such as the lungs, kidneys, and liver, capillaries form dense networks called capillary beds. These beds move a great deal of blood into and out of these organs.

Circulation and Blood Pressure

Blood pressure is the force with which blood pushes against the wall of an artery. A healthy resting blood pressure for a young adult is around 120/70 mm Hg (read as "120 over 70 millimeters of mercury"). The top, and higher, number is known as the **systolic pressure** (sih-STAHL-ihk). This is the amount of pressure on the walls of an artery when the left ventricle contracts to pump blood through the body. The bottom, and lower, number is known as the **diastolic pressure** (DY-uh-STAHL-ihk). This is the pressure in the artery when the left ventricle relaxes.

Blood pressure depends on how elastic and unblocked the arteries are and on the strength of the heart contraction. The less elastic the arteries and the more blockages that reduce blood flow, the harder the heart must pump. As a result, blood pressure rises. Blood pressure also rises naturally with activity, stress, and strong emotions, but it should drop again with rest. If the pressure remains high, there could be a problem in the circulatory system.

VISUAL VOCAB

Systolic pressure occurs when the left ventricle contracts. **Diastolic pressure** occurs when the ventricle relaxes. You can write these numbers as a fraction in which systolic pressure is always on top.

$$\frac{120}{70}$$ **systolic** = numerator; **diastolic** = denominator

***Connecting* CONCEPTS**

Differentiated Cells In **Chapter 28,** you learned that epithelial cells line most organs and structures in the body. These cells provide a protective layer that helps each organ or structure to do its job.

HANDS-ON ACTIVITY

Show students how to feel a person's pulse by gently pressing on the outside of the person's wrist with the middle and index fingers. Have pairs of students determine each other's pulse rate. Using a watch with a second hand, have them count the number of beats in 15 seconds and multiply that number by 4 to determine the number of beats per minute. **Ask,** What are you feeling with your fingers when you feel a person's pulse? expansion and relaxation of the blood vessel as blood is pumped through

PRE-AP

Have students compare the valve structure in veins, as shown in **FIGURE 30.11,** to the structure of the valves in the heart, shown in **FIGURE 30.9.** From an engineering point of view, have students evaluate the structures for the functions performed.

Biology Toolkit, Quick-Write, p. C19

Science Trivia

The coloration of the lips is due to the great number of capillaries found beneath the skin. The capillaries are full of oxygenated blood, which give the lips their reddish color. If a person is anemic or has lost a great deal of blood, the lips would be quite pale. Lips may appear blue in extreme cold when capillaries constrict and the blood loses oxygen.

Take It Further

Use the following table to discuss the normal ranges of **pulse rate** and **blood pressure.**

Normal Ranges for Pulse Rate and Blood Pressure by Age Group

Age Group	Pulse Rate (per minute)	Blood Pressure
Infant	129 to 150	not measured
2–6 yr	90 to 120	80/75 to 110/75
Children	85 to 100	75/40 to 120/75
Teenagers	70 to 100	85/45 to 130/89
Adults	60 to 100	100/50 to 119/79

Source: University of Nebraska Medical Center

Ask, Why is the pulse rate generally higher in infants and children than in adults? The rate of cellular respiration in infants and children is higher due to growth. The heart beats faster to supply tissues with adequate amounts of blood.

Answers

A Analyze Blood in arteries is under great pressure, which keeps it moving in one direction, and arteries have muscular walls that contract and relax to move blood.

▼ Teach *continued*

ONLINE BIOLOGY Go to the chapter Resource Center at **ClassZone.com** for additional resources and information on the circulatory system.

Take It Further

An **arterial stent** can be used to hold an artery open, allowing blood to flow through it. It consists of a small wire-mesh tube that is inserted into a blocked artery, and then expanded. This opens the artery, restoring adequate blood flow.

Answers

A Infer Two reasons: an artery has a thick wall that can withstand the pressure, and only arteries carry blood away from the heart.

B Provide Examples Poor diet can lead to blocked arteries as plaque builds up on their walls; smoking and lack of exercise can make artery walls thicker and less flexible.

▼ Assess and Reteach

Assess Use the Online Quiz or Section Quiz (*Assessment Book,* p. 594).

Reteach Have students come to the board to map out the movement of a blood cell as it picks up oxygen, delivers it, and then returns for more.

People with permanently high blood pressure have a condition called hypertension, which can lead to a heart attack or stroke. A heart attack occurs when the arteries to the heart muscle are damaged or blocked. A stroke can occur when blood flow to the brain is interrupted. Most people can lower their blood pressure through weight loss, proper diet, and exercise. If these remedies fail, people can use medications to reduce blood pressure.

A Infer Why do you think that blood moving from the heart to the lungs must be carried by an artery and not by a vein?

MAIN IDEA

Lifestyle plays a key role in circulatory diseases.

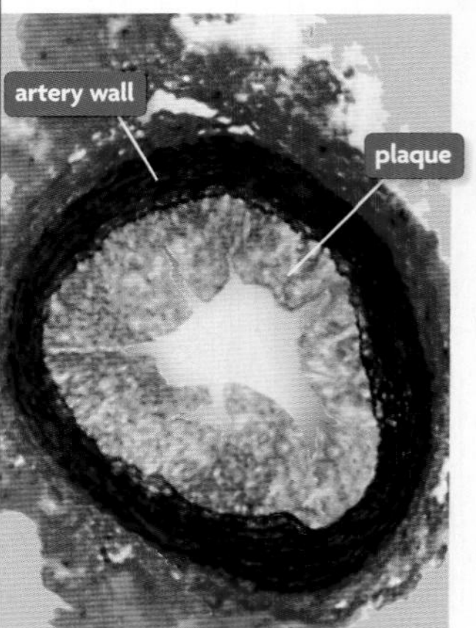

FIGURE 30.12 This micrograph clearly shows fatty deposits, called plaque, building up on an artery wall. If such deposits block blood flow, they can cause a heart attack or stroke. (LM; magnification 25×)

Lifestyle choices strongly influence the health of your circulatory system. Smoking, lack of exercise, excessive weight, long-term stress, and a diet low in fruits and vegetables but high in saturated fats are all linked to an increased risk of developing circulatory diseases. These diseases mainly affect the heart and the arteries. For example, in arteriosclerosis (ahr-TEER-ee-oh-skluh-ROH-sihs), the artery walls become thick and inflexible. In atherosclerosis (ATH-uh-roh-skluh-ROH-sihs), blood flow is partially or fully blocked by sticky material, called plaque, that collects on the walls of the arteries, as **FIGURE 30.12** shows. High blood pressure is often the only warning sign of these problems.

Both diseases can lead to a heart attack, stroke, or kidney damage. Some blocked arteries supplying the heart muscle can be opened using a surgical technique known as a balloon angioplasty (AN-jee-uh-PLAS-tee). A device is threaded into the artery and then inflated so that it squeezes the obstruction against the artery wall. If this procedure does not work, bypass surgery may be necessary. In this operation, a healthy blood vessel from another part of the body (usually the leg) is attached to the artery on either side of the blockage. Blood can then bypass the obstruction.

To reduce the risk of circulatory diseases, physicians urge people either not to smoke or to quit smoking, to maintain a healthy weight, and to exercise regularly. Medications can also help reduce the risks of heart disease.

B Provide Examples How can lifestyle choices affect the function of the arteries?

30.4 ASSESSMENT

ONLINE QUIZ ClassZone.com

REVIEWING MAIN IDEAS

1. How do the structures of arteries, veins, and capillaries relate to their functions?
2. How can lifestyle choices help reduce the risk of heart disease?

CRITICAL THINKING

3. **Infer** People who smoke often have cold hands and feet. What might explain this condition in terms of blood flow?
4. **Apply** Explain why narrowing of the arteries decreases blood flow but increases **blood pressure.**

***Connecting* CONCEPTS**

5. **Arthropods** The hard exoskeleton of an arthropod exerts pressure on the animal's circulatory system. In what way does the exoskeleton serve the same function as the heart does in mammals?

30.4 ASSESSMENT

1. Arteries: elastic, muscular structure helps them carry blood under great pressure and keep it moving; veins: under less pressure, are thinner, have valves to keep blood moving in one direction; capillaries: small size, thin walls, allow materials to move into and out of these vessels.
2. Good diet, proper weight, exercise, reduced stress, and not smoking can keep the heart and blood vessels healthy, preventing high blood pressure and damage to arteries.
3. Smoking can constrict blood vessels, reducing circulation to the hands and feet, which would make them feel cold.
4. Narrowing of the arteries restricts the amount of blood that can pass through the artery at that point. The narrower the opening, the more force needed to push the blood through, resulting in high blood pressure.
5. Like a mammal's heart, the exoskeleton acts like an external "pump" to keep fluid moving throughout the body.

Age Group and Disease

When scientists investigate some type of phenomenon, such as when they are trying to determine the cause of a disease, they often need to rule out variables that may or may not be important. This is especially helpful when many factors might play some role in the phenomenon, as is often the case, in the causes of disease.

The formation of a **null hypothesis** is useful during these types of investigations. The null hypothesis states that there is no difference among study groups for the independent variable being tested. The null hypothesis is always stated in the negative: one variable does *not* have an effect on the other variable. The null hypothesis is accepted or rejected based on the data. If the investigation shows that the one variable *does* affect the other, the null hypothesis is rejected. If the investigation shows that the one variable *does not* affect the other, then the null hypothesis is accepted.

EXAMPLE

A scientist investigates the rate of death from heart disease among different age groups. The null hypothesis for this investigation would be, "There is no difference in the rate of death from heart disease among different age groups." Consider the results listed below for the rate of death from heart disease per 100,000 people.

- Rate for ages 55–64 is 246.9
- Rate for ages 65–74 is 635.1
- Rate for ages 75–84 is 1725.7

In this case, the null hypothesis would be rejected because there is an obvious difference in the rate of death due to heart disease among different age groups. As people get older, the rate of death increases.

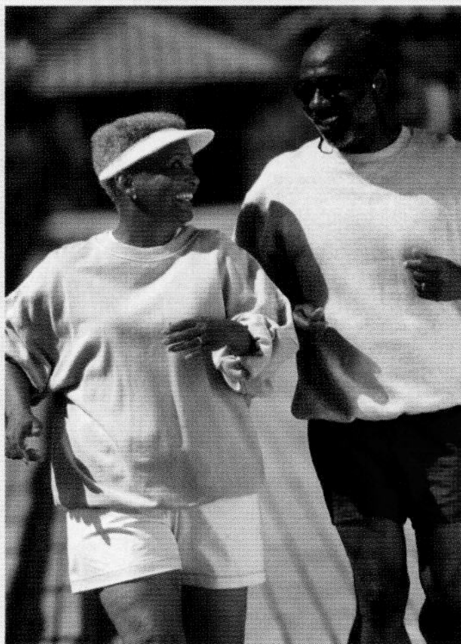

Exercise is an important factor in preventing heart disease.

ACCEPT OR REJECT THE NULL HYPOTHESIS

The graph at right shows the results of an investigation about differences in the rate of asthma based on age.

1. **Hypothesize** Form a null hypothesis for this investigation.
2. **Evaluate** Explain whether you accept or reject the null hypothesis, based on the data.

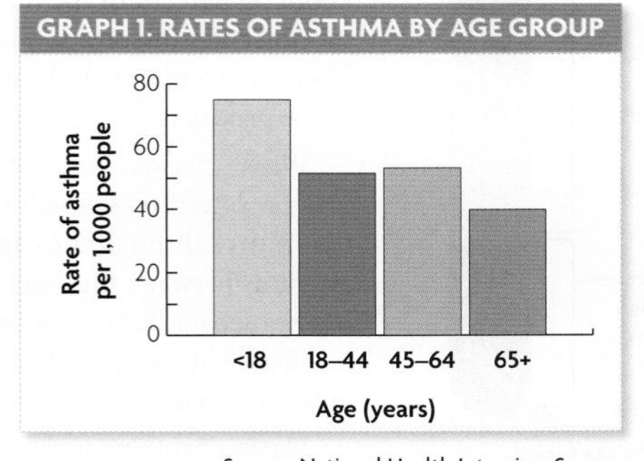

Source: National Health Interview Survey, National Center for Health Statistics

Answers

1. Answers may include any of the following: There is no difference in the rates of asthma among different age groups. The rates of asthma do not decline as people age. People over age 18 do not have higher rates of asthma than do people under age 18.
2. Students should be able to cite the data that would make them reject or accept their null hypothesis.

DATA ANALYSIS

Introduce

The null hypothesis is often the opposite of what the experimenter expects to find. It is put forward to allow the data to contradict it. This approach gives investigators somewhere to start, given a wide field of unknown variables. **Ask**

- From the example given, does rejection of the null hypothesis mean that aging causes heart disease? No, it only means that aging and heart disease may be related. How they are related would have to be a subject of further study.
- If the data support the null hypothesis and it is accepted, does that mean that the null hypothesis is true? No, it only means that there is not sufficient evidence against it.

Discuss

In actual clinical trials, an alternative hypothesis is set up along with the null hypothesis. For example, a null hypothesis (H_0) may state "The new drug has no effects different from those of the drug currently in use." An alternative hypothesis (H_1) might be "The two drugs have different effects." **Ask**

- If the data does not support H_0 and is rejected, does that mean that H_1 is true? No, rejecting the null hypothesis merely suggests that H_1 may be true.
- What are some possible reasons for rejecting the alternative hypothesis? One reason might be that there are too many possible variables that were not taken into account, or that the different results recorded may be caused by a factor unrelated to the new drug.

Unit Resource Book, Data Analysis, p. 81

SECTION 30.5

▼ Plan and Prepare

Objectives

- List the main components of blood.
- Describe the functions of platelets and different types of blood cells.

Section Resources

Unit Resource Book
Study Guide pp. 73–74
Power Notes p. 75
Reinforcement p. 76
Pre-AP Activity pp. 85–86

Interactive Reader Chapter 30
Spanish Study Guide pp. 309–310

Biology Toolkit pp. C19, C20, C40

Technology
Power Presentation 30.5
Media Gallery DVD
Online Quiz 30.5

Activate Prior Knowledge Tell students that crabs have blue blood, earthworms have green, starfish have yellow, and humans have red. **Ask,** What gives blood its color? its components Tell students the hemoglobin, a red pigment found in red blood cells, gives human blood its color.

▼ Teach

Science Trivia

- Blood travels 60,000 miles (96,540 km) per day throughout the body.
- Blood makes up 7–10 percent of a person's body weight.
- A newborn has about a cup of blood.
- There are one billion red blood cells in two to three drops of blood.
- A pint of blood is equivalent to a pound, so people lose a pound when they donate blood.
- Adult mosquitoes feed on flower nectar but mosquito eggs need protein to grow, so female mosquitoes suck blood to get the protein.

30.5 Blood

KEY CONCEPT Blood is a complex tissue that transports materials.

MAIN IDEAS
- Blood is composed mainly of cells, cell fragments, and plasma.
- Platelets and different types of blood cells have different functions.

VOCABULARY
platelet, p. 926
plasma, p. 926
ABO blood group, p. 927
Rh factor, p. 928
white blood cells, p. 928

Review
hemoglobin, red blood cell

Connect The adult human body contains about 5 liters (more than 5 qt) of blood. This fluid supplies your organs with gases and nutrients, helps you keep warm or cool off, and gets rid of waste products from your cells. Blood also has other components that help fight infections and control bleeding from damaged blood vessels. How can one substance accomplish all of these functions?

MAIN IDEA

Blood is composed mainly of cells, cell fragments, and plasma.

When you look at blood with the naked eye, it appears to be a single substance. Whole blood is actually a sticky mixture of cells, cell fragments, and fluid, along with particles of fat, other nutrients, and dissolved gases. If you put blood in a test tube and spin it in a centrifuge, it will separate into two main parts, as shown in **FIGURE 30.13.** At the bottom, a reddish-brown band contains red blood cells, white blood cells, and platelets. **Platelets** are cell fragments, produced in bone marrow, that help in blood clotting.

At the top of the tube is **plasma,** a clear pale-yellow fluid that makes up about 55 percent of the blood. Plasma is roughly 90 percent water. Many types of molecules dissolve in plasma and can be transported throughout the body. These molecules include amino acids, glucose, hormones, vitamins, salts, and waste products.

Why is plasma important? The concentration of molecules dissolved in plasma determines which substances will diffuse into and out of the blood that moves through the capillaries. The movement of water, gases, nutrients, and ions between the capillaries and the cells plays a critical role in maintaining homeostasis. For instance, as the concentration of glucose increases in the capillaries, it moves outward to an area of lower concentration and eventually enters the cells.

Plasma proteins such as albumin, fibrinogen, and immune proteins also help maintain homeostasis. Albumin, the same substance as in egg white, is the most abundant plasma protein. Its main role is to stabilize blood volume so that fluid in the blood does not leak out of the vessels. Fibrinogen is a clotting factor that works with platelets to stop the bleeding after an injury.

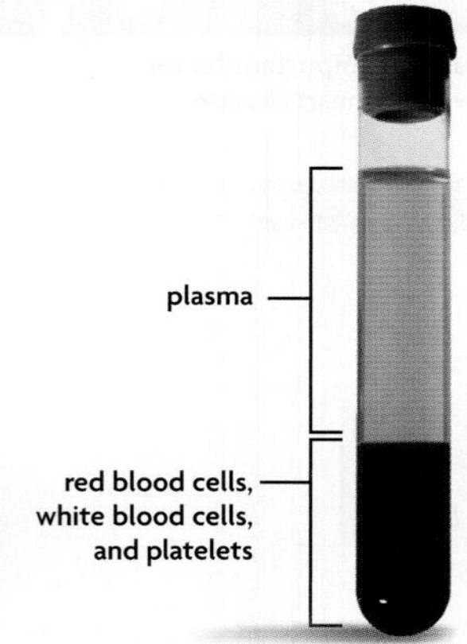

FIGURE 30.13 Whole blood is composed of several parts that help to fight infections, control bleeding, and transport gases, nutrients, waste products, and hormones.

Differentiated Instruction

ENGLISH LEARNERS

Have students create a concept map with these features:

- The central circle states, "Blood is a complex tissue that transports materials."
- Arrows show direction and verbs or phrases label them. At the end of each, in a square, is a property, or example of blood.
- Other concepts are placed in smaller squares with more arrows and verbs or phrases.
- An arrow from the center states, "It is a mixture of . . ." ending in a square, "cells, fluid, fat particles, nutrients, dissolved gases."
- Another arrow from the center states, "has two components" with two squares, "platelets" and "plasma."

Have students complete the concept map.

Biology Toolkit, Concept Map, p. C40

A group of specialized proteins made by the immune system fights infection or attacks foreign materials in the blood. You will learn more about these proteins in Chapter 31.

A Predict What do you think might happen to your blood if you become dehydrated?

MAIN IDEA

Platelets and different types of blood cells have different functions.

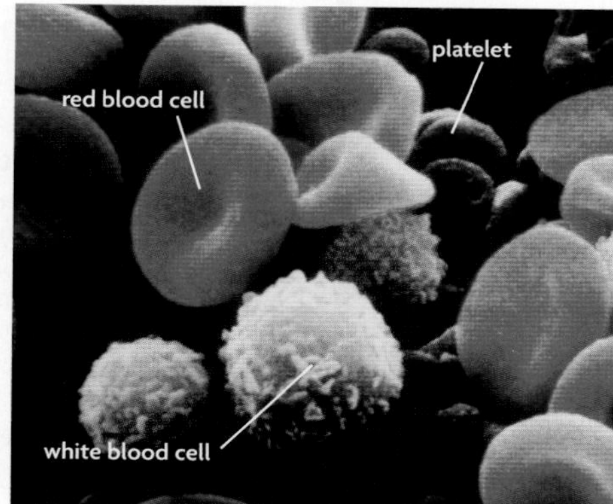

FIGURE 30.14 Red blood cells transport gases, white blood cells defend the body against pathogens and foreign materials, and platelets help seal wounds. (colored SEM; magnification 3,400×)

Blood contains red blood cells, several types of white blood cells, and platelets, as the photograph in **FIGURE 30.14** shows. These three blood components are manufactured mostly in the bone marrow. Each one has a specialized shape and function.

Red Blood Cells

Red blood cells make up 40 to 45 percent of all cells in the blood. Mature red blood cells are shaped like an inner tube with a solid center. They are produced from stem cells in bone marrow. As these cells mature, they gradually fill with hemoglobin and lose their nuclei and other organelles. Without nuclei, they cannot undergo cell division. Red blood cells circulate through the body for about 120 days before they begin to degrade. Degraded cells are carried to the liver and spleen, which break up the cells and recycle them.

The most important function of red blood cells is to transport O_2 to the cells and carry CO_2 away from them. As you read in Section 30.3, O_2 binds to the hemoglobin in red blood cells and is transported to all cells. When blood is returning to the heart, it picks up CO_2 and carries it to the lungs.

If red blood cells are damaged or misshapen, they cannot transport O_2 effectively. In sickle cell disease, for example, red blood cells are distorted into crescent shapes, as shown in **FIGURE 30.15**. They transport less O_2, last only 10 to 20 days, and tend to clump in blood vessels. This genetic disorder is most commonly found in people of African descent.

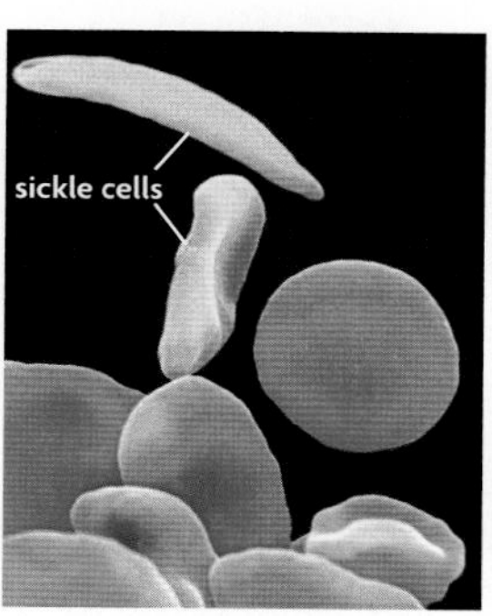

FIGURE 30.15 Sickle cell anemia is an inherited blood disease in which hemoglobin proteins clump together. This causes red blood cells to stiffen and curl into a crescent shape. (colored SEM; magnification 2,750×)

ABO Blood Group and Rh Factors

Red blood cells have surface protein markers that define your blood type. Blood type is very important when people give or receive blood for transfusions. If you receive blood with a protein marker different from your own, your immune system will attack the foreign blood cells, causing them to clump. The clumped blood can block vital blood vessels and result in death.

Protein markers exist for about 26 different blood types. The most common markers are A and B, which produce four blood types: A, B, AB, and O, also known as the **ABO blood group.** Type O has no protein marker and can be donated to a person with any other blood type. Type AB blood has both protein markers and can accept any type of blood. People with Type A and Type B blood can receive only their own blood type or type O blood.

ONLINE BIOLOGY Go to the chapter Resource Center at **ClassZone.com** for additional resources and information on blood.

The Inside Story

Charles Richard Drew pioneered a method for preserving blood to be stored for transfusions. He separated out blood plasma, which was dehydrated, then reconstituted the blood components when needed. It was Drew who organized Blood for Britain during World War II. He initiated the use of **bloodmobiles** to bank blood and plasma. This saved the lives of many suffering from war wounds.

As director of the American Red Cross blood bank he recruited 100,000 people to donate blood for American troops. However, he resigned from that position when the U.S. military insisted that the blood be segregated according to the donor's race. He argued, correctly, that blood has no race. Drew feared the policy would lead to needless deaths if soldiers and sailors went untreated as doctors waited for racially typed blood.

Answers

A Predict Students should reason that because the blood contains so much water, being dehydrated would make the blood thicker and less able to move through the smaller vessels of the circulatory system. Less water in the blood would also mean that materials could not diffuse into or out of the blood as easily, affecting homeostasis.

BELOW LEVEL

Have students make a two-column notes chart similar to the one on the right. Tell students to fill in the chart as they read this section, including as much detail as possible. Encourage students to write the functions of the blood components in their own words. When they have completed their charts, allow students to compare their charts and add to them or correct them.

Components of Blood	
Blood Component	**Function**
Plasma	
Red blood cells	
White blood cells	
Platelets	

Biology Toolkit, Two-Column Notes, p. C20

▼ Teach *continued*

ONLINE BIOLOGY Students can do a virtual lab on blood typing. See Options for Inquiry on page 933.

QUICK LAB

Time 20 minutes TEACHER TESTED

Lab Binder Human Bio, p. 35

Purpose Observe characteristics of different types of blood cells.

LAB MANAGEMENT

- It may be helpful to students to have references of the slides. A good college-level anatomy and physiology textbook should have micrographs of different blood cells for students to study.

Safety Caution students to handle the glass slides carefully. Remind them to wipe down the eyepieces with alcohol wipes after using them.

Answers

Analyze and Conclude

1. The shape of a red blood cell is round with a concave center on each side (biconcave).The concave shape on both sides provides more surface area for carrying gas molecules.
2. Red blood cells are the most numerous (about 4.8–5.4 million per cubic millimeter), and white blood cells are the least numerous (the ratio is about 1 white blood cell to every 700 red blood cells).

QUICK LAB OBSERVING NOS.3

Blood Cells

In this lab, you will examine different types of blood cells under the microscope.

MATERIALS
- slide of blood cells
- microscope

PROBLEM What are the different characteristics of blood cells?

PROCEDURE

1. Examine the slide under low power and high power on the microscope. Identify a red blood cell, a white blood cell, and a platelet. Notice the proportion of each type of cell on your slide.
2. Draw each type of cell and label its structures.

ANALYZE AND CONCLUDE

1. **Explain** What is the general shape of a red blood cell? How is this shape related to the function of a red blood cell?
2. **Infer** Based on the proportion of each type of cell on your slide, which type of cell is the most numerous in the blood of a healthy person? Which is least numerous?

***Connecting* CONCEPTS**

Genetics In **Chapter 7**, you read about the alleles that produce the different phenotypes in the ABO blood group.

Another blood protein, known as the **Rh factor,** is also critical in making a successful transfusion. People either are Rh positive (Rh^+) and have this protein or are Rh negative (Rh^-) and do not have it. Anyone can receive Rh^- blood without harm. However, if you are Rh^- and receive Rh^+ blood, your immune system will make proteins that cause the Rh^+ blood cells to swell and burst. As a result, blood must be matched for both the ABO group and the Rh group. The possible ABO/Rh blood combinations are shown in **FIGURE 30.16**.

FIGURE 30.16 ABO Rh BLOOD COMBINATIONS

BLOOD TYPE	CAN DONATE TO	CAN RECEIVE FROM
A	A, AB	A, O
B	AB, B	B, O
AB	AB	A, B, AB, O
O	A, B, AB, O	O
Rh FACTOR	**CAN DONATE TO**	**CAN RECEIVE FROM**
Rh^+ factor	Rh^+	Rh^+, Rh^-
Rh^- factor	Rh^+, Rh^-	Rh^-

White Blood Cells

White blood cells, which contain no hemoglobin, are cells that defend the body against infection and that remove foreign material and dead cells. Different kinds of white blood cells defend the body in different ways. Some surround and ingest microorganisms. Others produce proteins that act to destroy pathogens. Unlike red blood cells, white blood cells are not limited to the circulatory system. Some of these cells are able to pass through capillary

Differentiated Instruction

PRE-AP

Have students make the case for blood as a fluid form of connective tissue. Give them five minutes to write up their reasoning. Remind students that tissue types were introduced in Chapter 28.

Biology Toolkit, Quick-Write, p. C19

walls into the lymphatic system and attack pathogens in the body's tissues. For this reason, white blood cells are also considered part of the immune system.

Platelets and Blood Clotting

Platelets are cell fragments that help form clots that control bleeding. When you cut or tear a blood vessel, platelets quickly cluster around the wound.

Repairing injuries At the site of an injury, platelets form spiky extensions that intertwine into a complex net. The platelets then release proteins known as clotting factors, which begin the process of repair. One of the factors converts prothrombin, a plasma protein, into thrombin. Thrombin, in turn, converts fibrinogen into fibrin. Sticky threads of fibrin form a web that traps platelets and white blood cells, as the top photo shows in **FIGURE 30.17.**

The bottom photo shows how the tangle of fibrin, platelets, and blood cells has grown to form a plug, or clot, on the blood vessel. The clot seals the wound and prevents any further loss of blood. The steps in blood clotting are a good example of a positive feedback loop. The body increases the rate of change in clotting until the wound is sealed. Once the injury heals, other chemicals are released that dissolve the clot.

Blood clotting disorders Blood clots can also form inside blood vessels and present serious risks to a person's health. For example, clots that block arteries to the heart or brain can cause a heart attack or stroke. Medications that thin the blood or dissolve clots can help prevent these circulatory problems.

The inability to form clots can be equally serious. For example, hemophilia is a genetic disorder in which a key clotting factor is missing in the blood. For people with hemophilia, even a minor cut can cause life-threatening bleeding. As a result, they must guard against the slightest scrape or bruise. When injured, they must have the missing clotting factor injected into their blood to help seal the wound.

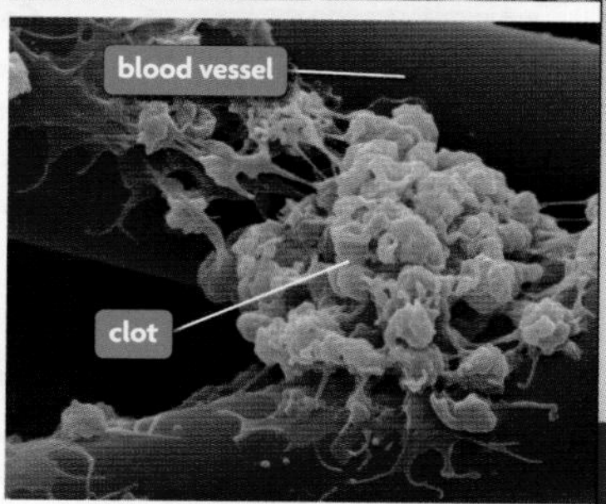

FIGURE 30.17 The top photograph shows platelets clustering at the site of a wound. Fibrin threads trap more cells until a plug, or clot, forms (bottom) and stops the bleeding from a blood vessel. (colored SEMs; magnifications: platelets and fibrin 6000×; clot 1900×)

A Apply Why might it be important for white blood cells to be part of a clot that seals an injury?

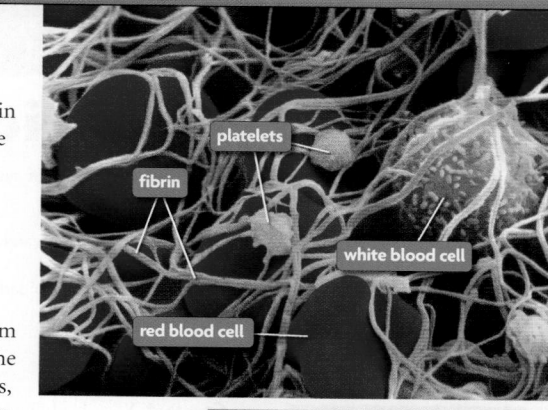

30.5 ASSESSMENT

ONLINE QUIZ ClassZone.com

REVIEWING MAIN IDEAS

1. List some of the substances dissolved in **plasma** and describe how they help maintain homeostasis.
2. What are the primary roles of red blood cells, **white blood cells,** and **platelets**?

CRITICAL THINKING

3. **Apply** What would happen if a person with type A Rh^- blood were transfused with type A Rh^+ blood?
4. **Infer** Some people must take medications that interfere with clotting factors. How might they need to change their activities?

***Connecting* CONCEPTS**

5. **Chemistry** Water is the most abundant component in human blood. What characteristic of water allows glucose, hormones, and many other materials to dissolve into it?

TEACH FROM VISUALS

FIGURE 30.17 Ask students to identify all the elements of a forming blood clot. Tell them that after bleeding stops, an external clot dries out. **Ask,** What do you call a dried clot on the surface of the skin? a scab

Answers

A Apply White blood cells would help prevent pathogens from infecting a wound.

Assess and Reteach ▼

Assess Use the Online Quiz or Section Quiz (*Assessment Book,* p. 595).

Reteach Have students make a shopping list for all the components needed to make blood. Tell them to justify their expenditures.

30.5 ASSESSMENT

1. Amino acids, glucose, hormones, vitamins, salts, and waste products dissolve in plasma. These substances diffuse into and out of the blood to help the body maintain homeostasis by regulating the amounts of fluid, nutrients, gases, and ions that the body requires for normal functioning.
2. Red blood cells carry oxygen; white blood cells help defend the body against pathogens and other foreign substances; platelets help seal wounds and prevent blood loss from torn or injured blood vessels.
3. The immune system of the person receiving the transfusion would attack the Rh^+ blood cells, causing them to swell and burst, which could result in a life-threatening condition.
4. They should avoid heavy-contact sports or other activities where there is a high risk of being injured, avoid surgical procedures, and try not to get cut or bruised. They would be at risk for severe bleeding because they would not have the normal clotting factors.
5. Water is the universal solvent, which means that a great variety of materials can dissolve in it.

SECTION 30.6

▼ Plan and Prepare

Objectives

- Describe the lymphatic system and its relationship to the circulatory system.
- Summarize the lymphatic system's function in the immune system.

Section Resources

Unit Resource Book Study Guide pp. 77–78 Power Notes p. 79 Reinforcement p. 80
Interactive Reader Chapter 30 **Spanish Study Guide** pp. 311–312
Biology Toolkit p. C39
Technology Power Presentation 30.6 Media Gallery DVD Online Quiz 30.6

Activate Prior Knowledge Find how many students had their tonsils removed when they were younger. **Ask,** What problems were the tonsils causing? Students may remember having difficulty breathing or swallowing. Tell students that tonsils are a collection of lymphatic tissues. They surround the top of the throat and can cause problems for small children when the tissue becomes swollen with infection.

30.6 Lymphatic System

KEY CONCEPT The lymphatic system provides another type of circulation in the body.

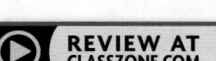

MAIN IDEAS

- Lymph is collected from tissues and returned to the circulatory system.
- The lymphatic system is a major part of the immune system.

VOCABULARY

lymphatic system, p. 930
lymph, p. 930
node, p. 930
lymphocyte, p. 931

Connect Your body has two transport networks that circulate fluids. The first is the circulatory system, which brings gases and nutrients to every cell. The second is the lymphatic system. While this system also helps to distribute nutrients, its main jobs are to absorb excess fluid, to fight disease, and to carry waste products away from the cells. These two systems work so closely together that almost everywhere there are blood vessels, there are also lymph vessels.

MAIN IDEA

Lymph is collected from tissues and returned to the circulatory system.

The **lymphatic system** (lihm-FAT-ihk) consists of a complex network of organs, vessels, and nodes throughout the body, as shown in **FIGURE 30.18.** The system collects excess fluid that leaks out of the blood capillaries into the area between the cells. This fluid, called interstitial (IHN-tuhr-STIHSH-uhl) fluid, brings nutrients to the cells and removes their wastes.

Although 90 percent of the fluid returns to the capillaries, up to 3 liters (3 qt) per day remain outside the blood vessels. Without the lymphatic system, your body would begin to swell as more fluid becomes trapped in your tissues. The system prevents this problem through a two-step process:

- It collects the fluid and filters it to remove dead cells and microorganisms.
- It returns the cleaned fluid to the circulatory system.

Lymphatic circulation begins when the fluid between the cells enters the lymphatic capillaries, where it becomes known as **lymph.** The lymph then flows into larger vessels within the lymphatic system. Without a heart to pump the fluid, the vessels rely on contractions of skeletal and smooth muscles to circulate the lymph. One-way valves similar to those in veins keep the fluid from flowing backwards.

From the vessels, lymph collects in small rounded structures called lymph **nodes.** The nodes filter the lymph and trap bacteria, viruses, fungi, and cell fragments. Specialized immune cells ingest and destroy this organic material. Vessels then carry the lymph out of the nodes. In the last stage of the journey, the lymph returns to the circulatory system. Two large vessels, one on either side of the body, enter veins located just under the collarbones. The lymph is returned to the blood and becomes part of the circulatory system again.

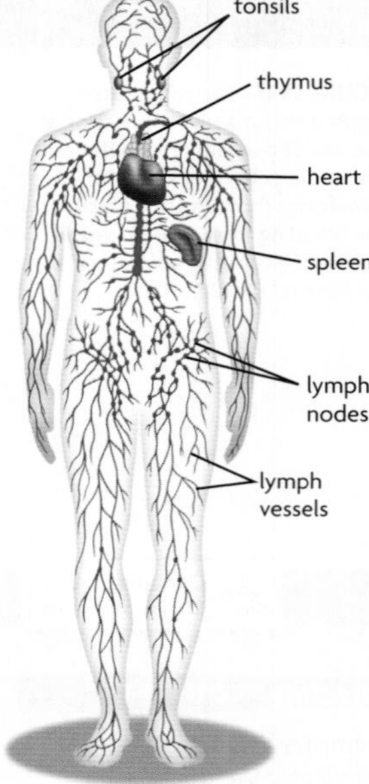

FIGURE 30.18 The lymphatic system collects fluid that leaks from the blood vessels and returns it to the heart. The spleen recycles old red blood cells; white blood cells mature in the thymus.

▼ Teach

TEACH FROM VISUALS

FIGURE 30.18 Point out the major features: lymphatic vessels, organs, and lymph nodes. Tell students that lymph nodes are found in groups near veins. Point out that lymph returns to the bloodstream by way of the left and right subclavian veins, just beneath the collarbones. **Ask,** Why does interstitial fluid have to be returned to the circulatory system? to maintain blood volume and keep body tissues from swelling

Differentiated Instruction

ENGLISH LEARNERS

Have students reinterpret the text describing lymphatic circulation as a cycle diagram. Model how you read the text, looking for words that describe circulation. Have students work in pairs, with one partner reading the text, and the other drawing the diagram.

Biology Toolkit, Cycle Diagram, p. C39

When lymphatic tissues and nodes are damaged or removed, lymph cannot drain normally from that area. The result is swelling as fluid accumulates. The swelling can be controlled by exercise, pressure bandages or garments, and massage. These treatments exert pressure on the tissues and nodes to "push" lymph into the vessels.

A Predict How would sitting for a long time affect the lymphatic circulation?

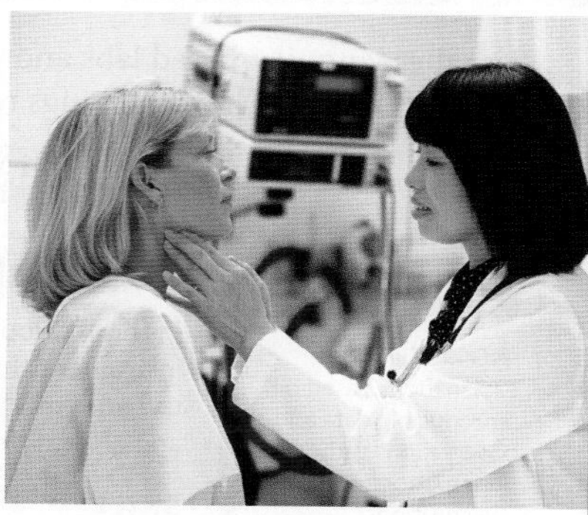

FIGURE 30.19 Doctors check your lymph nodes during a routine physical examination. Enlarged or lumpy nodes might indicate that your body is fighting an infection.

MAIN IDEA

The lymphatic system is a major part of the immune system.

Three structures in the lymphatic system—the tonsils, thymus, and spleen—also function as part of the immune system. Each of these structures has specialized functions that help the body to defend itself. The tonsils are lymph nodes set in the back of the throat on either side. These nodes help to filter out bacteria and viruses that have escaped the body's outer defenses. When too many pathogens collect in the tonsils, these nodes become swollen and infected and may have to be removed.

The thymus, located behind the breastbone, is important in developing certain types of white blood cells known as **lymphocytes** (LIHM-fuh-SYTS). These cells help the body fight pathogens, parasites, and other types of foreign organisms. Some immature lymphocytes migrate from the bone marrow to the thymus, where they develop the ability to recognize specific microorganisms. Most of these cells leave the thymus and circulate through the lymphatic and circulatory systems to protect the body.

The spleen is the largest organ in the lymphatic system. Its main job is to filter and clean the lymph of cell fragments and abnormal tissue. This organ also contains many lymphocytes and other white blood cells that destroy harmful bacteria and foreign organisms.

B Predict If the spleen is removed, how might the immune and lymphatic systems be affected?

Connecting CONCEPTS

Immune System You will read more in **Chapter 31** about how the body uses lymphocytes and other types of cells to fight pathogens.

30.6 ASSESSMENT

ONLINE QUIZ ClassZone.com

REVIEWING MAIN IDEAS

1. Describe the main organs and functions of the **lymphatic system.**
2. Give three examples of organs that are part of both the immune and lymphatic systems, and briefly describe their functions.

CRITICAL THINKING

3. **Compare and Contrast** How are the structures of an artery and a vein different from or similar to the structure of a **lymph** vessel?
4. **Infer** The circulatory system of the blood is a closed system. Is the lymphatic system a closed or an open system? Explain your answer.

Connecting CONCEPTS

5. **Immunology** Mononucleosis is a disease that causes the body to greatly increase the number of **lymphocytes** circulating in the blood and lymph. If you felt the spleen and looked at the tonsils of someone with mononucleosis, what might you observe and why?

30.6 ASSESSMENT

1. tonsils, thymus, spleen, lymph nodes, lymph vessels; main functions: collect excess fluid and return it to the circulatory system, filter and clean lymph, protect the body from pathogens
2. tonsils: help filter lymph and defend the body from disease; thymus: helps develop lymphocytes; spleen: filters and cleans lymph and helps the body defend itself against disease
3. Lymph vessels are similar to veins, but not arteries, because they have one-way valves and rely on skeletal and smooth muscles to keep lymphatic fluid circulating.
4. Open system; interstitial fluid enters the vessels from outside the system.
5. The tonsils and spleen would probably be swollen and tender, indicating the body is fighting a major infection.

ONLINE BIOLOGY Go to the chapter Resource Center at **ClassZone.com** for additional resources and information on the lymphatic system.

History of Science

Florence Rena Sabin (1871–1953) was a pioneering medical researcher in the field of **lymphatic system** development. Sabin discovered that lymphatic vessels arose from veins. She found that the outer layer of cells on veins sprouted buds, much like stems growing out of the branches of trees, proving that the lymphatic system developed entirely from existing vessels in the body.

Answers

A Predict Lymphatic circulation depends on the activity of skeletal muscles to pump the fluid throughout the body. If someone sits too long, lymph cannot move as efficiently, and fluid may pool in the legs, causing swelling.

B Predict Both systems would be impaired. The spleen cleans lymph and produces white blood cells. Removing it would mean that more debris might accumulate in the lymph. Also, fewer white blood cells would be produced, reducing the effectiveness of the immune system.

Assess and Reteach ▼

Assess Use the Online Quiz or Section Quiz (*Assessment Book,* p. 596).

Reteach Project on the board the image of **FIGURE 30.18** from the Media Gallery. Have students use the image to trace the movement of lymph from tissues to the circulatory system.

OPTIONS FOR INQUIRY

INVESTIGATION

Time 45 minutes	TEACHER TESTED
Teacher Preparation	
Student Difficulty	
Lab Binder Human Bio, pp. 30–32	

Purpose Determine whether lung capacity changes with exercise.

Overview Students will construct a respirometer to measure lung capacity. They will

- measure lung capacity at rest
- measure lung capacity after exercise
- construct and analyze a graph of the data

LAB PREPARATION

- Prepare the bottles by drilling a hole in the bottom of each bottle before class. The hole should be just big enough for the straw.

LAB MANAGEMENT

- Encourage students to pick a variety of exercises: low impact, moderate impact, and high impact.

Teacher Note "I've done this using respirometers from a biological supply company. This was much better, having students put the parts together to make one. Cool idea."

Inclusion Group students so that students with physical disabilities will have assistance with this lab.

POST-LAB DISCUSSION

Discuss the results of the tests and have students form conclusions. **Ask,** Why were the test subjects unable to blow into the straw as long after exercise as they were at rest? Breathing rate is faster after exercise. The test subjects most likely needed to breathe faster, so they could not blow into the straw as long after exercise, and even less able after more intense exercise.

Use these inquiry-based labs and online activities to deepen your understanding of how the lungs respond when you exercise.

NOS.1 Develop explanations based on reproducible data and observations gathered during laboratory investigations.

NOS.3 Clearly communicate their ideas and results of investigations verbally and in written form using tables, graphs, diagrams, and photographs.

INVESTIGATION

Making and Using a Respirometer

In this lab you will make a model respirometer, an instrument that measures your lung capacity. You will use your model to measure your lung capacity before and after different types of exercise.

SKILL Modeling

PROBLEM How might exercise affect a person's lung capacity?

MATERIALS

- 1 liter bottle with a hole in the bottom
- scissors
- white paper
- marker
- metric ruler
- 15 cm clear tape
- small paper cup
- plastic straw that bends
- clock with a second hand

PROCEDURE

1. Use the materials to construct a model like the one shown. In your finished model, you should be able to breathe into the straw and raise the cup.
2. Construct a data table in which to record your data.
3. Measure your lung capacity at rest. Take a deep breath and blow into the straw until the bottom of the cup reaches between 2 cm and 6 cm. Your partner will time how long you can keep the cup between these two points.
4. Decide on three types of exercises to perform during your investigation. You will perform each exercise for two minutes. After two minutes, immediately blow into your respirometer. Have your partner time how long you can keep the bottom of the cup between the 2 cm and 6 cm mark. Rest for three minutes, then start the next exercise.

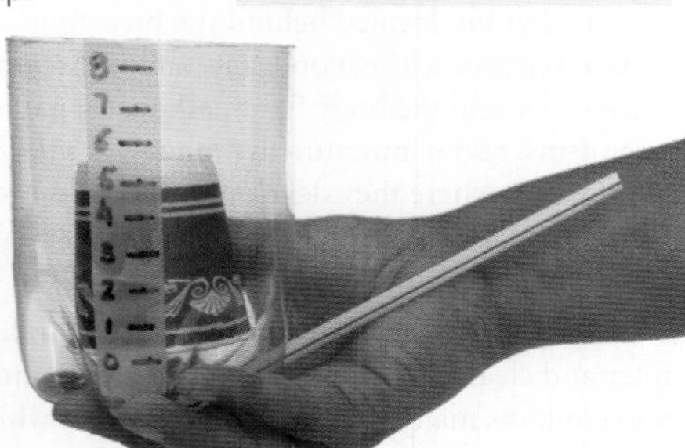

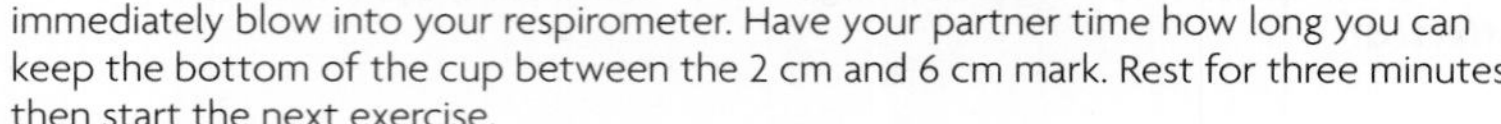

ANALYZE AND CONCLUDE

1. **Graph Data** Construct a bar graph to represent your data. What differences occurred in your lung capacity before and after you exercised?
2. **Contrast** What were the differences in your lung capacity after each type of exercise?
3. **Predict** How would you expect a person's lung capacity to change one week, two weeks, and three weeks after recovering from a minor cold?

EXTEND YOUR INVESTIGATION

Ask a sprinter and a long-distance runner, someone who plays a trumpet or trombone, and someone who is a singer to do this experiment. Which person would you expect to have the greatest lung capacity? After conducting the experiment, form a hypothesis based on your observations for further testing.

932 Unit 9: Human Biology

Answers

Sample Data

Effects of Exercise on Lung Capacity

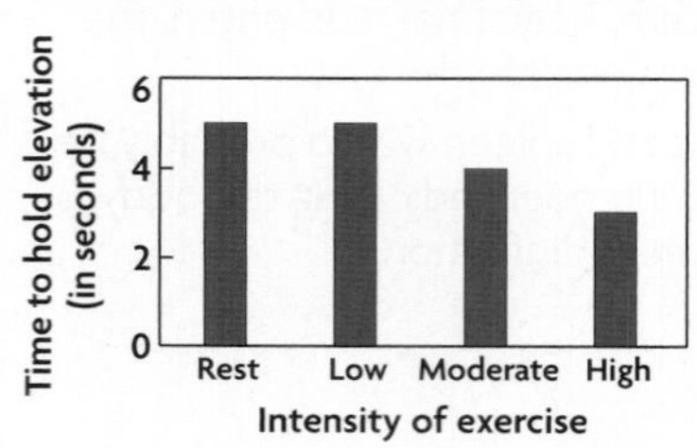

Analyze and Conclude

1. Students should create a bar or line graph with *Intensity of Exercise* on the *x*-axis and *Time (sec)* on the *y*-axis. Answers may show that lung capacity decreases after exercise, compared to lung capacity before exercise.
2. Usually the more rigorous the exercise, the less lung capacity students have.
3. A person having just got over a cold would have less lung capacity. Two or three weeks later, the lung capacity should be greater.

INVESTIGATION

Stimuli and Heart Rate

In this lab, you will test how different stimuli affect heart rate. You will expose the subject to two different stimuli—one that is intense and exciting and one that is calming and relaxing. You will then measure how the heart rate is affected before and after each stimulus.

SKILL Designing Experiments

PROBLEM How would the heart rate respond to two different types of stimuli?

MATERIALS
- CD player
- VCR or DVD player
- videos, DVDs, or CDs
- clock with a second hand (or stopwatch)

PROCEDURE

1. Determine a procedure for your experiment. You may want to compare the difference in results between music with a fast beat and music that is more relaxing. Or you may want to compare the difference between a video or DVD of an exciting sports competition and a video or DVD that shows beautiful scenery.
2. Identify your independent and dependent variables. How long will you expose the subject to each stimulus? How will you measure heart rate? At what points in the experiment will you measure the subject's heart rate?
3. Predict how the independent variables will affect the dependent variable. Construct a data table in which to record your data.
4. Have your teacher approve your procedure. Carry out your experiment.

ANALYZE AND CONCLUDE

1. **Analyze** Construct a graph to represent your data. What is the relationship between the independent and dependent variables? Was your prediction supported by the data?
2. **Evaluate** How could you improve the design of your experiment to obtain more accurate results? What variables could you control better?

Online BIOLOGY CLASSZONE.COM

VIRTUAL LAB
Blood Typing
How does a doctor find out the blood type of a blood sample? In this interactive lab, you will learn how to identify blood types, and then work on your own to identify the blood types of several samples.

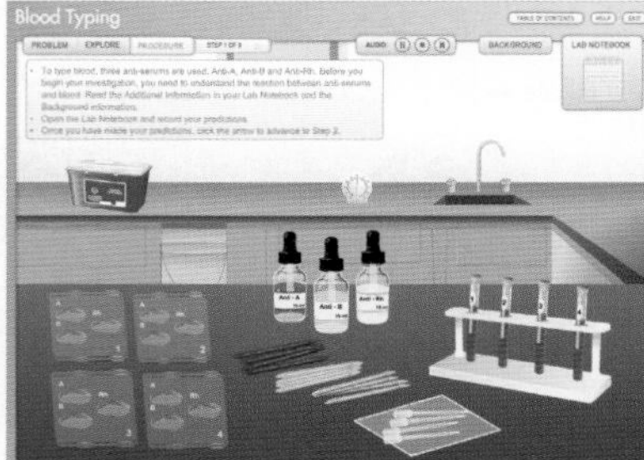

ANIMATED BIOLOGY
Build the Circulatory and Respiratory Systems
The respiratory system and circulatory system are closely connected. Build the two systems to get a better understanding of how they work together.

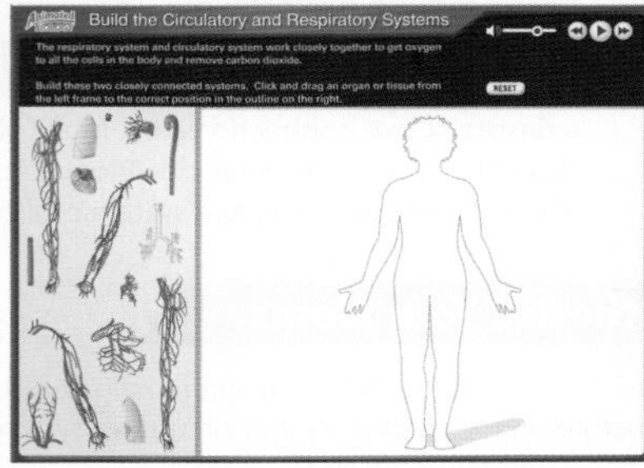

WEBQUEST
Asthma rates are increasing steadily across the country. Complete the WebQuest to learn what causes asthma, what triggers an episode, and why people with asthma can still live healthy, active lives.

Answers

Sample Data

For a sample of student data from this lab, go to page R110.

Analyze and Conclude

1. The relationship is direct, because heart rate (dependent variable) depends on the type of stimulus (independent variable). Usually the more exciting material caused the heart rate to increase, and the more calming material caused the heart rate to remain the same or even decrease.
2. In general, the variables that could be better controlled include background noise, experimental setting, and the initial mood of the subject (making sure the subject is in relatively the same physical, mental, and emotional state).

Online Biology ▼

VIRTUAL LAB Use this interactive lab to reinforce the concepts in **Section 30.5.**

ANIMATED BIOLOGY Use this interactive animation to reinforce the concepts in **Section 30.1.**

WEBQUEST The WebQuest takes one full class period. Students complete the activity online and then will need access to a printer to print their answers. Sample answers, teacher notes, and alternative assessment ideas are available on **ClassZone.com.** Use with **Section 30.2.**

INVESTIGATION

TEACHER TESTED

Time	45 minutes
Teacher Preparation	1 flask
Student Difficulty	1 flask
Lab Binder	Human Bio, pp. 33–34

Purpose Determine the effects of different stimuli on heart rate.

Overview Students will design an experiment that compares the effects of relaxing stimuli and exciting stimuli on heart rate.

LAB PREPARATION

- Borrow videos, CDs, or DVDs that have appropriate content—fast paced, exciting, thrilling; calm, serene, relaxing.
- Allow students to choose their own materials.

Safety Caution students to keep the volume of the music within normal hearing levels.

POST-LAB DISCUSSION

Discuss methods students used to plan their experiments. Compare the graphed data for each test. Discuss varied results.

CHAPTER REVIEW

Interactive Review

Encourage students to go to **ClassZone.com** for a detailed review of each section, including visuals and vocabulary practice.

Unit Resource Book, Vocabulary Practice, pp. 87–90

CHAPTER 30 **Interactive Review** @ CLASSZONE.COM

KEY CONCEPTS | Vocabulary Games | Concept Maps | Animated Biology | Online Quiz

30.1 Respiratory and Circulatory Functions

The respiratory and circulatory systems bring oxygen and nutrients to the cells. These two systems work together to maintain homeostasis. The respiratory system moves gases into and out of the blood. The circulatory system transports blood to all parts of the body.

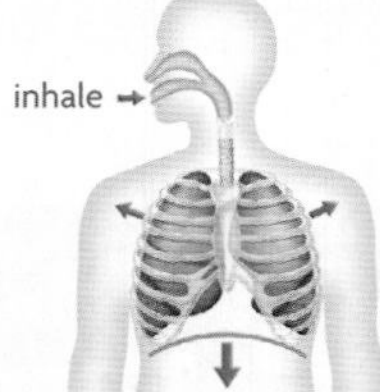

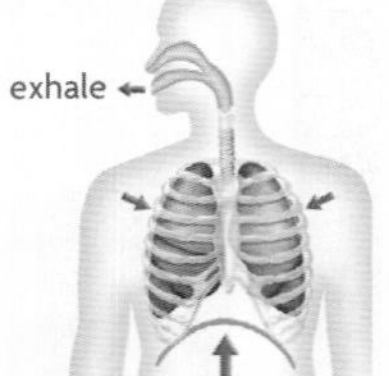

30.2 Respiration and Gas Exchange

The respiratory system exchanges oxygen and carbon dioxide. Gas exchange occurs in the alveoli of the lungs, where oxygen and carbon dioxide diffuse into and out of the blood. Respiratory diseases such as emphysema and asthma interfere with gas exchange.

30.3 The Heart and Circulation

The heart is a muscular pump that moves the blood through two pathways. The tissues and structures of the heart make it an efficient pump and allow it to work continuously. The heartbeat consists of two contractions that move blood from the atria to the ventricles. Blood circulates through the pulmonary and systemic pathways.

30.4 Blood Vessels and Transport

The circulatory system transports materials throughout the body. Arteries, veins, and capillaries transport blood to all the cells. The force with which blood pushes against the wall of an artery is known as blood pressure. The health of the circulatory system can be supported or harmed by lifestyle choices.

30.5 Blood

Blood is a complex tissue that transports materials. Blood is composed mainly of cells, platelets, and plasma. Red blood cells transport gases, white blood cells help fight diseases, and platelets help seal wounds. Proteins in blood determine blood type and Rh+ and Rh- factors. The ABO group is the most commonly used of all the blood grouping systems.

30.6 Lymphatic System

The lymphatic system provides another type of circulation in the body. The lymphatic system collects excess fluid between the cells, filters it, and returns it to the circulatory system. The lymphatic system is also an important part of the immune system.

Synthesize Your Notes

Venn Diagram Use a Venn diagram to help you compare structures in the respiratory and circulatory systems.

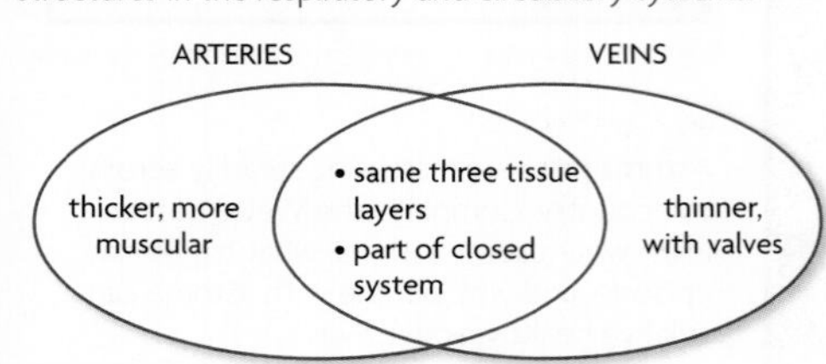

Concept Map A concept map is a good way to organize your notes on topics such as the components of blood.

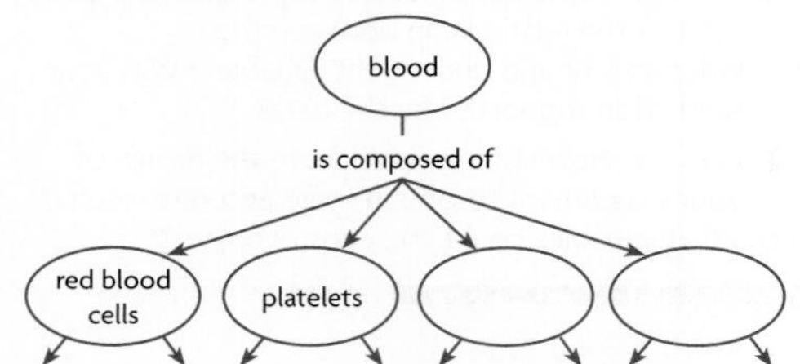

Reviewing Vocabulary

1. A capillary carries wastes away from cells to a vein.
2. Blood moves from an atrium to a ventricle in the heart.
3. An artery is a blood vessel that carries blood away from the heart.
4. Pulmonary circulation occurs between the lungs and heart, whereas systemic circulation occurs between the heart and the rest of the body.
5. Systolic pressure occurs when the left ventricle contracts, whereas diastolic pressure occurs when the left ventricle relaxes.
6. Blood contains several components, including platelets and plasma.
7. The trachea is the main airway leading to the vessels of the lungs.
8. White blood cells called lymphocytes circulate in lymph to help protect the body from microorganisms.
9. "Small hollow space" describes the structure of the tiny air sacs known as alveoli.
10. In emphysema, the lungs must work harder to take in air from the atmosphere, so people must breathe more deeply, or "inflate" their lungs more.
11. Hemoglobin is a protein that binds oxygen to red blood cells and gives blood its bright red color.
12. Plasma is a fluid, composed mostly of water, that helps thin the blood and allows it to flow through the vessels more easily.

Reviewing Main Ideas

13. Sensors in the artery walls and heart monitor O_2 and CO_2 levels. As the need for O_2 rises, the brain stem signals the heart and muscles of the rib cage and diaphragm to work harder, increasing breathing and heart rates to maintain O_2 and CO_2 levels.
14. Upon inhalation, the muscles of the rib cage and diaphragm contract, causing the rib cage to expand, increasing the lungs' volume. The lower air pressure in the lungs allows air to flow in. Upon exhalation, the muscles relax,

Chapter Assessment

Chapter Vocabulary

30.1 circulatory systems, p. 910
respiratory systems, p. 910
trachea, p. 911
lung, p. 911
alveoli, p. 911
diaphragm, p. 912
heart, p. 912
artery, p. 913
vein, p. 913
capillaries, p. 913

30.2 red blood cell, p. 915
hemoglobin, p. 915
emphysema, p. 916
asthma, p. 916

30.3 atrium, p. 917
ventricle, p. 917
valve, p. 917
pacemaker, p. 918
pulmonary circulation, p. 920
systemic circulation, p. 920

30.4 blood pressure, p. 923
systolic pressure, p. 923
diastolic pressure, p. 923

30.5 platelet, p. 926
plasma, p. 926
ABO blood group, p. 927
Rh factor, p. 928
white blood cells, p. 928

30.6 lymphatic system, p. 930
lymph, p. 930
node, p. 930
lymphocyte, p. 931

Reviewing Vocabulary

Term Relationships

For each pair of terms below, write a sentence that describes or explains a relationship between the two terms. For example, *oxygen, carbon dioxide:* All cells use oxygen and produce carbon dioxide as a waste product.

1. vein, capillary
2. atrium, ventricle
3. artery, heart
4. systemic circulation, pulmonary circulation
5. systolic pressure, diastolic pressure
6. platelet, plasma
7. lung, trachea
8. lymph, lymphocyte

Word Origins

For each term below, describe how its Latin or Greek meaning relates to its definition.

9. *Alveolus* comes from the Latin term *alveus*, which means "small hollow space."

10. *Emphysema* comes from the Greek term *emphysan*, which means "to inflate."

11. *Hemoglobin* is a combination of the Greek term *haima*, which means "blood," and the word *globin*, which refers to a protein.

12. *Plasma* comes from the Greek term *plassein*, which means "to mold or spread thin."

Reviewing MAIN IDEAS

13. When you exercise, your need for O_2 rises. How do your respiratory and circulatory systems react to maintain homeostasis in your body?

14. Describe how the diaphragm and muscles of the rib cage help bring air into and out of the lungs.

15. Explain how, in normal respiration, CO_2 and O_2 are able to diffuse in opposite directions through the alveolar and capillary walls.

16. How does damage to the alveoli from injury or disease affect the exchange of gases in the lungs?

17. Describe how the structures of the heart make it an efficient pump.

18. Explain how the circulatory system keeps oxygen-poor blood separate from oxygen-rich blood.

19. Compare the functions of arteries and veins.

20. Advice for maintaining a healthy circulatory system always includes proper diet and exercise. Explain what impact these two factors can have on the arteries.

21. Describe the main components of blood and the function of each component.

22. Explain what happens after a blood vessel is torn.

23. Why might it be important to know your blood type?

24. Explain what the lymphatic system is and why it is considered part of the immune system.

and the rib cage and lungs contract. As air pressure in the lungs increases, air flows out.

15. In normal respiration, CO_2 and O_2 can diffuse in opposite directions due to their concentrations. There is more CO_2 in the capillaries, so it diffuses into the alveolus. There is more O_2 in the alveolus, so it diffuses into the capillaries.

16. When alveoli are damaged, the surface area for gas exchange is reduced. A person would have to breathe more deeply and rapidly to maintain homeostasis.

17. The heart is an efficient pump because of its chamber and valve construction, its cardiac muscle fibers, and its relatively small size. Cardiac muscles can exert a large force on its small size.

18. Separate chambers in the heart, separation of arteries and veins, and a separate pulmonary circulation pathway keep oxygen-poor blood from mixing with oxygen-rich blood.

CHAPTER REVIEW

19. Arteries carry blood away from the heart and are more muscular and elastic than veins because the blood they carry is under great pressure. Veins carry blood to the heart. Because the blood is under much less pressure, veins have valves to keep blood from flowing backward.

20. Proper diet can prevent sticky buildup, called plaque, from collecting on artery walls. Exercise can strengthen the heart muscle and help keep blood circulating well in the body, particularly in the veins.

21. Blood is composed mainly of plasma, red blood cells, white blood cells, and platelets. Red blood cells carry O_2, white blood cells defend the body from microorganisms and foreign material, platelets aid in sealing wounds, and plasma helps maintain blood volume and contains many important substances that diffuse into and out of the blood.

22. Platelets develop spiky extensions and release proteins to activate clotting factors, such as fibrin. Fibrin creates a sticky net that traps other platelets and white blood cells, which form a clot to seal the wound. When the wound has healed, chemicals in the clot are activated to dissolve it.

23. If you ever need to give or receive blood in an emergency, knowing your blood type can prevent an incompatible mixing of blood types, which can result in a life-threatening immune reaction.

24. The lymphatic system is composed of the tonsils, thymus, spleen, and lymph nodes and vessels. It provides another type of circulatory system in the body. Its major function is to collect fluid that leaks out of the circulatory system and return it to the heart to maintain blood volume and fluid homeostasis. It also helps defend the body against disease and removes waste products and cell fragments from interstitial fluid.

Critical Thinking

25. When people lift or push a heavy weight, they are using their skeletal muscles more than usual, which exerts greater pressure on the veins. This pressure causes the veins to expand or puff out and become more visible.
26. You would test blood from an artery in the arm, which would show how much oxygen has been absorbed from the lungs and pumped from the heart. The only vein that could be tested is the pulmonary vein, which would clearly show how much oxygen is being absorbed from the lungs.
27. If the atmosphere were filled with CO_2, it would be inhaled by the animal. Diffusion would not take place between the alveoli and capillaries because the CO_2 concentrations would be similar. The lack of oxygen circulating through the body would suffocate and kill the animal.
28. The heavy weight would interfere with the movement of the rib cage muscles and the diaphragm, making it difficult for the rib cage to expand and contract.
29. The brain cells in the affected area would be starved of oxygen and nutrients and would quickly begin to cease functioning.

Interpreting Visuals

30. Oxygen-poor blood enters from the body into the right atrium and is pumped to the right ventricle, where it travels to the lungs. Oxygen-rich blood returns from the lungs and enters the left atrium, is pumped to the left ventricle, and from there is pumped to the rest of the body.
31. The right atrium needs two openings because blood returns from the lower and upper body through two separate veins.
32. The left ventricle and the aortic valve would be under the most stress from high blood pressure. The left ventricle contains the most blood, and the force exerted on it is larger because it must pump blood to the rest of the body. The aortic valve must seal the chamber to prevent blood from flowing backward. The higher the pressure, the more stress there would be on the muscle and valve of the left ventricle.

Critical Thinking

25. Infer When people lift or push a heavy weight, their veins often puff up and become visible under their skin. Why do you think this happens?

26. Synthesize A person who is exposed to high levels of smoke during a fire may be taken to a hospital for a test to determine whether he or she has enough oxygen in the blood. Would you test the blood from an artery or a vein in this case? Explain your answer.

27. Analyze In volcanic areas, certain depressions in the ground are filled with high levels of CO_2. Animals wandering into these areas die so quickly that they have no chance of getting out. Use your knowledge of diffusion and circulation to explain why death might occur so quickly.

28. Apply If someone has a heavy weight on his or her chest, explain why after a short time it becomes difficult to breathe, even though the person's mouth and nose are not affected.

29. Predict A stroke occurs when the blood supply to the brain is interrupted. What immediate impact would this event have on the brain cells?

Interpreting Visuals

Use the diagram of the heart to answer the next three questions.

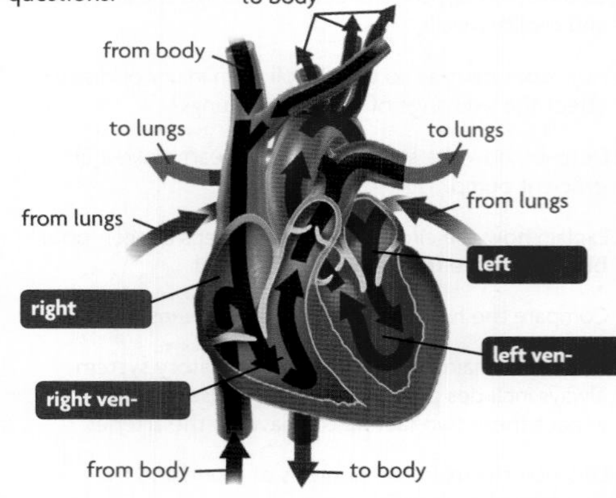

30. Identify Describe the path of blood in the heart.

31. Infer Why does the heart need two openings leading into the right atrium?

32. Analyze Which chamber(s) and valve(s) do you think would be under the most stress from high blood pressure? Explain.

Analyzing Data

A scientist is investigating the relationship between age and rates of smoking—light, medium, or heavy. Use the graph below about age and smoking rates to answer the next two questions about accepting or rejecting a null hypothesis.

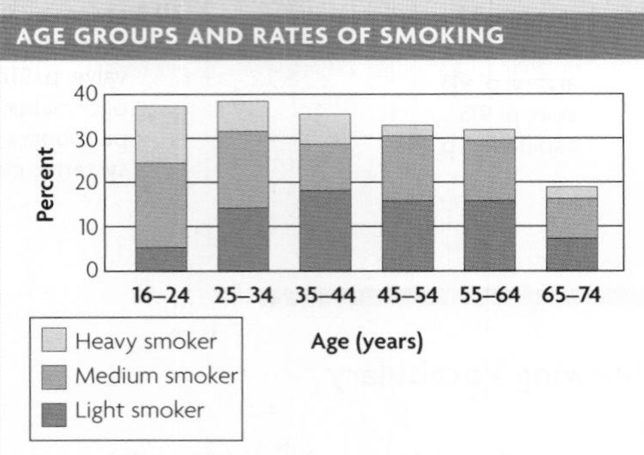

33. Evaluate One null hypothesis for this investigation might be: "There is no relationship between age and smoking rates." Based on the data, would you accept or reject this null hypothesis? Explain your answer.

34. Apply Form another null hypothesis for this investigation based on age and smoking rates. Explain whether the data would cause you to accept or reject your hypothesis.

Connecting CONCEPTS

35. Write a Proposal Suppose you are asked to make an animated film about the journey of an oxygen molecule from the time it is inhaled until it reaches a cell. Write a proposal describing your concept for the film. Include in your description the names of structures in the circulatory and respiratory systems, such as *trachea, alveoli, atrium, ventricle*, and so on.

36. Synthesize The heart and lungs work very efficiently, but they can be strengthened by exercise to work even better. For instance, the heart rate of an athlete at rest is actually lower than the resting heart rate of a person who does not regularly exercise. Why do you think this is so? Use your knowledge of the muscular, circulatory, and respiratory systems in your answer.

Analyzing Data

33. Reject; the data clearly show there is a direct relationship between age and whether a person is a light, medium, or heavy smoker.
34. *Sample Answer:* People over age 34 are heavier smokers than are people age 34 or under. The null hypothesis would be rejected; a lower percentage of people in the over-34 age groups are heavy smokers and thus smoke more cigarettes than do most people who are younger.

INDIANA ISTEP+ Test Prep

NOS.1

Test Practice For more test practice, go to ClassZone.com.

1

Blood Type Compatibility	
Blood Type	**Can Receive Blood From**
A	A or O
B	B or O
AB	A, B, AB, O
O	O

This chart shows compatibility between different blood types. What would happen if a person with type O blood received a blood transfusion of any other blood type?

A There would be no complications because any blood type can be exchanged for another.

B Complications would result as the immune system attacks the foreign blood cells.

C A larger amount of the different blood type would be needed to supply the missing protein.

D There would be complications only if type AB were given.

2 The circulatory and respiratory systems work together to provide cells with oxygen and nutrients and remove waste products such as carbon dioxide. When you need more oxygen, how does the circulatory system respond?

A More blood is sent to the lungs and less to the rest of the body.

B The blood vessels to the arms and legs constrict to conserve oxygen.

C The heart beats faster to match the rise in breathing rate.

D Blood moves more slowly through the organs to carry away more wastes.

3 In order for the body to maintain homeostasis, the intake of oxygen into the lungs must be followed by

A an increase in blood pressure.

B the exhalation of carbon dioxide.

C a decrease in gas exchange.

D a decrease in blood flow.

4 At higher elevations, the air has a lower concentration of oxygen. What effect would living at higher elevations have on a person's lung capacity?

A It would be larger to take in more oxygen.

B It would be smaller because the lungs need less oxygen.

C It would be larger because there is more carbon dioxide.

D It would be the same regardless of elevation.

THINK THROUGH THE QUESTION

Think about what *concentration* means in this context. At higher elevations, a standard breath of air would contain less oxygen than would the same volume of air at lower elevations.

5 The circulatory system helps to maintain a stable body temperature as you exercise. Which statement best describes this process?

A Heat produced by the muscles is absorbed by the surrounding blood, where it cools.

B Blood carries excess heat from the muscles to the skin, which allows heat to escape.

C The circulatory and lymphatic systems work together to remove heat from the muscles.

D Excess heat from the muscles is transported to the heart and lungs, where it cools.

6 What causes high blood pressure and why might it be a symptom of greater medical problems?

Standards-Based Assessment

1. B	4. A
2. C	5. B
3. B	6. See Below

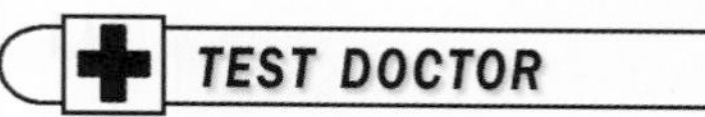

Question 3 Answer B is correct. Answers A, C, and D are incorrect because alterations to blood pressure, gas exchange, and blood flow would not directly help to eliminate carbon dioxide waste and maintain blood pH within acceptable limits.

Question 4 Answer A is correct. Answer B is incorrect because living at higher elevations does not decrease a person's need for oxygen. Answer C is incorrect because living at higher elevations does not increase carbon dioxide levels. Answer D is incorrect because the person at higher elevations would not get enough oxygen if lung capacity remains the same.

Question 5 Answer B is correct. Answers A and D are incorrect because they would keep heat trapped deep within the body. Answer C is incorrect because the lymphatic system helps the body fight infection, not maintain stable body temperature.

Question 6 Blood pressure is a measure of how much pressure is exerted on the inside of the artery walls by the blood. High blood pressure can mean that there is a block somewhere in the arteries, causing the blood pressure to build, or it can be a sign that the arteries are not elastic and have hardened or become brittle.

Connecting Concepts

35. The proposal should include the complete journey of the oxygen molecule from its entry into the nose or mouth, down the trachea through the lungs to the alveoli, binding to hemoglobin in red blood cells, journeying to the left atrium and ventricle of the heart, being pumped out of the heart into a major artery, and from there to an arteriole, to a capillary. It diffuses from the capillary to a cell.

36. Students should recall that the heart is a muscle and that muscles can be conditioned to be stronger and to work more efficiently. When a muscle is conditioned, it expends less energy to do the same amount of work. Therefore, an athlete's resting heart rate would be lower than an ordinary person's, because a stronger heart muscle requires less energy to pump.

ITEM CORRELATIONS	
Standard	**Items**
NOS.1	1

CHAPTER 31

Indiana Resource Preview

Print Resources

Immune System and Disease

INDIANA STANDARDS		Sections	PAGES and PACING	UNIT RESOURCE BOOK
	31.1	**Pathogens and Human Illness** **KEY CONCEPT** Germs cause many diseases in humans.	pp. 940–944 30 minutes	URB pages 91–94
	31.2	**Immune System** **KEY CONCEPT** The immune system consists of organs, cells, and molecules that fight infections.	pp. 945–948 30 minutes	URB pages 95–98
		DATA ANALYSIS: Identifying Experimental Design Flaws	p. 947 30 minutes	URB page 115
NOS.3		CHAPTER INVESTIGATION: Observing Normal and Diseased Tissue	p. 949 45 minutes	**Lab Binder** Human Bio pages 39–42
	31.3	**Immune Responses** **KEY CONCEPT** The immune system has many responses to pathogens and foreign cells.	pp. 950–954 30 minutes	URB pages 99–102
	31.4	**Immunity and Technology** **KEY CONCEPT** Living in a clean environment and building immunity help keep a person healthy.	pp. 955–956 30 minutes	URB pages 103–106
	31.5	**Overreactions of the Immune System** **KEY CONCEPT** An overactive immune system can make the body very unhealthy.	pp. 957–959 30 minutes	URB pages 107–110
	31.6	**Diseases That Weaken the Immune System** **KEY CONCEPT** When the immune system is weakened, the body cannot fight off diseases.	pp. 960–963 30 minutes	URB pages 111–114
NOS.6		OPTIONS FOR INQUIRY	pp. 964–965 30 minutes, 45 minutes	**Lab Binder** Human Bio pages 43–45
		Chapter Review	pp. 966–969	**Assessment Book** Chapter Tests A, B pp. 617–624

INDIANA STANDARDS

NOS.3 Clearly communicate their ideas and results of investigations verbally and in written form using tables, graphs, diagrams, and photographs.

NOS.6 Use analogies and models (mathematical and physical) to simplify and represent systems that are difficult to understand or directly experience due to their size, time scale, or complexity, and recognize the limitations of analogies and models.

Labs

PUPIL EDITION LABS

How Pathogens Spread, Section 1, p. 943 Students model the spread of a pathogen through a population. **Lab Binder** p.46	**Time:** 10 minutes **Materials:** 8-oz cup, 100 mL unknown solution, eyedropper, 3 drops "pathogen"-detecting solution
Observing Normal and Diseased Tissue, p. 949 Students compare healthy and diseased tissue by examining them under a microscope. **Lab Binder** pp. 39–42	**Time:** 45 minutes **Materials:** slide of normal lymph tissue, slide of diseased lymph tissue, slide of normal lung tissue, slide of diseased lung tissue (lung cancer or pneumonia), slide of normal red blood cells, slide of anemic red blood cells, slide of stomach tissue, slide of ulcer cells, slide of normal liver, slide of cinetosis of the liver, microscope

OPTIONS FOR INQUIRY

Modeling T Cell Activation, p. 964 Students use common materials to model how a T cell becomes activated. **Lab Binder** pp. 43–44	**Time:** 30 minutes **Materials:** sheet of white paper, 5 colors of construction paper, colored markers, glue, scissors
What Is an Autoimmune Disease?, p. 965 Students research the cause of an autoimmune disease, how the disease progresses, and possible treatments. **Lab Binder** p. 45	**Time:** 45 minutes **Material:** Computer with Internet access

LAB BINDER Unit 9 Human Biology

Additional Investigation: Simulating Viral Detection with ELISA, pp. 47–50

Biotechnology Lab: Food Allergies, Human Bio pp. 92–95

LAB GENERATOR

A searchable CD of all labs in the program in editable format, including forensic, probeware, and biotechnology labs.

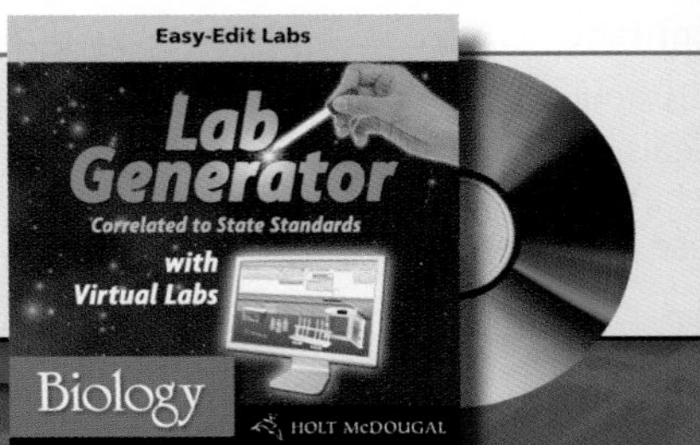

Presentation Tools

POWER PRESENTATIONS

Presentation Chapter 31
Power Presentations for each section incorporate images and clips from the Media Gallery: Includes Note Navigator for each section.

MEDIA GALLERY

Contains the following images and video clips, as well as animations, simulations and forms of visuals from the book.

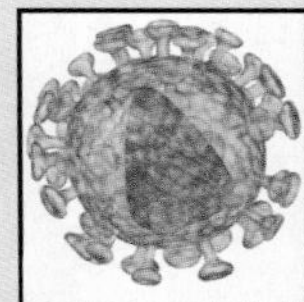
HIV

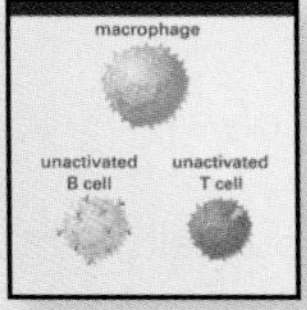

Immune responses

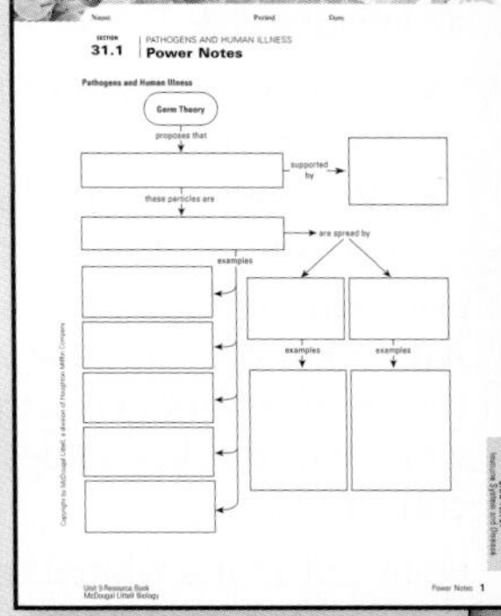

Power Notes

Computer model of antibody

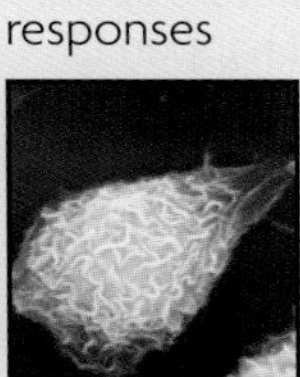
Phagocytosis

VIDEO

Review a set of short video clips exploring challenges to the immune system.

ANIMATED BIOLOGY

Vaccines and Active Immunity

Destroy the Invaders

TRANSPARENCIES

Cellular Immunity T129 **Vaccine Response** T131

Humoral Immunity T130 **HIV Infection** T132

BioZine
Animated Biology
Interactive Review
SciLinks
Resource Centers

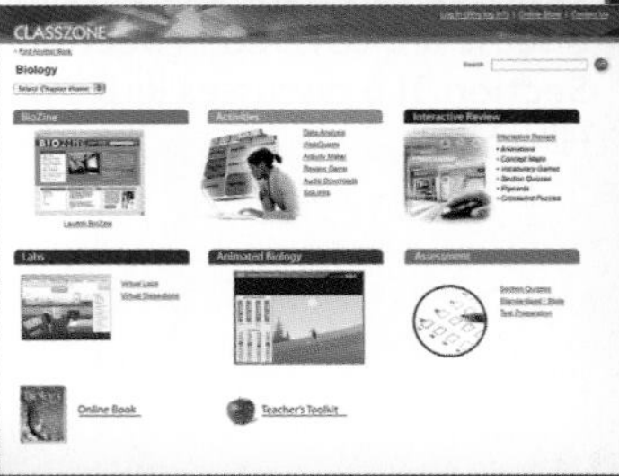

CHAPTER

31

▼ Focus and Motivate

How do your cells fight off invaders?

Students may answer that the white blood cell in the photograph is attacking an invader. **Ask**

- What is the invader? *E. coli,* a bacterium
- What other germs do your cells fight off? viruses, fungi, protozoa

Have students look at the picture again. **Ask,** What do you think will happen if the germs reproduce faster that your white blood cells can destroy them? You could get sick.

Point out that a white blood cell is only one way the immune system protects the body from invaders.

BIOZINE ClassZone.com

Students can access BioZine at **ClassZone.com** to learn about some of the latest research in the biological sciences.

In a Hurry?

You can have students review germ theory and modes of infection in **Section 31.1.** The critical material of the chapter is found in **Sections 31.2** and **31.3,** which cover the cells and proteins that fight pathogens, and the immune response. **Section 31.4** provides information on antiseptics, antibiotics, and vaccines. Allergens and autoimmune disease are covered in **Section 31.5; Section 31.6** discusses leukemia and HIV/AIDS.

31 Immune System and Disease

KEY CONCEPTS

31.1 Pathogens and Human Illness
Germs cause many diseases in humans.

31.2 Immune System
The immune system consists of organs, cells, and molecules that fight infections.

31.3 Immune Responses
The immune system has many responses to pathogens and foreign cells.

31.4 Immunity and Technology
Living in a clean environment and building immunity help keep a person healthy.

31.5 Overreactions of the Immune System
An overactive immune system can make the body very unhealthy.

31.6 Diseases That Weaken the Immune System
When the immune system is weakened, the body cannot fight off diseases.

BIOLOGY CLASSZONE.COM

Animated BIOLOGY
View animated chapter concepts.
- Vaccines and Active Immunity
- Destroy the Invaders

BIOZINE
Keep current with biology news.
- Featured stories
- News feeds
- Bio Bytes

RESOURCE CENTER
Get more information on
- Immune Response
- Allergies
- Autoimmune Disorders

Teacher Demo

Eye Opener Show how pathogens are spread by direct contact.

Note: This activity is similar to the Quick Lab on page 943 that deals with identifying the origin of a pathogen. You may choose to do one or both of these activities.

Materials
- hand lens (enough for class)
- cornstarch

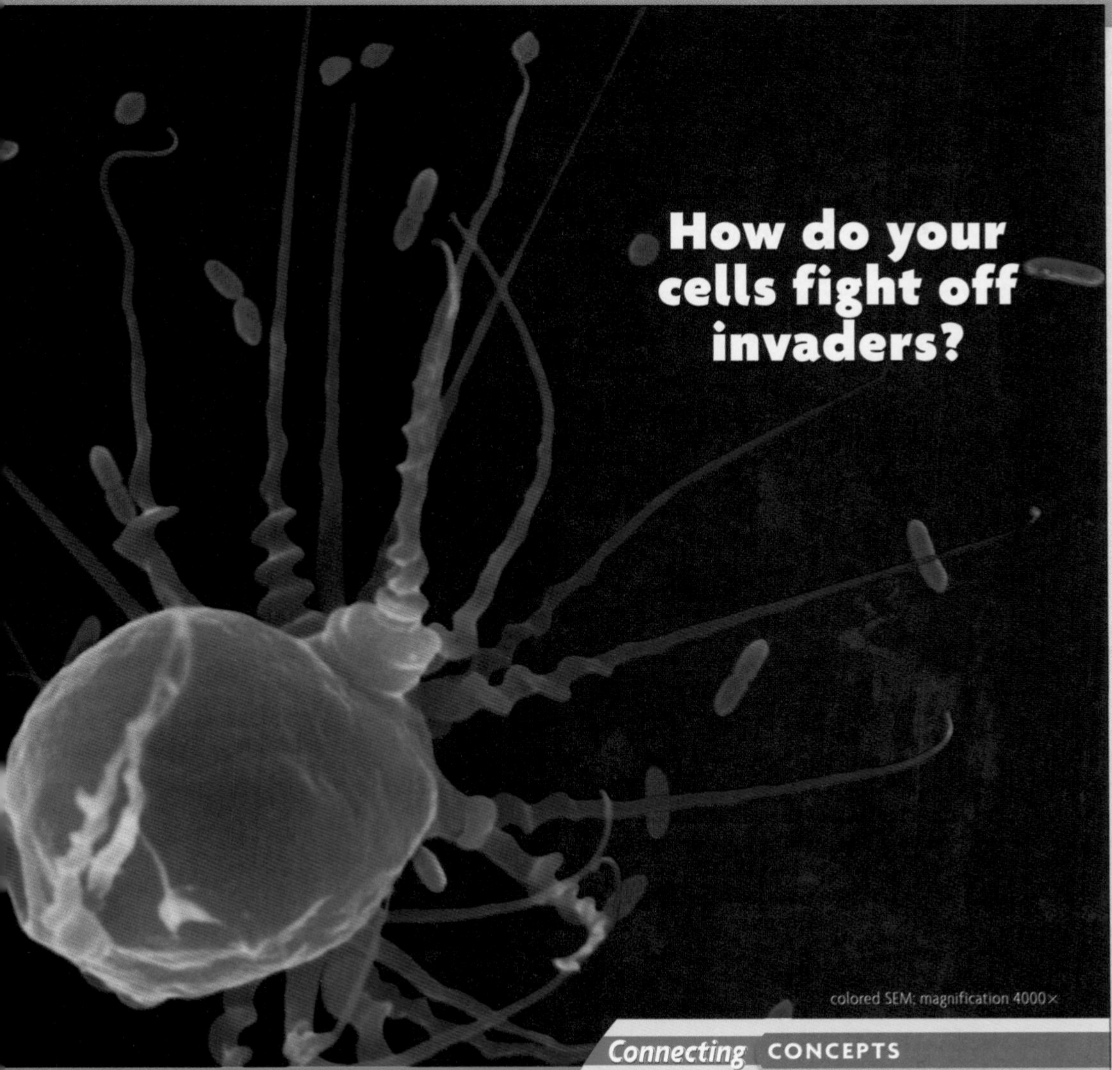

How do your cells fight off invaders?

colored SEM; magnification 4000×

Connecting CONCEPTS

You do not get sick every time disease-causing germs invade your body. Sometimes white blood cells, like the one in blue above, attack and destroy invaders without your feeling ill. Other times, you get sick because germs, such as the purple *E. coli* above, start winning. Fortunately, a healthy immune system can overpower many different types of germs—even when the germs temporarily gain the upper hand.

Plants Spots on a plant's leaves are evidence that the plant's immune system is fighting an infection. When a germ invades a plant, the infected cells release chemicals that kill the neighboring plant cells. With the surrounding cells dead, the germ is isolated and cannot infect the rest of the plant. Here, an English oak tree leaf has responded to a parasitic infection by causing its own cells around the infection sites to die (orange).

Demonstrate Before students enter class, put a small amount of cornstarch on the palms of your hands. As students enter class, stand by the door and greet them by randomly shaking some of their hands. After everyone has taken a seat, have students sitting next to one another shake hands. Discourage students from washing or wiping their hands until the end of this demonstration. Have students use the hand lens to examine their hands for cornstarch.

Discuss Tell students that the cornstarch represents a disease-causing pathogen. Find out how many students are "infected." **Ask**

- How was the "pathogen" spread? direct contact
- How could the "infection" have been prevented? avoiding contact, washing hands

Point out that infections can also spread by transferring pathogens to surfaces that might be touched by others.

Activate Prior Knowledge

Discuss with students what measures their parents or caregivers took to keep them from catching a cold or a "bug" when they were younger. **Ask,** What value is there to the common wisdom that you must dress warmly in cold or rainy weather to keep from catching a cold? Students may recognize that the body is spending energy to keep warm and so other body systems, such as the immune system, may be weakened. Point out another contributing factor are closed windows in your home or school, which keep out fresh air and keep in pathogens.

Preview Vocabulary

Greek and Latin Word Origins Tell students that two words important to this chapter are *disease* and *immunity.* Tell students that the word disease can be broken down into two familiar parts, *dis-* and *ease.* The prefix *dis-* means "not" and *ease* means "the condition of being comfortable." *Immunity* is related to the Latin word *immunis,* which means "exempt from public service." Discuss how these meanings apply to the words as they are used in this chapter.

Academic Vocabulary Students may be familiar with words based on the Greek word *pathos,* which means "suffering."

pathology, study of the nature of disease and its causes

pathetic, capable of arousing compassion or scornful pity

apathy, lack of emotion or feeling

sympathy, sharing the feelings of distress of another

English Learners Students may get confused by the number of terms used in this chapter that start with the prefix *anti-*:

antigen	*antibody*
antiviral	*antibacterial*
antibiotic	*antiseptic*

Make sure students understand that while most of these things are harmful to pathogens, they are not harmful to people. Remind students to look for context clues to help them derive meaning.

SECTION 31.1

▼ Plan and Prepare

Objectives

- Summarize the germ theory.
- Describe the different pathogens and the way they enter the body.

Section Resources

Unit Resource Book Study Guide pp. 91–92 Power Notes p. 93 Reinforcement p. 94
Interactive Reader Chapter 31 **Spanish Study Guide** pp. 313–314
Biology Toolkit pp. C6, C10, C11, C22, C38
Technology Power Presentation 31.1 Media Gallery DVD Online Quiz 31.1

Activate Prior Knowledge Discuss whether all diseases are able to be passed from one person to another. **Ask,** What are some causes of disease? genetics; outside agents such as alcohol, smoking, and chemicals; pathogens such as viruses and bacteria Tell students that they will be learning about diseases caused by pathogens in this chapter.

▼ Teach

Vocabulary

Academic Vocabulary The word *germ* comes from the Latin word *germen,* which means "embryo or germ," and is commonly used to refer to a microorganism. The word *germ* can also be used in different ways.

wheat germ, embryo of a wheat kernel

germ cell, sperm or egg cell

germ layer, cellular layer that differentiates in embryos

germicide, disinfectant

31.1 Pathogens and Human Illness

KEY CONCEPT Germs cause many diseases in humans.

MAIN IDEAS

- Germ theory states that microscopic particles cause certain diseases.
- There are different types of pathogens.
- Pathogens can enter the body in different ways.

VOCABULARY

germ theory, p. 941
pathogen, p. 941
vector, p. 944

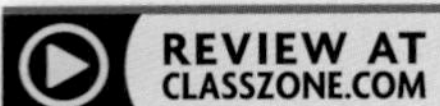

Connect Diseases caused by germs, such as the *E. coli* bacteria on the previous page, can be fatal. From 1330 to 1352, the bacteria that caused the Black Death killed 43 million people worldwide, or 13 percent of the population at the time. In 1918, a viral disease called the Spanish flu killed between 20 and 50 million people worldwide, or as much as 3 percent of the population. Because diseases can have devastating effects, scientists become concerned whenever a new disease such as HIV, SARS, or avian flu appears.

MAIN IDEA

Germ theory states that microscopic particles cause certain diseases.

A disease can be either infectious or noninfectious. Infectious diseases, such as flu and polio, can be passed from one person to another because infectious diseases are caused by germs. In contrast, cancer and heart disease are non-infectious diseases. These diseases are called noninfectious because a sick person cannot pass the disease to, or infect, a healthy person. Noninfectious diseases are not caused by germs; they result from a person's genetics or lifestyle.

FIGURE 31.1 History of Medicine

Most modern understanding about diseases occurred after Pasteur's germ theory.

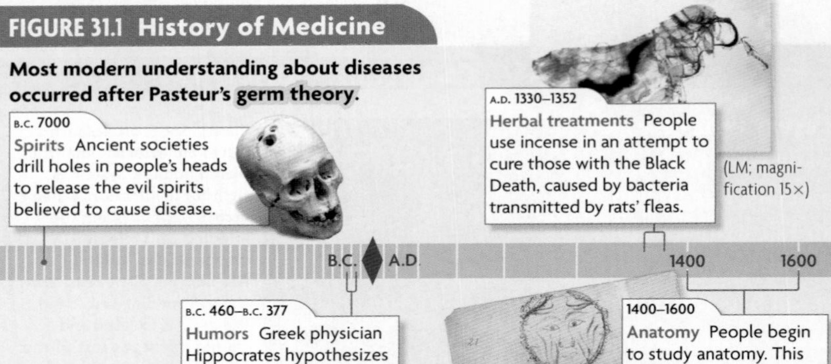

B.C. 7000
Spirits Ancient societies drill holes in people's heads to release the evil spirits believed to cause disease.
B.C. 460–B.C. 377
Humors Greek physician Hippocrates hypothesizes that fluids, called humors, cause disease.
A.D. 1330–1352
Herbal treatments People use incense in an attempt to cure those with the Black Death, caused by bacteria transmitted by rats' fleas.
(LM; magnification 15×)
1400–1600
Anatomy People begin to study anatomy. This drawing was made in the Middle East in 1555.
1857
Germ theory Louis Pasteur hypothesizes that disease is caused by small "animals."
1865
Antiseptic technique Joseph Lister finds that cleaning his surgical tools reduces patients' infections.
B.C.
A.D.
1400
1600
1800

Differentiated Instruction

BELOW LEVEL

Have students use the Directed Reading-Thinking Activity for this section. They should skim the pages to fill out the first three columns of a table marked: *What I know I know; What I think I know; What I think I'll learn; What I learned*

Once they have finished the section, they can make adjustments in the fourth column.

Biology Toolkit, DRTA, p. C6

ENGLISH LEARNERS

Write the topic *Immune System and Disease* on the board. Have students skim the chapter for a few minutes, then divide into several groups in different parts of the room. One student in each group gives a fact or an example related to the topic. Another student does the same. They cannot repeat statements. Continue for five minutes, then call time. Ask a student from each group to give the answers he or she can remember but not repeat ones from other groups. Create a class chart on the board or chart paper.

Biology Toolkit, Round Robin, p. C10

On the other hand, infectious diseases can be passed from one person to another because infectious diseases are caused by germs.

Today, it seems obvious that some germs cause infectious disease, but this concept is only a little more than 100 years old. It was not until the 1850s that French scientist Louis Pasteur helped make the connection between microorganisms and disease. His theory, called the **germ theory** of disease, proposed that specific microorganisms caused diseases. These disease-causing agents are called **pathogens.** Pasteur hypothesized that if pathogens were eliminated from the body, a person would not get sick.

Pasteur's germ theory led to rapid advances in our understanding of disease, as shown in **FIGURE 31.1.** But at the time, germ theory was not immediately accepted. It took the work of two other scientists to bring about the complete acceptance of Pasteur's germ theory.

Between 1861 and 1865, about half of British surgeon Joseph Lister's patients died from infections after otherwise successful operations. After hearing Pasteur's germ theory, Lister began using a weak acid to clean his operating tools and his patients' wounds before surgery. The number of his patients who died from infection dropped dramatically to near zero.

Meanwhile, German scientist Robert Koch found that he could make a healthy animal sick by injecting it with pathogens from a sick animal. From his experiments, he concluded that four conditions must be met before one can say that a certain pathogen causes a disease. These conditions are called Koch's postulates.

- The pathogen thought to cause the disease must be present in every case in which the disease is found.
- The pathogen must be isolated and grown outside the body in a pure, uncontaminated culture.
- Healthy animals infected with the pure culture must develop the disease.
- The pathogen must be re-isolated and cultured from the newly sick animals and must be identical to the original pathogen.

TAKING NOTES

Use a main idea diagram to study germ theory of disease.

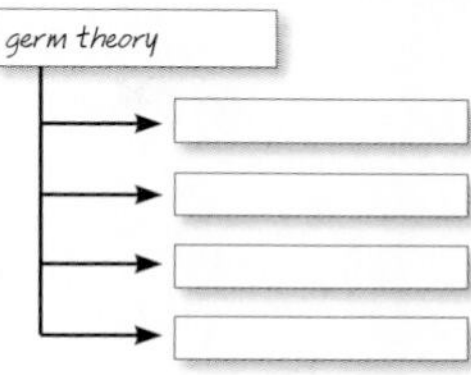

A Contrast How is germ theory different from earlier theories about disease?

1883 Koch's postulates Robert Koch finds four conditions that prove a pathogen causes a disease.

1900s Applying antiseptic technique Cities around the world start treating drinking water with chlorine, reducing the cases of cholera.

1928 Antibiotics Sir Alexander Fleming discovers penicillin.

1955 Polio vaccine Jonas Salk's vaccine against polio becomes available. The disease is eliminated in the U.S. in 1994.

2002 New diseases First cases of SARS, a disease that affects the respiratory system, spring up in China.

2005 Polio comeback Worldwide efforts increase to vaccinate people against polio, and the polio virus reemerges in fewer than ten people in the U.S.

1900

2000

The Inside Story

Louis Pasteur's early research involved working for wine makers to try to discover why some wine became sour during fermentation. He hypothesized that germs in the air got into the wine and caused it to sour. Pasteur discovered that the problem was solved by boiling the wine. This process of **pasteurization** is commonly used today to kill bacteria in milk and juices.

TEACH FROM VISUALS

FIGURE 31.1 Use the timeline to walk through the history of medicine. **Ask**

- Before Pasteur's hypothesis, what did people think caused disease? evil spirits, humors
- About how many years passed between Lister's use of an antiseptic technique to clean instruments and the use of an antiseptic technique to treat drinking water? about 40 years
- How many years passed between Pasteur's germ theory and the discovery of antibiotics? 71 years
- In comparison, how much time passed between the earliest studies of anatomy and the germ theory? more than 250 years

Answers

A Contrast Pasteur said that disease was caused by germs, or small living things. Earlier theories focused on the idea that evil spirits and humors caused disease.

PRE-AP

Tell students a new disease is infecting sheep in the Midwest. Have them apply Koch's postulates and use a sequence diagram to describe the procedure they would follow to identify the specific pathogen.

Biology Toolkit, Sequence Diagram, p. C38

Chapter 31: Immune System and Disease **941**

▼ Teach *continued*

Connecting CONCEPTS

Pathogens Having students understand the structure of viruses, bacteria, and fungi, and how they reproduce lays the groundwork for their understanding of how these organisms can enter the body, cause diseases, and be stopped by antibiotics and vaccines. Pathogens use nutrients in the body to reproduce, or, in the case of viruses, direct the DNA in body cells to reproduce viruses. Point out that not all bacteria living in the body are pathogens. Many bacteria thrive in and on the body, and some are very beneficial to humans.

Integrating Medical Science

Although cancers are noninfectious diseases, one exception is **cervical cancer.** It can be caused by the **human papillomavirus,** or HPV. Of the more than 100 identified types of HPV, all of which are sexually transmitted, 15 types cause almost all cases of cervical cancer. Not everyone who has one of these types of HPV will get cancer. In most cases, the body's immune system destroys the virus before the person ever gets sick. However, if the HPV infection remains, a woman's chance of getting cervical cancer increases significantly. New tests for detecting the virus and vaccines to prevent infection are now available.

MAIN IDEA

There are different types of pathogens.

Traditionally, bacteria and larger pathogens were isolated by straining them through a ceramic filter with tiny pores. The disease-causing bacteria would remain on the filter, and the solution that passed through the pores was harmless.

Sometimes, however, there were no visible pathogens on the filter, and the solution caused disease. By 1898, scientists had hypothesized that some disease-causing agents must be smaller than bacteria. They called these agents filterable viruses. As better technology was developed, scientists discovered a huge variety of tiny new pathogens, which are outlined below and in **FIGURE 31.2.**

Connecting CONCEPTS

Pathogens You can read more about microorganisms and viruses that cause disease in **Chapters 18 and 19.**

- **Bacteria** are single-celled organisms. They can cause illness by releasing chemicals that are toxic to the host or by destroying healthy body cells. Food poisoning, which causes a person to become nauseous, is a sickness caused by bacteria-released toxins.
- **Viruses** are disease-causing strands of DNA or RNA that are surrounded by protein coats. Viruses are so small that they could not be seen until the invention of the electron microscope in the 1930s. These particles enter and take over a healthy cell, forcing it to stop its normal activities and produce more viruses. Viruses cause illnesses such as flus, colds, and AIDS. You will learn more about AIDS in Section 31.6.
- **Fungi** can be multicellular or single-celled organisms, such as those you read about in Chapter 19. The fungi that cause disease do so by piercing healthy cells and taking the cell's nutrients. Fungal infections usually occur in places that are warm and damp. Athlete's foot, for example, is a fungus that invades the skin cells between the toes.

FIGURE 31.2 Common Infectious Diseases Worldwide

DISEASE	PATHOGEN TYPE	HOW IT SPREADS	AFFECTED BODY SYSTEMS	DEATHS ANNUALLY
HIV	virus	body fluids	immune	3,100,000
Pneumonia	virus, bacteria	airborne	respiratory	2,000,000
Tuberculosis	bacteria	airborne	respiratory, digestive	1,800,000
Malaria	protozoa	mosquito bite	digestive, circulatory, muscular	1,000,000
Hepatitis B	virus	contaminated food/water	digestive, immune	1,000,000
Measles	virus	airborne	respiratory, nervous	500,000
Influenza	virus	airborne, direct contact	respiratory	400,000

Source: World Health Organization

Differentiated Instruction

BELOW LEVEL

Have students list the five types of pathogens: bacteria, viruses, fungi, protozoa, and parasites. Then have groups of students list what they know about each type of pathogen. After they read the text, have them make changes and additions to their lists.

Remind students that they were first introduced to these organisms in Chapter 19.

Biology Toolkit, Brainstorming, p. C11

PRE-AP

Students can use a content frame to contrast information about the five types of pathogens. Tell students to use the first column to identify the pathogen, the second column to describe its structure, the third column to list how it causes disease, and any remaining columns they choose to add more detail.

Biology Toolkit, Content Frame, p. C22

- **Protozoa** are single-celled organisms that prey on other cells. Like viruses, protozoa need healthy cells to complete their life cycles. Malaria is a blood disease that is caused by a protozoan. Chapter 19 includes a description of how the protozoan that causes malaria uses red blood cells to complete its life cycle.
- **Parasites** are organisms that grow and feed on a host. Some parasites kill the host, while others drain the body's resources without killing the host. **FIGURE 31.3** shows a filaria, a parasitic worm found in tropical climates. Filaria will rarely kill its host, although some forms, such as heartworm, can be fatal in mammals. You can read more about parasitic worms in Chapter 23.

Although each of these pathogens is different, they all cause disease by attacking healthy cells. However, the way by which they attack varies.

A Summarize **What do all of these pathogens do that makes a person sick?**

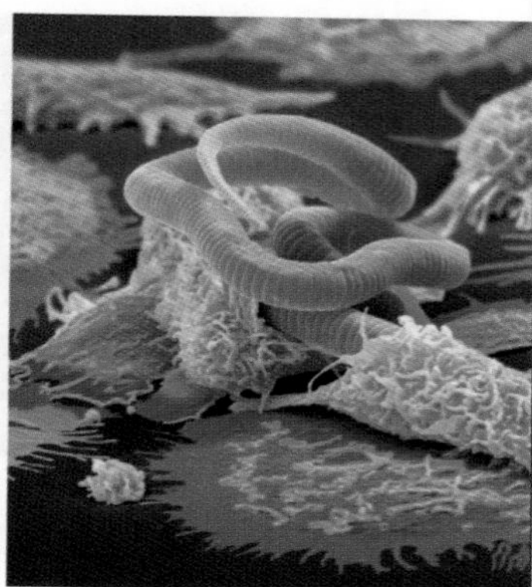

FIGURE 31.3 Filaria, such as this one, enter the body through contaminated food and can grow to be a meter long. (colored SEM; magnification 2500×)

MAIN IDEA

Pathogens can enter the body in different ways.

Before a pathogen can make a person sick, it must get inside the body. Some pathogens can be transferred by direct or indirect contact. Pathogens that spread by direct contact are those that require an infected person or animal to physically touch a healthy person. Rabies, for example, is transferred when an infected animal bites a healthy animal. HIV is transmitted through an exchange of bodily fluids, such as during sexual intercourse or sharing of infected needles. It can also be transmitted from a mother to her child through the placenta or breast milk.

QUICK LAB **MODELING**

How Pathogens Spread

Pathogens are disease-causing particles. In this lab, you will model how a pathogen spreads through a population.

PROBLEM From whom did the pathogen originate?

PROCEDURE

1. Obtain a cup filled with an unknown solution. Pour half your solution into a classmate's cup. Then pour the same amount from your classmate's cup back into your cup. Now your cup contains a mixture of the two solutions.
2. Repeat step 1 two more times with different classmates. Keep a record of with whom you exchanged solutions and in which order.
3. After you have exchanged solutions with three classmates, add three drops of "pathogen"-detecting solution to your cup. If your solution becomes pink, your cup contains the pathogen.

ANALYZE AND CONCLUDE

1. **Analyze** If your cup contained the pathogen, can you identify its origin? If your cup did not contain the pathogen, is it possible that any of the other solutions poured into your cup contained the pathogen?
2. **Analyze** Only one person in your class began with the pathogen in his or her cup. How can you determine whose cup had it?

MATERIALS

- 8-oz cup
- 100 mL unknown solution
- eyedropper
- 3 drops "pathogen"-detecting solution

TEACH WITH TECHNOLOGY

Use a computer or overhead projector to show photographs of a variety of each type of pathogen. For each pathogen shown, tell students what disease it causes. You may want to include photographs of vectors discussed on page 944. Reinforce the concept that infectious diseases are caused by pathogens.

Answers

A Summarize attack healthy cells

QUICK LAB

Time 10 minutes

Lab Binder Human Bio, p. 46

Purpose Model the spread of a pathogen through a population.

LAB PREPARATION

- Stir 1000 mg of baking soda into 100 mL of water as the pathogen source.
- Add the source solution to one cup to make it half full.
- Fill the rest of the cups halfway with distilled water.
- Provide a dropper and phenolphthalein in a cup. Each student will need three drops.

LAB MANAGEMENT

- Observe and identify the student who gets the source solution.
- Make sure the infecting student is not teased once the source is identified.

Safety Tell students to avoid spills. Make sure they wash their hands after the lab.

Teacher Note "Nice opportunity to revisit spontaneous generation."

Answers

Analyze and Conclude

1. Yes, if your cup contained the virus, you could identify its origin through the process of elimination. If your cup did not contain the virus, it is not possible that any other solutions poured into your cup contained the virus.
2. Retrace your steps; find who you shared solutions with and who they shared solutions with before you; and put together everyone's data to find the origin.

▼ Teach *continued*

ONLINE BIOLOGY Students can graph the number of West Nile virus cases and study the spread of the disease. See Data Analysis Online on page 965.

Take It Further

Another type of pathogen, called a **prion,** causes **mad cow disease** in cows, scrapie in sheep, chronic wasting disease in deer, and Creutzfeldt-Jakob disease in humans. A prion is an infectious protein that converts normal cell proteins into prions, disrupting cell function. Diseases caused by prions are fatal, but can be prevented in humans and domestic animals by avoiding food from infected animals. Prions are not affected by high temperatures and cooking, and are virtually indestructible.

Answers

A Infer Some pathogens live in human blood and are spread by insects that bite. Others must complete part of their life cycle in the body of an insect.

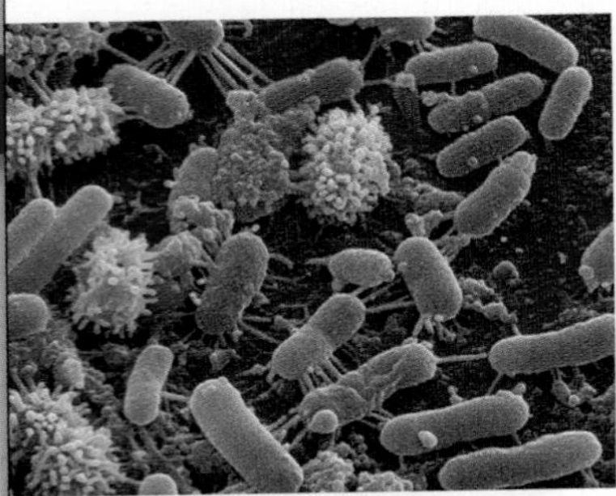

FIGURE 31.4 Sometimes even surfaces that we think are clean are covered with pathogens. Here you can see different types of pathogens clinging to a kitchen sponge. (colored SEM; magnification 6000×)

Pathogens that are spread by indirect contact can survive on nonliving surfaces, such as tables, door knobs, or kitchen sponges—as shown in **FIGURE 31.4.** Some parasitic worm larvae live in the soil and can burrow through the skin of a victim's bare foot. Once inside the body, the larvae travel into the victim's intestines. Species that remain in the intestines throughout their life cycle can cause discomfort, nausea, and diarrhea.

Other pathogens are spread through the air. When you cough or sneeze, you release droplets into the air around you. When you are sick, these droplets might contain pathogens. Other airborne pathogens are lightweight and hearty enough that they can survive in the air on dry particles. Respiratory diseases such as tuberculosis and SARS are examples of airborne diseases.

Still other pathogens are spread by vectors. A **vector** is anything that carries a pathogen and transmits it into healthy cells. Insects are examples of vectors. Insects can transmit bacteria, viruses, and protozoa. The Black Death, which killed millions of people in the 1300s, is caused by a bacterium that lives in the stomach of a rat's flea. People got sick with the Black Death when they were bitten by a contaminated flea. Mosquitoes can also pass diseases between animals. The protozoan that causes malaria, for example, completes a part of its life cycle in the gut of a mosquito. Mosquitoes can also transmit diseases between species. West Nile virus originally affected birds, but when an infected mosquito bites a person with a weak immune system, the virus can cause the person's brain to swell. However, insects cannot transmit pathogens, such as HIV, that die when the insect digests the infected human blood cells.

Pathogens can also be transmitted through food. Some diseases are caused by pathogens that were alive when the food-animal lived. Mad cow disease, which causes neurological problems in humans, is caused by an abnormal protein that is found in some beef cattle. Salmonella, which causes vomiting, is found in the intestines of some pigs and other animals. Most parasitic worm eggs enter the body through the mouth, as when a person eats contaminated food. Other diseases, such as various types of food poisoning, are caused by bacteria or fungi that decompose food.

 Infer **Why are some diseases only spread by insect bites?**

▼ Assess and Reteach

Assess Use the Online Quiz or Section Quiz (*Assessment Book,* p. 611).

Reteach Have pairs of students take turns quizzing each other on the main ideas and terms in this section. Let one student write a question and the other student answer it. Have partners switch roles and repeat the activity until they have covered all the main ideas and terms.

31.1 ASSESSMENT

ONLINE QUIZ ClassZone.com

REVIEWING MAIN IDEAS

1. What conditions must be met before a specific **pathogen** is proved to cause a disease?
2. Name five general types of pathogens.
3. What are some ways in which pathogens spread?

CRITICAL THINKING

4. **Contrast** How do bacteria and viruses differ in the ways they affect cells in the body?
5. **Synthesize** How did the work of Lister and Koch support Pasteur's **germ theory** of disease?

Connecting CONCEPTS

6. **Viruses** Viruses infect healthy cells by injecting their genetic material into them. How are viruses similar to **vectors**? If the virus is the vector, what is the pathogen?

31.1 ASSESSMENT

1. The conditions in Koch's postulates; the pathogen must be found in all individuals with the disease, be cultured, be reintroduced into a healthy individual and make that individual sick, and then be reisolated from the newly sick individual.
2. bacteria, viruses, fungi, protozoa, parasites
3. Answers will vary, but should include some examples of direct and indirect contact.
4. Bacteria release chemicals that are toxic to the body or destroy healthy body cells. Viruses enter and take over healthy cells, forcing them to stop their normal activity and produce more viruses. Both bacteria and viruses destroy healthy cells.
5. Lister showed that living things cause infection because when he applied an acid that would kill cells, infection was prevented in his patients. Koch showed that living things cause illness by isolating germs from animals and proving that these germs would cause the same illness if injected into a healthy animal.
6. Viruses are similar to vectors because they are the things that carry the disease-causing agent and transfer it to healthy cells. The pathogen is the genetic material the virus carries.

31.2 Immune System

KEY CONCEPT The immune system consists of organs, cells, and molecules that fight infections.

MAIN IDEAS
- Many body systems protect you from pathogens.
- Cells and proteins fight the body's infections.
- Immunity prevents a person from getting sick from a pathogen.

VOCABULARY

immune system, p. 945
phagocyte, p. 946
T cell, p. 946
B cell, p. 946
antibody, p. 947
interferon, p. 947
passive immunity, p. 948
active immunity, p. 948

Review
pathogen, lymphocyte

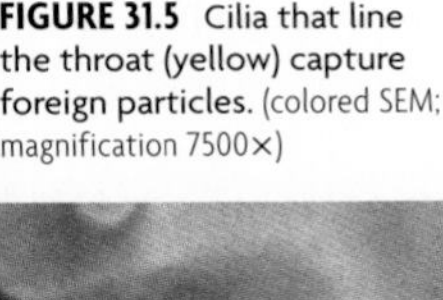

Connect Think of your body as a heavily guarded castle. When pathogens come to invade, they must first break down the outer wall or find a way around it. If the intruders get past the physical barriers, they must face your body's fighters in hand-to-hand combat. When the invaders gain the upper hand, you become sick. When the body's defenses are winning the war, you remain healthy.

MAIN IDEA

Many body systems protect you from pathogens.

The **immune system** is the body system that fights off infection and pathogens. Just as a castle has several lines of defense, so does your body's immune system. The immune system relies on physical barriers to keep pathogens out. However, when pathogens get past the physical barriers, the warrior cells of the immune system travel through the lymphatic and circulatory systems to reach the site of infection.

Your skin is your body's first line of defense. Like a castle's outer wall, the skin surrounds and protects your insides. The skin physically blocks invading pathogens. The skin also secretes oil and sweat, which make the skin hypertonic and acidic. Many pathogens cannot survive in this kind of environment.

Just as a castle's walls have doors and windows, your skin also has openings. For example, your eyes, nose, ears, mouth, and excretory organs are open to the environment, and so they need extra protection. Mucous membranes in these organs use hairlike cilia that are covered with a sticky liquid to trap pathogens before they move into the body, as shown in **FIGURE 31.5.**

***Connecting* CONCEPTS**

Hypertonic You learned in **Chapter 3** that when the environment has more solutes than a cell, water will diffuse out of the cell and the cell could die.

FIGURE 31.5 Cilia that line the throat (yellow) capture foreign particles. (colored SEM; magnification 7500×)

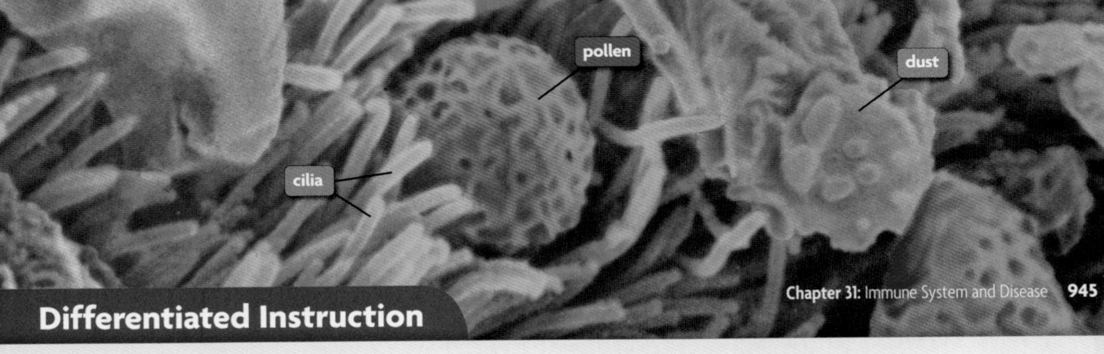

Differentiated Instruction

BELOW LEVEL

Have students place the Key Concept at the top of the page into a circle, then create a mind map to organize information in the section. They will include branches for body systems that protect the body and cells and proteins that provide immunity.

Biology Toolkit, Mind Map, p. C28

ENGLISH LEARNERS

To review, place sheets of chart paper with a question on each at stations around the room. Choose broad questions to elicit lots of information, for example, "What are some types of white blood cells, and what do they do?" In small groups, each with a different-colored marker, students go to an assigned station, discuss, and write a response without referring to books. After five minutes, they rotate, check answers they agree with, comment on those they do not, and add their own.

Biology Toolkit, Carousel Review, p. C12

SECTION 31.2

Plan and Prepare ▼

Objectives

- Identify the body systems that protect you from pathogens.
- Describe the cells and proteins that fight the body's infections.
- Compare the two types of immunity.

Section Resources

Unit Resource Book
Study Guide pp. 95–96
Power Notes p. 97
Reinforcement p. 98

Interactive Reader Chapter 31
Spanish Study Guide pp. 315–316

Biology Toolkit pp. C12, C19, C28, D9

Technology
Power Presentation 31.2
Media Gallery DVD
Online Quiz 31.2

Activate Prior Knowledge Discuss how physical barriers can be used for defense. **Ask**

- What are some examples of physical barriers in everyday life? doors, locks, fences, walls
- What physical barrier is your body's first line of defense? skin

Tell students that they will learn how their immune system defends them once the barrier of the skin has been breached.

Teach ▼

Take It Further

Mucous membranes form a lining in the respiratory, digestive, and genitourinary tracts. The membranes produce **antimicrobial proteins.** One antimicrobial protein, **lysozyme,** is an enzyme that can digest the cell walls of many types of bacteria. Lysozyme in saliva can kill bacteria present in food and water. Tears also contain lysozyme, killing some bacteria before they can enter the body through the eyes.

▼ Teach *continued*

The Inside Story

In 1971, **David Vetter** was born with a defective immune system. From his birth until shortly before his death in 1984, he lived in a "bubble," a sterile environment that offered protection from pathogens. Vetter suffered from **Severe Combined Immunodeficiency** (SCID), a rare genetic disease that causes defects in T and B cell responses. For a person suffering from SCID, any infection can be life threatening.

In 1976, John Travolta starred in a television movie called "The Boy in the Plastic Bubble." He portrayed a teenager with a similarly compromised immune system, who escapes his isolation by using a spacesuit. Vetter, who had a chance to see the movie, thought the spacesuit would have been dangerously unsterile. David Vetter died at the age of 12. His real-life drama was depicted in a PBS documentary as part of the *American Experience* series.

Answers

Ⓐ Summarize skin, blood vessels, lymph vessels, mucus membranes

Even with skin and mucous membranes to protect you, some pathogens still get into the body. Once pathogens are inside, the immune system relies on the circulatory system to send chemical signals to coordinate an attack and to transport specialized cells to the infection.

Ⓐ **Summarize Name some of the tissues that help to prevent and fight infection.**

MAIN IDEA

Cells and proteins fight the body's infections.

Once pathogens get past all of your outer defenses, the cells of your immune system spring into action. Just as a castle has many fighters and weapons, your immune system has many types of white blood cells and proteins.

White Blood Cells

White blood cells find and kill pathogens that have gotten past the body's external barriers. The six main types of white blood cells and their roles in fighting infection are summarized in **FIGURE 31.6**.

When a pathogen enters the body, basophils in the blood stream or mast cells found in other tissues release chemical signals. These signals attract other white blood cells to the site of the infection. If the pathogen is a parasite, eosinophils come and spray the parasite with poison. If the pathogen is a virus, bacterium, or fungus, neutrophils and macrophages go to work. These cells are phagocytes. A **phagocyte** (FAG-uh-SYT) is a cell that destroys pathogens by surrounding and engulfing them.

VISUAL VOCAB

A **phagocyte** is a cell that engulfs and destroys other cells. It comes from Greek words that translate to mean "cell eater."

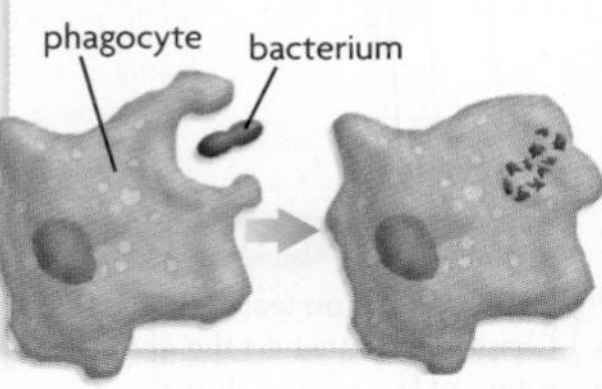

After phagocytes, lymphocytes reach the infection. Lymphocytes are white blood cells that initiate the specific immune responses, which you will read about in Section 31.3. There are two types of lymphocytes: T-lymphocytes and B-lymphocytes, also called T cells and B cells. **T cells** destroy body cells that are infected with pathogens. **B cells** produce proteins that inactivate pathogens that have not yet infected a body cell.

Connecting CONCEPTS

Lymphocytes Recall from **Chapter 30** that lymphocytes are cells of the lymphatic system that attack disease-causing particles.

FIGURE 31.6 White Blood Cells

NAME	FUNCTION
Basophil	makes chemicals that cause inflammation in the bloodstream
Mast cell	makes chemicals that cause inflammation in other body tissues
Neutrophil	engulfs pathogens and foreign invaders; phagocyte
Macrophage	engulfs dead or damaged body cells and some bacteria; phagocyte
Lymphocyte	destroys infected body cells or produces proteins that inactivate pathogens
Eosinophil	injects poisonous packets into parasites, such as protozoa

Differentiated Instruction

BELOW LEVEL

To help students understand the vocabulary involved with white blood cells, have them make a chart of the keywords and their definitions. Then have students come up with an analogy for each word to help them remember.

Biology Toolkit, Analogies, p. D9

DATA ANALYSIS

IDENTIFYING EXPERIMENTAL DESIGN FLAWS

Sometimes scientific investigations can be flawed as a result of how the experiments were designed. Such design problems could include having a sample that is not representative of the population or one that is too small. This can result in the collection of invalid data, incorrect conclusions, and the release of misleading information.

To study how common certain diseases are in the United States, a student interviews 100 people as they exit a small Midwestern hospital. The student asks them if they have ever had any of five specific infectious diseases. He calculates the percent of people who responded "yes" to each question and puts the data in the graph to the right.

Based on his data, the student concludes that chickenpox is the most contagious disease of the five diseases studied. He also concludes that people in the United States no longer get tuberculosis.

1. **Evaluate** What problems exist with the sample population in this investigation?
2. **Analyze** Are the conclusions drawn from this data accurate? Why or why not?
3. **Evaluate** How could this investigation be redesigned to produce valid results?

GRAPH 1. STUDENT DATA

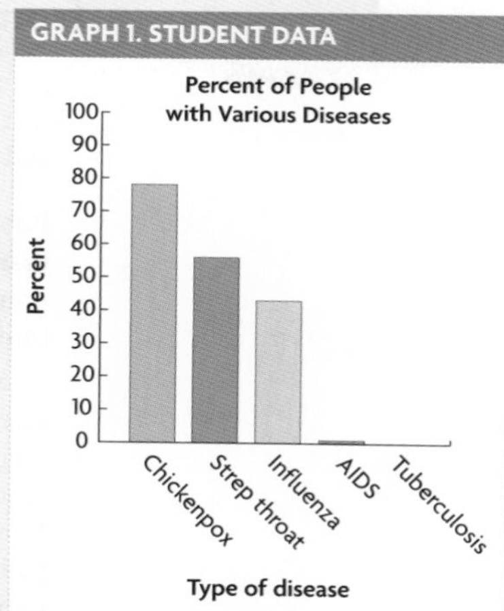

Proteins

The immune system uses three types of proteins to fight off invading pathogens: complement proteins, antibodies, and interferons.

- Complement proteins are made by white blood cells and by certain organs. Some complement proteins weaken a pathogen's cell membrane, allowing water to enter the cell and cause it to burst. Others attract phagocytes to the infected area. Still others cause microbes to stick to the walls of blood vessels, where they can more easily be found and destroyed by circulating phagocytes.
- **Antibodies** are proteins made by B cells. Antibodies destroy pathogens in one of three ways. Antibodies might make the pathogen ineffective by binding to the pathogen's membrane proteins. As **FIGURE 31.7** shows, antibodies might also cause pathogens to clump, making them easier for phagocytes to engulf and destroy. Other antibodies activate complement proteins that weaken the pathogen's cell membrane.
- **Interferons** (ihn-tuhr-FEER-AHNZ) are proteins produced by body cells that are infected by a virus. Cells release interferons, which stimulate uninfected body cells to produce enzymes that will prevent viruses from entering and infecting them. If viruses cannot enter healthy cells, they cannot reproduce. Other interferons stimulate an inflammation response.

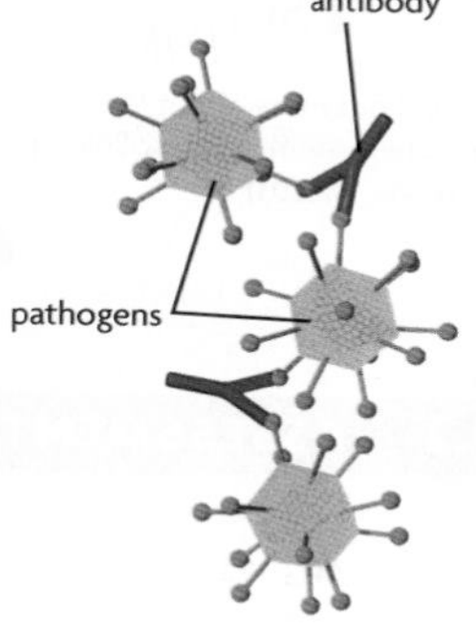

FIGURE 31.7 Antibodies help the immune system. Some types of antibodies cause pathogens to clump, making them easier to engulf and destroy.

A Compare and Contrast **What are some differences between the ways white blood cells and proteins fight infections?**

DATA ANALYSIS

Discuss

Have students discuss what locations might be more representative of a population as a whole. **Ask,** Can you think of any site that is neutral, in which a population has not been presorted? Students may find this hard to do.

Answers

1. The sample population is too small; biased because they were all leaving the hospital; not representative of the entire U.S. population in terms of age, gender, socioeconomic background, or ethnicity.
2. The conclusions are inaccurate due to sample bias and the fact that the sample is too small. The conclusion about chickenpox is inaccurate, because other variables aside from the level of contagiousness could be influencing why the rate of chickenpox is highest.
3. Conduct samples in several large U.S. cities. Sample size should be increased in each city. Samples should be obtained in a neutral location (over the phone, outside a store, and so on).

Unit Resource Book, Data Analysis, p. 115

Vocabulary

antibody Tell students that the body that an antibody acts against is a foreign body, a pathogen.

interferon Point out that what is being interfered with is the ability of a virus to reproduce.

PRE-AP

Tell students that phagocytes have surface receptors that attach to polysaccharides on the surface of bacteria. Once attached, the phagocyte engulfs the bacteria and fuses with a lysosome, whose toxic contents destroy the bacterium. Have students write for five minutes on adaptations bacterial populations might evolve to protect themselves from phagocytes. Some, in fact, "hide" their receptors with an outer capsule; others have defenses against the lysosome and reproduce in the phagocyte.

Biology Toolkit, Quick-Write, p. C19

INCLUSION

For students who might have trouble differentiating among cells and proteins that act in defense, suggest they create a "bestiary" in which they create their own mythology or imagery for the body's different types of defenses.

Answers

A **Compare and Contrast** *Sample Answer:* White blood cells engulf and destroy pathogens, and plasma proteins help white blood cells to work or signal to other body cells to protect themselves.

Teach *continued*

Integrating Zoology

Invertebrates do not have an active immunity, but they do have innate, nonspecific defenses to protect them. **Insects,** for example, have an open circulatory system, which circulates hemolymph. There are no white blood cells as such, but hemolymph has **hemocytes,** which are cells that have some protective functions. These include ingesting pathogens by phagocytosis; making antimicrobial peptides that attach to pathogens and kill them; and encapsulating parasites.

Answers

A Contrast Passive immunity is obtained without a person being exposed to a pathogen. Active immunity occurs when a person is infected with a pathogen and the body responds to the infection.

MAIN IDEA

Immunity prevents a person from getting sick from a pathogen.

If you are immune to a pathogen, it means that you will not get sick when that pathogen invades your body. There are two types of immunity—passive and active.

Passive Immunity

Passive immunity is immunity that occurs without the body's undergoing an immune response. Passive immunity is transferred between generations through DNA and between mother and child.

Some viruses can be spread between different species. A pathogen that infects a bird might infect a person as well. However, some viruses only make members of a specific species sick. Genetic immunity is immunity that a species has because a pathogen is not specialized to harming that species. Infants have another type of immunity. Inherited immunity occurs when pathogen-fighting antibodies in a mother's immune system are passed to the unborn baby through the umbilical cord or the mother's milk.

Active Immunity

Active immunity is immunity that your body produces in response to a specific pathogen that has infected or is infecting your body. Acquired immunity is a type of active immunity that occurs after your immune system reacts to a pathogen invasion. Acquired immunity keeps you from becoming sick by a particular pathogen more than once. We will look more closely at how the immune system produces acquired immunity in the next section.

Sometimes people get the same colds or flus over and over again throughout their lifetimes. This occurs because the viruses that cause these sicknesses mutate very quickly. Each time a different strain of virus invades, your immune system has to start from the beginning again. On the other hand, your immune system destroys repeat invaders before you get sick.

NSTA SCILINKS scilinks.org
To find out more about the immune system, go to scilinks.org.
Keycode: MLB031

 Contrast **How do passive and active immunity differ?**

Assess and Reteach

Assess Use the Online Quiz or Section Quiz (*Assessment Book*, p. 612).

Reteach On the board, make three columns: *Body Systems That Protect the Body from Pathogens; White Blood Cells and Proteins That Fight Infection;* and *Difference Between Active and Passive Immunity.* Have students volunteer information to fill in the columns.

31.2 ASSESSMENT

ONLINE QUIZ ClassZone.com

REVIEWING MAIN IDEAS

1. How does the **immune system** work with other body systems to prevent and fight disease?
2. How do **phagocytes** help to fight infections?
3. Which of the two types of immunity requires white blood cells? Explain.

CRITICAL THINKING

4. **Contrast** How do complement proteins differ from **antibodies**?
5. **Predict** If a person had a disease that prevented lymphocytes from maturing, how would the immune system's response to infection change?

***Connecting* CONCEPTS**

6. **Protein Synthesis** How might a person's immune system be affected if a portion of the DNA that codes for **interferons** has mutated?

31.2 ASSESSMENT

1. The skin and mucous membranes help to keep pathogens out of the body. However, once a pathogen is inside the body, the immune system requires the circulatory and lymphatic systems to transport the cells of the immune system to the site of infection.
2. Phagocytes destroy pathogens by surrounding and engulfing them.
3. Active immunity; a person's white blood cells respond to a pathogen invasion.
4. *Sample Answer:* Complement proteins are made by white blood cells and certain organs, and may weaken a pathogen's cell membrane. Antibodies are made by B cells and may bind to the pathogen's membrane proteins.
5. The immune system might not be able to fight off infections because the infected body cells would not be destroyed and pathogens would not be deactivated.
6. If the DNA mutated, some interferons might not be made properly. Without interferons, cells cannot be stimulated to protect themselves against pathogens, or an inflammation response might not be produced. This will limit the immune system's ability to fight viruses.

Observing Normal and Diseased Tissue

MATERIALS
- slide of normal lymph tissue
- slide of diseased lymph tissue
- slide of normal lung tissue
- slide of diseased lung tissue (lung cancer or pneumonia)
- slide of normal red blood cells
- slide of anemic red blood cells
- slide of healthy stomach tissue
- slide of ulcer cells
- slide of normal liver
- slide of sclerosis of the liver
- microscope

PROCESS SKILLS
- Observing
- Analyzing

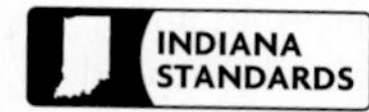

NOS.3 Clearly communicate their ideas and results of investigations verbally and in written form using tables, graphs, diagrams, and photographs.

In this lab, you will examine different cells and tissues under the microscope and compare the appearance of normal tissue with that of diseased tissue.

PROBLEM How do diseased tissues differ from normal ones?

PROCEDURE

1. Choose three slides of different healthy tissues and three slides of the same types of tissues with disease.
2. Examine a slide of normal tissue under low power and high power on the microscope. Draw the cells that you see.
3. Examine a slide of the same kind of tissue, but diseased, under low power and high power on the microscope. Draw the cells that you see.
4. Repeat steps 2 and 3 with each of the remaining slides that contain the different types of tissues.

ANALYZE AND CONCLUDE

1. **Contrast** How do each of the diseased tissues you observed differ from the normal tissues?
2. **Compare** What do the diseased tissues have in common with one another?
3. **Infer** Using what you know about pathogens, why do you think a tissue's appearance changes when it is infected?
4. **Infer** Using what you know about the function of each tissue, how do you think each of the diseased tissues is affected by the pathogen?

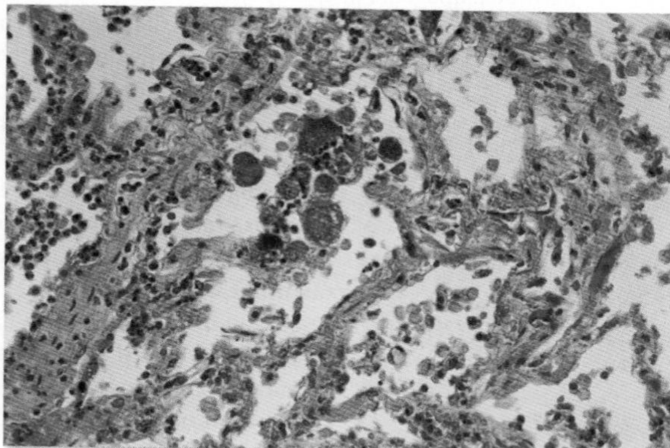

Many different viruses, bacteria, and fungi can cause pneumonia, a disease characterized by inflammation of the lungs. (colored LM; magnification: 220×)

INVESTIGATION

Time 45 minutes	TEACHER TESTED
Teacher Preparation	
Student Difficulty	
Lab Binder Human Bio, pp. 39–42	

Purpose Compare healthy and diseased tissue by examining them under a microscope.

Overview Students will use the low power and high power of a microscope to examine a slide of healthy tissue and a slide of the same kind of tissue, but diseased. Students will then
- draw the cells they see
- examine and draw two more kinds of healthy and diseased tissues
- compare healthy and diseased tissues
- draw conclusions about how each of the diseased tissues is affected by pathogens

LAB PREPARATION

- Provide some content background about the diseases represented in the slides of diseased tissues or allow students time to search for information.

Safety Remind students to wipe down the eyepieces with alcohol wipes after using them.

Teacher Note "Excellent hands-on activity for lower-level learners."

Inclusion For students who lack fine motor skills, focus the microscope or have a team member focus it for them. For students who are visually impaired, have team members describe what they see or make enlarged pictures of the tissues.

POST-LAB DISCUSSION

Discuss results. **Ask,** What could you add to this investigation to learn more about the effects of pathogens on these tissues? Examine slides at different stages of the disease.

Answers

Analyze and Conclude

1. Answers should include a visual description and comparison of the healthy and diseased slides.
2. The diseased tissues all had cells that looked damaged, discolored, or deformed in some way.
3. Students' answers should demonstrate an understanding that pathogens take resources from the cells, thus damaging and destroying them.
4. Answers will vary, depending on the tissues chosen.

SECTION 31.3

▼ Plan and Prepare

Objectives

- Identify nonspecific immune responses and the body systems that produce them.
- Summarize how the cells of the immune system respond to pathogens.
- Explain how the immune system rejects foreign tissues.

Section Resources

Unit Resource Book Study Guide pp. 99–100 Power Notes p. 101 Reinforcement p. 102 Pre-AP Activity pp. 117–118
Interactive Reader Chapter 31 **Spanish Study Guide** pp. 317–318
Biology Toolkit pp. C3, C5, C17, C19, C34, C38, D9
Technology Power Presentation 31.3 Media Gallery DVD Online Quiz 31.3

Activate Prior Knowledge Discuss with students the symptoms of the flu and how they feel when they have it. **Ask,** Why is a fever a common symptom of the flu? The body is fighting infection. Tell students this is an example of a nonspecific response to a pathogen.

▼ Teach

TEACH FROM VISUALS

FIGURE 31.8 Have students find the part of the white blood cell on the left of the capillary wall. This part is in the blood inside the capillary. Then have them find the part of the same white blood cell that has moved across the capillary wall. **Ask,** What else can move through the capillary wall? oxygen, carbon dioxide, plasma **Ask,** How does the size of a white blood cell compare to these other substances that can pass through the capillary wall? much larger

31.3 Immune Responses

KEY CONCEPT The immune system has many responses to pathogens and foreign cells.

MAIN IDEAS

- Many body systems work to produce nonspecific responses.
- Cells of the immune system produce specific responses.
- The immune system rejects foreign tissues.

VOCABULARY

inflammation, p. 950
antigen, p. 951
memory cell, p. 951
cellular immunity, p. 952
humoral immunity, p. 953
tissue rejection, p. 954

Review
T cell, B cell

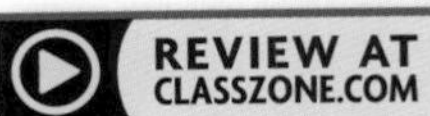

Connect Your body responds to pathogens in several different ways. For example, when you get a mosquito bite, your skin might swell and itch. After you are bitten, the skin around the bite becomes swollen, and the cells of your immune system attack the pathogens that entered the skin through the bite.

MAIN IDEA

Many body systems work to produce nonspecific responses.

The body responds to pathogens and foreign particles with specific and nonspecific responses. Responses that occur on the cellular level are called specific defenses. Specific responses are slightly different for each pathogen. Nonspecific immune responses are those that happen in the same way to every pathogen. Some examples of nonspecific defenses are inflammation and fever.

Inflammation

Inflammation is a nonspecific response that is characterized by swelling, redness, pain, itching, and increased warmth at the affected site. Inflammation occurs when a pathogen enters the body or when the body's other tissues become damaged. For example, if you scrape your knee, it swells up. This occurs because the body is trying to head off pathogens that enter the body through the newly broken skin.

FIGURE 31.8 When pathogens invade your body, white blood cells squeeze through the capillary wall and move toward the infection. (magnification unknown)

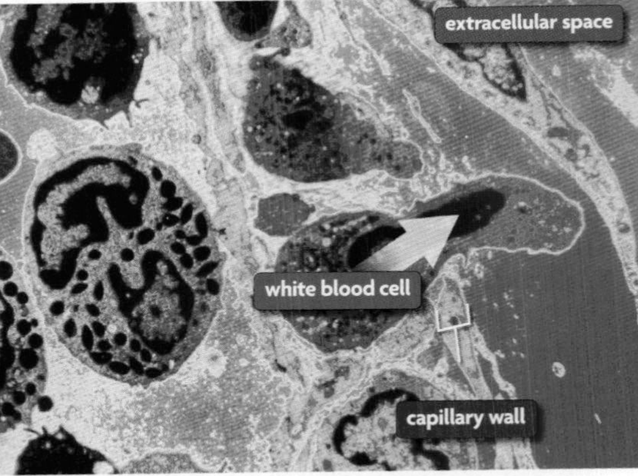

An inflammation response begins when mast cells or basophils release chemicals called histamines in response to a pathogen invasion. Histamines cause the cells in blood vessel walls to spread out. When this happens, fluids can move out of the blood vessel and into the surrounding tissues. White blood cells squeeze out of the capillary and move toward the site of infection, as shown in **FIGURE 31.8.** Once outside of the circulatory system, the white blood cells fight off the infection. When the pathogens are defeated, swelling stops, and tissue repair begins. Inflammation is a normal body response, but sometimes it occurs in response to things other than pathogens, as you will read in Section 31.5.

Differentiated Instruction

PRE-AP

To test students' understanding, write five to ten statements about the main points of the section. Focus on the body's nonspecific responses and the specific responses (cellular and humoral immunity). Have students react to the statements as being true or false before reading the section and then again after reading the section.

Biology Toolkit, Anticipation Guide, p. C3

ENGLISH LEARNERS

Before beginning, have students read just the orientation section at the top of the first page, with the Key Concept, Main Ideas, vocabulary list, and the Connect paragraph. Then have them close their books and individually make a three-column chart with the heads *K (Know), W (Want to Know),* and *L (Learned).* Give students five minutes to complete the *K* column and another five to complete the *W* column.

Biology Toolkit, KWL, p. C5

Fever

Fevers develop when mast cells or macrophages release chemicals that cause the hypothalamus to increase the body's temperature. When the infection is controlled and the mast cell's chemicals are no longer being made, the body temperature returns to normal.

Fever is a response that affects the entire body. Low fevers, around 37.7°C (100°F), stimulate the production of interferons. Recall that interferons are proteins that prevent viruses from reproducing. Low fevers also increase the activity of white blood cells by increasing the rate at which they mature, as shown in **FIGURE 31.9.** Having many mature white blood cells is important because only mature cells can destroy pathogens. The more mature white blood cells in the body, the more quickly the body can fight off an infection.

While low fevers speed up pathogen destruction, high fevers—more than 39°C, or 103°F—are dangerous. Under high fever conditions, the hypothalamus can no longer regulate body temperature. Enzymes that control chemical reactions in the body stop functioning. High fever can cause seizure, brain damage, and even death.

FIGURE 31.9 WHITE BLOOD CELL MATURATION

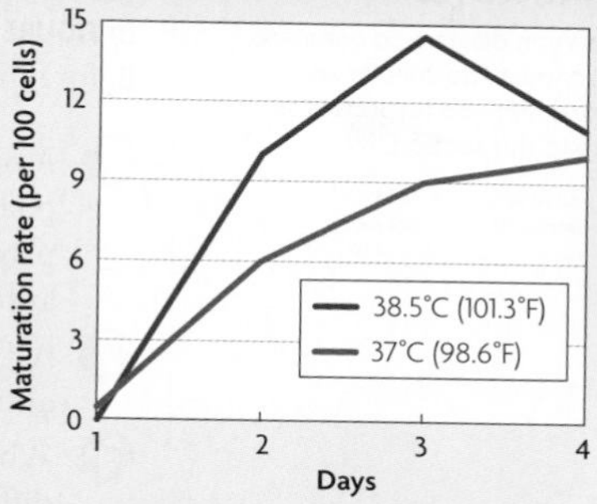

Scientists put immature white blood cells in a nutrient solution and found that they matured faster when the cells were heated as in a low fever (red line).

Source: Roberts, N. J. Jr. and R. T. Stergbigel. *American Society of Microbiology*

A Connect What body systems, other than the immune system, help to produce inflammation and fever?

MAIN IDEA

Cells of the immune system produce specific responses.

Specific immune defenses lead to acquired immunity, and they occur on the cellular level. For these specific immune defenses to work, the body must be able to tell the difference between its own healthy cells and foreign or infected cells. **Antigens** (AN-tih-juhnz) are protein markers on the surfaces of cells and viruses that help the immune system identify a foreign cell or virus. If pathogens are the invading army that is waging war on the immune system, then you can think of antigens as the pathogens' uniforms.

When the immune system detects a pathogen, it triggers an immune response. There are two types of specific immune system responses: cellular and humoral immune responses. Although the two responses are different, as you will read on the next page, they both produce acquired immunity. Immunity is acquired when your body produces memory cells after fighting off an infection. **Memory cells** are specialized T and B cells that provide acquired immunity because they "remember" an antigen that has previously invaded your body. So when memory cells come across this antigen a second time, they quickly destroy the pathogen before the body has a chance to get sick. You will learn more about how memory cells work in Section 31.4, when you read about vaccines. Now, we will discuss how the immune system fights a pathogen that it is encountering for the first time.

***Connecting* CONCEPTS**

T cells and B cells Recall from the previous section that T and B cells are lymphocytes that are specialized to fight off pathogens.

- T cells destroy infected body cells.
- B cells produce proteins that inactivate pathogens.

ONLINE BIOLOGY Go to the chapter Resource Center at **ClassZone.com** for additional resources and information on immune response.

TEACH FROM VISUALS

FIGURE 31.9 Point out that the graph represents cells grown in a nutrient solution, not in the human body. **Ask**

- On day 2, what is the difference in maturation rate of white blood cells at the different temperatures? At the higher temperature, the rate is 10 per 100 cells instead of 6 at the lower temperature.
- On day 2, at what temperature is the maturation rate of white blood cells faster? the higher temperature (38.5°C or 101.3°F)
- On what day is the maturation rate the fastest? day 3

Vocabulary

inflammation The word *inflammation* comes for the Latin *īnflammāre,* which means "to set on fire." **Ask,** How does this description apply to an inflammation? area with redness and increased warmth

Answers

A Connect nervous and circulatory

BELOW LEVEL

Have students expand on the analogy of antigens as the uniform of a pathogen. Students might prefer to change the analogy to that of the uniforms worn by athletes on a team. Have them write for five minutes about the importance of being able to distinguish like from unlike. Remind them that analogies are typically structured A is to B as C is to D.

Biology Toolkit, Quick-Write, p. C19; Analogies, p. D9

▼ Teach *continued*

TEACH FROM VISUALS

FIGURE 31.10 To help students understand cellular immunity, have them read the first numbered paragraph of text and then the first numbered caption. Make sure they identify the process in the diagram before moving on to the next paragraph and caption. **Ask**

- What role do phagocytes play in cellular immunity? They engulf pathogens, display the pathogens' antigens, and activate T cells.
- What does the activated T cell do? It divides and differentiates into memory T cells and activated T cells, which bind to infected body cells and cause them to burst.

Science Trivia

T cells and B cells have antigen receptors in their plasma membranes.

- One T cell or B cell has about 100,000 antigen receptors.
- All 100,000 receptors on one cell are identical.
- A B cell has Y-shaped receptors. Each receptor can bind to two antigens.
- A T cell has receptors with two parallel parts. Each receptor can bind to only one antigen.

Answers

A **Analyze** The T cells must be activated by proteins released by antigen-presenting cells. This allows them to recognize the pathogen's antigens and find body cells infected with those antigens.

TAKING NOTES

Use a Venn diagram to compare and contrast the cellular and humoral immune responses as you read this section.

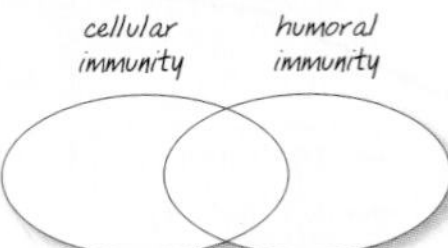

Cellular Immunity

Cellular immunity is an immune response that depends on T cells. As shown in **FIGURE 31.10**, T cells attach to infected body cells and cause them to burst. Before they can do this, however, T cells must become activated.

1. A phagocyte recognizes a foreign invader and engulfs it. Once inside the phagocyte, the invader's antigens are removed, and the phagocyte displays them on its cell membrane. A phagocyte that displays foreign antigens on its membrane is called an antigen-presenting cell.
2. A T cell encounters the antigen-presenting cell and binds to it. The antigen-presenting cell releases proteins that activate the T cell.
3. When a T cell is activated, it begins to divide and differentiate into two different types of T cells: activated and memory. The activated T cells will fight the current infection, but the memory T cells act as reserves that will wait for future invasions.
4. The activated T cells bind to and destroy infected body cells.

FIGURE 31.10 Cellular Immunity

In cellular immunity, T cells destroy infected body cells.

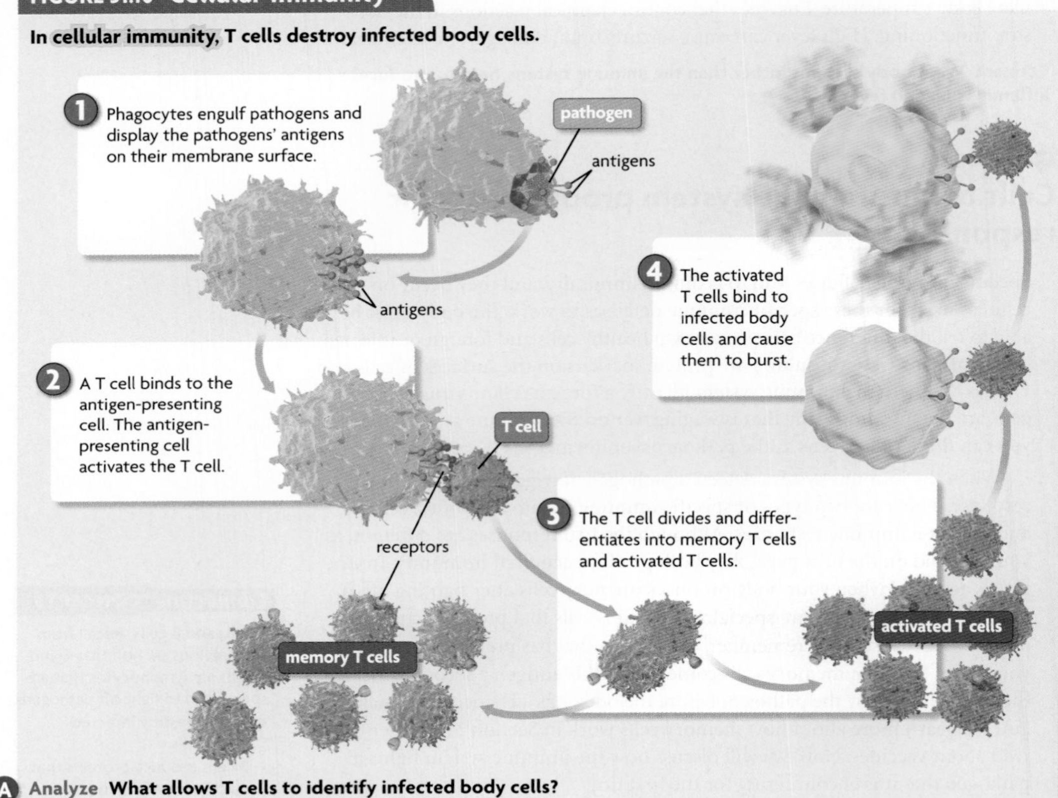

A Analyze **What allows T cells to identify infected body cells?**

Differentiated Instruction

INCLUSION

Have a visually impaired student pair up with a classmate, who will give a tour of cellular immunity and humoral immunity based on **FIGURES 31.10** and **31.11.** Encourage the student to ask for clarification as needed.

Biology Tookit, Connect to Content through Visuals, p. C17

BELOW LEVEL

For students who will have trouble differentiating details in **FIGURES 31.10** and **31.11,** suggest they redo each diagram as a chain of events.

Biology Tookit, Sequence Diagram, p. C38

Humoral Immunity

Humoral immunity is a type of immune response that depends on antibodies. Different types of antibodies fight pathogens by either causing them to burst, inactivating them, or causing them to clump, as shown in **FIGURE 31.11**.

1. A pathogen binds to a B cell. The B cell engulfs the pathogen and puts part of the antigen onto its surface.
2. When a T cell encounters the antigen-presenting B cell, it binds to the antigens. Then the T cell releases proteins that activate the B cell.
3. Once activated, the B cell divides and differentiates into activated B cells and memory B cells.
4. Activated B cells produce as many as 2000 pathogen-specific antibodies per second. In some cases, antibodies cause pathogens to clump.
5. Phagocytes engulf and destroy the pathogen clumps.

VOCABULARY
Humoral immunity comes from the Latin word *humor*, which means "fluid." *Humoral immunity* refers to the immunity given by antibodies that travel in the blood and other body fluids.

A Compare What are some similarities between the cellular and humoral responses?

FIGURE 31.11 Humoral Immunity

In humoral immunity, B cells produce antibodies that help destroy pathogens.

1 A pathogen binds to an antibody that is in an inactivated B cell's membrane. The B cell keeps a part of the antigen attached to its antibody.
B cell
pathogen
2 A T cell binds to the trapped antigen fragment and stimulates the B cell.
T cell
3 The B cell divides and differentiates into memory B cells and activated B cells.
memory B cells
activated B cells
4 The activated B cells produce antibodies that cause the pathogens to clump.
antibodies
5 Phagocytes eat the pathogen clumps.

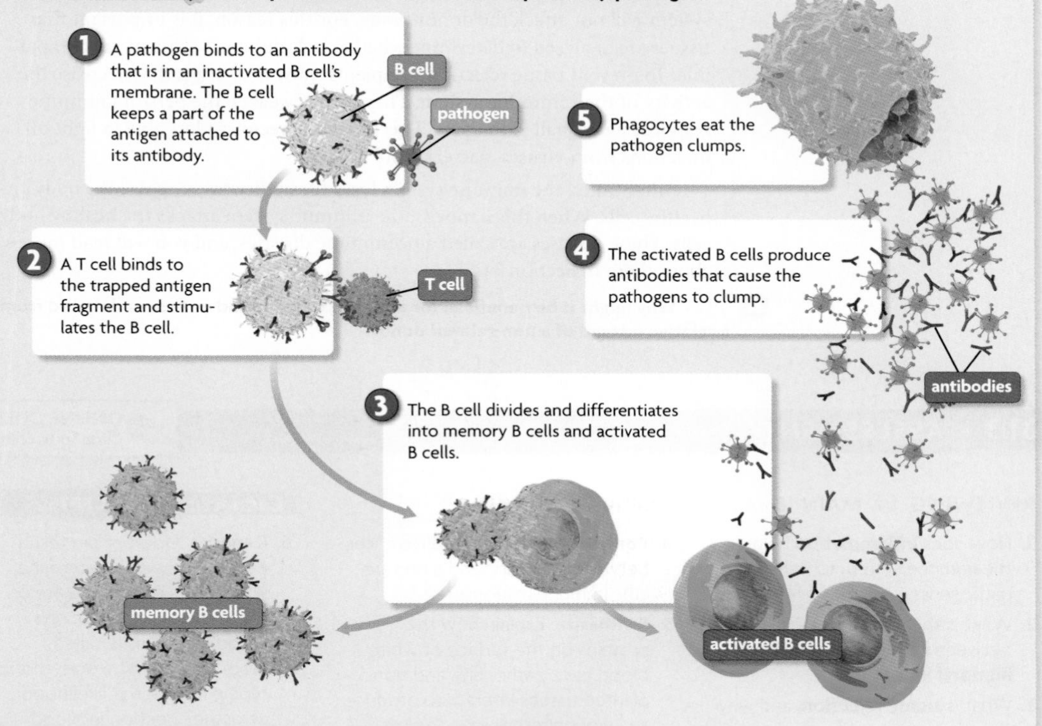

B Analyze How do T cells contribute to the humoral immune response?

ONLINE BIOLOGY Have students view the simulation to use a set of immune cells to mount an attack against a variety of pathogens. See Options for Inquiry on page 965.

TEACH FROM VISUALS

FIGURE 31.11 Help students to understand the differences between humoral and cellular immunity. **Ask**

- How do pathogens interact differently with cells of the immune system in cellular and humoral immune responses? cellular immunity: pathogens engulfed by phagocytes; humoral immunity: pathogen binds to a B cell
- What does the activated B cell do? It divides and differentiates into memory B cells and activated B cells, which produce antibodies.
- How do B cells fight pathogens? How is this different from the way T cells do in the cellular response? B cells produce antibodies that cause pathogens to clump and get destroyed by phagocytes; T cells bind to infected cells and cause them to burst.

Take It Further

Another name for an antibody is **immunoglobulin,** which is abbreviated *Ig.* The five major classes of antibodies are named IgA, IgD, IgE, IgG, and IgM. IgG is the most abundant class of antibodies in the blood and the only class of antibody that can cross the placenta. IgA is present in breast milk, mucus, and tears. **Ask,** How do you know that IgA and IgG antibodies provide passive immunity? passed from mother to child in breast milk or placenta

PRE-AP

Have students create a compare/contrast chart, using **FIGURES 31.10** and **31.11** for information.

Biology Toolkit, Compare/Contrast Chart, p. C34

Answers

A Compare Both require specific white blood cells to activate and produce memory cells.

B Analyze T cells bind to antigen fragments trapped by the antibody of an inactivated B cell and stimulate the B cell to divide and differentiate into memory and activated B cells.

▼ Teach *continued*

Take It Further

To help reduce the risk of tissue rejection, a **histocompatibility** antigen blood test is used to match a donor and a recipient. This test looks at inherited proteins on the surface of the blood cells. These proteins are human leukocyte antigens (HLA) found on every body cell with a nucleus. The body's immune system uses HLAs to determine what cells do not belong in the body. Because a person's HLAs are inherited from his or her parents, each person has a unique set of HLA. Identical twins have the closest match.

Answers

A Infer Relatives probably have more similar protein markers on the surfaces of their cells and more similar genes.

▼ Assess and Reteach

Assess Use the Online Quiz or Section Quiz (*Assessment Book*, p. 613).

Reteach Have student groups summarize nonspecific responses of the immune system to pathogens, cellular immunity, humoral immunity, and active and passive immunity. Assign each student a different immune response, or have students divide up the work among themselves.

MAIN IDEA

The immune system rejects foreign tissues.

***Connecting* CONCEPTS**

Blood Typing Blood cells have different proteins, called Rh factors, on their cell walls. Review **Chapter 30** for more information on how blood types affect a person's ability to receive blood transfusions.

All cells have protein markers on their surfaces. Your body must constantly decide whether your healthy cells are, in fact, your own or foreign cells. Sometimes you do not want your body to be able to identify foreign tissues and cells. For example, when you receive a blood transfusion or an organ transplant, you want to fool your body into ignoring the foreign tissues' protein markers. If protein markers on donated tissue differ from your cells' proteins, an immune response can occur and the transplanted tissue will be attacked and rejected. **Tissue rejection** occurs when the recipient's immune system makes antibodies against the protein markers on the donor's tissue.

Antigen receptors on the surface of your white blood cells determine whether your immune system will attack or ignore a transplanted tissue. Cells with protein markers that fit into the white blood cells' receptor molecules are foreign. Cells with protein markers that do not interact with white blood cells' receptor molecules are not detected by the immune system.

People have thousands of different combinations of protein markers on their cells. The fewer of these protein markers that differ between a donor's tissue and a recipient's, the better the chance that the recipient's immune system will not attack the donor tissue. For this reason, it is important that tissues are analyzed to determine whether a donor and recipient are compatible. To prevent tissue rejection, recipients must take drugs that decrease the activity of their immune system. These drugs weaken the person's immune response against all pathogens. This leaves the recipient less able to fight off infections from viruses, bacteria, and fungi.

Other times, the immune system loses the ability to recognize the body's healthy cells. When this happens, the immune system attacks the healthy body cells. These diseases are called autoimmune diseases, and you will read more about them in Section 31.5.

A Infer Why might it be beneficial for a person to get blood or tissues donated from a relative instead of a non-related donor?

31.3 ASSESSMENT

ONLINE QUIZ ClassZone.com

REVIEWING MAIN IDEAS

1. How does **inflammation** help the immune system to fight pathogens?
2. What is the main difference between **cellular immunity** and **humoral immunity**?
3. What is **tissue rejection,** and why does it occur?

CRITICAL THINKING

4. **Contrast** What are the differences between a specific and a nonspecific immune response?
5. **Synthesize** Explain how the proteins on the surface of white blood cells, pathogens, and transplanted tissues interact to produce an immune response.

***Connecting* CONCEPTS**

6. **Genetics** Doctors can test a person's blood to determine what types of proteins are on the surface of the person's blood cells. This is called blood typing. Why does blood typing reduce the likelihood of tissue rejection in blood transfusions?

31.3 ASSESSMENT

1. Inflammation allows white blood cells to move out of the capillaries toward the infection site to fight pathogens.
2. Cellular immunity uses T cells to destroy infected cells. Humoral immunity uses B cells to produce antibodies to clump or destroy pathogens.
3. Tissue rejection occurs when the recipient's immune system makes antibodies against the protein markers on the donor's tissue. It occurs because the protein markers on the donated tissue differ from the recipient's.
4. Specific immune responses are different for every pathogen, and they occur on a cellular level. Nonspecific immune responses are those that are the same for every pathogen.
5. If a protein on a transplanted tissue or pathogen fits into a protein receptor on white blood cells, then the white blood cell will attack. If the pathogen or tissue's proteins do not fit into the white blood cells' protein receptors, the white blood cells will ignore it.
6. Blood typing identifies donors whose blood is most similar to the recipient's. If the proteins on the blood cells are very similar, it is likely that the recipient's white blood cells will not attack the transfused blood.

31.4 Immunity and Technology

KEY CONCEPT Living in a clean environment and building immunity help keep a person healthy.

MAIN IDEAS
- Many methods are used to control pathogens.
- Vaccines artificially produce acquired immunity.

VOCABULARY
antiseptic, p. 955
antibiotic resistance, p. 955
vaccine, p. 956

Connect Because infectious diseases are spread from person to person, the risk of getting sick increases when there are many people in one area. Luckily, scientists have developed many different ways to control the spread of disease. Cleaning supplies, medicines, and vaccines are technologies that help to prevent against sickness or treat people who are already sick.

MAIN IDEA

Many methods are used to control pathogens.

Because pathogens can have such a negative effect on health, scientists have developed many ways to kill pathogens that our immune system might otherwise have a hard time fighting off. One way to prevent infection is to keep your environment clean. Cleaning can kill pathogens before they ever have a chance to enter your body and make you sick.

Heat and chemicals kill pathogens that are outside of the body. **Antiseptics** (an-tih-SEHP-tihks) are chemicals, such as soap, vinegar, and rubbing alcohol, that kill pathogens. Rubbing alcohol, for example, weakens cell membranes. Without a strong cell membrane, the microbe's nutrients leak out, and the microbe bursts. Antiseptics are not specific, meaning that they can kill many different types of pathogens.

FIGURE 31.12 Antibiotics have killed the bottom cell by weakening its cell wall and causing it to burst. (colored TEM; magnification 55,000×)

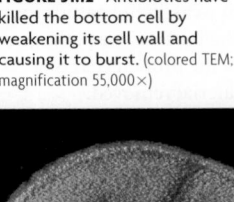

Once pathogens enter the body, sometimes they can be killed with medicines. Antibiotics are medicines that target bacteria or fungi and keep them from growing or reproducing. Antibiotics work in a variety of ways. For example, penicillin makes bacteria unable to form cell walls. The bacteria cannot divide successfully, and they burst, as shown in **FIGURE 31.12.**

Unlike antiseptics, antibiotics target one type of bacterium or fungus. As antibiotic use has become more common, antibiotic-resistant bacteria have evolved. As you read in Chapter 18, **antibiotic resistance** occurs when bacteria mutate so that they are no longer affected by antibiotics. Mutations make the bacteria resistant to the effects of antibiotics. When bacteria become resistant, scientists must find new medicines that can kill these mutant bacteria.

A **Compare and Contrast What are the similarities and differences between antiseptics and antibiotics?**

Differentiated Instruction

ENGLISH LEARNERS
Have students organize the information in this section as a cluster diagram.

Biology Toolkit, Cluster Diagram, p. C30

PRE-AP
Have students format the information in this section as a concept map.

Biology Toolkit, Concept Map, p. C40

Plan and Prepare ▼

Objectives

- Identify methods used to control pathogens.
- Explain how vaccines artificially produce acquired immunity.

Section Resources

Unit Resource Book
Study Guide pp. 103–104
Power Notes p. 105
Reinforcement p. 106

Interactive Reader Chapter 31
Spanish Study Guide pp. 319–320

Biology Toolkit pp. C30, C40

Technology
Power Presentation 31.4
Media Gallery DVD
Online Quiz 31.4

Activate Prior Knowledge Discuss vaccinations that are typically given to children. **Ask,** What vaccinations do young children get? chicken pox, diphtheria, tetanus, pertussis, polio, measles, mumps, rubella **Ask,** What vaccinations are often given to teenagers? hepatitis B, bacterial meningitis Discuss that many school systems and youth camps require proof of vaccinations.

Teach ▼

Take It Further

People use **antibacterial soap** to kill bacteria that could enter their bodies and make them sick. However, studies have shown that washing hands with regular soap and water is just as effective. Use of antibacterial soaps may result in bacteria that have antibiotic resistance.

Answers

A **Compare and Contrast** Both kill pathogens; however, antiseptics are non-specific and kill pathogens outside the body, and antibiotics target specific pathogens inside the body.

▼ Teach *continued*

History of Science

Tell students that *vaccine* comes from the Latin *vacca,* which means "cow." In the 1700s, **Edward Jenner** developed a vaccine for **smallpox,** which was a disease that killed many people. He observed that people who were exposed to **cowpox,** a disease in cows, had a mild case of a disease that seemed similar to smallpox. Using careful experimentation methods, he developed a vaccine for smallpox from the viruses that cause cowpox.

Answers

A Apply Viruses mutate rapidly, and the body cannot identify the new strains from year to year.

B Compare The memory B cells recognize the pathogen and begin to make antibodies right away, without having to go through the entire humoral immune response.

MAIN IDEA

Vaccines artificially produce acquired immunity.

Vaccination cannot cure a person who is sick because vaccines only work to prevent infection. Vaccination allows a person to develop memory cells and acquired immunity against an illness without actually contracting the disease.

A **vaccine** is a substance that contains the antigen of a pathogen. The antigen causes your immune system to produce memory cells, but you will not get sick. You do not get sick because the pathogen is weakened, and it cannot reproduce or attack your cells. When you are exposed to a pathogen and have not been vaccinated, you get sick because the pathogen reproduces faster than your immune system can respond. You stop being sick when your B or T cells win the fight over the infection.

If the pathogen enters your body after you are vaccinated, your memory B cells make antibodies right away, as shown in **FIGURE 31.13.** If you have not been vaccinated, your body must go through the entire humoral immune response, and the pathogen has enough time to make you feel sick.

There are four main types of vaccines.

- Some vaccines contain whole dead bacteria or viruses.
- Live attenuated vaccines contain weak living pathogens.
- Component vaccines use only the parts of the pathogen that contain the antigen, such as the protein coat of a virus that has had its genetic material removed.
- Toxoid vaccines are made from inactivated bacterial toxins, which are chemicals a bacterium produces that causes a person to become ill.

A Apply Why do you think that some vaccines, such as the flu vaccine, need to be given every year?

FIGURE 31.13 Vaccine Response

Vaccines stimulate an immune response so that you will not get sick if the real pathogen infects you.

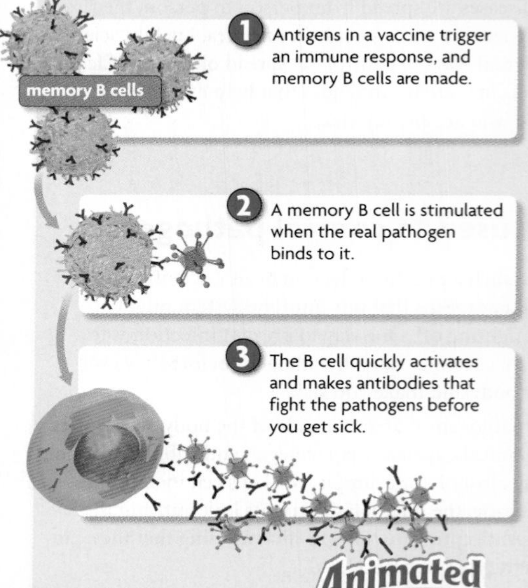

memory B cells
1 Antigens in a vaccine trigger an immune response, and memory B cells are made.
2 A memory B cell is stimulated when the real pathogen binds to it.
3 The B cell quickly activates and makes antibodies that fight the pathogens before you get sick.

B Compare How do memory cells cause a faster immune response?

Animated BIOLOGY
Watch how vaccines and active immunity work at ClassZone.com.

▼ Assess and Reteach

Assess Use the Online Quiz or Section Quiz (*Assessment Book,* p. 614).

Reteach Have groups of students summarize methods used to control pathogens and artificially produce acquired immunity.

31.4 ASSESSMENT

ONLINE QUIZ ClassZone.com

REVIEWING MAIN IDEAS

1. Under what circumstances might antibiotics not be useful in treating a disease caused by a pathogen?
2. How does the immune system respond to a pathogen that the person has been vaccinated against?

CRITICAL THINKING

3. **Summarize** Write out and describe the steps that your immune system takes when you are vaccinated.
4. **Apply** Why is the immune response faster after vaccination than the response that occurs the first time a pathogen invades?

Connecting CONCEPTS

5. **Evolution** Explain why **antibiotic resistance** is considered to be evidence of evolution. (**Hint:** Review Chapter 18 and the information about natural selection.)

31.4 ASSESSMENT

1. Antibiotics are ineffective against viruses and bacteria that have become resistant to some antibiotics.
2. Vaccines cause the immune system to produce memory B cells for specific pathogens. If the specific pathogen enters the body after the vaccine, the memory B cells make antibodies right away and the person will not get sick.
3. First, a specific immune response takes place. Then memory cells are produced. When the pathogen enters again, the memory cells are stimulated immediately to produce antibodies.
4. The first time a pathogen invades, the pathogen's antigens have to be displayed on a cell, and then a T cell must come and activate the immune system. Once memory cells are made, pathogens themselves stimulate the immune response.
5. Some bacteria survive the antibiotics, are able to reproduce, and pass on their genetic material to the next generation. Over time, natural selection results in a population of bacteria that is not killed by antibiotics and that are antibiotic resistant. The bacteria have evolved because of natural selection of bacteria that survive antibiotics.

31.5 Overreactions of the Immune System

KEY CONCEPT An overactive immune system can make the body very unhealthy.

MAIN IDEAS
- Allergies occur when the immune system responds to harmless antigens.
- In autoimmune diseases, white blood cells attack the body's healthy cells.

VOCABULARY
allergy, p. 957
allergen, p. 957
anaphylaxis, p. 958

Connect Eating a peanut can be deadly for a person who has an allergy. People who are allergic to peanuts can have their immune response activated by eating just one peanut or some peanut butter. An allergy is an overreaction in which the immune system produces an extreme response to a harmless protein marker. Other times, the immune system overreacts because it loses its ability to recognize the body's own healthy tissues.

MAIN IDEA

Allergies occur when the immune system responds to harmless antigens.

More than half of all Americans have an allergy. You probably know someone who is allergic to something—dogs, bee stings, or drugs, such as penicillin. An **allergy** is an oversensitivity to a normally harmless antigen. When someone has an allergy, the immune system produces antibodies in response to an allergen. **Allergens** are antigens that cause an allergic reaction.

When an allergen enters the body, mast cells or basophils release histamine, as shown in **FIGURE 31.14.** Histamine is a chemical that causes nonspecific immune responses, such as inflammation. Another type of white blood cell, eosinophils, also seems to have a role in allergic reactions. Eosinophils normally release poisonous chemicals that kill parasites that they encounter. These chemicals can also cause an inflammation response. Recall from Section 31.3 that in a normal inflammation response, cells release histamine. When histamine is released in response to a pathogen, the inflammation helps fight infection. When inflammation occurs in response to an allergen, the inflammation is unnecessary because it provides no benefit to the individual.

Scientists and doctors do not know why some individuals have allergies but others do not. Research suggests that some allergies are triggered by the overabundance of a certain type of antibody, and that a person's genetic makeup determines if a person has allergies. Other studies suggest that allergies are triggered when an allergen, such as one found in food, is given to a child at a certain stage in life.

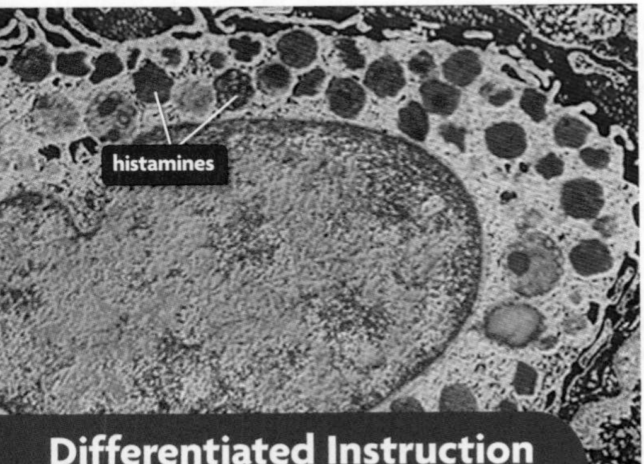

FIGURE 31.14 A basophil cell produces histamine, a chemical that triggers inflammation. (colored TEM; magnification 11,500×)

Differentiated Instruction

ENGLISH LEARNERS

Create on chart paper a three-column content frame with the heads *Problem, Cause(s),* and *Solutions.* Ask students how they could organize the chart. Guide them to list in the left-hand column the two broad heads *Allergens* and *Autoimmune Diseases,* with the three classes of allergens under the first head and the five autoimmune diseases from **FIGURE 31.16** under the second.

Biology Toolkit, Content Frame, p. C22

Plan and Prepare

Objectives
- Explain what happens when the immune system responds to harmless antigens.
- Describe autoimmune diseases.
- Identify common autoimmune diseases.

Section Resources

Unit Resource Book Study Guide pp. 107–108 Power Notes p. 109 Reinforcement p. 110
Interactive Reader Chapter 31 **Spanish Study Guide** pp. 321–322
Biology Toolkit pp. C19, C22
Technology Power Presentation 31.5 Media Gallery DVD Online Quiz 31.5

Activate Prior Knowledge Discuss what students know about allergies and the range of reactions people experience. **Ask,** What are some common allergens? pollen, animal dander, certain foods

Teach

TEACH FROM VISUALS

FIGURE 31.14 Have students notice that histamines are being produced. Remind students that histamines also are released as a nonspecific response to an injury that may or may not involve pathogens. In the case of an injury, the response is helpful because histamines protect the body from the possible presence of pathogens. **Ask,** Why are the histamines not helpful in allergies? There are no pathogens.

▼ Teach continued

ONLINE BIOLOGY Go to the chapter Resource Center at **ClassZone.com** for additional resources and information on allergies.

Science Trivia

- Approximately 10 million Americans are allergic to cat dander, making it the most common pet allergy.
- Allergies are the sixth leading cause of chronic disease in the United States, costing the health-care industry $18 billion annually.
- Peanut allergies affect about 0.6 percent of the U.S. population, causing the most severe food-induced allergic reactions.

Take It Further

Delayed hypersensitivity is a type of allergy that does not occur for about two days after exposure to an allergen. **Poison ivy,** oak, and sumac cause delayed hypersensitivity in people who are allergic to substances in the oils in the plants' leaves, stems, and roots. These oils can be transferred to the skin by touch or can be transferred to another surface, and then to a person's skin. Blisters on the skin appear later and are caused by lymphokines instead of histamines.

Answers

A Compare and Contrast Basophils release histamines, causing inflammation in both reactions. Allergic response occurs with non-disease-causing antigens; inflammation response occurs with disease-causing antigens.

Food Allergens

An allergic reaction can occur when a person eats a specific type of food. In the United States, one to two adults in every 100 have a severe allergy to at least one type of food, and five to eight children out of 100 have a food allergy. Although any type of food can cause an allergy, the most common food allergens are milk, eggs, peanuts and tree nuts, soy, wheat, fish, and shellfish.

If a person's allergic response is severe, he or she may experience anaphylaxis. **Anaphylaxis** (AN-uh-fuh-LAK-sihs) is a condition that occurs when the immune system releases a large amount of histamine, which causes airways to tighten and blood vessels to become porous. When the airways tighten, air cannot enter the lungs or other tissues. When blood vessels become porous, blood leaks out of the circulatory system, causing the body to shut down. If not treated immediately, anaphylaxis can cause death.

FIGURE 31.15 Common airborne allergens include pollen, animal dander, and dust mite wastes. (colored SEMs; magnifications: ragweed 1000×; cat dander about 300×; dust mite 300×)

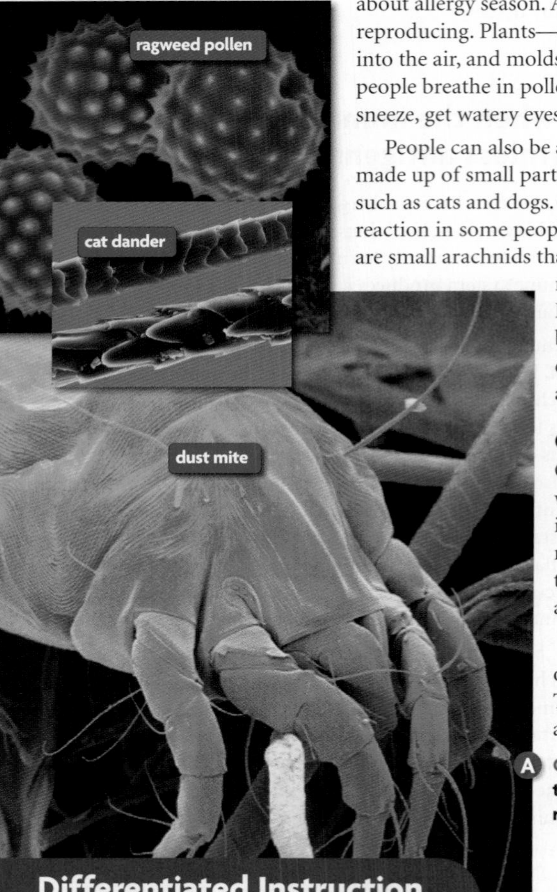

Airborne Allergens

Airborne allergens, such as the ones shown in **FIGURE 31.15**, are those that cause allergic responses when they are breathed in. You may have heard people talk about allergy season. Allergy season occurs when certain plants and molds are reproducing. Plants—such as ragweed, dandelions, and grass—release pollen into the air, and molds release spores as part of their reproductive cycle. When people breathe in pollen or spores, the histamine response may make them sneeze, get watery eyes, or become congested.

People can also be allergic to things that are indoors. Dander, which is made up of small particles in animal hair, makes some people allergic to pets, such as cats and dogs. Chemicals in animal saliva can also trigger an allergic reaction in some people. Others are allergic to the feces of dust mites, which are small arachnids that live in dust balls and cloth. In some cases, allergic reactions to airborne allergens can cause asthma. During an asthma attack the airways tighten, and breathing becomes difficult. Some people with asthma carry inhalers containing medicine that opens up the airways, reversing the effects of an asthma attack.

Chemical Allergens

Chemical allergens include metals that come in contact with the skin or those that enter the blood through injection or digestion. In metal allergies, people develop rashes when certain types of metal rest on their skin for too long. Ten percent of people in the United States are allergic to nickel, a metal that is common in jewelry.

Other chemicals, such as the venom from bee stings or drugs such as penicillin, can cause allergic reactions. These chemicals can cause anaphylaxis in a person with a severe allergy.

A Compare and Contrast How is an allergic response the same as and different from a normal inflammation response?

Differentiated Instruction

PRE-AP

Tell students to think about a man who suddenly starts sneezing and becomes congested. He thinks he is getting a cold. Based on the immune responses discussed in this chapter, have students write a brief essay explaining what is causing the symptoms if the man is getting a cold, and what is causing the symptoms if the man has an allergy.

Biology Toolkit, Quick-Write, p. C19

MAIN IDEA

In autoimmune diseases, white blood cells attack the body's healthy cells.

Autoimmune diseases are those that occur when the immune system cannot tell the difference between the body's healthy and unhealthy cells. Normally, immune system cells attack only foreign substances, such as pathogens and infected or abnormal cells. With autoimmune diseases, the body treats its own cells as though they are foreign invaders.

In Type 1 diabetes, the immune system destroys cells in the pancreas. As a result, the pancreas makes less insulin. Without insulin, the body cannot remove glucose from the blood. Type 1 diabetes can cause death if a person does not get extra insulin into the body. There are more than 60 other autoimmune diseases. Some of the most common ones are described in **FIGURE 31.16.**

FIGURE 31.16 Common Autoimmune Diseases

AUTOIMMUNE DISEASES	BODY SYSTEMS AFFECTED	THE IMMUNE SYSTEM . . .	HOW MANY AFFECTED
Rheumatoid arthritis	integumentary	breaks down tissues that line joints, making movement difficult	70 in 10,000
Type 1 diabetes mellitus	endocrine, digestive	attacks the pancreas, stopping the digestion of sugars	60 in 10,000
Hashimoto's thyroiditis	endocrine	attacks the thyroid gland, causing it to make fewer hormones	15 in 10,000
Multiple sclerosis (MS)	nervous	breaks down myelin sheaths, disrupting nerve communication	10 in 10,000
Graves' disease	endocrine	stimulates the thyroid gland, causing it to make more hormones	5 in 10,000

Scientists do not know why some people develop autoimmune diseases. Research suggests that a person's genes may make them more likely to get an autoimmune disease, but that the actual immune system attack is triggered by another factor—a virus, a drug, or an environmental toxin. Currently, doctors cannot cure autoimmune diseases, but they can provide treatments that lessen the diseases' effects.

A Apply How do autoimmune diseases disrupt other body systems?

ONLINE BIOLOGY Go to the chapter Resource Center at **ClassZone.com** for additional resources and information on autoimmune disorders.

Vocabulary

Greek and Latin Word Origins

Students may make positive associations to the Greek prefix *auto-*, given words such as *autotroph, automatic,* and *autobiography.* However, in the word **autoimmune,** students need to realize that the word literally means "to be immune to one's self," in the sense that the self fights itself.

Answers

A Apply Autoimmune diseases are those in which the immune system attacks healthy tissues. Body systems need organs and tissues to function properly, so if tissues in a body system are attacked, the system cannot function properly.

31.5 ASSESSMENT

ONLINE QUIZ ClassZone.com

REVIEWING MAIN IDEAS

1. Under what conditions is an antigen called an **allergen**?
2. Why might an autoimmune disease be considered a failure of the immune system?

CRITICAL THINKING

3. **Infer** Some **allergies** are treated with drugs called antihistamines. How do you think antihistamines might work?
4. **Analyze** Why does someone experiencing **anaphylaxis** need to receive medicine through injection instead of swallowing a pill?

***Connecting* CONCEPTS**

5. **Ecology** Bee stings can be deadly for people who are allergic to them, but in most people, a bee sting simply hurts and warns the person to leave the insect alone. How are stingers beneficial to the survival of bee species?

Assess and Reteach ▼

Assess Use the Online Quiz or Section Quiz (*Assessment Book,* p. 615).

Reteach In pairs, have students brainstorm about allergens and autoimmune diseases. Make a list of their information on the board to review.

31.5 ASSESSMENT

1. An antigen is called an allergen when the immune system produces antibodies in response to it, causing an allergic reaction.
2. The immune system can no longer recognize its own healthy cells.
3. Students should hypothesize that antihistamines might block histamine production. Answers should include some indication that students understand that histamines cause the inflammation response.
4. When a person is experiencing anaphylaxis, the throat tightens. When this happens, it may become difficult to swallow. An injection would also deliver the medicine more quickly.
5. The pain that people and animals experience from bee stings is probably enough to keep the person or animal, which the bee sees as a predator, away. Even if the bee dies after stinging its victim, the memory of the sting will probably keep the person or animal from bothering other bees in the future.

SECTION 31.6

▼ Plan and Prepare

Objectives

- Explain what leukemia is and how it weakens the immune system.
- Summarize how HIV affects the immune system.

Section Resources

Unit Resource Book Study Guide pp. 111–112 Power Notes p. 113 Reinforcement p. 114 Pre-AP Activity pp. 119–120
Interactive Reader Chapter 31 **Spanish Study Guide** pp. 323–324
Biology Toolkit pp. C3, C17, C19, C31
Technology Power Presentation 31.6 Media Gallery DVD Online Quiz 31.6

Activate Prior Knowledge Students have probably read about or seen movies dramatizing the stories of people who have AIDS. **Ask,** What is a common concern of people who have AIDS? Students may mention susceptibility to infection. Often the focus is on T cell counts.

▼ Teach

Vocabulary

anemia Anemia is a deficiency of the oxygen-carrying component in red blood cells, hemoglobin. The suffix *-emia* derives from a Greek word meaning "blood."

leukemia The prefix *leuk-* means "white." People with leukemia have abnormally high counts of white blood cells as compared to red blood cells.

31.6 Diseases That Weaken the Immune System

KEY CONCEPT When the immune system is weakened, the body cannot fight off diseases.

MAIN IDEAS
- Leukemia is characterized by abnormal white blood cells.
- HIV targets the immune system.

VOCABULARY
leukemia, p. 960
opportunistic infection, p. 961
human immunodeficiency virus (HIV), p. 961
acquired immune deficiency syndrome (AIDS), p. 963

Review
T cells

Connect There is no cure for AIDS. But people who are infected with HIV do not die directly from it—some people don't know that they're infected for more than ten years. Instead, as HIV weakens the immune system, they become sick with other diseases. Illnesses that weaken the immune system, such as an AIDS infection, make it easy for other pathogens to infect the body and take over.

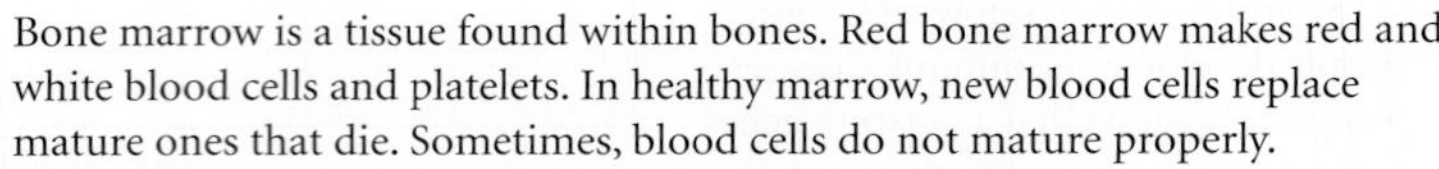

MAIN IDEA
Leukemia is characterized by abnormal white blood cells.

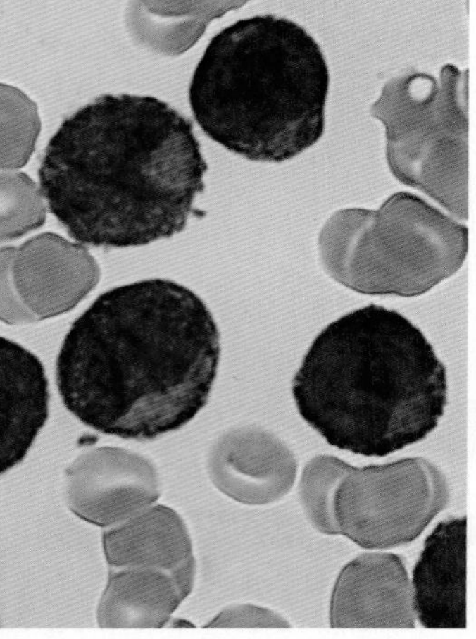

FIGURE 31.17 The blood of a person infected with leukemia contains an abnormally high number of immature white blood cells, dyed purple in this micrograph. (magnification needed)

Bone marrow is a tissue found within bones. Red bone marrow makes red and white blood cells and platelets. In healthy marrow, new blood cells replace mature ones that die. Sometimes, blood cells do not mature properly.

Leukemia is cancer of the bone marrow. Unlike other cancers, leukemia does not form tumors. Instead, it prevents the bone marrow from functioning properly. In one type of leukemia, the bone marrow produces white blood cells that do not develop properly. Because the cells are immature, they cannot fight infections. Here is how leukemia weakens the immune system.

- Bone marrow produces white blood cells that don't mature. These cells are shown in **FIGURE 31.17.**
- In effort to replace the defective white blood cells, the bone marrow produces more and more white blood cells. However, none of these new cells mature into effective white blood cells.
- Eventually, the bone marrow spends all of its time making white blood cells. As a result, it makes fewer red blood cells and platelets than are needed to replace those that die or become damaged.

To cure leukemia, the cancerous bone marrow must be replaced with healthy marrow from a donor. Before a bone marrow transplant takes place, the recipient is given large doses of radiation and chemotherapy to kill all the abnormal bone marrow cells. Then the donor marrow is put into the body. If the transplant is successful, the donor marrow will make healthy blood cells.

Differentiated Instruction

PRE-AP

To test students' understanding, write five to ten statements about the main points of the section. Focus on how leukemia and HIV weaken the immune system, and the results of a weakened immune system. You may also want to see if students understand the relationship beween HIV and AIDS. Have students react to the statements as being either true or false before reading the section and then again after reading the section.

Biology Toolkit, Anticipation Guide, p. C3

However, problems can arise from bone marrow transplants. In graft-versus-host disease (GVHD), the donor marrow makes antibodies against the host's healthy tissues. Chemotherapy and radiation treatments also kill both cancerous cells and healthy cells, leaving the immune system weak and open to opportunistic infections. An **opportunistic infection** is an infection caused by a pathogen that a healthy immune system would normally be able to fight off. When the immune system is weakened, an opportunistic infection can make a person very sick.

A Analyze **Shortness of breath and inability to form blood clots are common symptoms of leukemia. How does the disease lead to these symptoms?**

MAIN IDEA

HIV targets the immune system.

The World Health Organization estimates that more than 40 million people in the world have HIV/AIDS. During the 1980s, fewer than 2 million people had the virus. The **human immunodeficiency virus (HIV),** illustrated in **FIGURE 31.18,** is a retrovirus that attacks and weakens the immune system. A retrovirus is a type of virus that contains RNA instead of DNA. HIV is a retrovirus that has nine genes. HIV weakens the immune system, and the body is likely to get opportunistic infections.

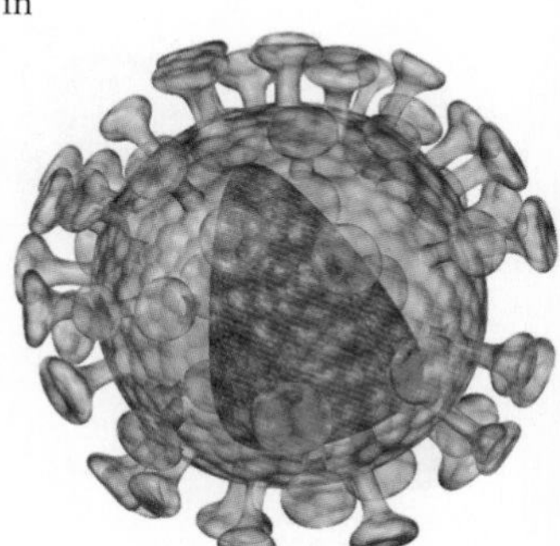

FIGURE 31.18 HIV is a small retrovirus that is covered with bumps, which are its antigens. This illustration shows an HIV about 500,000 times its actual size.

HIV Transmission

Although HIV is a very dangerous pathogen, it can only live in human blood cells and thus will not survive for long outside of the human body. For this reason, HIV is not transmitted through shaking hands with an infected individual, or swimming in a pool with an infected person. HIV cannot be transmitted through insect bites either. Insects that suck blood, such as ticks or mosquitoes, quickly digest the blood cells in their guts. Once the blood is digested, HIV dies.

A person becomes infected with HIV when the virus enters his or her bloodstream. HIV is passed from person to person through the mixing of blood and other body fluids. HIV is transmitted through sexual intercourse with an infected individual. It can also be passed from mothers to their unborn babies through the umbilical cord. A person might also get HIV if his or her skin is pierced by a needle that an infected individual recently used. Hypodermic needles used for injecting some illegal drugs and needles used for body piercing and tattooing have transmitted HIV between individuals. However, needles that your doctor uses to give shots or take blood do not transmit HIV because doctors use a new needle for every patient.

HIV Reproduces in T Cells

HIV infects T cells, the white blood cells that trigger the body's immune responses. When HIV enters a T cell, the T cell becomes ineffective and can no longer stimulate an immune response. While the T cell cannot function in the immune system, it remains alive as a host and produces new HIV. A single T cell can give rise to thousands of HIV viruses before it eventually dies.

ONLINE BIOLOGY Have students look at ongoing research into HIV and AIDS by doing the WebQuest in Options for Inquiry on page 965.

Vocabulary

opportunistic infection Tell students that opportunistic infections are a concern whenever the immune system is weakened. Pathogens have a better opportunity to survive the immune system's weakened defenses. Discuss the word *opportunity* to help students understand and remember *opportunistic.*

Address Misconceptions

Common Misconception Students often think that HIV is not transmitted between heterosexuals. They think HIV is mainly transmitted by homosexuals and drug addicts.

Correcting the Misconception Anyone who has any unprotected sex with someone who has the HIV virus can become infected. People who are infected with an HIV infection can look, act, and feel healthy. They may not know they have the virus.

Answers

A Analyze When there are too many immature white blood cells in a person's body, the red bone marrow makes fewer platelets, which form clots, and red blood cells, which carry oxygen, than are needed to replace those that die or become damaged.

BELOW LEVEL

Have students write a brief paragraph or list that summarizes leukemia and HIV, and their effects on the body. Then have students share their summaries with a partner.

Biology Toolkit, Quick-Write, p. C19

▼ Teach *continued*

TEACH FROM VISUALS

FIGURE 31.19 To help students understand what happens after HIV enters the body, have them read the description under stage 1 and view the diagram. **Ask,** How does this process compare to what occurs when any other virus enters the body? It is the same. Then move on to the next two numbered descriptions and diagrams and repeat the process. **Ask**

- What makes HIV different from other viruses? It kills T cells.
- What is the end result? opportunistic diseases

Help students interpret the graph. **Ask,** How are the number of T cells and HIV related? As the number of HIV increases, the number of T cells decreases. Note that at some time during year 3, AIDS had set in. Point out that the graph ends because the person had died.

Take It Further

Here are some daunting statistics about **HIV** and **AIDS:**

- More than 10 billion HIV can be produced in an infected person's body each day.
- Twenty-five million people worldwide have died of AIDS since 1981, and over four million were newly infected in 2005.
- An estimated 38 million people worldwide are infected with HIV. Almost half of them are women and children between the ages of 15 and 24.

Answers

A Critical Viewing T cells activate B cells, which produce antibodies. With fewer T cells, B cells cannot be activated to make antibodies.

FIGURE 31.19 HIV Destroys T cells

HIV reproduces within T cells, killing T cells and weakening the immune system.

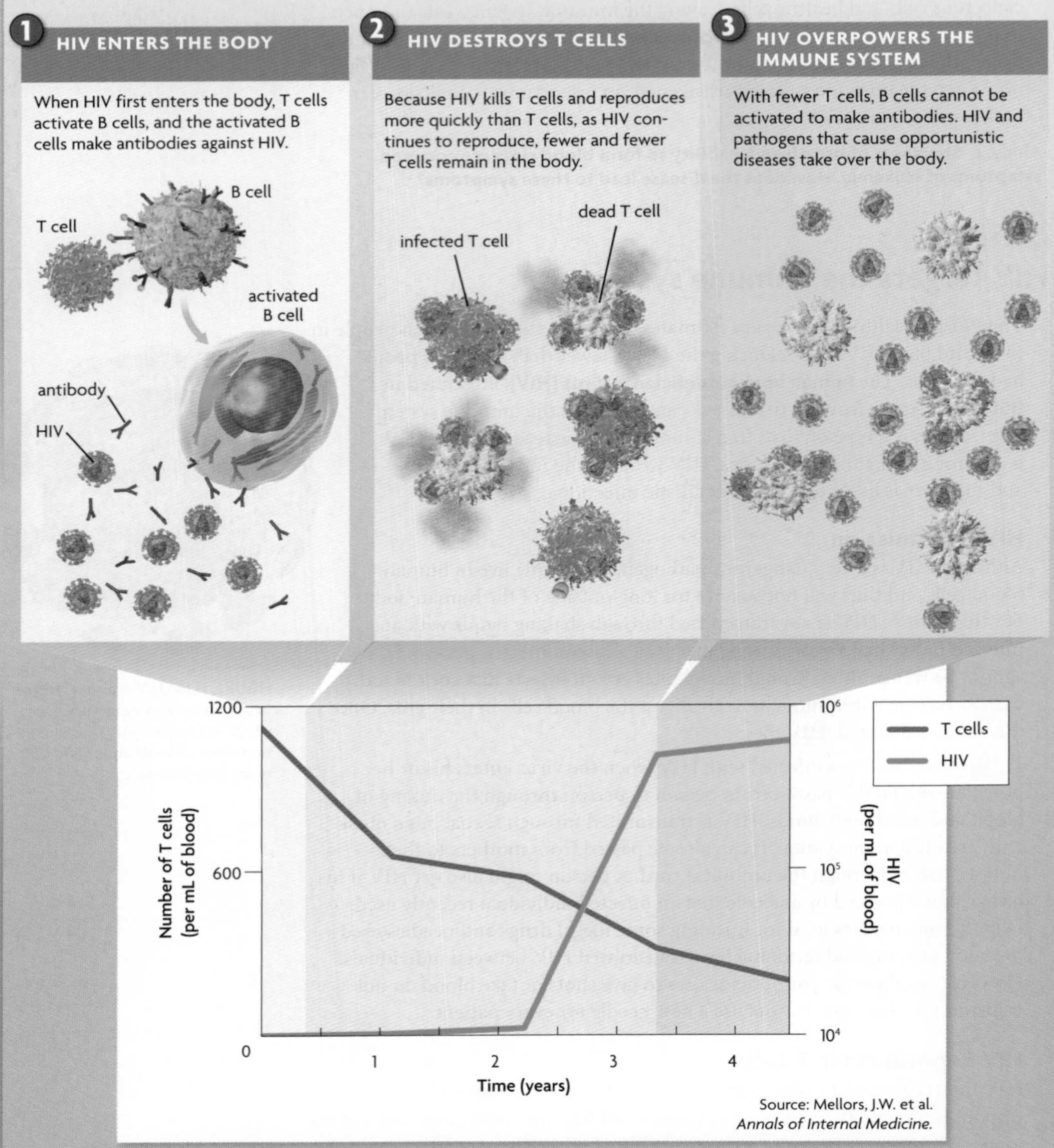

1 HIV ENTERS THE BODY
When HIV first enters the body, T cells activate B cells, and the activated B cells make antibodies against HIV.
B cell
T cell
activated B cell
antibody
HIV
2 HIV DESTROYS T CELLS
Because HIV kills T cells and reproduces more quickly than T cells, as HIV continues to reproduce, fewer and fewer T cells remain in the body.
dead T cell
infected T cell
3 HIV OVERPOWERS THE IMMUNE SYSTEM
With fewer T cells, B cells cannot be activated to make antibodies. HIV and pathogens that cause opportunistic diseases take over the body.
1200
600
0
Number of T cells (per mL of blood)
10^6
10^5
10^4
HIV (per mL of blood)
1
2
3
4
Time (years)
T cells
HIV
Source: Mellors, J.W. et al. *Annals of Internal Medicine.*

A CRITICAL VIEWING **Why might a graph comparing HIV and antibodies have a similar shape to the one above, which compares HIV and T cells?**

Differentiated Instruction

ENGLISH LEARNERS

Focus on the drawings and labels in **FIGURE 31.19.** Have students use their fingers to point to the drawings and follow along, as you read the description. Make sure they identify and understand each step before moving on. Then help students understand the connection between HIV and T cells in the graph. Make sure they know what each line and axis represents.

Biology Toolkit, Connect to Content through Visuals, p. C17

PRE-AP

Have students analyze the drawings and graph in **FIGURE 31.19.** Then have them combine the two in a timeline. The dates of the timeline should reflect the years in the graph. Above the timeline, have students draw what is going on in the person's body at different times during the four and one-half years, adding captions and labels to their drawings.

Biology Toolkit, Timeline, p. C31

As HIV reproduces, the body cannot make replacement T cells fast enough. As the immune system weakens, opportunistic infections begin to take over.

During the first few weeks of infection, a person usually does not feel sick. Although HIV is infecting some T cells, there are still enough healthy T cells that B cells can be activated to produce antibodies against HIV, as shown in **FIGURE 31.19.** At this stage, HIV is diagnosed by determining whether a person's blood contains antibodies against HIV.

After the initial infection, an infected person can have HIV for ten years or more without experiencing any symptoms. During this stage, more and more T cells become infected, and each cell produces thousands of HIV cells, as shown in **FIGURE 31.20.** Soon, the bone marrow cannot replace dead T cells quickly enough, and the body develops opportunistic infections and AIDS.

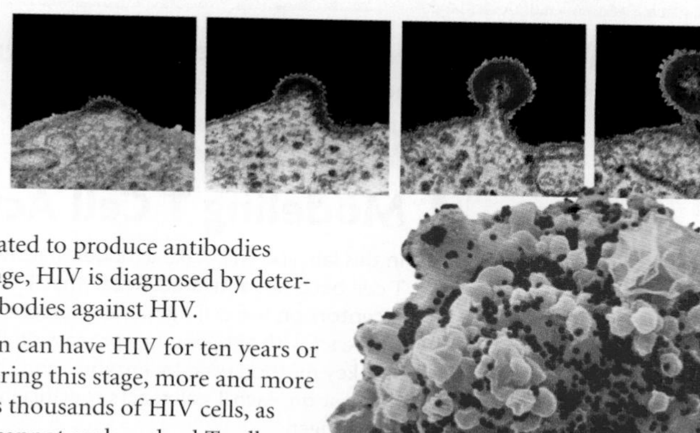

FIGURE 31.20 **Thousands of HIV, shown in red, will bud off a T cell before the T cell dies.** (top: colored TEM, magnification 105,000×; bottom: colored SEM, magnification 5000×)

HIV Leads to AIDS

Acquired immune deficiency syndrome (AIDS) is the final stage of the immune system's decline due to HIV. Whereas HIV is a virus, AIDS is the condition of having a worn-out immune system. A person with AIDS can have several opportunistic infections—such as fungal infections, tuberculosis, pneumonia, viral infections, and cancers—and very few T cells. AIDS always results in death because a person's body cannot fight off its many infections.

Treatment of an HIV infection is expensive, complicated, and only slows—but does not cure—the disease. Treatment involves a combination of three to four antiviral drugs that are taken as often as five times each day. These drugs can cause many unpleasant side effects and can be very expensive. What's more, as HIV mutates, a patient might need to use many different drug combinations to keep the infection under control. Also, HIV mutates rapidly, and so far no vaccine has provided complete protection against the new strains of HIV that are constantly evolving.

A Apply How does the destruction of T cells lead to the failure of the overall immune system?

31.6 ASSESSMENT

ONLINE QUIZ ClassZone.com

REVIEWING MAIN IDEAS

1. How does **leukemia** affect a person's entire body?
2. How do **HIV** and **AIDS** differ?

CRITICAL THINKING

3. **Analyze** Why won't people who take multiple medications to treat HIV infections ever be cured?
4. **Compare and Contrast** Which cells of the immune system are affected by HIV and leukemia, and what parts of the immune response do these cells influence?

Connecting CONCEPTS

5. **Antibiotics** You learned in Chapter 18 that viruses cannot be treated with antibiotics. Why, then, might doctors prescribe antibiotics to patients with HIV anyway?

31.6 ASSESSMENT

1. White blood cells do not mature. The circulatory system distributes these immature cells throughout the body, which prevents the immune system from effectively fighting pathogens. There are also fewer red blood cells and platelets than are needed, resulting in less oxygen for body cells and a reduced ability for blood to clot.
2. HIV is a virus that destroys T cells. AIDS is the final stage of the immune system's decline due to HIV.
3. Medicines cannot cure viruses; they just treat the symptoms.
4. HIV destroys T cells that are needed to activate the humoral and cellular immune responses. Leukemia affects the bone marrow, which produces white blood cells that do not mature and cannot fight infections.
5. The antibiotics fight off the opportunistic infections that occur because HIV has weakened the immune system.

Address Misconceptions

Common Misconception Students may think that HIV and AIDS are the same thing.

Correcting the Misconception HIV is the human immunodeficiency virus. It is the virus and viral infection that causes the human immune system to become deficient. During the viral infection, the HIV causes T cells to reproduce viruses and then kill the T cells. In the later stages of an HIV infection, the body's immune system cannot fight off other pathogens, and AIDS results.

AIDS is acquired immune deficiency syndrome. A syndrome is a group of symptoms that collectively indicate a disease. In the case of AIDS, the symptoms are the opportunistic diseases against which the body's immune system can no longer defend itself.

Answers

A Apply T cells are necessary for activating the humoral and cellular immune responses. If there are no T cells, neither response can occur.

Assess and Reteach ▼

Assess Use the Online Quiz or Section Quiz (*Assessment Book*, p. 616).

Reteach Help students to summarize the effects of leukemia and HIV on the immune system.

OPTIONS FOR INQUIRY

INVESTIGATION

Time 30 minutes	TEACHER TESTED
Teacher Preparation	
Student Difficulty	
Lab Binder Human Bio, pp. 43–44	

Purpose Use common materials to model how a T cell becomes activated.

Overview Students will decide how to model each of the components involved in T cell activation. They will

- decide how to represent T cell receptors on the surface of a T cell
- decide how to represent a macrophage with antigen fragments on its cell surface
- decide how to represent chemicals released by the macrophage and T cell
- make a model of T cell activation

LAB PREPARATION

- Review with students the information on page 952 about T cells, antigens, and T cell activation.
- Use any alternative materials that may be available in your classroom.

LAB MANAGEMENT

- Make sure students have decided on appropriate components before they make their models.
- Remind students to wash their hands after the investigation.

Inclusion For students who have difficulty with fine motor skills or students who are visually impaired, provide larger materials with different textures.

POST-LAB DISCUSSION

Discuss the importance of the T cell receptors having a "lock-and-key method" of recognizing antigens. **Ask,** What does this mean? A T cell receptor can recognize and bind to an antigen, because its structure fits that specific antigen.

Use these inquiry-based labs and online activities to deepen your understanding of immune system response.

NOS.6 Use analogies and models (mathematical and physical) to simplify and represent systems that are difficult to understand or directly experience due to their size, time scale, or complexity, and recognize the limitations of analogies and models.

INVESTIGATION

Modeling T Cell Activation

In this lab, you will make a model that shows how a T cell becomes activated. Recall that T cells have receptors on the cell membrane surface that recognize and react with antigens. In a process similar to the lock-and-key method used by enzymes and the substrates they act on, each T cell reacts specifically with only one antigen.

MATERIALS

- sheet of white paper
- 5 colors of construction paper
- colored markers
- glue
- scissors

SKILL Modeling

PROBLEM How does a T cell become activated?

PROCEDURE

1. Decide how you will model each of the components involved in T cell activation. Keep in mind that
   - You will need to represent a T cell with receptors on the surface of the cell membrane.
   - You will also need to represent a macrophage that has ingested an antigen and has antigen fragments on its cell surface.
   - You will also need to represent chemicals released by the macrophage and the T cell that lead to the production of more T cells.
2. Refer to Section 31.3 for more information and diagrams about T cell activation as you determine which materials you will use for constructing your models.
3. Make your model.

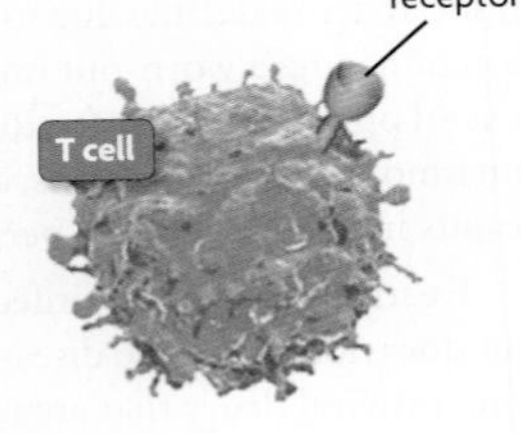

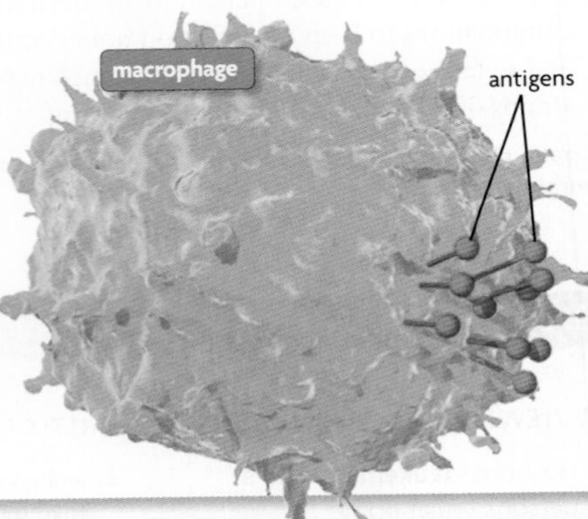

ANALYZE AND CONCLUDE

1. **Evaluate** What are the limitations of your model?
2. **Evaluate** How would your model change if you wanted to show how a T cell is involved in the activation of a B cell?

Answers

Analyze and Conclude

1. The size, ratio of the size, and number of parts are not accurate.
2. Other materials will be needed to represent a B cell and its antibodies. Refer students to page 953.

INVESTIGATION

What Is an Autoimmune Disease?

Sometimes the immune system attacks and damages the body's own healthy tissues. An autoimmune disorder is a disease that occurs when the immune system can no longer tell the difference between the body's own cells and foreign cells. Graves' disease, a disorder in which antibodies attach to receptors on cells in the thyroid gland, results in an overactive thyroid gland that must be treated with medication, surgery, or radiation.

SKILL Researching

PROBLEM What is the nature of the autoimmune disease?

PROCEDURE

1. Choose one of the following autoimmune diseases:
   - **a.** Myasthenia gravis
   - **b.** Lupus
   - **c.** Rheumatoid arthritis
   - **d.** Rheumatic fever
2. Perform research to find the cause of the disease.
3. How does the disease progress?
4. What are the possible treatments?

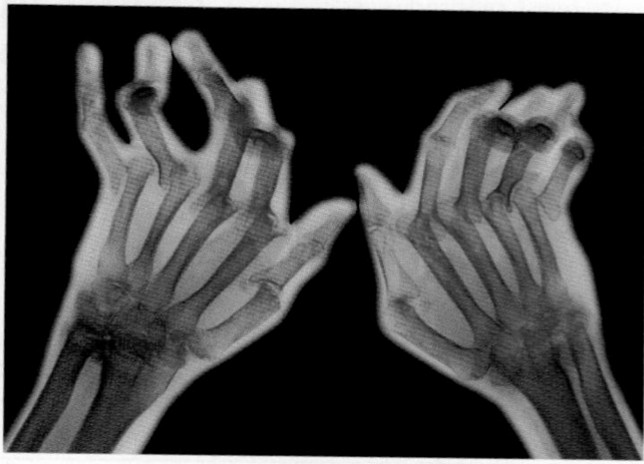

This x-ray image shows the hands of a person who is affected with rheumatoid arthritis.

Online BIOLOGY CLASSZONE.COM

ANIMATED BIOLOGY

Destroy the Invaders

Can you keep someone from contracting an illness? Use a set of immune cells to mount attacks against a variety of pathogens to keep the person healthy.

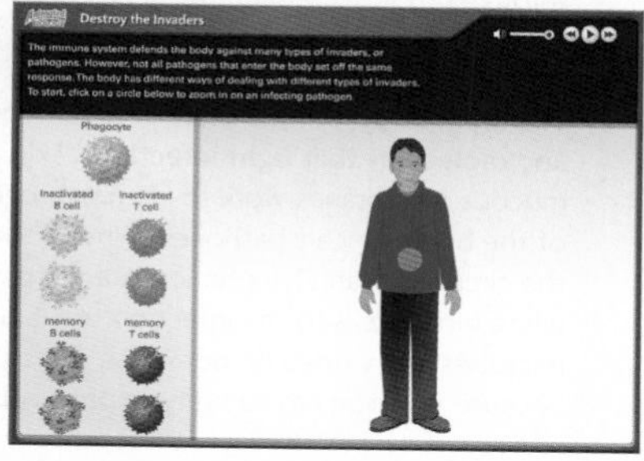

WEBQUEST

HIV infects people all over the world. You will learn more about how this deadly virus works and causes AIDS. Explore how HIV is treated and look into ongoing research devoted to overcoming HIV.

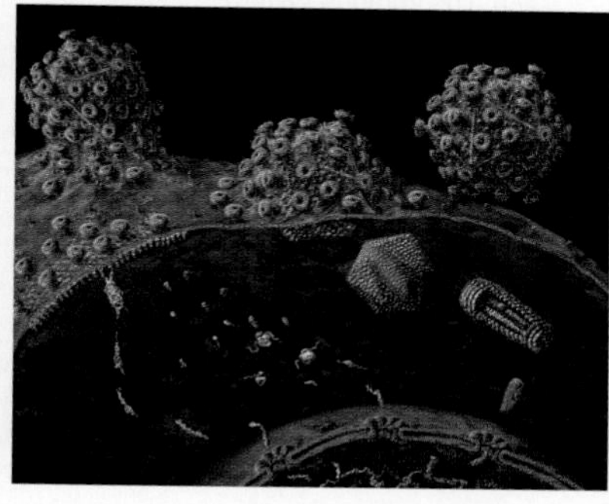

DATA ANALYSIS ONLINE

The West Nile virus first appeared in North America in 1999. The first reported infections were in the New York City area. Since then, it has spread across the United States. Graph the number of West Nile virus cases and discover just how quickly the virus spread.

Online Biology ▼

ANIMATED BIOLOGY Use this simulation to reinforce the concepts in **Section 31.2.**

WEBQUEST The WebQuest takes one full class period. Students complete the activity online and then will need access to a printer to print their answers. Sample answers, teacher notes, and alternative assessment ideas are available on **ClassZone.com.** Use with **Section 31.6.**

DATA ANALYSIS ONLINE

The graphs will show a substantial increase, from 83 cases (1999–2000) to over 3000 in 2005. Use this activity to reinforce the concepts in **Section 31.1.**

INVESTIGATION

Time	45 minutes (TEACHER TESTED)
Teacher Preparation	(1 flask)
Student Difficulty	(1 flask)
Lab Binder	Human Bio, p. 45

Purpose Research the cause of an autoimmune disease, how the disease progresses, and possible treatments.

POST-LAB DISCUSSION

Have students share their research with the class.

Answers

Research

Sample information for lupus:

Lupus is an autoimmune disease in which the body's immune system turns against healthy tissue, causing inflammation and damage to various parts of the body, such as the joints, skin, kidneys, heart, lungs, blood vessels, and brain. A combination of factors, such as heredity, environment, and hormones, may trigger lupus, but the disease is not well understood.

The progress and treatment of lupus is unpredictable and varies with the type of lupus a person has, and with each individual. A person with lupus experiences different symptoms at different times. Without treatment, lupus can cause life-threatening complications, which include kidney failure, infections of the heart muscle, certain cancers, and bone tissue death. A variety of medicines can be used to reduce the symptoms.

CHAPTER REVIEW

Interactive Review

Encourage students to go to **ClassZone.com** for a detailed review of each section, including visuals and vocabulary practice.

Unit Resource Book, Vocabulary Practice, pp. 121–124

CHAPTER 31 **Interactive Review** @ CLASSZONE.COM

KEY CONCEPTS | Vocabulary Games | Concept Maps | Animated Biology | Online Quiz

31.1 Pathogens and Human Illness

Germs cause many diseases in humans. Germ theory hypothesized that microbes—not spirits—caused disease. Viruses, bacteria, fungi, protozoa, and parasitic worms are examples of pathogens. These pathogens can be spread through physical contact, the air, or vectors.

31.2 Immune System

The immune system consists of organs, cells, and molecules that fight infections. Skin and mucous membranes work to keep pathogens out of the body. Once a pathogen is inside the body, the circulatory and lymphatic systems transport white blood cells to the infection site. Some microbes and viruses do not cause illness because a person has some type of immunity.

31.3 Immune Responses

The immune system has many responses to pathogens and foreign cells. Nonspecific responses, such as inflammation and fever, are those that react the same to every pathogen. Specific responses, such as the cellular and humoral responses, are different for every pathogen. The immune system might initiate a specific response against transplanted tissues.

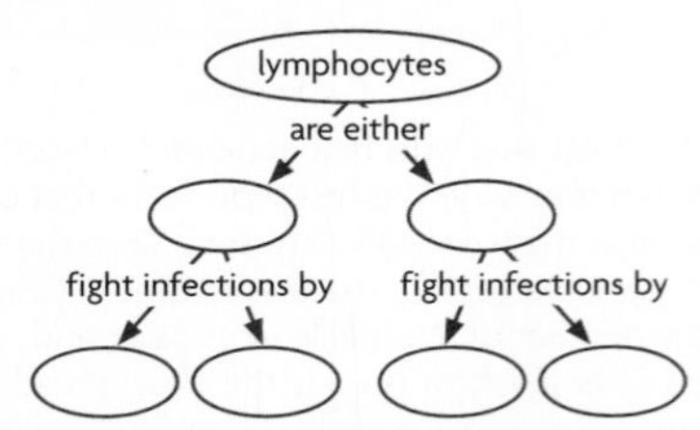

31.4 Immunity and Technology

Living in a clean environment and building immunity help keep a person healthy. Antiseptics destroy pathogens outside of the body, and antibiotics destroy pathogens inside of the body. Vaccines activate an immune response without getting a person sick. When the pathogen does invade, a vaccinated person's immune response is so quick that the person will not get sick.

31.5 Overreactions of the Immune System

An overactive immune system can make the body very unhealthy. Allergies occur when the immune system responds to a harmless antigen. In autoimmune diseases, white blood cells attack the body's healthy cells.

31.6 Diseases That Weaken the Immune System

When the immune system is weakened, the body cannot fight off diseases. Leukemia is characterized by immature white blood cells. HIV attacks T cells so that other pathogens can take over the body. When a person has very few T cells and several opportunistic diseases, the person has a condition called AIDS.

Synthesize Your Notes

Concept Map Use a concept map to organize your notes about lymphocytes.

lymphocytes
are either
fight infections by
fight infections by

Chart Use a three-column chart to compare similar concepts.

Word	Definition	How It Is Different from Others
antigen		
allergen		
protein marker		

Reviewing Vocabulary

1. A pathogen might be spread by a vector.
2. T cells can directly destroy unhealthy body cells, while B cells produce antibodies that fight pathogens.
3. Antibodies are proteins made by lymphocytes to respond to the presence of foreign antigens.
4. protein that keeps viruses from reproducing
5. nonspecific response to a pathogen
6. immune response that depends on T cells
7. chemical that kills pathogens outside of the body
8. A phagocyte is a cell that eats other cells.
9. An antibiotic is a substance that destroys living pathogens. Antibiotic resistance means the pathogen is unaffected by the substance.

Reviewing Main Ideas

10. In order to use Koch's postulates, the cause of the disease must be a pathogen. Pathogens cause infectious disease, but genetics, chemicals, and other non-pathogens cause noninfectious disease.
11. Bacteria, fungi, viruses, protozoa, parasites; pathogens cause disease by taking nutrients from cells and disrupting cells' normal activities.
12. direct contact: touching, kissing, sexual intercourse; indirect contact: touching an infected, nonliving surface

Chapter Assessment

Chapter Vocabulary

31.1 germ theory, p. 941
pathogen, p. 941
vector, p. 944

31.2 immune system, p. 945
phagocyte, p. 946
T cell, p. 946
B cell, p. 946
antibody, p. 947
interferon, p. 947
passive immunity, p. 948
active immunity, p. 948

31.3 inflammation, p. 950
antigen, p. 951
memory cell, p. 951
cellular immunity, p. 952
humoral immunity, p. 953
tissue rejection, p. 954

31.4 antiseptic, p. 955
antibiotic resistance, p. 955
vaccine, p. 956

31.5 allergy, p. 957
allergen, p. 957
anaphylaxis, p. 958

31.6 leukemia, p. 960
opportunistic infection, p. 961
human immunodeficiency virus (HIV), p. 961
acquired immune deficiency syndrome (AIDS), p. 963

Reviewing Vocabulary

Vocabulary Connections

For each group of words below, write a sentence or two to clearly explain how the terms are connected. For example, for the terms *HIV* and *AIDS,* you could write, "HIV weakens the immune system and leads to AIDS."

1. pathogen, vector
2. T cells, B cells
3. antibody, antigen

Keep It Short

For each vocabulary term below, write a short, precise phrase that describes its meaning. For example, a short phrase to describe *leukemia* could be "cancer of the bone marrow."

4. interferon
5. inflammation
6. cellular immunity
7. antiseptic

Greek and Latin Word Origins

8. The term *phagocyte* comes from the Greek word *phagos,* meaning "to eat." Explain how this meaning relates to the word *phagocyte.*

9. The word *antibiotic* contains the prefix *anti-,* from a Greek word meaning "opposite," and the Greek word *bios,* meaning "life." Explain how, together, these meanings relate to the term *antibiotic resistance.*

Reviewing MAIN IDEAS

10. Why do Koch's postulates and germ theory apply to infectious diseases but not noninfectious diseases?

11. What are some types of pathogens, and how do they attack the body?

12. What are some ways that pathogens spread?

13. How do other body systems help the immune system respond to infections?

14. How do phagocytes, antibodies, and interferons help to fight pathogens?

15. How are passive immunity and active immunity similar and different?

16. How does fever help to fight infections?

17. How do specific immune responses lead to active immunity?

18. How might organ transplants, which are meant to save a person's life, endanger the person?

19. People say, "Too much of a good thing can be bad." How does this statement relate to the use of antibiotics?

20. How does a vaccine produce active immunity without making a person sick?

21. How do autoimmune diseases disrupt homeostasis?

22. How does leukemia weaken the immune system?

23. What is the difference between HIV and AIDS?

CHAPTER REVIEW

13. The skin and mucous membrane block pathogens from entering. The lymphatic and circulatory systems help transport cells and proteins of the immune system.

14. Phagocytes engulf pathogens. Antibodies inactivate pathogens. Interferons stop viruses from reproducing.

15. Both types of immunity fight pathogens to help keep you from getting sick. Passive immunity can be passed through the umbilical cord to a nursing baby through breast milk or through genetics. Active immunity occurs after a person's immune system has fought off an invasion of a specific pathogen and pathogen-fighting memory cells that remember the particular pathogen are ready to fight it immediately if it invades again.

16. A low fever speeds the maturation rate of white blood cells, which fight infection.

17. A specific response involves the development of both T and B memory cells. This results after interacting with the pathogen's antigen. The memory cells then "remember" the particular antigen and if they encounter it again, the immune response occurs before the person gets sick. This is active immunity.

18. The immune system of the recipient will recognize the antigens on the donor cells as foreign and will make antibodies to fight them. This could cause the destruction of the tissue, also called tissue rejection.

19. Antibiotics can kill disease-causing bacteria and fungi. This is very good. But the continued use of antibiotics leads to microbes mutating into forms that can resist the antibiotic. This is called antibiotic resistance, and this is bad.

20. Vaccines trigger the same type of immune response from B cells as when you are exposed to a disease. However, you do not get sick because the antigens in the vaccine are either dead, very weak, pieces of the pathogens, or inactivated.

21. Autoimmune diseases are those in which cells of the immune system attack healthy body cells. Once attacked, the otherwise healthy cells cannot complete their normal activities.

22. Leukemia stops white blood cells from maturing. Immature white blood cells cannot fight disease. As the bone marrow makes more white blood cells to make up for the immature ones, the new ones also do not mature. The body has less and less ability to fight disease.

23. HIV is a virus that infects T cells, which begin the body's immune responses. AIDS is a condition that results from the person having a weakened immune system.

Critical Thinking

24. In order for one to conclude that a pathogen causes a specific disease, the pathogen must cause the disease in every case.
25. As viruses mutate, new vaccines must be developed. When bacteria evolve, new antibiotics must be found.
26. The stinger is a vector that carries weak poisons. These are recognized by white blood cells as foreign, but because they are not disease-causing pathogens, they are called allergens. White blood cells release chemicals that cause inflammation around the sting site.
27. In the humoral response, white blood cells detect antigens that indicate the presence of a pathogen. T cells stimulate B cells to produce antibodies to destroy the foreign substances. The humoral response can cause tissue rejection when donor tissue is identified as foreign. It also enables a person to fight disease.
28. Although HIV stimulates the production of antibodies, it also prevents T cells from performing their roles in the immune response. But the T cells can still act as hosts for the invading HIV, and this allows more HIV to be produced. HIV is produced faster than new T cells, so the number of needed antibodies can never catch up to the amount of HIV in the person. Eventually, there is hardly anything left in the inmune system to fight any kinds of diseases.
29. When a person becomes vaccinated, they undergo the entire humoral immune response, but they do not get sick because the antigens in the vaccine are weakened or dead. After a person is vaccinated, if they become infected by the pathogen, the body's memory cells will immediately mature and fight off the infection.
30. A humoral response after a person is vaccinated does not include the steps necessary to activate B cells. These steps, which require B cells to detect antigens, and T cells to bind with the B cells, must be what takes longest and allows the pathogen time to make a person sick.

Critical Thinking

24. Apply In 1918, scientists found a bacterium in the lungs of some people who died of flu. The bacteria were given to healthy volunteers, but only some volunteers developed flulike symptoms. Using germ theory, decide whether this bacterium caused flu.

25. Connect How does the evolution of pathogens, specifically bacteria and viruses, negatively affect humans' ability to stay healthy?

26. Synthesize If you get stung by a bee, the skin around the bite will swell. Explain the process that produced the swelling. Use and define the terms *vector, allergen, inflammation,* and *white blood cell* in your answer.

27. Compare and Contrast How can the humoral immune response both help and hurt the body?

28. Analyze People infected with HIV are said to be HIV-positive because they have the antibodies for the virus. Why don't antibodies, which normally protect the body against pathogens, protect people who are HIV-positive from developing AIDS?

29. Explain Summarize the process by which a vaccine helps the body fight off pathogens. Begin with what happens when a person gets vaccinated, and conclude with the destruction of the invading pathogen.

30. Infer Compare the normal humoral immune response to the response after someone is vaccinated. Which steps of the humoral response probably take the longest, allowing the pathogen to make the body sick?

Interpreting Visuals

Use the diagram below to answer the next three questions.

31. Summarize What is happening in each numbered part of the process shown above?

32. Apply Before this process could take place, one of two events must have occurred. What are the two events?

33. Analyze What kind of immunity is shown here?

Analyzing Data

Use the graph below to identify data flaws and answer the next two questions.

A researcher designs an experiment to determine what dose of a new antibiotic must be given to patients to kill the bacteria that cause pneumonia. The researcher infects three groups of mice with three different strands of pneumonia bacteria. Group 1 is not given any antibiotic. The researcher gives Groups 2 and 3 different doses of the antibiotic. The results are shown below.

MICE CURED WITH ANTIBIOTICS

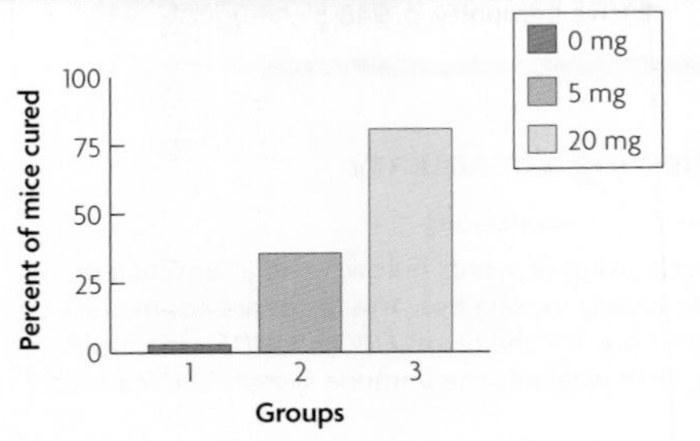

34. Analyze Can the researcher conclude that the largest dose of antibiotic is necessary to cure pneumonia? Why or why not?

35. Evaluate How could this investigation be redesigned to better answer the researcher's question?

Connecting CONCEPTS

36. Design a Video Game Imagine that you are creating a video game in which the player can choose to be a T cell or a B cell. Describe the player's goals for each version of the game. How will the player direct the cells in their mission to seek out and destroy the invading pathogens?

37. Design an Experiment One fall, children who live in a wooded area become ill. They develop an itchy rash, a hacking cough, and a sick feeling in their stomachs. One local doctor tells concerned parents that their children had an allergic reaction to something in the woods and advises that the children rest in bed. Another doctor thinks that a bacterium causes the sickness and prescribes medicine for the children. Design an experiment to determine who is correct. (**Hint:** What evidence do you need to prove a pathogen caused a disease?)

Interpreting Visuals

31. In step one, a B cell is detecting a pathogen. In step two, the B cell is maturing and dividing. In step three, the B cell is producing antibodies that fight pathogens.
32. A person must have been infected by this pathogen before, or the person must have been vaccinated.
33. acquired immunity

Analyzing Data

34. The researcher doesn't understand that antibiotic resistance means that a pathogen doesn't respond at all to the drug. The antibiotic cannot fight the pathogen. The researcher only questioned people who were cured by amoxicillin. That automatically eliminated anyone who was affected by antibiotic resistance.

INDIANA ISTEP+ Test Prep

NOS.1; NOS.8

Test Practice
For more test practice, go to ClassZone.com.

1 In the 1850s, Louis Pasteur conducted many experiments and based on his results, proposed that specific microorganisms cause disease. This proposal is an example of a scientific

A hypothesis.
B guess.
C theory.
D experiment.

2

Set Up for Chicken Pox Experiment

Volunteer	Injected with Dead Chicken Pox Virus	Injected with Distilled Water
A	X	
B		X
C	X	X

A scientist studies three volunteers who never had chicken pox by injecting each with a dead virus, distilled water, or a combination of the two. The experimental design is described in the table above. After the injection, whose blood stream would ***most*** likely contain antibodies for the chicken pox virus?

A volunteer A only
B volunteer B only
C volunteers A and B
D volunteers A and C

3 A person infected with HIV is more likely to become sick with other diseases because

A people infected with HIV must take drugs to suppress the immune system.
B pathogens can enter the bodies of people infected with HIV during surgery.
C HIV mutates quickly into other diseases that affect the immune system.
D HIV attacks the cells that produce immune responses.

4 Mucous membranes and the skin are nonspecific defenses against infection. The functions of the skin in immunity are to block the entry of pathogens and to

A release white blood cells.
B produce antibodies.
C secrete sweat and oil.
D activate active immunity.

5

antibodies
help — immune system
are — proteins
destroy — ??
proteins made by — B-cells

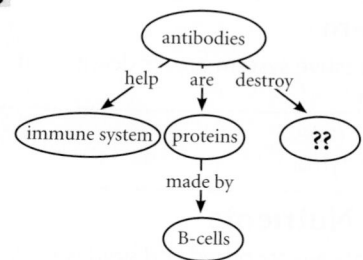

Which word ***best*** completes this concept map?

A white blood cells
B red blood cells
C pathogens
D vectors

6 Some interferons stimulate noninfected cells to produce thick coats that prevent viruses from infecting the cells. Why are interferons effective against viruses but not bacteria?

THINK THROUGH THE QUESTION

To answer this question, think about how bacteria and viruses are different. Which of these differences is related to the way interferons act?

Standards-Based Assessment

1. C	4. C
2. D	5. C
3. D	6. See Below

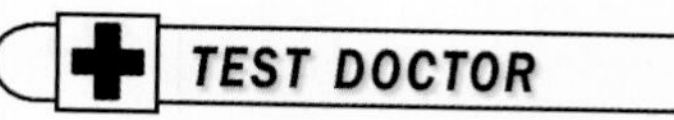

Question 1 Answer C is correct because a theory is a proposed explanation for a wide variety of observations and experimental results. Answer A is incorrect because a hypothesis is a proposed explanation for a scientific question, so it is not well supported by data. Answer B is incorrect because a guess is an attempt to answer a question, but it is also not well supported by data. Answer D is incorrect because an experiment is a methodical approach to generating data to help answer a scientific question.

Question 2 Answer D is correct. Answer A is incorrect because volunteer C has also been injected with dead chicken pox virus and would also likely have antibodies. Answers B and C are incorrect because volunteer B has never been exposed to the virus and would not have developed antibodies to it.

Question 3 Answer D is correct. Answer A is incorrect because people infected with HIV take drugs to help strengthen their immune system. Answer B is incorrect because pathogens can enter the bodies of anyone having surgery, and the answer fails to explain why people with HIV are more likely to become sick. Answer C is incorrect because HIV does not mutate into other diseases.

Question 6 Viruses need to enter a cell to reproduce, but bacteria do not.

35. The sample needs to be much larger. The criteria for inclusion in the sample needs to be that a person had one of the bacterial infections, and not that they were cured by the drug. Each bacterial infection and the effectiveness of amoxicillin needs to be looked at separately.

Connecting Concepts

36. Answers will vary. All answers, however, should properly sequence the events of an immune response in constructing the video game.

37. Answers will vary, but can include information on keeping clean, using antiseptics, properly cooking food, using bug spray to prevent insect bites, covering your mouth when you sneeze or cough, taking medicines only when prescribed.

ITEM CORRELATIONS

Standard	Items
NOS.1	2
NOS.8	1

CHAPTER 32

Indiana Resource Preview

Print Resources

Digestive and Excretory Systems

INDIANA STANDARDS		Sections	PAGES and PACING	UNIT RESOURCE BOOK
	32.1	**Nutrients and Homeostasis** **KEY CONCEPT** Cells require many different nutrients.	pp. 972–976 30 minutes	URB pages 125–128
	32.2	**Digestive System** **KEY CONCEPT** The digestive system breaks down food into simpler molecules.	pp. 977–980 30 minutes	URB pages 129–132
NOS.1, NOS.3		CHAPTER INVESTIGATION: Testing a Digestive Enzyme	p. 981 60 minutes	**Lab Binder** Human Bio pages 51–54
	32.3	**Absorption of Nutrients** **KEY CONCEPT** Nutrients are absorbed and solid wastes eliminated after digestion.	pp. 982–984 30 minutes	URB pages 133–136
NOS.1		DATA ANALYSIS: Identifying Outliers Outliers in Data Sets	p. 985 30 minutes	URB page 141
	32.4	**Excretory System** **KEY CONCEPT** The excretory system removes wastes and helps maintain homeostasis.	pp. 986–991 30 minutes	URB pages 137–140
NOS.1, NOS.3		OPTIONS FOR INQUIRY	pp. 992–993 45 minutes, 15 minutes	**Lab Binder** Human Bio pages 55–57
		Chapter Review	pp. 994–997	**Assessment Book** Chapter Tests A, B pp. 635–642

INDIANA STANDARDS

NOS.1 Develop explanations based on reproducible data and observations gathered during laboratory investigations.
NOS.3 Clearly communicate their ideas and results of investigations verbally and in written form using tables, graphs, diagrams, and photographs.

Labs

PUPIL EDITION LABS

Testing a Digestive Enzyme, p. 981 Students test the effectiveness of the enzyme pepsin in digesting different foods under different conditions. **Lab Binder** pp. 51–54	**Time:** 60 minutes **Materials:** 4 100-mL beakers, 10 cm tape, 2 100-mL graduated cylinders, 160 mL water, 80 mL 1% hydrochloric acid solution, 80 mL pepsin, 4 pecans, balance, 4 pieces of potato, 4 pieces of beef jerky, warm water bath, clock
Villi in the Small Intestine, Section 3, p. 983 Students design a model of the intestinal villi. **Lab Binder** p. 58	**Time:** 15 minutes **Materials:** 4 large paper cups, water, 8 paper towels, timer

OPTIONS FOR INQUIRY

Antacid Effectiveness, p. 992 Students test the effectiveness of several types of antacids. **Lab Binder** pp. 55–56	**Time:** 45 minutes **Materials:** 4 large paper cups, marker, 50-mL graduated cylinder, 100 mL white vinegar, 8 pH test strips, antacid A, antacid B, antacid C, antacid D, knife, mortar and pestle, scale, stirrer, timer
Digesting Milk, p. 993 Students analyze digestibility of milk. **Lab Binder** p. 57	**Time:** 15 minutes **Materials:** 2 test tubes, 5 cm tape, marker, 2 eyedroppers, 20 drops of nonfat milk, 20 drops of lactose-free milk, 4 glucose test strips, 2 drops lactase, 2 stirrers, timer

LAB BINDER Unit 9 Human Biology

Additional Investigation: Factors Affecting Digestion, pp. 59–62

LAB GENERATOR

A searchable CD of all labs in the program in editable format, including forensic, probeware, and biotechnology labs.

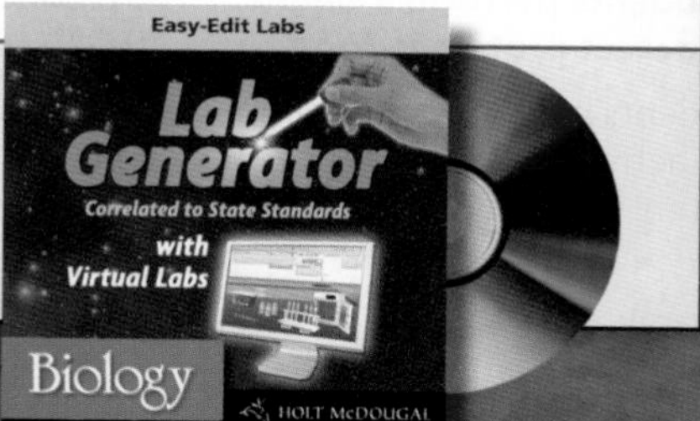

Presentation Tools

POWER PRESENTATIONS

Presentation Chapter 32
Power Presentations for each section incorporate images and clips from the Media Gallery: Includes Note Navigator for each section.

MEDIA GALLERY

Contains the following images and video clips, as well as animations, simulations and forms of visuals from the book.

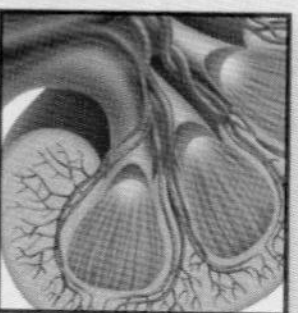
Kidney structure

Digestive system

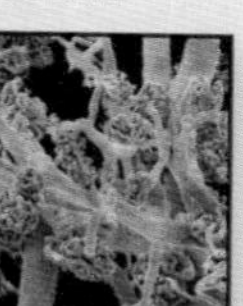
Glomeruli

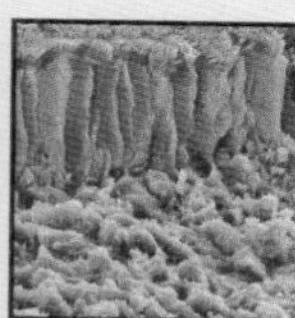
Microvilli

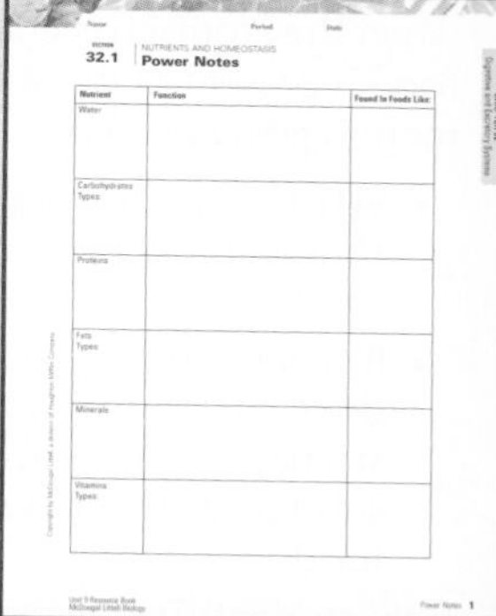

Power Notes

ANIMATED BIOLOGY

Digestive System
Run the Digestive System

TRANSPARENCIES

Reading a Food Label T133
Digestive System T134
Excretory System T135
Structure of the Kidney T136
Structure of the Nephron T137

Online BIOLOGY CLASSZONE.COM

BioZine
Animated Biology
Interactive Review
SciLinks
Resource Centers

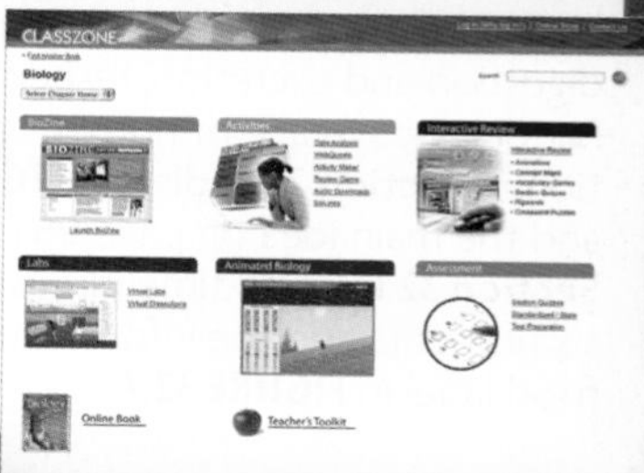

CHAPTER

32

▼ Focus and Motivate

What is that gut feeling inside of you?

Students can feel—and sometimes hear—smooth muscle contractions when the stomach is empty. But when food is present in the stomach, a lot more is going on. **Ask**

- What is the stomach doing when it churns? breaking down and mixing food
- Besides churning food, how else does the stomach digest food? The stomach's epithelial cells secrete substances that help break down food.

Help students understand that the food we eat must be broken down, or digested, in order to be usable. Everything we eat, even liquid foods such as soups, must be digested into simple molecules, such as sugars and amino acids, in order to be absorbed into the blood. The blood then carries the nutrients to all the cells of the body.

BIOZINE ClassZone.com

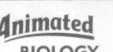

Students can access BioZine at **ClassZone.com** to learn about some of the latest research in the biological sciences.

In a Hurry?

The critical material of the chapter is found in **Sections 32.2** and **32.4,** which cover the organs and processes of digestion and excretion, respectively. For quick coverage of nutrient absorption in **Section 32.3,** discuss **FIGURE 32.13** and the main idea on page 984. In **Section 32.1,** spend time discussing the six nutrients and the information on the food label in **FIGURE 32.7.**

CHAPTER

32 Digestive and Excretory Systems

KEY CONCEPTS

32.1 Nutrients and Homeostasis
Cells require many different nutrients.

32.2 Digestive System
The digestive system breaks down food into simpler molecules.

32.3 Absorption of Nutrients
Nutrients are absorbed and solid wastes eliminated after digestion.

32.4 Excretory System
The excretory system removes wastes and helps to maintain homeostasis.

Online BIOLOGY CLASSZONE.COM

Animated BIOLOGY
View animated chapter concepts.
- Digestive System
- Run the Digestive System

BIOZINE
Keep current with biology news.
- Featured stories
- Strange Biology
- Polls

RESOURCE CENTER
Get more information on
- Nutrition
- Urinary System

Student Activity

Purpose Have students perform a simple chemical test to detect protein in food.

Safety Note Students must wear goggles and gloves during this activity. Sodium hydroxide is caustic and can burn. Tell students not to eat the food samples.

Materials (per team)

- variety of food samples, such as hamburger, tofu, cheese, bread, peas, yogurt, egg, apple
- test tubes (one for each food sample)
- balance or scale
- mortar and pestle
- 10-mL graduated cylinder
- water
- 0.1 *M* sodium hydroxide solution (Add 0.4 g NaOH to 100 mL distilled water.)
- 1% copper(II) sulfate solution (Add 1 g anhydrous cupric sulfate ($CuSO_4$) to 100 mL distilled water.)
- latex gloves
- goggles

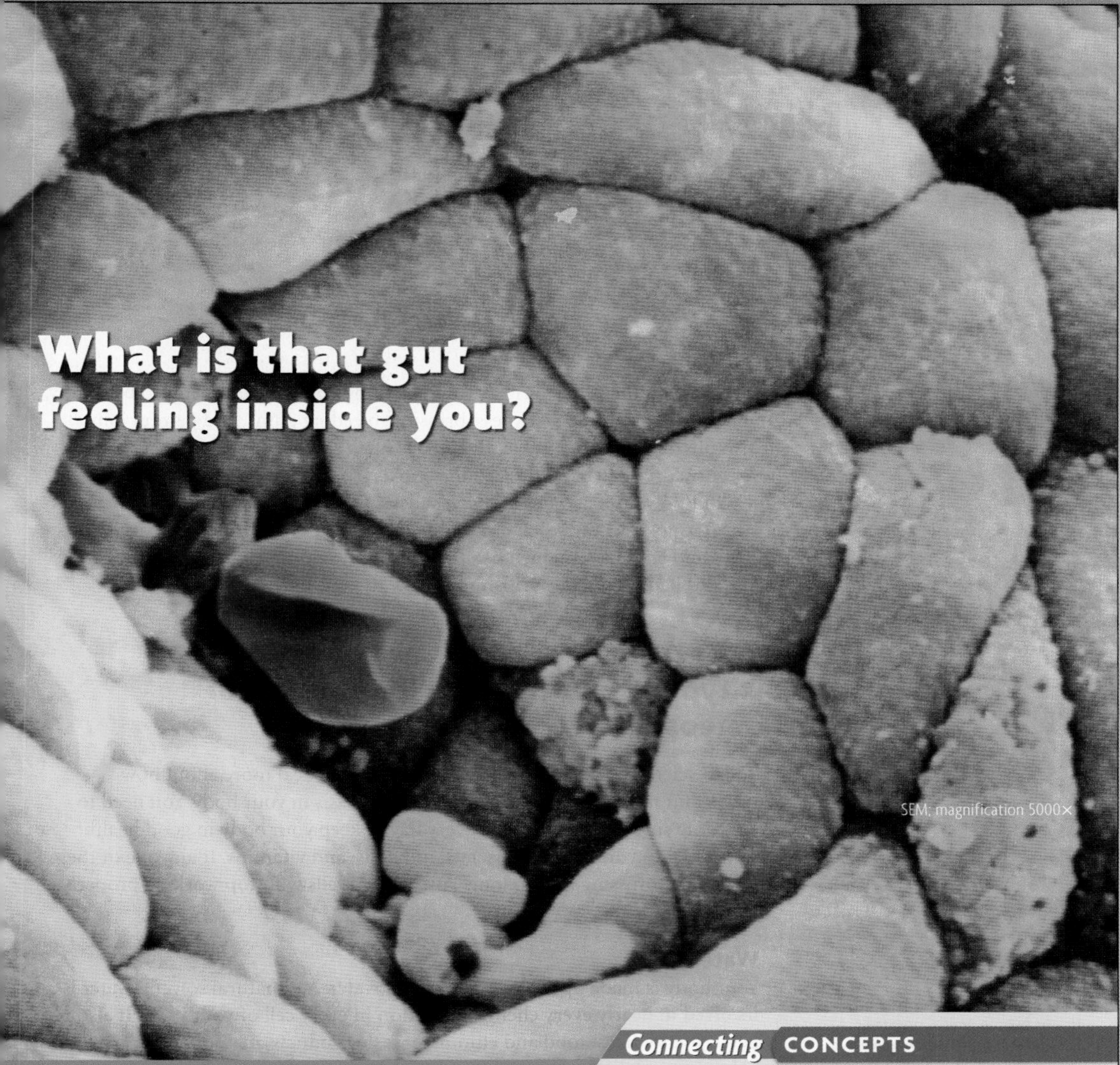

What is that gut feeling inside you?

SEM; magnification 5000×

A lot is going on in your stomach when you eat. For instance, epithelial cells, shown in the close-up above, secrete four types of substances: stomach acid; a protective mucus that keeps the stomach from digesting itself; enzymes that break down many types of food; and hormones that control the process.

Connecting CONCEPTS

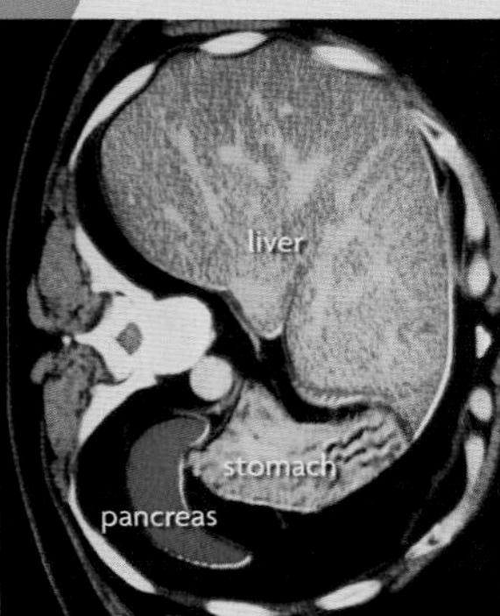

Organ Systems This colored CT scan is a cross-section of the digestive system as seen from above. The vertebrae and rib bones (white) help to protect the liver, stomach, and pancreas. The small and large intestines (not shown) are below these organs. The whole system breaks down food into simpler molecules that the body can absorb and use.

Introduce Divide students into teams, and give each team one or two different food samples. Have students use a mortar and pestle to crush about 3 g of a sample in 5 mL of water and then pour the mixture into a test tube. Tell them to add 5 mL of sodium hydroxide solution to the tube, and then slowly add 1 mL of copper(II) sulfate solution. Have teams record their observations on the board to share with the class. Students should wash their hands after completing the activity.

Discuss Tell students that copper sulfate changes color when it reacts with certain amino acids in proteins. In solution with sodium hydroxide, it goes from blue green to violet, depending on the amount of protein present. The darker violet the solution, the more protein present. **Ask,** Among the food tested, which foods have proteins? probably all at varying levels **Ask,** Why is it important to eat protein? The body uses proteins to help build enzymes and hormones, to build and repair tissue, and to make cell structures.

Activate Prior Knowledge

Students will no doubt think the subject distasteful, but mention that the human digestive system seamlessly connects with the excretory system. **Ask**

- From an engineering or architectural point of point of view, why wouldn't you ever build a building or house where food preparation, delivery, and waste disposal were far apart? more efficient to keep them close together, even if in different areas or rooms
- At what point in the process of eating does food become waste? when all that is useful to the body has been removed

Mention that the body is still extracting salts and water as material moves through the large intestine.

Preview Vocabulary

Academic Vocabulary The words *excretion* and *elimination* are sometimes thought of as being synonymous. However, these words refer to two distinct and separate biological processes. *Excretion* refers to the removal of nonsolid wastes by the kidneys, lungs, and skin. *Secretion* shares the same Latin root meaning "separate" and is similar in meaning to *excretion,* except it describes the release of material that is produced by the body, not waste material. *Elimination* refers to the removal of solid wastes through the large intestine. The root of the word comes from the Latin for "banish," and in everyday language its synonyms include *eradicate* and *purge.*

English Learners Students' ideas about what a *nutrient* is may be limited to those materials that provide energy and material: fats, carbohydrates, and proteins. Remind students that the body also needs water, minerals, and vitamins, all of which are important to the biochemical processes of the body.

SECTION 32.1

▼ Plan and Prepare

Objectives

- Identify six types of nutrients that help maintain homeostasis.
- Describe ways of meeting nutritional needs that support good health.

Section Resources

Unit Resource Book
Study Guide pp. 125–126
Power Notes p. 127
Reinforcement p. 128

Interactive Reader Chapter 32
Spanish Study Guide pp. 325–326

Biology Toolkit pp. C10, C19, C35, D6

Technology
Power Presentation 32.1
Media Gallery DVD
Online Quiz 32.1

Activate Prior Knowledge Discuss diets that students may have heard about that focus on certain foods. **Ask**

- Why do most of these diets have little long-term success? People like to eat a variety of foods, and some diets are not tailored to individual needs.
- How might such diets be detrimental? Extreme diets lack nutrients a person needs, while other diets may create imbalances in the body and disrupt homeostasis.

▼ Teach

Address Misconceptions

Common Misconception You can never drink too much water.

Correcting the Misconception Drinking more than 1.5 liters/hour over-dilutes the blood and causes sodium concentration to drop and osmotic pressure to increase, causing hyponatremia. Water enters cells, causing them to swell. Brain cells swell rapidly and cease functioning.

32.1 Nutrients and Homeostasis

KEY CONCEPT Cells require many different nutrients.

MAIN IDEAS

- Six types of nutrients help to maintain homeostasis.
- Meeting nutritional needs supports good health.

VOCABULARY

mineral, p. 973
vitamin, p. 974
Calorie, p. 975

Review
carbohydrate, protein, fat

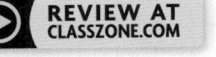

Connect Until the 1740s, British sailors on long voyages were crippled by scurvy, an illness that produced weakness, bruising, bleeding gums, and painful joints. British physician James Lind learned that Dutch sailors who ate oranges at sea never got scurvy. He hypothesized that citrus fruits might not only cure the illness but prevent it as well. To test his ideas, Lind divided the crew of one ship into six groups and gave each group different foods. Only the sailors eating oranges and lemons remained healthy. By simply adding vitamin C to the sailors' diets, Lind had shown the British navy how to wipe out scurvy at sea.

MAIN IDEA

Six types of nutrients help to maintain homeostasis.

Today, scientists and health experts know a great deal more about how important nutrients are to maintain homeostasis in your body. You need to consume six types of nutrients every day to keep your body in good health: water, carbohydrates, proteins, fats, minerals, and vitamins. If any one of these nutrients is missing for too long, your body's cells will stop working properly, which also affects your organs.

Water

Your body is made up of 55 to 60 percent water. As a natural solvent, water is involved in nearly every chemical reaction in every cell of your body. It also helps you to digest food and eliminate waste products, maintain your blood volume, regulate your body temperature, and keep your skin moist. To maintain your fluid balance, you need to drink about 2 liters (8 cups) of water a day to replace the amount you lose through sweat, urine, and respiration.

FIGURE 32.1 Complex carbohydrates (whole grains, potatoes, vegetables) must be broken down into sugars to be used as fuel. Simple carbohydrates, such as those found in fruits, do not need to be broken down as much.

Carbohydrates

Carbohydrates, shown in **FIGURE 32.1**, are the main source of energy for your body. Simple carbohydrates are sugars found in sugar cane, honey, and fruits. Complex carbohydrates are starches found in vegetables, grains, and potatoes. To be absorbed by your body, starches must be broken down during digestion into simple sugars, such as glucose. Excess supplies of glucose are converted to glycogen and are stored in the liver and muscle tissues for future use. Many grains, fruits, and vegetables also contain cellulose, a dietary fiber. Fiber cannot be digested, but it helps move food through your digestive system.

Differentiated Instruction

ENGLISH LEARNERS

Before beginning the section, have students form home groups and number off. Write on the board the chapter topic, "The Digestive and Excretory System." Allow students five minutes to scan the chapter. Then with books closed, have all 1's write on a piece of paper a fact they know about the topic. At a timed signal, have the 1's pass the paper to the 2's. Each person writes something they know but cannot repeat what others wrote. Have the groups copy their work on chart paper or the board and then discuss the responses.

Biology Toolkit, Round Table, p. C10

Proteins

Proteins are the raw materials used for the growth and repair of the body's cells and tissues. In addition, proteins make up all enzymes and many hormones that are vital for cell metabolism. Proteins are composed of chains of amino acids. Your body can make only 12 of the 20 amino acids it needs to build proteins. The other 8, called essential amino acids, must come from the foods you eat. Foods such as meat, cheese, and eggs contain all eight essential amino acids. However, most plant proteins lack at least one essential amino acid. Vegans—people who do not eat meat, dairy products, or eggs—must eat plant foods in combination to obtain all the amino acids they need. For example, red beans and rice together contain all 20 amino acids.

FIGURE 32.2 Proteins and fats are often found in the same foods. Beef, chicken, and eggs contain protein and saturated fats. Fish, nuts, beans, and seeds contain protein and unsaturated fats.

Fats

Fats provide energy and key components in cell membranes, myelin sheaths for neurons, and certain hormones. Fats consist of long chains of fatty acids hooked to glycerol molecules. Your body can make some fatty acids, but you must obtain all of the essential fatty acids from the foods you eat. Fats are classified as either saturated or unsaturated, depending on the structure of their fatty acid chains. Saturated fats are solid at room temperature and are found in animal products. Most unsaturated fats are liquid at room temperature and are found in plant oils, such as corn or olive oils, and in some fish, such as cod or salmon. In general, unsaturated fats are considered more beneficial to people's health than are saturated fats.

Minerals

Small amounts of minerals and vitamins are also needed to maintain homeostasis. **Minerals** are inorganic materials the body uses to carry out processes in cells and to build or repair tissues. Some of the more common minerals are listed in **FIGURE 32.3.** Calcium, for example, is essential for bone and tooth formation, muscle contraction, and nerve transmission. Sodium and potassium help to maintain the body's fluid homeostasis. You are constantly losing minerals in sweat, urine, and other waste products. You can replace them by eating a variety of plant foods or by combining plant and animal foods.

TAKING NOTES

Use a two-column chart to organize your notes about different nutrients and their functions.

Water	- makes up 55 to 60% of body - maintains blood volume

FIGURE 32.3 Important Minerals

MINERALS	SOURCES	IMPORTANT FOR
Calcium	dairy products, salmon, sardines, dark leafy greens	blood clotting, bone/tooth formation; muscle/nerve function
Iron	liver, dark leafy greens, whole grains	component in hemoglobin
Iodine	iodized salt, seafoods, sea vegetables	component in thyroid hormones
Magnesium	nuts, whole grains, leafy green vegetables	bone/tooth formation; coenzyme in protein synthesis
Phosphorus	meats, dairy products, nuts, dried peas and beans	bone/tooth formation; active in many metabolic processes
Potassium	meats, dairy products, many fruits and vegetables	regulation of pH, fluid balance, and muscle/nerve function
Sodium	table salt, seafoods, processed foods	regulation of pH, fluid balance, and muscle/nerve function
Zinc	meats, seafoods, grains	activation of many enzymes in metabolic processes

Integrating Nutritional Science

Both **omega-6 fatty acids** (O6FAs) and **omega-3 fatty acids** (O3FAs) are essential for good health because they help maintain cell membranes and are critical for the synthesis of certain hormones. Yet many studies have linked O6FAs with inflammatory diseases, including heart disease, arthritis, and some cancers. The bad effects of O6FAs arise when they are consumed at high levels in proportion to O3FAs. O6FAs, which are found in meats and in nuts and seeds and their oils, promote inflammation and clot formation, increase blood pressure, and promote growth of some tumors.

O3FAs, which are found in flax seeds, canola oil, and oily fish such as salmon and tuna, tend to decrease inflammation and clot formation and offer other important benefits. The benefits of O3FAs emerge at an O6-to-O3 ratio of around 4:1 or less. This ratio is common in diets high in fruits, whole grains, olive oil, and vegetables and relatively low in meat. The typical Western diet, which is high in meats and relatively low in fruits, vegetables, and whole grains, has a ratio between 15:1 and 16.7:1. Evidence shows that eating this kind of diet explains the high incidence of inflammatory diseases in the United States.

TEACH FROM VISUALS

FIGURE 32.3 Use the table to discuss the importance of a balanced diet as a means of getting the minerals needed to maintain homeostasis. **Ask**

- How can vegans (people who eat no animal-based foods) keep their bones strong? by eating plenty of green leafy vegetables, nuts, whole grains, and dried peas and beans
- What mineral deficiencies might you find in a person who eats mostly meat and processed foods and few vegetables? calcium, iodine, magnesium, iron
- What problems might this person have? clotting disorders, weak teeth and bones, nerve dysfunction, low hemoglobin

BELOW LEVEL

Some students may have difficulty sorting out the information in **FIGURES 32.3** and **32.4.** Have them list and group minerals and vitamins in a way that will help them associate these nutrients with their sources. For some students, color coding may be useful; other students may find it more helpful to make flash cards with pictures of sources, such as dairy products or green leafy vegetables.

Biology Toolkit, List-Group-Label, p. D6

PRE-AP

Have students write for five minutes on the question of whether the words *food* and *nutrient* are synonymous. Have them consider whether food and nutrients function in the same way. You may want to suggest students adopt the terminology *macronutrient* (large, energy-yielding) and *micronutrient* (small, nonenergy-yielding).

Biology Toolkit, Quick-Write, p. C19

▼ Teach *continued*

ONLINE BIOLOGY Go to the chapter Resource Center at **ClassZone.com** for additional resources and information about nutrition.

Vocabulary

vitamin The word *vitamin* was coined by a Polish biochemist, Kazimierz Funk, in 1911. *Vitamin* comes from the Latin word *vita,* meaning "life," and the biochemical term *amine.* Funk believed substances that were essential to life were amines and therefore called them *vitamines.* When it was realized these substances were not necessarily amines, the *e* was dropped from the word.

Science Trivia

- Shark liver oil is rich in vitamin A.
- The polar bear's liver could kill a human being if eaten because of the lethal amount of vitamin A.
- High doses of vitamin B_6 can cause nerve damage.
- Eight strawberries contain more vitamin C than a medium-sized orange.
- Vitamin K is produced by intestinal bacteria, so taking antibiotics can result in a vitamin K deficiency.

Answers

A Apply Complex carbohydrates; these nutrients would break down slowly and release energy over a long time. Proteins, on the other hand, are used mainly for growth and repair.

Vitamins

Vitamins are organic molecules that work with enzymes to regulate cell functions, growth, and development. As shown in **FIGURE 32.4,** these nutrients are divided into fat-soluble vitamins and water-soluble vitamins. Fat-soluble vitamins dissolve in fatty acids. The fat-soluble vitamins A, D, E, and K can be stored in the body's fatty tissues for future use. For this reason, taking high doses of these vitamins can actually create harmful, or toxic, levels in the body.

Water-soluble vitamins dissolve in water. The water-soluble vitamin C and the B vitamins cannot be stored and are excreted in urine and feces. As a result, you need to eat foods rich in these nutrients to keep replenishing them. The National Academy of Sciences publishes recommended daily amounts of minerals and vitamins based on your age, gender, and level of activity.

A Apply **Would a diet higher in protein or in complex carbohydrates give you more energy? Explain your answer.**

FIGURE 32.4 Essential Vitamins

VITAMIN	SOURCES	IMPORTANT FOR
Fat-Soluble (Dissolves in Fat)		
A (retinol)	dark green, yellow, and orange vegetables, fortified milk, fish and liver oils	healthy skin, mucous membranes, vision
D (calciferol)	fortified dairy and whole grain products, egg yolks, fish and liver oils	bone and tooth formation, increase in calcium and phosphorus absorption
E (tocopherol)	vegetable oils, nuts, fish oils, meats, leafy green vegetables	prevention of cell damage
K	leafy green vegetables, egg yolks, liver; also made by intestinal bacteria	blood clotting and synthesis of clotting factors
Water-Soluble (Dissolves in Water)		
B_1 (thiamine)	pork and red meats, whole grains, dried beans and peas, eggs	metabolism of carbohydrates
B_2 (riboflavin)	dairy products, liver and organ meats, enriched whole grains	metabolism of carbohydrates and proteins, normal growth in skin, lips, and mucous membranes
B_3 (niacin)	meats, dried peas and beans, whole grains	metabolism of glucose, fats, and proteins
B_6 (pyridoxine)	meats, fish, peanuts, eggs, bran cereal	metabolism of amino acids
B_{12}	liver, meats, eggs, dairy products	protein synthesis and red blood cell production
C (ascorbic acid)	citrus fruits, berries, tomatoes, broccoli, cabbage, potatoes, melons	antioxidant, maintenance of cartilage and bone, iron absorption, tissue repair, wound healing, healthy gums
Pantothenic acid	meats, dairy products, whole grains	metabolism of glucose, fats, and proteins
Folic acid	leafy green vegetables, liver, nuts, oranges, broccoli, peas, fortified cereals	amino acid synthesis and metabolism, prevention of neural tube defects in fetuses
Biotin	egg yolks, liver, soybeans	metabolism of carbohydrates, proteins, and fats
Choline	egg yolks, liver, whole grains	production of phospholipids and neurotransmitters

Differentiated Instruction

PRE-AP

Have students use the information in **FIGURES 32.3** and **32.4** to draw cause and effect diagrams showing possible causes of certain mineral or vitamin deficiencies and possible effects of these deficiencies. For example, a possible cause of vitamin C deficiency is not eating enough fruits or vegetables that are rich in vitamin C. A possible effect of vitamin C deficiency is unhealthy gums.

Biology Toolkit, Cause and Effect Diagram, p. C35

MAIN IDEA

Meeting nutritional needs supports good health.

A balanced diet is important throughout your life, but particularly during pre-teen and early teen years. During these years, you are growing and developing faster than at any other time since the first two years of your life. Your bone mass is increasing nearly 40 percent, you are gaining most of your adult body mass, and you are developing sexual characteristics.

To fuel this growth spurt, your body requires considerably more nutrients and more energy in the form of Calories consumed, as shown in **FIGURE 32.5.** A calorie, with a small *c*, is the amount of energy required to raise one gram of water one degree Celsius. One **Calorie** (capital *C*) from food equals one kilocalorie, or 1000 calories. Different foods contain different amounts of energy. One gram of protein or carbohydrate yields four Calories, while one gram of fat yields nine Calories.

Calories alone are not the whole story, however. The rapid changes in your body require adequate amounts of all six nutrients. Dietary experts recommend that most of your Calories come from eating whole grains, fruits, and vegetables, which are rich in fiber, vitamins, and minerals. Also, experts suggest drinking more low-fat milk or soy drinks and water, and fewer high-sugar soft drinks and juices. High-sugar foods provide Calories but very little nutritional value. Dietary experts also recommend eating more lean meats and fish, while cutting down on foods high in saturated fat.

It is also important to find a balance between food and physical activity so that you use about as many Calories as you consume. The U.S. Department of Agriculture (USDA) Web site provides information on how to develop a balanced diet.

Connecting CONCEPTS

Cellular Respiration You read in **Chapter 4** about the different ways that plant and animal cells obtain energy. In nearly all plant and animal cells, mitochondria use molecules broken down by digestion to build ATP, the main power source for cells.

FIGURE 32.6 Your food choices can help you consume high-quality energy and nutrients at a time when your body needs them the most.

FIGURE 32.5 Growth and Energy Needs

During rapid growth, the body requires significantly more energy.

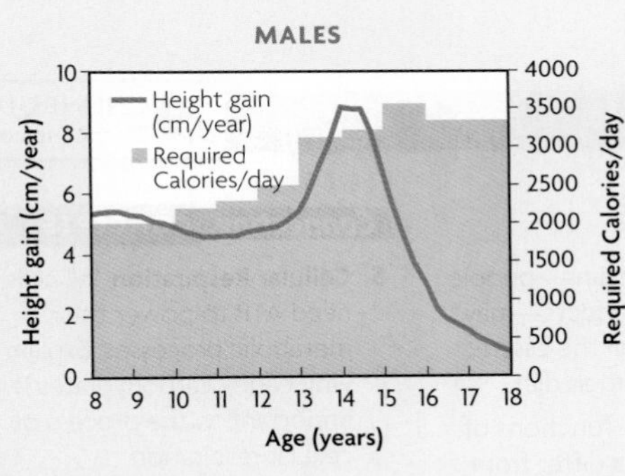

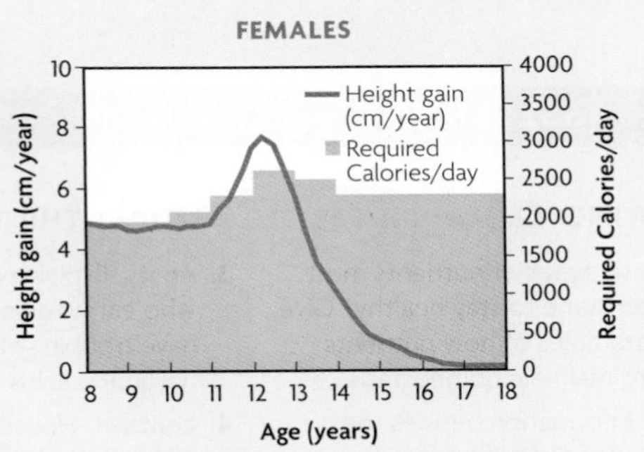

Sources: Adapted from JM Tanner: *Growth at adolescence*, ed.2, Oxford; Food and Nutrition Board: *Recommended dietary allowances*, ed. 10, National Academy Press; Institute of Medicine, Food and Nutrition Board, *Dietary reference*, National Academies Press.

A Contrast **What differences do you notice between the two charts?**

TEACH WITH TECHNOLOGY

Show students The Nutrition Source, Harvard School of Public Health's Website on healthy eating. The site explains all aspects of a healthy lifestyle and compares the USDA's MyPyramid with the one that the Harvard School of Public Health has created called the Healthy Eating Pyramid. A link is provided in the chapter resources at **ClassZone.com.**

TEACH FROM VISUALS

FIGURE 32.5 Use the graphs to discuss differences in Calorie requirements for females and males at different ages of adolescence. **Ask**

- At what age do most teenage girls need the most Calories per day? About 12 years of age; growth rate peaks at this age, requiring more Calories per day.
- When do teenage boys experience the greatest growth rate? about 14 years of age
- Why might the daily Calorie requirement for boys continue to increase after height gain peaks? Extra Calories are needed for other growth processes, such as muscle and bone growth.

Integrating Chemistry

Scientists use a **bomb calorimeter** to determine the Calorie content of different foods. A bomb calorimeter is a closed-system device in which food is burned completely in the presence of oxygen. The reaction releases heat, which is measured and expressed in Calories or joules (one Calorie = 4186 joules).

Answers

A Contrast Girls start their growth spurts and reach peak heights earlier than boys do, but their Calorie intake does not rise as high. This reflects the fact that boys gain more muscle and bone mass than do girls during this time.

▼ Teach *continued*

TEACH FROM VISUALS

FIGURE 32.7 Review the key elements of the food label with students. Emphasize that the Calories, fat, and other nutrient counts shown on the label are per serving. **Ask,** If you eat the whole package of macaroni and cheese, how many grams of fat will you consume? 24 grams Point out the % Daily Value column and the explanation of Percent Daily Values at the bottom of the food label. Explain that the percentages on the food label compare the amount of each nutrient present in the food with the recommended amount of that nutrient per day for a person who consumes about 2000 calories per day.

Answers

A Analyze Unprocessed foods contain more fiber, water, and nutrients, such as vitamins and minerals, than do most processed foods.

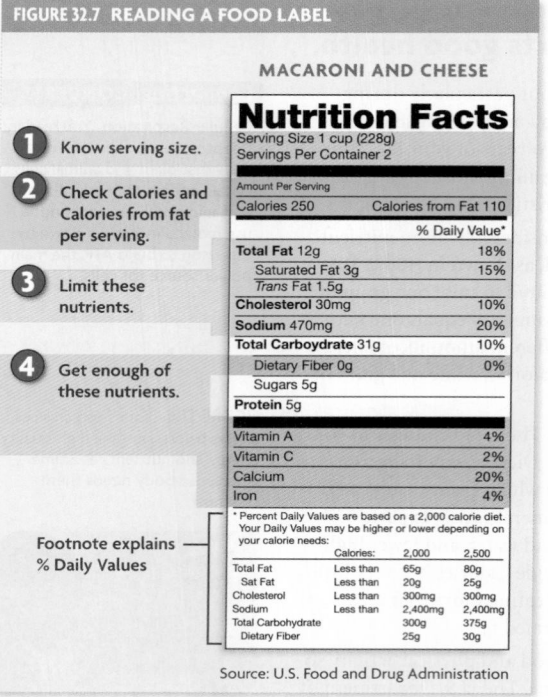

FIGURE 32.7 READING A FOOD LABEL

MACARONI AND CHEESE

Nutrition Facts

Serving Size 1 cup (228g)
Servings Per Container 2

Amount Per Serving

Calories 250	Calories from Fat 110
	% Daily Value*
Total Fat 12g	18%
Saturated Fat 3g	15%
Trans Fat 1.5g	
Cholesterol 30mg	10%
Sodium 470mg	20%
Total Carbohydrate 31g	10%
Dietary Fiber 0g	0%
Sugars 5g	
Protein 5g	
Vitamin A	4%
Vitamin C	2%
Calcium	20%
Iron	4%

* Percent Daily Values are based on a 2,000 calorie diet. Your Daily Values may be higher or lower depending on your calorie needs:

	Calories:	2,000	2,500
Total Fat	Less than	65g	80g
Sat Fat	Less than	20g	25g
Cholesterol	Less than	300mg	300mg
Sodium	Less than	2,400mg	2,400mg
Total Carbohydrate		300g	375g
Dietary Fiber		25g	30g

1 Know serving size.

2 Check Calories and Calories from fat per serving.

3 Limit these nutrients.

4 Get enough of these nutrients.

Footnote explains % Daily Values

Source: U.S. Food and Drug Administration

The information on a food label, such as the one in **FIGURE 32.7**, can help you make good choices and compare the values of different foods. The label shown here is from a box of macaroni and cheese.

1. **Serving size and number** This measurement varies from one product to another. In this case, one serving equals one cup. Notice that this container holds *two* servings.
2. **Calories and Calories from fat** The numbers listed on the label are for *one serving only.* If you eat both servings, you are actually getting 500 Calories, nearly half from fat.
3. **Nutrients to limit** Americans usually consume too much saturated fat, trans fat, cholesterol, and sodium. Trans fat is a type of fat that can cause cell damage. A diet high in these nutrients is linked to obesity, which affects more and more Americans of all ages. Too much sodium can raise blood pressure by causing the body to retain water.
4. **Nutrients to target** Americans need to consume enough of these nutrients each day. Notice that this product is low in vitamins and minerals, except for calcium, and has no dietary fiber. The wheat used in the macaroni has been processed until there is no fiber left.

As the label shows, if you eat this product, you will also need to eat whole grains, vegetables, and fruits during the day to obtain the nutrients that are missing from this food.

A Analyze **What nutritional advantages do unprocessed foods offer over processed foods?**

32.1 ASSESSMENT

ONLINE QUIZ ClassZone.com

REVIEWING ▶ MAIN IDEAS

1. What six types of nutrients must you consume to stay healthy? Give two examples of how nutrients help to maintain homeostasis.
2. What information besides the number of **Calories** can help you make good food choices?

CRITICAL THINKING

3. **Apply** Explain why vegans—people who eat no animal products—may have trouble getting all the essential amino acids from their diet.
4. **Contrast** How do the functions of **vitamins** and **minerals** differ from the functions of proteins and carbohydrates?

Connecting CONCEPTS

5. **Cellular Respiration** All cells need ATP to power their metabolic processes. Explain why eating carbohydrates is so important to the process of cellular respiration.

▼ Assess and Reteach

Assess Use the Online Quiz or Section Quiz (*Assessment Book,* p. 631).

Reteach Ask students to bring food labels to class. Have them use the information on the food labels to compare the nutritional value of the different foods, using **FIGURE 32.7** as a guide.

32.1 ASSESSMENT

1. Proteins, carbohydrates, water, fats, vitamins, and minerals; water and minerals helps to maintain fluid balance in the body.
2. Information regarding serving size, number of servings, Calories from fat, and available nutrients can help you make good food choices.
3. Unlike animal proteins, plant proteins usually lack one or more essential amino acids. Vegans must combine two or more plant proteins to obtain all essential amino acids.
4. Carbohydrates and proteins provide energy and building materials for the body. Vitamins and minerals facilitate chemical reactions and help maintain water balance.
5. Carbohydrates break down into simple sugars, such as glucose. Glucose is necessary to perform cellular respiration and produce ATP.

32.2 Digestive System

KEY CONCEPT The digestive system breaks down food into simpler molecules.

MAIN IDEAS

- Several digestive organs work together to break down food.
- Digestion begins in the mouth and continues in the stomach.
- Digestion is completed in part of the small intestine.

VOCABULARY

digestion, p. 977
digestive system, p. 977
sphincter, p. 977
esophagus, p. 978
peristalsis, p. 978
stomach, p. 978
chyme, p. 979
small intestine, p. 980
bile, p. 980

Connect In June 1822, Alexis St. Martin was shot in the stomach and treated by William Beaumont, an Army surgeon. The 28-year-old St. Martin recovered, but the bullet wound left a small hole in his stomach. Beaumont covered the hole and persuaded St. Martin to let him observe the digestive process by tying foods to a string, dropping them into the stomach hole, and retrieving them at different times to see how quickly different foods were digested. Over ten years, the experiments yielded a wealth of information about the digestive process. St. Martin married, had children, and lived to the age of 86.

MAIN IDEA

Several digestive organs work together to break down food.

Digestion is the process by which the large complex molecules in food are broken down into smaller molecules that can be used by the body. The **digestive system** is a collection of organs that breaks down food into energy that can be used in cells. It is like a factory that takes things apart instead of putting them together. The major organs of this "disassembly line" include the mouth, esophagus, stomach, pancreas, liver, gallbladder, large and small intestines, rectum, and anus, as shown in **FIGURE 32.8.** Rings of muscle, called **sphincters** (SFIHNGK-tuhrs), separate one section from another. The opening and closing of these sphincters and the contractions of smooth muscle in the walls of the organs keep food moving in one direction.

Digestion takes place through the interactions of enzymes, stomach acid, hormones, bile from the liver, and a network of nerves and muscles throughout the digestive system. Each organ contributes to breaking food down. For instance, in the mouth, salivary glands secrete an enzyme that helps to digest starches. The stomach releases enzymes that break down proteins.

Once digestion is complete, nutrients are absorbed by the body and transported by the circulatory system and lymphatic system to all the cells. Finally, undigested materials are eliminated as liquid and solid wastes. The entire process—from food entering the mouth to wastes leaving the body—takes about 24 to 33 hours per meal.

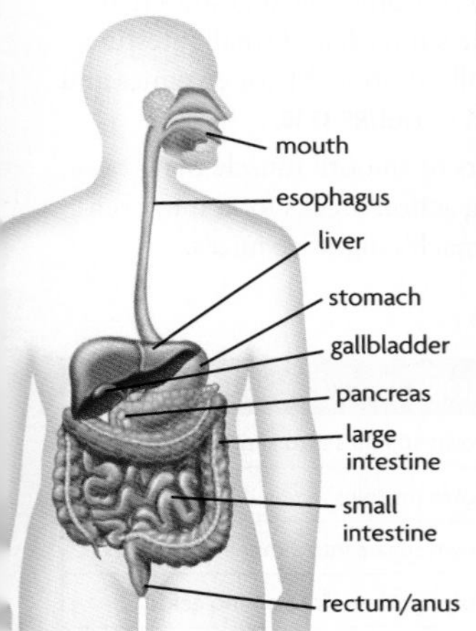

FIGURE 32.8 The major digestive organs are separated by sphincters, which help keep food moving in one direction.

A Predict What might happen if the digestive sections were not divided by sphincters?

Differentiated Instruction

ENGLISH LEARNERS

Have students structure their notes for this section around drawings of the digestive system. Suggest students organize their notes around the processes, structures, and products of the digestive system. They should do the same for the excretory system when they get to Section 32.4.

Biology Toolkit, Combination Notes, p. C23

BELOW LEVEL

Have students use the heads in this section as the basis for a concept map. Tell students to start with the Key Concept at the top of the page and then use the Main Concepts to help them structure the concept map. Remind them that the circles contain the "subject" words and the connecting arrows are labeled with "verbs."

Biology Toolkit, Concept Map, p. C40

Plan and Prepare ▼

Objectives

- Describe the organs of the digestive system.
- Summarize the difference between mechanical and chemical digestion.

Section Resources

Unit Resource Book Study Guide pp. 129–130 Power Notes p. 131 Reinforcement p. 132 Pre-AP Activity pp. 143–144
Interactive Reader Chapter 32 **Spanish Study Guide** pp. 327–328
Biology Toolkit pp. C13, C23, C40
Technology Power Presentation 32.2 Media Gallery DVD Online Quiz 32.2

Activate Prior Knowledge Have students visualize eating a sandwich. **Ask**

- What parts of the body are involved in the digestion of the sandwich? mouth, teeth, tongue, esophagus, stomach, small intestine
- What nutrients may be gained? It would depend on the type of sandwich, but most likely carbohydrates, protein, water, minerals, vitamins, and fats.

Teach ▼

TEACH FROM VISUALS

FIGURE 32.8 Have students study the figure. Point out that food moves through all the organs shown except the liver, gallbladder, and pancreas. These three organs release substances into the small intestine that aid digestion.

Answers

A Predict Instead of food moving in one direction only, it would be able to back up into the previous organ, which could damage the organ's lining.

▼ Teach *continued*

Vocabulary

Academic Vocabulary In everyday usage, the word **mechanical** relates to the use of machinery. In science, the word *mechanical* relates to phenomena or actions that are physical rather than chemical.

- A *mechanical process* is one in which a physical change takes place. The substance may change state, such as changing from a solid to a liquid, but its chemical composition remains the same.
- In a *chemical process,* a substance undergoes one or more chemical reactions that change its chemical composition, forming a different substance.

History of Science

Digestion was originally believed to be a mechanical process that ground up food particles in the stomach. In 1752, **René-Antoine Ferchault de Réaumur** conducted an experiment on digestion, using his pet falcon. Réaumur fed the falcon pieces of meat encased in a perforated metal tube to protect the meat from any friction. When he removed the tube several hours later, the meat was gone but the tube was undamaged. This led Réaumur to the idea that digestion was a chemical process, not a mechanical one.

In the 1780s, **Lazzaro Spallanzani** also conducted studies on digestion, using falcons. He extracted gastric juices from the falcon's stomachs to digest pieces of meat. Spallanzani's experiment was possibly the first time a vital reaction took place outside of the body of a living organism.

▶ MAIN IDEA

Digestion begins in the mouth and continues in the stomach.

You may have heard someone telling their children, "Chew your food—don't just gulp it!" This is actually good advice, because the first step in breaking down food is mechanical and chemical digestion in the mouth.

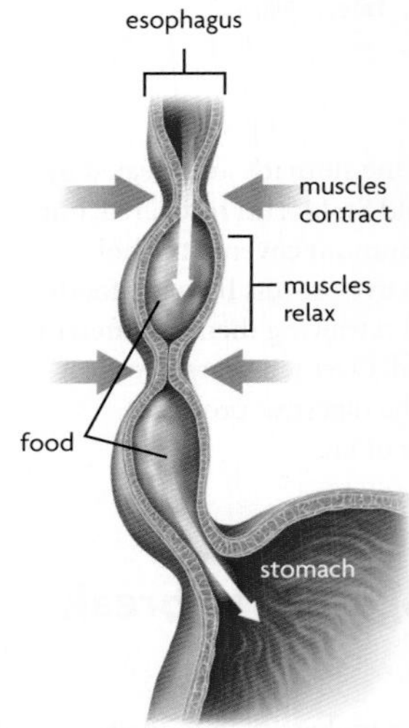

FIGURE 32.9 As food enters the esophagus, muscles behind the food contract, pushing it forward, while the muscles in front of the food relax. This rhythmic squeezing, called peristalsis, keeps food moving in one direction.

Digestion in the Mouth

You unwrap the sandwich you brought for lunch and bring it up to your mouth. Mechanical digestion begins the moment you bite into the sandwich and start chewing. Your teeth shred and grind the food into smaller pieces. Your tongue keeps the pieces positioned between your teeth. Chemical digestion, on the other hand, involves the action of enzymes. As you chew your food, the salivary glands release saliva that moistens the food and contains an enzyme called amylase (AM-uh-LAYS). Amylase begins the breakdown of complex starch molecules into sugars.

Once food has been chewed and mixed with saliva, the tongue pushes it to the back of the mouth. As you swallow, the food moves into the **esophagus** (ih-SAHF-uh-guhs), a tube that connects the mouth to the stomach. Food is kept moving down the esophagus by the action of peristalsis, as **FIGURE 32.9** shows. **Peristalsis** (PEHR-ih-STAWL-sihs) is the rhythmic, involuntary contraction of the smooth muscles in the walls of digestive organs.

Digestion in the Stomach

The next stop for your thoroughly chewed sandwich is the stomach. The **stomach** is a muscular sac that can stretch to nearly twice its original size and holds up to 2 liters (2 qt) of food. The stomach continues the digestion that began in the mouth. Proteins are digested in the stomach and small intestine, but fats and sugars are digested only in the small intestine. Major enzymes and their functions in the digestive system are listed in **FIGURE 32.10.**

The walls of the stomach contain three layers of smooth muscle that contract about every 20 seconds. This churning action breaks food into even smaller pieces and mixes the food with the stomach's digestive juices.

FIGURE 32.10 Major Digestive Enzymes

ENZYME	DIGESTIVE ORGAN	FUNCTION
Salivary amylase	mouth	breaks down starches into simpler sugars
Pepsin	stomach	breaks down proteins
Maltase, lactase, sucrase	small intestine	breaks down sugars into simpler molecules
Peptidase		breaks down proteins into amino acids
Trypsin	small intestine, pancreas	continues breakdown of proteins
Amylase		continues breakdown of starches
Lipase		aids in breaking down fats

Differentiated Instruction

HANDS-ON ACTIVITY

Give each student two equal-sized pieces of white bread. Tell students to chew one of the pieces quickly and record how it tastes. Then have them chew the second piece slowly until it becomes mushy, recording how it tastes. **Ask,** How did the two pieces compare in taste? The piece of bread that was chewed for a longer time tasted sweeter. **Ask,** Why was there a difference? When the bread was chewed longer, the amylase in saliva had more time to break down the starch in the bread into sugar.

As **FIGURE 32.11** summarizes, chemical digestion occurs along with the churning of mechanical digestion. The stomach lining secretes gastric juice containing hydrochloric acid (HCl) and the digestive enzyme pepsin. Gastric juice is acidic enough to kill most bacteria found on food and to break the bonds between protein molecules. Pepsin also breaks some chemical bonds between the amino acids in proteins. Digestive juices and enzymes turn your partly digested sandwich into a semi-liquid mixture called **chyme** (kym).

The stomach empties as peristaltic actions push the chyme against the sphincter that separates the stomach from the small intestine. With each contraction, the sphincter opens slightly, and chyme squirts into the small intestine, where digestion continues. It takes from two to six hours to empty the stomach after a meal.

Once the stomach is empty, the production of gastric juice stops. What keeps the stomach from digesting itself? First, pepsin is active only when there is food to digest. Second, the stomach secretes a layer of mucus to protect itself from its own acidic environment. Even so, cells in the stomach lining are replaced every few days to maintain the protective layer of mucus.

Connecting CONCEPTS

Chemistry Hydrochloric acid (HCl) is so strong that it can dissolve an iron nail in a matter of hours. To protect your stomach lining, specialized epithelial cells secrete bicarbonate, a base substance. Bicarbonate neutralizes the acid to keep it from burning through your stomach lining.

A Apply **If you ate a meal of spaghetti and meatballs, where would digestion of the pasta and meat begin?**

FIGURE 32.11 Mechanical and Chemical Digestion

The digestive organs use mechanical and chemical digestion to break food down into simple molecules.

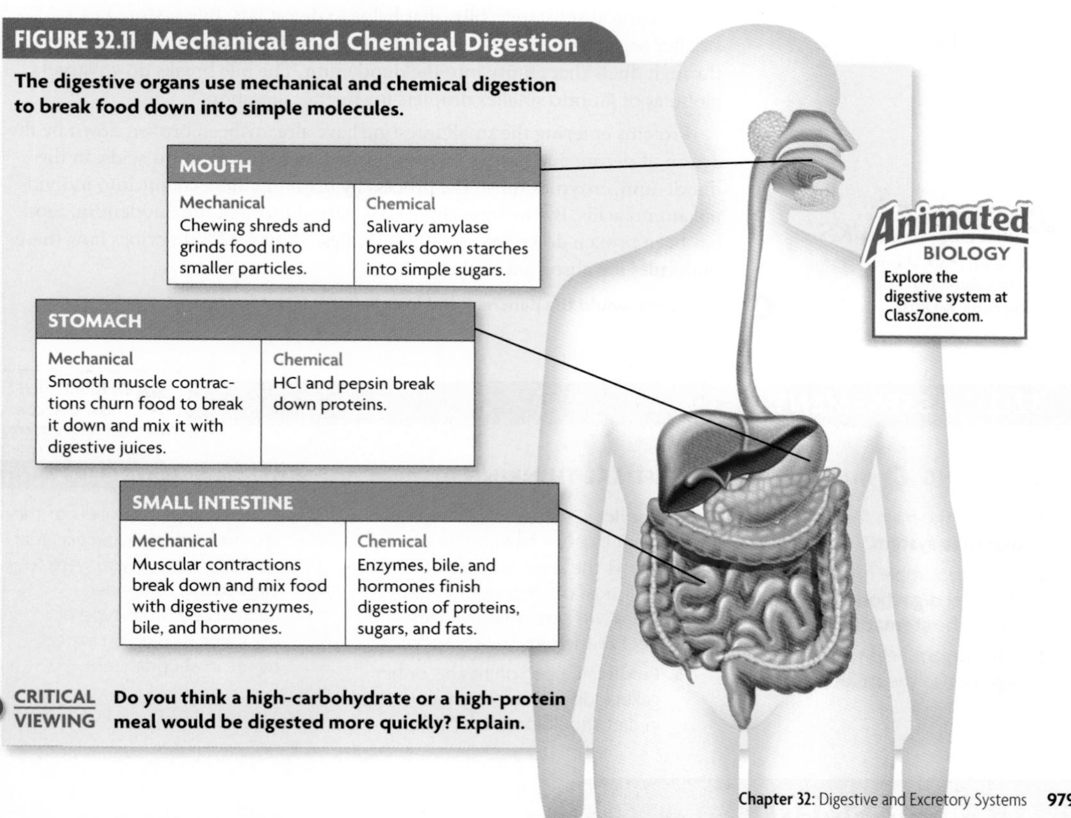

MOUTH
Mechanical
Chewing shreds and grinds food into smaller particles.
Chemical
Salivary amylase breaks down starches into simple sugars.
STOMACH
Mechanical
Smooth muscle contractions churn food to break it down and mix it with digestive juices.
Chemical
HCl and pepsin break down proteins.
SMALL INTESTINE
Mechanical
Muscular contractions break down and mix food with digestive enzymes, bile, and hormones.
Chemical
Enzymes, bile, and hormones finish digestion of proteins, sugars, and fats.
Animated BIOLOGY
Explore the digestive system at ClassZone.com.

B CRITICAL VIEWING **Do you think a high-carbohydrate or a high-protein meal would be digested more quickly? Explain.**

ONLINE BIOLOGY Have students follow the movement and digestion of food in the digestive system. Go to the Animated Biology in Options for Inquiry on page 993.

Integrating Medical Science

Heartburn occurs when the lower esophageal sphincter relaxes too much, allowing the reflux, or backflow, of stomach acid into the lower esophagus. Most people experience mild indigestion or heartburn occasionally. However, frequent or persistent heartburn may indicate GERD, or **gastroesophageal reflux disease,** a serious disorder causing a wide range of effects. These include severe inflammation, esophageal bleeding, and erosions, or ulcers, in the esophageal lining. As these heal, the damaged lining is replaced with scar tissue that can lead to narrowing of the esophagus. In some cases, the damaged esophageal cells are replaced with an abnormal cell type that can precede development of esophageal cancer.

Answers

A **Apply** Digestion of spaghetti (starch) would begin in the mouth. Digestion of meat (protein) would begin in the stomach.

B **Critical Viewing** A high-carbohydrate meal would be digested more quickly. Digestion begins in the mouth and finishes in the small intestine. Digestion of a high-protein meal would not begin until it reaches the stomach and would take longer to break down into amino acids.

BELOW LEVEL

Model the process of peristalsis for students. Using a tube of toothpaste, show how applying pressure behind the toothpaste at the bottom of the tube pushes the toothpaste forward. **Ask**

- What part of the model represents the muscles of the esophagus? the tube
- the food in the esophagus? toothpaste

PRE-AP

Have students work in pairs to isolate each enzyme described in **FIGURE 32.10** by digestive organ or by function. Have them repeat this for **FIGURE 32.11,** isolating each digestive organ and associating it with the primary activities that occur during the digestive process. Then have students put the two figures together, matching each enzyme from **FIGURE 32.10** with the appropriate organ or activity described in **FIGURE 32.11.**

Biology Toolkit, Think-Pair-Share, p. C13

▼ Teach continued

TEACH FROM VISUALS

FIGURE 32.12 Have students trace the flow of substances into the small intestine. **Ask**

- What three substances are secreted into the small intestine? bile, an alkaline fluid, digestive enzymes
- What organs secrete these substances? bile: liver via gallbladder; alkaline fluid and digestive enzymes: pancreas
- In general, what is the function of the bile and pancreatic enzymes? digest the fats and remaining proteins and sugars in chyme

Science Trivia

- The liver is the largest glandular organ in the body and performs more than 100 distinct functions.
- People with high cholesterol are at risk for forming gallstones—pebble-sized stones made of bile, cholesterol, and salts.
- The largest known gallstone weighed more than 6 kilograms (about 13 lb) and was removed from an 80-year-old woman.

Answers

Ⓐ **Apply** From the pancreas, enzymes such as lactase and lipase would break down the milk sugars and fats in the dairy product. Bile from the liver would also help break down the milk fat.

▼ Assess and Reteach

Assess Use the Online Quiz or Section Quiz (*Assessment Book,* p. 632).

Reteach Have students view the animation of the digestive system at **ClassZone.com.** Ask them to make a graphic of their choice that summarizes the movement of food through the digestive system and its digestion.

MAIN IDEA

Digestion is completed in part of the small intestine.

FIGURE 32.12 The liver and pancreas help digest fats, carbohydrates, and proteins in the small intestine. The liver secretes bile through the gallbladder, and the pancreas secretes an alkaline fluid and digestive enzymes.

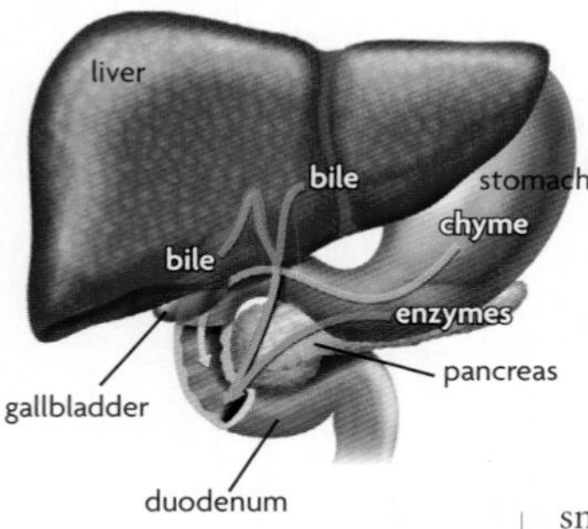

The remaining carbohydrates, proteins, and fats from your sandwich are digested in the duodenum (DOO-uh-DEE-nuhm), the section of small intestine closest to the stomach. The **small intestine** is a long, narrow tube in which most digestion takes place. Smooth muscle contractions churn the food, and chemical digestion further breaks down the complex molecules. As shown in **FIGURE 32.12**, enzymes and hormones from the pancreas, liver, and gallbladder flow through ducts into the duodenum to help complete the digestive process.

The pancreas is a small gland located behind the stomach. When chyme first enters the small intestine, the pancreas releases an alkaline fluid to help neutralize the acid and stop the action of pepsin. The pancreas also releases enzymes to break down starches further into simple sugars. For example, lactase is an intestinal enzyme that breaks down lactose, a sugar found in milk. The pancreas also produces an enzyme, lipase, that splits fat into fatty acids and smaller molecules.

The liver, which filters blood, is also a digestive organ. It produces a chemical substance, **bile,** that helps to digest fats. Bile is stored in a smaller organ, the gallbladder. When bile is needed to digest fats, it is released through ducts that empty into the duodenum. The bile breaks down large globules of fat into smaller droplets for further digestion.

Proteins entering the small intestine have already been broken down by the action of pepsin and gastric juice into smaller chains of amino acids. In the duodenum, enzymes finish the process by breaking these chains into individual amino acids. By the time chyme has passed through the duodenum, food has been broken down into small molecules. Section 32.3 describes how these molecules are absorbed by the body.

To learn more about digestion, visit scilinks.org.
Keycode: MLB032

Ⓐ **Apply How would the pancreas and liver help to digest ice cream?**

32.2 ASSESSMENT

REVIEWING MAIN IDEAS

1. What is the main function of the **digestive system**?
2. Give an example of mechanical and chemical **digestion** in the mouth and in the **stomach.**
3. What organs help to continue digestion in the **small intestine**?

CRITICAL THINKING

4. **Predict** One person eats a beef steak in a few bites, while another chews the same amount of beef well. If all other conditions are equal, will both people digest their beef at the same rate? Explain.
5. **Predict** If a person has his or her gallbladder removed, what changes in diet should be made? Why?

6. **Cell Structure** The cells of the stomach lining produce a great deal of mucus. If you were to view such a cell under a microscope, what type of organelle would you expect to see in abundance?

32.2 ASSESSMENT

1. to break down food into smaller molecules for the body to absorb and use
2. Mouth: mechanical digestion—teeth chew food and the tongue moves food to keep it between the teeth; chemical digestion—enzymes such as amylase in the salivary glands break down starches. Stomach: mechanical digestion—smooth muscles in the stomach churn chyme; chemical digestion—pepsin and HCl act on proteins to break them into smaller amino acid chains.
3. gallbladder, liver, pancreas
4. Yes, protein is not broken down in the mouth but in the stomach.
5. The gallbladder concentrates and releases bile made by the liver. The doctor may suggest that the person eat fewer fatty foods or only small amounts of fatty foods at any one time.
6. Vesicles would be in abundance in cells that secrete mucus.

MATERIALS

- 4 100-mL beakers
- 10 cm tape
- marker
- 2 100-mL graduated cylinders
- 160 mL water
- 80 mL 1% hydrochloric acid solution
- 80 mL pepsin
- 4 pecans
- balance
- 4 pieces of potato
- 4 pieces of beef jerky
- warm water bath
- clock

PROCESS SKILL
Analyzing Data

INDIANA STANDARDS

NOS.1 Develop explanations based on reproducible data and observations gathered during laboratory investigations.
NOS.3 Clearly communicate their ideas and results of investigations verbally and in written form using tables, graphs, diagrams, and photographs.

Testing a Digestive Enzyme

In this lab, you will test the effectiveness of the digestive enzyme pepsin under different conditions. You will also determine whether pepsin acts on carbohydrates, fats, or proteins.

PROBLEM Under which conditions is pepsin most effective?

PROCEDURE

1. Label the beakers A, B, C, and D. Add 80 mL of water to beaker A.
2. Add 40 mL of water and 40 mL of the hydrochloric acid solution to beaker B.
3. Add 40 mL of water and 40 mL of pepsin to beaker C.
4. Add 40 mL of the hydrochloric acid solution and 40 mL of pepsin to beaker D.
5. Measure and record the mass of four pecans. Find the average of the four masses. Obtain four pieces each of potato and beef jerky that are about the same mass as the average mass of the pecans.
6. Place one of each piece of food in beaker A. Repeat this step with beakers B, C, and D.
7. Place the beakers in a warm water bath at a temperature of about 37°C.
8. Observe and record the condition of the food in each beaker after 15 minutes, 30 minutes, 45 minutes, and 24 hours. Create a data table like the one below for each beaker. Use the following phrases to describe your observations of the condition of each piece of food: "not dissolving," "beginning to dissolve," "partly dissolved," "mostly dissolved," "completely dissolved." If the condition does not change at all, write "nothing happened."

TABLE 1. CONDITIONS OF FOOD PIECES

Beaker A	Potato	Pecan	Beef Jerky
15 min			
30 min			
45 min			
24 hr			

ANALYZE AND CONCLUDE

1. **Experimental Design** What were the independent and dependent variables in this experiment? Which beaker was the control? Why were the beakers placed in the warm water bath?
2. **Analyze** Compare the condition of each of the same pieces of food in each beaker. Which piece of food in which beaker was the most digested?
3. **Analyze** Hydrochloric acid has a low pH. What conclusion can you draw about the relationship between the effectiveness of pepsin and pH?
4. **Infer** Potatoes are about 90 percent carbohydrate and 10 percent protein. Pecans are about 87 percent fat, 5 percent protein, and 8 percent carbohydrate. Beef jerky is about 80 percent protein and 20 percent carbohydrate. On which molecule does pepsin act?
5. **Predict** If you were to repeat this experiment, replacing the pepsin with salivary amylase, which breaks down carbohydrates, how would you expect your results to change? The pH of saliva is about 7.4.

Answers

Sample Data

For a sample of student data from this lab, go to page R110. Be aware that the student used cooked chicken in place of beef jerky.

Analyze and Conclude

1. Independent variables: the food samples and the different solutions in the beakers; dependent variable: the condition of the food samples over time; the control was the beaker with water only. The warm water bath was used to simulate body temperature and maintain a constant temperature so that temperature was not a variable in the experiment.
2. The beef jerky in beaker D should be digested the most.
3. Pepsin works best at a low pH.
4. protein
5. The potato in beaker C would be the most digested.

INVESTIGATION

Time 60 minutes	TEACHER TESTED
Teacher Preparation	
Student Difficulty	
Lab Binder Human Bio, pp. 51–54	

Purpose Test the effectiveness of the enzyme pepsin in digesting different foods under different conditions.

Overview Students will compare the digestion of potato, pecans, and beef jerky by pepsin under varying conditions. They will

- place each type of food sample in a beaker with water only; with hydrochloric acid solution only; with pepsin only; and with pepsin and hydrochloric acid solution
- compare the digestion of the food samples over a period of 24 hours
- make conclusions about the type of food molecule pepsin acts on and the relationship between pepsin and pH

LAB PREPARATION

- Obtain enough food samples for each lab group to have about 10 grams of each.

LAB MANAGEMENT

Safety Notes Students must wear safety goggles and use heat-resistant gloves when handling beakers. Remind them not to eat in the lab.

POST-LAB DISCUSSION

Discuss the lab with the class. **Ask**

- Why was hydrochloric acid added to one of the beakers? to test the effect of lower pH on pepsin's activity
- Why was it important that the food samples have approximately the same mass? to eliminate size variables, to ensure valid comparisons are made between samples

▼ Plan and Prepare

Objectives

- Describe how nutrients are absorbed in the small intestine.
- Describe water absorption and solid-waste elimination in the large intestine.

Section Resources

Unit Resource Book Study Guide pp. 133–134 Power Notes p. 135 Reinforcement p. 136 Pre-AP Activity pp. 145–146
Interactive Reader Chapter 32 **Spanish Study Guide** pp. 329–330
Biology Toolkit pp. C19, C22, C24
Technology Power Presentation 32.3 Media Gallery DVD Online Quiz 32.3

Activate Prior Knowledge Discuss claims that manufacturers make for the absorbency of paper towels, such as "quilting" or ridges. **Ask,** What do these features do? increase surface area Tell students that the small intestine has features that produce a large surface area for absorption of nutrients.

▼ Teach

Vocabulary

Academic Vocabulary The word **intestine** comes from a Latin root meaning "within." It can also be used as an adjective meaning internal or civil, as in the *intestine* affairs of a nation. It is more commonly used in the expression *intestinal fortitude,* which suggests a particular strength of mind that allows one to endure adversity.

Answers

Ⓐ **Analyze** It would be greatly reduced.

32.3 Absorption of Nutrients

KEY CONCEPT Nutrients are absorbed and solid wastes eliminated after digestion.

MAIN IDEAS

- Most absorption of nutrients occurs in the small intestine.
- Water is absorbed and solid wastes are eliminated from the large intestine.

VOCABULARY

absorption, p. 982
villi, p. 983
microvilli, p. 983

Connect Suppose you tried to wipe up spilled water with a "sponge" made of solid plastic. Without the ability to absorb water, your sponge is useless. People with celiac disease face a similar, but more life-threatening, problem. Celiac disease is an autoimmune disorder that makes people unable to tolerate the protein gluten found in wheat, rye, and barley. Their immune systems produce antibodies to destroy it. The antibodies also damage the surfaces of cells lining the small intestine. This means that no matter how much a person eats, the body cannot absorb the food and becomes malnourished. The only treatment is to eliminate all gluten from the diet to protect the lining of the small intestine.

MAIN IDEA

Most absorption of nutrients occurs in the small intestine.

Food moving through the "disassembly line" of the digestive system is only part of the process. Your body must absorb the nutrients in order for the food you digest to do you any good. **Absorption** is the process by which nutrients move out of the digestive organs into the circulatory and lymphatic systems. As shown in **FIGURE 32.13,** the small intestine has three main structures—the lining, villi, and microvilli—that absorb most of the nutrients from chyme.

FIGURE 32.13 Small Intestine Structures

Specialized structures in the small intestine increase surface area and absorption.

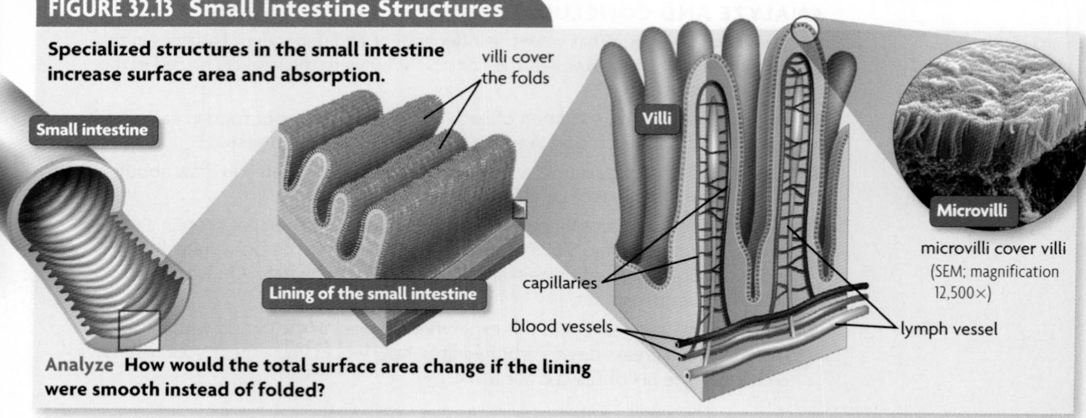

Analyze **How would the total surface area change if the lining were smooth instead of folded?**

Differentiated Instruction

ENGLISH LEARNERS

Ask groups of students to write a section summary. Have them look at the headings, keywords, visuals, and final questions, identify main points, and restate them in concise language. Example: After food is digested, it moves into the small intestine. Blood carries nutrients to the liver, where enzymes use some nutrients to build complex molecules needed by cells. The colon absorbs water and salts to maintain body fluid balance. Undigested material forms feces, which pass out through the anus.

Biology Toolkit, Summarizing, p. C24

Specialized Structures for Absorption

As you look over the diagram in **FIGURE 32.13**, notice that the lining of the small intestine is ridged and folded. These structures increase the surface area and slow the passage of material through the intestine. Slower motion allows more time for nutrients to be absorbed. The folds of the lining are covered with villi. **Villi** (VIHL-eye) are small fingerlike projections, covered with epithelial cells, that absorb nutrients.

In turn, every epithelial cell on the villi has thousands of tiny projections called **microvilli** that add even more surface area to absorb nutrients. Each microvillus is smaller than the period at the end of this sentence. The photograph in the diagram shows microvilli covering the epithelial cells like a dense carpet.

TAKING NOTES

Use a main idea and supporting detail diagram to help you remember the facts about absorption.

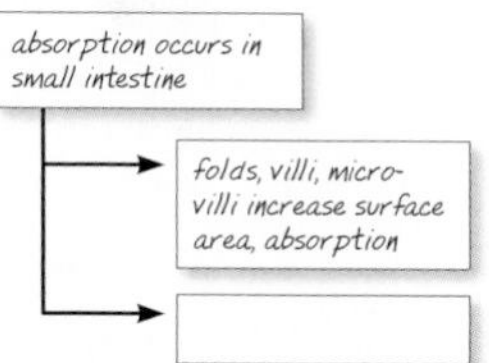

Absorption of Different Nutrients

As digestion is completed, nutrients are absorbed in each of the three parts of the small intestine: the duodenum, the jejunum, and the ileum. Together, these parts measure about 6 meters (about 20 ft) long. Villi in each of the three sections absorb different nutrients.

Duodenum Most simple sugars, amino acids, and minerals such as calcium and iron are absorbed by villi in the duodenum. These nutrients diffuse into the circulatory system and are carried to the liver.

Jejunum The villi in the jejunum (juh-JOO-nuhm) absorb glucose along with some amino acids, vitamin C, most B vitamins, and some water. These nutrients diffuse into the circulatory system to be distributed throughout the body.

Ileum The villi in the ileum (IHL-ee-uhm) absorb fat-soluble vitamins and vitamin B_{12}, fatty acids, cholesterol, and some water. The nutrients empty into lymph and blood vessels and are distributed to the cells.

***Connecting* CONCEPTS**

Cell Structure As you read in **Chapter 3,** plant cell walls are made of cellulose, or fiber. These tough cell walls cannot be broken down or absorbed in the small intestine. Instead, fiber moves through the small intestine to the large intestine.

QUICK LAB DESIGNING EXPERIMENTS NOS.6

Villi in the Small Intestine

In this lab, you will design a model of the villi in the lining of the small intestine.

PROBLEM How can you model the function of villi in the small intestine?

PROCEDURE

1. Use a paper cup, water, and paper towel to make a model of the villi in the lining of the small intestine.
2. Make three new models that are different. To do this, change one material to determine which model most effectively shows the action of the villi.
3. Determine which of your models most effectively models the villi.

ANALYZE AND CONCLUDE

1. **Summarize** Explain how this experiment models the action of the villi in the small intestine.
2. **Apply** Write a definition to describe how you measured each model's effectiveness.
3. **Analyze** Which model was most effective? How do you know?

MATERIALS

- 4 large paper cups
- water
- 8 paper towels
- timer

BELOW LEVEL

Have students make a four-column chart that lists the three sections of the small intestine plus the large intestine, identifies nutrients that are absorbed in each section, and describes what happens to the nutrients after they are absorbed.

Biology Toolkit, Content Frame, p. C22

PRE-AP

Tell students that the word *efficiency* describes the ratio of output to input in a system. Have students address the question of how a complete digestive system increases an animal's amount of activity (output) relative to the amount of food needed to fuel that activity (input). Students should realize that a complete digestive tract enables continuous feeding and processing of food for energy. You may want to remind them that radial invertebrates have only a single opening for handling food and waste.

Biology Toolkit, Quick-Write, p. C19

Vocabulary

Academic Vocabulary Have students write the following words in their notebooks and read them aloud:

absorb	*absorption*
reabsorb	*reabsorption*
resorb	*resorption*

The similarity between *reabsorption* and *resorption* can be confusing. The words are often used interchangeably to describe reuptake. However, in biology, the word *resorption* is used to describe a process in which a structure is broken down and its constituent tissues are taken up and repurposed. For example, in bone resorption, bone is broken down, and the calcium and other minerals that composed it are taken up and used in other parts of the body.

QUICK LAB

Time 15 minutes TEACHER TESTED

Lab Binder Human Bio, p. 58

Purpose Design a model of the intestinal villi.

Answers

Analyze and Conclude

1. The villi are the major structures that absorb nutrients from chyme. The experiment uses an absorbent material to model the action of absorption.
2. Students should describe the quantity of water absorbed by the models or the speed of water absorption.
3. The most effective model will be the one that absorbs the most water in the shortest amount of time. Students will use their method of measurement to determine the most effective model.

▼ Teach *continued*

Integrating Zoology

Unlike humans, animals that graze on grasses and other forms of vegetation are able to get nutrients from the tough cellulose in plant cell walls. Cows, sheep, goats, and kangaroos are examples of **foregut fermenters.** They have a complex multi-chambered digestive organ that harbors a rich community of microbes in the chambers preceding the true acid-secreting stomach. The microbes break down (ferment) the cellulose in the ingested plant matter before it reaches the true stomach. In **hindgut fermenters,** a group that includes horses, possums, and rabbits, the fermenting microbes are located in the cecum, posterior to the true acid-secreting stomach.

Answers

A Analyze Thousands of microvilli cover the surface of each villus, greatly increasing the surface area available to absorb nutrients.

B Infer A diet high in plant foods, such as fruits, vegetables, and whole grains; the fiber in these foods helps to move food through the digestive tract and forms the bulk of solid waste.

▼ Assess and Reteach

Assess Use the Online Quiz or Section Quiz (*Assessment Book,* p. 633).

Reteach As a class, make a concept map using the following terms: *small intestine, duodenum, jejunum, ileum, liver, large intestine.* Have students supply details about nutrient absorption for each part of the digestive system listed on the concept map and draw arrows to show connections between the parts.

Absorbed Nutrients and the Liver

Nutrient-rich blood leaves the small intestine and enters the liver. Enzymes in the liver use some nutrients to build more complex molecules that are needed by cells. The liver also stores some nutrients in liver tissues. For example, excess glucose is turned into glycogen and stored for future use. When you need large amounts of energy, glycogen can be converted back into glucose to keep the glucose levels in your blood relatively stable.

A Analyze Explain how the microvilli add more surface area to the small intestine to absorb nutrients.

MAIN IDEA

Water is absorbed and solid wastes are eliminated from the large intestine.

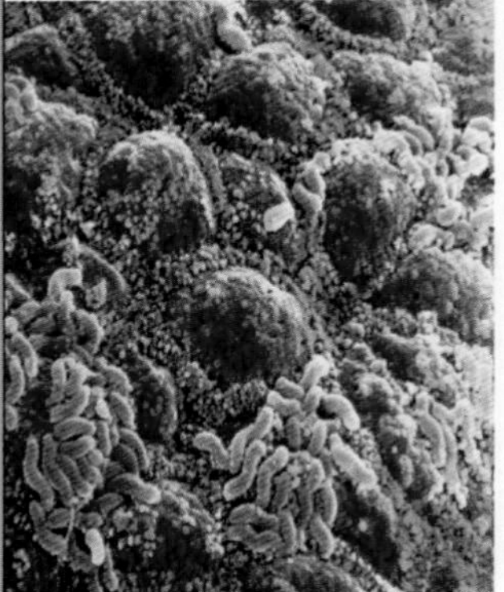

FIGURE 32.14 This micrograph shows the surface of the large intestine colonized by normally harmless bacteria, such as *Escherichia coli* (shown in pink clusters). (colored SEM: magnification 2500×)

The large intestine, or colon, is 1.5 meters (5 ft) long and about twice the diameter of the small intestine. The large intestine absorbs about 1 liter of water a day, along with some salts, which helps to maintain the body's fluid balance. The remaining undigested material forms into a solid mass, called feces. This material is partly composed of undigested fiber from plant foods, dead bacteria, and traces of undigested fat and protein. Bile pigments from the liver give feces its brownish color. The feces is stored in the rectum, a tube that connects the large intestine to the anus. Feces is then eliminated through the anus.

The large intestine also contains many types of bacteria. Some synthesize a few B vitamins and vitamin K (a blood-clotting factor). Other bacteria, such as *Escherichia coli,* shown in **FIGURE 32.14,** live harmlessly in the colon until some disturbance, such as an illness, allows them to overgrow other bacteria. An overgrowth of *E. coli* can reduce water absorption and cause severe diarrhea.

Your sandwich has taken roughly 24 to 33 hours to move through your digestive system. Now some of the water absorbed by the large intestine must be filtered through the kidneys and excreted, as described in Section 32.4.

B Infer A diet high in which types of foods might help the colon to function well?

32.3 ASSESSMENT

ONLINE QUIZ ClassZone.com

REVIEWING MAIN IDEAS

1. Explain the purposes of the lining, **villi,** and **microvilli** in the small intestine.
2. What are the main functions of the large intestine?

CRITICAL THINKING

3. **Contrast** Explain the difference between digestion and **absorption.** What role does each process play in maintaining homeostasis?
4. **Apply** Which nutrients would take longer to digest and absorb: sugars, proteins, or fats? Explain.

***Connecting* CONCEPTS**

5. **Animals** The desert kangaroo rat in Arizona eats plants but doesn't drink water. Yet even in summer, it doesn't suffer from dehydration. How do you think the rat's digestive system helps it to obtain water to maintain homeostasis?

32.3 ASSESSMENT

1. Folds increase the surface area and slow the movement of food through the small intestine. Villi and microvilli also increase the surface area of the intestine and absorb nutrients from chyme.
2. absorb water and eliminate solid wastes
3. Digestion uses mechanical and chemical means to break down food into simpler molecules. Absorption is the means by which nutrients move out of the digestive system and into the circulatory and lymphatic systems. Digestion makes nutrients available from food to maintain cell functions. Absorption allows nutrients to be carried to cells throughout the body.
4. Fats would take longer to digest and absorb. Digestion of most fats does not begin until it reaches the small intestine, where bile and other enzymes break globules of fat into smaller droplets.
5. The rat's digestive system must be able to absorb all of the water from the plants as they are broken down in the digestive tract.

NOS.1

Outliers in Data Sets

Sometimes in a scientific investigation, one or more unusual data points are recorded. A data point that is outside of the pattern of data is called an **outlier.** Outliers can result from human error in reading or recording data, from equipment failure, or from rare events such as a 31°C (70°F) day in Wisconsin in January.

To rule out the possibility that the outlier is a valid data point, scientists check their equipment, the laboratory set-up, and the recording process. If the outlier seems to be valid, further research may be needed. Simply ignoring or deleting outliers are not appropriate ways of handling these data.

EXAMPLE

A scientist measured the body temperatures of 1 person over time. As shown in the scatterplot at the right, nearly every temperature was between 36.9°C (98.4°F) and 37.8°C (98.6°F). Notice, however, that one temperature was recorded at 36.8°C (98.2°F). This outlier could be the result of equipment failure or human error. In cases of outliers, scientists must always ask, "What other explanations could there be for the data point? Do these data warrant further investigation?" Investigating the outlier further might lead to new discoveries.

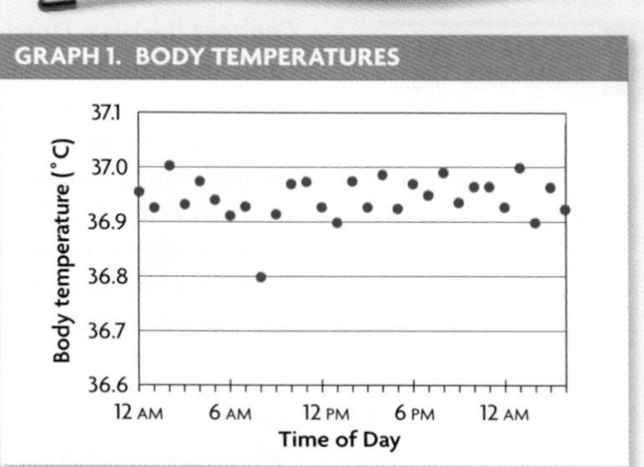

IDENTIFY OUTLIERS

Scientists investigated how the mass of an antacid affects its ability to raise the pH of gastric juices in the stomach. They recorded their data in the graph below. Examine the graph, and answer the questions that follow.

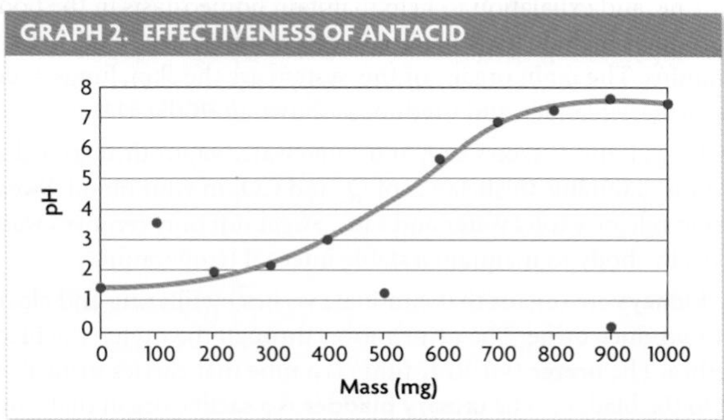

1. **Analyze** What is the trend in the data? Which points might be the outliers?
2. **Evaluate** What are some possible explanations for these outliers? How should the scientists proceed?

Answers

1. The trend is that as the mass of the antacid increases, it neutralizes the gastric juices more effectively. As the mass increases, the pH of the gastric juice increases. The outliers are at 100 mg and 500 mg.
2. The equipment used to measure the mass or the pH could be faulty. The sample could be contaminated. Human error could have led to improper collection or recording of data. Scientists should check the equipment, laboratory setup, and data-recording process. If the data points seem valid, further investigation should be carried out.

DATA ANALYSIS

Introduce

An outlier is a data point that lies at some distance from other values in a random sample of data. Outliers can result from errors in the experiment itself, equipment errors, or errors in data reading or recording. Students may find it frustrating when they find an outlier in their data and may be tempted to dismiss the anomaly as a fluke with no real meaning. This is poor science. Unless ruled out as due to human error, outliers in a data set indicate that something is wrong with the study, which might require further research.

Discuss

Have students look at the data and the outliers shown in the graph. **Ask**

- What is it about these two points that makes them outliers? Both are fairly distant from the rest of the results; neither follows the trend shown by the rest of the data.
- If the *y*-values at 100 mg and 500 mg each were near pH 2.5, would you still consider these outliers? Probably yes; while data points do not have to lie precisely on the trend line, the suggested *y*-values would still lie outside the general trend, which would make them suspicious.

Unit Resource Book, Data Analysis, p. 141

▼ Plan and Prepare

Objectives

- Identify the main organs of the excretory system and their functions.
- Explain how the kidneys help maintain homeostasis.
- Describe treatments for kidney diseases and injuries.

Section Resources

Unit Resource Book Study Guide pp. 137–138 Power Notes p. 139 Reinforcement p. 140
Interactive Reader Chapter 32 **Spanish Study Guide** pp. 331–332
Biology Toolkit pp. C8, C13, C19, C20, C23, C38
Technology Power Presentation 32.4 Media Gallery DVD Online Quiz 32.4

Activate Prior Knowledge Discuss the task of clearing the table after dinner. **Ask,** Do you dispose of liquid and solid trash differently? Yes, liquids can be poured down the drain; solids are put into a trash can. Point out that solid waste is eliminated through the digestive system and that fluid wastes, both gases and liquids, are removed by the excretory system.

▼ Teach

Vocabulary

Academic Vocabulary Remind students that the word **fluid** applies to both liquids and gases.

fluid (n.), continuous, amorphous substance that tends to assume the shape of its container

fluid (adj.), smooth and flowing

Answers

A Connect Lungs eliminate CO_2 and H_2O vapor; sweat glands release excess water and salts; kidneys clean blood of metabolic wastes and produce urine.

32.4 Excretory System

KEY CONCEPT The excretory system removes wastes and helps maintain homeostasis.

MAIN IDEAS

- The excretory system eliminates nonsolid wastes from the body.
- The kidneys help to maintain homeostasis by filtering the blood.
- Nephrons clean the blood and produce urine.
- Injury and disease can damage kidney functions.

VOCABULARY

excretory system, p. 986
kidney, p. 986
ureter, p. 986
urinary bladder, p. 986
nephron, p. 987
glomerulus, p. 988
dialysis, p. 991

Connect In 1943, Dutch physician Willem Kolff, who treated kidney patients, constructed the first machine to filter the blood of patients whose kidneys had temporarily stopped functioning. Kolff circulated their blood through synthetic sausage skins submerged in a saltwater bath. The high concentration of salt in the water drew metabolic wastes out of the blood through tiny pores in the synthetic skins. The filtered blood was then returned to the patients. However, Kolff's machine worked well only for people with temporary kidney failure. Today, modern kidney machines can help people even when their kidneys have permanently failed.

MAIN IDEA

The excretory system eliminates nonsolid wastes from the body.

If the digestive system is like a disassembly and distribution line, the excretory system is a like a group of waste treatment and disposal facilities. The **excretory system** is the body system that eliminates nonsolid wastes through sweat, urine, and exhalation to help maintain homeostasis in the body. The waste products include toxic materials, excess water, salts, CO_2, urea, minerals, and vitamins. The main organs of this system are the skin, lungs, kidneys, ureters, urinary bladder, and urethra, as shown in **FIGURE 32.15.**

The lungs remove excess CO_2 and some water vapor through exhalation. This action maintains the balance of O_2 and CO_2 in your blood. Sweat glands in the skin release excess water and salts. Sweat not only removes wastes but also cools the body to maintain a stable internal temperature.

The **kidneys** are organs that eliminate wastes by filtering and cleaning the blood to produce urine. The urine moves through the ureter, the bladder, and the urethra. The **ureter** (yu-REE-tuhr) is a tube that carries urine from each kidney to the bladder. The **urinary bladder** is a saclike organ that can store up to half a liter (over 2 cups) of urine at one time. The urine is released through a single tube, the urethra, into the outside environment.

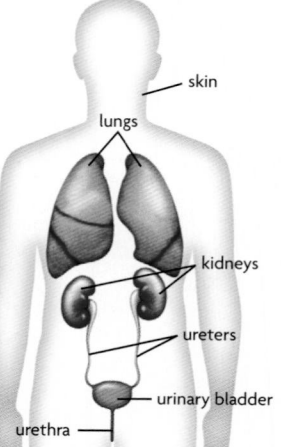

FIGURE 32.15 The excretory system not only excretes nonsolid wastes but also maintains the body's homeostasis.

Connect **When you are exercising, what organs of the excretory system are eliminating wastes?**

Differentiated Instruction

PRE-AP

Have students use the SQ3R strategy for learning the material in this section. Have them survey the text and come up with questions for each subsection. Direct them to read the text and then recite the answers to their questions. When they have answered all of their questions, have them review what they learned.

Biology Toolkit, SQ3R, p. C8

BELOW LEVEL

For students having difficulty keeping up with the details of the material, have them copy **FIGURE 32.15** into their notebooks. Then have students label each organ and what waste it eliminates from the body.

Biology Toolkit, Combination Notes, p. C23

MAIN IDEA

The kidneys help to maintain homeostasis by filtering the blood.

The kidneys are among the main organs responsible for maintaining fluid and chemical balances in your body within the limits that support life. One quarter of your blood supply passes through your kidneys every minute. Once the blood is filtered, cleaned, and chemically balanced by the kidneys, it is returned to the circulatory system.

Structure of the Kidneys

Your kidneys are a pair of bean-shaped organs, each about the size of your fist. They are located on the right and left sides of the lower back. Each kidney weighs about as much as a baseball. Most people are born with two kidneys. However, if one is damaged or must be removed, you can still live comfortably with only one kidney.

The main parts of the kidney are illustrated in **FIGURE 32.16.** Each kidney has an inner layer, called the medulla, and an outer layer, called the cortex. The cortex is packed with nephrons, which extend through the cortex and partly into the medulla. A **nephron** (NEHF-rahn) is the individual filtering unit of the kidney. Each of your kidneys contains about 1 million nephrons.

A large volume of blood continually enters the kidneys through the renal artery and exits through the renal vein. The word *renal* means "relating to the kidneys." The function of the kidneys is largely controlled by how much water, salts, and other materials are concentrated in the blood. Hormones released in response to these concentrations help to regulate kidney function.

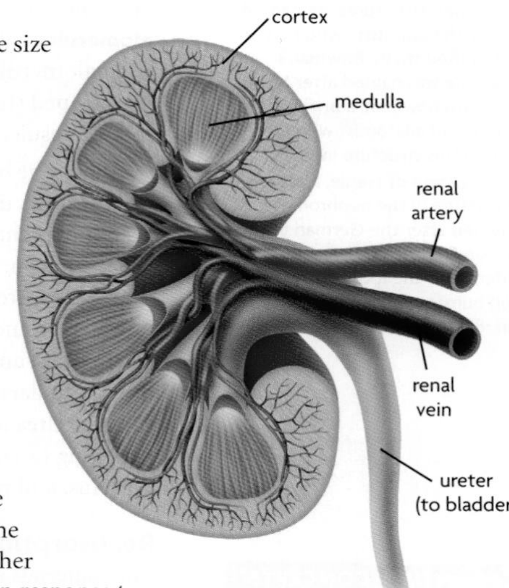

FIGURE 32.16 The bean-shaped kidneys are the main blood filtration and chemical balancing organs in the body. The cortex and medulla layers contain over 1 million nephrons, which are the kidneys' main filtering units.

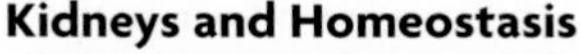

Kidneys and Homeostasis

The kidneys have three basic functions in maintaining homeostasis.

- They remove waste products from the blood, such as those produced from digestion and cell respiration.
- They help to maintain electrolyte, pH, and fluid balances in the body.
- They release hormones that help to keep bones healthy, to produce red blood cells, and to regulate blood pressure.

What if the kidneys fail to work properly? Waste products quickly build up in the blood, causing serious disruptions in homeostasis in many organ systems. For example, imbalances in electrolytes such as sodium and potassium could disrupt the rhythm of the heart, causing the organ to fail. A buildup of toxic substances such as ammonium salts in the blood can impair the functioning of neurons in the brain. Someone with this condition would quickly become confused and disoriented.

A Infer **What might be one reason why so many nephrons are needed in the kidneys?**

ONLINE BIOLOGY Go to the chapter Resource Center at **ClassZone.com** for additional resources and information on the urinary system.

Integrating Comparative Biology

With a few exceptions, such as sponges and jellyfish, animal cells are bathed in an internal extracellular layer of fluids that are made up in large part of water and various salts. The ability of an animal to control this internal environment as well as the availability of salt and water in a given environment are important factors in determining where an animal can live.

Osmoregulation is the control of the volume of water and salt content in extracellular fluids. Osmoregulatory and excretory functions in an animal correspond to the habitat it lives in.

Octopus: Extracellular fluid is similar in water–salt concentration to seawater; nitrogenous wastes diffuse through skin.

Saltwater fish: Drinks seawater and secretes excess salt through gills, kidney produces little urine.

Freshwater fish: Drinks little, absorbs salts through gills and some water through skin, kidney produces large amounts of urine.

Sea bird: Drinks seawater, secretes salt through salt gland; kidneys produce little urine, instead uric acid is eliminated in white excrement.

Frog: Absorbs salts through skin, which secretes waterproofing mucus; kidneys produce large amounts of urine.

Insect: Uric acid crystallizes in hindgut and salts and water move back into the body cavity; eliminates only solid waste.

ENGLISH LEARNERS

Help students create a sequence diagram showing how the kidneys eliminate process liquid wastes. Have students list the events and their order as you fill in boxes and draw arrows between them. Possible steps: (1) Blood enters kidneys through renal artery and exits through renal vein. (2) Kidneys filter and clean blood to produce urine. (3) Urethra carries urine from kidney to urinary bladder. (4) Bladder stores it until it is ready to be released. (5) Urine leaves body through urethra.

Biology Toolkit, Sequence Diagram, p. C38

Answers

A Infer The kidneys filter a huge quantity of blood; so many nephrons would greatly increase the area available to filter the blood and produce urine.

Chapter 32: Digestive and Excretory Systems **987**

▼ Teach *continued*

ONLINE BIOLOGY Students can observe the effect of antidiuretic hormone (ADH) on urine output. Go to Data Analysis Online in Options for Inquiry on page 993.

Integrating Sports Medicine

Drinking too much water during strenuous athletic events, such as a marathon, can pose an even greater health risk than dehydration. Scientists base this conclusion on a study of 488 runners who participated in the 2002 Boston Marathon. Roughly 13 percent of the runners had **hyponatremia,** an abnormally low blood plasma sodium level, after the race. The runners with the lowest post-race plasma sodium levels drank nearly 13 cups of fluids during the race. The rate of intake overshot the kidneys' ability to eliminate the excess water. While fluids are vitally important during exercise, particularly strenuous races, experts now suggest replenishing fluids less frequently.

Vocabulary

Academic Vocabulary The word **filter** shares the same root as the word **felt,** which is a fabric of matted, compressed animal fibers, such as wool or fur.

filter, porous material through which a liquid or gas is passed to separate fluid from suspended particulate matter

The **filtrate** is the gas or liquid that remains. Students will probably be familiar with the word *filter* in the context of computers, a filter being a program that blocks unwanted data or denies access to uninvited users.

MAIN IDEA

Nephrons clean the blood and produce urine.

The nephrons clean the blood in a three-step process: filtration, reabsorption, and excretion. First, water and other materials move out of the capillaries and into the nephron. Next, some of these materials are reabsorbed and returned to the blood. Finally, the remaining waste products are excreted in the urine.

VOCABULARY

At times, structures are named after the scientists who first identified them. **Bowman's capsule** was named after Sir William Bowman, a British surgeon and anatomist who identified this structure in 1831.

The **loop of Henle**, another structure in the nephron, was named after the German physician Friedrich G. J. Henle. He identified the loop in his book on human anatomy, published in 1873.

Filtration

As shown in **FIGURE 32.17**, each nephron is supplied with blood through an arteriole, a venule, and a tangled ball of capillaries that is known as the **glomerulus** (gloh-MEHR-yuh-luhs). Each glomerulus is tucked into a cup-shaped structure called Bowman's capsule.

VISUAL VOCAB

Glomerulus, a tangled ball of capillaries, is a word based on the Latin *glomus,* which means "ball."

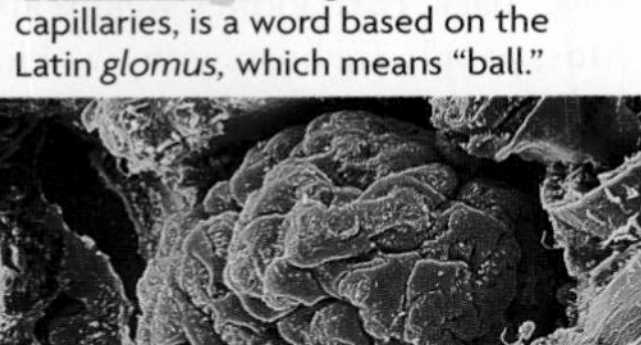

When the blood enters the kidneys, it flows into the arterioles and then moves into the glomerulus of each nephron. Because the blood is under pressure, small molecules such as water, amino acids, salts, glucose, electrolytes, and urea are pushed out of the capillaries and into Bowman's capsule. Urea is a waste product produced by the breakdown of proteins. Anything too large to move out of the capillaries—such as blood cells, plasma proteins, and platelets—stays in the blood.

***Connecting* CONCEPTS**

Cell Membranes You read in **Chapter 3** that materials diffuse into and out of cell membranes from areas of higher concentration to areas of lower concentration. In the glomerulus, molecules diffuse through capillary walls.

Reabsorption of Materials

The materials in Bowman's capsule are called the filtrate. The nephrons process about 180 liters (48 gal) of filtrate every day, yet only about 1 percent is excreted as urine. What happens to the other 99 percent?

Most of the filtrate is reabsorbed into the capillaries and returns to the blood. This process ensures that nutrients such as water, amino acids, glucose, and sodium (Na^+) are made available to the body. The reabsorption of water and Na^+ helps to maintain your fluid balance. For example, if you drink too much water, the nephrons will reabsorb less of the fluid and produce more urine. If you drink too little water, the nephrons will reabsorb more fluid and produce less urine.

Excretion of Materials

Finally, the waste products that are not reabsorbed are excreted in the urine. Urine is made up of water, urea, excess salts, and other materials that remain in the filtrate. These materials include ions such as potassium and hydrogen. Removal of some of these ions helps to maintain homeostasis by keeping the pH of the blood within normal limits. Filtrate moves out of Bowman's capsule and is concentrated in the loop of Henle. The loop of Henle is where water is removed one final time to reduce the volume of urine.

Differentiated Instruction

PRE-AP

Point out to students that the kidneys are vital to homeostasis. Briefly review some of the characteristics of homeostasis, and then have students write a five-minute essay describing the functions of the urinary system as applied to homeostasis.

Biology Toolkit, Quick-Write, p. C19

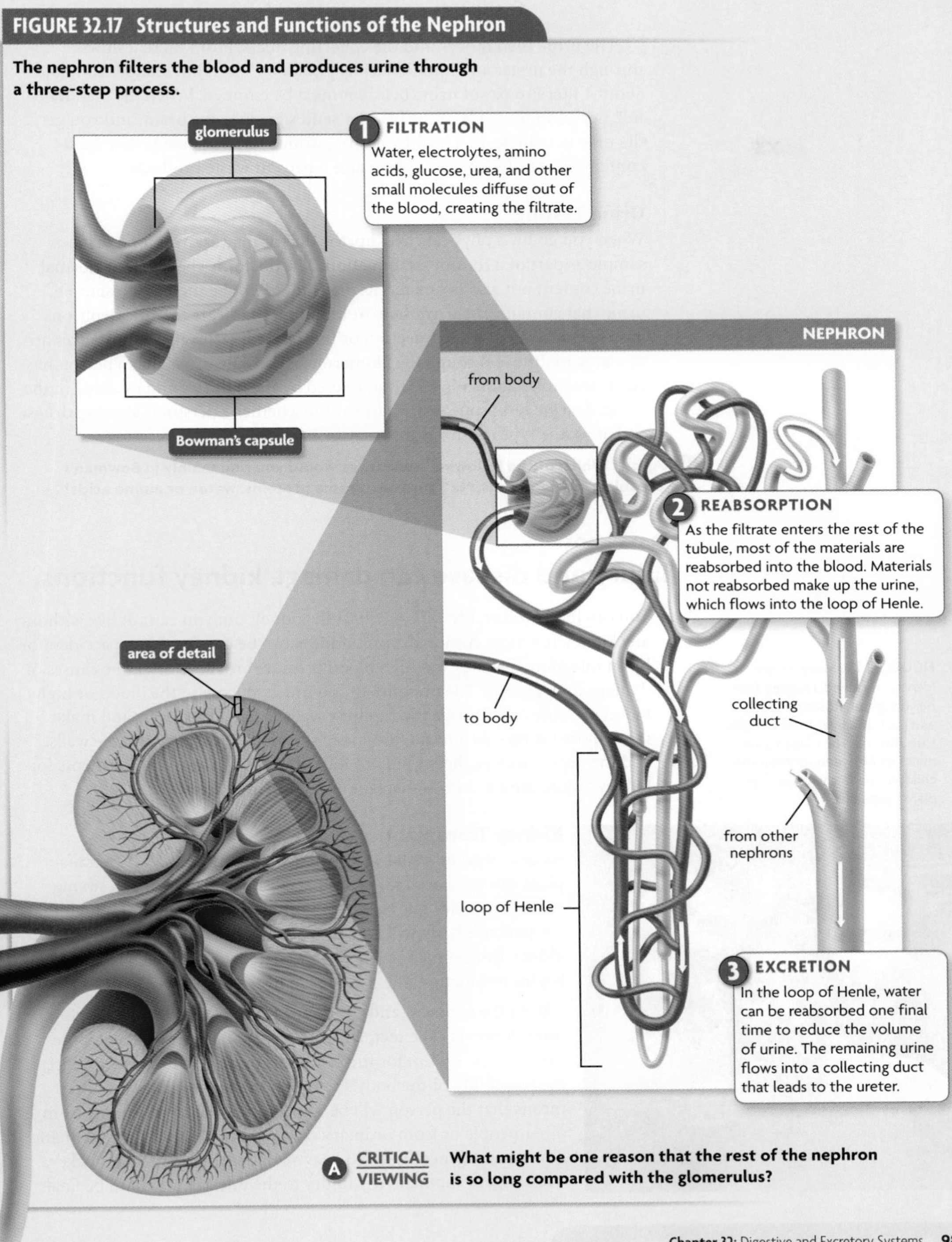
FIGURE 32.17 Structures and Functions of the Nephron
The nephron filters the blood and produces urine through a three-step process.
glomerulus
1 FILTRATION
Water, electrolytes, amino acids, glucose, urea, and other small molecules diffuse out of the blood, creating the filtrate.
Bowman's capsule
NEPHRON
from body
2 REABSORPTION
As the filtrate enters the rest of the tubule, most of the materials are reabsorbed into the blood. Materials not reabsorbed make up the urine, which flows into the loop of Henle.
area of detail
to body
collecting duct
from other nephrons
loop of Henle
3 EXCRETION
In the loop of Henle, water can be reabsorbed one final time to reduce the volume of urine. The remaining urine flows into a collecting duct that leads to the ureter.

A CRITICAL VIEWING **What might be one reason that the rest of the nephron is so long compared with the glomerulus?**

TEACH FROM VISUALS

FIGURE 32.17 Point out the shading next to the enlarged view of the nephron. Help students find the parts of the nephron that make up the kidney's cortex (glomerulus, tubule) and those that extend into the kidney's medulla (loop of Henle, collecting duct). **Ask**

- Why don't blood cells, proteins, and platelets diffuse into the glomerulus? They are too large to diffuse through the capillary walls.
- Why are the capillaries outside the glomerulus intertwined with the nephron tubule? to increase contact with the tubule, thereby allowing for more reabsorption

Integrating Medical Science

Bladder cancer is on the rise in the United States and is the fourth most common cancer in men. Researchers have found a relatively easy way to minimize the risk of developing this disease: drink plenty of fluids. A ten-year study of 48,000 men showed that men who drank more than ten 8-ounce glasses of fluids each day decreased their risk of bladder cancer by half compared to men who drank fewer than six glasses of fluids a day. It has been noted that compounds in green tea may reduce the risk of bladder cancer.

Answers

A Critical Viewing The length allows the body several chances to diffuse materials into and out of the nephron to maintain fluid and chemical homeostasis.

BELOW LEVEL

Students who have difficulty focusing on details will need to decode **FIGURE 32.17.** Have students work in pairs to isolate each section of the nephron depicted. Ask them to describe the activities that occur in each section. Then have students put the sections together to describe how a nephron cleans blood and produces urine.

Biology Toolkit, Think-Pair-Share, p. C13

▼ Teach *continued*

ONLINE BIOLOGY Students can do a WebQuest that examines the health risks associated with obesity. See Options for Inquiry on page 993.

Integrating Genetics

Some kidney diseases result from lifestyle choices, such as excessive drug use. Others may be genetically transmitted. **Polycystic kidney disease (PKD)** is a serious disorder that may be inherited or acquired. PKD is characterized by the growth of many large, fluid-filled cysts on and in the kidneys. Over time, the cysts replace functional kidney cells, leading to decreased kidney function and eventually kidney failure.

Almost 90 percent of all PKD cases are inherited as an autosomal dominant form. The rest are either inherited as an autosomal recessive form or are acquired. Autosomal dominant PKD usually has an onset after the age of 30, whereas the autosomal recessive form begins in infancy. The acquired form generally develops late in life, particularly among people who have been on long-term dialysis. PKD is the fourth leading cause of kidney failure in the United States.

Take It Further

- More than 70,000 Americans die each year from causes related to kidney failure.
- Each year, approximately 300,000 people in the United States received dialysis because of end-stage renal disease.
- More than 60,000 Americans are currently on waiting lists for a kidney transplant.

Answers

A Apply everything but red blood cells and plasma proteins

The urine then moves into the collecting ducts. From there it flows through the ureter and into the urinary bladder. The adult bladder can hold about 1 liter (16 oz) of urine before it must be emptied. When the bladder is full, nerves in the walls of the bladder send signals to the brain, and you get the urge to urinate. In a healthy person, urine is a clear, pale-yellow fluid containing about 95 percent water and 5 percent waste products.

Urine Testing

When you go for a physical checkup, the doctor may ask you for a urine sample as part of a routine examination. The doctor is checking for normal urine content but also for materials that should not be there. For example, urine that contains sugar, protein, or blood may indicate that the nephrons have been damaged by an infection or injury. Ordinarily, these substances are too large to diffuse through the glomerulus. Also, any drugs that a person has taken are broken down in the liver, filtered by the kidneys, and excreted in the urine. A urine test is one way to determine whether a person is abusing drugs, and, if so, the types of drugs that may be involved.

A Apply **Which of the following substances would you find mainly in Bowman's capsule: red blood cells, Na^+, glucose, plasma proteins, water, or amino acids?**

MAIN IDEA

Injury and disease can damage kidney functions.

You can live comfortably with one healthy kidney, but you cannot live without any kidney function. Although your kidneys can be damaged in an accident or by an infection, diabetes and high blood pressure are more often the causes of damage to nephrons. The presence of too much glucose in the blood or high blood pressure can damage the capillary walls in the glomerulus and make them more porous. As a result, too many substances pass through the walls, and the nephrons lose their ability to filter the blood. The only treatments for kidney failure are a kidney transplant or the use of dialysis.

FIGURE 32.18 Maria Alverez (center) received a kidney from her daughter, Rosario Proscia, and part of a liver from her son, José Alvarez. The close tissue matches between mother and children made the organ transplants possible.

Kidney Transplant

As described in **FIGURE 32.18**, a patient who needs a kidney transplant can receive a kidney from a close relative, such as a sibling, parent, or child. The tissues of both people are similar enough that the patient's body will accept the new kidney more easily than a kidney from someone who is not related. Once the new kidney begins to function, the patient can live a fairly normal life.

Both the recipient and the donor must live with some restrictions, however. The recipient will have to take drugs that suppress the immune system for the rest of his or her life to guard against the possibility of the body's rejecting the new organ. This also means that the person will be more vulnerable to infections from other people or from ordinary cuts and bruises. Both recipient and donor must generally avoid heavy contact sports, such as hockey, wrestling, or football. Any injury to the one kidney could be fatal.

Differentiated Instruction

BELOW LEVEL

Ask students to compare **FIGURES 32.16** and **32.19.** Have them make a T-chart that lists the parts of the dialysis apparatus in the left column and the corresponding parts of the urinary system in the right column. For example, the renal artery corresponds to the tube carrying blood to the dialysis unit. The kidney corresponds to the dialysis unit.

Biology Toolkit, T-Chart, p. C20

Kidney Dialysis

If a kidney donor is not available or the patient cannot have surgery, dialysis can save the person's life. **Dialysis** is a treatment in which a patient's blood is cleaned and chemically balanced through a mechanical process. The blood is then returned to the patient's body.

The main unit of a dialysis machine, as shown in **FIGURE 32.19**, acts like the glomerulus. Blood moves from a vein in the arm into the filtering unit. The tubing in the unit is porous, like the capillary walls, which allows waste materials to diffuse into the dialysis fluid. The fluid is continually replaced to carry wastes out of the unit. The chemical makeup of the fluid is as close to normal blood as possible. The process takes 3 to 5 hours and is done three times a week in the hospital or with a smaller dialysis machine in a patient's home.

FIGURE 32.19 Dialysis Process

The basic unit of a dialysis machine filters wastes from the blood.

A trap prevents air bubbles from entering patient's blood before it is returned to the body.
filter and bubble trap
Clean dialysis fluid flows in.
roller pump
dialysis unit
A pump pushes blood through dialysis unit.
Waste materials diffuse out of the blood, through membranes, and into the dialysis fluid.
Used dialysis fluid flows out.

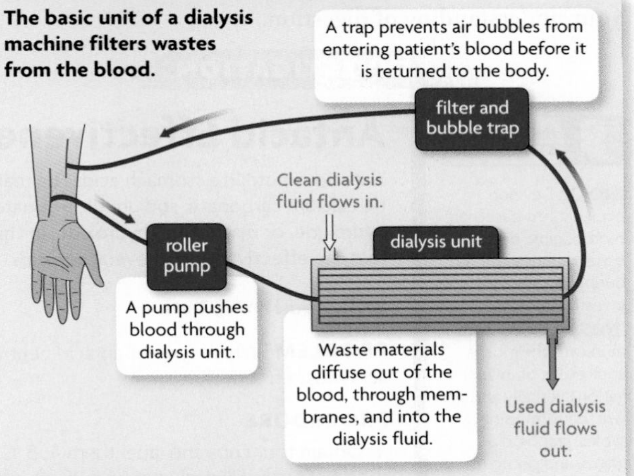

A Analyze **Why does the dialysis fluid need to be continually replaced?**

A few patients may prefer not to use a dialysis machine. Instead, they may be given peritoneal (PEHR-ih-tuhn-EE-uhl) dialysis, in which the lining of the patient's abdomen acts as a blood filter. Dialysis fluid is pumped through tubing into the abdomen. Waste products and excess fluid move from the bloodstream into the dialysis solution. The waste-filled fluid is drained from the abdomen and replaced several times until the blood is cleaned and chemically balanced.

B Summarize **Explain why people without kidney function would need to have dialysis at least three times a week.**

32.4 ASSESSMENT

ONLINE QUIZ ClassZone.com

REVIEWING MAIN IDEAS

1. How do the main organs of the **excretory system** get rid of wastes?
2. Give two examples of how **kidneys** help to maintain homeostasis.
3. Describe the main structures of the **nephron** and their functions.
4. Explain how the process of **dialysis** is similar to the way the kidneys filter the blood.

CRITICAL THINKING

5. **Apply** When kidney function is impaired, the pH level in the blood is disrupted. How would this loss of homeostasis affect the body's cells?
6. **Explain** Briefly explain the following sentence: "Filtration of the blood is relatively nonselective, but reabsorption of materials is selective."

***Connecting* CONCEPTS**

7. **Respiration** Compare the alveoli in the lungs to the nephrons in the kidneys. List the ways in which their structures and functions may be similar.

TEACH FROM VISUALS

FIGURE 32.19 Have students trace the flow of blood in the figure. Point out the arrows showing the dialysis fluid flowing into and out of the dialysis unit. **Ask,** Why do wastes diffuse out of the person's blood and into the dialysis fluid? The concentration of wastes is higher in the blood than in the dialysis fluid.

Answers

A Analyze Wastes continuously diffuse into the fluid. If it was not changed, the concentrations of the waste products would be higher in the fluid and would diffuse back into the blood.

B Summarize Waste products from digestion and cellular activity continuously build up in the blood and need to be filtered out regularly to prevent a disruption of homeostasis.

Assess and Reteach ▼

Assess Use the Online Quiz or Section Quiz (*Assessment Book*, p. 634).

Reteach Refer students to **FIGURES 32.15, 32.16,** and **32.17.** Have them synthesize the information in the figures to make a flow chart that summarizes the movement of blood to the kidneys, the removal of wastes from the blood in the kidneys, the return of cleaned blood to the body, and the passing of urine out of the body. When students are finished, put an example on the board and discuss it.

32.4 ASSESSMENT

1. skin: through sweat; lungs: through respiration; urinary system: through filtration of the blood to produce urine
2. Any two of the following: They remove waste products from the blood; they help to maintain electrolyte, pH, and fluid balances; they release hormones to help keep bones healthy, produce red blood cells, and regulate blood pressure.
3. Glomerulus—ball of capillaries that filters the blood; Bowman's capsule—cup that holds the filtrate; loop of Henle—long tubule where water is reabsorbed if necessary, and urine moves on to the collecting duct.
4. Like the kidneys, a dialysis unit filters the blood. When blood enters the unit, waste products diffuse through porous tubing into the dialysis fluid, just as waste products diffuse from the blood into Bowman's capsule. In both the kidneys and the dialysis unit, blood is rebalanced chemically and returned to the body.
5. A change in pH would disrupt the function of nearly every cell in the body by disrupting the process of diffusion of materials into and out of the cells.
6. Nonselective filtration means that everything that is small enough to get through the capillary wall moves into Bowman's capsule. Selective reabsorption means that different amounts of material move back into the capillaries, depending on what the body needs to maintain homeostasis.
7. The alveoli and nephrons serve similar functions. Both are structures that come in close contact with the blood, where materials are exchanged to maintain homeostasis in the body, and where waste products are removed from the blood.

INVESTIGATION

Time 45 minutes	TEACHER TESTED
Teacher Preparation ⚗	
Student Difficulty ⚗	
Lab Binder Human Bio, pp. 55–56	

Purpose Test the effectiveness of several types of antacids.

Overview Students will test four types of antacids for effectiveness. They will

- calculate the amount of active ingredient in one dosage of each antacid
- calculate the amount of each antacid needed to test equal amounts of the different active ingredients
- determine the effectiveness of the different antacids in neutralizing acid (vinegar) by recording changes in pH

LAB PREPARATION

- Obtain samples of four different types of antacid, each with a different active ingredient: sodium bicarbonate, calcium carbonate, aluminum hydroxide, and magnesium hydroxide.
- Explain to students that the vinegar, which has a pH of about 3, represents stomach acid (HCl), which has a pH of about 2.

LAB MANAGEMENT

Safety Remind students to exercise care when handling the acid and the knife, and wash their hands at the end of the lab.

POST-LAB DISCUSSION

Discuss the lab with students. **Ask**

- Why did you grind the antacid tablets with a mortar and pestle? increases the surface area
- Would you expect to see the same results if you did not grind the tablets? Depending on the active ingredients' strength, unground tablets could have the same effect on the acid, though it might take longer to work.

Use these inquiry-based labs and online activities to deepen your understanding of digestion.

NOS.1 Develop explanations based on reproducible data and observations gathered during laboratory investigations.

NOS.3 Clearly communicate their ideas and results of investigations verbally and in written form using tables, graphs, diagrams, and photographs.

INVESTIGATION

Antacid Effectiveness

Antacids neutralize stomach acid. The main ingredient may be calcium carbonate, sodium bicarbonate, aluminum hydroxide, or magnesium hydroxide. In this lab, you will test the effectiveness of several antacids.

SKILL Analyzing Data

PROBLEM Which type of antacid neutralizes stomach acid most effectively?

MATERIALS

- 4 large paper cups
- marker
- 50-mL graduated cylinder
- 100 mL white vinegar
- 8 pH test strips
- antacid A
- antacid B
- antacid C
- antacid D
- knife
- mortar and pestle
- scale
- stirrer
- timer

PROCEDURE

1. Obtain four cups and label them A, B, C, and D, respectively. Fill each cup with 25 mL of vinegar and measure and record the vinegar's pH in each cup.
2. Read the ingredients label and identify the active ingredient in each antacid. Determine how much of the active ingredient is in one dosage.
3. Your teacher will tell you the amount of each active ingredient you will be testing. Determine how much of each antacid you will need in order to test equal amounts of the different active ingredients. You might need to cut tablets into halves or quarters to make the amounts equal. Place tablet antacids in the pestle and grind them into powder. Design a data table like the one shown to the right.
4. Add antacid A to cup A. Stir the solution thoroughly. Wait one minute, then measure and record the pH in your data table. Record any observations of what occurs in the cup as the antacid dissolves. Clean the stirrer and the mortar and pestle (if needed).
5. Repeat step 4 with antacid B and cup B, antacid C and cup C, and antacid D and cup D, respectively.

TABLE 1. ANTACID OBSERVATIONS

Antacid	A	B	C	D
Active ingredient (__mg)				
pH of vinegar before adding antacid				
pH of vinegar after adding antacid				
Observations				

ANALYZE AND CONCLUDE

1. **Analyze** Which antacid was most effective in neutralizing the acid in the vinegar? How do you know? What is the active ingredient in that antacid?
2. **Experimental Design** Identify the independent and dependent variables in this experiment. What is the operational definition of the dependent variable? What variables were constants in the experiment?
3. **Infer** Why is it important for the environment of the stomach to be acidic? What health effects might a person experience if too little hydrochloric acid were released in the stomach?

Answers

Sample Data

For a sample of student data from this lab, go to page R110.

Analyze and Conclude

1. The antacid with sodium bicarbonate may be the most effective, as evidenced by the greatest increase in pH.
2. Independent variable: active ingredient in the antacids; dependent variable: pH; The operational definition is how much the pH increases after the antacid is added to the vinegar. The amount of vinegar and the amount of active ingredient were constant.
3. An acidic environment is necessary to break down protein molecules. Protein would not be digested as quickly or as well in the stomach, which, over the long term, would result in malnutrition and a disruption of homeostasis.

INVESTIGATION

Digesting Milk

In this lab, by testing two types of milk, you will try to determine why some people cannot digest milk.

SKILL Analyzing Data

PROBLEM Why are some people unable to digest milk?

MATERIALS

- 2 test tubes
- 5 cm tape
- marker
- 2 eye droppers
- 20 drops of milk A
- 20 drops of milk B
- 4 glucose test strips
- 2 drops of unknown solution
- 2 stirrers
- timer

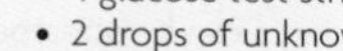

PROCEDURE

1. Label one test tube A and one test tube B. Fill test tube A with 20 drops of milk A. Using a new dropper, fill test tube B with 20 drops of milk B.
2. Use a glucose test strip to test and record the concentration of glucose in test tube A. Use a new strip to test and record the concentration of glucose in test tube B.
3. Add one drop of the unknown solution into test tube A. Mix the milk and solution with a stirrer. After one minute, measure the concentration of glucose in the solution.
4. Using a new stirrer, repeat step 3 with test tube B.

ANALYZE AND CONCLUDE

1. **Contrast** What is the difference between milk A and milk B before the unknown solution was added? What happened to the milk in test tube A after the unknown solution was added?
2. **Infer** The unknown solution is not glucose. What could it be? (**Hint**: Identify the type of sugar naturally found in milk.)
3. **Analyze** What type of milk is milk B?
4. **Summarize** Explain why some people cannot digest regular milk.

Online BIOLOGY CLASSZONE.COM

ANIMATED BIOLOGY

Run the Digestive System

The digestive system must get nutrients and water from food to the rest of the body. Move a snack from the mouth through the large intestine and get as much nourishment out of the food as possible.

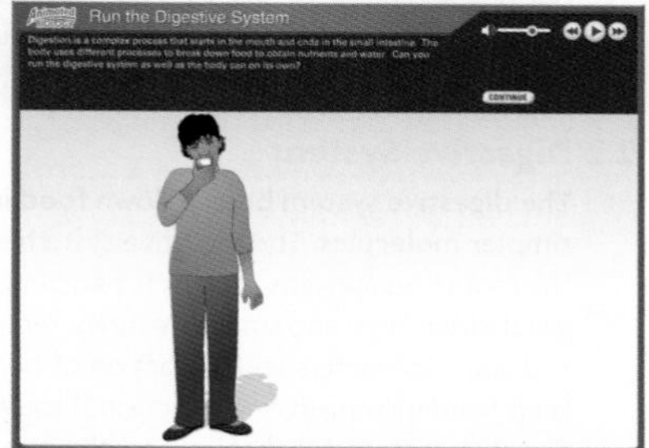

WEBQUEST

Obesity is on the rise, but is the answer as simple as "eat less and exercise more"? In the WebQuest, you will examine the causes and health risks of obesity. How can people take control of their weight?

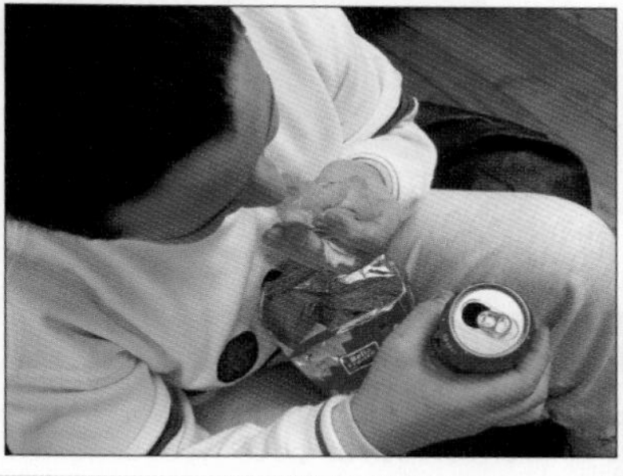

DATA ANALYSIS ONLINE

The hormone insulin helps to regulate glucose levels in the bloodstream. Graph the rate at which the pancreas releases insulin in response to changing glucose levels to see how quickly insulin acts to maintain homeostasis.

Answers

Analyze and Conclude

1. Milk A does not contain glucose, whereas milk B does. Glucose was present.
2. lactase, the enzyme that breaks down lactose (the sugar in milk) into galactose and glucose
3. Milk B is milk that does not contain any lactose; it is already broken down into galactose and glucose.
4. These people lack enough of the enzyme lactase; therefore, they cannot easily digest the lactose in regular milk.

Online Biology ▼

ANIMATED BIOLOGY Use this animation to reinforce concepts in **Sections 32.2** and **32.3.**

WEBQUEST The WebQuest takes one full class period. Students complete the activity online and will need access to a printer to print their answers. Sample answers, teacher notes, and alternative assessment ideas are available on **ClassZone.com.** Use with **Section 32.4.**

DATA ANALYSIS ONLINE

A positive correlation exists between ADH and water reabsorption; an inverse correlation exists between water reabsorption and urine output. Use with **Section 32.4.**

INVESTIGATION

Time 15 minutes	TEACHER TESTED ✓
Teacher Preparation	
Student Difficulty	
Lab Binder Human Bio, p. 57	

Purpose Analyze digestibility of milk.

Overview Students will examine the relative digestibility of milk in human adults. They will

- measure glucose concentrations in milk
- identify an unknown solution

LAB PREPARATION

- Milk A is nonfat milk, milk B is lactose-free milk, and the unknown solution is lactase.

Safety Remind students not to eat or drink in the lab.

POST-LAB DISCUSSION

Point out that between 30 and 50 million Americans are lactose intolerant. The disorder is usually transmitted by a single mutation in one gene.

Interactive Review

Encourage students to go to **ClassZone.com** for a detailed review of each section, including visuals and vocabulary practice.

Unit Resource Book, Vocabulary Practice, pp. 147–150

CHAPTER 32 Interactive Review @ CLASSZONE.COM

KEY CONCEPTS | Vocabulary Games | Concept Maps | Animated Biology | Online Quiz

32.1 Nutrients and Homeostasis

Cells require many different nutrients. Six types of nutrients are important to maintain homeostasis in the body: water, carbohydrates, proteins, fats, minerals, and vitamins. These nutrients help to maintain fluid balance, cell processes, functions such as digestion and elimination, and tissue building and repair. A balanced diet and adequate Calories are especially important during puberty, a time of rapid growth and development.

32.2 Digestive System

The digestive system breaks down food into simpler molecules. The digestive system includes the mouth, esophagus, stomach, pancreas, liver, gallbladder, large and small intestines, rectum, and anus. Sphincters and the action of peristalsis keep food moving in one direction through the digestive system. Mechanical and chemical digestion help to break down food into simpler molecules. The process of digestion begins in the mouth, continues in the stomach, and is completed in the duodenum of the small intestine.

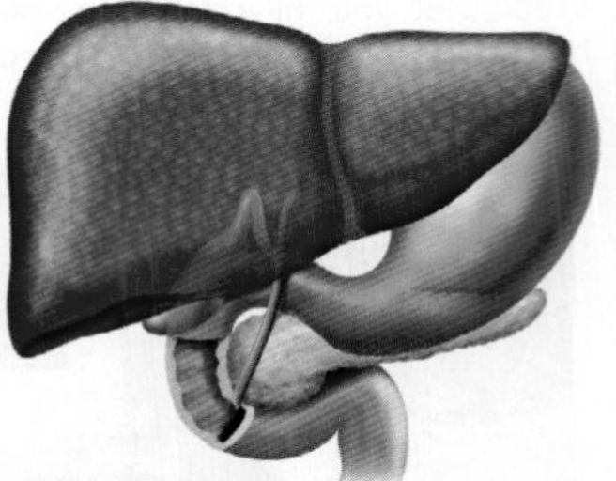

32.3 Absorption of Nutrients

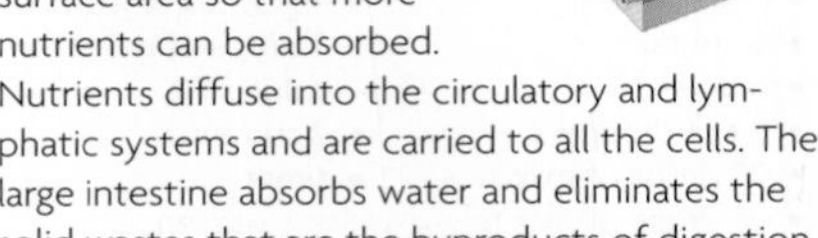

Nutrients are absorbed and solid wastes eliminated after digestion. Most absorption of nutrients occurs in the small intestine. The small intestine has specialized structures—folds, villi, and microvilli—that increase the surface area so that more nutrients can be absorbed. Nutrients diffuse into the circulatory and lymphatic systems and are carried to all the cells. The large intestine absorbs water and eliminates the solid wastes that are the byproducts of digestion.

32.4 Excretory System

The excretory system removes wastes and helps maintain homeostasis. The excretory system includes the skin, lungs, kidneys, ureter, bladder, and urethra. The nephrons in the kidneys filter the blood, reabsorb needed materials, and excrete waste materials in the urine. A person whose kidneys stop functioning must have a kidney transplant or dialysis treatment to maintain the body's homeostasis.

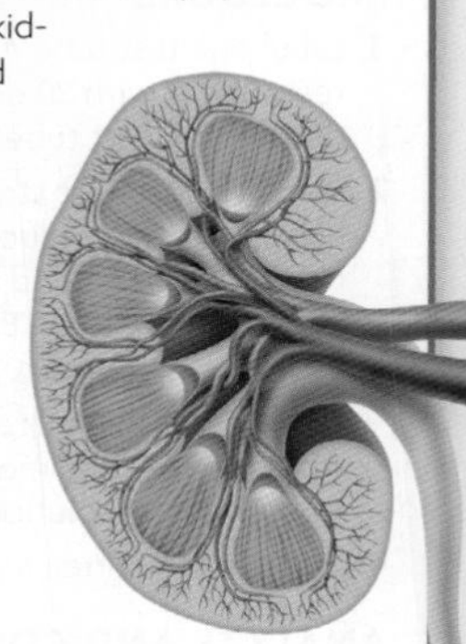

Synthesize Your Notes

Concept Map Use this graphic organizer to help you recall the functions of each of the six types of nutrients.

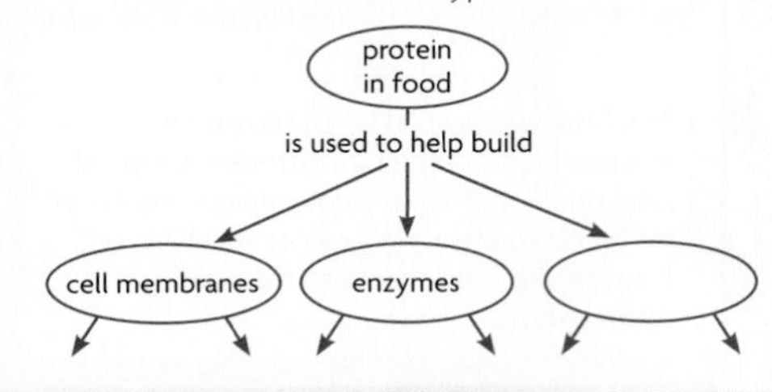

Flow Chart A flow chart like the one below can help you remember the steps in digestion.

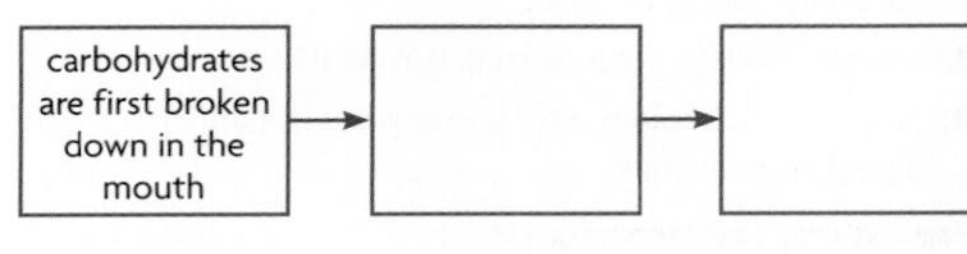

Reviewing Vocabulary

1. *Sample Answer:* The muscular actions that move food through the esophagus are called peristalsis.
2. *Sample Answer:* The villi on the surface of the small intestine are involved in the absorption of nutrients.
3. *Sample Answer:* The ureter carries urine to the urinary bladder, from which it is excreted.
4. *Sample Answer:* Bile secreted by the liver and gallbladder helps in the digestion of fats.
5. *Sample Answer:* Microvilli further increase the surface area of the small intestine.
6. *Sample Answer:* vitamin—organic molecule
7. *Sample Answer:* Calorie—measure of the energy stored in food
8. *Sample Answer:* nephron—structure in the kidneys that filters blood
9. *Sample Answer:* glomerulus—ball of capillaries in a nephron
10. Chyme is food that has been broken down and mixed with fluids until it is semiliquid, more like a juice than a solid.
11. Dialysis involves the diffusion of materials out of the blood and into the dialysis fluid, which is similar to the action of materials dissolving in a fluid.

Chapter Assessment

Chapter Vocabulary

32.1 mineral, p. 973
vitamin, p. 974
Calorie, p. 975

32.2 digestion, p. 977
digestive system, p. 977
sphincter, p. 977
esophagus, p. 978
peristalsis, p. 978
stomach, p. 978
chyme, p. 979
small intestine, p. 980
bile, p. 980

32.3 absorption, p. 982
villi, p. 983
microvilli, p. 983

32.4 excretory system, p. 986
kidney, p. 986
ureter, p. 986
urinary bladder, p. 986
nephron, p. 987
glomerulus, p. 988
dialysis, p. 991

Reviewing Vocabulary

Vocabulary Connections

For each pair of words below, write a sentence to clearly show how the terms are connected. For example, for the terms *stomach* and *chyme*, you might write, "Digestive juices in your stomach turn food into a semiliquid substance called chyme."

1. esophagus, peristalsis
2. absorption, villi
3. ureter, urinary bladder
4. digestion, bile
5. small intestine, microvilli

Keep It Short

For each vocabulary term below, write a short phrase that describes its meaning. For example, a short phrase to describe *sphincter* might be "ring of muscle separating digestive sections."

6. vitamin
7. Calorie
8. nephron
9. glomerulus

Word Origins

10. The term *chyme* comes from the Greek word *khūmos*, meaning "juice." Using this meaning, explain how it relates to what chyme is.

11. The term *dialysis* is based on the Greek word *dialūein*, meaning "to break up or to dissolve." Explain how this meaning relates to the process of dialysis.

Reviewing MAIN IDEAS

12. List the six types of nutrients the body needs to maintain homeostasis. Which nutrients are the main sources of energy for the body?

13. Explain why meeting nutritional needs is particularly important during pre-teen and teen years.

14. Explain the main purpose of the digestive system. In which organs does the digestion of carbohydrates, proteins, and fats take place?

15. What is the difference between mechanical and chemical digestion? Give three examples of enzymes involved in chemical digestion.

16. Describe how the digestion of food is completed in the duodenum. What digestive organs are involved in this process?

17. How are the nutrients from digested foods transported from the small intestine to the body's cells?

18. What are the two main functions of the colon? How can diet affect the functions of this organ?

19. List the main organs of the excretory system. Give two examples of how this system helps the body maintain homeostasis.

20. The main functions of the kidneys are to maintain fluid and chemical balances in the body. Explain how the structure of the kidney helps it carry out these functions.

21. The nephrons filter the blood and produce urine. Describe the steps involved in this process.

22. How does diabetes or high blood pressure affect kidney function?

Reviewing Main Ideas

12. The six nutrients are water, carbohydrates, fats, proteins, vitamins, and minerals. Carbohydrates and fats are the body's main sources of energy.

13. During pre-teen and teen years, the body grows and develops more rapidly than during any other time. This rapid growth requires the intake of more food to provide the body with more nutrients and energy.

14. The main purpose of the digestive system is to break down food into simpler molecules that the body can absorb. Digestion of carbohydrates—in the mouth and small intestine; digestion of proteins—in the stomach and small intestine; digestion of fats—in the small intestine.

15. Mechanical digestion involves the action of smooth muscle and teeth to break down and mix food. Chemical digestion involves the action of enzymes, hormones, and digestive juices. Amylase: carbohydrates; pepsin: proteins; lactase: milk sugars.

16. Enzymes and bile secreted by the liver, gallbladder, and pancreas help to break down proteins, fats, and remaining carbohydrates in the duodenum.

17. The nutrients move by absorption into the microvilli and villi of the small intestine and then into the circulatory and lymphatic systems. From there, they are distributed throughout the body.

18. The colon absorbs water and eliminates solid wastes. A diet high in fluids and dietary fiber will help form the bulk of solid waste and allow waste to move more easily through the organ.

19. The main organs are the skin, lungs, kidneys, ureters, urethra, and bladder. The excretory system regulates CO_2 and O_2 exchange, helps regulate body temperature, maintains fluid balance, and eliminates nonsolid wastes.

20. Most of the blood in the body flows to and from the kidneys through the renal artery and renal vein, respectively. Nephrons within the kidneys filter wastes from the blood and reabsorb materials needed by the body, excreting the rest as urine.

21. Blood enters the glomerulus from the arterioles, and all small molecules are forced out of the capillaries and into Bowman's capsule, forming the filtrate. As the filtrate moves out of the glomerulus into the rest of the nephron, materials are reabsorbed into the blood. In the loop of Henle, water is reabsorbed for the final time. Urine then flows out of the loop and into collecting ducts.

22. Too much glucose in the blood or too much pressure can damage the capillary walls in the glomerulus. This allows too many substances to pass through the walls, and the blood is no longer properly filtered, as more nephrons are damaged, kidney function declines.

Critical Thinking

23. The kidneys are responsible for chemically balancing the blood, which includes maintaining critical levels of minerals such as calcium. Students should be able to reason that if the kidneys are not functioning well, the chemical balance in the woman's blood will be off, which could be why she has a calcium deficiency.
24. An infection or overuse of certain medications creates an open sore, which means that this area of the stomach is unprotected against stomach acid. As stomach acid damages the lining, the stomach is less able to secrete pepsin and digestive fluids, which impairs its ability to digest food properly.
25. He is probably not eating enough vegetable matter, which would give him fiber. The fiber would help move wastes through his system and make elimination easier. He can correct the problem by including more fruits, vegetables, and whole grains in his diet.

Interpreting Visuals

26. yes, because Na^+ moves by active transport, so ions can be pumped into areas regardless of concentration
27. The body needs to reabsorb water, not excrete it. As a result, the membrane needs to change to let more water diffuse from an area of higher concentration in the tubule to an area of lower concentration outside the tubule.
28. H_2O would move from an area of higher concentration outside the tubule into an area of lower concentration inside the tubule.

Critical Thinking

23. **Analyze** A deficiency in calcium can cause spasms in the calf muscles at night. A woman complains to her doctor about this problem, yet she gets plenty of calcium in her diet. The doctor wants to check her kidney functions. Why would he suspect a problem with her kidneys?

24. **Infer** A gastric ulcer is a type of sore that appears in the stomach lining. The ulcer can be caused by infection or by overuse of products like aspirin or ibuprofen. How might a gastric ulcer affect a person's ability to digest food in the stomach?

25. **Infer** A teenager wants to build muscle so he can compete better on the wrestling team. He decides to eat a diet of mostly meat and fruit juices. Within a week, he is constipated. What probably happened, and how can the problem be corrected?

Interpreting Visuals

Molecules move across a membrane by means of active or passive transport. In active transport, molecules can be pumped across a membrane into areas of higher or lower concentration. In passive transport, molecules can move only from an area of higher concentration to an area of lower concentration. Use the following diagram to answer the next three questions.

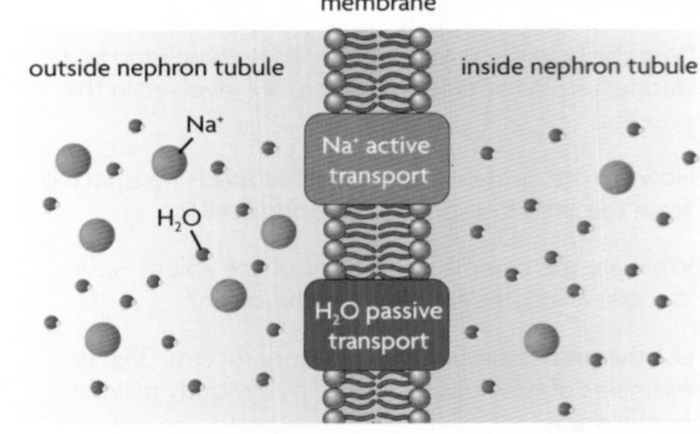

26. **Analyze** Look at the concentrations of Na^+ ions and H_2O in the diagram. Can more Na^+ ions move out of the tubule? Explain your answer.

27. **Infer** The membrane can change to let more or less water through. If a person were dehydrated, how might the membrane change? Explain.

28. **Evaluate** If the body contains too much fluid, which way would H_2O molecules move across the membrane? Explain your answer.

Analyzing Data

To educate young people about diet and health, a local hospital offered glucose testing so teenagers could learn more about how their bodies were functioning. Testing was done one to two hours after each meal so that the food was digested and nutrients were absorbed into the body. In a healthy person, glucose levels should be 80–120 mg/dL of blood before a meal and less than 180 mg/dL after food is digested. The graph below shows the results for one teenager. Use the graph to answer the next two questions.

GLUCOSE LEVELS

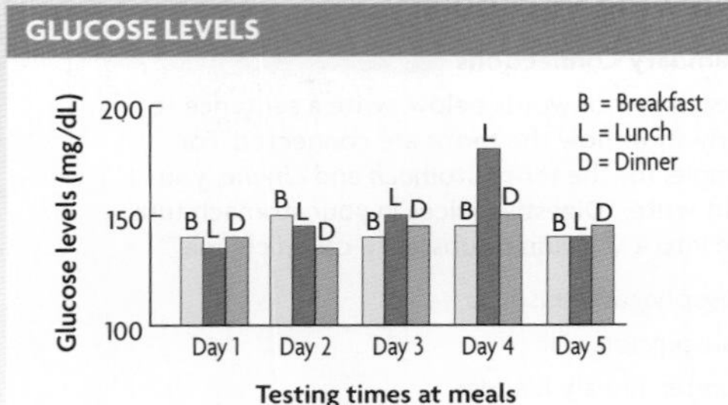

29. **Analyze** What is the typical glucose range for this teenager after meals? Which point is the outlier in this data set?

30. **Evaluate** What are some possible explanations for the outlier data? How should the scientists proceed?

Connecting CONCEPTS

31. **Blog a Snack-Food Challenge** More companies are offering alternative, "healthier" snack foods, such as protein bars or fruit strips. Your challenge: Use your knowledge of food labels to compare the nutritional information on these products with other snack foods such as candy bars and potato chips. Write a blog entry on your findings, including each product's nutritional content, its cost, and where you can buy it.

32. **Synthesize** The photo on page 971 shows the specialized cells in the lining of the stomach. Use what you know about the digestive process and the digestive tract to explain why the processes that occur in the stomach could not occur anywhere else.

Analyzing Data

29. The values range from 135 to 150, with the exception of lunch on day 4, which shows a value of 180. This is the outlier.
30. The teenager could have eaten a high-carbohydrate meal or dessert rich in sugar, which would elevate his or her blood glucose levels. Scientists will have to control the teenager's diet more carefully when testing the blood.

996 Unit 9: Human Biology

INDIANA ISTEP+ Test Prep

NOS.6

Test Practice For more test practice, go to ClassZone.com.

1 A student made a simple model to demonstrate digestion. A plastic bag and mallet were used to represent the chewing action of teeth in the mouth. A deflated balloon that could be twisted to churn food represented the stomach. Pantyhose that could be squeezed and stretched were used as a small intestine. One limitation of this model is that

- **A** it does not include chemical digestion.
- **B** it does not include mechanical digestion.
- **C** the order of the organs in incorrect.
- **D** model parts are each made of the same thing.

2 In order for cells of the body to receive nutrients from the food that we eat, digestion must be followed by

- **A** excretion.
- **B** fluid retention.
- **C** respiration.
- **D** absorption.

3 Chemical digestion occurs throughout the digestive tract. The stomach releases pepsin, the liver and gallbladder release bile, the salivary glands release amylase, and the pancreas releases an alkaline fluid. Together, these processes are an example of

- **A** the release of unnecessary chemicals.
- **B** coordinated function within an organ system.
- **C** a positive feedback loop between organs.
- **D** a negative feedback loop between organs.

4 Lungs are part of both the respiratory system and the excretory system. In their function as excretory organs, the lungs help remove which waste products from your body?

- **A** oxygen and water vapor
- **B** oxygen and carbon dioxide
- **C** carbon dioxide and water vapor
- **D** water vapor only

THINK THROUGH THE QUESTION

Think about what is present in the air that is not required by the respiratory system, and therefore would be removed by the excretory system.

5

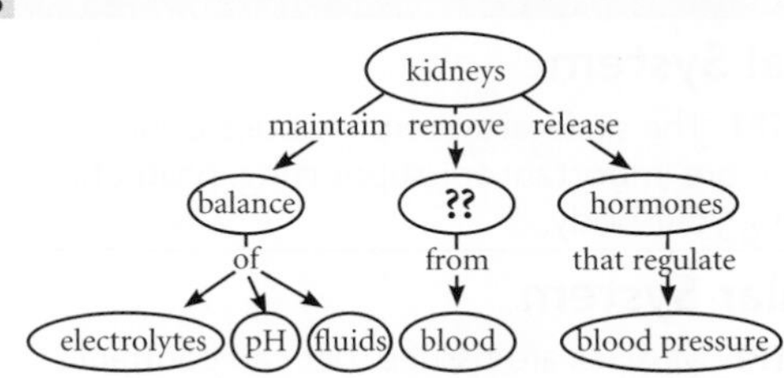

Which of these terms best completes this concept map?

- **A** nutrients
- **B** water
- **C** waste products
- **D** red blood cells

6 The digestive enzyme pepsin breaks down proteins but has no effect on starches. Why might this be?

CHAPTER REVIEW

Standards-Based Assessment

1. A	4. C
2. D	5. C
3. B	6. See Below

TEST DOCTOR

Question 1 Answer A is correct. Answer B is incorrect because chewing, churning, and squeezing are parts of mechanical digestion. Answer C is incorrect because the order of the organs is correct. Answer D is incorrect because the model parts were each made of different items well suited to what they represented.

Question 4 Answer C is correct. Answer A is incorrect because oxygen is primarily taken in by the lungs, not excreted by them. Answer B is incorrect because carbon dioxide is primarily excreted by the lungs, not taken in by them. Answer D is incorrect because both carbon dioxide and water vapor are excreted by the lungs.

Question 5 Answer C is correct. Answers A, B, and D are incorrect because the kidneys do not remove nutrients, water, or red blood cells from blood, which would be detrimental rather than helpful to the health of the body.

Question 6 Enzymes each have a unique shape and amino acid sequence so they interact with only certain substrates. Pepsin can recognize and act on proteins but not starches.

Connecting Concepts

31. Students should note in their blog whether the healthier products live up to their claims by noticing, on a per serving basis, how many grams of sugar are in each product, how many vitamins and minerals, how much fiber, and how few Calories from fat. Comparisons of prices and availability would also be measures of how likely teenagers are to substitute healthier snacks for their usual snack foods.

32. The stomach, unlike other parts of the digestive tract, is a sac-like organ whose specialized cells secrete pepsin, HCl, and other specialized fluids that are not secreted by any other digestive organ. It is where proteins are first broken down. Its layer of smooth muscle provides a mechanical action that not only moves food through the stomach but also churns the food and helps to turn it into a semiliquid substance, chyme, that can be further broken down in the duodenum.

ITEM CORRELATIONS

Standard	Items
NOS.6	1

CHAPTER 33

Indiana Resource Preview

Print Resources

Protection, Support, and Movement

INDIANA STANDARDS		Sections	PAGES and PACING	UNIT RESOURCE BOOK
	33.1	**Skeletal System** **KEY CONCEPT** The skeletal system includes bones and tissues that are important for supporting, protecting, and moving your body.	pp. 1000–1005 30 minutes	URB pages 151–154
	33.2	**Muscular System** **KEY CONCEPT** Muscles are tissues that can contract, enabling movement.	pp. 1006–1011 30 minutes	URB pages 155–158
NOS.3, NOS.5		CHAPTER INVESTIGATION: Muscle Fatigue	p. 1012 60 minutes	**Lab Binder** Human Bio pages 63–64
	33.3	**Integumentary System** **KEY CONCEPT** The integumentary system has many tissues that protect the body.	pp. 1013–1015 30 minutes	URB pages 159–162
NOS.1		DATA ANALYSIS: Analyzing Trends in Data	p. 1014 30 minutes	URB page 163
NOS.3		OPTIONS FOR INQUIRY	pp. 1016–1017 45 minutes, 15 minutes	**Lab Binder** Human Bio pages 65–70
		Chapter Review	pp. 1018–1021	**Assessment Book** Chapter Tests A, B pp. 653–660

INDIANA STANDARDS

NOS.1 Develop explanations based on reproducible data and observations gathered during laboratory investigations.
NOS.3 Clearly communicate their ideas and results of investigations verbally and in written form using tables, graphs, diagrams, and photographs.
NOS.5 Apply standard techniques in laboratory investigations to measure physical quantities in appropriate units and convert known quantities to other units as necessary.

Labs

PUPIL EDITION LABS

Muscles and Bones of the Skull, Section 2, p. 1011 Students observe contractions of muscles attached to the skull and relate them to movements of the jaw and face. **Lab Binder** pp. 71–72	**Time:** 30 minutes **Materials:** model skull, Muscle and Bone Drawings
Muscle Fatigue, p. 1012 Students test how long it takes for muscles in the hand to become fatigued. **Lab Binder** pp. 63–64	**Time:** 45 minutes **Materials:** tennis ball, timer with a second hand

OPTIONS FOR INQUIRY

Muscles in Action, p. 1016 Students identify the bones, muscles, and tendons involved in a particular action. **Lab Binder** pp. 65–68	**Time:** 45 minutes **Materials:** Muscle and Bone Charts
Bone and Muscle Cells, p. 1017 Students compare various cell types. **Lab Binder** pp. 69–70	**Time:** 45 minutes **Materials:** slide of smooth muscle, slide of skeletal muscle, slide of bone cells, slide of tendon tissue, slide of ligament tissue, slide of skin cells, compound light microscope

LAB BINDER Unit 9 Human Biology

Additional Investigation: Chicken Wing Dissection, pp. 73–75

Forensics Lab: Analyzing Identifying Features: Fingerprints, pp. 89–91

LAB GENERATOR

A searchable CD of all labs in the program in editable format, including forensic, probeware, and biotechnology labs.

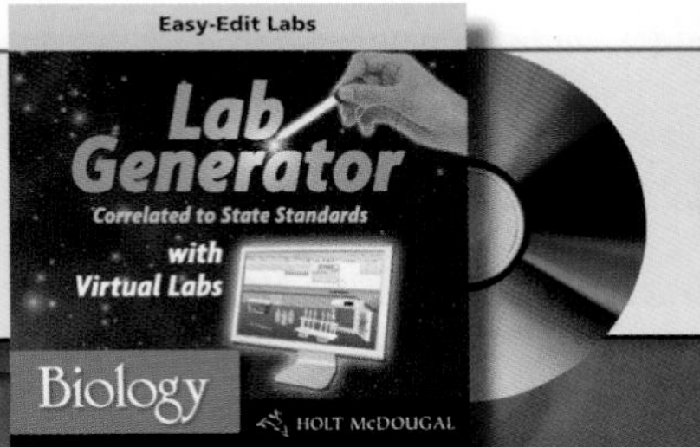

Presentation Tools

POWER PRESENTATIONS

Presentation Chapter 33
Power Presentations for each section incorporate images and clips from the Media Gallery: Includes Note Navigator for each section.

MEDIA GALLERY

Contains the following images and video clips, as well as animations, simulations and forms of visuals from the book.

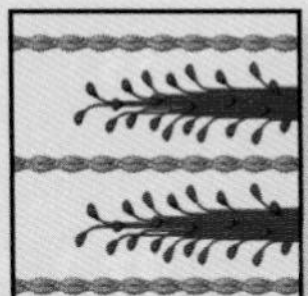
Muscle structure and function

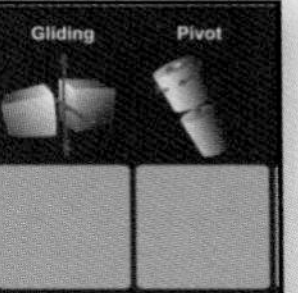

Joint types

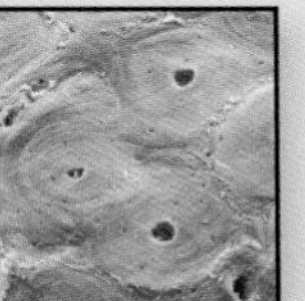
Compact bone

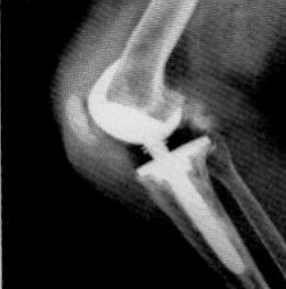
X-ray of knee replacement devices

Power Notes

VIDEO

Find a set of short video clips exploring muscle types, muscle function, and the skin.

ANIMATED BIOLOGY

Muscle Contraction
What Kind of Joint Is It?

TRANSPARENCIES

Skeletal System T138	**Muscular System** T141
Joints of the Body T139	**Muscle Structure** T142
Bone Structure T140	**Skin Structure** T143

Online BIOLOGY CLASSZONE.COM

BioZine
Animated Biology
Interactive Review
SciLinks
Resource Centers

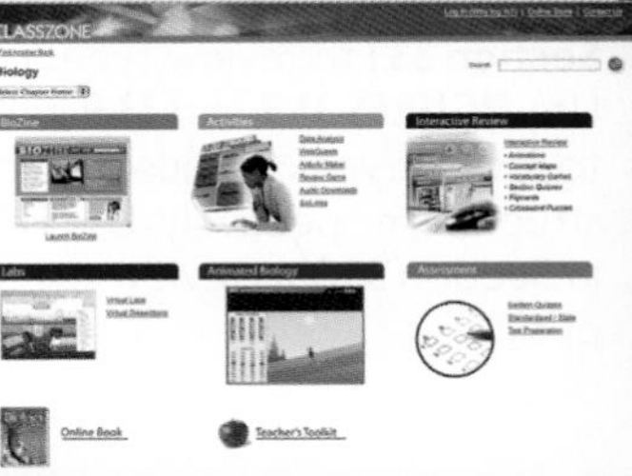

CHAPTER 33

▼ Focus and Motivate

Could you jump this hurdle if you didn't have bones?

After students state the obvious answer, elicit their reasons for answering this way. Tell students that, in terms of the mechanics of movement, bones are often compared to a system of levers. **Ask,** How is the skeleton similar to a system of levers? Like a system of levers, the skeleton moves in such ways as to increase the amount of force acting on something, in this case the legs. Tell students that joints act as fulcrums and that bones act as levers. When muscle pulls on bone, force is applied to move a part of the body.

Have students look at the photo of the red lily beetle. **Ask,** How does the red lily beetle's exoskeleton form a system of levers? The appendages of the exoskeleton are levers, and the joints act as fulcrums. While a human's muscles pull on bones, a beetle's muscles pull on its exoskeleton, providing the force needed for movement.

BIOZINE ClassZone.com

Students can access BioZine at **ClassZone.com** to receive updates to featured topics in the book.

In a Hurry?

Students may be familiar with some of the material in this chapter. For quick coverage, use **FIGURE 33.3** in **Section 33.1** to review types of joints. Use **FIGURES 33.7** and **33.9** in **Section 33.2** to review types of muscle and muscle structure, respectively. Use **FIGURE 33.13** in **Section 33.3** to review the structures of skin.

CHAPTER 33

Protection, Support, and Movement

KEY CONCEPTS

33.1 Skeletal System
The skeletal system includes bones and tissues that are important for supporting, protecting, and moving your body.

33.2 Muscular System
Muscles are tissues that can contract, enabling movement.

33.3 Integumentary System
The integumentary system has many tissues that protect the body.

Online BIOLOGY CLASSZONE.COM

Animated BIOLOGY
View animated chapter concepts.
- Muscle Contraction
- What Kind of Joint Is It?

BIOZINE
Keep current with biology news.
- News feeds
- Strange Biology
- Bio Bytes

RESOURCE CENTER
Get more information on
- Skeletal System
- Muscular System
- Integumentary System

Teacher Demo

Eye Opener Demonstrate the role of sweating in maintaining body temperature.

Materials
- 2 test tubes
- 2 strips of newspaper
- 4 rubber bands
- hot water
- timer
- medicine dropper
- 2 thermometers

Demonstrate
- Wrap each test tube in newspaper and secure with two rubber bands.
- Fill test tubes with hot water, taking care not to spill any water on the newspaper.
- Insert a thermometer into each test tube.
- Use the medicine dropper to saturate the newspaper around one of the test tubes with water.
- Measure the temperature of the water in each test tube every minute for ten minutes.

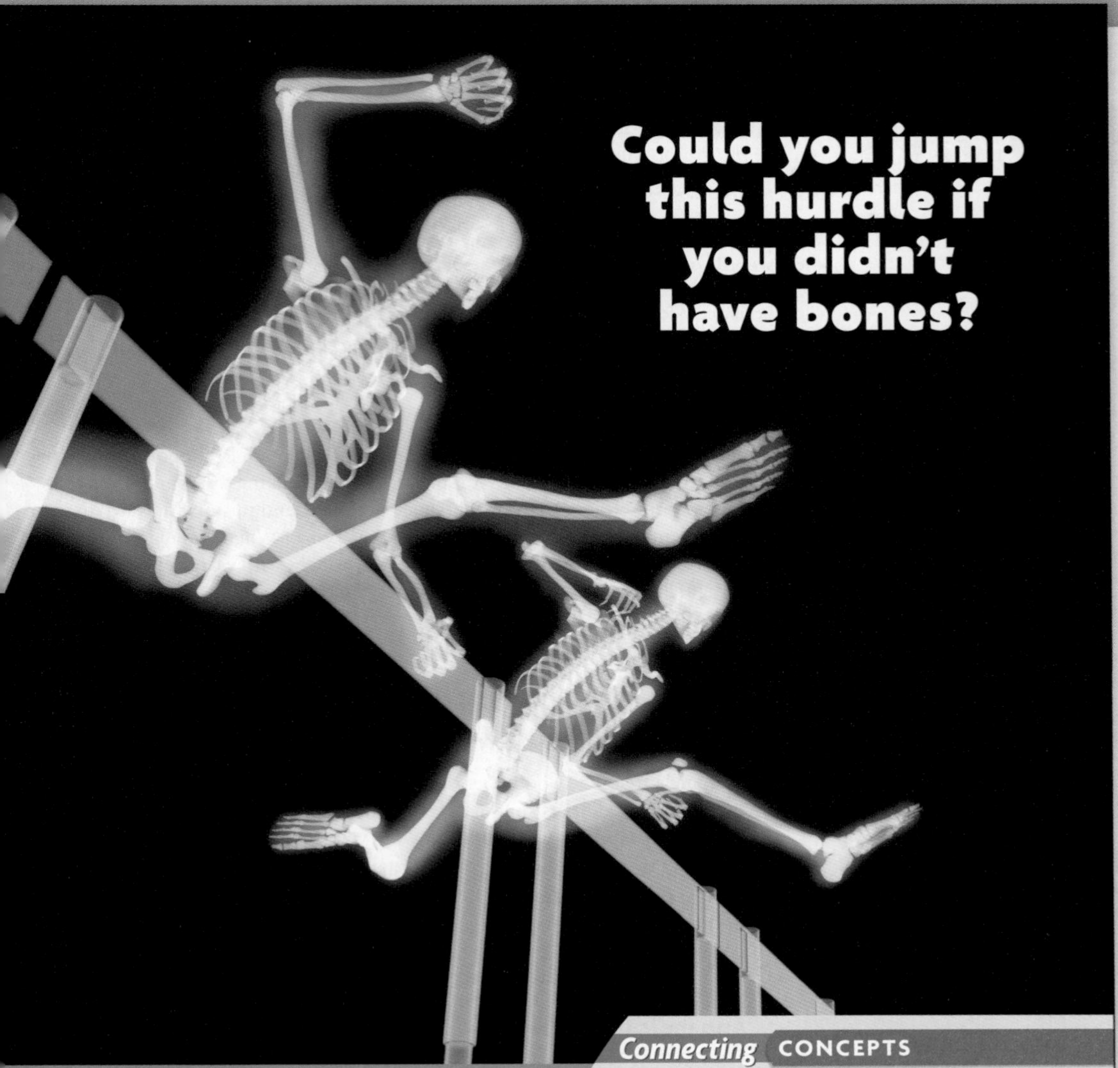

Could you jump this hurdle if you didn't have bones?

Connecting CONCEPTS

This dramatic image of the skeletal system is a composite of many x-ray images. As you can see, your bones form a system of levers to which your muscles attach. Without this system of bones, you would not be able to move around the way that you normally do.

Exoskeleton You don't have to take an x-ray to see an insect's skeleton. Unlike people and other vertebrates, an insect has a skeleton on the outside of its body. The exoskeleton, which is red and black on the red lily beetle to the left, is a hard protective covering. Muscles attached to the inside of the jointed exoskeleton pull at it, allowing movement.

Discuss The temperature of the water in the wet test tube decreases faster than in the dry test tube. Point out that water transfers heat more quickly than air does. Mention the following points:

- Living systems either exist in an aqueous solution or have internal mechanisms for dispersing heat.
- The internal mechanisms for dispersing heat in humans prevent the body from overheating.
- Sweating is one of the mechanisms that are controlled internally.

Ask, How does sweating help you to keep cool? It carries heat away from the body.

Activate Prior Knowledge

Direct students' attention to the red lily beetle shown at the bottom of the page. **Ask,** What happens when a beetle gets turned on to its back? often cannot right itself **Ask,** How does the structure of its exoskeleton contribute to the problem? not flexible Have students comment on the structure of the human skeleton, the number of bones involved, and the many places where it can turn or pivot.

Preview Vocabulary

Greek and Latin Word Origins Point out to students these important prefixes that appear in this chapter:

vertere = to turn
myo- = muscle
sarco- = flesh
epi- = on; upon
derma = skin
integere = to cover

Academic Vocabulary Write the following words on the board:

axial
appendicular

Have students think about the location of Earth's *axis.* It runs through the center of Earth, much as an *axle* runs through the center of a wheel. Have students point out the axial skeleton in the photograph. Then tell students that the word *append* means "to add or attach." Have students point out the appendicular skeleton.

English Learners Write the following words on the board: *cartilage, epidermis, integument, joint, ligament, myofibril, tendon.* Have students divide the words into three groups according to body system. Suggest students preview the vocabulary lists at the beginning of each section and prepare word squares as a way to preview the chapter.

SECTION 33.1

▼ Plan and Prepare

Objectives

- Compare the axial and appendicular skeletons.
- Describe the different types of joints.
- Describe bone structure and growth.

Section Resources

Unit Resource Book
Study Guide pp. 151–152
Power Notes p. 153
Reinforcement p. 154

Interactive Reader Chapter 33
Spanish Study Guide pp. 333–334

Biology Toolkit pp. C19, C21, C30, C32

Technology
Power Presentation 33.1
Media Gallery DVD
Online Quiz 33.1

Activate Prior Knowledge Have students look at the diagram of the skeleton in **FIGURE 33.1. Ask,** How many bones are there in the male skeleton compared to the female skeleton? both have 206 Where would you expect the two skeletal systems to differ? pelvic area; not the chest area, though some students may think so

▼ Teach

Take It Further

Males and females have the same number of bones. The differences between male and female skeletons include overall size, the size and shape of the pelvis, and bone density.

33.1 Skeletal System

KEY CONCEPT The skeletal system includes bones and tissues that are important for supporting, protecting, and moving your body.

MAIN IDEAS

- Your skeletal system is made up of the appendicular and axial skeletons.
- Bones connect to form joints.
- Bones are living tissue.

VOCABULARY

skeletal system, p. 1000
appendicular skeleton, p. 1000
axial skeleton, p. 1001
vertebrae, p. 1001
cartilage, p. 1001
joint, p. 1001
ligament, p. 1002
calcification, p. 1005

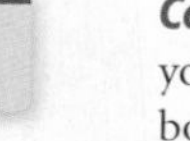
REVIEW AT CLASSZONE.COM

Connect Your bones and muscles must be strong enough to support more than your body's weight. Each time you move, whether walking or running, your bones and muscles must absorb the force of the ground pushing upward on your foot. How much force do your bones need to absorb? When you jog, your body absorbs a force of more than twice your body weight with each step. When you jump and land, this force is about 12 times your body weight.

MAIN IDEA

Your skeletal system is made up of the appendicular and axial skeletons.

Imagine a tree. The wood fibers support the tree and protect the tree's internal tissues. As wood fibers support a tree, your skeletal system protects your organs and supports your body, allowing your body to keep its shape. Unlike the wood in a tree, however, your skeletal system allows you to move.

The **skeletal system,** shown in **FIGURE 33.1,** is an organ system that includes the bones and the connective tissues that hold the bones together. The human skeleton has 206 bones, which can be categorized as part of either the appendicular or axial skeletons.

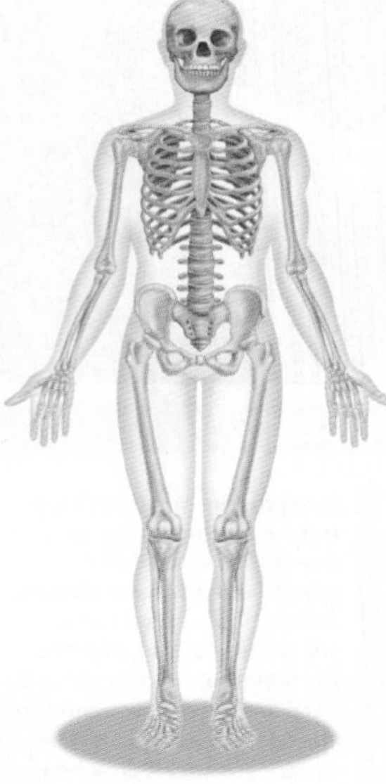

FIGURE 33.1 The skeletal system is composed of an appendicular skeleton (white) and an axial skeleton (red).

Appendicular Skeleton

Unlike the branches of a tree, which cannot move much, parts of your skeleton allow for wide ranges of movement. The **appendicular skeleton** is the part of your skeleton that is adapted to allow the body to move. It includes the bones in the limbs that extend from the trunk of your body—your legs, arms, feet, and hands.

The appendicular skeleton also includes two sets of bones, called girdles, that connect your limbs to your body. The girdles attach the bones of the arms and legs to the body loosely enough that these limbs have a wide range of motion. Your arm, for example, can rotate from the floor to the ceiling, as when a swimmer does the backstroke or a baseball pitcher "winds up" during a pitch. Your leg is connected loosely enough that your knee can be raised high in front of your body, as when you are running, or it can move away from your body, as when a basketball player shuffles sideways down a court.

Differentiated Instruction

ENGLISH LEARNERS
Have students create a two-column chart to summarize the section. Tell them to list the main ideas on the left side and related details on the right. Remind them that the main ideas are already identified in the text. They should use the black headings to organize the detail notes and key vocabulary.

Biology Toolkit, Main Idea/Detail Notes, p. C21

BELOW LEVEL
Have students use a Y diagram to compare the structures and functions of the axial and appendicular skeletons. For example, the appendicular skeleton could include movement, limbs, and girdles. The axial skeleton could include support, protection, trunk, head, and vertebrae. Features in common could include bones, connective tissues, joints, and cartilage.

Biology Toolkit, Y Diagram, p. C32

Axial Skeleton

The **axial skeleton** is made up of the bones found in the trunk and head of the body. The bones of the axial skeleton support the weight of the body and protect the internal tissues. The axial skeleton includes the 27 bones in the skull, the 33 bones that form the spine, the 12 pairs of ribs, and the breastbone, the flat bone in the front of the chest that connects the ribs.

The bones of the axial skeleton cover most of the body's vital organs. **Vertebrae** are the bones that surround the spinal cord. The bones of the skull protect the brain, and the ribs and breastbone protect the heart and lungs, as shown in **FIGURE 33.2.**

Although the main functions of the axial skeleton are protection and support, it also provides some limited movement. The ribs are connected with flexible tissue that allows the chest to expand while breathing. Flexible tissue in the spine allows people to bend or to turn and look behind them.

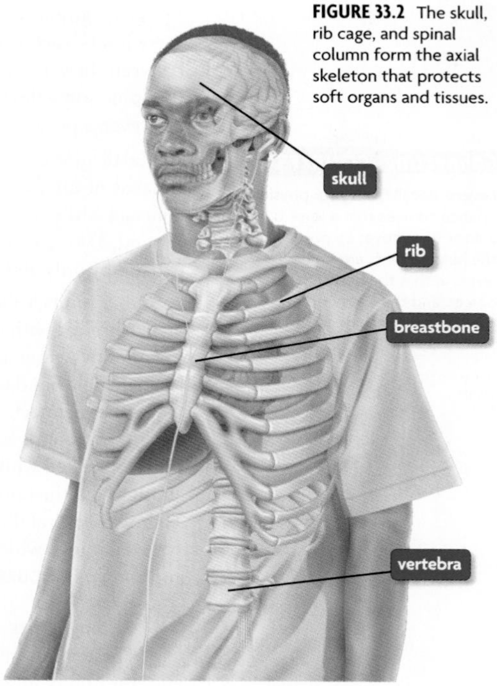

skull
rib
breastbone
vertebra

FIGURE 33.2 The skull, rib cage, and spinal column form the axial skeleton that protects soft organs and tissues.

Cartilage

Bones are very hard organs. If two bones in your finger fused into one, your muscles would not be able to move your finger. But if the two bones were in contact with one another, they would rub together every time you moved, and eventually, the ends of the bones would wear down. Fortunately, the ends of your bones are protected from wear by cartilage.

Cartilage is flexible connective tissue that is found between your bones. It cushions your bones and allows for smooth movements. Sometimes cartilage physically connects two bones. The cartilage found in your chest, for example, holds neighboring ribs together into one strong rib cage. Because the ribs are held together with cartilage and not bone, the rib cage is flexible too. Cartilage is also found between neighboring bones that move relative to one another.

A **Analyze** **Why is it important that the ribs are connected by cartilage?**

MAIN IDEA

Bones connect to form joints.

A **joint** is the place where two bones meet. Joints allow for different amounts of movement. Some joints are made of very strong fibers that do not allow movement. These joints, called fibrous joints, are made of the same dense material that bone is made of, and they act like a tough glue that connects the bones and holds them in place. Fibrous joints in your jawbone hold your teeth in your mouth. Fibrous joints also connect the plates of your skull into one large structure that surrounds your brain.

TAKING NOTES

Use a main idea diagram to organize your notes about joints.

Joints are places where two bones meet.

Fibrous joints occur in places such as the skull, where bones are fused together so they cannot move.

PRE-AP

Remind students that among primates, only humans can walk on two legs for long periods of time. Bipedalism is an adaptation made possible by changes in skeletal structure. Have students look at pictures of nonhuman primates on page 380 of Chapter 12 and pages 817, 825, 830, and 838 of Chapter 27. Ask them to write for five minutes on what they infer are likely differences between human and other primate skeletons. These include a shorter, more flexible back bone as well as differences in knee and ankle joints and pelvic bones.

Biology Toolkit, Quick-Write, p. C19

TEACH FROM VISUALS

FIGURE 33.2 Ask students to find the cartilage in this illustration. Cartilage is found where the ribs meet the breastbone and in the discs between the vertebrae. **Ask,** Where else can you find cartilage? possible answers include any joint: finger and toe joints, knees, elbows, shoulders, hip, ankles, wrists

Science Trivia

- Bones can be classified into four main groups: long, short, flat, and irregular.
- Babies are born with more than 270 bones; many fuse together as children get older.
- The longest bone in the human body is the femur (thigh bone) and is about one-fourth a person's height.
- The femur can withstand a compressional force of up to 2500 lb.
- The stapes, or stirrup bone, in the ear is the smallest bone in the human body; it is about 2.5–3.3 millimeters (0.10–0.13 in.) long.

Take It Further

Cartilage consists of collagen fibers embedded in a rubbery matrix of chondroitin sulfate, which is a protein compound. This protein makes cartilage strong yet flexible. Chondroitin sulfate found in dietary supplements is extracted from animal cartilage, such as shark cartilage or cattle tracheas.

Answers

A **Analyze** Cartilage allows flexibility for the rib cage to expand while breathing, yet it gives the rib cage additional strength to protect the heart and lungs.

▼ Teach *continued*

Connecting CONCEPTS

Levers Most levers in the body are third-class levers, in which the effort force is located between the resistance force (or weight) and the fulcrum. Third-class levers increase distance but do not change the direction of the force. An example of a third-class lever is the forearm, where the elbow is the fulcrum; see VISUAL VOCAB. **Ask,** What provides the effort force, and what is the weight (resistance force) in the example of a forearm? The biceps provide the effort force, and the resistance force is the arm, hand, and whatever the hand might be holding.

Integrating Medical Science

Rheumatology is the medical specialty dealing with conditions that involve the musculoskeletal system. One of the most common rheumatological conditions is **arthritis.** Arthritis is a disorder that can cause inflammation, degeneration, and deformity of the joints and can affect muscles, ligaments, cartilage, and tendons.

There are over 100 forms of arthritis, with the most common being osteoarthritis and rheumatoid arthritis. More than 350 million people worldwide have some form of arthritis. There are about 40 million Americans with arthritis, including over a quarter million children. Arthritis costs the United States more than $50 billion dollars as a result of missed work, doctor visits, medications, physical therapy, and hospitalization.

Answers

A Infer Ligaments are connective tissue that allow bones to have a wide range of movement across a joint. Only the appendicular skeleton allows for such a wide range of movement.

Connecting CONCEPTS

Levers Recall from your physical science courses that a lever is like a door that moves by pivoting at the hinges. Joints are similar to levers in that the bone is the rigid object, and the ligaments and joints allow the bone to pivot.

Cartilaginous (KAHR-tuhl-AJ-uh-nuhs) joints allow partial movement. In these joints, cartilage physically holds bones together. Discs of cartilage between the vertebrae keep the bones stacked on top of one another and give the spine some flexibility. A person can bend slightly to one side at the waist. However, a person cannot fold in half by bending to the right or left.

Cartilaginous joints are also found where the breastbone and ribs meet. Because of cartilage's flexibility, these joints allow the chest to expand and contract while you breathe. But there is a limit to how far your chest can expand. Taking in a deep breath will cause the circumference of your chest to expand by only about 7 cm (3 in.).

Other joints, called synovial joints, are cushioned with cartilage and held together by ligaments. A **ligament** is a long, flexible band of connective tissue that connects two bones across a joint. Ligaments keep bones physically connected while remaining loose enough that the bones can move. There are several different types of synovial joints, which are listed below and shown in **FIGURE 33.3.**

VISUAL VOCAB

A **ligament** is a long band of connective tissue that connects two bones across a joint.

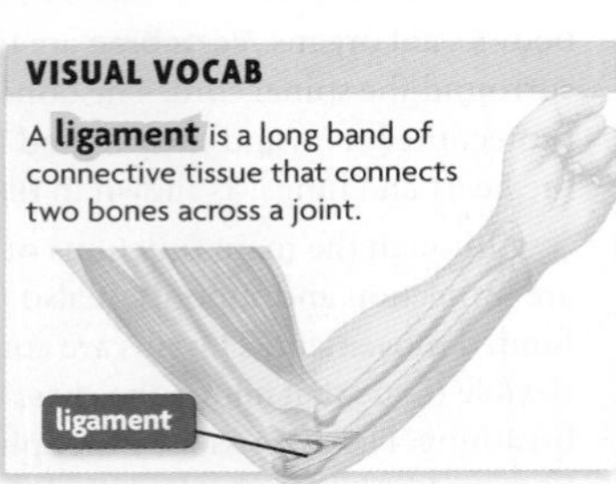

1. **Gliding joints** allow the flat surfaces of bones to slide over each other. These joints give flexibility to the ankle and wrist. These joints give you the ability to walk on uneven surfaces and move your hand to the right and left.
2. **Pivot joints** are found where two bones turn on each other and allow rotation. The top two vertebrae that support the skull form a pivot joint that allows the head to turn to the right and left.
3. **Ball-and-socket joints** are found in the hip and shoulder. In these joints, the knoblike end of an arm or thigh bone fits into a bony cup in the shoulder blade or hip bone. Ball-and-socket joints allow the arm or leg to move in almost any direction.
4. **Saddle joints** allow a bone to move front to back and left to right. Your thumbs are connected to your hands by saddle joints. The saddle joint in your thumb is what gives your thumb the ability to reach across the palm of your hand and touch your other fingers.
5. **Hinge joints** allow bones to move in one direction, like a swinging door. These joints are found in the knees, fingers, and toes.

Some bones in the body are connected by more than one type of synovial joint. These are called compound joints. In your elbow, for example, a hinge joint connects your forearm to your upper arm and allows you to extend and retract your forearm. Your elbow also has a pivot joint that allows the arm to rotate so that your hand can face up or down.

A Infer **Why do you think that ligaments are found in the appendicular skeleton but not the axial skeleton?**

Differentiated Instruction

PRE-AP

Ask students to identify and diagram other third-class levers in the body and describe how they work. Some examples are the thigh, elbow, and knee joints—the joint is the fulcrum. Ask students if they can identify the action of a first-class lever, where the fulcrum is between the effort force and resistance force—tilting head up. Ask about second-class levers, where the resistance force is between the effort force and fulcrum—standing on tiptoes.

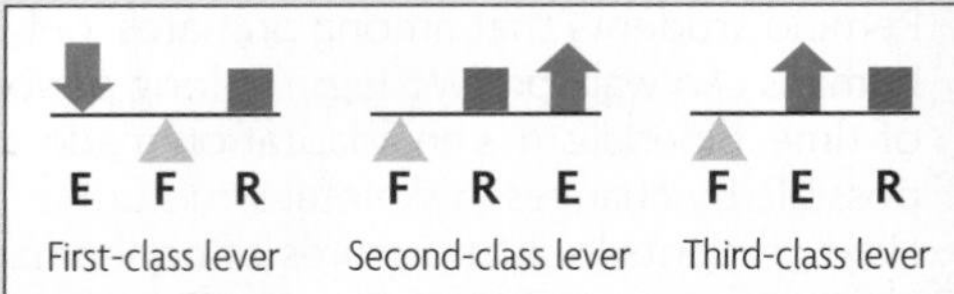

FIGURE 33.3 Joints

Some joints allow for movement.

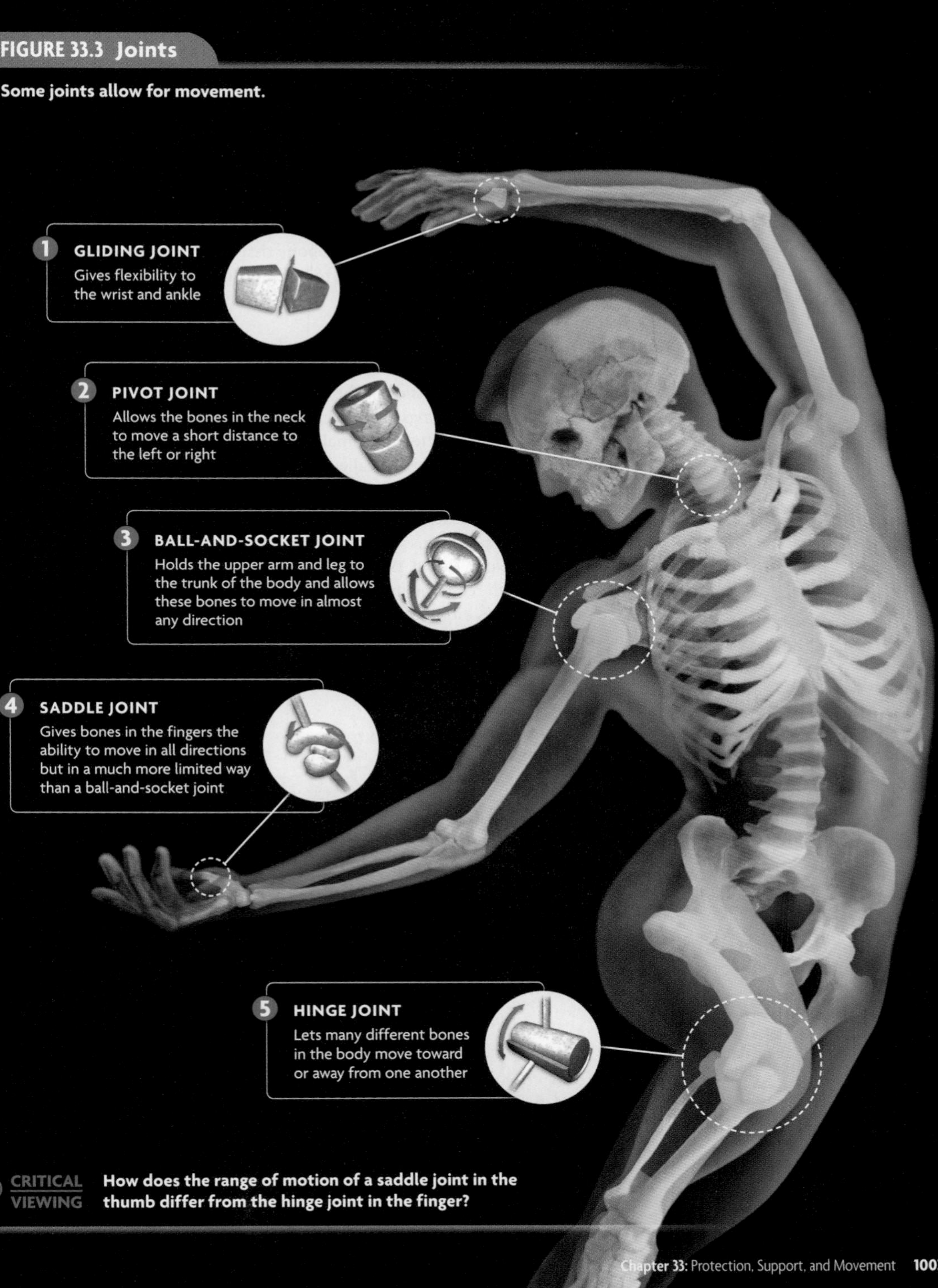

1 GLIDING JOINT
Gives flexibility to the wrist and ankle
2 PIVOT JOINT
Allows the bones in the neck to move a short distance to the left or right
3 BALL-AND-SOCKET JOINT
Holds the upper arm and leg to the trunk of the body and allows these bones to move in almost any direction
4 SADDLE JOINT
Gives bones in the fingers the ability to move in all directions but in a much more limited way than a ball-and-socket joint
5 HINGE JOINT
Lets many different bones in the body move toward or away from one another

CRITICAL VIEWING **How does the range of motion of a saddle joint in the thumb differ from the hinge joint in the finger?**

ONLINE BIOLOGY Have students categorize joints by their structure and the type of movement they allow. Go to Animated Biology in Options for Inquiry on page 1017.

TEACH FROM VISUALS

FIGURE 33.3 The figure shows several types of synovial joints. As you call out each joint in the figure, ask students to describe the movement it allows and to give examples of where it can be found. **Ask**

- What are examples of joints you use when you pick up a book? gliding (wrist), saddle (thumb), hinge (fingers)
- What are examples of joints you use when you swing your leg back to kick a ball? ball-and-socket (hip), hinge (knee)

You may wish to have students carry out these actions to help them identify the joints.

History of Science

One of the first weight-bearing **artificial joints,** made in 1923, was a piece of molded glass that fit over the ball of the hip joint. It quickly failed because the glass was too fragile. Scientists continued to search for more durable materials for artificial joints and better techniques to implant them. In the 1960s, **John Charnley,** a surgeon, came upon the solution when he tried hip sockets made of polyethylene. Charnley also used bone cement, commonly used by dentists, to fix the joint.

Today, doctors can replace joints in the shoulders, fingers, ankles, elbows, knees, and spinal discs, in addition to hips. Materials used for modern joint replacements include titanium, cobalt, and chromium mixtures; high-density polyethylene, pyrolytic carbon, and graphite; ceramics made from aluminum or zirconium; and silicone.

BELOW LEVEL

Help students visualize joints by having them use various materials to construct a model joint. For example, they can use washers and pencils to make a pivot joint. Two wooden blocks that have been waxed can be used to model a gliding joint. Modeling clay can be used to fashion a saddle joint. Give students a door hinge and an old TV antenna to model a hinge joint and ball-and-socket joint, respectively. Ask students to demonstrate how the model joints work.

Answers

A Critical Viewing The thumb can move in more than two directions, but fingers can only extend outward or curl inward.

▼ Teach *continued*

Address Misconceptions

Common Misconception Students may think that spongy bone is soft like a bath sponge.

Correcting the Misconception It is called spongy bone because, like a bath sponge, spongy bone contains numerous pores. (The pores in a bath sponge are passageways for water, whereas the pores in spongy bone contain marrow.) However, spongy bone is not soft like a bath sponge. Remind students that many living sponges contain structures, also made of calcium, that make them hard.

Vocabulary

Academic Vocabulary Students will learn that the word *calcification* relates to bone growth. It may be easier for them to remember this term if they recall that to *calcify* means "to add calcium to something." Because of the association to bones, the words *calcification* and *calcify* are also used in everyday language to indicate that someone's attitude or position has become inflexible or hardened.

Answers

A Analyze Compact bone surrounds and protects blood vessels that are found within Haversian canals. Spongy bone protects bone marrow, which makes blood cells.

MAIN IDEA

Bones are living tissue.

In addition to their role in providing support, allowing movement, and protecting internal organs, bones are living tissue that produce blood cells and act as a storage bank for minerals. Bones are covered by a layer of connective tissue called periosteum (PEHR-ee-AHS-tee-uhm), which holds and protects blood vessels that run alongside of the bone tissue. Just like any other tissue in the body, bones rely on blood vessels to bring nutrients and remove wastes.

Bone Structure

There are two types of bone tissue: compact and spongy. Compact bone is the hard, dense layer that protects against jolts and bumps. It is found inside the periosteum but on the outside of the spongy bone. Compact bone is made up of several calcium-rich rings. These rings are maintained by bone cells called osteocytes, which are scattered in small spaces throughout the rings. At the center of the rings are channels called Haversian canals, each of which contains a small blood vessel.

Spongy bone is the less dense bone that is surrounded by compact bone. Spongy bone is a porous tissue that holds and protects red or yellow bone marrow, as shown in **FIGURE 33.4.** When a person is young, most of the spongy bone is filled with red bone marrow. Red marrow is a part of the circulatory system. It produces blood cells. As a person matures and grows, some of the red bone marrow in their bones is replaced with yellow bone marrow.

FIGURE 33.4 Bone Structure

Bones have many layers for protection and transport.

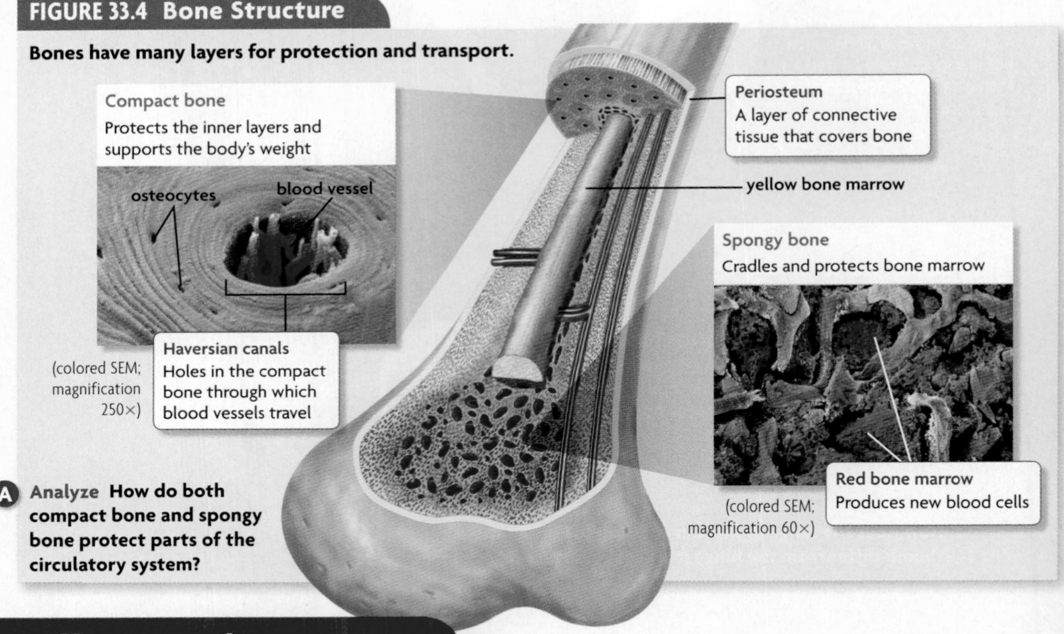

A Analyze How do both compact bone and spongy bone protect parts of the circulatory system?

Differentiated Instruction

BELOW LEVEL

Have students study the SEMs in **FIGURE 33.4** and compare the structure of compact bone to the structure of spongy bone. Have students write for five minutes on the question of how the structure of bone can be strong yet lightweight enough for a person to do activities such as walking and running. Make sure students differentiate between Haversian canals of compact bone and porous tissue of spongy bone.

Biology Toolkit, Quick-Write, p. C19

ENGLISH LEARNERS

Have pairs of students close their books and create a cluster diagram for each vocabulary word. Each diagram should take two or three minutes. In the map for *joint,* students should include the five types of joints in **FIGURE 33.3.** When they finish, ask each pair to copy one diagram on the board. Then have all students discuss, check, and add to the diagram.

Biology Toolkit, Cluster Diagram, p. C30

Yellow marrow is mostly fat, but it can change back into red marrow and produce blood cells if the body suddenly loses blood.

Bone Growth

Human embryos do not have bones at first. Instead, when they are developing, their skeletal system is made mostly of cartilage. Over time, the flexible cartilage becomes hardened bone.

Bones form when cells called osteoblasts secrete chemicals that cause cartilage to harden. Osteoblasts release a mixture of collagen, a strong fibrous connective tissue, and calcium phosphate, a mineral that hardens the collagen. The process of creating hard bone by combining collagen and calcium phosphate is called **calcification.** Once bone calcifies, the trapped osteoblast is called an osteocyte, shown in **FIGURE 33.5.**

Bones grow from their ends, where the cartilage is located. After birth, two bands of cartilage remain at either end of the bone. Until puberty, children's bones grow longer, wider, and thicker. In adolescence, sex hormones stimulate bones to become more dense. Bones are strongest when a person is between 18 and 30 years old. After that, bones lose density because calcium is taken from the bones and used elsewhere in the body.

Depositing and removing calcium from bones is a continual process that reshapes bones and helps maintain chemical homeostasis in the body. New bone can be created by osteoblasts to heal fractures even after a person matures and the bones stop growing. Bones also serve as storage areas for calcium that the body uses in many metabolic activities such as muscle movement, which you will read about in Section 33.2. Calcium removal from and deposit into bones is regulated by calcitonin, a hormone produced by the thyroid gland, and parathyroid hormone (PTH), which is produced by the parathyroid gland. Calcitonin stimulates osteoblasts to remove calcium from the blood and deposit it in bone. PTH stimulates other bone cells called osteoclasts to remove calcium from bone and make it available for use in the body.

Ⓐ **Infer How are Haversian canals important to the function of spongy bone?**

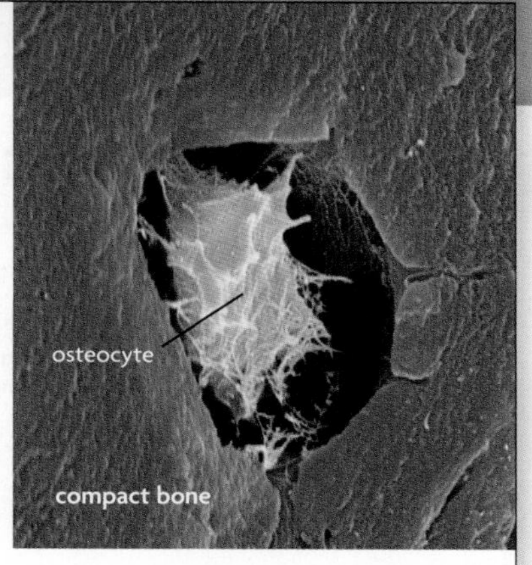

FIGURE 33.5 Osteocytes are specialized bone cells that have produced compact bone. (colored SEM; magnification 4500×)

To find out more about joints, go to scilinks.org.
Keycode: MLB033

ONLINE BIOLOGY Go to the chapter Resource Center at **ClassZone.com** for additional resources and information on the skeletal system.

TEACH FROM VISUALS

FIGURE 33.5 Point out that osteocytes are trapped in compact bone. **Ask,** What sequence of events led to the formation of osteocytes? Osteoblasts released a mixture of collagen and calcium phosphate. Calcium phosphate caused the collagen to harden. Compact bone formed around the osteoblasts, creating osteocytes.

Answers

Ⓐ **Infer** Haversian canals transport blood cells produced in spongy bone.

33.1 ASSESSMENT

ONLINE QUIZ ClassZone.com

REVIEWING MAIN IDEAS

1. What are the differences between the **axial skeleton** and the **appendicular skeleton**?
2. How are **ligaments** and **cartilage** functionally similar in **joints**?
3. How is **calcification** important for growth and protection?

CRITICAL THINKING

4. **Analyze** Some scientists say that a person's bones will never contain more calcium than they had when the person was 18 years old. How might they explain this hypothesis?
5. **Compare and Contrast** How are the joints of the axial skeleton similar to and different from the joints of the appendicular skeleton?

***Connecting* CONCEPTS**

6. **Nervous System Vertebrae** protect the spinal cord, the organ that sends messages to and gets messages from the brain. Why do you think it is beneficial for vertebrae to have cartilaginous joints that limit movement?

Assess and Reteach ▼

Assess Use the Online Quiz or Section Quiz (*Assessment Book,* p. 649).

Reteach Draw a stick figure on the board and tell students you want to give it a full range of motion. Have students come to the board to "redesign" your stick figure. In the process, tell them they need to make use of all the key vocabulary for this section.

33.1 ASSESSMENT

1. The axial skeleton provides protection and support, whereas the appendicular skeleton allows for movement.
2. Both connect bones at joints and allow for at least some movement.
3. By adding calcium to bone, the bones are stronger and can better protect the body. Calcium is also important because it transforms cartilage into bone.
4. Students should conclude that most people stop growing at 18, so their bones are fully developed. Because bones are finished growing at age 18, most of the calcification that will occur in the body has already taken place.
5. Students should define joints and explain how they provide less movement in the axial skeleton compared to the appendicular skeleton. Students should also discuss the role of cartilage in the two skeletal systems.
6. Cartilaginous joints allow enough flexibility in the trunk of the body to facilitate movement, yet movement is limited enough to prevent any damage to the spinal cord.

▼ Plan and Prepare

Objectives

- Describe the three types of muscle in humans.
- Explain how muscles contract.

Section Resources

Unit Resource Book
- Study Guide pp. 155–156
- Power Notes p. 157
- Reinforcement p. 158
- Pre-AP Activity pp. 165–166

Interactive Reader Chapter 33
Spanish Study Guide pp. 335–336

Biology Toolkit pp. C17, C19, C23, C38, D3, D7

Technology
- Power Presentation 33.2
- Media Gallery DVD
- Online Quiz 33.2

Activate Prior Knowledge Have students think of the different muscles they use in gym class. **Ask,** What are the names of some of these muscles? Students may say the tricep, bicep, quadricep, heart, and abdominals. Remind students that various parts of the body respond to signals from the nervous system. **Ask,** What kind of neuron sends signals to the muscles? motor neuron Tell students they will be studying the association between motor neurons and muscles more closely in this section.

▼ Teach

Science Trivia

- There are approximately 650 muscles in the human body.
- The largest muscle is the gluteus maximus.
- The smallest muscle is the stapedius, at 5.08 millimeters (0.2 in.). The stapedius is located in the middle ear and controls the smallest bone in the body, the stapes.

33.2 Muscular System

KEY CONCEPT Muscles are tissues that can contract, enabling movement.

MAIN IDEAS
- Humans have three types of muscle.
- Muscles contract when the nervous system causes muscle filaments to move.

VOCABULARY
- **muscular system,** p. 1006
- **muscle fiber,** p. 1006
- **skeletal muscle,** p. 1006
- **tendon,** p. 1006
- **smooth muscle,** p. 1007
- **cardiac muscle,** p. 1008
- **myofibril,** p. 1008
- **sarcomere,** p. 1008
- **actin,** p. 1008
- **myosin,** p. 1008

Connect Make a muscle with your arm. The biceps you see is one type of muscle. Your beating heart is another. You also have muscles that line other organs. Some of these muscles push food through your digestive organs. Others change the size of the blood vessels to allow more oxygenated blood to reach the other muscles of the body that are doing hard work.

MAIN IDEA

Humans have three types of muscle.

The **muscular system** is the body system that moves bones at joints and pushes substances such as blood, food, and fluids throughout the body. Muscle fibers perform a lot of hard work, and so they contain many mitochondria to power their contractions. Your muscle contractions also help regulate your body temperature. While you're at rest, as much as 25 percent of your body heat comes from the energy used as your various muscles contract. When your body temperature falls below a set point, you shiver. The involuntary muscles that cause shivering generate even more heat that helps raise your body temperature. The part of your muscular system that moves your bones and allows you to shiver is shown in **FIGURE 33.6.**

All muscles are longer than they are wide, and they are divided into fibers. **Muscle fibers** are muscle cells that contract, or shorten, when they are stimulated by the nervous system. Because muscle fibers can only shorten and not elongate, muscles only work in a pulling action. There are three types of muscle tissue: skeletal muscle, smooth muscle, and cardiac muscle.

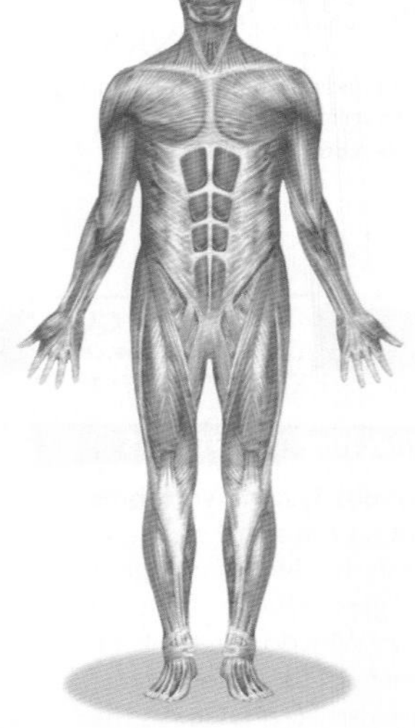

FIGURE 33.6 Muscle tissue moves matter in the body.

Skeletal Muscle

The muscles you are most familiar with are skeletal muscles. **Skeletal muscle** is a type of muscle that attaches to the skeleton by tendons. A **tendon** is a connective tissue that begins within the muscle and continues into the bone or other muscle tissue. It physically connects the two, allowing for movement.

Skeletal muscle cells are rectangular and have many nuclei. Under a microscope, skeletal muscle appears striped, or striated, as you can see in **FIGURE 33.7.** The stripes result from a regular pattern of the protein filaments that cause skeletal muscle contraction, as you will read later in this section.

Differentiated Instruction

ENGLISH LEARNERS

Have groups of three students compare skeletal, smooth, and cardiac muscles in a matrix. Have students choose features to compare such as these: *striped, voluntary, control body temperature, spindle shaped.* Tell students to verify their answers in the text. Help them use the chart to make statements such as "Skeletal and cardiac muscles are striped, but smooth muscles are not."

Biology Toolkit, Semantic Feature Analysis, p. D7

HANDS-ON ACTIVITY

Have students tightly press on the middle of their right forearm using the index finger and thumb of the left hand. Tell them to wiggle the fingers of their right hand, make a fist, and move each finger independently. Students should be able to feel the muscles acting in their forearm. Next, have them straighten their fingers and tell them to bend just the pinky finger. In most cases, the ring finger will bend too. **Ask,** Why do you think you cannot raise your pinky finger without moving your ring finger? The muscles of the pinky finger and ring finger are connected.

FIGURE 33.7 TYPES OF MUSCLE

SKELETAL MUSCLE	CARDIAC MUSCLE	SMOOTH MUSCLE
Muscle that moves bones has dark bands across it and is rectangular in shape.	Muscle in the heart has dark bands and oval-shaped cells.	Muscle in the arteries and intestines has spindle-shaped cells and no bands.
	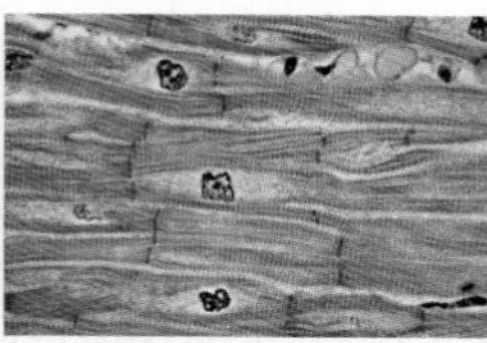	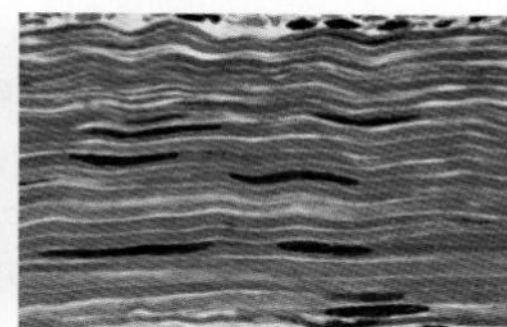
colored TM; magnification 150×	colored TM; magnification 300×	colored TM; magnification 400×

Skeletal muscles are mostly under voluntary control, which means that you can tell yourself to move your arm or wiggle an eyebrow, and it will happen. Some skeletal muscles, such as those in the spinal column, are involuntary. Muscles in your spine help maintain your posture, and muscles in your legs and feet allow you to remain balanced without your needing to think about it.

Skeletal muscles are made of two different types of muscle fibers: fast-twitch fibers and slow-twitch fibers. Fast-twitch fibers respond quickly to nerve impulses, and they make quick, sudden movements. Slow-twitch fibers respond slowly and are responsible for sustained movements. Your eye, for example, contains the quickest fast-twitch fiber. It can make you blink in less than one one-hundredth of a second. On the other hand, muscles in your leg can take several seconds to contract when you walk slowly.

A person with a high percentage of fast-twitch fibers would be a good sprinter, while a person with more slow-twitch fibers would do better as a distance runner. Individuals are born with certain amounts of fast-twitch and slow-twitch fibers. These amounts cannot be changed. With exercise, however, both fiber types can develop more mitochondria and become more efficient.

Smooth Muscle

Smooth muscle is found in many body systems and, unlike striated muscle, it is not striped. Smooth muscle moves food through the digestive system, empties the bladder, and helps push out a baby during birth. It also plays an important homeostatic role by controlling blood flow by regulating the width of blood vessels, as shown in **FIGURE 33.8.** When the smooth muscle cells surrounding a blood vessel contract, the blood vessel becomes narrow. When the muscle cells relax, the blood vessel becomes wider, and more blood can pass through. Smooth muscle cells are spindle-shaped, meaning they are wide in the middle and taper at the ends. Also, smooth muscle cells have only one nucleus.

No smooth muscle is under voluntary control. Hormones or the nervous system stimulate smooth muscle, as you read in Chapter 29. The contractions of smooth muscle are slower than those of skeletal muscle, but they can be sustained for longer periods of time.

FIGURE 33.8 Smooth muscle around this artery allows the artery to regulate blood flow by shrinking and expanding. (colored SEM; magnification 1430×)

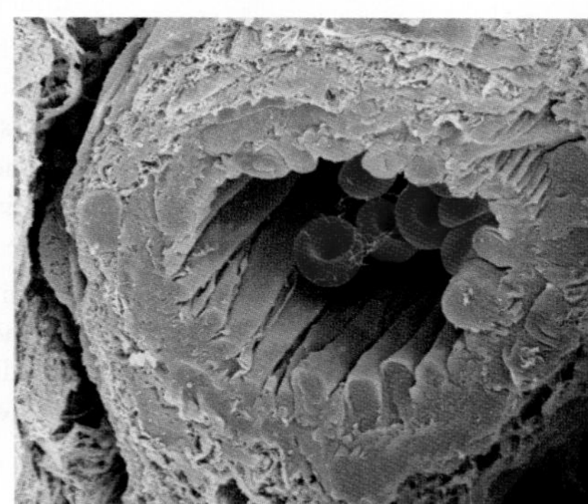

BELOW LEVEL

Suggest that students use context to compare their own sense of a word's meaning to the way it is used in the text. For example, have them consider the use of the words *voluntary* and *involuntary* or *striated* and *smooth* to describe muscles. Have students use a dictionary to get the correct definitions. Suggest they use drawings to help them remember.

Biology Toolkit, Student Vocabulary, p. D3

ONLINE BIOLOGY Go to the chapter Resource Center at **ClassZone.com** for additional resources and information on the muscular system.

The Inside Story

The mightiest warrior of the mythical Trojan War was **Achilles.** His super-human strength came from being dipped into the river Styx by his mother. Unfortunately, the heel she held never touched the water. Achilles died when this heel was struck by an arrow. The **Achilles tendon** that connects the calf muscles to the heel is named after him. It is the largest tendon in the human body and can be subjected to forces exceeding 1000 lbs. These tendons are workhorses worthy of their name. Calf muscles pull on the Achilles tendon to maintain balance, push forward when walking, spring forward when running, or push upwards when jumping. Ironically, injuries to the Achilles tendon are common due to the pressure and stress placed upon it.

Vocabulary

Academic Vocabulary Have students compare the meanings of these words:

involuntary, against one's will, not subject to control

voluntary, normally controlled by or subject to individual will

conscious, aware of one's environment, sensations, and thoughts

reflexive, produced as an automatic response or reaction

Point out that one may not always be conscious of the movement made by voluntary muscles.

▼ Teach *continued*

ONLINE BIOLOGY Students can learn about the causes and symptoms of muscular dystrophy in the WebQuest in Options for Inquiry on page 1017.

Take It Further

Cardiac muscle cells are shorter than skeletal muscle cells. Cardiac muscles have branching processes and are joined end to end. The areas where the cells join are called **gap junctions.** Gap junctions coordinate the contraction of cardiac muscle such that when one muscle cell contracts, the others quickly follow suit.

Integrating Sports Medicine

On average, the skeletal muscles are composed of about 50 percent **fast-twitch** and 50 percent **slow-twitch muscle fibers.** Natural athletes tend to be born with different proportions of fast-twitch and slow-twitch fibers, with sprinters having as much as 80 percent fast-twitch fibers and marathoners having as much as 80 percent slow-twitch fibers. Slow-twitch muscle fibers have more mitochondria, and thus are more efficient at generating ATP without lactic acid buildup. This also helps to explain why distance runners tend to have more slow-twitch fibers. Slow-twitch and fast-twitch fibers produce about the same amount of force per contraction. However, fast-twitch fibers contract more rapidly, which is advantageous to a sprinter.

Answers

A Compare and Contrast All three types of muscle cause movement within the body. Skeletal muscle moves bone and is under voluntary control. Cardiac muscle pumps the heart and is involuntary. Smooth muscle is also under involuntary control, but it controls movement of matter through organs and blood vessels.

Connecting **CONCEPTS**

Pacemaker The pacemaker is the part of the heart that stimulates contractions. To learn more about how the heart works, review **Section 30.3.**

Cardiac Muscle

Your heart is a muscle that pumps blood throughout your body, and it uses a specific kind of muscle cell. **Cardiac muscle** is muscle that is found only in the heart, and it looks like a combination of the two other muscle types. It is striated, like skeletal muscle, but its cells are oval-shaped and have multiple nuclei. Cardiac muscle cells use a huge amount of ATP and have more mitochondria than do skeletal muscles.

Cardiac muscle cells are under involuntary control. The impulse to contract comes from a pacemaker within the heart, and signals from the brainstem can only modify the rate at which the pacemaker causes contractions.

A Compare and Contrast How are the three types of muscle both similar and different in their functions?

MAIN IDEA

Muscles contract when the nervous system causes muscle filaments to move.

When you play tug-of-war, your team must hold on to a rope and pull the other team toward you. Each player on your team reaches down to the rope, grabs onto it, and pulls. The filaments in muscles work in a similar way during contractions. Some filaments act like the players in a game of tug-of-war and pull at other filaments, which are like the ropes that connect the teams. To understand how these filaments work, let's take a look at the smallest functional unit of a muscle, which is called a myofibril.

Muscle Structure

Myofibrils are long strands of protein found within a muscle fiber, as shown in **FIGURE 33.9.** Each myofibril contains a complex set of filaments that are arranged in a regular pattern. The protein filaments within these myofibrils cause muscle contraction.

Myofibrils can be further divided into sarcomeres. A **sarcomere** is a section of a myofibril that contains all of the filaments necessary to make that section of the muscle contract. You can see sarcomeres if you look at muscle tissue under a microscope; they are bounded by a dark stripe on each side.

The dark stripes occur where the filaments are located in the muscle cell. These filaments are called actin filaments. **Actin** filaments are thin protein fibers that are pulled to cause muscle contraction. The ends of the actin filaments are anchored to the sarcomere by a plate of structural protein called a Z line. Because actin filaments are attached to the sarcomere, when they are pulled, they drag the ends of the sarcomere along with them.

In the center of the sarcomere are thick filaments, called myosin. **Myosin** filaments are protein fibers that pull actin. The myosin is anchored to the middle of the sarcomere at the M line. By being anchored to the center of the of the sarcomere, myosin can pull the actin without moving itself.

Differentiated Instruction

TEACH WITH TECHNOLOGY

If you have a square-wave stimulator, you can demonstrate the electrical nature of muscle contraction. Ask a volunteer who is willing to experience a mild electrical stimulation of the forearm. **Caution:** *Do not allow anyone with a heart condition or other health problem to volunteer for this activity.* Stimulators can be hooked up to a computer to observe the wave action that corresponds to the electrical activity at the neuromuscular junction.

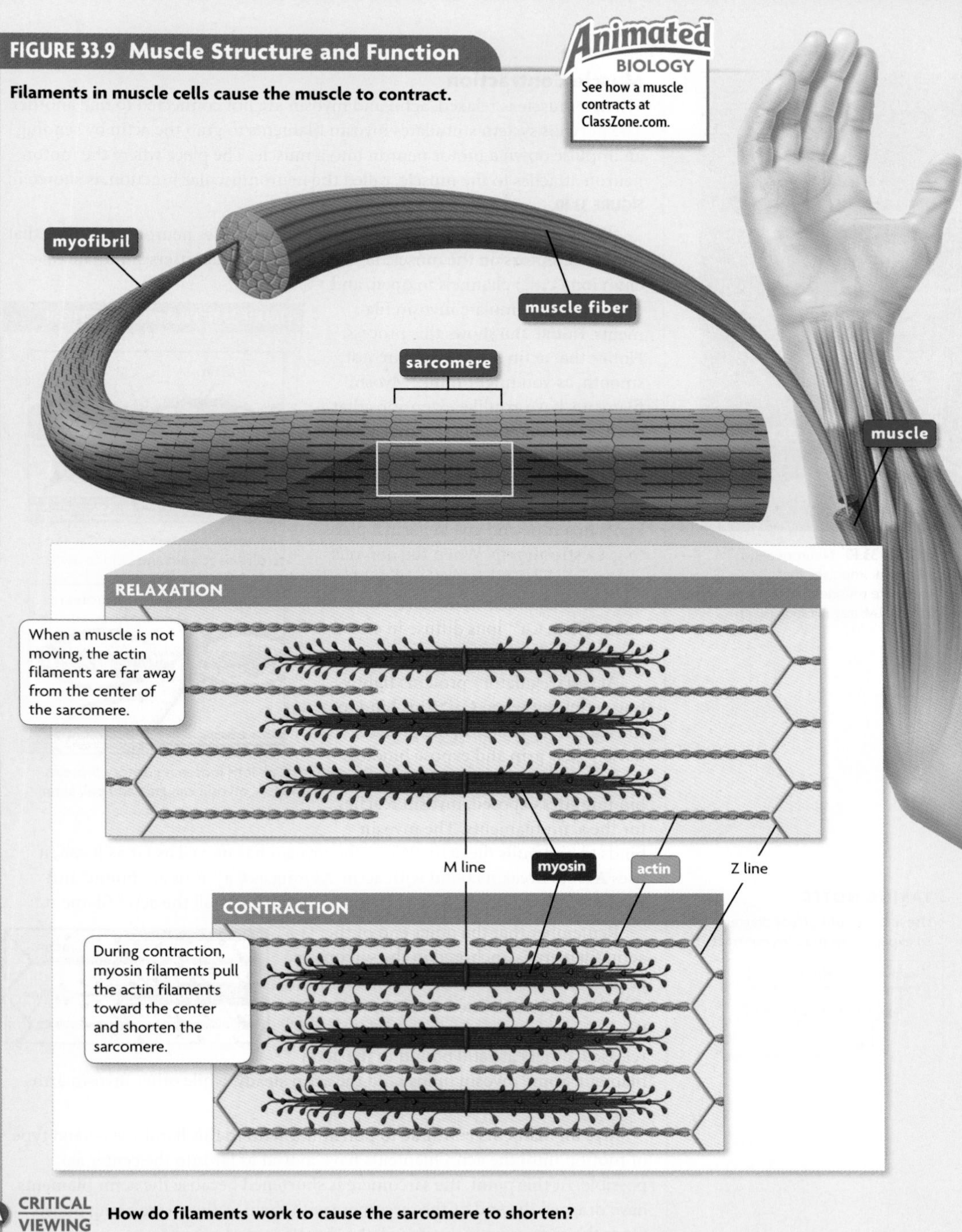

FIGURE 33.9 Muscle Structure and Function
Filaments in muscle cells cause the muscle to contract.
Animated BIOLOGY
See how a muscle contracts at ClassZone.com.
myofibril
muscle fiber
sarcomere
muscle
RELAXATION
When a muscle is not moving, the actin filaments are far away from the center of the sarcomere.
M line
myosin
actin
Z line
CONTRACTION
During contraction, myosin filaments pull the actin filaments toward the center and shorten the sarcomere.

A CRITICAL VIEWING How do filaments work to cause the sarcomere to shorten?

TEACH FROM VISUALS

FIGURE 33.9 Make sure students understand the structural relationship among sarcomeres, myofibrils, muscle fibers, and muscles. Remind students that a muscle fiber is equivalent to a muscle cell. Myofibrils are arranged in parallel bundles within the cytoplasm of the muscle fiber. **Ask**

- How do the lengths of the myosin filaments and actin filaments compare during relaxation and contraction? The lengths do not change.
- How does the distance between Z lines compare during relaxation and contraction? shorter during contraction
- What are the white bands that go from the muscle to the wrist in the illustration? What do they do? tendons; pull on bone

Take It Further

Myoblasts are undifferentiated, mononucleated cells that originate from the muscle stem cells. When myoblasts fuse together, they create a single, multinucleated, skeletal muscle cell. Myoblasts have the ability to take on the properties of other cells, regenerate, and repair themselves. Because cardiac muscle cells cannot repair themselves or regenerate, research is being conducted to see if transplanting skeletal muscle cells into the heart will create new cardiac muscle. Scientists hope that this treatment will help repair damaged hearts in the future.

Vocabulary

Greek and Latin Word Origins The word **muscle** is derived from the Latin *musculus,* meaning "little mouse." A muscle's shape and the movement of some muscles, such as the biceps, resemble that of a mouse. The scientific name for the house mouse is *Mus musculus.*

Answers

A Critical Viewing Myosin filaments pull actin filaments, which are attached to the ends of sarcomeres, at the Z lines.

INCLUSION

Have students who are visually impaired work with a classmate to go through the mechanism of muscle contraction and relaxation and how that relates to the structure of a muscle. Students should work to come up with analogies to describe the structures and their actions, as depicted in **FIGURES 33.9** and **33.11.**

Biology Toolkit, Connect to Content Through Visuals, C17

ENGLISH LEARNERS

Suggest that students create a single diagram that incorporates details of both **FIGURES 33.9** and **33.11.** This will help them to understand the relationship between the different components of a muscle. Tell them go from a muscle's macroscopic structure to its microscopic structure.

Biology Toolkit, Combination Notes, p. C23

▼ Teach *continued*

ONLINE BIOLOGY Have students graph the speed at which different people move their legs and determine whether fast runners move their legs more quickly than slow runners do. Go to Data Analysis Online in Options for Inquiry on page 1017.

Integrating Forensic Science

The interaction of actin and myosin filaments during a muscle contraction is powered by ATP. When a muscle is stimulated, calcium enters the cell and opens up a binding site on actin to which a myosin filament can attach, creating the pull on the actin filament. ATP provides the energy for this bond to be broken and the action to be repeated.

When a person dies, the cells stop making ATP. After several hours, all remaining ATP has been used up and the actin and myosin filaments remain locked together, causing the skeletal muscles to stiffen. This is the state known as **rigor mortis.** Approximately 20 to 60 hours after death, the muscles begin to atrophy and rigor mortis disappears.

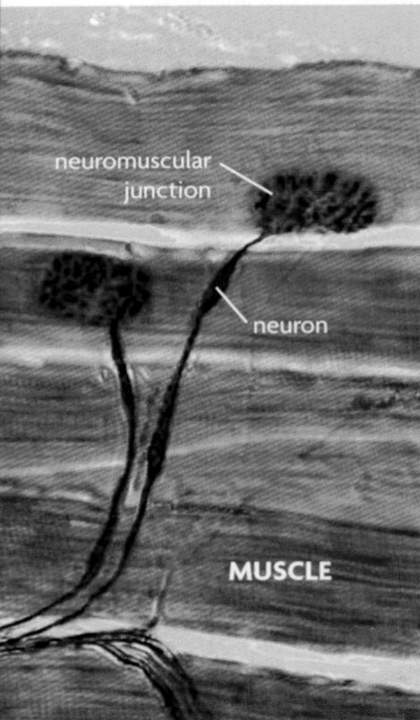

FIGURE 33.10 Neurons send electrical impulses that stimulate muscle contractions. (colored LM; magnification 150×)

TAKING NOTES

Use a cause-and-effect diagram to explain how muscles contract.

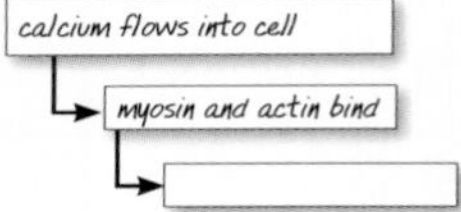

Muscle Contraction

When a muscle is relaxed, actin and myosin are not connected to one another. The nervous system stimulates myosin filaments to grab the actin by sending an impulse down a motor neuron into a muscle. The place where the motor neuron attaches to the muscle, called the neuromuscular junction, is shown in **FIGURE 33.10.**

At the neuromuscular junction, the neuron releases neurotransmitters that bind to receptors on the muscle fiber. The neurotransmitters stimulate calcium ion (Ca^{2+}) channels to open, and the Ca^{2+} ions stimulate myosin filaments. **FIGURE 33.11** shows this process. Notice that actin and myosin are not smooth, as you might think. Myosin filaments have armlike extensions that act like little hands. These hands grab onto and pull the actin filaments. Actin filaments also have bumps on their surface. These bumps act like knots in a rope and give myosin a place to get a strong grip. When the nervous system stimulates a muscle, calcium ion (Ca^{2+}) channels in the sarcomere open. Then, Ca^{2+} ions diffuse in and bind to regulatory proteins.

FIGURE 33.11 FILAMENT ACTION

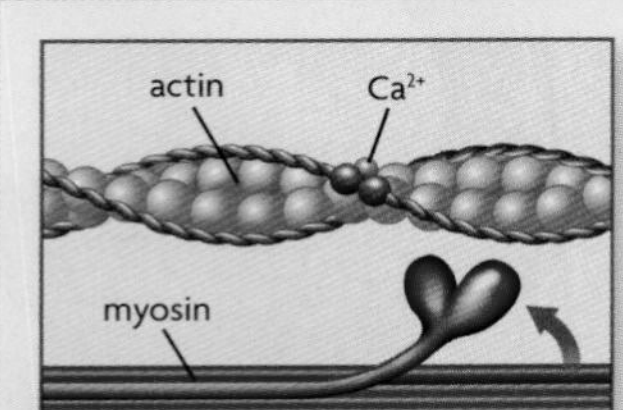

The nervous system causes Ca^{2+} ions to diffuse toward and bind to actin.

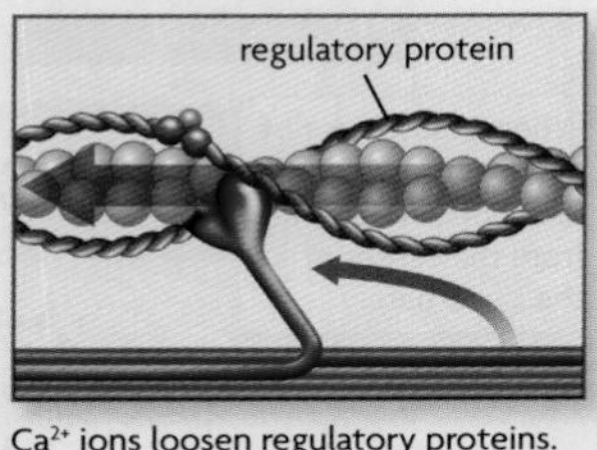

Ca^{2+} ions loosen regulatory proteins. Now, myosin can grab and pull actin.

At rest, regulatory proteins tightly hug actin. But when Ca^{2+} ions bind to the regulatory proteins, the proteins loosen their grip and expose binding sites on the actin filament. With the binding sites exposed, myosin reaches for the actin filaments. The myosin binds to and pulls the actin. When the myosin has moved as far as it can, it uses ATP to break its bond with actin. As long as Ca^{2+} ions are bound and binding sites are exposed, the myosin will grab and pull the actin filament.

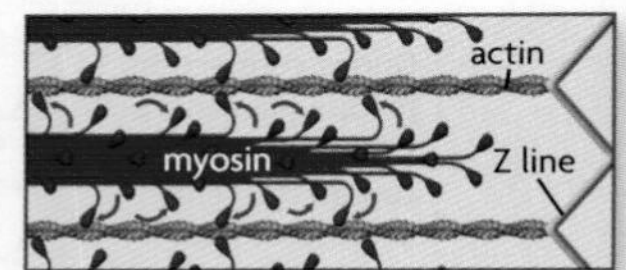

Remember that the other end of the actin filament is anchored in the sarcomere at the Z line. However, the actin filament does not slip when one myosin bulb lets go, because although one myosin bulb has released, others are still bound to the actin filament. Some myosin bulbs hold the actin steady, while other myosin arms reach farther down the actin filament.

Myosin filaments continue to pull at the actin in this hand-over-hand type of motion until the actin filaments have moved as far into the center as possible. At this point, the sarcomere is shortened because the actin filaments have dragged the end of the sarcomere with them as they were being pulled. Once the sarcomere is shortened, the muscle is contracted.

Differentiated Instruction

BELOW LEVEL

If students are having difficulty determining cause and effect during the process of muscle contraction, have them first make a sequence diagram for muscle contraction. After they have the steps in the correct order, they can add notes about cause and effect.

Biology Toolkit, Sequence Diagram, p. C38

PRE-AP

Ask students to write for five minutes, comparing the process by which calcium ions move into the sarcomere (facilitated diffusion) with the process by which calcium ions move away from the actin filaments (active transport). Have students explain why these two different processes are necessary. They should include the concept of concentration gradients in their explanation.

Biology Toolkit, Quick-Write, p. C19

QUICK LAB INTERPRETING GRAPHICS

Muscles and Bones of the Skull

In this lab, you will learn about the muscles that attach to the skull.

MATERIALS
- model skull
- Muscle and Bone Drawings

PROBLEM What is the arrangement of muscles and bones in the skull?

PROCEDURE

1. Place your fingers on the side of your jaw. Clench and unclench your jaw several times. You can feel your masseter muscle moving beneath your finger.
2. Place your fingers on either side of your mouth. Open and close your mouth and smile several times. You can feel your orbicularis ori moving beneath your fingers.
3. Place your fingers under your eye. Wink several times. You can feel your obivularis oculi moving beneath your fingers.
4. Look at the model skull and the muscle drawings. Identify the muscles you felt, and to which bones they were attached.

ANALYZE AND CONCLUDE

1. **Analyze** What type of muscles (skeletal or smooth) are the three muscles you identified in this lab? How do you know?
2. **Infer** What do you think the word *orbicular* means?
3. **Evaluate** What are some of the limitations to using models and illustrations in this lab?

The contraction stops when the nervous system stops stimulating the muscle tissue. When this happens, the Ca^{2+} ions unbind and are actively transported away from the actin. The myosin binding sites on the actin filament become covered and myosin can no longer grab the actin. So the actin filaments slide outward to where they began before the contraction.

The contraction of a muscle fiber is an all-or-nothing event. This means that an entire muscle will move only when many individual muscle fibers contract. Muscle contractions require the shortening of millions of sarcomeres. The coordination of these multiple sarcomeres is controlled by the nervous system.

(A) Apply **Explain why getting enough calcium in your diet is important for muscle function.**

33.2 ASSESSMENT

ONLINE QUIZ ClassZone.com

REVIEWING MAIN IDEAS

1. How do **skeletal muscle, cardiac muscle,** and **smooth muscle** differ in their structure and function?
2. How do **actin** and **myosin** filaments work together to cause muscle contractions?

CRITICAL THINKING

3. **Synthesize** How does muscle help keep the body warm?
4. **Synthesize** How does the number of mitochondria in a muscle cell relate to the amount of work the cell can do?

Connecting CONCEPTS

5. **Nervous System** Sensory neurons gather information. Interneurons process information. Motor neurons produce responses. Which type of neuron stimulates each of the three types of muscle tissue? Explain.

33.2 ASSESSMENT

1. Skeletal muscle is rectangular, striated, and can move bones. Cardiac muscle is oval-shaped, striated, and pumps blood. Smooth muscle is spindle-shaped, not striped, and can regulate the size of blood vessels.
2. Myosin filaments pull the actin filaments. Actin filaments drag the ends of the sarcomere behind them.
3. Student should explain that muscles release heat as they contract and that shivering and expanding and contracting blood vessels can increase the amount of heat in the body.
4. Mitochondria produce energy and that the more energy available, the stronger is the muscle contraction.
5. Motor neurons stimulate contraction of skeletal, smooth, and cardiac muscles.

QUICK LAB

TEACHER TESTED

Time 30 minutes

Lab Binder Human Bio, pp. 71–72

Purpose Observe contractions of muscles attached to the skull and relate them to movements of the jaw and face.

LAB PREPARATION

- Make copies of the Facial Muscles datasheet for students, *Lab Binder*, p. 72.
- Gather muscle and bone diagrams and a model skull before the lab.

Answers

Analyze and Conclude

1. Skeletal; the bones to which these muscles are attached can be moved voluntarily.
2. *Orbicular* means "spherical" or "circular."
3. Actual contraction of the muscles and movement of the associated bones cannot be observed.

Answers

(A) **Apply** Calcium ions are required for muscle contraction. They bind to proteins on actin filaments, thus allowing myosin to pull the filaments and result in contraction.

Assess and Reteach ▼

Assess Use the Online Quiz or Section Quiz (*Assessment Book*, p. 650).

Reteach On the board, construct a three-circle Venn diagram to compare skeletal, cardiac, and smooth muscle. The diagram should include:

- cardiac: oval cells, found in heart
- skeletal: rectangular cells, voluntary, connected to skeleton by tendons
- smooth: spindle-shaped cells
- where cardiac and skeletal overlap: striated, many nuclei
- where cardiac and smooth overlap: involuntary
- where all three overlap: contraction, movement, fibers

INVESTIGATION

Time 45 minutes	TEACHER TESTED ✓
Teacher Preparation	
Student Difficulty	
Lab Binder Human Bio, pp. 63–64	

Purpose Test how long it takes for muscles in the hand to become fatigued.

Overview Students will repeatedly squeeze a tennis ball in their hand for at least 120 seconds. They will

- make a data table to record the number of squeezes per ten-second time intervals
- collect data and observe changes in the number of squeezes over time

LAB PREPARATION

- Collect tennis balls and timers with second hands.
- You can substitute light weights and have students lift them until muscles are fatigued, or have them pull on an elastic band used for exercising.

LAB MANAGEMENT

- Make sure students watch the time and count carefully so that they do not introduce excessive error.

Teacher Note "The lab uses graphs to make its point. Interpreting graphs is a critical skill for standardized testing."

POST-LAB DISCUSSION

Discuss students' results. **Ask**

- What causes muscles to become fatigued during exercise? The muscles are breaking down glucose to make ATP faster than they can get the oxygen they need.
- What causes the burn you feel in your muscles during exercise? It is caused by a buildup of lactate as muscles work anaerobically in the absence of oxygen.

CHAPTER 33 INVESTIGATION

MATERIALS
- tennis ball
- timer with a second hand

PROCESS SKILLS
- Collecting Data
- Analyzing Data
- Graphing

NOS.3 Clearly communicate their ideas and results of investigations verbally and in written form using tables, graphs, diagrams, and photographs.
NOS.5 Apply standard techniques in laboratory investigations to measure physical quantities in appropriate units and convert known quantities to other units as necessary.

Muscle Fatigue

In Chapter 4, you learned that as your muscles do continuous activity, they will eventually begin to feel tired and fatigued. Muscles get fatigued because they need more oxygen than the blood vessels can supply them with, and they begin to work anaerobically, or without the necessary oxygen. In this lab, you will measure how long it takes before muscle fatigue begins.

PROBLEM How much time does it take for muscles to become fatigued?

PROCEDURE
1. Construct a data table like the one shown below. Extend the table to at least 120 seconds.
2. Hold a tennis ball in your nonwriting hand. When your partner tells you to begin, start squeezing the tennis ball as fast as you can, and count the number of squeezes.
3. Every 10 seconds, your partner will record the number of times you squeezed the tennis ball during that 10-second interval. Continue the activity for at least 120 seconds.
4. Switch roles with your partner and repeat steps 1–3.

TABLE 1. TIME AND NUMBER OF BALL SQUEEZES

Time (sec)	Number of Squeezes
0–10	
11–20	
21–30	
31–40	

ANALYZE AND CONCLUDE
1. **Graph Data** Construct a graph that displays your data. How did the number of squeezes change over time?
2. **Infer** How long did it take for your forearm muscles to become fatigued?
3. **Predict** How might your data be different if you performed the experiment with your writing hand instead of your nonwriting hand?

Answers

Sample Data

Table 1. Time and Number of Ball Squeezes

Time (sec)	Number of Squeezes	Time (sec)	Number of Squeezes
0–10	14	61–70	15
11–20	14	71–80	15
21–30	14	81–90	15
31–40	14	91–100	14
41–50	15	101–110	11
51–60	15	111–120	11

Analyze and Conclude

1. Answers will vary. Graphs should reflect a decrease in the number of squeezes when fatigue sets in.
2. Answers will vary (about 101 seconds).
3. It probably would take longer for fatigue to set in.

33.3 Integumentary System

KEY CONCEPT The integumentary system has many tissues that protect the body.

MAIN IDEAS
- The integumentary system helps maintain homeostasis.
- The integumentary system consists of many different tissues.

VOCABULARY

integumentary system, p. 1013
keratin, p. 1013
epidermis, p. 1014
dermis, p. 1015
hair follicle, p. 1015

Connect Have you ever noticed that when you are warm, your face becomes reddish? This is not an optical illusion. It is your skin helping you to maintain a constant body temperature. When you are warm, nerves in your skin signal blood vessels to expand and rise to the surface of the skin. At the surface, blood vessels release heat into the environment. When your body temperature drops, the blood vessels sink into your skin, keeping the heat in your body.

MAIN IDEA

The integumentary system helps maintain homeostasis.

Skin is a part of your integumentary system. The **integumentary system** is the body system that surrounds all of your other organ systems, and it includes the skin, hair, nails, oil glands, and sweat glands. Together, these tissues protect your body and help your body maintain homeostasis.

Your integumentary system consists of many tissues that protect your body. Oil glands in the skin release acidic oils that stop fungi and bacteria from growing on the skin, thereby preventing infection. Your fingernails and hair also have protective qualities. Fingernails and hair are made up of keratin. **Keratin** is a tough, waterproof protein that gives your hair and nails the ability to grow away from the body but still maintain their shape and sturdiness. In nails, keratin allows your nails to absorb some of the impact if you accidentally stub your toe. The microscopic view of a fingernail in **FIGURE 33.12** shows that these structures are actually many layers of thin, dead cells that are stacked on top of one another. In hair, keratin proteins are long and twisted around one another. Hair on top of the head shades your skin and keeps you cool.

FIGURE 33.12 Fingernails are dense layers of dead cells that protect the fingers from injury. (colored SEM; magnification 650×)

Nerves in your skin can help maintain temperature homeostasis, but your integumentary system maintains homeostasis in other ways as well. It removes water, salts, and urea from the bloodstream. Sweat glands help maintain homeostasis by cooling the body as the sweat evaporates off the skin. The average person has 2,600,000 sweat glands. During an intense hourlong workout, these glands allow your body to sweat out more than a liter of water.

Ⓐ Connect **When have your fingernails helped to protect you from injury?**

Differentiated Instruction

BELOW LEVEL

Prepare five to ten true/false statements to test what students know about skin. Have them revisit their responses after reading the section. For example,

1. The integumentary system is the only body that has no organs. F
2. Skin is made up of a single type of tissue. F
3. Skin is both living and nonliving. T
4. Skin is as important for homeostasis as other structures. T

Biology Toolkit, Anticipation Guide, p. C3

Plan and Prepare

Objectives
- Explain how the integumentary system helps maintain homeostasis.
- Describe the structures of the integumentary system.

Section Resources

Unit Resource Book	
Study Guide	pp. 159–160
Power Notes	p. 161
Reinforcement	p. 162
Pre-AP Activity	pp. 167–168
Interactive Reader	Chapter 33
Spanish Study Guide	pp. 337–338
Biology Toolkit	pp. C3, C13, C19
Technology	
Power Presentation	33.3
Media Gallery DVD	
Online Quiz	33.3

Activate Prior Knowledge Have students think of doing hard physical activity. **Ask**
- What do you look and feel like afterwards? sweaty, flushed, possibly odorous
- What is your body doing? trying to main homeostasis by cooling off, also removing impurities
- Which organ is directly involved in these reactions? skin

Teach

Vocabulary

integumentary The word *integumentary* comes from the Latin word *integumentum,* meaning "a covering."

keratin The word *keratin* comes from the Greek word *keras,* meaning "horn." Besides making up fingernails and hair, keratin is found in horns, feathers, and hooves.

Answers

Ⓐ **Connect** Students' answers will likely include descriptions of hitting their hand on a surface.

▼ Teach *continued*

ONLINE BIOLOGY Go to the chapter Resource Center at **ClassZone.com** for additional resources and information on the integumentary system.

DATA ANALYSIS

Discuss

Discuss the applications of bar graphs. **Ask**

- Why is a bar graph used to depict the data shown here? The time data is discrete, not continuous.
- What does the label for the *y*-axis mean? the number of people in a group of 100,000 who get the disease
- What information would you need to determine the total number of people who get the disease? incidence rates and the total population sizes for both men and women

Answers

1. In men, it increased until 1985–1989, then decreased; in women, it increased since 1980–1984.
2. Both show an incidence rate of about 24 per 100,000 people in the first years of the study, 1976–1979. However, the incidence rate was higher for men than for women during the second and third time periods, but lower or the same during all the other time periods. Since the 1990s, the incidence rate for women is much higher.
3. Duration of exposure to ultraviolet rays has increased for women and decreased for men. Possible factors could include more men working indoors and more women sunbathing or using tanning beds.

Unit Resource Book, Data Analysis, p. 163

MAIN IDEA

The integumentary system consists of many different tissues.

Connecting CONCEPTS

Immune System You read in **Chapter 31** that the skin and its various tissues are also part of the immune system; they help keep germs out of the body.

All of the tissues of your integumentary system are housed in the skin. Your skin is the largest organ in your body. It covers from 1 to 2 square meters (10 to 15 ft^2) and makes up about 15 percent of your body mass. The skin has three layers: the epidermis, the dermis, and the subcutaneous fat. The skin layers and the structures contained in them are shown in **FIGURE 33.13.**

The **epidermis** is the outermost layer of the skin, and it provides the first layer of protection for the tissues that are in deeper skin layers. The epidermis also contains pores through which sweat, salts, and oils can leave the body. The surface of the epidermis consists mostly of dead cells that continually flake off. Below the surface are new, living cells that are constantly dividing. The new cells pile on top of one another and push up to the surface over a period of two to four weeks to replace old, dead cells.

Cells in the epidermis also produce protective proteins, such as keratin and melanin. Almost every type of cell in the epidermis produces keratin. Keratin causes the skin to feel thick or hard, and it builds thicker layers in areas of the skin that come into frequent contact with the outer environment. The soles of your feet, for example, have a thick layer of keratin, and so the skin on your feet is tougher than the skin on your face. Although keratin is produced by almost every epidermal cell, only specialized cells, called melanocytes, produce melanin. Melanin is a dark pigment that absorbs harmful ultraviolet sunlight that would otherwise reach and damage internal organs. When a person's skin is exposed to more and more sunlight, melanocytes produce more melanin to block the additional rays. In other words, the skin tans.

DATA ANALYSIS

NOS.1

ANALYZING TRENDS IN DATA

Analyzing trends in data is a critical component of a scientific investigation. The graph below shows data about the incidence of basal cell skin cancer in men and women ages 26–30.

1. **Evaluate** What is the trend in the data for the incidence of this type of cancer in men in this age group? What is the trend for women of this age group?
2. **Compare and Contrast** How are these trends similar and different?
3. **Infer** Give a possible explanation for the trends.

GRAPH 1. INCIDENCE OF BASAL CELL SKIN CANCER

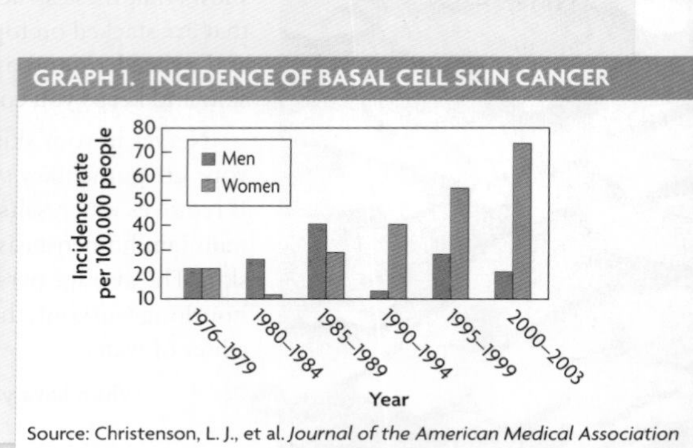

Source: Christenson, L. J., et al. *Journal of the American Medical Association*

Differentiated Instruction

ENGLISH LEARNERS

After students read the section, then have them write for five minutes on the question of how skin functions as a body system. Tell them that they should write without stopping and not worry about grammar, spelling, or punctuation. Have students check their work with one another, then have them discuss their ideas with the class.

Biology Toolkit, Quick-Write, p. C19; Think-Pair-Share, p. C13

The next layer of skin, the **dermis,** contains glands and the cells that maintain the skin's structure by producing elastin and collagen. Elastin is a protein that gives the skin flexibility, allowing it to stretch without tearing. Collagen is a dense protein that gives skin its shape. As a person ages, collagen molecules become weak and clump. Clumping collagen is one factor that contributes to wrinkles.

The dermis also contains sweat glands, oil glands, and hair follicles. A **hair follicle** is an elongated pit under the skin's surface that contains cells that produce the keratin that forms hair. Each hair follicle has a pain receptor associated with it, which is why it hurts when you pull out a hair.

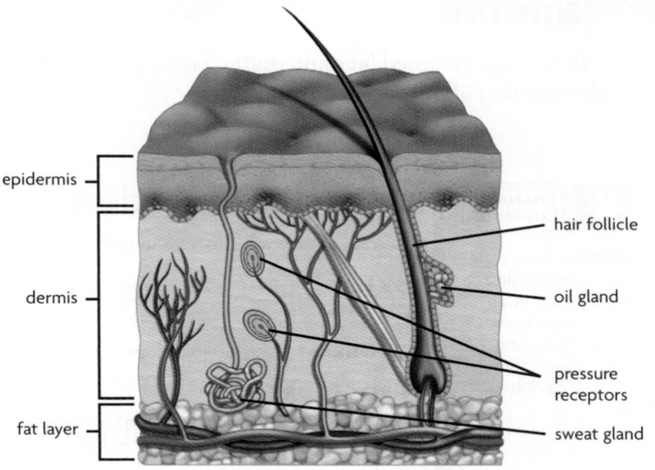

FIGURE 33.13 Skin has many structures that protect internal organs and sense the world around you.

Sweat and oil glands in the dermis also protect your body. Each person has 2 to 5 million glands—that's more than 10 glands for every square millimeter of skin. Sweat glands are called eccrine glands. Eccrine glands are found all over the body and help control body temperature. They also produce sweat that prevents damage that might occur when a person moves. When a person sweats from their armpits, for example, this sweat is protecting the skin by preventing the skin under the arm from rubbing too hard on the skin around the rib cage. Other glands, called sebaceous glands, produce oils that lubricate the skin and keep it waterproof.

Beneath the epidermis and dermis is a layer of subcutaneous fat. This layer of fat cells protects and cushions larger blood vessels and neurons. It also insulates the muscles and internal organs from temperature changes in the body's surrounding environment. These cells are connected to the muscles and bones by a layer of connective tissue.

A Summarize **What structures are found in each of the three layers of skin?**

33.3 ASSESSMENT

ONLINE QUIZ ClassZone.com

REVIEWING MAIN IDEAS

1. How does the **integumentary system** help your body maintain homeostasis?
2. What are three types of tissue that can be found in the **dermis**?

CRITICAL THINKING

3. **Infer** Why might it be beneficial to have dead skin cells on the outermost layer of the **epidermis**?
4. **Infer** What kind of sensory receptors are associated with **hair follicles**?

Connecting CONCEPTS

5. **Plants** Although the epidermises of plants and humans have different structures, some of these structures have the same function. How are pores in human skin functionally similar to stomata on plants?

33.3 ASSESSMENT

1. The integumentary system regulates body temperature and blocks pathogens from invading the body.
2. The dermis contains hair follicles, oil glands, and sweat glands.
3. Students should discuss how dead skin cells provide an additional layer between the body and pathogens.
4. Pain receptors are associated with hair follicles.
5. Pores and stomata are openings to the body through which water can escape to cool the surface.

Address Misconceptions

Common Misconceptions Ask students whether the following statements are true or false:

- Tanning beds are safer than the Sun.
- People with dark or olive-colored skin do not sunburn.
- You do not need to worry about sunburn on a cloudy day.
- A base tan protects you against sunburn.

Correcting the Misconceptions These statements are all false. Excessive exposure to ultraviolet rays damages the skin and can lead to skin cancer regardless of the source of exposure, your natural skin color, the amount of cloud cover, or how tanned you are.

Take It Further

A **pilosebaceous unit** (PSU) is made up of a hair, hair follicle, and sebaceous gland. **Acne** is caused when a PSU becomes inflamed. In teenagers, acne is caused when androgen hormones increase the production of sebum. The bacteria *Propionibacterium acnes* is attracted to the sebum, which in turn attracts white blood cells, leading to inflammation. When the follicle breaks down, it spills the bacteria and sebum onto the skin, producing a pimple. Acne is most common on the face, upper neck, and chest because these areas have the greatest numbers of PSUs.

Answers

A Summarize epidermis: pores, dead skin cells, keratin and melanin producing cells; dermis: elastin and collagen producing cells, hair follicles, sweat glands, oil glands; fat layer: fat cells, blood vessels, neurons

Assess and Reteach ▼

Assess Use the Online Quiz or Section Quiz (*Assessment Book*, p. 651).

Reteach Project **FIGURE 33.13** from the Media Gallery. Cover the labels and ask students to identify the structures and their homeostatic functions.

OPTIONS FOR INQUIRY

INVESTIGATION

Time 45 minutes	TEACHER TESTED
Teacher Preparation	
Student Difficulty	
Lab Binder Human Bio, pp. 65–68	

Purpose Identify the bones, muscles, and tendons involved in a particular action.

Overview Students will choose an action, such as kicking a ball. They will

- decide which bones, muscles, and tendons are involved in their chosen action
- diagram the action and the relevant bones, muscles, and tendons

LAB PREPARATION

- Make student copies of the Muscle Charts in the *Lab Binder*, p. 68.
- Have anatomy books available for students to use.

LAB MANAGEMENT

Teacher Note "Trying to figure out actions related to muscles and bones was a fun way to get students to think about the relationship."

Teacher Note "Students recognize how many muscles are used in each action and how interrelated they are. They have more trouble finding tendons."

POST-LAB DISCUSSION

Have several students come to the board and copy the illustration they made for this investigation, but without the labels in step 3. Then ask volunteers to explain each illustration, including which muscles are contracting and which are relaxed. You may want to have students demonstrate what their illustration shows as another student explains the motion.

Use these inquiry-based labs and online activities to deepen your understanding of muscles and bones.

NOS.3 Clearly communicate their ideas and results of investigations verbally and in written form using tables, graphs, diagrams, and photographs.

INVESTIGATION

Muscles in Action

In this lab, you will illustrate muscles in action.

MATERIALS
Muscle and Bone Charts

SKILLS Analyzing Relationships, Interpreting, Modeling

PROBLEM Which muscles are used in an action?

PROCEDURE

1. Choose an appropriate action to illustrate, such as a person getting ready to kick a soccer ball, throw a football, or hold a guitar.
2. Determine which bones, muscles, and tendons are involved in the motion. Identify which muscles are contracting and which are extending.
3. Illustrate the part of the body frozen in the motion. Draw and label the relevant bones, muscles, and tendons involved in the action. Indicate the role of each structure in the action.

ANALYZE AND CONCLUDE

1. **Analyze** What is the function of a tendon? What would happen if one of the tendons involved in the action were torn?
2. **Infer** Suppose one of the muscles used in the action were stretched. How might that affect the performance of that muscle as the action is repeated?
3. **Infer** How does the overall structure of the body part (including the type of joint and the shapes of the bones and muscles) you drew allow for the motion that it made?

Answers

Expected Results

Student diagrams should show actively contracting muscles bulging.

Analyze and Conclude

1. Tendons attach muscles to bones. Skeletal muscles produce body movements by exerting force on tendons, which then pull on bones. If the tendon is torn, aside from pain, the tendon cannot function properly; therefore, the muscle action cannot be performed properly.
2. The muscle may become swollen and sore, and performance would decrease.
3. Answers will vary with body part. Answers should take into account the type of joint(s) involved and where the tendons are inserted.

INVESTIGATION

Bone and Muscle Cells

Imagine an injured athlete undergoing knee surgery. In this lab, you will use a microscope to examine the skin, the compact bone cells, and the different types of cells that the surgeon will see.

SKILL Modeling

MATERIALS
- slide of smooth muscle
- slide of skeletal muscle
- slide of bone cells
- slide of tendon tissue
- slide of ligament tissue
- slide of skin cells
- compound light microscope

PROBLEM What differences exist between different types of cells?

PROCEDURE
1. Examine the first slide under low power and high power on the microscope.
2. Draw and label one cell and its structures.
3. Repeat steps 1 and 2 for the remaining slides.

ANALYZE AND CONCLUDE
1. **Compare and Contrast** What are the similarities and differences in the structures of the two types of muscle cells you viewed?
2. **Analyze** How do nutrients and oxygen reach bone cells that are surrounded by calcitic bone?
3. **Contrast** How do the slides of ligament and tendon tissue differ from skeletal muscle tissue?
4. **Summarize** Draw and label in the correct order the layers of the skin that the surgeon will cut through to reach the kneecap.

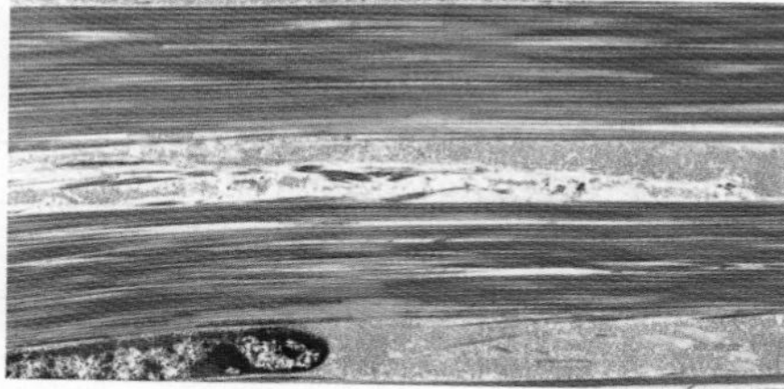

Tendon tissue, pictured above, connects muscles to bones. (colored TEM; magnification 15,000×)

Online BIOLOGY CLASSZONE.COM

ANIMATED BIOLOGY
What Kind of Joint Is It?
Can you tell a gliding joint from a hinge joint? Explore different joints in the body and learn how they move. Then categorize each joint based on its movement and structure.

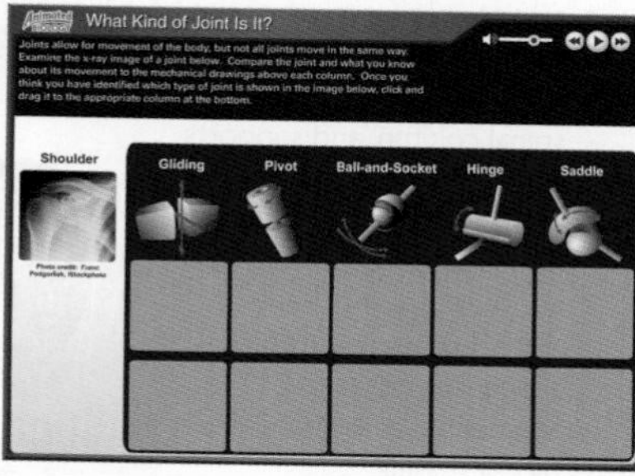

WEBQUEST
Every year there is a telethon to raise money for muscular dystrophy. What exactly is muscular dystrophy? Why should we worry about money for research? Complete this WebQuest to find out. Learn the causes and symptoms of muscular dystrophy, and the treatment options available to those afflicted with it.

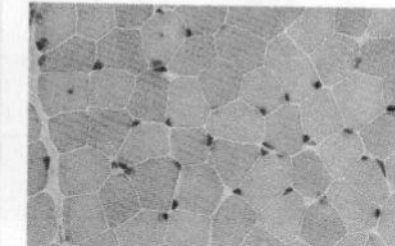

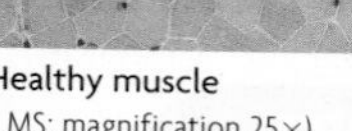

Healthy muscle (LMS; magnification 25×)

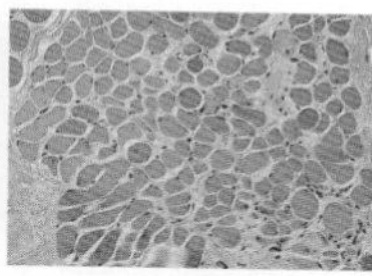

Muscle affected by muscular dystrophy (LMS; magnification 25×)

DATA ANALYSIS ONLINE
Some runners can run a mile in less than 4 minutes, while others might take 13 minutes to run the same distance. Graph the speed at which different people move their legs versus each person's top speed. Determine whether fast runners move their legs more quickly than slow runners.

Answers

Analyze and Conclude

1. Both are long, thin cells that contract. Skeletal muscle cells are rectangular, contain many nuclei, and are striated. Smooth muscle cells are spindle-shaped, not striated, and have only one nucleus.
2. Nutrients and oxygen reach bone cells through blood vessels that are contained in the Haversian canals found in the center of the calcium-rich rings that make up compact bone.
3. Ligaments and tendons are made up of connective tissue that is arranged in a regular pattern.
4. Students should illustrate the epidermis, the dermis, and the subcutaneous layer beneath the dermis.

Online Biology ▼

ANIMATED BIOLOGY Use this interactive animation to have students classify joints based on movement and structure. Use with **Section 33.1.**

WEBQUEST The WebQuest takes one full class period. Students complete the activity online and will need access to a printer to print their answers. Sample answers, teacher notes, and alternative assessment ideas are available on **ClassZone.com.** Use with **Section 33.2.**

DATA ANALYSIS ONLINE
Using a bar graph, students should see that the speed at which runners move their legs does not have an impact on their top speed. The force with which they push off the ground is what makes some runners faster than others. Use with **Section 33.2.**

INVESTIGATION

Time	45 minutes (TEACHER TESTED)
Teacher Preparation	1 flask
Student Difficulty	1 flask
Lab Binder	Human Bio, pp. 69–70

Purpose Compare various cell types.

Overview Students will use a microscope to view slides of different cell types.

Safety Have students wipe down the eyepieces with alcohol wipes after use.

POST-LAB DISCUSSION

Discuss the relationship between structure and function of the various cells.

CHAPTER REVIEW

Interactive Review

Encourage students to go to **ClassZone.com** for a detailed review of each section, including visuals and vocabulary practice.

Unit Resource Book, Vocabulary Practice, pp. 169–172

CHAPTER 33 Interactive Review @ CLASSZONE.COM

KEY CONCEPTS | Vocabulary Games | Concept Maps | Animated Biology | Online Quiz

33.1 Skeletal System

The skeletal system includes bones and tissues that are important for supporting, protecting, and moving your body. The skeletal system has two parts: the appendicular skeleton and the axial skeleton. The appendicular skeleton is responsible for most of the body's movements and includes the arms and legs. The axial skeleton includes bones such as the skull, rib cage, and spinal column, and supports the body and protects internal organs. Individual bones are connected to one another by joints. Each individual bone is living tissue that contains specialized cells and blood vessels.

33.2 Muscular System

Muscles are tissues that can contract, enabling movement. Humans have three types of muscles: skeletal, smooth, and cardiac. Skeletal muscle attaches to bones. Smooth muscle surrounds blood vessels and the organs of the digestive system. Cardiac muscle is only found in the heart. The various types of muscles contract when the nervous system stimulates muscle filaments to move. The nervous system causes Ca^{2+} to enter the sarcomere, allowing myosin filaments to bind to actin filaments. The muscle contracts when the myosin filaments pull the actin toward the sarcomere's center.

33.3 Integumentary System

The integumentary system has many tissues that protect the body. The integumentary system is the body system that acts as a barrier between the body's internal and external environments. It helps to maintain homeostasis by regulating the body's temperature and blocking out pathogens. The skin has three layers: the dermis, the epidermis, and the layer of subcutaneous fat. The skin also contains proteins, such as keratin and melanin, that protect the skin's cells and maintain its structure.

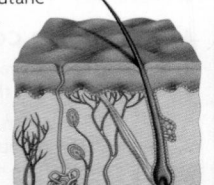

Synthesize Your Notes

Concept Map Organize your notes on the skeletal system using a concept map like the one below.

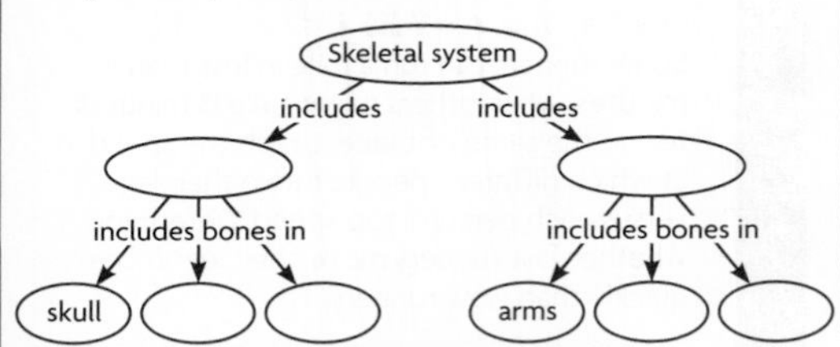

Three-Column Chart Study the integumentary system using a three-column chart like the one below.

Parts of the Integumentary System

Parts	Structures	Functions
skin	dermis epidermis	
nails		
hair		

Reviewing Vocabulary

1. *Sample Answer:* What protein is produced in a hair follicle?
2. *Sample Answer:* What type of connective tissue is found in joints of the appendicular skeleton?
3. *Sample Answer:* A tendon connects which type of muscle to bone?
4. *Sample Answer:* What does myosin pull to cause muscle contraction?
5. cardiac muscle
6. smooth muscle
7. epidermis
8. dermis
9. protects internal organs
10. shortens during muscle contraction
11. process that forms compact bone

Chapter Assessment

Chapter Vocabulary

33.1 skeletal system, p. 1000
appendicular skeleton, p. 1000
axial skeleton, p. 1001
vertebrae, p. 1001
cartilage, p. 1001
joint, p. 1001
ligament, p. 1002
calcification, p. 1005

33.2 muscular system, p. 1006
muscle fibers, p. 1006
skeletal muscle, p. 1006
tendon, p. 1006
smooth muscle, p. 1007
cardiac muscle, p. 1008
myofibrils, p. 1008
sarcomere, p. 1008
actin, p. 1008
myosin, p. 1008

33.3 integumentary system, p. 1013
keratin, p. 1013
epidermis, p. 1014
dermis, p. 1015
hair follicle, p. 1015

Reviewing Vocabulary

Write Your Own Questions

Write a question about the first term that uses the second term as the answer. For the pair *skeletal system, appendicular skeleton,* the question could be, "What part of the skeletal system is responsible for most of your movements?"

1. hair follicle, keratin
2. joint, ligament
3. tendon, skeletal muscle
4. myosin, actin

Category Clues

For each clue, list the appropriate vocabulary term from the chapter.

Category: Types of Muscle

5. found only in the heart
6. regulates width of blood vessels

Category: Parts of the Skin

7. consists mostly of dead cells
8. contains glands

Keep It Short

For each vocabulary term below, write a short, precise phrase that defines it. For example, a short phrase to describe *vertebrae* could be "protect spinal cord."

9. axial skeleton
10. sarcomere
11. calcification

Reviewing MAIN IDEAS

12. Which organs do each of the three collections of bones in the axial skeleton protect?

13. How does cartilage protect bones from wearing out while allowing muscles to move bones?

14. What type of joint is found in the hips and shoulders? How does this type of joint allow these body parts to move the way that they do?

15. How do compact and spongy bone interact with the circulatory system?

16. Bone is formed when flexible cartilage is transformed into hard bone. How do specialized cells create compact bone from cartilage?

17. Ligaments and tendons are connective tissues that help the body move. What are some differences between ligaments and tendons?

18. Humans have three types of muscle: skeletal, smooth, and cardiac. How are the three types of muscle cells different from one another?

19. Both the Z line and the M line have important roles in muscle contraction. What are the differences in the function and placement of the Z line and the M line in the sarcomere?

20. How do actin and myosin work together to produce muscle contractions?

21. How does the integumentary system help to maintain homeostasis?

22. What are the three layers of skin, and how do they work to protect the body?

23. What roles do elastin and collagen play in the connective tissue of the dermis?

CHAPTER REVIEW

Reviewing Main Ideas

12. Vertebrae protect the spinal cord. The skull protects the brain. The rib cage protects the heart and lungs.
13. Cartilage cushions bones at joints so that the bones do not rub against one another.
14. The hip and shoulder joints are ball-and-socket joints that allow movement in almost any direction.
15. Compact bone protects the blood vessels that carry nutrients and new blood cells produced in the bone marrow to the rest of the body. Spongy bone protects the bone marrow.
16. Osteoblasts secrete collagen and calcium phosphate that harden cartilage into bone. The calcium phosphate causes the collagen to harden. The trapped osteoblast is called an osteocyte. Osteocytes maintain the calcium-rich rings that create compact bone.
17. Tendons connect a bone to a muscle. Ligaments connect two bones across a joint.
18. Students should explain the differences in appearance and function of the three types of cells.
19. The M line is found in the middle of the sarcomere, and it connects the myosin to the sarcomere. The Z line is found at the edge of the sarcomere, and it connects the actin to the sarcomere.
20. Myosin pulls actin, which in turn pulls the ends of the sarcomere.
21. The integumentary system regulates body temperature and blocks out pathogens.
22. The epidermis blocks pathogens, sunlight, and other damaging environmental factors. The dermis produces protective sweat, oil, and hairs. The subcutaneous fat layer insulates the muscles and internal organs, and cushions neurons and blood vessels.
23. Elastin and collagen are proteins that contribute to the structure of skin. Elastin is a protein that gives skin flexibility, while collagen is a dense protein that gives skin its shape.

Critical Thinking

24. Sensory neurons are found in the skin, because the skin detects the external environment. Motor neurons are found in the muscles, because muscles respond to signals from the nervous system.
25. Hair follicles could be a good target for infection because they are open to the external environment. Oil glands probably help keep pathogens from entering the hair follicle.
26. Calcium moves out of bone and into the blood when blood calcium is low, and vice versa. Haversian canals contain blood vessels and allow materials, such as calcium, to be transported between the interior of a bone to the circulatory system.
27. The more mitochondria in a cell, the more ATP is available to it.
28. Students should indicate an understanding that myosin pulls actin, which because it is secured at the Z line, pulls the sarcomere. Muscle contractions pull the Z line toward the middle of the sarcomere and cause the sarcomeres to shorten. When a muscle relaxes, the myosin lets go of the actin, and the sarcomere returns to its original shape.
29. Calcium would be removed from bones.

Interpreting Visuals

30. Myosin is pulling actin.
31. The sarcomere will shorten, and the muscle will contract.
32. The Z line is toward the right, and the M line is toward the left. Students know this because myosin pulls actin away from the Z line toward the M line.

Critical Thinking

24. **Connect** Neurons are specialized cells of the nervous system. Sensory neurons sense the internal and external environments. Motor neurons cause the body to respond to a stimulus. Which neurons do you think are found in the integumentary system? the muscular system? How do you know?

25. **Infer** A hair on your arm emerges through a pore and onto the surface of your skin. Within your skin, the hair follicle has an oil-secreting gland associated with it. Why might hair follicles be good targets for infections? How do glands prevent hair follicles from becoming infected?

26. **Infer** Calcium is an important nutrient in the body. It allows for the nervous, muscular, and skeletal systems to work. How do Haversian canals work with bone cells to maintain calcium homeostasis?

27. **Connect** What is the relationship between ATP and the number of mitochondria in muscle cells?

28. **Summarize** Several things must happen to make a sarcomere shorten and a muscle contract. Describe the steps involved in contracting and relaxing a muscle. In your answer, discuss the following: sarcomeres, actin filaments, myosin filaments, M lines, and Z lines.

29. **Predict** Your body stores extra calcium in your bones. What might happen to your bones if there weren't enough calcium in your muscle fibers to stimulate muscle contractions?

Interpreting Visuals

Use the diagram to answer the next three questions.

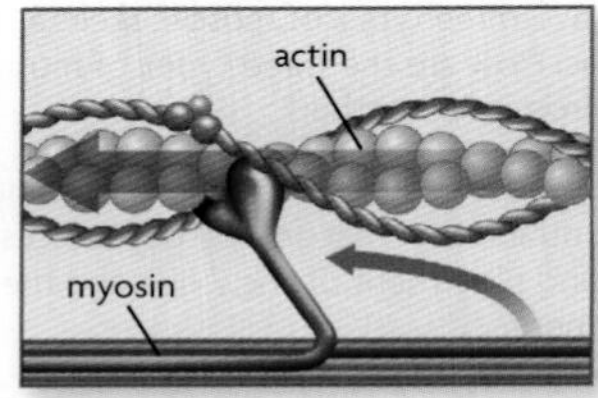

30. **Analyze** What is happening in the diagram?

31. **Apply** What will result from the action shown in the diagram?

32. **Infer** Assume that the actin filament is moving to the left. On which side of the picture would the Z line be? The M line? How do you know?

Analyzing Data

For a research project, a student asked 200 students at her school to record some of their physical activities. Each student recorded if they walked, rode a bicycle, or went swimming at least three times a week. The recording sheets were handed out in March and collected shortly after the students returned to school in the fall. Use the data to answer the next three questions.

STUDENTS' ACTIVITIES EACH MONTH

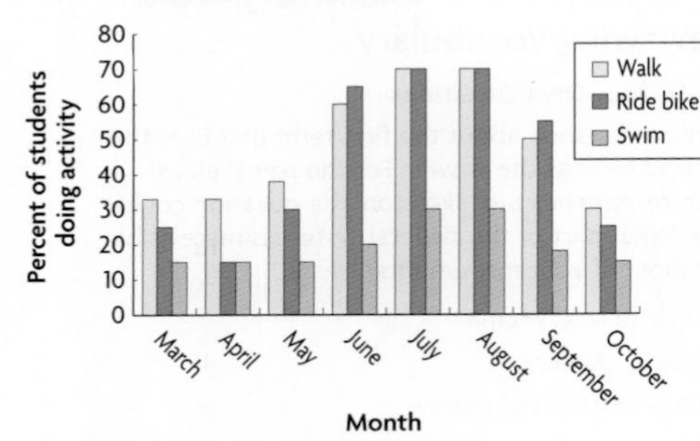

33. **Evaluate** What are the trends for physical activities from spring through early fall?

34. **Contrast** How do the trends differ between activities?

35. **Hypothesize** What might be possible explanations for these trends and differences?

Connecting CONCEPTS

36. **Write a Help Wanted Ad** Figure 33.3 on page 1003 shows the different types of joints and describes how they work. Write Help Wanted ads for two of the joints. Each ad should include the type of joint that is needed, what it must be able to do (job description), and the kinds of tasks it should expect to perform.

37. **Compare** Look at the pictures on page 999. How do an insect's skeletal and muscular systems compare with those of humans? (**Hint:** Consider the physical structures of the skeletons, their types of movement, and their relationships to the animal's muscles.)

Analyzing Data

33. Students should indicate that during the warmest months, people are more active for all activities studied.
34. There are always half as many people swimming as there are walking or riding their bikes. During the spring and fall, more people walk than ride bikes.
35. *Sample Answers:* There is more variation for walking and riding a bike because these are outdoor activities and weather dependent. Swimming is either indoor or outdoor. More people ride bikes or walk because they are more accessible.

1020 Unit 9: Human Biology

INDIANA ISTEP+ Test Prep

NOS.6

Test Practice For more test practice, go to ClassZone.com.

1

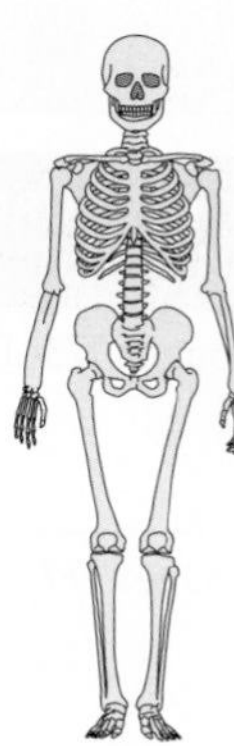

Three-dimensional models of human skeletons are useful learning tools. However, they do ***not*** help to show how the

A axial and appendicular skeletons join.
B vertebrae form the spinal column.
C bones meet to form joints.
D bones adjust to support the body's weight.

2 When you run a race, the muscles in your legs need extra oxygen. To get oxygen to your muscles, your lungs breathe harder. Your heart pumps more blood. The muscles that line your blood vessels change the size of the blood vessel to direct more blood to the active muscles and less blood to the inactive muscles. This situation is an example of

A positive feedback.
B operant conditioning.
C multiple body systems working together.
D anaerobic respiration.

3 Which of these is the ***best*** example of the skin maintaining the body's stable environment, or homeostasis?

A becoming sunburned after a day in the sun
B releasing acidic oils that prevent infection
C breaking out in acne after eating certain foods
D freckles appearing after sun exposure

4 Calcium is an important nutrient that is involved in stimulating muscle contraction and sending nerve impulses. Depositing and removing calcium from bones is a continual process that reshapes bones and sends calcium to other parts of the body where it is needed. Which of the following events would ***most*** likely result in calcium moving into bones?

A bone injury
B intense exercise
C digestion
D thinking

THINK THROUGH THE QUESTION

Read the first part of the question carefully. Then consider which one of the answer choices would *not* require calcium to be sent to another part of the body.

5 In amyotrophic lateral sclerosis (ALS), or Lou Gehrig's disease, motor neurons lose their ability to send impulses. Which of the following is ***most*** likely to occur due to this disease?

A The patient will lose sensory ability.
B The patient will lose memory ability.
C The patient will lose thought ability.
D The patient will lose speaking ability.

6 How does the skin keep pathogens from surviving on the body's surface?

Standards-Based Assessment

1. D	4. A
2. C	5. D
3. B	6. See Below

TEST DOCTOR

Question 1 Answer D is correct. Answers A, B, and C are incorrect because the human skeleton model can show how the axial and appendicular skeletons join, how the vertebrae form the spinal column, and how the bones meet to form joints, which are all visible in a static figure; it does not, however, show how the skeleton adjusts during motion.

Question 3 Answer B is correct. Answers A, C, and D are incorrect because while they may be the consequences of those actions, they do not help the body maintain stable conditions.

Question 5 Answer D is correct. Answers A, B, and C are incorrect because motor neurons are responsible for motion, not for sensory, memory, and thinking abilities.

Question 6 Skin secretes oil and sweat that create an environment in which pathogens cannot survive.

Connecting Concepts

36. Students can choose any two of the following: gliding, pivot, ball-and-socket, hinge, saddle. *Sample Answer:* The gliding joint will need to assist the person in walking, jumping, riding a bike, and other activities involving the ankle by providing flexibility. The ball-and-socket joint needs to be able to move in almost any direction to perform tasks such as throwing a ball, swinging a bat, swimming, kicking a soccer ball, or dancing.

37. Both types of skeletons protect the animal's internal organs. In the exoskeleton, the muscles attach directly to the exoskeleton and pull on it to make it move. The exoskeleton is hard, not flexible. The muscles are within the exoskeleton. In the internal skeleton, muscles are attached to bones by tendons. Cartilage cushions bones and sometimes connects bones. It also helps provide flexibility to parts of the skeleton, such as the ribs. The internal skeleton has joints in which the bones are connected by ligaments.

ITEM CORRELATIONS

Standard	Items
NOS.6	1

CHAPTER 34

Indiana Resource Preview

Print Resources

Reproduction and Development

INDIANA STANDARDS		Sections	PAGES and PACING	UNIT RESOURCE BOOK
	34.1	**Reproductive Anatomy** **KEY CONCEPT** Female and male reproductive organs fully develop during puberty.	pp. 1024–1026 30 minutes	URB pages 173–176
	34.2	**Reproductive Processes** **KEY CONCEPT** Human reproductive processes depend on cycles of hormones.	pp. 1027–1032 30 minutes	URB pages 177–180
NOS.3		CHAPTER INVESTIGATION: Hormones in the Human Menstrual Cycle	p. 1033 45 minutes	**Lab Binder** Human Bio pages 77–79
B.6.3	34.3	**Fetal Development** **KEY CONCEPT** Development progresses in stages from zygote to fetus.	pp. 1034–1039 30 minutes	URB pages 181–184
NOS.1		DATA ANALYSIS: Interpreting Graphs	p. 1038 30 minutes	URB page 189
	34.4	**Birth and Development** **KEY CONCEPT** Physical development continues through adolescence and declines with age.	pp. 1040–1043 30 minutes	URB pages 185–188
NOS.3		OPTIONS FOR INQUIRY	pp. 1044–1045 30 minutes, 30 minutes	**Lab Binder** Human Bio pages 80–83
		Chapter Review	pp. 1046–1049	**Assessment Book** Chapter Tests A, B pp. 671–678

INDIANA STANDARDS

B.6.3 Explain that in multicellular organisms the zygote produced during fertilization undergoes a series of cell divisions that lead to clusters of cells that go on to specialize and become the organism's tissues and organs.
NOS.1 Develop explanations based on reproducible data and observations gathered during laboratory investigations.
NOS.3 Clearly communicate their ideas and results of investigations verbally and in written form using tables, graphs, diagrams, and photographs.

Labs

PUPIL EDITION LABS

Human Sex Cells, Section 2, p. 1031 Students examine the structures of a mammalian sperm cell and egg cell, using prepared slides and a microscope. **Lab Binder** p. 84	**Time:** 15 minutes **Materials:** slide of mammalian sperm cells, slide of mammalian egg cells, microscope
Hormones in the Human Menstrual Cycle, p. 1033 Students analyze changes in the blood levels of hormones during the menstrual cycle. **Lab Binder** pp. 77–79	**Time:** 45 minutes **Materials:** graph paper, colored markers, Hormone Blood Levels Datasheet

OPTIONS FOR INQUIRY

Development of an Embryo, p. 1044 Students observe the development of a sea star embryo by examining prepared slides. **Lab Binder** pp. 80–82	**Time:** 30 minutes **Materials:** slide of sea star embryo in early cleavage, slide of sea star embryo in late cleavage, slide of sea star blastula, slide of sea star gastrula, microscope
Effects of Chemicals on Reproductive Organs, p. 1045 Students research the effects of a toxic chemical on male and female reproductive systems. **Lab Binder** p. 83	**Time:** 30 minutes **Material:** Computer with Internet access

LAB BINDER Unit 9 Human Biology

Additional Investigation: Stages of Human Development, pp. 85–88

LAB GENERATOR

A searchable CD of all labs in the program in editable format, including forensic, probeware, and biotechnology labs.

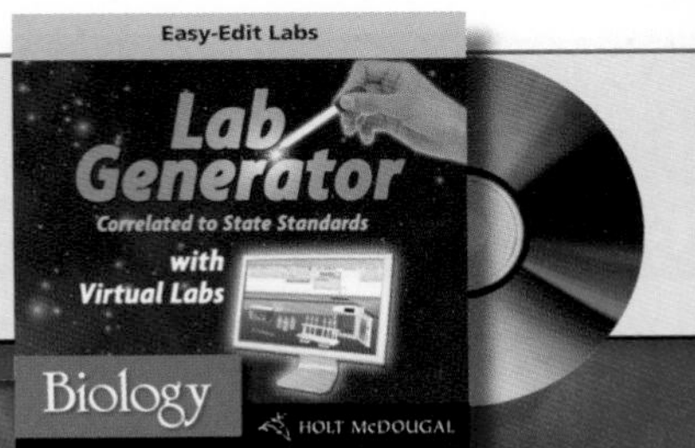

Presentation Tools

POWER PRESENTATIONS

Presentation Chapter 34
Power Presentations for each section incorporate images and clips from the Media Gallery: Includes Note Navigator for each section.

MEDIA GALLERY

Contains the following images and video clips, as well as animations, simulations and forms of visuals from the book.

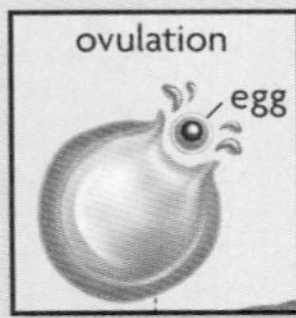

Menstrual cycle

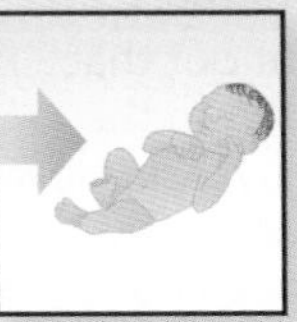
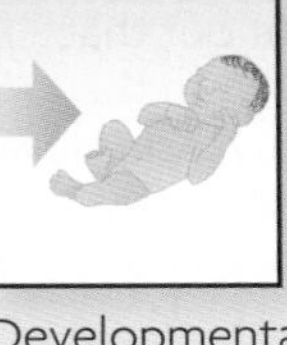
Developmental timeline

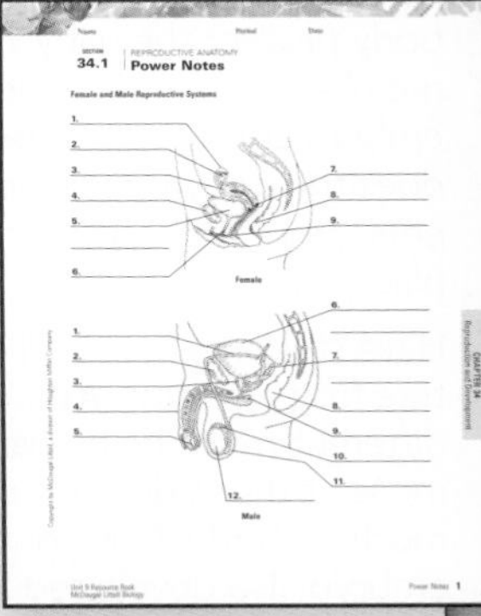

Power Notes

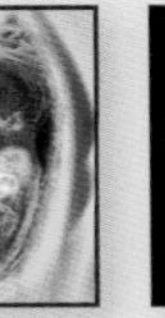
MRI of fetus

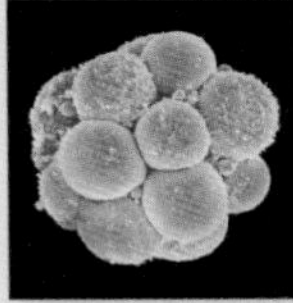
Embryo, 16 cells

VIDEO

View a series of short video clips exploring the journey from ovum to fetus.

ANIMATED BIOLOGY

Embryonic Development

Human Aging

Developmental Time Line

TRANSPARENCIES

Female Reproductive System T144

Male Reproductive System T145

Online BIOLOGY CLASSZONE.COM

BioZine

Animated Biology

Interactive Review

SciLinks

Resource Centers

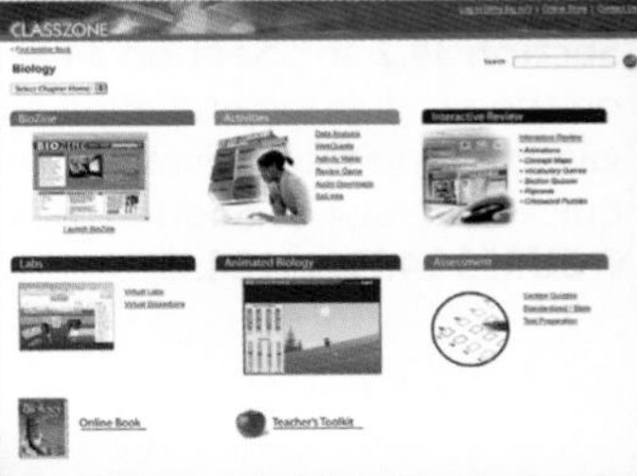

CHAPTER

34

▼ Focus and Motivate

What protects this developing baby?

Students may answer that the liquid the baby is floating in and the mother's body protect the baby. Point out that membranes that developed from the embryo also protect the baby. **Ask,** How does this baby get oxygen and nutrients? from the mother, through the placenta

Have students look at the picture of the tree frog embryos. **Ask,** How are they different from the human baby? smaller, more of them, develop outside their mother's body Point out that each frog embryo also developed from a single cell that contained the genetic instructions for developing into a frog. **Ask,** What is the advantage of having multiple embryos? increases the chances of the species surviving

BIOZINE ClassZone.com

Students can access BioZine at **ClassZone.com** to learn about some of the latest research in the biological sciences.

In a Hurry?

Students may be familiar with the material on reproductive anatomy in **Section 34.1.** To review this section, use the highlighted vocabulary words and **FIGURES 34.1** and **34.2.** The critical material in this chapter is found in **Section 34.2** and **Section 34.3,** focusing on the production and release of gametes and fetal development. For quick coverage of **Section 34.4,** use **FIGURES 34.13** and **34.15.**

CHAPTER

34 Reproduction and Development

KEY CONCEPTS

34.1 Reproductive Anatomy
Female and male reproductive organs fully develop during puberty.

34.2 Reproductive Processes
Human reproductive processes depend on cycles of hormones.

34.3 Fetal Development
Development progresses in stages from zygote to fetus.

34.4 Birth and Development
Physical development continues through adolescence and declines with age.

Online BIOLOGY CLASSZONE.COM

Animated BIOLOGY
View animated chapter concepts.
- Embryonic Development
- Human Aging
- Developmental Timeline

BIOZINE
Keep current with biology news.
- Featured stories
- Careers
- Polls

RESOURCE CENTER
Get more information on
- Gametes, or Sex Cells
- Fetal Monitoring
- Human Development

Student Activity

Purpose Have students do a biological cost-benefit analysis of asexual reproduction compared to sexual reproduction.

Materials (per team)
- chart paper
- markers

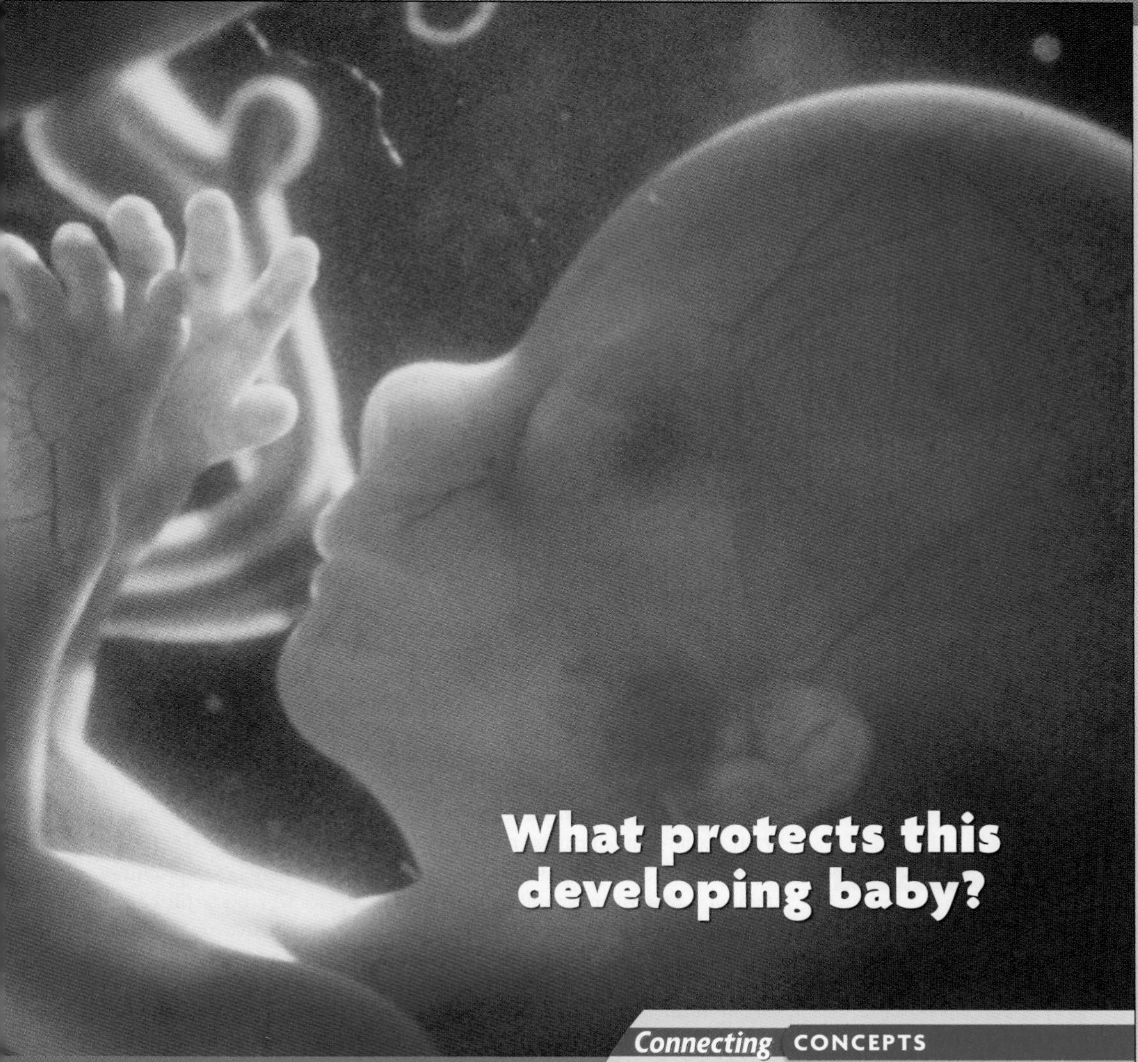

What protects this developing baby?

Connecting CONCEPTS

This developing baby, only about four months old, floats in a liquid world, receiving all its oxygen and nutrients from its mother's body. The journey from a single cell to a fully developed human being is guided by genetic instructions, environmental influences, and the complex actions of hormones in both mother and baby.

Amphibians This photograph shows a cluster of nine-day-old embryos of a tree frog. Unlike human babies, these embryos do not develop completely within the mother's body. Instead, they are deposited in special underwater nurseries. Once these eggs hatch, the tiny tadpoles are left to fend for themselves.

Introduce Remind students that with asexual reproduction, there is one organism involved and no special reproductive organs. With sexual reproduction, two organisms are involved whose bodies must have structures capable of producing gametes. Give students a few minutes to compare the biological cost and benefits of each type of reproduction.

Discuss Go over student lists and quantify the costs and benefits of each. It will probably be apparent from the lists that there are far greater costs to sexual reproduction in terms of energy, materials, and time, and primarily a single benefit, genetic diversity. **Ask,** What does this suggest about the value of genetic diversity? worth the cost

Activate Prior Knowledge

Have students look at the photograph. Remind them that many animals, as they develop, go through a period of metamorphosis. For example, frog eggs are deposited in water, and a tadpole spends its first weeks in water before developing into a frog that will live primarily on land. **Ask,** In what sense does a fetus go through a metamorphosis when it leaves the mother's womb? Answers should include that it goes from a protected enclosed aqueous environment to an open one, must breath through its lungs, take in nutrients through its mouth, process its own wastes.

Preview Vocabulary

Greek and Latin Word Origins The words commonly used to describe stages of human development are *infant, adolescent,* and *adult.* The Latin origin for the word *infant* translates into "not able to speak." The words *adolescent* and *adult* come from the same Latin source, meaning "to grow up." However, adolescence is associated with sexual immaturity, whereas adults are sexually mature. The word *puberty,* also derived from a Latin wording meaning "adult," is the stage of adolescence in which an individual becomes physiologically capable of sexual reproduction.

Academic Vocabulary Tell students that the word *mature* has many applications. It derives from a root that means "timely, seasonable" and so is suggestive of something that has ripened or reached its development:

a *mature* cheese

a *mature* audience

a *mature* bond

The word *immature,* meaning not fully developed, takes on the added connotation of being silly or childish.

English Learners Have students list all terms that they can relate to biological reproduction and development. Help them identify terms that relate specifically to mammals. Have them categorize terms according to different stages: gamete production, fertilization, and embryonic development.

SECTION 34.1

▼ Plan and Prepare

Objectives

- Describe the structure and function of the female reproductive system.
- Identify the structure and function of the male reproductive system.

Section Resources

Unit Resource Book Study Guide pp. 173–174 Power Notes p. 175 Reinforcement p. 176
Interactive Reader Chapter 34 **Spanish Study Guide** pp. 339–340
Biology Toolkit pp. C3, C38, D6
Technology Power Presentation 34.1 Media Gallery DVD Online Quiz 34.1

Activate Prior Knowledge Remind students that sexual reproduction is a feature common to most multicellular organisms. **Ask,** How is sexual reproduction in plants and animals similar? requires male and female reproductive structures, meiosis, gametes, fertilization

▼ Teach

Vocabulary

Word Origins Mention the two words in this chapter that derive from a person's name.

fallopian tube The duct is named after the 16th-century Italian anatomist, Gabriele Fallopio, who studied the reproductive organs of both sexes.

cesarean section A cesarean section is the delivery of a fetus by making a surgical incision in the mother's abdominal wall and uterus. This procedure is named after Julius Caesar, or one of his ancestors, who was believed to have been born by this method.

34.1 Reproductive Anatomy

KEY CONCEPT Female and male reproductive organs fully develop during puberty.

MAIN IDEAS

- The female reproductive system produces ova.
- The male reproductive system produces sperm.

VOCABULARY

reproductive system, p. 1024
puberty, p. 1024
ovum, p. 1024
ovary, p. 1024
uterus, p. 1024
estrogen, p. 1024
fallopian tube, p. 1024
testis, p. 1025
testosterone, p. 1025
scrotum, p. 1026
epididymis, p. 1026
vas deferens, p. 1026
semen, p. 1026

Connect You have something in common with every person ever born. Like everyone else, you began life as a single cell, produced when one male sex cell joined with one female sex cell. Sexual reproduction is the means by which the human species passes on genetic information to each generation.

MAIN IDEA

The female reproductive system produces ova.

The **reproductive system** is a collection of specialized organs, glands, and hormones that help to produce a new human being. Females and males reach sexual maturity, or the ability to produce offspring, only after puberty. **Puberty** marks a time in your life when your hypothalamus and your pituitary gland release hormones, such as follicle-stimulating hormone (FSH) and luteinizing hormone (LH). Such hormones begin the process of developing your sexual characteristics and reproductive system.

***Connecting* CONCEPTS**

Endocrine System You read in **Chapter 29** that the hypothalamus and pituitary glands are part of the endocrine system. These two glands are considered "master" glands because the hormones they secrete affect other glands that play key roles in human reproduction, growth, and development.

The main functions of the female reproductive system are to produce ova (singular, **ovum**), or egg cells, and to provide a place where a fertilized egg can develop. Unlike males, females have all of their reproductive organs located inside their bodies. This organization helps to protect a fertilized egg while it develops. The egg cells are produced in the ovaries. The **ovaries** are paired organs located on either side of the **uterus,** or womb, as shown in **FIGURE 34.1.** When a female baby is born, she already has about 2 million potential egg cells stored in her ovaries.

In the ovaries, FSH and LH stimulate the release of another important hormone, estrogen. **Estrogen** is a steroid hormone that has three main functions. First, it controls the development of female sexual characteristics, including widening the pelvis, increasing fat deposits and bone mass, and enlarging the breasts. Second, it is needed for egg cells to develop fully before they leave the ovaries. Third, estrogen helps to prepare the uterus for pregnancy every month and helps to maintain a pregnancy when it occurs.

When an egg cell matures each month, it is released from an ovary and enters the fallopian tube. The **fallopian tube** (fuh-LOH-pee-uhn) is an organ about 10 centimeters (4 in.) long that ends in the uterus. An egg takes several days to travel through this tube. During that time, it can be fertilized by sperm

Differentiated Instruction

BELOW LEVEL

Have students list and then group key terms that describe the female and male reproductive systems in this section, for example,

ovaries-ovum-fallopian tube-uterus-cervix-vagina

scrotum-testes-sperm-epididymis-vas deferens-semen-penis

Tell students to label each group of terms. Then help students define each term.

Biology Toolkit, List-Group-Label, p. D6

PRE-AP

Have students construct two sequence diagrams—one for a sperm cell and one for an egg cell. The diagrams should include the origins and the paths of the cells. Then have students write captions for each step in their diagrams, describing what happens to the cell in each location.

Biology Toolkit, Sequence Diagram, p. C38

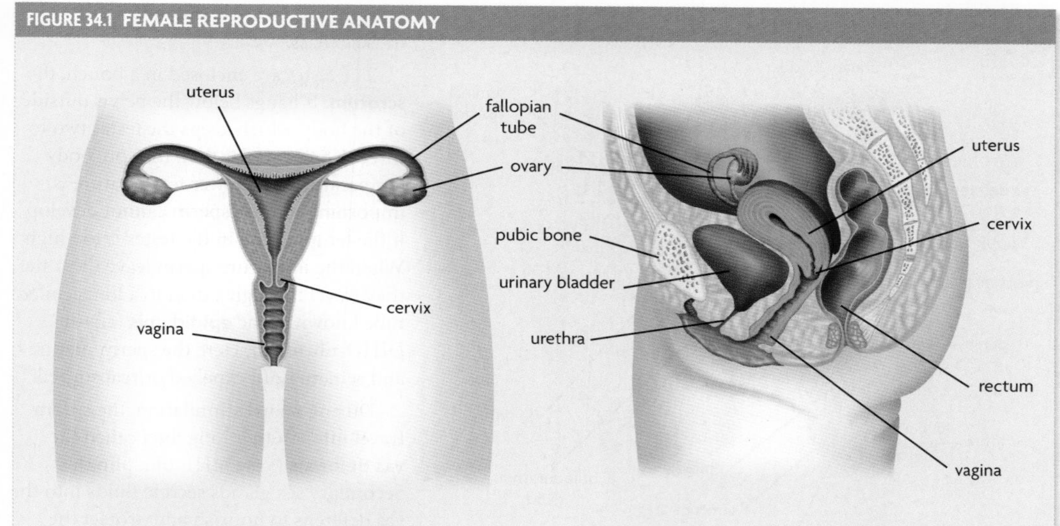

that enter the tube. A fertilized egg will attach to the wall of the uterus, but an unfertilized egg will eventually be broken down and discarded.

The uterus is about the size and shape of a pear. It is composed of three layers: a thin inner layer of epithelial cells, a thick middle layer of muscle, and an outer layer of connective tissue. The lower end of the uterus is called the cervix, which opens into the vagina. In a normal birth, a baby is pushed down the canal of the vagina to exit the mother's body. The complex processes of fertilization and human development are described in Sections 34.2 and 34.3.

TAKING NOTES

Use a two-column chart to list the major parts and functions of the female and male reproductive anatomy.

Female	Male
Ovaries — Paired organs where eggs are produced	Testes — Paired organs that produce sperm cells

A Analyze **How does the release of estrogen affect the female reproductive system during puberty?**

MAIN IDEA

The male reproductive system produces sperm.

The main functions of the male reproductive system are to produce sperm cells and to deliver them to the female reproductive system. The diagram in **FIGURE 34.2,** on the following page, shows the organs in which sperm are produced and stored and the organs that deliver the sperm.

Males do not produce sperm until puberty but afterward can produce sperm all their lives. Sperm production takes place in the testicles, or **testes** (TEHS-teez), which are paired organs. Each testis (singular of testes) contains hundreds of tiny tubules where millions of sperm cells are produced. In the testes, LH stimulates the release of testosterone. **Testosterone** (tehs-TAHS-tuh-ROHN) is a steroid hormone that, along with FSH, stimulates the production of sperm cells. Testosterone also controls the development of male sexual characteristics. These include a deeper voice than a female's, more body hair,

ENGLISH LEARNERS

Distribute a three-column chart with the heads *Statement, My Answer,* and *Text Answer.* Write six short true/false statements such as these that activate prior knowledge about main ideas: (1) Unlike males, females have all reproductive organs inside their bodies. (2) Mature egg cells are released from the uterus. (3) Semen is sperm. Have students write in the statements and their *true* or *false* answers. Students can fill in the third column after reading the section.

Biology Toolkit, Anticipation Guide, p. C3

TEACH FROM VISUALS

FIGURE 34.1 Have students locate the parts of the female reproductive system. **Ask,** Which labeled parts are not part of the female reproductive system? pubic bone, urinary bladder, urethra, rectum

Integrating Comparative Biology

The **female reproductive structures** in other mammals are similar to human structures but are different in some interesting ways. Cats and dogs have a cervix that leads to a uterus that divides into two parts called horns. Each horn ends at a fallopian tube and an ovary. Mice and rabbits have two cervixes, each leading to a separate uterus. Marsupials have two of everything—vaginas, cervixes, uteruses, fallopian tubes, and ovaries.

The Inside Story

In 1996, **Lance Armstrong** was diagnosed with an aggressive form of **testicular cancer** that eventually spread to his lungs and brain. Following chemotherapy and two surgeries, he went on to win the Tour de France seven times, from 1999 to 2005.

Although testicular cancer makes up only 1% of all the cancers found in men, it is the most common form of cancer in men aged 15 to 34. If found early, it is almost always curable.

Answers

A Analyze helps egg cells develop before leaving ovaries; helps prepare uterus for pregnancy every month.

▼ Teach *continued*

TEACH FROM VISUALS

FIGURE 34.2 Have students locate the parts of the male reproductive system. **Ask,** Which labeled parts are not part of the male reproductive system? pubic bone, urinary bladder, rectum Point out that the urethra is part of the male reproductive system as well as the excretory system because sperm and urine leave the body through the urethra. However, in females, the urethra is not part of the female reproductive system or connected to it.

Vocabulary

Greek and Latin Word Origins The term **epididymis** comes from the Greek word *epididumis,* which is a combination of *epi-* and *didumoi.* The root *didumoi* means "twins," but also translates to "testicles." The term **vas deferens** comes from two Latin words. The word *vas* means "duct"; *deferens* comes from *deferre,* which means "to carry away." *Deferens* shares the same root as the word *defer,* which means "to yield."

Answers

A Apply A fever raises the body temperature, and sperm need cooler temperatures to mature.

▼ Assess and Reteach

Assess Use the Online Quiz or Section Quiz (*Assessment Book,* p. 667).

Reteach Have students summarize the section's content by identifying the parts of the male and female reproductive systems and explaining the role of each part in reproduction. Write their responses on the board.

FIGURE 34.2 MALE REPRODUCTIVE ANATOMY

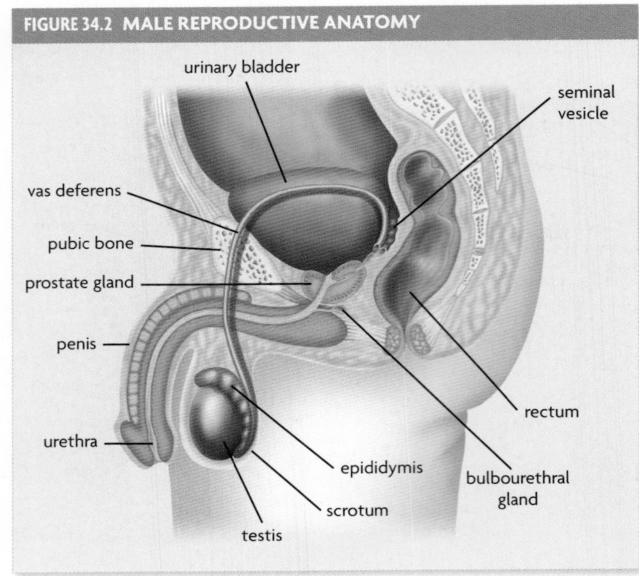

greater bone density, and increased muscle mass.

The testes are enclosed in a pouch, the **scrotum.** It hangs below the pelvis outside of the body, which keeps the testes two to three degrees cooler than the core body temperature. The lower temperature is important because sperm cannot develop if the temperature in the testes is too high. When the immature sperm leave the testes, they travel through a duct to a long, coiled tube known as the **epididymis** (EHP-ih-DIHD-uh-mihs). Here the sperm mature and remain until expelled or reabsorbed.

During sexual stimulation, the sperm travel into another long duct called the **vas deferens** (vas DEHF-uhr-uhnz). Secondary sex glands secrete fluids into the vas deferens to nourish and protect the sperm. The prostate gland, which surrounds the urethra, produces a fluid that helps sperm move more easily. The bulbourethral gland (BUHL-boh-yu-REE-thruhl) and the seminal vesicle secrete basic fluids that help to neutralize the acidity in the urethra and in the female's vagina. The fluids from all three glands, together with the sperm, form a milky white substance known as **semen.**

NSTA SCILINKS scilinks.org
For more information on the human reproductive systems, go to scilinks.org.
Keycode: MLB034

During sexual arousal, blood flows into the penis, making it rigid. Semen moves from the vas deferens into the urethra, which runs the length of the penis. When ejaculation occurs, a muscle closes off the bladder to prevent urine from mixing with the semen in the urethra. Smooth muscle contractions then propel the semen along the urethra and eject it from the penis.

A Apply **Why might having a high fever affect sperm production?**

34.1 ASSESSMENT

ONLINE QUIZ ClassZone.com

REVIEWING MAIN IDEAS

1. Explain the function of the following parts of the female reproductive system: **ovary, fallopian tube, uterus**.
2. Explain the function of the following parts of the male reproductive system: **testes, scrotum, epididymis, vas deferens**.

CRITICAL THINKING

3. **Compare** In what ways are the effects of **testosterone** on males and **estrogen** on females similar?
4. **Infer** Both males and females have paired organs that produce sex cells. What survival advantage for our species might this pairing of organs provide?

***Connecting* CONCEPTS**

5. **Plants** You read in Chapter 22 that flowering plants reproduce sexually. The stamen produces pollen grains, and the carpel contains an ovary where eggs are produced. How do these structures compare with human reproductive organs?

34.1 ASSESSMENT

1. The ovary produces ova (eggs), which travel through the fallopian tubes where they can be fertilized. The uterus provides an environment for a fertilized egg to develop.
2. The scrotum is a sac that helps keep testes cool. The testes produce sperm, which mature and are stored in the epididymis. The vas deferens is a duct that conveys semen to the urethra.
3. Both cause the development of sexual characteristics and are involved in the production of reproductive cells.
4. If one is damaged or destroyed, the other can still produce sex cells to enable species survival.
5. Stamen compares to testes because it produces male sex cells; the ovary and eggs compare to the same structures in females.

34.2 Reproductive Processes

KEY CONCEPT Human reproductive processes depend on cycles of hormones.

MAIN IDEAS
- Eggs mature and are released according to hormonal cycles.
- Sperm production in the testes is controlled by hormones.
- Fertilization occurs when a sperm cell joins an egg cell.
- Sexually transmitted diseases affect fertility and overall health.

VOCABULARY
follicle, p. 1028
ovulation, p. 1028
menstrual cycle, p. 1028
endometrium, p. 1028
corpus luteum, p. 1029
menopause, p. 1029
zygote, p. 1031
infertility, p. 1031
sexually transmitted disease, p. 1032

Review
meiosis, ovary, uterus, ovum, fallopian tube, sperm, vas deferens

Connect You may have heard the phrase "Timing is everything." In football, for instance, precise timing between players can mean the difference between catching or dropping a key pass. Likewise, timing is everything for the hormones that regulate the reproductive processes in your body. Numerous feedback loops among these hormones help ensure that each process occurs at the right time and in the right order.

MAIN IDEA

Eggs mature and are released according to hormonal cycles.

A female's reproductive cycle is controlled by hormones released by the hypothalamus, the pituitary gland, and the ovaries. Each month, the levels of these hormones rise and fall in well-timed feedback loops that regulate the development and release of an egg and prepare the uterus to receive it.

FIGURE 34.3 Potential eggs go through meiosis I and II to produce mature ova, or eggs with 23 chromosomes each.

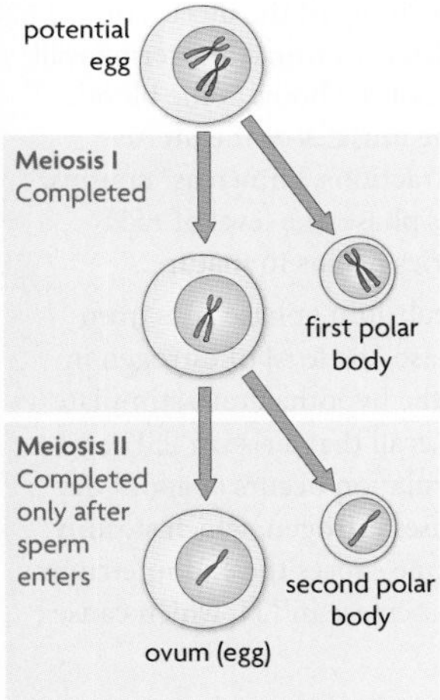

Production of Eggs

The production of eggs, or ova, begins before a female is born, as described in Section 34.1. Recall from Chapter 6 that meiosis is a type of cell division that produces sex cells, or gametes. After the chromosomes in each of the cells are duplicated, meiosis I can begin. The potential eggs then enter a resting phase that lasts until puberty. At birth, a female has about 2 million of these partially developed eggs in her ovaries. Before puberty begins, many of these cells break down until only about 400,000 are left.

At puberty, a monthly hormone cycle begins the second stage of egg production. Every 28 days or so, an increase in FSH stimulates a potential egg to complete meiosis I, as shown in **FIGURE 34.3.** The potential egg divides unevenly, producing two sex cells. The larger cell receives most of the organelles, cytoplasm, and nutrients an embryo will need when an egg is fertilized. The smaller cell, or polar body, simply breaks down. The larger sex cell completes meiosis II only after a sperm enters it. The cell divides again to produce an ovum, or egg, and a second polar body that also breaks down. Both the ovum and the second polar body contain 23 chromosomes from the mother.

Differentiated Instruction

BELOW LEVEL

Students can preview this section using this strategy:
- Predict what the section will be about by using the headings.
- Locate key terms.
- Add details and definitions while reading.
- Note how the text supports the section's main ideas, writing a paragraph for each main idea.

Biology Toolkit, PLAN, p. C7

SECTION 34.2

Plan and Prepare ▼

Objectives
- Explain the role of hormones in the reproductive process.
- Describe fertilization.
- Summarize how sexually transmitted diseases affect an individual.

Section Resources

Unit Resource Book
Study Guide pp. 177–178
Power Notes p. 179
Reinforcement p. 180
Pre-AP Activity pp. 191–192

Interactive Reader Chapter 34
Spanish Study Guide pp. 341–342

Biology Toolkit pp. C7, C19, C20, C22, C39

Technology
Power Presentation 34.2
Media Gallery DVD
Online Quiz 34.2

Activate Prior Knowledge Tell students that the word *parsimony* refers to excessive frugality, even stinginess.
Ask, Why is *parsimony* a good word to describe gamete production in human females but not males? Females produce far fewer eggs than males do sperm.
Ask, What does this form of frugality in females preserve? energy, resources

Teach ▼

TEACH FROM VISUALS

FIGURE 34.3 Have students relate the stages shown in the figure to the time frame described in the text for completion of meiosis I and II. **Ask**
- At a minimum, how much time elapses between prophase I in the potential egg and the completion of meiosis I? occurs with the onset of puberty, for most girls between ages 10 and 14 years
- When does the egg complete meiosis? upon fertilization

▼ Teach *continued*

Address Misconceptions

Common Misconception Students might think that an average of 28 days for a menstrual cycle equates to 28 days being normal and anything other than that being abnormal.

Correcting the Misconception Tell students that the length of a menstrual cycle and its phases varies not only among individuals but also can vary in an individual from cycle to cycle. A normal menstrual cycle can range from 23 days to 35 days. The average length of the flow phase is 5 days but can vary greatly from woman to woman.

Vocabulary

Word Origins The word **menstrual** derives from words associated with the word *month.* A menstrual cycle, which is counted from day 1 of one flow phase to day 1 of the next, roughly equates to a month's time. Menstrual cramps are also called **dysmenorrhea,** which incorporates the word parts *dys-* meaning "bad" and *-rrhea* meaning "flow." **Amenorrhea** refers to the suppression or absence of menstruation.

Answers

A Infer It provides more time for the egg to be fertilized.

FIGURE 34.4 Release of Egg

After an egg is released, it travels through the fallopian tube, where it might be fertilized.

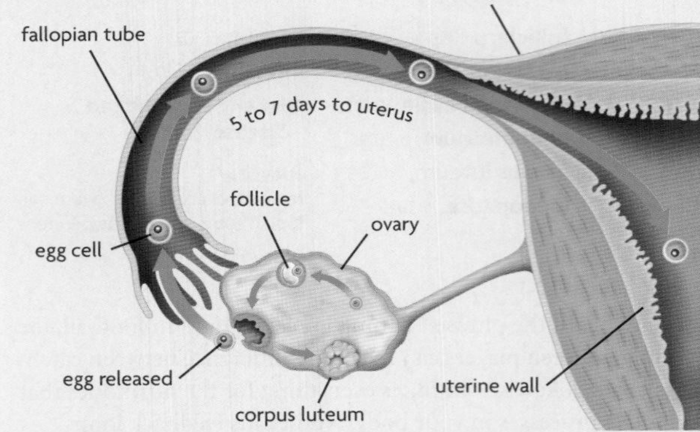

A Infer Why might it be an advantage that the egg takes several days to travel through the fallopian tube?

Release of Egg

Each developing sex cell, which you can think of as an egg, is surrounded by a group of cells called a **follicle** that helps the egg to mature. When an egg is ready to be released, the follicle ruptures, and the egg breaks through the ovary wall, as shown in **FIGURE 34.4.** The release of an egg from the ovary is called **ovulation.** The egg is swept into the fallopian tube, where it can be fertilized by a sperm. Over the next five to seven days, the egg moves through the tube to the uterus. An unfertilized egg is discarded during menstruation.

In most cases, only one egg is released during ovulation. About 400 to 500 eggs are released over a female's reproductive life. Which ovary releases an egg each month is entirely random. If one ovary is damaged, however, the other may take over and release an egg each month.

The Menstrual Cycle

The **menstrual cycle** is a series of monthly changes in the reproductive system that include producing and releasing an egg and preparing the uterus to receive it. The length of the cycle is slightly different for each female, but averages about 28 days. The cycle has three main phases—flow phase, follicular phase, and luteal phase, as **FIGURE 34.5** shows. The timing of each phase is regulated by specific hormones.

Connecting CONCEPTS

Animal Behavior As you read in **Chapter 27,** hormone cycles control more than reproduction. Certain glands and proteins in some animals detect seasonal changes in temperature and in the hours of daylight. As a result, the glands secrete hormones that control when an animal will hibernate or migrate.

1. **Flow phase** Day 1 of the menstrual cycle is the first day that the menstrual flow begins. The flow occurs when the lining of the uterus, or **endometrium** (EHN-doh-MEE-tree-uhm), detaches from the uterine wall and passes through the vagina to the outside of the body. Some blood, mucus, and tissue fluid are also expelled. The muscles of the uterus contract to help expel the lining. These contractions, known as "cramps," can be painful for some females. During this phase, the level of FSH starts to rise, and another follicle in the ovaries begins to mature.
2. **Follicular phase** The follicular (fuh-LIHK-yuh-luhr) phase lasts from about day 6 to day 14. At the start of this phase, the level of estrogen in the blood is relatively low. Hormones from the hypothalamus stimulate the pituitary to release more FSH and LH. Recall that a rise in FSH and LH causes the egg and follicle to mature. Ovulation occurs at about day 14. As the egg is developing, the follicle releases estrogen, which steadily increases over the next few days. This hormone causes the endometrium to thicken. Estrogen also stimulates a sharp increase in LH, which causes the follicle to rupture, releasing the egg.

Differentiated Instruction

ENGLISH LEARNERS

Have students create a T-chart, using the first three main ideas and **FIGURES 34.3, 34.4, 34.6,** and **34.7.** Tell students to omit "The Menstrual Cycle." Students should title the left column *Process,* and the right column *Steps.* Entries in the *Process* column could be (1) Eggs are produced and mature according to hormonal cycles; (2) Eggs are released according to hormonal cycles; and so on. By reading through the corresponding section of the text, students will be able to include details under *Steps.*

Biology Toolkit, T-Chart, p. C20

BELOW LEVEL

Tell students that sometimes unfamiliar scientific terms are derived from the same word. Have students consider these words:

ovum *ovary* *ovulation*

Ovum is from the Latin word *ovum,* which means "egg." *Ovary* and *ovulation* are derived from *ovum.* Have students remember the sentence "The release of an ovum (egg) from an ovary is ovulation."

3 Luteal phase In the luteal (LOO-tee-uhl) phase, the release of hormones is now timed to stop egg production and to develop the endometrium to receive a fertilized egg. After ovulation, the empty follicle turns yellow and is called the **corpus luteum** (KAWR-puhs LOO-tee-uhm), or "yellow body." The corpus luteum releases estrogen and another hormone, progesterone, which limits the production of LH. Progesterone and estrogen also increase the number of blood vessels in the endometrium. If the egg is not fertilized, rising levels of estrogen and progesterone cause the hypothalamus to stop releasing FSH and LH. The corpus luteum then breaks down and stops secreting estrogen and progesterone. As a result, the uterus lining begins to shed, and the next flow phase starts.

For most women, the menstrual cycle continues throughout their reproductive years, which may last from preteen years to the late 50s. Eventually, however, the levels of hormones decline with age. This decline disrupts the normal timing of the menstrual cycle. In a process called **menopause,** the cycle gradually becomes more and more irregular and finally stops altogether. Menopause can occur as early as a woman's mid-30s.

VOCABULARY

Menstruation and *menopause* are based on the Latin word *mensis,* which means "month."

A Summarize What are the main functions of estrogen and progesterone during the follicular and luteal phases?

FIGURE 34.5 Menstrual Cycle

Hormones cause changes in the follicle, egg, and lining of the uterus.

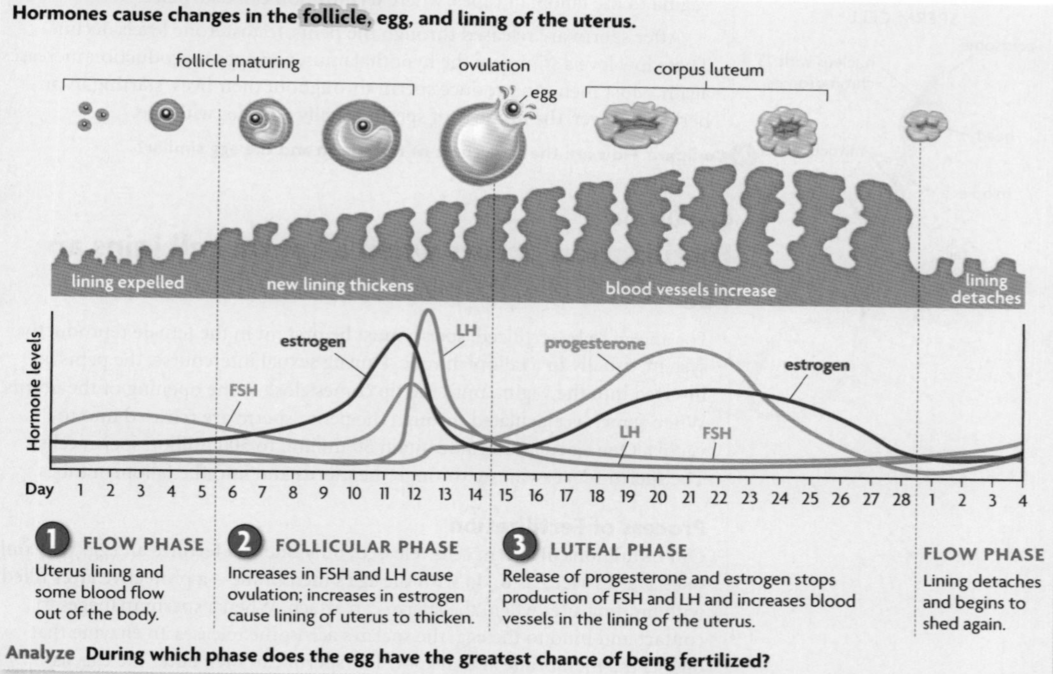

1 FLOW PHASE Uterus lining and some blood flow out of the body.

2 FOLLICULAR PHASE Increases in FSH and LH cause ovulation; increases in estrogen cause lining of uterus to thicken.

3 LUTEAL PHASE Release of progesterone and estrogen stops production of FSH and LH and increases blood vessels in the lining of the uterus.

FLOW PHASE Lining detaches and begins to shed again.

B Analyze During which phase does the egg have the greatest chance of being fertilized?

Integrating Medical Science

Endometriosis is a common problem in women. Endometriosis involves the endometrium of the uterus and occurs when endometrial cells become implanted in other areas of the body, such as on the ovaries, behind the uterus, or on the bowel or urinary bladder. The hormones that affect the endometrium also affect the implanted endometrial cells. Tissue and blood vessels build up in those areas each month, but they have no way to leave the body. The resulting growth can cause inflammation, scarring, and pain. **Ask,** Why might a woman with endometriosis have trouble becoming pregnant? The growth could cover an ovary or block a fallopian tube.

TEACH FROM VISUALS

FIGURE 34.5 Have students analyze the diagram and graph to understand the connections among the levels of hormones, the lining of the uterus, and the ovary. Remind students that the hypothalamus stimulates the pituitary gland to release FSH and LH, and the ovaries release estrogen and progesterone. **Ask**

- During what phase are most hormone levels the lowest? flow phase
- What hormones cause ovulation? FSH and LH
- What hormones stop the production of FSH and LH? progesterone and estrogen

PRE-AP

Have students make their own cycle diagrams that summarize the phases of a 28-day menstrual cycle. Each phase in the diagram should include the days, the hormone levels, and a description of what is occurring in the ovary and uterine lining.

Biology Toolkit, Cycle Diagram, p. C39

BELOW LEVEL

Have students use a content frame to help them understand and remember the hormones involved in the menstrual cycle. Tell students to list the hormones in the first column, where the hormones are produced in the second column, and in the third column, what each hormone does during the menstrual cycle.

Biology Toolkit, Content Frame, p. C22

Answers

A Summarize Follicular phase: estrogen causes the endometrium to thicken and stimulates a sharp increase in LH; progesterone has no function. Luteal phase: both limit production of LH, increase the number of blood vessels in the endometrium, and, if the egg is not fertilized, cause the hypothalamus to stop releasing FSH and LH.

B Analyze luteal, because the egg has been released and is in the fallopian tube

▼ Teach *continued*

ONLINE BIOLOGY Go to the chapter Resource Center at **ClassZone.com** for additional resources and information on gametes.

TEACH FROM VISUALS

FIGURE 34.6 Using the diagram, have students compare the process of meiosis in producing an egg and a sperm. **Ask**

- How does the number of sperm produced compare to the number of eggs produced from one specialized cell? one egg, four sperm
- How does the number of chromosomes in an egg compare to the number of chromosomes in a sperm? Both have 23 chromosomes.
- Why is this number important? The offspring will have 46 chromosomes.

History of Science

Preformation was a theory of embryonic development popular until the 18th century. It assumed that all parts of an organism existed completely formed in a germ cell and that prenatal development consisted only of increasing size. For humans, some believed that the sperm contained the miniature infant, called a **homunculus;** others believed the miniature infant was contained in the egg.

Advancements in technology made it possible to observe that an egg does not start with a fully formed individual, but rather goes through incremental stages of development. This successive differentiation of an egg is called **epigenesis.** The idea is not a new one; **Aristotle** proposed the theory 2000 years ago.

Answers

A Compare sex cells; 23 chromosomes

FIGURE 34.6 Each potential sperm cell that undergoes meiosis produces four mature sperm cells with 23 chromosomes each. A mature sperm has a head, midpiece, and whiplike tail that enables it to move.

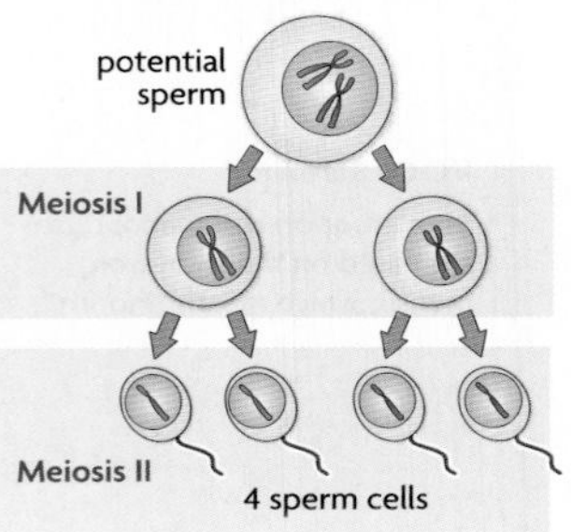

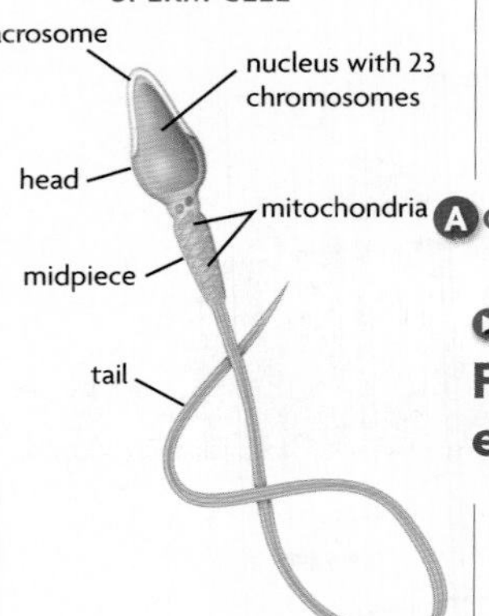

MAIN IDEA

Sperm production in the testes is controlled by hormones.

The reproductive cycles for males and females are different in two ways. First, females begin to produce eggs before they are born, but males do not produce sperm until they reach puberty. Second, females usually produce only one egg a month to be fertilized, while males produce millions of sperm almost daily.

The production of sperm begins when hormones from the hypothalamus stimulate the pituitary to release FSH and LH, which circulate to the testes. The testes start releasing testosterone, which causes specialized cells to go through meiosis to develop into mature sperm. As the levels of testosterone rise, the levels of FSH and LH begin to decline. This feedback loop among the hormones helps to control the number of sperm that are produced.

Unlike eggs, which produce polar bodies, the developing sperm divide into four equal sperm cells, as shown in **FIGURE 34.6.** Each cell is haploid, with 23 chromosomes. Sperm cells then fully mature in the epididymis. As the diagram shows, each sperm has a head, midpiece, and tail. The head contains a nucleus and a cap region called the acrosome. When a sperm cell contacts an egg, the acrosome releases enzymes that allow the sperm to penetrate the egg's membrane. The midpiece holds the mitochondria that supply the sperm with ATP for the energy it needs. The tail, or flagellum, propels the sperm from the vagina to the fallopian tubes, where fertilization can take place.

After sperm are released through the penis, testosterone levels decline. These low levels stimulate the hypothalamus, and sperm production increases again. Most men can produce sperm throughout their lives, starting in puberty. However, the number of sperm usually declines with age.

A Compare **How are the structures of the sperm and the egg similar?**

MAIN IDEA

Fertilization occurs when a sperm cell joins an egg cell.

For an egg to be fertilized, sperm must be present in the female reproductive system, usually in a fallopian tube. During sexual intercourse, the penis is inserted into the vagina until the tip comes close to the opening of the uterus. When semen is ejaculated through the penis, sperm are released into the vagina. One ejaculation can contain 50 million to 500 million sperm cells. The sperm must swim up through the uterus and into the fallopian tubes.

Process of Fertilization

Out of millions of sperm cells released, only one will fertilize an egg. Why only one? The answer has to do with the egg's membrane—a protective layer filled with binding sites where the sperm can attach. When a sperm manages to contact and bind to the egg, the sperm's acrosome releases an enzyme that digests the membrane at that spot. The sperm can then enter the egg, as

Differentiated Instruction

ENGLISH LEARNERS

Have students use a graphic organizer to compare and contrast the production of eggs and sperm. To get students started, have them consider these questions:

- What hormone feedback loops regulate each production?
- How does meiosis differ?
- When and how often is each produced?

Biology Toolkit, T-Chart, p. C20

QUICK LAB OBSERVING

Human Sex Cells

In this lab, you will examine prepared slides of mammalian male and female sex cells.

PROBLEM How do male and female sex cells differ?

PROCEDURE

1. Examine a slide of sperm cells under low power and high power. Draw a sperm cell and label its structures.
2. Examine a slide of egg cells under low power and high power. Draw an egg cell and label its different structures.

MATERIALS

- slide of mammalian sperm cells
- slide of mammalian egg cells
- microscope

ANALYZE AND CONCLUDE

1. **Analyze** Why is the flagellum an important structure in a sperm cell?
2. **Contrast** How is the egg structurally different from the sperm?

shown in **FIGURE 34.7.** Once the egg is penetrated, its surface changes to form a barrier that stops other sperm from entering. In effect, the egg lets in one sperm, then closes the door on the others. The egg then completes meiosis II. Then the 23 chromosomes of the sperm join with the 23 chromosomes of the egg to form a fertilized egg called a **zygote.** This combination of chromosomes helps preserve genetic diversity because chromosomes in a pair often have different alleles of genes. This is one reason children are never exact genetic copies of their parents.

In rare cases, more than one egg may be released into the fallopian tubes. If two eggs are fertilized, they will develop into fraternal twins. Fraternal twins are not genetically the same. They are just like any other siblings who are born separately.

Genetically identical twins occur only when a single fertilized egg splits into two zygotes, each one with 46 chromosomes. As a result, two identical but separate embryos develop in the uterus. In even rarer cases, a fertilized egg may split into three, four, or more zygotes. If they all develop, the mother will give birth to several genetically identical babies.

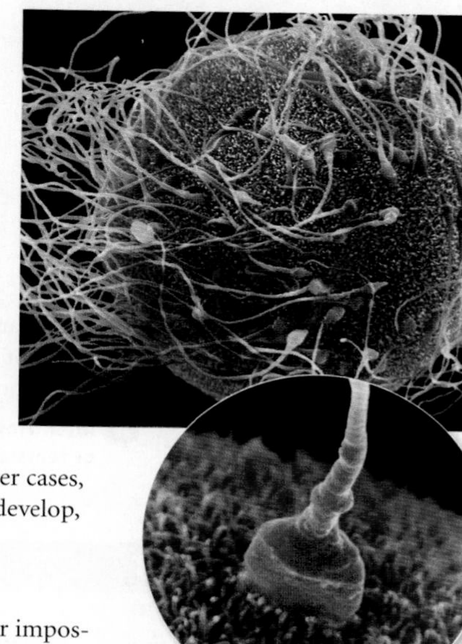

FIGURE 34.7 In the top image, sperm surround an egg. The bottom image shows one sperm penetrating an egg's membrane. (colored SEM; magnifications: egg with sperm 600×; sperm detail 4,000×)

Problems in Fertilization

Infertility refers to any condition that makes reproduction difficult or impossible. In the male, for instance, the vas deferens may be too narrow or blocked, which prevents sperm from leaving the body. If the sperm count is too low or the sperm are weakened or deformed, fertilization may not occur. Certain illnesses, such as mumps in adults, can destroy the testes' ability to produce sperm. In females, diseases that damage the ovaries or fallopian tubes can prevent eggs from being produced or reaching the uterus. The eggs themselves may have defects that keep the sperm from getting through the membrane. Many infertility problems can be corrected through treatments such as medications, surgery, or even dietary changes.

(A) Apply **If twins are born and one is a boy and one is a girl, are they identical or fraternal siblings? Explain your answer.**

PRE-AP

Have students write for five minutes on how the structure and size of a sperm cell compare to an egg cell. Students can use the information in this section as well as refer to information introduced in the plant and animal chapters. Have students think in terms of form following function.

Biology Toolkit, Quick-Write, p. C19

QUICK LAB

Time 15 minutes	TEACHER TESTED
Lab Binder Human Bio, p. 84	

Purpose Examine the structures of a mammalian sperm cell and egg cell, using prepared slides and a microscope.

LAB PREPARATION

- Review the production of egg cells and sperm cells with students.

LAB MANAGEMENT

Safety Caution students to handle the slides carefully. Remind students to wipe down the eyepieces with alcohol wipes before and after use.

Answers

Analyze and Conclude

1. The flagellum is used to propel the sperm through the female reproductive system to reach the egg.
2. Students' responses will depend on the slide viewed. Eggs are larger, have no tail, contain material to nourish a zygote, and are surrounded by a thick membrane. Sperm are small and have a tail to propel them, a head containing DNA and the acrosome, and a midpiece containing mitochondria.

Answers

(A) **Apply** Fraternal siblings; identical siblings are genetically alike, so they would be the same sex.

▼ Teach *continued*

Vocabulary

Academic Vocabulary You may want to point out the distinction between the words **sex** and **gender.** *Sex* refers to a classification based on the reproductive system. *Gender* was originally a grammatical category of masculine, feminine, and neuter, but is now used to describe social roles. So sex is defined biologically, and gender is defined culturally.

Answers

A Infer Bacterial STD can damage or destroy the sexual organs and may impair the release of key hormones, causing hormone feedback loops to be affected. These effects would make it impossible to be fertile.

MAIN IDEA

Sexually transmitted diseases affect fertility and overall health.

Diseases passed from one person to another during sexual contact are called **sexually transmitted diseases,** or STDs. These diseases affect millions of people in their peak reproductive years and cause thousands of deaths. Some STDs in the early stages produce few symptoms. People do not realize they are carrying the disease and continue to infect others through sexual contact.

Bacterial STDs include chlamydia, syphilis, and gonorrhea. Chlamydia is the most common infection in the United States. Bacterial STDs attack the reproductive organs, such as the ovaries, and often cause infertility. In the case of syphilis, an untreated infection can even be fatal. Another infection, trichomoniasis, is caused by a parasite, shown in **FIGURE 34.8.** Trichomoniasis and chlamydia mostly affect young women aged 15 to 24 and can cause a serious condition known as pelvic inflammatory disease. People with these infections show few symptoms at first. This may be one reason why rates for trichomoniasis and chlamydia are increasing. Most parasitic and bacterial STDs can be treated with antibiotics.

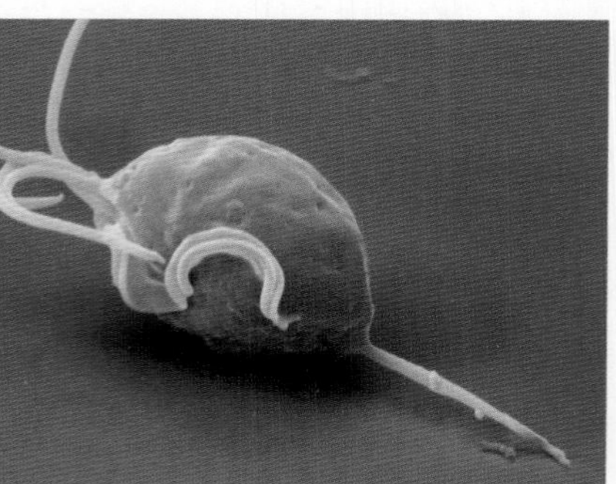

FIGURE 34.8 The parasite *Trichomonas vaginalis* causes a common STD infection, trichomoniasis, that can affect fertility. (colored SEM; magnification 9000×)

Viral STDs include hepatitis B, genital herpes, human papillomavirus (HPV), and human immunodeficiency virus (HIV), which causes AIDS. Although medications can control these diseases, there are no cures. Antibiotics have no effect on viruses. HPV has been linked to cervical cancer, and AIDS has caused millions of deaths worldwide.

People can avoid STDs, just as they avoid other diseases. The surest ways are to abstain from sexual contact before marriage and for partners who do not have STDs to remain faithful in a committed relationship. Using a condom is the next safest choice; however, a condom can break or tear.

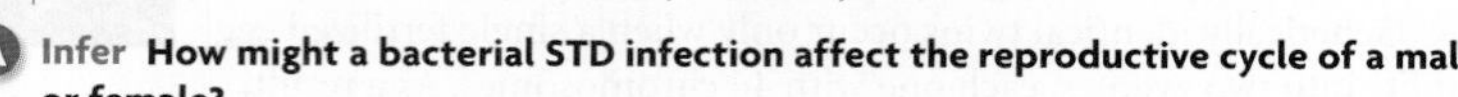

A Infer How might a bacterial STD infection affect the reproductive cycle of a male or female?

34.2 ASSESSMENT

ONLINE QUIZ ClassZone.com

REVIEWING MAIN IDEAS

1. What is the main function of each phase in the **menstrual cycle**?
2. How does the structure of the sperm cell aid its function?
3. Describe how an egg is fertilized.
4. **Sexually transmitted diseases** can affect fertility. Explain why.

CRITICAL THINKING

5. **Contrast** Name two ways that the production of eggs differs from the production of sperm.
6. **Apply** A woman gives birth to quadruplets, or four infants. Two of her children are identical twins. The other two are fraternal twins. How could this have happened?

Connecting CONCEPTS

7. **Developmental Biology** Every egg contains one X chromosome. Each sperm contains either one X or one Y chromosome. Explain why the sperm always determines a baby's gender.

▼ Assess and Reteach

Assess Use the Online Quiz or Section Quiz (*Assessment Book,* p. 668).

Reteach Project on the board the image of **FIGURE 34.5** (Menstrual Cycle) from the Media Gallery. Place a sticky note over each caption below each phase of the menstrual cycle. Have students describe each phase in terms of the approximate number of days of duration, hormone levels, condition of the uterine lining, and changes in the ovary.

34.2 ASSESSMENT

1. Flow phase: shed the lining of uterus. Follicular phase: release an egg, thicken the uterine lining. Luteal phase: further prepare the uterus to receive a fertilized egg.
2. The acrosome in the head makes it possible for the sperm to enter the cell. Mitochondria in the neck provide energy to the tail of the sperm. The tail moves back and forth, propelling the sperm forward.
3. A sperm contacts and binds to the egg; the acrosome digests the membrane and allows the sperm to enter. The 23 chromosomes in the sperm join with the 23 chromosomes in the egg to form a zygote.
4. These diseases can damage or destroy reproductive organs. Untreated infections can even cause death.
5. Eggs are produced before the female is born; sperm is produced when the male reaches puberty. Female has a limited number of eggs; male has a vast quantity of sperm. Female meiosis produces one ovum and two polar bodies; male produces four functional sperm cells.
6. Three eggs were fertilized by three different sperm. One fertilized egg separated into two genetically identical zygotes. The fraternal twins each developed from a separate fertilized egg.
7. If a sperm contributes an X chromosome, the child will be XX, or female. If a sperm contributes a Y chromosome, the child will be XY, or male.

MATERIALS
- graph paper
- colored markers
- Hormone Blood Levels Datasheet

PROCESS SKILLS
- **Graphing**
- **Interpreting Graphs**

NOS.3 Clearly communicate their ideas and results of investigations verbally and in written form using tables, graphs, diagrams, and photographs.

Hormones in the Human Menstrual Cycle

Hormones, including follicle-stimulating hormone (FSH), luteinizing hormone (LH), estrogen, and progesterone, play critical roles in the human menstrual cycle. As blood levels of these hormones rise and fall, the follicle, the egg, and the lining of the uterus go through different stages of development. In this lab, you will graph and analyze the changes in the blood levels of these four hormones during a menstrual cycle.

PROBLEM How do the blood levels of hormones change during the menstrual cycle?

PROCEDURE
1. Using the data sheet, construct a graph that shows the changes in the blood levels of hormones during a 28-day menstrual cycle in which fertilization does not occur.
2. Plot all hormones on one set of axes, and use different colors to represent the different hormones.

ANALYZE AND CONCLUDE
1. **Summarize** Describe the changes in levels that occur in each of the hormones throughout the month.
2. **Analyze** On what day of the cycle does LH peak? What is the significance of this fact?
3. **Analyze** When does the level of estrogen peak? What is the source of estrogen during this time?
4. **Explain** What is the significance of the rise in levels of estrogen and progesterone between days 10 and 22 of the cycle?
5. **Predict** How would the levels of hormones be affected if the egg were fertilized?

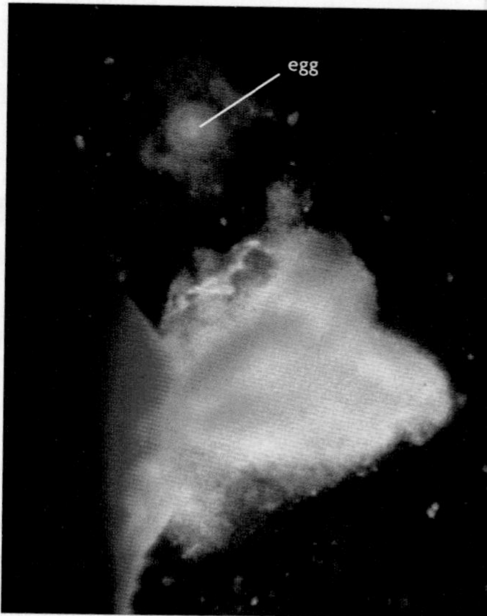

This micrograph captures the process of an egg breaking free from a rupturing follicle in the ovary. (LM; magnification unknown)

INVESTIGATION

Time 45 minutes	TEACHER TESTED
Teacher Preparation	
Student Difficulty	
Lab Binder Human Bio, pp. 77–79	

Purpose Analyze changes in the blood levels of hormones during the menstrual cycle.

Overview Students will graph data on the blood levels of FSH, LH, estrogen, and progesterone during each day of the menstrual cycle in which fertilization does not occur. They will
- analyze the changes in each hormone
- explain the significance of the changes
- predict how fertilization would affect the levels of hormones

LAB PREPARATION
- Make copies of the Hormone Table datasheet for students, *Lab Binder*, p. 79.
- Review with students the menstrual cycle and the role of each of the hormones: FSH, LH, estrogen, and progesterone.

LAB MANAGEMENT
- Remind students to label each axis of the graph and to include a title and a key.

POST-LAB DISCUSSION
Discuss students' results. **Ask,** How did making a graph help you analyze the changes in the level of each hormone? The separate lines on the graph make it easy to distinguish the levels of the four different hormones and to see whether the level of each hormone increases, decreases, or stays the same.

Answers

Expected Results
For a sample graph, see page R110.

Analyze and Conclude
1. FSH: rises on days 3–5, then falls; peaks on day 12; low on days 13–22; rises at day 23. LH: levels low, then peak on day 13; levels rapidly decline; low again by day 16; stable on days 19–24 and begins to rise. Estrogen: rises and peaks by day 12; drops between days 13–15; rise and fall in levels between days 16 and 28. Progesterone: low and stable until day 12; rises on days 13–21; peaks on day 22, then falls again.
2. day 13; when ovulation occurs
3. day 12; secreted by ovarian follicles
4. Uterus is prepared for a fertilized egg.
5. progesterone, estrogen levels remain high; corpus luteum releases more progesterone, estrogen; FSH and LH remain low

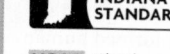

▼ Plan and Prepare

Objectives

- Describe development following implantation.
- Explain how an embryo gets nourishment.
- Explain how the mother and fetus affect each other's health.

Section Resources

Unit Resource Book Study Guide pp. 181–182 Power Notes p. 183 Reinforcement p. 184
Interactive Reader Chapter 34 **Spanish Study Guide** pp. 343–344
Biology Toolkit pp. C3, C19, C20, C26, D2
Technology Power Presentation 34.3 Media Gallery DVD Online Quiz 34.3

Activate Prior Knowledge Remind students that cells with the potential to differentiate into any body cell are described as totipotent. Those that can form into any cell of a given tissue are pluripotent. **Ask,** What type of cells are shown in the photograph in the VISUAL VOCAB? totipotent **Ask,** At what point do totipotent cells become pluripotent? upon implantation

▼ Teach

Vocabulary

Greek and Latin Word Origins The Greek word *blastos* means "bud." The **blastocyst** is also sometimes referred to as a **blastosphere.** By comparison, the word **embryo** derives, in part, from the Greek word *bruein,* which means "full to bursting."

34.3 Fetal Development

KEY CONCEPT Development progresses in stages from zygote to fetus.

MAIN IDEAS

- The fertilized egg implants into the uterus and is nourished by the placenta.
- A zygote develops into a fully formed fetus in about 38 weeks.
- The mother affects the fetus, and pregnancy affects the mother.

VOCABULARY

blastocyst, p. 1034
embryo, p. 1034
amniotic sac, p. 1035
placenta, p. 1035
umbilical cord, p. 1035
trimester, p. 1036
fetus, p. 1036

B.6.3 Explain that in multicellular organisms the zygote produced during fertilization undergoes a series of cell divisions that lead to clusters of cells that go on to specialize and become the organism's tissues and organs.

Connect A human zygote develops from a single cell into a fully formed human in about nine months. The rate of growth in the first few weeks is astonishing. If you grew at the same rate after birth, you would be 4 meters (13 ft) tall at one month of age. The zygote's growth is directed by its DNA. However, the environment of the uterus and the mother's overall health also have a strong impact on how well the zygote develops.

MAIN IDEA

The fertilized egg implants into the uterus and is nourished by the placenta.

After fertilization, the zygote begins to divide through mitosis as it travels down the fallopian tube. During this time, the corpus luteum continues to secrete progesterone and some estrogen. These hormones increase the number of blood vessels in the lining of the uterus and prepare it to receive the fertilized egg. After the zygote reaches the uterus, another chain of events takes place that helps it to develop.

Implantation in the Uterus

The zygote continues to undergo cell division until a hollow ball of cells called the **blastocyst** is formed. Cells on the surface of the blastocyst attach, or implant, into the uterine lining, as shown in **FIGURE 34.9.** Once the blastocyst is implanted, it goes through another stage in which three cell layers develop: the ectoderm, the mesoderm, and the endoderm.

The ectoderm layer develops into the skin and nervous system. The mesoderm layer forms many of the internal tissues and organs. The endoderm layer develops into many of the digestive organs and the lining of the digestive system. Once these structures begin to form, the ball of cells is known as an **embryo.**

blastocyst
uterine wall
implantation of blastocyst

FIGURE 34.9 About seven days after fertilization, the blastocyst enters the uterus and attaches, or implants, into the uterine wall. Implantation is the beginning of a pregnancy.

VISUAL VOCAB

The **blastocyst** is a hollow ball of cells that implants in the uterus.

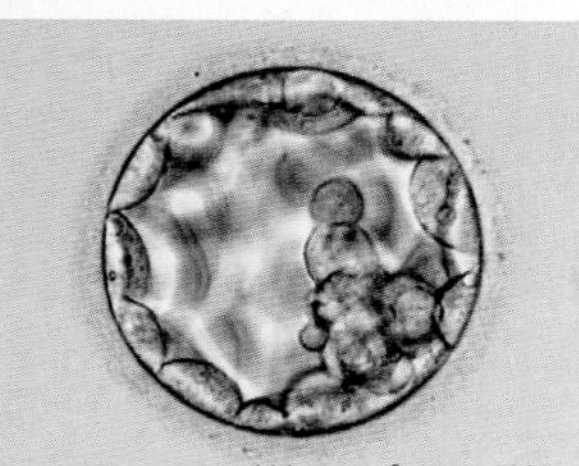

Differentiated Instruction

BELOW LEVEL

To assess students' understanding, write five to ten statements about the main points of the section. Focus on the implantation of the blastocyst in the uterus, the embryonic membranes, and fetal development during each trimester. Have students determine if the statements are true or false before reading the section, and then again after.

Biology Toolkit, Anticipation Guide, p. C3

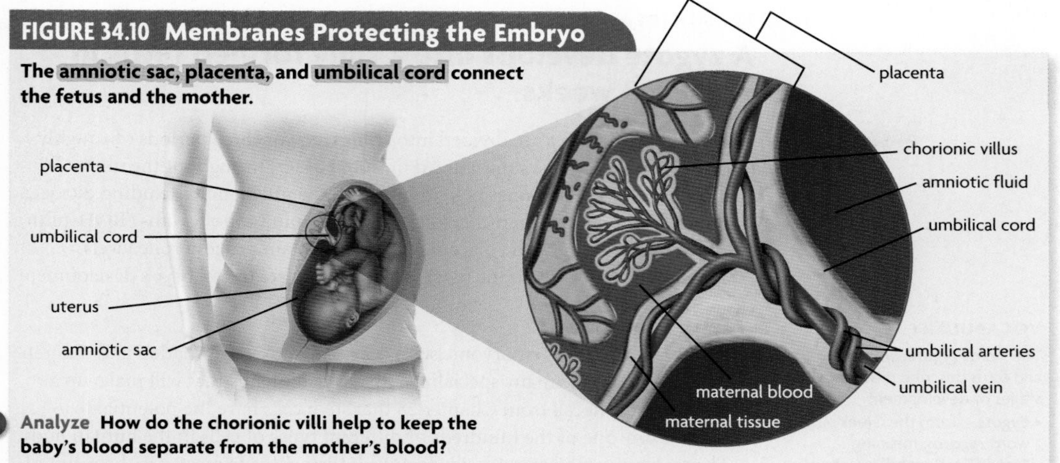

FIGURE 34.10 Membranes Protecting the Embryo

The amniotic sac, placenta, and umbilical cord connect the fetus and the mother.

A Analyze **How do the chorionic villi help to keep the baby's blood separate from the mother's blood?**

Embryonic Membranes

As the pregnancy continues, membranes form that nourish and protect the developing embryo, as shown in **FIGURE 34.10.** One membrane, the amnion, becomes filled with fluid and is called the **amniotic sac** (AM-nee-AHT-ihk). This sac cushions the embryo within the uterus and protects it from sudden temperature changes. The amniotic sac surrounds the embryo until birth. Another membrane, the chorion (KAWR-ee-AHN), also begins to form. The chorion helps to nourish the embryo as it develops. The outer surface of the chorion has small projections called chorionic villi that extend into the uterine lining.

Together, the chorionic villi and the lining of the uterus form an important organ called the placenta. The **placenta** (pluh-SEHN-tuh) connects the mother and embryo to allow for the exchange of oxygen, nutrients, and wastes between them. Another structure, the **umbilical cord,** consists of two arteries and a vein that are twisted together. This cord connects the embryo inside the amniotic sac to the placenta. Nutrients and oxygen from the mother's blood diffuse into the chorionic villi, which contain blood from the embryo. The nutrients are carried to the embryo along the umbilical cord. In turn, wastes from the embryo are carried back along the umbilical cord to the chorionic villi. From there, the wastes diffuse into the mother's blood and are excreted in her urine.

The blood flows of the mother and the embryo move past each other but never mix. The placenta keeps the two flows separated. If proteins from the embryo leaked into the mother's circulatory system, they might be detected as foreign invaders by her immune system. The mother's immune system would then attack the proteins, which could end the pregnancy. The placenta provides a protective barrier for the embryo as it develops.

B Apply **Why might a pregnant woman need to be concerned about what she eats or drinks during pregnancy?**

***Connecting* CONCEPTS**

Circulatory System Like the pulmonary arteries and veins that you read about in **Chapter 30,** the umbilical arteries carry oxygen-poor blood and the umbilical vein carries oxygen-rich blood. The umbilical arteries carry blood away from the fetus's heart, and the umbilical vein carries blood to the fetus's heart.

ENGLISH LEARNERS

Have pairs of students use Cornell notes to outline this section. In the right-hand column, students should make the section outline, following the blue and black heads and key points. In the left-hand column, students should list key terms—section vocabulary or other related words—and their definitions across from the part of the outline where the terms first appear. At the bottom, across both columns, students should add a short section summary.

Biology Toolkit, Cornell Notes, p. C26

Integrating Medical Science

In a normal pregnancy, the blastocyst implants in the lining of the uterus. In an **ectopic pregnancy,** the blastocyst implants elsewhere in the body, such as the fallopian tube, abdominal cavity, ovary, or cervix. A blastocyst that is not implanted in the uterus cannot survive and can mean serious health risks for the woman. If an ovary or fallopian tube ruptures, it can result in severe bleeding.

Vocabulary

Word Origins Tell students that the words **navel** and **umbilical** both derive from related Latin roots, *nobh-* and *ombh-* that refer to the "hub of a wheel" or "central knob." A related word, **nave,** refers to the central part of a church.

Tell students that the umbilical cord attaches to the abdomen. When the umbilical cord is removed, a small portion, called the *umbilicus,* is left behind. The umbilicus is more commonly known as the *belly button* or *navel.*

Answers

A Analyze The chorionic villi allows for oxygen, nutrient, and waste diffusion between mother and baby, keeping the two blood flows separate and preventing any of the baby's proteins from entering the mother and causing an immune response.

B Apply Substances broken down from what the mother eats or drinks can enter the embryo's blood through the chorionic villi.

▼ Teach *continued*

Address Misconceptions

Common Misconception A missed flow phase means a woman is pregnant.

Correcting the Misconception
Although pregnancy is the most common cause of a missed flow phase, the absence of menstruation or a menstrual period can have other causes, such as stress, medications, low body weight, excessive exercise, and health problems. An occasional missed period is not uncommon. **Ask,** How is it possible for someone to be pregnant if she has not yet had her first menstrual period? Ovulation occurs before a period.

Integrating Genetics

Until embryos are about two months old, their **embryonic gonads** are similar and can become testes or ovaries. A gene on the Y chromosome, called the **SRY gene** (for sex-determining region of the Y chromosome) triggers changes. In an embryo with an SRY gene, the embryonic gonads develop into testes. In an embryo without an SRY gene, the embryonic gonads develop into ovaries.

Answers

A Infer The fetus is undergoing cell determination and differentiation at this time; genetic errors and toxic chemicals can interfere with normal cell division and development.

MAIN IDEA

A zygote develops into a fully formed fetus in about 38 weeks.

Human pregnancies are divided into **trimesters,** or three periods of roughly three months each, as summarized in **FIGURE 34.11.** Throughout the nine months, several hormones help to maintain the pregnancy, including estrogen, progesterone, and human chorionic gonadotropin (goh-NAD-uh-TROH-pihn), which is produced by the placenta to help maintain progesterone levels. Thyroid hormones from the mother help to regulate the embryo's development.

VOCABULARY

The words *zygote, embryo,* and *fetus* describe different stages of development.

- **Zygote**—from the Greek word *zugotos,* meaning "yoked," or "joined," as when the sperm joins the egg and cell division begins
- **Embryo**—from the Greek word *embruon,* meaning "to be full to bursting." This stage covers weeks 1 to 8 when the entire body plan is developed.
- **Fetus**—from the Latin word *fetus,* meaning "offspring." This stage covers weeks 9 to 36.

TAKING NOTES

Use a timeline to help you take notes on early fetal development.

Weeks 1–12: egg fertilized; zygote forms; blastocyst implants; 3 layers form

Weeks 13–17

First Trimester

In the first trimester, embryonic stem cells undergo determination and differentiation to form the many specialized tissues and organs that will make up a human body. Recall from Chapter 28 that stem cells have the potential to become any one of the hundreds of different types of cells in the human body. The embryo can be more easily damaged during this trimester as the result of genetic errors or mutations, nutritional deficiencies in the mother, and any toxic chemicals, such as alcohol or drugs, that the mother may consume.

Even at this early stage, the complete body plan is already becoming visible. The heart begins beating at about five weeks. The early structures for the vertebrae and spinal cord have been formed. The brain is developing, many internal organs have appeared, and the arms and legs are evident. The embryo at nine weeks—now called a **fetus**—is only about 3 centimeters (about 1 in.) long, but is beginning to look like a small human being.

Second Trimester

The second trimester is a time of continuing development and increased physical activity. The heartbeat can now be heard by placing a stethoscope over the uterus. As the fetus flexes its muscles, the mother can feel movement within her uterus. During these three months, the uterus expands enough to make the mother's pregnancy noticeable. As the fetus develops, the uterus continues to expand until it reaches four to five times its original size. At the end of the second trimester, the fetus may be only 30 centimeters (12 in.) long, but it looks more and more like a full-sized baby. Even its fingers and toes are fully formed, as shown in **FIGURE 34.11.**

Third Trimester

In the third trimester, the fetus grows to its largest size. At birth, most babies weigh about 3 to 4 kilograms (7 to 9 lb) and are about 50 centimeters (20 in.) long. Babies born prematurely at the beginning of the third trimester have a difficult time surviving. Their organs, especially their lungs, are often too immature to function well. Babies born prematurely toward the middle of the third trimester often survive and thrive. In the last month, the lungs are strengthened as the fetus sucks in and pushes out the amniotic fluid.

A Infer Why might a fetus be more easily damaged by genetic errors or toxic chemicals during the first trimester than during any other trimester?

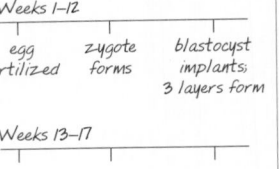

Differentiated Instruction

BELOW LEVEL

Ask students to identify words in the text that are unfamiliar or that they do not remember. Have students use context clues to write their own definitions of these words. Then have students use a dictionary and the Glossary to make any necessary corrections or additions to their definitions. Possible unfamiliar words include *determination, differentiation, potential, nutritional deficiencies, toxic, flexes,* and *prematurely.*

Biology Toolkit, New Word Analysis, p. D2

PRE-AP

Have students use a T-chart to compare the hormone feedback loops of a menstrual cycle and pregnancy. To get students started, have them consider these questions:

- What hormones trigger the different phases of the menstrual cycle?
- What hormones maintain a pregnancy and stop the menstrual cycle?

Biology Toolkit, T-Chart, p. C20

FIGURE 34.11 Trimesters of Development

During each trimester, the fetus goes through different stages of growth and development.

See embryo development in action at ClassZone.com.

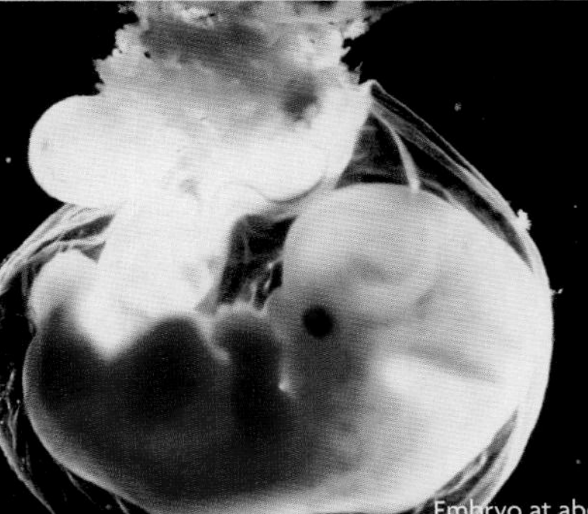
Embryo at about 8 weeks

FIRST TRIMESTER: WEEKS 1–12
Heart, brain, intestines, pancreas, kidneys, liver are forming.
Heartbeat can be detected after week 5.
Arms and legs begin to develop.
Lenses of the eye appear; eyelids will later fuse shut to allow irises to develop.
Individual fingers and toes begin to form.
Hair, fingernails, and toenails develop.
Cerebral hemispheres begin to form.
Early structure of bronchi begin to develop.
External sex organs show sex of the fetus.

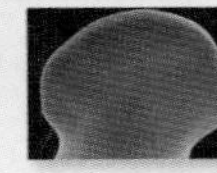
Hand at week 6

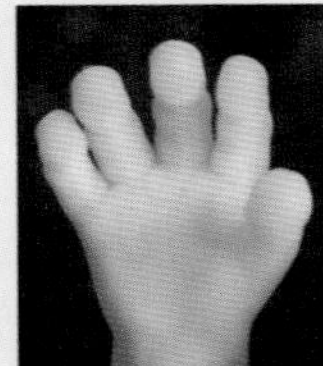
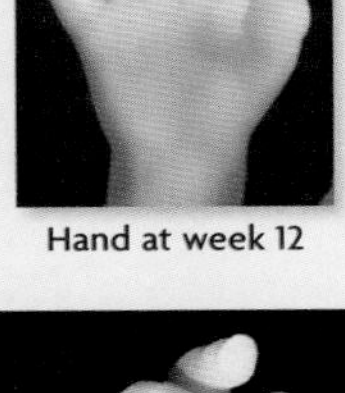
Hand at week 12

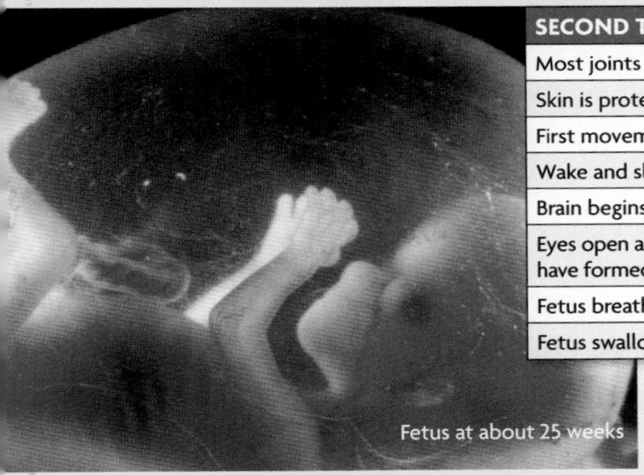

Fetus at about 25 weeks

SECOND TRIMESTER: WEEKS 13–27
Most joints and bones have started to form.
Skin is protected by fine hair and waxy substance.
First movements are felt by mother.
Wake and sleep cycles are more regular.
Brain begins a stage of rapid growth.
Eyes open and blink; eyebrows and eyelashes have formed.
Fetus breathes in amniotic fluid, which strengthens lungs.
Fetus swallows amniotic fluid and makes urine.

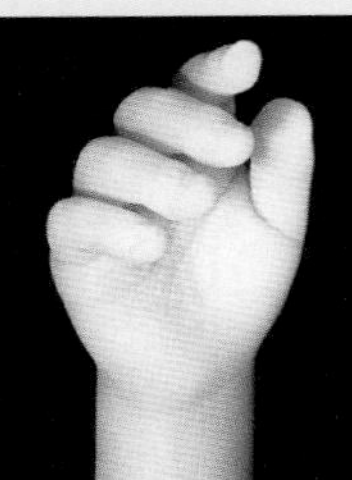
Hand at week 20

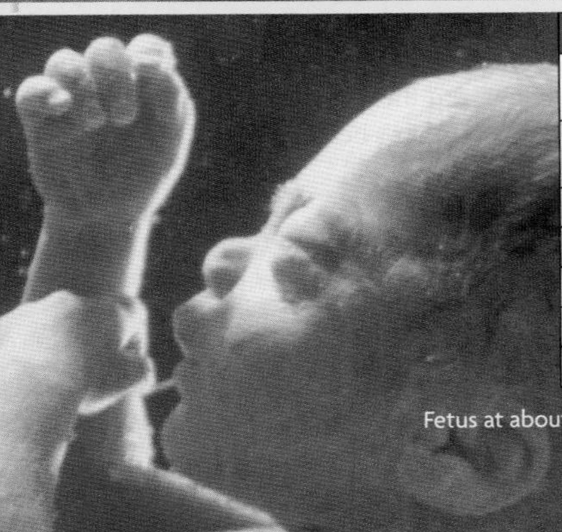
Fetus at about 32 weeks

THIRD TRIMESTER: WEEKS 28–40
Fetus responds more strongly to light and sound outside the uterus.
Fetus has periods of dreaming; eyes are open when awake and closed when asleep.
Fine body hair thins and scalp hair grows in.
Bones are growing and hardening.
Synapses between neurons form in huge numbers.
Lungs complete development.
Fetus turns to head-down position.

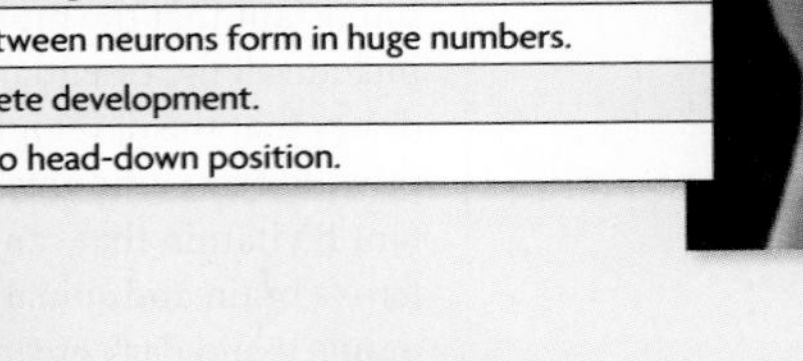
Hand at week 32

A CRITICAL VIEWING **Study the pictures of the embryo and fetus. What are some of the structural changes that have taken place from week 8 to week 32?**

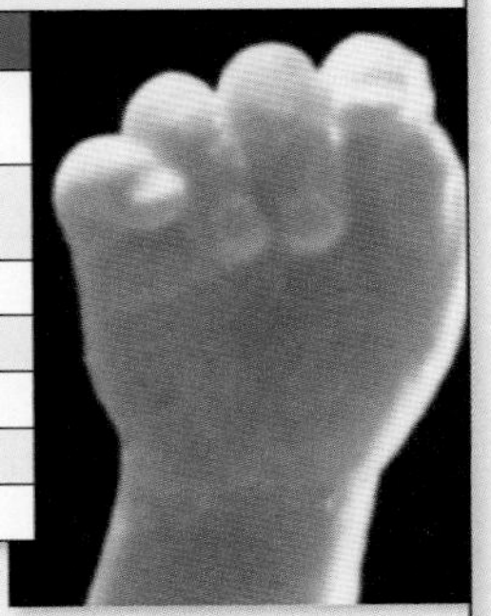

TEACH WITH TECHNOLOGY

There are several Internet resources that will help students see the progression of embryological and fetal development. The University of Pennsylvania and the University of New South Wales provide images and movies depicting development in the uterus up to the end of the third trimester. Links are provided in the chapter resources at **ClassZone.com.**

ONLINE BIOLOGY Have students test their knowledge of fetal development. They can use physical changes and other clues to place images along a developmental timeline. Go to the Animated Biology in Options for Inquiry on page 1045.

Take It Further

A **premature baby** is born more than three weeks before the mother's due date and has not had time to develop fully. With advances in technology, even fetuses that are 23 weeks along in their development and weigh only 1 pound have a chance of surviving. Underdeveloped lungs are the most common problem, but bleeding in the brain, retinal problems, and intestinal problems also are common. Babies born between 23 weeks and 26 weeks of development have the greatest risks of having serious medical problems if they survive. **Ask,** Why does every few days that a fetus stays in the uterus increase its chances of surviving and being healthy when it is born? A fetus develops so rapidly that even a few days can allow a fetus's organs and systems to become more developed.

Answers

A Critical Viewing *Sample Answers:* Facial features—eyes, nose, mouth, ears—are defined by week 32; head hair is evident; arms, legs, hands, and feet are developed; body and head have reached the proportions of a newborn.

▼ Teach *continued*

ONLINE BIOLOGY Have students learn about the importance of good eating habits for a pregnant woman and what a pregnant woman should and should not eat or drink. Go to the WebQuest in Options for Inquiry on page 1045.

DATA ANALYSIS

Discuss

Have students read the data in the graph. **Ask,** During which week does the fetus's immune system seem to produce TSH? week 22 **Ask,** How could TSH be in the fetus's blood if the fetus was not producing TSH? The TSH entered the chorionic villi from the mother's blood.

Answers

1. The mother's levels remain relatively stable throughout the pregnancy. Fetal levels start out low, then rise sharply after week 22, then decrease slightly after week 34.
2. Between weeks 18 and 34, there is a direct relationship; as the fetus grows, the hormone levels increase. After week 34, the fetus continues to develop, but hormone levels decrease slightly near the end of the term.

Unit Resource Book, Data Analysis, p. 189

Take It Further

Drinking any amount of alcohol during pregnancy can cause a range of disorders called **fetal alcohol spectrum disorders** (FASDs). The fetus can suffer damage that results in a range of physical, mental, behavioral, and learning disorders. One of the most severe effects of alcohol is **fetal alcohol syndrome** (FAS). Babies born with FAS have a range of mental retardation and birth defects. In the United States, the FAS rate is between 0.2 and 1.5 per 1000 live births.

DATA ANALYSIS

NOS.1

INTERPRETING GRAPHS

Scientists collected data on the amounts of thyroid-stimulating hormone (TSH) in mothers and in their developing fetuses. Researchers wanted to determine the point at which a fetus's own endocrine system begins to work independently of its mother's. The *x*-axis shows the different times during the pregnancy that levels of TSH were measured.

- The *y*-axis shows the amount of TSH in microliters per milliliter ($\mu L/mL$).
- The blue bar represents the fetus's levels of TSH.
- The orange bar represents the mother's levels of TSH.

1. **Analyze** What happens to both the mother's TSH levels and the fetus's TSH levels as the pregnancy progresses?
2. **Analyze** What is the relationship between the week of pregnancy and fetal TSH levels?

GRAPH 1. HORMONE LEVELS OF MOTHER AND FETUS

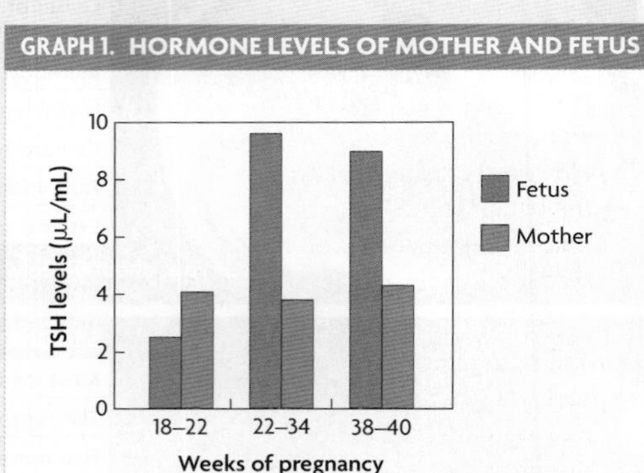

Source: D. Fisher, C. Hobel, R. Garza, C. Pierce, *Pediatrics*

MAIN IDEA

The mother affects the fetus, and pregnancy affects the mother.

Throughout pregnancy, the mother and the fetus continually affect each other's health. For the most part, whatever the mother eats or drinks, the baby is exposed to through the placenta and the umbilical cord. On the other hand, the hormones released during pregnancy and the nutritional needs of the fetus present their own challenges to the mother's health.

Health of the Fetus

The fetus depends on the mother for all its nutrition. As a result, it is vitally important that the mother eat well throughout pregnancy. Her diet must include all the essential amino acids, vitamins, minerals, fats, and carbohydrates that the developing fetus needs. Vitamin and mineral supplements can provide extra amounts of these nutrients. For example, folic acid is an important B vitamin that can significantly lower the risk of serious birth defects in a fetus's brain and spinal cord. Folic acid is found in such foods as poultry, oranges, and dark green leafy vegetables. In contrast, toxic chemicals in alcohol, tobacco, and many other drugs can diffuse through the placenta and harm the fetus. These substances often interfere with fetal development and can cause many types of birth defects and produce learning disabilities in a child.

Differentiated Instruction

BELOW LEVEL

Have students write a list that summarizes what a mother can do to help keep her fetus healthy.

Biology Toolkit, Quick-Write, p. C19

PRE-AP

Tell students to suppose that a pregnant woman suddenly has trouble maintaining a stable blood sugar level. Have students write a brief essay describing the possible effects the pregnancy could be causing, based on the information in this section.

Biology Toolkit, Quick-Write, p. C19

Studies have shown that many of these problems can be completely prevented if the mother avoids alcohol, tobacco, and drugs during the pregnancy. Even some over-the-counter medications can harm the fetus. As a result, the mother must check with a health care provider to be sure any medications she needs to take are safe for the fetus.

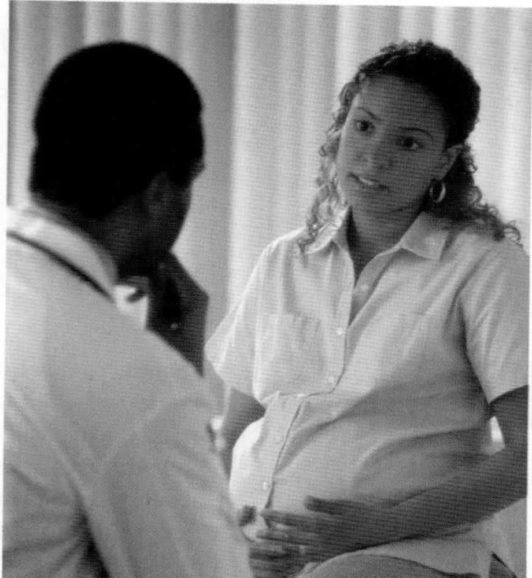

FIGURE 34.12 Routine medical tests can be used to check the mother's blood pressure, glucose levels, nutrition, and other factors. The baby's growth and development in the uterus can also be monitored.

Health of the Mother

The mother's health is affected by pregnancy in a number of ways. To supply enough energy for herself and her baby, the mother must add roughly 300 more Calories a day to her diet after the first trimester. During pregnancy, most women will gain on average about 12 kilograms (26 lb). However, gaining too much or too little weight can affect the fetus. Women who gain too little weight often have underweight babies who may have impaired immune systems, learning disabilities, and delayed development.

Hormone levels also fluctuate, affecting the mother's ability to maintain homeostasis. For example, some pregnant women are unable to control their glucose levels and may develop pregnancy-related diabetes. This type of diabetes normally disappears after the pregnancy is over. Hormones may also affect the digestive tract, causing what is known as morning sickness, or vomiting, for a time. This condition generally clears up as the pregnancy progresses. After the baby is born, some women may experience some depression during the time that their hormone levels are stabilizing. To help ensure a healthy pregnancy, the mother should have regular physical checkups. The normal challenges of pregnancy can be managed through proper diet, exercise, and medical care.

A Infer **When a woman first learns that she is pregnant, what lifestyle changes might she need to make?**

34.3 ASSESSMENT

ONLINE QUIZ ClassZone.com

B.6.3

REVIEWING MAIN IDEAS

1. Explain the main functions of the **placenta** during a pregnancy.
2. List two milestones of fetal growth and development achieved in each **trimester.**
3. Give two examples of how the mother and **fetus** affect one another during pregnancy.

CRITICAL THINKING

4. **Apply** A woman doesn't want to gain more than 6 kg (13 lbs) during her pregnancy. What effects might this decision have on the fetus?
5. **Infer** A baby is born 12 weeks premature. The organs are developed, but the baby must breathe using a ventilator. Explain why this treatment is necessary.

***Connecting* CONCEPTS**

6. **Tissue Rejection** A woman with type O Rh^- blood is pregnant for a second time. During her first pregnancy, she developed antibodies for Rh^+ factor. Her second baby's blood is type O Rh^+. What might happen if some fetal blood leaks into the mother's blood?

34.3 ASSESSMENT

1. The placenta connects the mother and fetus, to allow for exchange of oxygen, nutrients, and wastes.
2. Answers can include any items listed in Figure 34.11 for each trimester.
3. The mother affects the fetus through her diet and overall health. The fetus affects the mother by causing weight gain and through hormone fluctuations that affect her homeostasis.
4. The woman may give birth to an underweight baby, who may have an impaired immune system, learning disabilities, and delayed development.
5. The lungs are not fully developed yet, so the baby needs help to breathe.
6. The mother's antibodies would regard the type O Rh blood as foreign and mount an immune attack, which would put the baby's life in danger.

Take It Further

During a regular prenatal checkup, medical tests may be recommended to study the fetus. **Ultrasound, amniocentesis,** and **chorionic villus sampling (CVS)** are three common tests. A fetal ultrasound is a noninvasive test that uses sound waves to produce an image of the fetus and placenta. Among other information, an ultrasound can determine the fetus's age and gender, and can evaluate its development. Amniocentesis and CVS are used to test for genetic disorders. During amniocentesis, a needle is used to remove a sample of amniotic fluid. During CVS, a small sample of the placenta is removed with a thin tube or needle. **Ask,** How can a sample of amniotic fluid and chorionic villus provide information about genetic defects in the fetus? Both contain fetal cells that can be analyzed for genetic defects.

Answers

A Infer seek a physician's care; avoid toxic chemicals, such as household cleansers; avoid alcohol, tobacco, and even some over-the-counter drugs; eat properly; exercise

Assess and Reteach

Assess Use the Online Quiz or Section Quiz (*Assessment Book,* p. 669).

Reteach Have students view the animation of embryo development at **ClassZone.com.** Then have them present oral summaries based on the animation and the main ideas of this section.

SECTION 34.4

▼ Plan and Prepare

Objectives

- Describe the three stages of birth.
- Describe the stages of human growth and aging.

Section Resources

Unit Resource Book
Study Guide pp. 185–186
Power Notes p. 187
Reinforcement p. 188
Pre-AP Activity pp. 193–194

Interactive Reader Chapter 34
Spanish Study Guide pp. 345–346

Biology Toolkit pp. C19, C30, C31, C38

Technology
Power Presentation 34.4
Media Gallery DVD
Online Quiz 34.4

Activate Prior Knowledge Have students think about how a puppy or a kitten changes as it gets older. **Ask,** How have you changed from the time you were born until now? Students might describe physical, intellectual, and emotional changes as well as increased independence from parents. **Ask,** How might you change as you continue to get older? Students might describe declining physical, intellectual, and emotional conditions as well as an increased dependency on their children.

▼ Teach

Take It Further

Many **fetal monitoring** techniques can be used to measure the baby's heart rate and evaluate the baby's level of stress during labor and birth. These techniques range from a special stethoscope, called a **fetoscope,** to an electrode attached to the baby's head inside the uterus.

ONLINE BIOLOGY Go to the chapter Resource Center at **ClassZone.com** for additional resources and information on fetal monitoring.

34.4 Birth and Development

KEY CONCEPT Physical development continues through adolescence and declines with age.

MAIN IDEAS

- Birth occurs in three stages.
- Human growth and aging also occur in stages.

VOCABULARY

infancy, p. 1042
childhood, p. 1042
adolescence, p. 1042
adulthood, p. 1043

Connect After birth, you will spend nearly two decades learning how to live on your own. Until recently, scientists thought that the most important learning period happened in the first three years of life. Now they have discovered that in adolescence the brain goes through a second period of development. During this time, you are maturing emotionally and mentally, not just physically. This may be one reason why humans take so long to grow up.

MAIN IDEA

Birth occurs in three stages.

When the fetus has fully developed, the placenta can no longer provide enough nourishment. The time has come for the baby to be born. The birth process involves three stages: dilation of the cervix, emergence of the baby, and expulsion of the placenta, as shown in **FIGURE 34.13.** The physical changes that the mother's body goes through are known as labor.

Dilation of the Cervix

Labor begins with regular contractions of the uterus. The hormone oxytocin (AHK-sih-TOH-sihn), released by the mother and the fetus, stimulates the muscles in the wall of the uterus. However, not all contractions mean that the baby is about to be born. Expectant mothers are usually taught to count the number and strength of these contractions. When they become more frequent, intense, and painful over time, then true labor has begun. The amniotic sac usually breaks in the early stages of labor, although it can break earlier. The amniotic fluid is released through the vagina, which is also called the birth canal.

The contractions serve to push the walls of the cervix apart. The baby cannot leave the uterus until the cervix dilates, or widens, to at least 10 centimeters (4 in.). This space allows most babies to pass through. If the cervix does not dilate, the doctor must make an incision through the abdominal wall to remove the baby, a procedure called a cesarean section, or c-section.

Connecting CONCEPTS

Marsupials In **Chapter 26,** you read about marsupial mammals that give birth to young that are little more than embryos. These tiny life forms must then find their way into the mother's pouch to complete their development. In contrast, human babies are born at an advanced stage of development.

Emergence of the Baby

This stage of the birth process is often the most stressful for the mother and the baby. If everything goes well, the powerful contractions of the uterus help rotate the baby so that its head is toward the cervix. In some cases, the baby

Differentiated Instruction

BELOW LEVEL

To organize notes for this section, have students use a sequence diagram depicting different stages of development.

Biology Toolkit, Sequence Diagram, p. C38

PRE-AP

Have students use a cluster diagram to identify the behaviors and attitudes they associate with different stages of development. Then as they read the text, have them include the hormones that affect these stages. Ask students if they can draw any conclusion from their diagram.

Biology Toolkit, Cluster Diagram, p. C30

FIGURE 34.13 Three Stages of Birth

Birth begins with contractions and continues until the baby and placenta emerge.

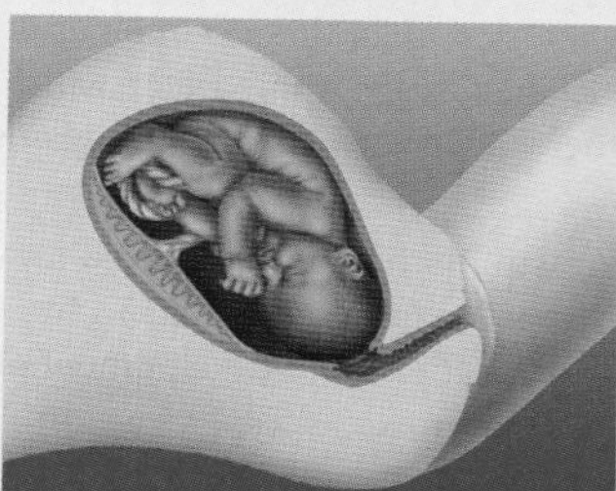

STAGE 1
As regular, strong contractions occur, the cervix dilates and the baby turns.

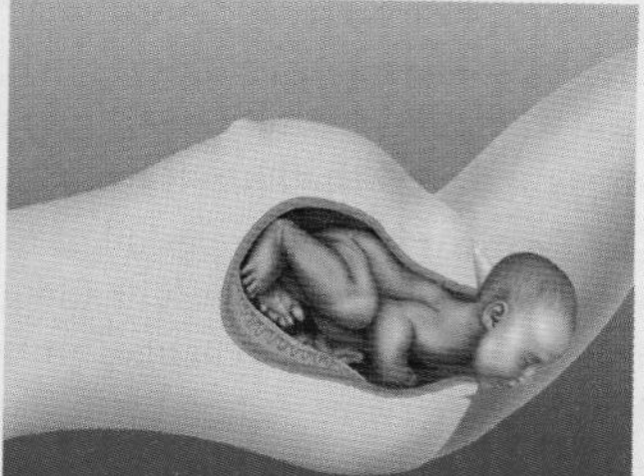

STAGE 2
The baby is pushed through the cervix and out of the vaginal canal.

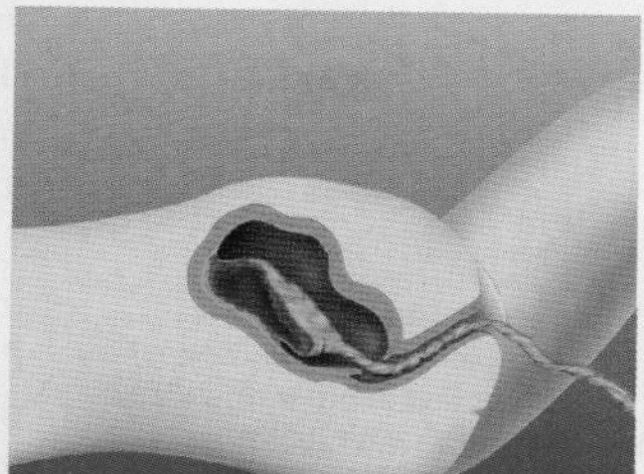

STAGE 3
Contractions continue, expelling the placenta and helping to control bleeding.

A Predict At what point might the baby begin to breathe on its own?

does not turn and is born feet first, which is a more difficult birth process. Usually, however, the baby is in the right position. The muscles of the uterus then push the baby into the birth canal. Once the head emerges, the rest of the body usually slips out quickly. Within a short time, the baby is breathing on its own. The hormone oxytocin also stimulates the mother's breasts to produce milk and increases her desire to bond with her infant. This bond helps to ensure that she will care for the baby after it is born.

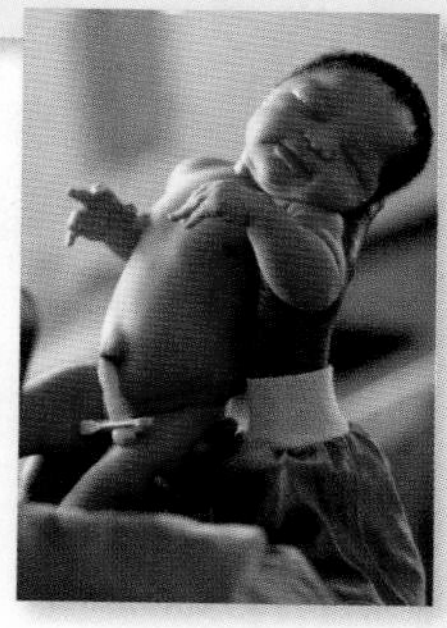

After living in the uterus for nine months, this newborn is breathing air for the first time. From now on it must live outside the protected environment of its mother's body.

Expulsion of the Placenta

The third stage of birth happens soon after the baby emerges. As the uterine contractions continue, the placenta detaches from the wall of the uterus and is expelled. These contractions also help to constrict blood vessels and reduce the amount of bleeding the mother experiences. The baby's umbilical cord is clamped and cut a few inches from the abdomen. This bit of cord eventually dries up and falls away, leaving a scar called the navel, or belly button.

B Infer Why might a head-first delivery be the safest for both mother and baby?

MAIN IDEA

Human growth and aging also occur in stages.

Just as hormones regulate human reproduction, they are also involved in human growth after birth. Most children follow the same pattern of growth and development, but each child matures at his or her own pace. Rates of growth are also affected by factors such as genetics, nutrition, and environment.

Key hormones involved in growth include thyroxin, estrogen, testosterone, and human growth hormone (hGH), which is secreted by the pituitary gland. Human growth hormone increases the body's rate of fat metabolism and protein synthesis. These processes cause all body cells to divide, particularly bone and skeletal muscle cells. However, as a person ages, the pituitary secretes less and less hGH.

ENGLISH LEARNERS

Have pairs of students create a timeline for human development, using the information in this section and their own prior knowledge. They could include birth, infancy, childhood, adolescence, young adulthood, middle age, and older adulthood by marking off points on the line and labeling them with as many characteristics as possible. Review and assess students' work and then use students' timelines to create a timeline on chart paper.

Biology Toolkit, Timeline, p. C31

Vocabulary

Academic Vocabulary The word *labor* is a commonly used word with many meanings. As a noun, *labor* can mean "physical or mental exertion, especially when difficult or exhausting; work; workers considered as a group" and "the process of childbirth." As a verb, *labor* can mean "to work, to strive painstakingly," and "to suffer distress or disadvantage." **Ask,** Why do you think the word *labor* is used to describe childbirth? Childbirth is hard work.

Take It Further

During pregnancy, hormones cause the mammary glands to develop and prepare for **lactation,** or the production of milk, but cause negative feedback to the pituitary gland, which prevents lactation. After the placenta is discharged, hormones levels drop and allow the pituitary to secrete **prolactin,** which stimulates the mammary glands to produce milk. Suckling by the baby sends signals that trigger the pituitary gland to release **oxytocin,** which causes the mammary glands to secrete milk in a milk-ejection reflex. The milk produced during the first few days is a yellowish fluid called **colostrum,** which contains antibodies from the mother. If a mother does not breastfeed her baby, an accumulation of milk in the mammary glands causes the pituitary to stop secreting prolactin.

Answers

A Predict when it exits the mother's body

B Infer If the head is as large as the rest of the body and it fits through the cervix first, the rest of the body should easily follow. If a leg is first, the body will have a harder time fitting through the cervix.

▼ Teach *continued*

ONLINE BIOLOGY Have students use the Data Analysis Online to compare growth hormone levels in girls and boys from infancy to adolescence. See Options for Inquiry on page 1045.

Science Trivia

- Around 3 months of age, infants can sit, hold their head up, grasp, and smile.
- Around 12 months of age, infants can stand, scribble, and speak one word.
- Around 24 months of age, infants can throw a ball, wash and dry their hands, and combine words.

Integrating Developmental Biology

In 1998, psychologists **Amy Wolfson** and **Mary Carskadon** studied the relationship between poor grades and sleep deprivation in 3000 high school students. They discovered that students who reported receiving C's, D's, and F's went to bed about 40 minutes later and got about 25 minutes less sleep than students who reported receiving A's and B's. Of the students studied, 26 percent said that they slept less than 6.5 hours a night, while only 15 percent stated that they slept more than 8.5 hours.

Most adolescents need more than 9 hours of sleep a night, compared to the 7.5 to 8 hours adults need. At the beginning of puberty, the **circadian rhythm** in adolescents changes, causing them to fall asleep later. Carskadon surmised that this may be due to the adolescent brain's sensitivity to light, which alters melatonin production. Some schools have changed their start times until later in the morning to better accommodate their students' needs.

Infancy and Childhood

Infancy lasts from birth to about age 2. When babies are born, their homeostatic mechanisms are not completely developed. As a result, a newborn's body temperature, heart rate, and breathing rate vary more than they do in older children. Also, an infant's kidneys are less efficient at reabsorbing water, which can lead to rapid dehydration. As infancy progresses, homeostatic mechanisms mature and these variations decrease.

The first year of life is a period of rapid growth. Both male and female infants usually triple their weight and grow about 25 centimeters (10 in.) by their first birthday. Other changes are equally dramatic. Rapid development of the brain and nervous system occurs, and vision improves as babies learn to focus their eyes. They begin to coordinate muscle groups to sit, stand, and finally walk. By the end of infancy, children usually have a vocabulary of several words and may even express themselves using short sentences.

FIGURE 34.14 The child (top) is learning to control major muscle groups in her legs in order to walk. The adolescent skater (below) is adapting her knowledge of walking to learn a more sophisticated skill.

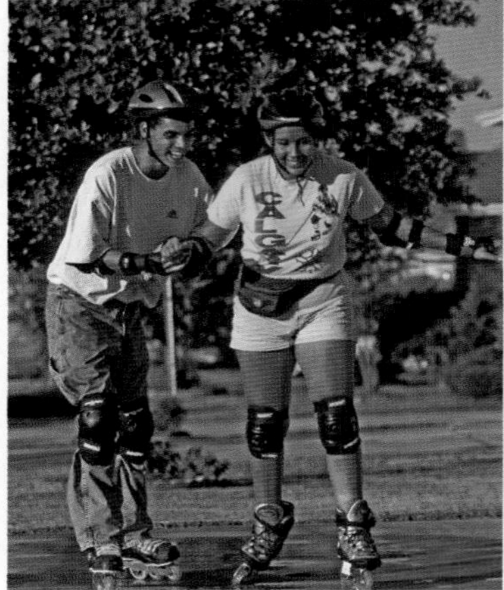

Childhood begins at age 2 and extends to about age 12. During childhood, physical growth slows down. Each year, most children grow only about 6 centimeters (3 in.) and gain about 4 kilograms (6 lb). Childhood is a time during which muscle skills and coordination improve as the nervous system matures. The continued development of sensory receptors, nerves, and muscles mean that children can learn both fine-motor skills such as writing and large-motor skills such as walking, as shown in **FIGURE 34.14.** Language and abstract reasoning abilities improve. Children begin to express more complex and varied emotions and become better able to understand the emotions of others.

Puberty and Adolescence

Puberty marks the beginning of sexual maturity and the development of sexual characteristics. As you read in Section 34.1, puberty begins when the hormones FSH and LH are released by the pituitary gland. For girls, the average age range for the onset of puberty is 10 to 14. For boys, the average age range is 10 to 16. During this time, young people experience a period of rapid growth stimulated by the release of testosterone and estrogen. Growth averages 5 to 7 centimeters (2 to 3 in.) and can reach up to 15 centimeters (6 in.) in one year. Young people often feel clumsy as they adjust to their changing bodies. They also experience rapid changes in their emotions and in their reasoning abilities as the brain continues to make new neural connections.

Adolescence begins at sexual maturity. In girls, sexual maturity is marked by ovulation and the first menstrual cycle. Although boys can ejaculate before sexual maturity, sexual maturity is indicated by the presence of sperm in the semen. During adolescence, bone growth continues until about age 15 in girls and about age 17 in boys. Adolescent boys and girls often experience greater strength and physical endurance in these years, and their coordination often improves. Although the brain stops increasing in size, the rearrangement of neural connections continues. In a very real sense, the adolescent brain is being "rewired" in preparation for adulthood.

Differentiated Instruction

HANDS-ON ACTIVITY

Provide students with pictures of different stages in human development. Include pictures of an egg, a blastocyst, an embryo, a fetus, an infant, a one-year-old child, a nine-year-old child, an adolescent, a young adult, and an older adult. Also provide a label on an index card for each stage. Have students arrange the pictures and their labels in the correct order. Discuss the growth that takes place during each stage.

PRE-AP

Point out that humans are unique among animals in that we live long past our reproductive years. In 1900, for example, people in the United States had a life expectancy of 47.3 years. In 2003, the life expectancy had increased to about 77.5 years. Have students write for five minutes about the unique ecological niche of the human species and whether it has redefined the concept of adaptation.

Biology Toolkit, Quick-Write, p. C19

Adulthood and Aging

You might think that **adulthood** marks a time when people reach their peak in terms of skills and abilities. For the most part, you would be right. During these years, most people establish independent lives, and many raise their own families. However, adulthood, like other life stages, also marks a time of distinct physical changes, as you can see in **FIGURE 34.15.**

Scientists are only now beginning to unlock the mysteries of how the body ages. As a person grows older, some of the most important changes include a decline in immune functions and in the production of many key hormones, such as growth hormone, testosterone, and estrogen. Most women around age 50 or so go through menopause. In men, the sperm count gradually decreases. For both sexes, the body's rates of metabolism and digestion slow down. Skin becomes thinner and less elastic, bones lose calcium, and muscle mass decreases and is replaced by fat deposits.

However, scientists are also finding that how one experiences the aging process may depend as much on genetics, lifestyle, and environment as it does on chronological age. In general, those who eat a healthy diet, remain physically active, and keep learning may be able to slow down or even counteract many of the changes that aging brings about. For example, regular weight-bearing exercise such as walking several miles a week can help to maintain bone and muscle mass. Also, studies have shown that if a person keeps learning throughout life, the brain continues to make new neural connections just as it did when the person was younger.

A Compare Describe some of the ways that the process of aging is the reverse of the processes that occur during puberty and adolescence.

FIGURE 34.15 These photos show the changes that occur in the same person's face from childhood to the 70s.

ONLINE BIOLOGY Go to the chapter Resource Center at **ClassZone.com** for additional resources and information on human development.

Answers

A Compare Puberty: gain muscle and bone mass; sex and growth hormone levels rise; reproductive cycles begin; need for Calories increases. Aging: lose muscle and bone mass; hormone levels decline; reproductive cycle in women stops and in men may stop or decline; need for Calories decreases.

34.4 ASSESSMENT

ONLINE QUIZ ClassZone.com

REVIEWING MAIN IDEAS

1. Briefly describe the three stages of the birth process. What are the signs that true labor has begun?
2. What are the basic stages of development after birth? During which stage(s) does the greatest amount of physical growth usually occur?

CRITICAL THINKING

3. **Compare and Contrast** What are some similarities and differences between the first year of life and the first year of puberty?
4. **Connect** Most large prey species, such as elk or antelope, are eutherian (placental), and not marsupial. What survival advantage might this give the offspring of the prey species?

Connecting CONCEPTS

5. **Reproductive Strategies** Many insects and fish give birth to hundreds of young at one time but do little to care for them. Most birds and mammals give birth to only one or a few young, but care for them until they are independent. What are some advantages and disadvantages to each type of reproduction?

Assess and Reteach

Assess Use the Online Quiz or Section Quiz (*Assessment Book,* p. 670).

Reteach Have pairs of students quiz one another on the main ideas and terms in this section. Let one student write a question and the other student answer it. Have partners switch roles and continue until all main ideas and terms are covered.

34.4 ASSESSMENT

1. Oxytocin is released, stimulating contractions and dilation of the cervix; contractions push the baby through the birth canal leading to the emergence of the baby; contractions cause the detachment and expulsion of the placenta. Contractions of the uterus become more frequent, intense, and painful over time in true labor.
2. infancy, childhood, adolescence, adulthood; during infancy and adolescence
3. Both are periods of intense physical growth. During the first year of life, many organs mature, while during puberty, only the sex organs mature. Also, puberty causes a recontouring of body shape as male and female sexual characteristics develop.
4. enables the offspring to be able to stand and run within hours of birth, thus escaping predators
5. Advantages: More offspring means more will survive to reproduce. A small number of offspring is easier to care for, which increases survivorship. Disadvantages: Lack of parental care increases loss of offspring to predators. Parental care requires energy and time. Reproductive rate is lower. Species is more affected by loss of individuals.

OPTIONS FOR INQUIRY

INVESTIGATION

Time 30 minutes	TEACHER TESTED
Teacher Preparation	
Student Difficulty	
Lab Binder Human Bio, pp. 80–82	

Purpose Observe the development of a sea star embryo by examining prepared slides.

Overview Students will examine prepared slides of a sea star embryo in the first two stages of development. They will

- examine each stage under high and low powers of a microscope
- draw and label the embryo and its structures at each stage
- compare the stages of development

LAB MANAGEMENT

Safety Caution students to handle the slides carefully and to clean the microscope's eyepiece with alcohol wipes before and after use.

Inclusion Images from the Internet of sea star embryo development can be used to supplement the slides.

POST-LAB DISCUSSION

Discuss the importance of the development of the embryo from closely packed cells to a hollow ball of cells with three layers. **Ask,** What would happen if the closely packed cells did not develop into a blastula? Cells would not differentiate, and an embryo would not develop. There would be just a mass of identical cells.

Use these inquiry-based labs and online activities to deepen your understanding of reproductive systems.

NOS.3 Clearly communicate their ideas and results of investigations verbally and in written form using tables, graphs, diagrams, and photographs.

INVESTIGATION

Development of an Embryo

Animals from echinoderms to humans go through three main stages of development after fertilization. In the first stage, cleavage, the embryo in an echinoderm divides to form the blastula, called a blastocyst in mammals. In the second stage, the blastula develops three distinct layers and becomes known as the gastrula. In the third stage, the embryo's internal organs begin to form. In this lab, you will examine slides of sea stars in the first two stages of embryonic development.

MATERIALS
- slide of sea star embryo in early cleavage
- slide of sea star embryo in late cleavage
- slide of sea star blastula
- slide of sea star gastrula
- microscope

SKILLS Observing, Analyzing

PROBLEM How does a sea star embryo develop?

PROCEDURE

1. Obtain the slide of a sea star embryo in early cleavage and examine it under low power and high power on the microscope. Draw and label the cell and its structures.
2. Repeat step 1 with each of the remaining slides.

ANALYZE AND CONCLUDE

1. **Describe** What does a sea star embryo look like in the early stages of cleavage?
2. **Analyze** What type of cell division occurred to produce the multicellular embryo after fertilization?
3. **Compare** How does the appearance of the cells in the late stages of cleavage compare with the appearance of the cells in the blastula?
4. **Contrast** Sketch the different cell layers in the gastrula. What differences do you see among them?
5. **Compare** How are the developmental stages of a sea star embryo similar to the stages of development in a human embryo?

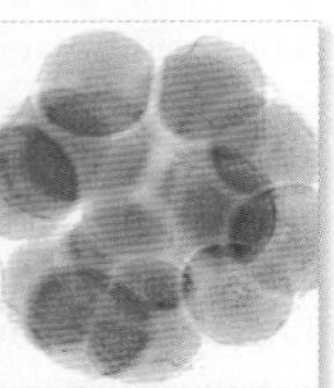

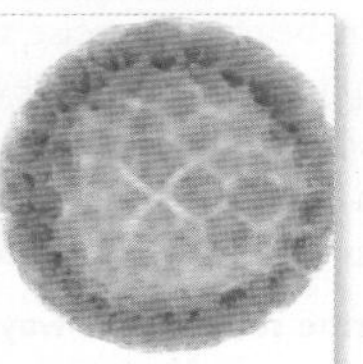

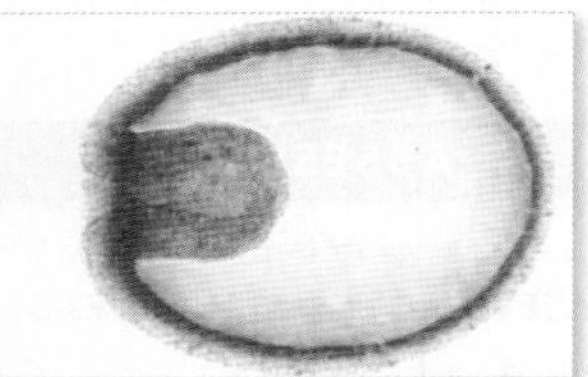

Sea stars undergo several stages of development including the 16-cell stage (*top*), blastula stage (*middle*), and gastrula stage. (LM; magnification unknown)

Answers

Analyze and Conclude

1. The embryo consists of 4 to 16 cells packed together.
2. mitotic division
3. In the late stages of cleavage, the cells are still closely packed together. The blastula consists of smaller cells that form a ring around a cavity.
4. *Sample Answer:* The ectoderm is the outermost layer, the mesoderm is the middle layer, and the endoderm is the innermost layer. Students should also describe differences relating to cell size and appearance.
5. A human embryo undergoes cleavage in which mitotic cell division leads to a multicellular embryo. Similar to the blastula in sea stars, the human embryo forms a blastocyst, which is a ball of cells that surrounds a hollow center. Both embryos continue to develop to adult forms.

INVESTIGATION

Effects of Chemicals on Reproductive Organs

Like other organs in the human body, including the liver, kidneys, and lungs, reproductive organs can be harmed by chemicals. Exposure to certain chemicals or toxins through the use of alcohol, tobacco, or drugs or from the environment can affect the structure and functioning of both the male and female reproductive systems.

SKILL Researching

PROBLEM What effects do certain toxic chemicals have on the male and female reproductive systems?

PROCEDURE

1. Choose one of the substances listed below to research.
   - Anabolic steroids
   - Alcohol
   - Cocaine
   - Tobacco
   - Pesticides (herbicides and/or insecticides)
   - Environmental toxins (benzene, toluene)
2. Describe the chemical's effects on male and female reproductive organs.
3. Explain whether scientists know if the effects are permanent or reversible.
4. Identify what effects, if any, the chemical might have on future offspring.

Toxic chemicals sprayed on fruits and vegetables to control pests may remain inside the plants. When a mother eats these foods, some of these toxic chemicals could harm her growing fetus.

Online BIOLOGY
CLASSZONE.COM

ANIMATED BIOLOGY
Developmental Timeline
Does the heart develop in the first month or second month of pregnancy? When do fingers form? Use physical changes and other clues to place images along a developmental timeline.

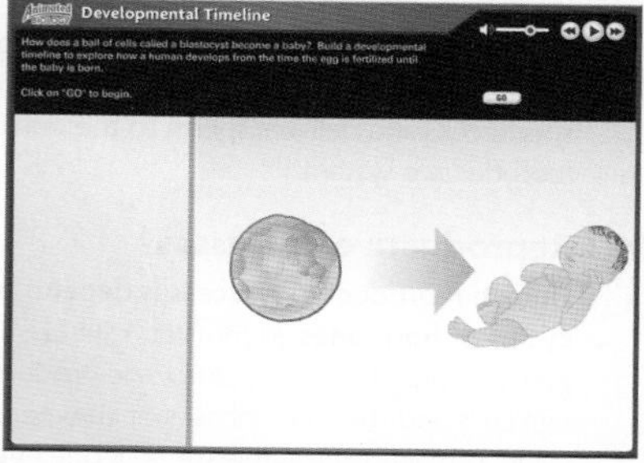

WEBQUEST
Developing fetuses depend on their mothers for nutrition. In this WebQuest, you will find out why expectant mothers must get balanced, proper nutrition. Explore what a pregnant woman should eat and what she should avoid.

DATA ANALYSIS ONLINE
Graph the rise and fall of human growth hormone through adolescence for both girls and boys.

Online Biology ▼

ANIMATED BIOLOGY Use this interactive animation to reinforce the concepts in **Section 34.3.**

WEBQUEST The WebQuest takes one full class period. Students complete the activity online and will need access to a printer to print their answers. Sample answers, teacher notes, and alternative assessment ideas are available on **ClassZone.com.** Use with **Section 34.3.**

DATA ANALYSIS ONLINE
In girls: level builds slowly, reaching a low peak between ages 12 and 15, then levels off to adult values. In boys, level quickly rises to a higher peak between ages 15 and 17, then descends quickly to adult values. Childhood and adult levels are similar in both sexes. Use with **Section 34.4.**

INVESTIGATION

Time	30 minutes
Teacher Preparation	1 flask
Student Difficulty	1 flask
Lab Binder	Human Bio, p. 83

Purpose Research the effects of a toxic chemical on male and female reproductive systems.

POST-LAB DISCUSSION

Have students share their research.

Answers

Sample Research

- Anabolic steroids can reduce the size of testicles and reduce sperm count. In women, they affect the menstrual cycle and decrease breast size.
- Alcohol abuse in men can lead to fewer or defective sperm and impotence. In women, it is associated with the cessation of menstruation and ovulation.
- Cocaine use can lead to low sperm counts or abnormally shaped sperm in men. In women, it can disrupt the menstrual cycle.
- Tobacco use can cause lower sperm counts in men. In women, smoking may reduce estrogen levels, and cause uterine and cervical cancer.
- Pesticides may decrease sperm production and increase the risk of testicular cancer. In women, hormone function and the menstrual cycle are disrupted.
- Environmental toxins may lead to reduced sperm counts and testicular cancer. In women, they can lead to miscarriage, and breast or ovarian cancer.

CHAPTER REVIEW

Interactive Review

Encourage students to go to **ClassZone.com** for a detailed review of each section, including visuals and vocabulary practice.

Unit Resource Book, Vocabulary Practice, pp. 195–198

CHAPTER 34

Interactive Review @ CLASSZONE.COM

KEY CONCEPTS | Vocabulary Games | Concept Maps | Animated Biology | Online Quiz

34.1 Reproductive Anatomy

Female and male reproductive organs fully develop during puberty. Puberty in both males and females begins with the release of two hormones: FSH and LH. These two hormones stimulate the release of estrogen in females and of testosterone in males. The female reproductive system produces ova, or egg cells, and provides an environment for a fertilized egg to develop. The male reproductive system produces sperm cells and delivers sperm to the female reproductive system.

34.2 Reproductive Processes

Human reproductive processes depend on cycles of hormones. In females, FSH, LH, estrogen, and progesterone control the production of egg cells and the three phases of the menstrual cycle. Females usually release only one egg a month until menopause.

In males, FSH, LH, and testosterone control the production of sperm cells. Males release millions of sperm on ejaculation and can continue to produce sperm all their lives. When a sperm penetrates an egg and the two nuclei fuse, fertilization occurs. Reproductive organs can be damaged or destroyed by STDs.

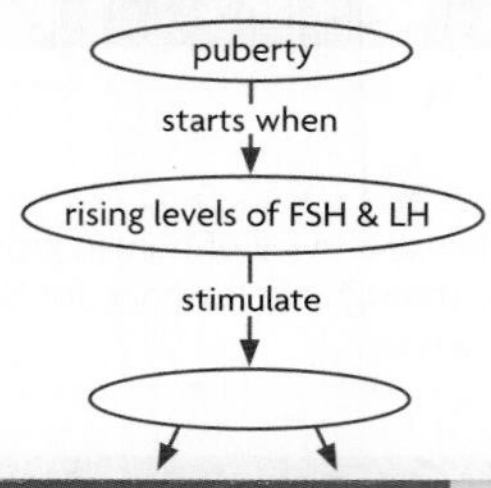

34.3 Fetal Development

Development progresses in stages from zygote to fetus. The fetus is nourished and protected by the amniotic fluid, placenta, and umbilical cord, which connect the mother and fetus. Development takes roughly nine months, divided into three trimesters. To ensure the health of her baby, a mother needs to eat well, exercise, and have regular medical checkups.

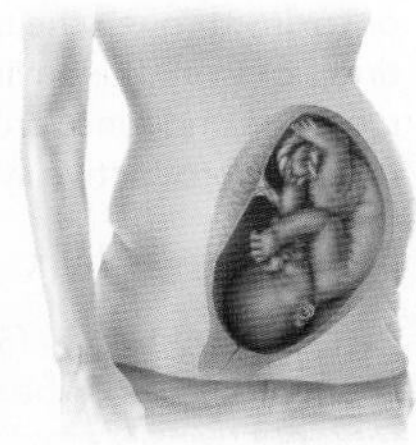

34.4 Birth and Development

Physical development continues through adolescence and declines with age. The birth process takes place in three stages: dilation of the cervix, emergence of the baby, and expulsion of the placenta. Key hormones regulate human growth and development throughout infancy, childhood, adolescence, and adulthood.

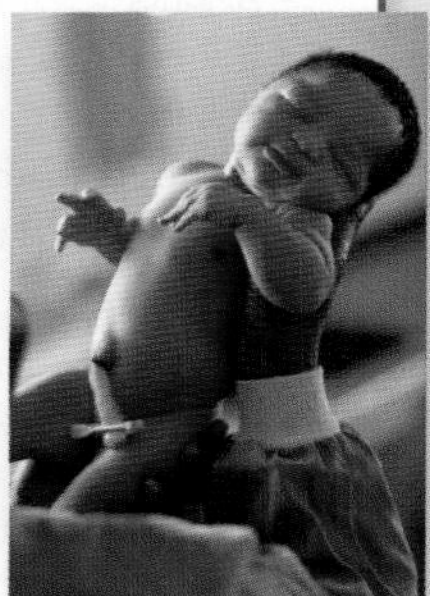

Synthesize Your Notes

Concept Map Use a concept map like the one below to take notes on topics such as puberty.

puberty → starts when → rising levels of FSH & LH → stimulate → [ ]

Process Diagram A process diagram like the one below is a good way to remember the steps in reproductive processes.

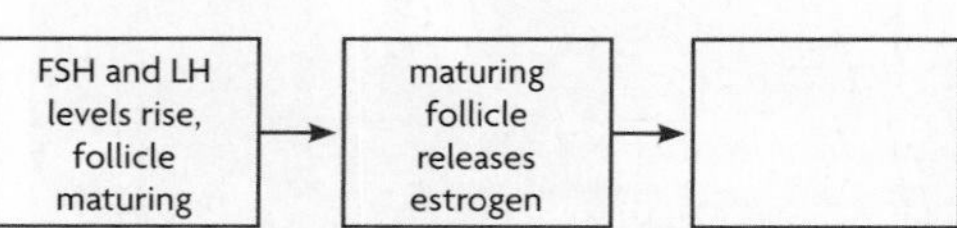

Reviewing Vocabulary

1. With the beginning of puberty in males, increased testosterone production helps stimulate sperm production.
2. In ovulation, the follicle ruptures and the egg is released.
3. In the follicular phase of the menstrual cycle, the endometrium thickens.
4. The embryo is cushioned and protected by fluid in the amniotic sac.
5. A woman goes through menopause during later adulthood, usually during her forties or fifties.
6. vas deferens
7. epididymis
8. testis
9. ovary
10. uterus
11. cervix

Chapter Assessment

Chapter Vocabulary

34.1 reproductive system, p. 1024
puberty, p. 1024
ovum, p. 1024
ovary, p. 1024
uterus, p. 1024
estrogen, p. 1024
fallopian tube, p. 1024
testis, p. 1025
testosterone, p. 1025
scrotum, p. 1026
epididymis, p. 1026
vas deferens, p. 1026
semen, p. 1026

34.2 follicle, p. 1028
ovulation, p. 1028
menstrual cycle, p. 1028
endometrium, p. 1028
corpus luteum, p. 1029
menopause, p. 1029
zygote, p. 1031
infertility, p. 1031
sexually transmitted disease, p. 1032

34.3 blastocyst, p. 1034
embryo, p. 1034
amniotic sac, p. 1035
placenta, p. 1035
umbilical cord, p. 1035
trimester, p. 1036
fetus, p. 1036

34.4 infancy, p. 1042
childhood, p. 1042
adolescence, p. 1042
adulthood, p. 1043

Reviewing Vocabulary

Term Relationships

For each pair of terms below, write a sentence that contains both terms and shows a relationship between them. For example, *fetus, umbilical cord: The fetus obtains nutrients through the umbilical cord.*

1. puberty, testosterone
2. follicle, ovulation
3. menstrual cycle, endometrium
4. embryo, amniotic sac
5. menopause, adulthood

Label Diagrams

In your notebook, write the vocabulary term that matches each item pointed out in the diagrams below.

MALE

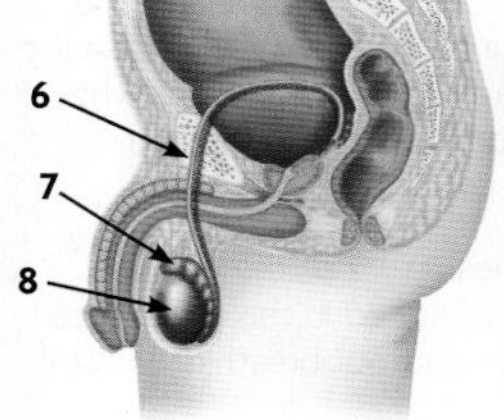

FEMALE

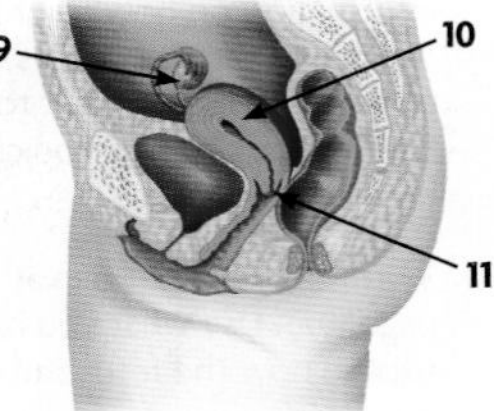

Reviewing MAIN IDEAS

12. Describe the three main functions of estrogen.
13. The sperm move from the testes to the epididymis to the vas deferens as they develop. What happens at each location?
14. Explain what happens to the endometrium during the three phases of the menstrual cycle.
15. What process of cell division do eggs and sperm undergo to become mature sex cells?
16. What happens to their chromosomes when one sperm joins with an egg?
17. Why can chlamydia and syphilis be cured with antibiotics, but genital herpes and HIV cannot?
18. Explain how nutrients and oxygen from the mother's blood are transported to the embryo.
19. A premature baby is born near the end of the second trimester. Why would it have a harder time surviving than one born during the middle of the third trimester?
20. Discuss two ways in which a fetus's health could be harmed by a mother's actions during pregnancy.
21. Describe what marks the beginning of the birth process and what marks the end of the process.
22. In what two phases of human development might human growth hormone be the most active? Explain.

CHAPTER REVIEW

Reviewing Main Ideas

12. The three main functions of estrogen; first: controls development of female sexual characteristics; second: needed for egg cells to develop fully before they leave the ovaries; third: helps prepare the uterus for pregnancy every month and helps maintain a pregnancy.
13. In the testes, specialized cells develop into immature sperm. They mature in the epididymis. Glands in the vas deferens secrete fluids that protect and nourish the sperm.
14. During phase one, the endometrium detaches from the uterine wall and is expelled from the body. In phase two, estrogen causes the endometrium to thicken. In phase three, progesterone and estrogen increase the number of blood vessels in the endometrium. If the egg is not fertilized, levels of estrogen and progesterone drop, and the cycle begins again.
15. meiosis
16. The 23 chromosomes in the sperm join with the 23 chromosomes in the egg to form a new organism with 46 chromosomes.
17. Chlamydia and syphilis are bacterial diseases and therefore, they respond to antibiotics. Genital herpes and HIV are viral diseases, and antibiotics have no effect on viruses.
18. The placenta is formed from the chorionic villi and the lining of the uterus. The umbilical cord connects the placenta to the embryo. Nutrients and oxygen diffuse from the mother's blood into the chorionic villi, which contain blood from the embryo. Nutrients and oxygen are transported from the chorionic villi through the umbilical cord to the embryo.
19. Toward the end of the second trimester, the baby's organs, especially the lungs, are often too immature to function well. By the middle of the third trimester, the organs are more developed.
20. Any two of the following: A mother who uses tobacco or alcohol will pass on toxic chemicals to her fetus, which can cause birth defects and learning disabilities, and can interfere with fetal development. A fetus might be born underweight if the mother does not eat enough. The fetus's spinal cord, brain, and nervous system will not develop properly if the mother does not get enough folic acid.
21. Labor, which causes dilation of the cervix, begins the birth process. The expulsion of the placenta ends the birth process.
22. Human growth hormone is most active in infancy and adolescence, when the greatest periods of growth occur.

Critical Thinking

23. The hypothalamus, pituitary, or thyroid may not be functioning well. The hypothalamus secretes hormones that stimulate the pituitary gland to secrete FSH and LH, which stimulate the follicles to mature. The thyroid regulates metabolism.
24. If the hypothalamus is damaged, it cannot send the proper signals to the pituitary to release FSH and LH. If levels of these two hormones are low, they cannot stimulate the release of testosterone, which means that specialized cells in the testes will not undergo meiosis to develop into mature sperm.
25. The amniotic sac is also a fluid-filled organ that protects the fetus. There is no comparable organ to the yolk. Nourishment for the fetus is also provided by extensions of the chorion, called chorionic villi, that join with the lining of the uterus to form the placenta. The placenta and the umbilical cord function for transport of nutrients, gas exchange, and waste removal. Waste materials move to the chorionic villi, where they diffuse into the mother's blood and are eliminated.
26. Answers will vary, but may include the ability to express feelings with words instead of acting them out, to understand the consequences of actions, to make choices based on an understanding of those consequences, to solve problems, and to sequence behavior to accomplish a task.

Critical Thinking

23. Infer A young woman discovers that she is not ovulating. What endocrine glands might a doctor suspect are not functioning well? Explain your answer.

24. Analyze Alcohol and drug abuse can damage the brain, including the hypothalamus. How would this condition affect sperm production?

25. Synthesize In a bird egg, the developing embryo is inside the *amnion,* which contains fluid. The embryo gets nourishment from the *yolk.* The *chorion* lines the inside of the shell and helps protect the embryo. What structures in a human provide the same functions as these structures in the bird egg?

26. Connect How do you think your ability to express complex emotions and use abstract reasoning changed between the ages of 5 and 15?

Interpreting Visuals

The structures shown below supply a fetus with oxygen and nutrients and remove its waste products. Use the diagram to answer the next three questions.

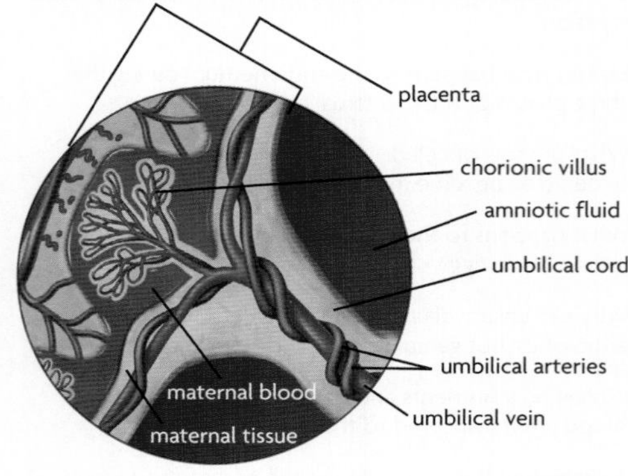

27. Apply Explain how the chorionic villi help move nutrients from the maternal blood to the fetus.

28. Analyze Look carefully at the umbilical arteries and vein. Which of these carries oxygen to the fetus? Explain.

29. Predict Suppose the umbilical arteries became blocked. Describe one way this condition would immediately affect the health of the fetus.

Analyzing Data

Puberty is a time of rapid physical development. The graph below shows average height increases for boys and girls in centimeters per year from ages 8 to 19. Study the data to answer the next two questions.

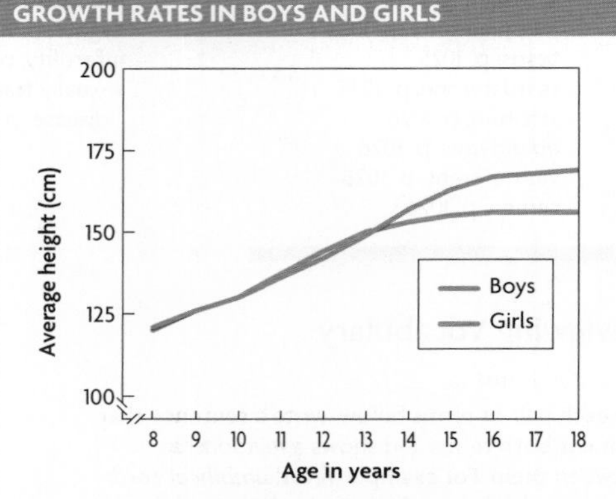

Source: Centers for Disease Control and Prevention

30. Analyze What does the graph show about the growth rates of boys and girls?

31. Analyze According to the graph, at about what age does the growth rate peak for boys? for girls?

Connecting CONCEPTS

32. Write a Brochure This chapter explained how a pregnant woman can affect the health of her fetus. Write the text for a brochure that gives women information on how to promote their own health and the health of their babies during pregnancy. Include a list of what to do and what to avoid and the reasons why. Be sure to cover the topics of food, checkups, and unhealthy activities.

33. Synthesize Look again at the picture of the fetus on page 1023. Use what you have learned in this chapter to explain how the fetus can live without breathing while it is in the uterus.

Interpreting Visuals

27. Nutrients diffuse from the maternal blood into the chorionic villi, which contain the fetus's blood. The nutrients are then transported through the umbilical cord to the fetus.
28. The umbilical vein, like the pulmonary vein, is colored red, which means it carries oxygen-rich blood to the fetus.
29. The umbilical arteries carry away waste products. A blockage would pose a serious threat because toxic materials would build up in the fetus, threatening its life.

Analyzing Data

30. At puberty, both boys and girls grow faster than in the previous few years. Boys start their growth spurt later than girls, but grow more during their spurt.
31. The growth rate for boys is still peaking at age 18; the growth rate for girls peaks at about age 16.

1048 Unit 9: Human Biology

INDIANA ISTEP+ Test Prep

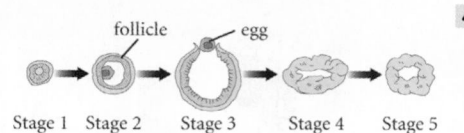

B.5.2; B.6.4; NOS.1

Test Practice For more test practice, go to ClassZone.com.

1

follicle egg

Stage 1 Stage 2 Stage 3 Stage 4 Stage 5

The release of an egg from the ovary is called ovulation. A female's body temperature typically rises significantly when ovulation occurs. Above is an illustration of the development of the follicle and egg. At which stage would you expect to plot the highest temperature?

A Stage 2
B Stage 3
C Stage 4
D Stage 5

2 Each month, the levels of hormones in the female's reproductive system rise and fall. The precise coordination of these hormone levels is responsible for the timing and release of an egg. These hormones are coordinated through a series of

A mitotic divisions.
B meiotic divisions.
C feedback loops.
D fallopian tubes.

3 Sex cells are produced during a specific type of cell division known as

A mitosis.
B meiosis.
C ovulation.
D implantation.

4

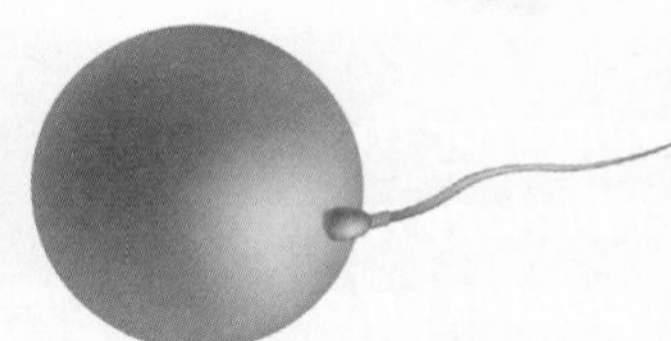

During fertilization, a sperm enters an egg, and the two join to form a zygote. Which statement is true regarding the combination of alleles in the zygote?

A All of the alleles come from the mother's egg.
B All of the alleles come from the father's sperm.
C New combinations of alleles are formed.
D Allele combinations depend on when the egg is fertilized.

5 The placenta is an organ that allows for the exchange of oxygen, nutrients, and wastes between the mother and the developing embryo. In other words, the placenta is responsible for

A allowing the mother and the embryo to maintain homeostasis at the same time.
B repairing genetic damage due to mutation in the embryo.
C ensuring that no fluids leave or enter the uterus.
D serving as a barrier to keep out all toxic materials.

6 What would happen if during meiosis, chromosomes did not divide equally into the new cells, producing cells that contained too many, or not enough chromosomes?

Standards-Based Assessment

1. B	4. C
2. C	5. A
3. B	6. See Below

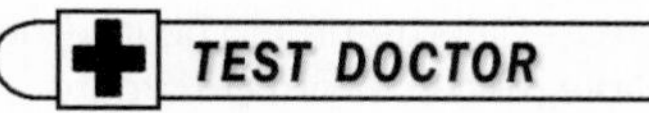

Question 4 Answer C is correct. Answer A is incorrect because half of the alleles come from the father's sperm. Answer B is incorrect because half of the alleles come from the mother's egg. Answer D is incorrect because both parents contribute half of the alleles to the zygote regardless of when the egg is fertilized.

Question 5 Answer A is correct. Answers B, C, and D are incorrect because the placenta cannot repair genetic damage, stop the movement of fluids, or prevent toxins from entering the embryo's body.

Question 6 The resulting egg or sperm cells would contain too much or not enough genetic information. They would not be viable at all, they would produce a zygote that would not survive, or they would produce a zygote that would develop into a fetus with a genetic malformation.

Connecting Concepts

32. Answers will vary, but should include the need for a balanced diet that includes essential amino acids, vitamins, minerals, proteins, fats, and carbohydrates. Special mention should be made of folic acid and its role in preventing spinal cord deformities and undeveloped nervous systems. Women should avoid tobacco and alcohol because these substances can cause learning disabilities and other problems. Women should check with their doctors before taking any kind of medication. Pregnant women should add about 300 Calories to their daily diet and have regular physical checkups.
33. The mother breathes in oxygen, and it circulates through her body in her blood. The oxygen diffuses into the chorionic villi, which contain blood from the fetus, and then is carried by the umbilical cord to the fetus. As a result, the fetus "breathes" by means of the umbilical cord.

ITEM CORRELATIONS

Standard	Items
B.5.2	4
B.6.4	3, 6
NOS.1	1

UNIT
9

Introduce

Tell students that the science knowledge base increases all the time. The Internet is a valuable resource for up-to-date scientific information, but students need to know how to evaluate these websites and the quality of the information they provide.

The URL, or address of a website, may provide a clue to how reliable, reputable, and well known a source is. For example, .gov and .us are government sites, .edu is an educational site, and .org often represents a nonprofit organization. Sites with these domains may be reliable sources of science information. Sites with a .com domain may be from a company selling a product or from an individual presenting a specific point of view and should be evaluated with that in mind.

Some URLs may indicate the specific source of the information. For example, nih.gov is the site of the National Institutes of Health, berkeley.edu and cornell.edu are the official sites of well-known universities, and mayoclinic.com is the site of the Mayo Clinic.

Tell students that once they open a page at a website, they should identify the author, organization, institution, or agency responsible for the page. They should also look for the date the page was written or last updated. Scientific information changes quickly, and up-to-date information is important. **Ask**

- How can evaluating URLs help save you time? You can choose which sites to open and avoid sites that would not be useful or reliable.
- What questions might you consider when evaluating the information at a website? Can I understand it? Does it describe the research method used? Is it objective? Does it contain facts, or is it someone's opinion?
- What is a "wiki," and why must you be careful using the information? A type of website that allows visitors to add, remove, or edit online content; wikis can carry misinformation.

UNIT 9: HUMAN BIOLOGY

BIOZINE at CLASSZONE.COM

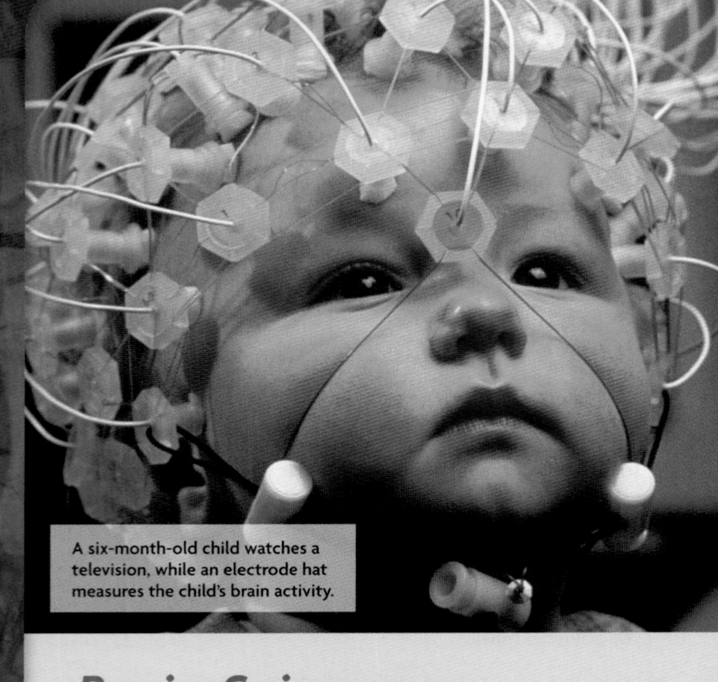

A six-month-old child watches a television, while an electrode hat measures the child's brain activity.

Brain Science—We Are Wired to Learn!

Your brain has more than 100 billion cells, called neurons. Together, the neurons in your brain are so powerful that they can process more information than the most powerful existing computer can in the same amount of time. Your brain can accomplish so much because you've spent years—every second of your life—learning from and interpreting the world around you.

Current News

Using the computer lab, have students look for stories about the human body in the Current News section of BioZine at **ClassZone.com.** Have students pick stories that interest them and ask them to share the information with their classmates.

Opinion Poll

Do boys learn differently than girls do? Should schools teach them in different ways? Ask students to share their opinions on these questions. Also have students take the online poll at BioZine. Have students think about polls they see on television or at their favorite websites. **Ask**

- How common is it that the polls you see are trying to sell you something or determine your level of interest in a product?
- How truthful do you think people are in taking polls, and does it matter?

Plasticity of the Brain

What factors affect the brain's plasticity, or ability to learn new things? How does the brain change with age? These are some of the questions neuroscientists addressed in the early years of brain research.

During the first three years of life, the neurons in the brain rapidly form connections, or synapses, between each other. Neurons and synapses are overproduced in babies' brains because their brains are taking in a lot of new information. At three years old, the brain begins to prune, or reduce the number of, these connections so that only the most used connections are intact. On average, three-year-olds have two times more synapses than adults have.

Of course, the brain does not lose all of its plasticity after the age of three. Even adults can learn a new skill, such as how to speak a foreign language. But neuroscientists have recently found a surprising second wave of brain growth and plasticity that begins just before puberty, similar to that observed in infants. Then, during the teenage years, some connections are pruned. The remaining connections become stronger and more efficient by the addition of more insulation around the neurons. This period of pruning and strengthening continues until a person is about 30. Connections that are used least are pruned away, and connections that are used the most are strengthened.

So how teenagers spend their time can affect their brain's wiring. One researcher says, "If a teen is doing music or sports or academics, those are the cells and connections that will be hard-wired. If they're lying on the couch or playing video games . . . those are the connections that are going to survive."

Although researchers agree that playing video games affects the brain, they do not agree on how the brain is affected. Some studies suggest that video games could strengthen beneficial connections. Other studies imply that some beneficial connections could become weakened.

TECHNOLOGY

Scanning the Brain

Much of today's research on brain function uses functional magnetic resonance imaging (fMRI). In a traditional MRI, computers use information from a magnetic field to make a three-dimensional image of the brain. An fMRI uses an MRI machine together with computer software that can analyze which part of the brain is active while a person performs different tasks.

A person lies in an MRI machine and thinks about something, observes images, listens to music, or does arithmetic. While the person thinks, the largest quantity of oxygenated blood gets directed to the part of the brain that is doing the most work.

The magnets detect molecules of hemoglobin, which bind oxygen in red blood cells. The hemoglobin contains atoms of iron, a metal that is attracted to magnets. When the magnetic field encounters the iron in hemoglobin, the magnetic field bends slightly.

Sensors in the MRI machine record the bending and send the information to a computer. The computer calculates, based on the amount of bending in the magnetic field, how much oxygen is present and calculates where in the brain the oxygen is located.

The computer maps this information on a three-dimensional model of the brain as shown in the photograph. The orange highlighted area on the model indicates the area of the brain that the person was using during the experiment.

Read More >> at CLASSZONE.COM

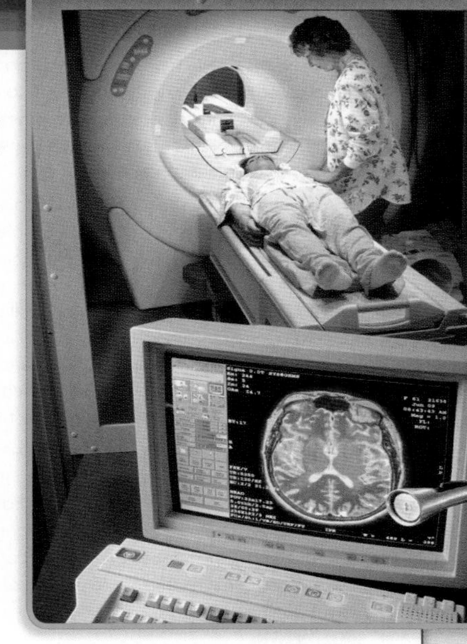

A patient emerges from an MRI machine as a computer maps oxygen (orange) in the patient's brain.

Vocabulary of Brain Research

Students may need clarification of some of the terms used in describing brain research.

neuron—a nerve cell. A neuron is specialized to generate and conduct electrical impulses, which allow communication with other neurons. Neurons in the brain send messages from one part of the brain to another and to organs and tissues throughout the body.

synapse—a tiny gap between two neurons across which neurons communicate. An electrical impulse in one neuron causes the release of a neurotransmitter at the synapse, which moves across the gap and triggers an electrical impulse in the next neuron.

neurotransmitter—chemical substances that carry messages from one neuron to the next neuron. Neurotransmitters are found in the synapse between neurons.

myelin—the insulation around neurons. Because myelin is an electrical insulator, it allows nerves to carry information faster and more efficiently. Connections in the brain become stronger during the teenage years when more myelin is added around neurons.

plasticity—in a general sense, the capability of being shaped or formed. Plasticity in the brain, or **neuroplasticity,** is the ability of the brain to change in response to internal and external stimuli or conditions.

magnetic resonance imaging (MRI)—a technique that uses a magnetic field and radio waves to create cross-sectional images of the brain or other parts of the body. A traditional MRI shows the structure or anatomy of the brain. A functional MRI shows brain activity. It allows researchers to measure the activity of neurons and locate what area of the brain is being used.

Strange Biology

Humans have the greatest number of brain cells between the third and sixth months of development in utero. Unnecessary brain cells are pruned before birth. Some scientists speculate that certain disorders, such as autism, might be a result of incorrect pruning of brain cells before birth. Have students discuss the importance of pruning. Then have students go to BioZine at **ClassZone.com** to read another strange biology fact. **Ask**

- Why does this information seem strange?
- How is this biology useful?

Careers

Have students go to BioZine and review the different careers highlighted there. **Ask**

- Which career would you be most interested in and why?
- Which career would you be least interested in and why?

UNIT

9

Take It Further

While the behavior of teenagers has long been attributed to hormonal changes, studies by neuroscientists have led to the conclusion that teenage behavior is also affected by their still developing brains. Studies have shown the following:

- The development of the teenage brain occurs in stages from the back of the brain to the front.
- The last part of the brain to mature is the prefrontal cortex in the front of the brain. This part of the brain is responsible for such functions as setting priorities, organizing thoughts, controlling behavior, and weighing the consequences of one's actions.
- Teenagers use a different part of the brain, the part responsible for emotion and gut response, than adults do when making decisions about what to do.
- The emotional part of the brain that is utilized in teenagers can lead to impulsive behavior since the consequences of their actions cannot be fully appreciated yet.

The Multitasking Brain

How can some video games strengthen connections in your brain? Some video games present the player with complicated puzzles and patterns. The player must take in visual messages from the computer or television screen, while using problem-solving skills to analyze patterns at the same time. This multitasking requires the player to use different areas of the brain at the same time. Using language has a similar effect on the brain as playing video games in that both activate many areas of the brain at the same time.

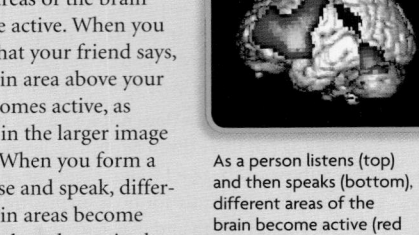

CAREERS

Neuroscientist in Action

DR. RAE NISHI
TITLE Director, Neuroscience Graduate Program, University of Vermont
EDUCATION Ph. D., Biology, University of California, San Diego

Dr. Rae Nishi's research proves that you do not need complicated technology, such as fMRIs, to make discoveries in neuroscience. Through observation and experiment, Dr. Nishi's research tries to answer the question: What causes brain cells to die?

Although the question is too broad to answer completely, Dr. Nishi has discovered a molecule that seems to keep alive brain cells in dying chick embryos. She also found that by blocking a certain receptor on the surface of neurons, dying neurons will stop showing signs of decline. Studies of how and why brain cells might die are important in understanding Alzheimer's and Parkinson's diseases, which cause certain areas of the brain to become inactive.

"There is no profession as exciting as being a scientist," Dr. Nishi says. "You get to learn new things every day. You get to make discoveries. You get to solve puzzles." Dr. Nishi is currently working to determine how the molecules released during one neuron's death might trigger the growth of new, neighboring neurons.

Read More >> at CLASSZONE.COM

When you have a conversation with a friend, many areas of the brain become active. When you hear what your friend says, the brain area above your ear becomes active, as shown in the larger image above. When you form a response and speak, different brain areas become activated, as shown in the smaller image at right. The front of the brain is activated when you interpret your friend's words and form a response. When you begin to respond, an area in the back of the brain becomes active. This area becomes more and more active as you talk.

As a person listens (top) and then speaks (bottom), different areas of the brain become active (red and yellow).

Reading is another complicated activity. The same areas of your brain that are active when you talk to your friend are active when you read. But another area is also activated. This third area is farther back in the brain. It allows you to see and interpret the printed words in front of you. Even people who read Braille use the visual part of their brain to interpret what is on the page.

Unanswered Questions

Every new discovery in neuroscience brings with it new questions. Some of these include the following:

- Can the plasticity of an adult brain be used to help adults recover from brain injuries and diseases?
- Can neuroscientists find ways to treat, or even cure, disorders such as Alzheimer's disease?
- Why are humans, and not other primates, good at learning words and systems of grammar?

Read More >> at CLASSZONE.COM

BIOZINE ClassZone.com

Have students use the resources available in the Unit 9 BioZine at **ClassZone.com** to report about recent discoveries in brain research. In addition to the sources available in BioZine, have students use the Internet and a search engine to find additional information. Remind students to evaluate URLs before opening websites. **Ask**

- What type of site did you find to be most useful?
- What discoveries about brain research did you find most interesting?
- What are some potential uses suggested for the discoveries that have been made?
- How is brain research being used to shape the way children are taught?

Student Resources

LAB HANDBOOK R2

- Safety R2
- Safety Symbols R4
- The Metric System and SI Units R5
- Measuring in the Lab R6
- Using a Light Microscope R8
- Designing Experiments R11

MATH AND DATA ANALYSIS HANDBOOK R14

- Calculating Mean, Median, and Mode R14
- Significant Figures and Scientific Notation R14
- Data Tables and Line Graphs R15
- Bar Graphs and Combination Graphs R16
- Histograms, Scatterplots, and Circle Graphs R17

VOCABULARY HANDBOOK R18

- Greek and Latin Word Parts R18
- Academic Vocabulary R20

NOTE-TAKING HANDBOOK R22

- Process and Cycle Diagrams and Supporting Main Ideas Notes R22
- Main Idea Webs, Two-Column Notes, Cause-and-Effect Diagrams, and Content Frames R23
- Venn Diagrams, Y Diagrams, and Concept Maps R24

APPENDICES R25

- A Classification R25
- B Life Cycles R32
    - Moss R32
    - Fern R33
    - Conifer R34
    - Flowering Plant R35
- C Periodic Table R36
- D Biology Careers R38

R1

Lab Handbook

Safety

Before you work in the laboratory, read these safety rules. Ask your teacher to explain any rules that you do not completely understand. Refer to these rules later on if you have questions about safety in the science classroom.

Directions

- Know where the fire extinguisher, fire blanket, shower, and eyewash are located in your classroom.
- Read all directions and make sure that you understand them before starting an investigation or lab activity. If you do not understand how to do a procedure or how to use a piece of equipment, ask your teacher.
- Do not begin any investigation or touch any equipment until your teacher has told you to start.
- Never experiment on your own. If you want to try a procedure that the directions do not call for, ask your teacher for permission first.
- If you are hurt or injured in any way, tell your teacher immediately.

Dress Code

- Wear goggles when using glassware, sharp objects, or chemicals; heating an object; or working with anything that can easily fly up into the air and hurt someone's eye.
- Tie back long hair or hair that hangs in front of your eyes.
- Remove any article of clothing—such as a loose sweater or a scarf—that hangs down and may touch a flame, chemical, or piece of equipment.
- Observe all safety icons calling for the wearing of eye protection, gloves, and aprons.

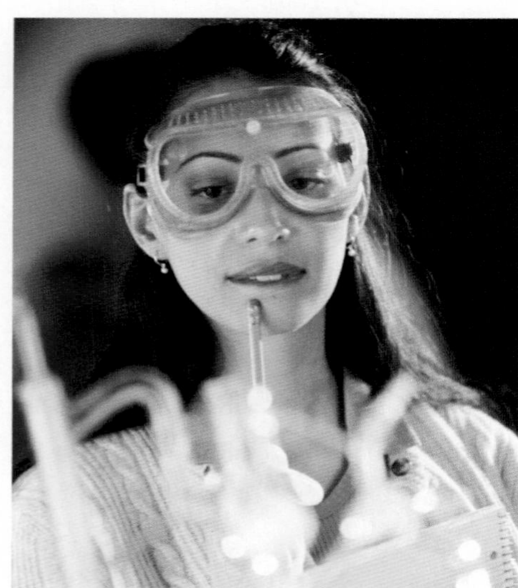

Heating and Fire Safety

- Keep your work area neat, clean, and free of extra materials.
- Use only borosilicate glass for heating substances.
- Never reach over a flame or heat source.
- Point objects being heated away from you and others.
- Never heat a substance or an object in a closed container.
- Use oven mitts, clamps, tongs, or a test tube holder to hold heated items.
- Never touch an object that has been heated. If you are unsure whether something is hot, treat it as though it is.
- After heating test tubes, place them in a test tube rack.
- Do not throw hot substances into the trash. Wait for them to cool and dispose of them in the container provided by your teacher.

Chemical Safety

- Always wear goggles when working with any type of chemical, even household items such as baking soda.
- Stand when you are working with chemicals. Pour them over a sink or your work area, not over the floor. If you spill a chemical or get it on your skin, tell your teacher right away.
- If you get a chemical in your eye, use the eyewash immediately.
- Never touch, taste, or sniff any chemicals in the lab. If you need to determine odor, waft. To waft, hold the chemical in its container 15 cm (6 in.) away from your nose, and use your fingers to bring fumes from the container to your nose.
- Keep lids on all chemicals you are not using.
- Use materials only from properly labeled containers.
- Never use more chemicals than the procedure calls for.
- When diluting acid with water, always add acid to water.
- Never put unused chemicals back into the original containers. Dispose of extra chemicals in the container provided by your teacher.
- Always wash your hands after handling chemicals.

Electrical Safety

- Never use lamps or other electrical equipment with frayed cords.
- Make sure no cord is lying on the floor where someone can trip over it.
- Do not let a cord hang over the side of a counter or table so that the equipment can easily be pulled or knocked to the floor.
- Never let cords hang into sinks or other places where water can be found.
- Turn off all power switches before plugging an appliance into an outlet.
- Never touch electrical equipment with wet hands.
- Never try to fix electrical problems. Immediately inform your teacher of any problems.
- Unplug an electrical cord by pulling on the plug, not the cord.

Glassware and Sharp-Object Safety

- Use only clean glassware that is free of chips and cracks.
- If you break glassware, tell your teacher right away.
- If you use a microscope that has a mirror, do not aim the mirror directly at the sun as you can damage your eyes.
- Use knives and other cutting instruments carefully. Always wear eye protection and cut away from yourself.
- Clean glassware according to your teacher's instructions after you use it.
- Use an appropriately sized test tube for the quantity of chemicals you are using, and store test tubes in a test tube rack.

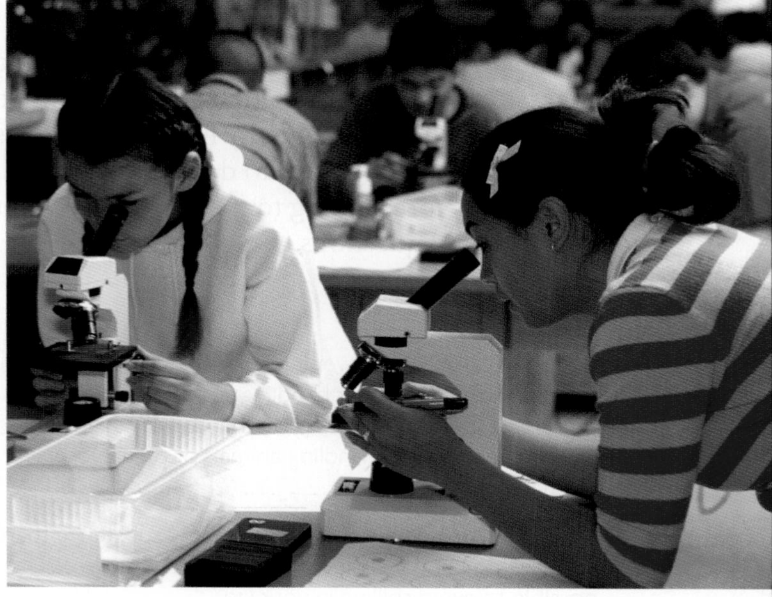

Animal Safety

- Never hurt an animal.
- Touch animals only when necessary. Follow your teacher's instructions for handling animals.
- Wear gloves when handling animals or preserved specimens.
- Specimens for dissection should be properly mounted and supported.
- Do not cut a specimen while holding it in your hands.
- Do not open containers of live microorganisms unless you are directed to do so.
- Dispose of preserved specimens as directed by your teacher.
- Always wash your hands with soap and water after working with animals or specimens.

Cleanup

- Follow your teacher's instructions for the disposal or storage of supplies.
- Clean your work area and pick up anything that has dropped to the floor.
- Wash your hands.

R3

Lab Handbook

Safety Symbols

Safety is the priority in the science classroom. In all of the activities in this textbook, safety symbols are used to alert you to materials, procedures, or situations that could be potentially hazardous if the safety guidelines are not followed. Learn what you need to do when you see these icons, and read all lab procedures before coming to the lab so you are prepared. Always ask your teacher if you have questions.

ANIMAL SAFETY Never injure an animal. Follow your teacher's instructions for handling specific animals or preserved specimens. Wash your hands with soap and water when finished handling animals or preserved specimens.

APRON Wear an apron when using any substance that could cause harm if spilled on you. Stand whenever possible to avoid spilling in your lap.

BREAKAGE Use caution when handling items that may break, such as glassware and thermometers. Always store test tubes in a test tube rack.

CHEMICAL SAFETY Always wear goggles when working with chemicals. Stand whenever possible when working with chemicals to avoid spilling on your lap. Tell your teacher immediately if you spill chemicals on yourself, the table, or floor. Never taste any substance or chemical in the lab. Always wash your hands after working with chemicals.

DISPOSAL Follow your teacher's instructions for disposing of all waste materials, including chemicals, specimens, or broken glass.

ELECTRICAL SAFETY Keep electrical cords away from water to avoid shock. Do not use cords with frayed edges. Unplug all equipment when done.

FIRE SAFETY Put on safety goggles before lighting flames. Remove loose clothing and tie back hair. Never leave a lit object unattended. Extinguish flames as soon as you finish heating.

FUMES Always work in a well-ventilated area. Bring fumes up to your nose by wafting with your fingers instead of sniffing.

GENERAL SAFETY Always follow the safety rules and ask your teacher if you are unsure about something. If you are designing your own experiment, get your teacher's approval on your plan before you start. Think about which safety rules you must follow in your experiment.

GLOVES Always wear gloves to protect your skin from possible injury when working with substances that may be harmful or when working with animals.

HAND WASHING Wash your hands with soap and water after working with soil, chemicals, animals, or preserved specimens.

HEATING SAFETY Wear goggles and never leave any substance while it is being heated. Use tongs, hot pads, or test tube holders to hold hot objects. Point any materials being heated away from you and others. Place hot objects such as test tubes in test tube racks while cooling.

HOT/GLOVE Always wear gloves such as oven mitts when handling larger hot materials.

POISON Never touch, taste, or inhale chemicals. Most chemicals are toxic in high concentrations. Wear goggles and wash your hands.

SAFETY GOGGLES Always wear safety goggles when working with chemicals, heating any substance, or using a sharp object or any material that could fly up and injure you or others.

SHARP OBJECTS Use scissors, knives, or razor tools with care. Wear goggles when cutting something with scalpels, knives, or razor tools. Always cut away from yourself.

The Metric System and SI Units

Scientists around the world use the metric system of measurement. The official name for the metric system is the International System of Units (SI). The short name SI comes from the French name, Système International d'Unitès.

SI Units

SI includes units for measuring length, mass, volume, temperature, and many other properties. The most commonly used SI units are shown in Table 1.

TABLE 1: COMMON SI UNITS	
PROPERTY	NAME
Length	meter (m)
Volume	liter (L)
Mass	kilogram (kg)
Temperature	Kelvin (K)

The relationships between all SI units are based on powers of 10. In most cases, an SI unit has a prefix that shows its relationship to the base unit. For example, 1 kilometer is 1000 meters, and 1 centimeter is one-hundredth of a meter. Table 2 lists the commonly used SI prefixes along with their symbols and values.

TABLE 2: SI PREFIXES		
PREFIX	SYMBOL	VALUE
giga-	G	1,000,000,000
mega-	M	1,000,000
kilo-	k	1000
hecto-	h	100
deca-	da	10
deci-	d	0.1
centi-	c	0.01
milli-	m	0.001
micro-	μ	0.000001
nano-	n	0.000000001
pico-	p	0.000000000001

For your reference, the mass of a paper clip is about 1 g. The diameter of a red blood cell is very small—about 10 μm.

Mass of paper clip = 1 g

Diameter of a red blood cell = 10 μm

Customary to SI Conversion

Although all scientists use the metric system, in the United States the customary system of measurements is still widely used. Table 3 provides useful equivalents for making conversions between these two systems of measurement.

TABLE 3: CUSTOMARY AND SI EQUIVALENTS	
U.S. CUSTOMARY	SI
1 inch (in.)	2.54 centimeters (cm)
39.37 inches (in.)	1 meter (m)
0.62 miles (mi)	1 kilometer (km)
1.06 quarts (qt)	1 liter (L)
1 fluid ounce (oz)	236 milliliters (mL)
2.2 pounds (lb)	1 kilogram (kg)
1 ounce (oz)	28.3 grams (g)

Temperature

Use the formulas at right for converting between Celsius and Fahrenheit temperatures.

$$°C = \frac{5}{9} \times (°F - 32)$$

$$°F = (\frac{9}{5} \times °C) + 32$$

Measuring in the Lab

Collecting accurate and precise data in the lab requires the skillful use of some basic lab equipment. Be sure that you know how to use all equipment correctly in the lab, not only to obtain accurate results but also to ensure your safety.

Metric Rulers

- Use metric rulers or meter sticks to measure length.
- Because the end of a meter stick or ruler is often imperfect, begin the measurement from the 1 cm mark.
- Lay a ruler flat on top of the object so that the 1-centimeter mark lines up with one end. Make sure the ruler and the object do not move between the time you line them up and the time you take the measurement.
- Estimate the reading to one place value beyond what is marked on the ruler. The ruler is marked to the tenths place value, so estimate to the hundredths. The stem of the leaf hits the ruler about halfway between the 4.2 and 4.3 cm marks, so it is estimated at 4.25 cm. However, it is necessary to subtract 1 cm from the edge of the ruler not used in the measurement, so the leaf measures 3.25 cm.

Graduated Cylinder

- Use a graduated cylinder to measure the volume of a liquid.
- You can use a graduated cylinder to find the volume of a solid object by measuring the increase in a liquid's level after you add the object to the cylinder.
- Be sure that the graduated cylinder is on a flat surface. Your eye level should be even with the surface of the liquid.
- Read the volume of the liquid at the bottom of the curve, or meniscus (muh-NIHS-kuhs).
- The volume of liquid is on the 96 mL mark. Estimate to one place value beyond what is marked on the graduated cylinder. The volume of liquid is 96.0 mL.

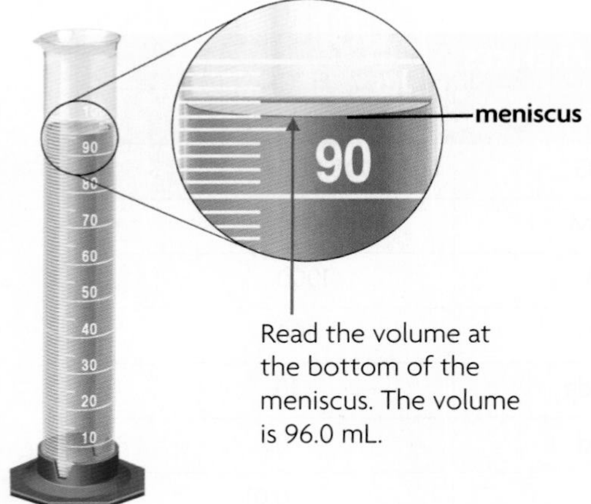

Read the volume at the bottom of the meniscus. The volume is 96.0 mL.

Thermometer

- To measure the temperature of a liquid, place a thermometer into the container without letting the thermometer touch the bottom of the container. Attach a clip to hold the thermometer in place, especially if the liquid is hot.
- As the liquid moves up or down inside the thermometer, rotate the thermometer for more accurate results.
- Stop recording measurements when the liquid in the thermometer stops moving. Take note of the highest point of liquid by estimating to the nearest tenth of a degree.
- The temperature on this thermometer is 24.5°C.

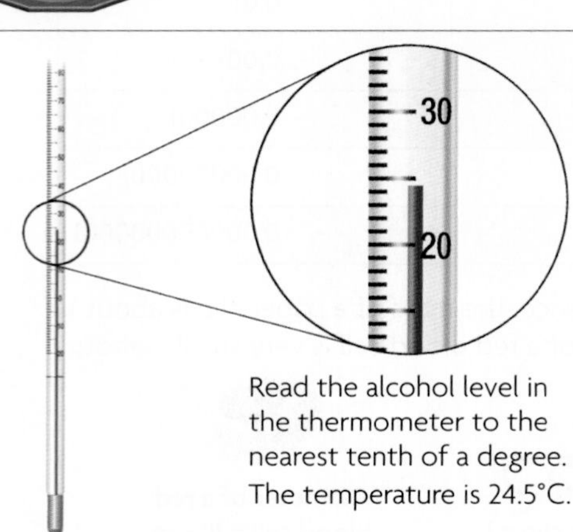

Read the alcohol level in the thermometer to the nearest tenth of a degree. The temperature is 24.5°C.

Triple-Beam Balance

This balance has a pan and three beams with sliding masses, called riders. Each beam is calibrated to a different level of mass, allowing the balance to be accurate to a tenth of a gram. At one end of the beams, a pointer indicates whether the mass on the pan is equal to the masses shown on the beams.

1. Place the balance on a stable, level surface.
2. Make sure the balance is zeroed before measuring the mass of an object. The balance is zeroed if the pointer is at zero when nothing is on the pan and the riders are at their zero points. Use the adjustment knob under the pan of the balance to zero it.
3. Place the object to be measured on the pan. Do not place a hot object or chemical on the pan. The changing temperature may have a direct impact on your measurement and can also be dangerous.
4. Move the riders one notch at a time away from the pan. Begin with the largest rider. If moving the largest rider one notch brings the pointer below zero, move the mass back and then begin measuring the mass of the object with the next smaller rider.
5. Change the positions of the riders until they balance the mass on the pan and the pointer is at zero. Then add the readings from the three beams to determine the mass of the object.
6. The balance below is being used to measure a beaker of water. To find the mass of the water inside the beaker, a student moved the riders to the positions shown. The total mass of the beaker and water is 163.0 g, but you must also subtract the mass of the empty beaker from the total.

Mass of water = Mass of beaker + water		**= 163.0 g**
	– Mass of beaker =	**63.0 g**
Mass of water		**= 100.0 g**

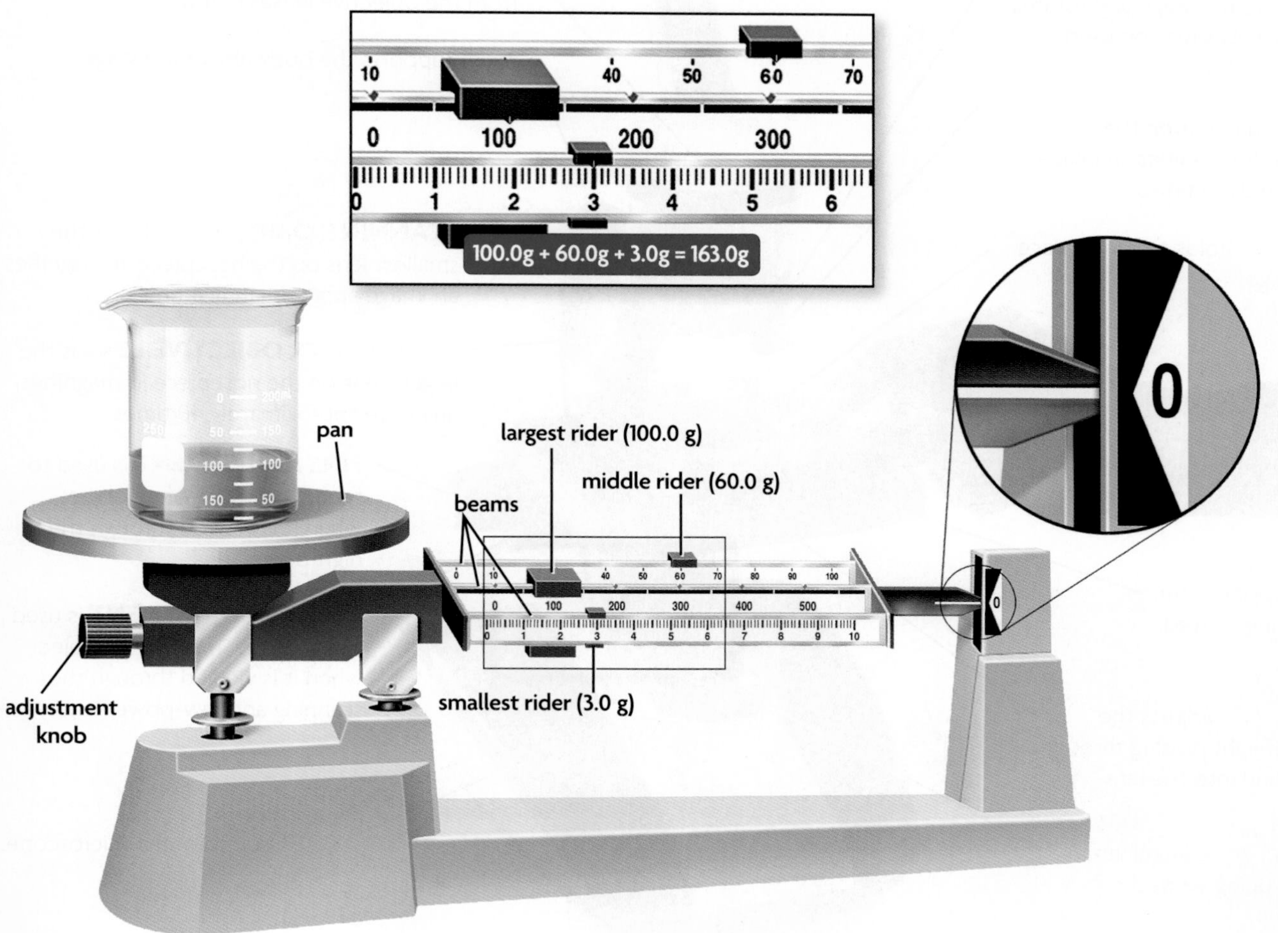

Using a Light Microscope

Microscopes are used to view objects too small to be seen with the naked eye.

Viewing an Object

Use these directions to view your specimen.

1. Use the coarse adjustment to raise the body tube.
2. Adjust the diaphragm so that you can see a bright circle of light through the eyepiece.
3. Place the slide on the stage. Be sure to center it over the hole in the stage and secure it with the stage clips.
4. Turn the nosepiece to click the scanning objective lens into place.
5. Using the coarse adjustment knob, slowly lower the lens and focus on the specimen being viewed. Be sure not to touch the slide or object with the lens.
6. When using the high power lens, use only the fine adjustment knob.
7. Move the slide on the stage with very small movements to view other parts of it. You may need to refocus using the fine adjustment.

EYEPIECE contains a lens that commonly magnifies an image 10 times. Objects are viewed through the eyepiece.

NOSEPIECE holds the objective lenses above the stage and rotates so that all lenses may be used.

BODY separates the lens in the eyepiece from the objective lenses below.

ARM supports the body above the stage.

LOW-POWER OBJECTIVE LENS is the medium lens on the nosepiece. It magnifies an image approximately 10 times.

STAGE CLIP holds a slide in place on the stage.

SCANNING OBJECTIVE LENS is the smallest lens on the nosepiece. It magnifies an image approximately 4 times.

HIGH-POWER OBJECTIVE LENS is the largest lens on the nosepiece. It magnifies an image approximately 40 times.

FINE ADJUSTMENT is used to focus the image of an object when it is viewed through the high-power lens.

STAGE supports the object being viewed.

COARSE ADJUSTMENT is used to focus the image of an object when it is viewed through the scanning and low-power lenses.

DIAPHRAGM adjusts the amount of light passing through the slide and into the lens.

LIGHT SOURCE illuminates specimen being viewed.

BASE supports the microscope.

R8

Making a Wet Mount

Use these steps to prepare a specimen to be viewed under a microscope.

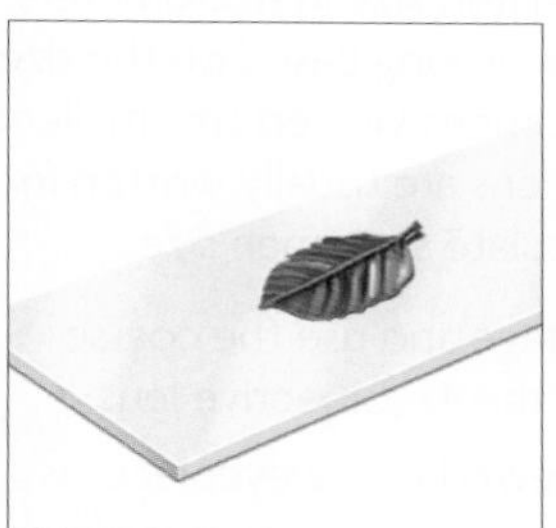

Place the specimen in the center of a clean slide.

Place a drop of water on the specimen.

Place a cover slip on the slide. Put one edge of the cover slip into the drop of water, and slowly lower the cover slip over the specimen.

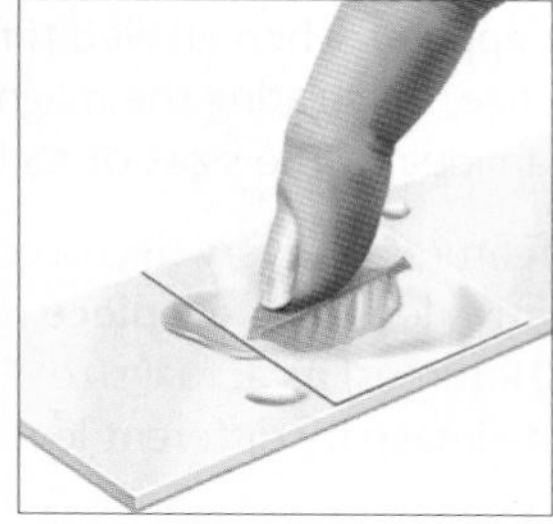

Remove any air bubbles from under the cover slip by gently tapping the cover slip.

Dry any excess water before placing the slide on the microscope stage for viewing.

Staining a Specimen

After you make a wet mount, use these steps to stain the specimen.

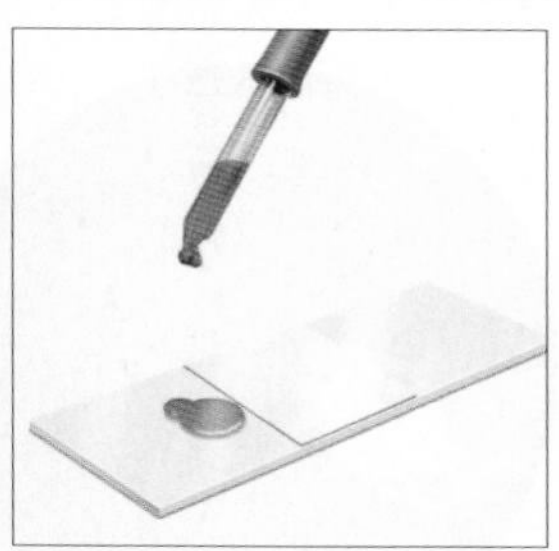

Place a drop of stain at one end of the cover slip.

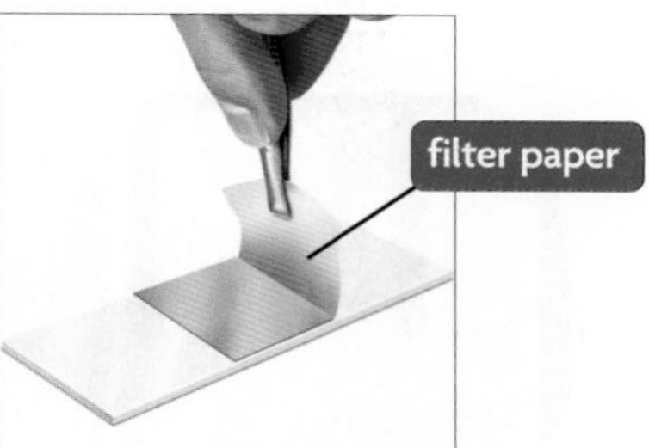

Hold a piece of filter paper with forceps at the other end of the cover slip. The stain will flow underneath the cover slip and stain the specimen.

Calculating Magnification

When you look through a microscope, you see a magnified image of the specimen on the slide. Magnification describes how much larger an object appears when viewed through a microscope than its actual size. Calculating the magnification of the image will give you an idea of the sizes of its features.

There are two magnifying features of every microscope: the eyepiece and the objective lens. The **eyepiece** has a lens that magnifies the image 10× (times) its actual size. The objective lenses magnify the image by different levels.

		Scanning Objective	4×
Eyepiece 10×	•	Low-Power Objective	10×
		High-Power Objective	40×

The total magnification of the image is the product of multiplying the eyepiece magnification by the objective lens magnification.

The examples below show how to calculate the total magnification of the daphnia under each lens.

EXAMPLE

Eyepiece • Scanning Objective = Total Magnification
(10×) • (4×) = 40×
This image is magnified 40× its actual size.

EXAMPLE

Eyepiece • Low-Power Objective = Total Magnification
(10×) • (10×) = 100×
The image is magnified 100× its actual size.

EXAMPLE

Eyepiece • High-Power Objective = Total Magnification
(10×) • (40×) = 400×
This image is magnified 400× its actual size.

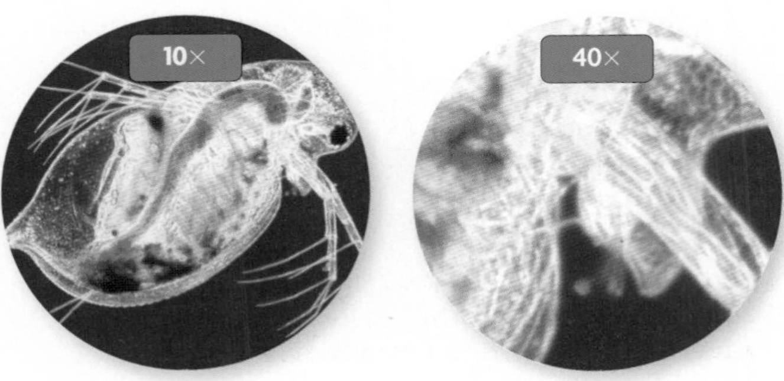

Calculating Specimen Size

The field of view is the area seen through the microscope eyepiece. You can calculate the estimated size in micrometers (µm) of a specimen or object you are viewing based on the size of the field of view. Since many specimens viewed are smaller than a millimeter, the sizes of specimens are usually written in micrometers. Use these steps to calculate specimen size.

1. Place a ruler on the microscope stage and use the coarse adjustment to focus the image in the 4× objective lens.
2. Look at the markings on a ruler viewed in the eyepiece, as shown in the image below.
3. Estimate the diameter of the field of view to the nearest millimeter, which is approximately 4 mm in this example.
4. Remove the ruler and put the slide specimen on the stage.
5. Adjust the slide so the specimen is at one side of the field of view. Estimate the size of the specimen based on the field of view. The length of the daphnia specimen viewed under the scanning objective lens is about 2 mm.
6. Convert mm to µm.

length of specimen • 1000 µm/mm = ?
2 mm • 1000 µm/mm = 2000 µm

Designing Experiments

Biologists continually make observations about the natural world around them and raise questions about these observations. Designing experiments to answer these questions serves as the basis of scientific discovery.

An **experiment** is a test under controlled conditions that is made to find a cause-and-effect relationship between variables. Every well-designed experiment has a purpose and an organized, step-by-step procedure.

Determining a Purpose

A simple observation that sparks your interest can lead to a purpose for an experiment. An observation can lead to many questions, but you should choose just one question to study. From that starting point, you can do background research and examine the results of previous experiments.

- Write the purpose of your experiment as a question or problem that you want to investigate.
- Write down specific questions that you will research to find information that will help you design your experiment.

EXAMPLE

Suppose you notice that different patches of plants appear to grow better in different areas around your school. How could you use this observation to design an experiment?

Problem: How does fertilizer affect plant growth?

Research Questions
What nutrients do plants need?
Which fertilizers contain those nutrients?

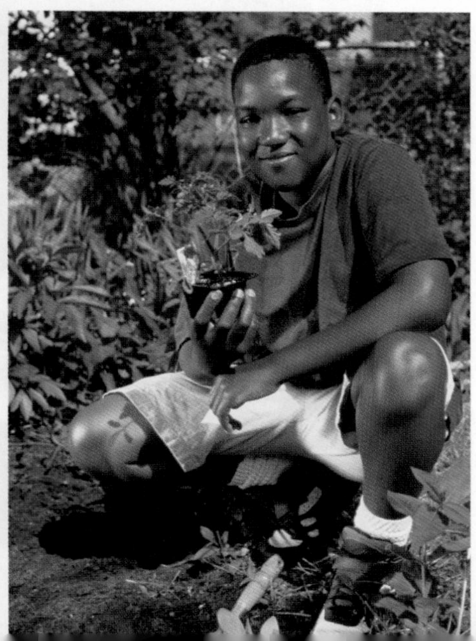

Writing a Hypothesis

A **hypothesis** is a tentative explanation for an observation. A hypothesis leads to testable predictions of what would happen if the hypothesis is valid.

An experiment is designed to test a hypothesis, not to prove that a hypothesis is correct. An experiment cannot prove a hypothesis; data from the experiment can only support it or fail to support it. Keep in mind that there are no "good-or-bad, right-or-wrong" experimental results. Even when results fail to support a hypothesis, they can lead to an idea for another experiment. Hypotheses can be written in several ways.

EXAMPLE

Hypothesis: Nitrogen is a nutrient that plants need for growth.

Testable prediction: If plants are given fertilizer that contains nitrogen, plant growth will increase.

Formalized hypothesis: If plants need the nutrient nitrogen to grow, then plants given fertilizer with nitrogen will experience an increase in growth.

Identifying Variables and Constants

All experiments include constants and variables. **Constants** are all of the factors that are kept the same—held constant—during the entire experiment. A variable is any factor that changes. The **independent variable** is the factor that you are testing and that you manipulate, or change. The **dependent variable** is the factor that you measure. The dependent variable changes, or "depends on," the independent variable. In the example below, plant growth (the dependent variable) is measured and depends on the amount of fertilizer with nitrogen (the independent variable) the plant is given.

EXAMPLE

Independent variable: amount of fertilizer with nitrogen

Dependent variable: plant growth

Constants: temperature, amount of light, intensity of light, type of plant, amount of water, frequency and time of watering, time when dependent variable is measured, amount of soil, type of soil

Lab Handbook

Determining Experimental and Control Groups

An experiment to determine how two factors are related always has at least two groups—a control group and an experimental group.

- The control group is exactly the same as the experimental group—except for the factor that is being tested.
- An experiment can have one or more experimental groups. With one experimental group, you are testing whether the independent variable has an effect. With more than one experimental group, you are testing the presence of the independent variable and different amounts of it.

EXAMPLE

In our example, there are three experimental groups—each tests a different amount of fertilizer.

Experimental Groups

5 g fertilizer
10 g fertilizer
15 g fertilizer

Control Group
0 g fertilizer

Identifying Types of Data

There are two types of data: qualitative and quantitative.

- **Qualitative data** are descriptions of the dependent variable, such as color, or sound. Qualitative data can also be a simple "yes-or-no" observation about whether something happens, such as whether a plant grows.
- **Quantitative data** are numerical measurements of the dependent variable. Quantitative data include measurements of size, mass, frequency, temperature, rate, and many other factors.

Qualitative data are useful, but they cannot be statistically analyzed. No experiment is based on qualitative data alone.

Forming Operational Definitions

An **operational definition** is a description of the exact way in which you will measure the dependent variable. Your operational definition will help you determine how you will do your experiment.

EXAMPLE

Quantitative operational definition: Height of the plant's main stem (in mm) is the operational definition for the effect of fertilizer on plant growth.

Writing a Procedure

All experiments need a step-by-step written procedure. The procedure should be detailed and clear so that someone else could exactly repeat the experiment. You can think of your procedure as a cookbook recipe that has to be followed exactly. A procedure should include

- a detailed materials list
- how and when to make observations

Even if you are planning to collect only quantitative data, you can still make qualitative observations. These observations may help you to explain your data and can provide clues toward a new experiment.

If something goes wrong during your experiment, make sure you record and report it. Not following the procedure exactly can produce errors in your results that you will need to explain.

Analyzing Data

You have carried out your experiment and collected data. Do the data support your hypothesis? You cannot answer that question by looking at a list of numbers and making a guess at what they show. Without organizing and analyzing your data, it is difficult to draw conclusions from your experiment.

- Organize all of the individual measurements, or data points, in a table. Data tables provide a person evaluating your experiment with a summary of your data.
- Analyze the raw data that you organized in your table. Calculate the mean, median, mode, and range for each group in the experiment. Use whatever type of statistics are appropriate for your data.

EXAMPLE

TABLE 1. PLANT GROWTH – CONTROL GROUP

Day	Plant 1 Height (cm)	Plant 2 Height (cm)	Plant 3 Height (cm)
0	12.40	11.30	11.90
3	12.45	11.40	12.20
6	13.25	12.00	13.10
9	14.75	12.75	14.25
12	15.35	13.40	15.65
15	16.85	14.95	16.95
18	18.00	15.90	17.25
21	19.75	16.50	17.80
Total growth	7.35	5.20	5.90

Mean Growth = 6.15 cm

Presenting Results

To present your results, look at your organized and analyzed data. Look for ways to most accurately and effectively show your results. You might make a graph to show and compare the groups' means. You might make several graphs that show each group separately. When possible, use spreadsheet software to present your data.

EXAMPLE

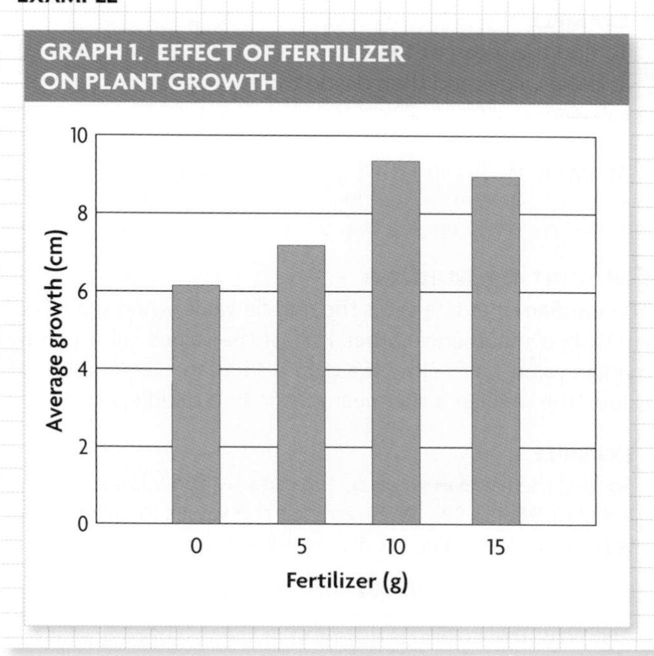

Drawing Conclusions

Compare your results with your hypothesis to determine whether your results support your hypothesis. Discuss what your results show about a relationship between the independent variable and the dependent variable. It is important to draw conclusions from your results, but do not make inferences about factors that you did not test.

EXAMPLE

Adding a fertilizer with nitrogen to soil tends to increase plant growth. Both high and moderate amounts of fertilizer tend to increase plant growth more than a low amount of fertilizer. However, high and moderate amounts of fertilizer appear to have the same effect on growth.

R13

Math and Data Analysis Handbook

Common Math Skills Used in Science

Some math skills that are often used in science are presented below.

Calculating Mean

The **mean** of a data set is the average: the sum of the values divided by the number of values.

EXAMPLE

To find the mean of the data set {14, 6, 10, 8, 4, 11, 6, 3, 5, 13}, add the values and then divide the sum by the number of values.

ANSWER $\frac{14 + 6 + 10 + 8 + 4 + 11 + 6 + 3 + 5 + 13}{10} = \frac{80}{10} = 8$

Calculating Median

The **median** of a data set is the middle value when the values are ranked in numerical order. Half of the values fall above the median value, half below. If a data set has an even number of values, the median is the mean of the two middle values.

EXAMPLE

To find the median value of the data set {582, 133, 207, 87, 164, 290, 98, 155, 196, 278 }, arrange the values in order from least to greatest. The median is the middle value.

87, 98, 133, 155, 164, 196, 207, 278, 290, 582

ANSWER The median is the mean of the two middle values, $\frac{164 + 196}{2} = 180$.

Finding Mode

The **mode** of a data set is the value that occurs most often. A data set can have more than one mode if two or more values are repeated the same number of times. A data set can have no mode if no values are repeated.

EXAMPLE

To find the mode of the data set {6, 7, 6, 4, 4, 4, 3, 6, 4, 6}, arrange the values in order from least to greatest and determine the value that occurs most often:

3, 4, 4, 4, 4, 6, 6, 6, 6, 7

ANSWER There are two modes, 4 and 6.

Using Significant Figures

The number of **significant figures** in a measurement or calculation is equal to the number of digits that are known with some degree of confidence plus the next digit, which is an estimate. When multiplying or dividing measurements, the answer should have only as many significant figures as the value with the fewest significant figures.

EXAMPLE

A density calculation is made in which 5.31 g is divided by 22 mL. The calculator output was 0.2413636 g/mL.

ANSWER There are three significant figures in the mass, but only two in the volume measurement. The density should have two significant figures: 0.24 g/mL.

Using Scientific Notation

Scientific notation is a shorthand way to write very large or very small numbers as a product of a number times a power of 10.

EXAMPLE

To convert from standard form to scientific notation:

Standard Form	**Scientific Notation**
720,000	7.2×10^5
5 decimal places left	Exponent is 5
0.000291	2.91×10^{-4}
4 decimal places right	Exponent is -4

To convert from scientific notation to standard form:

Scientific Notation	**Standard Form**
4.63×10^7	46,300,000
Exponent is 7	7 decimal places right
1.08×10^{-6}	0.00000108
Exponent is -6	6 decimal places left

Presenting Data

Scientists often communicate results of their experiments through tables and graphs. Tables and graphs organize and display information so that it can be easily interpreted.

Data Tables

A **data table** is used to organize and record data that are collected. Data tables can also help identify trends in data. Tables are organized according to the independent and dependent variables in the experiment. The **dependent variable** changes as a result of a change in the **independent variable.** The independent variable is listed in rows. The dependent variable is in columns. When repeated trials are conducted, they are recorded in subdivisions of the dependent variable column. When recording data in a table, the values of the independent variable are ordered. Most data are arranged from the smallest to largest.

The information given in each column is identified with a heading at the top of each column. When units are used, they are also included at the top of the column. Data tables should always have a title that clearly communicates what is being shown in the table. The title should make reference to the variables in the experiment.

TABLE 2. EFFECT OF HORMONES ON CELL GROWTH

Concentration of Hormone Solution (%)	Diameter of Cell Clump After 24 Hours (mm)	
	Trial 1	Trial 2
0	3	4
25	4	4
50	8	7
75	9	8

EXAMPLE
Table 2 shows data from a hypothetical experiment in which growth hormones were added to clumps of cells in a laboratory. The growth of the cell clumps was measured. In this example, the independent variable is the concentration of hormone solution. The values of the independent variable are listed in rows from lowest to highest concentration. The dependent variable, the diameter of the cell clumps after 24 hours, is in columns.

Line Graphs

A **line graph** is used to show a relationship between two variables. Line graphs are particularly useful for showing changes in variables over time. Line graphs are used when variables are continuous—that is, they can have any value including fractional values. For example, the height of a growing plant changes continuously. As a plant grows from 10 cm to 11 cm, its height can be 10.2 cm, 10.537 cm, or any other value between 10 and 11.

Line graphs are useful for representing trends. Two values are inversely related or have a **negative correlation** if an increase in the value of one variable is associated with a decrease in the value of the other variable. If an increase in one variable is associated with an increase in another variable, there is a **positive correlation** between the two variables. If there is no relationship between the two variables, they are said to have **no correlation.**

EXAMPLE
The level of the hormone insulin and length of exercise time have a negative correlation. As length of time increases, levels of insulin decrease.

GRAPH 2. BLOOD INSULIN LEVELS AND EXERCISE

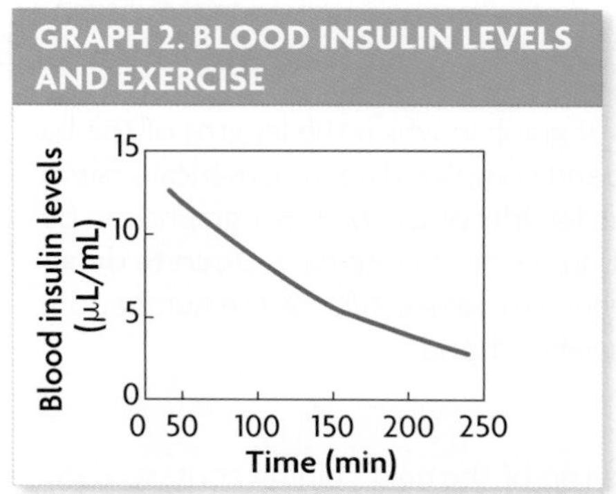

Math and Data Analysis Handbook

The level of the hormone glucagon and length of exercise time have a positive correlation. As length of time increases, levels of glucagon increase.

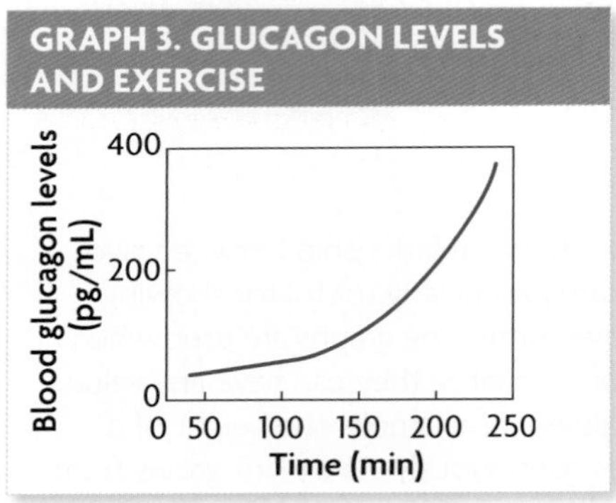

The level of the hormone ghrelin and length of exercise time have no correlation. The levels of ghrelin do not increase or decrease over time.

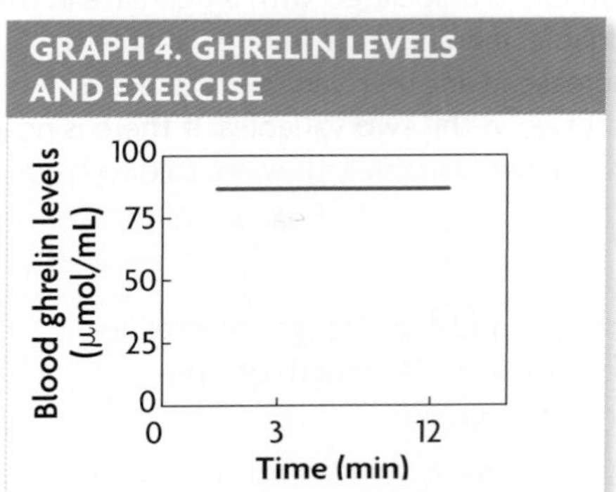

Bar Graphs

A **bar graph** is a type of graph in which the lengths of the bars are used to represent and compare data. A numerical scale is used to determine the lengths of the bars. Bar graphs can be used with either continuous or discrete data. **Discrete data** can have only whole-number values, such as the number of people or trees in a neighborhood.

EXAMPLE

The bar graph at the top of the next column contains data about the frequency of various genetic disorders in the human population. For each syndrome on the x-axis, the bar extends vertically on the y-axis to represent the incidence per 100,000 births. For example, out of 100,000 births, 111 children are born with Down syndrome.

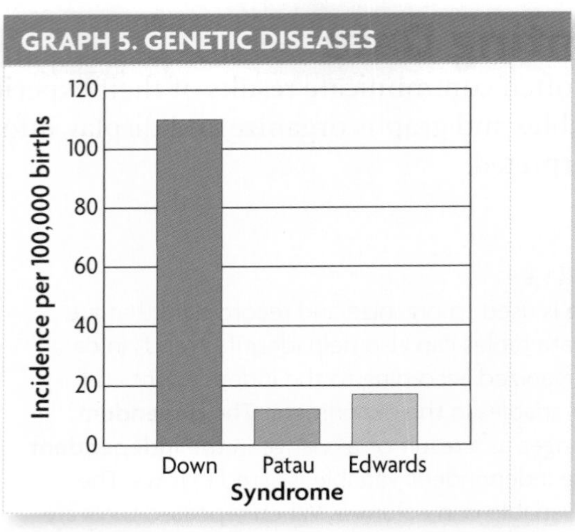

Combination Graphs

Combination graphs show two sets of data on the same graph. One set of data may be shown as a bar graph, and the other set may be shown as a line graph. The two data sets must share the same independent variable on the x-axis. Sharing the same independent variable makes it possible to determine if a relationship exists between two dependent variables.

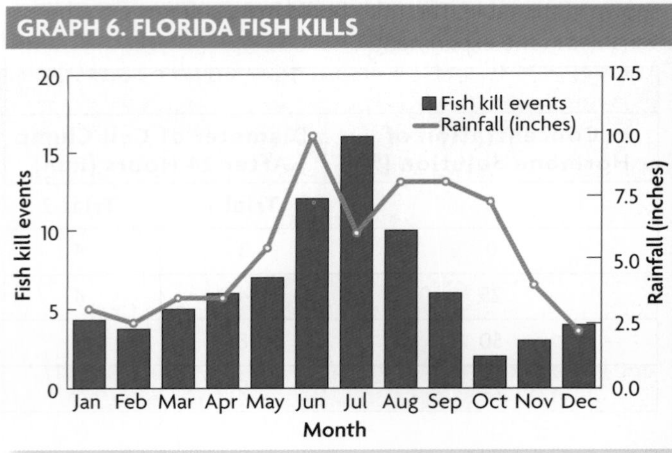

EXAMPLE

The combination graph above displays data about fish kill events and monthly rainfall in Florida.

- The y-axis on the left side of the graph represents the number of fish kill events.
- The y-axis on the right side of the graph represents rainfall amounts.
- The x-axis shows the month of data collection.

For example, the graph shows that in January there were four fish kill events and about 2.7 inches of rain.

Histograms

A **histogram** is a type of bar graph used to show the frequency distribution of data. A **frequency distribution** displays the number of cases that fit into each category of a variable.

EXAMPLE

The histogram below shows the frequency distribution of body fat in adult men. According to the histogram, the percentage body fat with the greatest frequency is 20 percent. When interpreting histograms, it is important to note that how the histogram is constructed can affect how the data are interpreted.

GRAPH 7. BODY FAT IN MEN

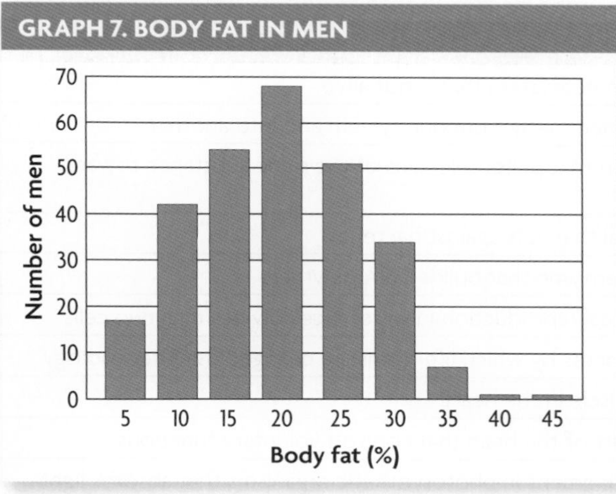

Scatterplots

A **scatterplot** is a type of graph used to identify a trend or correlation between two variables. The origin is usually at zero on both the *x*-axis and the *y*-axis. On a scatterplot, the data points are plotted but not joined together as they are on a line graph. Three types of relationships between variables that can be shown on a scatterplot are positive, negative, and no relationship. In a positive relationship, as one variable increases or decreases, the other variable increases or decreases, respectively. In a negative relationship, as one variable increases, the other variable decreases. For some variables, there is no consistent change in one variable as the other variable increases or decreases. Thus, there is no relationship between those two variables.

EXAMPLE

The scatterplot below of butter clam shell measurements shows that as the width of the clam's shell increases, its length also increases. This is a positive relationship, because as the value of one variable increases, the value of another variable increases. If it were a negative relationship, one of the variables would increase as the other decreased.

GRAPH 8. PUGET SOUND BUTTER CLAMS

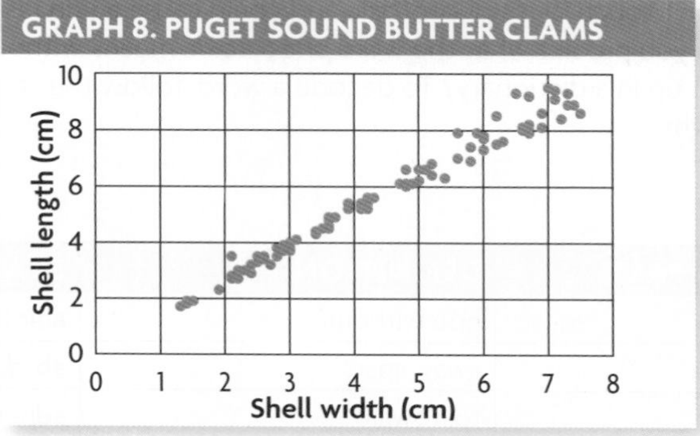

Circle Graphs

A **circle graph,** or pie chart, is a type of graph used to represent parts of a whole. It is made of a circle divided into sections that represent the frequency of each category's occurrence. To determine how much of the circle each section should cover, divide the number of occurrences for that category by the total number that the circle represents. When the result is multiplied by 100, it gives the percentage of the circle covered by the category.

EXAMPLE

In the circle graph below, the diversity of invertebrates is illustrated. Notice that all of the percentages for each category of invertebrate can be added together to equal 100. This is always the case in a circle graph, unless the values have been rounded after calculation.

GRAPH 9. INVERTEBRATE SPECIES BY GROUP

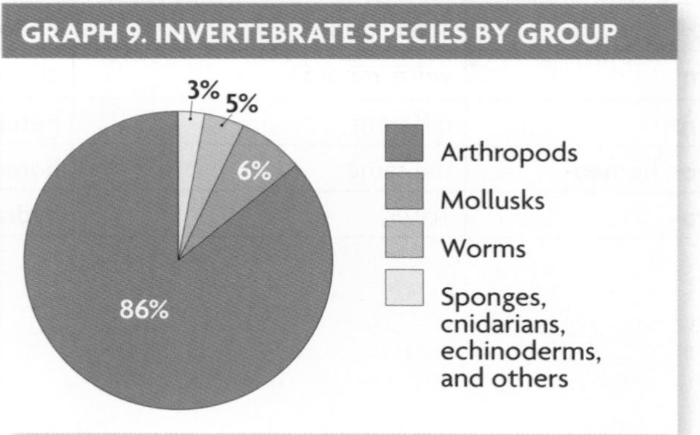

Vocabulary Handbook

Greek and Latin Word Parts

Many words in the English language developed from Greek and Latin words. If you know some common Greek and Latin word parts, you can decode the meanings of other unknown words.

Suppose you read a magazine article that says, "If you see this plant, don't touch it! It's phototoxic and could cause a skin rash." How can you predict what the word *phototoxic* means without looking it up in a dictionary? To decode a word, follow the steps to the right.

Break the word into parts. Try to find the Greek or Latin word parts within the word. In the word *phototoxic,* you can find two word parts: *photo-* and *tox-*.

Look up the word parts in the table below. You will find that *photo-* means "light" and *tox-* means "poisonous."

Analyze the clues to determine a definition. In this example, your word clues are "light" and "poisonous." But there is also a clue in the sentence, "skin rash." You might guess that a phototoxic plant is one that can poison a person's skin when a chemical in the plant reacts with sunlight, and that's just what it means!

WORD PART	DEFINITION	EXAMPLE
a-	not, without	**a**biotic: factor in an ecosystem that is not alive
ab-	away, apart	**ab**sorption: movement away from one system and into another
ad-	to, toward	**ad**hesion: attraction that pulls molecules of the same substance toward one another
anti-	against	**anti**biotic: chemical that acts against bacteria
-ase	enzyme	DNA polymer**ase**: enzyme that builds DNA polymers
bi-	two	**bi**nary fission: asexual reproduction in which a cell divides into two cells
bio-	life	**bio**engineering: process by which life forms are changed using technology
cardio-	of or relating to the heart	**cardi**ac muscle: muscle in the heart
cerebr-	brain	**cerebr**al cortex: part of the brain that controls voluntary functions
chloro-	green	**chloro**phyll: green pigment in photosynthetic organisms that absorbs light
-cide	kill	insecti**cide**: chemical that kills insects
con-, co-, com-	with, together	**co**dominance: both genes expressed together
cyto-	cell	**cyto**plasm: jellylike substance within a cell
di-	two	**di**cot: plant whose seeds have two cotyledons
diplo-	double	**diplo**id: having double genetic information
ecto-	outer, outside	**ecto**therm: organism that uses the outer environment to regulate body temperature
endo-	inner, inside	**endo**skeleton: skeleton found inside of the body
-gram	write, record	clado**gram**: record of proposed evolutionary relationships
hetero-	different	**hetero**zygous: having two different alleles
homo-, homeo-	the same	**homo**zygous: having two of the same alleles
hydro-	water	**hydro**logic cycle: water cycle

WORD PART	DEFINITION	EXAMPLE
hyper-	above, over	**hyper**tonic: having a concentration above that of another solution
hypo-	below, under	**hypo**tonic: having a concentration below that of another solution
im-, in-	with, into	**im**migration: movement of individuals into a population
iso-	equal	**iso**tonic: having a concentration equal to that of another solution
-itis	inflammation	appendic**itis**: inflammation of the appendix
-lysis	decomposition, dissolving	glyco**lysis**: breakdown of glucose
meso-	middle	**meso**phyll: layer of tissue in the middle of the plant leaf
mono-	one	**mono**hybrid cross: mating that examines inheritance of one trait
-morph	form	meta**morph**osis: change in body form
neuro-	neuron	**neuro**transmitter: chemical that signals neurons
-osis	condition or process	mit**osis**: process of cell division
path-	disease	**path**ogen: disease-causing agent
peri-	around	**peri**pheral nervous system: nerves found around, or outside, the central nervous system
phago-	to eat	**phago**cytosis: engulfing, or eating, of bacteria or foreign bodies by phagocytes
-philic	having a preference for	hydro**philic**: having an attraction to water
-phobic	having an aversion for	hydro**phobic**: having an aversion to water
photo-	light	**photo**synthesis: process that uses light to make sugars
phyto-	plants	**phyto**plankton: plantlike plankton
-pod	foot	pseudo**pod**: fake foot
poly-	many	**poly**genic trait: trait resulting from the interaction or many genes
re-	again, new	**re**generation: regrowth of lost or destroyed parts or organs
sperma-	relating to sperm or seeds	**sperma**togenesis: process that forms sperm
tel-, telo-	end	**telo**phase: ending phase of mitosis
-therm	heat	endo**therm**: animal that uses its internal tissues to produce its body heat
tox-	poisonous	**tox**in: poisonous substance that can destroy cells
trans-	across	**trans**genic: an organism that contains a gene from a different species
-troph	nutrition	auto**troph**: organism that makes its own source of nutrition
-tropism	response	geo**tropism**: growth response to gravity
uni-	single, one	**uni**cellular: organism made up of one cell
zoo-	animal	**zoo**logy: study of animals

R19

Vocabulary Handbook

Academic Vocabulary

Academic vocabulary words are words that occur frequently in textbooks, instructions, and standardized tests. The words can have many meanings. Some of these words are defined below and grouped into categories. These words appear in all subject areas. The simple definitions below give only one meaning of each word, the way it might be used in this book. Learn to recognize and understand these words.

Words Used in Lab Instructions

affect to produce a change
alter to change
analyze to study the parts
assemble to put together
characteristic a distinct part or feature
component part
conduct to manage or control
confirm to use data to support a statement
consequence a result
constraint a limit
control a part of the experiment that keeps all variables constant
criteria standards for judging
demonstrate to show
dominant having the most influence or control
emerge to rise from or to come forth
extract to draw or pull out
factor an individual part of a combination, ingredient
function a job, duty, or activity
indirect not direct or to the point
method a way of doing something
model a small object made to look like the real one
modify to change
monitor to watch closely
objective a goal
obtain to get
parameter a measurable factor that can vary
potential possible but does not yet exist
process a series of actions
produce to bring forth or create
property a trait or characteristic
prove to show as true by using evidence
purpose a reason to do
represent to stand for
restrict to keep within limits
reveal to show, to make known
signal a sign for communicating
source the origin or place something began
spatial having to do with space
structure the way the parts are put together
sufficient enough, as much as needed
technique a procedure, the way something is done
trace tiny amount
trait a feature
transfer to move from one to another
variation the result of changing
vary to change or to show change

Words About Math and Measuring

approximate nearly
compile to put together into one
convert to change something to another form
cumulative increasing by adding
derive to arrive at by reasoning
dimension measurement of one part
diminish to make less or smaller
equivalent equal to
pace the rate of speed
proportion an equation stating that two ratios are equal
range the difference between the smallest and largest amounts
reduce to make smaller
solve to find the answer to a problem

Words About Importance

core the center part
crucial a must-have, extremely important
essential necessary or basic
regular usual or normal
requisite necessary, required
significance the importance
standard the usual and accepted measure for comparing

Words Found in Test Directions

analyze to study the parts
apply to put on; to be relevant
assess to figure out the value of
clarify to make clear
compose to create or write something new
critique to judge carefully
define to tell what it means
demonstrate to show
develop to add detail, to fill out
evaluate to judge or decide the value of
exhibit to show or display
indicate to point out
interpret to explain the meaning of
relate to tell; to hook to something else
revise to review and change for the better
summarize to reduce to the main points in a few words
synthesize to combine parts into a whole

Other Words Used in Tests

alternative another choice
analogy a comparison to something similar
approach to come near; the way of getting near
articulate to say or write clearly
aspect appearance from one point of view
background the knowledge behind something
concise in a few words
confirm to make sure it's true
convey to communicate or show
correspond to be similar in nature
detail an individual part
detect to discover or learn about
determine to learn the facts; to decide
emphasize to stress
establish to set up
explicit fully and clearly expressed
focus to direct to one point
general about the whole or entire thing
imply to express indirectly
optional left to a person's choice
refer to direct to a source for help
specific definite and particular
succinct in a few words
symbolize to act as a sign that stands for something else
technical used in a special job or subject
topic a subject
transition the words that link one part to the next
valid correct or well-grounded
verify to prove the truth of

Words About Organization

category a class or special division
compile to put together
consist to be made up of
correlate to put into relation to something else
differentiate to separate by differences
dominant the strongest
integrate to put together
organize to put in order
primary first or most important
sequence order
series one after another
subsequent ones coming after

Words About Ideas

abstract cannot be touched
analogy a comparison to something else
authentic real
claim a statement that says something is a fact
complex not simple
conceive to form an idea
concept an idea
concrete actual or real
credible believable
deduce to figure out by reasoning
devise to form, plan, or design
discover to notice or learn; to be the first to learn
innovation a new idea or thing
irrelevant off the point
logical reasoning in a clear manner
origin the beginning; where something began to exist
principle a basic truth, rule, or standard
relevant to the point
strategy a plan of action
subjective depends on a person's viewpoint
topic the subject of writing or speech

Words About Time

intermittent off and on
invariably always, every time
prior before
typically usually

R21

Note-taking Handbook

Graphic organizers are tools to help you take notes. Some graphic organizers are best used as you read to help you understand concepts. Others are best used to summarize or review information. Using a variety of graphic organizers will help you to understand and remember what you have learned.

During Reading

Use these graphic organizers while you are reading. They help you organize ideas in paragraphs and sections as you read them.

Process Diagrams

What is it? A process is series of steps that produces a result. Process diagrams show these steps.

How do you make it? Start with the first step, and then draw each step, one after the other, and connect them with arrows.

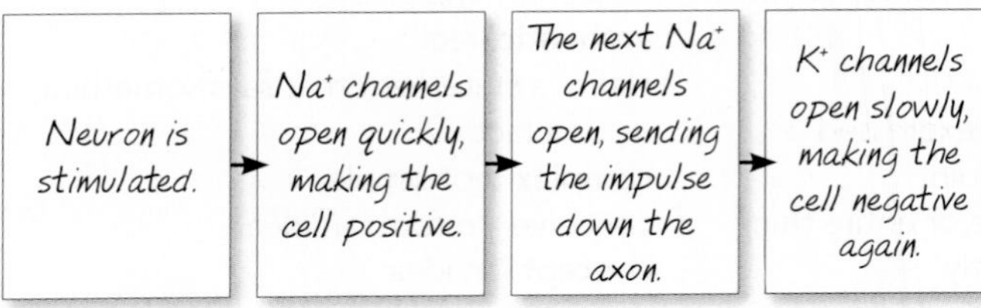

Cycle Diagrams

What is it? A cycle, such as the cell cycle, is a repeating series of events that happen one after another. Cycles do not have a beginning or an end. Cycle diagrams identify the steps in a cycle or process that repeat regularly.

How do you make it? Draw a cycle diagram to show processes that repeat without a beginning or ending. Use the arrows between the boxed steps to show the direction or order in which the cycle happens.

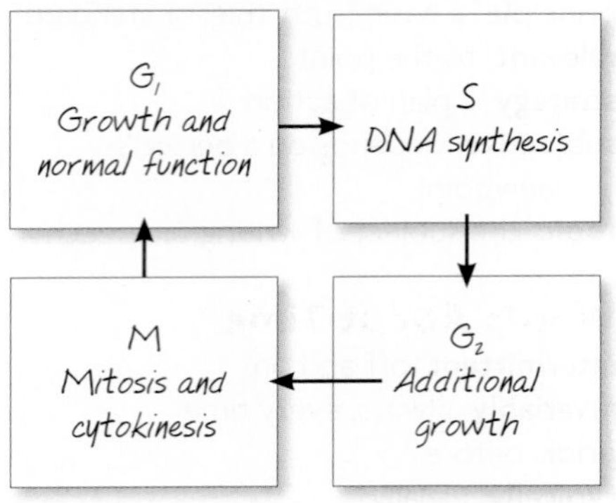

Supporting Main Ideas Notes

What is it? A main idea graphic helps separate and organize reading material into important concepts and related details of support. You can choose the main idea graphic that best fits the material. The first strategy is useful when details follow some type of order.

How do you make it? First, find the main idea. The main idea may be the title of the section, it may be labeled "main idea" or "key concept" in your book, or it may be the topic sentence in a paragraph. Write the main idea in the top box. Next, summarize or paraphrase details that help explain that idea in the boxes that follow.

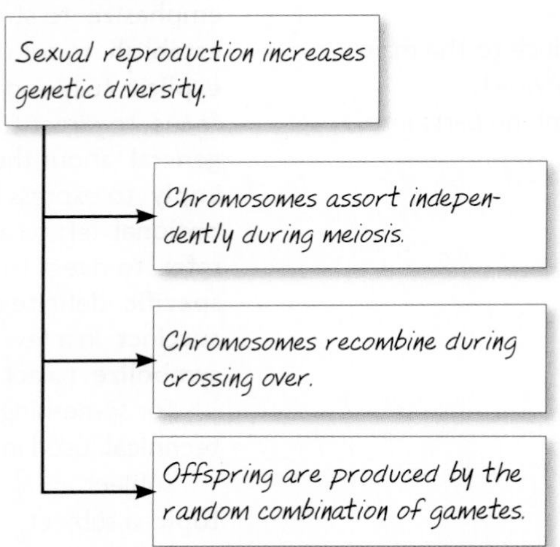

Main Idea Webs

Another way you can take notes on main ideas is to draw a web. Write the main idea in the center and the details in the web around it. This is useful when the details do not occur in any particular order.

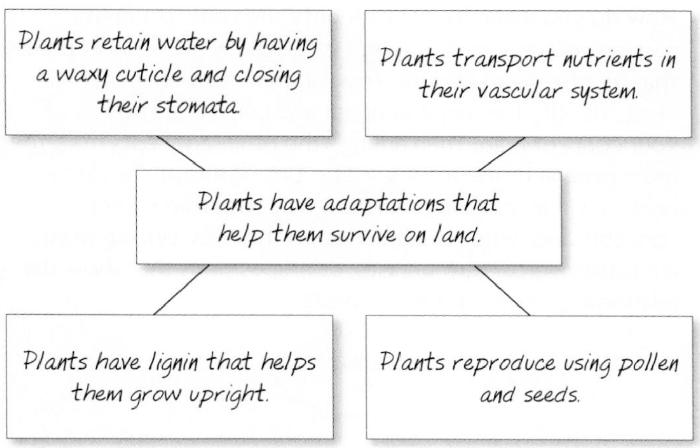

Plants retain water by having a waxy cuticle and closing their stomata.
Plants transport nutrients in their vascular system.
Plants have adaptations that help them survive on land.
Plants have lignin that helps them grow upright.
Plants reproduce using pollen and seeds.

Two-Column Notes

What is it? Two-column notes is a strategy for taking notes to show

- vocabulary and their definitions
- processes or cycles and their steps
- main ideas and supporting details
- questions and possible answers
- causes and effects
- comparisons and contrasts

How do you make it? List processes, concepts, main ideas, or vocabulary in the left column of a two-column table. Write the description or explanation of the words or concepts in the right-hand column across from the words in the left column. You can also draw pictures in the right-hand column.

Leave enough space between words or concepts in the left-hand column so that you can write notes in the right column.

To study for quizzes and tests, fold your two-column notes in half vertically so you can only see the left column. Ask yourself to describe and explain the word in the left column.

Cellular Respiration	*produces ATP* *occurs in mitochondria* $C_6H_{12}O_6 + 6O_2 \rightarrow 6CO_2 + 6H_2O$
Photosynthesis	*absorbs sunlight* *occurs in chloroplasts* $6CO_2 + 6H_2O \rightarrow C_6H_{12}O_6 + 6O_2$

After Reading

Use these graphic organizers after you have read material and have taken notes on it. These organizers help you summarize the most important concepts and relate them to each other.

Cause-and-Effect Diagrams

What is it? This strategy shows cause and effect relationships. In the diagram below, several effects result from a single cause. Those effects can cause more effects. A cause-and-effect diagram can also be drawn to show how multiple causes can produce a single effect.

How do you make it? Write the cause in the first box, and write the effects in the boxes connected to the cause. Then think about what effects can result from the first effects, and connect them.

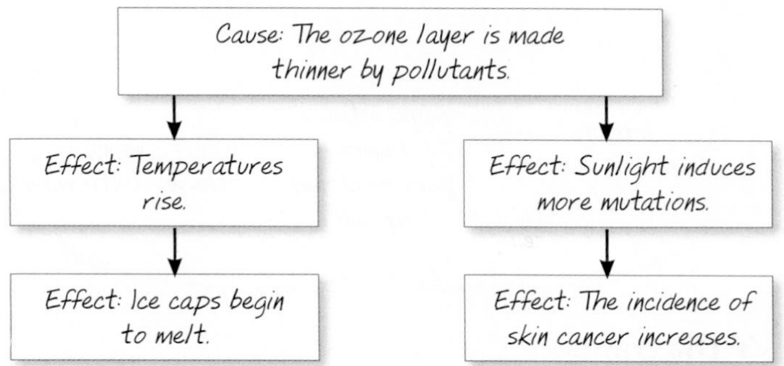

Cause: The ozone layer is made thinner by pollutants.
Effect: Temperatures rise.
Effect: Sunlight induces more mutations.
Effect: Ice caps begin to melt.
Effect: The incidence of skin cancer increases.

Content Frames

What is it? Content frames are tables that help you organize and condense large amounts of information.

How do you make it? To make a content frame, make a table. Label the rows along the side with characteristics. Label the columns with the topics or categories. You can also include a column for drawings or sketches.

Biome	*Tropical*	*Temperate*	*Tundra*
Climate	*Warm and rainy*	*Hot summers, cold winters*	*Cold and dry*
Vegetation	*Lush, thick forests*	*Broadleaf forests*	*Mosses and similar*
Example	*Manaus, Brazil*	*Burlington, Vermont*	*Barrow, Alaska*

R23

Venn Diagrams

What is it? Venn diagrams help you show how two processes, ideas, or things are alike and different.

How do you make it? Draw two circles that overlap, such as the ones below. Write one of the words or processes that you are going to compare in each circle. For example, the word *arteries* is written in the left circle and the word *veins* is written in the right circle. Under *arteries,* list characteristics or traits that only arteries possess. Under *veins,* list characteristics or traits that only veins possess. In the intersection of the two circles, list the traits that both arteries and veins share.

When you finish the diagram, write a sentence to summarize the similarities and differences: "Both veins and arteries have three-tissue layers and are each part of the closed circulatory system, but arteries are thicker and more muscular, and veins are thinner and have valves."

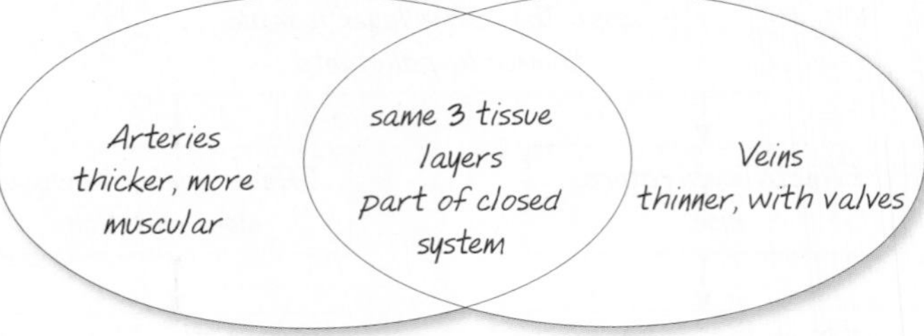

Y Diagrams

What is it? Y diagrams can be used instead of Venn diagrams to show how two processes, ideas, or things are alike and different.

How do you make it? On the top parts of the Y, list the characteristics of each topic separately. Then find the characteristics that are the same in both halves. Write them at the bottom part of the Y, and cross them out from the top half. When you finish, the top limbs of the Y show differences, and the bottom part shows similarities between the two topics.

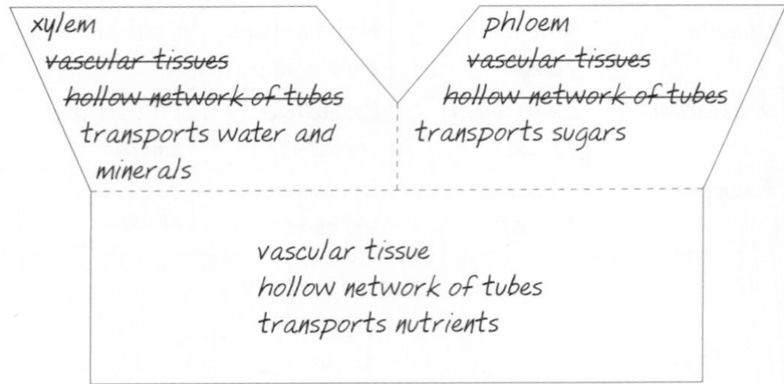

Concept Maps

What is it? A concept map is a diagram that shows the main concepts from a passage you've read as well as the relationships between those concepts. Concept maps are useful tools for organizing and reviewing information.

How do you make it? First, identify the concepts in the section you've read. A concept is a single word or short phrase that represents an idea, process, or important characteristic. Next, identify the major concept and place it at the top of your concept map. Then arrange the other concepts from the most general to the most specific. Each concept should be enclosed in an oval or box. Finally, use lines to connect concepts and write linking words on the lines. Linking words are usually verbs, verb phrases, or prepositions that show the relationship between the concepts.

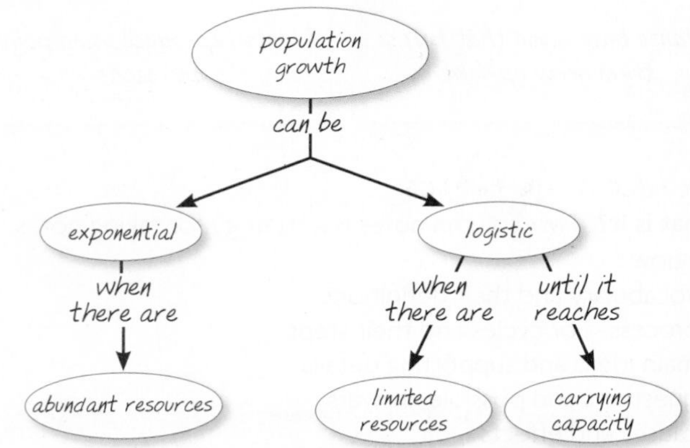

R24

Appendix A: Classification

Living things are classified into three domains. These domains are further divided into kingdoms, and then phyla. Major phyla are described in the table below, along with important features that are used to distinguish each group.

KINGDOM	PHYLUM	COMMON NAME AND DESCRIPTION
DOMAIN ARCHAEA		
ARCHAEA		**Archaea** Single-celled prokaryotes (no nucleus or other membrane-bound organelles) with distinct rRNA sequences. Lack peptidoglycan cell walls. Reproduce asexually. Live in some of Earth's most extreme environments, including salty, hot, acidic, and the deep ocean. They are often grouped according to where they live. Examples: *Sulfolobus solfataricus, Pyrococcus.*
DOMAIN BACTERIA		
BACTERIA		**Bacteria** Single-celled prokaryotes (no nucleus or other membrane-bound organelles), most with peptidoglycan cell walls. Live in all types of environments, including the human body. Reproduce by binary fission or budding. Examples: blue-green bacteria (cyanobacteria), *Streptococcus, Bacillus, Escherichia.*
KINGDOM	**PHYLUM**	**COMMON NAME AND DESCRIPTION**
DOMAIN EUKARYA		
		Eukaryotes Cells are larger than archaea or bacteria and are eukaryotic (have a nucleus containing DNA, as well as other membrane-bound organelles). Can be single-celled, colonial, or multicellular.
PROTISTA		**Protists** Usually single-celled, but sometimes multicellular or colonial. Many phyla resemble animals, plants, or fungi but are usually smaller or simpler in structure.
Animal-like Protists: Unicellular, heterotrophic, most can move.		
	Ciliophora	**Ciliates** Have many short, hairlike extensions called cilia, which they use for feeding and movement. Example: *Paramecium.*
	Zoomastigophora	**Zooflagellates** Have usually one or two long, hairlike extensions called flagella. Sometimes called Zoomastigina. Example: *Trichomonas.*
	Apicomplexa	**Sporozoans** Parasites that can move by body flexion or gliding. Cause diseases in animals such as birds and humans. Example: *Plasmodium.*

Pyrococcus

Escherichia

Paramecium

R25

Appendix A: Classification

KINGDOM	PHYLUM	COMMON NAME AND DESCRIPTION
PROTISTA (continued)	Rhizopoda	**Rhizopods** Use footlike extensions called pseudopods to move and feed. Phylum sometimes called Sarcodina. Example: *Amoeba.*
	Foraminifera	**Forams** Use footlike extensions called pseudopods to move. Have multi-chambered shells made of organic material. Most are marine. Example: *Rosalina globularis.*
Plantlike Protists: Many are photosynthetic autotrophs, but none have roots, stems, or leaves.		
	Euglenozoa	**Euglenoids** Single-celled, with one or two flagella. Most live in fresh water. Some are heterotrophs, others are photosynthetic autotrophs. Examples: *Euglena, Trypanosoma.*
	Dinoflagellata	**Dinoflagellates** Single-celled, with two flagella that allow cell to turn over and change direction. Some species are autotrophic, some are heterotrophic. In great numbers, some species can cause red tides along coastlines. Example: *Noctiluca.*
	Chrysophyta	**Chrysophytes** Also called yellow algae or golden-brown algae. Single-celled. Named for the yellow pigments in their chloroplasts (*chrysophyte,* in Greek, means "golden plant"). Example: *Thallasiosira.*
	Bacillariophyta	**Diatoms** Single-celled with glasslike shells made of silica. Shells serve as external skeleton. Example: *Amorpha ovalis.*
	Chlorophyta	**Green algae** May be single-celled, colonial, or multicellular. Contain both chlorophyll-*a* and chlorophyll-*b,* which are the same photosynthetic pigments found in land plants. Examples: *Pediastrum, Ulva, Spirogyra.*
	Phaeophyta	**Brown algae** Multicellular, photosynthetic. Live mainly in salt water. Contain the pigment fucoxanthin, which is the source of their brown color. Includes kelp. Example: *Sargassum.*
	Rhodophyta	**Red algae** Multicellular, photosynthetic. Most live in salt water. Contain a red pigment called phycoerythrin that makes these organisms red, purple, or reddish-black. Example: coralline algae.
Funguslike Protists: Most are decomposers that can move during part of their life cycle.		
	Acrasiomycota	**Cellular slime molds** Live partly as free-living single-celled organisms, often in the soil. When food is scarce, they can fuse together to form a many-celled mass that moves as if it's one organism. Example: *Dictyostelium.*

Euglena

Diatom

Red Algae

KINGDOM	PHYLUM	COMMON NAME AND DESCRIPTION
	Myxomycota	**Plasmodial slime molds** Live most of their lives as a mass of cytoplasm that is actually one large, slimy cell with many nuclei. Example: *Physarium* (dog-vomit slime mold).
	Oomycota	**Water molds and downy mildews** Produce thin, cottonlike extensions called hyphae. Feed from dead or decaying material, often in water. Some are parasites of plants or fish. Example: *Phytophthora infestans* (cause of potato blight).
FUNGI		**Fungi** Eukaryotic, heterotrophic, usually multicellular but some are single-celled. Cells have a thick cell wall usually containing chitin. Obtain nutrients through absorption. Often function as decomposers.
	Chytridiomycota	**Chytrids** Oldest and simplest fungi, usually aquatic. Have flagellated spores. Some are decomposers, some are parasitic. Example: chytrid frog fungus.
	Ascomycota	**Sac fungi** Reproduce with spores formed in an ascus. Includes single-celled yeasts as well as morels, truffles, and molds. Example: *Penicillium*.
	Zygomycota	**Bread molds** Obtain food by decomposing dead or decaying matter. Mold hyphae grow into food source and digest it. Some are parasitic. Example: black bread molds.
	Basidiomycota	**Club fungi** Multicellular with club-shaped fruiting bodies. Examples: mushrooms, puffballs, bracket fungi, rusts, smuts.
PLANTAE		**Plants** Multicellular photosynthetic autotrophs. Most have adapted to life on land. Cells have thick cell walls made of cellulose.
	Bryophyta	**Mosses** Nonvascular plants. Gametophyte generation is a grasslike plant. Most live in moist environments. Example: sphagnum (peat) moss.
	Hepatophyta	**Liverworts** Nonvascular plants named for the liver-shaped gametophyte generation. Most live in moist environments. Example: *Marchantia*.
	Anthocerotophyta	**Hornworts** Nonvascular plants named for the visible hornlike structures with which they reproduce. Live in moist, cool environments. Example: *Dendroceros*.
	Lycophyta	**Club mosses** Seedless vascular plants. Some resemble tiny pine trees. Live in wooded environments. Example: *Lycopodium* (ground pine).

Slime mold

Sac fungus

Toad stool mushroom

R27

Appendix A: Classification

KINGDOM	PHYLUM	COMMON NAME AND DESCRIPTION
PLANTAE (continued)	Pterophyta	**Ferns, whisk ferns, and horsetails** Seedless vascular plants. Most have fringed leaves. Whisk ferns sometimes classified in phylum Psilotophyta; horsetails sometimes classified in phylum Sphenophyta. Example: *Psilotum* (whisk fern).
	Cycadophyta	**Cycads** Gymnosperms; reproduce with seeds produced in large cones. Slow-growing, palmlike plants that grow in tropical environments. Example: sago palms
	Ginkgophyta	**Ginkgo biloba** Only species in phylum, a tree often planted in urban environments. Gymnosperm; reproduces with seeds that hang from branches.
	Coniferophyta	**Conifers** Gymnosperms; reproduce with seeds produced in cones. Usually evergreen. Examples: pines, spruces, firs, sequoias.
	Anthophyta	**Flowering plants** Also called angiosperms. Reproduce with seeds produced in flowers. Seeds are surrounded by fruit, which is the ripened plant ovary. **CLASS: Monocotyledonae** Monocots. Embryos have one cotyledon. Leaves with parallel veins, flower parts in multiples of three, and vascular bundles scattered throughout the stem. Examples: irises, tulips, grasses. **CLASS: Dicotyledonae** Dicots. Embryos have two cotyledons. Leaves with netlike veins, flower parts in multiples of four or five, and vascular bundles arranged in rings. Examples: roses, daisies, deciduous trees, foxgloves.
ANIMALIA		**Animals** Multicellular, eukaryotic heterotrophs with cells supported by collagen. Cells lack cell walls. Most have cells that are organized into specialized tissues, which make up organs. Most reproduce sexually.
	Porifera	**Sponges** Spend most of their lives fixed to the ocean floor. Feed by filtering water (containing nutrients and small organisms) through their body. Reproduce sexually and asexually. Example: *Euplectella* (Venus's flower basket).
	Cnidaria	**Cnidarians** Aquatic animals with a radial (spokelike) body shape; named for their stinging cells (cnidocytes). Have two basic body forms: the polyp and the medusa. May produce sexually and asexually. **CLASS: Hydrozoa** Alternate between polyp and medusa stages. Medusas reproduce sexually, polyps reproduce asexually. Example: hydras. **CLASS: Scyphozoa** Dominant medusa form. Example: jellyfish. **CLASS: Anthozoa** Dominant polyp form; there is no medusa stage. May be colonial or solitary. Central body surrounded by tentacles. Examples: sea anemones, corals. **CLASS: Cubozoa** Dominant cube-shaped medusa form with well-developed eyes. Examples: tropical box jellyfish, sea wasps.

Sago palm

Foxglove

Giant anemone

KINGDOM	PHYLUM	COMMON NAME AND DESCRIPTION
	Ctenophora	**Comb jellies** Resemble jellyfish; named for the comblike rows of cilia (hairlike extensions) that are used for movement. Example: *Pleurobrachia.*
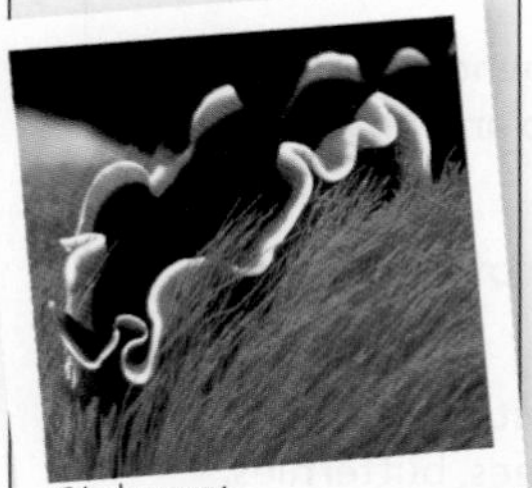 Flatworm	Platyhelminthes	**Flatworms** Thin, flattened worms with simple tissues and sensory organs. Includes planaria and tapeworms, which cause diseases in humans and other hosts. **CLASS: Turbellaria (turbellarians)** Free-living carnivores or scavengers that move with cilia. Example: planarians. **CLASS: Trematoda (flukes)** Internal parasites; life cycle often includes alternation of hosts. Example: *Schistosoma.* **CLASS: Cestoda (tapeworms)** Internal parasites; segmented body and head with suckers or hooks for attaching to host. Example: dog tapeworm.
 Nautilus	Mollusca	**Mollusks** Soft-bodied aquatic animals that usually have an outer shell. **CLASS: Gastropoda (gastropods)** Use muscular foot for movement. Have a distinct head and complete digestive tract. Most have a chambered shell. Examples: snails and slugs. **CLASS: Pelecypoda (bivalves)** Soft body protected by two hard shells that are hinged together. Most are filter feeders. Examples: clams, oysters, mussels, scallops. **CLASS: Cephalopoda (cephalopods)** Carnivores with well-developed eyes and nervous systems. Examples: squids, octopuses, nautiluses.
 Leeches	Annelida	**Segmented worms** Body is made of many similar segments. **CLASS: Polychaeta (polychaetes)** Marine worms with a pair of appendages on each segment. Have many setae. Examples: fan worms, featherduster worms. **CLASS: Oligochaeta (oligochaetes)** Earthworms; live in soil or fresh water. Have no appendages. Have few setae. Example: *Tubifex tubifex* (sludge worm). **CLASS: Hirudinea (leeches)** Most live in fresh water. Have flattened body with no appendages. Suckers at both ends; carnivores or blood-sucking parasites. Example: *Macrobdella decora* (medicinal leech).
	Nematoda	**Roundworms** Small, round worms; many species are parasites, causing diseases in humans, such as trichinosis and elephantiasis. Example: *Trichinella.*

R29

Appendix A: Classification

KINGDOM	PHYLUM	COMMON NAME AND DESCRIPTION
ANIMALIA (continued)  Scorpion  Dragonfly	Arthropoda	Animals with an outer skeleton called an exoskeleton, and jointed appendages such as legs or wings. **SUBPHYLUM: Trilobita (trilobites)** Includes the trilobites, which are all extinct. Important part of the Paleozoic marine ecosystems for 300 million years. Bodies divided into three lobes. Bottom feeders. **SUBPHYLUM: Crustacea (crustaceans)** Live in all of the oceans, freshwater streams, and on land. Have chewing mouthparts and two pairs of antennae. Examples: crabs, lobsters, copepods, pill bugs. **SUBPHYLUM: Chelicerata (chelicerates)** First pair of appendages specialized as daggerlike mouthparts that are used for tearing food; no antennae. Examples: horseshoe crabs, scorpions, spiders, mites, ticks. **SUBPHYLUM: Uniramia** Most live on land. Have one pair of antennae and chewing mouthparts. **CLASS: Insecta (insects)** Have three body segments with three pairs of legs attached to second segment. Examples: ants, bees, butterflies, cockroaches, flies, mosquitoes. **CLASS: Chilopoda (centipedes)** Body divided into many segments with one pair of legs per segment. Carnivores; first pair of legs bears fangs for capturing prey. Example: *Scutigera coleoptrata* (common house centipede). **CLASS: Diplopoda (millipedes)** Body divided into many segments with two pairs of legs per segment. Most are herbivores. Example: *Glomeris* (pill millipede).
 Sea star	Echinodermata	Adults are slow-moving marine animals with radial symmetry; larvae have bilateral symmetry. Have an internal skeleton, a water vascular system, and a complete digestive system. Some can regenerate limbs. **CLASS: Crinoidea (crinoids)** Filter feeders that remain attached to a surface such as the ocean floor. Examples: feather stars, sea lilies. **CLASS: Asteroidea (sea stars)** Star-shaped bottom dwellers that may be suspension feeders, opportunistic feeders, or carnivorous predators. Example: *Acanthaster planci* (crown-of-thorns starfish). **CLASS: Ophiuroidea** Most have five long spindly arms that they use to help move and feed; tube feet lack suckers. Examples: brittle stars, basket stars. **CLASS: Echinoidea** Have a five-part body plan but no arms; body covered with projections or spines. Most graze for food on ocean floor. Examples: sea urchins, sea biscuits, sand dollars. **CLASS: Holothuroidea (sea cucumbers)** Fleshy animals with long, cylindrical shape. Tentacles are used to capture food; also feed on sediment from ocean floor. Example: *Holothuria.*

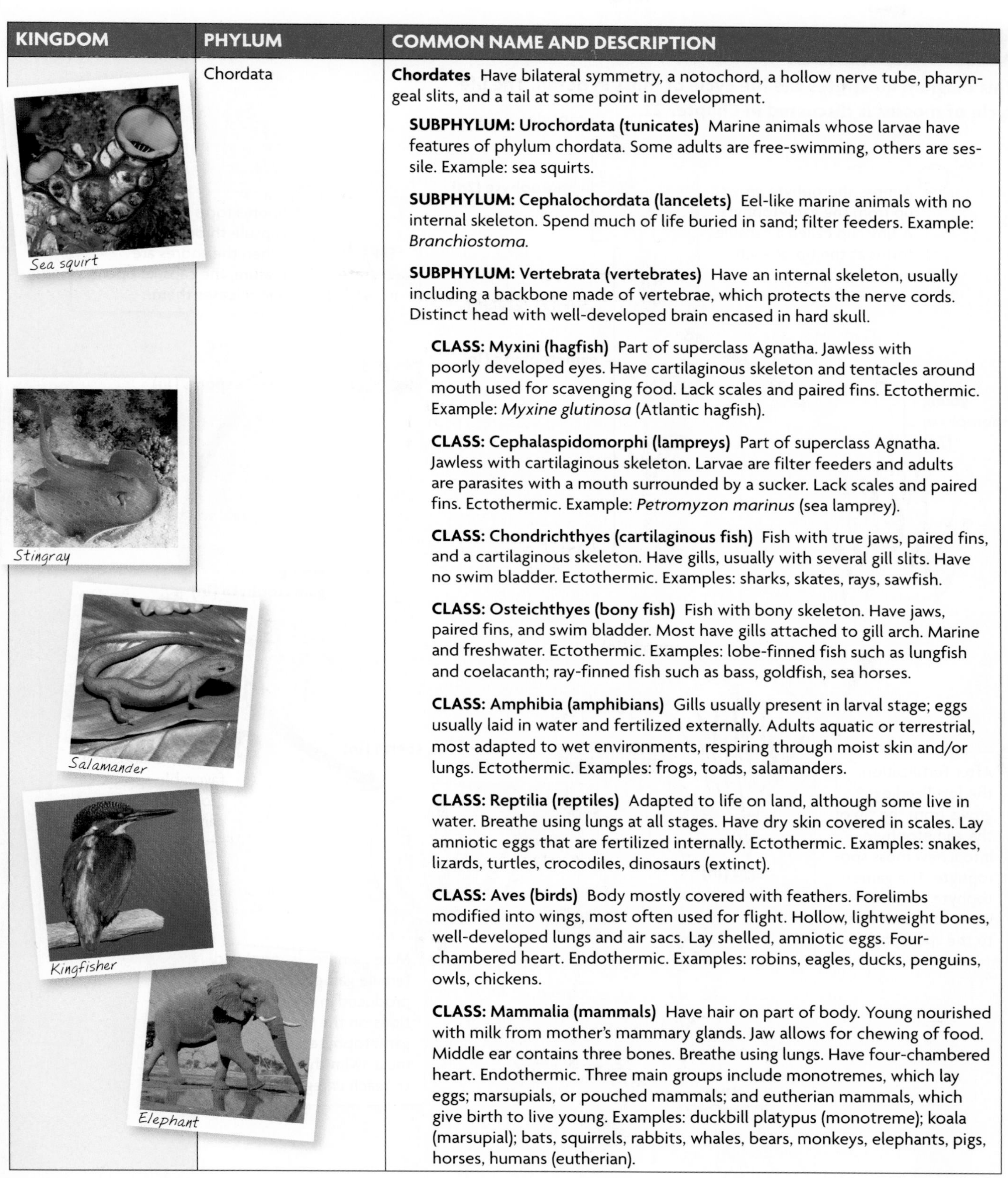

KINGDOM	PHYLUM	COMMON NAME AND DESCRIPTION
	Chordata	**Chordates** Have bilateral symmetry, a notochord, a hollow nerve tube, pharyngeal slits, and a tail at some point in development. **SUBPHYLUM: Urochordata (tunicates)** Marine animals whose larvae have features of phylum chordata. Some adults are free-swimming, others are sessile. Example: sea squirts. **SUBPHYLUM: Cephalochordata (lancelets)** Eel-like marine animals with no internal skeleton. Spend much of life buried in sand; filter feeders. Example: *Branchiostoma.* **SUBPHYLUM: Vertebrata (vertebrates)** Have an internal skeleton, usually including a backbone made of vertebrae, which protects the nerve cords. Distinct head with well-developed brain encased in hard skull. **CLASS: Myxini (hagfish)** Part of superclass Agnatha. Jawless with poorly developed eyes. Have cartilaginous skeleton and tentacles around mouth used for scavenging food. Lack scales and paired fins. Ectothermic. Example: *Myxine glutinosa* (Atlantic hagfish). **CLASS: Cephalaspidomorphi (lampreys)** Part of superclass Agnatha. Jawless with cartilaginous skeleton. Larvae are filter feeders and adults are parasites with a mouth surrounded by a sucker. Lack scales and paired fins. Ectothermic. Example: *Petromyzon marinus* (sea lamprey). **CLASS: Chondrichthyes (cartilaginous fish)** Fish with true jaws, paired fins, and a cartilaginous skeleton. Have gills, usually with several gill slits. Have no swim bladder. Ectothermic. Examples: sharks, skates, rays, sawfish. **CLASS: Osteichthyes (bony fish)** Fish with bony skeleton. Have jaws, paired fins, and swim bladder. Most have gills attached to gill arch. Marine and freshwater. Ectothermic. Examples: lobe-finned fish such as lungfish and coelacanth; ray-finned fish such as bass, goldfish, sea horses. **CLASS: Amphibia (amphibians)** Gills usually present in larval stage; eggs usually laid in water and fertilized externally. Adults aquatic or terrestrial, most adapted to wet environments, respiring through moist skin and/or lungs. Ectothermic. Examples: frogs, toads, salamanders. **CLASS: Reptilia (reptiles)** Adapted to life on land, although some live in water. Breathe using lungs at all stages. Have dry skin covered in scales. Lay amniotic eggs that are fertilized internally. Ectothermic. Examples: snakes, lizards, turtles, crocodiles, dinosaurs (extinct). **CLASS: Aves (birds)** Body mostly covered with feathers. Forelimbs modified into wings, most often used for flight. Hollow, lightweight bones, well-developed lungs and air sacs. Lay shelled, amniotic eggs. Four-chambered heart. Endothermic. Examples: robins, eagles, ducks, penguins, owls, chickens. **CLASS: Mammalia (mammals)** Have hair on part of body. Young nourished with milk from mother's mammary glands. Jaw allows for chewing of food. Middle ear contains three bones. Breathe using lungs. Have four-chambered heart. Endothermic. Three main groups include monotremes, which lay eggs; marsupials, or pouched mammals; and eutherian mammals, which give birth to live young. Examples: duckbill platypus (monotreme); koala (marsupial); bats, squirrels, rabbits, whales, bears, monkeys, elephants, pigs, horses, humans (eutherian).

R31

Appendix B: Life Cycles

Moss Life Cycle

This diagram illustrates the life cycle of moss in detail. The life cycle of mosses is discussed in Chapter 22.

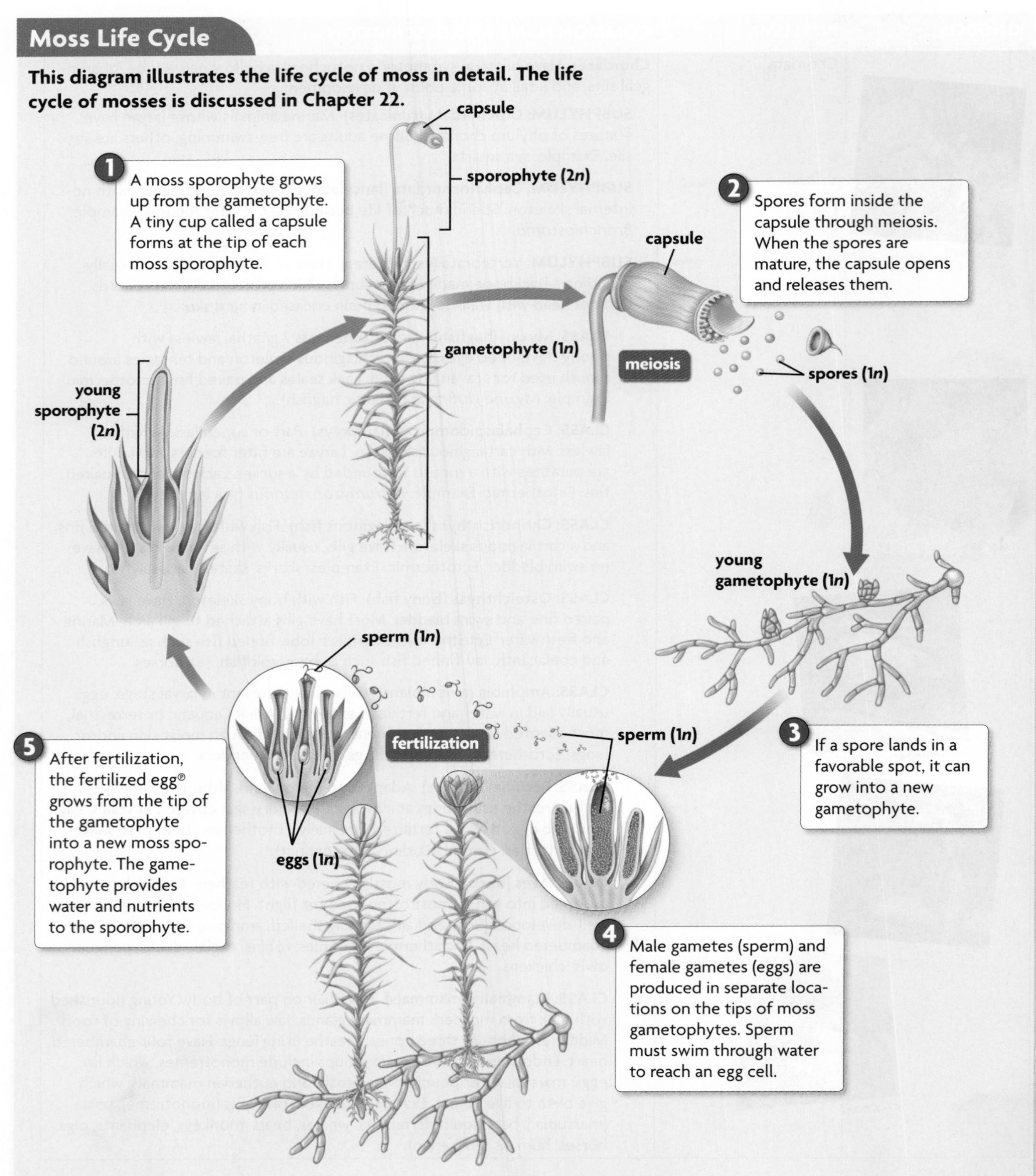

capsule
sporophyte (2n)
1 A moss sporophyte grows up from the gametophyte. A tiny cup called a capsule forms at the tip of each moss sporophyte.
capsule
2 Spores form inside the capsule through meiosis. When the spores are mature, the capsule opens and releases them.
gametophyte (1n)
meiosis
spores (1n)
young sporophyte (2n)
young gametophyte (1n)
sperm (1n)
fertilization
sperm (1n)
3 If a spore lands in a favorable spot, it can grow into a new gametophyte.
5 After fertilization, the fertilized egg® grows from the tip of the gametophyte into a new moss sporophyte. The gametophyte provides water and nutrients to the sporophyte.
eggs (1n)
4 Male gametes (sperm) and female gametes (eggs) are produced in separate locations on the tips of moss gametophytes. Sperm must swim through water to reach an egg cell.

Fern Life Cycle

This diagram illustrates the life cycle of ferns in detail. The life cycle of ferns is discussed in Chapter 22.

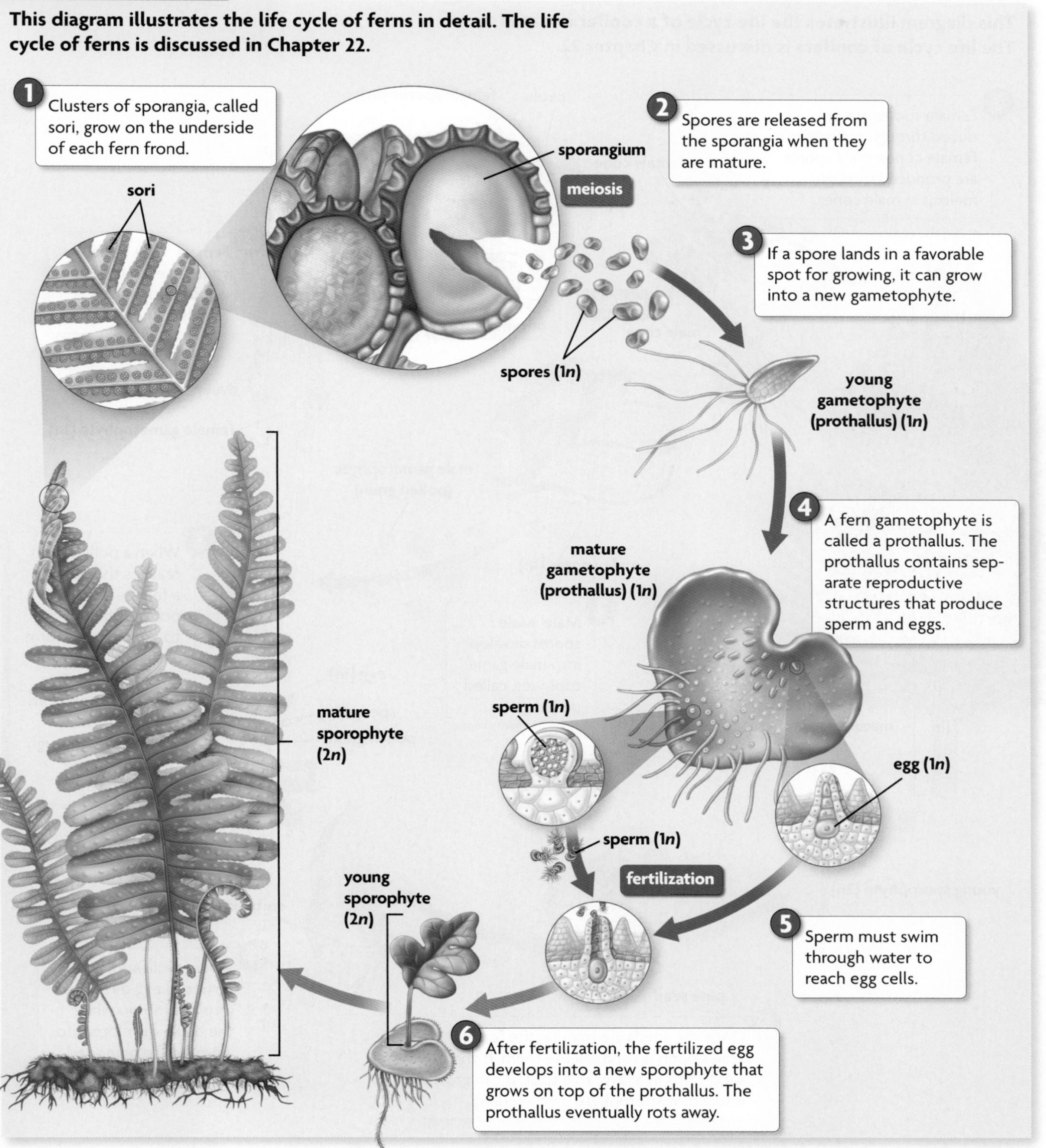

1 Clusters of sporangia, called sori, grow on the underside of each fern frond.
sori
sporangium
meiosis
2 Spores are released from the sporangia when they are mature.
3 If a spore lands in a favorable spot for growing, it can grow into a new gametophyte.
spores (1n)
young gametophyte (prothallus) (1n)
4 A fern gametophyte is called a prothallus. The prothallus contains separate reproductive structures that produce sperm and eggs.
mature gametophyte (prothallus) (1n)
mature sporophyte (2n)
sperm (1n)
egg (1n)
sperm (1n)
fertilization
young sporophyte (2n)
5 Sperm must swim through water to reach egg cells.
6 After fertilization, the fertilized egg develops into a new sporophyte that grows on top of the prothallus. The prothallus eventually rots away.

Appendix B: Life Cycles

Conifer Life Cycle

This diagram illustrates the life cycle of a conifer in detail. The life cycle of conifers is discussed in Chapter 22.

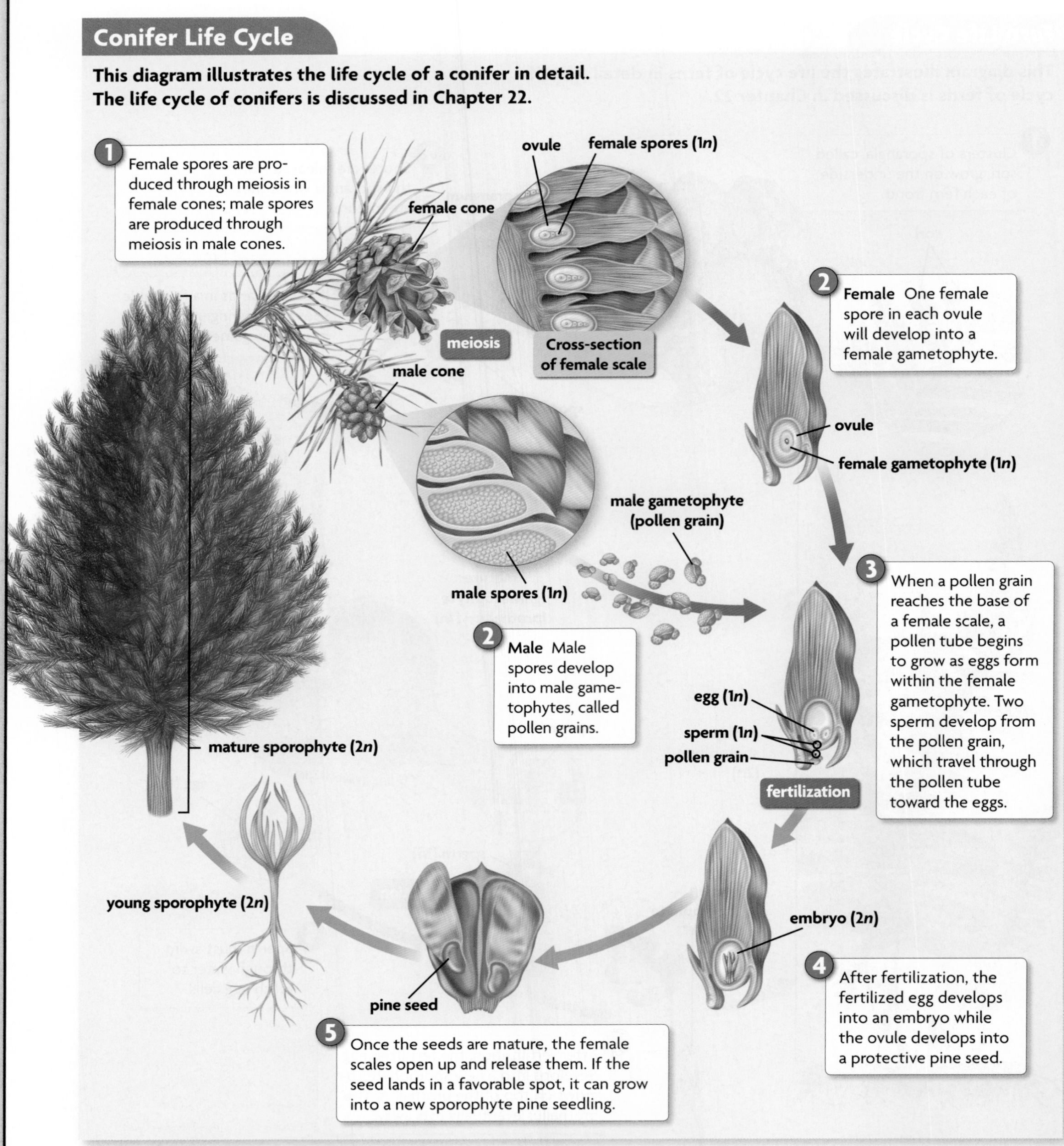

1 Female spores are produced through meiosis in female cones; male spores are produced through meiosis in male cones.
ovule
female spores (1n)
female cone
meiosis
Cross-section of female scale
male cone
2 Female One female spore in each ovule will develop into a female gametophyte.
ovule
female gametophyte (1n)
male gametophyte (pollen grain)
male spores (1n)
2 Male Male spores develop into male gametophytes, called pollen grains.
3 When a pollen grain reaches the base of a female scale, a pollen tube begins to grow as eggs form within the female gametophyte. Two sperm develop from the pollen grain, which travel through the pollen tube toward the eggs.
egg (1n)
sperm (1n)
pollen grain
fertilization
mature sporophyte (2n)
young sporophyte (2n)
embryo (2n)
4 After fertilization, the fertilized egg develops into an embryo while the ovule develops into a protective pine seed.
pine seed
5 Once the seeds are mature, the female scales open up and release them. If the seed lands in a favorable spot, it can grow into a new sporophyte pine seedling.

Flowering Plant Life Cycle

This diagram illustrates the life cycle of a flowering plant in detail. The life cycle of flowering plants is discussed in Chapter 22.

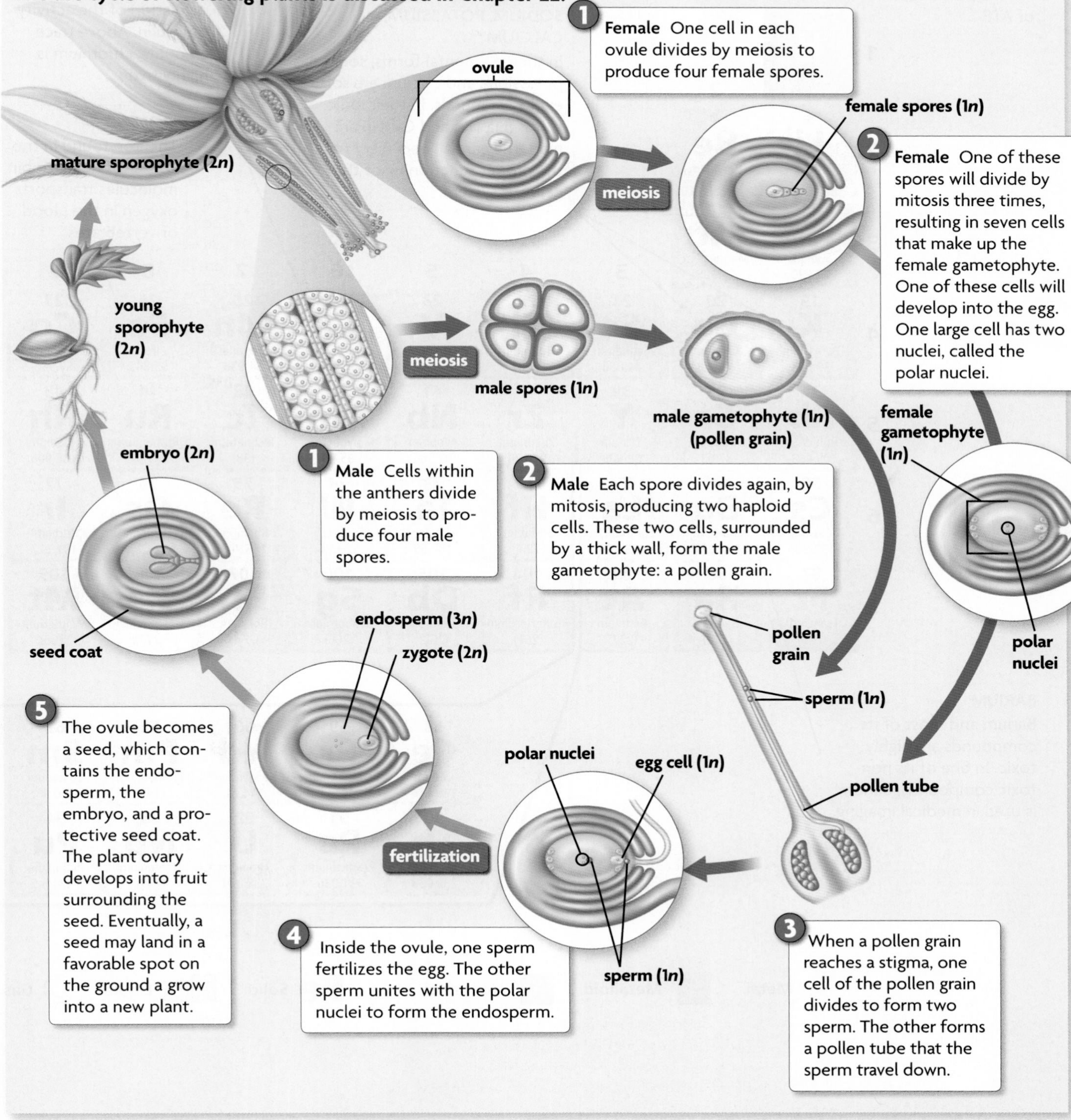

1 Female One cell in each ovule divides by meiosis to produce four female spores.

2 Female One of these spores will divide by mitosis three times, resulting in seven cells that make up the female gametophyte. One of these cells will develop into the egg. One large cell has two nuclei, called the polar nuclei.

1 Male Cells within the anthers divide by meiosis to produce four male spores.

2 Male Each spore divides again, by mitosis, producing two haploid cells. These two cells, surrounded by a thick wall, form the male gametophyte: a pollen grain.

3 When a pollen grain reaches a stigma, one cell of the pollen grain divides to form two sperm. The other forms a pollen tube that the sperm travel down.

4 Inside the ovule, one sperm fertilizes the egg. The other sperm unites with the polar nuclei to form the endosperm.

5 The ovule becomes a seed, which contains the endosperm, the embryo, and a protective seed coat. The plant ovary develops into fruit surrounding the seed. Eventually, a seed may land in a favorable spot on the ground a grow into a new plant.

ovule
mature sporophyte ($2n$)
meiosis
female spores ($1n$)
young sporophyte ($2n$)
meiosis
male spores ($1n$)
male gametophyte ($1n$) (pollen grain)
female gametophyte ($1n$)
polar nuclei
embryo ($2n$)
seed coat
endosperm ($3n$)
zygote ($2n$)
pollen grain
sperm ($1n$)
pollen tube
polar nuclei
egg cell ($1n$)
fertilization
sperm ($1n$)

Appendix C: Periodic Table

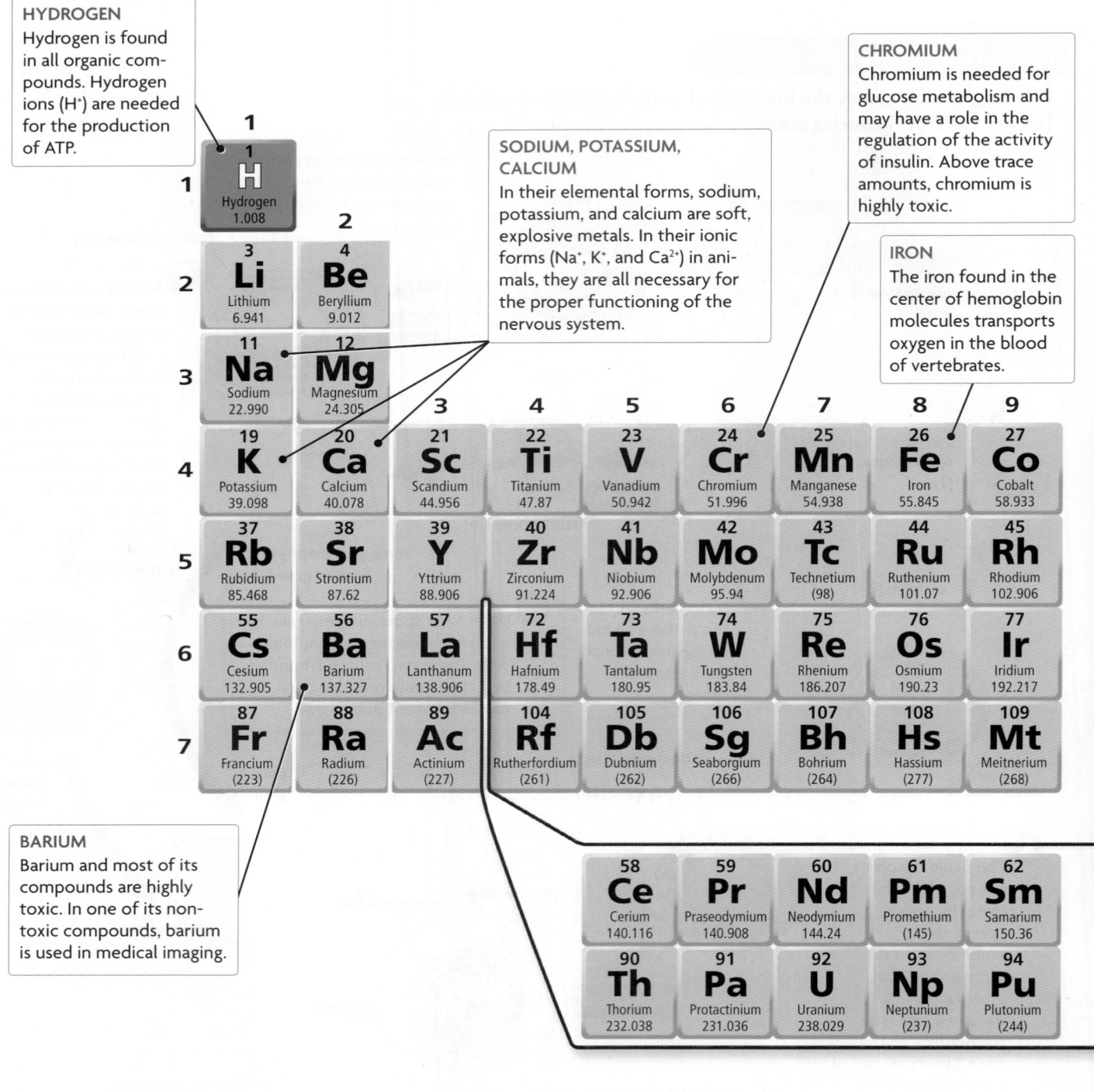

HYDROGEN
Hydrogen is found in all organic compounds. Hydrogen ions (H^+) are needed for the production of ATP.

SODIUM, POTASSIUM, CALCIUM
In their elemental forms, sodium, potassium, and calcium are soft, explosive metals. In their ionic forms (Na^+, K^+, and Ca^{2+}) in animals, they are all necessary for the proper functioning of the nervous system.

CHROMIUM
Chromium is needed for glucose metabolism and may have a role in the regulation of the activity of insulin. Above trace amounts, chromium is highly toxic.

IRON
The iron found in the center of hemoglobin molecules transports oxygen in the blood of vertebrates.

	1	2	3	4	5	6	7	8	9
1	1 H Hydrogen 1.008								
2	3 Li Lithium 6.941	4 Be Beryllium 9.012							
3	11 Na Sodium 22.990	12 Mg Magnesium 24.305							
4	19 K Potassium 39.098	20 Ca Calcium 40.078	21 Sc Scandium 44.956	22 Ti Titanium 47.87	23 V Vanadium 50.942	24 Cr Chromium 51.996	25 Mn Manganese 54.938	26 Fe Iron 55.845	27 Co Cobalt 58.933
5	37 Rb Rubidium 85.468	38 Sr Strontium 87.62	39 Y Yttrium 88.906	40 Zr Zirconium 91.224	41 Nb Niobium 92.906	42 Mo Molybdenum 95.94	43 Tc Technetium (98)	44 Ru Ruthenium 101.07	45 Rh Rhodium 102.906
6	55 Cs Cesium 132.905	56 Ba Barium 137.327	57 La Lanthanum 138.906	72 Hf Hafnium 178.49	73 Ta Tantalum 180.95	74 W Tungsten 183.84	75 Re Rhenium 186.207	76 Os Osmium 190.23	77 Ir Iridium 192.217
7	87 Fr Francium (223)	88 Ra Radium (226)	89 Ac Actinium (227)	104 Rf Rutherfordium (261)	105 Db Dubnium (262)	106 Sg Seaborgium (266)	107 Bh Bohrium (264)	108 Hs Hassium (277)	109 Mt Meitnerium (268)

58 Ce Cerium 140.116	59 Pr Praseodymium 140.908	60 Nd Neodymium 144.24	61 Pm Promethium (145)	62 Sm Samarium 150.36
90 Th Thorium 232.038	91 Pa Protactinium 231.036	92 U Uranium 238.029	93 Np Neptunium (237)	94 Pu Plutonium (244)

BARIUM
Barium and most of its compounds are highly toxic. In one of its nontoxic compounds, barium is used in medical imaging.

Metal  Metalloid  Nonmetal  Fe Solid  Liquid O Gas

OXYGEN
Oxygen is found in many organic molecules, and is needed for the aerobic stages of cellular respiration. Oxygen is also a waste product of photosynthesis and in some cases it is even toxic to cells.

NITROGEN
Proteins and nucleic acids both contain nitrogen. Although nitrogen makes up almost 80 percent of Earth's atmosphere, plants and animals cannot directly use nitrogen gas.

CARBON
All organic molecules, which are the basic building blocks of life, contain carbon.

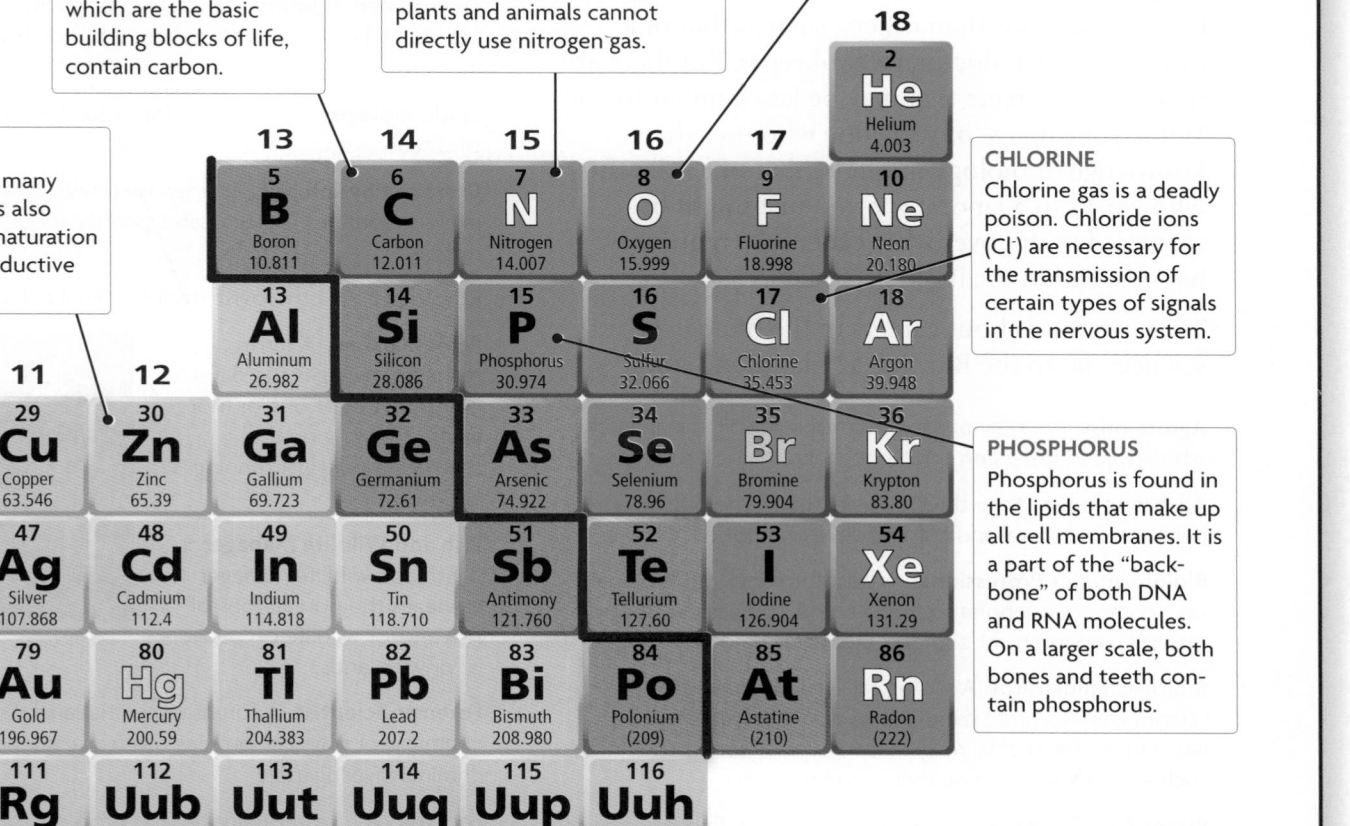

ZINC
Zinc is found in many enzymes. Zinc is also important for maturation of human reproductive systems.

CHLORINE
Chlorine gas is a deadly poison. Chloride ions (Cl^-) are necessary for the transmission of certain types of signals in the nervous system.

PHOSPHORUS
Phosphorus is found in the lipids that make up all cell membranes. It is a part of the "backbone" of both DNA and RNA molecules. On a larger scale, both bones and teeth contain phosphorus.

10	11	12	13	14	15	16	17	18
								2 He Helium 4.003
			5 B Boron 10.811	6 C Carbon 12.011	7 N Nitrogen 14.007	8 O Oxygen 15.999	9 F Fluorine 18.998	10 Ne Neon 20.180
			13 Al Aluminum 26.982	14 Si Silicon 28.086	15 P Phosphorus 30.974	16 S Sulfur 32.066	17 Cl Chlorine 35.453	18 Ar Argon 39.948
28 Ni Nickel 58.69	29 Cu Copper 63.546	30 Zn Zinc 65.39	31 Ga Gallium 69.723	32 Ge Germanium 72.61	33 As Arsenic 74.922	34 Se Selenium 78.96	35 Br Bromine 79.904	36 Kr Krypton 83.80
46 Pd Palladium 106.42	47 Ag Silver 107.868	48 Cd Cadmium 112.4	49 In Indium 114.818	50 Sn Tin 118.710	51 Sb Antimony 121.760	52 Te Tellurium 127.60	53 I Iodine 126.904	54 Xe Xenon 131.29
78 Pt Platinum 195.078	79 Au Gold 196.967	80 Hg Mercury 200.59	81 Tl Thallium 204.383	82 Pb Lead 207.2	83 Bi Bismuth 208.980	84 Po Polonium (209)	85 At Astatine (210)	86 Rn Radon (222)
110 Ds Darmstadtium (281)	111 Rg Roentgenium (272)	112 Uub Ununbium (285)	113 Uut Ununtrium (284)	114 Uuq Ununquadium (289)	115 Uup Ununpentium (288)	116 Uuh Ununhexium (292)		

63 Eu Europium 151.964	64 Gd Gadolinium 157.25	65 Tb Terbium 158.925	66 Dy Dysprosium 162.50	67 Ho Holmium 164.930	68 Er Erbium 167.26	69 Tm Thulium 168.934	70 Yb Ytterbium 173.04	71 Lu Lutetium 174.967
95 Am Americium (243)	96 Cm Curium (247)	97 Bk Berkelium (247)	98 Cf Californium (251)	99 Es Einsteinium (252)	100 Fm Fermium (257)	101 Md Mendelevium (258)	102 No Nobelium (259)	103 Lr Lawrencium (262)

Atomic number Number of protons in the nucleus of the element

1
H
Hydrogen
1.008

Symbol Each element has a symbol. The symbol's color represents the element's state at room temperature.

Name

Atomic mass Average mass of isotopes of this element

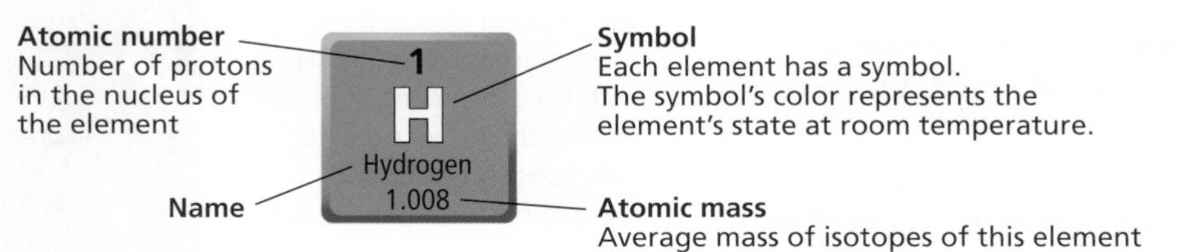

Appendix D: Biology Careers

Careers in Biology

A number of careers require a background knowledge of biology. Some of these career choices may be more obvious than others, such as that of a biology teacher, doctor, or zookeeper. But there are many more careers that may be less familiar to you. While your image of someone who uses their knowledge of biology might be that of a scientist who works in a laboratory, you just might be surprised to discover what other jobs require a background in the biological sciences.

To learn more about careers in the biological sciences, go to the BioZine at ClassZone.com.

Agronomist An agronomist is an expert in soil management who advises farmers on how to manage their crops.

Anthropologist An anthropologist studies the origin, behavior, and social and cultural development of humans.

Bioinformatics Professional A bioinformatics professional uses computers, laboratory robots, and software to develop, manage, and interpret complex biological data.

Biological Illustrator A biological illustrator provides scientifically accurate hand-drawn or computer-aided illustrations for clients, ranging from web sites to publications such as textbooks, newspapers, or magazines.

Biomedical Engineer A biomedical engineer develops devices and procedures that solve medical and health-related problems.

Conservation Biologist A conservation biologist manages, improves, and protects natural resources.

Ecotourism Guide An ecotourism guide leads groups of tourists on trips to natural areas to promote conservation and sustain the livelihood of local people.

Emergency Medical Technician An emergency medical technician provides emergency medical services to critically ill and injured persons.

Environmental Economist An environmental economist uses the principles of economics to determine the impact of such things as species loss, pollution, and climate change.

Environmental Health Professional An environmental health professional inspects the health and safety of establishments such as restaurants and housing areas.

Environmental Journalist An environmental journalist writes articles or books on environmental topics, frequently in an investigatory manner.

Epidemiologist An epidemiologist studies causes and control of diseases.

Exercise Physiologist An exercise physiologist develops exercise routines and educates people about the benefits of exercise.

Ethologist An ethologist studies animal behavior.

Farm Manager A farm manager manages the day-to-day activities of one or more farms, focusing on the business aspects of running a farm.

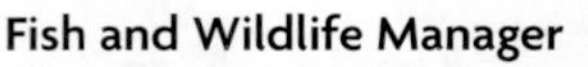

Fish and Wildlife Manager A fish and wildlife manager manages the populations of fish and/or wildlife on public or private lands.

Forensic Scientist A forensic scientist analyzes biological, chemical, or physical samples taken as evidence during a criminal investigation.

Forester A forester manages and protects forests and supervises tree harvesting.

Genetic Counselor A genetic counselor is a health professional who specializes in telling families about the nature and risks of inherited conditions and syndromes.

Geneticist A geneticist specializes in the study of genes and their influence on health, as well as the treatment of genetic disorders.

Immunologist An immunologist is a medical scientist who studies the immune system.

Landscape Architect A landscape architect plans the location of buildings, roads, and walkways along with the placement of plants so that the designs are not only functional but also compatible with the natural environment.

Medical Transcriptionist A medical transcriptionist listens to dictated recordings made by doctors and other health care workers and transcribes them into medical reports.

Medical Device Sales Representative A medical device sales representative sells medical devices to health professionals.

Molecular Biologist A molecular biologist studies the structure and function of biological molecules, such as DNA and proteins.

Nature Photographer A nature photographer takes photographs of natural settings and wildlife for publication online and in print material such as books and magazines.

Neuroscientist A neuroscientist specializes in the study of the structure and function of the brain and nervous system.

Nutritionist A nutritionist plans food and nutrition programs and provides advice to those with food allergies or those seeking weight loss.

Oceanographer An oceanographer studies the world's oceans and their inhabitants.

Park Ranger A park ranger supervises, manages, and performs work in the conservation and use of resources in national, state, and city parks.

Pharmacist A pharmacist distributes drugs prescribed by doctors and other health workers and provides information to patients about medications and their use.

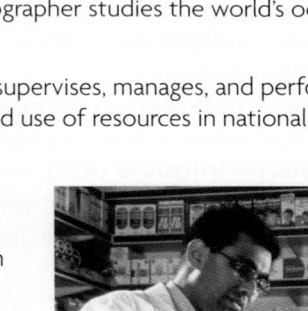

Phlebotomist A phlebotomist collects blood samples.

Physician Assistant A physician assistant takes medical histories, examines and treats patients, orders and interprets laboratory tests and x-rays, and makes diagnoses, all under the supervision of a doctor.

Physical Therapist A physical therapist provides services that help restore function, improve mobility, relieve pain, and prevent or limit permanent physical disabilities of patients suffering from injuries or disease.

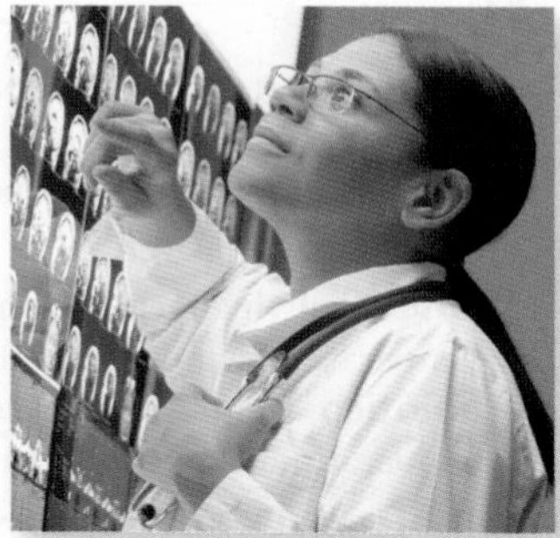

Radiologist A radiologist is a doctor who specializes in the interpretation of x-rays and other medical images.

Respiratory Therapist A respiratory therapist evaluates, treats, and cares for patients with breathing or other cardiopulmonary disorders.

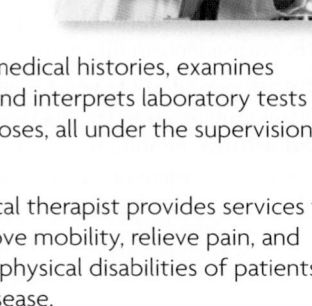

Science Editor A science editor edits scientific writing, ranging from academic journals to works meant for a general audience.

Science Museum Curator A science museum curator oversees the development and management of museum exhibits.

Science Patent Lawyer A science patent lawyer represents clients in legal proceedings, draws up legal documents, and advises clients on legal transactions.

Science Policy Analyst A science policy analyst advises lawmakers with regard to legislation focused on scientific issues such as biomedical research or environmental regulations.

Science Writer A science writer specializes in writing about scientific topics for both academic and general audiences.

Speech-Language Pathologist A speech-language pathologist tests, diagnoses, treats, and helps to prevent speech, language, and other voice-related disorders.

Sports Trainer A sports trainer helps athletes in the prevention of injury and provides initial management of a sports-related injury.

Surgical Technician A surgical technician assists in surgeries by preparing the surgical room, providing support to surgical workers, and monitoring the patient during surgery.

Ultrasound Technician An ultrasound technician operates an ultrasound machine, which collects reflected echoes and forms an image that may be videotaped, transmitted, or photographed for interpretation and diagnosis by a doctor.

X-Ray Technician An x-ray technician takes x-rays and administers nonradioactive materials into patients' bloodstreams for diagnostic purposes.

R39

Glossary

A

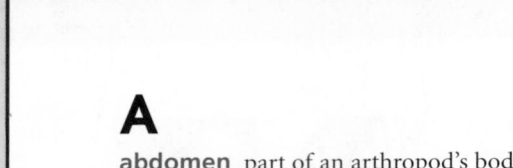

abdomen part of an arthropod's body that is behind the thorax. (p. 735)
abdomen parte del cuerpo de un artrópodo situada detrás del tórax.

abiotic nonliving factor in an ecosystem, such as moisture, temperature, wind, sunlight, soil, and minerals. (p. 402)
abiótico factor inerte de un ecosistema, como la humedad, la temperatura, el viento, la luz solar, el suelo y los minerales.

ABO blood group four common blood types (A, B, AB, and O) and the protein markers that distinguish them. (p. 927)
grupo sanguíneo ABO sistema que contiene los cuatro tipos de sangre comunes (A, B, AB y O) y los marcadores proteicos que los distinguen.

absorption process by which nutrients move out of one system and into another. (p. 982)
absorción proceso mediante el cual los nutrientes pasan de un sistema del organismo a otro.

abyssal zone (uh-BIHS-uhl) depth of the ocean that lies below 2000 meters and is in complete darkness. (p. 469)
zona abisal región del océano por debajo de los 2000 metros de profundidad que se encuentra en total oscuridad.

acid compound that donates a proton (H^+) when dissolved in a solution. (p. 42)
ácido compuesto que cede un protón (H^+) al ser disuelto en una solución.

acid rain precipitation produced when pollutants in the atmosphere cause the pH of rain to decrease. (p. 489)
lluvia ácida precipitación que se produce cuando los contaminantes de la atmósfera hacen que el pH de la lluvia disminuya.

acquired immune deficiency syndrome (AIDS) condition characterized by having several infections and very few T cells; caused by HIV. (p. 963)
síndrome de inmunodeficiencia adquirida (SIDA) enfermedad caracterizada por falta de defensa contra varias infecciones y muy pocas células T; causada por el VIH.

actin filament that is pulled by myosin filaments to cause muscle contraction. (p. 1008)
actina filamento que al ser accionado por los filamentos de miosina provoca una contracción muscular.

action potential fast, moving change in electrical charge across a neuron's membrane; also called an impulse. (p. 878)
potencial de acción cambio rápido en la descarga eléctrica a lo largo de la membrana de las neuronas; también llamado impulso.

activation energy energy input necessary to initiate a chemical reaction. (p. 53)
energía de activación energía necesaria para iniciar una reacción química.

active immunity immunity that occurs after the body responds to an antigen. (p. 948)
inmunidad activa inmunidad que se produce después de que el cuerpo haya respondido a un antígeno.

active transport energy-requiring movement of molecules across a membrane from a region of lower concentration to a region of higher concentration. (p. 89)
transporte activo desplazamiento de moléculas a través de una membrana desde un medio de baja concentración a un medio de alta concentración.

adaptation inherited trait that is selected for over time because it allows organisms to better survive in their environment. (pp. 10; 302)
adaptación rasgo heredado durante un periodo de tiempo mediante selección natural, que facilita la supervivencia de los organismos en su medio ambiente.

adaptive radiation process by which one species evolves and gives rise to many descendant species that occupy different ecological niches. (p. 351)
radiación adaptativa proceso evolutivo mediante el cual una especie da lugar a varias nuevas especies que ocupan distintos nichos ecológicos.

addiction uncontrollable physical and mental need for something. (p. 893)
adicción necesidad física y mental incontrolable de alguna sustancia o actividad.

adenosine diphosphate (ADP) low-energy molecule that can be converted to ATP. (p. 101)
adenosín difosfato (ADP) molécula con poca energía que puede convertirse en ATP.

adenosine triphosphate (ATP) high-energy molecule that contains, within its bonds, energy that cells can use. (p. 100)
adenosín trifosfato (ATP) molécula de alta energía en cuyos enlaces se almacena energía para las células.

adhesion attraction between molecules of different substances. (p. 41)
adhesión atracción que se produce entre moléculas de diferentes sustancias.

adolescence period of life beginning at puberty and ending at adulthood. (p. 1042)
adolescencia periodo de la vida que comienza en la pubertad y que termina en la edad adulta.

ADP *see* adenosine diphosphate. (p. 101)
ADP *véase* adenosín difosfato.

adulthood period of life when a person is fully developed and physical growth stops. (p. 1043)
edad adulta período de la vida en el que un individuo alcanza su completo desarrollo y en el que cesa el crecimiento.

aerobic (ay-ROH-bihk) process that requires oxygen to occur. (p. 113)
aeróbico proceso que requiere la presencia de oxígeno para ocurrir.

airfoil surface, such as a bird's wing, whose shape moves air faster over the top than underneath it, allowing for flight. (p. 799)
superficie aerodinámica superficie de ala cuya forma, como en el caso de las aves, permite que el aire se mueva más rápido por arriba que por abajo, facilitando así el vuelo.

air sac air-filled space that connects to a bird's lungs, aiding in breathing. (p. 801)
sacos aéreos órganos llenos de aire conectados a los pulmones de las aves para facilitar la respiración.

algae (singular: *alga*) photosynthetic plantlike protists. (p. 581)
alga protista fotosintética de aspecto vegetal.

alkaloid chemical produced by plants that contains nitrogen, many of which are used in medicines. (p. 631)
alcaloide compuesto químico, producido por las plantas, que contiene nitrógeno y es usado en muchos medicamentos.

allele (uh-LEEL) any of the alternative forms of a gene that occurs at a specific place on a chromosome. (p. 180)
alelo cualquier variante de un gen que ocupa la misma posición en un cromosoma.

allele frequency proportion of one allele, compared with all the alleles for that trait, in the gene pool. (p. 328)
frecuencia alélica proporción de un alelo determinado con respecto a los demás alelos del mismo rasgo en una misma población.

allergen antigen that does not cause disease but still produces an immune response. (p. 957)
alérgeno antígeno que, si bien no causa una enfermedad, produce una respuesta inmune.

allergy immune response that occurs when the body responds to a nondisease-causing antigen, such as pollen or animal dander. (p. 957)
alergia respuesta inmune producida cuando el organismo responde a aquellos antígenos que no causan enfermedades, como el polen o la caspa de ciertos animales.

alternation of generations plant life cycle in which the plant alternates between haploid and diploid phases. (p. 664)
alternancia generacional ciclo de vida de las plantas en el que la planta alterna fases haploides y diploides.

altruism behavior in which an animal reduces its own fitness to help the other members of its social group. (p. 833)
altruismo patrón de comportamiento animal, en el cual un individuo sacrifica su integridad para beneficiar a otros miembros de su grupo social.

alveolus (al-VEE-uh-luhs) (plural: *alveoli*) tiny, thin-walled structure across which oxygen gas is absorbed and carbon dioxide is released in the lungs. (p. 911)
alvéolo pequeña estructura de paredes delgadas a través de la cual se absorbe oxígeno gaseoso y se libera dióxido de carbono en los pulmones.

amino acid molecule that makes up proteins; composed of carbon, hydrogen, oxygen, nitrogen, and sometimes sulfur. (p. 47)
aminoácido molécula que forma las proteínas; está compuesta de carbono, hidrógeno, oxígeno, nitrógeno y, a veces, de azufre.

amniote vertebrate whose embryo or fetus is enclosed by a thin, tough membranous sac. (p. 778)
amniota vertebrado cuyo embrión o feto está envuelto en un saco membranoso delgado y resistente.

amniotic egg waterproof container that allows an embryo to develop out of water and externally from the mother without drying out. (p. 779)
huevo amniótico envoltura impermeable que permite el desarrollo del embrión fuera del agua y de la propia madre sin que éste se deshidrate.

amniotic sac fluid-filled organ that cushions and protects the developing embryo of some vertebrates. (p. 1035)
saco amniótico membrana que contiene líquido y que amortigua y protege el embrión de ciertos vertebrados.

amphibian vertebrate that can live on land and in water. (p. 773)
anfibio vertebrado que puede vivir en el agua y en tierra firme.

anaerobic process that does not require oxygen to occur. (p. 113)
anaeróbico proceso que no requiere oxígeno para ocurrir.

analogous structure body part that is similar in function as a body part of another organism but is structurally different. (p. 313)
estructura análoga parte del cuerpo que cumple una función similar a la parte del cuerpo de un organismo diferente, pero que tiene una estructura diferente.

anaphase third phase of mitosis during which chromatids separate and are pulled to opposite sides of the cell. (p. 140)
anafase tercera fase de la mitosis, en la cual las cromátidas se separan y se dirigen hacia los polos opuestos de la célula.

anaphylaxis (AN-uh-fuh-LAK-sihs) severe allergic reaction that causes airways to tighten and blood vessels to leak. (p. 958)
anafilaxis reacción alérgica grave que produce rigidez de las vías aéreas y el drenaje de líquido de los vasos sanguíneos.

angiosperm (AN-jee-uh-SPURM) seed plant whose embryos are enclosed by fruit. (p. 621)
angiosperma planta cuyos embriones se encuentran encerrados en el fruto.

Glossary

anthropoid humanlike primate. (p. 380)
antropoide primate semejante al ser humano.

antibiotic chemical that kills or slows the growth of bacteria. (p. 564)
antibiótico compuesto químico que mata o inhibe el desarrollo de las bacterias.

antibiotic resistance process by which bacteria mutate so that they are no longer affected by an antibiotic. (p. 955)
resistencia antibiótica proceso mediante el cual una bacteria sufre mutaciones y para hacerse resistente a los antibióticos.

antibody protein produced by B cells that aids in the destruction of pathogens. (p. 947)
anticuerpo proteína producida por las células B que contribuye a la destrucción de los patógenos.

anticodon set of three nucleotides in a tRNA molecule that binds to a complementary mRNA codon during translation. (p. 245)
anticodón grupo de tres nucleótidos de la molécula de ARNt que se acopla a un codón complementario de ARNm durante la traslación.

antigen (AN-tih-juhn) protein marker that helps the immune system identify foreign particles. (p. 951)
antígeno marcador proteico que ayuda al sistema immune a identificar sustancias extrañas tales como los virus.

antiseptic (AN-tih-SEHP-tihk) chemical, such as soap, vinegar, or rubbing alcohol, that destroys pathogens outside of the body. (p. 955)
antiséptico compuesto químico, como el jabón, el vinagre o el alcohol, que destruyen los patógenos fuera del cuerpo.

apoptosis (AP-uhp-TOH-sihs) programmed cell death. (p. 145)
apoptosis muerte celular programada.

appendage extension, such as an antenna or arm, that is attached to the body. (p. 730)
apéndice prolongación del cuerpo, como una antena o un brazo, unida o contigua al mismo.

appendicular skeleton part of the skeletal system that allows for most of the body's movements; includes bones of the arms, shoulders, legs, and pelvis. (p. 1000)
esqueleto apendicular parte del sistema esquelético que permite la mayor parte de los movimientos del cuerpo; consta, entre otros, de los huesos de los brazos, hombros, piernas y la pelvis.

arachnid terrestrial chelicerate, such as a spider. (p. 740)
arácnido quelicerado terrestre, como la araña.

Archaea one of the three domains of life, containing single-celled prokaryotes in the kingdom Archaea. (p 534)
Arqueas uno de los tres dominios de la vida, compuesto de procariontes unicelulares del reino Archaea.

artery large blood vessel that carries blood away from the heart. (p. 913)
arteria gran vaso sanguíneo que transporta la sangre desde el corazón.

arthropod invertebrate with an exoskeleton, jointed appendages, and a segmented body. (p. 730)
artrópodo invertebrado con exoesqueleto, apéndices articulados y cuerpo segmentado.

artificial selection process by which humans modify a species by breeding it for certain traits (p. 304)
selección artificial proceso mediante el cual los seres humanos modifican una especie al criarla para obtener ciertos rasgos.

asexual reproduction process by which offspring are produced from a single parent; does not involve the joining of gametes. (p. 148)
reproducción asexual proceso mediante el cual se producen descendientes de un solo progenitor, sin necesidad de la unión de gametos.

asthma (AZ-muh) condition in which air pathways in the lungs constrict, making breathing difficult. (p. 916)
asma enfermedad que, al estrechar las vías aéreas de los pulmones, dificulta la respiración.

atmosphere air blanketing Earth's solid surface. (p. 456)
atmósfera envoltura de aire que rodea la superficie sólida de la Tierra.

atom smallest basic unit of matter. (p. 36)
átomo unidad básica más pequeña de la materia.

ATP *see* adenosene triphosphate. (p. 100)
ATP *véase* adenosín trifosfato.

ATP synthase enzyme that catalyzes the reaction that adds a high-energy phosphate group to ADP to form ATP. (p. 110)
ATP sintetasa enzima que cataliza la reacción para enlazar un grupo fosfato de alta energía al ADP y formar así el ATP.

atrium (plural: *atria*) small chamber in the human heart that receives blood from the veins. (p. 917)
aurícula pequeña cavidad del corazón humano que recibe sangre de las venas.

autonomic nervous system division of the peripheral nervous system that controls involuntary functions. (p. 890)
sistema nervioso autónomo parte del sistema nervioso periférico que controla las funciones involuntarias.

autosome chromosome that contains genes for characteristics not directly related to the sex of the organism. (p. 169)
autosoma cromosoma cuyos genes no rigen los rasgos relacionados directamente con el sexo del organismo.

autotroph organism that obtains its energy from abiotic sources, such as sunlight or inorganic chemicals. (p. 406)
autótrofo organismo que obtiene su energía a partir de fuentes abióticas como, por ejemplo, la luz solar o sustancias inorgánicas.

auxin (AWK-sihn) plant hormone that stimulates the lengthening of cells in the growing tip. (p. 681)
auxina hormona vegetal que estimula la elongación de las células y regula el crecimiento de las plantas.

axial skeleton part of the skeletal system that supports the body's weight and protects the body's internal tissues; includes the bones of the skull, spinal column, and rib cage. (p. 1001)
esqueleto axial parte del sistema esquelético que da soporte al peso corporal y que protege los tejidos internos del organismo; consta de los huesos del cráneo, la columna vertebral y la caja torácica.

axon long extension of the neuron membrane that carries impulses from one neuron to another. (p. 876)
axón prolongación de la membrana de la neurona que transmite impulsos eléctricos de una neurona a otra.

B

Bacteria one of the three domains of life, containing single-celled prokaryotes in the kingdom Bacteria. (p. 534)
Bacteria uno de los tres dominios en los que se dividen los seres vivos, que consta de procariontes unicelulares del reino Bacteria.

bacteriophage virus that infects bacteria. (pp. 228; 549)
bacteriófago virus que infecta a las bacterias.

bacterium (plural: *bacteria*) organism that is within the kingdom Bacteria. (p. 534)
bacteria organismo perteneciento al reino Bacteria.

base compound that accepts a proton (H^+) when dissolved in solution. (p. 42)
base compuesto que al disolverlo en una solución acepta un protón (H^+).

base pairing rules rule that describes how nucleotides form bonds in DNA; adenine (A) always bonds with thymine (T), and guanine (G) always bonds with cytosine (C). (p. 232)
reglas de apareamiento de bases regla que describe cómo se enlazan los nucleótidos en el ADN; la adenina (A) siempre se enlaza con la timina (T), y la guanina (G) siempre se enlaza con la citosina (C).

bathyal zone (BATH-ee-uhl) zone of the ocean that extends from the edge of the neritic zone to the base of the continental shelf. (p. 469)
zona batial region océanica que se extiende desde el límite de la zona nerítica hasta la base de la plataforma continental.

B cell white blood cell that matures in the bone marrow and produces antibodies that fight off infection; also called a B-lymphocyte. (p. 946)
célula B glóbulo blanco que madura en la médula osea y que produce los anticuerpos que combaten las infecciones; también se conoce como linfocito B.

behavioral isolation isolation between populations due to differences in courtship or mating behavior. (p. 345)
aislamiento etológico aislamiento entre poblaciones debido a diferencias en los rituales de cortejo o apareamiento.

benign having no dangerous effect on health, especially referring to an abnormal growth of cells that are not cancerous. (p. 146)
benigno que no tiene efectos graves sobre la salud; se refiere particularmente al crecimiento anormal de células que no son cancerosas.

benthic zone lake or pond bottom, where little to no sunlight can reach. (p. 474)
zona béntica fondo de un lago o estanque, adonde llega poca o ninguna luz.

bilateral symmetry body plan of some organisms in which the body can be divided equally along only one plane. (p. 701)
simetría bilateral se observa en los organismos que pueden dividirse en partes iguales a lo largo de un plano único.

bile fluid released by the liver and gallbladder into the small intestine that aids in the digestion and absorption of fats. (p. 980)
bilis fluido segregado por el hígado y almacenado en la vesícula biliar, y que es liberado al intestino delgado para facilitar la digestión y la absorción de las grasas.

binary fission (BY-nuh-ree FIHSH-uhn) asexual reproduction in which a cell divides into two equal parts. (p. 148)
fisión binaria reproducción asexual en la que una célula se divide en dos partes iguales.

binomial nomenclature naming system in which each species is given a two-part scientific name (genus and species) using Latin words. (p. 519)
nomenclatura binomial sistema de denominación de especies mediante el cual se les otorga un nombre científico que consta de dos palabras en latín (género y especie).

biodiversity variety of life within an area. (pp. 5; 403)
biodiversidad variedad de las formas de vida en una zona determinada.

biogeochemical cycle movement of a chemical through the biological and geological, or living and nonliving, parts of an ecosystem. (p. 413)
ciclo biogeoquímico movimiento de una sustancia química a través de los componentes biológicos y geológicos, o vivos e inertes, de un ecosistema.

biogeography study of the distribution of organisms around the world. (p. 311)
biogeografía estudio de la distribución de los organismos en el mundo.

bioinformatics use of computer databases to organize and analyze biological data. (p. 282)
bioinformática utilización de bases de datos de computación para organizar y analizar datos biológicos.

Glossary

biological clock internal mechanism that controls an animal's activity patterns. (p. 820)
reloj biológico mecanismo interno que controla el ritmo de actividad de un animal.

biology scientific study of all forms of life. (p. 5)
biología estudio científico de todas las formas de vida.

biomagnification condition of toxic substances being more concentrated in tissues of organisms higher on the food chain than ones lower in the food chain. (p. 495)
biomagnificación condición en la cual la concentración de sustancias tóxicas en los tejidos de los organismos que pertenecen a eslabones más altos de la cadena alimentaria es mayor que la concentración en los organismos de los eslabones más bajos.

biomass total dry mass of all organisms in a given area. (p. 417)
biomasa masa deshidratada total de todos los organismos de un área determinada.

biome regional or global community of organisms characterized by the climate conditions and plant communities that thrive there. (p. 397)
bioma comunidad regional o global de organismos caracterizada por las condiciones climáticas y el tipo de vegetación del área.

bioremediation process by which humans use living things to break down pollutants. (p. 561)
biorremediación proceso mediante el cual los seres humanos emplean organismos vivos para descomponer sustancias contaminantes.

biosphere all organisms and the part of Earth where they exist. (pp. 4; 456)
biosfera todos los seres vivos y las partes de la Tierra en las que existen.

biota collection of living things. (p. 456)
biota conjunto de seres vivos.

biotechnology use and application of living things and biological processes. (p. 26)
biotecnología aprovechamiento y aplicación de los seres vivos y de sus procesos biológicos.

biotic living things, such as plants, animals, fungi, and bacteria. (p. 402)
biótico referente a los seres vivos, tales como las plantas, los animales, los hongos y las bacterias.

bipedal animal that walks on two legs. (p. 381)
bípedo animal que camina sobre dos patas.

blade broad part of a leaf where most of the photosynthesis of a plant takes place. (p. 652)
lámina parte ancha de la hoja donde ocurre la mayor parte de la fotosíntesis de una planta.

blastocyst stage of development during which the zygote consists of a ball of cells. (p. 1034)
blastocisto fase de desarrollo en la que el cigoto consta de células apelotonadas.

blood pressure force with which blood pushes against the wall of an artery. (p. 923)
presión sanguínea fuerza que ejerce la sangre contra las paredes de las arterias.

bond energy amount of energy needed to break a bond between two particular atoms; or the amount of energy released when a bond forms between two particular atoms. (p. 51)
energía de enlace energía necesaria para romper un enlace entre dos partículas atómicas; energía liberada al formarse un enlace entre dos átomos determinados.

book lung respiratory organ that has several membranes that are arranged like the pages in a book. (p. 740)
pulmón en libro órgano respiratorio compuesto por una serie de membranas dispuestas como las páginas de un libro.

botany study of plants. (p. 629)
botánica estudio de las plantas.

bottleneck effect genetic drift that results from an event that drastically reduces the size of a population. (p. 336)
efecto de cuello de botella deriva genética resultante de un acontecimiento que reduce drásticamente el tamaño de una población.

brain stem structure that connects the brain to the spinal cord and controls breathing and heartbeat. (p. 888)
tronco del encéfalo estructura que conecta el cerebro con la médula espinal y que controla la respiración y los latidos del corazón.

C

calcification process that hardens bones by adding calcium phosphate and collagen. (p. 1005)
calcificación proceso que endurece los huesos mediante depósitos de fosfato cálcico y colágeno.

Calorie measure of energy released from digesting food; one Calorie equals one kilocalorie of heat. (p. 975)
caloría medida de energía liberada al digerir la comida; una caloría equivale a una kilocaloría de calor.

Calvin cycle process by which a photosynthetic organism uses energy to synthesize simple sugars from CO_2. (p. 111)
ciclo de Calvin proceso mediante el cual un organismo fotosintético usa energía para sintetizar monosacáridos a partir del CO_2.

Cambrian explosion earliest part of the Paleozoic era, when a huge diversity of animal species evolved. (p. 376)
explosión Cámbrica periodo inicial de la era paleozoica, en la que surgió una enorme diversidad de especies animales.

cancer common name for a class of diseases characterized by uncontrolled cell division. (p. 146)
cáncer nombre común de una clase de enfermedades caracterizadas por una división descontrolada de las células.

canopy dense covering formed by the uppermost branches of trees. (p. 464)
cobertura arbórea tupido entramado formado por las ramas más altas de los árboles.

capillary tiny blood vessel that transports blood between larger blood vessels and other tissues in the body. (p. 913)
capilar diminuto vaso sanguíneo que transporta la sangre entre vasos sanguíneos más grandes y otros tejidos del cuerpo.

capsid protein shell that surrounds a virus. (p. 547)
cápsida cubierta proteica que envuelve al virus.

carapace (KAR-uh-PAYS) plate of exoskeleton that covers the head and thorax of a crustacean. (p. 735)
caparazón parte del exoesqueleto de los crustáceos que cubre la cabeza y el tórax.

carbohydrate molecule composed of carbon, hydrogen, and oxygen; includes sugars and starches. (p. 45)
carbohidrato molécula compuesta de carbono, hidrógeno y oxígeno; incluye los azúcares y los almidones.

carcinogen substance that produces or promotes the development of cancer. (p. 146)
carcinógeno sustancia que estimula o contribuye a inducir el cáncer.

cardiac muscle muscle tissue that is only found in the heart. (p. 1008)
músculo cardíaco tejido muscular, también conocido como miocardio, que sólo se halla en el corazón.

carnivore organism that obtains energy by eating only animals. (p. 409)
carnívoro organismo que obtiene energía al alimentarse únicamente de otros animales.

carpel female structure of flowering plants; made of the ovary, style, and stigma. (p. 668)
carpelo estructura reproductora femenina de las plantas con flor; consta de ovario, estilo y stigma.

carrier organism whose genome contains a gene for a certain trait or disease that is not expressed in the organism's phenotype. (p. 201)
portador organismo cuyo genoma contiene un gen de cierto rasgo o enfermedad que no se encuentra expresado en el fenotipo de dicho organismo.

carrying capacity number of individuals that the resources of an environment can normally and persistently support. (p. 442)
capacidad de carga de población número de individuos que los recursos de un ambiente pueden sustentar normalmente de manera continua.

cartilage tough, elastic, and fibrous connective tissue found between bones. (p. 1001)
cartílago tejido conectivo resistente, fibroso y elástico que se encuentra entre los huesos.

catalyst (KAT-uhl-ihst) substance that decreases activation energy and increases reaction rate in a chemical reaction. (p. 54)
catalizador sustancia que disminuye la energía de activación y aumenta la tasa de reacción de una reacción química determinada.

catastrophism theory that states that natural disasters such as floods and volcanic eruptions shaped Earth's landforms and caused extinction of some species. (p. 301)
catastrofismo teoría según la cual la configuración actual de los accidentes geográficos de la Tierra y la extinción de algunas especies se debió a inundaciones, erupciones volcánicas y otras catástrofes naturales.

cell basic unit of life. (p. 5)
célula unidad básica de la vida.

cell cycle pattern of growth, DNA replication, and cell division that occurs in a eukaryotic cell. (p. 134)
ciclo celular proceso de crecimiento, replicación de ADN y división celular que ocurre en las células eucarióticas.

cell differentiation processes by which unspecialized cells develop into their mature form and function. (p. 152)
diferenciación celular proceso mediante el cual las células no especializadas adquieren una forma y una función determinada.

cell membrane double-layer of phospholipids that forms a boundary between a cell and the surrounding environment and controls the passage of materials into and out of a cell. (p. 81)
membrana celular capa doble de fosfolípidos que forma una barrera entre la célula y el medio que la rodea, y que controla el flujo de materiales hacia dentro y hacia fuera de la célula.

cell theory theory that states that all organisms are made of cells, all cells are produced by other living cells, and the cell is the most basic unit of life. (p. 71)
teoría celular establece que todos los organismos están formados por células, que todas las células proceden de otras células vivas y que la célula es la unidad básica de la vida.

cellular immunity immune response that relies on T cells to destroy infected body cells. (p. 952)
inmunidad celular respuesta inmune que depende de las células T para atacar las células infectadas del cuerpo.

cellular respiration process of producing ATP by breaking down carbon-based molecules when oxygen is present. (p. 113)
respiración celular proceso de producción de ATP mediante la descomposición de moléculas de carbono en presencia de oxígeno.

cell wall rigid structure that gives protection, support, and shape to cells in plants, algae, fungi, and bacteria. (p. 79)
pared celular estructura rígida que proteje, sustenta y da forma a las células de las plantas, algas, hongos y bacterias.

Glossary

Cenozoic geologic time period that began 65 million years ago and continues today. (p. 378)
Cenozoico período geológico que empezó hace 65 millones de años y que se extiende hasta la actualidad.

central dogma theory that states that, in cells, information only flows from DNA to RNA to proteins. (p. 239)
dogma central teoría que formula que la información en las células siempre fluye del ADN al ARN y luego a las proteínas.

central nervous system (CNS) part of the nervous system that interprets messages from other nerves in the body; includes the brain and spinal cord. (p. 875)
sistema nervioso central parte del sistema nervioso encargada de interpretar los mensajes recibidos de otros nervios del cuerpo; consta del cerebro y de la médula espinal.

centriole (SEHN-tree-OHL) small cylinder-shaped organelle made of protein tubes arranged in a circle; aids mitosis. (p. 78)
centriolo orgánulo celular con forma de pequeño cilindro formado por una serie de tubos de proteínas en disposición circular; participa en la reproducción celular.

centromere (SEHN-truh-MEER) region of condensed chromosome that looks pinched; where spindle fibers attach during meiosis and mitosis. (p. 139)
centrómero región de condensación del cromosoma donde se une el huso durante la meiosis y la mitosis.

cephalothorax (SEHF-uh-luh-THAWR-AKS) region of a crustacean body where the head and thorax meet. (p. 735)
cefalotórax región del cuerpo de los crustáceos donde se unen la cabeza y el tórax.

cerebellum (SEHR-uh-BEHL-uhm) part of the brain that coordinates and regulates all voluntary muscle movement and maintains posture and balance. (p. 888)
cerebelo parte del encéfalo que coordina y regula todos los movimientos musculares voluntarios, y que permite mantener la postura y el equilibrio.

cerebral cortex layer of gray matter on the surface of the cerebrum that receives information and generates responses. (p. 887)
corteza cerebral capa de material gris situada en la superficie del cerebro que se encarga de recibir información y de generar respuestas.

cerebrum (SEHR-uh-bruhm) largest part of the brain, coordinating movement, thought, reasoning, and memory; includes the cerebral cortex and the white matter beneath it. (p. 886)
cerebro la parte más grande del encéfalo que se encarga de coordinar el movimiento, el pensamiento, el razonamiento y la memoria; incluye la corteza cerebral y la materia blanca que se encuentra debajo de ésta.

chaparral (SHAP-uh-RAL) biome characterized by hot, dry summers and cool, moist winters; also called Mediterranean shrubland. (p. 466)
chaparral bioma caracterizado por veranos secos y calurosos e inviernos frescos y húmedos; también se conoce como matorral mediterráneo.

chelicerate arthropod that lacks antennae and has four pairs of walking legs and a pair of fanglike mouth parts. (p. 740)
quelicerado artrópodo sin antenas con cuatro pares de patas y una boca de dos piezas en forma de colmillos.

chemical reaction process by which substances change into different substances through the breaking and forming of chemical bonds. (p. 50)
reacción química proceso mediante el cual una sustancia se transforma en otra sustancia diferente al romperse sus enlaces químicos y formarse otros nuevos.

chemosynthesis (KEE-mo-SIHN-thih-sihs) process by which ATP is synthesized by using chemicals as an energy source instead of light. (pp. 102, 407)
quimiosíntesis proceso de síntesis del ATP cuya fuente de energía no es la luz, sino determinadas sustancias químicas.

childhood period of life from age two until puberty. (p. 1042)
infancia periodo de la vida comprendido entre los dos años y la pubertad.

chitin tough, protective polysaccharide that makes up arthropod skeletons and the cell walls of some fungi. (pp. 589; 730)
quitina polisacárido duro que forma los exoesqueletos de los artrópodos y las paredes celulares de algunos hongos.

chlorophyll (KLAWR-uh-fihl) light-absorbing pigment molecule in photosynthetic organisms. (p. 103)
clorofila molécula pigmentaria de los organismos fotosintéticos que absorbe la luz.

chloroplast (KLAWR-uh-PLAST) organelle composed of numerous membranes that are used to convert solar energy into chemical energy; contains chlorophyll. (p. 79)
colorplasto orgánulo compuesto de numerosas membranes cuya funcción es transformer la energía solar en energía química; contiene clorofila.

chordate any animal having, at some stage in development, a hollow nerve cord, pharyngeal slits, and tail. (p. 758)
cordado todo tipo de animal que en alguna fase de su desarrollo tiene un cordón nervioso dorsal, hendiduras faríngeas y cola.

chromatid (KROH-muh-tihd) one half of a duplicated chromosome. (p. 139)
cromátida mitad de un cromosoma duplicado.

chromatin loose combination of DNA and proteins that is present during interphase. (p. 139)
cromatina conjunto de ADN y proteínas que se manifiesta durante la interfase.

chromosome long, continuous thread of DNA that consists of numerous genes and regulatory information. (p. 138)
cromosoma un largo y continuo filamento de ADN formado por numerosos genes y que almacena información genética.

chyme (kym) partially digested, semi-liquid mixture that passes from the stomach to the small intestine. (p. 979)
quimo mezcla semi líquida parcialmente digerida que pasa del estómago al intestino delgado.

cilia (singular: *cilium*) short hairlike structures that cover some or all of the cell surface and help the organism swim and capture food. (p. 578)
cilios estructuras en forma de pelillos cortos que cubren total o parcialmente la superficie de determinadas células y que ayuda a los organismos a nadar y capturar alimentos.

circadian rhythm daily cycle of activity that occurs over a 24-hour period of time. (p. 820)
ritmo circadiano ciclo diario de actividad que abarca 24 horas.

circulatory system body system that transports nutrients and wastes between various body tissues; includes heart, blood, and blood vessels. (p. 910)
sistema circulatorio sistema corporal encargado de transportar nutrientes y desechos entre diversos tejidos corporales; consta del corazón, la sangre y los vasos sanguíneos.

citric acid cycle *see* Krebs cycle. (p. 115)
ciclo del ácido cítrico *véase* ciclo de Krebs.

cladistics method of organizing species by evolutionary relationships in which species are grouped according to the order that they diverged from their ancestral line. (p. 525)
cladismo método de clasificación de las especies según su parentesco evolutivo en el que las especies son agrupadas en el orden en que se separaron de su linaje ancestral.

cladogram diagram that displays proposed evolutionary relationships among a group of species. (p. 525)
cladograma diagrama en el que se presentan los parentescos evolutivos propuestos de un grupo determinado de especies.

classical conditioning process by which an organism learns to associate a previously neutral stimulus with a reward or punishment. (p. 826)
condicionamiento clásico proceso mediante el cual un organismo aprende a asociar un estímulo, que previamente había sido neutro, con un premio o castigo.

climate average long-term weather pattern of a region. (p. 458)
clima promedio de valores del tiempo en una región a largo plazo.

clone genetically identical copy of a single gene or an entire organism. (p. 275)
clon copia genéticamente exacta de un gen o de un organismo completo.

codominance heterozygous genotype that equally expresses the traits from both alleles. (p. 205)
codominancia genotipo heterocigoto que expresa equitativamente los rasgos de ambos alelos.

codon sequence of three nucleotides that codes for one amino acid. (p. 243)
codón secuencia de tres nucleotides que codifica un aminoácido.

coelom fluid-filled space that is completely covered by muscle. (p. 714)
celoma cavidad llena de líquido cubierta enteramente por el músculo.

coevolution process in which two or more species evolve in response to changes in each other. (p. 349)
coevolución proceso mediante el cual dos o más especies evolucionan a consecuencia de cambios producidos en cada uno de ellas.

cognition mental process of knowing, including aspects such as awareness, perception, reasoning, and judgment. (p. 837)
cognición conjunto de procesos mentales cuya función es el conocimiento y que incluyen la conciencia, la percepción, el razonamiento y el juicio.

cohesion attraction between molecules of the same substance. (p. 41)
cohesión atracción entre moléculas de una misma sustancia.

cohesion tension theory theory that explains how the physical properties of water allow it to move through the xylem of plants. (p. 643)
teoría de la tensión-cohesión teoría que explica el modo en que las propiedades físicas del agua permiten que ésta fluya a través del xilema de las plantas.

collagen three-stranded protein, unique to animals, that combines to form strong, flexible fibers. (p. 697)
colágeno proteína animal compuesta por tres cadenas que se enlazan para formar fibras resistentes y flexibles.

collenchyma cell elongated cells with unevenly thick walls that form a supportive tissue of plants. (p. 640)
célula del colénquima célula alargada con paredes de grosor irregular que forma el tejido de sostén de las plantas.

commensalism ecological relationship in which one species receives a benefit but the other species is not affected one way or another. (p. 432)
comensalismo relación ecológica entre dos especies en la que una se beneficia sin perjudicar ni beneficiar a la otra.

community collection of all of the different populations that live in one area. (p. 397)
comunidad conjunto de todas las poblaciones que viven en un área determinada.

competition ecological relationship in which two organisms attempt to obtain the same resource. (p. 431)
competencia relación ecológica en la que dos organismos tratan de obtener el mismo recurso.

competitive exclusion theory that states that no two species can occupy the same niche at the same time. (p. 429)
exclusión competitiva teoría según la cual dos especies distintas no pueden ocupar el mismo nicho al mismo tiempo.

Glossary

complete digestive tract digestive system that has two openings, a mouth and an anus, that are at opposite ends of a continuous tube. (p. 712)
tubo digestivo completo sistema digestivo con dos aperturas, la boca y el ano, situadas en los extremos opuestos de un tubo continuo.

complete metamorphosis process by which immature organisms change their body form before becoming an adult. (p. 744)
metamorfosis completa proceso mediante el cual se van produciendo cambios en los organismos inmaduros antes de llegar a adultos.

compound substance made of atoms of different elements that are bonded together in a particular ratio. (p. 37)
compuesto sustancia formada por átomos de diversos elementos combinados en una proporción determinada.

concentration gradient difference in the concentration of a substance from one location to another. (p. 85)
gradiente de concentración diferencia en la concentración de una sustancia entre un lugar y otro.

cone reproductive structure of gymnosperms inside of which the female gamete is fertilized and seeds are produced. (p. 621)
cono estructura reproductora de las gimnospermas en cuyo interior se fertiliza el gameto femenino y se producen semillas.

cone cell sensory neuron in the eye that detects color. (p. 881)
cono (célula) neurona sensorial del ojo que detecta el color.

coniferous tree that retains its needles year-round and reproduces with cones. (p. 465)
conífera árbol que mantiene sus hojas durante todo el año y que se reproduce mediante conos.

conjugation process by which a prokaryote transfers part of its chromosome to another prokaryote. (p. 558)
conjugación proceso mediante el cual un procarionte transfiere parte de su cromosoma a otro procarionte.

constant condition that is controlled so that it does not change during an experiment. (p. 16)
constante condición controlada de un experimento que no varía en el transcurso del mismo.

consumer organism that obtains its energy and nutrients by eating other organisms. (p. 406)
consumidor organismo que obtiene su energía y nutrientes mediante la ingestión de otros organismos.

convergent evolution evolution toward similar characteristics in unrelated species, resulting from adaptations to similar environmental conditions. (p. 348)
evolución convergente evolución hacia características similares en especies no relacionadas, que resulta de adaptaciones a condiciones ambientales similares.

coral reef ocean habitat found in the shallow coastal waters in a tropical climate. (p. 470)
arrecife de coral hábitat oceánico que se encuentra en aguas costeras poco profundas de climas tropicales.

corpus luteum (KAWR-puhs LOO-tee-uhm) follicle after ovulation; also called a yellow body because of its yellow color. (p. 1029)
cuerpo lúteo folículo que aparece después de la ovulación; se conoce también como cuerpo amarillo a causa de su color.

cotyledon (KAHT-uhl-EED-uhn) embryonic leaf inside of a seed. (p. 625)
cotiledón hoja embriónica que se forma en el interior de la semilla.

countercurrent flow flow of water opposite that of the flow of blood in a fish's gills. (p. 764)
flujo contracorriente flujo de agua en sentido opuesto al flujo de la sangre en las branquias de los peces.

covalent bond chemical bond formed when two atoms share one or more pairs of electrons. (p. 39)
enlace covalente enlace químico que se forma cuando dos átomos comparten uno o más pares de electrones.

cross mating of two organisms. (p. 178)
cruzamiento apareamiento de dos organismos.

crossing over exchange of chromosome segments between homologous chromosomes during meiosis I. (p. 190)
entrecruzamiento intercambio de segmentos de cromosomas entre cromosomas homólogos durante la meiosis I.

crustacean any of the aquatic arthropods, such as lobsters, crabs, and shrimps, that has a segmented body, an exoskeleton, and paired, jointed limbs. (p. 735)
crustáceo artrópodo acuático, como las langostas, los cangrejos y los camarones, que se caracteriza por tener un cuerpo segmentado, un exoesqueleto y pares de extremidades articuladas.

cultural behavior behavior that is passed between members of the same population by learning and not natural selection. (p. 839)
comportamiento cultural comportamiento que se transmite entre los miembros de una misma población, no por selección natural, sino mediante un proceso de aprendizaje.

cuticle in plants, a waxy layer that holds in moisture; in insects, a tough exoskeleton made of nonliving material. (pp. 614; 716)
cutícula en las plantas, es una capa de cera que mantiene la humedad; en los insectos, exoesqueleto duro de material inerte.

cyanobacteria (singular: *cyanobaterium*) bacteria that can carry out photosynthesis. (p. 372)
cianobacteria bacteria capaz de realizar la fotosíntesis.

cytokinesis (SY-toh-kuh-NEE-sihs) process by which the cell cytoplasm divides. (p. 135)
citocinesis proceso mediante el cual el citoplasma celular se divide.

cytokinin (SY-tuh-KY-nihn) plant hormone that stimulates the final stage of cell division, cytokinesis; also involved in the growth of side branches. (p. 681)
citoquinina hormona vegetal que estimula la última fase de la división celular: la citocinesis; también participa en el crecimiento de las ramas laterales.

cytoplasm jellylike substance inside cells that contains molecules and in some cells organelles. (p. 72)
citoplasma sustancia gelatinosa del interior de las células que contiene diversos tipos de moléculas y, en algunas células, orgánulos.

cytoskeleton network of proteins, such as microtubules and microfilaments, inside a eukaryotic cell that supports and shapes the cell. (p. 73)
citoesqueleto red proteica, como los microtúbulos y los microfilamentos, dentro de una célula eucariótica que da soporte y define la forma de la célula.

D

data (singular: *datum*) observations and measurements recorded during an experiment. (p. 14)
datos observaciones y medidas registrados en el transcurso de un experimento.

deciduous tree that has adapted to winter temperatures by dropping its leaves and going dormant during the cold season. (p. 465)
caducifolio árbol que pierde su foliaje y entra en un período de letargo para adaptarse a las temperaturas invernales.

decomposer detritivore that breaks down organic matter into simpler compounds, returning nutrients back into an ecosystem. (p. 409)
descomponedor detritívoro que, al descomponer la materia orgánica en compuestos más sencillos, devuelve al ecosistema sus nutrientes básicos.

dendrite branchlike extension of a neuron that receives impulses from neighboring neurons. (p. 876)
dendrita prolongación ramificada de la neurona que recibe impulsos eléctricos de las neuronas adyacentes.

density-dependent limiting factor environmental resistance that affects a population that has become overly crowded. (p. 443)
factor limitativo dependiente de la densidad resistencia ambiental que afecta a una población sometida a una densidad demográfica excesiva.

density-independent limiting factor environmental resistance that affects a population regardless of population density. (p. 444)
factor limitativo independiente de la densidad resistencia ambiental que afecta a una población sin importar su densidad demográfica.

dependent variable experimental data collected through observation and measurement. (p. 16)
variable dependiente datos de una investigación recolectados por medio de la observación y de la medición.

depressant drug that causes fewer signals to be transmitted between neurons. (p. 894)
depresor medicamento que reduce la transmisión de señales entre las neuronas.

derived characteristic trait that differs in structure or function from that found in the ancestral line for a group of species; used in constructing cladograms. (p. 525)
caracter derivado rasgo que difiere, en su estructura o función, del hallado en un linaje ancestral de un grupo de especies; se usa para crear cladogramas.

dermal tissue tissue system that covers the outside of plants and animals. (p. 642)
tejido dérmico sistema de tejidos que cubre la superficie de los animales y las plantas.

dermis second layer of skin that includes structural proteins, blood vessels, glands, and hair follicles. (p. 1015)
dermis segunda capa de piel formada por proteínas estructurales, vasos sanguíneos y folículos capilares.

desensitization process by which neurons in the brain break down neurotransmitter receptors in response to a larger amount of neurotransmitter in the synapse than usual. (p. 893)
desensibilización proceso mediante el cual las neuronas del cerebro inactivan los receptores de los neurotransmisores como respuesta a una cantidad de neurotransmisores mayor de lo habitual en la sinapsis.

desert biome characterized by a very dry climate. (p. 464)
desierto bioma caracterizado por un clima muy seco.

determination process by which stem cells become committed to develop into only one type of cell. (p. 852)
determinación celular proceso mediante el cual las células madre se desarrollan en un tipo específico de célula.

detritivore organism that eats dead organic matter. (p. 409)
detritívoro organismo que se alimenta de materia orgánica muerta.

deuterostome animal development in which the animal's anus develops before the mouth. (p. 702)
deuterostomia desarrollo animal en el que el ano del animal se desarrolla antes que la boca.

dialysis treatment in which a patient's blood is filtered through a machine, the waste is removed, and the cleaned blood is returned to the patient's body. (p. 991)
diálisis tratamiento médico que consiste en filtrar la sangre del paciente mediante una máquina que elimina los desechos y devuelve la sangre purificada al cuerpo del paciente.

diaphragm thin muscle below the rib cage that controls the flow of air into and out of the lungs. (p. 912)
diafragma músculo delgado situado debajo de la caja torácica que controla el flujo de aire hacia el interior y el exterior de los pulmones.

R49

Glossary

diastolic pressure (DY-uh-STAHL-ihk) pressure in an artery when the left ventricle relaxes. (p. 923)
presión diastólica presión en la arteria en el momento en que se relaja el ventrículo izquierdo.

dicot (DY-KAHT) flowering plant whose embryos have two cotyledons. (p. 626)
dicotiledónea planta con flor cuyos embriones tienen dos cotiledones.

differentiation process by which committed cells acquire the structures and functions of highly specialized cells. (p. 853)
diferenciación celular proceso mediante el cual ciertas células adquieren estructuras y funciones altamente especializadas.

diffusion movement of dissolved molecules in a fluid or gas from a region of higher concentration to a region of lower concentration. (p. 85)
difusión movimiento de las moléculas disueltas en un líquido o gas desde una región de alta concentración a otra región de menor concentración.

digestion process by which large, complex molecules are broken down into smaller molecules that can be used by cells. (p. 977)
digestión proceso mediante el cual grandes y complejas moléculas se descomponen en moléculas más pequeñas que pueden ser absorbidas por las células.

digestive system body system that digests food; includes mouth, esophagus, stomach, pancreas, intestines, liver, gallbladder, rectum, and anus. (p. 977)
sistema digestivo sistema corporal encargado de la digestión de los alimentos; consta de la boca, el esófago, el estómago, el páncreas, los intestinos, el hígado, la vesícula biliar, el recto y el ano.

dihybrid cross cross, or mating, between organisms involving two pairs of contrasting traits. (p. 186)
cruzamiento dihíbrido cruzamiento o apareamiento entre organismos que tienen dos pares de rasgos opuestos.

diploid (DIHP-LOYD) cell that has two copies of each chromosome, one from an egg and one from a sperm. (p. 170)
diploide celula que tiene dos copias de cada cromosoma, una proveniente de un óvulo y la otra de un espermatozoide.

directional selection pathway of natural selection in which one uncommon phenotype is selected over a more common phenotype. (p. 331)
selección direccional proceso de selección natural en el que se favorece un fenotipo menos común sobre un fenotipo más común.

disruptive selection pathway of natural selection in which two opposite, but equally uncommon, phenotypes are selected over the most common phenotype. (p. 333)
selección disruptiva proceso de selección natural en el que se favorece a dos fenotipos opuestos, pero igualmente poco comunes, sobre el fenotipo común.

divergent evolution evolution of one or more closely related species into different species; resulting from adaptations to different environmental conditions. (p. 348)
evolución divergente evolución de una o más especies afines que lleva a la formación de especies diferentes como resultado de adaptaciones a diversas condiciones ambientales.

DNA; deoxyribonucleic acid (dee-AHK-see-RY-boh-noo-KLEE-ihk) molecule that stores genetic information in all organisms. (p. 6)
ADN (ácido desoxirribonucleico) molécula que almacena la información genética de todos los organismos.

DNA fingerprint unique sequence of DNA base pairs that can be used to identify a person at the molecular level. (p. 272)
identificación por ADN secuencia única de pares de bases de ADN que permite la identificación de una persona a nivel molecular.

DNA microarray research tool used to study gene expression. (p. 282)
micromatriz de material genético (biochip) instrumento de investigación usado para estudiar la expresión de los genes.

DNA polymerase (PAHL-uh-muh-RAYS) enzyme that makes bonds between nucleotides, forming an identical strand of DNA during replication. (p. 236)
ADN polimerasa enzima que establece enlaces entre los nucleótidos y que permite la formación de cadenas idénticas de ADN durante el proceso de replicación.

dominant allele that is expressed when two different alleles are present in an organism's genotype. (p. 181)
dominante el alelo que se expresa de entre dos alelos diferentes que integran el genotipo de un organismo determinado.

dormancy state of inactivity during which an organism or embryo is not growing. (p. 674)
letargo periodo de inactividad durante el cual un organismo o embrión no crece.

double fertilization process by which two sperm of a flowering plant join with an egg and a polar body, forming an embryo and endosperm. (p. 670)
fertilización doble proceso mediante el cual dos gametos masculinos de una planta angiosperma se combinan con un óvulo y un núcleo polar para dar lugar al embrión y al endosperma.

double helix model that compares the structure of a DNA molecule, in which two strands wind around one another, to that of a twisted ladder. (p. 232)
doble hélice modelo mediante el cual se representa la estructura molecular del ADN como dos cadenas que giran sobre sí mismas, como una escalera espiroidal.

R50

E

ecological equivalents organisms that share a similar niche but live in different geographical regions. (p. 430)
equivalentes ecológicos organismos que tienen nichos ecológicos similares, pero que viven en diferentes zonas geográficas.

ecological footprint amount of land necessary to produce and maintain enough food, water, shelter, energy, and waste. (p. 487)
huella ecológica espacio que requiere una población humana para producir y mantener suficiente alimento, agua, alojamiento y energía, y para contener sus desperdicios.

ecological niche all of the physical, chemical, and biological factors that a species needs to survive, stay healthy, and reproduce in an ecosystem. (p. 428)
nicho ecológico conjunto de factores físicos, químicos y biológicos que una especie requiere para sobrevivir de manera saludable y reproducirse en un ecosistema determinado.

ecology study of the interactions among living things and their surroundings. (p. 396)
ecología estudio de las interacciones entre los seres vivos y su entorno.

ecosystem collection of organisms and nonliving things, such as climate, soil, water, and rocks, in an area. (pp. 7; 397)
ecosistema conjunto de organismos y factores físicos, como el clima, el suelo, el agua y las rocas, que caracterizan una zona determinada.

ectotherm organism that regulates its body temperature by exchanging heat with its environment. (p. 791)
poiquilotermo organismo que regula su temperatura corporal mediante el intercambio de calor con el ambiente.

egg female gamete. (p. 176)
óvulo gameto femenino.

electron transport chain series of proteins in the thylakoid and mitochondrial membranes that aid in converting ADP to ATP by transferring electrons. (p. 109)
cadena de transporte de electrones serie de proteínas de las membranas de las mitocondrias y los tilacoides que contribuyen a transformar ADP en ATP mediante la transferencia de electrones.

element substance made of only one type of atom that cannot be broken down by chemical means. (p. 36)
elemento sustancia formada por un solo tipo de átomo que no se puede descomponer por medios químicos.

embryo stage of development after the fertilized cell implants into the uterus but before the cells take on a recognizable shape. (p. 1034)
embrión fase de desarrollo a partir de la implantación del óvulo fertilizado en el útero, anterior a la etapa en que las células adquieren una forma reconocible.

emigration movement of individuals out of a population. (p. 440)
emigración flujo de individuos que abandonan una población.

emphysema (EHM-fih-SEE-muh) condition of the lungs in which the surface area of alveoli decreases, making breathing difficult. (p. 916)
enfisema enfermedad de los pulmones que causa una reducción en la superficie de los alvéolos y, en consecuencia, dificulta la respiración.

endocrine system (EHN-duh-krihn) body system that controls growth, development, and responses to the environment by releasing chemical signals into the bloodstream. (p. 874)
sistema endocrino sistema corporal que controla el crecimiento, el desarrollo y las respuestas al entorno, mediante la liberación de señales químicas al torrente sanguíneo.

endocytosis (EHN-doh-sy-TOH-sihs) uptake of liquids or large molecules into a cell by inward folding of the cell membrane. (p. 90)
endocitosis captación celular de líquidos o de grandes moléculas mediante una invaginación de la membrana hacia el interior de la célula.

endometrium (EHN-doh-MEE-tree-uhm) lining of the uterus. (p. 1028)
endometrio recubrimiento interior del útero.

endoplasmic reticulum (EHN-duh-PLAZ-mihk rih-TIHK-yuh-luhm) interconnected network of thin, folded membranes that produce, process, and distribute proteins. (p. 76)
retículo endoplasmático red de finas membranas interconectadas y plegadas que producen, procesan y distribuyen proteínas.

endoskeleton internal skeleton built of bone or cartilage. (p. 759)
endoesqueleto esqueleto interno formado por huesos y cartílagos.

endosperm tissue within seeds of flowering plants that nourishes an embryo. (p. 670)
endosperma tejido de reserva dentro de las semillas de las plantas con flor que abastece el embrión.

endospore prokaryotic cell with a thick, protective wall surrounding its DNA. (p. 558)
endospora célula procariótica cuyo ADN está protegido por una gruesa pared.

endosymbiosis ecological relationship in which one organism lives within the body of another. (p. 373)
endosimbiosis relación ecológica en la que un organismo vive en el interior de otro.

endotherm organism that produces its own heat through metabolic processes. (p. 791)
endotermo organismo que regula la temperatura de su cuerpo mediante sus propios procesos metabólicos.

R51

endothermic chemical reaction that requires a net input of energy. (p. 53)
endotérmica reacción química que requiere un aporte neto de energía.

energy pyramid diagram that compares energy used by producers, primary consumers, and other trophic levels. (p. 418)
pirámide de energía diagrama mediante el cual se compara la energía usada por los productores, los consumidores primarios y otros niveles tróficos.

enzyme protein that catalyzes chemical reactions for organisms. (p. 55)
enzima proteína que cataliza reacciones químicas para los organismos.

epidemic rapid outbreak of a disease that affects many people. (p. 553)
epidemia aparición repentina de una enfermedad que afecta a muchas personas.

epidermis outermost layer of skin that consists mainly of dead skin cells, and provides a barrier to pathogens. (p. 1014)
epidermis primera capa de piel, que consta principalmente de células epiteliales muertas y que constituye una barrera para los patógenos.

epididymis coiled tube through which sperm leave the testes and enter the vas deferens. (p. 1026)
epidídimo tubo enrollado a través del cuál los espermatozoides salen de los testículos y pasan al conducto deferente.

epoch smallest unit of geologic time, lasting several million years. (p. 367)
época unidad más pequeña de tiempo geológico, que dura varios millones de años.

equilibrium (EE-kwuh-LIHB-ree-uhm) condition in which reactants and products of a chemical reaction are formed at the same rate. (p. 51)
equilibrio químico estado en el que los reactivos y los productos de una reacción química se forman a la misma velocidad.

era second largest unit of geologic time, lasting tens to hundreds of millions of years and consisting of two or more periods. (p. 367)
era segunda unidad más amplia de tiempo geológico; que abarca entre decenas y cientos de millones de años y consta de dos o más períodos.

esophagus (ih-SAHF-uh-guhs) tube-shaped tissue of the digestive system that connects the mouth to the stomach. (p. 978)
esófago tejido en forma de tubo del sistema digestivo que conecta la boca con el estómago.

estrogen steroid hormone that is found in greater quantities in women than men and contributes to female sexual characteristics and development. (p. 1024)
estrógeno hormona esteroide que abunda más en las mujeres que en los hombres, y que contribuye al desarrollo de las características sexuales femeninas.

estuary partially enclosed body of water found where a river flows into the ocean. (p. 471)
estuario masa de agua parcialmente cerrada donde un río desemboca en el océano.

ethnobotany study of how various cultures use plants. (p. 629)
etnobotánica estudio del conocimiento que tienen las culturas sobre el uso de las plantas.

ethylene (EHTH-uh-LEEN) plant hormone that is produced in fruits and causes them to ripen. (p. 681)
etileno hormona vegetal que se produce en las frutas y que las hace madurar.

Eukarya one of the three domains of life, contains all eukaryotes in kingdoms Protista, Plantae, Fungi, and Animalia. (p. 534)
Eukarya uno de los tres dominios de la vida; consta de todos los eucariotas de los reinos protistas, plantashongos y animales.

eukaryotic cell (yoo-KAR-ee-AHT-ihk) cell that has a nucleus and other membrane-bound organelles. (p. 72)
célula eucariota célula que consta de un núcleo y de otros orgánulos limitados por una membrana.

eusocial organism population in which the role of each organism is specialized and not all of the organisms will reproduce. (p. 834)
eusocial población de organismos en la que todos tienen una función especializada y en la que algunos de ellos no se reproducen.

eutherian mammal that gives birth to live young that have completed fetal development. (p. 809)
euterio mamífero cuyas crías nacen tras un desarrollo fetal completo.

evolution change in a species over time (p. 10); process of biological change by which descendents come to differ from their ancestors. (p. 298)
evolución proceso de cambio de las especies a través del tiempo; proceso de cambios biológicos a través del cual los descendientes se diferencian de sus ancestros.

excretory system body system that collects and eliminates wastes from the body; includes the kidneys and bladder. (p. 986)
sistema excretor sistema corporal que recoge y elimina los desechos del organismo; consta de los riñones y la vejiga urinaria.

exocytosis (EHK-soh-sy-TOH-sihs) release of substances out a cell by the fusion of a vesicle with the membrane. (p. 91)
exocitosis expulsión de sustancias de una célula mediante la fusión de una vesícula citoplasmática con la membrana celular.

exon sequence of DNA that codes information for protein synthesis. (p. 251)
exón secuencia de ADN que codifica la información para la síntesis de las proteínas.

exoskeleton hard outer structure, such as the shell of an insect or crustacean, that provides protection and support for the organism. (p. 730)
exoesqueleto estructura exterior dura como, por ejemplo, el caparazón de un crustáceo, que protege y sustenta al organismo.

exothermic chemical reaction that yields a net release of energy in the form of heat. (p. 53)
exotérmica reacción química que, al producirse, libera energía en forma calor.

experiment process that tests a hypothesis by collecting information under controlled conditions. (p. 16)
experimento procedimiento mediante el cual se trata de comprobar una hipótesis mediante la recolección de datos bajo condiciones controladas.

exponential growth dramatic increase in population over a short period of time. (p. 441)
crecimiento exponencial intenso incremento de población en un breve espacio de tiempo.

extinction elimination of a species from Earth. (p. 350)
extinción desaparición de una especie o grupo de especies de la Tierra.

F

facilitated diffusion diffusion of molecules assisted by protein channels that pierce a cell membrane. (p. 87)
difusión facilitada difusión de moléculas asistida mediante canales de proteínas que perforan la membrana celular.

facultative aerobe organism that can live with or without oxygen. (p. 555)
aerobio facultativo organismo capaz de vivir con o sin oxígeno.

fallopian tube tube of connective tissue that attaches the ovary to the uterus in the female reproductive system and in which fertilization occurs. (p. 1024)
trompa de Falopio conducto de tejido conjuntivo que conecta el ovario con el útero en el sistema reproductor femenino, y donde se produce la fertilización.

fatty acid hydrocarbon chain often bonded to glycerol in a lipid. (p. 46)
ácido graso cadena de hidrocarbono que suele enlazarce con los glicéridos de un lípido.

feedback information that is compared with a set of ideal values and aids in maintaining homeostasis. (p. 859)
retroalimentación información que se compara con un grupo de valores ideales y que contribuye al mantenimiento de la homeóstasis.

fermentation anaerobic process by which ATP is produced by glycolysis. (p. 122)
fermentación proceso anaeróbico que da lugar al ATP mediante la glicólisis.

fertilization fusion of an egg and sperm cell. (p. 170)
fertilización fusión de un gameto masculino y uno femenino.

fetus unborn offspring from the end of the eighth week after conception to the moment of birth. (p. 1036)
feto cría no nacida desde el final de la octava semana después de la concepción hasta el momento del nacimiento.

fibrous root root system made up of many threadlike members of more or less equal length. (p. 649)
raíces fibrosas sistema radical compuesto de una multitud de filamentos que tienen una longitud aproximadamente igual.

filter feeder animal that eats by straining particles from water. (p. 706)
organismo filtrador animal que se alimenta mediante la filtración de partículas del agua.

fitness measure of an organism's ability to survive and produce offspring relative to other members of a population. (p. 307)
aptitud biológica capacidad de un organismo determinado para sobrevivir y producir descendencia en relación con los demás miembros de una población.

flagellum (plural: *flagella*) whiplike structure outside of a cell that is used for movement. (p. 556)
flagelo estructura en forma de látigo del exterior de determinadas células que les permite moverse en su medio.

flower reproductive structure of an angiosperm. (p. 622)
flor sistema reproductor de una angiosperma.

fluid mosaic model model that describes the arrangement and movement of the molecules that make up a cell membrane. (p. 82)
modelo de mosaico fluido modelo que describe la disposición y movimiento de las moléculas que conforman la membrana celular.

follicle collection of cells that surrounds and nourishes an egg while it is in the ovary. (p. 1028)
folículo conjunto de células que rodean y nutren al óvulo mientras éste permanece en el ovario.

food chain model that links organisms by their feeding relationships. (p. 408)
cadena alimentaria modelo que relaciona los organismos según sus interacciones alimentarias.

food web model that shows the complex network of feeding relationships within an ecosystem. (p. 411)
red alimentaria modelo que representa una red compleja de relaciones alimentarias en un ecosistema determinado.

fossil trace of an organism from the past. (p. 300)
fósil huella de un organismo del pasado.

R53

founder effect genetic drift that occurs after a small number of individuals colonize a new area. (p. 336)
efecto fundador deriva genética que se produce cuando un pequeño número de individuos coloniza una nueva región.

frameshift mutation mutation that involves the insertion or deletion of a nucleotide in the DNA sequence. (p. 252)
mutación del marco de lectura mutación que implica la incorporación o la eliminación de un nucleótido en una secuencia de ADN.

fruit fertilized and mature ovary of a flower. (p. 622)
fruto ovario fertilizado y maduro de una flor.

fruiting body spore-producing structure of a fungus that grows above ground. (p. 590)
esporocarpo estructura productora de esporas de un hongo que crece sobre la tierra.

G

gamete sex cell; an egg or a sperm cell. (p. 168)
gameto célula sexual; óvulo o espermatozoide.

gametogenesis (guh-MEE-tuh-JEHN-ih-sihs) process by which gametes are produced through the combination of meiosis and other maturational changes. (p. 176)
gametogénesis proceso de producción de gametos mediante una combinación de meiosis y otros cambios de maduración.

gametophyte (guh-MEE-tuh-FYT) haploid, gamete-producing phase in a plant life cycle. (p. 664)
gametofito fase de producción de gametos o células sexuales haploides en el ciclo de vida de las plantas.

gastrovascular cavity saclike digestive space. (p. 708)
cavidad gastrovascular espacio digestivo en forma de bolsa.

gel electrophoresis (ih-LEHK-troh-fuh-REE-sihs) method of separating various lengths of DNA strands by applying an electrical current to a gel. (p. 266)
electroforesis en gel método de separación de fragmentos de ADN mediante la aplicación de una corriente eléctrica a un gel.

gene specific region of DNA that codes for a particular protein. (pp. 23; 180)
gen parte específica del ADN con información codificada para sintetizar una proteína.

gene flow physical movement of alleles from one population to another. (p. 335)
flujo génico desplazamiento físico de alelos de una población a otra.

gene knockout genetic manipulation in which one or more of an organism's genes are prevented from being expressed. (p. 279)
supresión génica manipulación genética mediante la cual se anula la capacidad de expresarse de uno o más genes de un organismo determinado.

gene pool collection of alleles found in all of the individuals of a population. (p. 328)
acervo genético colección de alelos de todos los individuos de una población determinada.

generalist species that does not rely on a single source of prey. (p. 409)
generalista especie que no depende de un solo tipo de presa.

gene sequencing process of determining the order of DNA nucleotides in genes and genomes. (p. 280)
secuenciación génica proceso de determinación del orden de los nucleótidos de ADN en los genes y en los genomas.

gene therapy procedure to treat a disease in which a defective or missing gene is replaced or a new gene is inserted into a patient's genome. (p. 285)
terapia génica procedimiento para el tratamiento de una enfermedad en el que un gen defectuoso o ausente se reemplaza por uno sano que se inserta en el genoma del paciente.

genetic drift change in allele frequencies due to chance alone, occurring most commonly in small populations. (p. 336)
deriva genética cambio en las frecuencias de alelos que se produce, sobre todo, en poblaciones pequeñas.

genetic engineering process of changing an organism's DNA to give the organism new traits. (p. 276)
ingeniería genética proceso de modifación del ADN de un organismo con el fin de dotarlo de nuevos rasgos.

genetic linkage tendency for genes located close together on the same chromosome to be inherited together. (p. 191)
ligamiento genético tendencia de los genes que se encuentran muy próximos en un cromosoma a ser transmitidos juntos a la descendencia.

genetics study of the heredity patterns and variation of organisms. (p. 177)
genética estudio de los patrones hereditarios y de la variación de los organismos.

genetic screening process of testing DNA to determine the chance a person has, or might pass on, a genetic disorder. (p. 284)
análisis genético proceso de análisis de ADN para determinar las probabilidades que tiene una persona de contraer o transmitir una enfermedad genética.

genome all of an organism's genetic material. (p. 181)
genoma todo el material genético de un organismo determinado.

genomics (juh-NOH-mihks) study and comparison of genomes within a single species or among different species. (pp. 23, 280)
genómica estudio comparativo de los genomas de una misma especie y de especies diferentes.

genotype (JEHN-uh-TYP) collection of all of an organism's genetic information that codes for traits. (p. 181)
genotipo conjunto de todos los rasgos codificados en la información genética de un organismo.

genus first name in binomial nomenclature; the second-most specific taxon in the Linnaean classification system that includes one or more physically similar species, which are thought to be closely related. (p. 519)
género primera palabra de la nomenclatura binomial; segundo taxón más específico del sistema de clasificación de las especies de Linneo, que consta de dos o más especies físicamente semejantes consideradas muy próximas.

geographic isolation isolation between populations due to physical barriers. (p. 346)
aislamiento geográfico separación entre poblaciones debido a barreras físicas.

geologic time scale time scale representing the history of Earth. (p. 367)
escala de tiempo geológico escala de tiempo para representar la historia de la Tierra.

geosphere features of Earth's surface—such as continents and the sea floor—and everything below Earth's surface. (p. 456)
geosfera componentes de la superficie de la Tierra, es decir, los continentes, el suelo oceánico y el interior mismo de la Tierra.

germination process by which seeds or spores sprout and begin to grow. (p. 675)
germinación proceso mediante el cual las semillas o esporas brotan y empiezan a crecer.

germ theory theory that states that diseases are caused by microscopic particles called pathogens. (p. 941)
teoría de los gérmenes teoría según la cual las enfermedades son causadas por unas partículas microscópicas llamadas patógenos.

gibberellin (JIHB-uh-REHL-ihn) plant hormone that stimulates cell growth. (p. 680)
giberelina hormona vegetal que estimula el crecimiento celular.

gill respiratory organ of aquatic animals that allows breathing underwater. (p. 763)
branquia órgano respiratorio de numerosos animales acuáticos que permite respirar bajo el agua.

gland organ that produces and releases chemicals that affect the activities of other tissues. (p. 896)
glándula órgano que produce y secreta compuestos químicos que afectan el funcionamiento de otros tejidos.

global warming worldwide trend of increasing average temperatures. (p. 492)
calentamiento global incremento del promedio de la temperatura en toda la Tierra.

glomerulus (gloh-MEHR-yuh-luhs) tangled ball of capillaries that circulates blood in the kidneys. (p. 988)
glomérulos ovillo de vasos capilares por los que circula la sangre en los riñones.

glycolysis (gly-KAHL-uh-sihs) anaerobic process in which glucose is broken down into two molecules of pyruvate and two net ATP are produced. (p. 113)
glicólisis proceso anaeróbico en el que la glucosa se descompone en dos moléculas de piruvato y se producen dos moléculas de ATP.

Golgi apparatus (GOHL-jee) stack of flat, membrane-enclosed spaces containing enzymes that process, sort, and deliver proteins. (p. 76)
aparato de Golgi conjunto de sacos apilados y aplanados rodeados de una membrana que contienen enzimas que procesan, clasifican y distribuyen proteínas.

gradualism principle that states that the changes in landforms result from slow changes over a long period of time. (p. 301)
gradualismo principio que postula que los cambios en los accidentes geográficos resultan de pequeños cambios graduales durante extensos períodos de tiempo.

grassland biome in which the primary plant life is grass. (p. 464)
pradera bioma en la que las forma de vida vegetal predominante son las hierbas y los pastos.

gravitropism growth of plants in response to gravity; plant stems grow upward, against gravity, and roots grow toward the gravitational pull. (p. 682)
gravitropismo crecimiento de las plantas condicionado por la gravedad; el tallo crece hacia arriba, en sentido inverso a la fuerza de gravedad, y las raíces crecen hacia abajo, en el mismo sentido que la gravedad.

greenhouse effect normal warming effect produced when gases, such as carbon dioxide and methane, trap heat in Earth's atmosphere. (p. 490)
efecto invernadero calentamiento producido cuando ciertos gases, como el dióxido de carbono y el metano, atrapan el calor en la atmósfera terrestre.

ground tissue tissue system that makes up the majority of a plant. (p. 642)
tejido fundamental sistema de tejidos que comprende la parte principal del cuerpo de la planta.

growth factor broad group of proteins that stimulate cell division. (p. 144)
factor de crecimiento grupo numeroso de proteínas que estimulan la división celular.

guard cell one of a pair of cells that controls the opening and closing of a stoma in plant tissue. (p. 653)
células oclusivas las dos células que controlan la apertura y cierre de los estomas en el tejido vegetal.

gymnosperm (JIHM-nuh-SPURM) seed plant whose seeds are not enclosed by fruit. (p. 621)
gimnosperma planta productora de semillas que no están encerradas en una fruta.

R55

Glossary

H

habitat combined biotic and abiotic factors found in the area where an organism lives. (p. 428)
hábitat conjunto de factores bióticos y abióticos de la zona donde vive un organismo determinado.

habitat fragmentation process by which part of an organism's preferred habitat range becomes inaccessible. (p. 499)
fragmentación del hábitat proceso mediante el cual una parte del hábitat de un organismo se hace inaccesible.

habituation process of eventually ignoring a repeated stimulus. (p. 823)
habituación proceso que eventualmente conduce a ignorar un estímulo que se repite.

hair cell mechanoreceptor in the inner ear that detects sound waves when bent. (p. 882)
célula ciliada mecanoreceptor del oído interno que detecta las ondas sonoras que lo accionan.

hair follicle pit in the dermis of the skin that contains cells that produce hair. (p. 1015)
folículo piloso estrecha cavidad de la piel que contiene células que forman el cabello.

half-life amount of time it takes for half of the isotope in a sample to decay into its product isotope. (p. 362)
vida mitad intervalo de tiempo necesario para que la mitad de los átomos de una muestra de isótopos se desintegren.

haploid (HAP-LOYD) cell that has only one copy of each chromosome. (p. 170)
haploide célula que sólo tiene una copia de cada cromosoma.

Hardy-Weinberg equilibrium condition in which a population's allele frequencies for a given trait do not change from generation to generation. (p. 340)
equilibrio de Hardy-Weinberg condición en la que las frecuencias alélicas de un rasgo determinado en una población determinada se mantienen constantes de una generación a otra.

heart muscle in the chest that moves blood throughout the body. (p. 912)
corazón músculo situado en el pecho que hace circular la sangre por el cuerpo.

hemocoel open space between cells in animal tissues. (p. 712)
hemocele cavidad intracelular de los tejidos animales.

hemoglobin (HEE-muh-GLOH-bihn) iron-rich protein in red blood cells that allows the cell to absorb oxygen gas. (p. 915)
hemoglobina proteína rica en hierro de los glóbulos rojos que permite a las células absorber oxígeno gaseoso.

herbivore organism that eats only plants. (p. 409)
herbívoro organismo que sólo se alimenta de plantas.

heritibility ability of a trait to be passed from one generation to the next. (p. 304)
heredabilidad propiedad de un rasgo determinado de ser transmitido de una generación a la siguiente.

heterotroph organism that obtains its energy and nutrients by consuming other organisms. (p. 406)
heterótrofo organismo que obtiene su energía y sus nutrientes alimentándose de otros organismos.

heterozygous characteristic of having two different alleles that appear at the same locus of sister chromatids. (p. 180)
heterocigoto característica que consiste en tener dos alelos diferentes en el mismo locus de cromátidas hermanas.

histone protein that organizes chromosomes and around which DNA wraps. (p. 139)
histona proteína que ordena los cromosomas y alrededor de la cual se enrolla el ADN.

homeobox (HOH-mee-uh-BAHKS) genes that define the head-to-tail pattern of development in animal embryos; also called *Hox* genes. (p. 698)
homeobox genes que definen el desarrollo de los embriones animales organizado de cabeza a cola; también se conocen como genes *Hox*.

homeostasis (HOH-mee-oh-STAY-sihs) regulation and maintenance of constant internal conditions in an organism. (pp. 9; 858)
homeostasis regulación y mantenimiento de condiciones internas constantes en un organismo determinado.

homeotic (hoh-mee-AH-tihk) genes that control early development in animals. (p. 698)
homeóticos genes que controlan la primera fase del desarrollo de los animales.

hominid primate that walks upright, has long lower limbs, thumbs that oppose the other four fingers, and a relatively large brain. (p. 380)
homínido primate que camina erguido, que tiene extremidades inferiores largas, pulgar desarrollado y alineado con los cuatro dedos restantes y un cerebro relativamente grande.

homologous chromosomes chromosomes that have the same length, appearance, and copies of genes, although the alleles may differ. (p. 169)
cromosomas homólogos cromosomas de la misma longitud, aspecto y secuencia de genes, aunque los alelos de uno y otro cromosoma pueden ser distintos.

homologous structure body part that is similar in structure on different organisms but performs different functions. (p. 312)
estructura homóloga estructura anatómica similar de organismos diferentes pero que cumplen funciones diferentes.

homozygous characteristic of having two of the same alleles at the same locus of sister chromatids. (p. 180)
homocigoto característica que consiste en tener los mismos alelos en el mismo locus de cromátidas hermanas.

hormone chemical signal that is produced in one part of an organism and affects cell activity in another part. (pp. 680; 896)
hormona señal química producida en una parte del organismo que afecta a la actividad celular en otra parte del cuerpo.

Human Genome Project project whose goal is to map, sequence, and identify all of the genes in the human genome. (p. 281)
Proyecto Genoma Humano proyecto cuya meta consiste en cartografiar un mapa, identificar y hallar la secuencia de todos los genes del genoma humano.

human immunodeficiency virus (HIV) virus that weakens the immune system by reproducing in and destroying T cells; causes AIDS. (p. 961)
virus de inmunodeficiencia humana (VIH) virus que debilita el sistema inmune al reproducirse en las células T y destruirlas; causa el SIDA.

humoral immunity immune response that relies on B cells to produce antibodies to help fight infection. (p. 953)
inmunidad humoral respuesta inmune basada en los anticuerpos producidos por las células B para combatir las infecciones.

hydrogen bond attraction between a slightly positive hydrogen atom and a slightly negative atom. (p. 41)
enlace de hidrógeno atracción entre un átomo de hidrógeno con una carga parcial positiva y otro con una carga parcial negativa.

hydrologic cycle pathway of water from the atmosphere to Earth's surface, below ground, and back. (p. 412)
ciclo hidrológico movimiento del agua desde la atmósfera hasta la superficie de la Tierra, al subsuelo y de vuelta a la atmósfera.

hydrosphere collection of Earth's water bodies, ice, and water vapor. (p. 456)
hidrosfera conjunto de las masas de agua líquida, sólida y gaseosa de la Tierra.

hypertonic solution that has a higher concentration of dissolved particles compared with another solution. (p. 86)
hipertónica solución con una concentración mayor de partículas disueltas que otra solución.

hypha (plural: *hyphae*) threadlike filament forming the body and mycelium of a fungus. (p. 589)
hifa filamento que forman el cuerpo y el micelio de los hongos.

hypothalamus small area of the midbrain that plays a role in the nervous and endocrine systems. (p. 898)
hipotálamo área reducida del cerebro medio que participa en las funciones de los sistemas nervioso y endocrino.

hypothesis (plural: *hypotheses*) proposed explanation or answer to a scientific question. (p. 14)
hipótesis proceso de explicación o respuesta a una pregunta científica.

hypotonic solution that has a lower concentration of dissolved particles compared with another solution. (p. 87)
hipotónica solución con una concentración menor de partículas disueltas que otra solución.

I

imitation process by which an organism learns a behavior by observing other individuals. (p. 825)
imitación proceso mediante el cual un organismo aprende un determinado comportamiento mediante la observación de otros individuos.

immigration movement of individuals into a population. (p. 440)
inmigración desplazamiento de individuos hacia una población establecida.

immune system body system that fights off infections. (p. 945)
sistema inmune sistema encargado de combatir las infecciones.

imprinting process by which a newborn animal quickly learns to recognize another animal, such as a parent. (p. 824)
impronta filial proceso mediante el cual un animal recién nacido aprende rápidamente a reconocer a otro como, por ejemplo, su progenitor.

inclusive fitness total number of genes an animal contributes to the next generation. (p. 834)
aptitud inclusiva número total de genes que un animal transmite a la siguiente generación.

incomplete dominance heterozygous phenotype that is a blend of the two homozygous phenotypes. (p. 204)
dominancia incompleta fenotipo heterocigoto que resulta de la mezcla de dos fenotipos homocigotos.

incomplete metamorphosis process by which immature arthropods look similar to their adult form. (p. 744)
metamorfosis incompleta proceso mediante el cual los especímenes jóvenes de los artrópodos son muy similares en forma a los adultos.

independent variable condition or factor that is manipulated by a scientist during an experiment. (p. 16)
variable independiente condición o factor que es manipulado en el transcurso de un experimento científico.

index fossil fossil of an organism that existed during only specific spans of geologic time across large geographic areas. (p. 365)
fósil índice fósil de un organismo que existió en el pasado geológico durante un intervalo corto con una amplia distribución geográfica.

indicator species species whose presence in an ecosystem gives clues about the condition of that ecosystem. (p. 494)
especies indicadoras especies cuya presencia en un ecosistema proporcionan claves sobre el estado en que se encuentra dicho ecosistema.

Glossary

infancy period of life from birth until the ability to walk has been acquired. (p. 1042)
infancia periodo de vida comprendido entre el nacimiento y los primeros pasos.

infertility persistent condition in which offspring cannot be produced. (p. 1031)
esterilidad incapacidad recurrente de un individuo para reproducirse.

inflammation immune response that is characterized by swelling, redness, pain, and itching. (p. 950)
inflamación respuesta inmune caracterizada por hinchazón, rubor, dolor y picazón.

innate behavior that is not learned through experience. (p. 822)
innato comportamiento que no se aprende a través de la experiencia.

insecticide chemical that is used to kill insects. (p. 747)
insecticida compuesto químico usado para matar insectos.

insight ability to solve a problem without repeated trial and error. (p. 838)
perspicacia capacidad para resolver un problema sin necesidad de pasar por procesos reiterados de prueba y error.

instinct inborn pattern of behavior that is characteristic of a species. (p. 822)
instinto patrón innato de comportamiento característico de cada especie.

integumentary system body system that separates the other body systems from the external environment; includes the skin and the tissues found within it. (p. 1013)
sistema tegumentario sistema que delimita los sistemas corporales del medio exterior; consta de la piel y de los tejidos que la conforman.

interferon type of protein, produced by body cells, that prevents viruses from replicating in infected cells. (p. 947)
interferón tipo de proteína generada por las células corporales que impide la replicación de los virus en el interior de las células infectadas.

intertidal zone strip of land between the high and low tide lines. (p. 468)
zona intermareal banda de tierra comprendida entra las líneas de pleamar y de bajamar.

introduced species species that is not native and was brought to an area as a result of human activities. (p. 500)
especie introducida especie no autóctona que llega a otras regiones como resultado de actividades humanas.

intron segment of a gene that does not code for an amino acid. (p. 251)
intrón región de un gen que no participa en la codificación de amino ácidos.

invertebrate animal without a backbone. (p. 699)
invertebrado animal sin columna vertebral.

ion atom that has gained or lost one or more electrons. (p. 38)
ión átomo que ha ganado o perdido uno o más electrones.

ionic bond chemical bond formed through the electrical force between oppositely charged ions. (p. 38)
enlace iónico enlace químico que se establece mediante la fuerza eléctrica ejercida entre dos iones de cargas opuestas.

isotonic solution that has an equal concentration of dissolved particles compared with another solution. (p. 86)
isotónica solución que tiene la misma concentración de partículas disueltas que otra solución.

isotope form of an element that has the same number of protons but a different number of neutrons as another element. (p. 362)
isótopo átomo de un elemento químico que tiene el mismo número de protones, pero una cantidad diferente de neutrones que otro átomo del mismo elemento.

J

joint location in the body where two bones meet. (p. 1001)
articulación área del cuerpo en la que se unen dos huesos.

K

karyotype (KAR-ee-uh-TYP) image of all of the chromosomes in a cell. (p. 217)
cariotipo imagen de todos los cromosomas de una célula.

kelp forest ocean habitat that exists in cold, nutrient-rich shallow coastal waters, composed of large communities of kelp, a seaweed. (p. 470)
bosques de quelpo hábitat oceánico de frías aguas costeras de poca profundidad que son ricas en nutrientes y en las que abundan grandes comunidades de algas pardas llamadas quelpos.

keratin protein that binds to lipids inside a skin cell, forming a waterproof layer within the skin. (pp. 778; 1013)
queratina proteína que se enlaza con los lípidos dentro de las células epiteliales creando una capa impermeable en el interior de la piel.

keystone species organism that has an unusually large effect on its ecosystem. (p. 403)
especie clave organismo que tiene una rol dominante en su ecosistema.

kidney organ of the excretory system that removes waste from the blood and helps to maintain stable water levels in the body. (p. 986)
riñón órgano del sistema excretor que elimina los desechos de la sangre y contribuye a mantener niveles estables de agua en el organismo.

kinesis random movement that results from an increase in activity levels due to a stimulus. (p. 819)
quinesia movimiento aleatorio que resulta de un incremento en los niveles de actividad producidos por un estímulo.

kin selection when natural selection acts on alleles that favor the survival of close relatives. (p. 834)
nepotismo selección natural de los alelos que favorece la supervivencia de los familiares más próximos.

Krebs cycle process during cellular respiration that breaks down a carbon molecule to produce molecules that are used in the electron transport chain. (p. 115)
ciclo de Krebs proceso de respiración celular en el que se desintegra una molécula de carbono para generar moléculas que intervienen en la cadena de transporte de electrones.

L

lactic acid product of fermentation in many types of cells, including human muscle cells. (p. 123)
ácido láctico producto de fermentación de muchos tipos de células como, por ejemplo, las células musculares humanas.

lateral line sensory system in fish that allows them to sense distant movements in the water. (p. 767)
línea lateral sistema sensorial de los peces que les permite captar movimientos lejanos en el agua.

law of independent assortment Mendel's second law, stating that allele pairs separate from one another during gamete formation. (p. 186)
ley de transmisión independiente segunda ley de Mendel, según la cual los pares de alelos se separan durante la formación de los gametos.

law of segregation Mendel's first law, stating that (1) organisms inherit two copies of genes, one from each parent, and (2) organisms donate only one copy of each gene in their gametes because the genes separate during gamete formation. (p. 179)
ley de la segregación primera ley de Mendel, según la cual (1) los organismos heredan dos copias de cada gen, una de cada progenitor, y (2) que los organismos sólo reciben una copia de cada gen de los gametos de sus progenitores ya que los genes se separan durante la formación de gametos.

leukemia cancer of the bone marrow that weakens the immune system by preventing white blood cells from maturing. (p. 960)
leucemia cáncer de la medula ósea que debilita el sistema inmune al impedir que maduren los glóbulos blancos.

lichen fungus that grows symbiotically with algae, resulting in a composite organism that grows on rocks or tree trunks. (p. 598)
liquen organismo compuesto por un hongo y una alga que viven en y que crece sobre las rocas y los troncos de los árboles.

ligament long, flexible band of connective tissue that joins two bones across a joint. (p. 1002)
ligamento tira alargada y flexible de tejido conjuntivo que une dos huesos a través de una articulación.

light-dependent reactions part of photosynthesis that absorbs energy from sunlight and transfers energy to the light-independent reactions. (p. 105)
reacciones lumínicas etapa de la fotosíntesis en la que se absorbe energía solar para luego usarse en las reacciones oscuras.

light-independent reactions part of photosynthesis that uses energy absorbed during the light-dependent reactions to synthesize carbohydrates. (p. 105)
reacciones oscuras etapa de la fotosíntesis en que se aplica la energía absorbida durante las reacciones lumínicas para la síntesis de carbohidratos.

lignin (LIHG-nihn) complex polymer that hardens cell walls of some vascular tissues in plants. (p. 614)
lignina polímero complejo que endurece las paredes celulares de determinados tejidos vasculares de las plantas.

limiting factor environmental factor that limits the growth and size of a population. (p. 443)
factor limitante factor ambiental que limita el crecimiento y tamaño de una población determinada.

limnetic zone open water of a lake or pond that is located away from shore. (p. 474)
zona limnética aguas abiertas de un lago o estanque alejadas de las orillas.

linkage map diagram that shows the relative locations of genes on a chromosome. (p. 210)
mapa de ligamiento diagrama que representa la situación relativa de los genes en un cromosoma determinado.

lipid nonpolar molecule composed of carbon, hydrogen, and oxygen; includes fats and oils. (p. 46)
lípido molécula apolar compuesta de carbono, hidrógeno y oxígeno; las grasas y los aceites son lípidos.

littoral zone area between the high and low water marks along the shoreline of a lake or pond. (p. 474)
zona litoral área de aguas de profundidad intermedia a lo largo de la orilla de un lago o estanque.

lobe-fin paired limblike fin that is round in shape. (p. 770)
aleta lobulada tipo de aleta de forma redondeada que se presenta en pares y que se asemeja a una extremidad.

logistic growth population growth that is characterized by a period of slow growth, followed by a period of exponential growth, followed by another period of almost no growth. (p. 441)
crecimiento logístico crecimiento de población que se caracteriza por un período de crecimiento lento, seguido por un período de crecimiento exponencial al que le sigue un período de crecimiento insignificante.

lung organ that absorbs oxygen gas from air that an organism inhales. (p. 911)
pulmón órgano que absorbe el oxígeno gaseoso que inhala un organismo.

R59

Glossary

lymph collection of interstitial fluid and white blood cells that flows through the lymphatic system. (p. 930)
linfa conjunto de los fluidos intersticiales y de glóbulos blancos que circulan por el sistema linfático.

lymphatic system (lihm-FAT-ihk) body system that consists of organs, vessels, and nodes through which lymph circulates. (p. 930)
sistema linfático sistema corporal que consta de órganos, vasos y nódulos a través de los cuales circula la linfa.

lymphocyte (LIHM-fuh-SYT) white blood cell that plays a role in an immune response; *see* B cell and T cell. (p. 931)
linfocito glóbulo blanco que participa en la respuesta inmune; *véanse* célula B y célula T.

lysogenic infection infectious pathway of a virus in which host cells are not immediately destroyed. (p. 551)
infección lisogénica infección vírica en la que las células huésped no son destruidas de inmediato.

lysosome (LY-suh-SOHM) organelle that contains enzymes. (p. 78)
lisosoma orgánulo que contiene enzimas.

lytic infection infectious pathway of a virus in which host cells are destroyed. (p. 551)
infección lítica infección vírica en la que se destruyen las células huésped.

M

malignant cancerous tumor in which cells break away and spread to other parts of the body, causing harm to the organism's health. (p. 146)
maligno tumor canceroso en el que las células se desprenden y se diseminan a otras partes del cuerpo provocando daños a la salud del organismo.

mammal endothermic organism that has hair, mammary glands, bones in the ear that allow for hearing, and a jaw for chewing food. (p. 805)
mamífero organismo endotérmico que tiene pelo y glándulas mamarias, además de huesos en el oído que le permiten oír y una mandíbula para masticar.

mammary gland gland that produces milk. (p. 806)
glándula mamaria glándula productora de leche.

mandible appendage that is used to crush and bite food. (p. 737)
mandíbula apéndice empleado para triturar y morder la comida.

marsupial mammal whose young complete fetal development in the mother's external pouch. (p. 808)
marsupial mamífero cuyas crías terminan su desarrollo fetal en una bolsa exterior de la madre.

medusa umbrella-shaped body form of a cnidarian in which the mouth and tentacles are on the underside. (p. 707)
medusa organismo cnidario en forma de paraguas que tiene la boca y los tentáculos en la superficie cóncava.

meiosis (my-OH-sihs) form of nuclear division that divides a diploid cell into haploid cells; important in forming gametes for sexual reproduction. (p. 170)
meiosis forma de división nuclear en la que una célula diploide se divide en células haploides; importante en la formación de gametos para la reproducción sexual.

memory cell specialized white blood cell that contributes to acquired immunity by acting quickly to a foreign substance that infected the body previously. (p. 951)
célula de memoria glóbulo blanco que participa en el proceso de inmunización mediante una respuesta rápida ante una sustancia extraña que ya había infectado el organismo anteriormente.

menopause period of life when the female reproductive system permanently stops the menstrual cycle. (p. 1029)
menopausia período de la vida en que el sistema reproductor femenino deja de producir el ciclo menstrual.

menstrual cycle series of changes in the female reproductive system that takes place over the course of one month. (p. 1028)
ciclo menstrual sucesión de cambios en el sistema reproductor femenino que ocurre en el plazo de un mes.

meristem undifferentiated plant tissue from which new cells are formed. (p. 648)
meristemo tejido indiferenciado de las plantas en el que se forman nuevas células.

mesoglea jellylike material that separates the two tissue layers of a cnidarian. (p. 707)
mesoglea matriz gelatinosa que separa las dos capas de tejidos de un cnidario.

mesophyll photosynthetic tissue of a leaf, located between the upper and lower epidermis. (p. 652)
mesófilo tejido fotosintético de la hoja, situado entre la epidermis superior y la epidermis inferior de la hoja.

Mesozoic era during which dinosaurs roamed Earth (from 248 million years ago to 65 million years ago). (p. 377)
Mesozoico era de la Tierra que se inició hace unos 248 millones de años y que finalizó hace 65 millones de años en la que abundaron los dinosaurios.

messenger RNA (mRNA) form of RNA that carries genetic information from the nucleus to the cytoplasm, where it serves as a template for protein synthesis. (p. 240)
ARN mensajero (ARNm) forma de ARN que transporta la información genética del núcleo al citoplasma, donde sirve de patrón para la síntesis de las proteínas.

metabolism all chemical processes that synthesize or break down materials within an organism. (p. 6)
metabolismo conjunto de procesos químicos que sintetizan o descomponen sustancias en el interior de los organismos.

metaphase second phase of mitosis when spindle fibers align the chromosomes along the cell equator. (p. 140)
metafase segunda fase de la mitosis en la que las fibras de los husos alinean los cromosomas en el plano ecuatorial de la célula.

metastasize (mih-TAS-tuh-SYZ) to spread by transferring a disease-causing agent from the site of the disease to other parts of the body. (p. 146)
metástasis diseminación de una enfermedad causada por un agente patógeno del foco en que se origina a otras partes del cuerpo.

microclimate climate of a specific location within a larger area. (p. 458)
microclima clima de un lugar específico enclavado en un área más extensa.

microevolution observable change in the allele frequencies of a population over a few generations. (p. 331)
microevolución cambio observable en las frecuencias alélicas de una población en el transcurso de unas pocas generaciones.

microscope tool that provides an enlarged image of an object. (p. 19)
microscopio instrumento que permite ver una imagen amplificada de un objeto.

microvillus (plural: *microvilli*) small hairlike projection on the surface of a villus in the small intestine. (p. 983)
microvellosidad proyección pilosa muy pequeña que recubre las vellosidades del intestino delgado.

mineral inorganic material, such as calcium, iron, potassium, sodium, or zinc, that is essential to the nutrition of an organism. (p. 973)
mineral material inorgánico, como el calcio, el hierro, el potasio, el sodio o el zinc, que resulta esencial en la nutrición de los organismos.

mitochondrial DNA DNA found only in mitochondria, often used as a molecular clock. (p. 532)
ADN mitocondrial ADN propio de las mitocondrias que suele actuar a modo de reloj molecular.

mitochondrion (MY-tuh-KAHN-dree-uhn) (plural: *mitochondria*) bean-shaped organelle that supplies energy to the cell and has its own ribosomes and DNA. (p. 77)
mitocondria orgánulo en forma de fríjol que suministra energía a la célula y que tiene sus propios ribosomas y ADN.

mitosis (my-TOH-sihs) process by which a cell divides its nucleus and contents. (p. 135)
mitosis proceso en el cual tanto el núcleo como los demás elementos de la célula se duplican.

molecular clock theoretical clock that uses the rate of mutation to measure evolutionary time. (p. 530)
reloj molecular reloj teórico que emplea la tasa de mutación para medir el tiempo evolutivo.

molecular genetics study of DNA structure and function on the molecular level. (p. 23)
genética molecular estudio de la estructura y función del ADN a nivel molecular.

molecule two or more atoms held together by covalent bonds; not necessarily a compound. (p. 39)
molécula dos o más átomos unidos mediante enlaces covalentes; no forman necesariamente un compuesto.

monocot (MAHN-uh-KAHT) flowering plant whose embryos have one cotyledon. (p. 626)
monocotiledónea planta angiosperma cuyos embriones tienen un solo cotiledón.

monohybrid cross cross, or mating, between organisms that involves only one pair of contrasting traits. (p. 184)
cruzamiento monohíbrido cruzamiento o apareamiento entre dos organismos que sólo involucra un par de rasgos diferentes.

monomer molecular subunit of a polymer. (p. 45)
monómero subunidad molecular del polímero.

monotreme mammal whose offspring complete fetal development in laid eggs. (p. 807)
monotrema mamífero que pone huevos donde sus crías completan su desarrollo fetal.

muscle fiber cell of the muscular system that shortens when it is stimulated by the nervous system. (p. 1006)
fibra muscular célula del sistema muscular que se contrae al ser estimulada por el sistema nervioso.

muscular system body system that moves bones within and substances throughout the body. (p. 1006)
sistema muscular sistema corporal que mueve los huesos y que hace circular sustancias a través del cuerpo.

mutagen agent that can induce or increase the frequency of mutation in organisms. (p. 255)
mutágeno agente que puede inducir mutaciones en un organismo o incrementar la frecuencia de éstas.

mutation change in the DNA sequence. (p. 252)
mutación cambio en la secuencia de ADN.

mutualism ecological relationship between two species in which each species gets a benefit from the interaction. (p. 432)
mutualismo relación ecológica entre dos especies que resulta beneficiosa para ambas.

mycelium vegetative part of a fungus, consisting of a mass of branching, threadlike hyphae that grows underground. (p. 590)
micelio parte vegetativa del hongo compuesta de un entramado de filamentos ramificados, llamados hifas, que crece bajo tierra.

mycorrhizae ecological relationship between the mycelium of a fungus and the roots of certain plants. (p. 591)
micorriza relación ecológica entre el micelio de un hongo y las raíces de determinadas plantas.

myofibril long strand of protein within a muscle fiber. (p. 1008)
miofibrilla larga cadena proteica dentro de una fibra muscular.

R61

myosin filament that pulls actin filaments to cause muscle contraction. (p. 1008)
miosina filamento que al tensar los filamentos de actina causa la contracción muscular.

N

natural selection mechanism by which individuals that have inherited beneficial adaptations produce more offspring on average than do other individuals. (p. 305)
selección natural mecanismo mediante el cual los organismos que han heredado adaptaciones beneficiosas producen un promedio más alto de descendientes que los demás individuos.

nebula rotating cloud of gas and dust. (p. 368)
nebulosa nube giratoria de polvo y gases.

negative feedback control system for homeostasis that adjusts the body's conditions when the conditions vary from the ideal. (p. 860)
retroalimentación negativa sistema de control de la homeostasis que regula las condiciones del cuerpo cuando éstas no son óptimas.

nematocyst capsule containing a thin, coiled tubule with a poisonous barb at one end. (p. 707)
nematocisto cápsula que contiene un fino túbulo enrollado con un aguijón venenoso en la punta.

nephron (NEHF-rahn) individual filtering unit of the kidney that removes waste from the blood. (p. 987)
nefrona unidad de filtración del riñón que retira los desechos de la sangre.

neritic zone zone of the ocean that extends from the intertidal zone out to the edge of the continental shelf. (p. 468)
zona nerítica zona del océano que se extiende desde la zona intermareal hasta el límite de la plataforma continental.

nervous system body system that controls sensation, interpretation, and response; includes the brain, spinal cord, and nerves. (p. 874)
sistema nervioso sistema corporal que controla las sensaciones, las interpretaciones y las respuestas; incluye el encéfalo, la médula espinal y los nervios.

neuron cell of the nervous system that transmits impulses between the body systems as well as interprets and stores some messages in the brain. (p. 876)
neurona célula del sistema nervioso que transmite impulsos entre los diversos sistemas del organismo y que, además, interpreta y almacena información en el cerebro.

neurotransmitter (NUR-oh-TRANS-miht-uhr) chemical that transmits a nervous system's signal across a synapse. (p. 879)
neurotransmisor compuesto químico que transmite una señal del sistema nervioso a través de la sinapsis.

nitrogen fixation process by which certain types of bacteria convert gaseous nitrogen into nitrogen compounds. (p. 415)
fijación del nitrógeno proceso mediante el cual ciertos tipos de bacterias transforman el nitrógeno gaseoso en compuestos nitrogenados.

node organ located along the lymphatic vessels that filters bacteria and foreign particles from lymph. (p. 930)
ganglio linfático órgano situado a lo largo de los vasos linfáticos encargado de filtrar bacterias y sustancias extrañas de la linfa.

nonrenewable resource natural resource that is used more quickly than it can be formed. (p. 485)
recurso no renovable recurso natural que se consume con más rapidez de la que se puede reponer.

normal distribution distribution in a population in which allele frequency is highest near the mean range value and decreases progressively toward each extreme end. (p. 330)
distribución normal distribución de la población en la que la frecuencia alélica es mayor en la zona de valor medio y disminuye progresivamente hacia ambos extremos.

notochord flexible skeletal support rod embedded in an animal's back. (p. 758)
notocordio bastón esqueletal flexible que proporciona sostén y que está situado en el dorso de los animales.

nucleic acid polymer of nucleotides; the genetic material of organisms. (p. 48)
ácido nucleico polímero de nucleótidos; material genético de los organismos.

nucleotide (NOO-klee-oh-TYD) monomer that forms DNA and has a phosphate group, a sugar, and a nitrogen-containing base. (p. 230)
nucleótido monómero que forma el ADN y que tiene un grupo fosfato, un azúcar y una base nitrogenada.

nucleus (NOO-klee-uhs) (plural: *nuclei*) organelle composed of a double membrane that acts as the storehouse for most of a cell's DNA. (p. 75)
núcleo orgánulo compuesto de una doble membrana que almacena la mayor parte del ADN de la célula.

O

obligate aerobe prokaryote that cannot survive without the presence of oxygen. (p. 555)
aerobio obligado procariota que no puede sobrevivir en un entorno sin oxígeno.

obligate anaerobe prokaryote that cannot survive in the presence of oxygen. (p. 555)
anaerobio obligado procariota que no puede sobrevivir en un entorno oxigenado.

observation using the senses to study the world; using tools to collect measurements; examining previous research results. (p. 13)
observación utilización de los sentidos para estudiar el mundo; uso de instrumentos de medición; análisis de resultados de investigación.

omnivore organism that eats both plants and animals. (p. 409)
omnívoro organismo que se alimenta tanto de animales como de plantas.

operant conditioning process by which a behavior increases or decreases as the result of a reward or punishment. (p. 826)
condicionamiento operante proceso mediante el cual varía la frecuencia de un comportamiento como resultado de un premio o un castigo.

operculum protective bony plate that covers a fish's gills. (p. 767)
opérculo placa protectora ósea que recubre las branquias de los peces.

operon section of DNA that contains all of the code to begin transcription, regulate transcription, and build a protein; includes a promotor, regulatory gene, and structural gene (p. 248)
operon sección de ADN que contiene todos los códigos necesarios para iniciar y regular el proceso de transcripción y para sintetizar una proteína: consta de un promotor, de un gen regulador y de un gen estuctural.

opportunistic infection infection caused by a pathogen that a healthy immune system would normally be able to fight off. (p. 961)
infección oportunista infección causada por un patógeno que un sistema inmune saludable podría combatir con eficacia.

optimal foraging theory that states that natural selection will favor organisms that have behaviors that can gather the best food sources. (p. 829)
abastecimiento óptimo teoría según la cual la selección natural favorece a aquellos organismos cuyos comportamientos les permiten acceder a las mejores fuentes de alimento.

organ group of different types of tissues that work together to perform a specific function or related functions. (pp. 151; 854)
órgano grupo de diversos tipos de tejidos que funcionan de manera coordinada para desarrollar una función específica o funciones relacionadas.

organelle membrane-bound structure that is specialized to perform a distinct process within a cell. (p. 72)
orgánulo estructura intracelular que se especializa en una función específica.

organism any individual living thing. (p. 5)
organismo cualquier ser vivo.

organ system two or more organs that work in a coordinated way to carry out similar functions. (pp. 151; 854)
sistema de órganos dos o más órganos que funcionan de manera coordinada para realizar funciones similares.

osmosis diffusion of water molecules across a semipermeable membrane from an area of higher water concentration to an area of lower water concentration. (p. 86)
ósmosis difusión de moléculas de agua a través de una membrana semipermeable, desde un área de mayor concentración de agua a otra de menor concentración de agua.

ossicle small bone, especially one of the three found in the middle ear of mammals. (p. 718)
huesecillo en los mamíferos, cada uno de los tres huesos pequeños que se encuentran en el oído medio.

ovary organ in which female gametes develop prior to fertilization. (pp. 668; 1024)
ovario órgano en el que se desarrollan los gametos femeninos antes de la fertilización.

oviparous reproductive strategy in which the embryos develop outside of the mother's body. (p. 793)
ovíparo organismo que se reproduce mediante un sistema en el que los embriones se desarrollan fuera del cuerpo materno.

ovulation process by which an egg is released from the ovary and becomes available for fertilization. (p. 1028)
ovulación proceso mediante el cual se libera un óvulo del ovario, quedando susceptible a ser fertilizado.

ovum (plural: *ova*) egg cell that is produced by the female reproductive system. (p. 1024)
óvulo ovocito producido en el sistema reproductor femenino.

P

pacemaker collection of cells that stimulates the pumping action of the heart. (p. 918)
nódulo sinusal conjunto de células que estimula los latidos del corazón; también conocido como marcapaso natural.

paleontology study of fossils or extinct organisms. (p. 316)
paleontología estudio de los fósiles o de los organismos extinctos.

Paleozoic era of geologic time (from 544 to 248 million years ago) during which members of every major animal group alive today evolved. (p. 376)
Paleozoico era geológica (desde hace 544 a 248 millones de años) durante la cual evolucionaron especies de los principales grupos de animales de la actualidad.

parasitism ecological relationship in which one organism benefits by harming another organism. (p. 432)
parasitismo relación ecológica en la que un organismo se beneficia perjudicando al otro organismo.

parasympathetic nervous system division of the peripheral nervous system that calms the body and helps the body to conserve energy. (p. 890)
sistema nervioso parasimpático parte del sistema nervioso periférico encargado de mantener un estado corporal de descanso y ayudar al cuerpo a conservar energía.

Glossary

parenchyma cell cell with thin walls that forms tissues within leaves, roots, stems, and fruit of plants. (p. 640)
célula del parénquima célula de paredes delgadas que forma tejidos en el interior de las hojas, raíces, tallos y frutas de las plantas.

particulate microscopic bits of dust, metal, and unburned fuel produced by industrial processes. (p. 488)
materia particulada partículas microscópicas de polvo, metal y combustibles sin quemar, que se generan en los procesos industriales.

passive immunity immunity that occurs without the body undergoing an immune response. (p. 948)
inmunidad pasiva inmunidad que tiene lugar sin que el cuerpo experimente una reacción inmune.

passive transport movement of molecules across the cell membrane without energy input from the cell. (p. 85)
transporte pasivo movimiento de moléculas a través de la membrana celular, que se produce sin aporte de energía celular.

pathogen agent that causes disease. (pp. 544; 941)
patógeno agente que causa una enfermedad.

pedigree chart of the phenotypes and genotypes in a family that is used to determine whether an individual is a carrier of a recessive allele. (p. 214)
pedigrí diagrama de los fenotipos y genotipos de una familia que se emplea para determinar si un individuo es portador de un alelo recesivo.

period unit of geologic time that lasts tens of millions of years and is associated with a particular type of rock system. (p. 367)
periodo unidad de tiempo geológico que abarca decenas de millones de años y que suele asociarse a tipos determinados de formaciones rocosas.

peripheral nervous system (PNS) division of the nervous system that transmits impulses between the central nervous system and other organs in the body. (p. 875)
sistema nervioso periférico (SNP) división del sistema nervioso que transmite impulsos entre el sistema nervioso central y otros órganos del cuerpo.

peristalsis (PEHR-ih-STAWL-sihs) wavelike involuntary muscle contractions that push food through the organs of the digestive system. (p. 978)
peristaltismo contracciones involuntarias en forma de ondas que impulsan los alimentos a través de los órganos del sistema digestivo.

petal modified leaf that surrounds a flower's reproductive structures. (p. 668)
pétalo hoja modificada que rodea las estructuras reproductivas de la flor.

petiole stalk that attaches a leaf blade to a stem. (p. 652)
peciolo rabillo que une la lámina de la hoja al tallo.

pH measurement of acidity; related to free hydrogen ion concentration in solution. (p. 42)
pH medida de acidez; relacionada con la concentración de los iones libres de hidrógeno en una solución.

phagocyte cell that destroys other cells by surrounding and engulfing them. (p. 946)
fagocito célula que destruye a otras células rodeándolas y engulléndolas.

phagocytosis (FAG-uh-sy-TOH-sihs) uptake of a solid particle into a cell by engulfing the particle; *see* endocytosis. (p. 90)
fagocitosis absorción de una partícula sólida por parte de una célula que la envuelve: *véase* endocitosis.

pharmacology study of drugs and their effects on the body. (p. 631)
farmacología estudio de los medicamentos y de los efectos que causan en el cuerpo.

phenotype collection of all of an organism's physical characteristics. (p. 181)
fenotipo conjunto de todas las características físicas de un organismo determinado.

pheromone chemical released by an organism that stimulates a behavior in other organisms of the same species. (p. 832)
feromona compuesto químico liberado por un organismo que estimula ciertos comportamientos en otros organismos de la misma especie.

phloem tissue that transports sugars in vascular plants. (p. 642)
floema tejido transportador de azúcares en las plantas vasculares.

phospholipid molecule that forms a double-layered cell membrane; consists of a glycerol, a phosphate group, and two fatty acids. (p. 81)
fosfolípido molécula que forma una membrana de capa doble; consta de glicerol, un grupo fosfato y dos ácidos grasos.

photoperiodism response of an organism to changes in the length of the day. (p. 683)
fotoperiodismo respuesta de un organismo a las variaciones de luz en un período de 24 horas.

photosynthesis process by which light energy is converted to chemical energy; produces sugar and oxygen from carbon dioxide and water. (p. 103)
fotosíntesis proceso mediante el cual la energía del sol se convierte en energía química; produce azúcar y oxígeno a partir de dióxido de carbono y agua.

photosystem series of light-absorbing pigments and proteins that capture and transfer energy in the thylakoid membrane. (p. 108)
fotosistema conjunto de pigmentos y proteínas que capturan y transfieren energía en la membrana tilacoide.

phototropism growth of a plant toward a light source. (p. 682)
fototropismo crecimiento de la planta hacia la luz.

phylogeny evolutionary history of a group of related species. (p. 524)
filogenia historia evolutiva de un grupo de especies relacionadas.

phylum group of animals defined by structural and functional characteristics that are different from every other animal phylum. (p. 699)
división grupo de animales definidos por una serie de características estructurales y funcionales que se diferencian de cualquier otra división; también se conoce como filum.

phytoplankton photosynthetic microscopic protists, such as algae. (p. 469)
fitoplancton colonia de protistas microscópicas fotosintéticas, como las algas.

pioneer species organism that is the first to live in a previously uninhabited area. (p. 446)
especie pionera primer organismo que vive en una zona hasta entonces deshabitada.

pituitary gland area in the middle of the brain that makes and releases hormones that control cell growth and osmoregulation, water levels in the blood. (p. 898)
glándula pituitaria zona en el centro del cerebro que produce y segrega hormonas que controlan el crecimiento celular y la osmorregulación, es decir, la regulación de los niveles de líquidos en la sangre.

placenta (pluh-SEHN-tuh) organ that develops in female mammals during pregnancy and carries nutrients from the mother to the embryo. (pp. 779; 1035)
placenta órgano que se desarrolla en las hembras de los mamíferos durante la gestación y que lleva nutrientes de la madre al embrión.

plankton microscopic, free-floating organisms, which may be animals or protists, that live in the water. (p. 469)
plancton organismos microscópicos, animales o protistas, que flotan libremente en el agua.

plant multicellular eukaryote that produces its own food through photosynthesis. (p. 612)
planta organismo eucariota multicelular que produce su propio alimento mediante la fotosíntesis.

plasma clear yellowish fluid, about 90 percent water, that suspends cells in the blood. (p. 926)
plasma líquido de color amarillento pálido que consisten en un 90 por ciento deagua en el que están suspendidas las células sanguíneas.

plasmid circular piece of genetic material found in bacteria that can replicate separately from the DNA of the main chromosome. (pp. 276; 556)
plásmido cadena de material genético en forma circular que se encuentra en las bacterias y que se replica independientemente del ADN cromosómico.

platelet cell fragment that is produced in the bone marrow and is important for blood clotting. (p. 926)
plaqueta fragmento celular que se produce en la médula ósea y que cumple una función importante en la coagulación de la sangre.

point mutation mutation that involves a substitution of only one nucleotide. (p. 252)
mutación puntual mutación que involucra la sustitución de un solo nucleótido.

polar body haploid cell produced during meiosis in the female of many species; these cells have little more than DNA and eventually disintegrate. (p. 176)
cuerpo polar célula haploide producida durante la meiosis en las hembras de muchas especies; esta célula tiene poco más que ADN y termina por desintegrarse.

pollen grain two-celled structure that contains the male form of the plant's gamete. (p. 614)
grano de polen estructura formada por dos células que contiene el gameto masculino de la planta.

pollination process by which seed plants become fertilized without the need for free-standing water. (p. 620)
polinización proceso mediante el cual las plantas con semillas se fertilizan sin depender del agua del suelo.

pollution anything that is added to the environment and has a negative affect on the environment or its organisms. (p. 488)
contaminación cualquier sustancia que se libera en el medio ambiente con efectos negativos para los organismos que lo habitan y su entorno.

polygenic trait trait that is produced by two or more genes. (p. 206)
rasgo poligénico rasgo producido por dos o más genes.

polymer large, carbon-based molecule formed by monomers. (p. 45)
polímero gran molécula de carbono formada por monómeros.

polymerase chain reaction (PCR) method for increasing the quantity of DNA by separating it into two strands and adding primers and enzymes. (p. 269)
reacción en cadena de la polimerasa (RCP) método para obtener un gran número de copias de ADN separándolo en dos hebras y añadiendo cebadores y enzimas.

polyp tube-shaped body form of a cnidarian in which the mouth and tentacles face upward. (p. 707)
pólipo cuerpo de forma tubular de un cnidario con la boca y los tentáculos orientados hacia arriba.

population all of the individuals of a species that live in the same area. (p. 306)
población conjunto de individuos de la misma especie que viven en la misma zona.

population crash dramatic decline in the size of a population over a short period of time. (p. 442)
colapso poblacional reducción drástica del tamaño de una población en un breve período de tiempo.

R65

Glossary

population density measure of individuals living in a defined area. (p. 436)
densidad de población cantidad de habitantes que viven en un área determinada.

population dispersion way in which individuals of a population are spread out over an area or volume. (p. 437)
dispersión de población manera en la que los individuos de una población determinada se han distribuido en una área o en un volumen.

positive feedback control system in which sensory information causes the body to increase the rate of change away from homeostasis. (p. 861)
retroalimentación positiva sistema de control mediante el cual la información sensorial estimula el cuerpo a incrementar la tasa de cambio, alejándola de valores homeostáticos.

predation process by which one organism hunts and kills another organism for food. (p. 431)
predación proceso mediante el cual un organismo acecha, mata y se come a otro organismo.

pressure-flow model model for predicting how sugars are transported from photosynthetic tissue to the rest of a plant. (p. 645)
modelo de flujo de presión modelo para predecir la forma en que los azúcares son transportados del tejido fotosintético al resto de una planta.

primary growth growth in vascular plants resulting in elongation of the plant body. (p. 651)
crecimiento primario crecimiento de las plantas vasculares que resulta de la elongación del cuerpo de la planta.

primary succession establishment and development of an ecosystem in an area that was previously uninhabited. (p. 446)
sucesión primaria establecimiento y desarrollo de un ecosistema en una zona hasta entonces deshabitada.

primate mammal with flexible hands and feet, forward-looking eyes, and enlarged brains relative to body size. (p. 379)
primate mamífero de manos y pies flexibles, mirada frontal y un cerebro grande en relación con el tamaño del cuerpo.

primer short segment of DNA that initiates replication by DNA polymerase. (p. 271)
cebador pequeño segmento de ADN que inicia la replicación mediante ADN polimerasa.

prion infectious agent that consists of a protein fragment that can cause other proteins to fold incorrectly. (p. 545)
prión agente infeccioso que consta de una partícula proteica que induce a otras proteínas a plegarse de forma incorrecta.

probability likelihood that a particular event will happen. (p. 187)
probabilidad posibilidad de que ocurra un suceso en particular.

producer organism that obtains its energy from abiotic sources, such as sunlight or inorganic chemicals. (p. 406)
productor organismo que obtiene su alimento de fuentes abióticas, como la luz solar o compuestos inorgánicos.

product substance formed by a chemical reaction. (p. 50)
producto sustancia formada por una reacción química.

prokaryotic cell (proh-KAR-ee-AHT-ihk) cell that does not have a nucleus or other membrane-bound organelles. (p. 72)
célula procarionta célula que no tiene núcleo ni orgánulos limitados por membranas.

promoter section of DNA to which RNA polymerase binds, starting the transcription of mRNA. (p. 248)
promotor sección de ADN a la que se enlaza el ARN polimerasa al inicio del proceso de transcripción de ARNm.

prophage DNA of a bacteriophage inserted into a host cell's DNA. (p. 551)
profago ADN de un bacteriófago insertado en el ADN de la célula huésped.

prophase first phase of mitosis when chromatin condenses, the nuclear envelope breaks down, the nucleolus disappears, and the centrosomes and centrioles migrate to opposite sides of the cell. (p. 140)
profase primera fase de la mitosis, en la que la cromatina se condensa, la membrana nuclear se desintegra, el nucleolo desaparece y los centrosomas y los centriolos migran a lados opuestos de la célula.

prosimian oldest primate group that includes mostly small, nocturnal primates such as lemurs. (p. 379)
prosimio grupo de primates más antiguo que consta, principalmente, de pequeños primates nocturnos, como los lemures.

protein polymer composed of amino acids linked by peptide bonds; folds into a particular structure depending on bonds between amino acids. (p. 47)
proteína polímero compuesto de aminoácidos unidos por enlaces peptídicos; se pliega formando una estructura determinada según sean los enlaces que hay entre los aminoácidos.

proteomics (PROH-tee-AH-mihks) study and comparison of all the proteins produced by an organism's genome. (p. 283)
proteómica estudio y comparación de todas las proteínas producidas por el genoma de un organismo determinado.

protist eukaryote that is not an animal, plant, or fungus. (p. 574)
protista organismo eucariota que no es un animal, una planta, ni un hongo.

protostome animal development in which the animal's mouth develops before the anus. (p. 702)
protóstomo animal en el que la boca se desarrolla antes que el ano.

protozoa animal-like protist. (p. 577)
protozoo protista con características animales.

pseudocoelom fluid filled space with mesoderm only on one side of the space. (p. 716)
pseudoceloma cavidad llena de fluido que tiene mesodermo en un solo lado de la cavidad.

pseudopod temporary extension of cytoplasm and plasma membrane that helps protozoa move and feed. (p. 578)
pseudópodo extensión temporal del citoplasma y de la membrana plasmática que permite a los protozoos moverse y alimentarse.

puberty stage of adolescence that is marked by the production of hormones involved in reproduction. (p. 1024)
pubertad fase de la adolescencia marcada por la producción de hormonas involucradas en la reproducción.

pulmonary circuit (PUL-muh-NEHR-ee) collection of blood vessels that carries blood between the lungs and heart. (pp. 789; 920)
circuito pulmonar conjunto de vasos sanguíneos que transporta sangre entre los pulmones y el corazón.

pulmonary circulation *see* pulmonary circuit.
circulación pulmonar *véanse* circuito pulmonar.

punctuated equilibrium theory that states that speciation occurs suddenly and rapidly followed by long periods of little evolutionary change. (p. 351)
equilibrio puntuado teoría según la cual la especiación se produce repentinamente y va seguida de largos períodos de escasa actividad evolutiva.

Punnett square model for predicting all possible genotypes resulting from a cross, or mating. (p. 183)
cuadrado de Punnet modelo de predicción de todos los genotipos posibles que se pueden obtener a partir de un determinado cruzamiento o apareamiento.

pupa stage of metamorphosis in which the organism reorganizes into a completely new body form. (p. 744)
pupa fase de la metamorfosis en la que el organismo adopta una nueva forma corporal.

purebred type of organism whose ancestors are genetically uniform. (p. 178)
pura raza organismo de ancestros con uniformidad genética.

R

radial symmetry arrangement of body parts in a circle around a central axis. (p. 701)
simetría radial disposición de las partes del cuerpo en un círculo que rodea un eje central.

radiometric dating technique that measures the natural decay rate of isotopes to calculate the age of material. (p. 362)
fechado radiométrico técnica para medir la tasa natural de decaimiento de los isótopos para calcular la edad de los materiales.

radula filelike feeding organ found in mollusks. (p. 712)
rádula órgano raspador con el que se alimentan los moluscos.

ray-fin fan-shaped arrangement of bones in a fish's fin. (p. 768)
aleta radial disposición en abanico de las espinas de una aleta de pez.

reactant substance that is changed by a chemical reaction. (p. 50)
reactante sustancia que cambia a consecuencia de una reacción química.

receptor protein that detects a signal molecule and performs an action in response. (p. 84)
receptor proteína que detecta la señal de una molécula y responde con una acción concreta.

recessive allele that is not expressed unless two copies are present in an organism's genotype. (p. 181)
recesivo alelo que no se expresa, a menos que en el genotipo del organismo en cuestión estén presenten dos copias de dicho gen.

recombinant DNA (ree-KAHM-buh-nuhnt) genetically engineered DNA that contains genes from more than one organism or species. (p. 276)
ADN recombinante ADN manipulado geneticamente que contiene genes de más de un organismo o especie.

red blood cell cell that carries oxygen gas from the lungs to the rest of the body. (p. 915)
glóbulo rojo célula encargada de transportar oxígeno gaseoso de los pulmones al resto del cuerpo.

reflex arc nerve pathway in which an impulse crosses only two synapses before producing a response. (p. 889)
arco reflejo circuito nervioso en el que un impulso sólo atraviesa dos simpasis antes de producir una respuesta.

regeneration process by which a new plant can grow from a fragment of a nonreproductive structure, such as a root, stem, or leaf. (p. 678)
regeneración proceso mediante el cual una nueva planta puede desarrollarse a partir de un fragmento de una estructura no reproductora, como una raíz, un tallo o una hoja.

relative dating estimate of the age of a fossil based on the location of fossils in strata. (p. 362)
datación relativa estimación de la edad de un fósil según la ubicación de los fósiles en los estratos.

releaser stimulus that triggers a specific behavior. (p. 822)
estímulo liberador que suscita un comportamiento específico.

releasing hormone chemical that stimulates other glands to release their hormones. (p. 900)
hormona liberadora sustancia química que estimula otras glándulas para que secreten hormonas.

renewable resource resource that replenishes itself quickly enough so that it will not be used faster than it can be produced. (p. 485)
recurso renovable recurso natural que se restablece a un ritmo superior del ritmo al que se consume.

replication process by which DNA is copied. (p. 235)
replicación proceso mediante el cual se copian las moléculas de ADN.

R67

Glossary

reproductive isolation final stage in speciation, in which members of isolated populations are either no longer able to mate or no longer able to produce viable offspring. (p. 344)
aislamiento reproductor fase final de la especiación en la que los miembros de poblaciones aisladas pierden la capacidad de aparearse o no pueden producir crías viables.

reproductive system body system that allows for sexual reproduction; includes testes, ovaries, uterus, and other male and female sex organs. (p. 1024)
sistema reproductor sistema corporal que permite la reproducción sexual; consta de testículos, ovarios, útero y otros órganos sexuales masculinos y femeninos.

reptile ectotherm that is covered with dry scales, breathes with lungs, and reproduces by laying eggs. (p. 793)
reptil vertebrado ectotermo con la piel cubierta de escamas, que respira con pulmones y que pone huevos para reproducirse.

respiratory system body system that brings oxygen into the body and removes carbon dioxide; includes the nose, trachea, and lungs. (p. 910)
sistema respiratorio sistema corporal que lleva oxígeno al cuerpo y elimina el dióxido de carbono; consta de nariz, tráquea y pulmones.

resting potential difference in electrical charge between the inside and outside of a neuron; contains the potential energy needed to transmit the impulse. (p. 877)
potencial de reposo diferencia de carga eléctrica entre el interior y el exterior de una neurona; energía potencial necesaria para transmitir un impulso.

restriction enzyme enzyme that cuts DNA molecules at specific nucleotide sequences. (p. 265)
enzima de restricción enzima que fragmenta moléculas de ADN en secuencias específicas de nucleótidos.

restriction map diagram that shows the lengths of fragments between restriction sites in the strand of DNA. (p. 267)
mapa de restricción diagrama que representa las longitudes de los fragmentos entre los sitios de corte de una hebra de ADN.

retrovirus virus that contains RNA and uses the enzyme called reverse transcriptase to make a DNA copy. (p. 553)
retrovirus virus que contiene ARN y que usa una enzima llamada transcriptasa para hacer una copia del ADN.

Rh factor surface protein on red blood cells in the ABO blood group; people can be Rh^+ or Rh^-. (p. 928)
factor Rh proteína de la superficie de los glóbulos rojos de los grupos sanguíneos ABO; el factor Rh de las personas puede ser Rh^+ o Rh^-.

ribosomal RNA (rRNA) RNA that is in the ribosome and guides the translation of mRNA into a protein; also used as a molecular clock. (pp. 240; 532)
ARN ribosómico (ARNr) ARN presente en los ribosomas que guía el proceso de síntesis de las proteínas a partir del ARNm; también denominado reloj molecular.

ribosome (RY-buh-SOHM) organelle that links amino acids together to form proteins. (p. 76)
ribosoma orgánulo que enlaza las moléculas de aminoácidos para formar proteínas.

ribozyme RNA molecule that can catalyze specific chemical reactions. (p. 370)
Ribozima molécula de ARN que tiene la capacidad de catalizar determinadas reacciones químicas.

RNA nucleic acid molecule that allows for the transmission of genetic information and protein synthesis. (p. 239)
ARN molécula de ácido nucleico encargada de la transmisión de información genética y de la síntesis de las proteínas.

RNA polymerase enzyme that catalyzes the synthesis of a complementary strand of RNA from a DNA template. (p. 240)
ARN polimerasa enzima que cataliza la síntesis de una hebra complementaria de ARN a partir de un patrón de ADN.

rod cell photoreceptor in the eye that detects light intensity and contributes to black and white vision. (p. 881)
bastoncillo célula fotosensible del ojo que detecta la intensidad de la luz y contribuye a la visión en blanco y negro.

root cap mass of cells that covers and protects the tips of plant roots. (p. 648)
ápice de la raíz masa de células que cubre y protege las puntas de las raíces de las plantas.

root hair thin hairlike outgrowth of an epidermal cell of a plant root that absorbs water and minerals from the soil. (p. 648)
pelos radicales finas extensiones de la célula epidérmica en las raíces de una planta encargada de absorber agua y minerales del suelo.

S

sarcomere section of a muscle fiber that contains all of the filaments necessary to cause muscle contraction. (p. 1008)
sarcómero sección de fibra muscular con todos los filamentos necesarios para generar una contracción muscular.

sclerenchyma cell thick-walled, lignin-rich cells that form a supportive plant tissue. (p. 641)
esclereida célula rica en lignina que constituye el esclerénquima, un tejido de sostén de las plantas.

scrotum skin that encloses the testes outside of the male body. (p. 1026)
escroto piel que envuelve las gónadas masculinas en el exterior del cuerpo.

secondary growth growth in woody plants resulting in wider roots, branches, and stems. (p. 651)
crecimiento secundario crecimiento de las plantas que produce un engrosamiento de las raíces, de las ramas y de los tallos.

secondary succession reestablishment of a damaged ecosystem in an area where the soil was left intact. (p. 447)
sucesión secundaria desarrollo de un ecosistema dañado en una zona donde el suelo permanece inalterado.

seed structure used by some land plants to store and protect the embryo. (p. 614)
semilla estructura empleada por algunas plantas para almacenar y proteger al embrión.

segmentation repeated sections of an annelid's long body that contain the same set of body structures, apart from its distinct head and tail region. (pp. 714; 730)
segmentación secciones repetidas del cuerpo alargado de un anélido, cada una de las cueles contiene el mismo conjunto de estructuras corporales, con excepción de la cabeza y de la cola.

selective permeability condition or quality of allowing some, but not all, materials to cross a barrier or membrane. (p. 83)
permeabilidad selectiva condición o cualidad que permite discriminar el flujo de determinados materiales a través de una membrana o barrera.

semen white substance that contains sperm and fluids produced by sex glands of the male reproductive system. (p. 1026)
semen sustancia blanca que contiene espermatozoides y fluidos generados por las glándulas sexuales del sistema reproductor masculino.

sepal modified leaf that covers and protects the flower while it develops. (p. 668)
sépalo hoja modificada que cubre la flor durante su desarrollo.

sensitization process by which a neuron adds more receptors to its surface in response to consistently lower amounts of a neurotransmitter in the synapse. (p. 893)
sensibilización proceso mediante el cual una neurona incorpora a su superficie más receptores en respuesta a una insuficiencia sostenida de neurotransmisores en el espacio sináptico.

sessile unable to move from a fixed point. (p. 705)
sésil fijo a un punto, que no se mueve.

sex chromosome chromosome that directly controls the development of sexual characteristics. (p. 169)
cromosoma sexual cromosoma que controla directamente el desarrollo de las características sexuales.

sex-linked gene gene that is located on a sex chromosome. (p. 201)
gen ligado al sexo gen ubicado en un cromosoma sexual.

sexually transmitted disease (STD) disease that is passed from one person to another during sexual contact. (p. 1032)
enfermedad de transmisión sexual (ETS) enfermedad que se transmite de una persona a otra durante el contacto sexual.

sexual reproduction process by which two gametes fuse and offspring that are a genetic mixture of both parents are produced. (p. 170)
reproducción sexual proceso mediante el cual se unen dos gametos que dan lugar a crías cuyo genoma es una mezcla del de los dos progenitores.

sexual selection selection in which certain traits enhance mating success; traits are, therefore, passed on to offspring. (p. 338)
selección sexual selección en la que determinados rasgos incrementan el éxito del apareamiento; en consecuencia, tales rasgos se transmiten a las crías.

skeletal muscle muscle tissue that is attached to the skeletal system and, when contracted, moves bones. (p. 1006)
músculo esquelético tejido muscular adherido al sistema esquelético que, al contraerse, mueve los músculos.

skeletal system body system that includes bones and the connective tissues that hold the bones together in the body. (p. 1000)
sistema esquelético sistema que consta de los huesos y de los tejidos conjuntivos que mantienen unidos a los huesos.

slime mold protist with a slimelike amoeboid stage that grows on decaying vegetation and in moist soil. (p. 587)
moho mucoso protista de aspecto gelatinoso con una fase ameboide, que crece en material vegetal en descomposición y en la tierra húmeda.

small intestine organ of the digestive system that connects the stomach to the large intestine and in which chemical digestion takes place. (p. 980)
intestino delgado órgano del sistema digestivo que conecta el estómago al intestino grueso y en el que se produce la digestión química.

smog air pollution in which gases released from burning fossil fuels form a fog when they react with sunlight. (p. 488)
smog contaminación atmosférica en la que los gases liberados por la combustión de hidrocarburos reaccionan con la luz creando una niebla.

smooth muscle muscle tissue that moves substances, such as food and blood, through organs and tissues, such as the digestive system organs and blood vessels. (p. 1007)
músculo liso tejido muscular que mueve los alimentos y la sangre por los órganos y los tejidos como, por ejemplo, los órganos del sistema digestivo y los vasos sanguíneos.

sodium potassium pump active transport protein in neurons that carries sodium (Na^+) ions out of the cell and bring potassium (K^+) ions into the cell. (p. 877)
bomba sodio-potasio transporte activo de proteínas en las neuronas, en el que se extrae de la célula iones de sodio (Na^+) y se mete iones de potasio (K^+).

solute substance that dissolves in a solvent and is present at a lower concentration than the solvent. (p. 42)
soluto sustancia que se disuelve en un solvente y que aparece en menor concentración que éste.

solution mixture that is consistent throughout; also called a homogeneous mixture. (p. 42)
solución mezcla uniforme en toda su extensión; también se conoce como mezcla homogénea.

solvent substance in which solutes dissolve and that is present in greatest concentration in a solution. (p. 42)
solvente sustancia en la que se disuelve un soluto y que se presenta en mayor concentración que éste.

somatic cell (soh-MAT-ihk) cell that makes up all of the body tissues and organs, except gametes. (p. 168)
célula somática célula que conforma todos los tejidos y órganos del organismo, excepto los gametos.

somatic nervous system division of the peripheral nervous system that transports signals from the brain to the muscles that produce voluntary movements. (p. 889)
sistema nervioso somático parte del sistema nervioso periférico que transporta señales del encéfalo a los músculos para producir los movimientos voluntarios.

specialist consumer that eats only one type of organism. (p. 409)
especialista consumidor que se alimenta de un solo tipo de organismo.

speciation evolution of two or more species from one ancestral species. (p. 344)
especiación evolución de dos o más especies a partir de una sola especie ancestral.

species group of organisms so similar to one another that they can breed and produce fertile offspring. (pp. 5; 298)
especie grupo de organismos tan semejantes entre sí que pueden reproducirse y tener descendencia fértil.

sperm male gamete. (p. 176)
espermatozoide gameto masculino.

sphincter (SFIHNGK-tuhr) ring of muscle that separates the different organs of the digestive system. (p. 977)
esfínter músculo en forma de anillo que separa a los diversos órganos del sistema digestivo.

spiracle (SPIHR-uh-kuhl) hole on the body of an insect's exoskeleton through which air can be taken in or released. (p. 741)
espiráculo orificio en el cuerpo del exoesqueleto de los insectos a través del cual entra y sale aire.

sporangia spore-forming structures found in fungi, algae, and some plants. (p. 592)
esporangio estructura que produce esporas y que se encuentra en los hongos, las algas y algunas plantas.

sporophyte (SPAWR-uh-FYT) diploid, spore-producing phase of a plant life cycle. (p. 664)
esporofita fase diploide de producción de esporas en el ciclo de vida de una planta.

stabilizing selection pathway of natural selection in which intermediate phenotypes are selected over phenotypes at both extremes. (p. 332)
selección estabilizadora proceso de selección natural en el que se da preferencia a los fenotipos intermedios sobre los fenotipos de ambos extremos.

stamen male structure of flowering plants; includes the stalk and anther, which produces pollen. (p. 668)
estambre estructura floral masculina de las gimnospermas; consiste de una antera productora de polen unida a un pedicelo.

start codon codon that signals to ribosomes to begin translation; codes for the first amino acid in a protein. (p. 244)
codón de iniciación codón que da la señal a los ribosomas para que inicien el proceso de traducción; codifica el primer aminoácido de la proteína.

stem cell cell that can divide for long periods of time while remaining undifferentiated. (p. 153)
célula madre célula capaz de dividirse durante largos periodos de tiempo sin diferenciarse.

sternum long, flat bone that connects the ribs in front of the chest and to which the chest muscle attaches. (p. 801)
esternón hueso plano y alargado que conecta las costillas a la altura del pecho y al que van adheridos los músculos pectorales.

stimulant drug that increases the number of impulses that neurons generate. (p. 894)
estimulante droga que incrementa el número de impulsos que generan las neuronas.

stimulus (STIHM-yuh-luhs) (plural: *stimuli*) something that causes a physiological response. (pp. 818; 874)
estímulo cualquier cosa capaz de provocar una respuesta fisiológica.

stomach muscular sac in the digestive system that breaks down food into a liquidlike mixture. (p. 978)
estómago saco muscular del sistema digestivo donde se descompone la comida en una mezcla líquida.

stomata (singular: *stoma*) pores in the cuticle of a plant through which gas exchange occurs. (p. 614)
estoma poro en la cutícula de una planta a través del cual se produce el intercambio gaseoso.

stop codon codon that signals to ribosomes to stop translation. (p. 244)
codón de terminación codón que indica a los ribosomas que detengan el proceso de traducción.

substrate reactant in a chemical reaction upon which an enzyme acts. (p. 56)
sustrato reactivo de una reacción química sobre el que actúa un enzima.

succession sequence of biotic changes that regenerate a damaged community or start a community in a previously uninhabited area. (p. 445)
sucesión secuencia de cambios bióticos que regeneran una comunidad dañada o que crean una nueva comunidad en una zona hasta entonces deshabitada.

survivorship probability of surviving to a particular age. (p. 827)
supervivencia probabilidad de sobrevivir hasta una edad determinada.

survivorship curve graph showing the surviving members of each age group of a population over time. (p. 438)
curva de sobrevivencia gráfica que representa los sobrevivientes de una población por grupos de edad durante un periodo determinado.

sustainable development practice of not using natural resources more quickly than they can be replenished. (p. 502)
desarrollo sostenible práctica que consiste en no utilizar los recursos naturales más rápidamente de lo que pueden ser generarlos.

swim bladder buoyancy organ that helps fish to swim at different depths in the water. (p. 769)
vejiga natatoria órgano de flotación que permite a los peces nadar a diferentes profundidades.

symbiosis ecological relationship between members of at least two different species that live in direct contact with one another. (p. 432)
simbiosis relación ecológica en la que los miembros de al menos dos especies diferentes viven en contacto directo.

sympathetic nervous system part of the autonomic nervous system that prepares the body for action and stress. (p. 890)
sistema nervioso simpático sistema que forma parte del sistema nervioso autónomo y que se encarga de preparar el cuerpo para situaciones de acción y de estrés.

synapse tiny gap between neurons through which chemical signals are sent. (p. 879)
sinapsis pequeño espacio entre las neuronas a través del cual se envían señales químicas.

system changing, organized group of related parts that interact to form a whole. (p. 7)
sistema conjunto organizado y dinámico de partes que interactúan entre sí para formar un todo.

systemic circuit (sihs-STEHM-ihk) collection of blood vessels that carries blood between the heart and the rest of the body, except for the lungs. (pp. 789; 920)
circuito sistémico conjunto de vasos sanguíneos que transporta la sangre entre el corazón y el resto del cuerpo, excepto los pulmones.

systemic circulation *see* systemic circuit.
circulación sistémica *véanse* circuito sistémico.

systolic pressure (sih-STAHL-ihk) measure of pressure on the walls of an artery when the left ventricle contracts to pump blood through the body. (p. 923)
presión sistólica medida de la presión de las paredes arteriales cuando el ventrículo izquierdo se contrae para bombear sangre a través del cuerpo.

T

tadpole aquatic larva of frogs or toads. (p. 774)
renacuajo larva acuática de las ranas y los sapos.

taiga (TY-guh) biome with long and cold winters, lasting up to six months; also called a boreal forest. (p. 465)
taiga bioma propio de zonas de largos y fríos inviernos de hasta seis meses de duración; también se conoce como bosque boreal.

taproot main root of some plants, usually larger than other roots and growing straight down from a stem. (p. 649)
raíz pivotante raíz principal de determinadas plantas, normalmente más grande que las demás raíces y que crece en en línea recta hacia abajo a partir del tallo.

taxis movement in a particular direction, either toward or away from a stimulus. (p. 819)
taxismo movimiento en una dirección determinada, ya sea hacia un estímulo o en sentido opuesto a éste; conocido también como taxis.

taxon (plural: *taxa*) level within the Linnaean system of classification (kingdom, phylum, class, order, family, genus, or species) that is organized into a nested hierarchy. (p. 518)
taxón cualquiera de los niveles del sistema de clasificación jerárquico de Linneo, (reino, división, clase, orden, familia, género o especie).

taxonomy science of classifying and naming organisms. (p. 518)
taxonomía ciencia dedicada a la clasificación y nomenclatura de los organismos.

T cell white blood cell that matures in the thymus and destroys infected body cells by causing them to burst; also called a T-lymphocyte. (p. 946)
célula T glóbulo blanco que madura en el timo y que destruye las células infectadas haciéndolas reventar; también se conoce como linfocito T.

telomere (TEHL-uh-MEER) repeating nucleotide at the ends of DNA molecules that do not form genes and help prevent the loss of genes. (p. 139)
telómero extremo de la molécula de ADN compuesto de nucleótidos repetidos que no producen genes pero que ayudan a prevenir la pérdida de éstos.

telophase last phase of mitosis when a complete set of identical chromosomes is positioned at each pole of the cell, the nuclear membranes start to form, the chromosomes begin to uncoil, and the spindle fibers disassemble. (p. 140)
telofase última fase de la mitosis en que un conjunto completo de cromosomas idénticos se sitúa en los polos opuestos de la célula; empiezan a formarse las membranas nucleares; los cromosomas empiezan a desenrollarse y el huso mitótico se desintegra.

temporal isolation isolation between populations due to barriers related to time, such as differences in mating periods or differences in the time of day that individuals are most active. (p. 346)
aislamiento temporal aislamiento entre poblaciones que se produce por motivos de índole temporal como, por ejemplo, diferencias en los períodos de apareamiento o de las horas del día en que los individuos son más activos.

Glossary

tendon band of connective tissue that joins a muscle to the bone that it moves. (p. 1006)
tendón banda de tejido conjuntivo que conecta cada músculo con el hueso que mueve.

terminal end of the neuron's axon from which neurotransmitters are released to stimulate an adjacent cell. (p. 879)
terminal extremo del axón de la neurona desde el cual se segregan neurotransmisores para estimular a la célula adyacente.

territoriality behavior pattern in which an organism controls and defends a specific area. (p. 828)
territorialidad patrón de comportamiento mediante el cual un organismo determinado controla y defiende un área específica.

testcross cross between an organism with an unknown genotype and an organism with a recessive phenotype. (p. 185)
cruzamiento de prueba cruzamiento entre un organismo de genotipo desconocido y un organismo de fenotipo recesivo.

testis (plural: *testes*) organ of the male reproductive system that produces sperm. (p. 1025)
testículo órgano del sistema reproductor masculino encargado de la producción de espermatozoides.

testosterone (tehs-TAHS-tuh-ROHN) steroid hormone that is found in greater quantities in men than women and contributes to male sexual characteristics and development. (p. 1025)
testosterona hormona esteroide que se encuentra en mayor cantidad en el hombre que en la mujer y que contribuye al desarrollo de las características sexuales masculinas.

tetrapod vertebrate with four limbs. (p. 773)
tetrápodo vertebrado con cuatro extremidades.

theory proposed explanation for a wide variety of observations and experimental results. (p. 16)
teoría explicación de un fenómeno a partir de una amplia gama de observaciones y resultados experimentales.

thermoregulation (THUR-moh-REHG-yoo-LAY-shuhn) process of the body maintaining a stable internal temperature under various conditions. (p. 863)
termorregulación proceso que permite mantener una temperatura interna constante bajo diferentes condiciones.

thigmotropism turning or bending of a plant in response to contact with an object. (p. 682)
tigmotropismo giro o flexión de una planta como respuesta al contacto con un objeto.

thylakoid (THY-luh-KOYD) membrane-bound structure within chloroplasts that contains chlorophyll and other light-absorbing pigments used in the light-dependent reactions of photosynthesis. (p. 104)
tilacoide estructura de la membrana interna de los cloroplastos que contiene clorofila y otros pigmentos fotoabsorbentes que intervienen en las reacciones captadoras de luz de la fotosíntesis.

tissue group of cells that work together to perform a similar function. (pp. 151; 854)
tejido grupo de células similares que trabajan juntas para desempeñar la misma función.

tissue rejection process by which a transplant recipient's immune system makes antibodies against the protein markers on the donor's tissue; can result in the destruction of the donor tissue. (p. 954)
rechazo de tejidos proceso mediante el cual el sistema inmune de un individuo receptor de un transplante genera anticuerpos contra los marcadores proteicos del tejido donante; puede producir la destrucción del tejido donante.

tolerance drug resistance that occurs when cells adapt, requiring larger doses of the drug to produce the same effect. (p. 893)
tolerancia resistencia a una droga producida cuando las células se adaptan a ella, lo cual requiere un aumento de la dosis para producir el mismo efecto.

toxin poison released by an organism. (p. 563)
toxina sustancia tóxica producida por un organismo.

trachea (TRAY-kee-uh) (plural: *tracheae*) long structure made of soft tissue that connects the mouth and nose to the lungs in humans (p. 911); a system of thin branching tubes in the bodies of insects that allow for breathing. (p. 741)
tráquea tubo alargado de tejido blando que conecta la boca y la nariz con los pulmones de los humanos; sistema de finos tubos ramificados en el cuerpo de los insectos que les permite respirar.

trait characteristic that is inherited. (p. 177)
rasgo característica heredada.

transcription process of copying a nucleotide sequence of DNA to form a complementary strand of mRNA. (p. 240)
transcripción proceso donde se copia una secuencia de ADN para formar una cadena complementaria de ARNm.

transfer RNA (tRNA) form of RNA that brings amino acids to ribosomes during protein synthesis. (p. 240)
ARN de transferencia (ARNt) tipo de ARN que transporta aminoácidos a los ribosomas durante el proceso de síntesis proteica.

transgenic organism whose genome has been altered to contain one or more genes from another organism or species. (pp. 26; 277)
transgénico organismo cuyo genoma ha sido alterado mediante la incorporación de uno o más genes de otro organismo o especie.

translation process by which mRNA is decoded and a protein is produced. (p. 243)
traducción proceso mediante el cual se decodifica el ARNm y se produce una proteína.

transpiration release of vapor through the pores of the skin or the stomata of plant tissue. (p. 645)
transpiración liberación de vapor a través de los poros de la piel o, en los tejidos vegetales, de los estomas.

trimester one of three periods of approximately three months each into which a human pregnancy is divided. (p. 1036)
trimestre uno de los períodos de aproximadamente tres meses en que se divide la gestación humana.

trophic level level of nourishment in a food chain. (p. 409)
nivel trófico nivel de alimentación de la cadena trófica.

tropism movement or growth of a plant in response to an environmental stimulus. (p. 681)
tropismo movimiento o crecimiento determinado por un estímulo ambiental.

tundra biome found at far northern latitudes where winters last as long as ten months per year. (p. 466)
tundra bioma de latitudes septentrionales extremas donde los inviernos duran hasta diez meses.

U

umbilical cord structure that connects an embryo to its mother and provides the embryo with nourishment and waste removal. (p. 1035)
cordón umbilical estructura que conecta el embrión con su madre y que le suministra alimento y un sistema de eliminación de residuos.

umbrella species species whose being protected under the Endangered Species Act leads to the preservation of its habitat and all of the other organisms in its community. (p. 503)
especie paraguas especie protegida por la Ley de Especies en Peligro de Extinción cuya salvaguarda conlleva la protección de su hábitat y la de todos los otros organismos que viven en él.

uniformitarianism theory that states that the geologic processes that shape Earth are uniform through time. (p. 301)
uniformitarismo teoría según la cual los procesos geológicos que dan forma a la Tierra se producen de manera uniforme a lo largo del tiempo.

ureter (yu-REE-tuhr) tube of connective tissue that carries urine from each of the kidneys to the bladder. (p. 986)
uréter tubo de tejido conjuntivo que transporta la orina desde los riñones hasta la vejiga.

urinary bladder saclike organ that collects and stores urine before it is excreted from the body. (p. 986)
vejiga urinaria órgano en forma de bolsa donde se recoge y se almacena la orina antes de ser excretada del cuerpo.

uterus organ of the female reproductive system in which a fertilized egg attaches and a fetus develops. (p. 1024)
útero órgano del sistema reproductor femenino al que se adhiere el huevo fertilizado y dónde se desarrolla el feto.

V

vaccine substance that stimulates an immune response, producing acquired immunity without illness or infection. (pp. 553; 956)
vacuna sustancia que estimula una respuesta inmune y que proporciona inmunidad ante una enfermedad o infección determinada sin provocarla.

vacuole (VAK-yoo-OHL) organelle that is used to store materials, such as water, food, or enzymes, that are needed by the cell. (p. 77)
vacuola orgánulo encargado de almacenar diversos materiales necesarios para la célula, como el agua, nutrientes o enzimas.

valve flap of tissue that prevents blood from flowing backward into a blood vessel or heart chamber. (p. 917)
válvula tejido membranoso encargado de evitar que la sangre refluya por el vaso sanguíneo en que circula o hacia una cavidad del corazón.

variation differences in physical traits of an individual from the group to which it belongs. (p. 302)
variación diferencia en rasgos físicos que presenta un individuo con respecto al grupo al que pertenece.

vascular cylinder center of a root or stem that contains phloem and xylem. (p. 648)
cilindro vascular cilindro en el centro de una raíz o tallo que contiene el floema y el xilema.

vascular system collection of specialized tissues in some plants that transports mineral nutrients up from the roots and brings sugars down from the leaves. (p. 614)
sistema vascular conjunto de tejidos especializados de determinadas plantas que transportan nutrientes minerales desde las raíces hacia arriba y que conducen el azúcar de las hojas hacia abajo.

vascular tissue supportive and conductive tissue in plants, consisting of xylem and phloem. (p. 642)
tejido vascular tejido conductor y de sostén de las plantas que consta de xilema y de floema.

vas deferens duct in which sperm mixes with other fluids before reaching the urethra. (p. 1026)
conducto deferente conducto en el que el esperma se mezcla con otros fluidos antes de alcanzar la uretra.

vector organism, such as a mosquito or tick, that transfers pathogens from one host to another. (pp. 748; 944)
vector organismo, como o el mosquito o la garrapatas que puede transferir patógenos de un huésped a otro.

vegetative reproduction asexual reproduction in which a stem, leaf, or root will produce a new individual when detached from a parent plant. (p. 678)
reproducción vegetativa reproducción asexual en la que un tallo, una hoja o una raíz producen un nuevo individuo cuando se separan de la planta de la cual forman parte.

R73

Glossary

vein large blood vessel that carries blood from the rest of the body to the heart. (p. 913)
vena vaso sanguíneo de gran caudal que transporta la sangre desde todas las partes del cuerpo hasta el corazón.

ventricle large chamber in the heart that receives blood from an atrium and pumps blood to the rest of the body. (p. 917)
ventrículo amplia cámara del corazón que recibe sangre de la aurícula y la impulsa al resto del cuerpo.

vertebra (plural: *vertebrae*) bone that makes up the spinal column. (p. 1001)
vértebra hueso que compone la columna vertebral.

vertebrate animal with an internal segmented backbone. (p. 699)
vertebrado animal con una columna vertebral interna y segmentada.

vesicle (VEHS-ih-kuhl) small organelle that contains and transports materials within the cytoplasm. (p. 77)
vesícula pequeño orgánulo que contiene y transporta materiales en el interior del citoplasma.

vestigial structure remnants of an organ or structure that functioned in an earlier ancestor. (p. 314)
estructura vestigial restos de algún órgano o estructura en una especie determinada que cumplieron alguna función en un ancestrode ésta.

villus (VIHL-uhs) (plural: *villi*) small fingerlike projection in the small intestine that absorbs nutrients. (p. 983)
vellosidades pequeñas proyecciones en forma de dedo del intestino delgado encargadas de absorber los nutrientes.

viroid infectious particle made of single-stranded RNA without a protein coat, that almost always use plants as their host. (p. 544)
viroide partícula infecciosa que consta de un solo filamento de ARN sin envoltura de proteínas, que casi siempre se hospeda como parásito en las plantas.

virus infectious particle made only of a strand of either DNA or RNA surrounded by a protein coat. (p. 544)
virus partícula infecciosa que consta de un sólo filamento de ADN o ARN y rodeado por una envuelta de proteína.

vitamin organic molecule that works with enzymes to regulate cell function, growth, and development. (p. 974)
vitamina molécula orgánica que funciona con enzimas para regular el funcionamiento, el crecimiento y el desarrollo de las células.

viviparous reproductive strategy in which the embryo develops within the mother's body. (p. 793)
vivíparo modalidad de reproducción en la que los embriones se desarrollan en el interior de la madre.

W

water mold fungus that is either a parasite or decomposer and lives in fresh water or moist soil. (p. 588)
moho acuático hongo acuático o de suelos húmedos que actúa como parásito o descomponedor de materia orgánica.

watershed region of land that drains into a river, river system, or other body of water. (p. 473)
cuenca hidrográfica área terrestre que vierte sus aguas hacia un río, una red fluvial o cualquier otra masa acuática.

water vascular system system of water-filled canals that extend down each arm of a echinoderm, such as a sea star. (p. 718)
sistema ambulacral sistema formado por una serie de tubos llenos de agua que se prolongan por los brazos de los equinodermos como, por ejemplo, la estrella de mar.

white blood cell cell that attacks pathogens. (p. 928)
glóbulo blanco célula cuya funcíon es atacar a los patógenos.

wood fibrous material made of dead cells that are part of the vascular system in some plants. (p. 627)
madera material fibroso formado por células muertas que forman parte del sistema vascular de algunas plantas.

X

X chromosome inactivation process that occurs in female mammals in which one of the X chromosomes is randomly turned off in each cell. (p. 203)
inactivación X proceso en los mamíferos del sexo femenino en que uno de los cromosomas X de cada célula se desactiva aleatoriamente.

xylem tissue that transports water and dissolved minerals in vascular plants. (p. 642)
xilema tejido de las plantas vasculares que transporta agua y sales minerales disueltas.

Z

zooplankton animal plankton. (p. 469)
zooplancton plancton animal.

zygote cell that forms when a male gamete fertilizes a female gamete. (p. 1031)
cigoto célula formada cuando un gameto masculino fertiliza un gameto femenino.

Index

Page numbers for definitions are printed in **boldface** type. Page numbers for illustrations, maps, and charts are printed in *italics.*

A

abdomen, 735
abiotic factor, 402–405, 457, 458
ABO blood group, 927–928, *928*
absorption, *644*, 649, **982**
abyssal zone, 469
acacia, 349, *349*
Acanthodian, 765
Acanthostega, 773
acetylcholine, 892
acid, 42–43
acid rain, *483*, **489**, *489*, 493
acne, *564*
Acoelomorpha, 704
acquired characteristics, inheritance of, 299. ***See also*** **heredity.**
acquired immune deficiency syndrome (AIDS), 960, **963**, 965, 1032
acquired immunity, 948, 951
Acrasiomycota, 587
acrosome, 1030
actin filament, 1008–1011, *1009*, *1010*
action potential, *878*, **879**, 893–894
activation energy, *52*, **53**, *54*, 54–55
active immunity, 948
active transport, 89–90, *89*, 877, *877*
adaptation, 10–11, **302**–303, *307*, 353
  and animal behavior, 818–821, 825–826
  of birds, 799–803
  to climate, 461
  as compromise, 309
  to ecosystem, 473
  environmental, 305–306, 321
  of finches, 308–309, 311
  of freshwater organisms, 473
  of insects, 744–746
  of leaves, 655
  online animation, 477
  of plants, 613–614, *615*, 624–625, *625*, 657
adaptive radiation, 351, 367
addiction, 893, 903
Addison's disease, 901
adenine, 230–233, *231*, *233*, 240
adenosine diphosphate, 101
adenosine triphosphate, 100
adhesion, 41, *41*, 643–645, *644*
adolescence, 1042
ADP, 101, *102*
adrenal gland, 898, *899*, 901
adulthood, 1043
adult stem cell, 154
advantageous characteristics. *See* natural selection.
aerobic process, 113
aflatoxin, 590
African swallowtail, 334
African violet, 679
agar, 584
agave plant, 680, *680*
aging, 1043
Agnatha, 760, *765*. ***See also*** **jawless fish.**
agriculture, 565, 567, 629–630
AIDS, 960, **963**, 965, 1032
Ailurus fulgens, *521*
airfoil, 799
air movement, 460
air quality, 488–492
air sac, 801
alanine, 244
albatross, 436
albinism, 59, 207, *207*
albumin, 926
alcoholic fermentation, 124–125
aldosterone, 84
algae, *410*, 411, **581**–586, 601
  green, 612–613, *613*
  limiting nutrients for, 448
  photosynthetic, 99, *99*
  red, 584, *R26*
  and pollution, 494
alkaloid, 631
allele, 180–184, 187. ***See also*** **genetics.**
  codominance, 205–206, *205*, 208
  dominant/recessive, 341
  in gene pool, 328–329
  and genetic disorders, 201
  incomplete dominance, 204–205, *205*, 219
  and phenotypes, 204–207
  and probability, 193
allele frequency, 328–331, *329*, 341–343
allergen, 957–958
allergy, 692, **957**
Allosaurus, 798
aloe vera, 631
alternation of generations, 664, *664*
Altman, Sidney, 370
altruism, 833–836
Alvarez, José and Maria, *990*
alveolus, 911–912, *914*, 914–916, *915*
Alzheimer's disease, 1052
amber-preserved fossil, 360
Ambulocetus natans, *318*
amino acid, 47–48, *47*, 369
  essential, 973
  and molecular clocks, 530–531, *531*
  and species' relatedness, 529
  and translation, 243–247
Amish communities, 336
ammonia, 415
ammonification, 415
amniote, 778–779, 786–809
  anatomy and circulation, 789–790, *790*
  birds, 798–804
  body temperature regulation, 791–792
  embryos, 788, *788*
  mammals, 805–809
  reptiles, 793–797
amniotic egg, 779, 788, *788*
amniotic sac, 526, 788, **1035**, *1035*
amoeba, 578, *578*
amoebocyte, 706
Amphibia, 760
amphibian, 430, 526, **773**–777, 781
  online animation, 477
amygdala, 888
amylase, 55, 56, 978, *978*
anaerobic process, 113
analogies, drawing, 353
analogous structure, 313, *313*
analyzing data. *See* data analysis.
anaphase, 140, *141*
anaphylaxis, 958
anapsid, 794
ancestry, common, 244, 299, 310–313, 317, 524–525
Andes mountains, 303
anemone, sea, 150, 468, 707–708, 827, *R28*
angioplasty, 924
angiosperm, 621, 622. ***See also*** **flowering plant.**
anhinga, 395, *395*
animal
  and allergies, 958
  arthropods, 704, 716, 728–749, **730**
  body structures, 696, *696*, 699–700, 723
  body temperature regulation, 863, 875, 900, 913
  cells, *74*, 78, *113*, 140
  characteristics of, 696–698
  classification of, 701–702
  developmental patterns of, 702, *702*
  embryo growth, 153, *153*
  and fungi, 697
  genetic engineering in, 278–279
  invertebrates, 699, 705–720
  and neurons, *873*
  online animation, 723
  phyla, 699, 703–704, *761*
  and sensory organs, 882
  vertebrates, 699, 756–779
animal behavior, 816–839
  adaptive value of, 818–821, 825–826
  and cognition, 837–839
  costs of, 827–828, 831, 833–834
  evolution of, 827–829, 833–834
  and hormone cycles, 1028
  instinct and learning, 822–826
  mate selection, 832
  online animation, 841
  problem-solving, 838
  social, 831–836, 838–839
animalcule, *71*
animal fat, 46
Animalia, *R28–R31*

R75

Index

Animated Biology, 21, 29, 41, 52, 59, 74, 93, 104, 114, 127, 157, 175, 182, 193, 219, 233, 237, 246, 257, 266, 270, 287, 307, 321, 337, 342, 353, 373, 385, 406, 421, 430, 449, 474, 477, 484, 491, 507, 531, 537, 550, 567, 579, 583, 601, 633, 644, 657, 685, 723, 732, 745, 751, 763, 775, 781, 800, 811, 828, 841, 855, 867, 878, 889, 903, 912, 919, 933, 956, 965, 993, 1017, 1037, 1043, 1045
anino acid, 243
annelid, 714–715, *715*, 734. *See also* **segmented worm.**
annual plant, 627
anole lizard, 352, 820, *820*
***Anopheles* mosquito,** 580
ant
  honeypot, 4, 4
  leafcutter, 599, *599*
  social behavior of, 834, *835*
  stinging, 349, *349*
  weaver, 834
antacid, 992
Antarctica, 467
antelope, 429
antenna, 733, 736
Antennapedia, 698
anther, 668
Anthocerophyta, 617
Anthophyta, 622
anthozoa, 708
anthrax, *564*
anthropoid, **380**, *380*
antibiotic, **564**, *941*, **955**, *955*
  and fungi, 597, 599
  online animation, 567
  resistance, 331, 353, 391–392, 565, **955**
antibody, **947**, *947*, 953, *953*
anticodon, **245**
antidiuretic hormone (ADH), 993
antigen, **951**
antigen-presenting cell, 952, *952*
antiseptic, *941*, **955**
anus, 984
aorta, 918
ape, 380, *380*
aphid, 747, *747*
aphotic zone, 468
apical meristem, 648, 651
Apicomplexa, 580
aplacophora, 713
Aplomado Falcon, 848
apoptosis, **145**, 157, 853
appendage, **730**
appendicular skeleton, **1000**, *1000*
apple, 679, 681
apple snail, 409, *409*
arachnid, 740–742, *741*
Archaea domain, **534**–535, *535*, 555–557, *R25*
Archaeopteryx, 798, *798*
archosaur, 797
Arctic, 467
Arctic Sea, 492, *492*
Arctic tern, 811
Armadillidium vulgare, 840
armadillo, 303, *524*, 525
Armidillidium vulgare, 519
Armillaria ostoyae, 589
arteriole, 922
arteriosclerosis, 924
artery, **913**
arthropod, 376, 528, 704, 716, 728–749, **730**
  and annelid worms, 734
  arachnids, **740**–742, *741*
  characteristics of, 730–734
  crustaceans, 731, *731*, **735**–738
  fossils, 359
  groups, 731, 751
  and humans, 747–749
  insects, 313, 731, *731*, 743–746
  online animation, 751
articular bone, 807
artificial selection, **304**–305, 308, 630
Ascomycota, 590, 594
ascorbic acid, *974*
ascus, 591, 594
asexual reproduction, **148**–150, 373, 678–679
  of algae, 584–585
  of animals, 698
  of fungi, 591–594
  of invertebrates, 705–707, 715
Aspergillis flavus, 590
aspirin, 631
associative learning, 825
Asteroidea, 719
asthma, **916**, 933
athlete's foot, 942
atmosphere, **456**
atom, **36**–37, *37*
  and bond energy, **51**
  covalent bonds, **39**, *39*
ATP, **100**–102, *102*, 975
  and active transport, 90
  and cellular respiration, 113, 115, 117–118, 120
  and photosynthesis, 108, 110–111
ATP synthase, **110**, *110*
atrioventricular (AV) node, 918
atrium, **917**
Australia, *441*
australopithecine, 382
Australopithecus afarensis, 382, *383*
autoimmune disease, 959, *959*, 965
autonomic nervous system, **890**
autosome, **169**, 200–201, *201*, 214, *215*
autotroph, **406**
auxin, **681**–682
Avery, Oswald, 227, 229
Aves, 760. *See also* **birds.**
avian flu, 553, 608
axial skeleton, *1000*, **1001**, *1001*
axillary bud, 652
axolotl, 776
axon, **876**, *876*
azalea, 43

B

Bacillariophyta, 583
bacillus, 556
Bacillus anthracis, *564*
Bacillus thuringiensis, 748
background extinction, 350, *350*, 847
bacteria, 79, 544. *See also* **prokaryote.**
  and antibiotics, 564–565
  cyanobacteria, *366*, 372
  and digestion, 125
  and disease, 942
  drug-resistant, 149, 331, 353, 391–392, 565
  and endosymbiosis, 373
  in esophagus, *543*
  generation times of, 375
  and genetics, 227–228, 276–278
  growth of, *149*
  and humans, 11
  and infections, 563–564, *564*
  in intestine, *559*
  leaf print, 562
  and oil, 561, 566
  online lab, 157, 287, 567
  and plants, 616
  and restriction enzymes, 265, *265*
  shapes of, *556*
  and viral infection, 549
Bacteria domain, **534**–535, *535*, 555–557, *R25*
bacteriophage, **228**, *228*, 391, **549**
bald eagle, 335, *335*, 504
ball-and-socket joint, 1002, *1003*
bandicoot, 190, *190*
band 3 protein, 84
banyan fig, 639
baobab tree, *650*
bar graph, 172, 210, 339, 497, 836, 895, 1038, R16
bark, 650, *651*
barnacle, 311, *311*, 738
barn owl, 519, *519*
barracuda, *768*
base, **42**–43
base pair, 230–233, 265
basidia, 592
Basidiomycota, 590, 592
Basilosaurus isis, 316, *316*
basket star, 720, *720*
basophil, 957, *957*
bat
  vampire, 833
  wings of, *312*, 312–313, *313*
  Yuma myotis, *805*
Bateson, William, 209
bathyal zone, **469**
B cell, **946**, 947, 951, 953, *953*
beak, 321, 803, 811

bear
  grizzly, *396*
  polar, 9, *9*, 467, *467*, *512*
Beaumont, William, 977
beaver, 403
bee, *429*, 432, *669*, *746*, 823, 832
beetle
  elm bark, 597, *597*
  red leaf, *696*
  red lily, *999*
  rhino, *730*
  snout, *8*, 9
behavior, animal. ***See* animal behavior.**
behavioral isolation, 345
Beijerinck, Martinus, 547
Belding's ground squirrel, *833*, 833–834
beluga whale, 496
Bengal tiger, *809*
benign tumor, 146
benthic zone, 468, **474**
best-fit line, 142
betta fish, 205, *205*
bichir, 769
biennial plant, 627
bighorn sheep, 338
bilateral symmetry, 701, *701*, *703*
bile, 980
binary fission, 148–149, *149*, 558
binomial nomenclature, 519
biochemistry. ***See* chemistry of life.**
biochip, 293
biodegradable material, 561
biodiversity, 5, 11, **403**, 498–501, 846–848
  and genetics, 276
  online analysis, 29, 537
bioethics, 26–27, 29, 63–64
biogeochemical cycle, 413, 587
biogeography, 311
bioindicator, 494
bioinformatics, 282–283
biological clock, 820
biology, 5
  characteristics of organisms, 5–6
  and ethics, 26–27
  and health, 24–25
  and scientific thinking, 13–17
  tools and technology, 19–23
  unifying themes of, 7–11
biomagnification, 495–496, *495*
biomass, 417–418, *418*, 470
biome, 397, *397*, 462–467, 476
bioreactor, 26
bioremediation, *561*, 847
biosphere, 4, 454–474, **456**
  biomes, 397, *397*, 462–467, 476
  and climate, 458–461
  and Earth's systems, 456–457
  estuaries and freshwater ecosystems, 471–474
  marine ecosystems, 411, 468–471
biota, 456
biotechnology, 26, 262–285. ***See also* DNA.**
  and bacteria, 543
  bioinformatics, 282–283
  gene therapy, 285, 293–294
  genetic engineering, 275–279, **276**, 286
  genetic screening, 63–64, **284**, 287
  genomics, 280–281
biotic factor, 402–405, 457
biotin, *974*
BioZine, 62–64, 162–164, 292–294, 390–392, 512–514, 606–608, 690–692, 846–848, 1050–1052
bipedal animal, 381
bird, 798–803
  adaptation of, 799–803
  anatomy of, *800*
  beaks of, 321, 803, 811
  bones of, *800*, 801
  competition, 431
  and estuaries, 472
  evolution of, 798–799
  flight hypotheses, 799
  heart of, 790, *790*
  migration, 811, 821
  mobbing by, 832
  online animation, 800, 811
  radiation of, 378
  response, 841
  wings of, 799, 802, 804
bird flu, 553, 608
birth, human, 1040–1041, *1041*
Bishop pine, 346
bivalve, 713
Black Death, 940, *940*, 944
black-footed ferret, 398
black widow spider, 741
bladder, urinary, 986, 990
blade, 652
blastocyst, 1034, *1034*
blood, 926–929
  and carbonic acid, 51, *51*
  circulation, 917–920
  clotting, 861, 929, *929*
  and kidney function, 987–991
  online lab, 933
  plasma, 42, *51*
  pressure, 923–924
  and smooth muscle, 1007
  types, 205–206, 927–928, *928*, 933, 954
  vessels, 922–923, *923*
blood cell
  and erythropoietin, 145
  microscopic observation of, 928
  red, 8–9, *852*, **915**, 927, *927*
  white, *55*, 553, 898, **928**, 931, *939*, 946, *946*, *950*, 950–951, 959–960
blue-footed booby, 803, *803*
blue-spotted ray, *766*
bluestem, *627*
blue whale, 696, *696*
B-lymphocyte, 946, 947, 951, 953, *953*
body heat, 851
body temperature
  of amniotes, 791–792
  and blood, 920, 1013
  homeostasis, 858, 859, *859*, 867, 1013
  and human skin, 883
  and muscular system, 1006
  online graphing, 811
  regulation of, 9, 863, 875, 900, 913
bog, 359
Bohr, Niels, *37*
bond energy, 51
bonding, chemical, 50–51, *51*
  online animation, 59
bone, 759, *800*, 801, 1000–1005, *1004*. ***See also* skeletal system.**
bone marrow, 145, 960–961, *1004*, 1004–1005
bony fish, 765, 767, 768–771, *769*, 780. ***See also* Osteichthye.**
booby, blue-footed, 803, *803*
book lung, 740
boreal forest, 465
Borlaug, Norman, 691
Borrelia Burgdorferi, *564*
botany, 629
bottleneck effect, 336
bottlenose dolphin, 838
botulism, 563
bovine spongiform encephalopathy (BSE), 545
bowerbird, satin, 832, *832*
Bowman's capsule, 988, *989*
box turtle, *760*
bracket fungus, 591
braconid wasp, 432, *433*
brain, 886–888, *887*, 1050–1052. ***See also* nervous system.**
  cell, 317
  chemistry of, 891–894
  disorders of, 892, 903
  and drugs, 893–894
  lobe, *887*
  multitasking, 1052
  plasticity of, 1051
  size, 382–383
  stem, 888, 915
braincase, 759
bread mold, 591–592, *592*, *593*
breast cancer, 146, 294
breathing, 860, *860*, 912, *912*
breeding, 193, 304–305, 308
brine shrimp, 739
bristlecone pine, 622
brittle star, 720
bronchiole, 911, *911*, *914*, 916
bronchus, 911, *911*
brown algae, 584, *584*
brown pelican, 471
brown recluse spider, 741

Index

Bryophyta, 617
Bt, 278, 692
bubonic plague, 748
budding, 150, 591
buffer, 43
Buffon, Georges Louis Leclerc de, 299, *299*
bugeye squid, *53*
bulb, 679
bulbourethral gland, 1026, *1026*
bull-thorn acacia, 349, *349*
buoyancy, 769
Burgess Shale, 359, 376
Burmese python, 500, *500*
burr, 673, *673*
butterfly, *429*, *731*
 monarch, 616, *745*
 swallowtail, 334, *748*
bypass surgery, 924

C

cactus, 465, 640, 650, *650*, 655, *678*
caecilian, 777, *777*
calciferol, *974*
calcification, 1005
calcitonin, 1005
calcium, 38, 973, *973*, 1005
calculating, 106–107, 188, 218, 384. ***See also*** **data analysis.**
Calorie, 975
calorimetry, 59
Calvin cycle, 105, **111**
Cambrian explosion, 376, 700, 734
Cambrian period, 366
Canada goose, 821
cancer, 146
 breast, 146, 294
 cell, *133*, *144*, *146*, 147
 cervical, 146
 lung, 133, *133*
 online animation, 157
 and plant compounds, 631
 skin, 256
 treatments for, 705
cancer geneticist, 294
Candida, 597
Canis lupis, 520, 521
canopy, 464
Cape sugarbird, *611*
capillary, 913
capillary action, 645
capsid, 547
capuchin monkey, 838, *838*
carapace, 735
carbohydrate, 45–46, *46*, 101–102
 in cell membrane, 82, *82*
 complex/simple, 972
carbon
 atom, 44
 and fatty acids, 46
 radiometric dating, 362–363
 sinks and sources, 414
carbon-based molecule, *44*, 44–48
 and ATP, 101–102
 and cellular respiration, 118
 chains and rings, 44, *44*
 and energy, 100
 and photosynthesis, 111
carbon cycle, 112, 414, *414*, 499
 online lab, 127
carbon dioxide, 39, *39*, 414, 457
 and carbonic acid, 51
 and exercise, 921
 and photosynthesis, 105, 112
 and respiratory and circulatory systems, 50, 911, 914–915
 and temperature change, *490*, 490–492, 514
carbonic acid, 51, 915
Carboniferous period, 366, *376*, 377, 619, 794
carcinogen, 146
cardiac muscle, 917–918, *1007*, **1008**
careers
 in Biology, R38–R39
 cancer geneticist, 294
 cell biologist, 164
 conservation biologist, 848
 epidemiologist, 608
 evolutionary biologist, 392
 geneticist, 64
 neuroscientist, 1052
 oceanographer, 514
 research engineer, 692
carnivore, 409
carotenoid, 584
carpel, 668
carrageenan, 584
Carribean Sea, 402
carrier, 201
carrying capacity, 442, 484–485
Carson, Rachel, *255*, 502
cartilage, 1001
cartilaginous fish, 765–767. ***See also*** **Chondrichthye.**
cartilaginous joint, 1002
cast, natural, 360
cat, 203, *203*, 275, *275*, 789, *789*
catalase, 57
catalyst, 54–55, *54*
catastrophism, *300*, **301**
caterpillar, hornworm, 432, *433*
Caulerpa taxifolia, 601
causation, 895
Cech, Thomas, 370
cecum, 314
celery, 640
celiac disease, 982
cell, 5–6, 68–91, 98–125. ***See also*** **blood cell; cellular respiration; somatic cell.**
 active transport, 89–90, *89*
 ADP, 101, *102*
 animal, *74*, *113*
 ATP, 90, **100**–102, *102*
 binary fission, 558
 brain, 317
 cycle, 235
 determination, 852–853
 differentiation, 152–153, *153*, **853**–854, *853*
 diffusion, 85–88
 diploid, 170–171, 664
 endocytosis and exocytosis, 90
 eukaryotes, 373–374
 and fermentation, 118, **122**–125, 127
 formation of first cells, 370
 haploid, 170–171, 175–176, 664
 host, 373
 membrane, 8, 47, **81**–84, *82*, 88, 93, 370, 897, 988
 metabolism, 851, 860
 microscopic examination of, 866
 multicellular organisms, 376
 online animation, 93
 organelles, 72, 73–79, 93
 osmosis, 85–87, **86**
 and photosynthesis, 102, **103**–112
 plant, *71*, *74*, *100*, *640*, 640–642, *641*
 prokaryotes, 372–374
 sex, 1031
 size, 136–137, *137*, 156
 sperm, 853, *1030*
 stem, 153–155, 852–853
 structure and function, 8–9, 35, 38, 46, 92–93, 148
 theory, 70–72, **71**
 wall, 79, *79*, 87, 142, 983
 zygote, 852, **1031,** 1034
cell biologist, 164
cell division, 132–150, 173. ***See also*** **meiosis.**
 and asexual reproduction, 148–150
 and cancer, 146–147, *146*
 cell cycle, 134–137, *134*, *140*, 140–142, *142*
 cytokinesis, 135, 138–142, *141*
 and growth factors, 144–145
 mitosis, 134, **135,** 138–142, *141*, 143
 rate of, 136, *136*
 regulation of, 144–147
cellular immunity, 952, *952*
cellular respiration, 50, 53, **113**–121, *114*, 126, 417
 and ATP, 113, 115, 117–118, 120
 of birds, 801
 and electron transport, *114*, 119–121, *120*
 and glycolysis, 113, 117–118, 122–123
 and Krebs cycle, *114*, **115,** 118–*119*
 and photosynthesis, 112, 114–115, *115*, 121, *121*
cellular slime mold, 588
cellulose, 45–46, 112, 314
 in cell walls, 79
 in food, 972
 plant, 732
Celsius
 conversion to Fahrenheit, R5

Cenozoic era, 366–367, **378**
centipede, *731*
central dogma, 239, *239*
central nervous system (CNS), 875, *885,* 885–890
central tendency, 628
centriole, 78, *78*
centromere, 139, *139*
centrosome, 78
cephalochordate, 758
cephalopoda, 713
cephalothorax, 735
cerebellum, 888
cerebral cortex, 887
cerebrum, 886–887, *887*
cervical cancer, 146
cervix, 1025, 1040
Cesarean section, 1040
chaparral, 466, *466*
Chara, *612*
Chargaff, Erwin, 231, 257
Chargaff's rules, 231, 257
charophycean, 612, *612*
Chase, Martha, 228, 230, 231
cheese, 123, *125*
chelicerate, 731, *731,* 734, **740**
cheliped, 736
chemical energy, 6, 100–102. ***See also*** **cellular respiration; photosynthesis.**
chemical reaction, 50–53
chemiosmotic gradient, 110
chemistry of life, 34–56
atoms, ions, and molecules, 36–39
bonding, 50–51
carbon-based molecules, *44,* 44–48
catalysts, 54–55, *54*
chemical reactions, 50–53
enzymes, 54–56, **55**
isotopes, 362
water, 40–43
chemoreceptor, 881
chemosynthesis, 102, 407
chemotherapy, 147, 163
chickenpox, *554*
chigger, 741
childhood, 1042
chimera, 766
chimpanzee, 380, *380, 817,* 838
chitin, 79, **589, 730,** 732
chiton, 713
chlamydia, 1032
Chlamydomonas, *584,* 584–585, *585*
chloride ion, 38, *38*
chlorine, 38
chlorophyll, 79, **103**–105, 582, 584
fluorescence, 654
and green algae, 612
Chlorophyta, 584
chloroplast, 79, *79,* 80, *103,* 103–104, *104,* 114, 373
choanocyte, 706
choanoflagellate, 705
cholesterol, 82, *82*
choline, *974*
Chondrichthye, 760, 766. ***See also*** **cartilaginous fish.**
Chordata, 702, 758
chordate, 758, 888
chorion, 1035
chromatid, 139, *139,* 173, *173,* 175, *175,* 190
chromatin, 139, *139*
chromosomal mutation, 253–254
chromosome, 138–139, *138, 139,* 168–171. ***See also*** **genetics.**
autosomes, 169, 200–201, *201,* 214, *215*
cross-overs, 190–191, *190,* 210–211, *211*
for eye color, *199*
and fertilization, 1031
homologous, 169, *173,* 173–174, *174,* 190
and linked genes, 209
mapping, 216–217
and phenotype, 200–203
sex, 169, 200–201, *201*
X and Y, 169, 201–203, 213, *213*
X chromosome inactivation, 203
chyme, 979
chytrid, 590
Chytridiomycota, 590
cigarette smoke, 25, 916
cilia, 78, 578–579, *855,* 911, 945, *945*
ciliate, 578–579
Ciliophora, 579
circadian rhythm, 820
circle graph, R17
circulatory system, 614, *856,* **910**–913, *913*
of amniotes, 789–790, *790*
of amphibians, 774
of arthropods, 733
and blood transport, 922–924
diseases of, 924
of fish, 763
and gas exchange, 914–915
and heart, 917–920
and lymphatic system, 930
online animation, 933
citric acid, 118, 599
citrus fruit, 972
clade, 525–526, *527*
cladistics, 525
cladogram, 525–526, *527*
online animation, 537
clam, 714
classical conditioning, 826
classification, *R25–R31*
of animals, 701–702
domains and kingdoms, 533–535, 575
and evolutionary relationships, 524–528
genus, 383
Linnaean, 298, 518–521
and molecular evolution, 530–532
of plants, 617–622, 632
of vertebrates, 758–760, *761*
classifying, 522, 525. ***See also*** **data analysis.**
class taxon, *520,* 520–521
Clean Air Act, 504
cleaner shrimp, *7*
Clever Hans, 837
climate, 458–461
cloaca, *797,* 808
clone, 275–276, 287
Clostridium botulinum, *563,* 563–564
Clostridium tetani, *564*
clotting, blood, 861, 929, *929*
clover, 561, *561*
clown anemone fish, *764*
club fungus, 591–592, *592, 593*
club moss, 619, *619*
clumped dispersion, 437, *437*
cnidarian, *707,* 707–708, *708*
cnidocyte, 707
coal, 377
coastal ecosystem, 470
cocaine, *894*
cocci, 556
cochlea, 882
coconut, 673
coconut crab, *737*
codominance, 205–206, *205,* 208
codon, 243–245
coelacanth, 771
coelom, 714
coenzyme A, 118
coevolution, 349
cognition, animal, 837–839, 841
cohesion, 41, *41,* 643–645, *644*
cohesion-tension theory, 643–645
cold desert, 465
cold virus, 552, *552,* 864
collagen, 697, *697,* 1015
collecting data, 28, 57, 126, 143, 405, 493, 497, 647, 709, 739, 750, 857, 884, 902, 1012. ***See also*** **data analysis.**
collenchyma cell, 640, *641*
colon, 984, *984*
Colorado River, *473*
colorblindness, 214–216, *215*
combination graph, 442, **R16**
commensalism, 432, *433,* 663
common ancestor, 244, 299, 310–313, 317, 524–525
communicating, 59, 157. ***See also*** **data analysis.**
communication
animal, 832
in human organism, 859
nervous and endocrine systems, 875
community, 397, *397*
compact bone, 1004, *1004*
comparing, 92, 147, 477, 506, 733. ***See also*** **data analysis.**
competition, 306, 429, **431,** 443, 639, 828
competitive exclusion, 429–430
complement protein, 947

Index

complete metamorphosis, 744, *745*
complex tissue, 643
component vaccine, 956
compound, 37
  buffer, 43
  ionic, 38, 42
  online animation, 59
compound joint, 1002
compound microscope, 70, *70*
computerized tomography (CT), 891, *891*
computer modeling, 3, 22, 282
concentration gradient, 85, 89–90
conclusions, drawing, 320. *See also* data analysis.
conditioning, behavioral, 825–826
cone, 621, 666–667, *667*
cone cell, *881*
conidia, 594
conifer. *See also* gymnosperm.
  life cycle, *R34*
Coniferophyta, 621
coniferous tree, 465, 622, *622*, 666–667, *667*
conjugation, 391, **557**
connective tissue, 854
conservation, 502–505, 847–848
conservation biologist, 848
constant, 16, R11
consumer, 406, 409
continuous data, 497
control center, 859
control group, 16, R12
convergent evolution, 348, *348*, 517, 744
coordination. *See* muscular system; skeletal system.
Copeland, Herbert, 533
copepod, 735, 737
coral, 583, *707*, 707–708
coral larva, 586
coral reef, 402, *410*, 411, **470,** *470*
Cordyceps, 594
cork, 70
corn, 188, *630*, 748
cornea, 881
coronary artery disease, *254*
corpus callosum, 887
corpus luteum, 1029
correlation, 895
cortisol, 901, 903
cotyledon, 625, 672, 675
countercurrent flow, 764
covalent bond, 39, *39*, 232
cow, *555*
coyote, 438
crab, 311, *311*, 349, *731*
  coconut, *737*
  fiddler, 736
  hermit, 736
  spider, 730
crane
  sandhill, 444
  whooping, 824, *824*
crayfish, 751
Cretaceous period, 351, 366, 795
Creutzfeld-Jakob disease (CJD), 545
Crick, Francis, 231–232, *232*, 235, 239, 264
crinoid, *360*
Crinoidea, 719
crocodile, 432, *433*
crocodilian, 797
cropper, *305*
cross, genetic, 178–179, *178*, *179*, 184–186
crossing over, chromosome, 190–191, *190*, 210–211, *211*
crustacean, 731, *731*, **735**–738
ctenidia, 712
CT scan, 891, *891*
cubozoa, 708
cultural behavior, 383, **839**
Curry, Eddy, 63
Curry, Ruth, 514
curly-tail lizard, 352
Curvier, Georges, 300–301
Cushing's syndrome, 901
cuticle, 614, *615*, 652, **716,** 732, 740
cutting, plant, 679
cyanobacteria, *366*, **372,** 560–561
cycad, 621, *621*
Cycadophyta, 621
cyclin, 145
cycling of matter, 412–416
cypsela, *673*
cystic fibrosis (CF), 201, *252*, 916
cytokinesis, 135, 138–142, *141*, 175
cytokinin, 681
cytoplasm, 72, *72*, 75
cytosine, 230–233, *231*, *233*
cytoskeleton, 73
cytosol, 75

D

daffodil, 679
dander, 958
Daphnia, 737, 750
Darwin, Charles, 298–306, *302*, 309–312, 316, 803
data, 14, R15–R17
  continuous, R15
  discrete, R16
  qualitative, R12
  quantitative, R12
data analysis, 18, 58, 88, 92, 116, 147, 156, 185, 188, 192, 202, 208, 218, 229, 268, 287, 435, 438, 448, 475, 506, 525, 529, 536, 546, 562, 566, 586, 600, 623, 632, 647, 654, 656, 674, 676–677, 709, 714, 722, 723, 733, 739, 751, 804, 824, 857, 866, 884, 886, 949, 964, 981, 992, 993, 1016, 1017, 1044. *See also* graphing.
  bioinformatics, 282–283
  causation, 895
  central tendency, 628
  collecting and interpreting data, 28, 57, 126, 143, 405, 493, 497
  correlation, 895
  dichotomous keys, 522
  frequency distributions, 234
  identifying patterns, 320, 339
  identifying variables, 28, 49, 57, 256
  inverse relationships, 865
  null hypothesis, 925
  online, 29, 219, 257, 321, 353, 449, 477, 507, 601, 781, 811, 903, 965, 993, 1017, 1045
  operational definitions, 80
  outliers, 985
  qualitative and quantitative data, 12, 14, 497
  repeated trials, 649
  sampling, 398–399, 401, 420, 947
  trends, 1014
  types of, 12
data mining, 23
data tables, R15, R15–R17
dating, fossil, 362–365, 385
daughter cell, 140–142, *141*, 149
DDT, 502
decapod, 737
deciduous forest, *463*, **465**
decomposer, 409, 471, 474, 596
deep-sea sediment coring, 513
deep-sea vent, 102, 407
deer, 436
deer tick, 740
definition, operational, R12
demodicid, 432, *433*
dendrite, 876, *876*
density-dependent limiting factor, 443
density-independent limiting factor, 444
deoxyribonucleic acid (DNA). *See* **DNA.**
deoxyribose, 230
dependent variable, 16, R11, R15
depressant, 894
depression, 892
derived character, 525–526, *527*, 528
dermal tissue, 642
dermis, 1015
descent with modification, 306, *307*
desensitization, 893, *893*
desert, 408, *463*, **464**–465
desert cottontail, *408*, 408–409
designing experiments, 28, 88, 106–107, 124, 127, 493, 566, 586, 600, 674, 933. *See also* data analysis.
determination, 852–853
detritivore, 409
deuterostome, 702, *702*, *703*
Devonian period, 366, 621, 770
dewlap, 820
diabetes mellitus, 864–865, 959, *959*
  pregnancy-related, 1039
  and stem cell research, 155

dialysis, 991, *991*
diaphragm, 789, **912**
diapsid, 794
diastolic pressure, 923
diatom, 99, *99*, 583, *583, R26*
dichtomous key, 522
dicot, 626, *626*, 632, 650
Didinium, *573*, 574
diet, 973
differential survival. *See* **natural selection.**
differentiation, 853–854, *853*
diffusion, 85–88, 764
digestion, 977
digestive system, *856*, *971*, **977**–984, *977*
  digestive enzymes, *978*
  and fermentation, 125
  online animation, 993
digestive tract, complete, 712
digger wasp, *729*
dihybrid cross, 186, *186*
Dimetrodon, *360*
Dinoflagellate, 582–583, *583*
dinosaur, 795
  Dimetrodon, *360*
  extinction of, 351
  ichthyosaurs, 377, 794
  Mononykus, *366*
  online animation, 321
  pterosaurs, *377*, 795
  Velociraptor, *360*, 798
diploid cell, 170–171, 664
diploid organism, 698
directional selection, 331, *331*
discrete data, 497
disease, 443, *940*, 940–941, *941*
  and arthropods, 748–749
  germ theory of, 17
  and kidney function, 990–991
  and protists, 580
dispersion, population, 437, *437*
disruptive selection, 333, *333*
dissecting, 669, 685, 722, 780
divergent evolution, 348, *348*
division, 617
division taxon, 520, *520*
DNA, 6, 23, 48. *See also* **gene; RNA.**
  base pairing rules, 230–233, **232**, 265
  blunt/sticky ends, 265–266
  and cell nucleus, 75
  chromosomes in, 138–139, *138*, *139*, *169*
  copying, 269–271
  and evolutionary tree, 528
  extracting, 229
  fingerprinting, 236, *263*, **272**–274, *272*, *273*
  and gametes, 168
  and gene expression, 248–251
  as genetic material, 228
  and genetic variations, 199
  hybridization, 536
  manipulating, 264–267
  microarray, 282–283, *283*
  mitochondrial, 532, *532*
  mutations, 252–255
  nuclear, 532
  online animation, 233, 237, 241, 257
  polymerase, 236, 269–271
  and proteins, 138–139
  recombinant, 276–277, *277*, 287
  replication, 135, **235**–238, *237*, *238*, 242, 255, 271
  sequencing, 280–281, 317
  structure of, 230–233
  transcription, 239–242, **240**, *241*, *242*, 248–251
  as transforming principle, 226–227, *227*
  and translation, 243–247, *246*
  of ungulates, *318*
  and viral infection, 551
  of whales, *318*
Dobzhansky, Theodosius, 319, 353
dog-vomit slime mold, 574, *574*, 587
dogwood, *624*
dolphin, 12, *12*, 348, *348*, 838
domain, 520, 533–535, R25
domed tortoise, 302, *303*
dominant allele, 181–182, 187, 201, 204
dopamine, 892
dormancy, 674, 683
dormouse, *821*
dorsal surface, 701
Dorudon, *318*
double fertilization, 670, *671*
double helix, *139*, 232
Down syndrome, 172, 217, *217*
downy woodpecker, 332, *332*
dragonfly, *R30*
drawing conclusions, 320, 656, 865. *See also* **data analysis.**
Drosophila melanogaster, 209, 344. *See also* **fruit fly.**
drug reaction, 292–293
drug-resistant bacteria, 149, 331, 353, 390–392, 565
drug treatment, 392, 893–894
Duchenne's muscular dystrophy (DMD), 284, *284*
duck-billed platypus, 807–808, *808*
duodenum, 980, 983
dust mite, 958
Dutch elm disease, 597, *597*
dwarfism, 336
dynamic equilibrium, 85

E

eagle, bald, 335, *335*, 504
eagle owl, *799*
ear, 806–807, 882, *882*
Earth. *See also* **evolution.**
  age of, 299–301, 303, 363
  biomes of, 462–467
  biosphere, 456
  climate zones of, *459*, 459–460
  geologic time scale, 365–**367**, *366*, 381
  multicellular life on, 376–378
  natural resources of, 485–487, 504–505
  origin of life on, 368–371
  and photosynthesis, 112
  and population growth, 484–486
  single-cellular organisms on, 372–375
  systems of, 456–457
earthworm, 704, 714–715, *715*
Easter Island, 486, *486*
eccrine gland, 1015
Ecdysozoa, 702, 716, 734
echinoderm, *718*, 718–720, *719*, *720*
Echinodermata, 702
Echinoidea, 720
E. coli, *265*, 375, *375*, *544*, 549, *549*, *939*, 984
ecological equivalent, 430
ecological footprint, 487, *487*
ecological niche, 315, **428**–429, 697
ecology, 395–400, **396**
  levels of organization, 397, *397*
  research methods, 398–401
ecoparasite, 434, *434*
ecosystem, 7–8, **397**, *397*, 402–419, 427–447. *See also* **biosphere.**
  air quality, 488–492
  biodiversity, 403, 498–501, 847–848
  biotic and abiotic factors, 402–405, 457, 458
  community interactions, 431–434
  competitive exclusion, 429–430
  conservation of, 502–505
  cycling of matter, 412–416
  ecological equivalents, 430
  ecological niche, 351, **428**–429
  energy in, 406–407, 417–418
  food chains and webs, 408–411
  freshwater, 471–474
  and fungi, 596–599
  habitat, 428–429, 499
  marine, 411, 468–471
  modeling, 400, 417–419, 421
  online animation, 477
  population density of, 436–439
  population growth in, 440–444, 484–487
  and prokaryotes, 560–561
  pyramid models, 417–419
  water quality, 494–496, 506, 507
  wetland, 404, *404*
ectoderm, 701, 1034
ectotherm, 791–793
eel, *7*
egg
  amniotic, 788, *788*, 810
  human, *167*, **176**, 1024, *1027*, 1027–1028, *1028*, 1030–1031, *1031*
Egyptian plover, 432, *433*
ejaculation, 1026

Index

Elasmobranch, 766
elastin, 1015
Eldredge, Niles, 351
electron, 36–37, 108
electron microscope, 3, 19–20
electron tomography, 607
electron transport, *114*, 119–121, *120*
electron transport chain, **109**
  online animation, 127
electroreceptive cell, 767
element, **36**–37
  cycling of, 413
  in organisms, 37
elephant, *400*, 832, 839, *839*, *R31*
elephant seal, 336, 436
elk, Irish, 338
Ellis-van Creveld syndrome, 336
elm bark beetle, 597, *597*
embryo
  amniote, 788, *788*
  and cell differentiation, **152**–153
  human, 145, *145*, *167*, 176, *1023*, **1034**–1035, *1035*, 1044
embryology, 311–312, 318
embryonic membrane, 1035, *1035*
embryonic stem cell, 154–155, *155*, 852–853, 1036
embryo sac, 670
emigration, **440**
emperor penguin, *831*
emperor tamarin, *846*
emphysema, **916**
Endangered Species Act, 503–504
endocrine system, *856*, **874**, *874*
  glands of, 896, *896*, 898–900, *899*
  and homeostasis, 874–875
  and hormones, 896–901
  and hypothalamus, 900, *900*
endocytosis, **90**
endoderm, 701, 1034
endometrium, **1028**
endoparasite, 434, *434*
endoplasmic reticulum, **76**, *76*
endoskeleton, **759**
endosperm, **670**
endospore, **558**
endosymbiosis, **373**, *373*
endotherm, **791**–792
endothermic reaction, *52*, **53**
energy
  atomic, 37
  bond, **51**
  chemical, 6, 50–53, *52*, 100–102
  in ecosystems, 406–407, 417–418
  and food, *102*
  and natural resources, 485–486
energy pyramid, 417–**418**, *418*, 495
Enterococcus faecalis, *331, 556*
environment, response to, 6
Environmental Protection Agency, 504
enzyme, 8, 54–57, **55**, 59, *371*
  as catalyst, 236
  digestive, *978*, 978–979, 981
  and germination, 675
  lysosomes, 78
  restriction, **265**–266, *265*, *266*, 278
eosinophil, 957
epidemic, *553*
epidemiologist, 608
epidemiology, 22
epidermis, 642, **1014**
epididymis, **1026**
epiglottis, 911, *911*
epinephrine, 819
epiphyte, 464
episodic speciation, **351**, 367
epistatic gene, 206–207
epithelial cell, 923, *971*, 983
epithelial tissue, 854, *855*
epoch, geologic, 367
equilibrium
  chemical, **51**
  dynamic, 85
era, geologic, 367
erythropoietin, 145
Escherichia coli, *265*, 375, *375*, *544*, 549, *549*, *939*, 984, *R25*
esophagus, *543*, **978**, *978*
estrogen, 494, **1024**, 1028–1029, 1036
estuary, **471**–472, *471*
ethnobotany, **629**
ethogram, 830
ethylene, **681**, 684
euglena, 582, *582*, 819, *R26*
euglenoid, 582
Euglenophyta, 582
Eukarya domain, **534**, *535*, 575, *R25–R31*
eukaryote, 373–374, 534
  and protists, 575–576, *576*
  and viral infection, 549
eukaryotic cell, **72**, *72*, 73–75, 135, 150
  and DNA, 239, 249–251
Euplotes, 575, *575*
European rabbit, 441, *441*
eusocial species, **834**–836
eutherian mammal, **809**
eutrophication, 494, *494*
evaporation, 412
Everglades, *397*
evolution, **10**–11, 296–319, **298**, 328–351, 359–383. ***See also*** **adaptation.**
  age of Earth, 299–301, 303, 363
  of altruism, 833–834
  of animals, 702–704, 827–829, 833–834
  of arthropods, 734
  and classification, 524–528
  coevolution, **349**
  convergent/divergent, **348**, *348*, 517, 744
  descent with modification, 306
  evidence of, 310–319
  and fossils, **300**, 310, 316, 360–364
  and genetic variation, 328–329
  geologic time scale, 365–**367**, *366*, 381, 385
  Hardy-Weinberg equilibrium, 340–343
  human, 378–383
  of mammals, 377–378
  mechanisms of, 335–339, *342*, 343
  microevolution, **331**
  molecular, *530*, 530–532
  of multicellular life, 376–378
  by natural selection, 304–309, **305**, 330–334, *342*, 343
  online animation, 353
  and origin of life, 368–371
  patterns in, 347–351
  of plants, 455, 612–616, *613*
  pre-Darwinian theories of, 298–301
  primate, 379–383, *380*
  of reptiles, 794–795
  of sexual reproduction, 374
  of single-celled organisms, 372–375
  speciation, 344–346, 351
  and species varation, **302**, 306, *307*, 308–309
evolutionary biologist, 392
evolutionary biology, 316–319
evolutionary response, 429
excretory system, *856*, *986*, 986–991
experiment, **R11.** ***See also*** **lab experiment.**
  designing an, R11–R13
experimental group, R12
exercise, 921
exocytosis, **90**
exon, **251**
exoskeleton, **730**, 732–733, *999*
exothermic reaction, *52*, **53**
experiment, **16**, 399
exponential growth, **441**
extinction of species, 299–301, **350**–351, *350*
  background, 350, *350*, 847
  mass, 367, 377, 778
eye, *880*, 880–881, *881*, 1007
  of arthropod, 733
  of cephalopod, 713
  color, *199*, 206, *206*
  of vertebrates, 317
eyelash mite, 432, *433*

F

facilitated diffusion, **87**, *87*
facultative aerobe, **555**
Fahrenheit
  conversion to Celsius, R5
falcon, 848
fallopian tube, **1024**
family taxon, *520*, 520–521
fantail, *305*
farming, 629–630
fast-twitch fiber, 1007

fat, 46
and homeostasis, 973
trans, 976
fatty acid, **46**, *46*, 973
feather, 798, *800*, 802
feather star, 719, *719*
feces, 984
feedback, **859**–861, 900, 903
feedback loop, 457
female reproductive system, 1024–1025, *1025*, 1038. ***See also*** **human reproduction.**
fermentation, 118, **122**–125, 127, 559
fern, 619, *619*, 666, *666*
life cycle, *R33*
ferret, black-footed, 398
fertilization, **170**, 184, **670**, *671*, 1030–1031
fetal development, 1034–1039
fetus, **1036**
fiber, dietary, 972
fibrin, 929
fibrinogen, 926
fibrous joint, 1001
fibrous root, **649**
Ficus, 639
fiddlehead, 619, *619*, 666
fiddler crab, 736
field experiment, 399
field guide, 449
field mice, 315, *315*
fight-or-flight response, 819, 890, 898
fig tree, *639*
filaria, 943, *943*
filter feeder, **706**
filtrate, 988
fin, 764, *764*
finch, Galapagos, 302, 308–309
cactus finch, *311*
tree finch, *311*
fingernail, 1013, *1013*
fingerprinting, DNA, 236, *263*, **272**–274, *272*, *273*
fire, *447*, 464, 466
firefly, 345
fish, 763–771
bony, 765, 767, 768–771, *769*, 780
characteristics of, 763–764
early, 762, 771
fin shape in, *341*, 348
gill slits in, 312
groups of, 765–767
jaw evolution of, 762, 765, *765*
jawless, *366*, 376
lobe-finned, 770–771
online animation, 781
radiation of, 378
ray-finned, 768–769
schools of, *437*
fishing industry, 503
fission, 558, 591
fitness, **307**
flagellum, 78, **556**, 577, 1030
flamingo, *472*
flatfish, 769
flatworm, 150, 704, *710*, 710–711, *711, R29*
flea, 434, 750
Fleming, Sir Alexander, *941*
flight
bird, 799–801
insect, 746
Florida snail kite, 409, *409*
flower, **622**, 624, *668*
flowering plant, 378, 622, 624–627, 668–672
life cycle, *671, R35*
flow phase, 1028, *1029*
fluid mosaic model, **82**
fluke, 711, *711*
fluorescence, 654
"fluropig", *62*
flu virus, 607–608
flying frog, *777*
folic acid, *974*, 1038
follicle, 1015, *1015*, **1028**
follicle-stimulating hormone (FSH), 1024, 1025, 1028–1030
follicular phase, 1028, *1029*
food, 973
allergen, 958
and energy, 100–102
labels, 976, *976*
and photosynthesis, 113
poisoning, 563–564, 942
food chain, **408**–409, *408*, 417
food web, *410*, **411**, 513
online animation, 421, 507
foot
of birds, 803
human, 9
length, 384
foraging, 828–829
foram, 578, *578*
foraminifera, 578, *578*
forensic model, 268
forest
conservation of, 502–503
deciduous, *463*, **465**
rain, 403, 455, *455*, *463*, 464, 499
Forsteronia refracta, 633
Forster's tern, 495
fossil, **300**, 310
amber-preserved, 360
arachnid, 740
arthropod, 734
bird, 798–799
in bogs, 359
fish, 762, 771
footprints, 384
of hominids, 382
index, **365**
and molecular clocks, 531
plant, *366*, 613, 619
record, *360*, 360–364
sponge, 705
stromatolites, 372, *372*
trace, 360
transitional, 316
types of, 360
of vertebrates, 760–762, 773
whale, 318
fossil fuel, 485, 488
founder effect, **336**, *337*
four-chambered heart, 790, *790*
four o'clock plant, 204
fox, 348, *348*
foxglove, *627, R28*
fragmentation, 150
frameshift mutation, **252**
Franklin, Rosalind, 231, *231*
frequency distribution, 234, **R17**
freshwater ecosystem, 473–474
frigate bird, 338
frog, *531*, 774–777
anatomy of, *775*
deformities, 25, *25*
flying, *777*
glass, *757*
as indicator species, 494
leaf nesting, *498*, 499
mantella, 430, *430*
metamorphosis of, 775, *775*
poison dart, 430, *430*
pygmy marsupial, *774*
red-legged, 438–439
water-holding, 461, *461*
frond, 619, 666
frontal lobe, *887*
fructose, 45
fruit, 621, **622**, 625, 672–673
fruit fly, *209*, 209–211, *211*, 281, 344–345, *345*, *700*, *733*
fruiting body, **590**
Fu, Tong-Jen, 692
Fuligo septica, 574, *574*, 587
functional MRI, 20, 1051
fungicide, 597
Fungi, *R27*
fungus, 79, 409, 533, 589–599, *R27*
and animals, 697
and disease, 942
online animation, 601
and plants, 589, 597, 616
reproduction of, 591–594, *592*, *593*
types of, 590–591
fur color, 206–207
furcula, 798
fusulinids, 365, *365*

G

Gaia hypothesis, 457
Galapagos finch, 302, 308–309
cactus finch, *311*
tree finch, *311*

Index

Galapagos Islands, 302
gall fly, 332, *332*
gamete, 148, **168**, 170, 664
gametogenesis, 152, 176, **176**
gametophyte, **664**–667, 670
gamma amino butyric (GABA), 892
gannet, *437*
gap 1 stage, 135
gap 2 stage, 135
gas exchange, 914–916, *915*
gasoline engine, *118*
gastropoda, 713
gastrovascular cavity, **708**
gecko, *779*
gel electrophoresis, **266**–267, *267*
  online animation, 287
gene, 23, **180**–182. ***See also* DNA.**
  autosomal, **169**, 200–201, *201*, 214, *215*
  bacterial, 692
  brain-related, 383
  duplication, 253
  epistatic, 206–207
  expression and regulation, 248–251, 823
  homeobox, 250, 317, **698**, 700, *701*
  knockout, **279**
  mutations, 252–254, 267, 329
  pesticide resistant, 692
  and phenotypes, 330
  pool, 328–329
  pseudogene, 317
  recombination, 329, 374
  sequencing, **280**–281
  sex-linked, **201**–203, 213–216, *215*
  therapy, **285**, 293–294
gene flow, **335**, *342*, 343–344, 436
gene frequency. ***See* allele frequency.**
gene gun, 691
generalist, **409**, 573
genetic drift, **336**–337, *342*, 343
genetic linkage, **191**, 209–211
geneticist, 64
genetics, **177**, 278–279. ***See also* allele; chromosome.**
  and biodiversity, 276
  genetically modified (GM) crops, 278–279, 294, 690–692
  genetic disorders, 200–201, 212–213, 284, 287
  genetic engineering, 62, 275–279, **276**, 286
  genetic immunity, 948
  genetic screening, 26–27, 63–64, 214, **284**, 287
  genetic variation, 189–191, 254, 328–329, 337, 374
  heredity, 177–179, 181, 183–187, 204–207
  meiosis, **170**–176, 189–191
  Mendelian, 340
  molecular, **23**
  and natural selection, 319
  online lab, 287
  and pedigrees, **214**–218, *215*
genome, **181**, 273, 280, *281*
genomics, **23**, **280**–281
genotype, **181**, 183–185, 207
  frequency, 341
  online animation, 219
  and phenotypes, 214–216, *215*
genus, 383, **519**–521, *519*, *520*
Geochelone elephantopus, *303*
geographic dispersion, 437
geographic isolation, 346, *346*
geologic time scale, **365**–**367**, *366*, 381
  online animation, 385
geosphere, **456**
germ cell, 140, 168
germination, **675**–676, *675*
germ theory, 17, **941**
giant anemone, *R28*
giant panda, 521
Giardia, 580
gibberellin, **680**
gibbon, 380, *380*
gigantism, 867, *867*
gill, **763**
gill arch, 759, 765
gill slit, 312
ginger, *650*
Ginkgo biloba, 621, *621*
giraffe, 299, *696*, 832
girdle, 1000
Glacier Bay, *446*
gland, **896**, *896*, 898–900, *899*, 1015
glass frog, *757*
gliding joint, 1002, *1003*
global warming, *491*, **492**, *492*, 512–514
glomerulus, **988**, *988*, *989*
glucagon, 864
glucose, 45, *45*, 50, 105, 113, 984
  and diabetes, 864–865
  and PET scans, 891
  in plasma, 926
glutamate, 892
glycerol, 46
glycogen, 45, 984
glycolysis, **113**, 117–118, 122–123
Glyptodon, 303, *524*, 525
Glyptotherium arizonae, *524*
golden rice, 691
goldenrod, 332, *332*
gold-specs jawfish, 6, *6*
Golgi apparatus, **76**, *76*, 142
gonad, **898**, *899*
gonadotropin, 1036
Goodall, Jane, *830*
Goodman's mouse lemur, *29*
goose
  Canada, 821
  graylag, 824
gorilla, 13, *13*, 380, *380*
Gould, Stephen Jay, 351
GPS transmitter, *400*
graduated cylinder, R8, *R8*
gradualism, *300*, **301**, 303
grafting, 679
graft versus host disease (GVHD), 961
grama grass, *408*
Gram staining, 557, *557*
Grant, Peter and Rosemary, 308, 321
granum, 104, *104*
grape, 680
graphic organizers. ***See* note-taking strategies.**
graphics, interpreting, 1011
graphing, 29, 106–107, 126, 364, 601, 649, 750, 804, 902, 1012, 1033. ***See also* data analysis.**
  bar graph, 830, 836, R16, *R16*
  bar graphs, 172, 210, 339
  best-fit lines, 142
  choice of graph, 792
  combination graphs, 442, 461, R16, *R16*
  continuous data, R15, *R15*
  discrete data, R16
  histograms, 234, 282, R17, *R17*
  line graphs, 308, 334, 1038
  online, 29, 219, 257, 321, 353, 449, 477, 507, 601, 781, 811, 903, 965, 993, 1017, 1045
  scales of axes, 375
  scatterplots, 721, 742, 770, R17, *R17*
  survivorship curves, 438
grass, grama, *408*
grasshopper, 442
grassland, *463*, **464**
Graves' disease, *959*, 965
gravitropism, **682**
gravity, 682
graylag goose, 824
gray matter, 886
gray mold, 597
gray squirrel, 429
gray wolf, 400, 406, 409, 443, *443*, 520, 521
Greek word parts, R18
green algae, *584*, 584–585, *585*, 612–613, *613*
green fluorescent protein (GEP), *225*
greenhouse effect, **490**, *491*
Green Revolution, 691
green woodpecker, 803, *803*
grey reef shark, 766, *766*
Griffith, Frederick, 226–227
grizzly bear, *396*
ground-level ozone, 488–489
ground tissue, **642**
"ground-up" hypothesis, 799
group
  control, R12
  experimental, R12
growth, human, 975, *975*, 1041–1043
growth factor, cell, **144**–145
growth hormone, 145
guanine, 230–233, *231*, *233*

guard cell, 653, *653*
Guinea worm, 717
gull
  black-backed, 823, *823*
  herring, 823
guppy, 339
gymnosperm, 621. *See also* **conifer.**

H

habitat, 428–429
habitat fragmentation, 499
habituation, 823
Hadean eon, 368
Haeckel, Ernst, 396, 533
hagfish, 762, *762*
hair, 1013
  cell, *882*
  follicle, 1015, *1015*
  line, 212, *212*, 214, *215*
  of mammals, 806
  texture, *200*
half-life, 362
Hamilton, William, 833
hand, human, 312, *312*, 853
hantavirus, 608
haplodiploid species, 834
haploid cell, 170–171, 175–176, 664
HapMap, 281
Hardy, Godfrey, 340
Hardy-Weinberg equilibrium, 340–343
Harris's hawk, *408*, 408–409
Harvey, William, 922
Hashimoto's thyroiditis, *959*
Haversian canal, 1004, *1004*
Hawaiian honeycreeper, 828
Hawaiian Islands, 445
hawk
  Harris's, *408*, 408–409
  sparrow, 803, *803*
hawk moth, 616, *616*
hearing, 882
heart, 912, 917–920
  amniote, 790, *790*
  attack, *22*
  blood flow in, 918–920, *919*
  cardiac muscle, 1008
  coronary artery disease, *254*
  and nervous system, *909*
  structures of, *917*, 917–918
heartwood, 650, *651*
hedgehog, *207*
HeLa cell, 147
helicase enzyme, 269, *371*
hemocoel, 712
hemoglobin, 48, *48*, 530–531, **915**
hemophilia, 213, 929
Henle, loop of, 988, *989*
hepatitis A, *554*
hepatitis B, *942*, 1032
Hepatophyta, 617
herbaceous plant, 627, 650
herbicide, 681
herbivore, 409, 432, 616
heredity, 177–179, 181, 183–187, 204–207. *See also* **genetics.**
heritability, 299, **304**
hermaphrodite, 713
hermit crab, 736
herpes, 1032
herring gull, *495*, 823
Hershey, Alfred, 228, 230, 231
heterotroph, 406, 575, 697
heterozygous allele, 180, 182, 184–185, 201, 204
hibernation, 821
hinge joint, 1002, *1003*
hippocampus, 888
Hippocrates, *940*
hippopotamus, *318*, 319
histamine, 950, 957, *957*, 958
histogram, 234, 282, **R17**
histone, 139, *139*
history of life. *See* **evolution.**
HIV, 553, *553*, *942*, 943, **961**–963, *961*, *962*, 965, 1032
Holocephalus, 766
Holothuroidea, 720
homeobox gene, 250, 317, **698**, 700, *700*
homeostasis, 9, 43, 83, 151, 327, **858**–865
  and animal behavior, 819
  body temperature, 858, 859, *859*, 867
  disruption of, 864–865
  and exercise, 857
  and hormones, 867
  and integumentary system, 1013
  and kidneys, 987
  mechanisms of, 858–861
  and nervous and endochrine systems, 874–875
  and nutrients, 972–976
  online animation, 867
  and organ systems, 862–865
  and respiratory and circulatory systems, 910, 913
  and senses, 880
homeotic gene, 698
hominid, 380–383, *380*, *383*
hominoid, 380, *380*
  online animation, 385
Homo habilis, 382, *383*
homologous chromosome, 169, *173*, 173–174, *174*, 190
homologous structure, 312–313, 736
Homo neanderthalensis, 382, *383*
Homo sapiens, 378, 382, *383*
homozygous allele, 180, 182, 184–185, 201, 204
honeybee, *429*, 432, *669*, 746, 823, 832
honeycreeper, 828
honeypot ant, 4, *4*
Hooke, Robert, 70, *71*
hookworm, 434, *434*, 717
hormone, 680, 896, *896*
  and endocrine system, 896–901
  feedback loop, 903
  and fetal development, 1036
  and glands, 898, *899*
  and growth, 145, 1041, 1045
  and homeostasis, 867
  and illness, 901
  and menstrual cycle, 1024, 1027–1029, 1033
  online animation, 903
  plant, 680–681, 684
  and pregnancy, 1039
  releasing, 900
  and sperm production, 1030
  steroid and nonsteroid, 897, *897*
hornworm caterpillar, 432, *433*
hornwort, 618
horse, 378, 837
horsetail, 619, *R28*
host, 434
host cell, 373
hot desert, 464
***Hox* gene, 698**, 700, *700*
H. pylori, *17*
human. *See also* **hominid.**
  appendix, 314
  behavior, 824
  brain size of, 382–383
  evolution of, 378–383
  hands of, 312, *312*
  ice-preserved remains of, *360*
  parasites, *433*, *434*
human biology
  circulatory system, *856*, **910**–913, *913*, 917–924
  digestive system, *856*, *971*, **977**–984, *977*
  endocrine system, *856*, **874**–875, *874*, 896–901
  excretory system, *856*, *986*, 986–991
  fetal development and birth, 1034–1041
  homeostasis, 858–865, 972–976, 987
  immune system, *856*, **945**–963
  integumentary system, *856*, **1013**–1015
  lymphatic system, 930–931, *930*
  muscular system, *856*, **1006**–1011, *1006*
  nervous system, *856*, **874**–894, *874*
  online news, 867
  reproductive system, *856*, 898, **1024**–1032
  respiratory system, *855*, *856*, **910**–916
  skeletal system, *865*, *999*, **1000**–1005, *1000*, *1001*, *1003*
human body. *See also* **human biology.**
  control systems, 859–860
  development of, 1041–1043
  growth and energy needs, 975, *975*
  levels of organization, 852–855
human embryo, 145, *145*, *167*, 176, *1023*, **1034**–1035, *1035*, 1044

R85

Index

Human Genome Project, 181, **281**, *281*
human growth hormone (hGH), 1041
human immunodeficiency virus (HIV), 553, *553*, *942*, 943, **961**–963, *961*, *962*, 965, 1032
human papillomavirus (HPV), 1032
human population growth, 484–487
human reproduction, 1022–1043, **1024**
  anatomy of, 1024–1026, *1025*, *1026*
  birth and development, 1040–1043
  and exposure to chemicals, 1038–1039, 1045
  fertilization, 1030–1031
  fetal development, 1034–1039
  and hormones, 1024, 1027–1029, 1030, 1033, 1036, 1039
  menstrual cycle, 1028, 1028–1029, *1029*
  online animation, 1045
hummingbird, ruby-throated, 811
humoral immunity, 953, *953*
humpback whale, 99, *99*, *318*, *319*, 738, *738*
Huntington's disease, 201
hurricane, *444*, 472
Hutton, James, 301
hybridization, 298, 329
hydra, 150, *150*, 698, 708, 709, *709*
hydrochloric acid, 979
hydrogen, 36, *37*
  and fatty acids, 46
  ions, 38, 42–43
  in water, 40
hydrogen bond, 40–**41**, 48, 81
  and cohesion, 643
  and protein shape, 75
hydrologic cycle, 412, 486
hydrosphere, 456
hydrostatic skeleton, 714
hydrothermal pool, 407, *407*
hydrothermal vent, 102
hydrozoa, 708
Hyman, Libbie, 702, 704
hypertension, 924
hypertonic solution, 86, *86*
hypha, 589–590
hypothalamus, 888, **898**, *899*, 900, *900*
  and reproduction, 1024
  temperature regulation, 863
hypothermia, 867
hypothesis, 14–16, 925, **R11**
  online animation, 29
hypothyroidism, 901
hypotonic solution, *86*, **87**, 945

I

Iberian lynx, *350*
ice, 40, 513
ice cap, 467
Iceland, 64
ice-preserved man, *360*
ichthyosaur, 377, 794
ileum, 983
imaging, 20
imitation, 825
immigration, 440
immortal cell, 133
immune system, *856*, **945**–963
  autoimmune diseases, 959, *959*, 965
  cells of, 951–952
  and circulatory system, 946
  and cold virus, 864
  diseases of, 960–963
  and lymphatic system, 931
  online animation, 965
  overreactions of, 957–959
  and pathogens, 945–946
  of plants, 939
  and proteins, 947
  responses, 950–954
  and skin, 1014
  and technology, 955–956
  and vaccines, 554, 564
immunity, 948, 951–953
imprinting, 824
inclusive fitness, 834
incomplete dominance, 204–205, *205*, 219
incomplete metamorphosis, 744
incus, 806–807, 882
independent assortment, law of, 186, 191
independent variable, 16, 18, **R11**, R15
index fossil, 365
indicator species, 494, 781
industrialization, *483*. ***See also*** **conservation; pollution.**
infancy, 1042
infant mortality, 439, 485
infectious disease, 391–392, 940–941, *942*
  bacterial, 563–564, *564*
  and protists, 580
  types of, 549–551, *550*
  viral, 544–546, 552–554, *554*
inferring, 28, 58, 106–107, 156, 185, 208, 218, 313, 320, 321, 384, 595, 857, 884. ***See also*** **data analysis.**
infertility, 1031
inflammation, 950, 957
influenza, 553, 607–608, *942*
inheritance. ***See also*** **genetics; heredity.**
  of acquired characteristics, 299
  patterns of, 177–179, 181, 183–187, 204–207
inherited immunity, 948
innate behavior, 822–823
Innocence Project, 274
inoculation, 946, *946*, *950*, 950–951, *951*
insect, 731, *731*, 743–746. ***See also*** **arthropod.**
  flight and feeding, 313, *313*, 746
  and fungi, 599
  online lab, 751
  social, 834, *835*
  as vector, 944
insecticide, 747–748
insight, 838
instinct, 822
insulin, 91, 277
  and diabetes, 864–865
integrated pest management (IPM), 748
integumentary system, *856*, **1013**–1015
interferon, 947, 951
International System. ***See*** **SI units.**
interneuron, 877
interphase, 134, 140, *141*
interpreting data, 364, 384. ***See also*** **data analysis.**
interstitial fluid, 930
intertidal zone, 468
intestine
  large, 984, *984*
  small, *979*, 980, *982*, 982–984
introduced species, 429, 441, 444, **500**, 507
intron, 251
invertebrate, 699, *699*, 705–720. ***See also*** **arthropod.**
  annelids, 714–715, *715*, 734
  cnidarians, *707*, 707–708, *708*
  echinoderms, *718*, 718–720, *719*, *720*
  flatworms, 704, *710*, 710–711, *711*
  larval stage of, 469
  marine, 376
  mollusks, *712*, 712–713, *713*
  online news, 723
  roundworms, 704, *716*, 716–717
  sexual reproduction of, 705–707, 713, 715, 717, 719
  sponges, *695*, *705*, 705–706, *706*
iodine, *973*
ion, 38, *38*
ionic bond, 38, *38*, 42
iris, *627*, 678
Irish elk, 338
iron, *973*
iron sulfide, 370
isolation, population, 344–346
isopod, 738
isotonic solution, 86, *86*
isotope, 362, *362*
Ivanovksy, Dmitri, 547
ivory-billed woodpecker, 5

J

jackal, 12, *12*
jacobin, *305*
Jacobson's organ, 796, *796*
jaguar, 306–307, *307*
Janssen, Hans and Zacharias, 70
jaw, mammalian, 807
jawfish, 6, *6*
jawless fish, *366*, 376. ***See also*** **Agnatha.**
jejunum, 983
jellyfish, *410*, **707**, *707*, 708, *708*
joint, 1001–1002, *1003*
  online animation, 1017
jumping spider, 832
Jurassic period, 366, 377, 621

K

kangaroo, red, *808*
kangaroo rat, 409, 471
karyotype, 217, *217*
Kawaoka, Yoshihiro, 607
kelp, 584
kelp forest, 470
keratin, 778, 1013–1014
key, dichotomous, 522
keystone species, 403–404, *404*, 472
  online animation, 421
kidney, 84, 986–987, *987*, 990–991
kinase, 145
kinesis, 819
kingdom, *520*, 520–521, 533–536, 575, *R25–R31*
kingfisher, *R31*
king penguin, *327*, 327–328
kin selection, 834
kit fox, 348, *348*
knee, human, *20*
Koch, Robert, 941, *941*
Kolff, Willem, 986
Komodo dragon, *789*
Krebs cycle, *114*, **115**, 118–*119*
krill, 99, 735
kudu, *819*
kudzu, 501, *501*

L

lab equipment, R6–R9
  graduated cylinder, R6, *R6*
  light microscope, R8, *R8*
  metric ruler, R6, *R6*
  thermometer, R6, *R6*
  triple-beam balance, R7, *R7*
lab experiment, 399
lab safety, R2–R4
  animal, R3
  chemical, R2
  clean up, R3
  directions, R2
  dress code, R2
  electrical, R3
  glassware and sharp-object, R3
  heating and fire, R2
  symbols, R4, *R4*
labor, birth, 1040
laboratory methods. ***See* Virtual Lab.**
Lacks, Henrietta, 147
***lac* operon, 248**–249
lactase, *978*, 980
lactic acid, 123–124
Lactobacilli, *556*
lactose, 249, 980
lake, 474
lake trout, *495*
Lamarck, Jean-Baptiste, *299*, 299–300
lamprey, *529*, 762
lancelet, 758, 760
land bridge, 499, *499*
land management, 502–505. ***See also* natural resource.**
landmass, 460
large intestine, 984, *984*
larva, 311, *311*, 744, *745*
lateral growth, 681
lateral line, 767
lateral meristem, 648, 651
Latin word parts, R18
lava flow, *445*
lazuli bunting, 333, *333*
leaf, *5*, *21*, *103*, *547*, 652–655, *655*
  characteristics, 653, *653*
  online animation, 657
  and photoperiodism, 683
  print, 562
  stomata, 614, *615*, 647, 652–653, *653*
leafcutter ant, 599, *599*
leaflet, 653
leaf nesting frog, *498*, 499
learning, animal, 822–826
leech, 434, *434*, 714, *R29*
Leeuwenhoek, Anton van, 70, *71*
leg length, 384
legume, 561
lemur, *29*, 379, *837*
Lenski, Richard, 392
leucine, 244
leukemia, 960, *960*
levels of organization, 151, *152*, 852–855, *855*
lever, 1002
lichen, 598, *598*
ligament, 1002
ligand, 84, *84*
ligation, 277
liger, 537, *537*
light, 103
light-dependent reaction, *104*, **105**, 108–110, *109*
light-independent reaction, *104*, **105**, 110–112, *111*
lightning, 415
lignin, 614, *615*
lily, *668*
limbic system, 888
limiting factor, 443
limnetic zone, 474
limpet, 522, *523*
Lind, James, 972
line graph, 116, 308, 375, 497, 865, **R15**
linkage map, 210–211
Linnaean system of classification, 298, 518–521
Linnaeus, Carolus, 298, *299*, 518
lion, *428*, 428–429, *819*
lipase, *978*
lipid, 46–47, *47*, 102
lipid membrane, 370
liposome, *370*
Lister, Joseph, *940*, 941
littoral zone, 474
liver, 980, *980*, 984
liverwort, 617, *617*
lizard, 789, 796, *796*, 819
  anole, 352, 820, *820*
  curly-tailed, 352
  whiptail, 698
lobe, brain, *887*
lobe-fin, 770
lobe-finned fish, 770–771
lobster, 735, *735*, 736, *736*, 737
lock-and-key model, 56
locus, genetic, 180
logistic growth, 441
loop of Henle, 988, *989*
Lophotrochozoa, 702, 710
Lorenz, Konrad, 824
loris, 379
Lovelock, James, 457
lumen, 76
lung, 854, *909*, 910–913, **911**, *911*
  cancer, 133, *133*
  effects of smoking on, 916, *916*
  epithelial cells, *855*
  and waste elimination, 986
lungfish, 771, *771*
luteal phase, 1029, *1029*
luteinizing hormone (LH), 1024, 1025, 1028–1030
Lycophyta, 619
Lycopodium, 619, *619*
Lyell, Charles, 299, 301, 302, 303
Lyme disease, *564*
lymph, 930
lymphatic system, 930–931, *930*
lymphocyte, 136, **931**, 946
lynx, Iberian, *350*
lysogenic infection, *550*, **551**
lysosome, 78, *78*, 90
lytic infection, *550*, **551**

M

macaque, Japanese, 825, *825*
macronucleus, 579
macrophage, *69*, 90
Madagascar periwinkle, 631, 633
mad cow disease, 545, 944
magnesium, 649, *973*
magnetic resonance imaging (MRI), 20, *873*, 891, *891*, 1051
malaria, 580, 748, *942*, 943
male reproductive system, 1025–1026, *1026*. ***See also* human reproduction.**
malignant tumor, 146
malleus, 806–807, 882
malpighian tubule, 740
maltase, *978*
Malthus, Thomas, 305, 484

Index

mammal, 805–809
characteristics of, 805–807
early, 351
evolution of, 377–378
gill slits of, 312
heart of, 790, *790*
placental, 378
types of, 807–809
Mammalia, 760
mammary gland, 806
manatee, West Indian, *503*, 503–504
mandible, 737
mangrove tree, 402, *402*, *631*
mantella frog, 430, *430*
mantis shrimp, 736, *736*
mantle, 712
manzanita, 471
mapping chromosomes, 216–217
Margulis, Lynn, 373, 457
marine ecosystem, 411, 468–471
marine worm, 317, *317*
mark-recapture, 398
marmot, yellow-bellied, 831
Marmota flaviventris, 831
Marmota monax, 831
marsupial, 377, **808**, 1040
marsupium, 808
Martin, Gail, 164
Martin, William, 370
mass extinction, 350, *350*, 367, 377, 778
mating, 338. ***See also*** **reproduction.**
mean, 628, **R14**
measles, *942*
measuring, 18, 57, 126, 384, 506, 676–677, 804, 921. ***See also*** **data analysis.**
mechanoreceptor, 881
median, 628, **R14**
medicine, history of, *940*, 941, *941*
Mediterranean shrubland, 466
medulla, 915, 920
medulla oblongata, 888, *888*
medusa, 707, *707*
meiosis, 170–176, 179, 329, 670. ***See also*** **genetics.**
crossing over, 190–191, *190*
and genetic variation, 189–191
and human reproduction, 1027, *1027*
meiosis I, 174, *174*
meiosis II, 175, *175*
and mitosis, 170–171, *171*
modeling, 192
and probability, 187, 193
melanin, 59, 1014
melanocyte, 1014
membrane
amniotic, 788, *788*
cell, 47, **81**–84, *82*, 88, 93, 897, 988
channels, 8
embryonic, 1035, *1035*
online animation, 93
memory cell, 951
memory deficit, 895
Mendel, Gregor, *177*, 177–182, 191, 193, 200–201, 204, 209
Mendelian genetics, 340
Mendel's laws, 179, **186**, 191
meninge, 886
meniscus, R6, *R6*
menopause, 1029
menstrual cycle, 1028, 1028–1029, *1029*, 1033
meristem, 648, 650–651
mesoderm, 701, 1034
mesoglea, 707
mesophyll, 652, 654, *655*
Mesozoic era , 366–367, **377**, 621, 802
mesquite, 465
messenger RNA (mRNA), 240, *243*, 243–247, *244*, 250–251, *251*
metabolism, 6, 417, 801. ***See also*** **cellular respiration; chemistry of life.**
metamorphosis, 744, *744*, *745*, 775, *775*
metaphase, 140, *141*
metastasis, 146
meteorite, 363, 369
methamphetamine, 894
methane worm, 27, *27*
methaqualone, 894
metric system, R5, *R5*
prefixes, *R5*
microarray, 282–283
microclimate, 458, *458*, 460
microevolution, 331
microfilament, 73, *73*
micrograph, *21*
microgravity, 685
micronucleus, 579
microscope, 3, **19**–20, *19*, 22, *70*, 70–71
calculating magnification, R10, *R10*
calculating specimen size, R10, *R10*
light, R8, *R8*
making a wet mount, R9, *R9*
parts of, *R9*
staining specimen for, R9, *R9*
viewing objects, R9
microtubule, 73, *73*, 78
microvilli, *982*, **983**
midbrain, 888, *888*
middle ear, 806–807
migration, 513, 811, 821
milk, 993
milk products, 123
milkweed, 616
Miller, Stanley, 369
Miller-Urey experiment, 369, *369*
millipede, 409, 730
mimosa, 683
mineral, 973, *973*
mineral nutrient, 649
miotic reproduction, 150
Mississippian period, 455
mite, 432, *433*, 741–742, 958
mitochondrial DNA, 532, *532*
mitochondrion, 77, *77*, *113*, 113–115, *114*, 119–120, 373
mitosis, 134, **135**, 138–142, *141*, 143, 631
and binary fission, 148–149, *149*
and meiosis, 170–171, *171*
online animation, 157
mockingbird, 819, *819*
mode, 628, **R14**
modeling, 3, 18, 83, 93, 156, 192, 257, 268, 278, 282, 286, 315, 334, 337, 352, 364, 381, 385, 400, 417–419, 421, 435, 476, 496, 507, 536, 567, 772, 861, 932, 943, 964, 1016, 1017. ***See also*** **data analysis.**
mold, 600, *R27*. ***See also*** **fungi; protist.**
mole, 312
forefoot of, 312, *312*
star-nosed, 297, *297*
molecular clock, 530–532
molecular fingerprinting, 317
molecular genetics, 23
molecule, 39
carbon-based, 44–48
polar and nonpolar, 40–42
water, *40*, 40–41
mole rat, 836
mollusk, *712*, 712–713, *713*
molting, arthropod, 732, *732*
monarch butterfly, 616, *745*
Monera kingdom, 533–534
monkey, 380, *759*
capuchin, 838, *838*
snow, 825, *825*
monoamine oxidase, 25
monocot, 626, *626*, 632, 650
monohybrid cross, 184
monomer, 45
Mononykus, *366*
monosaccharide, 45
monotreme, 378, **807**–808, 1035
Monterey pine, 346
Montoya, Angel, 848
moose, *443*
moray eel, *7*
morel, 590, *590*
Morgan, Thomas Hunt, 209–210
morning sickness, 1039
Morowitz, Harold, 370
Morro Bay estuary, 471, *471*
mortality, infant, 485
mortality rate, 439
mosaic disease, 547
mosquito, *3*, *42*, 580, 748, 944
moss, 617–619, *618*, *619*, 665, *665*
life cycle, *R32*
moss cup fungus, *590*
moth orchid, *663*
motor cortex, 887, *887*
motor neuron, 877

mountain climate, 460, 467
mountain habitat, 419, *419*
mouse, 206–207, 278–279, *279*, 315, *315*, *500*, 501, *821*
mouse lemur, *29*
mouth, 978, *979*
MRI scan, 20, *873*, 891, *891*, 1051
mRNA, **240**, *243*, 243–247, *244*, 250–251, *251*
mucus, 911
Mullis, Kary, 269, *269*
multicellular life, 376–378
multicellular organism, 5, 151–155
  algae, 581
  fungi, 592–594
  levels of organization, 852–856
multiple sclerosis (MS), *959*
multipotent stem cell, 154, *154*
multitasking, 1052
mumps, *554*
Muneta, Ben, 608
murex snail, 349
muscle
  of birds, 801
  cells, 853
  fatigue, 1012
  and fermentation, 122–123
  microscopic examination of, 1017
  online animation, 127
  structure and function, 1008–1011, *1009*, 1016
  tissue, 854
  types of, 1006–1008, *1007*
muscle fiber, **1006**, *1009*
muscular dystrophy, 284, *284*
muscular system, *856*, **1006**–1011, *1006*
mushroom, *458*, 589, *589*, 595, *R27*
mutagen, **255**
mutation, **252**–255, *342*, 343
  and cancer, 146
  gene, 252–254, 267
  in homeotic genes, 698, 700
  and molecular clocks, 530–532
  online lab, 193
  and phenotypes, 329, 330
  and reproductive isolation, 344–345
  silent, 254
  types of, 252–253, *253*
mutualism, **432**, *433*, 616
mutualist, 598–599
mycelium, **590**, 598
Mycobacterium tuberculosis, 563
Mycomycota, 598
mycorrhizae, **591**, 598
myelin sheath, 877, 886
myofibril, **1008**, *1009*
myosin filament, **1008**–1011, *1009*, *1010*
myriapod, 731, *731*, 734
Myxomycota, 587

N

NADH, 117–118
NADPH, 108, 110–111
naked mole rat, 836
names, scientific, 519, *519*. ***See also* classification.**
nanoball, 392
natural resource, 485–487, 504–505
natural selection, 10, 304–309, **305**, *307*
  and artificial selection, **304**–305, 308
  and fishing techniques, 503
  forms of, 330–333
  and genetics, 319
  and genetic variation, 190, 308–309
  and mammals, 806
  and mutations, 254
  online animation, 321
  patterns in, 347, *347*
  and phenotypes, 328, 330–334
  and population evolution, *342*, 343
  principles of, 306
  and sexual reproduction, 374
nauplius larva, 738
Nautilus, *R29*
navel, 1041
Neanderthal, 382
nebula, **368**, *368*
nectar, 624
negative feedback, 9, **860**, *860*, 861
negative reinforcement, 826
nematocyst, **707**–708, *708*
nematode, 716
nephron, **987**–990, *989*
neritic zone, **468**
nerve cell. ***See* neuron.**
nerve cord, 758
nervous system, *856*, **874**–894, *874*
  and brain chemistry, 891–894
  central and peripheral, **875**, *885*, 885–890
  and gas exchange, 915
  and homeostasis, 874–875
  and hypothalamus, 900, *900*
  and interference, 884
  subsystems of, 889–890, *890*
  tissue of, 854
neural crest, 760
neuromuscular junction, 1010
neuron, *852*, *873*, **876**–879, *876*, 1052
  adaptation of, 893, *893*
  and cell division, 136
  exocytosis, 91
  and learning, 823
  and muscle contractions, 1010, *1010*
  types of, 877
neuroscientist, 1052
neurotransmitter, *878*, **879**, 892, *893*, 893–894
  and muscular contraction, 1010
  and spider venom, 741
neutron, 36
new world monkey, 380, *380*
niacin, *974*
niche, ecological, 351, **428**–429, 559, 697
niche partitioning, 429
Nile crocodile, 432, *433*
nine-banded armadillo, *524*
Nishi, Rae, 1052
nitrate, 415
nitrification, 415
nitrogen, 649
nitrogen cycle, 415, *415*
nitrogen fixation, **415**
nitrogen-fixing bacteria, 560–561, *561*
nitrogen oxide, 415, 489
node, cladogram, 526, *527*
node, lymph, **930**–931
nondisjunction, 192
noninfectious disease, 940
nonnative species, 429, 441, 444, 500, 507
nonpolar molecule, 40, 42
nonrenewable resource, **485**–486
nonspecific immune response, 950
nonsteroid hormone, 896–897, *897*
nonvascular plant, 620, 665
nori, 584
normal distribution, **330**
North Atlantic current, 514
northern pike, *507*
note-taking strategies
  cause-and-effect diagram, 361, 818, 1010, **R23**, *R23*
  combination notes, 654, 665
  concept map, 30, 60, 94, 128, 158, 220, 258, 288, 322, 354, 379, 386, 422, 450, 478, 508, 538, 568, 602, 634, 686, 752, 782, 812, 842, 868, 904, 934, 941, 966, 994, 1018, 1046, **R24**, *R24*
  content frame, 30, 44, 724, **R23**, *R23*
  cycle diagram, 135, 194, 236, 568, 686, 868, **R22**, *R22*
  diagrams, 414, 429, 456, 485, 697, 775, 842
  examples, 432
  flow chart, 877, 994
  levels of organization, 397, 422
  main ideas, 36, 60, 94, 101, 139, 220, 264, 322, 450, 478, 518, 538, 602, 613, 658, 681, 731, 737, 748, 801, 812, 853, 886, 910, 983, 1001, **R23**, *R23*
  mind map, 24, 123, 280, 328
  outlining, 70
  process diagram, 508, 752, 782, 1046, **R22**, *R22*
  sketches, 701, 764
  summarizing, 258, 306
  supporting main ideas notes, **R22**, *R22*
  tables, 226, 831
  three-column chart, 534, 574, 634, 641, 658, 904, 966, 1018
  timeline, 386, 1036
  two-column chart, 5, 75, 128, 168, 202, 288, 298, 354, 545, 789, 922, 973, 1025
  Venn diagram, 158, 173, 556, 746, 934, 952, **R24**, *R24*
  Y diagram, 194, **R24**, *R24*

R89

Index

notochord, 758–759
nuclear division, 170–171, 173
nuclear DNA, 532
nuclear transfer, 163, 275
nucleic acid, 48, 138. ***See also* DNA; RNA.**
nucleolus, 75
nucleotide, 48, 138–139, **230,** 232–233, 240
nucleus, 36, **75,** *75*
null hypothesis, 925
nutrient
  absorption, 89, 982–984
  and homeostasis, 972–976
  limiting, 448
nutrition, 1045
nymph, 744

O

oak, 519, *519, 627, 939*
obesity, 976, 993
obligate aerobe, 555
obligate anaerobe, 555
obligate pathogen, 597
observing, 13, 15, 28, 57, 58, 92, 143, 147, 229, 315, 398, 449, 460, 522, 560, 562, 579, 595, 623, 632, 647, 656, 657, 676–677, 709, 714, 722, 723, 751, 776, 780, 802, 804, 824, 830, 857, 866, 884, 921, 928, 1031, 1044. ***See also* data analysis.**
occipital lobe, *887*
ocean
  deep-sea vents, 407
  online animation, 477
  plankton, 444
  sediment coring, 513
  zones of, 468–470
oceanographer, 514
oil, 46
old world monkey, 380, *380*
olfactory cell, 883
Olopade, Olufunmilayo, 294
omnivore, 409
Onchyophora, 734
oncogene, 146
oncomouse, 278–279
onion, 679
online lab. ***See* Virtual Lab.**
On the Origin of Species, 306
operant conditioning, 826
operational definition, 80, R12
operator, 248
operculum, 767, *767*
operon, 248–249
Ophiuroidea, 720
opossum, Virginia, 808
opportunistic infection, 961, 963
opportunity cost, 828
optimal foraging, 829
orange, 679
orangutan, 380, *380*
orchid, 10, *10, 663*
order taxon, *520,* 520–521
Ordovician period, 366
organ, 151, *152,* **854**
organelle, 72, 73–79, 93
organic life, 369
organism, 5, 397, *397,* 854
organ system, 151, *152,* **854,** 856, *856,* 874–875. ***See also* human biology.**
organ transplant, 990
origin of life, 368–371. ***See also* earth; evolution.**
  early cell structure hypotheses, 370
  organic molecule hypotheses, 369
  RNA hypothesis, 370–371
osculum, 706
osmosis, 85–87, **86,** *86,* 646
ossicle, 718
Osteichthye, 760, 767. ***See also* bony fish.**
osteoblast, 1005
osteocyte, 1004–1005, *1005*
ostrich, 314, *314*
otter, sea, 421
outgroup, 525
outlier, 985
ovary, 668, 898, *899,* **1024**
overproduction, 306, *307*
oviparous reptile, 793
ovulation, 1028
ovum, 168, **1024,** *1027,* 1027–1028, *1028,* 1030–1031, *1031*
owl, 315, *315, 799*
oxygen, 36, *37*
  and cell metabolism, 851, 860
  and cellular respiration, 117–118, 120, 122
  cycle, 413, *413*
  diffusion of, 86
  and energy, 50
  molecules, 39
  and ozone, 489
  and prokaryotes, 555
  and respiratory and circulatory systems, 911, 914–915, 920
  in water, 40
oxytocin, 1040, 1041
oystercatcher, 829, *829*
ozone, ground-level, 488–489
ozone layer, 489

P

Pace, Betty, 285, *285*
pacemaker, 918, *918,* 1008
Pacific salmon, 396, *396*
Pacific yew, 631
pain receptor, 881, 883
Pakicetus, *318*
paleontology, 316
Paleozoic era, 366–367, **376**–377
palisade mesophyll, 654, *655*
Panama, Isthmus of, 346
pancreas, 91, 864–865, **898,** *899,* 980, *980*
panda, 309, *309*
  giant, 521
  red, *521*
pandemic, 606–607
pangolin, *517*
panic attack, 895
pantothenic acid, *974*
paper wasp, *729*
papilla, 883
Paramecium, *573,* 574, 579, *579, R25*
parasite, 943
  flukes and tapeworms, 711, *711*
  online animation, 723
  roundworms, *716,* 716–717
  tongue worms, 738
parasitic wasp, 332, *332*
parasitic worm, 943, *943,* 944
parasitism, 432–434, *433,* 443
parasympathetic nervous system, 890
parathyroid hormone (PTH), 1005
parenchyma cell, 640, *641*
parietal lobe, *887*
Parkinson's disease, 892, 1052
parrot, 803
parrotfish, *410,* 411
particulate, 488
passive immunity, 948
passive transport, 85, *85*
Pasteur, Louis, *940,* 941
pathogen, 544, 940–944, **941,** 947, 955. ***See also* bacteria; virus.**
  fungi as, 597
  and immune system, 945–946
  and white blood cells, 946, *946, 950,* 950–951, *951*
patterns
  identifying, 339
  predicting from, 320
Pauling, Linus, 231, 530
Pavlov, Ivan, 826
PCB, 495, 496
peach scab, 597
peacock, 338
peanut, 626, 957
pea plant, 178
peat, 618
Pediastrum, 575, *575*
pedigree, 214–218, *215,* 287
pedipalp, 740
peer review, 14–15
pelagic zone, 468, 474
pelecypoda, 713
pelican, 471, 803
pellicle, 582
Pelomyxa palustris, 578
pelvic inflammatory disease, 1032
pelycosaur, 794
penguin
  emperor, *831*
  king, *327,* 327–328

penicillin, 955
Penicillium, 590
pepsin, *978*, 979, 981
peptidase, *978*
peptide bond, 47, *47*
peptidoglycan, 79, 557, *557*
peregrine falcon, *848*
perennial plant, 627
period, geologic, 367
periodic table, *R36–R37*
periosteum, 1004, *1004*
peripheral nervous system (PNS), **875**, *885*, 885–890
peristalsis, **978**
peritoneal dialysis, 991
permafrost, 466
Permian period, 366
permineralization, 360–361, *361*
pesticide, 278
petal, **668**
petiole, **652**
PET scan, 891, *891*, *892*
pH, **42**–43, *43*, 58
  and acid rain, 489
  and enzymes, 55
Phaeophyta, 584
phage, 228
phagocyte, **946**
phagocytosis, **90**, 578
pharmacogenomics, 293–294
pharmacology, **631**
pharming, 276
pharyngeal slit, 758–759
pharynx, 710
phenotype, **181**–186, 328
  in ABO blood group, 928
  and alleles, 204–207
  and chromosomes, 200–203
  and genotypes, 214–216, *215*
  and mutations, 254, 329, 330
  and natural selection, 330–334
  online animation, 219
pheromone, 344, **832**
phloem, **642**, *645*, 645–646, *646*
phosphate group, 100–101, 416
phospholipid, 47, *47*, **81**–82, *82*
phosphorus, *973*
phosphorus cycle, 416, *416*
photic zone, 468
photon, 42
photoperiodism, **683**
photoreceptor, 881
photosynthesis, 53, 102, **103**–112, 372, 407, 413, *413*, 469
  Calvin cycle, **111**
  and cellar respiration, 112, 114–115, *115*, 121, *121*
  and cynobacteria, 560
  and diatoms, 583
  functions of, 112
  and leaves, 654–656
  light-dependent reactions, *104*, **105**, 108–110, *109*
  light-independent reactions, *104*, **105**, 110–112, *111*
  overview of, 103–105, *104*
  and phloem, 645
  rates of, 106
  and sugars, 105, 110–111
photosynthetic algae, 99, *99*
photosystem, **108**–110, *109*
phototropism, **682**, *682*
Photuris fairchildi, 345
Photuris frontalis, 345
Photuris hebes, 345
phycoerythrin, 584
phylogeny, **524**, 702–704, *703*
phylum, *520*, 520–521, **699**, *R25–R31*
Phytophthora infestans, 588, *588*
phytoplankton, *410*, 411, 444, **469**, 495, *495*, 513, 581
Picrophilus, 43
pigeon, 304, *305*
piglet, *806*
pigment, flower, 182
pili, 556
pill bug, 519, 738, 819, 840
pinacocyte, 706
pine, 655, 666–667, *667*
  Bishop, 346
  bristlecone, 620
  Monterey, 346
  Ponderosa, 622
pinna, 882
pinworm, 717
pioneer species, **446**
pistil, 668
pitcher plant, 655
pituitary gland, **898**, *899*, 900, *900*, 901
  and growth, 1041
  and reproduction, 1024
pivot joint, 1002, *1003*
placenta, **779**, 809, **1035**, *1035*, 1041
placental mammal, 378
Placoderm, 765, *765*
plaice, *769*
planarian, 710, *710*
plankton, **469**, 582
plant, **612**–631, 638–655
  abiotic factors, 405
  adaptation, 613–614, *615*, 624–625, *625*, 657
  and allergies, 958
  and carbon cycle, 414
  and cell differentiation, **152**–153
  cells, *71*, *74*, 77, *77*, 78–79, *100*, *483*, *640*, 640–641, *641*
  and chlorophyll, 103
  classification, 617–622, 630
  cloning, 275
  epiphytes, 464
  evolution of, 455, 610–614, *611*
  flowering, 378, 622, 624–627, 668–672, *R35*
  fossils, *366*, 611, 617
  and fungi, 589, 597, 616
  genetic engineering in, 277–278
  habitat, 623
  herbaceous, 627, 650
  and herbivores, 616
  hormones, 680–681, 684
  and human culture, 629–631
  insect repelling, 692
  life cycle and lifespan, 170, 627, 664–667, *R32. R33, R34, R35*
  medicinal uses of, 631, 633
  online animation, 633, 685
  organ systems, 151
  origins of, 612–616
  and phosphorus, 416
  and photosynthesis, 102, 112
  population sampling, 398
  purebred, **178**, *178*
  reproduction, 614, 620, 668–679
  roots, *639*, *648*, 648–649, *649*
  seeds, 620–622
  stems, *650*, 650–651
  structure and function, 657
  tissues, 151, 641–642, *642*
  vascular system of, **614**, *615*, 620, 643–646
Plantae, *R27–R28*
planula, 707
plaque, 924, *924*
plasma, 42, *51*, **926**, *926*
plasma membrane, 81
plasmid, **276**–278, *276*, *277*, 391, **556**
plasmodesmata, 641
plasmodial slime mold, *587*, 587–588
Plasmodium, 580, *580*
platelet, 145, **926**
Platyhelminthes, 704
platypus, duck-billed, 807–808, *808*
plesiosaur, 794
plover, Egyptian, 432, *433*
plumule, 675
pluripotent stem cell, 154, *154*
pneumonia, *942*, *949*
poinsetta, 683
point mutation, **252**
poison dart frog, 430, *430*
polar bear, 9, *9*, 467, *467*, *512*
polar body, **176**
polar climate, *459*, 467
polar ice cap, 467, 492, *492*
polar molecule, 40–42
polar nucleus, 670
polio, *941*
pollen grain, **614**, *615*, *669*, 669–670
pollination, **620**, 624, 669
  online animation, 633

Index

pollution, 488
air, 488–493
water, 494–496
polychlorinated biphenyl (PCB), 495, 496
polydactyly, *181*
polygenic trait, 206
polymer, 45
polymerase
DNA, **236**, 269–271
enzyme, *371*
RNA, **240**, *241*, 242
polymerase chain reaction (PCR), 269–271, *270*
polyp, 707
polypeptide, *47*, 47–48, 239, 243
polyplacophora, 713
polysaccharide, 45
pond ecosystem, 418, *418*, 474
Ponderosa pine, 622
pons, 888, *888*, 915
population, 397, *397*. *See also* evolution.
crash, **442**
density, **436**–439
dispersion, **437**
evolving, 352, 392
growth, 305, **306**, 440–444, 449
Hardy-Weinberg model, 340–343
human, 484–487
isolation, 344–346
online animation, 353, 421, 449
sampling, 398, 401, 421
Portuguese man-of-war, 708
positive feedback, 861, 929
positive reinforcement, 826
positron emission tomography (PET), 891, *891*, *892*
potassium, 973, *973*
potato, 150, *650*, 679, *679*
potato blight, 588
potter wasp, *743*
power consumption, 485–486
PPFM bacteria, 562
prairie dog, 398, 417
prairie ecosystem, 418, *418*
Precambrian time, 366
precipitation, 412, 460, 464–466
predation, 431–432, 435, 443
predator-prey pursuit, 315
predicting, 202, 208, 219, 268, 315, 320, 595, 739. *See also* data analysis.
pregnancy, 1038–1039
preserved remains, 360
pressure-flow model, 645–646, *646*
prickly pear, 678, *678*
primary growth, 651
primary sensory cortex, 886
primary succession, 446, *446*, 598, 618
primate, *366*, **379**
primate evolution, 379–383, *380*
primer, 271
primitive fungus, 590
Principles of Geology, 301
prion, 17, 59, **545**
probability, 187, 193, 218, 273–274
problem-solving behavior, 838
proboscis, 746
process skill. *See* data analysis.
producer, 103, **406**–407
product, 50
progesterone, 1029, 1036
prokaryote, 372–374, 533–534, 544, *544*, 555–561
flagella of, 577
functions of, 559–561
structure of, 556–557, *557*
prokaryotic cell, 72, *72*, 136
and DNA, 239, 248
promoter, 248
prophage, 551
prophase, 140, *141*
Propionibacterium, *564*
prop root, *639*
prosimian, 379, *380*
prostate gland, 1026, *1026*
protea, *611*, 612
protein, 8, **47**–48, *47*, 102
and blood types, 927–928, 954
in cell membrane, 82, *82*
complement, 947
and DNA, 138–139
and homeostasis, 973
molecular fingerprinting, 317
online animation, 59, 257
and organelles, 75–77
and pathogens, 947
and prions, 545
as transforming principle, *227*, 227–228
translation, **243**–247, *246*
transport, 87, 89–90
proteomics, 283
prothallus, 666
protist, 572–588, *573*, **574**, 697
animal-like, 577–579
choanoflagellates, 705
funguslike, 587–588
online animation, 601
and other eukaryotes, 575–576, *576*
plantlike, 581–585
types of, 575
Protista kingdom, 533, 574, 575, *R25–R27*
proton, 36
proton pump, 90
protostome, 702, *702*, *703*
protozoa, 577–579, 943
pseudocoelom, 716
pseudogene, 317
Pseudomonas putida, 847
Pseudomyrmex ferrugineus, 349
pseudoplasmodium, 588
pseudopod, 578
Pteranodon, 795
Pterophyta, 619
pterosaur, *377*, 795
puberty, 861, **1024**, 1042
puffball, 591, *591*
pufferfish, 818, *818*
pulmonary ciculation, 920, *920*
pulmonary circuit, 789
pumpkin, 672, *672*
punctuated equilibrium, 351
Punnett, R. C., 183, *183*, 209
Punnett square, 183–188, *183*, *184*, *185*, *187*, 340
pupa, 744, *745*
pupil of eye, *880*
purebred plant, 178, *178*
pygmy marsupial frog, *774*
pyramid, energy, 417–**418**, *418*, 495
pyramid model, 417–419
pyramid of numbers, 419, *419*
pyridoxine, *974*
pyrococcus, *R25*
Pyrococcus furiosus, 534
pyruvate, 117–118
python, Burmese, 500, *500*

Q

quadrate bone, 807
quadrat sampling, 398–399
qualitative data, 12, 14, **R12**
quantitative data, 12, 14, **R12**
Quaternary period, 366, 378
Quercus alba, 519, *519*

R

rabbit, 441, *441*
rabbit-eared bandicoot, 190, *190*
rabies, *554*, 943
racoon, 521
radial symmetry, 701, *701*, *703*
radiation, adaptive, 351, 367
radiation therapy, 147
radicle, 675
radioactive decay, 364
radiometric dating, 362–363, *363*
radio telemetry, 398, *398*
radula, 712
rainfall, 412, 460, 464–466
rain forest, 403, 455, *455*, *463*, 464, 499, 846
random dispersion, 437, *437*
random event, 347
random sampling, 420
rat, kangaroo, 409, 471
ratfish, 766
ray, 766, *766*
ray-fin, 768–769
R bacteria, 226–227
reactant, 50
reaction time, 902
reading frame, 244
receptor, 84, *84*, *167*, 552, 680, 859, 881
recessive allele, 181–182, 187, 201, 204
recombinant DNA, 276–277, *277*
recombination, 329, 374
rectum, 984
red algae, 584, *R26*

redback spider, 828, *828*
red blood cell, 8–9, *852*, **915**, 927, *927*
red fox, 348, *348*
red leaf beetle, *696*
red-legged frog, 438–439
red lily beetle, *999*
red panda, *521*
red squirrel, 429
red tide, 583, *583*
reduction division, 171
reef shark, *410*, 411
reflex arc, 889
regeneration, 678
reindeer, 443
relative dating, 362
releaser, 822
releasing hormone, 900
renal function, 987
renewable resource, 485–486
replication, DNA, 235–238, *237*, *238*, 242, 255, 271
repressor protein, 249
reproduction, 6. ***See also*** **asexual reproduction; human reproduction; sexual reproduction.**
  of algae, 584–585
  of amphibians, 774
  of birds, 801
  of fish, 772
  of fungi, 591–594, *592*, *593*
  miotic, 150
  of plants, 614, 620, 668–679
  and stimulus, 820
  strategy, 438–439
  vegetative, 678–679
reproductive isolation, 334, 344, *345*
reptile, 377, **793**–797
  anatomy of, *797*
  ear bone of, *807*
  heart of, 790, *790*
  phylogenic tree of, 794, *795*
Reptilia, 760
research engineer, 692
researching, 29, 601, 633, 781, 811, 841, 867, 903, 965, 1045. ***See also*** **data analysis.**
respiration, 413, *413*, 414. ***See also*** **cellular respiration.**
respiratory system, *855*, *856*, **910**–916
  of birds, 801
  and cellular respiration, 911
  diseases of, 916
  and gas exchange, 914–916
  online animation, 933
  organs and tissues, *911*
respirometer, 932
resting potential, 877
restriction enzyme, 265–266, *265*, *266*, 278
restriction map, 267, *267*, 272
restriction site, 265
retina, 881
retinol, *974*
retrovirus, 553, *553*, 961
reverse transcriptase, 553
rheumatoid arthritis, *959*
Rh factor, 928, 954
rhino beetle, *730*
rhizoid, 618
rhizome, 619, 678
Rhizopoda, 578
Rhodophyta, 584
riboflavin, *974*
ribonucleic acid (RNA). ***See*** **RNA.**
ribosomal RNA (rRNA), 240, 532
ribosome, 75, **76,** 245, *245*, *247*
ribozyme, 370–371
rice, 691
risk cost, 828
river ecosystem, 457, 473
RNA, 48. ***See also*** **DNA.**
  base pairing, 240
  and DNA, 239–240, 370–371, *371*
  and gene expression, 248–251
  hypothesis, 370–371
  mRNA, 240, *243*, 243–247, *244*, 250–251, *251*
  online animation, 246
  polymerase, 240, *241*, 242
  rRNA, 240, 532
  translation, 243–247, *246*
  tRNA, 240, *245*, 245–247
  and viral infection, 553
rod cell, *881*
root, *639*, *648*, 648–649, *649*
root cap, 648
root hair, 648, *648*
rotifer, 696, *696*
roundworm, 704, *716*, 716–717
Royal, Charmaine, 64
rRNA, 240, 532
ruby-throated hummingbird, 811
runner, plant, 150, 678
Russell, Michael, 370

S

Saccharomyces cerevisiae, 590
sac fungus, 590, *590*, *592*, 594, *594*, *R27*
saddle-back tortoise, 302, *303*
saddle joint, 1002, *1003*
safety, R2–R4
sago palm, *R28*
Sahelanthropus tchadensis, *382*
St. Martin, Alexis, 977
salamander, 776, *776*, *R31*
salicin, 631
salinity, 472
saliva, 55, 826, 978
salmon, Pacific, 396, *396*
salmonella, 944
salt, 38
samara, *673*
sampling, 947. ***See also*** **data analysis.**
  and population size, 398, 401
  quadrat, 398–399
  random, 420
sand dollar, 720
sandhill crane, 444
Sanger, Frederick, 280
sap, 645
sapwood, 650, *651*
sarcomere, 1008–1011, *1009*
SARS, 553, *941*
saturated fat, 46, 973
savanna, 464
S bacteria, 226–227
scanning electron microscope (SEM), 3, 20, *21*, 69
scaphopoda, 713
scarlet elf cup, *590*
scatterplot, 721, 742, 770, **R17**
schistosomiasis, 711
schizophrenia, 892
Schleiden, Matthias, 71, *71*
Schwann, Theodor, 71, *71*
Schwann cell, 877
scientific inquiry, 399. ***See also*** **data analysis.**
  computers in, 817
  scientific thinking, 13–17, *15*
  surveys, 398
  terminology, 519, *519*
  and theories, 299, 301
scientific notation, R14
sclerenchyma cell, 641, *641*
scorpion, *731*, 741–742, *R30*
scrotum, 1026
scurvy, 972
scyphozoa, 708
sea. ***See*** **ocean.**
sea anemone, 150, 468, 707–708, 827
sea biscuit, 720
sea cucumber, 537, 720, *720*
sea dragon, 769
seahorse, *757*
sea ice, 513
seal, elephant, 336, 436
sea lily, 719
sea otter, 421
sea slug, *695*
season, climatic, 459
sea sponge, *410*
sea squid, 713, *713*
sea squirt, *758*, 759, *759*, *R31*
sea star, *718*, 718–719, *719*, 722, *R30*
sea turtle, 207, *410*, 796, *796*, 811, 822, *822*
sea urchin, 720, *720*
sea wasp, 708
sebaceous gland, 1015
secondary growth, 651
secondary succession, 447, *447*
second messenger, 897
sediment coring, 513

seed, 614, *615*, 620, 625–626, 672
seed dispersal, 673–674
  online animation, 685
seedling, 675
seed plant, 620, *620*, 620–622
segmentation, 714, 730
segmented worm, 528. ***See also* annelid.**
segregation, law of, 179, 186
selective permeability, 83
semen, 1026
semiarid desert, 465
seminal vesicle, 1026, *1026*
semipermeable membrane, 83
sensitization, 893, *893*
sensor, 859
sensory cortex, 887, *887*
sensory neuron, 877
sensory organs, 880–883
sepal, 668
septum, 714
sequoia tree, 622
serine, *47*
serotonin, 892
sessile, 705
severe acute respiratory syndrome (SARS), 553
sex chromosome, 169, 200–201, *201*
sex-linked gene, 201–203, 213, 214–216, *215*
sexually transmitted disease (STD), 1032
sexual reproduction, 148, **170**
  of algae, 584–585
  of animals, 698
  and chemical signals, 898
  evolution of, 374
  of fungi, 591–594
  and genetic variation, 189–190
  hermaphroditism, 713
  of invertebrates, 705–707, 713, 715, 717, 719
  meiosis, 329
  and reproductive strategy, 438–439
sexual selection, 338–339, *342*, 343, 832
shark, 348, *348*, 766, *766*
  reef, *410*, 411
sheep, bighorn, 338
shrimp, *7*, *410*, 411
  brine, 739
  mantis, 736, *736*
  snapping, 346, *346*, 836
Siberian tiger, *827*
sickle cell anemia, 48, *48*, 208, *208*, 927, *927*
Sierra Nevada, 460, *460*
significant figures, R14
Silent Spring, 502
silk, 741
Silurian period, 366
single-celled organism, 5, 372–375, 533
  algae, 581
  fungi, 591
sinoatrial (SA) node, 918
sister chromatid, 173, *173*, 175, *175*, 190
SI units, R5, *R5*
  conversion from customary system, *R5*
skate, 766
skeletal muscle, 1006–1007, *1007*
skeletal system, *865*, *999*, **1000**–1005, *1000*, *1001*, *1003*
  of birds, *800*, 801
  comparisons, 312–313, 383, *383*
skepticism, 13
skin, 883, *883*, 1013–1015, *1015*
  cancer, 146, *146*, 157, 256
  color, 206
  and pathogens, 945
Skinner, B. F., 826
Skinner box, 826
skull
  hominid, 383, *383*
  muscles of, 1011
  of reptiles, 794, *794*
sleeping sickness, 580
slime mold, 574, *574*, **587**–588, *R27*
sloth, tree, *437*
slow-twitch fiber, 1007
small intestine, *979*, 980, *982*, 982–984
smell, 882–883
smelt, *495*
Smith, William, 365
smog, *488*, 488–489
smooth muscle, 1007, *1007*
snail, *712*
  apple, 409, *409*
  murex, 349
snail kite, 409, *409*
snake, 314, 796, *796*
  timber rattlesnake, *431*, 432
snapping shrimp, 346, *346*, 836
snout beetle, *8*, 9
snow monkey, 825, *825*
social behavior, animal, 831–836, 838–839
sodium, 38, *38*, 973, *973*, 976
sodium chloride, 38, *38*
sodium-potassium pump, 90, **877**–879
soil, 477
solar car, *108*
solar system, 368
solute, 42
solution, 42
solvent, 42
somatic cell, 140, 163, **168**, 170
somatic cell nuclear transfer (SCNT), 163
somatic nervous system, 889
somatic stem cell, 154
sonic hedgehog, 250
sorus, 666
Spanish flu, 607
sparrow hawk, 803, *803*
Spassky, N. P., 353
specialist, 409, 573
speciation, 344–346. ***See also* evolution.**
  adaptative radiation, 351, 367
  online animation, 353
  patterns in, 351
species, 5, 298
  coevolution, 349
  common ancestors of, 299, 310–313, 317, 524–525
  and competition, 429, **431**, 443
  defining, 537
  ecological equivalents of, 430
  endangered, 503–504
  extinction of, 299–301, *350*, 350–351, 367, 377
  indicator, 494, 781
  introduced, 500, 507
  keystone, 403–404, *404*, 421, 472
  in Linnaean system, 518–521, *519*, *520*
  nonnative, 429, 441, 444
  pioneer, 446
  survival strategies of, 438–439
  symbiotic relationships among, 432–434
  umbrella, 503–504
  variation, 302, 306, *307*, 308–309
specific immune response, 950
sperm, 1025–1026, 1030–1031
spermatozoa, 168
sperm cell, *167*, **176**, 853, *1030*
sphagnum, 618
sphenodont, 796
sphincter, 977
spice, 630, *630*
spider, 695, 740–742. ***See also* arachnid.**
  amber-preserved, *360*
  Australian redback, 828, *828*
  black widow, 741
  brown recluse, 741
  jumping, 832
  spiny, 740, *740*
spider crab, 730
spinal cord, *875*, *888*, 888–889
spiny spider, 740, *740*
spiracle, 741, 744
spirillus, 556
Spirochaeta, *556*
spirochete, 556
spleen, 931
sponge, *695*, *705*, 705–706, *706*
spongin, 706
spongy bone, 1004, *1004*
spongy mesophyll, 654, *655*
sporangia, 592, 666
spore, fungus, 594
sporophyte, 664–667
sporozoan, 580
squid, *53*, 713, *713*
squirrel
  Belding's ground, *833*, 833–834
  gray, 429
  red, 429
Sri Lanka, 499

stabilizing selection, 332, *332*
stamen, 668
standards-based assessment, 33, 63, 97, 131, 161, 197, 223, 261, 291, 325, 357, 389, 425, 453, 481, 511, 541, 571, 605, 637, 661, 689, 727, 755, 785, 815, 845, 871, 907, 937, 969, 997, 1021, 1049
stapes, 774, 806–807, *807*, 882
staph infection, 391
Staphylococcus aureus, 391, 563
starch, 45, 56, 112
starfish, 150
star-nosed mole, 297, *297*
start codon, 244
statistical analysis, 14
Steller's jay, *696*
stem cell, 153–155, *154*, *155*, 162–164, 852–853, 1036
  embryonic, *162*
sternum, 801
steroid hormone, 896–897, *897*
stewardship, 504–505
stick insect, 730
stigma, 668
stimulant, 894
stimulus, 818–820, **874**, 933
stinging ant, 349, *349*
sting ray, *R31*
stolon, 678
stoma, *21*, 151, **614**, *615*, 647, 652–653, *653*, 744
stomach, 978–979, *979*
stomach ulcer, *17*
Stomphia, 827
stonefly, 473
stop codon, 244
strangler fig, *639*
strawberry, 150, *650*, 678
Streptococcus, 564, *564*
stride inference, 384
stroma, 104, *104*
stromatolite, 372, *372*
Stroop, John, 884
Sturtevant, Alfred, 210
style, 668
subcutaneous fat, 1015
substrate, 56
succession, 445–447
sucrase, *978*
sugar, 45, 103
  and photosynthesis, 105, 110–111
  sources and sinks, 645–646, *646*
sulphur atom, 48
sunflower, 624
sunlight, 102, 368, 407, 417. ***See also*** **photosynthesis.**
  and climate, 459
  and plants, 681–682
  in tropical rain forest, 464
superbug, 565
superposition, law of, 300
surface tension, 41, *41*
survey, scientific, 398
survival strategy, 438–439
survivorship, 827
survivorship curve, 438–439
sustainable development, 502–503
swallowtail butterfly, 334, *748*
sweat, 986, 1013
sweat gland, 1015, *1015*
swim bladder, 769
swimmeret, 737
swimming, 764
symbiosis, 432, 433, 706
  lichens, 446
  mutualistic, 559
symmetry, animal, 701, *701*
sympathetic nervous system, 890
synapse, *878*, **879**
synapsid, 794, 805, 806
synovial joint, 1002
synthesis stage, 135
syphilis, 1032
system, 7–8
systematics, 704
systemic ciculation, 920, *920*
systemic circuit, 789
systolic pressure, 923

T

tadpole, 473, **773**–774, *774*, *1023*
taiga, *463*, **465**
tail, 758
tamarin, *846*
tapeworm, 711
taproot, 649
Tardigradia, 734
target, 859, 896
tarsier, 379, *379*, *787*
taste, 882–883
TATA box, 250
taxis, 819
taxol, 631
taxon, 518
taxonomy, 518
T cell, 946, 951–952, *952*, 961–963, *962*, *963*, 964
technology, 485
Tejo Estuary, *472*
telomere, 139, *139*
telophase, 140, *141*
temperate climate, *459*, *463*, 465
temperature, 460. ***See also*** **body temperature.**
  and enzymes, 55
  global warming, *491*, **492**, *492*, 512–514
  greenhouse effect, 490, *490*
  and hydrogen bonds, 41
temporal isolation, 346
temporal lobe, *887*
tendon, 1006, *1017*
teosinte, *630*
tepal, 668
terminal, 879
termite, 578, 836
tern, Arctic, 811
terrapin, 796
terrarium, 421
territoriality, 828
Tertiary period, 366, 378
testcross, 185
testes, 898, *899*, **1025**–1026, 1030
testicle, 1025
testoterone, 1025, 1030
tetanus, *564*
tetraploidy, 170
tetrapod, 312, 526, *527*, **773**
thalamus, 888
thallose liverwort, 617, *617*
theory, 16–17
therapeutic cloning, 163
thermoreceptor, 881
thermoregulation, 863
thermostat, 860
Thermotoga maritima, 535
theropod, 798–799
thiamine, *974*
thigmotropism, 682
thorn bug, 10, *10*
threatened species, 503–504
three-chambered heart, 790, *790*
threshold, neuron, 879
thylakoid, 79, **104**–105, 110
thymine, 230–233, *231*, *233*, 240
thymus, 898, *899*, 931
thyroid gland, 898, *899*, 901
thyroid hormone, 91, 1036
thyroxine, *851*
tick, 434, 740–742, *749*
tide pool, *468*
tiger, *827*
  Bengal, *809*
Tiktaalik roseae, 773
timber rattlesnake, *431*, 432
time, geologic, 365–367, *366*, 381, 385
Tinbergen, Niko, 823
tissue, 151, *152*, **854**
  animal, 701, *703*
  of integumentary system, 1014
  leaf, 652
  microscopic observation of, 949
  rejection, 954
  system, 641–642, *642*
titan arum plant, *663*
T-lymphocyte, 946, **946**, 952, *952*, 961–963, *962*, *963*, 964
toad, *777*
toadstool mushroom, *R27*
tobacco, 916
tobacco mosaic virus (TMV), *547*
tocopherol, *974*

Index

tolerance, 893
Tollund Man, 359, *359*
tomato, *671*, 681, *681*
tongue worm, 738
tonsil, 931
tool use, 383, 838
tooth decay, *564*
tortoise, *263*, 796
  domed, 302, *303*
  saddle-back, 302, *303*
  skull of, 794, *794*
totipotent stem cell, 154, *154*
touch, 883
toxin, 563
toxoid vaccine, 956
trace fossil, 360
trachea, 741, 911, *911*
tracheid cell, 643, *643*
trait, 177, 181, 183–187. ***See also* phenotype.**
transcription, 239–242, **240,** *241*, *242*, 248–251, 257
transcription factor, 250
transdifferentiation, 154
trans fat, 976
transfer RNA (tRNA), 240, *245*, 245–247
transgenic organism, 26, 257, **277**–279, 294
transitional fossil, 316
translation, 243–247, *246*
translocation, 253
transmission electron microscope (TEM), 20, *21*
transpiration, 412, *644*, **645**
  online animation, 657
transplant, kidney, 990
transport
  active, 89–90, *89*
  electron, 109, *114*, 119–121, *120*, 127
transport protein, 87, 89–90
tree
  and acid rain, 489, *489*
  coniferous, 465
  deciduous, 465
  ecosystem, 419
  rings, 651, *651*
tree of life. ***See* classification.**
"trees-down" hypothesis, 799
tree sloth, *437*
Triassic period, 366, 377
tribolite, *310*, *366*, 731, *731*, 734
Trichomonas vaginalis, 1032, *1032*
trichomoniasis, 1032
triggerfish, *410*, 411
triglyceride, 46–47, *47*
trimester, 1036, *1037*
triploblastic animal, 701
tRNA, 240, *245*, 245–247
trochophore, 710
trophic level, 409, 418–419
tropical climate, *459*, *463*
tropical rain forest, 403, 455, *455*, *463*, 464
tropism, 681, 819
trout, 473
tryblidia, 713
Trypanosoma, 580
trypsin, *978*
tsetse fly, 580
tsunami, 444
tuatara, 796
tube foot, 718
tuber, 679
tuberculosis (TB), 563, *942*
tube worm, *696*
tulip, 679
tumor, 146
tundra, *463*, **466**
tunicate, 758, 760
turtle, *760*, 796
  sea, 796, *796*, 811, 822, *822*
  skull of, 794, *794*
tusk shell, 713
tympanic membrane, 882
type 1 diabetes, *864*, 864–865
type 2 diabetes, 864–865
Tyrannosaurus rex, 798, 805
Tyto alba, 519, *519*

U

ultraviolet (UV) radiation, 255, 256
umbilical cord, 1035, *1035*, 1041
umbrella species, 503–504
ungulate, *318*
uniform dispersion, 437, *437*
uniformitarianism, *300*, **301,** *301*
unsaturated fat, 973
uracil, 240
urea, 913
ureter, 986
urethra, 986, 1026, *1026*
Urey, Harold, 369
urinary bladder, 986, 990
urine, 986, 988–990
urochordate, 758
uterus, 1024–1025, 1036

V

vaccine, 294, **553,** 554, 564, 749, *941*, **956,** *956*
vacuole, 77, *77*, 578
vagina, 1025, 1040
valve, 917
vampire bat, 833
vancomycin, 391
variable, 49
  dependent, R10, R15
  independent, R10, R15
variation, 302, 306, *307*
  in bird beaks, 321, 811
  genetic, 189–191, 254, 328–329, 337, 374
  and natural selection, 308–309
vascular cylinder, 648
vascular system
  of plants, 614, *615*, 620, 640–646
  water, 718
vascular tissue, 642
vas deferens, 1026
vector, 748, *749*, **944**
vegan, 973
vegetative propagation, 679
vegetative reproduction, 150, **678**–679
vein, 913
Velociraptor, *360*, 798
velvet worm, 734, *734*
ventral surface, 701
ventricle, 917
Venus flytrap, *35*, 54, 683, *683*
vertebra, 759, **1001**
vertebrate, 395, **699,** 756–779
  amniotes, 778–779, 786–809
  amphibians, 773–777, 781
  cell differentiation in, 153
  classification, 758–760, *761*
  eye of, 317
  fish, 763–771
  land, 778–779
  origins of, 760–762, 773
vesicle, 77, *77*, 90–91
vessel, blood, 922–923, *923*
vessel element, 643, *643*
vestigial structure, 314, *314*, 318
Victoria, Queen, 213
villi, *982*, **983**
vinblastine, 633
vincristine, 633
violet, 679
violet-spotted reef lobster, 735, *735*
Virchow, Rudolf, 71, *71*
virion, 547
viroid, 544
Virtual Lab, 59, 127, 157, 193, 287, 385, 421, 567, 657, 685, 751, 841, 933
virus, *3*, *17*, **544**–554, 606–608
  and disease, 942
  genetic material of, 548–549
  and infection, 544–546, 552–554, *554*
  shapes and sizes of, *545*, *548*
  structure and reproduction, 547–551, 567
vision, 881
vitamin, 974, *974*
vitamin D production, 862, *863*
viviparous reptile, 793
vocabulary. ***See* word parts.**
  academic, R20–R21
Volvocales, 581
Volvox, 581, *581*

W

Wadlow, Robert, 867
walking upright, 381
Wallace, Alfred Russel, 306

wasp
braconid, 432, *433*
digger, *729*
paper, *729*
parasitic, 332, *332*
potter, *743*
waste elimination, *856*, *986*, 986–991
waste production, 486–487
air pollution, 488–493
water pollution, 494–496
water
and algae, 613
and cells, 22
cohesion-tension theory, 643–645
heating and cooling, 477
and homeostasis, 972
hydrologic cycle, **412**, *413*
ice, 40
molecules, *40*, 40–41, 51
movement of, 460
and nutrient absorption, 984, 988
osmosis, 86–87
plant absorption of, *644*, 649
properties of, 40–43, 412
and temperature change, 475
water bear, 734, *734*
water dragon, 793, *793*
water flea, 737, 750
water-holding frog, 461, *461*
water lily, 655
water mold, **588**
water quality, 494–496, 506, 507
watershed, **473**
water vascular system, **718**
Watson, James, 231–232, *232*, 235, 264
weather, 444
online animation, 449
weaver ant, 834
Webquest, 29, 59, 93, 127, 157, 193, 219, 257, 287, 321, 353, 385, 421, 449, 477, 507, 537, 567, 601, 633, 657, 685, 723, 751, 781, 811, 841, 867, 903, 933, 965, 993, 1017, 1045
Weinberg, Wilhelm, 340
West Nile virus, *554*, 749, 944, 965
wetland ecosystem, 404, *404*, 473, 499
whale, 319
Basilosaurus isis, 316
beluga, 496
blue, 696, *696*
evolution of, *318*
humpback, 99, *99*, *318*, *319*, 738, *738*
wheat, *627*
whiptail lizard, 698
whisk fern, 619
white blood cell, *55*, 553, 898, **928**, 931, *939*
autoimmune diseases, 959, *959*
and leukemia, 960
and pathogens, 946, *946*, *950*, 950–951, *951*
white matter, 886
white oak, 519, *519*
white stork, 15
Whittaker, Robert, 533
whooping crane, 824, *824*
widowbird, 339
widow's peak, 212, *212*, 214, *215*
wildtype fly, 698, *698*
Wilkins, Maurice, 231
willow tree, 631
wind turbine, 485, *485*
wing, bird, 799, 802, 804
Woese, Carl, 532, 533–534
wolf, gray, 400, 406, 409, 443, *443*, 520, 521
wood, **627**
woodchuck, 831
wood lice, 738
woodpecker
downy, 332, *332*
green, 803, *803*
ivory-billed, 5
word parts, R18, *R18–R19*
Greek, R18–R19
Latin, R18–R19
world population, *484*, 484–485
worm
marine, 317, *317*
methane, 27, *27*
parasitic, 943, *943*, 944
segmented, 528
velvet, 734, *734*

X

X chromosome, 169, 201–203, 213, *213*
X chromosome inactivation, **203**
x-ray, 20
x-ray crystallography, 231
xylem, **642**, 643–645, *644*, *645*, *646*

Y

Y chromosome, 169, 201–203, 213, *213*, 219
yeast, 125, 135, 150, *150*, 281, 590–591, *591*, 599
yellow fever, 748
Yellowstone ecosystem, 400, 407
yew, Pacific, 629
yogurt, 560
Yosemite National Park, *504*, 504–505
Yuma myotis bat, *805*

Z

zebra, *427*, 427–428
zebra flatworm, *710*
zinc, *973*
zooflagellate, *577*, 577–578
Zoomastigophora, 577
zoonose, 608
zooplankton, *410*, 444, **469**, 495, *495*, 735
zoospore, 584
Zuckerkandl, Emile, 530
Zygomycota, 590, 592
zygote, 852, **101**, 1034

R97

Acknowledgments

PHOTOGRAPHY

Unit Openers **1** *Chapter 1 image* © Eye of Science/Photo Researchers, Inc.; *Chapter 2 image* © OSF/Photolibrary.com; *red blood cells, banner* © Royalty-Free/Corbis; *red blood cells, background* © William Fowle/Electron Microscopy Center, Northeastern University; *all others* © Getty Images; **67** *Chapter 3 image* © Eye of Science/Photo Researchers, Inc.; *Chapter 4 image* © Andrew Syred/Photo Researchers, Inc.; *Chapter 5 image* © SPL/Photo Researchers, Inc.; *rabbit colon cell* © 2006 JupiterImages Corporation; *red blood cells, background* © Royalty-Free/Corbis; *onion cell* © Getty Images; *neuron* © Francois Paquet-Durand/Photo Researchers, Inc.; *amoeba* © www.micrographia.com; *red blood cells, banner* © William Fowle/Electron Microscopy Center, Northeastern University; **165** *Chapter 6 image* © David M. Phillips/Photo Researchers, Inc.; *Chapter 7 images, left to right* © Jupiter Images; © Getty Images; © Gazimal/Getty Images; © Kaz Mori/Getty Images; © Diana Koenigsberg/Getty Images; © Getty Images; © James Woodson/Getty Images; © Kaz Chiba/Getty Images; © Nancy Honey/Getty Images; © Blend Images/Alamy; © Hans Neleman/Getty Images; © Navaswan/Getty Images; *bottom* © CNRI/Photo Researchers, Inc.; *Chapter 8 image* © Eye of Science/Photo Researchers, Inc.; *Chapter 9 image* © Getty Images; *DNA sequence* © Royalty-Free/Corbis; *DNA GATTACA* Image used under license from Shutterstock, Inc.; *fruit fly* © Dwight Kuhn; **295** *Chapter 10 image* © Ken Catania; *Chapter 11 image* © Theo Allofs/Corbis; *Chapter 12 image* © Silkeborg Museum, Denmark; *fossil fish, archaeopteryx* Images used under license from Shutterstock, Inc.; *all others* © Getty; **393** *Chapter 13 image* © www.richardettlinger.com; *Chapter 14 image* © Anup and Manoj Shah; *Chapter 15 image* © Andrew Brown/Photo Researchers, Inc.; *Chapter 16 image* © Simon Fraser/Photo Researchers, Inc.; *all others* © Getty; **515** *Chapter 17 image* © Frans Lanting/Minden Pictures; *Chapter 18 image* © Steve Gschmeissner/Photo Researchers, Inc.; *Chapter 19 image* © Eye of Science/Photo Researchers, Inc.; *filaments, diatoms* © University of Wisconsin-Madison; *lichen* © Sue Baugh; *mushrooms* Image used under license from Shutterstock, Inc.; **609** *Chapter 20 image* © Martin Harvey/Corbis; *Chapter 21 image* © José Fuste Raga/Age Fotostock; *Chapter 22 image* Image used under license from Shutterstock, Inc.; *all others* © Getty; **693** *Chapter 23 image* © Jez Tryner 2005/Image Quest Marine; *Chapter 24 image* © Dan Tenaglia Photography/missouriplants.com; *Chapter 25 image* © Gregory G. Dimijian/Photo Researchers, Inc.; *Chapter 26 image* © F. Stuart Westmorland/Photo Researchers, Inc.; *Chapter 27 image* © Cyril Ruoso/JH Editorial/Minden Pictures; *reptile skin* © Royalty-Free/Corbis; *wing, honeybee* © Getty; *all others* Images used under license from Shutterstock, Inc.; **849** *Chapter 28 image* © Ken Redding/Corbis; *Chapter 29 image* © ISM/Phototake; *Chapter 30 image* © Martin Dohrn/Royal College of Surgeons/Photo Researchers, Inc.; *Chapter 31 image* © Dennis Kunkel/Phototake Inc./Alamy Ltd; *Chapter 32 image* © Prof. Cinti and V. Gremet/Photo Researchers, Inc.; *Chapter 33 image* © Gusto/Photo Researchers, Inc.; *Chapter 34 image* © Nestle/Petit Format/Photo Researchers, Inc.; *skull* © Artville; *red blood cells, banner* © Royalty-Free/Corbis; *red blood cells, background* © William Fowle/Electron Microscopy *Center*, Northeastern University; *brain, x-ray* Images used under license from Shutterstock, Inc.; *all others* © Getty.

Unit 1 **2–3** © Eye of Science/Photo Researchers, Inc.; **3** Provided by Michael G. Rossman and Richard J. Kuhn of the Department of Biological Sciences, Purdue University; **4** *left* © Mitsuhiko Imamori/Minden Pictures; *bottom* © Leo Meier/Australian Picture Library/Corbis; **5** *top* © Getty Images ; *bottom* © R.B. Taylor/Photo Researchers, Inc.; **6** © David Fleetham/Bluegreen; **7** © Doug Perrine/naturepl.com; **8** *left* © Andrew Syred/Photo Researchers, Inc.; *right* © Steve Gschmeissner/Photo Researchers, Inc.; **9** *bottom* © Fritz Polking/Peter Arnold, Inc.; *center right* © Andrew Syred/Photo Researchers, Inc.; **10** *left* © Martin Gabriel/naturepl.com; *right* © Michael and Patricia Fogden/Corbis; **12** *top* © Doug Perrine/naturepl.com; *bottom* © Laurent Geslin/naturepl.com; **13** Michael Nichols/National Geographic Image Collection; **14** © Colin Cuthbert/Photo Researchers, Inc.; **17** *top inset* © Dr. E. Walker/Photo Researchers, Inc.; *top* © David McCarthy/Photo Researchers, Inc.; **19** Photograph by Sharon Hoogstraten; **20** *left* © SPL/Photo Researchers, Inc.; *right* © Susan Leavines/Photo Researchers, Inc.; **21** *top left* © ISM/Phototake; *bottom left, right* © Dr. Jeremy Burgess/Photo Researchers, Inc.; *background* © Aflo/naturepl.com; **22** *left* © James King-Holmes/Photo Researchers, Inc.; *top right* Photograph by Sharon Hoogstraten **23** *top* © David Parker/Photo Researchers, Inc.; *right* © Kevin Curtis/Photo Researchers, Inc.; **25** *bottom* © Frans Lanting/Minden Pictures; *top* Courtesy of Brookhaven National Laboratory; **26** *all* © Pascal Goetgheluck/Photo Researchers, Inc.; **27** Charles Fisher, The Pennsylvania State University; **29** © Robert Zingg/Zoo Zurich; **30** *left* © Martin Gabriel/naturepl.com; *right* © Michael and Patricia Fogden/Corbis; **32** © Martin Harvey/Foto Natura/Minden Pictures; **34–35** © OSF/Photolibrary.com; **35** James Mauseth, University of Texas; **41** *top right* © Gary Meszaros/Photo Researchers, Inc.; *bottom right* © Sinclair Stammers/Photo Researchers, Inc.; **42** *center left* © Roger Eritja/Alamy; **45** *bottom right* © Mike Powell/Getty Images; **46** © ISM/Phototake; **48** *top left* © Eye of Science/Photo Researchers, Inc.; **49** *top right* © Tom and Dee Ann McCarthy/Corbis; **50** *bottom left* © AFP/Getty Images; **51** *bottom right* © Rapho Agence de Presse/Phototake; *top right* Photograph by Sharon Hoogstraten; **53** *right* © Peter Batson/ExploreTheAbyss.com; **55** *center right* © Biology Media/Photo Researchers, Inc.; *bottom right* © Dr. Gopal Murti/Photo Researchers, Inc.; **57–59** Photographs by Sharon Hoogstraten **64, 65** AP/Wide World Photos; **66** © Ron Ceasar.

Unit 2 **68–69** © Eye of Science/Photo Researchers, Inc.; **69** © Eye of Science/Photo Researchers, Inc.; **70** © Science Museum London/HIP/The Image Works; **71** *center right* © HIP/Art Resource, New York; *top* Library of Congress, Prints and Photographs Division, #LC-USZ62-95187; *all others* The Granger Collection, New York; **72** *top left* © LSHTM/Photo Researchers, Inc.; *center left* © Dr. Kari Lounatmaa/Photo Researchers, Inc.; **73** *bottom left* © Albert Tousson/Phototake; **75** *bottom right* © Dr. Elena Kiseleva/Photo Researchers, Inc.; **76** *top left* © Dennis Kunkel/Phototake; *bottom left* © Dennis Kunkel/Phototake; **77** *center* © Bill Longcore/Photo Researchers, Inc.; *top* © Don W. Fawcett/Photo Researchers, Inc.; *bottom right* © ISM/Phototake; **78** *top left* © CNRI/Photo Researchers, Inc.; *bottom* © Don W. Fawcett/Photo Researchers, Inc.; **79** *top* © ISM/Phototake; *center right* © Dr. Kari Lounatmaa/Photo Researchers, Inc.; **80** *both* © Herman Eisenbeiss/Photo Researchers, Inc.; **83** Photograph by Sharon Hoogstraten; **86** *top left* Photograph by Sharon Hoogstraten; *all others* © David M. Phillips/Photo Researchers, Inc.; **88** Photograph by Sharon Hoogstraten; **90** DoD/US Air Force; **92** Photograph by Sharon Hoogstraten; **93** © P. Motta & T. Naguro/Photo Researchers, Inc.; **98–99** © Andrew Syred/Photo Researchers, Inc.; **99** © Francois Gohier/Photo Researchers, Inc.; **100** © Biophoto Associates/Photo Researchers, Inc.; **102** © Jack Hollingsworth/PictureQuest/Royalty-Free; **103** © Royalty-Free/Corbis; **106** Photographs by Sharon Hoogstraten; **108** Photo by Stefano Paltera/North American Solar Challenge; **110** *both* © Medical Research Council, UK; **113** © Biophoto Associates/Photo Researchers, Inc.; **116** *all* © Tommaso Guicciardini/Photo Researchers, Inc.; **118** © Yellow Dog Productions/Getty Images; **121, 122** AP/Wide World Photos; **125** © Rob Fiocca/PictureArts Corporation; **132–133** © SPL/Photo Researchers, Inc.; **133** *left* © Science Source/Photo Researchers, Inc.; *right* © VideoSurgery/Photo Researchers, Inc.; **136** © Jose Luis Pelaez, Inc./Corbis; **138** *bottom right* © Biophoto Associates/Photo Researchers, Inc.; **141** *all* © Michael W. Davidson at Florida State University; **143** © Carolina Biological Supply Company/Alamy Ltd; **145** *center right* © Anatomical Travelogue/Photo Researchers, Inc.; *bottom right* © Royalty-Free/Corbis; **146** © CNRI/Photo Researchers, Inc.; **149** © Dr. Gopal Murti/Photo Researchers, Inc.; **150** *top* © Roland Birke/Phototake Inc./Alamy Ltd; *bottom* © J. Forsdyke/Gene Cox/Photo Researchers, Inc.; **152** *left* © Dennis Kunkel Microscopy, Inc.; *center* © Andrew Syred/Photo Researchers, Inc.; *right* © Ken Davies/Masterfile; **153** *left* © Andrew Syred/Photo Researchers, Inc.; *center* © Susumu Nishinaga/Photo Researchers, Inc.; *right* © David Scharf/Photo Researchers, Inc.; **157** *bottom left* © Dr. Gopal Murti/Photo Researchers, Inc.; *webquest, left* © Michael Abbey/Photo Researchers, Inc.; *webquest, second from left* © Carolina Biological/Phototake; *webquest, third from left* © Carolina Biological/Phototake; *webquest, third from right* © Carolina Biological/Phototake; *webquest, second from right* © Carolina Biological/Phototake; *webquest, right* © Carolina Biological/Phototake; **160** © Ed Reschke/Peter Arnold, Inc.; **162** © Miodrag Stojkovic/Photo Researchers, Inc.; **164** *top right* © Chris Stewart/San Francisco Chronicle/Corbis; *bottom left* © 2006 Seth Affoumado.

Unit 3 **166–167** © David M. Phillips/Photo Researchers, Inc.; **167** © K.H. Kjeldsen/Photo Researchers, Inc.; **169** *top* © CNRI/Photo Researchers, Inc.; **172** © CNRI/Photo Researchers, Inc.; **174** © Adrian T. Sumner/Photo Researchers, Inc.; **177** © Bettmann/Corbis; **178** *purple flowers* © David Hosking/Alamy; *white flowers* © George D. Lepp/Corbis; **181** © CNRI/Photo Researchers, Inc.; **182** © Gilbert S. Grant/Photo Researchers, Inc.; **183** © John Innes Archives courtesy of the John Innes Foundation; **184** *purple flowers* © David Hosking/Alamy; *white flower* © George D. Lepp/Corbis; **185** *top left* © David Hosking/Alamy; *top right* © George D. Lepp/Corbis; **187** Photographs by Sharon Hoogstraten; **188** © Phototake Inc./Alamy; **189** © Chuck Savage/Corbis; **190** © Martin Harvey/Peter Arnold, Inc.; **192, 193** *top left* Photograph by Sharon Hoogstraten; **198** *top* © Jupiter Images; *bottom* © Blend Images/Alamy; *center* © Diana Koenigsberg/Getty Images; **199** *first row, left* © Getty Images; *first row, center* © Gazimal/Getty Images; *first row, right* © Kaz Mori/Getty Images; *second row, left* © Getty Images; *second row, right* © Kaz Chiba/Getty Images; *second row, center* © James Woodson/Getty Images; *third row, left* © Nancy Honey/Getty Images; *third row, center* © Hans Neleman/Getty Images; *third row, right* © Navaswan/Getty Images; *bottom* © CNRI/Photo Researchers, Inc.; **200** © Dimitri Vervits/Getty Images; **202** Photograph by Sharon Hoogstraten; **203** © John Daniels/Ardea London Limited; **205** Photos by Atison Phumchoosri; **206** *first row, left* © Matthew Wiley/Masterfile; *first row, center* © David Greenwood/Getty Images; *first row, right* © Steve Dunwell/Getty Images; *second row, left* © BSIP, Chassenet/Photo Researchers, Inc.; *second row, center* © Jon Feingersh/zefa/Corbis; *second row, right* © Martin Dohrn/Photo Researchers, Inc.; **207** © Jose Fuste Raga/zefa/Corbis; **208** © Eye of Science/Photo Researchers, Inc.; **209** *both* © Dwight Kuhn; **211** © Dennis Kunkel Microscopy, Inc.; **212** © Stockbyte/Getty Images ; **213** © Biophoto Associates/Photo Researchers, Inc.; **214** Photograph by Sharon Hoogstraten; **216** *both* © Reuters/Corbis; **217** *right* © Leonard Lessin/Peter Arnold, Inc.; *top inset* Courtesy of Professor Christine Harrison/University of Southampton, UK; *center inset* © CNRI/Photo Researchers, Inc.; **219** *top right* © Elliott Kimmel, Science Teacher; *bottom right* © Biophoto Associates/Photo Researchers, Inc.; **220** *left* © John Daniels/Ardea London Limited; *right, both* © Dwight Kuhn; **224–225** © Eye of Science/Photo Researchers, Inc.; **225** © Kenneth Eward/BioGrafx/Photo Researchers, Inc.; **227** © Bettmann/Corbis; **228** © Biozentrum, University of Basel/Photo Researchers, Inc.; **229** Photographs by Sharon Hoogstraten; **231** © Jewish Chronicle Ltd/HIP/The Image Works; **232** *top left* © A. Barrington Brown/Photo Researchers, Inc.; *top right* © SPL/Photo Researchers, Inc.; **234** © Ted Spiegel/Corbis; **237** © Dr. Gopal Murti/Science Photo Library/Photo Researchers, Inc.; **242** © Don Fawcett/Science Photo Library/Photo Researchers, Inc.; **252** © Janie Airey/Getty Images ; **254** *both* © SPL/Photo Researchers, Inc.; **255** © Time Life Pictures/Getty Images; **256** Photograph by Sharon Hoogstraten; **257** *bottom right* © U. S. Grains Council; **262–263** © Getty Images; **263** © 2005 Peter Menzel/Menzelphoto.com; **265** © Torunn Berge/Photo Researchers, Inc.; **267** © Eurelios/Phototake; **269** © MarkRobertHalper.com; **270, 271** Photographs by Sharon Hoogstraten; **272** © David Parker/Photo Researchers, Inc.; **274** © Tek Image/Photo Researchers, Inc.; **275** AP/Wide World Photos; **276** © Professor Stanley Cohen/Photo Researchers, Inc.; **277** © Dr. Gopal Murti/Photo Researchers, Inc.; **278** From *The Beast That Ate the Earth.* © Chris Madden; **279** © 1995 Amgen, Inc.; **281** © Alfred Pasieka/Photo Researchers, Inc.; **283** Arnold Greenwell/Environmental Health Perspectives; **284** © National Centre for Medical Genetics, Dublin, Ireland; **285** © John Scott Glass; **286** Photograph by Sharon Hoogstraten; **292** © Bernardo Bucci/Corbis; **293** © Sam Ogden/Photo Researchers, Inc.; **294** *left* © Dan Dry/University of Chicago; *right* © Jim Richardson/Corbis.

Unit 4 **296–297** © Ken Catania; **297** © Ken Catania; **299** *bottom left* Plant Sexual System, Carl Linnaeus. Natural History Museum, London. © The Bridgeman Art Library; *second from right* Portrait of Dr. Erasmus Darwin, Joseph Wright of Derby. Oil on canvas. 76.2 cm x 63.5 cm. Private collection. © The Bridgeman Art Library; *second from left* Histoire Naturelle des Oiseaux - Le Courly Rouge, Georges de Buffon. Christie's Images. © The Bridgeman Art Library; *third from left* Skunk, from Histoire Naturelle, Georges Louis Leclerc Buffon. Colored engraving. Bibliotheque Nationale, Paris. © Lauros/Giraudon/The Bridgeman Art Library; *bottom right* © The Granger Collection, New York; **300** *bottom right* © Richard Hamilton Smith/Corbis; *bottom left* © Jim Sugar/Corbis; *bottom center* © Robert Glusic/Corbis; **301** © Richard Hamilton Smith/Corbis; **302** © The Granger Collection, New York; **303** *top left* © Stephen Frink/Corbis; *top right* © Mark Jones/Roving Tortoise Photography; **305** *bottom left* © Lynda Richardson/Corbis; *second from right* © Australian National Pigeon Association; *second from left* © Australian National Pigeon Association; *bottom right* © Australian National Pigeon Association; **309** *bottom right* © Keren Su/Corbis; *top right* AP/Wide World Photos; **310** *bottom* AP/Wide World Photos; *top left* AP/Wide World Photos; **311** *bottom center* © DLILLC/Corbis; *bottom right* © Walter E. Harvey/Photo Researchers, Inc.; **312** *center right* © Science Photo Library/Photo Researchers, Inc.; *center* © Dietmar Nill/naturepl.com; **313** *bottom right* © Gusto/Photo Researchers, Inc.; *bottom left* © Dietmar Nill/naturepl.com; **314** *top left* © Tony Heald/naturepl.com; **315** *top right* © Joe McDonald/Corbis; **316** *bottom left* © Philip D. Gingerich/University of Michigan; **317** *right* © Douglas P. Wilson/Frank Lane Picture Agency/Corbis; **318** *bottom left* Photograph by Dale W. Rice. From *The Life History and Ecology of the Gray Whale (Eschrichtius robustus)* by Dale W. Rice and Allen A. Wolman. © 1971 by The American Society of Mammologists; *top right* © Will Darnell/Animals Animals - Earth Scenes; **319** *top right* © Paul A. Souders/Corbis; **321** *bottom right* © James L. Amos/Corbis; **322** *left* © Stephen Frink/Corbis; *second from left* © Mark Jones/Roving Tortoise Photography; *center, second from right* © Science Photo Library/Photo Researchers, Inc.; *right* © Dietmar Nill/naturepl.com; *bottom right* © Will Darnell/Animals Animals - Earth Scenes; **325** © Mountain High Maps; **326–327** © Theo Allofs/Corbis; **327** © Laura Riley/Bruce Coleman, Inc.; **331** © Mark Thomas/Photo Researchers, Inc.; **332** *bottom right* © Gary W. Carter/Corbis; *center* © M.F. Claridge; *top left* photo by W. Abrahamson; *top left, inset* © Peter Harris, Agriculture and Agri-Food Canada/www.forestryimages.org; **333** *center right* © C. Allan Morgan/Peter Arnold, Inc.; **334** © Patti Murray/Animals Animals; **335** © Randy Wells/Corbis; **338** © Pete Oxford/naturepl.com; **339** © Peter Blackwell/naturepl.com; **345** *top left* © Royalty-Free/Corbis; *top center* © Royalty-Free/Corbis; *flies* © Oliver Meckes/Nicole Ottawa/Photo Researchers, Inc.; **346** © Fred Bavendam/Minden Pictures; **348** *second from right* © Kolar, Richard/Animals Animals - Earth Scenes; *right* © Bennett, Darren/Animals Animals - Earth Scenes; *second from bottom left* © Alexis Rosenfeld/Photo Researchers, Inc.; *bottom left* © Jeffrey L. Rotman/Corbis; **349** *top right* © Phil Savoie/Nature Picture Library; **350** *top left* © John Cancalosi/Nature Picture Library; **353** *bottom right* © NaturePics/Alamy Images; **358–359** © Silkeborg Museum, Denmark; **359** Waptia fieldensis. Photo © Chip Clark/National Museum of Natural History/Smithsonian Institution; **360** *left* © Louie Psihoyos/Corbis; *second from left* © Jim Jurica, 2006. Used under license from Shutterstock, Inc.; *center* © Lester V. Bergman/Corbis; *second from right* © Colin Keates/Dorling Kindersley/Getty Images; *right* © Corbis; **364** *top right* © James King-Holmes/Photo Researchers, Inc.; **365** *center left* © Ron Sturm; **366** *top* © Nick Garbutt/Nature Picture Library; *second from top* © Louie Psihoyos/Corbis; *third from top* © James L. Amos/Corbis; *second from bottom* © OSF/Paling, J./Animals Animals - Earth Scenes; *bottom* © James L. Amos/Corbis; *bottom left* © S. Stammers/Photo Researchers, Inc.; **368** *bottom left* © David A. Hardy/Photo Researchers, Inc.; **370** *bottom left* © David McCarthy/Photo Researchers, Inc.; *center right* Emory Kristof/National Geographic Image Collection; **372** *bottom left* © Mitsuaki Iwago/Minden Pictures; **373** Courtesy of David H. Walker, M.D. an Vsevolod L. Popov, Ph.D.; **375** *top right* © Photo Researchers, Inc.; **377** *center right* © John Cancalosi/Peter Arnold, Inc.; **378** *center Hyracotherium vasacciensis.* Photo © Chip Clark/National Museum of Natural History/Smithsonian Institution; **379** *right* © Michael & Patricia Fogden/Corbis; **380** *left* © Pete Oxford/Nature Picture Library; *third from left* © David A. Northcott/Corbis; *second from left* © Pete Oxford/Nature Picture Library; *fourth from left* © Sohns, Juergen and Christine/Animals Animals - Earth Scenes; *fourth from right* © Kenneth W. Fink/Ardea London Ltd.; *right* © Wegner, Jorg and Petra/Animals Animals - Earth Scenes; *second from right* © Anup Shah/Nature Picture Library; *third from right* © PictureQuest; **381** © Brand X Pictures/Alamy Images; **382** *bottom* © MPFT; *top* © MPFT; **384** © David Hecker/AFP/Getty Images; **385** *top* Illustration by Six Red Marbles; **390** *top* © Francisco Leong/AFP/Getty Images; *bottom* © Hannah Gleghorn, 2006. Used under license from Shutterstock, Inc.; **391** © Hank Morgan/Photo Researchers, Inc.; **392** *left* Photo courtesy of Bruce Fox, MSU; *right* © Gary Gaugler/The Medical File/Peter Arnold, Inc.

Unit 5 **394–395** © www.richardettlinger.com; **395** *bottom right* © Jeff Gynane/Alamy; **396** *bottom left* © Hal Beral/Corbis; **398** *top left* © Jim West/Alamy Ltd; **400** *top left* © Reuters/Corbis; **401** *top right* © Paul Glendell/Peter Arnold, Inc.; **402** *bottom left* © Louise Murray/Getty Images; **405** Photograph by Sharon Hoogstraten; **406** *center left* gene@seawifs.gstc.nasa.gov; **407** *right* © Dennis Frates/Alamy Images; **408** *bottom left* © Frank Oberle; *center* © D. Robert & Lorri Franz/Corbis; *right* © Tom Brakefield/Corbis; **409** *top right* © Arthur Morris/Corbis; **426–427** © Anup and Manoj Shah; **427** *bottom right* © Jeremy Woodhouse/Masterfile; **428** *bottom left* © Paul A. Souders/Corbis; **429** *bottom* © WizData, Inc./Alamy; **430** *top left* © David A. Northcott/Corbis; *top right* © Michael & Patricia Fogden/Corbis; **431** *bottom left* © Bianca Lavies/National Geographic Image Collection; **433** *top* © Scott Camazine/Alamy; *center* © Steve Gschmeissner/Photo Researchers, Inc.; *bottom* © Merlin D. Tuttle/Bat Conservation International; **434** *top left* © Martin Dohrn/Photo Researchers, Inc.; *top right* © David Scharf/Peter Arnold, Inc.; **435** *top right* © Lynn M. Stone/Nature Picture Library; **437** *left* © Franklin Viola/Animals Animals; *center* © Wolfgang Kaehler/Corbis; *right* © Buddy Mays/Corbis; **441** *bottom right* © M. W. Mules/CSIRO; **443** *center right* © Rolf O. Peterson; **444** AP Photo by Michael Spooneybarger, Tampa Tribune; **445** *bottom left* © Frans Lanting; *bottom right* © Frans Lanting; **446** *top right* © Getty Images; **447** *top right* © Raymond Gehman/National Geographic Image Collection; **448** Photograph by Sharon Hoogstraten; **449** *bottom right* © Jacques Descloitres, MODIS Rapid Response Team, NASA/GSFC; **450** © M. W. Mules/CSIRO; **454–455** © Andrew Brown/Photo Researchers, Inc.; **455** © Frank Krahmer/zefa/Corbis; **457** © Corbis; **458** © Frank Zullo/Photo Researchers, Inc.; **459** NASA; **460** *top* © Andrew Brown; Ecoscene/Corbis; *bottom* © Dennis Flaherty/Photo Researchers, Inc.; **461** © Jason Edwards/Getty Images; **463** *first from top left* © Corbis; *fifth from top left* © Ed Reschke/Peter Arnold, Inc.; *seventh from top left* © John Cancalosi/Peter Arnold, Inc.; *ninth from top left* © Getty Images; *eleventh from top left* © Comstock; *thirteenth from top left* © Getty Images; *fifteenth from top left* © Getty Images; *second from top left* © Michael Fogden/Animals Animals; *fourth from top left* © Frank Krahmer/zefa/Corbis; *eighth from top left* © Andrew Brown; Ecoscene/Corbis; *sixth from top left* © Layne Kennedy/Corbis; *fourteenth from top left* © Getty Images; *sixteenth from top left* © Wolfgang Kaehler/Corbis; *third from top left* © Corbis; *twelfth from top left* © Getty Images; *tenth from top left* © Brand X Pictures; **466** © Andrew Brown; Ecoscene/Corbis; **467** © Norbert Rosing/National Geographic Image Collection; **468** © Don Geyer/Alamy Images; **470** *top left* © Wolf Hilbertz/Global Coral Reef Alliance; **471** © Morro Bay National Estuary Program; **472** *center left* © John R. MacGregor/Peter Arnold, Inc.; *top* © Paulo Magalhaes/Getty Images; **473** *top* © John Kelly/The Image Bank/Getty Images; *bottom* © Royalty-Free/Corbis; **474** © NHPA/David Woodfall; **475** © Jorma Luhta/naturepl.com; **476** Photograph by Sharon Hoogstraten; **477** *bottom* © Susan Berg/SJB Photography; **478** *bottom left* NASA; **482–483** © Simon Fraser/Photo Researchers, Inc.; **483** © Alfred Pasieka/Photo Researchers, Inc.; **485** © Alan Sirulnikoff/Photo Researchers, Inc.; **486** © Bill Bachmann/Alamy Images; **488** © Nik Wheeler/Corbis; **489** © Adam Hart-Davis/Photo Researchers, Inc.; **491** *background* © G. Baden/zefa/Corbis; *bottom left* © Dennis MacDonald/Alamy Images; **492** NASA © 2005 NRDC; **493** Photograph by Sharon Hoogstraten; **494** © Chris Howes/Wild Places Photography/Alamy Images; **496** © age fotostock/SuperStock ; **497** © Michael & Patricia Fogden/Corbis; **498** AP Photo/Courtesy Wild Life Heritage Trust, HO; **499** © Joel Sartore; **500** *bottom* © John Mitchell/Photo Researchers, Inc.; *top* Photo courtesy CSIRO; **501** © Cameron Marlow; **502** © China Tourism Press/Getty Images; **503** © Brandon D. Cole/Corbis; **504** © Susan Berg/SJB Photography; **505** © Raymond Gehman/Corbis; **507** *bottom* © Wil Meinderts/Foto Natura/Minden Pictures; **508** *top right* AP Photo/Courtesy Wild Life Heritage Trust, HO; *bottom right* © Raymond Gehman/Corbis; **512** *top right* © Thomas Nilsen/Science Photo Library/Photo Researchers, Inc.; *bottom left* © Tom Van Sant/Photo Researchers, Inc.; **513** AP/Wide World Photos/ Katsumi Kasahara; **514** *top left* © Peter Essick/Aurora/Getty Images; *top right* Photo by Tom Kleindinst/Woods Hole Oceanographic Institution.

Unit 6 **516–517** © Frans Lanting/Minden Pictures; **517** © Jen & Des Bartlett/Oxford Scientific/Jupiter Images; **519** *top right* © Digital Vision/Robert Harding; *bottom right* © Larry Michael/naturepl.com; **521** *top right* © Sohns, Juergen and Christine/Animals Animals - Earth Scenes; **523** Photographs by Sharon Hoogstraten; **524** *bottom left* © The Natural History Museum; *bottom right* © Pontier, John/Animals Animals - Earth Scenes; **529** © Gary Meszaros/Photo Researchers, Inc.; **531** © Michael Durham/Minden Pictures; **534** © Eye of Science/Photo Researchers, Inc.; **536** Photograph by Sharon Hoogstraten; **537** *bottom left* © Bill Dow/Shambala Preserve; *bottom right* © Fred Bavendam/Minden Pictures; **538** *bottom left* © The Natural History Museum; *bottom center* © Pontier, John/Animals Animals - Earth Scenes; **542–543** © Steve Gschmeissner/Photo Researchers, Inc.; **543** © Andrew Syred/Photo Researchers, Inc.; **544** © Dr. Linda Stannard, UCT/Photo Researchers, Inc.; **547** *top* © Duncan Smith/Photo Researchers, Inc.; *bottom* © Norm Thomas/Photo Researchers, Inc.; **548** *center left* © Nibsc/Photo Researchers, Inc.; *center* © Em Unit, CVL Weybridge/Photo Researchers, Inc.; *center right* © Alfred Pasieka/Photo Researchers, Inc.; **549** *top* © Eye of Science/Photo Researchers, Inc.; *top, inset* © Eye of Science/Photo Researchers, Inc.; **552** © Dr. Steve Patterson/Photo Researchers, Inc.; **553** *center* © Reuters/Corbis; *bottom right* © Nibsc/Photo Researchers, Inc.; **555** © Stephen Ausmus/Agricultural Research Service/USDA; **556** *bottom left* © SciMAT/Photo Researchers, Inc.; *bottom center* © SciMAT/Photo Researchers, Inc.; *bottom right* © Eye of Science/Photo Researchers, Inc.; **557** *bottom left, bottom right* © CNRI/Science Photo Library/Photo Researchers, Inc.; **558** *center right* © Dr. L. Caro/Photo Researchers, Inc.; **559** *right* © Dr. Gary Gaugler/Photo Researchers, Inc.; **561** *top right* © Dr. Jeremy Burgess/Photo Researchers, Inc.; *center* © Dr. Jeremy Burgess/Photo Researchers, Inc.; **562** Photograph by Sharon Hoogstraten; **563** © Dr. Gary Gaugler/Photo Researchers, Inc.; **564** *bottom left* © Dr. P. Marazzi/Science Photo Library/Photo Researchers, Inc.; **568** *center* © Eye of Science/Photo Researchers, Inc.; **572–573** © Eye of Science/Photo Researchers, Inc.; **573** *all three bottom* © Biophoto Associates/Photo Researchers, Inc.; © Biophoto Associates /Photo Researchers, Inc.; © Biophoto Associates/Photo Researchers, Inc.; **574** © Jarrod Erbe Photography/Alamy Ltd; **575** *top right* © Steve Gschmeissner/Science Photo Library/Photo Researchers, Inc.; *center right* © SPL/Photo Researchers, Inc.; **577** © SPL/Photo Researchers, Inc.; **578** *all four top* © Biophoto Associates/Photo Researchers, Inc.; *bottom right* © Astrid & Hanns-Frieder Michler/Photo Researchers, Inc.; **579** © Eric Grave/Photo Researchers, Inc.; **581** © Roland Birke/Peter Arnold, Inc.; **582** © Andrew Syred/Photo Researchers, Inc.; **583** *top inset* © Steve Gschmeissner/Science Photo Library/Photo Researchers, Inc.; *top right* © Bill Bachman/Photo Researchers, Inc.; *bottom left* © Andrew Syred/Photo Researchers, Inc.; *bottom center, bottom right* © Susumu Nishinaga/Photo Researchers, Inc.; **584** *bottom* © Andrew Syred/Photo Researchers, Inc.; *top* © Gary Bell/oceanwideimages.com; **587** *left* © Eye of Science/Photo Researchers, Inc.; *right* © David Scharf/Science Photo Library/Photo Researchers, Inc.; **588** *inset* © Andrew Syred/Photo Researchers, Inc.; *top left* © Scott Bauer/USDA/Agricultural Research Service; **590** *top* © Royalty-Free/Corbis; *bottom* © Vaughan Fleming/Photo Researchers, Inc.; **591** *top* © Kenneth H. Thomas/Photo Researchers, Inc.; *bottom* © J. Forsdyke/Gene Cox/Photo Researchers, Inc.; **592** *top* © Orla, 2006. Used under license from Shutterstock, Inc.; *center* © Mauritius, GMBH/Phototake; *bottom* © Vaughan Fleming/Photo Researchers, Inc.; **593** *top left* © Orla, 2006. Used under license from Shutterstock, Inc.; *center* © Mauritius, GMBH/Phototake; **594** *top left* © Ray Coleman/Photo Researchers, Inc.; *inset* © Ed Reschke /Peter Arnold, Inc.; **596** © Merryl Brackstone, 2006. Used under license from Shutterstock, Inc.; **597** *center* © Roger Tidman/Corbis; *center* © Stephen Dalton/Minden Pictures; **598** © Pat O'Hara/Corbis; **599** © Michael & Patricia Fogden/Corbis; **601** *bottom right* © Eye of Science/Photo Researchers, Inc.; **602** *right* © Orla, 2006. Used under license from Shutterstock, Inc.; **606** *top right* © age fotostock/SuperStock; *center right* © Pasieka/Photo Researchers, Inc.; **607** *top left* © The Art Archive/Culver Pictures; *top right* © By Ian Miles-Flashpoint Pictures/Alamy; *bottom right* Courtesy of Drs. Takeshi Noda and Yoshihiro Kawaoka; **608** *top left* Photo of Dr. Ben Muneta courtesy of Jana Muneta; *top right* © Ali Imam/Reuters/Corbis.

Unit 7 **610–611** © Martin Harvey/Corbis; **611** © Nigel J. Dennis; Gallo Images/Corbis; **612** © Ken Wagner/Phototake; **613** *top left* © Ken Wagner/Phototake; *second from top left* © Stuart Westmorland/Corbis; *top center* © Gusto/SPL/Photo Researchers, Inc.; *second from top right* © Stephen P. Parker/Photo Researchers, Inc.; *top right* © Lynn Watson, 2006. Used under license from Shutterstock, Inc.; **615** *top left* © Magdalena Bujak, 2006. Used under license from Shutterstock, Inc.; *top right* © John Walmsley/Education Photos/Alamy Ltd; **616** *top left* © Colin Keates/Dorling Kindersley, Courtesy of the Natural History Museum, London; *left* © Paul Harcourt Davies/Photo Researchers, Inc.; **617** *bottom right* © Harold Taylor/PictureQuest; **618** *top right* Olympic National Park Site/National Park Service, U.S. Dept. of the Interior; *bottom* © Stuart Westmorland/Corbis; **619** *top right* © Philip Gould/Corbis; *bottom right* © Gusto/SPL/Photo Researchers, Inc.; *bottom* © Steve Kaufman/Corbis; **620** © Martha Cooper/Peter Arnold, Inc.; **621** *center* © Chris Jones/PictureQuest; *bottom left* © Science Pictures Limited/Photo Researchers, Inc.; *bottom right* © Joseph Malcolm Smith/Photo Researchers, Inc.; **622** *inset* © Stephen P. Parker/Photo Researchers, Inc.; *top left* © Andrew Brown; Ecoscene/Corbis; **623** Photograph by Sharon Hoogstraten; **624** © Royalty-Free/Corbis; 625 *top left* © Michael and Patricia Fogden/Corbis; *top right* © Michael Quinton/Minden Pictures; **627** *left* © Lynn Watson, 2006. Used under license from Shutterstock, Inc.; *second from top left* © Yare Marketing, 2006. Used under license from Shutterstock, Inc.; *top second from right* © BananaStock/PictureQuest; *top right* © Matt, 2006. Used under license from Shutterstock, Inc.; *bottom center* © Ross Frid/Alamy Ltd; **628** © Royalty-Free/Corbis; **629** *bottom* © Charles O'Rear/Corbis; **630** *top left* © Andrew McRobb/Dorling Kindersley; *center left* © Helmut Partsch/Photo Researchers, Inc.; *bottom* © Hanan Isachar/Corbis; **631** © Bojan Brecelj/Corbis; **633** *bottom left* © Chris Hellier/Corbis; *bottom right* © Gunter Marx Photography/Corbis; **634** *top left* © Ken Wagner/Phototake; *top right* © BananaStock/PictureQuest; *bottom right* © Hanan Isachar/Corbis; **638–639** © José Fuste Raga/Age Fotostock; **639** © Walter H. Hodge/Peter Arnold, Inc.; **641** *left, center, right* © Biophoto Associates/Photo Researchers, Inc.; **643** © Andrew Syred/Photo Researchers, Inc.; **646** *left* © Olga Shelego, 2006. Used under license from Shutterstock, Inc.; *top* © Laurin Rinder, 2006. Used under license from Shutterstock, Inc.; **648** *left* © M.I. Walker/Photo Researchers, Inc.; *right* © Andrew Syred/Photo Researchers, Inc.; **649** *top right* © Scott Sinklier/Alamy Images; *center right* © David Wasserman/Alamy Images; **650** *top left* © Nick Garbutt/naturepl.com; *top center* © B.S.P.I./Corbis; *center left* © Dwight R. Kuhn; *center* © Ron Chapple/Alamy Images; *top right* © TPH/Alamy Images; *bottom left* © Ed Reschke/Peter Arnold, Inc.; *second from bottom left* © Carolina Biological Supply Company/Phototake, Inc./Alamy Ltd; **651** *center right* © Alan Linn, 2006. Used under license from Shutterstock, Inc.; **652** © Mark A. Schneider/Photo Researchers, Inc.; **653** *top center, top right* © Dr. Jeremy Burgess/Photo Researchers, Inc.; *parallel* © Brian Tan, 2006. Used under license from Shutterstock, Inc.; *pinnate* © Adam Hart-Davis/Photo Researchers, Inc.; *double compound* © Runk/Schoenberger/Alamy Ltd; *simple, compound, toothed, entire* © Melba Photo Agency/Alamy Ltd; *lobed* © Mark A. Schneider/Photo Researchers, Inc.; **656** Photograph by Sharon Hoogstraten; **657** *bottom* © LEAF - Wisconsin's K–12 Forestry Education Program; **658** *top right* © Scott Sinklier/Alamy Images; **660** © Alan Linn, 2006. Used under license from Shutterstock, Inc.; **662–663** Image used under license from Shutterstock, Inc.; **663** © Reuters/Corbis; **665** *bottom left* © Ed Reschke/Peter Arnold, Inc.; *bottom right* © Dwight R. Kuhn; **666** *top left inset* © Wolfgang Kaehler/Corbis; *top left* © Craig Tuttle/Corbis; *center left* © Biophoto Associates/Photo Researchers, Inc.; **667** *top right* © Darrell Gulin/Corbis; *right* © Dr. Jeremy Burgess/Photo Researchers, Inc.; **669** *top right* © Darwin Dale/Photo Researchers, Inc.; *top left* © Susumu Nishinaga/Photo Researchers, Inc.; *bottom right* © Archie Young/Photo Researchers, Inc.; **672** © Ingram Publishing/Alamy Images; *top left* © Scott Camazine/Photo Researchers, Inc.; *top center* © Tonis Valing, 2006. Used under license from Shutterstock, Inc.; *top right* © Royalty-Free/Corbis; **673** *bottom left* © Scott Camazine/Alamy Images; *bottom right* © Anette Linnea Rasmussen, 2006. Used under license from Shutterstock, Inc.; *bottom center* © Dwight R. Kuhn; **675** *top left* © Andrew Syred/Photo Researchers, Inc.; *second from top left* © Andrew Syred/Photo Researchers, Inc.; *second from top right* © Andrew Syred/Photo Researchers, Inc.; *top right* © Andrew Syred/Photo Researchers, Inc.; **677** © Dwight R. Kuhn; **678** © Joseph Sohm/Corbis; **679** *top* © Dwight R. Kuhn; **680** © Richard Cummins/Corbis; **681** *top right* © Stockbyte Platinum/Alamy; *center right* © Chris Howes/Wild Places Photography/Alamy; **682** © Cathlyn Melloan/Getty Images; **683** © Dr. Jeremy Burgess/Photo Researchers, Inc.; **684** Photograph by Sharon Hoogstraten; **686** *top right* © Dwight R. Kuhn; **688** © Dan Rosandich/CartoonStock; **690** *top* © Nick Cobbing/Peter Arnold, Inc.; *bottom left* © Anastassios Mentis/FoodPix/Jupiter Images; **691** *top right* © Leonard Lessin/Peter Arnold, Inc.; *bottom right* © Matt Meadows/Peter Arnold, Inc.; **692** *top left* Photo courtesy of Dr. Tong-Jen Fu; *bottom right* Noah Berger/AP/Wide World Photos.

Unit 8 **694–695** © Jez Tryner 2005/Image Quest Marine; **695** © James D. Watt/SeaPics.com; **696** *first row left* © Roland Birke/Phototake, Inc./Alamy Ltd; *first row right* © George Grall/National Geographic Image Collection; *second row left* © Mike VanDeWalker/Alamy; *first row center* © D. Allen Photography/Animals Animals; *second row right* © Phillip Colla/SeaPics.com; *second row center* © Jurgen Freund/naturepl.com; **697** *bottom right* © David M. Phillips/The Population Council/Photo Researchers, Inc.; *bottom right inset* © Kenneth Eward/Photo Researchers, Inc.; **698** *both* © F. R. Turner, Indiana University; © F. R. Turner, Indiana University; **701** *bottom* © Sue Daly/naturepl.com; *top* © National Geographic/Getty Images; **704** © Deco/Alamy Images; **705** © Carlos Villoch 2004/Image Quest Marine; **707** *bottom* © Phillip Colla/www.OceanLight.com; *top* © Jeff Rotman/naturepl.com; **709** *top right* © Biophoto Associates/Photo Researchers, Inc.; *center right* © Image Source/Getty Images; **711** *top left* © Alan Towse; Ecoscene/Corbis; *top right* © David Scharf/Science Faction/Getty Images; *far right* © John Durham/Photo Researchers, Inc.; *center* © Peter Arnold, Inc./Alamy Images; **713** © Brian J. Skerry/National Geographic Image Collection; **717** © David Cooney/www.CartoonStock.com; **719** *top* © Alexis Rosenfeld/Photo Researchers, Inc.; *bottom* © Fred Bavendam/Minden Pictures; **720** *top left* Southeastern Regional Taxonomic Center/South Carolina Department of Natural Resources; *top center* © Flip Nicklin/Minden Pictures; *top right* © Fred Bavendam/Minden Pictures; **721** © Dynamic Graphics Group/IT Stock Free/Alamy; **723** *bottom* © 2004 Dennis Kunkel Microscopy, Inc.; **724** *left* © National Geographic/Getty Images; *center* © Sue Daly/naturepl.com; *top right* © David Scharf/Science Faction/Getty Images; **729–730** © Dan Tenaglia Photography/missouriplants.com; **729** © Bartomeu Borrell/Age Fotostock; **730** © Hans Christoph Kappel/naturepl.com; **731** *top* © Sinclair Stammers/Photo Researchers, Inc.; *second from bottom right* © Holger Wulschlaeger, 2006. Used under license from Shutterstock, Inc.; *bottom right* © Tom McHugh/Photo Researchers, Inc.; *bottom left* © Pete Oxford/naturepl.com; *second from bottom left* © Stephen Dalton/Photo Researchers, Inc.; **732** © Breck P. Kent/Animals Animals; **733** *inset* © Holt Studios International Ltd/Alamy; *top* © Susumu Nishinaga/Photo Researchers, Inc.; **734** *bottom* © Andrew Syred/Photo Researchers, Inc.; *top* © Dr. Morley Read/Photo

R99

Acknowledgments

Researchers, Inc.; **735** © Roger Steene/Image Quest Marine; **736** © Peter Lange/www.fotofish.at; **737** © Pete Oxford/naturepl.com; **738** © Wayne Levin/Getty Images; **739** Photograph by Sharon Hoogstraten; **740** © Piotr Naskrecki/Minden Pictures; **742** © The Garden Picture Library/Alamy; **743** © WoodyStock/Alamy Ltd; **746** © Mitsuhiko Imamori/Minden Pictures; **747** © Mike Wilkes/naturepl.com; **748** © Bruce Marlin/cirrusimage.com; **749** *top left* © Volker Steger/Photo Researchers, Inc.; *second from left* © Rod Planck/Photo Researchers, Inc.; *second from right* © Chu Tours-Joubert/Photo Researchers, Inc.; *right* © Scott Camazine/Photo Researchers, Inc.; **751** *bottom inset* Photo by Scott Bauer/Agricultural Research Service, USDA; **752** *top left* © Hans Christoph Kappel/naturepl.com; *top right* © Piotr Naskrecki/Minden Pictures; **756–757** © Gregory G. Dimijian/Photo Researchers, Inc.; **757** © Dr. Paul A. Zahl/Photo Researchers, Inc.; **759** *top* © Robert Yin/Corbis; *bottom* © Untitled/Alamy; **760** © Ingram Publishing/Alamy; **762** © Tom McHugh/Photo Researchers, Inc.; **764** © David Fleetham/Bluegreen; **766** *top* © David Fleetham/Bluegreen; *bottom* © blickwinkel/Alamy; **767** © Roberto Rinaldi/Bluegreen; **768** © Eric Haucke/Photo Researchers, Inc.; **769** © 2006 Kaere Telnes/Image Quest Marine; **770** © Steve Maslowski/Photo Researchers, Inc.; **771** © Reg Morrison/Auscape/Minden Pictures; **772** © blickwinkel/Alamy; **773** © Ted Daeschler/Academy of Natural Sciences/VIREO Stock Photography; **774** © Michael & Patricia Fogden/Corbis; **776** © Gary Meszaros/Photo Researchers, Inc.; **777** *bottom* © Michael & Patricia Fogden/Minden Pictures; *top* © Stephen Dalton/Photo Researchers, Inc.; **779** © Zigmund Leszczynski/Animals Animals; **781** *left* © 2006 S. K. Sessions; *bottom right* © Jeffrey L. Rotman/Corbis; *top right inset* Duane Raver/U.S. Fish and Wildlife Service; **784** © Jane Burton/naturepl.com; **786–787** © F. Stuart Westmorland/Photo Researchers, Inc.; **787** © Fabio Liverani/naturepl.com; **789** *top right* © Cyril Ruoso/JH Editorial/Minden Pictures; *top left* © Aaron Shimer; **791** *top* © David R. Parks (http://www.mobot.org/mobot/madagascar); *bottom* © Flip Nicklin/Minden Pictures; **793** © Michael Maconachie/Alamy Images; **794** California Academy of Sciences Department of Ornithology and Mammalogy /Valley Anatomical Preparations. Photo © Valley Anatomical Preparations, Inc.; **796** *top* © Gerard Soury/OSF/photolibrary. All Rights Reserved.; *bottom* © Joe McDonald/Corbis; **799** © Dietmar Nill/Foto Natura/Minden Pictures; **802** © Nguyen Thai, 2006. Used under license from Shutterstock, Inc.; **803** *left bottom* © dkimages.com; *left center* © Arthur Morris/Corbis; *right bottom* © William Osborn/naturepl.com; *right center* © Royalty-Free/Corbis; *top left* © Frans Lanting/Minden Pictures; *top right* © Pete Oxford/naturepl.com; **804** Photograph by Sharon Hoogstraten; **805** © Michael Durham/Minden Pictures; **806** © Jose Azel/Getty Images; **807** *top* © John Cancalosi/naturepl.com; *bottom* © Tony Heald/naturepl.com; **808** *top* © Tom McHugh/Photo Researchers, Inc.; *bottom left* © Charles Philip Cangialosi/Corbis; *bottom center* © Mitsuaki Iwago/Minden Pictures; **809** © Terry Whittaker; Frank Lane Picture Agency/Corbis; **810** Photograph by Sharon Hoogstraten; **811** *top right* John J. Mosesso/NBII; *bottom right* © Fred Bavendam/Minden Pictures; *top left* © Tim Davis/Corbis; **812** *center right* © Terry Whittaker; Frank Lane Picture Agency/Corbis; *left* © Joe McDonald/Corbis; **816–817** © Cyril Ruoso/JH Editorial/Minden Pictures; **817** © Frans Lanting/Minden Pictures; **818** © Jeffrey L. Rotman/Corbis; **819** *top right* © Martin Harvey/Foto Natura/Minden Pictures; *center* © Dwight Kuhn; *bottom* © Alan Schein Photography/Corbis; **820** Max Feken; **821** © George McCarthy/naturepl.com; **822** © Mike Parry/Minden Pictures; **823** © John Cancalosi/Ardea London Limited; **824** © Martin Harvey/NHPA; **825** © Heather Angel/Natural Visions; **826** *center* © Elmer Parolini/www.CartoonStock.com; *top* © Scott Tysick/Masterfile; **827** © Steve Bloom/Alamy; **828** © Ken Jones/MCB Andrade 2003; **829** © Martin Woike/Foto Natura/Minden Pictures; **830** © Michael Neugebauer/mine@netway.at; **831** © Doug Allan/naturepl.com; **832** © Staffan Widstrand/naturepl.com; **833** © Marie Read; **835** *background* © Wayne Lawler; Ecoscene/Corbis; *bottom* © Alex Wild 2006; *center left* © Richard Seaman; *top* © D. Clyne/OSF/Animals Animals; **837** © Jim Wallace/Duke University Photography; **838** © Pete Oxford/Minden Pictures; **839** © Michael Brooke/OSF/Animals Animals/Earth Scenes. All rights reserved.; **840** *both* © Dwight Kuhn; **841** *top left* © Nigel J. Dennis/Photo Researchers, Inc.; **842** *left* © Scott Tysick/Masterfile; *right* © Staffan Widstrand/naturepl.com; **844** © Gallo Images/Corbis; **846** © Claus Meyer/Minden Pictures; **847** *top right* © Gerry Ellis/Minden Pictures; *bottom right* © Sally A. Morgan; Ecoscene/Corbis; *center right* © Manfred Kage/Peter Arnold, Inc.; *cleanup* © Getty Images; **848** *center right* © The Peregrine Fund; *top right* © blickwinkel/Alamy.

Unit 9 **850–851** © Ken Redding/Corbis; **851** © Dennis Kunkel/Phototake; **852** *top left* © Susumu Nishinaga/Photo Researchers, Inc.; *bottom* © David McCarthy/Photo Researchers, Inc.; **853** *center* © Dr. Yorgos Nikas/Photo Researchers, Inc.; *3 o'clock position* © Ed Reschke/Peter Arnold, Inc.; *1 o'clock position* © Ed Reschke/Peter Arnold, Inc.; *bottom* © CNRI/Photo Researchers, Inc.; *7 o'clock position* © Ed Reschke/Peter Arnold, Inc.; *9 o'clock position* © Carolina Biological Supply company/Phototake Inc./Alamy Ltd; *4 o'clock position* © Ed Reschke/Peter Arnold, Inc.; *11 o'clock position* © Educational Images/Custom Medical Stock Photo; **855** *top* © SPL/Photo Researchers, Inc.; *second from top* © Dr. Gladden Willis/Getty Images; *right* © RubberBall/Alamy Images; **857** *bottom left* © WidStock/Alamy Images; **859** *bottom right* © Steve Mason/Getty Images (Royalty-Free); *center right* © age fotostock/SuperStock; *top right* © Lori Adamski Peek/Getty Images; **862** *center left* © Kevin Fleming/Corbis; **867** *top left* © Bettmann/Corbis; *bottom right* © Michael Krasowitz/Getty Images; **868** *center* © Dr. Yorgos Nikas/Photo Researchers, Inc.; *3 o'clock position* © Ed Reschke/Peter Arnold, Inc.; *1 o'clock position* © Ed Reschke/Peter Arnold, Inc.; *bottom* © CNRI/Photo Researchers, Inc.; *7 o'clock position* © Ed Reschke/Peter Arnold, Inc.; *9 o'clock position* © Carolina Biological Supply company/Phototake Inc./Alamy Ltd; *4 o'clock position* © Ed Reschke/Peter Arnold, Inc.; *11 o'clock position* © Educational Images/Custom Medical Stock Photo; **872–873** © ISM/Phototake; **873** *bottom right* © Francois Paquet-Durand/Photo Researchers, Inc.; **875** © Anatomical Travelogue/Photo Researchers, Inc.; **876** *bottom right* © James Cavallini/Photo Researchers, Inc.; **880** *top* © Custom Medical Stock Photo; *bottom* © Custom Medical Stock Photo; **881** © Omikron/Photo Researchers, Inc.; **882** © Steve Gschmeissner/Photo Researchers, Inc.; **883** © CNRI/Photo Researchers, Inc.; **887** *bottom left* © Wellcome Dept. of Cognitive Neurology/Photo Researchers, Inc.; *bottom center* © WDCN/Univ. College London/Photo Researchers, Inc.; *bottom right* © Wellcome Dept. of Cognitive Neurology/Photo Researchers, Inc.; **888** *top center* © Dr. Fred Hossler/Getty Images; bell, *top right* © Fotolistic, 2006. Used under license from Shutterstock, Inc.; *top right* © Dr. Fred Hossler/Getty Images; **891** *bottom left* © Du Cane Medical Imaging Ltd./Photo Researchers, Inc.; *bottom center* © ISM/Phototake; *bottom right* © Tim Beddow/Photo Researchers, Inc.; **892** *all* © Science Source/Photo Researchers, Inc.; **903** *left* © Howard Sochurek/Corbis; *bottom right* Courtesy of National Institute of Drug Abuse/National Institutes of Health; **908–909** © Martin Dohrn/Royal College of Surgeons/Photo Researchers, Inc.; **909** © David Arky/Corbis; **914** © Photo Insolite Realite/Photo Researchers, Inc.; **916** *top* © Dachez/Photo Researchers, Inc.; *bottom* © Kent Wood/Photo Researchers, Inc.; **919** © Custom Medical Stock Photo; **921** © SW Productions/Getty Images ; **924** © ISM/Phototake; **925** © Paul Barton/Corbis; **926** © Yoav Levy/Phototake; **927** *top* © Kenneth Eward/BioGrafx/Photo Researchers, Inc.; *bottom* © Dr. Gopal Murti/Photo Researchers, Inc.; **929** *center right* © CNRI/Photo Researchers, Inc.; *top* © SPL/Photo Researchers, Inc.; **931** © Dynamics Graphics Group/Creatas/Alamy Images; **932** Photograph by Sharon Hoogstraten; **934** © Kenneth Eward/BioGrafx/Photo Researchers, Inc.; **938–939** © Dennis Kunkel/Phototake Inc./Alamy Ltd; **939** © Ross Hoddinott/naturepl.com; **940** *left* © Science Museum/Science and Society Picture Library; *second from left* Ms Pesan 1555 Anatomical diagram of the human circulatory and digestive system (1425-1450), Mansour b. Eliyas Chirazi. Vellum. 26.5 x 18. Biblioteque Nationale, Paris. © Bridgeman Art Library; *third from left* Louis Pasteur, about 1865, Charles Reutlinger. Photograph. © Adoc-photos/Art Resource, New York; *bottom* © Archivo Iconografico, S.A./Corbis; **941** *top left to right* © Bettmann/Corbis; © Bettmann/Corbis; © Garo/Photo Researchers, Inc.; *bottom left to right* © Yale Joel/Time Life Pictures/Getty Images; © Craig van der Lende/Photographer's Choice/Getty Images; © pixelman, 2006. Used under license from Shutterstock, Inc.; **943** © Oliver Meckes/Nicole Ottawa/Photo Researchers, Inc.; **944** © David Scharf/Photo Researchers, Inc.; **945** © E. Gray/Photo Researchers, Inc.; **949** © Carolina Biological Supply Company/Phototake Inc./Alamy Ltd; **950** © Joubert/Phanie/Photo Researchers, Inc.; **955** © CNRI/Photo Researchers, Inc.; **957** © Dr. Dorothea Zucker-Franklin, M.D./Phototake; **958** *top* © Ralph C. Eagle Jr./Photo Researchers, Inc.; *center* © Dennis Kunkel/Phototake; *bottom* © A. Syred/Photo Researchers, Inc.; **960** © Dr. Cecil H. Fox/Photo Researchers, Inc.; **963** *top* © Eye of Science/Photo Researchers, Inc.; *bottom* © Nibsc/Photo Researchers, Inc.; **965** *bottom left* © CNRI/Photo Researchers, Inc.; *bottom right* © Russell Kightley Media, rkm.com.au; **970–971** © Dr. Michael Webb/Visuals Unlimited/Getty Images; **971** © Alfred Pasieka/Science Photo Library/Photo Researchers, Inc.; **972** © Louis B. Wallach, Inc./The Image Bank/Getty Images; **973** © Comstock Production Department/Alamy Images; **975** © David Young-Wolff/PhotoEdit; **982** © Eye of Science/Photo Researchers, Inc.; **984** © Professors P. Motta & F. Carpino/University "La Sapienza", Rome/Science Photo Library/Photo Researchers, Inc.; **985** © Jason Smith, 2006. Used under license from Shutterstock, Inc.; **988** © Susumu Nishinaga/Photo Researchers, Inc.; **990** © Vince Bucci/AFP/Getty Images; **993** *bottom* © BSIP/Phototake; 998-999 © Gusto/Photo Researchers, Inc.; **999** © Steve Hopkin/Ardea London Limited; **1003** © Anatomical Travelogue/Photo Researchers, Inc.; **1004** *bottom left* © Andrew Syred/Photo Researchers, Inc.; *bottom right* © SPL/Photo Researchers, Inc.; **1005** © SPL/Photo Researchers, Inc.; **1007** *top all* © Ed Reschke/Peter Arnold, Inc.; *bottom right* © SPL/Photo Researchers, Inc.; **1010** © Kent Wood/Photo Researchers, Inc.; **1012** *ball* © Nina Shannon, 2006. Used under license from Shutterstock, Inc.; *timer* © Hannah Gleghorn, 2006. Used under license from Shutterstock, Inc.; **1013** © Andrew Syred/Photo Researchers, Inc.; **1016** © Anatomical Travelogue/Photo Researchers, Inc.; **1017** *webquest left* © Siebert/Custom Medical Stock Photo; *webquest right* © Siebert/Custom Medical Stock Photo; *bottom left* © Steve Gschmeissner/Photo Researchers, Inc.; *top right inset* © Franc Podgorsek/istockphoto.com; **1022–1023** © Nestle/Petit Format/Photo Researchers, Inc.; **1023** © Francois Gohier/Ardea London Limited; **1031** *top* © Dr. David M. Philips/Visuals Unlimited; *bottom* © D. Philips/Photo Researchers, Inc.; **1032** © Eye of Science/Photo Researchers, Inc.; **1033** © Claude Edelmann/Photo Researchers, Inc.; **1034** © Liz Sanders/Mississippi Fertility Institute; **1037** *top left, center left* © Claude Edelmann/Photo Researchers, Inc.; *bottom left* © Petit Format/Photo Researchers, Inc.; *Week 6 and Week 12* © SPL/Photo Researchers, Inc.; *Week 20* © Mediscan/Medical-on-line/Alamy Ltd; *Week 32* © Petit Format/Photo Researchers, Inc.; **1039** © Jose Luis Pelaez, Inc./Corbis; **1041** © David Turnley/Corbis; **1042** *center left* © Tom & Dee Ann McCarthy/Corbis; *bottom left* © Bob Daemmrich/PhotoEdit; **1043** all Courtesy of the Peel Family, Chicago, IL; **1044** © Science Source/Photo Researchers, Inc.; **1045** *bottom left* © Paul Grebliunas/Getty Images; *bottom right* © Marnie Burkhart/Masterfile; **1046** *bottom left* © D. Philips/Photo Researchers, Inc.; *bottom right* © David Turnley/Corbis; **1050** © Cary Wolinsky/National Geographic Image Collection; **1051** © Lester Lefkowitz/Corbis; **1052** *left* Courtesy of the Dept. of Anatomy and Neurobiology, University of Vermont College of Medicine; *top right* © WDCN/Univ. College London/Photo Researchers, Inc.; *center right* © Wellcome Dept. of Cognitive Neurology/Photo Researchers, Inc.

Backmatter **R2** © Comstock Images/Age Fotostock America, Inc.; **R3** *top right* © Michael Newman/PhotoEdit; *bottom left* © Andrew Lambert Photography/Photo Researchers, Inc.; **R5** *top right* © davies & starr/Getty Images; *center right* © MicroScan/Phototake; **R8** Photograph by Sharon Hoogstraten; **R10** *right* © M. I. Walker/Photo Researchers, Inc.; *center left* © M. I. Walker/Photo Researchers, Inc.; *left* © M. I. Walker/Photo Researchers, Inc.; **R11** © Cathlyn Melloan/Getty Images; **R12** © Martyn Chillmaid/OSF/photolibrary. All Rights Reserved.; **R25** *top* © Eye of Science/Photo Researchers, Inc.; *center* © NIAID/CDC/Photo Researchers, Inc.; *bottom* © M. I. Walker/Photo Researchers, Inc.; **R26** *top* © M. I. Walker/Photo Researchers, Inc.; *center* © Steve Gschmeissner/Photo Researchers, Inc.; *bottom* © Brandon D. Cole/Corbis; **R27** *top* © Laurie Knight/istockphoto.com; *center* © Bryan Eastham, 2006. Used under license from Shutterstock, Inc.; *bottom* © Galina Dreyzina, 2006. Used under license from Shutterstock, Inc.; **R28** *top* © David Hughes/Photo Researchers, Inc.; *center* © Cindy Haggerty, 2006. Used under license from Shutterstock, Inc.; *bottom* © Norbert Wu/Minden Pictures; **R29** *top* © Gary Bell/oceanwideimages.com; *center* © Norbert Wu/Minden Pictures; *bottom* © Kim Taylor/naturepl.com; **R30** *top* © F. Collet/Ardea London Limited; *center* © Rene Krekels/Foto Natura/Minden Pictures; *bottom* © Gary Bell/oceanwideimages.com; **R31** *top* © Gary Bell/oceanwideimages.com; *second from top* © eStock Photo; *center* © Joseph T. Collins/Photo Researchers, Inc.; *second from bottom* © Jeremy Early/FLPA/Minden Pictures; *bottom* © Frans Lanting/Minden Pictures; **R38** *bottom left* © Peter Oxford/naturepl.com; *top right* © Scott Bauer/USDA/Agricultural Research Service; *bottom right* © Aaron Haupt/Photo Researchers, Inc.; **R39** *top left* © Kim Heacox/Getty Images; *top right* © Ron Levine/The Image Bank/Getty Images; *bottom left* © Geoff Tompkinson/Photo Researchers, Inc.

ILLUSTRATIONS

Illustration by Argosy **29, 93, 127, 157, 193, 257, 321, 353, 385, 421, 449, 477, 507, 537, 567, 601, 633, 685, 723, 751, 781, 841, 867, 903, 933, 965, 993, 1017, 1045;** Illustration by Thomas Bayley/Sparks Arts & Literary Agents **307;** Illustration by Richard Bonson/Wildlife Art Ltd. 397 *bottom*, **446–447, 595, 732;** Illustration by Robin Boutell/Wildlife Art Ltd. **741;** Illustration by Peter Bull **83, 85, 87, 89, 90-91, 94, 139, 250, 325, 357, 361, 495, 520, 538, 541, 576, 580, 589, 598, 603, 605, 642, 646, 655, 658–659, 700, 702–703, 726, 750, 761, 763, 765, 769–770, 859–860, 874, 876–878, 885, 896, 904, 911–913, 915, 920, 923, 930, 934, 977, 979, 980, 982, 986, 994, 1000, 1002, 1004, 1006, 1010, 1015, 1018, 1025–1026, 1028–1029, 1034, 1047;** Illustration by Robin Carter/Wildlife Art Ltd. **708, 710, 715–716, 738, 758, 788, 796–797, 812;** Illustration by Stuart Carter /Wildlife Art Ltd. **348, 404, 706, 712, 718;** Illustration by Dan Cole/Wildlife Art Ltd. **800;** Illustration by Barry Croucher/Wildlife Art Ltd. **790, 814;** Illustration by Stephen Durke **CA10, 37–48, 60, 104, 114, 128, 146, 165, 233, 237, 241, 258, 260, 318, 369, 386, 545, 548–549, 557, 579, 582, 585, 602, 643, 911, 915, 947, 952–953, 956, 961–962, 964, 966, 968, 1030;** Illustration by Luigi Galante/Sparks Arts & Literary Agents **152, 329, 354, 644, 775, 782;** Illustration by Garth Glazier **CA24–25, 550, 565, 568, 570, 881–883, 887–888, 900;** Patrick Gnan **311;** Illustration by Sharon & Joel Harris **855, 863–864, 889, 899, 978, 987, 989, 994, 1001, 1009–1010, 1018, 1035, 1041, 1046;** Illustration by Inklink Studio/Sparks Arts & Literary Agents **413, 414, 415, 416, 418–419, 422, 469;** Illustration by Joel Ito **383;** Illustration by Ian Jackson/Wildlife Art Ltd. **744;** Illustration by Virge Kask **592–593;** Elliott Kimmel, Science Teacher **219;** Illustration by Debbie Maizels **178, 182, 615, 626, 644–645, 658, 664, 667–668, 671, 682, 686, 800–801, R32–R35;** Illustration by Alan Male **376, 377–378, 527, 795, 798;** Courtesy of National Institute of Drug Abuse/National Institutes of Health **903** *bottom right*; Illustration by Steve Oh/KO Studios **140–141;** MapQuest.com, Inc. **303, 311, 335, 346, 354, 397, 430, 462;** Illustration by Jun Park **52;** Illustration by Mick Posen/Wildlife Art Ltd. **349, 410;** Illustration by Six Red Marbles **C09, 59, 127, 193, 287, 567, 657, 685, 751, 841, 933;** Illustration by Mick Stevens **169;** Dan Stuckenschneider (Uhl Studios) **R2, R6–R7, R9;** Illustration by Myke Taylor/Wildlife Art Ltd. **CA42, 341, 736, 744, 752;** Illustration by Bart Vallecoccia **73–79, 82, 94–96, 104, 109, 111, 113–115, 119–120, 128, 130, 311, 373, 386, 640, 897, 917–919, 936;** Illustration by Jane Watkins/Wildlife Art Ltd. **615** Articulate graphics/Rep:Deborah Wolfe, Ltd. **666.**

Chapter 1

Manipulating Plant Growth, page 28

EFFECT OF LIGHT ON PLANT GROWTH			
Day	Plant A Growth (mm) (control)	Plant B Growth (mm)	Plant C Growth (mm)
1	0	0	0
2	1	2	2
3	3	3	4
4	4	4	5
5	5	5	6

Chapter 2

Enzymatic Activity, page 57

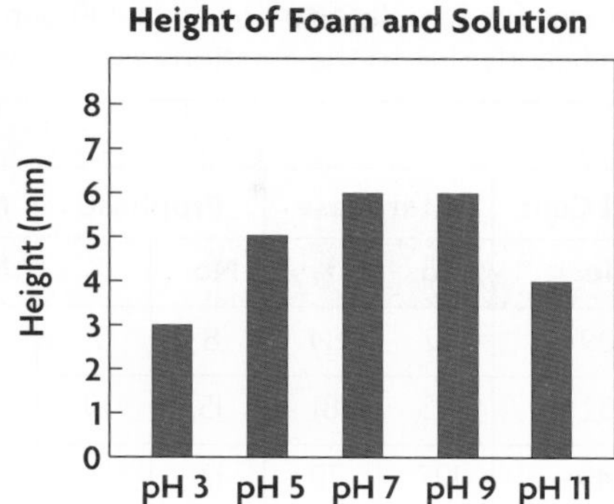

Chapter 3

Diffusion Across a Membrane, page 88

TABLE 1 CHANGES IN EGG MASS		
Solution	Observation	
Distilled water	Egg increases in mass.	**hypertonic**
5% NaCl	No change to egg.	**isotonic**
20% NaCl	Egg got smaller.	**hypertonic**
50% glucose	Egg shrinks.	**hypertonic**

Modeling the Cell, page 93

Material	Part	Reasoning	Function
Bags	Membrane	Outer structure is flexible and contains other materials.	Cell membrane maintains the cellular boundaries, protects the internal cellular environment, and regulates movement of materials into and out of cell.
Gelatin jigglers	Cytoplasm	Thick fluid fills the cell.	Internal medium of the cell
Balloon	Nucleus	Large circular organelle, very prominent in cell	Contains the DNA, the control center of the cell
(Marker)	Nucleolus	Used to draw a spot on the balloon	Region on the nucleus where ribosomes are assembled
Coffee straws	Microtubules	Long, thin tubes	Maintain cell shape
Wire	Microfilaments	Thin fiber strands	Gives the cell a sturdy, flexible framework
Sponge	ER	Kind of layered material	Involved in protein synthesis
Sponge	Golgi apparatus	Similar to ER	Involved in protein packaging and delivery
Beads	Ribosomes	Small, round structures	Involved in protein synthesis; in cytoplasm or associated with ER
Styrofoam peanuts	Mitochondria	Similar shape	Involved in energy production
Foil	Lysosomes	Foil can be shaped into it, and represents function (disposal).	Involved in breaking down of cellular waste
Drinking straw slices	Centriole	Roundish in shape—similar to relative size	Form cilia and flagella

Chapter 5

Mitosis in Onion Root Cells, page 143

Note the percentages for Sample 2 do not equal 100 percent. Also, the total number of cells viewed differ significantly due to the locations viewed on the root.

TABLE 1. STAGES OF THE CELL CYCLE

Sample	Total Cells	Interphase		Prophase		Metaphase		Anaphase		Telophase	
	No.	No.	%	No.	%	No.	%	No.	%	No.	%
1	109	92	84	8	7	5	5	3	3	1	1
2	152	123	81	15	10	6	4	4	3	4	3
3	249	197	79	17	7	12	5	20	8	3	1

Chapter 8

UV Light and Skin Cancer, page 256

Effectiveness of Sunscreen

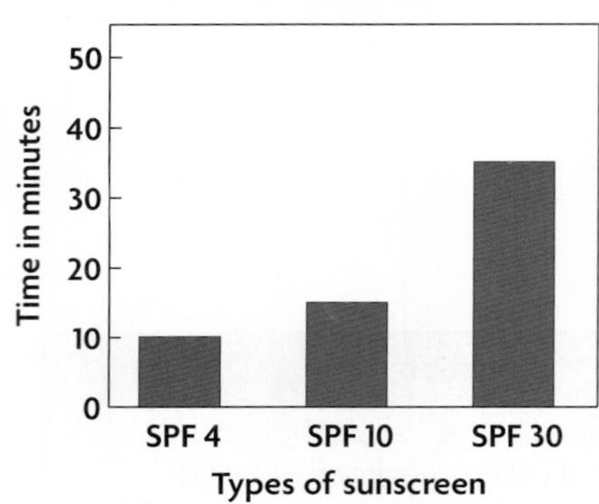

Chapter 9

Constructing Histograms, page 282

Human Chromosome Sizes

Number of human chromosomes
0
2
4
6
8
10
0–50
51–100
101–150
151–200
201–250
Millions of base pairs

Chapter 10

Predator-Prey Pursuit, page 315

Influence of Selective Predation on Field Mice

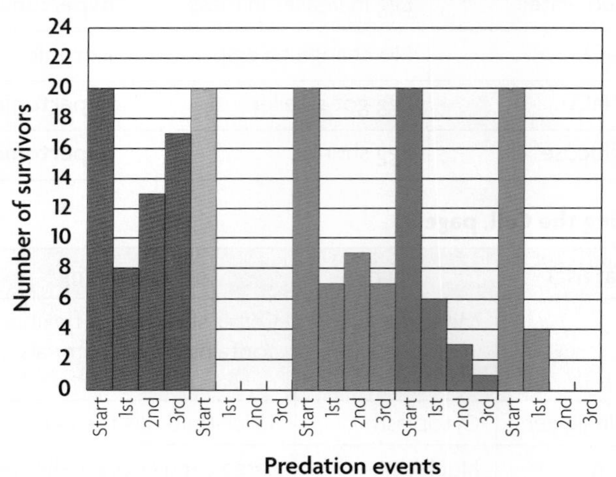

Chapter 11

Natural Selection in African Swallowtails, page 334

TABLE 1. NUMBER OF SWALLOWTAILS (MIMICS) OF EACH COLOR			
	Yellow	Orange	Red
Original population	2	5	2
Trial 1	4	6	2
Trial 2	8	0	4
Trial 3	16	0	8

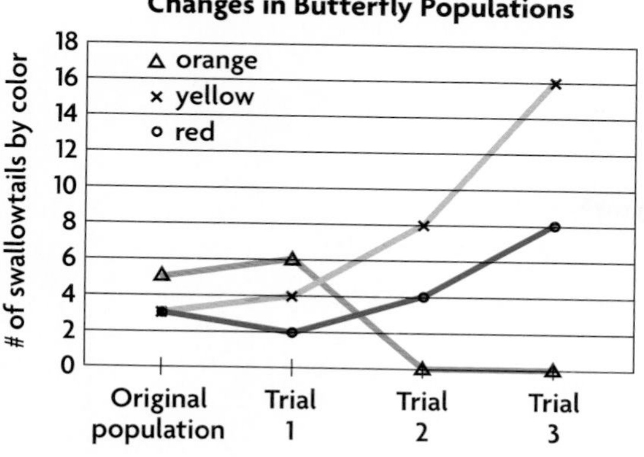

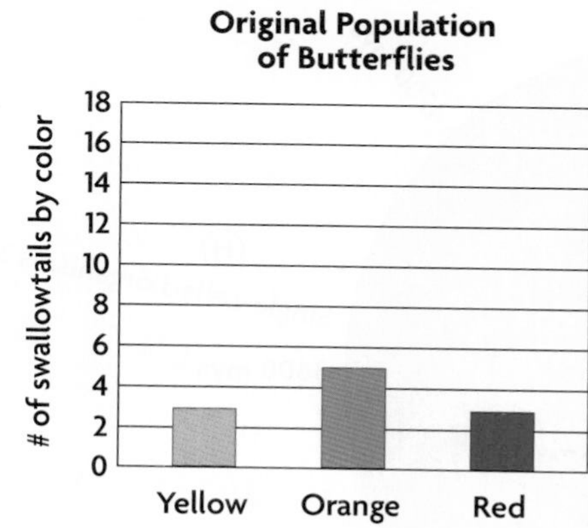

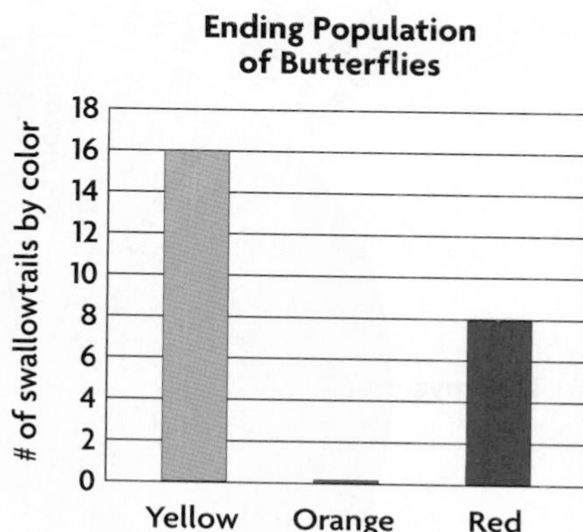

Chapter 12

Radioactive Decay, page 364

Trial		Start	1	2	3	4	5	6	7	8	9	10
Number of Tailsium Atoms	My Data	10	6	2	2	1	0					
	Class Average	10	6	5.4	2.6	1.8	0.2	0				
	Theoretical Data	10	5	2.5	1.25	0.625	0.313	0.156	0.078	0.039	0.019	0

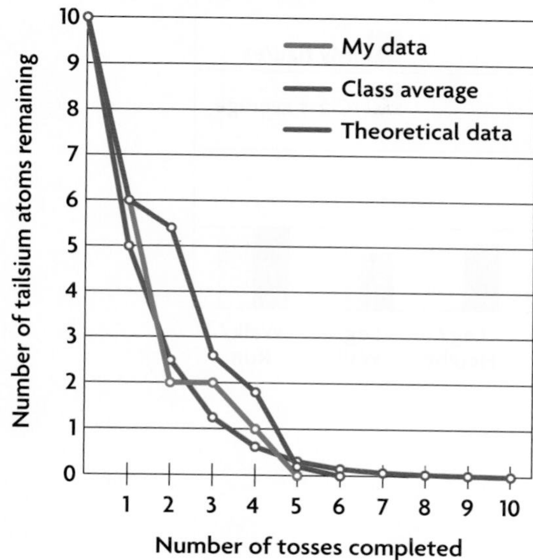

Chapter 12 *continued*

Geologic Clock, page 381

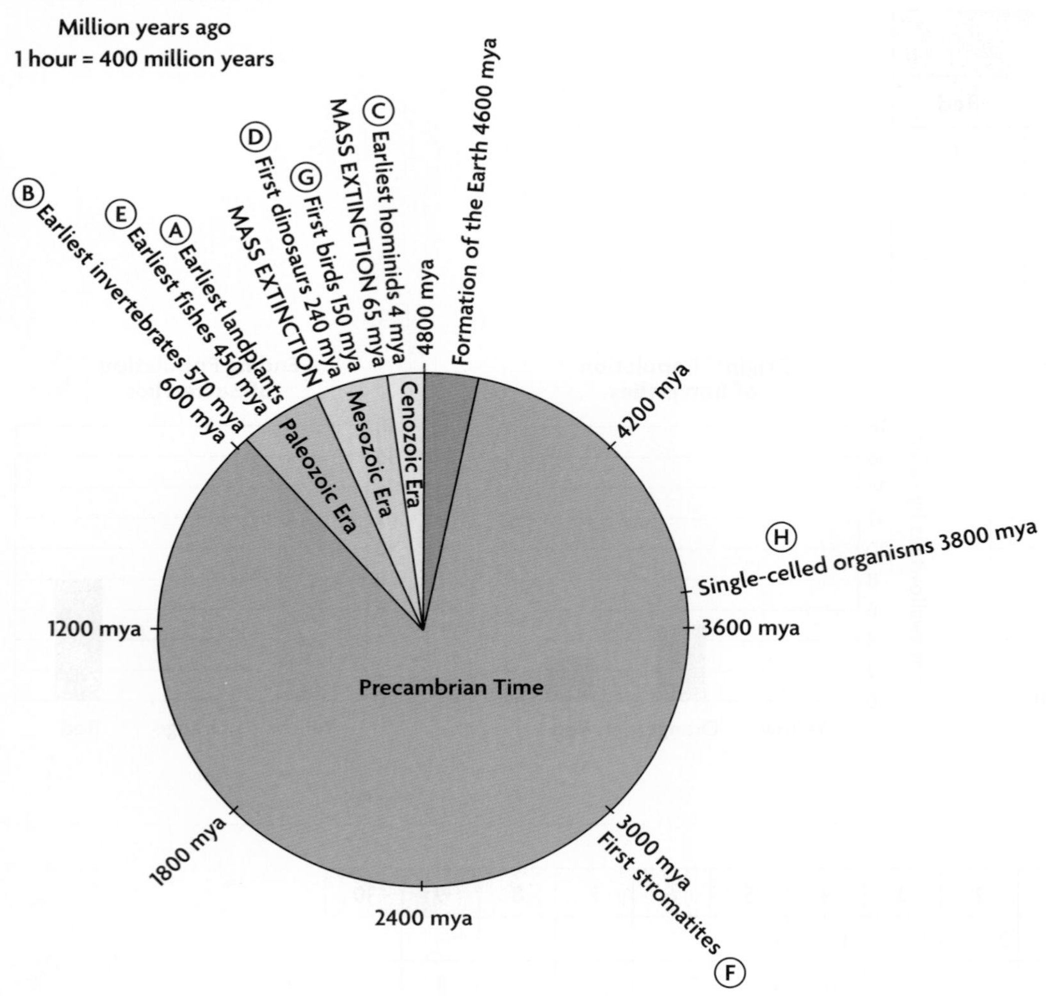

Stride Inferences, page 384

Stride Data	Team 1	Class Average
Measurements (cm)		
Height (cm)	159.0	162.8
Foot length	22.0	23.0
Leg length	92.5	90.7
Walking stride	125.0	125.0
Running stride	250.0	229.1
Ratios		
Foot/Leg	4.2	3.9
Foot/Height	7.2	7.1
Leg/Height	1.7	1.8
Leg/Walk Stride	1.4	1.4
Walk/Run Stride	2.0	1.9

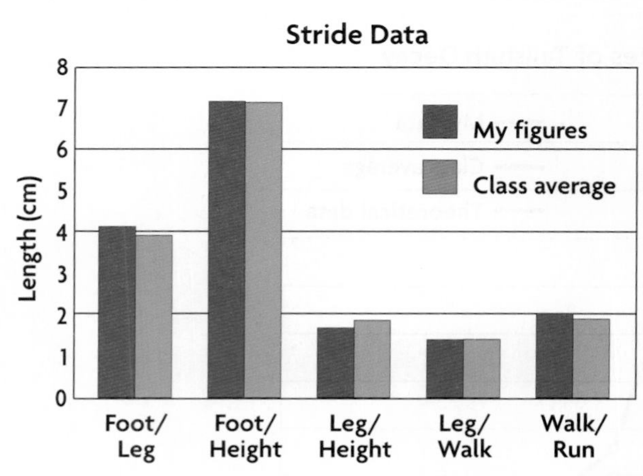

Chapter 13

Random Sampling, page 420

GRID COORDINATES		
Letter	Number	No. of Big Bluestems in Grid Segment
B	5	2
A	5	1
B	1	1
D	7	1
G	2	2
A	6	0
D	5	4
C	5	3
C	1	3
D	6	2
B	3	4
B	1	1
Result:		total: 24; avg.: 2.0; pop. est. 98

Actual number of Bluestems: 110

Percent error calculated = 10.90%

Chapter 14

Modeling Predation, page 435

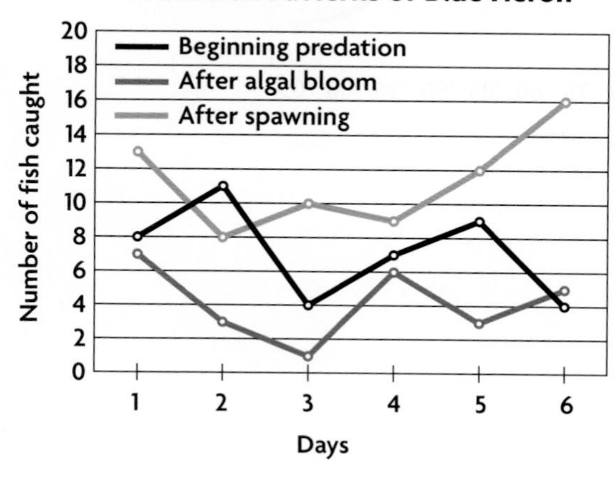

Survivorship Curves, page 438

TABLE 1. SURVIVORSHIP DATA			
Age (years)	Deaths	Survivors	% Surviving
0–5	|	35 – 1 = 34	97
6–10	0	34 – 0 = 34	97
11–15	||	34 – 2 = 32	91
16–20	|||	32 – 3 = 29	83
21–25	0	29 – 0 = 29	83
26–30	|	29 – 1 = 28	80
31–35	0	28 – 0 = 28	80
36–40	|	28 – 1 = 27	77
41–45	0	27 – 0 = 27	77
46–50	|	27 – 1 = 26	74
51–55	|	26 – 1 = 25	71
56–60	|||	25 – 3 = 22	63
61–65	||	22 – 2 = 20	57
66–70	||	20 – 2 = 18	51
71–75	||	18 – 2 = 16	46
76–80	||||||||	16 – 8 = 8	23
81–85	|	8 – 1 = 7	20
86–90	||||||	7 – 6 = 1	3
91–95	|	1 – 1 = 0	0
96–100	0	0 – 0 = 0	0

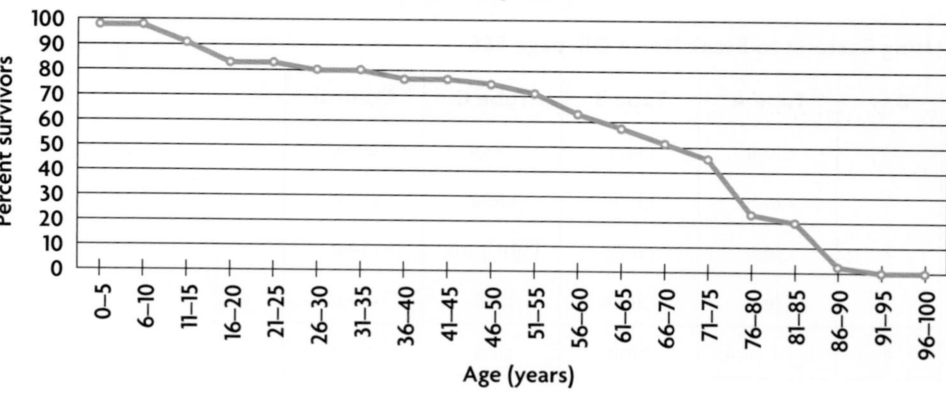

Chapter 16

Water Quality Testing, page 506

TABLE 1. TEST RESULTS AND EPA STANDARDS FOR DRINKING WATER			
Possible Contaminant	EPA Maximum Level (mg/L)	Sample A	Sample B
Chlorine	4	0	0
Copper	1.3	0	0.5
Iron*	0.3	0	0
Nitrate	100	0.5	50
Nitrite	1	0	0

*EPA Recommended Standard

Chapter 18

Trends in Infectious Disease, page 546

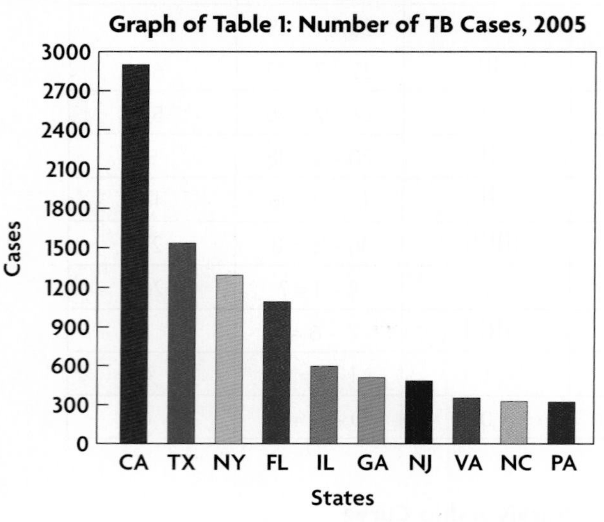

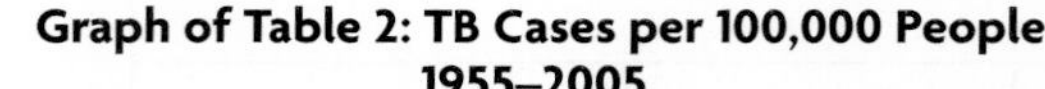

Graph of Table 2: TB Cases per 100,000 People
1955–2005

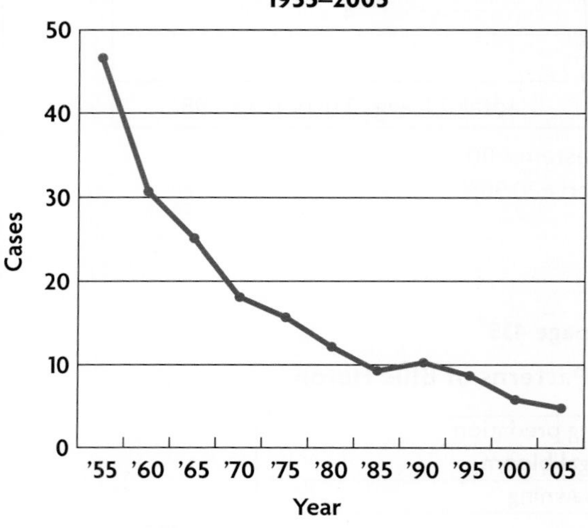

Using Bacteria to Break Down Oil, page 566

Day	Tube A	Tube B	Tube C	Control
0	clear	clear	clear	clear
1	clear	clear	clear	clear
2	clear	clear	light pink	clear
3	clear	clear	pink	clear
4	light pink	pink	pink	clear
5	pink	pink	pink	clear

Tube A = QT Garbage Disposal Cleaner and sunflower oil
Tube B = K47 Cesspool Treatment and sunflower oil
Tube C = Roebic Septic Cleaner and sunflower oil
Tube D = sunflower oil (control)

Chapter 19

Quantifying Mold Growth, page 600

Student	Initial Mass of Bread (g)	Final Mass of Bread (g)
1	30.2	38.1
2	29.0	44.1
3	29.0	36.0
4	30.6	37.6
5	28.9	29.9

Chapter 24

Constructing Scatterplots, page 742

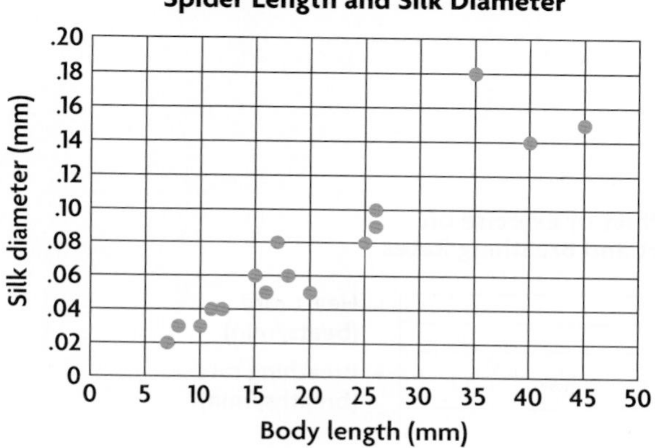

***Daphnia* and Heart Rate, page 750**

TABLE 1. HYDROGEN PEROXIDE SOLUTIONS		
Hydrogen Peroxide Concentration (mg/L)	Amount of Stock Solution (mL)	Amount of Spring Water (mL)
0	0.0	100.0
0.3	1.0	99.0
0.6	2.0	98.0
1.0	3.3	96.7
1.3	4.3	95.7
1.6	5.3	94.7
2.0	6.7	93.3
2.3	7.7	92.7
2.6	8.7	91.3
3.0	10.0	90.0

Chapter 26

Choosing Graphs, page 792

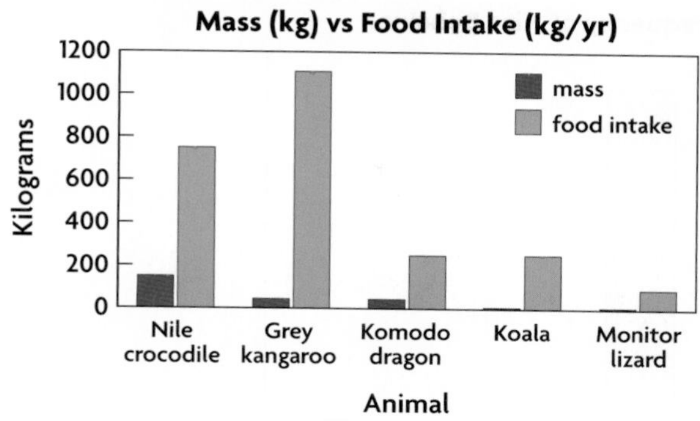

Chapter 27

Using an Ethogram to Describe Animal Behavior, page 830

CAT BEHAVIOR			
Behavior	Number of Times	Length of Time (min)	Total Length of Time (min)
resting	1	31	31
eating	1	9	9
cleaning	1	4	4
playing	2	8, 7	15

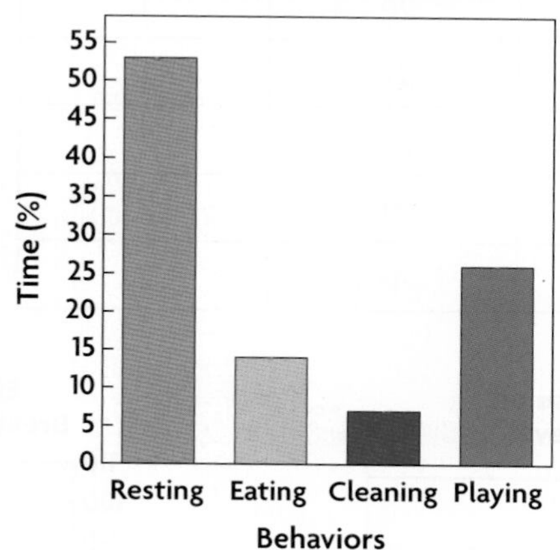

Chapter 27 *continued*

Constructing Bar Graphs, page 836

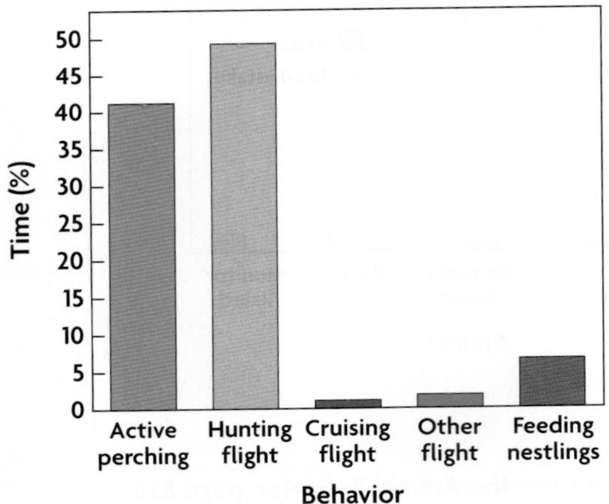

Chapter 28

Homeostasis and Exercise, page 857

TABLE 1. EFFECTS OF EXERCISE

Time (min)	Heart Rate (beats/min)	Breathing Rate (breaths/min)	Perspiration Level
0	50	11	1
2	64	20	1
4	76	27	2
6	82	30	2
8	96	33	2
9	105	43	2

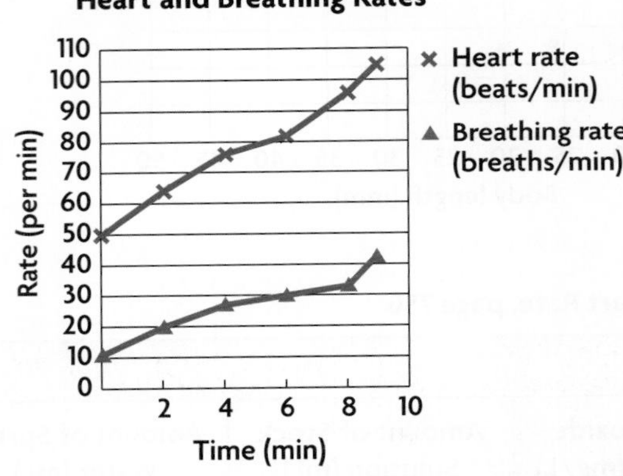

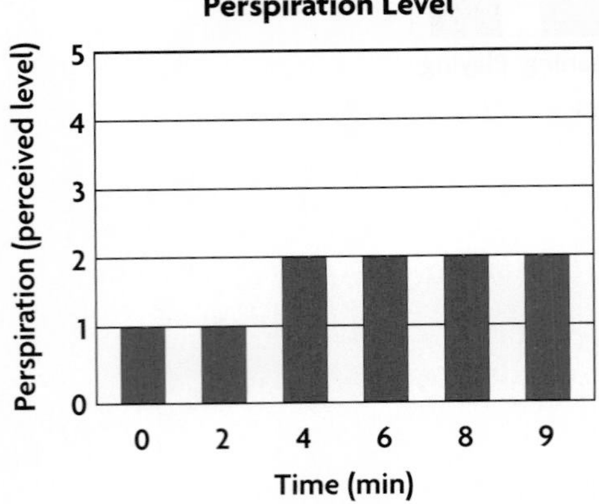

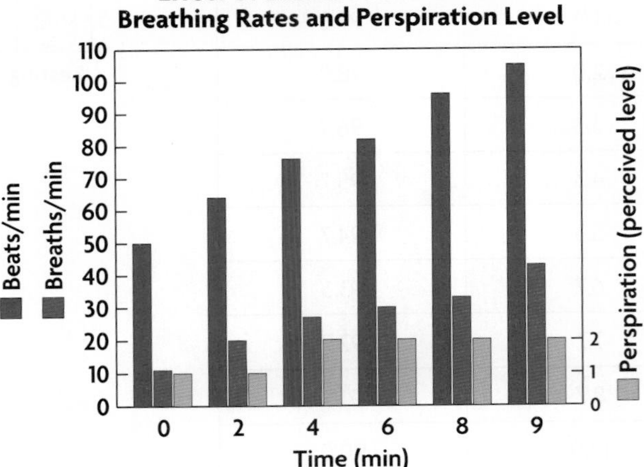

Chapter 28 *continued*

Examining Human Cells, page 866

Type of Cell	Function	Slide Description
Bone	Bone cells form bones in the skeletal system, which supports the body.	Series of rings closely packed together Dark spots scattered throughout the rings Canal in the center, which may contain blood cells
Skeletal muscle	Skeletal muscle cells receive impulses from the nervous system to contract.	Long, thin strands or fibers that lie in the same direction More than one nucleus Cross bands
Neuron	Neurons send and receive information by transmitting impulses between the body and the brain and spinal cord.	Central body with a nucleus Strands extend off the body in many directions.

Chapter 29

Reaction Time, page 902

Task	Time Without Distraction (sec)	Time With Distraction (sec)
Two even piles	26	28
Two piles (by color)	31	35
Four even piles	27	31
Four piles (by suit)	49	60

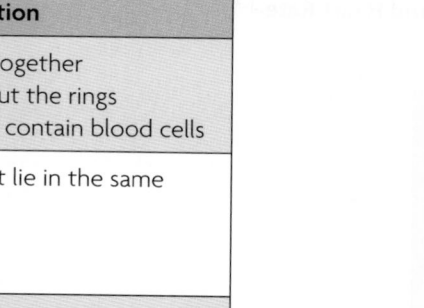

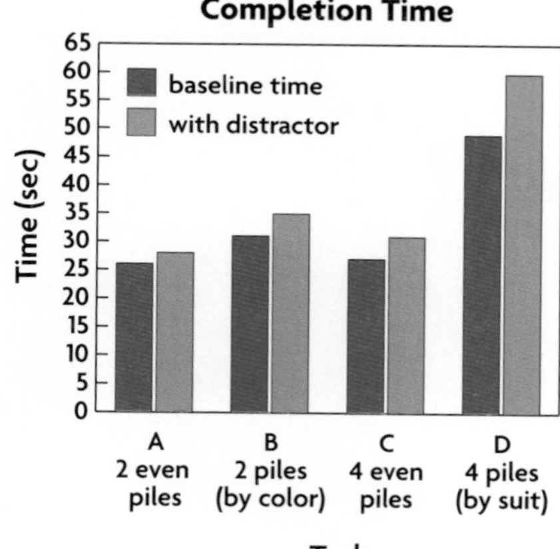

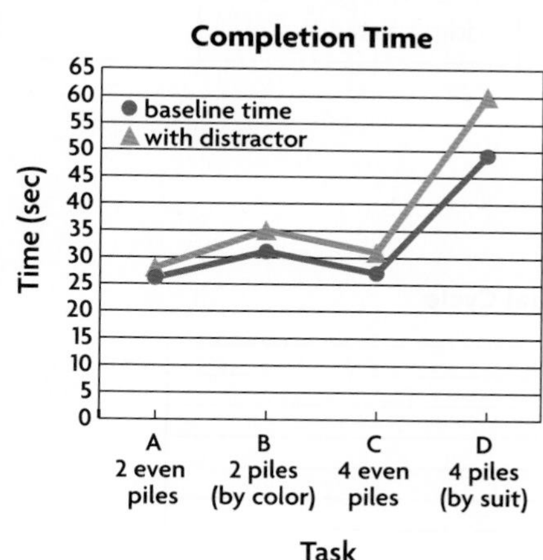

Chapter 30

Stimuli and Heart Rate, page 933

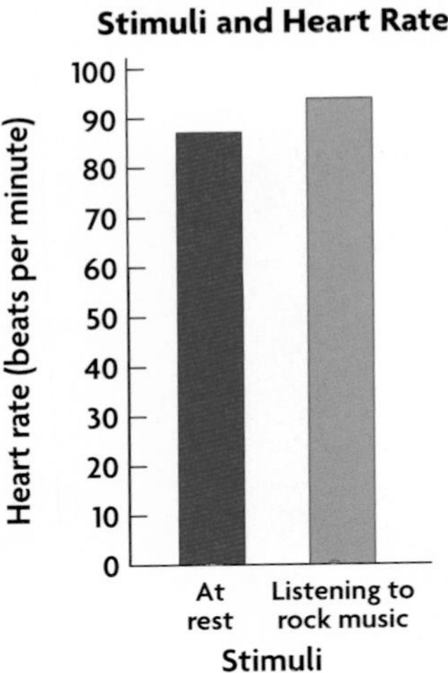

Chapter 32

Testing a Digestive Enzyme, page 981

Students in the test group used chicken instead of beef jerky. Also they did not extend their observations to a 24-hour period.

SUMAMRY TABLE OF OBSERVATIONS	
Beaker A	potato and pecan do not dissolve; chicken begins to dissolve after 30 minutes
Beaker B	potato and pecan moderately dissolve throughout; chicken moderately dissolves after 30 minutes, mostly dissolved after 45 minutes.
Beaker C	potato begins to dissolve throughout; pecan and chicken moderately dissolve after 30 minutes
Beaker D	potato, pecan, and chicken begin to dissolve after 15 minutes, moderately dissolve after 30 minutes, and are mostly dissolved after 45 minutes

Antacid Effectiveness, page 992

TABLE 1: ANTACID OBSERVATIONS				
Antacid	A	B	C	D
Active ingredient	aluminum hydroxide	magnesium hydroxide	calcium carbonate	sodium bicarbonate
pH of vinegar before adding antacid	3.1	3.1	3.2	3.2
pH of vinegar after adding antacid	4.2	4.0	5.1	5.6

Chapter 34

Hormones in the Human Menstrual Cycle, page 1033

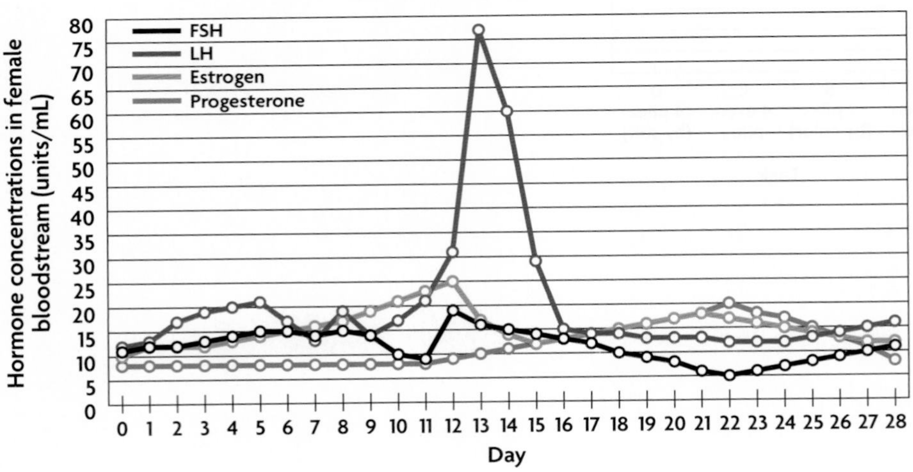